HORSES

IN TRAINING 2014

124th YEAR OF PUBLICATION

Raceform

INDEX TO GENERAL CONTENTS

Editor	Richard Lowther; Raceform Ltd., Compton, Newbury, RG20 6NL. Fax: 01635 578101 E-mail: richard.lowther@racingpost.com
Assistant Editor	Simon Turner
Production Editor	Adrian Gowling; Bloodstock Services, Weatherbys
Production Assistants	Emma Kerwin, Chris Hill, Alan Mosley, Jenni Graham and Lucy Brown
Typesetting	Maggie Elvie; Printing Services, Weatherbys, Sanders Road, Wellingborough, NN8 4BX.
Orders	Raceform Ltd., Sanders Road, Wellingborough, Northants NN8 4BX. Tel: 01933 304858 www.racingpost.com/shop E-mail: Shop@racingpost.com
Advertisements	Julian Brown; Raceform Ltd., Compton, Newbury, RG20 6NL. Tel: 01635 577603 E-mail: julian.brown@racingpost.com
ISBN	978-1-909471-27-6

Printed and bound by CPI GROUP (UK) Ltd, Croydon, CR0 4YY

INDEX TO ADVERTISERS

GO TO BED WITH A REAL PAGE TURNER

The Racing Post iPad edition.
Available from 8pm the night
before it's in the shops.

Free 30-day trial. On the app store now.

2014
RACING FIXTURES
AND SALE DATES

(SUBJECT TO ALTERATION)

Flat fixtures are in **Black Type**; Jump in Light Type; Irish in *Italic*;
asterisk (☆) indicates an evening or Twilight meeting;
† indicates an All Weather meeting. Sale dates are at foot of fixtures

MARCH

Sun	Mon	Tues	Wed	Thur	Fri	Sat
30	**31**					**1**
Ascot **Doncaster** *Leopardstown* *Limerick*	Hexham **Kempton Park**† Plumpton					Doncaster Kelso **Lingfield Park**† *Navan* Newbury
2	**3**	**4**	**5**	**6**	**7**	**8**
Huntingdon *Leopardstown* Sedgefield	**Kempton Park**† **Lingfield Park**† Southwell	Exeter Newcastle **Southwell**†	Catterick Bridge *Downpatrick* Fontwell Park **Kempton Park**†☆ **Lingfield Park**†	Carlisle *Clonmel* **Kempton Park**†☆ **Southwell**† Wincanton	Ayr *Dundalk*†☆ Leicester Sandown Park **Wolverhampton**†☆	Ayr Chepstow *Gowran Park* Sandown Park **Wolverhampton**†
9	**10**	**11**	**12**	**13**	**14**	**15**
Market Rasen *Naas* Warwick	Plumpton Stratford-on-Avon Taunton	Cheltenham Sedgefield **Southwell**† **Wolverhampton**†☆	Cheltenham Huntingdon **Kempton Park**†☆ **Southwell**†	Cheltenham Hexham Towcester **Wolverhampton**†☆	Cheltenham *Dundalk*†☆ Fakenham **Lingfield Park**† **Wolverhampton**†☆	Fontwell Park Kempton Park *Limerick* Newcastle Uttoxeter **Wolverhampton**†☆
16	**17**	**18**	**19**	**20**	**21**	**22**
Carlisle *Ffos Las* *Limerick* *Navan*	*Down Royal* **Kempton Park**† Southwell *Wexford* **Wolverhampton**†	Exeter **Southwell**† Wetherby	Haydock Park **Kempton Park**†☆ **Lingfield Park**† Warwick	Chepstow **Kempton Park**†☆ Ludlow *Thurles* **Wolverhampton**†	*Dundalk*†☆ **Lingfield Park**† Newbury Sedgefield **Wolverhampton**†☆ Doncaster (Newbury) Sale	Bangor-on-Dee *Gowran Park* Kelso **Lingfield Park**† Newbury Stratford-on-Avon
23	**24**	**25**	**26**	**27**	**28**	**29**
Curragh *Downpatrick* Market Rasen Wincanton	Taunton Towcester **Wolverhampton**† Fasig-Tipton Sale	Chepstow Fontwell Park **Southwell**†	Exeter **Kempton Park**†☆ **Lingfield Park**† **Southwell**†	*Cork* *Ffos Las* **Kempton Park**†☆ **Southwell**† **Wolverhampton**†	*Dundalk*†☆ **Lingfield Park**† Newcastle Wetherby **Wolverhampton**†☆	**Doncaster** **Kempton Park**† *Navan* Stratford-on-Avon Uttoxeter

APRIL

Sun	Mon	Tues	Wed	Thur	Fri	Sat
		1 Kempton Park† Newton Abbot **Southwell**† Fasig-Tipton Sale	**2** Kempton Park☆ *Leopardstown*☆ **Lingfield Park**† **Southwell**† Wincanton Ascot Sale	**3** Aintree *Clonmel*☆ **Lingfield Park**† Taunton **Wolverhampton**†☆	**4** Aintree *Dundalk*†☆ **Leicester** Sedgefield **Wolverhampton**†☆	**5** Aintree Chepstow *Gowran Park* **Lingfield Park**† Newcastle **Wolverhampton**†☆
6 *Cork* *Fairyhouse* *Ffos Las* Market Rasen	**7** Kelso **Redcar** Windsor	**8** Carlisle **Pontefract** **Southwell**†	**9** **Catterick Bridge** Kempton Park†☆ *Limerick* **Lingfield Park**† Nottingham Keeneland Sale	**10** Kempton Park†☆ *Limerick* Ludlow Taunton Towcester Keeneland Sale	**11** Ayr Fontwell Park **Newbury** *Wexford*☆ **Wolverhampton**†☆	**12** Ayr Bangor-on-Dee *Navan* **Newbury** **Thirsk** **Wolverhampton**†☆
13 *Curragh* Stratford-on-Avon *Tramore* Wetherby Wincanton	**14** Hexham **Pontefract** *Tramore*☆ **Windsor**	**15** Exeter Kempton Park **Southwell**† Tattersalls Sale Ascot Sale	**16** **Beverley** Cheltenham *Dundalk*☆ **Newmarket** Sedgefield☆ Southwell☆ Tattersalls Sale	**17** Cheltenham **Newmarket** **Ripon** *Tipperary*☆ Tattersalls Sale	**18** **Lingfield Park**† Musselburgh	**19** **Bath**☆ Carlisle *Cork* Haydock Park **Kempton Park**† Newton Abbot **Nottingham**☆
20 *Cork* *Fairyhouse* **Musselburgh** Plumpton Towcester	**21** Chepstow *Cork* *Fairyhouse* Fakenham Huntingdon Market Rasen Plumpton **Redcar** Yarmouth	**22** *Ballinrobe*☆ Kelso Ludlow Wetherby **Wolverhampton**†☆ **Yarmouth**☆ Doncaster Sale	**23** **Catterick Bridge** **Epsom Downs** Perth Southwell☆ Taunton☆ Doncaster Sale	**24** **Beverley** **Brighton**☆ **Newcastle**☆ Perth *Tipperary*☆ **Warwick** Doncaster Sale	**25** Chepstow☆ **Doncaster** *Dundalk*†☆ *Kilbeggan*☆ Newton Abbot☆ Perth **Sandown Park** Cheltenham Sale	**26** **Doncaster**☆ **Haydock Park** **Leicester** *Limerick* **Ripon** Sandown Park **Wolverhampton**†☆
27 Ayr *Gowran Park* **Kempton Park**† *Limerick*	**28** **Bath** **Kempton Park**† *Naas*☆ **Southwell**†☆ **Windsor**☆ **Wolverhampton**†	**29** **Lingfield Park**† **Newcastle**☆ **Nottingham** *Punchestown*☆ **Wolverhampton**†☆ Yarmouth	**30** **Ascot** **Brighton**☆ Cheltenham☆ **Pontefract** *Punchestown*☆ **Southwell**†			

MAY

Sun	Mon	Tues	Wed	Thur	Fri	Sat
■	■	■	■	**1** Ffos Las† **Lingfield Park†** *Punchestown* **Redcar** Sedgefield Towcester☆ Tattersalls Sale Goffs Sale	**2** Bangor-on-Dee☆ **Chepstow** Fontwell Park☆ **Lingfield Park†** **Musselburgh** *Punchestown☆* Tattersalls Sale	**3** Doncaster☆ Goodwood Hexham☆ Newmarket *Punchestown* Thirsk Uttoxeter
4 *Gowran Park* Hamilton Park Newmarket Salisbury *Sligo*	**5** Bath Beverley *Curragh* *Down Royal* Ffos Las Kempton Park **Warwick** **Windsor**	**6** Brighton Catterick Bridge☆ Exeter☆ *Fairyhouse☆* Fakenham **Kempton Park†**	**7** Brighton Chester Kelso **Kempton Park†☆** Worcester☆	**8** Carlisle☆ Chester *Clonmel☆* Newton Abbot **Southwell†** Wincanton☆	**9** Ascot☆ Chester *Cork☆* *Downpatrick☆* **Lingfield Park** Market Rasen **Nottingham☆** **Ripon☆** Arqana Sale	**10** Ascot☆ Haydock (Mixed) Hexham **Lingfield Park** Nottingham Thirsk☆ **Warwick☆** *Wexford* Arqana Sale
11 *Killarney* *Leopardstown* Ludlow Plumpton	**12** Doncaster *Killarney☆* **Musselburgh** Towcester☆ **Windsor☆** **Wolverhampton†**	**13** Beverley Ffos Las☆ *Killarney☆* Sedgefield Southwell☆ Wincanton	**14** Chepstow☆ *Naas☆* Perth☆ Uttoxeter Worcester **York**	**15** Fontwell Park☆ **Newmarket☆** Perth **Salisbury** *Tipperary☆* **York**	**16** Aintree☆ *Dundalk†☆* **Hamilton Park☆** *Kilbeggan☆* **Newbury** **Newmarket** **York**	**17** Bangor-on-Dee Doncaster☆ **Newbury** **Newmarket** *Punchestown* Thirsk Uttoxeter☆
18 *Limerick* Market Rasen *Navan* **Ripon** Stratford-on-Avon	**19** Leicester☆ **Redcar** *Roscommon☆* **Southwell†** Towcester **Windsor☆** Fasig-Tipton Sale	**20** Bath Newcastle Nottingham **Warwick☆** Yarmouth☆ Doncaster Sale Fasig-Tipton Sale	**21** Ayr **Kempton Park†☆** **Lingfield Park** Newton Abbot *Sligo☆* Worcester☆ Doncaster Sale	**22** Ayr *Clonmel☆* **Goodwood** **Salisbury☆** **Sandown Park☆** Wetherby Doncaster Sale Goresbridge Sale	**23** *Cork☆* **Goodwood** Haydock Park **Musselburgh☆** **Pontefract☆** Towcester☆ **Yarmouth** Goresbridge Sale	**24** Beverley Cartmel☆ Catterick Bridge *Curragh* Ffos Las☆ **Goodwood** Haydock Park
25 *Curragh* Fontwell Park Kelso Uttoxeter	**26** *Ballinrobe☆* **Carlisle** Cartmel **Leicester** **Redcar** **Windsor**	**27** *Ballinrobe☆* Hexham☆ Huntingdon☆ **Leicester** **Lingfield Park†☆** **Redcar**	**28** Beverley☆ Cartmel Chepstow Hamilton Park **Kempton Park†☆**	**29** Bath *Fairyhouse☆* **Haydock Park** **Sandown Park☆** Wetherby☆ Worcester Cheltenham Sale	**30** Brighton Catterick Bridge☆ *Down Royal☆* **Haydock Park☆** Newcastle **Newmarket** Stratford-on-Avon☆ *Tramore☆* Baden-Baden Sale	**31** Chester **Haydock Park** **Newbury☆** **Newmarket** Stratford-on-Avon☆ *Tramore* **York**

JUNE

Sun	Mon	Tues	Wed	Thur	Fri	Sat
1	**2**	**3**	**4**	**5**	**6**	**7**
Fakenham	Carlisle☆	Brighton	Fontwell Park	Ffos Las☆	Bath☆	Doncaster
Kilbeggan	Chepstow	Ripon	Kempton Park☆	Hamilton Park	Catterick Bridge	Epsom Downs
Listowel	Leicester	Southwell☆	Nottingham	Kempton Park☆	*Downpatrick☆*	Hexham
Nottingham	*Listowel*	Yarmouth☆	*Punchestown☆*	Lingfield Park	Epsom Downs	*Limerick☆*
	Naas		Ripon☆	*Tipperary☆*	Goodwood☆	Lingfield Park☆
	Windsor☆		Southwell†	Wolverhampton†	*Leopardstown☆*	Musselburgh
					Market Rasen	Newcastle☆
						Worcester
		Ascot Sale				
8	**9**	**10**	**11**	**12**	**13**	**14**
Curragh	Ayr	Fontwell Park	Beverley	Haydock Park☆	Aintree☆	Bath
Goodwood	Newton Abbot	Lingfield Park☆	*Fairyhouse☆*	*Leopardstown☆*	Chepstow☆	Chester
Perth	Pontefract☆	*Roscommon☆*	Hamilton Park☆	Newbury	*Clonmel☆*	Hexham
	Roscommon☆	Salisbury	Haydock Park	Nottingham	Goodwood☆	Leicester☆
	Windsor☆	Worcester☆	Kempton Park☆	Uttoxeter☆	Musselburgh	Lingfield Park☆
			Yarmouth	Yarmouth	Sandown Park	Musselburgh
					York	*Navan*
						Sandown Park
			Goffs Sale	*Goffs Sale*		York
15	**16**	**17**	**18**	**19**	**20**	**21**
Cork	Carlisle	Brighton☆	Hamilton Park	Ffos Las☆	*Down Royal☆*	Ayr
Doncaster	Newton Abbot	Nottingham☆	Ripon☆	Leicester☆	Goodwood☆	*Down Royal*
Downpatrick	Warwick☆	Royal Ascot	Royal Ascot	*Leopardstown☆*	*Limerick☆*	Gowran Park
Salisbury	Windsor☆	*Sligo☆*	Southwell☆	Lingfield Park†☆	Market Rasen	Haydock Park☆
		Stratford-on-Avon	Uttoxeter	Ripon	Newmarket☆	Lingfield Park☆
		Thirsk	*Wexford☆*	Royal Ascot	Redcar	Newmarket
				Wolverhampton†	Royal Ascot	Redcar
						Royal Ascot
	Goffs Sale					
	(Kempton Park)					
22	**23**	**24**	**25**	**26**	**27**	**28**
Gowran Park	Chepstow	*Ballinrobe☆*	Bath☆	Hamilton Park☆	Chester☆	Chester
Hexham	*Kilbeggan☆*	Beverley	Carlisle	Leicester☆	*Curragh☆*	*Curragh*
Pontefract	Thirsk☆	Brighton	Kempton Park☆	Newcastle	Doncaster	Doncaster☆
Worcester	Windsor☆	Newbury☆	*Naas☆*	*Tipperary☆*	Musselburgh	Lingfield Park☆
	Wolverhampton†	Newton Abbot☆	Salisbury	Warwick	Newcastle☆	Newcastle
			Worcester	Yarmouth	Newmarket☆	Newmarket
					Yarmouth	Windsor
				Tattersalls (IRE) Sale	*Tattersalls (IRE) Sale*	
29	**30**					
Curragh	Ffos Las☆					
Salisbury	Pontefract					
Uttoxeter	Windsor☆					
Windsor	Wolverhampton†					

JULY

Sun	Mon	Tues	Wed	Thur	Fri	Sat
		1 Bath☆ Brighton *Gowran Park*☆ **Hamilton Park** Stratford-on-Avon☆	**2** **Catterick Bridge** Chepstow☆ *Fairyhouse*☆ Kempton Park☆ Perth Worcester	**3** Epsom Downs☆ **Haydock Park** *Leopardstown*☆ Newbury☆ Perth **Yarmouth** *Arqana Sale*	**4** *Bellewstown*☆ Beverley☆ Doncaster **Haydock Park**☆ **Sandown Park** **Warwick** *Wexford*☆ *Arqana Sale*	**5** *Bellewstown*☆ **Beverley** Carlisle☆ **Haydock Park** Leicester Nottingham☆ **Sandown Park**
6 Ayr *Bellewstown* *Limerick* Market Rasen	**7** Ayr Newton Abbot **Ripon**☆ *Roscommon*☆ **Windsor**☆	**8** Brighton☆ Pontefract *Roscommon*☆ Uttoxeter☆ **Wolverhampton**† *Tattersalls Sale*	**9** **Catterick Bridge** Kempton Park☆ **Lingfield Park** *Naas*☆ Worcester☆ **Yarmouth** *Tattersalls Sale*	**10** Bath☆ **Doncaster** Epsom Downs☆ *Leopardstown*☆ **Newmarket** **Warwick** *Tattersalls Sale*	**11** Ascot Chepstow☆ **Chester**☆ *Cork*☆ *Navan*☆ **Newmarket** **York** *Tattersalls Sale*	**12** Ascot **Chester** *Dundalk* **Hamilton Park**☆ **Newmarket** Salisbury☆ *Tipperary* **York**
13 *Fairyhouse* Perth *Sligo* Southwell Stratford-on-Avon	**14** Ayr *Downpatrick* *Killarney*☆ Newton Abbot **Windsor**☆ **Wolverhampton**†☆ *Fasig-Tipton Sale*	**15** Bath **Beverley** *Killarney*☆ **Thirsk**☆ **Yarmouth**☆ *Ascot Sale*	**16** **Catterick Bridge** *Killarney*☆ **Lingfield Park** **Sandown Park**† Uttoxeter Worcester☆	**17** Brighton☆ Doncaster☆ Epsom Downs☆ **Hamilton Park** *Killarney* Leicester *Leopardstown*☆	**18** **Hamilton Park**☆ **Haydock Park** *Kilbeggan*☆ Newbury **Newmarket**☆ Nottingham **Pontefract**☆	**19** Cartmel *Curragh* **Haydock Park**☆ **Lingfield Park**☆ Market Rasen Newbury **Newmarket** Ripon
20 *Curragh* Newton Abbot **Redcar** Stratford-on-Avon *Tipperary*	**21** Ayr *Ballinrobe*☆ **Beverley**☆ Cartmel **Windsor**☆	**22** *Ballinrobe*☆ Bangor-on-Dee☆ **Carlisle**☆ **Musselburgh** Southwell	**23** **Catterick Bridge** Leicester☆ **Lingfield Park**† *Naas*☆ **Sandown Park**☆ Worcester	**24** Bath **Doncaster**☆ *Leopardstown*☆ *Limerick*☆ **Sandown Park** **Wolverhampton**†☆ **Yarmouth**	**25** Ascot Chepstow☆ *Down Royal*☆ **Newmarket**☆ **Thirsk** Uttoxeter *Wexford*☆ **York**☆ *Goresbridge Sale*	**26** Ascot **Lingfield Park**☆ Newcastle **Newmarket** Salisbury☆ *Wexford*☆ **York**
27 Ascot Carlisle Pontefract	**28** Ayr *Galway*☆ **Lingfield Park** Uttoxeter☆ **Windsor**☆	**29** **Beverley** *Galway*☆ **Goodwood** Perth☆ Worcester☆ **Yarmouth**	**30** *Galway*☆ **Goodwood** Leicester☆ Perth **Redcar** **Sandown Park**☆	**31** Epsom Downs☆ *Flos Las*☆ *Galway* **Goodwood** Nottingham Stratford-on-Avon		

AUGUST

Sun	Mon	Tues	Wed	Thur	Fri	Sat
31					**1**	**2**
Brighton *Cork* *Curragh* Worcester					Bangor-on-Dee **Bath**☆ *Galway*☆ **Goodwood** **Musselburgh**☆ **Newmarket**☆ **Thirsk**	Doncaster *Galway* **Goodwood** Hamilton Park☆ Lingfield Park☆ Newmarket Thirsk
3	**4**	**5**	**6**	**7**	**8**	**9**
Chester *Galway* Market Rasen **Newbury**	Carlisle☆ *Cork* **Kempton Park**† *Naas* **Ripon** Windsor☆	Catterick Bridge *Cork*☆ Ffos Las **Kempton Park**†☆ Ripon☆ *Roscommon*☆	Brighton Chepstow **Kempton Park**†☆ **Pontefract** *Sligo*☆ Yarmouth☆	Brighton Haydock Park *Leopardstown* Newcastle☆ Sandown Park☆ *Sligo*☆ **Southwell**†☆ **Yarmouth**	Brighton Haydock Park☆ Lingfield Park† Musselburgh **Newmarket**☆ *Tipperary*☆	Ascot☆ Ayr☆ **Haydock Park** *Kilbeggan*☆ Lingfield Park☆ **Newmarket** Redcar
	Fasig-Tipton Sale	*Fasig-Tipton Sale*				*Fasig-Tipton Sale*
10	**11**	**12**	**13**	**14**	**15**	**16**
Curragh *Downpatrick* Leicester **Windsor**	Ayr *Ballinrobe*☆ Thirsk☆ **Windsor**☆ **Wolverhampton**†	Carlisle Ffos Las Lingfield Park†☆ **Nottingham**☆	Beverley *Gowran Park*☆ **Kempton Park**†☆ Newton Abbot **Salisbury** Yarmouth☆	Beverley Chepstow Fontwell Park☆ *Leopardstown*☆ **Newmarket** Salisbury *Tramore*☆	Catterick Bridge☆ Newbury Newcastle **Newmarket**☆ Nottingham *Tramore*☆	Chester Doncaster Lingfield Park☆ Market Rasen☆ Newbury Newmarket Perth **Ripon** *Tramore*☆
Fasig-Tipton Sale		*Tattersalls (IRE) Sale*	*Tattersalls (IRE) Sale*			*Arqana Sale*
17	**18**	**19**	**20**	**21**	**22**	**23**
Dundalk† Pontefract Southwell *Tramore*	*Roscommon*☆ **Kempton Park**† Thirsk **Windsor**☆ **Wolverhampton**†☆	Brighton Leicester☆ *Sligo*☆ Worcester☆ Yarmouth	**Kempton Park**†☆ *Killarney*☆ **Lingfield Park** Musselburgh **Southwell**†☆ York	Bath Ffos Las *Killarney*☆ Newton Abbot **Wolverhampton**†☆ York	Ffos Las (Mixed) **Goodwood**☆ Hamilton Park☆ *Kilbeggan*☆ *Killarney*☆ Newcastle☆ Newmarket York	Cartmel *Curragh* **Goodwood** *Killarney* Newmarket Redcar☆ Windsor☆ York
Arqana Sale	*Arqana Sale*	*Ascot Sale* *Arqana Sale*				
24	**25**	**26**	**27**	**28**	**29**	**30**
Beverley *Curragh* **Goodwood** Yarmouth	Cartmel **Chepstow** *Downpatrick* **Epsom Downs** Huntingdon **Newcastle** **Ripon** **Warwick**	*Ballinrobe*☆ **Epsom Downs** **Ripon** Sedgefield☆ **Wolverhampton**†☆	*Bellewstown*☆ Carlisle **Catterick Bridge** **Kempton Park**†☆ Lingfield Park† Worcester☆	*Bellewstown*☆ **Ffos Las** Hamilton Park☆ Lingfield Park☆ Stratford-on-Avon *Tipperary*☆	Bangor-on-Dee *Down Royal*☆ Salisbury☆ **Sandown Park** **Thirsk** **Wolverhampton**†☆	**Bath**☆ Beverley Chester Market Rasen☆ Newton Abbot **Sandown Park** *Wexford*
	Fasig-Tipton Sale	*Doncaster Sale*	*Doncaster Sale*	*Doncaster Sale*		

SEPTEMBER

Sun	Mon	Tues	Wed	Thur	Fri	Sat
	1	**2**	**3**	**4**	**5**	**6**
	Brighton Huntingdon **Leicester** *Roscommon☆*	**Goodwood** **Hamilton Park** Kempton Park†☆ **Warwick**	**Bath** *Gowran Park☆* Kempton Park†☆ **Lingfield Park** Southwell	**Haydock Park** *Laytown☆* **Salisbury** Sedgefield Wolverhampton†☆	**Chepstow** **Haydock Park** Kempton Park† *Kilbeggan☆* **Musselburgh☆** **Newcastle**	**Ascot** **Haydock Park** Kempton Park† *Navan* Stratford-on-Avon **Thirsk** Wolverhampton†☆
		Doncaster Sale	Doncaster Sale	Doncaster Sale	Baden-Baden Sale	
7	**8**	**9**	**10**	**11**	**12**	**13**
Dundalk† Fontwell Park **York**	**Brighton** *Galway☆* Newton Abbot Perth	*Galway☆* **Leicester** Perth☆ **Redcar** Worcester	**Carlisle** **Doncaster** *Galway☆* Kempton Park†☆ Uttoxeter	**Chepstow** *Clonmel☆* **Doncaster** **Epsom Downs** Wolverhampton†☆	**Chester** **Doncaster** *Down Royal☆* **Salisbury☆** **Sandown Park**	**Bath** **Chester** **Doncaster** *Leopardstown* **Lingfield Park** Wolverhampton†☆
						Goffs Sale
Keeneland Sale	Keeneland Sale	Keeneland Sale	Keeneland Sale	Keeneland Sale	Keeneland Sale	Keeneland Sale
14	**15**	**16**	**17**	**18**	**19**	**20**
Bath *Curragh* **Ffos Las** *Listowel*	**Brighton** *Listowel* **Musselburgh** Wolverhampton†	**Chepstow** *Listowel* Sedgefield☆ **Thirsk** **Yarmouth**	**Beverley** Kelso☆ *Listowel* **Sandown Park** **Yarmouth**	Kempton Park†☆ *Listowel* **Pontefract** **Ayr** **Yarmouth**	*Listowel* **Newbury** Newton Abbot **Ayr** Worcester☆	**Catterick Bridge** *Listowel* **Newbury** **Newmarket** **Ayr** Wolverhampton†☆
					SGA Sale	SGA Sale
Keeneland Sale	Keeneland Sale	Keeneland Sale	Keeneland Sale	Keeneland Sale	Keeneland Sale	Keeneland Sale
21	**22**	**23**	**24**	**25**	**26**	**27**
Gowran Park **Hamilton Park** Plumpton Uttoxeter	**Hamilton Park** Kempton Park† **Leicester**	*Ballinrobe* **Beverley** **Lingfield Park†** Newcastle☆ **Nottingham**	**Goodwood** Kempton Park†☆ Perth **Redcar**	Kempton Park†☆ **Newmarket** Perth **Pontefract**	*Downpatrick* *Dundalk†☆* **Haydock Park** **Newmarket** Wolverhampton†☆ Worcester	**Chester** **Haydock Park** Market Rasen *Navan* **Newmarket** **Ripon** Wolverhampton†☆
Keeneland Sale		Tattersalls (IRE) Sale	Tattersalls (IRE) Sale			
28	**29**	**30**				
Curragh **Epsom Downs** **Musselburgh**	**Bath** **Hamilton Park** Newton Abbot *Roscommon*	**Ayr** Chepstow *Fairyhouse* Sedgefield				
	Fasig-Tipton Sale					

OCTOBER

Sun	Mon	Tues	Wed	Thur	Fri	Sat
			1 **Kempton Park**†☆ **Newcastle** **Nottingham** **Salisbury** *Sligo*	**2** Bangor-on-Dee *Clonmel* **Kempton Park**†☆ Southwell Warwick	**3** Ascot *Dundalk*†☆ Fontwell Park *Gowran Park* Hexham **Wolverhampton**†☆	**4** **Ascot** Fontwell Park *Gowran Park* **Newmarket** **Redcar** **Wolverhampton**†☆
				Goffs Sale	Goffs Sale	Goffs Sale	Arqana Sale
5 Huntingdon Kelso *Tipperary* Uttoxeter	**6** **Pontefract** Stratford-on-Avon **Windsor**	**7** **Brighton** **Catterick Bridge** **Leicester** *Tipperary* Tattersalls Sale Ascot Sale Fasig-Tipton Sale	**8** **Kempton Park**†☆ Ludlow *Navan* **Nottingham** Towcester Tattersalls Sale	**9** **Ayr** Exeter *Tramore* **Wolverhampton**†☆ Worcester Tattersalls Sale	**10** Carlisle *Dundalk*†☆ Newton Abbot **Wolverhampton**†☆ **York** Tattersalls Sale	**11** Chepstow Fairyhouse Hexham **Musselburgh** **Newmarket** **Wolverhampton**†☆ **York**
12 *Curragh* Ffos Las **Goodwood** *Limerick* Tattersalls Sale	**13** **Salisbury** Sedgefield **Windsor** Tattersalls Sale	**14** Huntingdon **Leicester** **Newcastle** Tattersalls Sale	**15** **Kempton Park**†☆ **Lingfield Park**† **Nottingham** *Punchestown* Wetherby Tattersalls Sale	**16** **Brighton** *Punchestown* Uttoxeter Wincanton **Wolverhampton**†☆	**17** Cheltenham *Downpatrick* *Dundalk*†☆ **Haydock Park** **Newmarket** **Redcar** **Wolverhampton**†☆ Tattersalls Sale Baden-Baden Sale	**18** **Ascot** **Catterick Bridge** Cheltenham *Cork* Kelso **Wolverhampton**†☆ Baden-Baden Sale
19 **Bath** *Cork* Kempton Park *Naas*	**20** Plumpton **Pontefract** **Windsor** Arqana Sale Fasig-Tipton Sale	**21** Exeter **Lingfield Park**† **Yarmouth** Arqana Sale Fasig-Tipton Sale	**22** Fontwell Park **Kempton Park**†☆ *Navan* **Newmarket** Worcester Goffs Sale Arqana Sale Fasig-Tipton Sale	**23** Carlisle **Kempton Park**†☆ Ludlow Southwell *Thurles* Goffs Sale	**24** **Doncaster** *Dundalk*†☆ Fakenham **Newbury** **Wolverhampton**†☆	**25** Aintree Chepstow **Doncaster** *Leopardstown* **Newbury** Stratford-on-Avon *Wexford* **Wolverhampton**†☆
26 Aintree *Galway* *Leopardstown* Wincanton	**27** Ayr *Galway* **Leicester** **Redcar** *Wexford* Tattersalls Sale	**28** **Catterick Bridge** Ffos Las **Yarmouth** Tattersalls Sale	**29** **Kempton Park**†☆ **Nottingham** *Punchestown* Taunton Worcester Tattersalls Sale	**30** *Clonmel* **Kempton Park**†☆ **Lingfield Park**† Sedgefield Stratford-on-Avon Tattersalls Sale	**31** *Down Royal* *Dundalk*†☆ **Newmarket** Uttoxeter Wetherby **Wolverhampton**†☆ Tattersalls Sale Goresbridge Sale	

NOVEMBER

Sun	Mon	Tues	Wed	Thur	Fri	Sat
30 Carlisle *Fairyhouse* Leicester						**1** Ascot Ayr *Down Royal* **Newmarket** Wetherby Tattersalls Sale
2 Carlisle *Cork* Huntingdon *Naas*	**3** Kempton Park Plumpton **Wolverhampton†** Doncaster Sale Fasig-Tipton Sale	**4** Exeter *Fairyhouse* **Redcar** **Southwell†** Doncaster Sale	**5** Chepstow *Dundalk†☆* **Kempton Park†☆** **Nottingham** Warwick Doncaster Sale Keeneland Sale	**6** Fakenham Musselburgh *Thurles* Towcester **Wolverhampton†☆** Ascot Sale Keeneland Sale	**7** *Dundalk†☆* Fontwell Park Hexham Musselburgh **Wolverhampton†☆** Keeneland Sale	**8** **Doncaster** Kelso *Naas* Sandown Park Wincanton Keeneland Sale
9 Ffos Las *Limerick* Market Rasen *Navan* Tattersalls (IRE) Sale Keeneland Sale	**10** Carlisle **Kempton Park†** Southwell Tattersalls (IRE) Sale Keeneland Sale	**11** Huntingdon Lingfield Park Sedgefield Tattersalls (IRE) Sale Keeneland Sale	**12** Ayr Bangor-on-Dee *Dundalk†☆* Exeter **Kempton Park†☆** Tattersalls (IRE) Sale Keeneland Sale	**13** *Clonmel* **Kempton Park†☆** Ludlow **Southwell†** Taunton Tattersalls (IRE) Sale Keeneland Sale	**14** Cheltenham *Dundalk†☆* **Lingfield Park†** Newcastle **Wolverhampton†☆** Tattersalls (IRE) Sale Cheltenham Sale Keeneland Sale SGA Sale	**15** Cheltenham **Lingfield Park†** *Punchestown* Uttoxeter Wetherby **Wolverhampton†☆** Tattersalls (IRE) Sale Keeneland Sale SGA Sale
16 Cheltenham *Cork* Fontwell Park *Punchestown* Tattersalls (IRE) Sale	**17** Leicester Plumpton **Wolverhampton†** Goffs Sale Arqana Sale	**18** Doncaster Fakenham **Southwell†** *Wexford* Goffs Sale Arqana Sale	**19** *Fairyhouse* Hexham **Kempton Park†☆** **Lingfield Park†** Warwick Goffs Sale	**20** Chepstow **Kempton Park†☆** Market Rasen *Thurles* Wincanton Goffs Sale	**21** Ascot *Dundalk☆* Ffos Las Haydock Park **Wolverhampton†☆** Goffs Sale	**22** Ascot *Gowran Park* Haydock Park Huntingdon **Lingfield Park†** **Wolverhampton†☆** Goffs Sale
23 Exeter *Navan* Towcester Goffs Sale	**24** Kempton Park Ludlow **Wolverhampton†** Tattersalls Sale	**25** Lingfield Park Sedgefield **Southwell†** 	**26** *Dundalk†☆* Fontwell Park **Kempton Park†☆** **Lingfield Park†** Wetherby Tattersalls Sale	**27** **Kempton Park†☆** Newbury Taunton *Thurles* Uttoxeter Tattersalls Sale	**28** Doncaster *Dundalk†☆* Musselburgh Newbury **Wolverhampton†☆** Tattersalls Sale	**29** Bangor-on-Dee *Fairyhouse* Newbury Newcastle Towcester **Wolverhampton†☆** Tattersalls Sale

DECEMBER

Sun	Mon	Tues	Wed	Thur	Fri	Sat
	1 **Kempton Park**† Plumpton **Wolverhampton**†	**2** Sedgefield Southwell **Wolverhampton**†	**3** Catterick Bridge **Kempton Park**†☆ **Lingfield Park**† Ludlow	**4** *Clonmel* **Kempton Park**†☆ Leicester Market Rasen Wincanton	**5** *Dundalk*†☆ Exeter **Lingfield Park**† Sandown Park **Wolverhampton**†☆	**6** Aintree Chepstow *Navan* Sandown Park Wetherby **Wolverhampton**†☆
Tattersalls Sale	Tattersalls Sale	Tattersalls Sale	Tattersalls Sale	Tattersalls Sale	Tattersalls Sale	Arqana Sale
7 *Cork* Huntingdon Kelso *Punchestown*	**8** **Kempton Park**† **Lingfield Park**† Musselburgh	**9** Fontwell Park **Southwell**† Uttoxeter	**10** *Dundalk*☆ Hexham **Kempton Park**†☆ Leicester **Lingfield Park**†	**11** **Kempton Park**†☆ Newcastle Taunton Warwick	**12** Bangor-on-Dee Cheltenham Doncaster *Dundalk*†☆ **Wolverhampton**†☆	**13** Cheltenham Doncaster Lingfield Park **Southwell**† *Tramore* **Wolverhampton**†☆
	Ascot Sale Fasig-Tipton Sale					
Arqana Sale	Arqana Sale	Arqana Sale	Goffs Sale	Goffs Sale	Cheltenham Sale	
14 Carlisle *Navan* Southwell	**15** Ffos Las Plumpton **Wolverhampton**†	**16** Catterick Bridge **Kempton Park**† **Southwell**†	**17** **Kempton Park**†☆ **Lingfield Park**† Ludlow Newbury	**18** Exeter **Kempton Park**†☆ **Southwell**† Towcester	**19** Ascot *Dundalk*†☆ **Southwell**† Uttoxeter **Wolverhampton**†☆	**20** Ascot *Fairyhouse* Haydock Park **Lingfield Park**† Newcastle
21 Fakenham Lingfield Park *Thurles*	**22** Bangor-on-Dee **Kempton Park**† **Wolverhampton**†	**23**	**24**	**25**	**26** *Down Royal* Fontwell Park Huntingdon Kempton Park *Leopardstown* *Limerick* Market Rasen Sedgefield Towcester Wetherby	**27** Chepstow Kempton Park *Leopardstown* *Limerick* **Southwell**† Wetherby **Wolverhampton**†☆ Wincanton **Wolverhampton**†
28 Catterick Bridge Leicester *Leopardstown* *Limerick* **Lingfield Park**†	**29** Doncaster Kelso *Leopardstown* *Limerick* Newbury **Southwell**†	**30** Haydock Park **Lingfield Park**† Taunton	**31** **Lingfield Park**† *Punchestown* Uttoxeter Warwick			

DATES OF PRINCIPAL RACES

(SUBJECT TO ALTERATION)

JANUARY

Cheltenham Pony Club Raceday Novices' Chase (Registered as Dipper Novices' Steeple Chase (Cheltenham)) 1st
Fairlawne Handicap Chase Steeple Chase (Handicap) (Cheltenham) 1st
EBF High Sheriff Of Gloucestershire's 'Junior' Standard Open NH Flat Race (Cheltenham) 1st
Holden Plant Handicap Steeple Chase (Tramore) 1st
32Red Tolworth Novices' Hurdle Race (Sandown Park) 4th
32Red.com Mares Hurdle Race (Sandown Park) 4th
Slaney Novices' Hurdle (Naas) 5th
Native Upmanship Steeple Chase (Thurles) 6th
Neptune Investment Management Novices' Hurdle Race (Registered As Leamington Novices Hurdle Race) (Warwick) 11th
Betfred Classic Steeple Chase (A Handicap) (Class 1) (Warwick) 11th
William Hill Lanzarote Hurdle (A Handicap) (Kempton Park) 11th
Williamhill.com Steeple Chase (Class 1) (Kempton Park) 11th
Moscow Flyer Novices' Steeple Chase (Punchestown) 11th
Foxrock Handicap Steeple Chase (Navan) 12th
Coolmore Anaglog's Daughter Mares Only Novices' EBF Steeple Chase (Thurles) 16th
Kinloch Brae Steeple Chase (Thurles) 16th
Clarence House Steeple Chase (Ascot) 18th
Warfield Mares' Hurdle Race (Ascot) 18th
Keltbray Holloway's Hurdle Race (A Limited Handicap) (Ascot) 18th
Williamhill.com Supreme Trial Rossington Main Novice Hurdle (Haydock Park) 18th
Stanjames.com Champion Hurdle Trial (Haydock Park) 18th
Altcar Novices' Steeple Chase (Haydock Park) 18th
Peter Marsh Steeple Chase (A Limited Handicap) (Haydock Park) 18th
Limestone Lad Hurdle (Naas) 18th
Woodlands Park 100 Naas Novices' Steeple Chase (Naas) 18th
Solerina Mares Only Novices' Hurdle (Fairyhouse) 19th
Dan Moore Memorial Handicap Steeple Chase (Fairyhouse) 19th
Galmoy Hurdle (Gowran Park) 23rd
Goffs Thyestes Handicap Steeple Chase (Gowran Park) 23rd
Neptune Investment Management Novices' Hurdle Race (Registered As Classic Novices' Hurdle Race) (Cheltenham) 25th
Cleeve Hurdle Race (Cheltenham) 25th
Argento Steeple Chase (Registered As Cotswold Steeple Chase) (Cheltenham) 25th
JCB Triumph Hurdle Trial (Registered As Finesse Juvenile Hurdle Race) (Cheltenham) 25th
Murphy Group Steeple Chase (A Handicap) (Cheltenham) 25th
Racing Post Lightning Novices' Steeple Chase ((Doncaster) 25th
Albert Bartlett Novices' Hurdle Race (Registered As River Don) (Doncaster) 25th
OLBG Doncaster Mares' Hurdle Race (Doncaster) 25th
Sky Bet Chase (A Handicap) (Formerly The Great Yorkshire Chase) (Doncaster) 25th
Boylesports Limited Handicap Hurdle (Leopardstown) 25th
Boylesports Killiney Novices' Steeple Chase (Leopardstown) 25th
Leopardstown Handicap Steeple Chase (Leopardstown) 25th
BHP Irish Champion Hurdle (Leopardstown) 26th
Synergy Golden Cygnet Novices' Hurdle (Leopardstown) 26th
Frank Ward Solicitors Arkle Novices' Steeple Chase (Leopardstown) 26th

FEBRUARY

Betfred Challengers Novices' Steeple Chase (Registered As Scilly Isles Novices' Steeple Chase) (Sandown Park) 1st
Betfred Heroes Handicap Hurdle Race (Sandown Park) 1st
Betfred Mobile Sports Contenders Hurdle Race (Sandown Park) 1st
Totepool Towton Novices' Steeple Chase (Wetherby) 1st
Burns Pet Nutrition Welsh Champion Hurdle (Limited Handicap) (Ffos Las) 1st
John Smith's Scottish Triumph Hurdle Trial (A Juvenile Hurdle Race) (Musselburgh) 2nd
EBF INHSO Series Novices' Hurdle (Punchestown) 2nd
Grand National Trial Handicap Steeple Chase (Punchestown) 2nd
Tied Cottage Steeple Chase (Punchestown) 2nd
Powerstown Novices' Hurdle (Clonmel) 6th
Betfair Denman Steeple Chase (Newbury) 8th
Betfair Super Saturday Game Spirit Steeple Chase (Newbury) 8th
Betfair Hurdle Race (Handicap) (Newbury) 8th
Betfair Commits £40 Million To British Racing Bumper Standard Open NH Flat Race (Newbury) 8th
Kingmaker Novices Steeple Chase (Warwick) 8th
Warwick Mares Hurdle Race (Warwick) 8th
Exeter Novices' Hurdle Race (Exeter) 9th
Spring 4yo Hurdle (Leopardstown) 9th
Deloitte Novices' Hurdle (Leopardstown) 9th
Dr P J. Moriarty Novices' Steeple Chase (Leopardstown) 9th
Hennessy Gold Cup Steeple Chase (Leopardstown) 9th

Jane Seymour Mares' Novices' Hurdle (Sandown Park) 14th
Betfair Ascot Steeple Chase (Ascot) 15th
RSA Novice Trials Steeplechase (Registered As Reynoldstown Novices Steeplechase) (Ascot) 15th
Weatherbys Hamilton Insurance Steeple Chase (Ascot) 15th
Albert Bartlett Novices' Hurdle Race (Registered As Prestige Novices' Hurdle Race) (Haydock Park) 15th
Betfred Hurdle Race (Registered As Rendlesham Hurdle Race) (Haydock Park) 15th
Betfred Grand National Trial (A Handicap Steeple Chase) (Haydock Park) 15th
Bathwick Tyres Kingwell Hurdle Race (Wincanton) 15th
Red Mills Trial Hurdle (Gowran Park) 15th
Red Mills Steeple Chase (Gowran Park) 15th
Ladbrokes Boyne Hurdle (Navan) 16th
Flyingbolt Novices' Steeple Chase (Navan) 16th
Ten Up Novices' Steeple Chase (Navan) 16th
Sidney Banks Memorial Novices' Hurdle (Huntingdon) 20th
Compare Bookmakers at Bookmakers.co.uk Cleves Stakes (Lingfield Park) 22nd
Coral App Download From The App Store Winter Derby Trial (Lingfield Park) 22nd
Williamhill.com Supreme Dovecote Novice Hurdle Trial (Kempton Park) 22nd
Adonis Juvenile Hurdle Race (Kempton Park) 22nd
Pendil Novices' Steeple Chase (Kempton Park) 22nd
Kempton Park Steeple Chase (Handicap) (Kempton Park) 22nd
Winning Fair 4yo Hurdle (Fairyhouse) 22nd
At The Races Bobbyjo Steeple Chase (Fairyhouse) 22nd
Totepool National Spirit Hurdle Race (Fontwell Park) 23rd
Paddy Power Johnstown Novice Hurdle (Naas) 23rd
Paddy Power Nas Na Riogh Novices' Steeple Chase (Naas) 23rd
Paddy Power Newlands Steeple Chase (Naas) 23rd
Michael Purcell Memorial Novices' Hurdle (Thurles) 27th

MARCH

Totepool Premier Kelso Novices' Hurdle Race (Kelso) 1st
Totepool Mobile Text 'TOTE' to 89660 Premier Steeple Chase (Kelso) 1st
Greatwood Gold Cup Handicap Steeple Chase (Newbury) 1st
William Hill - No.1 Downloaded Betting App Mares' Novices' Hurdle (Doncaster) 1st
Carrickmines Handicap Steeple Chase (Leopardstown) 2nd
Download The Ladbrokes App Lady Wulfruna Stakes (Wolverhampton) 8th
Paddy Power Imperial Cup Handicap Hurdle (Sandown Park) 8th
European Breeders' Fund Paddypower.Com 'National Hunt' Novices' Handicap Hurdle Race Final (Sandown Park) .. 8th
European Breeders' Fund Mares' Standard Open National Hunt Flat Race (Sandown Park) 8th
Shamrock Handicap Steeple Chase (Gowran Park) 8th
Kingsfurze Novices' Hurdle (Naas) 9th
Directors Plate Novices' Steeple Chase (Naas) 9th
Leinster Grand National Handicap Steeple Chase (Naas) 9th
William Hill Supreme Novices' Hurdle Race (Cheltenham) 11th
Arkle Challenge Trophy Novices' Steeple Chase (Cheltenham) 11th
Stan James Champion Hurdle Challenge Trophy (Cheltenham) 11th
OLBG David Nicholson Mares Hurdle Race (Cheltenham) 11th
Cheltenham Handicap Steeple Chase (Cheltenham) 11th
144th Year National Hunt Steeple Chase (Amateur Riders Novices' Steeple Chase) (Cheltenham) 11th
Rewards4Racing Novices' Handicap Steeple Chase (Cheltenham) 11th
Neptune Investment Management Novices' Hurdle Race (Registered As Baring Bingham Novices' Hurdle Race) (Cheltenham) .. 12th
RSA Novices' Steeple Chase (Cheltenham) 12th
Sportingbet.com Queen Mother Champion Steeple Chase (Cheltenham) 12th
Weatherbys Champion Bumper (A Standard Open National Hunt Flat Race) (Cheltenham) 12th
Fred Winter Novices' Handicap Hurdle Race (Cheltenham) 12th
Coral Cup (A Handicap Hurdle Race) (Cheltenham) 12th
Ladbrokes World Hurdle Race (Cheltenham) 13th
Ryanair Steeple Chase (Registered As Festival Trophy Steeple Chase) (Cheltenham) 13th
JLT Specialty Novices' Steeple Chase (Registered As Golden Miller Novices' Steeple Chase) (Cheltenham) .. 13th
Byrne Group Plate (A Handicap Steeple Chase) (Cheltenham) 13th
Pertemps Network Final (A Handicap Hurdle Race) (Cheltenham) 13th
Albert Bartlett Novices' Hurdle Race (Registered As Spa Novices' Hurdle Race) (Cheltenham) 14th
JCB Triumph Hurdle Race (Cheltenham) 14th
Betfred Cheltenham Gold Cup Steeple Chase (Cheltenham) 14th
Johnny Henderson Grand Annual Steeple Chase Challenge Cup (Handicap) (Cheltenham) 14th
Vincent O'Brien County Handicap Hurdle Race (Cheltenham) 14th
Martin Pipe Conditional Jockeys' Handicap Hurdle (Cheltenham) 14th
CGA Foxhunter Steeple Chase (Cheltenham) 14th
Betfred Midlands Grand National Steeple Chase (A Handicap) (Uttoxeter) 15th
Shannon Spray EBF Mares Only Novices' Hurdle (Limerick) 16th
Dawn Run EBF Mares Only Novices' Steeple Chase (Limerick) 16th
EBF Novices' Chase Series Final Handicap Steeple Chase (Navan) 16th
Coral Winter Derby (Lingfield Park) 22nd
Bookmakers.co.uk Hever Sprint Stakes (Lingfield Park) 22nd
32Red Spring Cup (Lingfield Park) 22nd
EBF Ultima Business Solutions Mares' 'National Hunt' Novices' Hurdle Finale (A Limited Handicap) (Newbury) 22nd

EBF Park Express Stakes (Curragh)..23rd
6 Places Eachway Grand National at BetVictor Magnolia Stakes (Kempton Park) 29th
William Hill Doncaster Mile (Doncaster)...29th
William Hill – New iPad App Cammidge Trophy (Doncaster)..29th
William Hill Lincoln (Heritage Handicap) (Doncaster)...29th
An Uaimh Steeple Chase (Navan)..29th
Ballysax Stakes (Leopardstown)...30th
Heritage Stakes (Leopardstown)...30th
1000 Guineas Trial (Leopardstown)...30th
2000 Guineas Trial (Leopardstown)...30th
Hugh McMahon Memorial Novices' Steeplechase (Limerick)..30th
Kevin McManus 4yo Only Bumper (Limerick)..30th

APRIL

Anniversary Juvenile Hurdle Race (Aintree) 3rd
Bowl Steeple Chase (Aintree) 3rd
Manifesto Novices' Steeple Chase (Aintree) 3rd
Aintree Hurdle (Aintree)..3rd
Red Rum Handicap Steeple Chase (Aintree)...3rd
Aintree Handicap Hurdle Race (Aintree)..3rd
Sefton Novices' Hurdle Race (Aintree)..4th
Melling Steeple Chase (Aintree)...4th
Mildmay Novices' Steeple Chase (Aintree)..4th
Top Novices' Hurdle Race (Aintree)..4th
Aintree Handicap Hurdle Race (Aintree)..4th
Crabbie's Topham Steeple Chase (Handicap) (Aintree)..4th
Mares' Standard Open National Hunt Flat Race (Aintree)..4th
Liverpool Hurdle Race (Aintree)...5th
Maghull Novices' Steeple Chase (Aintree)...5th
Mersey Novices' Hurdle Race (Aintree)...5th
Champion Standard Open National Hunt Flat Race (Aintree)...5th
Crabbie's Grand National Steeple Chase (Aintree)..5th
Aintree Handicap Steeple Chase (Aintree)...5th
International Trial Stakes (Class 1) (Lingfield Park) 5th
Cork Sprint (Cork)..6th
EBF Mares' Novices' Hurdle Final (Fairyhouse)...6th
Rathbarry & Glenview Studs Hardy Eustace Novices' Hurdle (Fairyhouse)..6th
Coolmore NH Sires Festival Novices' Hurdle (Fairyhouse)..6th
Normans Grove Steeple Chase (Fairyhouse)..6th
Arkle Bar Novices' Handicap Steeplechase (Fairyhouse)...6th
EBF Betfred Barry Hills 'Further Flight' Stakes (Nottingham)..9th
Arcadia Consulting William Dickie & Mary Robertson Future Champion Novices Steeple Chase (Ayr) 12th
QTS Scottish Champion Hurdle Race (A Limited Handicap) (Ayr)...12th
Coral Scottish Grand National Handicap Steeple Chase (Ayr)..12th
Scotty Brand Handicap Steeple Chase (Ayr)..12th
Aon Greenham Stakes (Newbury)..12th
Dubai Duty Free Stakes (Registered As Fred Darling Stakes) (Newbury) 12th
Dubai Duty Free Finest Surprise Stakes (Registered As John Porter Stakes) (Newbury) 12th
Salsabil Stakes (Navan)...12th
Gladness Stakes (Curragh)...13th
Alleged Stakes (Curragh)...13th
Ceres Estates Silver Trophy Steeple Chase (A Handicap) (Cheltenham) 16th
Lanwades Stud Nell Gwyn Stakes (Newmarket)..16th
CSP European Free Handicap (Newmarket)..16th
ebm-papst Feilden Stakes (Newmarket)...16th
Patton Stakes (Dundalk) 16th
Abernant Stakes (Newmarket)..17th
Novae Bloodstock Insurance Craven Stakes (Newmarket)...17th
Weatherbys Earl Of Sefton Stakes (Newmarket)...17th
EBF/TBA Mares' Novices' Steeple Chase Finale (A Handicap) (Cheltenham) 17th
OLBG.com Mares' Handicap Hurdle (Cheltenham)...17th
Thoroughbred Breeders' Association Mares' Novices' Hurdle (Cheltenham)...17th
All-Weather Championships (Finals) (Lingfield Park) 18th
EBF and Whitsbury Manor Stud Lansdown Fillies' Stakes (Bath) 19th
Betfred Snowdrop Fillies' Stakes (Kempton Park)..19th
Easter Handicap Hurdle (Cork)..20th
John Fowler Memorial Mares' Steeple Chase (Cork)...20th
thetote.ie Handicap Hurdle (Fairyhouse)...20th
INHSO Series Final Novices' Handicap Hurdle (Fairyhouse)..20th
Power Gold Cup Novices' Steeple Chase (Fairyhouse)..20th
Weatherbys 4yo Hurdle (Fairyhouse)..21st
Keelings Hurdle (Fairyhouse)...21st
Irish Grand National Limited Handicap Steeple Chase (Fairyhouse) 21st
Bet365 Mile (Sandown Park) 25th
Bet365 Classic Trial (Sandown Park) 25th

Bet365 Gordon Richards Stakes (Sandown Park) 25th
Bet365.com Celebration Steeple Chase (Sandown Park) 26th
Bet365 Gold Cup Steeple Chase (Handicap) (Sandown Park) 26th
EBF totepool.com King Richard III Stakes (Leicester) 26th
Martin Molony Stakes (Limerick) 26th
Prix Ganay (Longchamp) 27th
Victor McCalmont Stakes (Gowran Park) 27th
Woodlands Sprint Stakes (Naas) 28th
Evening Herald Champion Novice Hurdle (Punchestown) 29th
www.thetote.com Handicap Hurdle (Punchestown) 29th
Growise Novices' Steeple Chase (Punchestown) 29th
Boylesports Champion Chase (Punchestown) 29th
Longines Sagaro Stakes (Ascot) 30th
Battersea Dogs & Cats Home Paradise Stakes (Ascot) 30th
Battersea Dogs & Cats Home Pavilion Stakes (Ascot) 30th
Irish Daily Mirror War Of Attrition Novices' Hurdle (Punchestown) 30th
thetote.com Punchestown Gold Cup Steeple Chase (Punchestown) 30th
Guinness Handicap Steeple Chase (Punchestown) 30th
betchronicle Champion Bumper (Punchestown) 30th

MAY

Ladbrokes World Series Hurdle (Punchestown) 1st
Ryanair Novices' Steeple Chase (Punchestown) 1st
Bibby Financial Handicap Steeple Chase (Punchestown) 1st
Tattersalls Ireland Tickell Champion Novices' Hurdle (Punchestown) 2nd
Radobank Punchestown Champion Hurdle (Punchestown) 2nd
Glencaraig Lady Mares' Handicap Steeple Chase (Punchestown) 2nd
Aon Novices' Handicap Steeple Chase (Punchestown) 2nd
Qipco 2000 Guineas Stakes (British Champions Series) (Newmarket) 3rd
Qipco Jockey Club Stakes (Newmarket) 3rd
Pearl Bloodstock Palace House Stakes (Newmarket) 3rd
Qatar Racing Newmarket Stakes (Newmarket) 3rd
Betfred Mobile Casino British Stallion Studs EBF Conqueror Stakes (Goodwood) 3rd
Betfred The Bonus King EBF Daisy Warwick Stakes (Goodwood) 3rd
Aes Champion 4yo Only Hurdle (Punchestown) 3rd
ITBA Mares' Champion Hurdle (Punchestown) 3rd
Bragbet Handicap Hurdle (Punchestown) 3rd
3' Pat Taaffe Limited Handicap Steeple Chase (Punchestown) 3rd
Qipco 1000 Guineas Stakes (British Champions Series) (Newmarket) 4th
Qatar Bloodstock Dahlia Stakes (Newmarket) 4th
Tweenhills Pretty Polly Stakes (Newmarket) 4th
Mooresbridge Stakes (Curragh) 5th
Athasi Stakes (Curragh) 5th
Tetrarch Stakes (Curragh) 5th
Weatherbys Bank Cheshire Oaks (Chester) 7th
MBNA Chester Vase (Chester) 8th
Betfair Huxley Stakes (For Tradesman's Cup) (Chester) 8th
Stanjames.com Chester Cup (Heritage Handicap) (Chester) 8th
Stobart Barristers Dee Stakes (Chester) 9th
Boodles Diamond Ormonde Stakes (Chester) 9th
Betfred Victoria Cup (Heritage Handicap) (Ascot) 10th
Buckhounds Stakes (Ascot) 10th
Swinton Handicap Hurdle (Haydock Park) 10th
Pertemps Network Spring Trophy Stakes (Haydock Park) 10th
Betfred Chartwell Fillies' Stakes (Lingfield Park) 10th
Betfred Derby Trial Stakes (Lingfield Park) 10th
Betfred 'The Bonus King' Oaks Trial Stakes (Lingfield Park) 10th
EBF Weatherbys Hamilton Insurance Kilvington Fillies' Stakes (Nottingham) 10th
Poule d'Essai des Pouliches (Longchamp) 11th
Poule d'Essai des Poulains (Longchamp) 11th
Amethyst Stakes (Leopardstown) 11th
Derrinstown Derby Trial Stakes (Leopardstown) 11th
Derrinstown 1000 Guineas Trial Stakes (Leopardstown) 11th
Ladbrokes Handicap Hurdle (Killarney) 11th
British Stallion Studs Supporting British Racing EBF Stakes (Windsor) 12th
Duke Of York Clipper Logistics Stakes (York) 14th
Tattersalls Musidora Stakes (York) 14th
Blue Wind Stakes (Naas) 14th
Betfred Dante Stakes (York) 15th
Betfred Middleton Stakes (York) 15th
Betfred Hambleton Stakes (Class 1 Handicap) (York) 15th
Yorkshire Cup (British Champions Series) (York) 16th
Blade Amenity Fillies' Stakes (York) 16th
Langley Solicitors LLP EBF Marygate Stakes (York) 16th
Ginger Grouse Braveheart Stakes (Handicap) (Hamilton Park) 16th

Swettenham Stud Fillies' Trial Stakes (Newbury) 16th
Bathwick Tyres Carnarvon Stakes (Newbury) 16th
JLT Lockinge Stakes (British Champions Series) (Newbury) 17th
JLT Aston Park Stakes (Newbury) 17th
Coral King Charles II Stakes (Newmarket) 17th
Best Odds Guaranteed On Racing At coral.co.uk Fairway Stakes (Newmarket) 17th
Vintage Crop Stakes (Navan) 18th
Height Of Fashion Stakes (Goodwood) 22nd
Casco EBF Cocked Hat Stakes (Goodwood) 23rd
Timeform Jury Stakes (Registered As John Of Gaunt Stakes) (Haydock Park) 24th
Pinnacle Stakes (Haydock Park) 24th
BetVictor.com EBF Cecil Frail Stakes (Haydock Park) 24th
BetVictor No Lose Hughes Money Back Sandy Lane Stakes (Haydock Park) 24th
32Red Festival Stakes (Goodwood) 24th
Tapster Stakes (Goodwood) 24th
Weatherbys Ireland Greenlands Stakes (Curragh) 24th
TRI Equestrian Ridgewood Pearl Stakes (Curragh) 24th
Marble Hill Stakes (Curragh) 24th
Irish 2000 Guineas (Curragh) 24th
Airlie Gallinule Stakes (Curragh) 25th
Tattersalls Gold Cup (Curragh) 25th
Irish 1000 Guineas Stakes (Curragh) 25th
Prix Saint-Alary (Longchamp) 25th
Prix d'Ispahan (Longchamp) 25th
Betfair Henry II Stakes (Sandown Park) 29th
Betfair Brigadier Gerard Stakes (Sandown Park) 29th
Cantor Fitzgerald Corporate Finance Heron Stakes (Sandown Park) 29th
Cantor Fitzgerald Equities National Stakes (Sandown Park) 29th
Mere Golf Resort & Spa Achilles Stakes (Haydock Park) 30th
Betfred.com Temple Stakes (British Champions Series) (Haydock Park) 31st
Betfred Silver Bowl (Heritage Handicap) (Haydock Park) 31st
Stowe Family Law LLP Grand Cup (Class 1) (York) 31st

JUNE

Prix du Jockey Club (Chantilly) 1st
coral.co.uk Leisure Stakes (Windsor) 2nd
Whitehead Memorial Stakes (Naas) 2nd
Rochestown Stakes (Naas) 2nd
Coolmore Stud Juvenile Fillies' Stakes (Naas) 2nd
Investec Oaks (British Champions Series) (Epsom Downs) 6th
Investec Diomed Stakes (Epsom Downs) 6th
Princess Elizabeth Stakes (Sponsored By Investec) (Epsom Downs) 6th
Investec Surrey Stakes (Epsom Downs) 6th
Nijinsky (For King George V Cup) Stakes (Leopardstown) 6th
Seamus & Rosemary McGrath Memorial Savel Beg Stakes (Leopardstown) 6th
Investec Coronation Cup (British Champions Series) (Epsom Downs) 7th
Investec Derby (British Champions Series) (Epsom Downs) 7th
Investec Woodcote Stakes (Epsom Downs) 7th
Investec Entrepreneurial Class 'Dash' (Heritage Handicap) (Epsom Downs) 7th
Edinburgh Cup (Heritage Handicap) (Musselburgh) 7th
Silver Stakes (Curragh) 8th
Lord Weinstock Memorial Stakes (Newbury) 12th
Ballyogan Stakes (Leopardstown) 12th
Ballycorus Stakes (Leopardstown) 12th
Macmillan Charity Sprint Trophy (Heritage Handicap) (York) 14th
Novae Bloodstock Insurance Scurry Stakes (Sandown Park) 14th
Ian and Kate Hall Macmillan Ganton Stakes (York) 14th
Prix de Diane (Chantilly) 15th
European Breeders' Fund Cathedral Stakes (Salisbury) 15th
Midsummer Sprint (Cork) 15th
Kerry Group Noblesse Stakes (Cork) 15th
Voute Sales Warwickshire Oaks Stakes (Warwick) 16th
King's Stand Stakes (British Champions Series & Global Sprint Challenge) (Royal Ascot) 17th
Queen Anne Stakes (British Champions Series) (Royal Ascot) 17th
St James's Palace Stakes (British Champions Series) (Royal Ascot) 17th
Coventry Stakes (Royal Ascot) 17th
Windsor Castle Stakes (Royal Ascot) 17th
Prince Of Wales's Stakes (British Champions Series) (Royal Ascot) 18th
Queen Mary Stakes (Royal Ascot) 18th
Duke Of Cambridge Stakes (Previously Windsor Forest) (Royal Ascot) 18th
Jersey Stakes (Royal Ascot) 18th
Royal Hunt Cup (Heritage Handicap) (Royal Ascot) 18th
Sandringham Handicap Stakes (Royal Ascot) 18th
Gold Cup (British Champions Series) (Royal Ascot) 19th
Norfolk Stakes (Royal Ascot) 19th

Ribblesdale Stakes (Royal Ascot) 19th
Tercentenary Stakes (Royal Ascot) 19th
Britannia Stakes (Heritage Handicap) (Royal Ascot) 19th
Glencairn Stakes (Leopardstown) 19th
Coronation Stakes (British Champions Series) (Royal Ascot) 20th
King Edward VII Stakes (Royal Ascot) 20th
Albany Stakes (Royal Ascot) 20th
Queen's Vase (Royal Ascot) 20th
Wolferton Handicap Stakes (Royal Ascot) 20th
Diamond Jubilee Stakes (British Champions Series & Global Sprint Challenge) (Royal Ascot) 21st
Hardwicke Stakes (Royal Ascot) 21st
Wokingham Stakes (Heritage Handicap) (Royal Ascot) 21st
Chesham Stakes (Royal Ascot) 21st
Scottish Sun/EBF Stallions Land O'Burns Fillies' Stakes (Ayr) 21st
totepool Pontefract Castle Stakes (Pontefract) 22nd
Naas Oaks Trial Stakes (Naas) 25th
EBF Stallions / Arkle Finance Eternal Stakes (Warwick) 26th
Betfred / British Stallions Studs EBF Hoppings Stakes (Newcastle) 27th
Betfred.com Chipchase Stakes (Newcastle) 28th
John Smith's Northumberland Plate (Heritage Handicap) (Newcastle) 28th
Bet365 Criterion Stakes (Newmarket) 28th
bet365.com Fred Archer Stakes (Newmarket) 28th
bet365 Empress Stakes (Newmarket) 28th
totepool King Size Pools Midsummer Stakes (Windsor) 28th
Dubai Duty Free Celebration Stakes (Curragh) 28th
Woodies DIY Sapphire Stakes (Curragh) 28th
Dubai Duty Free Railway Stakes (Curragh) 28th
Dubai Duty Free Irish Derby Stakes (Curragh) 28th
Grand Prix de Saint-Cloud (Saint-Cloud) 29th
Grangecon Stud Balanchine Stakes (Curragh) 29th
At The Races Curragh Cup (Curragh) 29th
Pretty Polly Stakes (Curragh) 29th
International Stakes (Curragh) 29th

JULY

Brownstown Stakes (Fairyhouse) 2nd
Ambant Gala Stakes (Sandown Park) 4th
Coral Dragon Stakes (Sandown Park) 4th
Bet365 Lancashire Oaks (Haydock Park) 5th
Bet365 Old Newton Cup (Heritage Handicap) (Haydock Park) 5th
Coral-Eclipse (British Champions Series) (Sandown Park) 5th
Coral Charge (Registered As Sprint Stakes) (Sandown Park) 5th
Coral Challenge (Heritage Handicap) (Sandown Park) 5th
Coral Distaff Stakes (Sandown Park) 5th
Coral Marathon Stakes (Sandown Park) 5th
Lenebane Stakes (Roscommon) 7th
Weatherbys VAT Services Pipalong Stakes (Pontefract) 8th
Princess of Wales' Goldsmith Stakes (Newmarket) 10th
TNT July Stakes (Newmarket) 10th
Bahrain Trophy (Newmarket) 10th
Insure Pink Stubbs Stakes (Newmarket) 10th
Etihad Airways Falmouth Stakes (British Champions Series) (Newmarket) 11th
Duchess Of Cambridge Stakes (Formerly Cherry Hinton Stakes) (Newmarket) 11th
Betfred 'Bonus King' Heritage Handicap (Newmarket) 11th
Summer Stakes (York) 11th
Transformers & Rectifiers Summer Mile Stakes (Ascot) 12th
Darley July Cup (British Champions Series & Global Sprint Challenge) (Newmarket) 12th
32Red.com Superlative Stakes (Newmarket) 12th
32Red Bunbury Cup Handicap (Heritage Handicap) (Newmarket) 12th
John Smith's Cup (Heritage Handicap) (York) 12th
John Smith's City Walls Stakes (York) 12th
John Smith's Silver Cup Stakes (Class 1 Handicap) (York) 12th
Raymond Corbett Memorial City Plate Stakes (Chester) 12th
Grimes Hurdle (Tipperary) 12th
Tipperary Stakes (Tipperary) 13th
Grand Prix de Paris (Longchamp) 13th
Belgrave Stakes (Fairyhouse) 14th
Prix Jean Prat (Chantilly) 14th
Bourn Vincent Memorial Handicap Steeple Chase (Killarney) 17th
Silver Flash Stakes (Leopardstown) 17th
Challenge Stakes (Leopardstown) 17th
EBF Stallions Glasgow Stakes (Hamilton Park) 18th
Rose Bowl Stakes - Sponsored by Compton Beauchamp Estates Ltd Stakes (Newbury) 18th
Al Basti Equi World Stakes (Registered As Hackwood Stakes) (Newbury) 19th
Sharps Brewery Steventon Stakes (Newbury) 19th

Newsells Park Stud Stakes (Newmarket) 19th
Darley Irish Oaks Stakes (Curragh) 19th
Jebel Ali Anglesey Stakes (Curragh) 19th
Kilboy Estate Stakes (Curragh) 20th
Minstrel Stakes (Curragh) 20th
Sweet Mimosa Stakes (Naas) 23rd
Meld Stakes (Leopardstown) 24th
Tyros Stakes (Leopardstown) 24th
Irish Stallion Farms EBF Star Stakes (Sandown Park) 24th
Woodcote Stud EBF Valiant Stakes (Ascot) 25th
British Stallion Studs Supporting British Racing EBF Stakes (York) 25th
King George VI And Queen Elizabeth Stakes (Sponsored By Betfair) (British Champions Series) (Ascot) 26th
Princess Margaret Juddmonte Stakes (Ascot) 26th
International Stakes (Heritage Handicap) (Ascot) 26th
Titanic Belfast Winkfield Stakes (Ascot) 26th
Sky Bet York Stakes (York) 26th
Skybet Supporting The Yorkshire Racing Summer Festival Stakes (Pontefract) 27th
Bet365 Lennox Stakes (Goodwood) 29th
Bet365 Molecomb Stakes (Goodwood) 29th
Qipco Sussex Stakes (British Champions Series) (Goodwood) 30th
Veuve Clicquot Vintage Stakes (Goodwood) 30th
Neptune Investment Management Gordon Stakes (Goodwood) 30th
thetote.com Galway Plate (Handicap Chase) (Galway) 30th
Artemis Goodwood Cup (British Champions' Series) (Goodwood) 31st
Audi Richmond Stakes (Goodwood) 31st
Blackrock Fillies' Stakes (Registered As Lillie Langtry Stakes) (Goodwood) 31st
Corrib EBF Fillies' Stakes (Galway) 31st
Guinness Galway Hurdle (Handicap) (Galway) 31st

AUGUST

Gordon's King George Stakes (Goodwood) 1st
Coutts Glorious Stakes (Goodwood) 1st
Oak Tree Stakes (Goodwood) 1st
Bonhams Thoroughbred Stakes (Goodwood) 1st
Betfred Mile (Heritage Handicap) (Formerly Known As Golden Mile) (Goodwood) 1st
Markel Insurance Nassau Stakes (British Champions Series) (Goodwood) 2nd
Stewards' Cup (Heritage Handicap) (Goodwood) 2nd
Mervue Handicap Hurdle (Galway) 2nd
Winter Wonderland Queensferry Stakes (Chester) 3rd
British Stallion Studs EBF Chalice Stakes (Newbury) 3rd
Prix Rothschild (Deauville) 3rd
Give Thanks Stakes (Cork) 5th
Platinum Stakes (Cork) 5th
Ballyroan Stakes (Leopardstown) 7th
Abergwaun Stakes (Tipperary) 8th
El Gran Senor Stakes (Tipperary) 8th
Rose Of Lancaster Stakes (Haydock Park) 9th
Earlestown Handicap Stakes (Heritage Handicap) (Haydock Park) 9th
Betfred EBF Stallions Dick Hern Fillies' Stakes (Haydock Park) 9th
German-Thoroughbred.com Sweet Solera Stakes (Newmarket) 9th
Prix Maurice de Gheest (Deauville) 10th
Phoenix Stakes (Curragh) 10th
Patrick O'Leary Memorial Phoenix Sprint Stakes (Curragh) 10th
European Breeders' Fund Upavon Fillies' Stakes (Salisbury) 13th
Hurry Harriet Stakes (Gowran Park) 13th
Totepool.com Sovereign Stakes (Salisbury) 14th
Desmond Stakes (Leopardstown) 14th
Bathwick Tyres St Hugh's Stakes (Newbury) 15th
Betfred Hungerford Stakes (Newbury) 16th
Betfred 'Bonus King' Geoffrey Freer Stakes (Newbury) 16th
Denford Stud Stakes (Newbury) 16th
William Hill Great St Wilfrid Stakes (Heritage Handicap) (Ripon) 16th
Prix Jacques Le Marois (Deauville) 17th
EBF Highfield Farm Flying Fillies' Stakes (Pontefract) 17th
Juddmonte International Stakes (British Champions Series) (York) 20th
Neptune Investment Management Great Voltigeur Stakes (York) 20th
Pinsent Masons LLP Acomb Stakes (York) 20th
Ruby Stakes (Killarney) 20th
Darley Yorkshire Oaks (British Champions Series) (York) 22nd
Connolly's Red Mills Lowther Stakes (York) 22nd
Breeders Backing Racing EBF Galtres Stakes (York) 22nd
Coolmore Nunthorpe Stakes (British Champions Series) (York) 22nd
Weatherbys Hamilton Insurance Lonsdale Cup (British Champions Series) (York) 22nd
Sky Bet Strensall Stakes (York) 22nd
Lough Leane Handicap Chase (Killarney) 22nd

Betfair Celebration Mile (Goodwood) 23rd
Prestige Stakes (Goodwood) 23rd
Betfair Cash Out Stakes (Heritage Handicap) (Goodwood) 23rd
March Stakes (Goodwood) 23rd
Betfred Winter Hill Stakes (Windsor) 23rd
EBF Stallions August Stakes (Windsor) 23rd
Irish Thoroughbred Marketing Gimcrack Stakes (York) 23rd
Betfred Ebor (Heritage Handicap) (York) 23rd
Julia Graves Roses Stakes (York) 23rd
Betfred City Of York Stakes (York) 23rd
Stobart Members Club Hopeful Stakes (Newmarket) 23rd
Dance Design Stakes (Curragh) 23rd
Ballycullen Stakes (Curragh) 23rd
Galileo EBF Futurity Stakes (Curragh) 23rd
Curragh Stakes (Curragh) 23rd
Brandon Handicap Hurdle (Killarney) 23rd
Prix Morny (Deauville) 24th
Prix Jean Romanet (Deauville) 24th
Supreme Stakes (Goodwood) 24th
Debutante Stakes (Curragh) 24th
Royal Whip Stakes (Curragh) 24th
Irish Stallion Farms EBF Ripon Champion Two Years Old Trophy (Ripon).. 25th
Fairy Bridge Stakes (Tipperary) 28th
Weatherbys Bank Stonehenge Stakes (Salisbury) 29th
Solario Stakes (Sandown Park) 30th
Atalanta Stakes (Sandown Park) 30th
Betfred Beverley Bullet Sprint Stakes (Beverley) 30th
Golden Square Shopping Centre Chester Stakes (Chester).. 30th
Flame Of Tara Stakes (Curragh) 31st
Round Tower Stakes (Curragh) 31st
Flying Five Stakes (Curragh)... 31st

SEPTEMBER

EBF Stallions & Country Gentlemen's Association Dick Poole Fillies' Stakes (Salisbury).................. 4th
Betfred Sprint Cup (British Champions Series) (Haydock Park) 6th
Superior Mile Stakes (Haydock Park)... 6th
Betfred Bundles Old Borough Cup (Heritage Handicap) (Haydock Park).. 6th
Betfred TV Stakes (Haydock Park) 6th
Totepool September Stakes (Kempton Park) 6th
Totepool.com Sirenia Stakes (Kempton Park).. 6th
Betfred Garrowby Stakes (York) 7th
Oyster Stakes (Galway) 8th
Crown Hotel Bawtry Scarbrough Stakes (Doncaster).. 10th
Park Hill Stakes (Doncaster) 11th
Sceptre Stakes (Doncaster) 11th
May Hill Stakes (Doncaster) 12th
Doncaster Cup (British Champions Series) (Doncaster) 12th
Flying Childers Stakes (Doncaster) 12th
One Call Insurance Flying Scotsman Stakes (Doncaster) 12th
Ladbrokes St Leger Stakes (British Champions Series) (Doncaster) 13th
OLBG Park Stakes (Doncaster) 13th
Champagne Stakes (Doncaster) 13th
Ladbrokes Portland (Heritage Handicap) (Doncaster) 13th
Stella Artois Stand Cup (Chester) 13th
Coolmore Matron Stakes (Leopardstown) 13th
ICON Breeders' Cup Trial Golden Fleece Stakes (Leopardstown) 13th
Red Mills Irish Champion Stakes (Leopardstown) 13th
KPMG Kilternan Stakes (Leopardstown) 13th
Prix du Moulin de Longchamp (Longchamp) 14th
Prix Vermeille (Longchamp) 14th
Goffs Vincent O'Brien National Stakes (Curragh).. 14th
Gain Horse Feeds St Leger Stakes (Curragh) 14th
Renaissance Stakes (Curragh) 14th
Solonoway Stakes (Curragh) 14th
Blandford Stakes (Curragh) 14th
Moyglare Stud Stakes (Curragh) 14th
Listowel 4yo Handicap Hurdle (Listowel) 16th
Fortune Stakes (Sandown Park) 17th
EBF At The Races John Musker Fillies' Stakes (Yarmouth) 17th
Listowel Stakes (Listowel) 17th
Guinness Kerry National Handicap Chase (Listowel) 17th
Guinness Handicap Hurdle (Listowel) 18th
Shadwell Stud / EBF Stallions Harry Rosebery Stakes (Ayr) 19th
Dubai Duty Free Cup (Newbury)... 19th
William Hill Firth Of Clyde Stakes (Ayr) 20th

William Hill (Ayr) Gold Cup (Heritage Handicap) (Ayr) 20th
William Hill - Bet On The Move Doonside Cup Stakes (Ayr) 20th
Dubai Duty Free Mill Reef Stakes (Newbury) 20th
Dubai Duty Free Arc Trial (Newbury) 20th
Dubai International Airport World Trophy (Newbury) 20th
Dubai Duty Free Handicap Stakes (Heritage Handicap) (Newbury) 20th
DC Cordell Lavarack Stakes (Gowran Park) 21st
Greene King Foundation Stakes (Goodwood) 24th
Somerville Tattersall Stakes (Newmarket) 25th
Jockey Club Rose Bowl Stakes (Newmarket) 25th
Vision.ae Rockfel Stakes (Newmarket) 26th
Sakhee Oh So Sharp Stakes (Newmarket) 26th
Nayef Joel Stakes (British Champions Series) (Newmarket) 26th
Shadwell International Stallions Rosemary Stakes (Newmarket) 26th
Mawatheeq Godolphin Stakes (Newmarket) 26th
Jaguar Cars Cheveley Park Stakes (Newmarket) 27th
Kingdom Of Bahrain Sun Chariot Stakes (Newmarket) 27th
Juddmonte Royal Lodge Stakes (Newmarket) 27th
Princess Royal Richard Hambro EBF Stakes (Newmarket) 27th
Betfred Cambridgeshire (Heritage Handicap) (Newmarket) 27th
Loughbrown Stakes (Curragh) 28th
Blenheim Stakes (Curragh) 28th
CL Weld Park Stakes (Curragh) 28th
Juddmonte Beresford Stakes (Curragh) 28th
Kilbegnet Novices' Chase (Roscommon) 29th

OCTOBER

Ascot Underwriting Noel Murless Stakes (Ascot) 3rd
Diamond Stakes (Dundalk) 3rd
Grosvenor Casinos Cumberland Lodge Stakes (Ascot) 4th
John Guest Bengough Stakes (Ascot) 4th
EBF Stallions October Stakes (Ascot) 4th
Macquarie Group Rous Stakes (Ascot) 4th
EBF National Stud Boadicea Fillies' Stakes (Newmarket) 4th
totescoop6 EBF Guisborough Stakes (Redcar) 4th
totepool Two-Year-Old Trophy (Redcar) 4th
Gowran Champion Chase (Gowran Park) 4th
Kilkenny Racing Festival Handicap Hurdle (Gowran Park) 4th
Prix du Cadran (Longchamp) 5th
Prix de l'Abbaye de Longchamp (Longchamp) 5th
Prix Marcel Boussac (Longchamp) 5th
Prix Jean-Luc Lagardere (Longchamp) 5th
Prix de la Foret (Longchamp) 5th
Prix de l'Arc de Triomphe (Longchamp) 5th
Prix de l'Opera (Longchamp) 5th
Like A Butterfly Novices' Chase (Tipperary) 5th
Joe Mac Novices' Hurdle (Tipperary) 5th
Concorde Stakes (Tipperary) 5th
Tipperary Hurdle (Tipperary) 5th
Star Appeal Stakes (Dundalk) 10th
Autumn Stakes (Newmarket) 11th
Betfred Cesarewitch (Heritage Handicap) (Newmarket) 11th
TRM Pride Stakes (Newmarket) 11th
Coral Sprint Trophy (Heritage Handicap) (York) 11th
coral.co.uk Rockingham Stakes (York) 11th
Lanwades & Staffordstown Studs Silken Glider Stakes (Curragh) 12th
Finale Stakes (Curragh) 12th
Waterford Testimonial Stakes (Curragh) 12th
Greenmount Park Novices' Hurdle (Limerick) 12th
PricewaterhouseCooper Chase (Limerick) 12th
Ladbrokes Munster National Handicap Chase (Limerick) 12th
Grabel Mares Hurdle (Punchestown) 15th
Buck House Novices' Chase (Punchestown) 16th
Carvills Hill Chase (Punchestown) 16th
Shadwell Fillies' Mile (Newmarket) 17th
Vision.ae Middle Park Stakes (Newmarket) 17th
Dubai Dewhurst Stakes (Newmarket) 17th
Dubai Challenge Stakes (Newmarket) 17th
Jaguar XJ Cornwallis Stakes (Newmarket) 17th
Darley Stakes (Newmarket) 17th
Carlingford Stakes (Dundalk) 17th
Queen Elizabeth II Stakes Sponsored By Qipco (British Champions Mile) (Ascot) 18th
Qipco Champion Stakes (British Champions Middle Distance) (Ascot) 18th
Qipco British Champions Fillies' And Mares' Stakes (Ascot) 18th
Qipco British Champions Sprint Stakes (Ascot) 18th

Qipco British Champions Long Distance Cup (Ascot)..18th
Navigation Stakes (Cork)..18th
Kinsale Handicap Chase (Cork)..19th
Garnet Stakes (Naas)..19th
EBF Stallions / totepool Mobile Silver Tankard Stakes (Pontefract)..20th
Mercury Stakes (Dundalk)..24th
Betfred Monet's Garden Old Roan Steeple Chase (A Limited Handicap) (Aintree)................................25th
Totetentofollow Persian War Novices' Hurdle Race (Chepstow)..25th
Totepool Silver Trophy Handicap Hurdle Race (Chepstow)..25th
Racing Post Trophy (Doncaster)..25th
Scott Dobson Memorial Doncaster Stakes (Doncaster)..25th
Worthington's Whizz Kids Stakes (Registered As Horris Hill Stakes) (Newbury)....................................25th
Worthington's Champion Shield Stakes (Registered As St Simon Stakes) (Newbury)..............................25th
Free Bets freebets.co.uk Stakes (Newbury)..25th
Trigo Stakes (Leopardstown)..25th
Killavullan Stakes (Leopardstown)..25th
Bettyville Steeple Chase (Wexford)..25th
Prix Royal-Oak (Saint-Cloud)..26th
Criterium International (Saint-Cloud)..26th
Knockaire Stakes (Leopardstown)..26th
Eyrefield Stakes (Leopardstown)..26th
Ballybrit Novices' Chase (Galway)..27th
32Red / EBFstallions.com Fleur De Lys Fillies' Stakes (Lingfield Park)..30th
32Red.com / Choose EBF Nominated River Eden Fillies' Stakes (Lingfield Park)..................................30th
Irish Stallion Farms EBF Bosra Sham Fillies' Stakes (Newmarket)..31st
Hamptons EBF Mares' Novices' Hurdle (Down Royal)..31st
WKD Hurdle (Down Royal)..31st
Cooley Stakes (Dundalk)..31st

NOVEMBER

United House Gold Cup Handicap Steeple Chase (Ascot)..1st
Bet365 Charlie Hall Steeple Chase (Wetherby)..1st
Bet365 Hurdle Race (Registered As West Yorkshire Hurdle Race) (Wetherby)....................................1st
fasttracktosuccess Finjan James Seymour Stakes (Newmarket)..1st
fasttracktosuccess Finjan At Gazeley Stud Ben Marshall Stakes (Newmarket)....................................1st
EBF Stallions / Lanwades Montrose Fillies' Stakes (Newmarket)..1st
Mac's Joy Handicap Hurdle (Down Royal)..1st
Jnwine Champion Chase (Down Royal)..1st
Ladbrokes Skymas Chase (Down Royal)..1st
Paddy Power EBF Novices' Chase (Cork)..2nd
Paddy Power EBF Novices' Hurdle (Cork)..2nd
Paddy Power Cork Grand National Handicap Steeple Chase (Cork)..2nd
Brown Lad Handicap Hurdle (Naas)..2nd
Poplar Square Chase (Naas)..2nd
Haldon Gold Cup Steeple Chase (A Limited Handicap) (Exeter)..4th
Winners Are Welcome At Betdaq Floodlit Stakes (Kempton Park)..5th
Thurles Chase (Thurles)..6th
Criterium de Saint-Cloud (Saint-Cloud)..8th
Betfred November Handicap Stakes (Heritage Handicap) (Doncaster)..8th
Betfred Mobile / EBF Stallions Gillies Fillies' Stakes (Doncaster)..8th
Betfred Goals Galore Wentworth Stakes (Doncaster)..8th
Rising Stars Novices' Steeple Chase (Wincanton)..8th
Elite Hurdle Race (Wincanton)..8th
Fishery Lane Stakes (Naas)..8th
For Auction Novices' Hurdle (Navan)..9th
Lismullen Hurdle (Navan)..9th
Fortria Chase (Navan)..9th
Clonmel Oil Chase (Clonmel)..13th
EBF TA Morris Memorial Mares' Steeple Chase (Clonmel)..13th
JCB Triumph Hurdle Trial (Registered As Prestbury Juvenile Hurdle Race) (Cheltenham)....................15th
Neptune Investment Management Novices' Hurdle Race (Registered As Hyde Novices' Hurdle Race) (Cheltenham)....15th
Paddy Power Gold Cup Steeple Chase (A Handicap) (Cheltenham)..15th
Rewards4Racing Handicap Steeple Chase (Cheltenham)..15th
coral.co.uk Churchill Stakes (Lingfield Park)..15th
Best Odds At bookmakers.co.uk Golden Rose Stakes (Lingfield Park)..15th
Opus Energy Novices' Hurdle Race (Registered As Sharp Novices' Hurdle) (Cheltenham)....................16th
Racing Post Arkle Trial Novices' Steeple Chase (Registered As November Novices' Steeple Chase) (Cheltenham)....16th
Greatwood Handicap Hurdle Race (Cheltenham)..16th
Blackwater Handicap Hurdle (Cork)..16th
Ladbrokes Craddockstown Novices' Steeple Chase (Punchestown)..16th
Ladbrokes Morgiana Hurdle (Punchestown)..16th
Ladbrokes Florida Pearl Novices' Steeple Chase (Punchestown)..16th
Winners Are Welcome At Betdaq EBF Stallions Hyde Stakes (Kempton Park)....................................19th
Amlin 1965 Steeple Chase (Ascot)..22nd
Coral Hurdle Race (Registered As Ascot Hurdle Race) (Ascot)..22nd

Betfair Steeple Chase (Registered As Lancashire Chase) (Haydock Park) 22nd
Betfair.com "Fixed Brush" Handicap Hurdle Race (Haydock Park) 22nd
Proudstown Handicap Hurdle (Navan) 23rd
Mares' Bumper (Navan) 23rd
Ladbrokes Troytown Handicap Steeple Chase (Navan) 23rd
Monksfield Novices' Hurdle (Navan) 23rd
£500 Free Bets At Betdaq Wild Flower Stakes (Kempton Park) 26th
RSA Novices' Steeple Chase (Registered As Worcester Novices' Steeple Chase) (Newbury) 27th
Fuller's London Pride Novices' Steeple Chase (Registered As Berkshire Novices' Steeple Chase) (Newbury) 28th
Bet365 Long Distance Hurdle Race (Newbury) 29th
Hennessy Gold Cup Steeple Chase (Handicap) (Newbury) 29th
Stanjames.com Fighting Fifth Hurdle Race (Newcastle) 29th
New Stand Handicap Hurdle (Fairyhouse) 29th
Ballyhack Handicap Steeple Chase (Fairyhouse) 29th
Winter Festival Juvenile Hurdle (Fairyhouse) 30th
Bar One Drinmore Novices' Steeple Chase (Fairyhouse) 30th
Porterstown Handicap Steeple Chase (Fairyhouse) 30th
Bar One Hatton's Grace Hurdle (Fairyhouse) 30th
Bar One Royal Bond Novices' Hurdle (Fairyhouse) 30th

DECEMBER

Neptune Investment Management Novices' Hurdle Race (Registered As Winter Novices' Hurdle Race) (Sandown Park) 5th
Betfred Becher Handicap Chase (Aintree) 6th
Sportingbet Tingle Creek Steeple Chase (Sandown Park) 6th
Henry VIII Novices' Steeple Chase (Sandown Park) 6th
Betfred Peterborough Steeple Chase (Huntingdon) 7th
Cork Stayers' Novices' Hurdle (Cork) 7th
Hilly Way Steeple Chase (Cork) 7th
Lombardstown Mares' Novices' Steeple Chase (Cork) 7th
John Durkan Memorial Steeple Chase (Punchestown) 7th
Majordomo Hospitality Handicap Steeple Chase (Cheltenham) 12th
Albert Bartlett Novices' Hurdle Race (Registered As Bristol Novices' Hurdle Race) (Cheltenham) 13th
Stanjames.com International Hurdle Race (Cheltenham) 13th
Unicoin Homes Relkeel Hurdle Race (Cheltenham) 13th
December Gold Cup (A Handicap Steeple Chase) (Cheltenham) 13th
Summit Juvenile Hurdle Race (Doncaster) 13th
December Novices' Steeple Chase (Lingfield Park) 13th
Tara Handicap Hurdle (Navan) 14th
Navan Novices' Hurdle (Navan) 14th
Future Champions Bumper (Navan) 14th
Betfred Novices' Steeple Chase (Registered As Noel Novices' Steeple Chase) (Ascot) 19th
Mitie Kennel Gate Novices' Hurdle Race (Ascot) 19th
Coral App Download From The App Store Quebec Stakes (Lingfield Park) 20th
Long Walk Hurdle Race (Ascot) 20th
Ladbroke Handicap Hurdle (Ascot) 20th
Kauto Star Novices' Steeple Chase (Formerly Feltham, In Memory Of Nigel Clark) (Kempton Park) 26th
Williamhill.com Christmas Hurdle Race (Kempton Park) 26th
William Hill King George VI Steeple Chase (Kempton Park) 26th
Rowland Meyrick Handicap Steeple Chase (Wetherby) 26th
UAE Juvenile Hurdle (Leopardstown) 26th
Racing Post Novices' Steeple Chase (Leopardstown) 26th
Greenmount Park Novices' Steeple Chase (Limerick) 26th
Coral Future Champions Finale Juvenile Hurdle Race (Chepstow) 27th
Coral Welsh Grand National (A Handicap Steeple Chase) (Chepstow) 27th
Williamhill.com Desert Orchid Steeple Chase (Kempton Park) 27th
Williamhill.com Novices' Steeple Chase (Registered As Wayward Lad Novices' Steeple Chase) (Kempton Park) 27th
Paddy Power Dial-A-Bet Chase (Leopardstown) 27th
Paddy Power Future Champions Novices' Hurdle (Leopardstown) 27th
Paddy Power Handicap Steeple Chase (Leopardstown) 27th
Tim Duggan Memorial Handicap Steeple Chase (Limerick) 27th
Woodies DIY Christmas Hurdle (Leopardstown) 28th
Lexus Chase (Leopardstown) 28th
Dorans Pride Novices' Hurdle (Limerick) 28th
Betfred Challow Novices' Hurdle Race (Newbury) 29th
EBF Mares' Hurdle (Leopardstown) 29th
Istabraq December Hurdle (Leopardstown) 29th
Topaz Fort Leney Novices' Steeple Chase (Leopardstown) 29th

The list of Principal Races has been supplied by the BHA and Horse Racing Ireland and is provisional. In all cases, the dates, venues and names of sponsors are correct at the time of going to press, but also subject to possible alteration.

INDEX TO TRAINERS
†denotes Permit to train under N.H. Rules only

Name	Team No.	Name	Team No.
BRENNAN, MR BARRY	063	CARTER, MR LEE	102
BREWER, MISS ALI	064	CASE, MR BEN	103
BRIDGER, MR JOHN	065	CECIL, LADY JANE	104
BRIDGWATER, MR DAVID	066	CHAMINGS, MR PATRICK	105
BRISBOURNE, MR MARK	067	CHANNON, MR MICK	106
BRITTAIN, MR CLIVE	068	CHAPMAN, MR MICHAEL	107
BRITTAIN, MR MEL	069	CHAPPLE-HYAM, MS JANE	108
†BROOKE, LADY	070	CHAPPLE-HYAM, MR PETER	109
BROOKS, MR CHARLIE	071	CHARALAMBOUS, MR PETER	110
BROTHERTON, MR ROY	072	CHARLTON, MR GEORGE	111
BROWN, MR ALAN	073	CHARLTON, MR ROGER	112
BROWN, MR ANDI	074	CHISMAN, MR HARRY	113
BROWN, MR DAVID	075	†CLARK, MRS JANE	114
BROWN, MR GARY	076	†CLARKE, MRS ANGELA	115
†BROWN, MR REGINALD	077	CLINTON, MR PATRICK	116
†BRYANT, MISS MICHELLE	078	CLUTTERBUCK, MR K. F.	117
†BUCKETT, MRS KATE	079	COAKLEY, MR DENIS J.	118
BUCKLER, MR BOB	080	†COBB, MRS HEATHER	119
BUCKLEY, MR MARK	081	COLE, MR PAUL	120
BURCHELL, MR DAI	082	COLES, MR TOBIAS B. P.	121
BURGOYNE, MR PAUL	083	COLTHERD, MR STUART	122
BURKE, MR K. R.	084	COOGAN, MR ALAN	123
BURKE, MR KEIRAN	085	COOMBE, MR JOHN	124
†BURNS, MR HUGH	086	CORBETT, MRS SUSAN	125
BUTLER, MR JOHN	087	CORCORAN, MR LIAM	126
BUTLER, MR PADDY	088	†CORNWALL, MR JOHN	127
†BUTTERWORTH, MRS BARBARA	089	COWELL, MR ROBERT	128
BYCROFT, MR NEVILLE	090	COWLEY, MR PAUL	129
		COX, MR CLIVE	130
		COYLE, MR TONY	131

C

Name	Team No.	Name	Team No.
CAMACHO, MISS JULIE	091	CRAGGS, MR RAY	132
CAMPION, MR MARK	092	CRATE, MR PETER	133
CANDLISH, MS JENNIE	093	CREIGHTON, MR EDWARD	134
CANDY, MR HENRY	094	CROOK, MR ANDREW	135
CANN, MR GRANT	095	CROWLEY, MISS JO	136
CANTILLON, MR DON	096	CUMANI, MR LUCA	137
CAROE, MISS CLARISSA	097	CURRAN, MR SEAN	138
CARR, MRS RUTH	098	CURTIS, MISS REBECCA	139
CARROLL, MR DECLAN	099	CURTIS, MR ROGER	140
CARROLL, MR TONY	100	CUTHBERT, MR THOMAS	141
CARSON, MR TONY	101		

Name	Team No.
D	
D'ARCY, MR PAUL	142
DACE, MR LUKE	143
DALGLEISH, MR KEITH	144
DALY, MR HENRY	145
DANDO, MR PHILIP	146
DARTNALL, MR VICTOR	147
DASCOMBE, MR TOM	148
†DAVIDSON, MR TRISTAN	149
DAVIES, MR JOHN	150
†DAVIES, MR PAUL	151
DAVIES, MISS SARAH-JAYNE	152
†DAVIES, MR WILLIAM	153
DAVIS, MISS JOANNA	154
DAVISON, MISS ZOE	155
†DAY, MR ANTHONY	156
†DAY, MISS LISA	157
DE BEST-TURNER, MR WILLIAM	158
DE GILES, MR ED	159
DE HAAN, MR BEN	160
DEACON, MR GEOFFREY	161
DENNIS, MR DAVID	162
†DENNIS, MR TIM	163
DICKIN, MR ROBIN	164
†DIXON, MR JOHN	165
DIXON, MR SCOTT	166
DOBBIN, MRS ROSE	167
†DODGSON, MR ASHLEY	168
DODS, MR MICHAEL	169
DONOVAN, MR DESMOND	170
DORE, MR CONOR	171
DOUMEN, MR FRANCOIS	172
DOW, MR SIMON	172a
DOWN, MR CHRIS	173
†DRAKE, MR RICHARD	174
DREW, MR CLIVE	175
DU PLESSIS, MISS JACKIE	176
DUFFIELD, MRS ANN	177
DUKE, MR BRENDAN W.	178
DUNCAN, MR IAN	179
DUNLOP, MR ED	180

Name	Team No.
DUNLOP, MR HARRY	181
DUNN, MRS ALEXANDRA	182
DUNNETT, MRS CHRISTINE	183
DURACK, MR SEAMUS	184
DUTFIELD, MRS NERYS	185
DWYER, MR CHRIS	186
DYSON, MISS CLAIRE	187
E	
EARLE, MR SIMON	188
EASTERBY, MR MICHAEL	189
EASTERBY, MR TIM	190
†ECKLEY, MR BRIAN	191
EDDERY, MR PAT	192
EDDERY, MR ROBERT	193
†EDWARDS, MR GORDON	194
EGERTON, MR CHARLES	195
ELLISON, MR BRIAN	196
ELSWORTH, MR DAVID	197
ENRIGHT, MR GERRY	198
ETHERINGTON, MR TIM	199
EUSTACE, MR JAMES	200
EVANS, MR DAVID	201
†EVANS, MR HYWEL	202
EVANS, MR JAMES	203
†EVANS, MRS MARY	204
EVANS, MRS NIKKI	205
EWART, MR JAMES	206
F	
FAHEY, MR RICHARD	207
FAIRHURST, MR CHRIS	208
FANSHAWE, MR JAMES	209
FARRELLY, MR JOHNNY	210
FEILDEN, MISS JULIA	211
FELLOWES, MR CHARLIE	212
FENTON, MR PHILIP	213
FERGUSON, MR JOHN	214
FFRENCH DAVIS, MR DOMINIC	215
FIERRO, MR GIUSEPPE	216

Name	Team No.
FIFE, MRS MARJORIE	217
FITZGERALD, MR TIM	218
FITZPATRICK, MR JEREMIAH	219
FITZSIMONS, MR PAUL	220
FLINT, MR JOHN	221
FLOOD, MR DAVID	222
FORBES, MR TONY	223
FORD, MRS PAM	224
FORD, MR RICHARD	225
†FORD, MRS RICHENDA	226
FORSEY, MR BRIAN	227
FORSTER, MISS SANDY	228
FOSTER, MISS JOANNE	229
FOWLER, MRS LORNA	230
FOX, MR JIMMY	231
FRANCE, MISS SUZZANNE	232
†FRANKLAND, MR DEREK	233
FROST, MR JAMES	234
†FROST, MR KEVIN	235
FRY, MR HARRY	236
FRYER, MISS CAROLINE	237

G

Name	Team No.
GALLAGHER, MR JOHN	238
GANSERA-LEVEQUE, MRS ILKA	239
GARDNER, MRS SUSAN	240
GASK, MR JEREMY	241
†GASSON, MRS ROSEMARY	242
†GATES, MR MICHAEL	243
GEAKE, MR JONATHAN	244
GEORGE, MISS KAREN	245
GEORGE, MR TOM	246
GIBNEY, MR THOMAS	247
†GIBSON, MRS THERESA	248
GIFFORD, MR NICK	249
GILLARD, MR MARK	250
GILLIGAN, MR PATRICK	251
GIVEN, MR JAMES	252
†GLEDSON, MR J. L.	253
GOLDIE, MR JIM	254
†GOLDIE, MR ROBERT	255

Name	Team No.
GOLDSWORTHY, MR KEITH	256
GOLLINGS, MR STEVE	257
GORDON, MR CHRIS	258
GORMAN, MR J T	259
GOSDEN, MR JOHN	260
GRAHAM, MRS HARRIET	261
GRANT, MR CHRIS	262
GRASSICK, MR LIAM	263
GRASSICK, MR M. C.	264
GRAY, MR CARROLL	265
GRAYSON, MR PETER	266
GREATREX, MR WARREN	267
GREEN, MR PAUL	268
GRETTON, MR TOM	269
GRIFFIN, MR PATRICK	270
GRIFFITHS, MR DAVID C.	271
GRIFFITHS, MR SIMON	272
GRISSELL, MRS DIANA	273
GROUCOTT, MR JOHN BRYAN	274
GUBBY, MR BRIAN	275
GUEST, MR RAE	276
GUEST, MR RICHARD	277
GUNDRY, MISS POLLY	278

H

Name	Team No.
HAGGAS, MR WILLIAM	279
HALES, MR ALEX	280
HALFORD, MR MICHAEL	281
HALL, MISS SALLY	282
HAMBRO, MRS MARY	283
HAMER, MRS DEBRA	284
HAMILTON, MRS ALISON	285
†HAMILTON, MRS ANN	286
HAMILTON, MR B. R.	287
HAMMOND, MR MICKY	288
HAMMOND, MR MIKE	289
HANLON, MR JOHN JOSEPH	290
HANNON, MR RICHARD	291
HARKER, MR GEOFFREY	292
HARNEY, MR W.	293
†HARPER, MR RICHARD	294

Name	Team No.
HARRINGTON, MRS JESSICA	295
HARRIS, MR RONALD	296
HARRIS, MR SHAUN	297
HARRISON, MR GARY	298
HARRISON, MISS LISA	299
HASLAM, MR BEN	300
HASSETT, MR P. J.	301
HAWES, MRS FLEUR	302
HAWKE, MR NIGEL	303
HAWKER, MR RICHARD	304
HAYDN JONES, MR DEREK	305
†HAYNES, MR JONATHAN	306
HAYNES, MR TED	307
HEAD-MAAREK, MRS C.	308
HEDGER, MR PETER	309
HENDERSON, MR NICKY	310
HENDERSON, MR PAUL	311
HERRIES, LADY	312
HERRINGTON, MR MICHAEL	313
HIATT, MR PETER	314
HIDE, MR PHILIP	315
HILL, MRS LAWNEY	316
HILL, MR MARTIN	317
HILLS, MR CHARLES	318
HILLS, MR J. W.	319
HOAD, MR MARK	320
HOBBS, MR PHILIP	321
†HOBSON, MR RICHARD	322
HODGES, MR RON	323
HODGSON, MR SIMON	324
HOGAN, MR EAMONN	325
†HOGARTH, MR HENRY	326
HOLLINGSWORTH, MR ALAN	327
HOLLINSHEAD, MR ANDREW	328
HOLLINSHEAD, MRS STEPH	329
HOLMES, MR PATRICK	330
HOLT, MR JOHN	331
HONEYBALL, MR ANTHONY	332
HOURIGAN, MR MICHAEL	333
HOWE, MR STUART	334
HUGHES, MR D. T.	335

Name	Team No.
HUGHES, MRS JO	336
†HUGHES, MR STEPHEN	337
HUGO, MS N. M.	338
HUMPHREY, MRS SARAH	339
†HUNTER, MR KEVIN	340
†HURLEY, MISS LAURA	341
HUTCHINSON, MISS ALISON	342

I
Name	Team No.
INGRAM, MR ROGER	343
IVORY, MR DEAN	344

J
Name	Team No.
JACKSON, MISS TINA	345
†JACKSON, MRS VALERIE	346
JAMES, MR LEE	347
JARDINE, MR IAIN	348
JARVIS, MR ALAN	349
JARVIS, MR WILLIAM	350
JEFFERSON, MR MALCOLM	351
JENKINS, MR J. R.	352
†JESSOP, MR ALAN	353
JEWELL, MRS LINDA	354
JOHNSON, MR BRETT	355
JOHNSON, MR ROBERT	356
†JOHNSON, MRS SUSAN	357
JOHNSON HOUGHTON, MISS EVE	357a
JOHNSTON, MR MARK	358
JONES, MR ALAN	359
JONES, MR GEORGE	360
JONES, MS LUCY	361
JORDAN, MRS VIOLET M.	362

K
Name	Team No.
KEDDY, MR TOM	363
KEEVIL, MRS CAROLINE	364
KEIGHLEY, MR MARTIN	365
KELLETT, MR CHRISTOPHER	366
KELLEWAY, MISS GAY	367
†KENDALL, MISS LYNSEY	368

Name	Team No.
KENT, MR NICK	369
†KERSWELL, MISS SARAH	370
KING, MR ALAN	371
KING, MR NEIL	372
†KING, MR RICHARD	373
KINSEY, MR WILLIAM	374
KIRBY, MR PHILIP	375
KIRK, MR SYLVESTER	376
KITTOW, MR STUART	377
KNIGHT, MR WILLIAM	378
KUBLER, MR DANIEL	379

L

Name	Team No.
LAFFON-PARIAS, MR CARLOS	380
LAMPARD, MR NICK	381
LANIGAN, MR DAVID	382
LAVELLE, MISS EMMA	383
LEAVY, MR BARRY	384
LEE, MR RICHARD	385
LEECH, MRS SOPHIE	386
LIDDERDALE, MR ALASTAIR	387
LINES, MR CLIFFORD	388
LITTMODEN, MR NICK	389
LLEWELLYN, MR BERNARD	390
LLOYD-BEAVIS, MISS NATALIE	391
LOCKWOOD, MR ALAN	392
LONG, MR JOHN E.	393
LONGSDON, MR CHARLIE	394
LOUGHNANE, MR DANIEL MARK	395
LYCETT, MR SHAUN	396
LYONS, MR GER	397

M

Name	Team No.
MACAIRE, MR GUILLAUME	398
MACKIE, MR JOHN	399
†MACTAGGART, MR ALAN	400
MACTAGGART, MR BRUCE	401
MADGWICK, MR MICHAEL	402
MAIN, MRS HEATHER	403
MAKIN, MR PETER	404

Name	Team No.
MALZARD, MRS ALYSON	405
MANGAN, MR JAMES JOSEPH	406
MANN, MR CHARLIE	407
MARGARSON, MR GEORGE	408
MARTIN, MR A. J.	409
†MARTIN, MR ANDREW J.	410
MASON, MR CHRISTOPHER	411
MASON, MRS JENNIFER	412
†MATHEW, MR ROBIN	413
†MAUNDRELL, MR G. C.	414
MCAULIFFE, MR KEVIN	415
MCBRIDE, MR PHILIP	416
MCCABE, MR ALAN	417
MCCAIN, MR DONALD	418
MCCARTHY, MR TIM	419
MCCORMICK, MISS DANIELLE	420
MCENTEE, MR PHIL	421
MCGRATH, MR MURTY	422
MCGREGOR, MRS JEAN	423
MCLINTOCK, MS KAREN	424
MCMAHON, MR ED	425
MCPHERSON, MR GRAEME	426
MEADE, MR MARTYN	427
MEADE, MR NOEL	428
MEEHAN, MR BRIAN	429
MENZIES, MISS REBECCA	430
MIDDLETON, MR ANTHONY	431
†MIDDLETON, MR PHIL	432
MIDGLEY, MR PAUL	433
MILLMAN, MR ROD	434
MILLS, MR ROBERT	435
MITCHELL, MR NICK	436
MITCHELL, MR PHILIP	437
MITCHELL, MR RICHARD	438
MOFFATT, MR JAMES	439
MOHAMMED, MR ISMAIL	440
MONGAN, MRS LAURA	441
MOORE, MR ARTHUR	442
MOORE, MR GARY	443
MOORE, MR GEORGE	444
MOORE, MR J. S.	445

Name	Team No.
MORGAN, MR KEVIN	446
MORRIS, MR DAVE	447
MORRIS, MR M. F.	448
MORRIS, MR PATRICK	449
MORRISON, MR HUGHIE	450
MOSS, MR GARRY	451
MUIR, MR WILLIAM	452
MULHALL, MR CLIVE	453
MULHOLLAND, MR NEIL	454
MULLANEY, MR LAWRENCE	455
MULLINEAUX, MR MICHAEL	456
MULLINS, MR SEAMUS	457
MULLINS, MR WILLIAM P.	458
MURPHY, MRS ANABEL K.	459
MURPHY, MR COLM	460
MURPHY, MR MICHAEL	461
MURPHY, MR MIKE	462
MURPHY, MR PAT	463
MURTAGH, MR BARRY	464
MUSSON, MR WILLIE	465

N

Name	Team No.
NAYLOR, DR JEREMY	466
†NEEDHAM, MR JOHN	467
NELMES, MRS HELEN	468
NEWCOMBE, MR TONY	469
NEWLAND, DR RICHARD	470
NEWTON-SMITH, MISS ANNA	471
NICHOLLS, MR DAVID	472
NICHOLLS, MR PAUL	473
NIVEN, MR PETER	474
†NIXON, MR RAYSON	475
NORMILE, MRS LUCY	476
NORTON, MR JOHN	477
NOSEDA, MR JEREMY	478

O

Name	Team No.
O'BRIEN, MR A. P.	479
O'BRIEN, MR DANIEL	480
O'BRIEN, MR FERGAL	481

Name	Team No.
O'GORMAN, MR P. J.	482
O'KEEFFE, MR JEDD	483
O'MEARA, MR DAVID	484
†O'NEILL, MR JOHN	485
O'NEILL, MR JONJO	486
O'SHEA, MR JOHN	487
OLD, MR JIM	488
OLDROYD, MR GEOFFREY	489
OLIVER, MR HENRY	490
OSBORNE, MR JAMIE	491
OXX, MR JOHN M.	492

P

Name	Team No.
PALMER, MR HUGO	493
PANTALL, MR H. A.	494
PANVERT, MR JOHN	495
†PARROTT, MRS HILARY	496
PAULING, MR BEN	497
PEACOCK, MR RAY	498
PEARCE, MRS LYDIA	499
PEARS, MR OLLIE	500
†PEARSON, MR DAVID	501
PERRATT, MISS LINDA	502
PERRETT, MRS AMANDA	503
PHELAN, MR PAT	504
PHILLIPS, MR RICHARD	505
PICKARD, MISS IMOGEN	506
PIPE, MR DAVID	507
PITT, MR TIM	508
POGSON, MR CHARLES	509
POMFRET, MR NICHOLAS	510
PORTMAN, MR JONATHAN	511
POULTON, MR JAMIE	512
POWELL, MR BRENDAN	513
POWELL, MR TED	514
PRESCOTT BT, SIR MARK	515
PRICE, MR ANDREW	516
†PRICE, MR JOHN	517
PRICE, MR RICHARD	518
PRITCHARD, MR PETER	519
PURDY, MR PETER	520

Name	Team No.
Q	
QUINLAN, MR NOEL	521
QUINN, MR DENIS	522
QUINN, MR JOHN	523
QUINN, MR MICK	524
R	
†REED, MR W. T.	525
†REED, MR WILLIAM	526
REES, MR DAVID	527
†REES, MRS HELEN	528
REGAN, MR SEAN	529
REID, MR ANDREW	530
REVELEY, MR KEITH	531
†RICHARDS, MR DAVID	532
RICHARDS, MRS LYDIA	533
RICHARDS, MR NICKY	534
RIMELL, MR MARK	535
RIMMER, MR MARK	536
†ROBERTS, MISS BETH	537
ROBERTS, MR DAVE	538
ROBERTS, MR MIKE	539
ROBESON, MRS RENEE	540
ROBINSON, MISS SARAH	541
ROBSON, MISS PAULINE	542
ROHAUT, MR FRANCOIS	543
ROPER, MR W. M.	544
ROTHWELL, MR BRIAN	545
ROUGET, MR J. C.	546
ROWE, MR RICHARD	547
ROWLAND, MISS MANDY	548
ROYER-DUPRE, MR A. DE	549
RUSSELL, MS LUCINDA	550
RYALL, MR JOHN	551
RYAN, MR JOHN	552
RYAN, MR KEVIN	553
S	
SADIK, MR AYTACH	554
SANDERSON, MRS DEBORAH	555

Name	Team No.
SAUNDERS, MR MALCOLM	556
SAYER, MRS DIANNE	557
SCARGILL, DR JON	558
†SCOTT, MR DERRICK	559
SCOTT, MR JEREMY	560
†SCRIVEN, MR BERNARD	561
SCUDAMORE, MR MICHAEL	562
SEMPLE, MR IAN	563
SHAW, MR DEREK	564
†SHAW, MRS PATRICIA	565
†SHEARS, MR MARK	566
SHEPPARD, MR MATT	567
SHERWOOD, MR OLIVER	568
†SHIELS, MR RAYMOND	569
SHIRLEY-BEAVAN, MR SIMON	570
SIDDALL, MISS LYNN	571
SIMCOCK, MR DAVID	572
SKELTON, MR DAN	573
†SLACK, MRS EVELYN	574
SLY, MRS PAM	575
SMAGA, MR DAVID	576
SMART, MR BRYAN	577
SMITH, MR CHARLES	578
SMITH, MR JULIAN	579
SMITH, MR MARTIN	580
SMITH, MR MICHAEL	581
SMITH, MR R. MIKE	582
SMITH, MR RALPH	583
SMITH, MRS SUE	584
SMITH, MISS SUZY	585
SMYLY, MR GILES	586
SNOWDEN, MR JAMIE	587
SOWERSBY, MR MIKE	588
SPEARING, MR JOHN	589
SQUANCE, MR MICHAEL	590
STACK, MR TOMMY	591
STANFORD, MR EUGENE	592
†STEELE, MR DANIEL	593
†STEPHEN, MRS JACKIE	594
STEPHENS, MR ROBERT	595
STEVENS, MR OLLY	596

Name	Team No.	Name	Team No.
STIMPSON, MR JOHN	597	UPSON, MR JOHN	633
STOKELL, MISS ANN	598	USHER, MR MARK	634
STONE, MR WILLIAM	599		
STOREY, MR BRIAN	600		
STOREY, MR WILF	601	**V**	
STOUTE, SIR MICHAEL	602	VARIAN, MR ROGER	635
STUBBS, MISS KRISTIN	603	VAUGHAN, MR ED	636
SUMMERS, MR ROB	604	VAUGHAN, MR TIM	637
SUPPLE, MR JOHN A.	605	VON DER RECKE, MR CHRISTIAN	638
SWAN, MR C. F.	606		
SWINBANK, MR ALAN	607		
SYMONDS, MR TOM	608	**W**	
		WADE, MR JOHN	639
		WADHAM, MRS LUCY	640
T		WAGGOTT, MISS TRACY	641
TATE, MR JAMES	609	WAINWRIGHT, MR JOHN	642
TATE, MR TOM	610	WALFORD, MR MARK	643
†TAYLOR, MRS SUSAN	611	WALFORD, MR ROBERT	644
TEAGUE, MR COLIN	612	WALKER, MR ED	645
TEAL, MR ROGER	613	WALL, MR CHRIS	646
THOMPSON, MR DAVID	614	†WALL, MRS SARAH	647
†THOMPSON, MR VICTOR	615	WALL, MR TREVOR	648
THOMSON, MR SANDY	616	WALTON, MRS JANE	649
THORNTON, MR KARL	617	†WALTON, MR JASON	650
TINKLER, MR NIGEL	618	WALTON, MRS SHEENA	651
TIZZARD, MR COLIN	619	WARD, MR JASON	652
TODHUNTER, MR MARTIN	620	WATSON, MR FREDERICK	653
TOLLER, MR JAMES	621	WATT, MRS SHARON	654
TOMPKINS, MR MARK	622	WAUGH, MR SIMON	655
TORK, MR KEVIN	623	WEAVER, MISS AMY	656
TREGONING, MR MARCUS	624	†WEBB-BOWEN, MR ROBERT	657
TUER, MR EDWIN	625	WEBBER, MR PAUL	658
TUITE, MR JOSEPH	626	WELD, MR D. K.	659
TURNELL, MR ANDREW	627	WEST, MISS SHEENA	660
TURNER, MR BILL	628	WEST, MR SIMON	661
TURNER, MR JAMES	629	†WESTWOOD, MISS JESSICA	662
TUTTY, MRS KAREN	630	WEYMES, MR JOHN	663
TWISTON-DAVIES, MR NIGEL	631	WHEELER, MR ERIC	664
		WHILLANS, MR ALISTAIR	665
		WHILLANS, MR DONALD	666
U		WHITAKER, MR RICHARD	667
UNETT, MR JAMES	632	†WHITEHEAD, MR ARTHUR	668

PROPERTY OF HER MAJESTY

The Queen

Colours: Purple, gold braid, scarlet sleeves, black velvet cap with gold fringe

Trained by **Sir Michael Stoute**, Newmarket

  1 BOLD SNIPER, 4, b g New Approach (IRE)—Daring Aim
  2 ESTIMATE (IRE), 5, b m Monsun (GER)—Ebaziya (IRE)

THREE-YEAR-OLDS

  3 DALMATIA (IRE), gr f Cape Cross (IRE)—Dalataya (IRE)
  4 QUEEN'S PRIZE, b f Dansili—Daring Aim
  5 SHAMA (IRE), b f Danehill Dancer (IRE)—Shamadara (IRE)

TWO-YEAR-OLDS

  6 MUSTARD, b c 8/2 Motivator—Flash of Gold (Darshaan)

Trained by **Richard Hannon**, Marlborough

  7 PRINCE'S TRUST, 4, b g Invincible Spirit (IRE)—Lost In Wonder (USA)
  8 SEA SHANTY (USA), 4, b g Elusive Quality (USA)—Medley

THREE-YEAR-OLDS

  9 BOLD SPIRIT, b g Invincible Spirit (IRE)—Far Shores (USA)
  10 KINLOSS, ch f Kheleyf (USA)—Celtic Cross
  11 MUSICAL COMEDY, b g Royal Applause—Spinning Top

TWO-YEAR-OLDS

  12 PACK TOGETHER, b f 8/2 Paco Boy (IRE)—New Assembly (IRE) (Machiavellian (USA))
  13 PEACOCK, b c 11/3 Paco Boy (IRE)—Rainbow's Edge (Rainbow Quest (USA))

Trained by **Roger Charlton**, Beckhampton

  14 BORDER LEGEND, 5, ch g Selkirk (USA)—Bonnie Doon (IRE)

THREE-YEAR-OLDS

  15 DUMFRIES HOUSE, b g New Approach (IRE)—Bonnie Doon (IRE)
  16 SHARP LOOKOUT, b g Shamardal (USA)—Tempting Prospect

Trained by **Michael Bell**, Newmarket

THREE-YEAR-OLDS

  17 FIERY SUNSET, b f Galileo (IRE)—Five Fields (USA)
  18 GOOD HOPE, b f Cape Cross (IRE)—Fairy Godmother
  19 SILVER MIRAGE, b f Oasis Dream—Phantom Gold

PROPERTY OF HER MAJESTY

The Queen

TWO-YEAR-OLDS

20 TOUCHLINE, b f 29/2 Exceed And Excel (AUS)—Trianon (Nayef (USA))

Trained by **Andrew Balding**, Kingsclere

THREE-YEAR-OLDS

21 ENLIVEN, b f Dansili—Aurore (IRE)
22 MICRAS, b f Medicean—Purple Heather (USA)

Trained by **William Haggas**, Newmarket

THREE-YEAR-OLDS

23 PURPLE SPECTRUM, gr g Verglas (IRE)—Rainbow's Edge
24 TREPIDATION, ch g Danehill Dancer (IRE)—Trianon

TWO-YEAR-OLDS

25 THAMES PAGEANT, b f 22/2 Dansili—Golden Stream (IRE) (Sadler's Wells (USA))

Trained by **Mrs Gai Waterhouse**, Sydney, Australia

26 CARLTON HOUSE (USA), 6, b h Street Cry (IRE)—Talented

Trained by **Nicky Henderson**, Lambourn

27 OPEN HEARTED, 7, b g Generous (IRE)—Romantic Dream
28 SIDE STEP, 5, b m Norse Dancer (IRE)—Magic Score
29 SPECIAL AGENT, 5, b g Invincible Spirit (IRE)—Flight of Fancy

To be allocated

TWO-YEAR-OLDS

30 ANANAS, b f 1/4 Nayef (USA)—Anasazi (IRE) (Sadler's Wells (USA))
31 AWESOME POWER, b c 27/2 Dubawi (IRE)—Fairy Godmother (Fairy King (USA))
32 DEXTEROUS, b f 31/1 Mastercraftsman (IRE)—Daring Aim (Daylami (IRE))
33 FABRICATE, b c 13/2 Makfi—Flight of Fancy (Sadler's Wells (USA))
34 GALLEY PROOF, b c 27/2 Galileo (IRE)—Fictitious (Machiavellian (USA))
35 KINEMATIC, b f 19/4 Kyllachy—Spinning Top (Alzao (USA))
36 MARGINAL, ch c 22/4 Shamardal (USA)—Far Shores (USA) (Distant View (USA))
37 MOTION PICTURE, b f 28/3 Motivator—Starshine (Danehill Dancer (IRE))
38 ORANGE WALK (USA), b g 21/2 Bernardini (USA)—Sally Forth (Dubai Destination (USA))
39 PICK YOUR CHOICE, b c 29/2 Elusive Quality (USA)—Enticement (Montjeu (IRE))
40 PITCH, b f 23/3 Montjeu (IRE)—Five Fields (USA) (Chester House (USA))
41 RELAY MEDAL (USA), b c 21/2 Medaglia d'oro (USA)—Medley (Danehill Dancer (IRE))
42 SAMPLE (FR), b f 11/2 Zamindar (USA)—Sanabyra (FR) (Kahyasi)
43 STARBOARD BEAM (IRE), b f 11/4 Sea The Stars (IRE)—Behkiyra (IRE) (Entrepreneur)

SOME TRAINERS' STRINGS ARE TAKEN FROM THE BHA RACING ADMINISTRATION WEBSITE AND
INCLUDE HORSES LISTED ON THERE AS 'AT GRASS' OR 'RESTING'

---

1 MR N. W. ALEXANDER, Kinneston
Posta7l: Kinneston, Leslie, Glenrothes, Fife, KY6 3JJ
Contacts: **PHONE** (01592) 840774 **MOBILE** (07831) 488210
E-MAIL nicholasalexander@kinneston.com **WEBSITE** www.kinneston.com

1 **ALLFORTHELOVE**, 6, b g Alflora (IRE)—Powerlove (FR) **Kinneston Racing**
2 **ALWAYS TIPSY**, 5, b g Dushyantor (USA)—French Pick (USA) **JJ Cockburn AJ Wight P Home**
3 **ANOTHER MATTIE (IRE)**, 7, b g Zagreb (USA)—Silver Tassie (FR) **Quandt & Cochrane**
4 **BACK ON THE ROAD (IRE)**, 12, br g Broken Hearted—Special Trix (IRE) **J. F. Alexander**
5 **BERTIE MILAN (IRE)**, 9, b g Milan—Miss Bertaine (IRE) **Turcan Barber Douglas Miller Dunning**
6 **BLACKMORE**, 7, b g Rainbow Quest (USA)—Waki Music (USA) **Mr HW Turcan & Sir Simon Dunning**
7 **BUFFALO BALLET**, 8, b g Kayf Tara—Minora (IRE) **H W Turcan E MacGregor Sir S Dunning**
8 **CAUGHT IN THE ACT (IRE)**, 7, br g Overbury (IRE)—Catch Those Kisses **Turcan Barber Fletcher Dunning**
9 **CEILIDH (IRE)**, 6, b m Tamure (IRE)—Eyesabeatin (IRE) **J & S Dudgeon G & S Irwin W Alexander**
10 **CLAN CHIEF**, 5, ch g Generous (IRE)—Harrietfield **Clan Gathering**
11 **DAASIJ (IRE)**, 9, b g Dalakhani (IRE)—Alyakkh (IRE) **Stanistreet & Liddle**
12 **DUTCH CANYON (IRE)**, 4, b br g Craigsteel—Chitabe (IRE)
13 **FRANKIE'S PROMISE (IRE)**, 6, ch g Fruits of Love (USA)—According To Molly (USA) **Mr B. C. Castle**
14 **GOLD OPERA (IRE)**, 5, b g Gold Well—Flute Opera (IRE) **Macdonalds, Cardwell, Castle & Davies**
15 4, Ch g Midnight Legend—Harrietfield **Alexander Family**
16 **HUMPHREY BEE (IRE)**, 11, br g Oscar Schindler (IRE)—Gladriels Jem (IRE) **A. H. B. Hodge**
17 **ISLA PEARL FISHER**, 11, br g Supreme Sound—Salem Beach **Mrs P. M. Gammell**
18 **JET MASTER (IRE)**, 8, b g Brian Boru—Whats The Reason (IRE) **Mr HW Turcan & Sir Simon Dunning**
19 **KING BREX (DEN)**, 11, b g Primatico (USA)—Moon Shine (DEN) **N. W. Alexander**
20 **LANDECKER (IRE)**, 6, b g Craigsteel—Winsome Breeze (IRE) **Mrs N. J. Hodge**
21 **LITTLE GLENSHEE (IRE)**, 8, gr m Terimon—Harrietfield **Turcan Barber Douglas Miller Dunning 1**
22 **MAKHZOON (USA)**, 10, b br g Dynaformer (USA)—Boubskaia **The Ladies Who**
23 **MARLEE MASSIE (IRE)**, 5, b g Dr Massini (IRE)—Meadstown Miss (IRE) **A. J. Neill**
24 **MARLEE MOURINHO (IRE)**, 8, br g Pushkin (IRE)—Spur of The Moment **A. J. Neill**
25 **MILANO MAGIC (IRE)**, 8, b g Milan—Magical Mist (IRE) **Mr A. Cochrane**
26 **NATIVE COLL**, 14, ch g Primitive Rising (USA)—Harrietfield **N. W. Alexander**
27 **NOIR ET VERT (FR)**, 13, b g Silver Rainbow—Danse Verte (FR) **J. F. Alexander**
28 **NORTHERN ACRES**, 8, b g Mtoto—Bunting **C. Lysaght Media, Quandt & Cochrane**
29 **OCARINA (FR)**, 12, b g Bulington (FR)—Alconea (FR) **N. W. Alexander**
30 **OR DE GRUGY (FR)**, 12, b g April Night (FR)—Girlish (FR) **Lord Cochrane & Partners**
31 **PRESENT POTENTIAL (IRE)**, 7, b g Presenting—Calbrooke (IRE) **N. W. Alexander**
32 **ROSSINI'S DANCER**, 9, b g Rossini (USA)—Bint Alhabib **Turcan Barber Fletcher Dunning**
33 **STANDINTHEBAND (IRE)**, 7, b g Old Vic—Superior Dawn (IRE) **Michelle And Dan Macdonald**
34 **THE FLAMING MATRON (IRE)**, 8, b m Flemensfirth (USA)—The Mighty Matron (IRE) **The Ladies Who**
35 **THE ORANGE ROGUE (IRE)**, 7, br g Alderbrook—Classic Enough **Mrs S. M. Irwin**
36 **THE PADDY PREMIUM (IRE)**, 14, b g Glacial Storm (USA)—Miss Cripps (IRE) **Cochrane, Fleming & Alexander**
37 **WICKLOW LAD**, 10, gr g Silver Patriarch (USA)—Marina Bird **Clan Gathering**

Other Owners: J. M. Barber, Mr N. J. Cardwell, The Hon T. H. V. Cochrane, Lord Cochrane of Cults, Mr J. J. Cockburn, Mr D. J. Davies, Mrs J. Douglas Miller, J. G. Dudgeon, Mr A. W. B. Duncan, Sir Simon Dunning, Mr M. R. D. Fleming, Miss F. M. Fletcher, C. Lysaght, Miss E. G. MacGregor, Mrs M. Macdonald, Mr W. D. Macdonald, Miss S. Quandt, N. D. A. Stanistreet, Mrs L. C. A. Stanistreet, H. W. Turcan, Mr A. J. Wight.

Jockey (NH): Lucy Alexander. **Apprentice:** Lucy Alexander. **Amateur:** Mr Kit Alexander, Mr Blair Campbell.

---

2 MR JIM ALLEN, Tiverton
Postal: West Steart Farm, Stoodleigh, Tiverton, Devon, EX16 9QA
Contacts: **MOBILE** (07973) 243369
E-MAIL jallen@arenaracingcompany.co.uk

1 **BEACH RHYTHM (USA)**, 7, ch g Footstepsinthesand—Queen's Music (USA) **J. P. Allen**
2 **INCANTARE**, 4, gr f Proclamation (IRE)—Mythical Charm **J. P. Allen**

TWO-YEAR-OLDS
3 **TWELFTH DAN**, ch c 7/5 Proclamation (IRE)—Mythical Charm (Charnwood Forest (IRE)) **J. P. Allen**

3 MR ERIC ALSTON, Preston

Postal: Edges Farm Stables, Chapel Lane, Longton, Preston, Lancashire, PR4 5NA
Contacts: PHONE (01772) 612120 FAX (01772) 619600 MOBILE (07879) 641660
E-MAIL eric1943@supanet.com

1 BALLARINA, 8, b m Compton Place—Miss Uluwatu (IRE) **Mrs P. O. Morris**
2 BARKSTON ASH, 6, b g Kyllachy—Ae Kae Ae (USA) **The Selebians**
3 BEACON TARN, 4, b f Shamardal (USA)—Baize **Mr & Mrs G. Middlebrook**
4 CHESTER ARISTOCRAT, 5, ch g Sakhee (USA)—New Light **Paul Buist & John Thompson**
5 DIMAN WATERS (IRE), 7, br g Namid—Phantom Waters **Paul Buist & John Thompson**
6 KING OF EDEN (IRE), 8, b g Royal Applause—Moonlight Paradise (USA) **The Grumpy Old Geezers**
7 KING OF PARADISE (IRE), 5, b g Hurricane Run (IRE)—Silly Game (IRE) **P. G. Buist**
8 LITTLE ELI, 4, b g Green Desert (USA)—Princess Ellis **Whittle Racing Partnership**
9 LORD FRANKLIN, 5, ch g Iceman—Zell (IRE) **Liam & Tony Ferguson**
10 ORREST HEAD, 4, b g Sakhee (USA)—Saint Ann (USA) **Mr & Mrs G. Middlebrook**
11 RED BARON (IRE), 5, b h Moss Vale (IRE)—Twinberry (IRE) **J. W. Stephenson**
12 SEE THE STORM, 6, b br g Statue of Liberty (USA)—Khafayit (USA) **Keating Bradley Fold Limited**
13 SILVER LIGHTNING (IRE), 4, gr g Verglas (IRE)—Church Road (IRE) **Edges Farm Racing Stables Ltd**
14 SPAVENTO (IRE), 8, gr m Verglas (IRE)—Lanasara **Whitehills Racing Syndicate**
15 TENHOO, 8, b g Reset (AUS)—Bella Bambina **Edges Farm Racing Stables Ltd**

THREE-YEAR-OLDS

16 BLITHE SPIRIT, b f Byron—Damalis (IRE) **Liam & Tony Ferguson**
17 MIGUELA MCGUIRE, b f Sir Percy—Miss McGuire **Red Rose Partnership**
18 REEFLEX, b g Multiplex—Reem Two **Mr D Ellis & Mr R Pattison**
19 SPRING WILLOW (IRE), b g Camacho—Twinberry (IRE) **J. W. Stephenson**

TWO-YEAR-OLDS

20 B c 30/3 Pastoral Pursuits—Damalis (IRE) (Mukaddamah (USA))
21 NIQNAAQPAADIWAAQ, b c 23/3 Aqlaam—
　　　　　　Aswaaq (IRE) (Peintre Celebre (USA)) (36000) **Paul Buist & John Thompson**
22 TIME CONTINUUM, b f 18/3 Monsieur Bond (IRE)—Primum Tempus (Primo Dominie) **Mr G. M. & Mrs C. Baillie**

Other Owners: Mr G. M. Baillie, Mrs C. Baillie, Mrs J. E. Buist, Mr D. Ellis, M. L. Ferguson, Mr C. A. Ferguson, J. E. Jackson, M. S. Kelly, G. Middlebrook, Mrs L. A. Middlebrook, Mr R. Ormisher, R. Pattison, Mr A. J. Raven, M. M. Taylor, J. Thompson.

Assistant Trainer: Mrs Sue Alston

Jockey (flat): David Allan.

4 MR WILLIAM AMOS, Otterburn

Postal: Rochester House Farm, Rochester, Newcastle upon Tyne, Northumberland, NE19 1RH
Contacts: PHONE (01450) 850323 MOBILE (07810) 738149

1 ARC WARRIOR (FR), 10, b g Even Top (IRE)—What The Hell (IRE) **J. J. Paterson**
2 BILLSGREY (IRE), 12, gr g Pistolet Bleu (IRE)—Grouse-N-Heather **Mr J. M. Stenhouse**
3 BOB'S DREAM (IRE), 12, b g Bob's Return (IRE)—Back In Kansas (IRE) **Bonney, Elliot & Crook**
4 B g Generous (IRE)—Border Mist (IRE) **W. M. Aitchison**
5 BRIERYHILL BOY, 7, gr g Terimon—Bella Mary **Mr & Mrs D. S. Byers**
6 B m Enrique—Candello **W. Amos**
7 CYRUS DARIUS, 5, b g Overbury (IRE)—Barton Belle **J. W. Stephenson**
8 FORT CANNING, 5, b g Barathea (IRE)—Cream Tease **J. W. Stephenson**
9 ISAACSTOWN LAD (IRE), 7, b g Milan—Friends of Friends (IRE) **J. W. Stephenson**
10 Ch g Proclamation (IRE)—Kompete **Mr I. A. Gauld**
11 LOCHORE (IRE), 8, b g Morozov (USA)—Fulgina (FR) **Mr I. A. Gauld**
12 OIL BURNER, 9, b g Sir Harry Lewis (USA)—Quick Quote **Mr J. W. Clark**
13 PRINCE DALKING (IRE), 8, b g Desert Prince (IRE)—Notable Dear (ITY) **Mr J. M. Stenhouse**
14 SILVA SAMOURAI, 5, gr g Proclamation (IRE)—Ladykirk **Mr I. A. Gauld**
15 TUNERS (IRE), 7, ch g Green Tune (USA)—Tresor Russe (IRE)
16 WHAT A DREAM, 8, ch g Supreme Sound—Ben Roseler (IRE) **R. J. Kyle, D. & J. Byers**
17 WILLIE HALL, 10, b g Afflora (IRE)—G'ime A Buzz **R. H. Hall**

MR WILLIAM AMOS - Continued

THREE-YEAR-OLDS

18 B g Alflora (IRE)—Reivers Moon **W. Amos**

Other Owners: S. Bonney, D. S. Byers, Mrs M. J. Byers, Mr J. R. Crook, K. R. Elliott, R. J. Kyle.

MR CHARLIE APPLEBY, Newmarket
Postal: **Godolphin Management Co Ltd, Moulton Paddocks, Newmarket, Suffolk, CB8 7YE**
WEBSITE www.godolphin.com

The following list has not been supplied by the trainer and is as accurate as possible at the time of going to press. Some horses listed may not return to Britain from Dubai. Only 2yos entered in the 2015 Derby and/or Tattersalls Millions are shown. **For the latest information please visit www.godolphin.com**

1 AHTOUG, 6, b h Byron—Cherokee Rose (IRE)
2 ALDGATE (USA), 5, ch g Street Cry (IRE)—Adonesque (IRE)
3 ALTRUISM (IRE), 4, b g Authorized (IRE)—Bold Assumption
4 ARTIGIANO (USA), 4, ch c Distorted Humor (USA)—Angel Craft (USA)
5 BANNOCK (IRE), 5, b g Bertolini (USA)—Laoub (USA)
6 BELLO (AUS), 6, b g Exceed And Excel (AUS)—Cara Bella
7 BUCKWHEAT, 4, b c Manduro (GER)—Russian Snows (IRE)
8 BUSTOPHER (USA), 4, b br g Elusive Quality (USA)—Catstar (USA)
9 CAP O'RUSHES, 4, b c New Approach (IRE)—Valley of Gold (FR)
10 CAT O'MOUNTAIN (USA), 4, b br g Street Cry (IRE)—Thunder Kitten (USA)
11 CERTIFY (USA), 4, b f Elusive Quality (USA)—Please Sign In (USA)
12 COUNTERGLOW (IRE), 5, b g Echo of Light—Quintellina
13 DESERT WINGS (IRE), 4, ch g Raven's Pass (USA)—Rise and Fall (USA)
14 DRAGON FALLS (IRE), 5, b g Distorted Humor (USA)—Tizdubai (USA)
15 ENCKE (USA), 5, b h Kingmambo (USA)—Shawanda (IRE)
16 ENERGIZER (GER), 5, b h Monsun (GER)—Erytheis (USA)
17 ENNISTOWN, 4, b g Authorized (IRE)—Saoirse Abu (USA)
18 ENNOBLED FRIEND (USA), 4, b c Malibu Moon (USA)—Seek To Soar (USA)
19 FIREBEAM, 6, b g Cadeaux Genereux—Firebelly
20 FRENCH NAVY, 6, b h Shamardal (USA)—First Fleet (USA)
21 FULBRIGHT, 5, b h Exceed And Excel (AUS)—Lindfield Belle (IRE)
22 GENIUS BEAST (USA), 6, b h Kingmambo (USA)—Shawanda (IRE)
23 GROUNDBREAKING, 4, b c New Approach (IRE)—Ladeena (IRE)
24 HISTORY BOOK (IRE), 4, b f Raven's Pass (USA)—Pure Illusion (IRE)
25 IMPROVISATION (IRE), 4, b c Teofilo (IRE)—Dance Troupe
26 INTRIGO, 4, b g Medicean—A Thousand Smiles (IRE)
27 KALISPELL (IRE), 4, b f Singspiel (IRE)—Genovefa (USA)
28 LE BERNARDIN (USA), 5, b br h Bernardini (USA)—La Rosa (USA)
29 LIBERTARIAN, 4, b c New Approach (IRE)—Intrum Morshaan (IRE)
30 LIFE PARTNER (IRE), 4, b g Cape Cross (IRE)—Miss Intimate (USA)
31 LONG JOHN (AUS), 4, b g Street Cry (IRE)—Hosiery (AUS)
32 MAPUTO, 4, b c Cape Cross (IRE)—Insijaam (USA)
33 MIGHTY AMBITION (USA), 5, b h Street Cry (IRE)—New Morning (IRE)
34 MODERN HISTORY (IRE), 6, b g Shamardal (USA)—Fatefully (USA)
35 MOONWALK IN PARIS (FR), 6, b g Oratorio (IRE)—Shining Glory
36 NINE REALMS, 5, b g Green Desert (USA)—Bourbonella
37 NOT A GIVEN (USA), 5, b h Any Given Saturday (USA)—Any For Love (ARG)
38 OCEAN WAR, 6, gr g Dalakhani (IRE)—Atlantic Destiny (IRE)
39 PENGLAI PAVILION (USA), 4, b br c Monsun (GER)—Maiden Tower
40 PORT ALFRED, 4, b g Oasis Dream—Cape Merino
41 PRESS ROOM (USA), 4, ch g Street Cry (IRE)—Causeway Lass (AUS)
42 RESTRAINT OF TRADE (IRE), 4, br g Authorized (IRE)—Zivania (IRE)
43 ROSTRUM (FR), 7, b g Shamardal (USA)—En Public (FR)
44 SADEEK'S SONG (USA), 6, ch h Kingmambo (USA)—New Morning (IRE)
45 SAINT BAUDOLINO (IRE), 5, b h Pivotal—Alessandria
46 SNOWBOARDER (USA), 4, ch c Raven's Pass (USA)—Gaudete (USA)
47 SPECKLED (USA), 4, b f Street Cry (IRE)—Painted Lady (USA)
48 STEELER (IRE), 4, ch c Raven's Pass (USA)—Discreet Brief (IRE)
49 TAYLOR SAID (CAN), 6, b b g Stephanotis (CAN)—Fleet Amyanne (CAN)
50 TENENBAUM, 5, b g Authorized (IRE)—Al Hasnaa

MR CHARLIE APPLEBY - Continued

51 **TIMONEER (USA)**, 4, b br c Elusive Quality (USA)—Gentle Gale (USA)
52 **URBAN DANCE (IRE)**, 4, b g Street Cry (IRE)—Melikah (IRE)
53 **VAN ELLIS**, 5, b h Shamardal (USA)—Jalousie (IRE)
54 **VANCOUVERITE**, 4, b c Dansili—Villarrica (USA)
55 **WINTERLUDE (IRE)**, 4, b c Street Cry (IRE)—New Morning (IRE)
56 **ZIBELINA (IRE)**, 4, b f Dansili—Zaeema
57 **ZIP TOP (IRE)**, 5, b h Smart Strike (CAN)—Zofzig (USA)

THREE-YEAR-OLDS

58 **ABOUT TURN**, ch c Pivotal—Doctor's Glory (USA)
59 **ALPINE RETREAT (USA)**, ch c Distorted Humor (USA)—Indy's Windy (USA)
60 **ALPINE STORM (IRE)**, b f Raven's Pass (USA)—Lurina (IRE)
61 **ANGLOPHILE**, ch g Dubawi (IRE)—Anna Palariva (IRE)
62 **ARCTIC MOON (USA)**, b br f Raven's Pass (USA)—Golden Sphinx (USA)
63 **AUTUMN LILY (USA)**, b f Strect Cry (IRE)—Arlette (IRE)
64 **BILLINGSGATE (IRE)**, b c Exceed And Excel (AUS)—Island Babe (USA)
65 **BOMBARDMENT (USA)**, gr c War Front (USA)—Niceling (USA)
66 **CARIDADI (IRE)**, b g Invincible Spirit (USA)—Charity Belle (USA)
67 **CHORTLE**, b f Dubawi (IRE)—Portmanteau
68 **CLASSIC DEVOTION (USA)**, b c Street Cry (IRE)—Serenading (USA)
69 **CLEAN LIVING**, b g Sea The Stars (IRE)—Virtuosity
70 **CONQUERANT**, ch c Dubawi (IRE)—The World
71 **CRY JOY (USA)**, b c Street Cry (IRE)—Blushing Ogygian (USA)
72 **DEADLY APPROACH**, b c New Approach (IRE)—Speirbhean (IRE)
73 **DEVILMENT**, b g Cape Cross (IRE)—Mischief Making (USA)
74 **DULLINGHAM**, b g Dubawi (IRE)—Dixey
75 **EARL OF MENTEITH (IRE)**, b c Shamardal (USA)—Inchmahome
76 **EMIRATES JOY (USA)**, b f Street Cry (IRE)—Zofzig (USA)
77 **FEEDYAH (USA)**, b f Street Cry (IRE)—Red Dune (IRE)
78 **FIGURE OF SPEECH (IRE)**, b g Invincible Spirit (USA)—Epic Similie
79 **FIRE BLAZE (IRE)**, gr f Dubawi (IRE)—Nahoodh (IRE)
80 **FOLK MELODY (IRE)**, b f Street Cry (IRE)—Folk Opera (IRE)
81 **GILMER (IRE)**, b g Exceed And Excel (AUS)—Cherokee Rose (IRE)
82 **GOLD TRAIL (IRE)**, ch c Teofilo (IRE)—Goldthroat (IRE)
83 **INTENSE EFFORT (IRE)**, b c Acclamation—Pretty Demanding (IRE)
84 **INTERMEDIUM**, ro c Exceed And Excel (AUS)—Gweneira
85 **KIND INVITATION**, b f New Approach (IRE)—French Bid (AUS)
86 **MAJEYDA (USA)**, b br f Street Cry (IRE)—Alzerra (UAE)
87 **MARIA BELLA (IRE)**, ch f Raven's Pass (USA)—Infinite Spirit (USA)
88 **MINER'S LAMP (IRE)**, b c Shamardal (USA)—Truly Mine (IRE)
89 **MOONTIME**, b g Sea The Stars (IRE)—Time On
90 **MUSIC THEORY (IRE)**, b g Acclamation—Key Girl (IRE)
91 **OUTSTRIP**, gr ro c Exceed And Excel (AUS)—Asi Siempre (USA)
92 **PANTOLONI**, b c Dansili—Short Skirt
93 **PERSONAL OPINION**, ch c New Approach (IRE)—Sentimental Value (USA)
94 **PINZOLO (IRE)**, b c Monsun (GER)—Pongee
95 **PRETEND (IRE)**, b c Invincible Spirit (USA)—Fafinta (IRE)
96 **SAFETY CHECK (IRE)**, ch c Dubawi (IRE)—Doors To Manual (USA)
97 **SEQUINED (USA)**, b br f Street Cry (IRE)—Sunspangled (IRE)
98 **SIBLING HONOUR**, b f Bernardini (USA)—Porto Roca (AUS)
99 **SNOW SQUALL**, b g Dansili—Snow Ballerina
100 **SOLIDARITY**, b g Dubawi (IRE)—Assabiyya (IRE)
101 **SOUND REFLECTION (USA)**, b f Street Cry (IRE)—Echoes In Eternity (IRE)
102 **SPELLBIND**, b f Shamardal (USA)—Bedazzle (USA)
103 **SQUIRE**, b g Teofilo (IRE)—Most Charming (FR)
104 **STRATEGICAL (USA)**, b c More Than Ready (USA)—Mary Ellise (USA)
105 **SUDDEN WONDER (IRE)**, ch c New Approach (IRE)—Dubai Surprise (IRE)
106 **TENDER EMOTION**, ch f Pivotal—Silca's Sister
107 **TRYSTER (IRE)**, b g Shamardal (USA)—Min Alhawa (USA)
108 **WEDDING RING (IRE)**, b f Oasis Dream—Cast In Gold (USA)

TWO-YEAR-OLDS

109 **AD DABARAN (GER)**, b c 18/4 Dubawi (IRE)—Allure (GER) (Konigstuhl (GER)) (278745)
110 B c 27/2 Teofilo (IRE)—Al Joza (Dubawi (IRE)) (150000)
111 B c 24/1 Oasis Dream—Annabelle's Charm (IRE) (Indian Ridge) (625000)

MR CHARLIE APPLEBY - Continued

112 Gr ro c 17/5 Street Cry (IRE)—Blue Dress (USA) (Danzig (USA))
113 B c 20/2 Oasis Dream—Briolette (IRE) (Sadler's Wells (USA)) (650000)
114 B c 7/5 Echo of Light—Calando (USA) (Storm Cat (USA))
115 B c 22/3 New Approach (IRE)—Caro George (USA) (Distant View (USA)) (270000)
116 Ch c 24/2 New Approach (IRE)—Cheerleader (Singspiel (IRE)) (360000)
117 B c 21/4 Dubawi (IRE)—Country Star (USA) (Empire Maker (USA))
118 B c 27/1 Dubawi (IRE)—Demisemiquaver (Singspiel (IRE)) (650000)
119 B br c 10/2 Street Cry (IRE)—Love Charm (Singspiel (IRE))
120 B c 5/4 Oasis Dream—Love Divine (Diesis) (300000)
121 B f 7/3 Sea The Stars (IRE)—Mamonta (Fantastic Light (USA)) (180000)
122 B f 12/3 Dubawi (IRE)—Much Faster (USA) (Fasliyev (USA)) (300000)
123 Br c 6/4 Teofilo (IRE)—Neverletme Go (IRE) (Green Desert (USA)) (500000)
124 B f 4/2 New Approach (IRE)—Park Twilight (IRE) (Bertolini (USA)) (150000)
125 B c 20/2 Exceed And Excel (AUS)—Pickle (Piccolo) (220000)
126 Ch c 29/3 New Approach (IRE)—Purple Glow (IRE) (Orientate (USA)) (180000)
127 B c 8/2 Sea The Stars (IRE)—Que Puntual (ARG) (Contested Bid (USA)) (360000)
128 Ch c 16/4 Dubawi (IRE)—Rebelline (IRE) (Robellino (USA)) (200000)
129 B f 14/3 Shamardal (USA)—Sadima (IRE) (Sadler's Wells (USA)) (260000)
130 Ch c 6/2 New Approach (IRE)—Spring Oak (Mark of Esteem (IRE))
131 B f 31/1 Dubawi (IRE)—Sugar Free (IRE) (Oasis Dream) (300000)
132 B c 9/4 War Front (USA)—Superior Selection (USA) (Giant's Causeway (USA))
133 B c 18/2 Dubawi (IRE)—Zayn Zen (Singspiel (IRE))

---

6 **MR MICHAEL APPLEBY, Newark**
Postal: **Stubby Nook Lodge Bungalow, Danethorpe Lane, Danethorpe, Newark, Nottinghamshire, NG24 2PD**
Contacts: **MOBILE (07884) 366421**
E-MAIL appleby477@aol.com WEBSITE www.mickapplebyracing.com

1 **ALYS ROCK (IRE)**, 5, gr m Medaaly—Rock Slide (IRE) **M. Appleby**
2 **ANGEL CAKE (IRE)**, 5, b m Dark Angel (IRE)—Royal Jelly **Mr W. J. Sewell**
3 **ARABIAN FLIGHT**, 5, b m Exceed And Excel (AUS)—Emirates First (IRE) **Dallas Racing**
4 **BANCNUANAHEIREANN (IRE)**, 7, b g Chevalier (IRE)—Alamanta (IRE) **Dallas Racing**
5 **BE ROYALE**, 4, b f Byron—Sofia Royale **Mr Wayne Brackstone, Mr Steve Whitear**
6 **BEYEH (IRE)**, 6, b m King's Best (USA)—Cradle Rock (IRE) **T. R. Pryke**
7 **BITAPHON (IRE)**, 5, br g Acclamation—Pitrizzia **Dallas Racing**
8 **DEWALA**, 5, b m Deportivo—Fuwala **Goldform Racing**
9 **EURYSTHEUS (IRE)**, 5, b g Acclamation—Dust Flicker **Midest Partnership**
10 **EXPOSE**, 6, ch g Compton Place—Show Off **The Giggle Factor Partnership**
11 **FALCON'S REIGN (FR)**, 5, ch g Haafhd—Al Badeya (IRE) **M. Appleby**
12 **FAVORITE GIRL (GER)**, 6, b m Shirocco (GER)—Favorite (GER) **T. R. Pryke**
13 **FIRST GLANCE**, 5, br g Passing Glance—Lady Santana (IRE) **Sarnian Racing**
14 **GENES QUEST**, 7, b m Rainbow High—Polly Tino **Mr A. Jordan**
15 **GLAN LADY (IRE)**, 8, b m Court Cave—Vanished (IRE) **P Voce & C Voce**
16 **GUISHAN (USA)**, 4, b f Ishiguru (USA)—Fareham **B. D. Cantle**
17 **HONOURED (IRE)**, 7, ch g Mark of Esteem (IRE)—Traou Mad (IRE) **Dallas Racing**
18 **HOT SUGAR (USA)**, 5, b g Lemon Drop Kid (USA)—Plaisir Des Yeux (FR) **Mick Appleby Racing**
19 **HUZZAH (IRE)**, 9, b g Acclamation—Borders Belle (IRE) **Mr Richard Popplewell**
20 **IT MUST BE FAITH**, 4, b g Mount Nelson—Purple Rain (IRE) **M. Appleby**
21 **IVY PORT**, 4, b f Deportivo—Ivy Bridge (IRE) **Goldform Racing**
22 **JACOBS SON**, 6, ch g Refuse To Bend (IRE)—Woodwin (IRE) **The Rain Dancers**
23 **JIMMY SEWELL (IRE)**, 5, b g Catcher In The Rye (IRE)—Starway To Heaven (IRE) **Mr W. J. Sewell**
24 **JOHN COFFEY (IRE)**, 5, b g Acclamation—Appleblossom Pearl (IRE) **Mick Appleby Racing**
25 **KHAJAALY (IRE)**, 7, b g Kheleyf (USA)—Joyfullness (USA) **New Kids On The Trot**
26 **LAPWORTH (IRE)**, 7, b g Alflora (IRE)—La Bella Villa **K. D. Pugh**
27 **LIEUTENANT DAN (IRE)**, 7, b g Danroad (AUS)—Dakhira **Dallas Racing**
28 **LINCOLNROSE (IRE)**, 4, gr f Verglas (IRE)—Imelda (USA) **P C Coaches of Lincoln Limited**
29 **LUCY BEE**, 4, ch f Haafhd—Procession **Mrs L. B. K. Bone**
30 **MAGGIE PINK**, 5, b m Beat All (USA)—Top Notch **Mr A. W. Bult**
31 **MIAKO (USA)**, 4, ch g Speightstown (USA)—Bond Queen (USA) **Rod In Pickle Partnership**
32 **MINSKY MINE (IRE)**, 7, b g Montjeu (IRE)—Summer Trysting (USA) **T. R. Pryke**
33 **MR RED CLUBS (IRE)**, 5, b g Red Clubs (IRE)—Queen Cobra (IRE) **Ferrybank Properties Ltd**
34 **NELLIES QUEST**, 5, b m Rainbow High—Dream Seeker (IRE) **Mr A. Jordan**

MR MICHAEL APPLEBY - Continued

35 **NO WIN NO FEE**, 4, b g Firebreak—Milliscent **Mr S. Almond**
36 **OUR IVOR**, 5, gr g Cape Town (IRE)—Caprice **J&G Bacciochi, A Taylor, Bruce W Wyatt**
37 **QUEEN OF SKIES (IRE)**, 5, b m Shamardal (USA)—Attractive Crown (USA) **Ferrybank Properties Ltd**
38 **ROYAL PECULIAR**, 6, b h Galileo (IRE)—Distinctive Look (IRE) **T. R. Pryke**
39 **SHELFORD (IRE)**, 5, b g Galileo (IRE)—Lyrical **Mr C. Hodgson**
40 **SILENT SAM**, 6, b g Elusive City (USA)—Luisa Miller (IRE) **Mr M. Park**
41 **SIOUX CHIEFTAIN (IRE)**, 4, b g Mount Nelson—Lady Gin (IRE) **Ferrybank Properties Ltd**
42 **STAFF SERGEANT**, 7, b g Dubawi (IRE)—Miss Particular (IRE) **Mick Appleby Racing**
43 **STELLAR EXPRESS (IRE)**, 5, b m Royal Applause—Aitch (IRE) **Dallas Racing**
44 **SUPER SAY (IRE)**, 8, ch g Intikhab (USA)—Again Royale (IRE) **Castle Racing**
45 **THE BULL HAYES (IRE)**, 8, b g Sadler's Wells (USA)—No Review (USA) **Mr J. Wholey**
46 **THE LOCK MASTER (IRE)**, 7, b g Key of Luck (USA)—Pitrizza (IRE) **Kenneth George Kitchen**
47 **THORPE BAY**, 5, b g Piccolo—My Valentina **Dallas Racing**
48 **TONY HOLLIS**, 6, b g Antonius Pius (USA)—Seasons Parks **Mick Appleby Racing**

THREE-YEAR-OLDS

49 **BONNIE FAIRY**, b f Notnowcato—Cheviot Heights **Mrs L. B. K. Bone**
50 **CORDITE (IRE)**, ch c Footstepsinthesand—Marion Haste (IRE) **Shaw Greaves Gamble**
51 **DANDY MAID**, b f Dandy Man (IRE)—Cut Back **M. C. Wainman**
52 **DANZENO**, b g Denounce—Danzanora **Mr A. M. Wragg**
53 Ch f Denounce—Fuwala **Goldform Racing**
54 **HESKA (IRE)**, b g Rock of Gibraltar (IRE)—Sweet Sioux **Dennis & Andy Deacon**
55 Ch f Selkirk (USA)—Rubies From Burma (USA) **Ferrybank Properties Ltd**
56 **RURAL AFFAIR**, b f Pastoral Pursuits—Torcross **Dallas Racing & Mr T. R. Pearson**
57 **SLEET (IRE)**, b c Amadeus Wolf—Secret Justice (USA) **M. Appleby**

TWO-YEAR-OLDS

58 Ch f 18/3 Pivotal—Best Side (IRE) (King's Best (USA)) (15000) **Ferrybank Properties Ltd**
59 B f 6/4 Cape Cross (IRE)—Bezant (IRE) (Zamindar (USA)) (22000) **Ferrybank Properties Ltd**
60 B f 6/2 Monsieur Bond (IRE)—Jasmine Breeze (Saddlers' Hall (IRE)) (1428) **Pryke, Golding, Appleby**
61 B f 13/2 Approve (IRE)—Passage To India (IRE) (Indian Ridge) (9047) **Golding, Pryke, Appleby**
62 B c 21/4 Broken Vow (USA)—Platinum Preferred (CAN) (Vindication (USA)) (21000) **Ferrybank Properties Ltd**
63 **TOBOUGGAN**, b c 25/2 Tobougg (IRE)—Justbetweenfriends (USA) (Diesis) (2857) **Mr J. R. Theaker**
64 Ch f 18/2 Equiano (FR)—Whistful (First Trump) (2857) **Golding, Pryke**

Other Owners: Mr Michael Appleby, Mr J. Bacciochi, Mr Wayne Brackstone, Mr John Branson, Mr V. H. Coleman, Mrs N. Cooper, Mr Christopher Dixon, Mr D. R. Gardner, Mr Mark A. Glassett, Mr D. Greaves, Mr Mick Harris, Mr Nick Hoare, Mr Richard Hoiles, Mr James Holt, Mr A. W. Le Page, Mr C. Le Page, Mr Steven Nightingale, Mr T. R. Pearson, Mr O. Robinson, Mr Nigel Sennett, Mr P. Shaw, Mr J. Soiza, Mr J. R. Theaker, Mr P. Voce, Mrs C. Voce, Mr S. J. Whitear, Mr Denis Woodward, Mr Bruce W. Wyatt.

Assistant Trainer: Mr Jonathan Clayton **Head Lad:** Niall Nevin

Jockey (flat): Luke Morris, Robbie Fitzpatrick, Ben Curtis, Andrew Mullen. **Jockey (NH):** Ryan Mahon, Charlie Poste, Charlie Wallace. **Conditional:** Jonathan England. **Apprentice:** Ali Rawlinson. **Amateur:** Miss Serena Brotherton, Miss Emily Melbourn.

---

7   **MR DAVID ARBUTHNOT, Dorking**
Postal: Henfold House Cottage, Henfold Lane, Beare Green, Dorking, Surrey, RH5 4RW
Contacts: PHONE (01306) 631529 FAX (01306) 631529 MOBILE (07836) 276464
E-MAIL dwparbuthnot@hotmail.com WEBSITE www.henfoldracing.co.uk

1 4, Br g Kalanisi (IRE)—Clondalee (IRE) **Mr A T A Wates & Mrs S Wates**
2 **FEEL THE FORCE (IRE)**, 10, br g Presenting—Shipping News (IRE) **A. T. A. Wates**
3 **GANDALFE (FR)**, 9, b br g Laveron—Goldville (FR) **A. T. A. Wates**
4 **MAX MILAN (IRE)**, 5, b g Milan—Sunset Leader (IRE) **Mr P. M. Claydon**
5 **ROCKY ELSOM (USA)**, 7, b g Rock of Gibraltar (IRE)—Bowstring (IRE) **Mr A T A Wates & Mr J G M Wates**
6 **SHUIL ROYALE (IRE)**, 9, b g King's Theatre (IRE)—Shuil Na Lee (IRE) **R. P. Fry**
7 **SNOWBALL (IRE)**, 7, gr g Alderbrook—Rosafi (IRE) **Mr P Fry & Mr P Claydon**
8 **STROLLAWAYNOW (IRE)**, 7, b g Oscar (IRE)—Rose of Salome (IRE) **A. T. A. Wates**
9 **THE STRAWBERRY ONE**, 9, ch m Kadastrof (FR)—Peppermint Plod **Miss C. A. B. Allsopp**
10 **TINGO IN THE TALE (IRE)**, 5, b g Oratorio (IRE)—Sunlit Skies **G. S. Thompson**
11 **TOPOLSKI (IRE)**, 8, b g Peintre Celebre (USA)—Witching Hour (IRE) **Mr P. M. Claydon**
12 **URCALIN (FR)**, 6, b g Network (GER)—Caline So (FR) **Mr A T A Wates & Mrs S Wates**

MR DAVID ARBUTHNOT - Continued

13 **WESTAWAY (IRE)**, 7, b br g Westerner—I'llaway (IRE) **Mr P. M. Claydon**
14 **WHENINDOUBTDOIT (IRE)**, 7, ch g Shantou (USA)—Warning Cry (IRE) **A. T. A. Wates**

THREE-YEAR-OLDS

15 **DANGLYDONTASK**, b g Lucky Story (USA)—Strat's Quest **P. Banfield**

Other Owners: J. G. M. Wates, Mrs S. M. Wates.

Jockey (NH): Tom Cannon, Daryl Jacob.

MR PETER ATKINSON, Northallerton
Postal: Yafforth Hill Farm, Yafforth, Northallerton, North Yorkshire, DL7 0LT
Contacts: **PHONE (01609) 772598 MOBILE (07751) 131215**

1 **CROCO BAY (IRE)**, 7, b g Croco Rouge (IRE)—April Thistle (IRE) **Mr P. G. Atkinson**
2 **SPARKLING HAND**, 8, b m Lend A Hand—Sparkling Yasmin **Mr P. G. Atkinson**

---

9 **MR MICHAEL ATTWATER, Epsom**
Postal: Tattenham Corner Stables, Tattenham Corner Road, Epsom Downs, Surrey, KT18 5PP
Contacts: **PHONE (01737) 360066 MOBILE (07725) 423633**
E-MAIL Attwaterracing@hotmail.co.uk WEBSITE www.attwaterracing.com

1 **ASK THE GURU**, 4, b c Ishiguru (USA)—Tharwa (IRE) **Canisbay Bloodstock**
2 **BEAT ROUTE**, 7, ch g Beat Hollow—Steppin Out **Canisbay Bloodstock**
3 **BOWSTAR**, 5, b m Oasis Dream—Bold Empress (USA) **Canisbay Bloodstock**
4 **BRAVO ECHO**, 8, b g Oasis Dream—Bold Empress (USA) **Canisbay Bloodstock**
5 **BRONZE PRINCE**, 7, b g Oasis Dream—Sweet Pea **Canisbay Bloodstock**
6 **CAPONE (IRE)**, 9, b g Daggers Drawn (USA)—Order of The Day (USA) **Brooklands Racing**
7 **CUTHBERT (IRE)**, 7, ch g Bertolini (USA)—Tequise (IRE) **Canisbay Bloodstock**
8 **DISPATCH BOX**, 10, b g Dansili—Division Bell
9 **DIXIE GWALIA**, 6, b m Tobougg (IRE)—Dixieanna **Mr J. M. Duggan & Mr T. P. Duggan**
10 **ECHOES OF WAR**, 5, b g Echo of Light—Waraqa (USA) **Mr M. J. Evans**
11 **EMPIRE STORM (GER)**, 7, b h Storming Home—Emy Coasting (USA) **The Attwater Partnership**
12 **GEORGE GURU**, 7, b g Ishiguru (USA)—Waraqa (USA) **T. M. Jones**
13 **HOWLIN MOON**, 6, ch m Zamindar (USA)—Steppin Out **Canisbay Bloodstock**
14 **KINDIA (IRE)**, 6, b m Cape Cross (IRE)—Susu **Canisbay Bloodstock**
15 **L'HIRONDELLE (IRE)**, 10, b g Anabaa (USA)—Auratum (USA) **Canisbay Bloodstock**
16 **LET'S CONFER**, 5, ch m Doyen (IRE)—Vrennan **Canisbay Bloodstock**
17 **LION'S MAID**, 5, b m Iceman—Steppin Out **Canisbay Bloodstock**
18 **NOBLE DEED**, 4, ch g Kyllachy—Noble One **Canisbay Bloodstock**
19 **PARSONS GREEN**, 5, b m Sakhee (USA)—Anastasia Venture **Canisbay Bloodstock**
20 **PLOVER**, 4, b f Oasis Dream—Short Dance (USA) **Canisbay Bloodstock**
21 **PURFORD GREEN**, 5, ch m Kyllachy—Mo Stopher **Canisbay Bloodstock**
22 **ROLLIN 'N TUMBLIN**, 10, ch g Zaha (CAN)—Steppin Out **Canisbay Bloodstock**
23 **SALIENT**, 10, b g Fasliyev (USA)—Savannah Belle **Canisbay Bloodstock**
24 **SUNSHINE ALWAYS (IRE)**, 8, b gr g Verglas (IRE)—Easy Sunshine (IRE) **Miss M. E. Stopher**
25 **TITAN TRIUMPH**, 10, b g Zamindar (USA)—Triple Green **Canisbay Bloodstock**
26 **WHERE'S REILEY (USA)**, 8, b brg Doneraile Court (USA)—Plateau (USA) **Mr J. M. Duggan & Mr T. P. Duggan**

THREE-YEAR-OLDS

27 **BONGO BEAT**, ch c Beat Hollow—Steppin Out **Canisbay Bloodstock**
28 **REDY TO RUMBLE**, ch g Three Valleys (USA)—Sorara **The Attwater Partnership**
29 Ch f Byron—Royal Ivy **Canisbay Bloodstock**
30 **STORM OF CHOICE**, b g Shirocco (GER)—New Choice (IRE) **The Attwater Partnership**

Other Owners: Mr B. M. Attwater, Mr M. J. Attwater, Mr M. H. Bates, Mr James Michael Duggan, Mr T. P. Duggan, Mr T. M. Jones, Mr R. F. Kilby, Mr D. S. Lovatt, Mrs A. M. Mercs, Miss Maureen Stopher.

Assistant Trainer: K. F. Latchford

---

10 **MR NICK AYLIFFE, Minehead**
Postal: **Glebe Stables, Little Ham, Winsford, Minehead, Somerset, TA24 7JH**
Contacts: **PHONE (01643) 851265 MOBILE (07975) 657839**

1 DALRYMPLE (IRE), 8, ch g Daylami (IRE)—Dallaah **Mr M. J. Hayes**
2 HOLDEN CAULFIELD (IRE), 9, b g Catcher In The Rye (IRE)—God Speed Her **R. Allatt**
3 MIX N MATCH, 10, b g Royal Applause—South Wind
4 SPICE HILL (IRE), 8, b g Indian Danehill (IRE)—Histologie (FR) **Mrs M. A. Barrett**
5 VALONA STAR, 6, b m Man Among Men (IRE)—Valona Valley (IRE) **Mrs M. A. Barrett**

Other Owners: Mrs J. J. Young.

Assistant Trainer: Miss N. French

---

11 **MR ALAN BAILEY, Newmarket**
Postal: **Cavendish Stables, Hamilton Road, Newmarket, Suffolk, CB8 7JQ**
Contacts: **PHONE (01638) 664546 FAX (01638) 664546 MOBILE (07808) 734223**
WEBSITE www.alanbaileyracing.co.uk

1 BADDILINI, 4, b g Bertolini (USA)—Baddi Heights (FR) **Mrs M. Shone**
2 COINCIDENTLY, 4, b f Acclamation—Miss Chaussini (IRE) **Mr Tom Mohan & Allan McNamee**
3 DAZZLING VALENTINE, 6, b m Oratorio (IRE)—Bedazzling (IRE) **The Glenbuccaneers**
4 GO FAR, 4, b f Dutch Art—Carranita (IRE) **Mr R. J. H. West**
5 HANDSOME STRANGER (IRE), 4, ch g Tamayuz—Just Special **Mr J. F. Stocker**
6 MEGALEKA, 4, b f Misu Bond (IRE)—Peyto Princess **North Cheshire Trading & Storage Ltd**
7 MESPONE (FR), 5, b g Vespone (IRE)—Manon **T & Z Racing Club**
8 POPPY BOND, 4, b f Misu Bond (IRE)—Matilda Peace **North Cheshire Trading & Storage Ltd**
9 SIXTIES QUEEN, 4, b f Sixties Icon—Lily of Tagula (IRE) **Tregarth Racing & Partner**
10 ST IGNATIUS, 7, b g Ishiguru (IRE)—Branston Berry (IRE) **Allan McNamee & Alan Bailey**
11 STRICTLY SILVER (IRE), 5, gr g Dalakhani (IRE)—Miss Chaussini (IRE) **Allan McNamee & Alan Bailey**

THREE-YEAR-OLDS

12 ANYTIMEATALL (IRE), b f Kodiac—Under My Skin (IRE) **AB Racing Limited**
13 CRESTA RISE, br f Authorized (IRE)—Cresta Gold **P. T. Tellwright**
14 MASTERPAVER, gr g Mastercraftsman (IRE)—Most-Saucy **Mrs A. M. Riney**
15 SAFFIRE SONG, ch f Firebreak—Saffwah (IRE) **Mrs M. Shone**
16 SCRUFFY TRAMP (IRE), br g Kheleyf (USA)—Reem One (IRE) **Mr J. F. Stocker**
17 STEVENTON STAR, b g Pastoral Pursuits—Premiere Dance (IRE) **Mr J. F. Stocker**
18 TRINITY LORRAINE (IRE), b f Dark Angel (IRE)—Known Class (USA) **Dr S. P. Hargreaves**

TWO-YEAR-OLDS

19 Gr f 21/1 Zebedee—Alexander Family (IRE) (Danetime (IRE)) (24000) **Mr M. Lowther**
20 B c 28/3 High Chaparral (IRE)—Cool Catena (One Cool Cat (USA)) (95000) **Dr S. Hargreaves**
21 B c 30/4 Clodovil (IRE)—Idle Rich (USA) (Sky Classic (CAN)) (15000) **Mr J. Stocker & Mr A. McNamee**
22 MRS EVE (IRE), ch f 9/4 Bahamian Bounty—Catbells (IRE) (Rakti) **Mr & Mrs C. Martin**
23 B f 19/4 Fast Company—Suzi's A Smartlady (IRE) (Rakti) (11000) **Mr J. Stocker & Mr A. McNamee**

Other Owners: Mr A. Bailey, Mr P. Baker, Miss Zora Fakirmohamed, Mr H. Hall, Mr Allan McNamee, Mr T. Mohan, Mr P. M. Murphy, Mr Terrence White, Mr R. L. Williams.

Assistant Trainer: Mrs J. P. Bailey

Jockey (flat): Natasha Eaton.

---

12 **MRS CAROLINE BAILEY, Holdenby**
Postal: **Holdenby North Lodge, Spratton, Northamptonshire, NN6 8LG**
Contacts: **PHONE (01604) 883729 (Home) (01604) 770234 (Yard) FAX (01604) 770423**
MOBILE (07831) 373340
E-MAIL caroline.bailey4@btinternet.com WEBSITE www.carolinebaileyracing.co.uk

1 BRASSBOUND (USA), 6, b g Redoute's Choice (AUS)—In A Bound (AUS) **C. W. Booth**
2 CARLI KING (IRE), 8, br g Witness Box (USA)—Abinitio Lady (IRE) **Varley, Lloyd & Bailey**
3 CHASSE EN MER (FR), 4, b f Protektor (GER)—Cybertina (FR) **Mrs S. Carsberg**
4 DEALING RIVER, 7, b g Avonbridge—Greensand **Mrs S. M. Richards**

MRS CAROLINE BAILEY - Continued

5 **DENALI HIGHWAY (IRE)**, 7, ch g Governor Brown (USA)—Amaretto Flame (IRE) **Ian Payne & Kim Franklin**
6 **DERMATOLOGISTE**, 11, b m Kayf Tara—Poor Skin (IRE) **Mrs L. C. Taylor**
7 **GALWAY JACK (IRE)**, 9, b g Witness Box (USA)—Cooldalus (IRE) **Mrs M. E. Moody**
8 **GLOBAL BONUS (IRE)**, 5, b g Heron Island (IRE)—That's The Bonus (IRE) **Mrs S. Carsberg**
9 **HIGH HOLLOA**, 5, ch m Distant Music (USA)—Elmside Katie **Mr P. Dixon Smith**
10 **HIGH RON**, 9, b g Rainbow High—Sunny Heights **Mrs G. A. Burke**
11 **NOBLE LEGEND**, 7, b g Midnight Legend—Elmside Katie **Mr P. Dixon Smith**
12 **PRINCE DES MARAIS (FR)**, 11, b br g Network (GER)—Djeba Royale (FR) **C. W. Booth**
13 **QUEEN OLIVIA**, 6, b m King's Theatre—Queen's Leader **Mr R. Hunnisett**
14 **SCOLT HEAD ISLAND**, 8, ch m Alflora (IRE)—Auchendinny Jay **Mr A. J. Papworth**
15 **SMARTMAX (FR)**, 5, ch g Until Sundown (USA)—Quendora (FR) **C. Flinton**
16 **SPECKLED DOOR**, 6, b g Brian Boru—Monte Mayor Golf (IRE) **Mr A. & Mrs P. Hurn**
17 **TEETON BLACKVELVET**, 5, gr m Fair Mix (IRE)—Teeton Priceless
18 **TRAPPER PEAK (IRE)**, 5, b g Westerner—Banningham Blaze **R. & P. Scott & I. Payne & K. Franklin**

Other Owners: G. T. H. Bailey, Miss K. M. Franklin, A. Hurn, The Hon Mrs A. Hurn, Mr R. B. Lloyd, Mr I. T. Payne, R. Scott, Mrs P. M. Scott, Mr M. Varley.

Jockey (NH): Tom Messenger, Adam Pogson, Andrew Thornton. **Amateur:** Mr Jonathan Bailey.

---

13 MR KIM BAILEY, Cheltenham
Postal: **Thorndale Farm, Withington Road, Andoversford, Cheltenham, Gloucestershire, GL54 4LL**
Contacts: **PHONE** (01242) 890241 **FAX** (01242) 890193 **MOBILE** (07831) 416859
E-MAIL info@kimbaileyracing.com **WEBSITE** www.kimbaileyracing.com

1 **A SHADE OF BAY**, 6, b m Midnight Legend—Pulling Strings (IRE) **The Real Partnership**
2 **ABLE DEPUTY**, 7, b g Lomitas—Island Colony (USA) **W. J. Ives**
3 **AGENT FEDORA**, 6, b m Kayf Tara—Flora Poste **Mrs S. F. Dibben**
4 **ALMADIN (IRE)**, 6, b g Azamour (IRE)—Alamouna (IRE) **A & S Enterprises Ltd**
5 **AMAZING D'AZY (IRE)**, 6, br m Presenting—Shuil Mavourneen (IRE) **Mrs E. Ellis**
6 **AZURE AWARE (IRE)**, 7, b g Milan—Luck Penni (IRE) **J. F. Perriss**
7 **BALLYWATT (IRE)**, 8, b g Kayf Tara—Lady Arpel (IRE) **Mrs V. W. H. Johnson**
8 **BAY MAX**, 5, b g Fair Mix (IRE)—Suilven **I. F. W. Buchan**
9 **BISHOPHILL JACK (IRE)**, 8, b g Tikkanen (USA)—Kerrys Cross (IRE) **The On The Bridle Partnership**
10 **BY THE BOARDWALK (IRE)**, 6, br g Presenting—Peripheral Vision (IRE) **J. F. Perriss**
11 **CHARINGWORTH (IRE)**, 11, b g Supreme Leader—Quinnsboro Guest (IRE) **A & S Enterprises Ltd**
12 **DEVILS PAINTBRUSH (IRE)**, 6, b g Shantou (USA)—Back Log (IRE) **Racing For Research Partnership II**
13 **EARLY BONNET (IRE)**, 6, b m Old Vic—Superior Dawn (IRE) **Have Fun Racing Partnership**
14 **ELLIN'S TOWER**, 5, b m Kayf Tara—Lucia Forte **Mrs Julie Martin & David R. Martin**
15 **FINMERELLO**, 8, b m Definite Article—Belle Magello (FR) **K. Marsden & J. P. Lim**
16 **FLEMENSMIX**, 6, gr g Flemensfirth (USA)—Perfect Mix (FR) **The Perfect Mix Racing Club**
17 **GALLERY EXHIBITION (IRE)**, 7, b g Portrait Gallery (IRE)—Good Hearted (IRE) **The GFH Partnership**
18 **GRAND MARCH**, 5, b g Beat All (USA)—Bora Bora **Mme J. B. Baldanza**
19 **GRANDMA SMITH**, 6, b m Tobougg (IRE)—Grandma Lily (IRE) **J. W. Hardy**
20 **HANDSOME HARRY (IRE)**, 8, b g Broadway Flyer (USA)—Whistful Suzie (IRE) **Mrs E. A. Kellar**
21 **HARRY TOPPER**, 7, b g Sir Harry Lewis (USA)—Indeed To Goodness (IRE) **D. J. Keyte**
22 **JIMMY THE JETPLANE**, 6, b g Jimble (FR)—C'est Cool (IRE) **The Cool Silk Partnership**
23 **KIBO**, 4, b g Lucarno (USA)—Fantastisch (IRE) **Mrs M. C. Sweeney**
24 **KING'S OPUS (IRE)**, 5, b g King's Theatre—Kahysera **Mrs Julie Martin & David R. Martin**
25 **KNOCKANRAWLEY (IRE)**, 6, gr g Portrait Gallery (IRE)—Hot Lips (IRE) **Kim Bailey Racing Partnership VIII**
26 **LA BELLE SAUVAGE**, 7, ch m Old Vic—Lady Rebecca **Kinnersley Optimists**
27 **MAGIC MONEY**, 6, b m Midnight Legend—Sticky Money **M. D. C. Jenks**
28 **MAX BYGRAVES**, 11, ch g Midnight Legend—Smokey Diva (IRE) **J. F. Perriss**
29 **MIDNIGHT OSCAR (IRE)**, 7, br g Oscar (IRE)—Midnight Light (IRE) **The Oscar Partnership**
30 **MILORD (GER)**, 5, br h Monsun (GER)—Montserrat (GER) **Kim Bailey Racing Partnership VII**
31 **MOLLY'S A DIVA**, 5, ch m Midnight Legend—Smokey Diva (IRE) **J. F. Perriss**
32 **MRS PEACHEY (IRE)**, 7, b m Brian Boru—Maracana (IRE) **The Boom Syndicate**
33 **MULDOON'S PICNIC (IRE)**, 8, b g King's Theatre (IRE)—Going My Way **Mr C. A. Washbourn**
34 **NET WORK ROUGE (FR)**, 5, b g Network (GER)—
Lychee de La Roque (FR) **John Wills & David ReidScott Partnership**
35 4, B f Kayf Tara—Nile Cristale (FR) **Kim Bailey Racing Partnership**
36 **PATSYS CASTLE (IRE)**, 7, ch g Windsor Castle—Annienoora (IRE) **Mr P. P. Moorby**
37 **PREMIER PORTRAIT (IRE)**, 7, b g Portrait Gallery (IRE)—Shesnotthelast (IRE) **Mrs P. A. Perriss**
38 **SAVANT BLEU (FR)**, 8, ch g Agent Bleu (FR)—Avane Ili (FR) **Kim Bailey Racing Partnership III**

MR KIM BAILEY - Continued

39 **SILVER EAGLE (IRE)**, 6, gr g Presenting—Lady Lincon (IRE) **Kim Bailey Racing Partnership IV**
40 **SOUTH STACK**, 9, b g Alflora (IRE)—Mandy Chat (IRE) **Mrs Julie Martin & David R. Martin**
41 **SPARVILLE (IRE)**, 8, ch g Docksider (USA)—Play The Queen (IRE) **Racing For Research Partnership**
42 **SUCH A LEGEND**, 6, ch g Midnight Legend—Mrs Fizziwig **The Real Partnership**
43 **SUPREME PRESENT**, 6, b m Presenting—Deep Sunset (IRE) **Lucky Bin Racing & Little Lodge Farm**
44 **THE RAINBOW HUNTER**, 10, b g Rainbow High—Sobranie **May We Never Be Found Out Partnership**
45 **THE SCARLETT WOMAN**, 5, b m Kayf Tara—Double Red (IRE) **Mrs P. A. Perriss**
46 **TRUMIX**, 6, b g Fair Mix (IRE)—Indeed To Goodness (IRE) **Kim Bailey Racing Partnership II**
47 **TWELVE ROSES**, 6, ch g Midnight Legend—Miniature Rose **Jones Broughtons Wilson Weaver**
48 **UN ACE (FR)**, 6, b g Voix du Nord (FR)—First Ball (FR) **Ace In The Pack Partnership**
49 **UP FOR AN OSCAR (IRE)**, 7, b g Oscar (IRE)—Queen of Harts (IRE) **The Hon Mrs A. M. Cookson**
50 **WENLOCKS BOXER**, 5, b g Kayf Tara—Black Collar **W. J. Ives**
51 **WEST END (IRE)**, 7, b g Westerner—Brown Bess (IRE) **D. A. Hall**
52 **WRESTOW LADY (IRE)**, 6, b m Presenting—Christines Gale (IRE) **Kim Bailey Racing Partnership IX**

Other Owners: Mr K. C. Bailey, Mrs Kim Bailey, Mr Oliver Bell, Mr Charles Bithell, Sir Martin Broughton, Mr Stephen Broughton, Mr Michael J. Campbell, Mr Stephen Cannon, Mr M. Checketts, Mr R. D. Chugg, Mrs Robert Chugg, Mr Kevin T. Clancy, Mr Dermot M. Clancy, Mr Bob Clarke, Mr Gordon Farr, Mr N. R. Jennings, Mrs Nicholas Jones, Mr P. S. Kerr, Mr Henry Kimbell, Mr J-P. Lim, Mr K. Marsden, Mrs Julie Martin, Mr David R. Martin, Mr C. W. Mather, Mr B. Robbins, Mr A. N. Solomons, Mrs Sandra Steer-Fowler, Dr Martyn Steer-Fowler, Mr G. D. W. Swire, Mrs C. A. T. Swire, Mrs Nicky Van Dijk, Mrs Giles Weaver, Mr Duncan R. Williams, Mr Tom Wilson.

Assistant Trainer: Mathew Nicholls

Conditional: Ed Cookson.

---

14 MRS TRACEY L. BAILEY, Hungerford
Postal: **Soley Farm Stud, Chilton Foliat, Hungerford, Berkshire, RG17 0TW**
Contacts: **PHONE (01488) 683321**

1 **BROADWAY SYMPHONY (IRE)**, 7, ch g Broadway Flyer (USA)—Flying Hooves (IRE) **N. R. A. Sutton**
2 **MARUFO (IRE)**, 12, b g Presenting—Bucks Cregg (IRE) **N. R. A. Sutton**
3 **OFFSHORE ACCOUNT (IRE)**, 14, b g Oscar (IRE)—Park Breeze (IRE) **N. R. A. Sutton**

---

15 MISS EMMA BAKER, Cheltenham
Postal: **Brockhill, Naunton, Cheltenham, Gloucestershire, GL54 3BA**
Contacts: PHONE **(01451) 850714 (Home)** FAX **(01451) 850199** MOBILE **(07887) 845970**
E-MAIL **emmajbakerracing@hotmail.co.uk** WEBSITE **www.emmabakerracing.com**

1 **BACK BY MIDNIGHT**, 5, ch g Midnight Legend—Roberta Back (IRE) **Mrs J. Arnold**
2 **BAJARDO (IRE)**, 6, b g Jammaal—Bit of Peace (IRE) **Mrs J. Arnold**
3 **BOURDELLO**, 5, b m Milan—Haudello (FR) **Mrs J. Arnold**
4 **CHURCH HALL (IRE)**, 6, b g Craigsteel—Island Religion (IRE) **Mrs J. Arnold**
5 **CRACKERJACK**, 7, ch g Lahib (USA)—Tidesong **Mrs J. Arnold**
6 **MASTER CARDOR VISA (IRE)**, 9, br g Alderbrook—Princess Moodyshoe **Mrs J. Arnold**
7 **MIDNIGHT CHARMER**, 8, b g Midnight Legend—Dickies Girl **Mrs J. Arnold**
8 **NOVUS ORDO (IRE)**, 5, b g Olden Times—Ballybeg Charm (IRE)
9 **PADDLEYOUROWNCANOE (IRE)**, 13, b g Saddlers' Hall (IRE)—Little Paddle (IRE) **Miss E. J. Baker**
10 **PETRARCHICK (USA)**, 7, b m Arch (USA)—Tustin (USA) **Mr P. G. Horrocks**
11 **SOCIAL OVERDRIVE (IRE)**, 8, b g Alderbrook—La Grande Duchesse (IRE) **The Socialites**
12 **SUBTLE APPROACH (IRE)**, 9, b g Subtle Power (IRE)—Rotoruasprings (IRE) **Mrs J. Arnold**
13 **TIGNELLO (IRE)**, 9, b g Kendor (FR)—La Genereuse **Mrs J. Arnold**

Other Owners: Mrs C. P. Bedford, J. F. Perriss.

16 MR GEORGE BAKER, Manton

Postal: **Barton Yard, Manton House Estate, Marlborough, Wiltshire, SN8 4HB**
Contacts: **PHONE OFFICE: (01672) 515493 (01672) 516234 FAX (01672) 514938**
MOBILE (07889) 514881
E-MAIL gbakerracing@gmail.com WEBSITE www.georgebakerracing.com

1 **ABIGAIL LYNCH (IRE)**, 6, b m Oscar (IRE)—Tanit Lady (IRE) **Rose Tinted Racing**
2 **ALL ON RED (IRE)**, 4, b f Red Clubs (IRE)—Champion Tipster **PJL Racing**
3 **ANCIENT GREECE**, 7, b g Pivotal—Classicism (USA) **Inkin, Inkin, Byng, Baker & Partners**
4 **AQUA ARDENS (GER)**, 6, b g Nayef (USA)—Arduinna (GER) **M Khan X2**
5 **BELGIAN BILL**, 6, b h Exceed And Excel (AUS)—Gay Romance **PJL, Byrne & Baker**
6 **BOOMSHACKERLACKER (IRE)**, 4, gr c Dark Angel (IRE)—Allegrina (IRE) **PJL Racing**
7 **BOUNTYBEAMADAM**, 4, b f Bahamian Bounty—Madamoiselle Jones **Whitsbury Hopefuls**
8 **CAPITOL GAIN (IRE)**, 5, b g Bahamian Bounty—Emmas Princess (IRE) **Mrs L. O. Sangster**
9 **CHATTANOOGA LINE**, 4, b f Rail Link—Gay Romance **Wickfield Stud & Hartshill Stud**
10 **DANA'S PRESENT**, 5, ch g Osorio (GER)—Euro Empire (USA) **Whitsbury Racing Club**
11 **DEE AITCH DEE**, 4, gr f Sakhee's Secret—Fluttering Rose **Lady Cobham & Mr G. Irwin**
12 **DESTINY'S GOLD**, 4, b g Millenary—Knockhouse Rose (IRE) **Delancey & Mrs V Finegold**
13 **ETON RAMBLER (USA)**, 4, b br g Hard Spun (USA)—Brightbraveandgood (USA) **The Eton Ramblers**
14 **FOUR NATIONS (USA)**, 6, ch g Langfuhr (CAN)—Kiswahili **The Transatlantic USA Syndicate**
15 **GEORGE BAKER (IRE)**, 7, b g Camacho—Petite Maxine **George Baker**
16 **HALLEY (FR)**, 7, b g Loup Solitaire (USA)—Moon Glow (FR) **PJL Racing & TR George**
17 **HUMIDOR (IRE)**, 7, b g Camacho—Miss Indigo **Delancey Real Estate Asset Management Limited**
18 **I'M FRAAM GOVAN**, 6, ch g Fraam—Urban Dancer (IRE) **Sir A. Ferguson**
19 **I'M HARRY**, 5, b g Haafhd—First Approval **Wickfield Stud & Hartshill Stud**
20 **ISHIAMBER**, 4, ch f Ishiguru (USA)—Black And Amber **Mrs P Scott-Dunn**
21 **JACK'S REVENGE (IRE)**, 6, br g Footstepsinthesand—Spirit of Age (IRE) **PJL Racing**
22 **JOEY'S DESTINY (IRE)**, 4, ch g Kheleyf (USA)—
Maid of Ailsa (USA) **Delancey Real Estate Asset Management Limited**
23 **LAUGHING JACK**, 6, b g Beat Hollow—Bronzewing **Mr P. A. Downing**
24 **LITTLE PUDDING**, 6, b m Sleeping Indian—Neptunalia **Mrs M. C. Hambro**
25 **LUCKY BLACK STAR (IRE)**, 4, b g Lawman (FR)—Silver Bandana (USA) **Black Star Limited & Andy Luckhurst**
26 **MEDBURN CUTLER**, 4, ch g Zafeen (FR)—Tiegs (IRE) **Mr E. L. Evans**
27 **MISTER CARROT**, 4, b g Elusive City (USA)—It's Twilight Time **The Allotment Gang**
28 **MRS WARREN**, 4, b f Kyllachy—Bold Bunny **George Baker & Partners**
29 **NENGE MBOKO**, 4, b g Compton Place—Floppie (FR) **Russell Conrad Vail Wheeler Hippychick**
30 **PANDY**, 5, b m Sakhee—Ceiriog Valley **R. J. McAlpine**
31 **RED FOUR**, 4, ch f Singspiel (IRE)—Protectorate **Lady N. F. Cobham**
32 **REFRESHESTHEPARTS (USA)**, 5, ch m Proud Citizen (USA)—St Francis Wood (USA) **Mr M. R. de Carvalho**
33 **SINBAD THE SAILOR**, 9, b g Cape Cross (IRE)—Sinead (USA) **Baker, Coleman, Wand & Williams**
34 **SQUIRREL WOOD**, 6, b m Sadler's Wells—Didbrook **Mrs M. C. Hambro**
35 **UGANDA GLORY (USA)**, 4, b br f Hat Trick (JPN)—Febrile (USA) **George Baker & Partners**
36 **YUL FINEGOLD**, 4, b g Invincible Spirit (IRE)—Mascara **Mrs V. Finegold**

THREE-YEAR-OLDS

37 **CASTORIENTA**, ch f Orientor—The Lady Caster **D. P. Barrie**
38 Ch f Sakhee's Secret—Darling Daisy **Mrs P. A. Scott-Dunn**
39 **FIFTYSHADESDARKER (IRE)**, gr c Invincible Spirit (IRE)—Poetry In Motion (IRE) **Team Fifty**
40 **FIFTYSHADESFREED (IRE)**, gr g Verglas (IRE)—Vasilia **Team Fifty**
41 **FIFTYSHADESOFGREY (IRE)**, gr c Dark Angel (IRE)—Wohaida (IRE) **Team Fifty**
42 **HIPZ (IRE)**, br f Intense Focus (USA)—Radha **George Baker & Partners**
43 B f Nomadic Way (USA)—Jago's Girl **Mr & Mrs Giles**
44 **LAURELITA (IRE)**, b f High Chaparral (IRE)—Chervil **Mr & Mrs J Pittam & Peter Gleeson**
45 **LOVING YOUR WORK**, b g Royal Applause—Time Crystal (IRE) **The Loving Your Work Syndicate**
46 **MENDACIOUS HARPY (IRE)**, b f Dark Angel (IRE)—Idesia (IRE) **Mr R. Curry**
47 **MISTER MAYDAY (IRE)**, b g Kheleyf (USA)—Soxy Doxy (IRE) **Asprey, Kane & Thomas**
48 **REDLORRYELLOWLORRY (IRE)**, b g Bushranger (IRE)—Bronze Baby (USA) **PJL Racing**
49 **RORING SAMSON (IRE)**, b c Art Connoisseur (IRE)—Marju Guest (IRE) **Mr P. Bowden**
50 **SLEEPING VENUS (IRE)**, ch f Excellent Art—Sun Moon and Stars (IRE) **Equi ex Incertis Partners**
51 **SOCIETY DIVA (IRE)**, b f Kheleyf (USA)—Mistle Thrush (USA) **Mr A. G. Irwin**
52 **STAN NINETEEN (IRE)**, b c Kodiac—Redwood Forest (IRE) **The Villains**

MR GEORGE BAKER - Continued

TWO-YEAR-OLDS

53 B f 9/1 Approve (IRE)—Bakewell Tart (IRE) (Tagula (IRE)) (19357) **George Baker and Partners**
54 **DESTINY'S SHADOW (IRE)**, b c 22/3 Dark Angel (IRE)—
Lunar Love (IRE) (In The Wings) (25000) **Delancey Real Estate Asset Management Limited**
55 Gr f 29/2 Dark Angel (IRE)—Distant Piper (IRE) (Distant Music (USA)) (17034) **George Baker and Partners**
56 B c 17/4 Compton Place—Floppie (FR) (Law Society (USA)) **Russell, Hippychick & Baker**
57 **FLUTTERBEE**, b f 2/5 Equiano (FR)—Dunya (Unfuwain (USA)) (50000) **PJL Racing**
58 **HARRY HURRICANE**, b c 24/4 Kodiac—Eolith (Pastoral Pursuits) (36190) **PJL Racing**
59 Ch f 10/4 Lord Shanakill (USA)—
Highwater Dancer (IRE) (Sadler's Wells (USA)) (11614) **George Baker and Partners**
60 **ORLANDO ROGUE**, b c 13/4 Bushranger (IRE)—
Boston Ivy (USA) (Mark of Esteem (IRE)) (46457) **Mr and Mrs J Pittam**
61 Ch c 18/4 Zebedee—Playful (Piccolo) (32520) **PJL Racing**
62 B f 26/4 Kodiac—Summer Sunshine (Dubai Destination (USA)) (8517) **George Baker and Partners**
63 **ZUBAIDAH**, b f 10/3 Exceed And Excel (AUS)—
Bedouin Bride (USA) (Chester House (USA)) (30000) **Equi ex Incertis Partners**

Other Owners: Miss E. Asprey, Mr George Baker, Mrs C. E. S. Baker, Blackstar (Europe) Limited, Mr P. Bowden, Mr Justin Byrne, Mr Victor Chandler, Sean Clancy, Lady Cobham, Mr A. Coleman, Mr A. Conrad, Delancey, Mr Marcus Edwards-Jones, Mrs R. S. Evans, Mr Richard Evans, Mrs Virginia Finegold, Mr P. Gleeson, Hippychick Limited, Miss L Hurley, Mr Piers Inkin, Mr Giles Irwin, Mr David Jenks, Mr M. Khan, Mr Mustafa Khan, Mr Marcus Locock, Mr A. Luckhurst, Mr L. Lugg, Sir I. Magee, Erika Mitchell, Mr A. Nicolls, Mr Stephen Penny, Mr J. Pittam, Mrs A. J. Pittam, Mr Jamie Ritblat, Mr D. I. Russell, Mr W. A. B. Russell, Mr B. V. Sangster, Mr Tim Slade, Lord Spencer, Mr John Stockdale, Mr James Richard Terry, Mr G. D. Thorp, Mr L. R. Turland, Dominic Vail, Mr Toby Wand, Mr N. Wheeler, Mrs P. H. Williams, Mr Michael Wilson, Ms Camilla Wright.

Assistant Trainers: Patrick Murphy, Valerie Murphy.

Jockey (flat): Pat Cosgrave. **Jockey (NH):** Andrew Tinkler. **Conditional:** Trevor Whelan.

---

17   **MR ANDREW BALDING, Kingsclere**
Postal: Park House Stables, Kingsclere, Newbury, Berkshire, RG20 5PZ
Contacts: PHONE (01635) 298210 FAX (01635) 298305 MOBILE (07774) 633791
E-MAIL admin@kingsclere.com WEBSITE www.kingsclere.com

1 **A BOY NAMED SUZI**, 6, b g Medecis—Classic Coral **Qatar Racing Limited**
2 **ABSOLUTELY SO (IRE)**, 4, b c Acclamation—Week End **Mr & Mrs G. A. E. Smith**
3 **ANGELIC UPSTART (IRE)**, 6, b g Singspiel (IRE)—Rada (IRE) **Mr B. Burdett**
4 **BALLINDERRY BOY**, 4, b g Kayf Tara—Spring Dream (IRE) **Rainbow Racing**
5 **BEYOND CONCEIT (IRE)**, 5, b g Galileo (IRE)—Baraka (IRE) **Mrs F. H. Hay**
6 **BREAKHEART (IRE)**, 7, b g Shamardal—Exorcet (FR) **I. A. Balding**
7 **BUTTERFLY MCQUEEN (USA)**, 4, b f Curlin (USA)—Distant Roar (CAN) **A Ferguson, G Mason & P Done**
8 **CHIBERTA KING**, 8, b g King's Best—Glam Rock **The Pink Hat Racing Partnership**
9 **COMMUNICATOR**, 6, b g Motivator—Goodie Twosues **Lady S. Davis**
10 **DANDY (GER)**, 5, b g Nayef (USA)—Diacada (GER) **Mr R. E. Tillett**
11 **DAYLIGHT**, 4, ch g Firebreak—Dayville (USA) **Kennet Valley Thoroughbreds V**
12 **DEBDEBDEB**, 4, b f Teofilo (IRE)—Windmill **C. C. Buckley**
13 **DESERT COMMAND**, 4, b g Oasis Dream—Speed Cop **J. C. Smith**
14 **DUNGANNON**, 7, b g Monsieur Bond (IRE)—May Light **Dr E. Harris**
15 **GRAND PIANO (IRE)**, 7, b g Arakan (USA)—Stately Princess **I. A. Balding**
16 **HAVANA BEAT (IRE)**, 4, b g Teofilo (IRE)—Sweet Home Alabama (IRE) **Mick and Janice Mariscotti**
17 **HERE COMES WHEN (IRE)**, 4, b g Danehill Dancer (IRE)—Quad's Melody (IRE) **Mrs F. H. Hay**
18 **HIGHLAND COLORI (IRE)**, 6, b g Le Vie Dei Colori—Emma's Star (ITY) **Mr E.M. Sutherland**
19 **HIGHLAND KNIGHT (IRE)**, 7, b g Night Shift (USA)—Highland Shot **J. C. Smith**
20 **IMPERIAL GLANCE**, 4, br g Passing Glance—Juno Mint **Mrs J. S. Newton**
21 **INTRANSIGENT**, 5, b g Trans Island—Mara River **Kingsclere Racing Club**
22 **LADY OF THE VINE (USA)**, 4, b f Master Command (USA)—
Silverbulletlover (USA) **A Ferguson, G Mason & P Done**
23 **LIZZIE TUDOR**, 4, ch f Tamayuz—Silca Destination **Ms K. Gough**
24 **MODERN TUTOR**, 5, b g Selkirk (USA)—Magical Romance (IRE) **Mr D. E. Brownlow & Mr P. Fox**
25 **MY LEARNED FRIEND (IRE)**, 10, b g Marju—Stately Princess **I. A. Balding**
26 **MYSTERIOUS MAN (IRE)**, 5, b g Manduro (GER)—Edabiya (IRE) **Mr & Mrs R. M. Gorell**
27 **NEW FFOREST**, 4, b f Oasis Dream—Ffestiniog (IRE) **Elite Racing Club**
28 **OASIS SPIRIT**, 4, b f Oasis Dream—Fearless Spirit (USA) **A. M. Balding**

MR ANDREW BALDING - Continued

29 **OMAR KHAYYAM**, 5, b h Pivotal—Kithanga (IRE) **J. L. C. Pearce**
30 **PERFECT MISSION**, 6, b g Bertolini (USA)—Sharp Secret (IRE) **Mildmay Racing & D. H. Caslon**
31 **PERFECT SPELL**, 4, ch c Singspiel (IRE)—Flamjica (USA) **The Cadagan Partnership**
32 **POEM (IRE)**, 4, ch f Dylan Thomas (IRE)—Almarai (USA) **Mr R. J. C. Wilmot-Smith**
33 **PRAIRIE RANGER**, 4, b g Montjeu (IRE)—No Frills (IRE) **Dr P. J. Brown**
34 **PURCELL (IRE)**, 4, b g Acclamation—Lyca Ballerina **Highclere Thoroughbred Racing-John Porter**
35 **QUEEN'S STAR**, 5, ch m With Approval (CAN)—Memsahib **Sir Gordon Brunton**
36 **RACE AND STATUS (IRE)**, 4, b g Raven's Pass (USA)—Love Excelling (FR) **Mr & Mrs G. A. E. Smith**
37 **RAWAKI (IRE)**, 6, b g Phoenix Reach (IRE)—Averami **Kingsclere Racing Club**
38 **ROSERROW**, 5, ch g Beat Hollow—Sabah **Sir Roger Buckley, Mr Gerald Oury**
39 **SEA SOLDIER (IRE)**, 6, b g Red Ransom (USA)—Placement **Mrs C. J. Wates**
40 **SHAMASSIBA (IRE)**, 4, b f Shamardal (USA)—Nilassiba **Hillwood Racing**
41 **SIDE GLANCE**, 7, b g Passing Glance—Averami **Pearl Bloodstock Limited**
42 **SILVER POND (FR)**, 7, gr h Act One—Silver Fame (USA) **Saeed Nasser Al Romaithi**
43 **SOVIET ROCK (IRE)**, 4, b g Rock of Gibraltar (IRE)—Anna Karenina (USA) **Mr & Mrs G. A. E. Smith**
44 **STIRRING BALLAD**, 5, ch m Compton Place—Balnaha **G. Strawbridge**
45 **SWAN SONG**, 5, br m Green Desert (USA)—Lochsong **J. C. Smith**
46 **TULLIUS (IRE)**, 6, ch g Le Vie Dei Colori—Whipped Queen (USA) **Kennet Valley Thoroughbreds VI**
47 **VAN PERCY**, 4, b g Sir Percy—Enforce (USA) **Mrs L E Ramsden & Richard Morecombe**
48 **VICKSBURG**, 4, b f Cape Cross (IRE)—Totality **Mr R. J. C. Wilmot-Smith**
49 **WHIPLASH WILLIE**, 6, ch g Phoenix Reach (IRE)—Santa Isobel **J. C. & S. R. Hitchins**
50 **ZANETTO**, 4, b g Medicean—Play Bouzouki **Mick and Janice Mariscotti**

THREE-YEAR-OLDS

51 **ALUMINA (IRE)**, b f Invincible Spirit (IRE)—La Reine Mambo (USA) **Mr S. Mistry**
52 **BELFILO (IRE)**, ch g Teofilo (IRE)—Belsay **Mrs F. H. Hay**
53 **BISHOP OF RUSCOMBE**, b c Mount Nelson—Pain Perdu (IRE) **D. E. Brownlow**
54 **BORN IN BOMBAY**, b c Shamardal (USA)—Pearl Dance (USA) **G. Strawbridge**
55 **CAPE VICTORIA**, b f Mount Nelson—Victoria Montoya **Kingsclere Racing Club**
56 **CASUAL SMILE**, ch f Sea The Stars (IRE)—Casual Look (USA) **Mr W. S. Farish**
57 **CHESIL BEACH**, b f Phoenix Reach (IRE)—Seaflower Reef (IRE) **Kingsclere Racing Club**
58 **CHINOTTO (IRE)**, b c Duke of Marmalade (IRE)—Muskoka Dawn (USA) **Mick and Janice Mariscotti**
59 **COLLABORATION**, b g Halling (USA)—Red Shareef **Another Bottle Racing 2**
60 **COMANCHERO (IRE)**, b g Camacho—Trempjane **Kennet Valley Thoroughbreds VII**
61 **DARTING**, b f Shamardal (USA)—Dararita (IRE) **The Birdcage & Lloyd Webber Family**
62 **DER MEISTER (IRE)**, ro g Mastercraftsman (IRE)—Agnetha (GER) **James/Michaelson/Greenwood 1**
63 **EILEENLILIAN**, b f Authorized (IRE)—Welsh Diva **Mr & Mrs G. A. E. Smith**
64 **END OF LINE**, b c Pastoral Pursuits—Just Devine (IRE) **Qatar Racing Limited**
65 **ENLIVEN**, b f Dansili—Aurore (IRE) **Her Majesty The Queen**
66 **EVERY TIME**, b f Pivotal—Time Away (IRE) **R. Barnett**
67 **FEMME DE MENAGE**, ch f Bahamian Bounty—Duena **Mrs C. J. Wates**
68 **FIELD OF FAME**, b c Champs Elysees—Aswaaq (IRE) **Thurloe Thoroughbreds XXXI**
69 **FROM FROST**, b c Nayef (USA)—Salutare (IRE) **G. Strawbridge**
70 **GALLIC DESTINY (IRE)**, b c Champs Elysees—Cross Your Fingers (USA) **Dr P. J. Brown**
71 **GEORDAN MURPHY**, b g Firebreak—Sukuma (IRE)
72 **GRACE AND FAVOUR**, b f Montjeu (IRE)—Gryada **N. M. H. Jones**
73 **GRACIOUS LADY**, b f Royal Applause—Succinct **Dr P. J. Brown**
74 **GREY GEM (IRE)**, gr c Danehill Dancer (IRE)—Tiffany Diamond (IRE) **J. C. Smith**
75 **HANNINGTON**, ch g Firebreak—Manderina **I. A. Balding**
76 **HIGH DRAMA (IRE)**, b f High Chaparral (IRE)—Highland Shot **J. C. Smith**
77 **IMPULSIVE MOMENT (IRE)**, ch c Galileo (IRE)—Luas Line (IRE) **Weston Brook Farm Bromfield & Whitaker**
78 **INFORMALITY (IRE)**, b f Haafhd—Casual Glance **Kingsclere Racing Club**
79 **JEREMY'S JET (IRE)**, b g Jeremy (USA)—Double Vie (IRE) **Mr N Botica, Mr Rex & Mrs Wendy Gorell**
80 **JONNY RAE**, b c Shirocco (GER)—Lady Brora **Kingsclere Racing Club**
81 **KNOCKROON**, b c Royal Applause—Spring Touch (USA) **D. E. Brownlow**
82 **KOKOVOKO (IRE)**, br c Trans Island—Khazaria (FR) **Mrs T. L. Miller**
83 **LIBECCIO (FR)**, b g Shirocco (GER)—Francais **Mick and Janice Mariscotti**
84 **MAN OF HARLECH**, b c Dansili—Ffestiniog (IRE) **Elite Racing Club**
85 **MERRY ME (IRE)**, b f Invincible Spirit (IRE)—Thought Is Free **Mrs F. H. Hay**
86 **MICRAS**, b f Medicean—Purple Heather (USA) **Her Majesty The Queen**
87 **MIME DANCE**, b g Notnowcato—Encore My Love **D. E. Brownlow**
88 **MONTALY**, b c Yeats (IRE)—Le Badie (IRE) **The Farleigh Court Racing Partnership**
89 **MUIR LODGE**, ch g Exceed And Excel (AUS)—Miss Chaussini (IRE) **Mrs F. H. Hay**
90 **MYMATECHRIS (IRE)**, b c High Chaparral (IRE)—Splendeur (FR) **D. E. Brownlow**
91 **NABATEAN (IRE)**, b g Rock of Gibraltar (IRE)—Landinium (ITY) **Lord J. Blyth**

MR ANDREW BALDING - Continued

92 **OBSTINATE (IRE)**, b c Fastnet Rock (AUS)—Sangita **Mrs F. H. Hay**
93 **ON DEMAND**, ch f Teofilo (IRE)—Mimisel
94 **OPERA DUKE (IRE)**, ch g Duke of Marmalade (IRE)—Opera Glass **J. C. Smith**
95 **PACIFIC TRIP**, b c Tagula (IRE)—Marajuana **Kingsclere Racing Club**
96 **PASSOVER**, b g Passing Glance—Floriana **Kingsclere Racing Club**
97 **PICARDY (IRE)**, ch f Notnowcato—Sabah **Sir R. J. Buckley**
98 **POOL HOUSE**, b c Sakhee's Secret—Gitane (FR) **D. E. Brownlow**
99 **PRIORS BROOK**, b g Champs Elysees—Dyanita **Mrs L. Alexander**
100 **RESTRAINT**, b g Kheleyf (USA)—Inhibition **Kingsclere Racing Club**
101 **RIZAL PARK (IRE)**, b g Amadeus Wolf—Imelda (USA) **L. L. Register, Martin & Valerie Slade**
102 **ROSKILLY (IRE)**, ch c Hurricane Run (IRE)—Party Feet (IRE) **Mick and Janice Mariscotti**
103 **ROYAL PRESERVE**, ch g Duke of Marmalade (IRE)—Castaway Queen (IRE) **Mick and Janice Mariscotti**
104 **ROYAL WARRANTY**, ch f Sir Percy—Royal Patron **Sir Gordon Brunton**
105 **SCOPPIO DEL CARRO**, b g Medicean—Sadie Thompson (IRE) **Martin & Valerie Slade & Partner**
106 **SCOTLAND (GER)**, b c Monsun (GER)—Sqillo (IRE) **Mrs F. H. Hay**
107 **SECRET HINT**, b f Oasis Dream—Teeky **G. Strawbridge**
108 **SIGNAL**, b c Cape Cross (IRE)—Moon Sister (IRE) **Highclere Thoroughbred Racing - Conquest**
109 **SIGNPOSTED (IRE)**, b c Rock of Gibraltar (IRE)—Portentous **Mr N Botica, Mr Rex & Mrs Wendy Gorell**
110 **SMILING STRANGER**, b c Nayef (USA)—Carraigoona (IRE) **N. M. Watts**
111 **SPECTATOR**, br g Passing Glance—Averami **Kingsclere Racing Club**
112 **STORM FORCE TEN**, b g Shirocco (GER)—Stravinsky Dance **R. B. Waley-Cohen**
113 **STYBBA**, b f Medicean—Time Saved **Qatar Racing Limited**
114 **TELEGRAPH (IRE)**, b g Bushranger (IRE)—Vampire Queen (IRE) **Highclere Thoroughbred Racing - Alcove**
115 **VECHEKA (IRE)**, b g Lawman (FR)—Lidanski (IRE) **Mick and Janice Mariscotti**
116 **WILLY BRENNAN (IRE)**, br g Bushranger (IRE)—Miss Assertive **Dr P. J. Brown**
117 **WONDER WEAPON (GER)**, b c Konigstiger (GER)—Wurfspiel (GER) **Mr N Botica, Mr Rex & Mrs Wendy Gorell**
118 **WORTHY SPIRIT (GER)**, b g Shirocco (GER)—Wakytara (GER) **Mr N Botica, Mr Rex & Mrs Wendy Gorell**
119 **WYLYE**, gr f Dalakhani (IRE)—Tavy **Mrs A. Wigan**
120 **ZAMPA MANOS (USA)**, b g Arch (USA)—Doryphar (USA) **N. M. Watts**

TWO-YEAR-OLDS

121 B c 10/2 Royal Applause—Ada River (Dansili) (40000) **KTS**
122 Ch f 16/4 Kyllachy—Amanjena (Beat Hollow) **Mrs C. J. Wates**
123 B c 20/1 Halling (USA)—American Spirit (IRE) (Rock of Gibraltar (IRE)) **G. Strawbridge**
124 Ch c 9/4 Makfi—Arabian Spell (IRE) (Desert Prince (IRE)) (61943) **Mrs F. H. Hay**
125 B c 23/4 Oasis Dream—Attima (Zafonic (USA)) (69686) **Mrs F. H. Hay**
126 **BALLYNANTY (IRE)**, br c 15/4 Yeats (IRE)—Reina Blanca (Darshaan) (48005) **Mr R. J. C. Wilmot-Smith**
127 Ch c 3/4 Sleeping Indian—Balnaha (Lomond (USA)) **G. Strawbridge**
128 B c 31/1 Phoenix Reach (IRE)—Beat Seven (Beat Hollow) (28571) **Winterbeck Manor Stud**
129 B c 11/4 Makfi—Belle Reine (King of Kings) (75000) **Qatar Racing Limited**
130 **BERKSHIRE BEAUTY**, b f 3/5 Aqlaam—Salim Toto (Mtoto) (22000) **Berkshire Parts & Panels Ltd**
131 **BERKSHIRE HONEY**, br f 9/5 Sakhee's Secret—
    Sabrina Brown (Polar Falcon (USA)) (6000) **Berkshire Parts & Panels Ltd**
132 B c 27/4 Galileo (IRE)—Blue Symphony (Darshaan) (400000) **Qatar Racing Limited**
133 B c 28/4 Yeats (IRE)—Casual Glance (Sinndar (IRE)) **Kingsclere Racing Club**
134 B c 6/2 Dylan Thomas (IRE)—Chelsey Jayne (IRE) (Galileo (IRE)) (30000) **R P B Michaelson & Dr E Harris**
135 **COUNTERMAND**, b g 28/3 Authorized (IRE)—
    Answered Prayer (Green Desert (USA)) **Karen Gough & R Wilmot-Smith**
136 B c 4/2 Makfi—Crystal Reef (King's Best (USA)) **Qatar Racing Limited**
137 B c 10/5 Fastnet Rock (AUS)—Ela's Giant (Giant's Causeway (USA)) **Mr N. N. Botica**
138 Ch f 2/4 New Approach (IRE)—Exorcet (FR) (Selkirk (USA)) **J. C. Smith**
139 B f 19/4 Cape Cross (IRE)—Fearless Spirit (USA) (Spinning World (USA)) **G. Strawbridge**
140 Ch g 4/4 Norse Dancer (IRE)—Florida Heart (First Trump) **Kingsclere Racing Club**
141 **GALEOTTI**, ch c 29/4 Paco Boy (IRE)—Bella Lambada (Lammtarra (USA)) (50000) **Mick and Janice Mariscotti**
142 **HALA MADRID**, ch f 10/4 Nayef (USA)—Ermine (IRE) (Cadeaux Genereux) (30000) **N. M. Watts**
143 **HAVISHAM**, b c 11/2 Mount Nelson—Ile Deserte (Green Desert (USA)) (247773) **D. E. Brownlow**
144 Br c 13/3 High Chaparral (IRE)—Highland Shot (Selkirk (USA)) **J. C. Smith**
145 **HIT LIST (IRE)**, ch c 24/1 Makfi—Kassiopeia (IRE) (Galileo (IRE)) **Another Bottle Racing 2**
146 Ch f 15/2 Tamayuz—Holda (IRE) (Docksider (USA)) (65000) **Mr R. M. Gorell**
147 Ch f 14/4 New Approach (IRE)—Honorine (IRE) (Mark of Esteem (IRE)) **Qatar Racing Limited**
148 B gr f 19/2 Phoenix Reach (IRE)—Josie May (USA) (Aljabr (USA)) **D. E. Brownlow**
149 **KIND OF HUSH (IRE)**, b f 17/1 Marju (IRE)—Affinity (Sadler's Wells (USA)) **Elite Racing Club**
150 B c 23/1 Phoenix Reach (IRE)—Lady Brora (Dashing Blade) **Kingsclere Racing Club**
151 B f 17/3 Zamindar (USA)—Lady Donatella (Last Tycoon) **Mrs C. J. Wates**
152 **LUNAR LOGIC**, b c 12/2 Motivator—Moonmaiden (Selkirk (USA)) (20000) **Martin & Valerie Slade**

MR ANDREW BALDING - Continued

153 Ch c 18/2 Sir Percy—Memsahib (Alzao (USA)) **Sir Gordon Brunton**
154 MR QUICKSILVER, gr c 19/3 Dansili—Last Second (IRE) (Alzao (USA)) (300000) **J. L. C. Pearce**
155 MS GRANDE CORNICHE, ch f 1/2 Pivotal—Miss Corniche (Hernando (FR)) **J. L. C. Pearce**
156 NADDER, ch f 21/1 Notnowcato—Tavy (Pivotal) **Mrs A. Wigan**
157 Ch c 28/4 Major Cadeaux—Ocean Grove (IRE) (Fairy King (USA)) (13000) **Kennet Valley Thoroughbreds X**
158 OPTIMYSTIC (IRE), ch f 3/4 Exceed And Excel (AUS)—Psychic (IRE) (Alhaarth (IRE)) (45000) **BA Racing**
159 PRINCE OF CARDAMOM (IRE), b c 6/3 Nayef (USA)—Tiger Spice (Royal Applause) (40000) **Mr M. A. Burton**
160 RATTLING JEWEL, b c 20/2 Royal Applause—Mutoon (IRE) (Erhaab (USA)) (75000) **Mick and Janice Mariscotti**
161 ROSE ABOVE, b f 29/3 Yeats (IRE)—Sabah (Nashwan (USA)) **Sir Roger Buckley, Mr Gerald Oury**
162 ROYAL NORMANDY, b c 8/4 Royal Applause—Border Minstral (Sri Pekan (USA)) (50000) **M. Payton**
163 SCOTS FERN, b f 26/1 Selkirk (USA)—Ushindi (IRE) (Montjeu (IRE)) **Mrs P. I. Veenbaas & Hot to Trot**
164 B c 19/2 Passing Glance—Seaflower Reef (IRE) (Robellino (USA)) **Kingsclere Racing Club**
165 B c 25/3 Soviet Star (USA)—Shantalla Peak (IRE) (Darshaan) (14000)
166 B c 7/4 Mawatheeq (USA)—Silvereine (FR) (Bering) (10000)
167 SONNOLENTO (IRE), b c 14/2 Rip Van Winkle (IRE)—
Dreams Come True (FR) (Zafonic (USA)) (55000) **Mick And Janice Mariscotti**
168 Ch f 8/2 Pivotal—Speed Cop (Cadeaux Genereux) **J. C. Smith**
169 B c 26/1 Norse Dancer (IRE)—Strictly Dancing (IRE) (Danehill Dancer (IRE)) **J. C. Smith**
170 B br c 18/4 Sir Percy—Sweet Mandolin (Soviet Star (USA)) **J. C., J R & S. R. Hitchins**
171 B c 25/1 Danehill Dancer (IRE)—
Titivation (Montjeu (IRE)) (135000) **HighclereThoroughbredRacing(Jersey Lily)**
172 B c 10/3 Sleeping Indian—Vax Rapide (Sharpo) (10000) **Pink Star Racing**
173 B c 4/5 Acclamation—Venus Rising (Observatory (USA)) (34285) **Thurloe Thoroughbreds XXXIV**
174 B f 26/3 Sir Percy—Victoria Montoya (High Chaparral (IRE)) **Kingsclere Racing Club**
175 B c 30/4 Shamardal (USA)—Wedding Gift (FR) (Always Fair (USA)) (201316) **Dr P. J. Brown**
176 Ch c 24/1 New Approach (IRE)—Wosaita (Generous (USA)) (160000) **D. E. Brownlow**
177 B c 21/3 Teofilo (IRE)—Zeiting (IRE) (Zieten (USA)) (131629) **Mrs F. H. Hay**

Other Owners: Mrs I. A. Balding, Mr Paul Blaydon, Mr Peter Box, Mr John Bridgman, Mr John Bromfield, Sir Roger Buckley, Mr D. H. Caslon, Mr P. M. Claydon, Mr P. Coates, Mr Carl Conroy, Mr M. E. T. Davies, Mr Peter Done, Mr Bridget Drew, Mr N. R. R. Drew, Miss G. B. Drew, Mr John Drew, Mr P. E. Felton, Sir Alex Ferguson, Mr Jim Glasgow, Mrs W. Gorell, Mr B. Greenwood, Mr Peter W. Haddock, Mr S. Harding, Mr N. G. R. Harris, The Hon H. Herbert, Highclere Thoroughbred Racing Ltd, Mr S. Hill, Mr Tony Hill, Mr J. C. Hitchins, J. R. Hitchins, Mr S. R. Hitchins, Sir C. J. S. Hobhouse, Mr R. S. Hoskins, Mr G. R. Ireland, Ms Kate James, Ms S. Johnson, Mr Luke Lillington, Lady Lloyd-Webber, Mr Mick Mariscotti, Mrs Janice Mariscotti, Mr Ged Mason, Mr R. P. B. Michaelson, Mr Richard Morecombe, Mr John A. Newman, Miss M. Noden, Mr Gerald Oury, Mr O. J. W. Pawle, Miss J. Philip-Jones, Mrs L. E. Ramsden, Mr L. L. Register, Mr N. J. F. Robinson, Dr Felicity Simpson, Mr D. M. Slade, Mrs V. J. M. Slade, Mrs G. A. E. Smith, Mr J. A. B. Stafford, Mr Bruce Swallow, Mr A. J. Thomas, Mr S. R. Thomas, Mr C. Vigors, Mrs C. Vigors, Mr K. Weston, Mrs C. S. Whitaker.

Assistant Trainer: C. Bonner

Jockey (flat): Liam Keniry, David Probert, Jimmy Fortune. **Apprentice:** Thomas Brown, Jack Garritty, Rob Hornby, Oisin Murphy, Daniel Muscutt, Kieran Shoemark, Jonathan Willetts.

---

18 MR JOHN BALDING, Doncaster
Postal: **Mayflower Stables, Saracens Lane, Scrooby, Doncaster, South Yorkshire, DN10 6AS**
Contacts: **HOME (01302) 710096 FAX (01302) 710096 MOBILE (07816) 612631**
E-MAIL j.balding@btconnect.com

1 ALL GOOD NEWS (IRE), 5, gr g Moss Vale (IRE)—Blanche Neige (USA) **Bluegrass Racing Ltd**
2 FORTINBRASS (IRE), 4, b g Baltic King—Greta d'argent (IRE) **J. Balding**
3 IMAGINARY WORLD (IRE), 6, b m Exceed And Excel (AUS)—Plutonia **Hairy Gorrilaz**
4 POINT NORTH (IRE), 7, b g Danehill Dancer (IRE)—Briolette (IRE) **Mr W. Herring**
5 SILLY BILLY (IRE), 6, b g Noverre (USA)—Rock Dove (IRE) **R. L. Crowe**
6 SLEEPY BLUE OCEAN, 8, b g Oasis Dream—Esteemed Lady (IRE) **Tykes & Terriers Racing Club**

Other Owners: Mr K. Ackroyd, Mr P. Birley, M. V. Firth, Mr A. J. Sharp, Mr B. Topliss.

Assistant Trainer: Claire Edmunds, Jason Edmunds

19 **MR MICHAEL BANKS, Sandy**
Postal: **Manor Farm, Manor Farm Road, Waresley, Sandy, Bedfordshire, SG19 3BX**
Contacts: **PHONE (01767) 650563 FAX (01767) 652988 MOBILE (07860) 627370**
E-MAIL **waresleyfarms@btconnect.com**

1 **JODIES JEM**, 4, br g Kheleyf (USA)—First Approval **Mrs R. L. Banks**
2 **LOMBARDY BOY (IRE)**, 9, b g Milan—Horner Water (IRE) **M. C. Banks**
3 **MAX LAURIE (FR)**, 9, bl g Ungaro (GER)—Laurie Mercuriale (FR) **Mrs R. L. Banks**
4 **ROGUE DANCER (FR)**, 9, b g Dark Moondancer—Esperanza IV (FR) **M. C. Banks**

Other Owners: Mrs M C Banks.

20 **MR MARC BARBER, Amroth**
Postal: **Amroth Farm, Amroth, Narberth, Dyfed, SA67 8NJ**

1 **BEALLANDENDALL (IRE)**, 6, b g Beneficial—Railstown Lady (IRE) **Mrs J. Barber**
2 **BURNSWOOD (IRE)**, 10, b g Monsun (GER)—Banaja (IRE) **Mr A. D. Quinn**
3 **HUNKY DOREY**, 8, b g Clan of Roses—Somethingaboutmary (IRE) **Mr G. M. Barber**
4 **KILL VAN KULL (IRE)**, 5, b g Johannesburg (USA)—Stephanootz (USA) **Mrs J. Barber**
5 **KIMORA (IRE)**, 8, b m Bach (IRE)—Blue Gale (IRE) **Mr G. J. Barber**
6 **KUSADASI (IRE)**, 9, b g Beneficial—Otorum (IRE) **Mr G. M. Barber**
7 **NO MORE WHISPERS (IRE)**, 9, b g Kahyasi—Dizzy's Whisper (IRE) **Mr G. M. Barber**
8 **NOT MANY KNOW THAT (IRE)**, 8, b g Winged Love (IRE)—The Cree River (IRE) **Mr G. M. Barber**
9 **PELCOMB BRIDGE**, 9, b g King O' The Mana (IRE)—Flaming Katey **Mr G. J. Barber**
10 **PHILHARMONIC HALL**, 6, b g Victory Note (USA)—Lambast **Mr G. M. Barber**
11 **SPIN THE BEAT**, 4, b g Beat All (USA)—Little Red Spider **Mr G. M. Barber**
12 **SPUNKY**, 5, b g Invincible Spirit (IRE)—Passe Passe (USA) **Mr G. M. Barber**

21 **MRS TRACEY BARFOOT-SAUNT, Wotton-under-Edge**
Postal: **Cosy Farm, Huntingford, Charfield, Wotton-under-Edge, Gloucestershire, GL12 8EY**
Contacts: **PHONE (01453) 520312 FAX (01453) 520312 MOBILE (07976) 360626**

1 **ANMOSS (IRE)**, 11, ch m Anshan—Anmaca (IRE) **A Good Days Racing**
2 **BRUSLINI (FR)**, 9, gr g Linamix (FR)—Brusca (USA) **A Good Days Racing**
3 **LOUGHMORE VIC (IRE)**, 9, ch g Old Vic—Princess Lizzie (IRE) **A Good Days Racing**
4 **RAVENS SECRET**, 9, br g Overbury (IRE)—Secret Pearl (IRE) **A Good Days Racing**

THREE-YEAR-OLDS

5 **LAUGHING MUSKETEER (IRE)**, b g Azamour (IRE)—Sweet Clover **A Good Days Racing**

Other Owners: Mrs T. M. Barfoot-Saunt.

Amateur: Mr Geoff Barfoot-Saunt.

22 **MR MAURICE BARNES, Brampton**
Postal: **Tarnside, Farlam, Brampton, Cumbria, CA8 1LA**
Contacts: **PHONE/FAX (01697) 746675 MOBILE (07760) 433191**
E-MAIL **anne.barnes1@btinternet.com**

1 **APACHE PILOT**, 6, br g Indian Danehill (IRE)—Anniejo **Abbadis Racing**
2 **ATTYCRAN (IRE)**, 9, b g Snurge—Baltimore Lass (IRE) **Miss A. P. Lee**
3 **BOBS LADY TAMURE**, 7, b m Tamure (IRE)—Bob Back's Lady (IRE) **J. R. Wills**
4 **DIBDABS (IRE)**, 6, b g Royal Anthem (USA)—Leadaro (IRE) **The Edinburgh Woollen Mill Ltd**
5 **DYNAMIC DRIVE (IRE)**, 7, b g Motivator—Biriyani (IRE) **Ring Of Fire**
6 **EVERREADYNEDDY**, 4, ch g Ad Valorem (USA)—Maugwenna **Mr R. E. Wharton**
7 **FA'SIDE CASTLE (IRE)**, 5, br g Dylan Thomas (IRE)—Keyaki (IRE) **Mr M Barnes, Mr Scott Lowther**
8 **GARLETON (IRE)**, 13, b g Anshan—Another Grouse **Mr C Davidson Mr D Thorburn**
9 **HOWIZEE**, 8, gr g Baryshnikov (AUS)—Sendai **Mr G. Baird**
10 **I'LL BE FRANK**, 9, b g Fraam—Miss Opulence (IRE) **M. D. Townson**
11 **INDIAN VOYAGE (IRE)**, 6, b g Indian Haven—Voyage of Dreams (USA) **D. Carr**

MR MAURICE BARNES - Continued

12 **L'EMINENCE GRISE (IRE)**, 7, gr g Kahyasi—Belle Innocence (FR) **Mr C. Davidson**
13 **MY IDEA**, 8, b g Golan (IRE)—Ghana (GER) **The Whisperers**
14 **NINETYNINE (IRE)**, 7, b m Exit To Nowhere (USA)—Sparkling Jess **Mr M Barnes, Mr Scott Lowther**
15 **ODDSMAKER (IRE)**, 13, b g Barathea (IRE)—Archipova (IRE) **M. A. Barnes**
16 **OVERPRICED**, 8, b m Chocolat de Meguro (USA)—One Stop **M. A. Barnes**
17 **PAS TROP TARD (FR)**, 7, b g Caballo Raptor (CAN)—This Melody (FR) **Mr C. Davidson**
18 **PERFECT PRINT (IRE)**, 5, b g Kodiac—Naughtiness **Mr R. E. Wharton**
19 **QUICK BREW**, 6, b g Denounce—Darjeeling (IRE) **The Wizards**
20 **RED MYSTIQUE (IRE)**, 5, b g Red Clubs (IRE)—Sacred Love (IRE) **M. A. Barnes**
21 **SHE'S TALKIN**, 5, b m Fantastic View (USA)—Little Cascade **M. A. Barnes**
22 **TOLEDO GOLD (IRE)**, 8, ch g Needwood Blade—Eman's Joy **Mr M Barnes, Mr Scott Lowther**

Other Owners: Mr M. Barnes, Mr R. H. Briggs, Mr C. Davidson, Mr J. G. Graham, Mr Keith Greenwell, Mr Stevan Houliston, Mr S. G. Johnston, Mr Scott Lowther, Mr Nigel North, Mr Davidson Thorburn.

Conditional: Stephen Mulqueen.

23
MR BRIAN BARR, Sherborne
Postal: Tall Trees Stud, Longburton, Sherborne, Dorset, DT9 5PH
Contacts: **PHONE (01963) 210173 MOBILE (07826) 867881**

1 **BOSTIN (IRE)**, 6, ch g Busy Flight—Bustingoutallover (USA) **Miss D. Hitchins**
2 **CASTLEMORRIS KING**, 6, br g And Beyond (IRE)—Brookshield Baby (IRE) **Miss D. Hitchins**
3 **DON'T LOOK BACK (IRE)**, 9, b g Bach (IRE)—Buckalong (IRE) **Miss D. Hitchins**
4 **FOLLOW THE TRACKS (IRE)**, 6, b br g Milan—Charming Mo (IRE)
5 **FORGOTTEN PROMISE**, 7, b m Revoque (IRE)—Ivory's Promise **Miss D. Hitchins**
6 **GEORGE NYMPTON (IRE)**, 8, br g Alderbrook—Countess Camilla
7 **IN THE CROWD (IRE)**, 5, ch g Haafhd—Eliza Gilbert
8 **TUFFSTUFF**, 6, b g Generous (IRE)—Life Line **Miss D. Hitchins**

Assistant Trainer: Daisy Hitchins

Conditional: Gavin Sheehan.

24
MR RON BARR, Middlesbrough
Postal: Carr House Farm, Seamer, Stokesley, Middlesbrough, Cleveland, TS9 5LL
Contacts: **PHONE (01642) 710687 MOBILE (07711) 895309**
E-MAIL christinebarr1@aol.com

1 **A J COOK (IRE)**, 4, b g Mujadil (USA)—Undertone (IRE) **Mrs V. G. Davies**
2 **AL FURAT (USA)**, 6, b g El Prado (IRE)—No Frills (IRE) **Mrs V. G. Davies**
3 **FOREIGN RHYTHM (IRE)**, 9, ch m Distant Music (USA)—Happy Talk (IRE) **R. E. Barr**
4 **GRACEFUL ACT**, 6, b m Royal Applause—Minnina (IRE) **D. Thomson**
5 **KARATE QUEEN**, 9, b m King's Best (USA)—Black Belt Shopper (IRE) **C. Barr**
6 **MIDNIGHT WARRIOR**, 4, b g Teofilo (IRE)—Mauri Moon **Mr K. Trimble**
7 **MITCHUM**, 5, b g Elnadim (USA)—Maid To Matter **A. J. Duffield**
8 **TROPICAL DUKE (IRE)**, 8, ch g Bachelor Duke (USA)—Tropical Dance (USA) **R. E. Barr**

Other Owners: Mrs R. E. Barr, M. G. Bell, B. Cunningham.

Assistant Trainer: Mrs C. Barr

Amateur: Miss V. Barr.

25
MR DAVID BARRON, Thirsk
Postal: Maunby House, Maunby, Thirsk, North Yorkshire, YO7 4HD
Contacts: **PHONE (01845) 587435 FAX (01845) 587331**
E-MAIL david@harrowgate.wanadoo.co.uk

1 **ANTONIO GRAMSCI**, 4, b g Misu Bond (IRE)—La Corujera **Norton Common Farm Racing Ltd**
2 **BERTIEWHITTLE**, 6, ch g Bahamian Bounty—Minette **Norton Common Farm Racing II&JKB Johnson**
3 **BIG JOHNNY D (IRE)**, 5, ch g Alhaarth (IRE)—Bakiya (USA) **Mr C. A. Washbourn**
4 **COLONEL MAK**, 7, br g Makbul—Colonel's Daughter **Norton Common Farm Racing,O'Kane,Murphy**

MR DAVID BARRON - Continued

5 **COSMIC CHATTER**, 4, b g Paris House—Paradise Eve **Highclere T'Bred Racing & David Barron**
6 **ESTEAMING**, 4, b g Sir Percy—Night Over Day **D. E. Cook**
7 **FIELDGUNNER KIRKUP (GER)**, 6, b g Acclamation—Fire Finch **Harrowgate Bloodstock Ltd**
8 **HITCHENS (IRE)**, 9, b g Acclamation—Royal Fizz (IRE) **Mr Laurence O'Kane & Mr Paul Murphy**
9 **JOFRANKA**, 4, b f Paris House—Gypsy Fair **Mr M. R. Dalby**
10 **LONG AWAITED (IRE)**, 8, b g Pivotal—Desertion (IRE) **Peter Jones**
11 **MAGICAL MACEY (USA)**, 7, ch g Rossini (USA)—Spring's Glory (USA) **K. J. Alderson**
12 **MISSISSIPPI**, 5, b g Exceed And Excel (AUS)—Ruby Rocket (USA) **Van Der Hoeven, Pryde & O'Kane**
13 **MUFFIN MCLEAY (IRE)**, 6, b g Hawk Wing (USA)—Youngus (USA) **Harrowgate Bloodstock Ltd**
14 **NEWSTEAD ABBEY**, 4, b g Byron—Oatcake **Let's Be Lucky Partnership**
15 **NEXT DOOR (IRE)**, 4, b f Elusive City (USA)—Lamh Eile (IRE) **Oghill House Stud & Partner**
16 **NORSE BLUES**, 6, ch g Norse Dancer (IRE)—Indiana Blues **J Bollington & Partners**
17 **PEARL SECRET**, 5, ch h Compton Place—Our Little Secret (IRE) **Qatar Racing Limited**
18 **PRIMARY ROUTE (IRE)**, 4, ch f Primary—Ashtaroute (USA) **Twinacre Nurseries Ltd**
19 **PTOLEMY**, 5, b g Royal Applause—Rydal Mount (IRE) **R. S. E. Gifford**
20 **ROBOT BOY (IRE)**, 4, ch g Shamardal (USA)—Pivotal's Princess (IRE) **Mr Laurence O'Kane & Paul Murphy**
21 **SHADY MCCOY (USA)**, 4, b g English Channel (USA)—Raw Gold (USA) **Allwins Stables**
22 **SHESASTAR**, 6, b m Bahamian Bounty—Celestial Welcome **Star Alliance 4 - Lancs 2 Lincs**
23 **SIRVINO**, 9, b g Vettori (IRE)—Zenita (IRE) **Mr Theo Williams & Mr Charles Mocatta**
24 **SPES NOSTRA**, 6, b g Ad Valorem (USA)—Millagros (IRE) **Mr J. Cringan & Mr D. Pryde**
25 **SUBLIMATION (IRE)**, 4, ch g Manduro (GER)—Meon Mix **The Dream Team**
26 **SUITS ME**, 11, ch g Bertolini (USA)—Fancier Bit **D. E. Cook**
27 **TAROOQ (USA)**, 8, b g War Chant (USA)—Rose of Zollern (IRE) **EPL Investments**
28 **TRES CORONAS (IRE)**, 7, b g Key of Luck (USA)—Almanza (IRE) **Mr D. Pryde & Mr J. Cringan**

THREE-YEAR-OLDS

29 **ART OBSESSION (USA)**, b g Excellent Art—Ghana (IRE) **Mr D. Pryde & Mr J. Cringan**
30 **BOY IN THE BAR**, ch g Dutch Art—Lipsia (IRE) **S. Rudolf**
31 **CAVALLO BELLA**, gr f Bertolini (USA)—Crosby Millie **J. E. Raper**
32 **CENTRE HAAFHD**, b g Haafhd—Deira Dubai **D. G. Pryde, Jim Beaumont & James Callow**
33 **DUELLING DRAGON (USA)**, b g Henrythenavigator (USA)—Ometsz (IRE) **Qatar Racing Limited**
34 Ch c Sir Percy—Fantasy Princess (USA) **Norton Common Farm Racing Ltd**
35 **FAST TRACK**, b g Rail Link—Silca Boo **R. C. Miquel**
36 **FICKLE FEELINGS (IRE)**, b f Nayef (USA)—Caravan of Dreams (IRE) **P. D. Savill**
37 **FIRECRUISE**, b g Firebreak—Catmint **Profile Storage Ltd**
38 **INDY (IRE)**, b c Indian Haven—Maddie's Pearl (IRE) **Hardisty Rolls II**
39 **KASHSTAREE**, b f Sakhee (USA)—Celestial Welcome **Star Alliance 5**
40 **LUCY PARSONS (IRE)**, ch f Thousand Words—Consensus (IRE) **Norton Common Farm Racing Ltd**
41 **MISS SOPHISTICATED**, b f Bahamian Bounty—Miss Sophisticat **Wensleydale Bacon Limited**
42 **PRECARIOUSLY GOOD**, b f Oasis Dream—Danceabout **Qatar Racing Limited**
43 **PREMIUM PRESSURE (USA)**, b br c War Front (USA)—Judy's Magic (USA) **Qatar Racing Limited**
44 **RED STARGAZER (IRE)**, b g Intikhab (USA)—Autumn Star (IRE) **Twinacre Nurseries Ltd**
45 **ROZENE (IRE)**, b f Sleeping Indian—Few Words **Twinacre Nurseries Ltd**
46 **SEA SPEAR**, ch g Virtual—Fred's Dream **Mr J. Sagar**
47 **TIASTA (IRE)**, ch f Footstepsinthesand—La Stravaganza (USA) **Mr J. Sagar**
48 **TWIN APPEAL (IRE)**, b g Oratorio (IRE)—Velvet Appeal (IRE) **Twinacre Nurseries Ltd**
49 **VIVA VERGLAS (IRE)**, gr g Verglas (IRE)—Yellow Trumpet **R. C. Miquel**
50 **ZAC BROWN (IRE)**, b c Kodiac—Mildmay (USA) **Mr R. G. Toes**

TWO-YEAR-OLDS

51 B c 20/4 Holy Roman Emperor (IRE)—Big Swifty (IRE) (Intikhab (USA)) (19357) **Harrowgate Bloodstock Ltd**
52 **BUSHTIGER (IRE)**, b c 7/5 Bushranger (IRE)—Emma's Surprise (Tobougg (IRE)) (12388) **Billy & Debbie Glover**
53 B c 28/4 Bushranger (IRE)—Cloneden (IRE) (Definite Article) **Ms Colette Twomey**
54 Ch c 16/3 Lope de Vega (IRE)—Dehbanu (IRE) (King's Best (USA)) (38095) **Qatar Racing Limited**
55 **HANDSOME DUDE**, b c 7/3 Showcasing—Dee Dee Girl (IRE) (Primo Dominie) (21904) **Billy & Debbie Glover**
56 Ch c 7/2 Intense Focus (USA)—Kayak (Singspiel (IRE)) (24777) **L. G. O'Kane**
57 **MIGNOLINO**, b c 25/4 Kodiac—Caterina di Cesi (Cape Town (IRE)) (30971) **Mr R. G. Toes**
58 B c 24/4 Sir Percy—Monjouet (IRE) (Montjeu (IRE)) (56000) **Qatar Racing Limited**
59 B c 24/4 Captain Rio—Over The Ridge (IRE) (Indian Ridge) (11614) **Dr N. J. Barron**
60 Ch c 23/2 Tagula (IRE)—Shinko Dancer (IRE) (Shinko Forest (IRE)) (19047) **Qatar Racing Limited**
61 **SOMETHINGROYAL (IRE)**, b c 28/2 Paco Boy—Stellarina (IRE) (Night Shift (USA)) (17142) **S. Rudolf**
62 **STELLA ETOILE (IRE)**, b f 28/4 Duke of Marmalade (IRE)—Sangita (Royal Academy (USA)) (28571) **S. Rudolf**
63 B f 27/2 Kodiac—Suffer Her (IRE) (Whipper (USA)) (11428) **S. Rudolf**
64 B br c 13/3 Acclamation—Weekend Fling (USA) (Forest Wildcat (USA)) (52585) **S. Rudolf**

MR DAVID BARRON - Continued

Other Owners: T. D. Barron, J. J. Beaumont, Ms J. C. Bollington, J. R. Callow, Mr H. P. T. Chamberlain, J. A. Cringan, Dr P. A. I. Doro, J. A. Evans, Mr W. D. Glover, Mrs D. A. Glover, Mr R. A. Gorrie, Mr S. T. Gorrie, The Hon H. M. Herbert, Highclere Thoroughbred Racing Ltd, Mr I. Holroyd-Pearce, Mr P. Hyland, Mr H. D. Hyland, Mrs S. J. Mason, Mr C. T. Mocatta, Mr P. A. Murphy, D. G. Pryde, Mr P. Rolls, Mrs J. Rolls, Mr G. S. Slater, T. Williams, Mr A. Worrall, Mr D. P. van der Hoeven.

Assistant Trainer: Nicola-Jo Barron

---

26 **MR MICHAEL BARRY, Fermoy**
Postal: **Mondaniel, Fermoy, Co. Cork, Ireland**
Contacts: **PHONE (00353) 25 31577 FAX (00353) 25 31792 MOBILE (00353) 87 2536815**

1 COLLS CORNER (IRE), 11, ch g Beneficial—Pandoras Hope (IRE) **Michael Barry**
2 EARLY AND OFTEN (IRE), 7, b g Revoque (IRE)—Smart Approach (IRE) **Michael Barry**
3 GUTSIE H (IRE), 5, b g Indian Danehill (IRE)—Pretoria Cottage (IRE) **Michael Barry**
4 JIMMY SHAN (IRE), 6, b g Milan—Divine Prospect (IRE) **Michael Barry**

Assistant Trainer: John Fennessy

---

27 **MR P. BARY, Chantilly**
Postal: **5 Chemin des Aigles, 60500 Chantilly, France**
Contacts: **PHONE (0033) 3445 71403 FAX (0033) 3446 72015 MOBILE (0033) 6075 80241**
E-MAIL p-bary@wanadoo.fr

1 ART CONTEMPORAIN (USA), 4, gr c Smart Strike (CAN)—Super Lina (FR) **Ecurie J. L. Bouchard**
2 CHEYENNE HOME (USA), 4, b g Empire Maker (USA)—Cheyenne Dream **K. Abdullah**
3 CORYCIAN (IRE), 4, b c Dansili—Colza (USA) **Niarchos Family**
4 DAIVIKA (USA), 4, b f Dynaformer (USA)—Divine Proportions (USA) **Niarchos Family**
5 ENTREE, 4, b f Halling (USA)—West Dakota (USA) **K. Abdullah**
6 HASNA (FR), 5, ch m American Post—Harriet (FR) **G. Sandor**
7 MARKET SHARE, 4, b c Zamindar (USA)—Winter Solstice **K. Abdullah**
8 MORTGA (FR), 5, b h Anabaa (USA)—Cornelia (FR) **Saeed Nasser Al Romaithi**
9 NOTAIRE (IRE), 4, b c Nayef (USA)—Aiglonne (USA) **Skymarc Farm Inc.**
10 SHARED ACCOUNT, 4, br f Dansili—Imbabala **K. Abdullah**
11 SMOKING SUN (USA), 5, b br h Smart Strike (CAN)—Burning Sunset **Niarchos Family**
12 SPIRITJIM (FR), 4, b c Galileo (IRE)—Hidden Silver **Hspirit**
13 STRIX, 4, ch c Muthathir—Serandine (IRE) **Laghi France**
14 TANTRIS (FR), 4, ch c Turtle Bowl (IRE)—Tianshan (FR) **G. Sandor**
15 TERRUBI (IRE), 4, gr c Dalakhani (IRE)—Altruiste (USA) **Ecurie J. L. Bouchard**
16 UNNEFER (FR), 9, b h Danehill Dancer (IRE)—Mimalia (USA) **Niarchos Family**
17 YOGA (IRE), 4, ch f Monsun (GER)—Remote Romance (USA) **Niarchos Family**
18 ZHIYI (USA), 4, b g Henrythenavigator (USA)—Burning Sunset **Niarchos Family**

THREE-YEAR-OLDS

19 ALBAJULIA (IRE), b f Holy Roman Emperor (IRE)—Azorina Vidalii (GER) **Daria Camilla**
20 AMBROISIE (FR), b f Naaqoos—Aviane (GER) **Mme R. G. Ehrnrooth**
21 AZARIANE (FR), b f Sageburg (IRE)—Peace Talk (FR) **Ecurie J. L. Bouchard**
22 BOETIE'S DREAM (IRE), b c Oasis Dream—Source of Life (IRE) **Ecurie La Boetie**
23 BUSHIDO (FR), ro ch c Bernebeau (FR)—Belga Wood (USA) **G. Sandor**
24 CAGOULE, b c Oasis Dream—Pretty Face **K. Abdullah**
25 CASTAGNOU (IRE), b c Lawman (FR)—Around Me (IRE) **Ecurie J. L. Bouchard**
26 CONQUETE (FR), ch f Kyllachy—Chesnut Bird (IRE) **G. Sandor**
27 DELHI, br f High Chaparral (IRE)—Dream Day **Skymarc Farm Inc.**
28 DEMOISELLE (IRE), gr f Dalakhani (IRE)—Amonita **Hars du Mezeray**
29 DUKE AGAIN (IRE), ch g Duke of Marmalade (IRE)—Thanks Again (IRE) **Laghi France**
30 DURANO (FR), gr c Verglas (IRE)—Darasa (FR) **Ecurie J. L. Bouchard**
31 ENZINA, ch f New Approach (IRE)—Kyniska (IRE) **Ecurie J. L. Bouchard**
32 EQUIVALENT, b c Dansili—Proportional **K. Abdullah**
33 FAUFILER (IRE), b f Galileo (IRE)—Six Perfections (FR) **Niarchos Family**
34 FINGLASS (IRE), b f Elusive City (USA)—Samya **Laghi France**
35 HERON LAKE (IRE), b c Danehill Dancer (IRE)—Herboriste **Mme R. G. Ehrnrooth**
36 HIGGS BOSUN (FR), b c Turtle Bowl (IRE)—Epopee (IRE) **Galileo Racing**

MR P. BARY - Continued

37 **HONEYSUCKLE ROSE (FR)**, ch f Turtle Bowl (IRE)—Valleyrose (IRE) **Emmeline de Waldner**
38 **HOUSE OF DREAMS (JPN)**, bl f Neo Universe (JPN)—Second Happiness (USA) **Niarchos Family**
39 **LAKA (IRE)**, b f Oasis Dream—Mimalia (USA) **Niarchos Family**
40 **LOOK OVER**, b f Nayef (USA)—Half Glance **K. Abdullah**
41 **MISTERDAD (IRE)**, b c Cape Cross (IRE)—Flaming Cliffs (USA) **Niarchos Family**
42 **MONOCEROS (USA)**, b c Giant's Causeway (USA)—Divine Proportions (USA) **Niarchos Family**
43 **MYA MIMA (FR)**, b f Sir Percy—Pink Topaz (USA) **Niarchos Family**
44 **NACRE (JPN)**, b f Deep Impact (JPN)—Forest Rain (FR) **Niarchos Family**
45 **NARAM SIN (FR)**, b c Zafeen (FR)—Noemie (FR) **G. Sandor**
46 **PHENETIC**, b f Zamindar (USA)—Starfan (USA) **K. Abdullah**
47 **PREVALENT (USA)**, b f Empire Maker (USA)—Helstra (USA) **K. Abdullah**
48 **SAN SICARIO (USA)**, ch c Smart Strike (CAN)—Astrologie (FR) **Haras du Mezeray**
49 **ST OLAVS GATE (FR)**, b f Sageburg (IRE)—Final Whistle (IRE) **Moise Ohana**
50 **STELLA RIVER (FR)**, b f Stormy River (FR)—Montagne Magique (IRE) **D. Jacob**
51 **STEPHILL (FR)**, ch c Footstepsinthesand—Magic Hill (FR) **Laghi France**
52 **TATOOINE (FR)**, ch c Galileo (IRE)—Three Mysteries (IRE) **Niarchos Family**
53 **TELETEXT (USA)**, b c Empire Maker (USA)—Conference Call **K. Abdullah**
54 **THEME ASTRAL (FR)**, b c Cape Cross (IRE)—Lumiere Astrale (FR) **Haras du Mezeray**
55 **TOP OF THE MOON (IRE)**, b f Rock of Gibraltar (IRE)—Trip To The Moon **Ecurie J. L. Bouchard**
56 **WIRE (USA)**, b f Rock Hard Ten (USA)—Tsar's Pride **K. Abdullah**

TWO-YEAR-OLDS

57 B c 27/4 Teofilo (IRE)—Alsace (King's Best (USA)) (309717) **Hspirit**
58 **AMUSER (IRE)**, ch f 27/4 Galileo (IRE)—Six Perfections (FR) (Celtic Swing) **Niarchos Family**
59 B c 7/3 Galileo (IRE)—Apsara (FR) (Darshaan) **Niarchos Family**
60 **BERCHED (FR)**, gr f 8/4 Layman (USA)—Belga Wood (USA) (Woodman (USA)) (17034) **G. Sandor**
61 B f 25/2 Champs Elysees—Buffering (Beat Hollow) **K. Abdullah**
62 Br gr c 13/5 Galileo (IRE)—Dibenoise (FR) (Kendor (FR)) (387146) **Hspirit**
63 **DUCHESSE BLEUE (IRE)**, ch f 9/3 Duke of Marmalade (IRE)—
Blue Blue Sky (IRE) (Anabaa (USA)) (34843) **Laghi France**
64 B f 13/5 Big Bad Bob (IRE)—Ekadzati (FR) (Fasliyev (USA)) **Niarchos Family**
65 B f 30/1 Nayef (USA)—Fresh Laurels (IRE) (Rock of Gibraltar (IRE)) (108401) **Ecurie des Monceaux**
66 **GOLD LOCK (FR)**, b c 28/3 Iffraaj—Guarded (Eagle Eyed (USA)) (116144) **Sutong Pan**
67 **GOLDEN FASTNET (FR)**, b f 6/2 Fastnet Rock (AUS)—Militante (IRE) (Johannesburg (USA)) (61943) **Sutong Pan**
68 **GOLDMETAL JACKET (IRE)**, b c 8/2 Acclamation—Twinspot (USA) (Bahri (USA)) (90000) **Sutong Pan**
69 **HARVESTIDE (IRE)**, b f 22/2 Duke of Marmalade (IRE)—Herboriste (Hernando (FR)) **Mme R. G. Ehrnrooth**
70 B c 14/4 Zamindar (USA)—Heart of Hearts (Oasis Dream) **K. Abdullah**
71 **HELVETIA (USA)**, b f 26/2 Blame (USA)—Helstra (USA) (Nureyev (USA)) **K. Abdullah**
72 B c 13/3 Oasis Dream—Homepage (Dansili) **K. Abdullah**
73 **IF I DO (FR)**, b f 17/2 Iffraaj—Doriana (Kendor (FR)) (69686) **Sutong Pan**
74 B c 9/3 Oasis Dream—Indication (Sadler's Wells (USA)) **K. Abdullah**
75 **INORDINATE (USA)**, b c 5/3 Harlan's Holiday (USA)—Out of Reach (Warning) **K. Abdullah**
76 B f 5/3 Sea The Stars (IRE)—Lion Forest (Forestry (USA)) (140000) **K. Abdullah**
77 **MAJVER (IRE)**, b f 6/5 Mastercraftsman (IRE)—Marie de Blois (IRE) (Barathea (IRE)) (23228) **Laghi France**
78 **MEZAMOUR (FR)**, b f 17/2 Layman (USA)—
Minnaloushe (FR) (Black Minnaloushe (USA)) (23228) **Laurent Dassault**
79 Ch f 6/2 Shamardal (USA)—Milford Sound (Barathea (IRE)) **K. Abdullah**
80 **MOI MEME**, b f 6/4 Teofilo (IRE)—Di Moi Oui (Warning) **Scuderia Vittadini Srl**
81 **NIGHT OF LIGHT (IRE)**, b f 9/4 Sea The Stars (IRE)—
Celestial Lagoon (JPN) (Sunday Silence (USA)) **Niarchos Family**
82 B f 7/3 Teofilo (IRE)—Pietra Santa (FR) (Acclamation) (61943) **Ecurie La Boetie**
83 Br f 7/4 Manduro (GER)—Quenched (Dansili) **K. Abdullah**
84 **SAMIRE (IRE)**, ch c 29/2 American Post—Mizoram (USA) (23228) **G. Sandor**
85 B c 8/2 Iffraaj—Sandbar (Oasis Dream) (263259) **Hspirit**
86 B f 4/2 High Chaparral (IRE)—Serisia (FR) (Exit To Nowhere (USA)) **Lady O'Reilly**
87 **SEYFERT GALAXY**, b c 30/3 Dalakhani (IRE)—Three Mysteries (IRE) (Linamix (FR)) **Niarchos Family**
88 **SPREZZATURA**, b f 9/3 Mount Nelson—She of The Moon (Kingmambo (USA)) **Niarchos Family**
89 **STELWOOD (FR)**, b c 1/3 Falco (USA)—L'ensorceleuse (IRE) (Oasis Dream) (38714) **Ecurie Stella Maris**
90 B c 23/3 Fastnet Rock (AUS)—Sterope (FR) (Hernando (FR)) **Niarchos Family**
91 **TALE OF LIFE (JPN)**, br c 6/5 Deep Impact (JPN)—
Second Happiness (USA) (Storm Cat (USA)) **Flaxman Stables Ireland**
92 **TANTIVY (USA)**, ch f 27/2 Giant's Causeway (USA)—
Witching Hour (FR) (Fairy King (USA)) **Flaxman Stables Ireland**

MR P. BARY - Continued

93 **THINDY (FR)**, b c 12/4 Footstepsinthesand—Windy (FR) (Rock of Gibraltar (IRE)) (50329) **Laghi France**
94 **YOUNKOUNKOUN**, b c 13/4 Elusive City (USA)—Arbalette (IRE) (Anabaa (USA)) (51103) **Ecurie La Boetie**

Jockey (flat): Stephane Pasquier. **Apprentice:** Pierre Bazire.

---

28 **MR ROBIN BASTIMAN, Wetherby**
Postal: Goosemoor Farm, Warfield Lane, Cowthorpe, Wetherby, West Yorkshire, LS22 5EU
Contacts: **PHONE (01423) 359397 MOBILE (07976) 282976**
WEBSITE www.rbastimanracing.com

1 **BORDERLESCOTT**, 12, b g Compton Place—Jeewan **James Edgar & William Donaldson**
2 **COPPER TO GOLD**, 5, ch m Avonbridge—Faithful Beauty (IRE) **Mrs C. Steel**
3 **FAOLAN (IRE)**, 4, b g Amadeus Wolf—Sudden Interest (FR) **Ms M. Austerfield**
4 **GREEN HOWARD**, 6, ch g Bahamian Bounty—Dash of Lime **Ms M. Austerfield**
5 **HELLOLINI**, 4, b f Bertolini (USA)—Smiddy Hill **I. B. Barker**
6 **JACK BARKER**, 5, b g Danbird (AUS)—Smiddy Hill **I. B. Barker**
7 **KYLLACHYKOV (IRE)**, 6, ch g Kyllachy—Dance On **Ms M. Austerfield**
8 **LIZZY'S DREAM**, 6, ch g Choisir (AUS)—Flyingit (USA) **Mrs P. Bastiman**
9 **MONSIEUR PONTAVEN**, 7, b g Avonbridge—Take Heart **Mr E. N. Barber**
10 **NOVALIST**, 6, ch g Avonbridge—Malelane (IRE) **Ms M. Austerfield**
11 **SECRET CITY (IRE)**, 8, b g City On A Hill (USA)—Secret Combe (IRE) **Ms M. Austerfield**
12 **SEE VERMONT**, 6, b g Kyllachy—Orange Lily **Mr J. Smith**
13 **SINGEUR (IRE)**, 7, b g Chineur (FR)—Singitta **Ms M. Austerfield**
14 **TROY BOY**, 4, b g Choisir (AUS)—Love Thing **Ms M. Austerfield**

THREE-YEAR-OLDS

15 **SHIKARI**, ch g Sakhee's Secret—Hickleton Lady (IRE) **Ms M. Austerfield**

TWO-YEAR-OLDS

16 **BIG RED**, ch f 11/3 Sakhee's Secret—Hickleton Lady (IRE) (Kala Shikari) (2500) **Ms M. Austerfield**
17 **MADAM MAI TAI**, ch f 19/3 Compton Place—Dash of Lime (Bold Edge) **Ms M. Austerfield**
18 **ROYAL ACCLAIM (IRE)**, b c 26/4 Acclamation—Top Row (Observatory (USA)) (20000) **Ms. M. Austerfield**

Other Owners: Mrs P. Bastiman, Mr Robin Bastiman, Mr William Donaldson, Mr James Edgar.

Assistant Trainers: H. Bastiman & Miss R. Bastiman

Jockey (flat): Robert Winston, Daniel Tudhope. **Apprentice:** Jason Hart. **Amateur:** Miss R. Bastiman.

---

29 **MRS ALISON BATCHELOR, Petworth**
Postal: Down View Farm, Burton Park Road, Petworth, West Sussex, GU28 0JT
Contacts: **PHONE (01798) 343090 FAX (01798) 343090**
E-MAIL alison@alisonbatchelorracing.com WEBSITE www.alisonbatchelorracing.com

1 **BORDER STATION (IRE)**, 8, b g Shantou (USA)—Telemania (IRE) **Mrs A. M. Batchelor**
2 **LAMBRO RIVER (IRE)**, 9, b g Milan—Chaparral Reef (IRE) **Mrs A. M. Batchelor**
3 **MINNEAPOLIS**, 9, b g Sadler's Wells (USA)—Teggiano (IRE) **Mrs A. M. Batchelor**
4 **SEVENTH HUSSAR**, 8, b g Alflora (IRE)—Shuil Do (IRE) **Mrs A. M. Batchelor**
5 **TAGGIA (FR)**, 7, b m Great Pretender (IRE)—Ecossaise II (FR) **Mrs A. M. Batchelor**

Assistant Trainer: Jose Dos Santos

Amateur: Mr S. Hanson.

---

30 **MR BRIAN BAUGH, Stoke on Trent**
Postal: Brooklands Farm, Park Lane, Audley, Stoke on Trent
Contacts: **HOME (01782) 723144 MOBILE (07771) 693666**

1 **ACTON GOLD**, 5, b m And Beyond (IRE)—Antonia Bertolini **Magnate Racing**
2 **ART DZEKO**, 5, b g Acclamation—Delitme (IRE) **Mr B. P. J. Baugh**
3 **BABY QUEEN (IRE)**, 8, b m Royal Applause—Kissing Time **Mr G. B. Hignett**
4 **COMPTONSPIRIT**, 10, ch m Compton Place—Croeso Cynnes **Mr G. B. Hignett**

MR BRIAN BAUGH - Continued

5 **CONSISTANT**, 6, b g Reel Buddy (USA)—Compact Disc (IRE) **Miss J. A. Price**
6 **DEAR BEN**, 5, b g Echo of Light—Miss Up N Go **Mr B. P. J. Baugh**
7 **ECHOLOGIC**, 4, b g Echo of Light—Crown City (USA) **Miss J. A. Price**
8 **GOLDSTORM**, 6, ch m Storming Home—Antonia Bertolini **Magnate Racing**
9 **JOHN POTTS**, 9, b g Josr Algarhoud (IRE)—Crown City (USA) **Miss S. M. Potts**
10 **LEXI'S BEAUTY (IRE)**, 4, br f Kheleyf (USA)—Voyage of Dreams (USA) **Mr G. B. Hignett**
11 **MASTER OF DISGUISE**, 8, b g Kyllachy—St James's Antigua (IRE) **21C Telecom.co.uk**
12 **MISSFIRE**, 4, b f Firebreak—Gary's Indian (IRE) **Mr G. B. Hignett**
13 **PEARL NATION (USA)**, 5, b g Speightstown (USA)—Happy Nation (USA) **Mr C. Iddon**
14 **PICCOLO EXPRESS**, 8, b g Piccolo—Ashfield **Mr G. B. Hignett**
15 **SCAMPERDALE**, 12, br g Compton Place—Miss Up N Go **Saddle Up Racing**
16 **SEPTENARIUS (USA)**, 5, b g Empire Maker (USA)—Reams of Verse (USA) **Mr S. Holmes**
17 **TANFORAN**, 12, b g Mujahid (USA)—Florentynna Bay **Miss S. M. Potts**
18 **TYFOS**, 9, b g Bertolini (USA)—Warminghamsharpish **Mr G. Williams & Mrs L. E. Tomlinson**

THREE-YEAR-OLDS

19 **LUV U HONEY**, b f Captain Gerrard (IRE)—Lady Suesanne (IRE) **21C Telecom.co.uk**
20 **REFLECTION**, ch f Major Cadeaux—River Song (USA) **Mr B. P. J. Baugh**

Other Owners: Mr R. A. Hunt, Mrs N. Hunt, Mr G. Ratcliffe, Mrs M. Robinson, Mr K. V. Robinson, Mrs L. E. Tomlinson, Mr D. G. Williams.

Assistant Trainer: S Potts

---

31 | **MR CHRIS BEALBY, Grantham**
Postal: **North Lodge, Barrowby, Grantham, Lincolnshire, NG32 1DH**
Contacts: **OFFICE (01476) 564568 FAX (01476) 572391 MOBILE (07831) 538689**
E-MAIL chris@northlodgeracing.co.uk WEBSITE www.northlodgeracing.co.uk

1 **AWAREINESS (IRE)**, 8, b g Flemensfirth (USA)—Special Case (IRE) **R. A. Jenkinson**
2 **BENEVOLENT (IRE)**, 7, ch g Beneficial—Bobs Lass (IRE) **Paul Read & Dave Cook**
3 **CHAC DU CADRAN (FR)**, 8, b g Passing Sale (FR)—L'indienne (FR) **Bingley, Williams & Pepperdine**
4 **DIEGO SUAREZ (FR)**, 4, b g Astarabad (USA)—Shabada (FR) **Mrs M. J. Pepperdine**
5 **IFONLYALFIE**, 9, b g Alflora (IRE)—Ifni du Luc (FR) **Triumph In Mind**
6 **INTENT (IRE)**, 5, b m Jeremy (USA)—Cant Hurry Love **The Rann Family**
7 **LEGENDARY HOP**, 8, b m Midnight Legend—Hopping Mad **Messrs Duke,Umpleby,Holmes & Bealby**
8 **MACKESON**, 5, gr g Baryshnikov (AUS)—Travelling Lady **T. Urry**
9 **OVERRULE (USA)**, 10, b g Diesis—Her Own Way (USA) **Miss F. Harper**
10 **REARRANGE**, 5, b m Rail Link—New Order **The Rann Family**
11 **RUARAIDH HUGH (IRE)**, 5, b g Craigsteel—Decent Shower **C. C. Bealby**
12 **SIR LYNX (IRE)**, 7, gr g Amilynx (FR)—Minilus (IRE) **Sir Lynx Partnership**

Other Owners: Mrs E. A. Bingley, Mr D. M. Cook, B. G. Duke, F. M. Holmes, Mr G. P. D. Rann, Mrs L. E. Rann, Mr P. L. Read, Mr P. Umpleby, Mr T. Wendels, Mrs A. M. Williams, R. F. Wright.

Jockey (flat): Dane O'Neill. **Jockey (NH):** Tom Messenger, Noel Fehily. **Conditional:** Adam Wedge.
Amateur: Mr Olly Murphy.

---

32 | **MR RALPH BECKETT, Andover**
Postal: **Kimpton Down Stables, Kimpton Down, Andover, Hampshire, SP11 8QQ**
Contacts: **PHONE (01264) 772278 FAX (01264) 771221 MOBILE (07802) 219022**
E-MAIL trainer@rbeckett.com WEBSITE www.rbeckett.com

1 **ALDBOROUGH (IRE)**, 4, b g Danehill Dancer (USA)—Kitty O'shea **Mr & Mrs David Aykroyd**
2 **ASTRA HALL**, 5, ch m Halling (USA)—Star Precision **G. B. Balding**
3 **CROSS YOUR FINGERS (IRE)**, 4, b c Monsun (GER)—Capestar (IRE) **D & J Newell**
4 **CUBANITA**, 5, ch m Selkirk (USA)—Caribana **Miss K. Rausing**
5 **FLEUR DE LA VIE (IRE)**, 5, ch m Primary (USA)—Francophilia **Prime Of Life 3**
6 **FOXTROT JUBILEE (IRE)**, 4, b g Captain Marvelous (USA)—Cool Cousin (IRE) **Foxtrot Racing Partnership IV**
7 **HAAF A SIXPENCE**, 5, b g Haafhd—Melody Maker **Melody Racing**
8 **HURRY UP GEORGE**, 5, b g Intikhab—Digamist Girl (IRE) **A. E. Frost**
9 **INKA SURPRISE (IRE)**, 4, b g Intikhab (USA)—Sweet Surprise (IRE) **McDonagh Murphy & Nixon**
10 **LUNETTE (IRE)**, 4, b f Teofilo (IRE)—Princess Luna (GER) **Mr T D Rootes & Mr O F Waller**

MR RALPH BECKETT - Continued

11 **NICEOFYOUTOTELLME**, 5, b g Hernando (FR)—Swain's Gold (USA) **Mr R. J. Roberts**
12 **PEARL MIX (IRE)**, 5, gr h Oratorio (IRE)—Rosamixa (FR) **Qatar Racing Limited**
13 **POYLE THOMAS**, 5, b g Rail Link—Lost In Lucca **Cecil and Miss Alison Wiggins**
14 **ROYAL PRIZE**, 4, ch g Nayef (USA)—Spot Prize (USA) **J. C. Smith**
15 **SEASIDE SIZZLER**, 7, ch g Rahy (USA)—Via Borghese (USA) **I. J. Heseltine**
16 **SECRET GESTURE**, 4, b f Galileo (IRE)—Shastye (IRE) **Qatar Racing Ltd & Newsells Park Stud**
17 **SIZZLER**, 4, ch g Hernando (FR)—Gino's Spirits **Heseltine, Henley & Jones**
18 **TALENT**, 4, ch f New Approach (IRE)—Prowess (IRE) **Mr J L Rowsell & Mr M H Dixon**
19 **ZIPP (IRE)**, 4, b f Excellent Art—Subito **R. H. W. Morecombe**

THREE-YEAR-OLDS

20 B f Naaqoos—Beauty And Style (AUS) **R. A. Pegum**
21 **BELROG**, ch c New Approach (IRE)—Millennium Dash **Qatar Racing Limited**
22 **BOWIE BOY (IRE)**, b c Intikhab (USA)—Catatonic **I. J. Heseltine**
23 **CABIN FEVER**, ch f Medicean—Folly Lodge **T. D. Rootes**
24 **CALAMITY JANE**, b f Lawman (FR)—Yesteryear **The Quick Fill Partnership**
25 **CAPE CASTER (IRE)**, br g Cape Cross (IRE)—Playboy Mansion (IRE) **D P Barrie & D Redhead**
26 **CARNEVALE**, ch f New Approach (IRE)—Festivale (IRE) **Prince A. A. Faisal**
27 **CINNILLA**, b f Authorized (IRE)—Caesarea (GER) **J. L. Rowsell**
28 **CRYSTAL LAKE (IRE)**, gr c Verglas (IRE)—Entail (IRE) **The Pickford Hill Partnership**
29 **DARK REALITY (IRE)**, b f Intikhab (USA)—Sunny Slope **Qatar Racing Limited**
30 **DETER**, b f Nayef (USA)—Garah **Prince A. A. Faisal**
31 **DINNERATMIDNIGHT**, b g Kyllachy—The Terrier **The Rat Pack Partnership**
32 **EVITA PERON**, ch f Pivotal—Entente Cordiale (IRE) **Newsells Park Stud Limited**
33 **EXTRA NOBLE**, ch c Sir Percy—La Peinture (GER) **Ballymore Downunder Syndicate**
34 **FIALKA**, b f Cape Cross (IRE)—First **N. Bizakov**
35 **FREE REIN**, b f Dansili—Sant Elena **The Eclipse Partnership**
36 **GOLDENROD**, b g Pivotal—Prairie Flower (IRE) **J. H. Richmond-Watson**
37 **GOT TO DANCE**, b f Selkirk (USA)—Mullein **Landmark Racing Limited**
38 **HOLD HANDS**, b f Lawman (FR)—Tiponi (IRE) **D & J Newell**
39 **HONOR BOUND**, b f Authorized (IRE)—Honorine (IRE) **Ashley House Stud**
40 **KALLISHA**, b f Whipper (USA)—Shallika (IRE) **D & J Newell**
41 **KILLING TIME (IRE)**, b g Oratorio (IRE)—Enchanting Muse (USA) **Kennet Valley Thoroughbreds VIII**
42 **LABISE (IRE)**, b f Azamour (IRE)—What A Picture (FR) **Mrs E. Kennedy**
43 **LAST ECHO (IRE)**, b f Whipper (USA)—Priory Rock (IRE) **Mr R A Farmiloe & Partner**
44 **LIGHTNING SPEAR**, ch c Pivotal—Atlantic Destiny (IRE) **Qatar Racing Limited**
45 **LIKE A PRAYER**, b c Compton Place—Floating **The Rat Pack Partnership**
46 **LUNAR SPIRIT**, b f Invincible Spirit (IRE)—Kitty O'shea **Mr & Mrs David Aykroyd**
47 **MELROSE ABBEY (IRE)**, ch f Selkirk (USA)—Villa Carlotta (IRE) **J. H. Richmond-Watson**
48 **MERCURY MAGIC**, b g Oratorio (IRE)—Lochridge **J. C. Smith**
49 **MOLLY ON THE SHORE**, b f Halling (USA)—Zahrtee (IRE) **Mr D. J Macham**
50 **MONTAIGNE**, b c Exceed And Excel (AUS)—Autumn Pearl **Mr & Mrs Kevan Watts**
51 **MOONRISE LANDING (IRE)**, gr f Dalakhani (IRE)—Celtic Slipper (IRE) **P. D. Savill**
52 **MOUNTAIN DEW**, b f Tiger Hill (IRE)—Ecstasy **A D G Oldrey, G C Hartigan & S F Oldrey**
53 **MR BOSSY BOOTS (IRE)**, b c Teofilo (IRE)—Zelding (IRE) **Merriebelle Stables LLC**
54 **NIRVA (IRE)**, gr f Verglas (IRE)—Nirvana **Lady G. De Walden**
55 **NORSE LIGHT**, ch g Norse Dancer (IRE)—Dimelight **J. C. Smith**
56 **PERFECT ALCHEMY (IRE)**, b f Clodovil (IRE)—Desert Alchemy (IRE) **The Perfect Partnership & D H Caslon**
57 **PERFECT RHYTHM**, b f Halling (USA)—Bassinet (USA) **Dr Bridget Drew & Partners**
58 **PRINCIPLE EQUATION (IRE)**, b f Oasis Dream—Dame Alicia (IRE) **Clipper Group Holdings Ltd**
59 **RAGING BOB (IRE)**, br g Big Bad Bob (IRE)—Lanasara **A.W.A. Partnership**
60 **RAVENOUS**, b g Raven's Pass (USA)—Supereva (IRE) **The Prince of Wales & The Duchess of Cornwall**
61 **REGARDEZ**, b f Champs Elysees—Look So **J. H. Richmond-Watson**
62 **RIDEONASTAR (IRE)**, b c Manduro (GER)—Capestar (IRE)
63 **SEA GODDESS (IRE)**, b f Galileo (IRE)—Castara Beach (IRE) **Mrs J Magnier, Mr D Smith & Mr M Tabor**
64 **SEA HERE**, ch c Sea The Stars (IRE)—Look Here **J. H. Richmond-Watson**
65 **SECRET ARCHIVE (USA)**, gr ro g Arch (USA)—Mystic Miracle **Thurloe Thoroughbreds XXXII**
66 **SERIOUS DOWTH (IRE)**, b f Iffraaj—Zelda (IRE) **Merriebelle Stables LLC**
67 **SLEEPER**, b f Rail Link—Guermantes **The Millennium Madness Partnership**
68 **STARLIGHT SERENADE**, ch f Three Valleys (USA)—Melody Maker **Melody Racing**
69 **TAQUKA (IRE)**, b c Kodiac—Dubai Princess (IRE) **The Pickford Hill Partnership**
70 **TEA LEAF (IRE)**, b f Bushranger (IRE)—Boston Ivy (USA) **McCalmont and Drew**
71 **TINGA (IRE)**, ch f Galileo (IRE)—Tingling (USA) **N. Bizakov**
72 **VENUS GRACE**, b f Royal Applause—Basque Beauty **Lady Coventry & Partners**
73 **WELL FINISHED**, gr ro f Mastercraftsman (IRE)—Grain of Gold **R. Barnett**

MR RALPH BECKETT - Continued

74 **WHEELS OF FORTUNE**, ch c Exceed And Excel (AUS)—Be Free **Clipper Group Holdings Ltd**
75 **WITCH FROM ROME**, b g Holy Roman Emperor (IRE)—Spangle **Mr R. J. Roberts**

TWO-YEAR-OLDS

76 Gr c 17/2 Verglas (IRE)—Atlas Silk (Dansili) (27619) **Mrs I. M. Beckett**
77 **AZURE AMOUR (IRE)**, b f 12/5 Azamour (IRE)—Al Euro (FR) (Mujtahid (USA)) (19000) **The Dirham Partnership**
78 **BOLD APPEAL**, b c 24/1 Nayef (USA)—Shy Appeal (IRE) (Barathea (IRE)) (18000) **J. P. Repard**
79 B f 30/4 Exceed And Excel (AUS)—
              Bronze Star (Mark of Esteem (IRE)) (52000) **Qatar Racing Ltd & Mr N H Wrigley**
80 **CAMAGUEYANA**, b f 2/3 Archipenko (USA)—Caribana (Hernando (FR)) **Miss K. Rausing**
81 **CAPE CAY**, gr f 26/4 Cape Cross (IRE)—White Cay (Dalakhani (IRE)) (16000) **R. Barnett**
82 B c 7/3 Alfred Nobel (IRE)—Common Rumpus (IRE) (Common Grounds) (37000) **Mr R. Ng**
83 B c 17/1 Rock of Gibraltar (IRE)—Cordelia (Green Desert (USA)) (13333) **The Outlaws**
84 B f 27/2 Acclamation—Corps de Ballet (IRE) (Fasliyev (USA)) (50000) **Mr S. Pan**
85 B c 2/4 Pivotal—Coy (IRE) (Danehill (USA)) (20000) **What Asham Partnership**
86 **CRACKER**, b f 6/3 Smart Strike (CAN)—Tottie (Fantastic Light (USA)) **J. H. Richmond-Watson**
87 B f 19/2 Danehill Dancer (IRE)—Dark Missile (Night Shift (USA)) **J. C. Smith**
88 B c 12/4 Sir Percy—Dominica (Alhaarth (IRE)) (29000)
89 **DON'T TRY (IRE)**, b f 2/3 Galileo (IRE)—
              Bonheur (IRE) (Royal Academy (USA)) (371660) **M Al Kubaisi/Sheikh Suhaim Al Thani/QRL**
90 B c 15/2 Oasis Dream—Entente Cordiale (IRE) (Ela-Mana-Mou) (220000) **Newsells Park Stud Limited**
91 B c 19/1 Invincible Spirit (IRE)—Ermine And Velvet (Nayef (USA)) (135000) **Mr S. Pan**
92 Ch f 4/4 Raven's Pass (USA)—
              Fashion Rocks (IRE) (Rock of Gibraltar (IRE)) (70000) **Thurloe Thoroughbreds XXXIV**
93 B c 28/2 Kyllachy—Fluttering Rose (Compton Place) (108400) **Mr S. Pan**
94 B c 15/4 Arcano (IRE)—Folcara (IRE) (Brief Truce (USA)) (30000) **Mr R. Ng**
95 **FORTE**, ch f 23/2 New Approach (IRE)—Prowess (IRE) (Peintre Celebre (USA)) **Mr J L Rowsell & Mr M H Dixon**
96 B c 9/4 Big Bad Bob (IRE)—Gladiole (GER) (Platini (GER)) (46000) **Kennet Valley Thoroughbreds VIII**
97 Ch g 20/3 Duke of Marmalade (IRE)—Graduation (Lomitas) (30000) **Mr R. Ng**
98 **GREAT GLEN**, b c 14/2 High Chaparral (IRE)—Grand Opening (IRE) (Desert King (IRE)) **J. H. Richmond-Watson**
99 B f 4/2 New Approach (IRE)—Green Room (FR) (In The Wings)
100 **HARD TO HANDEL**, b c 10/4 Stimulation (IRE)—Melody Maker (Diktat) **Melody Racing**
101 **HAWKIN (IRE)**, b f 15/2 Big Bad Bob (IRE)—Margaux Magique (Xaar) (33333) **The Hawk Inn Syndicate 4**
102 B g 15/1 Duke of Marmalade (IRE)—Island Dreams (USA) (Giant's Causeway (USA)) (30000) **Mr R. Ng**
103 Ch c 11/2 Sea The Stars (IRE)—Jakonda (USA) (Kingmambo (USA)) (73557) **Qatar Racing Limited**
104 B c 2/2 Norse Dancer (IRE)—King's Siren (IRE) (King's Best (USA)) **J. C. Smith**
105 B c 14/3 Intikhab (USA)—Lady Docker (IRE) (Docksider (USA)) (26000)
106 B c 17/3 Equiano (FR)—Loch Verdi (Green Desert (USA)) (40000) **J. C. Smith**
107 **MAGIC CIRCLE (IRE)**, b c 1/5 Makfi—Minkova (IRE) (Sadler's Wells (USA)) **Mr & Mrs David Aykroyd**
108 B f 5/5 Dynaformer (USA)—Mambo Jambo (USA) (Kingmambo (USA)) **J. L. Rowsell**
109 B c 7/4 Kheleyf (USA)—My Golly (Mozart (IRE)) (60000) **Mr S. Pan**
110 B f 29/4 Dutch Art—Nine Red (Royal Applause) **R. C. Tooth**
111 **PACIFY**, b c 14/2 Paco Boy (IRE)—
              Supereva (IRE) (Sadler's Wells (USA)) **The Prince of Wales & The Duchess of Cornwall**
112 **PACKED HOUSE**, b f 14/2 Azamour (IRE)—Riotous Applause (Royal Applause) **The Eclipse Partnership**
113 **PARNELL'S DREAM**, b f 7/5 Oasis Dream—Kitty O'shea (Sadler's Wells (USA)) **Mr & Mrs David Aykroyd**
114 B c 20/2 Sir Percy—Pella (Hector Protector (USA)) (70000) **Mrs H. I. Slade**
115 **PERRAULT (IRE)**, b c 30/4 Rip Van Winkle (IRE)—La Persiana (Daylami (IRE)) **Lady G. De Walden**
116 B f 28/4 Fastnet Rock (AUS)—Playboy Mansion (IRE) (Grand Lodge (USA)) (42000) **Mrs E. Kennedy**
117 **PURE LINE**, b f 26/4 Zamindar (USA)—Pure Grain (Polish Precedent (USA)) **R. Barnett**
118 B f 14/3 High Chaparral (IRE)—
              Quiet Waters (USA) (Quiet American (USA)) (65000) **Ballymore Sterling Syndicate**
119 B c 4/3 Showcasing—Raggle Taggle (IRE) (Tagula (IRE)) (51428) **Qatar Racing Limited**
120 B c 3/2 Approve (IRE)—Rihana (IRE) (Priolo (USA)) (27000) **Highclere Thoroughbred Racing - Approve**
121 B f 12/4 Tobougg (IRE)—Roseum (Lahib (USA)) (34285) **Mr N H Wrigley & Qatar Racing Ltd**
122 **SHE IS NO LADY**, b f 27/3 Lope de Vega (IRE)—Capestar (IRE) (Cape Cross (IRE)) **D & J Newell**
123 **SINGULAR QUEST**, ch c 5/5 Dalakhani (IRE)—Singuliere (IRE) (Singspiel (IRE)) **J. L. Rowsell**
124 B c 22/2 Rip Van Winkle (IRE)—Steel Princess (IRE) (Danehill (USA)) (400000) **Qatar Racing Limited**
125 B f 12/3 Cape Cross (IRE)—Stormy Blessing (USA) (Storm Cat (USA)) **Mr C. McHale**
126 B f 22/4 Cape Cross (IRE)—Surval (IRE) (Sadler's Wells (USA)) (70000) **Mr R. Ng**
127 Gr c 2/4 Aqlaam—Vellena (Lucky Story (USA)) (20000) **A. E. Frost**

Other Owners: Mr D. Abraham, Mr A. R. Adams, Mr M. A. M. K. Al - Kubaisi, Sheikh S. A. K. H. Al Thani, Mrs L. M. Aykroyd, D. P. Aykroyd, D. P. Barrie, Mr R. D. Beckett, Mr T. Bennett, Mr J. A. Byrne, D. H. Caslon, Duchess of Cornwall, Countess R. Coventry, D. W. Dennis, M. H. Dixon, Dr S. B. Drew, J. R. Drew, Mr R. A. Farmiloe, N. J. Forman Hardy, Mr R

MR RALPH BECKETT - Continued

J. Fowler, Mrs M. R. Gregory, P. W. Haddock, B. P. Hammond, Mrs J. E. Hammond, G. C. Hartigan, M. G. H. Heald, The Hon H. M. Herbert, Highclere Thoroughbred Racing Ltd, Mr J. Hillier, Mr S. J. Kattau, Mr M. J. Kershaw, Mr E. A. M. Leatham, Mrs S. E. Leatham, Mr R. P. Legh, Mrs S. Magnier, Mr M. D. Moroney, Mr P. G. Murphy, D. J. M. Newell, Mrs J. Newell, A. D. G. Oldrey, S. F. Oldrey, R. L. Page, Mr M. Patel, Mr N. Patsalides, O. J. W. Pawle, Mr J. A. Randall, Mr D. P. Redhead, N. J. F. Robinson, D. Smith, Mrs H. L. Smyly, Mr J. A. B. Stafford, M. Tabor, H.R.H. The Prince Of Wales, O. F. Waller, Mr K. Watts, Mrs P. M. L. Watts, Mr R. Weston, C. Wiggins, Miss A. J. Wiggins, T. V. Wilkinson, N. H. T. Wrigley.

Assistant Trainers: Adam Kite, W. Jackson-Stops.

Jockey (flat): Jim Crowley. **Apprentice:** Patrick O'Donnell, Jane Elliott. **Amateur:** Miss S. West.

---

33 MR MICHAEL BELL, Newmarket
Postal: **Fitzroy House, Newmarket, Suffolk, CB8 0JT**
Contacts: PHONE (01638) 666567 FAX (01638) 668000 MOBILE (07802) 264514
E-MAIL office@fitzroyhouse.co.uk WEBSITE www.michaelbellracing.co.uk

1 **FASHION LINE (IRE),** 4, b f Cape Cross (IRE)—Shadow Roll (IRE) **Sheikh Marwan Al Maktoum**
2 **GEORGE CINQ,** 4, b g Pastoral Pursuits—Fairnilee **Tamdown Group Limited**
3 **HOT MUSTARD,** 4, b g Pastoral Pursuits—Lihou Island **Mrs G. E. Rowland-Clark**
4 **MADAME DEFARGE (IRE),** 4, b f Motivator—Friendlier **W. J. Gredley**
5 **RISKIT FORA BISKIT (IRE),** 4, b f Kodiac—
Miss Brief (IRE) **Mr Christopher Wright & The Hon Mrs J.M.Corbett**
6 **ROLE PLAYER,** 4, ch c Exceed And Excel (AUS)—Dresden Doll (USA) **Sheikh Marwan Al Maktoum**
7 **RUTLAND BOY,** 6, ch g Bertolini (USA)—Israar **Abdulla Ahmad Al Shaikh**
8 **SHANTI,** 4, b g Dansili—Maycocks Bay **Lady Bamford**
9 **SOVEREIGN DEBT (IRE),** 5, gr g Dark Angel (IRE)—Kelsey Rose **Mr Lawrie Inman**
10 **SWORD OF THE LORD,** 4, b g Kheleyf (USA)—Blue Echo **Saleh Al Homaizi & Imad Al Sagar**
11 **THE LARK,** 4, ch f Pivotal—Gull Wing **Lady Bamford**
12 **WIGMORE HALL (IRE),** 7, b g High Chaparral (IRE)—Love And Laughter (IRE) **Mr M. B. Hawtin**

THREE-YEAR-OLDS

13 **ACROSS THE CAPE,** ch f Manduro (GER)—Cape Marien (IRE) **Saif Ali**
14 **ALMAX,** b c Rock of Gibraltar (IRE)—Inya Lake **Karmaa Racing Limited**
15 **ASTRAL WEEKS,** b f Sea The Stars (IRE)—Miss Universe (IRE) **Mr Christopher Wright & Lordship Stud**
16 **BED BED,** b f Nayef (USA)—Bedara **M. L. W. Bell Racing Ltd**
17 **BIG ORANGE,** b g Duke of Marmalade (IRE)—Miss Brown To You (IRE) **W. J. Gredley**
18 **BORN TO REIGN,** b c Sir Percy—Oat Cuisine **Mrs G. E. Rowland-Clark**
19 **BOURBON PRINCE,** ch g Aqlaam—Good Enough (FR) **R. N. Frosell**
20 B c Fastnet Rock (AUS)—Bowstring (IRE) **Mr N. A. Jackson**
21 **BY JUPITER,** ch f Sea The Stars (IRE)—Maid of Killeen (IRE) **Lady Bamford**
22 B f Royal Applause—Cefira (USA) **Mr James Boughey**
23 **CHATHAM HOUSE RULE,** gr c Authorized (IRE)—Cozy Maria (USA) **Saleh Al Homaizi & Imad Al Sagar**
24 **EXCEEDING POWER,** b g Exceed And Excel (AUS)—Extreme Beauty (USA) **Dr Ali Ridha**
25 **FIERY SUNSET,** b f Galileo (IRE)—Five Fields (USA) **Her Majesty The Queen**
26 **FINN CLASS (IRE),** b c Exceed And Excel (AUS)—Finnmark (IRE) **Saif Ali**
27 **GALIZZI (USA),** b c Dansili—Dancing Abbie (USA) **Sheikh Marwan Al Maktoum**
28 **GAUCHITA,** b f Invincible Spirit—Rex Regina (USA) **Mrs Melba Bryce**
29 **GOOD HOPE,** b f Cape Cross (IRE)—Fairy Godmother **Her Majesty The Queen**
30 **GRAND MEISTER,** gr c Mastercraftsman (IRE)—Wait It Out (USA) **Mrs Doreen Tabor**
31 **HALA HALA (IRE),** b f Invincible Spirit (IRE)—Galistic (IRE) **Sultan Ali**
32 **INVOKE (IRE),** b f Kodiac—Tides **Highclere Thoroughbred Racing-Herbert Jones**
33 **JAYEFF HERRING (IRE),** b g Excellent Art—Biasca **M. L. W. Bell Racing Ltd**
34 C b Peintre Celebre (USA)—Kotdiji **Mr N. A. Jackson**
35 **MANTOU (IRE),** ch c Teofilo (IRE)—Shadow Roll (IRE) **Sheikh Marwan Al Maktoum**
36 **MARWEENA (IRE),** b f Cape Cross (IRE)—Dunes Queen (USA) **Jaber Abdullah**
37 **MISSISSIPPI QUEEN (USA),** b f Artie Schiller (USA)—Siempre Asi (USA) **Mr Christopher Wright**
38 **NEWMARKET WARRIOR (IRE),** b c Dalakhani (IRE)—Heavens Peak **W. J. Gredley**
39 **PIAZON,** br g Striking Ambition—Colonel's Daughter **R. P. B. Michaelson**
40 **RAVEN RIDGE (IRE),** b c High Chaparral (IRE)—Green Castle (IRE) **Saleh Al Homaizi & Imad Al Sagar**
41 **RHONDA (IRE),** b f Fastnet Rock (AUS)—Regal Darcey (IRE) **The Royal Ascot Racing Club**
42 **RIBBLEHEAD (USA),** b br c Arch—Moolakaya (FR) **Clipper Logistics**
43 **ROCK OF LEON,** b g Rock of Gibraltar (IRE)—Leonica **Mr Leon Caine & Mr & Mrs Ray Jenner**
44 **SALTWATER CREEK (IRE),** b f Marju (IRE)—Crossing **Dr Ali Ridha**
45 **SILVER MIRAGE,** b f Oasis Dream—Phantom Gold **Her Majesty The Queen**

MR MICHAEL BELL - Continued

46 **SPIRITOFTHEUNION**, b f Authorized (IRE)—Kahlua Kiss **Ahmad Abdulla Al Shaikh**
47 **SUGAR RUSH**, ch g Pastoral Pursuits—Panic Stations **D. W. & L. Y. Payne**
48 **TAUTIRA (IRE)**, b f Kheleyf (USA)—Ballantrae (IRE) **Sheikh Marwan Al Maktoum**
49 **THATCHEREEN (IRE)**, ro f Mastercraftsman (IRE)—Roof Fiddle (USA) **Mr Tim Redman & Mr Peter Philipps**
50 **VALEN (IRE)**, gr f Acclamation—Ardea Brave (IRE) **Mrs Melba Bryce**
51 **WEDDING WISH (IRE)**, b f Acclamation—Have Faith (IRE) **Saleh Al Homaizi & Imad Al Sagar**

TWO-YEAR-OLDS

52 B f 17/3 Iffraaj—Al Cobra (IRE) (Sadler's Wells (USA)) (52000) **Saif Ali**
53 B c 15/4 Exceed And Excel (AUS)—Always On My Mind (Distant Relative) (30000) **Karmaa Racing Limited**
54 **AROUSAL**, b f 10/2 Stimulation (IRE)—
        Midnight Mover (IRE) (Bahamian Bounty) (7619) **Mrs G Rowland-Clarke & Mr W E A Fox**
55 **AUSSIE BERRY (IRE)**, gr c 10/3 Aussie Rules (USA)—
        Berry Baby (IRE) (Rainbow Quest (USA)) (18000) **Mr Dermot Hanafin**
56 B c 24/1 Iffraaj—Badalona (Cape Cross (IRE)) **Sheikh Marwan Al Maktoum**
57 B br c 27/3 Cape Cross (IRE)—Ballantrae (IRE) (Diktat) **Sheikh Marwan Al Maktoum**
58 B f 19/4 Motivator—
        Bantu (Cape Cross (IRE)) (34000) **The Hon Major James Broughton and The Hon Peter Stanley**
59 **BAREFOOT DANCER**, b c 1/3 Dansili—Charlotte O Fraise (IRE) (Beat Hollow) **Racing Fillies**
60 **CHASING RUBIES (IRE)**, b f 21/2 Tamayuz—
        Laurdelean Lady (IRE) (Statue of Liberty (USA)) (40000) **Lordship Stud 4 & Christopher Wright**
61 B f 25/3 Equiano (FR)—Christmas Tart (IRE) (Danetime (IRE)) (80000) **Middleham Park Racing**
62 **DOWN TO EARTH**, gr c 3/3 Aussie Rules (USA)—
        May Fox (Zilzal (USA)) (41000) **P. A. Philipps & C. E. L. Philipps**
63 Ch f 28/4 Dutch Art—Drastic Measure (Pivotal) **Mr Dilip Rahulan**
64 **ELLA FITZ**, b f 26/1 Pivotal—Under The Rainbow (Fantastic Light (USA)) **W. J. Gredley**
65 **EMINENTT**, b c 5/4 Exceed And Excel (AUS)—Antediluvian (Air Express (IRE)) (60000) **W. J. Gredley**
66 B c 2/3 Vale of York (IRE)—Finnmark (Halling (USA)) (9000) **Sultan Ali**
67 Ch c 2/5 Dubawi (IRE)—Flashy Wings (Zafonic (USA)) **Jaber Abdullah**
68 B f 6/1 Elusive Quality (USA)—
        Flip Flop (FR) (Zieten (USA)) (60000) **Mrs Hugo Lascelles and Mrs Ben Sangster**
69 **FRANKLIN D**, ch c 16/2 Pivotal—Sabreon (Caerleon (USA)) (80000) **W. J. Gredley**
70 **FRIENDLIE**, b f 25/2 Motivator—Friendlier (Zafonic (USA)) **W. J. Gredley**
71 B c 18/2 Fast Company (IRE)—Good Lady (IRE) (Barathea (IRE)) **Jaber Abdullah**
72 **HO YAM LAY**, ch f 25/4 Sakhee's Secret—
        Winterbourne (Cadeaux Genereux) (12380) **Ahmad Abdulla Al Shaikh & Co**
73 **INDIA (IRE)**, b f 15/2 Authorized (IRE)—Miss Brown To You (IRE) (Fasliyev (USA)) **W. J. Gredley**
74 Ch c 14/4 New Approach (IRE)—Just Like A Woman (Observatory (USA)) (72000) **Mascalls Stud**
75 B c 17/4 Makfi—Maidin Maith (IRE) (Montjeu (IRE)) (230000) **Saleh Al Homaizi & Imad Al Sagar**
76 B c 21/3 Azamour (IRE)—Maramba (USA) (Hussonet (USA)) (17000)
77 **MY STRATEGY (IRE)**, b c 27/2 Strategic Prince—Mythie (FR) (Octagonal (NZ)) (30952) **W. E. A. Fox**
78 Ch c 9/3 Rip Van Winkle (IRE)—Night Haven (Night Shift (USA)) (90000) **Mr Michael Tabor**
79 **ON THE HUH**, b c 17/2 Avonbridge—Red Sovereign (Danzig Connection (USA)) (20000) **Mr Paddy Barrett**
80 **ORANGE BLOOM**, ch f 3/3 New Approach (IRE)—Fleur de Lis (Nayef (USA)) **W. J. Gredley**
81 B c 15/3 Dansili—Penang Pearl (FR) (Bering) (120000) **Mrs A. K. H. Ooi**
82 B c 27/3 Royal Applause—Poldhu (Cape Cross (IRE)) (36000) **Karmaa Racing Ltd**
83 Ch f 6/4 Mount Nelson—Red Roses Story (FR) (Pink (FR)) **Mr Dilip Rahulan**
84 **SAVOY SHOWGIRL (IRE)**, ch f 27/3 Kyllachy—
        The Strand (Gone West (USA)) (85171) **Christopher Wright & Miss Emily Asprey**
85 B f 15/2 Oasis Dream—Sewards Folly (Rudimentary (USA)) **Saleh Al Homaizi and Imad Al Sagar**
86 **SHERIFF**, b c 27/3 Lawman (FR)—Ammo (IRE) (Sadler's Wells (USA)) (28000) **W. J. Gredley**
87 B c 25/5 Dubawi (IRE)—Shy Lady (FR) (Kaldoun (FR)) **Jaber Abdullah**
88 B f 23/1 Hellvelyn—Startori (Vettori (IRE)) (20000) **M. L. W. Bell Racing Ltd**
89 **STONE ROSES (IRE)**, ch f 24/1 Zebedee—Blanche Dubois (Nashwan (USA)) (40000) **Tamdown Group Ltd**
90 **THUNDER IN MYHEART (IRE)**, gr f 15/2 Mastercraftsman (IRE)—
        Happy Land (IRE) (Refuse To Bend (IRE)) (38000) **C Wright, Mrs C Forsyth & Miss H Wright**
91 **TOUCHLINE**, b f 29/2 Exceed And Excel (AUS)—Trianon (Nayef (USA)) **Her Majesty The Queen**
92 **WHATWHAZZ**, b f 5/3 Nayef (USA)—Whazzat (Daylami (IRE)) **W. J. Gredley**

Assistant Trainer: Richard Spencer

Jockey (flat): Jamie Spencer, Tom Queally. **Apprentice:** Thomas Hemsley, Louis Steward.

34 **MR JAMES BENNETT, Wantage**
Postal: **2 Filley Alley, Letcombe Bassett, Wantage, Oxfordshire, OX12 9LT**
Contacts: **PHONE (01235) 762163 FAX (01235) 762163 MOBILE (07771) 523076**
E-MAIL jabennett345@btinternet.com

1 **IDOL DEPUTY (FR)**, 8, gr g Silver Deputy (CAN)—Runaway Venus (USA) **Miss J. C. Blackwell**
2 **PRINCESSE KATIE (IRE)**, 8, b m Presenting—Another Shot (IRE) **Miss J. C. Blackwell**

THREE-YEAR-OLDS

3 **STAR CLOUD**, b g Nayef (USA)—Space Quest **Miss J. C. Blackwell**

Assistant Trainer: Miss J. Blackwell

Jockey (flat): Racheal Kneller.

35 **MR ALAN BERRY, Cockerham**
Postal: **Moss Side Racing Stables, Crimbles Lane, Cockerham, Lancashire, LA2 0ES**
Contacts: **PHONE (01524) 791179 FAX (01524) 791958 MOBILE (07880) 553515**
E-MAIL mosssideracing@tiscali.co.uk WEBSITE www.alanberryracing.co.uk

1 **AMIS REUNIS**, 5, b m Bahamian Bounty—Spring Clean (FR) **A. B. Parr**
2 **BIX (IRE)**, 4, b g Holy Roman Emperor (IRE)—Belle Rebelle (IRE) **A. Berry**
3 **BUSY BIMBO (IRE)**, 5, b m Red Clubs (IRE)—Unfortunate **Do Well Racing**
4 **ECONOMIC CRISIS (IRE)**, 5, ch m Excellent Art—Try The Air (IRE) **Mr & Mrs T. Blane**
5 **GRETHEL (IRE)**, 10, b m Fruits of Love (USA)—Stay Sharpe (USA) **Mr J. P. Smith**
6 **I'LL BE GOOD**, 5, b g Red Clubs (IRE)—Willisa **Do Well Racing**
7 **JORDAURA**, 8, br g Primo Valentino (IRE)—Christina's Dream **A. B. Parr**
8 **KAY GEE BE (IRE)**, 10, b g Fasliyev—Pursuit of Truth (USA) **A. Berry**
9 **KINGSCROFT (IRE)**, 6, b g Antonius Pius (USA)—Handsome Anna (IRE) **Mr L. J. Mann**
10 **MYSTIFIED (IRE)**, 11, b g Raise A Grand (IRE)—Sunrise (IRE) **A. Willoughby**
11 **NOBLE MAXIMUS**, 4, b g Oratorio (IRE)—Perfect Peach **A. Berry**
12 **PARTNER'S GOLD (IRE)**, 4, b c Red Clubs (IRE)—Unfortunate **Partner's Brewery**
13 **PERFECT BLOSSOM**, 7, b m One Cool Cat (USA)—Perfect Peach **A. Berry**
14 **PLUNDER**, 4, ch g Zamindar (USA)—Reaching Ahead (USA) **Mr & Mrs D. Yates**
15 **RARE COINCIDENCE**, 13, ch g Atraf—Green Seed (IRE) **A. Willoughby**
16 **RED ROAR (IRE)**, 7, ch m Chineur (FR)—Unfortunate **Sporting Kings**
17 **SAMOAN (IRE)**, 5, b g Danehill Dancer (IRE)—Rain Flower (IRE) **A. B. Parr**
18 **SPEIGHTOWNS KID (USA)**, 6, gr ro g Speightstown (USA)—Seize the Wind (USA) **Ged & Daz**
19 **SPREAD BOY (IRE)**, 7, b g Tagula (IRE)—Marinka **A. Berry**
20 **WICKED WILMA (IRE)**, 10, b m Tagula (IRE)—Wicked **Mrs L. White**

THREE-YEAR-OLDS

21 **CASPER LEE (IRE)**, b g Kheleyf (USA)—Shallop **Mr & Mrs D. Yates**
22 **LUNESDALE BUDDY**, b c Indesatchel (IRE)—Darling Buds **Kirkby Lonsdale Racing**
23 **MILDENHALL**, ch f Compton Place—Night Kiss (IRE) **A. B. Parr**
24 **PENNY PURSUITS**, b f Pastoral Pursuits—Sattelight **A. R. White**
25 **RAISE A BILLION**, b c Major Cadeaux—Romantic Destiny **T Blane, F Flynn, H Rocks & M Rocks**
26 **RED FOREVER**, ch c Major Cadeaux—Spindara (IRE) **Sporting Kings**
27 **STRAIGHT GIN**, b g Major Cadeaux—Nee Lemon Left **J Berry/ W Burns**

Other Owners: Mr S. J. Allen, J. Berry, T. W. Blane, Mrs S. Blane, Mr G. D. Brown, W. Burns, Mr F. G. Flynn, Mr I. Griffiths, Mr I. D. Johnson, Mr B. J. Maxted, Mr G. O'Mahoney, Mr H. Rocks, Mr M. Rocks, Mr N. Sharp, Mr P. Stephenson, G. R. Taylor, Mr D. Yates, Mrs A. V. Yates.

36 **MR J. A. BERRY, Blackwater**
Postal: **Ballyroe, Blackwater, Enniscorthy, Co. Wexford, Ireland**
Contacts: **PHONE (00353) 53 27205 MOBILE (00353) 8625 57537**

1 **ACRIVEEN (IRE)**, 12, ch g Accordion—Raheen River (IRE) **J. A. Berry**
2 **ANOTHER NOTION (IRE)**, 6, b g Rashar (USA)—Dame Nancy (IRE) **M. Berry**
3 **BALLYROE RAMBLER (IRE)**, 7, br g Lahib (USA)—Victoria's Rose (IRE) **Fire & Ice Syndicate**
4 **BOOLAVARD KING (IRE)**, 5, b g Winged Love (IRE)—Eastender **P. McGovern**
5 **CARA VIC (IRE)**, 7, ch m Old Vic—Sonnerschien (IRE) **Go For It Syndicate**

MR J. A. BERRY - Continued

    6 CIVENA (IRE), 8, b m Oscar (IRE)—The Village Merc (IRE) Go For It Syndicate
    7 COOTAMUNDRA (IRE), 11, ch g Broken Hearted—Sigginstown Turbine Syndicate
    8 CROGHILL TUPPENCE (IRE), 9, gr g Great Palm (USA)—Shady's Rose (IRE) Turbine Syndicate
    9 DEEP INSPIRATION (IRE), 6, b g Heron Island (IRE)—The Wrens Nest (IRE) Mrs Joan Berry
   10 FAMOUS BALLERINA (IRE), 6, b m Golan (IRE)—World of Ballet (IRE) J. Berry
   11 GIVE US A HAND (IRE), 12, br g Anshan—Desperado Dawn (IRE) Mrs Joan Berry
   12 KOPI LUWAK (IRE), 6, b g Classic Cliche (IRE)—Strong Edition (IRE) M. Berry
   13 SEE IT AS IT IS (IRE), 7, b g Shantou (USA)—Opus One Not For Friends Syndicate
   14 SHINGLE BAY, 8, b g Karinga Bay—Riva La Belle J. A. Berry
   15 SILVER CAVALIER (IRE), 8, gr g Sonus (IRE)—Benaughlin (IRE) Not For Friends Syndicate
   16 TOMPATPEG (IRE), 7, b g Luso—River Grove (IRE) M. I. Cloney
   17 WHAT ABOUT THAT (IRE), 6, b g Spartacus (IRE)—Cajo (IRE) J. A. Berry
   18 WHATS ON THE MENU (IRE), 10, ch g Anshan—Leading Dream (IRE) Mrs J. Berry

Assistant Trainer: Blain Parnell **Conditional:** A. G. O'Neill. **Amateur:** Mr M. Scallan.

---

37 MR JOHN BERRY, Newmarket
Postal: Beverley House Stables, Exeter Road, Newmarket, Suffolk, CB8 8LR
Contacts: PHONE (01638) 660663
WEBSITE www.beverleyhousestables.com

    1 DOUCHKIRK (FR), 7, b g Prince Kirk (FR)—Douchka (FR) The Beverley Hillbillies
    2 ETHICS GIRL (IRE), 8, b m Hernando (FR)—Palinisa (FR) The 1997 Partnership
    3 FEN FLYER, 5, ch g Piccolo—Maraffi (IRE) Mr D. Tunmore
    4 GIFT OF SILENCE, 5, gr m Cadeaux Genereux—Not A Word J. C. De P. Berry
    5 JACK IRISH, 4, b g Bertolini (USA)—Desiree (IRE) Mrs E. L. Berry
    6 MAGIC ICE, 4, b f Royal Applause—Winter Ice J. C. De P. Berry
    7 OSCAR BERNADOTTE, 6, b g Sulamani (IRE)—Desiree (IRE) Emma Berry & Stephen Mccormick
    8 ROY ROCKET (FR), 4, gr g Layman (USA)—Minnie's Mystery (FR) McCarthy & Berry
    9 RUSSIAN LINK, 4, b f Rail Link—Zathonia Mrs E. L. Berry
   10 SALEAL, 5, b g Gentleman's Deal (IRE)—Sales Flow J. C. De P. Berry
   11 WASABI (IRE), 5, b m Tiger Hill (IRE)—Quinzey (JPN) Mr A. W. Fordham
   12 ZAROSA (IRE), 5, b m Barathea (IRE)—Shantalla Peak (IRE) Mr R. G. Vicarage

THREE-YEAR-OLDS

   13 INDIRA, ch f Sleeping Indian—Forever Loved Severn Crossing Partnership

TWO-YEAR-OLDS

   14 DELATITE, b c 7/3 Schiaparelli (GER)—Desiree (IRE) (Desert Story (IRE)) Mrs Emma Berry & Mr Mark Ritchie
   15 B f 17/5 Champs Elysees—Query (USA) (Distant View (USA)) (2000) Mr D. Tunmore
   16 B f 3/4 Dylan Thomas (IRE)—Rockahoolababy (IRE) (Kalanisi (IRE)) (5806) Mr J. A. Carver
   17 SO MUCH WATER (FR), gr f 3/4 Le Havre (IRE)—
                                Minnie's Mystery (FR) (Highest Honor (FR)) Mr J. C. De P. Berry
   18 B f 15/3 Motivator—White Turf (GER) (Tiger Hill (IRE)) (8000) Mr J. A. Carver

Other Owners: Mr W. F. Benter, Mr John Berry, Mrs Emma Berry, Mr C. de P. Berry, Mr J. Bond, Mr S. Bradie, Mrs J. Braithwaite, Mr R. Fleck, Mr H. Fraser, Mr K. Gibbs, Mr B. Granahan, Mr Gerry Grimstone, Mr J. Haggarty, Mr J. Hathorn, Mr D. J. Huelin, Mr Richard Jones, Mr S. Jones, Mr L. Kingston, Mr Kevan Leggett, Mr A. Mayne, Miss L. I. McCarthy, Mr Stephen F. McCormick, Mr A. McLeod, Mrs M. L. Parry, Mr T. O'Rourke, Mr P. Steele-Mortimer, Mr Larry Stratton, Mr T. Trounce, Mr C. Vautier, Mr L. C. Wadey.

Assistant Trainer: Hugh Fraser

Jockey (NH): Will Kennedy.

---

38 MR JIM BEST, Lewes
Postal: Grandstand Stables, The Old Racecourse, Lewes, East Sussex, BN7 1UR
Contacts: PHONE (01435) 882073 (01273) 480249 FAX (01435) 882073 MOBILE (07968) 743272
E-MAIL jimandtombest@btinternet.com WEBSITE www.jimandtombestracing.co.uk

    1 ACE FIGHTER PILOT, 8, b g Silver Patriarch (IRE)—Vedra (IRE) Odds On Racing
    2 BOLLIN JUDITH, 8, br m Bollin Eric—Bollin Nellie Mr J. J. Callaghan
    3 BUGSY'S GIRL (IRE), 6, ch m Desert King (IRE)—Icydora (FR) Mrs S. C. Head

MR JIM BEST - Continued

4 **CRANNAGHMORE BOY (IRE)**, 9, b g Pilsudski (IRE)—Glencairn Mist (IRE) **JAG Racing Elite**
5 **DORRY K (IRE)**, 5, b m Ad Valorem (USA)—Ashtaroute (USA) **The K Team**
6 **EASTER LAD**, 10, b g Shahrastani (USA)—Frozen Pipe **Elten Barker & Chris Dillon**
7 **GENEROUS JACK (IRE)**, 5, ch h Generous (IRE)—Yosna (FR) **Mr J. J. Callaghan**
8 **INTO THE WIND**, 7, ch m Piccolo—In The Stocks **Into The Wind Partnership**
9 **IT'S ONLY BUSINESS**, 4, ch g Haafhd—Noble Plum (IRE) **Mr J. J. Callaghan**
10 **LYSSIO (GER)**, 7, b g Motivator—Lysuna (GER) **Mr J. J. Callaghan**
11 **MISSILE MAN (IRE)**, 5, b h Winged Love (IRE)—Miss Ondee (FR) **Jack Callaghan & Christopher Dillon**
12 **MONEY MONEY MONEY**, 8, b m Generous (IRE)—Shi Shi **Money Money Money Partnership**
13 **ON THE FEATHER**, 8, br m Josr Algarhoud (IRE)—Fotheringhay **Elten Barker & Chris Dillon**
14 **PADDOCKS LOUNGE (IRE)**, 7, b g Oscar (IRE)—Sister Rosza (IRE) **Mrs R. Wenman**
15 **PLANETOID (IRE)**, 6, b g Galileo (IRE)—Palmeraie (USA) **Planetoid Partnership**
16 **RAMONA CHASE**, 9, b g High Chaparral (IRE)—Audacieuse **Fruits Incorporated**
17 **RED ORATOR**, 5, ch g Osorio (GER)—Red Roses Story (FR) **Wishful Thinkers Partnership**
18 **RELENTLESS (IRE)**, 4, b g Dylan Thomas (IRE)—Karamiyna (IRE) **Wishful Thinkers Partnership**
19 **RENAGISHA (IRE)**, 8, b g Luso—Slaney Rose (IRE) **Mr B. Reilly**
20 **ROBOBAR (IRE)**, 9, b g Passing Sale (FR)—Carvine d'or (FR) **Mark Callow & Mark Goldstein**
21 **ROCKY RYAN (IRE)**, 11, b g Even Top (IRE)—The Dara Queen
22 **SAINT HELENA (IRE)**, 6, b m Holy Roman Emperor (IRE)—Tafseer (IRE) **Mr A. K. Hosie**
23 **SCHOOL FOR SCANDAL (IRE)**, 6, b g Pivotal—Sensation **School For Scandal Partnership**
24 **SLANEY STAR (IRE)**, 6, b g Cloudings (IRE)—Slaney Rose (IRE) **Fruits Incorporated**
25 **SPEAR THISTLE**, 12, ch g Selkirk (USA)—Ardisia (USA) **Mrs S. C. Head**
26 **SPORTING CLUB GIRL**, 4, b f Kyllachy—Validate **The National Sporting Club**
27 **SUDDEN LIGHT (IRE)**, 8, b m Presenting—Coolshamrock (IRE) **M&R Refurbishments Ltd**
28 **SUGAR HICCUP (IRE)**, 6, b m Refuse To Bend (IRE)—Raysiza (IRE) **Jack Callaghan & Christopher Dillon**
29 **WESTERN HIGH**, 9, b g Rainbow High—Western Ploy **Mr J. J. Best**

Other Owners: Mr A. Achilleous, Mr E. Barker, Mr M. Callow, Mr J. Cumber, Mr C. J. Dillon, Mr P. E. Gardener, Mr P. J. Gardner, Mr F. W. Golding, Mrs M. J. Golding, Mr M. D. Goldstein, Mr T. J. Good, S. P. Graham, Mr J. Haste, Mr M. Jackson, Mr A. Maloney, Mr G. C. Sales.

Assistant Trainer: Mr T. Best

Jockey (NH): Marc Goldstein, A. P. McCoy.

---

39 **MR JOHN BEST, Maidstone**
Postal: **Scragged Oak Farm, Scragged Oak Road, Hucking, Maidstone, Kent, ME17 1QU**
Contacts: **PHONE (01622) 880276 FAX (01622) 880525 MOBILE (07889) 362154**
E-MAIL john.best@johnbestracing.com WEBSITE www.johnbestracing.com

1 **AZABITMOUR (FR)**, 4, b g Azamour (IRE)—Brixa (FR) **Mr G Jones & Mr B Malt**
2 **BIG MOZA**, 4, b f Pastoral Pursuits—Zaynah (IRE) **Watson & Malyon**
3 **CASUAL MOVER (IRE)**, 6, b g Diamond Green (FR)—Baileys On Line **Brian Goodyear & Rhonda Wilson**
4 **ELOUNTA**, 4, b f Dubawi (IRE)—Santiburi Girl **Laura Malcolm & Bob Malt**
5 **FEARLESS LAD (IRE)**, 4, b c Excellent Art—Souffle **Mrs J. O. Jones**
6 **GUNG HO JACK**, 5, b g Moss Vale (IRE)—Bijan (IRE) **Mr J. R. Best**
7 **HABESHIA**, 4, ch g Muhtathir—Lumiere Rouge (FR) **C. B. Goodyear**
8 **LEWAMY (IRE)**, 4, b c Amadeus Wolf—Thai Dye (UAE) **C. B. Goodyear**
9 **LUPO D'ORO (IRE)**, 5, b g Amadeus Wolf—Vital Laser (USA) **Mr S. Malcolm, Mr M. Winwright & Mr P. Tindall**
10 **MASTERED (IRE)**, 4, b g Refuse To Bend (IRE)—Woodmaven (USA) **Miss H. J. Williams**
11 **MOSSGO (IRE)**, 4, b g Moss Vale (IRE)—Perovskia (USA) **Hucking Horses V**
12 **SABRE ROCK**, 4, b g Dubawi (IRE)—Retainage (USA) **Mark Curtis & Rob Hemmens**
13 **SHEIKH THE REINS (IRE)**, 5, b g Iffraaj—Wychwood Wanderer (IRE) **Mr J. R. Best**
14 **SOWETO STAR (IRE)**, 6, ch g Johannesburg (USA)—Lady of Talent (USA) **Part Two Partnership**
15 **STONE OF FOLCA (IRE)**, 4, b g Kodiac—Soyalang (IRE) **Folkestone Racecourse Owners Group**
16 **YALDING DANCER**, 5, b m Zafeen (FR)—Daughters World

THREE-YEAR-OLDS

17 **BERRAHRI (IRE)**, b c Bahri (USA)—Band of Colour (IRE) **Curtis, Malt & Wykes**
18 **CHARLIES MATE**, br c Myboycharlie (IRE)—Retainage (USA) **Mrs J. O. Jones**
19 **DUBAI GOLD**, ch f Major Cadeaux—Cheap N Chic **24 Carrot Partnership**
20 **FOXIE GIRL**, b f Virtual—Santiburi Girl **Mrs Jackie Jones & Mr John Best**
21 **FRENCH ACCENT**, ch f Elnadim (USA)—Saralea (FR) **H. J. Jarvis**
22 **HIORNE TOWER (FR)**, b c Poliglote—Hierarchie (FR) **Mrs Jackie Jones & Mr John Best**

MR JOHN BEST - Continued

23 B f Virtual—Hucking Harmony (IRE) **Five In Harmony**
24 **IN SEINE,** b c Champs Elysees—Fancy Rose (USA) **Curtis, Malt & Williams**
25 **LINGFIELD LUPUS (IRE),** b g Amadeus Wolf—Clytha **Lingfield Park Owners Group**
26 B f Three Valleys (USA)—Loquacity **Curtis & Williams Bloodstock**
27 **MARPHILLY (IRE),** b f Amadeus Wolf—Pilda (IRE) **Embassy Racing**
28 **MR WICKFIELD,** b c Champs Elysees—First Approval **Fenlon, Jupp, Morley, Rogers & Malt**
29 B g Duke of Marmalade (IRE)—My Dream Castles (USA) **M. J. Ward**
30 **NICE FELLOW (FR),** ch g Redback—Clever Jo (USA)
31 **NINETY MINUTES (IRE),** b c Oratorio (IRE)—Fleeting Mirage (USA) **Andy Carroll, Kevin Nolan & Mark Curtis**
32 **TRIPLE O SEVEN (IRE),** b c Kodiac—Triple Zero (IRE) **Lingfield Park Owners Group**
33 **YANKEE RED,** b g Pastoral Pursuits—Miriam **Holl, Jenkins, Redknapp & Flint**
34 **ZEALAND (IRE),** b c Baltic King—Zafaraya (IRE) **Simon Malcolm & Malcolm Winwright**

TWO-YEAR-OLDS

35 B f 2/3 Mullionmileanhour (IRE)—Beechnut (IRE) (Mujadil (USA))
36 B f 7/4 Moss Vale (IRE)—Bijan (IRE) (Mukaddamah (USA)) (12000)
37 B f 14/5 Mullionmileanhour (IRE)—Hucking Harmony (IRE) (Spartacus (IRE)) **Five In Harmony**
38 B br c 25/2 Vision d'etat (FR)—Karmibola (FR) (Persian Bold) (17808)
39 **MULLIONHEIR,** b c 5/2 Mullionmileanhour (IRE)—Peyto Princess (Bold Arrangement) (13333) **Mr S. D. Malcolm**
40 B f 8/3 Mullionmileanhour (IRE)—Nala (USA) (Lion Heart (USA))
41 B c 20/3 Mullionmileanhour (IRE)—Neissa (USA) (Three Wonders (USA))
42 B f 26/2 Mullionmileanhour (IRE)—Numanthia (Barathea (IRE))
43 B c 28/3 Mullionmileanhour (IRE)—Santinari Girl (Casteddu) **Mr J. R. Best**
44 B c 1/3 Champs Elysees—Strike Lightly (Rainbow Quest (USA)) (17000) **Mrs L. C. G. Malcolm**

Other Owners: Mr M. B. Curtis, Mr R. E. Hemmens, Mr G. R. Jones, Mr R. C. Malt, Mr A. Watson, Ms R. L. Wilson, Mr M. J. Winwright.

Assistant Trainer: David Menuisier

---

40 **MR JAMES BETHELL, Middleham**
Postal: **Thorngill, Coverham, Middleham, North Yorkshire, DL8 4TJ**
Contacts: **PHONE (01969) 640360 FAX (01969) 640360 MOBILE (07831) 683528**
E-MAIL james@jamesbethell.co.uk WEBSITE www.jamesbethell.com

1 **BOBS HER UNCLE,** 5, b m Fair Mix (IRE)—Shazana **R. F. Gibbons**
2 **FAB LOLLY (IRE),** 4, b f Rock of Gibraltar (IRE)—Violet Ballerina (IRE) **Mr J. S. Lambert**
3 **GROUND GINGER,** 4, ch g Byron—Hoh Hedsor **Mrs N. F. Lee**
4 **HARTLEBURY,** 4, ch g Sakhee's Secret—Marakabei **Clarendon Thoroughbred Racing**
5 **MISTER BOB (GER),** 5, ch g Black Sam Bellamy (IRE)—Mosquera (GER) **R. F. Gibbons**
6 **PINTRADA,** 6, b g Tiger Hill (IRE)—Ballymore Celebre (IRE) **Scotyork Partnership**
7 **RICH AGAIN (IRE),** 5, b g Amadeus Wolf—Fully Fashioned (IRE) **Clarendon Thoroughbred Racing**
8 **RICH FOREVER (IRE),** 4, b g Camacho—Sixfields Flyer (IRE) **Clarendon Thoroughbred Racing**
9 **STARBOTTON,** 4, b f Kyllachy—Bonne Etoile **Clarendon Thoroughbred Racing**
10 **STEELRIVER (IRE),** 4, b g Iffraaj—Numerus Clausus (FR) **BNT Partnership**
11 **THANKYOU VERY MUCH,** 4, b f Lucky Story (USA)—Maid of Perth **R. F. Gibbons**
12 **TRUE PLEASURE,** 7, b m Choisir (AUS)—Absolute Pleasure **Clarendon Thoroughbred Racing**

THREE-YEAR-OLDS

13 **BELLE DE LAWERS,** b f Black Sam Bellamy (IRE)—Scotland The Brave **Mr J. A. Tabet**
14 **BRAIDLEY (IRE),** b g Dylan Thomas (IRE)—All Our Hope (USA) **Clarendon Thoroughbred Racing**
15 **CHINA IN MY HANDS,** gr f Dark Angel (IRE)—Cheap Thrills **Mr C. Wright**
16 **GOTCHA,** bl f Fair Mix (IRE)—Shazana **R. F. Gibbons**
17 **HALLOWEEN MOON,** b g Halling (USA)—Mamounia (IRE) **Clarendon Thoroughbred Racing**
18 **HOUSEWIVES CHOICE,** ch f Black Sam Bellamy (IRE)—Maid of Perth **R. F. Gibbons**
19 **KIRKMAN (IRE),** ch g Virtual—Validate **M. J. Dawson**
20 **PENHILL,** b g Mount Nelson—Serrenia (IRE) **Clarendon Thoroughbred Racing**
21 **SCRAFTON,** b g Leporello (IRE)—Some Diva **Clarendon Thoroughbred Racing**

TWO-YEAR-OLDS

22 **BURNESTON,** b c 19/4 Rock of Gibraltar (IRE)—
Grain of Gold (Mr Prospector (USA)) (26000) **Clarendon Thoroughbred Racing**
23 **COMIN UP ROSES,** b f 3/3 Schiaparelli (GER)—Shazana (Key of Luck (USA)) **R. F. Gibbons**

MR JAMES BETHELL - Continued

24 **KELLY'S FINEST (IRE)**, ch f 18/3 Intense Focus (USA)—
                        Priory Rock (IRE) (Rock of Gibraltar (IRE)) (25000) **Mr James Lambert**
25 B c 24/4 Arcano (IRE)—Marine City (JPN) (Carnegie (IRE)) (15000)
26 **MISTRAL (GER)**, b c 18/2 Shirocco (GER)—Marny (GER) (Dashing Blade) (19357) **Scotyork Partnership**
27 **NOBBLY BOBBLY (IRE)**, br c 20/2 High Chaparral (IRE)—
                        Rock Queen (IRE) (Rock of Gibraltar (IRE)) (34000) **Mr James Lambert**
28 **PRINCESS PEACHES**, ch f 25/3 Notnowcato—Miss Apricot (Indian Ridge) **Clarendon Thoroughbred Racing**
29 **THE MUNSHI**, b c 27/2 Multiplex—Maid of Perth (Mark of Esteem (IRE)) **R. F. Gibbons**

Other Owners: Mr J. D. Bethell, Mrs James Bethell, Mr J. Carrick.

MR EDWARD BEVAN, Hereford
Postal: **Pullen Farm, Ullingswick, Herefordshire, HR1 3JQ**
Contacts: **PHONE/FAX (01432) 820370 MOBILE (07970) 650347**

1 **BOLD CROSS (IRE)**, 11, b g Cape Cross (IRE)—Machikane Akaiito (IRE) **E. G. Bevan**
2 **BOLD DUKE**, 6, b g Sulamani (IRE)—Dominant Duchess **E. G. Bevan**
3 **FLAMENCO FLYER**, 5, b g Fantastic Spain (USA)—Magical Gift
4 **LEGAL PURSUIT**, 5, b g Proclamation (IRE)—Trysting Grove (IRE) **E. G. Bevan**

Assistant Trainer: Michelle Byrom

---

42 MR GEORGE BEWLEY, Hawick
Postal: **South Dean Farm, Bonchester Bridge, Hawick, Roxburghshire, TD9 8TP**
Contacts: **PHONE (01450) 860651 MOBILE (07704) 924783**
E-MAIL southdean.farm@btconnect.com

1 **BRAE ON (IRE)**, 6, ch g Presenting—Raphuca (IRE) **West Coast Racing Partnership**
2 4, Ch g Shirocco (GER)—Cream of Society (IRE) **G. T. Bewley**
3 **CUMBRIAN FARMER**, 7, ch g Alflora (IRE)—Quark Top (FR) **Southdean Racing Club**
4 **DARK CAVIAR (IRE)**, 6, b g Indian Danehill (IRE)—Whites Cross (IRE) **martingrayracing**
5 **DIAMOND D'AMOUR (IRE)**, 8, gr g Danehill Dancer (IRE)—
                        Diamond Line (FR) **Mr J Hope,Mr K Twentyman & Mr J Gibson**
6 **EASEMENT**, 11, b g Kayf Tara—Raspberry Sauce **Southdean Racing Club**
7 **INNIS SHANNON (IRE)**, 4, br f Stowaway—Put On Hold (IRE) **Mrs Lesley Bewley & Mr John Gibson**
8 **MESSINA STRAIGHTS**, 6, br g Blueprint (IRE)—Calabria **G. F. White**
9 **MISTER D (IRE)**, 8, ch g Anshan—Eleanors Joy **Beacon Hill Farm**
10 **OUR JOEY (IRE)**, 6, b g Wareed (IRE)—Put On Hold (IRE) **John Gibson,Kevin Twentyman & Bewley**
11 **REV UP RUBY**, 6, b m Revoque (IRE)—Kingennie **Mr R Fisher,Fools With Horses&Twentyman**
12 **ROMANY RYME**, 8, ch g Nomadic Way (USA)—Rakaposhi Ryme (IRE) **martingrayracing**
13 4, Gr f Mahler—Sika Trix (IRE) **G. T. Bewley**

THREE-YEAR-OLDS

14 B c Definite Article—Mrs Avery (IRE) **martingrayracing**

Other Owners: Mrs L. Bewley, Mr R. A. Fisher, Mr J. H. Gibson, Mr I. M. Gray, Mrs G. Gray, J. Hope, Mr D. Kerr, Mrs C. Moore, Mr A. B. Moore, Mr C. Thomason, Mr K. Twentyman, Mr A. L. Wilson.

Conditional: Jonathon Bewley. **Amateur:** Miss Joanna Walton.

---

43 MR JOSEPH BEWLEY, Jedburgh
Postal: **Newhouse Cottage, Camptown, Jedburgh, Roxburghshire, TD8 6RW**
Contacts: **PHONE (01835) 840273 MOBILE (07758) 783910**
E-MAIL bewley18@tiscali.co.uk

1 5, B g Exit To Nowhere (USA)—Aberdare **J. R. Bewley**
2 5, B g Overbury (IRE)—Evening Splash (IRE) **J. R. Bewley**
3 **INDIGO ISLAND (IRE)**, 5, b g Trans Island—Go Indigo (IRE) **J. R. Bewley**
4 5, B g Indian Danehill (IRE)—Native Novel (IRE) **J. R. Bewley**

Assistant Trainer: Mrs K Bewley **Jockey (NH):** Ryan Mania. **Conditional:** Callum Bewley.

44 MR SAEED BIN SUROOR, Newmarket

Postal: **Godolphin Office, Snailwell Road, Newmarket, Suffolk, CB8 7YE**
WEBSITE www.godolphin.com

The following list has not been supplied by the trainer and is as accurate as possible at the time of going to press. Some horses listed may not return to Britain from Dubai. Only 2yos entered in the 2015 Derby and/or Tattersalls Millions are shown. **For the latest information please visit www.godolphin.com**

1 **ACADEMUS (AUS)**, 5, br g Lonhro (AUS)—Youthful Presence (AUS)
2 **ADROITLY (AUS)**, 7, br g Octagonal (NZ)—Easy Out (AUS)
3 **AESOP'S FABLES (USA)**, 5, b g Distorted Humor (USA)—Abhisheka (IRE)
4 **AFRICAN STORY**, 7, ch g Pivotal—Blixen (USA)
5 **AHZEEMAH (IRE)**, 5, b g Dubawi (IRE)—Swiss Roll (IRE)
6 **AL SAHAM**, 5, b g Authorized (IRE)—Local Spirit (USA)
7 **ALBASHARAH (USA)**, 5, b m Arch (USA)—Desert Gold (USA)
8 **ALMAAS (USA)**, 5, ch g Hard Spun (USA)—Summer Dream Girl (USA)
9 **ASATIR (USA)**, 5, b g Elusive Quality (USA)—Valid Warning (USA)
10 **BIG AUDIO (IRE)**, 7, b g Oratorio (IRE)—Tarbela (IRE)
11 **BOLINGBROKE (IRE)**, 5, b g King's Best (USA)—Noble Rose (IRE)
12 **CAVALRYMAN**, 8, b h Halling (USA)—Silversword (FR)
13 **CAYMANS (AUS)**, 9, b g Secret Savings (USA)—Easy Out (AUS)
14 **CLON BRULEE (IRE)**, 5, ch g Modigliani (USA)—Cloneden (IRE)
15 **CODE OF HONOR**, 4, b c Zafeen (FR)—Verbal Intrigue (USA)
16 **COMPLICATE (AUS)**, 5, b g Commands (AUS)—Chaparra (AUS)
17 **DAAREE (IRE)**, 4, b c Teofilo (IRE)—Mawaakeb (USA)
18 **DESERT LAW (IRE)**, 6, b g Oasis Dream—Speed Cop
19 **DO IT ALL (USA)**, 7, b br h Distorted Humor (USA)—Stupendous Miss (USA)
20 **EXCELLENT RESULT (IRE)**, 4, b c Shamardal (USA)—Line Ahead (IRE)
21 **EXPERT FIGHTER (USA)**, 5, ch g Dubai Destination (USA)—Porto Roca (AUS)
22 **FAMOUS POET (IRE)**, 5, b h Exceed And Excel (AUS)—Asfurah (USA)
23 **FREE WHEELING (AUS)**, 6, b g Ad Valorem (USA)—Miss Carefree (AUS)
24 **FUTURE REFERENCE (IRE)**, 4, ch g Raven's Pass (USA)—Mike's Wildcat (USA)
25 **GOLD HUNTER (IRE)**, 4, b g Invincible Spirit (IRE)—Goldthroat (IRE)
26 **GREAT FIGHTER**, 4, b g Street Cry (IRE)—Evil Empire (GER)
27 **HAAFAGUINEA**, 4, ch c Haafhd—Ha'penny Beacon
28 **HANDSOME MAN (IRE)**, 5, ch g Nayef (USA)—Danceabout
29 **HOODNA (IRE)**, 4, b f Invincible Spirit (IRE)—Heaven's Cause (USA)
30 **HUNTER'S LIGHT (IRE)**, 6, ch h Dubawi (IRE)—Portmanteau
31 **I'M BACK (IRE)**, 4, b c Exceed And Excel (AUS)—Paracel (USA)
32 **INDUNA (AUS)**, 6, b g Elusive Quality (USA)—Camarena (NZ)
33 **KASSIANO (GER)**, 5, b g Soldier Hollow—Kastila (GER)
34 **LANDAMAN (IRE)**, 4, br g Cape Cross (IRE)—Mayoress
35 **LOCKWOOD**, 5, gr g Invincible Spirit (IRE)—Emily Bronte
36 **LOST IN THE MOMENT (IRE)**, 7, b h Danehill Dancer (IRE)—Streetcar (IRE)
37 **MAR MAR (IRE)**, 4, b f Invincible Spirit (IRE)—Queen of Tara (IRE)
38 **MUSADDAS**, 4, b g Exceed And Excel (AUS)—Zuleika Dobson
39 **MY FREEDOM (IRE)**, 6, b g Invincible Spirit (IRE)—Priere
40 **OUT OF BOUNDS (USA)**, 5, ch h Discreet Cat (USA)—Unbridled Elaine (USA)
41 **PAXIMADIA (USA)**, 4, br c Commands (AUS)—Latona
42 **PIED A TERRE (AUS)**, 6, b g Ad Valorem (USA)—Masonette (AUS)
43 **PRINCE BISHOP (IRE)**, 7, ch g Dubawi (IRE)—North East Bay (USA)
44 **QUICK WIT**, 7, b h Oasis Dream—Roo
45 **ROAYH (USA)**, 6, ch g Speightstown (USA)—Most Remarkable (USA)
46 **ROYAL EMPIRE (IRE)**, 5, b h Teofilo (IRE)—Zeiting (IRE)
47 **ROYAL FLAG**, 4, b c New Approach (IRE)—Gonbarda (GER)
48 **SAMAWI (IRE)**, 4, b g Street Cry (IRE)—Hi Dubai
49 **SAXO JACK (FR)**, 4, B G King's Best (USA)—Gamma (FR)
50 **SECRET NUMBER**, 4, b c Raven's Pass (USA)—Mysterial (USA)
51 **SHARESTAN (IRE)**, 6, b g Shamardal (USA)—Sharesha (IRE)
52 **SHURUQ (USA)**, 4, b f Elusive Quality (USA)—Miss Lucifer (FR)
53 **SONGCRAFT (IRE)**, 6, b g Singspiel (IRE)—Baya (USA)
54 **SOUL (AUS)**, 7, b g Commands (AUS)—Marvilha (AUS)
55 **STATUTORY (IRE)**, 4, b g Authorized (USA)—Mialuna
56 **TARIKHI (USA)**, 4, b g Bernardini (USA)—Caffe Latte (IRE)
57 **TASADAY (USA)**, 4, gr ro f Nayef (USA)—Tashelka (FR)
58 **TAWHID**, 4, gr c Invincible Spirit (IRE)—Snowdrops

MR SAEED BIN SUROOR - Continued

59 THA'IR (IRE), 4, b c New Approach (IRE)—Flashing Green
60 TRANSPARENT (USA), 4, b br c Bernardini (USA)—Habiboo (USA)
61 VALIDUS, 5, b g Zamindar (USA)—Victoire Finale
62 WADI AL HATTAWI (IRE), 4, b g Dalakhani (IRE)—Carisolo
63 WILLING FOE (USA), 7, b br g Dynaformer (USA)—Thunder Kitten (USA)
64 WINDHOEK, 4, b c Cape Cross (IRE)—Kahlua Kiss

THREE-YEAR-OLDS

65 ALMERZEM (USA), b br c Medaglia d'oro (USA)—Tashawak (IRE)
66 ARABIAN BEAUTY (IRE), b f Shamardal (USA)—Express Way (ARG)
67 BE READY (IRE), ch c New Approach (IRE)—Call Later (USA)
68 BEAUTIFUL FOREST, ch f Nayef (USA)—Baya (USA)
69 BETTER CHANCE (IRE), b f Shamardal (USA)—Victoria Star (IRE)
70 BRAVE BOY (IRE), b g Invincible Spirit (IRE)—Chan Tong (BRZ)
71 ELITE ARMY, b c Authorized (IRE)—White Rose (GER)
72 EMIRATES FLYER, b c Acclamation—Galapagar (USA)
73 EMIRATES GALLOPER (IRE), b g Dalakhani (IRE)—Emmy Award (IRE)
74 EXCELLENT VIEW, gr f Shamardal (USA)—Pearl Grey
75 FAJRY (USA), b br c Dixie Union (USA)—Tahfeez (USA)
76 FAST DELIVERY, b c Authorized (IRE)—Rosenreihe (IRE)
77 FIRST FLIGHT (IRE), b c Invincible Spirit (IRE)—First of Many
78 FLAG WAR (GER), ch g Dubawi (IRE)—Fantastic Flame (IRE)
79 FLIGHT OFFICER, b c New Approach (IRE)—Danuta (USA)
80 FURAS (IRE), br c Shamardal (USA)—Albaraari
81 GHAZI (IRE), b g Exceed And Excel (AUS)—Concordia
82 GOLDEN TOWN (IRE), b c Invincible Spirit (IRE)—Princesse Dansante (IRE)
83 IHTIMAL (IRE), b f Shamardal (USA)—Eastern Joy
84 IMPORTANT TIME (IRE), b f Oasis Dream—Satwa Queen (FR)
85 ISTIKSHAF (IRE), b c Exceed And Excel (AUS)—Shinko Hermes (IRE)
86 KING'S LAND, b br c New Approach (IRE)—Kazzia (GER)
87 MOUNTAIN FIGHTER, b g Dubawi (IRE)—River Pearl (GER)
88 MOUNTAIN LION (IRE), b c Invincible Spirit (IRE)—Tuzla (FR)
89 MY TARGET (IRE), b c Cape Cross (IRE)—Chercheuse (USA)
90 NABEEL (IRE), b g Invincible Spirit (IRE)—Screen Star (IRE)
91 NAJMA, b f Cape Cross (IRE)—Silkwood
92 NATURAL CHOICE, b f Teofilo (IRE)—Oiseau Rare (FR)
93 NICE LIFE (IRE), b f Invincible Spirit (IRE)—Rosa Parks
94 NIGHT PARTY (IRE), b f Dansili—La Salina (GER)
95 PROMISE YOU, b f Teofilo (IRE)—Eilean Ban (USA)
96 SILENT BULLET (IRE), b g Exceed And Excel (AUS)—Veil of Silence (IRE)
97 SUPER MOMENT (IRE), b f Oasis Dream—Philae (USA)
98 TAYMA (IRE), ch f Exceed And Excel (AUS)—Bergamask (USA)
99 THINK AHEAD, b c Shamardal (USA)—Moonshadow
100 TRUE MATCH (IRE), b f Cape Cross (IRE)—West Wind
101 TRUE STORY, b br c Manduro (GER)—Tanzania (USA)
102 WAHGAH (USA), b f Distorted Humor (USA)—Basaata (USA)

TWO-YEAR-OLDS

103 B c 2/4 King's Best (USA)—Anaamil (IRE) (Darshaan)
104 Ch c 4/4 King's Best (USA)—Born Something (IRE) (Caerleon (USA))
105 B c 17/3 Cape Cross (USA)—Copperbeech (IRE) (Red Ransom (USA))
106 Ch f 20/1 Lope de Vega (IRE)—Danielli (IRE) (Danehill (USA)) (280000)
107 B c 27/4 Shamardal (USA)—Deveron (USA) (Cozzene (USA)) (280000)
108 Ch c 30/1 New Approach (IRE)—Fann (USA) (Diesis)
109 Ch c 2/2 New Approach (IRE)—Gleam of Light (IRE) (Danehill (USA)) (140000)
110 B c 19/4 Pivotal—Gonbarda (GER) (Lando (GER))
111 IJMAALY (IRE), ch c 5/2 Makfi—Wedding Gown (Dubai Destination (USA)) (300000)
112 Ch c 15/2 Exceed And Excel (AUS)—Kangra Valley (Indian Ridge) (105000)
113 KATARO (GER), b c 21/3 Monsun (GER)—Katy Carr (Machiavellian (USA)) (232288)
114 B c 10/4 Lawman (FR)—Keriyka (IRE) (Indian Ridge) (120000)
115 KHUSOOSY (USA), b c 9/2 Hard Spun (USA)—Elmaleeha (Galileo (IRE))
116 B br c 6/2 Street Cry (IRE)—Lady Darshaan (IRE) (High Chaparral (IRE)) (300000)
117 B c 30/1 Cape Cross (IRE)—Local Talent (USA) (Lion Cavern (USA))
118 B c 15/4 New Approach (IRE)—Lunda (IRE) (Soviet Star (USA))
119 Ch c 21/4 Monsun (GER)—Mandellicht (IRE) (Be My Guest (USA))

MR SAEED BIN SUROOR - Continued

120 **MOAYADD (USA)**, b c 20/3 Street Cry (IRE)—Aryaamm (IRE) (Galileo (IRE))
121 B c 5/5 Dubawi (IRE)—Nabati (USA) (Rahy (USA))
122 B f 26/1 Shamardal (USA)—Nashmiah (IRE) (Elusive City (USA)) (150000)
123 B c 14/2 Shamardal (USA)—Pioneer Bride (USA) (Gone West (USA)) (250000)
124 B br c 9/2 New Approach (IRE)—Plaza (USA) (Chester House (USA))
125 B c 20/2 Cape Cross (IRE)—Queen Consort (USA) (Kingmambo (USA))
126 **SEE THE WHITE (GER)**, b c 25/4 Monsun (GER)—Sasuela (GER) (Dashing Blade) (278745)
127 Ch c 23/2 Raven's Pass (USA)—Sensationally (Montjeu (IRE)) (240000)
128 **SERAFIGLIO**, b c 30/1 Teofilo (IRE)—Seradim (Elnadim (USA)) (120000)
129 Ch c 26/3 Exceed And Excel (AUS)—Sharp Terms (Kris) (175000)
130 B br c 2/5 Dubawi (IRE)—Short Skirt (Diktat)
131 B c 12/3 Dubawi (IRE)—Silkwood (Singspiel (IRE))
132 Ch f 8/3 Pivotal—Vassiana (FR) (Anabaa (USA)) (320000)
133 B c 12/3 Cape Cross (IRE)—Villarrica (USA) (Selkirk (USA))
134 **WELL OFF (GER)**, b c 8/3 Monsun (GER)—Wells Present (GER) (Cadeaux Genereux) (300000)
135 Gr f 27/3 Dark Angel (IRE)—Win Cash (IRE) (Alhaarth (IRE)) (160000)

45

MR KEVIN BISHOP, Bridgwater
Postal: **Barford Park Stables, Spaxton, Bridgwater, Somerset, TA5 1AF**
Contacts: **PHONE/FAX (01278) 671437 MOBILE (07816) 837610**
E-MAIL hevbishop@hotmail.com

1 **COUNT VETTORI (IRE)**, 8, br g Vettori (IRE)—Alifandango (IRE) **K. Bishop**
2 **CROWCOMBE PARK**, 6, b m Overbury (IRE)—Just Jasmine **K. Bishop**
3 **CRUISE IN STYLE (IRE)**, 8, b m Definite Article—Henrietta Street (IRE) **Mr S. G. Atkinson**
4 **JUST SPOT**, 7, ch m Baryshnikov (AUS)—Just Jasmine **K. Bishop**
5 **PRECIOUS GROUND**, 4, b g Helissio (FR)—Wild Ground (IRE)
6 **QUEENS GROVE**, 8, gr m Baryshnikov (AUS)—Just Jasmine **Mrs E. K. Ellis**
7 **REDGRAVE DANCER**, 8, gr m Baryshnikov (AUS)—Redgrave Bay **W. Davies**
8 **TARA TAVEY (IRE)**, 9, gr m Kayf Tara—Slieve League (IRE) **K. Bishop**
9 **WITHY MILLS**, 9, gr m Baryshnikov (AUS)—Gipsy Rose **Slabs & Lucan**

Other Owners: C. J. Macey, C. H. Roberts.

Assistant Trainer: Heather Bishop

Conditional: James Best. **Amateur:** Mr Jo Park.

46

MISS LINDA BLACKFORD, Tiverton
Postal: **Shortlane Stables, Rackenford, Tiverton, Devon, EX16 8EH**
Contacts: PHONE **(01884) 881589** MOBILE **(07887) 947832**
E-MAIL overthelast@talktalk.net WEBSITE www.overthelast.com

1 **CHANCE ENCOUNTER (IRE)**, 8, br g Anshan—Glittering Grit (IRE) **The Profile Partnership**
2 **LOUIS PHILLIPE (IRE)**, 7, ch g Croco Rouge (IRE)—Presenting's Wager (IRE) **Over De Last Racing**
3 **MOUNTAIN OF MOURNE (IRE)**, 5, ch g Mountain High (IRE)—Katies Native (IRE) **Over De Last Racing**
4 **ROMANY QUEST**, 7, b g Nomadic Way (USA)—Dinkies Quest **18 Red Lions Partnership**
5 **SHADES OF AUTUMN (IRE)**, 9, ch g Anshan—Be Right (IRE) **The Profile Partnership**
6 **THATS YER MAN (IRE)**, 6, ch g Marignan (USA)—Glengarra Princess **Over De Last Racing**
7 **WOLFE MOUNTAIN (IRE)**, 5, b g Mountain High (IRE)—Rachel's Choice (IRE) **Over De Last Racing**

Other Owners: Miss L. A. Blackford, Mrs Sarah Child, Mr David Cocks, Mr Rob Pitcher, Mr M. J. Vanstone, Mr Terry Wheatley.

Assistant Trainer: M J Vanstone

Jockey (NH): Ian Popham, Nick Scholfield. **Conditional:** Micheal Nolan. **Amateur:** Mr Joshua Guerriero, Mr C. Smith.

47 **MR ALAN BLACKMORE, Hertford**
Postal: 'Chasers', Stockings Lane, Little Berkhamsted, Hertford
Contacts: **PHONE** (01707) 875060 **MOBILE** (07803) 711453

1 **COOL CHIEF**, 5, b g Sleeping Indian—Be Bop Aloha **A. G. Blackmore**
2 **MONROE PARK (IRE)**, 9, b g Spectrum (IRE)—Paloma Bay (IRE) **A. G. Blackmore**
3 **OCCASIONALLY YOURS (IRE)**, 10, b g Moscow Society (USA)—Kristina's Lady (IRE) **A. G. Blackmore**

Assistant Trainer: Mrs P. M. Blackmore

Jockey (NH): Marc Goldstein.

48 **MR MICHAEL BLAKE, Trowbridge**
Postal: Staverton Farm, Trowbridge, Wiltshire, BA14 6PE
Contacts: **PHONE** (01225) 782327 **MOBILE** (07971) 675180
E-MAIL mblakestavertonfarm@btinternet.com

1 **ABLE DASH**, 4, ch g Dutch Art—Evasive Quality (FR) **West Wilts Hockey Lads**
2 4, B f Rakti—Attymon Lill (IRE) **B. Dunn**
3 **BACK ON THE TRAIL**, 4, b g Singspiel (IRE)—Boleyna (USA) **M. J. Blake**
4 **BATHWICK JUNIOR**, 7, b m Reset (AUS)—Bathwick Babe (IRE) **H. M. W. Clifford**
5 **FLYING PHOENIX**, 6, b m Phoenix Reach (IRE)—Rasmalai **Mr F. Tieman**
6 **GILANTO (IRE)**, 7, b g Milan—Topham Gale (IRE) **H. M. W. Clifford**
7 **HASSADIN**, 8, ch g Reset (AUS)—Crocolat **Mrs J. M. Haines**
8 **HE'S A STRIKER (IRE)**, 4, br g Footstepsinthesand—Aiming Upwards **B Dunn & J Pierce**
9 **HIGH ASPIRATIONS (IRE)**, 6, b g Dr Massini (IRE)—Divining (IRE) **Mrs J. M. Haines**
10 **LAMPS**, 7, b g Dynaformer (USA)—Conspiring (USA) **The Moonlighters**
11 **MOONLIT ORCHARD (FR)**, 4, b f Apple Tree (FR)—Last Eclipse (FR) **The Moonlighters**
12 **MY SON MAX**, 6, b g Avonbridge—Pendulum **Kevin Corcoran Aaron Pierce Chris Weare**
13 **PICK A LITTLE**, 6, b g Piccolo—Little Caroline (IRE) **Mr C Weare and Mr A Pierce**
14 **ROCKY REBEL**, 6, b g Norse Dancer (IRE)—Gulchina (USA) **B Dunn & J Pierce**
15 **ROYAL CHATELIER (FR)**, 9, b g Video Rock (FR)—Attualita (FR) **The Moonlighters**
16 **SADLER'S STAR (GER)**, 11, b g Alwuhush (USA)—Sadlerella (IRE) **Mrs J. M. Haines**
17 **STOW**, 9, ch g Selkirk (USA)—Spry **Mrs J. M. Haines**
18 **TORRENTIAL RAINE**, 6, b g Storming Home—La Riverane (USA) **H. M. W. Clifford**
19 4, B f Pasternak—Twin Time **Dajam Ltd**
20 **TYPICAL OSCAR (IRE)**, 7, b g Oscar (IRE)—Kachina (IRE) **The Moonlighters**
21 **UMUSTBEJOKING (FR)**, 6, b m Lavirco (GER)—Arika (FR) **The Moonlighters**

THREE-YEAR-OLDS

22 **DESERT FLUTE**, b g Piccolo—Hawait Al Barr **Mrs J. M. Haines**
23 **LINCE SUERTUDO (FR)**, ch c Astronomer Royal (USA)—La Cibeles (FR) **B. Dunn**

Other Owners: Mrs S. E. Blake, Mrs V. A. Butcher, Mr R. C. Butcher, K. J. Corcoran, Mr A. T. Pierce, Mr J. V. Pierce, Mr C. E. Weare.

49 **MR MICHAEL BLANSHARD, Upper Lambourn**
Postal: Lethornes Stables, Upper Lambourn, Hungerford, Berkshire, RG17 8QP
Contacts: **PHONE** (01488) 71091 **FAX** (01488) 73497 **MOBILE** (07785) 370093
E-MAIL blanshard.racing@btconnect.com **WEBSITE** www.michaelblanshard.co.uk

1 **AMALFI DOUG (FR)**, 4, gr g Network (GER)—Queissa (FR) **C Buttery & W Garrett**
2 **BAJAN BEAR**, 6, ch g Compton Place—Bajan Rose **C. McKenna**
3 **CARRERA**, 4, b g Sixties Icon—Aileen's Gift (IRE) **D. Carroll**
4 **DISHY GURU**, 4, ch g Ishiguru (USA)—Pick A Nice Name **Clifton Partners**
5 **FAIR COMMENT**, 4, b f Tamayuz—Cliche (IRE) **Fair Comment Partnership**
6 **FAMOUS TALES**, 4, b f Zamindar (USA)—Fame Game (IRE) **M Beevor, K Bartlett**
7 **IVANHOE**, 4, b c Haafhd—Marysienka **The Lansdowners & N Price**
8 **JUST DUCHESS**, 4, b f Avonbridge—Red Countess **D. A. Poole**
9 **PETERSBODEN**, 5, b g Iceman—Bowden Rose **N. C. D. Hall**
10 **RED DRAGON (IRE)**, 4, b g Acclamation—Delphie Queen (IRE) **Lady E. Mays-Smith**
11 **SAMMYMAN**, 7, b g Tamure (IRE)—Bajan Rose **C. McKenna**

MR MICHAEL BLANSHARD - Continued

12 **TARARA**, 4, b f Royal Applause—Anneliina **J K Racing Club**
13 **THE COMPOSER**, 12, b g Royal Applause—Superspring **A. D. Jones**

THREE-YEAR-OLDS

14 **CONFITURE**, b f Duke of Marmalade (IRE)—Sandtime (IRE) **Ian Lewis & Partners**
15 **JUST RUBIE**, b f Refuse To Bend (IRE)—Island Rapture (IRE) **D. A. Poole**
16 **MONASHKA BAY (IRE)**, b g Kodiac—River Style (IRE) **W. D. S. Murdoch**
17 **STELLARTA**, b f Sakhee's Secret—Torgau (IRE) **Mr V. G. Ward**

TWO-YEAR-OLDS

18 B c 26/2 Intikhab (USA)—Greeley Bright (USA) (Mr Greeley (USA)) (4000) **L Hill**
19 B f 5/2 Avonbridge—Night Kiss (FR) (Night Shift (USA)) (6000)
20 **PERFECT CONCORD**, b f 9/1 Kheleyf (USA)—Perfect Flight (Hawk Wing (USA))
21 B c 2/4 Showcasing—Queensgate (Compton Place)
22 B f 30/1 Sakhee's Secret—Raindrop (Primo Dominie) (3000)
23 Br f 29/2 Showcasing—Treble Seven (USA) (Fusaichi Pegasus (USA))
24 Ch f 8/3 Monsieur Bond (IRE)—Tryptonic (FR) (Baryshnikov (AUS)) **J. Goodall**

---

50 MR J. S. BOLGER, Carlow
Postal: **Glebe House, Coolcullen, Carlow, Ireland**
Contacts: PHONE (00353) 56 4443150 (00353) 56 4443158 FAX (00353) 56 4443256
E-MAIL racing@jsb.ie

1 **ALPINIST**, 4, b c New Approach (IRE)—Alouette **Mrs J. S. Bolger**
2 **BUNREACHT (USA)**, 4, gr c Mr Greeley (USA)—Unbridled Treasure (USA) **Mrs J. S. Bolger**
3 **EDGE OF SANITY (IRE)**, 5, b h Invincible Spirit (IRE)—Saor Sinn (IRE) **Mrs June Judd**
4 **HUDSON'S BAY (IRE)**, 4, b c Teofilo (IRE)—Cache Creek (IRE) **Sheikh Mohammed**
5 **LEITIR MOR (IRE)**, 4, b c Holy Roman Emperor (IRE)—Christmas Letter (IRE) **Mrs J. S. Bolger**
6 **LIGHT HEAVY (IRE)**, 5, ch h Teofilo (IRE)—Siamsa (USA) **Mrs J. S. Bolger**
7 **LOCH GARMAN (IRE)**, 4, b c Teofilo (IRE)—Irish Question (IRE) **Mrs J. S. Bolger**
8 **NEOPHILIA (IRE)**, 4, b f Teofilo (IRE)—Tiffed (USA) **Mrs J. S. Bolger**
9 **NEW REGALIA (IRE)**, 4, b f New Approach (IRE)—Simonetta (IRE) **Mrs J. S. Bolger**
10 **PAENE MAGNUS (IRE)**, 5, ch h Teofilo (IRE)—Luminaria (IRE) **Mrs J. S. Bolger**
11 **PARISH HALL (IRE)**, 5, b h Teofilo (IRE)—Halla Siamsa (IRE) **Mrs J. S. Bolger**
12 **SYMMETRICAL (USA)**, 4, ch f Unbridled's Song (USA)—Pure Symmetry (USA) **Mrs J. S. Bolger**
13 **TOBANN (IRE)**, 4, b f Teofilo (IRE)—Precipitous (IRE) **Mrs J. S. Bolger**
14 **TRADING LEATHER (IRE)**, 4, b c Teofilo (IRE)—Night Visit **Godolphin**

THREE-YEAR-OLDS

15 **AERIALIST (IRE)**, ch c Sea The Stars (IRE)—Maoineach (USA) **Mrs J. S. Bolger**
16 **ANSWERED**, b c Authorized (IRE)—Dublino (USA) **Sheikh Mohammed**
17 **AUSTERE APPROACH (IRE)**, ch c New Approach (IRE)—Ovazione **Mrs J. S. Bolger**
18 **BEYOND INTENSITY (IRE)**, ch f Intense Focus (USA)—Beyond Compare (IRE) **Mrs J. S. Bolger**
19 **CEISTEACH (IRE)**, ch f New Approach (IRE)—Ceist Eile (IRE) **Craig Bernick**
20 **CLUB WEXFORD (IRE)**, b c Lawman (FR)—Masnada (IRE) **Dave Bernie**
21 **CONGRESSMAN (IRE)**, ch c New Approach (IRE)—Miss Marvellous (USA) **Sheikh Mohammed**
22 **CORRECT APPROACH (IRE)**, ch c New Approach (IRE)—Gleigeal (USA) **Mrs J. S. Bolger**
23 **COUNTY WEXFORD (IRE)**, b c Teofilo (IRE)—Tiffed (USA) **Mrs J. S. Bolger**
24 **CRAIC AGUS SPRAOI (IRE)**, b f Intense Focus (USA)—Halla Siamsa (IRE) **Mrs J. S. Bolger**
25 **DUSHLAN (IRE)**, ch f New Approach (IRE)—Duaisbhanna (IRE) **Mrs J. S. Bolger**
26 **EVASON**, b c Galileo (IRE)—Soneva **Mrs C. Jungo**
27 **FISCAL FOCUS (IRE)**, b c Intense Focus (USA)—Elida (IRE) **Mrs J. S. Bolger**
28 **FLIGHT RISK (IRE)**, ch c Teofilo (IRE)—Raghida (IRE) **Mrs J. S. Bolger**
29 **FOCAS MOR (IRE)**, ch f Intense Focus (USA)—Intriguing Humor (CAN) **Mrs J. S. Bolger**
30 **FOCUS ON VENICE (IRE)**, b c Intense Focus (USA)—Marina of Venice (IRE) **Mrs June Judd**
31 **FORT MOUNTAIN**, b c Montjeu (IRE)—Thinking Positive **Mrs J. S. Bolger**
32 **GOLD FOCUS (IRE)**, ch f Intense Focus (USA)—Gold Bust **Mrs J. S. Bolger**
33 **GREANTA (IRE)**, b f Intense Focus (USA)—Greannmhar (USA) **Mrs J. S. Bolger**
34 **HEART FOCUS (IRE)**, b f Intense Focus (USA)—Have A Heart (IRE) **Mrs J. S. Bolger**
35 **INTENSICAL (IRE)**, b c Intense Focus (USA)—Christmas Letter (IRE) **Mrs J. S. Bolger**
36 **INTENSIFIED (IRE)**, b br g Intense Focus (USA)—Sway Me Now (USA) **Mrs J. S. Bolger**
37 **IONSAI NUA (IRE)**, b f New Approach (IRE)—Toirneach (USA) **Mrs J. S. Bolger**

MR J. S. BOLGER - Continued

38 **LEAFY SUBURB (IRE)**, ch f Intense Focus (USA)—Dublin Six (USA) **Mrs J. S. Bolger**
39 **MANDATARIO**, br c Manduro (GER)—Crystal Mountain (USA) **Mrs June Judd**
40 **NOVEL APPROACH (IRE)**, b f New Approach (IRE)—Altarejos (IRE) **Mrs J. S. Bolger**
41 **PIANOTA (USA)**, ch f Birdstone (USA)—Paiota Falls (USA) **Mrs J. S. Bolger**
42 **PLAMAS (IRE)**, b f Teofilo (IRE)—Danemarque (AUS) **Mrs J. S. Bolger**
43 **PRINTHA (IRE)**, ch f New Approach (IRE)—Scarpetta (USA) **Mrs J. S. Bolger**
44 **PRUDENT APPROACH (IRE)**, b f New Approach (IRE)—Hymn of The Dawn (USA) **Paddy Spain**
45 **SAR OICHE (IRE)**, b f Teofilo (IRE)—Zavaleta (IRE) **Mrs J. S. Bolger**
46 **SPRING FOCUS (IRE)**, b c Intense Focus (USA)—Teacht An Earraig (USA) **Mrs J. S. Bolger**
47 **SUNDARA (IRE)**, b c Galileo (IRE)—Saoire **Mrs M. Joyce**
48 **TIRGHRA (IRE)**, b f Teofilo (IRE)—National Swagger (IRE) **Mrs J. S. Bolger**
49 **UPPER SILESIAN (IRE)**, b f Lawman (FR)—Silesian (IRE) **Mrs J. S. Bolger**
50 **WEXFORD TOWN (IRE)**, b c Teofilo (IRE)—Night Visit **Mrs J. S. Bolger**

TWO-YEAR-OLDS

51 **ALAINN (IRE)**, b f 28/3 Intense Focus (USA)—Aoibhneas (USA) (Dehere (USA)) **Mrs J. S. Bolger**
52 **ALERTNESS (IRE)**, b f 4/4 Teofilo (IRE)—Napping (Danzig (USA)) **Mrs J. S. Bolger**
53 **ALGONQUIN**, gr c 20/2 Archipenko (USA)—Alborada (Alzao (USA)) **Miss K. Rausing**
54 **ALTERNO (IRE)**, b c 10/3 Fastnet Rock (AUS)—Altarejos (IRE) (Vettori (IRE)) **Mrs J. S. Bolger**
55 **ARDNOSACH (IRE)**, b f 25/3 Teofilo (IRE)—Ard Fheis (IRE) (Lil's Boy (USA)) **Mrs J. S. Bolger**
56 B c 3/4 Iffraaj—Artisti (Cape Cross (IRE)) (100000) **Sheikh Mohammed**
57 B c 24/3 Dubawi (IRE)—Bedazzle (USA) (Dixieland Band (USA)) **Sheikh Mohammed**
58 **BRIDLE PATH (IRE)**, b f 28/4 Teofilo (IRE)—Twin Sails (USA) (Boston Harbor (USA)) **Mrs J. S. Bolger**
59 **BRIGHTLY SHINING (IRE)**, b c 24/1 Teofilo (IRE)—Gleigeal (USA) (Mr Greeley (USA)) **Mrs J. S. Bolger**
60 **BUN NA SPEIRE (IRE)**, b f 9/2 Lawman (FR)—Imeall Na Speire (USA) (Galileo (IRE)) **Mrs J. S. Bolger**
61 B c 27/2 Raven's Pass (USA)—Cache Creek (Marju (IRE)) **Sheikh Mohammed**
62 **CAILIUIL (IRE)**, ch f 13/3 New Approach (IRE)—Cailiocht (USA) (Elusive Quality (USA)) **Mrs J. S. Bolger**
63 **CREAKY VOICE (IRE)**, b f 24/2 Vocalised (USA)—Lavender Blue (Galileo (IRE)) (16260) **Mrs J. S. Bolger**
64 **CRUIDIN (IRE)**, b f 11/3 Intense Focus (USA)—Have A Heart (IRE) (Daggers Drawn (USA)) **Mrs J. S. Bolger**
65 **CUNEIFORM (IRE)**, br c 17/3 Vocalised (USA)—
              Maidin Moch (IRE) (High Chaparral (IRE)) (774) **Mrs J. S. Bolger**
66 B c 5/5 Pivotal—Danelata (IRE) (Danehill (USA)) (162600) **Sheikh Mohammed**
67 **DEFINED BENEFIT (IRE)**, b c 17/5 Teofilo (IRE)—Masnada (IRE) (Erins Isle) **Mrs J. S. Bolger**
68 **DEONTAS (IRE)**, b f 24/2 Teofilo (IRE)—Duaisbhanna (IRE) (Rock of Gibraltar (IRE)) **Mrs J. S. Bolger**
69 **EASTERN APPROACH (IRE)**, ch c 9/3 New Approach (IRE)—
              Key To Coolcullen (IRE) (Royal Academy (USA)) **Mrs J. S. Bolger**
70 **ELECTRIC MAIL (IRE)**, ch f 23/4 Teofilo (IRE)—Tintreach (CAN) (Vindication (USA)) **Mrs J. S. Bolger**
71 **ELUSIVE APPROACH (IRE)**, b f 20/1 New Approach (IRE)—
              Soilse Na Cathrach (IRE) (Elusive City (USA)) **Mrs J. S. Bolger**
72 B f 11/4 Shamardal (USA)—Emirates Girl (USA) (Unbridled's Song (USA)) **Sheikh Mohammed**
73 **FAMILY PRIDE (IRE)**, b c 23/3 Proud Citizen (USA)—Family (USA) (Danzig (USA)) **Mrs J. S. Bolger**
74 **FAST AND NOW (IRE)**, b c 24/2 Vocalised (USA)—
              Irish Question (IRE) (Giant's Causeway (USA)) **Mrs J. S. Bolger**
75 **FOCUS ON LIGHT (IRE)**, b c 1/5 Intense Focus (USA)—
              Go Hiontach (USA) (Speightstown (USA)) **Mrs J. S. Bolger**
76 **FRESH FOCUS (IRE)**, b br c 4/3 Intense Focus (USA)—
              Sway Me Now (USA) (Speightstown (USA)) **Mrs J. S. Bolger**
77 **GEORGIE HYDE**, b f 26/1 Yeats (IRE)—Edabiya (IRE) (Rainbow Quest (USA)) (112272) **Mrs June Judd**
78 **GOLD GAME (IRE)**, b c 26/4 Vocalised (USA)—Gold Mirage (IRE) (Galileo (IRE)) **Mrs J. S. Bolger**
79 **GOLDEN INK (IRE)**, ch c 10/3 New Approach (IRE)—Solasai (USA) (Malibu Moon (USA)) **Mrs J. S. Bolger**
80 **GOLDSMITH (IRE)**, b c 8/5 Teofilo (IRE)—Gold Bust (Nashwan (USA)) **Mrs J. S. Bolger**
81 **HALL OF FAME (IRE)**, ch c 18/5 Teofilo (IRE)—Halla Siamsa (IRE) (Montjeu (IRE)) **Mrs J. S. Bolger**
82 B c 4/2 Teofilo (IRE)—Hundred Year Flood (USA) (Giant's Causeway (USA)) **Sheikh Mohammed**
83 **ICY LADY (IRE)**, ch f 20/1 New Approach (IRE)—Kitty Kiernan (Pivotal) **Mrs June Judd**
84 **INTENSE DESIRE (IRE)**, b c 1/4 Intense Focus (USA)—Beachaire (CAN) (Speightstown (USA)) **Mrs June Judd**
85 **INTENSE STYLE (IRE)**, ch c 4/2 Intense Focus (USA)—Style Queen (IRE) (Galileo (IRE)) **Mrs J. S. Bolger**
86 **INTENSER (IRE)**, b c 17/4 Intense Focus (USA)—
              Nancy Rock (IRE) (Rock of Gibraltar (IRE)) (37165) **Mrs J. S. Bolger**
87 **INVOCATION (IRE)**, b c 12/5 Vocalised (USA)—Hymn of The Dawn (USA) (Phone Trick (USA)) **Mrs J. S. Bolger**
88 B f 11/4 Shamardal (USA)—Island Babe (USA) (Kingmambo (USA)) **Sheikh Mohammed**
89 **JALEO (GER)**, ch c 16/2 New Approach (IRE)—Jambalaya (GER) (Samum (GER)) (139372) **Sheikh Mohammed**
90 B c 21/2 Cape Cross (IRE)—Keladora (Crafty Prospector (USA)) **Sheikh Mohammed**
91 B c 20/4 Cape Cross (IRE)—Last Resort (Lahib (USA)) **Sheikh Mohammed**
92 **LAWYERS TALK (IRE)**, b f 30/1 Lawman (FR)—Lush Lashes (Galileo (IRE)) **Mrs June Judd**
93 **LEAFY APPROACH (IRE)**, ch f 4/5 New Approach (IRE)—Tiz The Whiz (USA) (Tiznow (USA)) **Mrs J. S. Bolger**

MR J. S. BOLGER - Continued

94 **LETTER FOCUS (IRE)**, b c 17/2 Intense Focus (USA)—Christinas Letter (IRE) (Galileo (IRE)) **Mrs J. S. Bolger**
95 Ch c 1/4 Teofilo (IRE)—Lia (IRE) (Desert King (IRE)) **Sheikh Mohammed**
96 **LOOK LIVELY (IRE)**, b c 28/5 Teofilo (IRE)—Sister Angelina (USA) (Saint Ballado (CAN)) **Mrs J. S. Bolger**
97 B c 22/3 Shamardal (USA)—Loving Kindness (USA) (Seattle Slew (USA)) **Sheikh Mohammed**
98 **LUCHT NA GAEILGE (IRE)**, b f 30/4 Teofilo (IRE)—Danemarque (AUS) (Danehill (USA)) **Mrs J. S. Bolger**
99 **LUMINIZE (IRE)**, b f 16/3 Vocalised (USA)—Luminous One (IRE) (Galileo (IRE)) **Mrs J. S. Bolger**
100 B f 24/4 Shamardal (USA)—Lura (USA) (Street Cry (IRE)) **Sheikh Mohammed**
101 **MAGNO CLAMORE (IRE)**, b c 28/5 Vocalised (USA)—Bronntanas (IRE) (Spectrum (IRE)) **Mrs J. S. Bolger**
102 **MAINICIN (IRE)**, b f 8/4 Teofilo (IRE)—Luminaria (IRE) (Danehill (USA)) **Mrs J. S. Bolger**
103 **MCGUIGAN (IRE)**, ch c 17/5 Teofilo (IRE)—Scribonia (IRE) (Danehill (USA)) **Mrs J. S. Bolger**
104 **MORNING MIX (IRE)**, b c 9/3 Teofilo (IRE)—Fainne (IRE) (Peintre Celebre (USA)) **Mrs J. S. Bolger**
105 **NEW ALLIANCE (IRE)**, b f 15/2 New Approach (IRE)—
                                  Dochas Is Gra (IRE) (High Chaparral (IRE)) **Mrs J. S. Bolger**
106 **NEW DIRECTION (IRE)**, b c 29/2 New Approach (IRE)—Gearanai (USA) (Toccet (USA)) **Mrs J. S. Bolger**
107 B f 31/3 Teofilo (IRE)—Night Visit (Sinndar (IRE)) **Godolphin**
108 **NOVIS ADVENTUS (IRE)**, b c 8/2 New Approach (IRE)—Tiffed (USA) (Seattle Slew (USA)) **Mrs J. S. Bolger**
109 **PIROLO (IRE)**, ch c 24/5 Teofilo (IRE)—Zavaleta (IRE) (Kahyasi) **Mrs J. S. Bolger**
110 **PLEASACH (IRE)**, b f 6/2 Teofilo (IRE)—Toirneach (USA) (Thunder Gulch (USA)) **Mrs J. S. Bolger**
111 **RAPID EYE (IRE)**, b f 26/3 Equiano (FR)—Hidden Meaning (Cadeaux Genereux) (34842) **Mrs J. S. Bolger**
112 Gr c 7/3 New Approach (IRE)—Requesting (Rainbow Quest (USA)) **Sheikh Mohammed**
113 **RING PRESENCE (IRE)**, ch c 13/4 Teofilo (IRE)—Maoineach (USA) (Congaree (USA)) **Mrs June Judd**
114 **RINGSIDE HUMOUR (IRE)**, b f 17/4 Teofilo (IRE)—
                                  Intriguing Humor (CAN) (Distorted Humor (USA)) **Mrs J. S. Bolger**
115 B c 4/2 Teofilo (IRE)—Sassy Gal (IRE) (King's Best (USA)) **Sheikh Mohammed**
116 **SELSKAR ABBEY (USA)**, b c 22/5 Street Sense (USA)—
                                  Saintly Hertfield (USA) (Saint Ballado (CAN)) **Mrs J. S. Bolger**
117 B c 27/2 Raven's Pass (USA)—Sogno Verde (IRE) (Green Desert (USA)) **Sheikh Mohammed**
118 **STAIR AN DAMHSA (IRE)**, ch f 11/5 Teofilo (IRE)—
                                  National Swagger (IRE) (Giant's Causeway (USA)) **Mrs J. S. Bolger**
119 **STEIP AMACH (IRE)**, b f 1/2 Vocalised (USA)—Ceist Eile (IRE) (Noverre (USA)) **Mrs J. S. Bolger**
120 **STRESS TEST (IRE)**, b c 16/5 Teofilo (IRE)—Simonetta (IRE) (Lil's Boy (USA)) **Mrs J. S. Bolger**
121 Ch c 14/5 Teofilo (IRE)—Sugarhoneybaby (IRE) (Docksider (USA)) **Sheikh Mohammed**
122 **SUN FOCUS (IRE)**, b c 9/5 Intense Focus (USA)—Solas Na Greine (IRE) (Galileo (IRE)) **Mrs J. S. Bolger**
123 **SUPER FOCUS (IRE)**, b f 21/2 Intense Focus (USA)—Super Hoofer (IRE) (Shamardal (USA)) **Mrs J. S. Bolger**
124 **TAP FOCUS (IRE)**, ch f 8/3 Intense Focus (USA)—Gilded Butterfly (USA) (Tapit (USA)) **Mrs J. S. Bolger**
125 **TAPERING (USA)**, gr c 3/4 Invasor (ARG)—Unbridled Treasure (USA) (Unbridled's Song (USA)) **Mrs J. S. Bolger**
126 **THREE GOLD (IRE)**, ch c 30/3 Teofilo (IRE)—Tamra Delight (Diesis) **Mrs J. S. Bolger**
127 **VITALIZED (IRE)**, b f 29/4 Vocalised (USA)—Astralai (IRE) (Galileo (IRE)) **Mrs J. S. Bolger**
128 **VOCAL ALERT (IRE)**, b f 4/5 Vocalised (USA)—Groves Royal (USA) (Royal Academy (USA)) **Mrs J. S. Bolger**
129 **VOCAL NATION (IRE)**, b f 13/4 Vocalised (USA)—Six Nations (USA) (Danzig (USA)) (13162) **Mrs J. S. Bolger**
130 **VOCAL SUPPORT (IRE)**, b f 18/4 Vocalised (USA)—Sanaara (USA) (Anabaa (USA)) **Mrs J. S. Bolger**
131 **VOCALISER (IRE)**, b c 11/2 Vocalised (USA)—Bring Back Matron (IRE) (Rock of Gibraltar (IRE)) **Mrs J. S. Bolger**
132 **VOCIFEROUSLY (IRE)**, b f 21/4 Vocalised (USA)—Azra (IRE) (Danehill (USA)) (13937) **Mrs J. S. Bolger**
133 **VOICE OF CHOICE (IRE)**, b c 27/4 Holy Roman Emperor (IRE)—
                                  Dream On Buddy (IRE) (Oasis Dream) **Mrs June Judd**
134 **VOYAGE TO ROME (IRE)**, b c 24/2 Vocalised (USA)—Abigail Pett (Medicean) **Mrs June Judd**

Other Owners: Mr John Corcoran, Mr Tom McGurk, Mr John Sikura.

Jockey (flat): R. P. Cleary, Kevin Manning. **Apprentice:** David Fitzpatrick, Killian Hennessy, Daniel Redmond, Dylan Robinson, R. P. Whelan.

---

51 MRS MYRIAM BOLLACK-BADEL, Lamorlaye
Postal: 20 Rue Blanche, 60260 Lamorlaye, France
Contacts: (0033) 9774 89044 FAX (0033) 3442 13367 MOBILE (0033) 6108 09347
E-MAIL myriam.bollack@gmail.com **WEBSITE** www.myriam-bollack.com

1 **AVIATOR (FR)**, 5, b h Motivator—Summer Wave (IRE) **Ecurie Noel Forgeard**
2 **CINDER'S POST (FR)**, 4, b f American Post—Cinders' Prize **Mr J. C. Smith**
3 **IRON SPIRIT (FR)**, 4, b c Turtle Bowl (IRE)—Irish Vintage (FR) **Mr Cecil Motschmann**
4 **KANOTIER (FR)**, 6, b h Daliapour (IRE)—Knout (FR) **Mme Guy de Chatelperron**
5 **KUKURUN (FR)**, 4, b c Kouroun (FR)—Knout (FR) **Mme Guy de Chatelperron**
6 **NORSE KING (FR)**, 5, ch g Norse Dancer (IRE)—Angel Wing **Mr J. C. Smith**

MRS MYRIAM BOLLACK-BADEL - Continued

    7 **SLICE OF LIFE (FR)**, 4, b f Nombre Premier—Cortiguera **Mr Alain Pinot**
    8 **ZIMRI (FR)**, 10, b g Take Risks (FR)—Zayine (IRE) **Mme M. Bollack-Badel**

THREE-YEAR-OLDS

    9 **ANGELIC NEWS (FR)**, b f American Post—Angel Wing **Mr J. C. Smith**
  10 **CAMONDO (IRE)**, ch c Champs Elysees—Brooklyn Academy (USA) **Mr Cecil Motschmann**
  11 **CHAMEUR (FR)**, ch c Shirocco (GER)—Crystals Sky (FR) **Mr Cecil Motschmann**
  12 **GREEN SPEED (FR)**, ch f Green Tune (USA)—Speed of Sound **Mr J. C. Smith**
  13 **MY VALLEY (FR)**, b f My Risk (FR)—Squadra Valley (FR) **H. d'Aillieres**
  14 **NORSE PRIZE (FR)**, ch c Norse Dancer (IRE)—Cinders' Prize **Mr J. C. Smith**
  15 **NORSE WAVE (FR)**, b f Norse Dancer (IRE)—Wave Goodbye (FR) **Mr J. C. Smith**
  16 **OUTBACK RACER (FR)**, b c Aussie Rules (USA)—Mary Linda **Mr J. C. Smith**
  17 **OWLAM**, b f Astronomer Royal (USA)—October Winds (USA) **P. Fellous**
  18 **WILD GUEST (FR)**, b f Azamour (IRE)—White House **Mme Guy de Chatelperron**
  19 **ZYGMUNT (FR)**, ch c Vespone (IRE)—Zython (FR) **Mme M. Bollack-Badel**

TWO-YEAR-OLDS

  20 **ALBICOCCA (FR)**, ch f 3/5 Naaqoos—Ashley River (Ashkalani (IRE)) **P. Fellous**
  21 **BRONZINO (FR)**, b c 10/3 Creachadoir (IRE)—Berenice Pancrisia (FR) (Kendor (FR)) **Mme M. Bollack-Badel**
  22 **CLOWN (FR)**, b c 27/1 Kouroun (FR)—Cleanaway (FR) (Kahyasi) **S. Plot**
  23 **EARTHRISE**, gr f 10/3 Naaqoos—Divine Promesse (FR) (Verglas (IRE)) (28648) **Mr Cecil Motschmann**
  24 **GALEOTTO (FR)**, b c 7/4 Naaqoos—Hay Amor (ARG) (Candy Stripes (USA)) **Mme M. Bollack-Badel**
  25 **HERACLEA (FR)**, b f 3/5 Panis (USA)—Hokey Pokey (FR) (Lead On Time (USA)) **Mr Cecil Motschmann**
  26 **SAINTE ADELE (FR)**, b f 12/5 Naaqoos—Sambala (IRE) (Danehill Dancer (IRE)) **Ecurie Noel Forgeard**
  27 B f 1/4 Lope de Vega (IRE)—Sasicha (IRE) (Montjeu (IRE)) (20905) **Mme M. Bollack-Badel / S. Caytan**
  28 B c 2/5 Elusive City (USA)—Scope (USA) (Devil's Bag (USA)) (30971) **Saleh Al Dugish**
  29 **VIKING RUNNER (FR)**, b f 25/3 Norse Dancer (IRE)—Speed of Sound (Zafonic (USA)) **Mr J. C. Smith**
  30 **WAVE POWER (FR)**, b c 12/3 Motivator—Wave Goodbye (FR) (Linamix (FR)) **Mr J. C. Smith**
  31 **ZAHAB (FR)**, b f 4/5 Naaqoos—Zython (FR) (Kabool) **Mme M. Bollack-Badel**
  32 **ZAMIYR (FR)**, b f 14/2 Naaqoos—Zayine (IRE) (Polish Patriot (USA)) **Mme M. Bollack-Badel**

Assistant Trainer: Alain Badel

Jockey (flat): Alexis Badel.

---

52 | **MR MARTIN BOSLEY, Chalfont St Giles**
Postal: Bowstridge Farm, Bowstridge Lane, Chalfont St Giles, Buckinghamshire, HP8 4RF
Contacts: PHONE (01494) 875533 FAX (01494) 875533 MOBILE (07778) 938040
E-MAIL martin@martinbosley.com WEBSITE www.martinbosleyracing.com

    1 **ALFRESCO**, 10, b g Mtoto—Maureena (IRE) **Mrs A. M. Riney**
    2 **BURNT CREAM**, 7, b m Exceed And Excel (AUS)—Basbousate Nadia **Mrs P. M. Brown**
    3 **CARLANDA (FR)**, ch f Lando (GER)—Carousel Girl (USA) **Mr C. Bacon**
    4 **CAROBELLO (IRE)**, 7, b g Luso—Vic's Queen (IRE) **Mr I. Herbert**
    5 **DRUSSELL (IRE)**, 8, b g Orpen (USA)—Cahermee Queen (USA) **Walid & Paula Marzouk**
    6 **FLASH TOMMIE (IRE)**, 6, b g City Honours (USA)—African Keys (IRE) **Mr C. Bacon**
    7 **JOYFUL RISK (IRE)**, 4, ch f Kheleyf (USA)—Joyfullness (USA) **Mrs B. M. Cuthbert**
    8 **LEMON GROVE**, 4, b f Compton Place—Lemon Tree (USA) **K. J. Quinn**
    9 **LITTLE RED NELL (IRE)**, 5, b m Red Clubs (IRE)—Naughty Nell **Mr S. Day**
  10 **MISS BISCOTTI**, 6, ch m Emperor Fountain—Bellacaccia (USA) **Mrs C. B. Herbert**
  11 **NEW YOUMZAIN (FR)**, 5, b g Sinndar (IRE)—Luna Sacra (FR) **Mr C. Bacon**
  12 **NIFTY KIER**, 5, b g Kier Park (IRE)—Yeldham Lady **Fairford Goes Racing**
  13 **PARK DANCER**, 7, b m Kier Park (IRE)—Kerry Dancer **J. Carey**
  14 **RANDALL**, 6, b g Superior Premium—Wilderness Bay (IRE) **Mrs J. M. O'Connor**
  15 **TOPTHORN**, 8, gr g Silver Patriarch (IRE)—Miss Traxdata **Stephenson-Vollaro-Clark-Bosley-Morris**

THREE-YEAR-OLDS

  16 **THANKS HARRY**, br c Lucky Story (USA)—Africa's Star (IRE) **Mrs P. A. Hall**

Other Owners: Mr M. R. Bosley, Mr G. F. Clark, Mrs S. H. Jones, Mr Walid Marzouk, Mrs Paula Marzouk, Mrs E. Morris, Mr I. H. Stephenson, Ms L. Vollaro.

Jockey (flat): George Baker. **Amateur:** Mr Zac Baker.

53 **MR MARCO BOTTI, Newmarket**
Postal: **Prestige Place, Snailwell Road, Newmarket, Suffolk, CB8 7DP**
Contacts: **PHONE (01638) 662416 FAX (01638) 662417 MOBILE (07775) 803007**
E-MAIL office@marcobotti.co.uk WEBSITE www.marcobotti.co.uk

1 CAMACHOICE (IRE), 4, b g Camacho—Nouvelle Reve (GER) **Mr J. Allison**
2 CENTURIUS, 4, ch c New Approach (IRE)—Questina (FR) **Mr M. A. M. Albousi Alghufli**
3 CHARITY LINE (IRE), 4, ch f Manduro (GER)—Holy Moon (IRE)
4 CHARLOTTE RHODES, 4, br f Halling (USA)—Kunda (IRE) **H.E. S. Al-kaabi**
5 DANDINO, 7, b br h Dansili—Generous Diana **Australian Thoroughbred Bloodstock**
6 DONT BOTHER ME (IRE), 4, br c Dark Angel (IRE)—Faleh (USA) **Mr N. Moran**
7 EDU QUERIDO (BRZ), 5, ch h Holzmeister (USA)—Kournikova (BRZ) **Mr S. Friborg**
8 ENERGIA DAVOS (BRZ), 6, gr g Torrential (USA)—Star Brisingamen (USA) **Mr S. Friborg**
9 ENERGIA EROS (BRZ), 5, b h Point Given (USA)—Super Eletric (BRZ) **Mr S. Friborg**
10 FOXTROT ROMEO (IRE), 5, b h Danehill Dancer (IRE)—Hawala (IRE) **Mr W. A. Tinkler**
11 GRENDISAR (IRE), 4, b c Invincible Spirit (IRE)—Remarkable Story **Mr M. A. M. Albousi Alghufli**
12 GREY MIRAGE, 5, b g Oasis Dream—Grey Way (USA) **G. Manfredini**
13 GUEST OF HONOUR (IRE), 5, b h Cape Cross (IRE)—Risera (IRE) **G. Manfredini**
14 HALFSIN (IRE), 6, b g Haafhd—Firesteed (IRE) **Dr M. B. Q. S. Koukash**
15 HASOPOP (IRE), 4, b g Haatef (USA)—Convenience (IRE) **G. Manfredini**
16 KELINNI (IRE), 6, b g Refuse To Bend (IRE)—Orinoco (IRE) **Unregistered Partnership**
17 MAGIKA, 4, b f Dubawi (IRE)—Aline's Wings (ITY) **Marco & Sara Moretti & Partner**
18 MASAMAH (IRE), 8, gr g Exceed And Excel (AUS)—Bethesda **Dr M. B. Q. S. Koukash**
19 MOOHAAJIM (IRE), 4, b c Cape Cross (IRE)—Thiella (USA) **Sheikh M. B. K. Al Maktoum**
20 MOUNT ATHOS (IRE), 7, b g Montjeu (IRE)—Ionian Sea **Dr M. B. Q. S. Koukash**
21 ODYSSEE (FR), 4, ch f Teofilo (IRE)—Uruk **Mr S. Friborg**
22 RENEW (IRE), 4, b c Dansili—Hold Me Love Me (IRE) **O.T.I. Racing**
23 SENAFE, 4, b f Byron—Kiruna **Mr A. N. Mubarak**
24 SHAMDARLEY (IRE), 5, b h Shamardal (USA)—Siphon Melody (USA) **Mr W. A. Tinkler**
25 SOLAR DEITY (IRE), 5, b h Exceed And Excel (AUS)—Dawn Raid (IRE) **Mr G Manfredini & Mr A Tinkler**
26 SPIFER (IRE), 6, gr g Motivator—Zarawa (IRE) **Op Center One**
27 STRING THEORY (IRE), 4, b c Medicean—Shebelia (GER) **Prince A. A. Faisal**
28 TAC DE BOISTRON (FR), 7, gr g Take Risks (FR)—Pondiki (FR) **Australian Thoroughbred Bloodstock**
29 WAKEUP LITTLE SUZY (IRE), 4, ch f Peintre Celebre (USA)—Maramba (USA) **P. Newton**
30 WHAILEYY (IRE), 6, b g Holy Roman Emperor (IRE)—Alshoowg (USA) **Saleh Al Homaizi & Imad Al Sagar**

THREE-YEAR-OLDS

31 ABDICATION, b g Royal Applause—Bowled Out (GER)
32 ADERFI (IRE), b c Pivotal—Princess Danah (IRE) **Saleh Al Homaizi & Imad Al Sagar**
33 AL BUSAYYIR (IRE), b c Amadeus Wolf—Helen Wells (IRE) **Mr A. N. Mubarak**
34 AL THAKHIRA (IRE), b f Dubawi (IRE)—Dahama **H.E. Sheikh J. B. H. B. K. Al Thani**
35 ALEXANOR (IRE), b c Pivotal—Butterfly Cove (USA) **Op Center One**
36 ATTENZIONE (IRE), b g Shamardal (USA)—Fig Tree Drive (USA) **Global First Racing**
37 BYRON GALA, b g Byron—Tenuta di Gala (IRE) **Scuderia Blueberry S. R. L.**
38 CAPTAIN MO, b c Captain Gerrard (IRE)—Plum Blossom **Mr M. A. M. Albousi Alghufli**
39 CAPTAIN SECRET, ch f Captain Gerrard (IRE)—Obsessive Secret (IRE) **Scuderia Blueberry S. R. L.**
40 CHAMPS D'OR, b f Champs Elysees—Shemriyna (IRE) **Miss Y. M. G. Jacques**
41 CHARMY DUKESSE (IRE), b f Duke of Marmalade (IRE)—Nashatara (USA) **La Tesa SPA**
42 CRAZY CHIC (IRE), gr g Exceed And Excel (AUS)—Martines (IRE) **Scuderia Vittadini SRL**
43 DAMASCENE, b c Oasis Dream—Acts of Grace (USA) **Prince A. A. Faisal**
44 DRAGOON GUARD (IRE), b c Jeremy—Elouges (USA) **K. A. Dasmal**
45 ESTEBAN, b g Cape Cross (IRE)—Young and Daring (USA) **Al Asayl Bloodstock Ltd**
46 EURO CHARLINE, b f Myboycharlie (IRE)—Eurolink Artemis **Scuderia Blueberry S. R. L.**
47 EXCEEDER, b c Exceed And Excel (AUS)—Norfolk Broads (IRE) **G. Manfredini**
48 FITZGERALD (IRE), b c Duke of Marmalade (IRE)—La Vida Loca (IRE) **Al Asayl Bloodstock Ltd**
49 GOLDEN STEPS (FR), b c Footstepsinthesand—Kocooning (USA) **Mr M. A. A. Al-Mannai**
50 GOLEADOR (USA), b g English Channel (USA)—Stormin' Home (USA) **El Catorce**
51 GWAFA (IRE), gr c Tamayuz—Atalina (FR) **Saleh Al Homaizi & Imad Al Sagar**
52 HAGREE (IRE), b c Haatef (USA)—Zuniga's Date (USA) **Mr Manfredini & Mohamed Albousi Alghufli**
53 HALATION (IRE), b g Azamour (IRE)—Ghenwah (FR) **Al Asayl Bloodstock Ltd**
54 HOLYSTONES (IRE), b c Holy Roman Emperor (IRE)—Cappagh Strand (USA) **G. Manfredini**
55 JOOHAINA (IRE), b f New Approach (IRE)—Rouge Noir (USA) **Sheikh M. B. K. Al Maktoum**
56 LATIN CHARM (IRE), b c Cape Cross (IRE)—Di Moi Oui **Grundy Bloodstock Ltd**
57 LIGHTNING SHOWER (USA), b c Mr Greeley (USA)—Lightning Show (USA) **Mr J. Allison**
58 LOCKEDOUTAHEAVEN (IRE), ch g Rock of Gibraltar (IRE)—Second Burst (IRE) **Mrs L. Botti**

MR MARCO BOTTI - Continued

59 **LUNGARNO PALACE (USA)**, b g Henrythenavigator (USA)—Good Time Sally (USA) **G. Manfredini**
60 **MAAHIR**, b c Cape Cross (IRE)—Trick Or Treat **Sheikh M. B. K. Al Maktoum**
61 **MAGNUS ROMEO**, b c Manduro (GER)—Chili Dip **Al Asayl Bloodstock Ltd**
62 **MANNARO (IRE)**, b g Manduro (GER)—Donoma (IRE) **La Tesa SPA**
63 **MARAAYILL (IRE)**, b c Sea The Stars (IRE)—Navajo Moon (IRE) **Sheikh M. B. K. Al Maktoum**
64 **MARITAL (IRE)**, b c Montjeu (IRE)—Fleeting Affair (USA) **Mr W. A. Tinkler**
65 **MEANING OF LIFE (IRE)**, b c Exceed And Excel (AUS)—Emirates Hills **Scuderia Effevi SRL**
66 **MIN ALEMARAT (IRE)**, ch c Galileo (IRE)—Baraka (IRE) **A. Al Shaikh**
67 **MOBHIRR**, br c Sea The Stars (IRE)—Silent Heir (AUS) **Sheikh M. B. K. Al Maktoum**
68 B c Shamardal (USA)—Mouriyana (IRE) **Mrs C. McStay**
69 **NAADIRR (IRE)**, b c Oasis Dream—Beach Bunny (IRE) **Sheikh M. B. K. Al Maktoum**
70 **NABATEO**, ch g Sea The Stars (IRE)—Rosa Del Dubai (IRE) **Scuderia Rencati Srl**
71 **NORAB (GER)**, b c Galileo (IRE)—Night Woman (GER) **Mr M. Keller**
72 **NORMANNA (IRE)**, b f Elusive City (USA)—Nantes (GER) **Mr U. M. Saini Fasanotti**
73 **NOVA PRINCESSE (GER)**, b f Desert Prince (IRE)—Nova Scotia (GER) **Scuderia Blueberry S. R. L.**
74 **PATENTAR (FR)**, b c Teofilo (IRE)—Poppets Sweetlove **Saleh Al Homaizi & Imad Al Sagar**
75 **PELERIN (IRE)**, ch f Shamardal (USA)—Fragrancy (IRE) **Mr Bruni & Mr Somma**
76 **PERSHING**, gr c Mount Nelson—La Gandilie (FR) **Mr M. Keller**
77 **QUEEN SARRA**, b f Shamardal (USA)—Grace O'malley (IRE) **Saleh Al Homaizi & Imad Al Sagar**
78 **QUIET WARRIOR (IRE)**, b g Kodiac—Pretty Woman (IRE) **Global First Racing**
79 **RASHEEDA**, ro f Mastercraftsman (IRE)—Violette **Mr A. N. Mubarak**
80 **RAYOUMTI (IRE)**, b f Lawman (FR)—Sveva (IRE) **Saleh Al Homaizi & Imad Al Sagar**
81 **ROSE KAZAN (IRE)**, ch f Teofilo (IRE)—Zahour Al Yasmeen **J. Abdullah**
82 **SAYED YOUMZAIN**, b c Dalakhani (IRE)—Silver Touch (IRE) **J. Abdullah**
83 **SERATA DI GALA (FR)**, b f Footstepsinthesand—Sea Sex Sun **Mr U. M. Saini Fasanotti**
84 **SILVER GALAXY**, b c Galileo (IRE)—Silver Pivotal (IRE) **Newsells Park Stud Limited**
85 **SIR ROBERT CHEVAL**, b c Green Desert (USA)—Aunt Ruby (USA) **Heart Of The South Racing**
86 **SMAGETA**, b f Shirocco (GER)—Sensibility **Scuderia Rencati Srl**
87 **SOTISE (IRE)**, br f Shamardal (USA)—Tropical Glamour (IRE) **Bloodstock Agency Limited**
88 **SPECIAL MISS**, b f Authorized (IRE)—Whatamiss (USA) **Team Valor LLC**
89 **SPEECHDAY (IRE)**, b f Kodiac—Privileged Speech (USA) **Miss Y. M. G. Jacques**
90 **SPIRIT OR SOUL (FR)**, b c Soldier of Fortune (IRE)—Far Across **Niarchos Family**
91 **STONECUTTER (IRE)**, gr c Mastercraftsman (IRE)—
                                                    Sparkle of Stones (FR) **Mrs J Magnier, Mr D Smith & Mr M Tabor**
92 **SUFRANEL (IRE)**, b c Galileo (IRE)—Noelani (IRE) **Scuderia Rencati Srl**
93 **THE OSTLER (IRE)**, ch c Mastercraftsman (IRE)—Awani **Mr N. A. Jackson**
94 **TRIBULINA**, b f Dansili—Wickwing **Mrs E. Locchi**
95 **TRIKALA (IRE)**, b f High Chaparral (IRE)—Thiella (USA) **Lady C. J. O'Reilly**
96 **TZHARR (IRE)**, gr c Teofilo (IRE)—Netrebko (IRE) **Mr M. A. M. Albousi Alghufli**

TWO-YEAR-OLDS

97 **AQLETTE**, ch f 16/4 Aqlaam—Violette (Observatory (USA)) (42857) **Scuderia Blueberry S. R. L.**
98 **BROUGHTONIAN**, b c 10/3 Invincible Spirit (IRE)—Quan Yin (IRE) (Sadler's Wells (USA)) **Niarchos Family**
99 **DREAM ON STAGE**, b c 4/5 Aqlaam—Star On Stage (Sadler's Wells (USA)) (20000) **Grundy Bloodstock Ltd**
100 B c 16/2 Paco Boy (IRE)—Gee Kel (IRE) (Danehill Dancer (IRE)) (57000) **Saleh Al Homaizi & Imad Al Sagar**
101 B c 31/3 Galileo (IRE)—Healing Music (FR) (Bering) **Qatar Racing Limited**
102 B f 28/3 Equiano (FR)—Lady Scarlett (Woodman (USA)) (30000) **Newsells Park Stud Limited**
103 B c 12/4 Cape Cross (IRE)—Lady Slippers (IRE) (Royal Academy (USA)) (162600) **Sheikh M. B. K. Al Maktoum**
104 Ch f 18/3 Arcano (IRE)—Luanas Pearl (IRE) (Bahri (USA)) (17000) **Mr C. McHale**
105 B c 7/3 Champs Elysees—Millistar (Galileo (IRE)) (105000) **Mr M. Keller**
106 **PLAISIR (IRE)**, b f 21/2 Elusive City (USA)—Sea Sex Sun (Desert Prince (IRE)) **Mr U. M. Saini Fasanotti**
107 B f 23/1 Cape Cross (IRE)—Queen of Mean (Pivotal) (260000) **Saleh Al Homaizi & Imad Al Sagar**
108 B c 3/3 Kodiac—Right After Moyne (IRE) (Imperial Ballet (IRE)) (130000) **Saleh Al Homaizi & Imad Al Sagar**
109 B f 12/3 Mount Nelson—Sakhee's Song (IRE) (Sakhee (USA)) (80952) **Saleh Al Homaizi & Imad Al Sagar**
110 B f 10/2 Acclamation—Secret History (USA) (Bahri (USA)) (100000) **Sheikh M. B. K. Al Maktoum**
111 B c 11/4 Rip Van Winkle (IRE)—Set Fire (IRE) (Bertolini (USA)) (52651) **Mr M. A. M. Albousi Alghufli**
112 B c 13/2 Galileo (IRE)—So Squally (GER) (Monsun (GER)) (400000) **Mr M. Keller**
113 B f 18/1 Henrythenavigator (USA)—Spring Heather (IRE) (Montjeu (IRE)) (38000) **Scuderia Rencati Srl**
114 B c 23/3 Royal Applause—Tia Mia (Dr Fong (USA)) (45000) **Scuderia Rencati Srl**
115 B c 12/2 Kodiac—Town And Gown (Oasis Dream) (152380) **Sheikh M. B. K. Al Maktoum**
116 Ch c 14/2 Nayef (USA)—Ulfah (USA) (Danzig (USA)) **Sheikh M. B. K. Al Maktoum**
117 **WARM RECEPTION**, b f 1/4 Acclamation—Feel (Rainbow Quest (USA)) (50000) **Scuderia Vittadini SRL**

Other Owners: I. J. Al-Sagar, Mr L. Biffi, Mr R. Bruni, Mr E. Bulgheroni, Mr D. P. Dance, Mr S. E. Duke, Mr S. C. Gereaux, Mr G. P. Gereaux, Mrs S. Grassick, Mr T. Henderson, Saleh Al Homaizi, Mr M. Johnston, R. M. Levitt, Mrs S. Magnier, Mr

MR MARCO BOTTI - Continued

M. G. Moretti, Mrs S. P. E. Moretti, Mr S. O'Donnell, J. R. Penny, Miss E. Penny, Mr C. Pizarro, Mrs K. Pizarro, Mr T. N. Porter, Mr A. Schutz, D. Smith, Mr A. Somma, M. Tabor.

Assistant Trainers: Lucie Botti, Mario Baratti

Jockey (flat): Martin Harley. **Apprentice:** Toby Atkinson.

---

54 **MR PETER BOWEN, Haverfordwest**
Postal: Yet-Y-Rhug, Letterston, Haverfordwest, Pembrokeshire, SA62 5TB
Contacts: PHONE (01348) 840486 FAX (01348) 840486 MOBILE (07811) 111234
E-MAIL info@peterbowenracing.com WEBSITE www.peterbowenracing.com

1 **AL CO (FR)**, 9, ch g Dom Alco (FR)—Carama (FR) **F. Lloyd**
2 **AWAYWITHTHEGREYS (IRE)**, 7, gr g Whipper (USA)—Silver Sash (GER) **W. Bryan**
3 **BALLYBOUGH GORTA (IRE)**, 7, b g Indian Danehill (IRE)—Eyelet (IRE) **Yeh Man Partnership**
4 **BEREA BORU (IRE)**, 6, b g Brian Boru—Wayward Venture (IRE) **Mr A. J. R. Hart**
5 **BOOK'EM DANNO (IRE)**, 8, ch g Moscow Society (USA)—Rifada **Roddy Owen & Paul Fullagar**
6 **BUACHAILL ALAINN (IRE)**, 7, b g Oscar (IRE)—Bottle A Knock (IRE) **Roddy Owen & Paul Fullagar**
7 **CHRISTMAS CRACKER (IRE)**, 6, b m Flemensfirth (USA)—
                                Laughing Lesa (IRE) **select-racing-club.co.uk & Mr C. Davies**
8 **CRUISING BYE**, 8, b g Afflora (IRE)—Althrey Flame (IRE) **F. Lloyd**
9 **CYGNET**, 8, b g Danisili—Ballet Princess **Mrs K. Bowen**
10 **DARK GLACIER (IRE)**, 9, b g Flemensfirth (USA)—Glacier Lilly (IRE) **Mrs N. Unsworth & Mr R. Greenway**
11 **DINEUR (FR)**, 8, ch g Discover d'auteuil (FR)—Sky Rocket (FR) **G. J. Morris**
12 **DIPITY DOO DAH**, 10, b m Slip Anchor—Lyra **C. G. R. Booth**
13 **DOUBLE DOUBLE (FR)**, 8, b g Sakhee (USA)—Queen Sceptre (IRE) **Roddy Owen & Paul Fullagar**
14 **DR ROBIN (IRE)**, 4, b g Robin des Pres (FR)—Inter Alia (IRE) **D. J. Robbins**
15 **FLYING EAGLE (IRE)**, 6, b g Oscar (IRE)—Fille d'argent (IRE) **West Coast Haulage Limited**
16 **G'DAI SYDNEY**, 6, b g Choisir (AUS)—Silly Mid-On **Mrs L. J. Williams**
17 **GAP OF DUNLOE (IRE)**, 6, b g Hurricane Run (IRE)—Karri Valley (USA) **Einsley & Angela Harries**
18 **GET HOME NOW**, 6, b g Diktat—Swiftly **Miss Jayne Brace & Mr Gwyn Brace**
19 **GHOST RIVER**, 4, ch g Flemensfirth (USA)—Cresswell Native (IRE) **Mr J. Andrews**
20 **GOLDEN CALF (IRE)**, 7, b g Gold Well—Cherry In A Hurry (IRE) **C. E. R. Greenway**
21 **GRAPE FLAME**, 6, ch m Grape Tree Road—Althrey Flame (IRE) **F. Lloyd**
22 **GULLIBLE GORDON (IRE)**, 11, ch g Anshan—Cronohill (IRE) **Yeh Man Partnership**
23 **GWILI SPAR**, 6, ch g Generosity—Lady of Mine **R. Morgans**
24 **HANDMAID**, 5, b m King's Theatre (IRE)—Hand Inn Glove **Patrick Burling Developments Ltd**
25 **HAROUET (FR)**, 9, ch g Vertical Speed (FR)—Lairna (FR) **Egan Waste & Karen Bowen**
26 **HENLLAN HARRI (IRE)**, 6, br g King's Theatre (IRE)—Told You So (IRE) **Einsley & Angela Harries**
27 **JUMP UP**, 8, b g Carnival Dancer—Taylor Green (USA) **Mr A. J. R. Hart**
28 **KIAN'S DELIGHT**, 6, b g Whipper (USA)—Desert Royalty (IRE) **Roddy Owen, Paul Fullagar & Karen Bowen**
29 **KINARI (IRE)**, 4, b g Captain Rio—Baraza (IRE) **Mr John Andrews**
30 **KING OF JAZZ (IRE)**, 6, b g Acclamation—Grand Slam Maria (FR) **Mrs S. Nicholls**
31 **LAMBORO LAD (IRE)**, 9, b g Milan—Orchard Spray (IRE) **Margaret and Raymond John**
32 **LAND OF VIC**, 6, b m Old Vic—Land of Glory **Mr W. G. A. Hill**
33 **MADE OF DIAMONDS**, 5, b m Afflora (IRE)—Posh Pearl **Mr. M. Bowen**
34 **MAN OF STEEL (IRE)**, 5, b g Craigsteel—Knappogue Honey (IRE) **Saith O Ni**
35 **MUMBLES BAY (IRE)**, 8, b g Oscar (IRE)—Klippersteet (IRE) **Ms J. Day**
36 **MUMBLES HEAD (IRE)**, 13, ch g Flemensfirth (USA)—Extra Mile (IRE) **Ms J. Day**
37 **PENSION PLAN**, 10, b g Afflora (IRE)—Dalbeattie **The Loppington Five**
38 **PRINCESS TARA (IRE)**, 4, b f Kayf Tara—Oscars Vision (IRE) **David Perkins & Kate Becton**
39 **PURE FAITH (IRE)**, 10, b g Anshan—Bolaney Girl (IRE) **P. Bowling, S. Scott & Mrs K. Bowen**
40 **REGAL DIAMOND (IRE)**, 6, b h Vinnie Roe (IRE)—
                                Paper Money (IRE) **Roddy Owen, Paul Fullagar & Karen Bowen**
41 **ROLLING MAUL (IRE)**, 6, b g Oscar (IRE)—Water Sports (IRE) **Roddy Owen & Paul Fullagar**
42 **RONS DREAM**, 4, b f Kayf Tara—Empress of Light **Mrs T. S. P. Stepney**
43 **SANDYNOW (IRE)**, 9, ch g Old Vic—Kasterlee (FR) **J. Martin, C. Morris, T. Stepney, K. Bowen**
44 **SIGN PRO (IRE)**, 6, b g Noverre (USA)—Sadalsud (IRE) **Mr E. O. Morgan**
45 **SIR DU BEARN (FR)**, 8, b br g Passing Sale (FR)—Girl du Bearn (FR) **Mr M. B. Bowen**
46 **SIR PITT**, 7, b g Tiger Hill (IRE)—Rebecca Sharp **G. D. Kendrick**
47 **SQUEEZE ME**, 7, b m Grape Tree Road—Ask Me Not (IRE) **F. Lloyd**
48 **STRUMBLE HEAD (IRE)**, 9, b g Anshan—Milan Moss **Mr J. A. Martin**
49 **TAFFY THOMAS**, 10, b g Afflora (IRE)—Tui **Mrs L. J. Williams**
50 **THE ROAD AHEAD**, 7, b m Grape Tree Road—Althrey Flame (IRE) **F. Lloyd**

MR PETER BOWEN - Continued

51 THUNDER AND RAIN (IRE), 6, b g Craigsteel—Old Cup (IRE) **Straightline Construction Ltd**
52 TONY DINOZZO (FR), 7, b g Lavirco (GER)—Arika (FR) **Mr J. Andrews**
53 VINNIE MY BOY (IRE), 6, ch g Vinnie Roe (IRE)—Copper Magic (IRE) **R. D. J. Swinburne**
54 WESTERN XPRESS (IRE), 6, b g Westerner—Lockersleybay (IRE) **Mrs K. Bowen**

Other Owners: Mr A. W. Barker, Mrs Kate Becton, Mr B. G. Bowen, Mrs Karen Bowen, Mr W. Bryan, Mr R. Burden, Mr C. Davies, Egan Waste Services Ltd, Mr P. Fullagar, Mr R. Greenway, Mrs M. B. A. John, Mr Raymond John, Mrs Joy Martin, Mrs C. Morris, Mr Roddy Owen, Mr David Perkins, www.Select-Racing-Club.co.uk, Mrs Tania Stepney, Mrs N. Unsworth, Mr P. R. Williams.

Assistant Trainers: K. Bowen, Michael Bowen

Jockey (NH): Donal Devereux, Jamie Moore, Tom O'Brien. **Amateur:** Mr Sean Bowen.

---

55 **MR ROY BOWRING, Edwinstowe**
Postal: **Fir Tree Farm, Edwinstowe, Mansfield, Nottinghamshire, NG21 9JG**
Contacts: **PHONE (01623) 822451 MOBILE (07973) 712942**
E-MAIL bowrings@btconnect.com

1 ACE MASTER, 6, ch g Ballet Master (USA)—Ace Maite **S. R. Bowring**
2 CLUBLAND (IRE), 5, b g Red Clubs (IRE)—Racjilanemm **S. R. Bowring**
3 DANCING MAITE, 9, ch g Ballet Master (USA)—Ace Maite **S. R. Bowring**
4 DIVERTIMENTI (IRE), 10, b g Green Desert (USA)—Ballet Shoes (IRE) **K. Nicholls**
5 FLYING APPLAUSE, 9, b g Royal Applause—Mrs Gray **K. Nicholls**
6 MARINA BALLERINA, 6, b br m Ballet Master (USA)—Marinaite **S. R. Bowring**
7 MASTER OF SONG, 7, ch g Ballet Master (USA)—Ocean Song **S. R. Bowring**
8 SOFIAS NUMBER ONE (USA), 6, b br g Silver Deputy (CAN)—Storidawn (USA) **S. R. Bowring**
9 SOLARMAITE, 5, b m Needwood Blade—Marinaite **S. R. Bowring**
10 WEST END LAD, 11, b g Tomba—Cliburnel News (IRE) **K. Nicholls**
11 XPRES MAITE, 11, b g Komaite (USA)—Antonias Melody **Charterhouse Holdings Plc**

THREE-YEAR-OLDS

12 BLACK GERONIMO, b c Sleeping Indian—Voice **K. Nicholls**
13 HICKSTER (IRE), br g Intense Focus (USA)—Surrender To Me (USA) **S. R. Bowring**
14 MISU'S MAITE, b f Misu Bond (IRE)—Magical Flute **Charterhouse Holdings Plc**
15 WALTA (IRE), b g Tagula (IRE)—Hi Katriona (IRE) **S. R. Bowring**

Jockey (flat): Mark Coumbe.

---

56 **MR JIM BOYLE, Epsom**
Postal: **South Hatch Stables, Burgh Heath Road, Epsom, Surrey, KT17 4LX**
Contacts: **PHONE (01372) 748800 FAX (01372) 739410 MOBILE (07719) 554147**
E-MAIL info@jamesboyle.co.uk & jimboylesec@hotmail.co.uk (Secretary)
WEBSITE www.jamesboyle.co.uk

1 ATLANTIS CROSSING (IRE), 5, b g Elusive City (USA)—Back At de Front (IRE) **The "In Recovery" Partnership**
2 CLEARING, 4, br f Sleeping Indian—Spring Clean (FR) **The Paddock Space Partnership**
3 FINAL DELIVERY, 5, b g Three Valleys (USA)—Bowled Out (GER) **M Khan X2**
4 GENTLEMAX (FR), 4, b c Gentlewave (IRE)—Marcela Howard (IRE) **A. B. Pope**
5 IDLE CURIOSITY (IRE), 4, b f Red Clubs (IRE)—Idle Fancy **Inside Track Racing Club**
6 INTOMIST (IRE), 5, ch g Strategic Prince—Fast Temper (USA) **The Clueless Syndicate**
7 KISSED BY FIRE, 4, ch f Sleeping Indian—Desert Cristal (IRE) **The Paddock Space Partnership**
8 LIBERTY JACK (IRE), 4, b g Sakhee (USA)—Azeema (IRE) **Mr M. Fitzgerald**
9 MARCUS ANTONIUS, 7, b g Mark of Esteem (IRE)—Star of The Course (USA) **The Grosvenor Club**
10 MEETHA ACHAR, 4, b f Sakhee (USA)—Sweet Pickle **M Khan X2**
11 PALOMA'S PRINCE (IRE), 5, ch g Nayef (USA)—Ma Paloma (FR) **Serendipity Syndicate 2006**
12 PERFECT PASTIME, 6, ch g Pastoral Pursuits—Puritanical (IRE) **Country Friends**
13 REE'S RASCAL (IRE), 6, gr g Verglas (IRE)—Night Scent (IRE) **Mr W. J. Hayford**
14 SONNETATION (IRE), 4, b f Dylan Thomas (IRE)—Southern Migration (USA) **The "In Recovery" Partnership**

THREE-YEAR-OLDS

15 CONFUCIUS LEGEND (IRE), b g Oratorio (IRE)—Midnight Partner (IRE) **Mr C. C. A. Kwok**
16 JALEBI, ch f Sleeping Indian—Sweet Pickle **M Khan X2**

MR JIM BOYLE - Continued

17 **SPEED SOCIETY**, b g Bertolini (USA)—Tamara **The "In Recovery" Partnership**
18 **WHAT A DANDY (IRE)**, b c Dandy Man (IRE)—Ibtihal (IRE) **Inside Track Racing Club**

TWO-YEAR-OLDS

19 Ch c 17/4 Rip Van Winkle (IRE)—For Evva Silca (Piccolo) (85171)
20 B c 16/4 Tagula (IRE)—Gypsy Royal (IRE) (Desert Prince (IRE)) (14285)
21 **INKE (IRE)**, br f 3/3 Intikhab (USA)—Chifney Rush (IRE) (Grand Lodge (USA)) (8517) **Harrier Racing 2**
22 **ONORINA (IRE)**, b f 4/4 Arcano (IRE)—Miss Honorine (IRE) (Highest Honor (FR)) (30971)
23 Ch c 28/3 Mount Nelson—Photographie (USA) (Trempolino (USA)) (3000) **Mr J. N. Reus**
24 B c 17/2 Approve (IRE)—Wonders Gift (Dr Devious (IRE)) (15485) **Harrier Racing 1**

Other Owners: Mr K. Booth, J. R. Boyle, Mrs P. Boyle, A. J. Chambers, Mr M. P. Chitty, Mrs H. Colraine, Mr K. Ferguson, Mr D. Ferguson, Ms J. E. Harrison, Mr D. J. Hegarty, Mr N. Higham, Mr J. Hillier, M. Khan, M. Khan, Mr K. J. Mackie, Mr P. O. Mooney, Mr S. D. O'Connell, Mr R. O'Dwyer, Miss V. J. Palmer, E. Sames, Mr P. A. Taylor.

Apprentice: Nathan Alison, Daniel Cremin.

 MR RICHARD BRABAZON, Curragh
Postal: **Rangers Lodge, The Curragh, Co. Kildare, Ireland**
Contacts: **PHONE 00353 (0) 45 441259 FAX 00353 (0) 45 441906 MOBILE 00353 (0) 87 2515626**
E-MAIL richardbrabazon@eircom.net WEBSITE www.richardbrabazon.ie

1 **FLOWING AIR (IRE)**, 4, b f Authorized (IRE)—Al Kamah (USA) **Mrs Alice Perry & Richard Brabazon**
2 **IMPERIAL BRAVE (IRE)**, 4, b g Antonius Pius (USA)—White Paper (IRE) **Richard Brabazon**
3 **KORBOUS (IRE)**, 5, ch g Choisir (AUS)—Puppet Play (IRE) **Mrs F. D. McAuley**
4 **PLACERE (IRE)**, 6, ch m Noverre (USA)—Puppet Play (IRE) **Mrs F. D. McAuley**

TWO-YEAR-OLDS

5 B g 26/3 Duke of Marmalade (IRE)—Quest For Eternity (IRE) (Sadler's Wells (USA)) (3871) **David Moran**

---

58 **MR DAVID BRACE, Bridgend**
Postal: **Llanmihangel Farm, Pyle, Bridgend, Mid-Glamorgan, CF33 6RL**
Contacts: **PHONE (01656) 742313**

1 **ALOTTAMO (IRE)**, 6, b m Zerpour (IRE)—Alottalady (IRE) **D. Brace**
2 **BAJAN BLU**, 6, b g Generous (IRE)—Bajan Girl (FR) **D. Brace**
3 **BOB THE BUTCHER**, 5, b g Needle Gun (IRE)—Brydferth Ddu (IRE) **D. Brace**
4 **BRINGINTHEBRANSTON**, 6, ch g Generous (IRE)—Branston Lily **D. Brace**
5 **COCK OF THE ROCK (IRE)**, 9, b g Pierre—Glynn View (IRE) **D. Brace**
6 **COOL STEEL (IRE)**, 8, br g Craigsteel—Coolafinka **D. Brace**
7 **DBOBE**, 5, br g Needle Gun (IRE)—Braceys Girl (IRE) **The Brace Family**
8 **DIRECT LINE (IRE)**, 9, ch g Moscow Society (USA)—Try Another Rose (IRE) **D. Brace**
9 **DOLMEL ROCK (IRE)**, 6, b g Danroad (AUS)—Amoli (IRE) **D. Brace**
10 **DUNRAVEN PRINCE (IRE)**, 7, b g Alderbrook—Lost Prairie (IRE) **D. Brace**
11 **ELYSIAN HEIGHTS (IRE)**, 6, b g Galileo (IRE)—Ziffany **D. Brace**
12 **HERE'S HENRY**, 5, b g Needle Gun (IRE)—Holly Oak **D. Brace**
13 **HOOPY (IRE)**, 12, ch g Presenting—Simply Joyful **D. Brace**
14 **JOHNNY OWEN (IRE)**, 8, b g Danehill Dancer (IRE)—Makarova (IRE) **D. Brace**
15 **KNIGHT BLAZE**, 7, b m Bach (IRE)—Braceys Girl (IRE) **D. Brace**
16 **LENNIE DA LION**, 6, b g Tamure (IRE)—Lynoso **D. Brace**
17 **MALCOLM THE MOON**, 4, b g Needle Gun (IRE)—Moon Catcher **D. Brace**
18 **MIKE THE POACHER**, 5, b g Needle Gun (IRE)—Poacher's Paddy (IRE) **D. Brace**
19 **MOON STREAM**, 7, b g Kayf Tara—Moon Catcher **D. Brace**
20 **NURSE BRACE**, 5, b m Milan—Bajan Girl (FR) **D. Brace**
21 **RESPECTUEUX (FR)**, 8, b g Robin des Pres (FR)—Rouge Folie (FR) **D. Brace**
22 **ROWDY RAMPAGE (IRE)**, 10, b g Lahib (USA)—Rowdy Nights (IRE) **D. Brace**
23 **SILVER TOKEN**, 9, gr g Silver Patriarch (IRE)—Commanche Token (IRE) **D. Brace**
24 **SON OF SWALLOW (IRE)**, 8, b g Swallow Flight (IRE)—Heresheis **D. Brace**
25 **VICTOR MERLYN (IRE)**, 14, b g Old Vic—Aberedw (IRE) **D. Brace**

Other Owners: Mr A. Brace, Mr M. Brace.

Assistant Trainer: Robbie Llewellyn

59 **MR MILTON BRADLEY, Chepstow**
Postal: **Meads Farm, Sedbury Park, Chepstow, Gwent, NP16 7HN**
Contacts: **PHONE (01291) 622486 FAX (01291) 626939**

1 **AVONDREAM**, 5, b g Avonbridge—Amazing Dream (IRE) **J. M. Bradley**
2 **COLOURBEARER (IRE)**, 7, ch g Pivotal—Centifolia (FR) **E. A. Hayward**
3 **COMPTON PRINCE**, 5, ch g Compton Place—Malelane (IRE) **E. A. Hayward**
4 **COURAGEOUS (IRE)**, 8, ch g Refuse To Bend (IRE)—Bella Bella (IRE) **J. M. Bradley**
5 **DANCING WELCOME**, 8, b m Kyllachy—Highland Gait **J. M. Bradley**
6 **DIVINE CALL**, 7, b g Pivotal—Pious **E. A. Hayward**
7 **EGOTIST (IRE)**, 6, ch g Halling (USA)—Devil's Imp (IRE) **E. A. Hayward**
8 **EMIRATESDOTCOM**, 8, b g Pivotal—Teggiano (IRE) **Ms S. A. Howell**
9 **FALASTEEN (IRE)**, 7, ch g Titus Livius (FR)—Law Review (IRE) **J. M. Bradley**
10 **FEDERAL BLUE (USA)**, 4, b g Elusive Quality (USA)—Blue Duster (USA) **E. A. Hayward**
11 **FLAXEN LAKE**, 7, b g Sampower Star—Cloudy Reef **Asterix Partnership**
12 **HAMIS AL BIN (IRE)**, 5, b g Acclamation—Paimpolaise (IRE) **P. Banfield**
13 **INDIAN AFFAIR**, 4, b c Sleeping Indian—Rare Fling (USA) **J. M. Bradley**
14 **ISLAND LEGEND (IRE)**, 8, b g Trans Island—Legand of Tara (USA) **J. M. Bradley**
15 **LADY RAIN**, 6, b m Resplendent Glory (IRE)—Devils Desire **Mrs V. James**
16 **LOYAL ROYAL (IRE)**, 11, b g King Charlemagne (USA)—Supportive (IRE) **J. M. Bradley**
17 **NEW DECADE**, 5, ch g Pivotal—Irresistible **J. M. Bradley**
18 **PANDAR**, 5, b g Zamindar (USA)—Pagnottella (IRE) **Dab Hand Racing**
19 **REGAL PARADE**, 10, ch g Pivotal—Model Queen (USA) **Dab Hand Racing**
20 **SOLE DANSER (IRE)**, 6, b g Dansili—Plymsole (USA) **E. A. Hayward**
21 **SOLEMN**, 9, b g Pivotal—Pious **E. A. Hayward**
22 **SPIRIT OF GONDREE (IRE)**, 6, b g Invincible Spirit (IRE)—
                                        Kristal's Paradise (IRE) **Paul & Ann de Weck & Partner**
23 **TELAMON (IRE)**, 4, b g Rock of Gibraltar (IRE)—Laureldean Express **Dab Hand Racing**
24 **TEMPLE ROAD (IRE)**, 6, b g Street Cry (USA)—Sugarhoneybaby (IRE) **J. M. Bradley**
25 **TRIPLE DREAM**, 9, ch g Vision of Night—Triple Joy **J. M. Bradley**
26 **VOLCANIC DUST (IRE)**, 6, b m Ivan Denisovich (IRE)—Top of The Form (IRE) **Miss D. Hill**

THREE-YEAR-OLDS

27 **BORDER GUARD**, b g Selkirk (USA)—Argent du Bois (USA) **E. A. Hayward**
28 **JAZRI**, b c Myboycharlie (IRE)—Read Federica **Dab Hand Racing**
29 **NOTNOW PENNY**, ch f Notnowcato—Tuppenny **J. M. Bradley**

TWO-YEAR-OLDS

30 B f 6/3 Arabian Gleam—Hansomis (IRE) (Titus Livius (FR)) **J. M. Bradley**
31 B c 19/3 Alfred Nobel (IRE)—Island Music (IRE) (Mujahid (USA)) (3809) **Mr R. Miles**
32 B gr c 29/3 Verglas (IRE)—Rhapsodize (Halling (USA)) (1500) **E. A. Hayward**
33 B c 16/3 Amadeus Wolf—Spring Glory (Dr Fong (USA)) (4000) **E. A. Hayward**

Other Owners: Mr J. M. Bradley, Mr Clifton Hunt, Mr Stephen McAvoy, Mr D. Pearson, Mr Alan Pirie, Mrs Ann E. de
Weck, Mr Paul de Weck.

Assistant Trainer: Mrs Hayley Wallis

Jockey (flat): Richard Kingscote, Adam Kirby, Luke Morris. **Jockey (NH):** Chris Davies, Charlie Wallis.
Apprentice: Leroy Lynch.

60 **MR MARK BRADSTOCK, Wantage**
Postal: **The Old Manor Stables, Letcombe Bassett, Wantage, Oxfordshire, OX12 9NB**
Contacts: **PHONE (01235) 760780 MOBILE (07887) 686697**
E-MAIL mark.bradstock@btconnect.com WEBSITE www.markbradstockracing.co.uk

1 **CARMINO (IRE)**, 5, ch g Stowaway—Fiddlers Pal (IRE) **North Star Partnership**
2 **CARRUTHERS**, 11, b g Kayf Tara—Plaid Maid (IRE) **The Oaksey Partnership**
3 **CONEYGREE**, 7, b g Karinga Bay—Plaid Maid (IRE) **The Max Partnership**
4 **DAHTESTE**, 6, b m Overbury (IRE)—Sunday News'n'echo (USA) **The Elgram Club**
5 **DAMBY'S STAR (IRE)**, 4, b g Kayf Tara—She Took A Tree (FR) **North Star Partnership**
6 **FLINTHAM**, 5, b g Kayf Tara—Plaid Maid (IRE) **The Rasher Partnership**
7 **LADY OVERMOON**, 5, b m Overbury (IRE)—Lady Fleur **The Lady Overmoon Partnership**
8 **MAID OF OAKSEY**, 6, br m Overbury (IRE)—Plaid Maid (IRE) **The Plaid Maid Partnership**
9 **ROBERT'S STAR (IRE)**, 4, b g Oscar (IRE)—Halona **North Star Partnership**

MR MARK BRADSTOCK - Continued

10 **STAR RIDE**, 5, b g Kayf Tara—Star Diva (IRE) **Dorchester On Thames Syndicate**
11 **SUPER VILLAN**, 9, ch g Afflora (IRE)—Country House **M. S. Tamburro**

Other Owners: Mr Mark Bradstock, Mr R. C. Douglas, Lady Dundas, Mr C. Elgram, Mrs D. Elgram, Mrs M. J. Kelsey Fry, Mr Duncan King, Rachel Lady Oaksey, Lord Oaksey, Miss J. Seaman, Mr Mark Tamburro, Mr Robert Tyrrell, Mr C. A. Vernon, Mr Alan Waller.

Assistant Trainer: Sara Bradstock

61

MR GILES BRAVERY, Newmarket
Postal: **2 Charnwood Stables, Hamilton Road, Newmarket, Suffolk, CB8 7JQ**
Contacts: **PHONE (01638) 454044 MOBILE (07711) 112345**
E-MAIL Braverygc@aol.com

1 **AMBER SPYGLASS**, 4, ch c Act One—Northern Bows **Hyphen Bloodstock**
2 **BISON GRASS**, 4, b g Halling (USA)—Secret Blend **Mr J. P. Carrington**
3 **CANTOR**, 6, b g Iceman—Choir Mistress **Mr J. F. Tew**
4 **JEMIMAVILLE (IRE)**, 7, b m Fasliyev (USA)—Sparkling Isle **Mr T. I. Mcintosh**
5 **PUZZLE TIME**, 4, b f Araafa (IRE)—Puzzling **J. J. May**
6 **SILK ROUTE**, 4, ch f Dubai Destination (USA)—Crinolette (IRE) **D. B. Clark**
7 **SPIRIT RIDER (USA)**, 4, b g Candy Ride (ARG)—Teenage Queen (USA) **Mr M. J. James**
8 **TRACKS OF MY TEARS**, 4, b f Rail Link—Policy Setter (USA) **D. B. Clark**
9 **TRIPLE AITCH (USA)**, 4, b g Harlan's Holiday (USA)—Hadley (USA) **Mr I. Collier**

THREE-YEAR-OLDS
10 **LITTLE MISS BECKY**, b f Piccolo—Boojum **Mr J. F. Tew**

Other Owners: Mrs F. E. Bravery, Hyphen Bloodstock, Mr Mark James.

62

MR PATRICK BREEN, Youghal
Postal: **Reanaskeha, Grange, Youghal, Co. Cork. Ireland**
Contacts: **MOBILE (00353) 868152523**
E-MAIL pjfbreen@gmail.com

1 **BALLYHASS (IRE)**, 8, ch m Classic Cliche (IRE)—Have Patience (IRE) **Cecilia Cunningham**
2 **BELL'S CROSS (IRE)**, 7, b m Dr Massini (IRE)—Disposen (IRE) **David Finn**
3 **DESIDERATA (IRE)**, 4, b g Alhaarth (IRE)—Erstwhile (FR) **Thomas Walsh**
4 **SON OF YORK (IRE)**, 5, b g King's Best (USA)—Canouan (IRE) **Pat Breen**
5 **TAMAM NAMOOSE (IRE)**, 5, b g Exceed And Excel (AUS)—Journey's End (IRE) **Pat Breen**

TWO-YEAR-OLDS
6 Ch g 1/2 Arcano (IRE)—Baileys Cream (Mister Baileys) **William Fitzgerald**
7 B f 25/3 Baltic King—Input (Primo Dominie) (619) **Regina Cunningham**
8 Ch f 6/3 Windsor Knot (IRE)—Tarziyma (IRE) (Kalanisi (IRE)) (928) **Stephen Keane**

Assistant Trainer: Cecilia Cunningham

Jockey (flat): Ben Curtis, Declan McDonagh. **Jockey (NH):** Patrick Mangan. **Conditional:** David Splaine.
Apprentice: Colin Keane, Conor King. **Amateur:** Mr P. F. Casey.

63

MR BARRY BRENNAN, Upper Lambourn
Postal: **Rowdown House, Upper Lambourn, Hungerford, Berkshire, RG17 8QP**
Contacts: **MOBILE (07907) 529780**
E-MAIL barrybrennan2@hotmail.co.uk WEBSITE barrybrennanracing.co.uk

1 **ADMIRALS WALK (IRE)**, 4, b g Tagula (IRE)—Very Racy (USA) **Miss R. L. K. Kavanagh**
2 **ALIZARI (IRE)**, 5, b g Oratorio (IRE)—Alaya (IRE) **P. M. Rich**
3 **BATHCOUNTY (IRE)**, 7, ch g Tobougg (IRE)—Seasons Estates **Dr I. A. Cragg**
4 **BEL AMI RICH**, 4, b g Black Sam Bellamy (IRE)—Granny Rich **P. M. Rich**
5 **BIN END**, 8, b g King's Best (USA)—Overboard (IRE) **D. R. T. Gibbons**
6 **BOOM TO BUST (IRE)**, 6, br g Big Bad Bob (IRE)—Forever Phoenix **P. M. Rich**

MR BARRY BRENNAN - Continued

7 **ELLA'S PROMISE**, 5, ch m Doyen (IRE)—Sweet N' Twenty **Dr I. A. Cragg**
8 **MANGER HANAGMENT (IRE)**, 9, br g Heron Island (IRE)—Island Religion (IRE) **F. J. Brennan**
9 **MOLAISE LAD (IRE)**, 8, b g Morozov (USA)—Artic Annie (IRE) **Mr D. J. Lewin**
10 **RUDINERO (IRE)**, 12, gr g Rudimentary (USA)—Cash Chase (IRE) **D. R. T. Gibbons**
11 **SERGEANT DICK (IRE)**, 9, b g Lord of Appeal—Darawadda (IRE) **Connect Eight**
12 **WELLFORTH (IRE)**, 10, b g New Frontier (IRE)—Faitch's Lady (IRE) **Miss Clare L. Ellam**

Other Owners: Exors of the Late Mr W. H. R. Grindle, Mr J. P. Hampson, Mr G. A. Morgan, Mr R. S. Parker, Mr A. Wells.

Amateur: Mr M. Ennis.

64
MISS ALI BREWER, Eastbury
Postal: **Castle Piece Racing Stables, Eastbury, Hungerford, Berkshire, RG17 7JR**
Contacts: **PHONE (01488) 72818 MOBILE (07779) 285205**
E-MAIL info@castlepiecestables.com WEBSITE www.castlepiecestables.com

1 **BARENGER (IRE)**, 7, b g Indian Danehill (IRE)—Build A Dream (USA) **Kings Of The Castle**
2 **CAMPBONNAIS (FR)**, 9, b g Sassanian (USA)—Kries du Berlais (FR) **Miss A. J. Brewer**
3 **CONIGRE**, 7, b g Selkirk (USA)—Mystify **Mr I. Kidger**
4 **HATTERS RIVER (IRE)**, 7, b g Milan—Curzon Ridge (IRE) **Susan & Gerard Nock**
5 **KATHLEEN FRANCES**, 7, b m Sakhee (USA)—Trew Class **Mrs B. V. Evans**
6 **MEETINGS MAN (IRE)**, 7, gr g Footstepsinthesand—Missella (IRE) **Mrs B. V. Evans**
7 **MONEYMIX**, 7, gr g Fair Mix (IRE)—Sticky Money **Miss A. J. Brewer**
8 **PROUD TIMES (USA)**, 8, b g Proud Citizen (USA)—Laura's Pistolette (USA) **Miss A. J. Brewer**
9 **ROYAL GUARDSMAN (IRE)**, 7, b g King's Theatre (IRE)—Lisa du Chenet (FR) **Camilla & Rosie Nock**
10 **SI BIEN (FR)**, 9, b g Solon (GER)—Secret Gold (GER) **Miss A. J. Brewer**
11 **SKINT**, 8, b g King's Theatre (IRE)—No More Money **Mrs B. V. Evans**
12 **UNCLE MUF (IRE)**, 4, b g Curlin (USA)—Peak Maria's Way (USA) **Mr R. W. Tyrrell**
13 **VICO (IRE)**, 10, b g Old Vic—Over The Glen (IRE) **Mrs V. Verdin**

Other Owners: Mr J. J. King, Mrs S. Nock, G. Nock, Miss C. D. Nock, Miss R. C. Nock, Mr F. W. Tulloch.

Assistant Trainer: Sam Stronge

65
MR JOHN BRIDGER, Liphook
Postal: **Upper Hatch Farm, Wheatsheaf Enclosure, Liphook, Hampshire, GU30 7EL**
Contacts: **PHONE (01428) 722528 MOBILE (07785) 716614**
E-MAIL jbridger@btconnect.com

1 **BYRD IN HAND (IRE)**, 7, b g Fasliyev (USA)—Military Tune (IRE) **Marshall Bridger**
2 **CHORAL FESTIVAL**, 8, b m Pivotal—Choirgirl **Mrs E. Gardner**
3 **COMMANDINGPRESENCE (USA)**, 8, b br m Thunder Gulch (USA)—Sehra (USA) **T Wallace & J J Bridger**
4 **FAIRY MIST (IRE)**, 7, b g Oratorio (IRE)—Prealpina (IRE) **Mr J. J. Bridger**
5 **LILY EDGE**, 5, b m Byron—Flaming Spirit **Mr J. J. Bridger**
6 **MEGALALA (IRE)**, 13, b g Petardia—Avionne **T. Ware**
7 **PHAROH JAKE**, 6, ch g Piccolo—Rose Amber **The Hair & Haberdasher Partnership**
8 **PRINCESS CAMMIE (IRE)**, 4, b f Camacho—Hawattef (IRE) **W. A. Wood**
9 **SHIFTING STAR (IRE)**, 9, ch g Night Shift (USA)—Ahshado **Night Shadow Syndicate**
10 **SILVEE**, 7, gr m Avonbridge—Silver Louie (IRE) **Mr & Mrs K. Finch**
11 **STARWATCH**, 7, b g Observatory—Trinity Reef **Mr J. J. Bridger**
12 **SURREY DREAM (IRE)**, 5, b g Oasis Dream—Trois Graces (USA) **P. Cook**
13 **WELSH INLET (IRE)**, 6, br m Kheleyf (USA)—Ervedya (IRE) **Mr J. J. Bridger**

THREE-YEAR-OLDS

14 **COMMANDING FORCE**, b g Authorized (IRE)—Ghazal (USA) **Mr T. Wallace**
15 **DESERT ISLAND DUSK**, b g Superior Premium—Desert Island Disc **W. A. Wood**
16 **JAZZ BAY**, ch g Refuse To Bend (IRE)—Shasta **P. Cook**
17 **LITTLE HERBERT**, ch g Avonbridge—Filemot **Miss K. Windsor-Luck**
18 **MOVIE MAGIC**, b f Multiplex—Alucica **Mr & Mrs K. Finch**
19 **SPIRITED SILVER**, gr f Proclamation (IRE)—Real Emotion (USA) **Mr & Mrs K. Finch**

MR JOHN BRIDGER - Continued

TWO-YEAR-OLDS

20 **BELLA ALAMOTO**, b f 27/3 Almaty (IRE)—Mtoto Girl (Mtoto)
21 **DISC PLAY**, b f 6/3 Showcasing—Gitane (FR) (Grand Lodge (USA)) **K. Finch**
22 **MOONSTONE LADY**, ch f 4/5 Observatory (USA)—Force In The Wings (IRE) (In The Wings) **K. Finch**
23 Ch f 28/2 Avonbridge—Too Grand (Zaha (CAN)) **Mr J. J. Bridger**

Other Owners: Mrs D. Ellison, Mrs D. Finch, T. M. Jones, C. Marshall, Mr A. P. Prockter, Mrs J. M. Stamp, Mrs D. Stewart.

Assistant Trainer: Rachel Cook

---

66 MR DAVID BRIDGWATER, Stow-on-the-Wold
Postal: **Wyck Hill Farm, Wyck Hill, Stow-on-the-Wold, Cheltenham, Gloucestershire, GL54 1HT**
Contacts: **PHONE (01451) 830349 FAX (01451) 830349 MOBILE (07831) 635817**
E-MAIL sales@bridgwaterracing.co.uk WEBSITE www.bridgwaterracing.co.uk

1 **ACADEMY GENERAL (IRE)**, 8, b g Beneficial—Discerning Air **Mr M. Bettis**
2 **ALL FOR FREE (IRE)**, 8, b g Atraf—Milain (IRE) **The Jesters**
3 **BAWDEN ROCKS**, 5, b g Anabaa (USA)—Late Night (GER) **Mr S. Hunt**
4 **BIG TALK**, 7, b g Selkirk (USA)—Common Request (USA) **Deauville Daze Partnership**
5 **CRAZY (GER)**, 5, b m Nicaron (GER)—Chato's Girl (GER) **Jobarry Partnership**
6 **DANISA**, 5, b m Shamardal (USA)—Divisa (GER) **Nigel Holder, Peter Glanville**
7 **DEFINITE MEMORIES (IRE)**, 7, b m Definite Article—Memories (FR) **D. A. Hunt**
8 **DIRTY BERTIE (FR)**, 8, ch g Dream Well (FR)—Ma Reilly (FR) **Mr R. P. Russell**
9 **DONT DO MONDAYS (IRE)**, 7, b g Rashar (USA)—Bit of A Chance **K. Griffin**
10 **ENGAI (GER)**, 8, b g Noroit (GER)—Enigma (GER) **Building Bridgies**
11 **FEARLESS LEADER**, 7, b g Dr Fong (USA)—Queen's Dancer **The Ferandlin Peaches**
12 **FERGAL MAEL DUIN**, 6, gr g Tikkanen (USA)—Fad Amach (IRE) **J Messenger S Kerwood J Buob-Aldorf**
13 **GARNACK (IRE)**, 6, b m Craigsteel—Sister Stephanie (IRE) **Mrs M. K. B. Turner**
14 **GINO TRAIL (IRE)**, 7, br g Perugino (USA)—Borough Trail **Mrs J. Smith**
15 **LORD NAVITS (IRE)**, 6, b g Golan (IRE)—Nanavits (IRE) **Jobarry Partnership**
16 **NO BUTS**, 6, b g Kayf Tara—Wontcostalotbut **Wontcostalot Partnership**
17 **NO IFS NO BUTS**, 5, b m Kayf Tara—Wontcostalotbut **Wontcostalot Partnership**
18 **OSCAR HILL (IRE)**, 8, b g Oscar (IRE)—Elizabeth Tudor (IRE) **K. W. Bradley**
19 **PLUM PUDDING (FR)**, 11, b g Fado (FR)—Tale (FR) **J Messenger S Kerwood J Buob-Aldorf**
20 **PRESENT TO YOU (IRE)**, 9, ch g Presenting—Charm of Toulon (IRE) **Deauville Daze Partnership**
21 **REGAL ONE (IRE)**, 6, b g Antonius Pius (USA)—Regal Dancer (IRE) **Terry & Sarah Amos**
22 **RINGA BAY**, 9, ch g Karinga Bay—Redgrave Wolf **Mr S. J. Corcoran**
23 **SAFFRON PRINCE**, 6, b g Kayf Tara—Jan's Dream (IRE) **Mrs J. A. Chenery**
24 **SPAGETTI WESTERN (IRE)**, 7, b g Luso—Shes Sharp (IRE) **The Ferandlin Peaches**
25 **SWINCOMBE ROCK**, 9, ch g Double Trigger (IRE)—Soloism **Mills & Mason Partnership**
26 **TEMPURAN**, 5, b gr g Unbridled's Song (USA)—Tenderly (IRE) **Mr D. J. Smith**
27 **THE GIANT BOLSTER**, 9, b g Black Sam Bellamy (IRE)—Divisa (GER) **Mr S. Hunt**
28 **UIOP**, 6, b g Caballo Raptor (CAN)—Qwertyze (FR) **Botany Bay**
29 **VINEMAN**, 7, b g Grape Tree Road—Great Ovation (FR) **Mr D. G. Bridgwater**
30 **VINNIESLITTLE LAMB (IRE)**, 6, b m Vinnie Roe—Polar Lamb (IRE) **D. A. Hunt**
31 **WAH WAH TAYSEE (IRE)**, 7, b g Saddlers' Hall (IRE)—Slieve Bernagh (IRE) **Dean Bostock & Raymond Bostock**
32 **WHISPERING BOY (IRE)**, 7, b g Talkin Man (CAN)—Dolphins View (IRE) **The Phelan Partnership**
33 **WYCK HILL (IRE)**, 10, b g Pierre—Willow Rose (IRE) **J. P. McManus**

Other Owners: Mr B. A. Adams, Mr T. P. Amos, Mrs S. P. Amos, Mr Robert Aplin, Mr J. R. Bostock, Mr Dean Graham Bostock, Mr P. Bowden, Mr R. J. Brennan, Mr Russell Bridgeman, Mr D. G. Bridgwater, Mrs Mary Bridgwater, Mr JM. Buob-Aldorf, Mr R. J. Chenery, Mr A. A. Clifford, Mr R. L. Clifford, Mr Steve Corcoran, Mrs Jane Frieze, Mr Mark Frieze, Mr Peter Glanville, Mr P. V. Harris, Ms R. J. Harris, Mr M. V. Hill, Mr Nigel Holder, Mrs S. Kerwood, Mr J. K. Llewellyn, Mr David Mason, Mr C. D. Massey, Mrs J. Massey, Mr James Messenger, Mr F. J. Mills, Mr W. R. Mills, Mr Tim Payton, Mr John Phelan.

Jockey (NH): Tom Scudamore, Robert Thornton. **Conditional:** Jake Hodson.

67 **MR MARK BRISBOURNE, Nesscliffe**
Postal: Ness Strange Stables, Great Ness, Shrewsbury, Shropshire, SY4 2LE
Contacts: **PHONE (01743) 741536/741360 MOBILE (07803) 019651**

1 **DANCING PRIMO**, 8, b m Primo Valentino (IRE)—Tycoon's Last **L. R. Owen**
2 **DUTCH BARNEY**, 4, b g Dutch Art—Celeb Style (IRE) **Celeb Style Racing**
3 **ELLA MOTIVA (IRE)**, 4, b f Motivator—Stormy View (USA) **Mr P. L. Mort**
4 **ELLE REBELLE**, 4, b f Cockney Rebel (IRE)—Lille Ida **The Bourne Connection**
5 **GIFTED SPIRIT**, 4, b f Indesatchel (IRE)—Dispol Verity **L. R. Owen**
6 **HIGH ON THE HOG (IRE)**, 6, b g Clodovil (IRE)—Maraami **Trevor Mennell & Kathie Gwilliam**
7 **LOWER LAKE (FR)**, 4, b g Medecis—Black Dahlia (FR) **R. C. Tooth**
8 **MARKET PUZZLE (IRE)**, 7, ch g Bahamian Bounty—Trempjane **Mark Brisbourne**
9 **OMOTESANDO**, 4, b g Street Cry (IRE)—Punctilious **P. G. Evans**
10 **PENDLE LADY (IRE)**, 5, b m Chineur (FR)—Rose of Battle **Mr P. L. Mort**
11 **ROYAL TROOPER (IRE)**, 8, b g Hawk Wing (USA)—Strawberry Roan (IRE) **W. M. Brisbourne**
12 **SILVAS ROMANA (IRE)**, 5, b m Holy Roman Emperor (IRE)—Triple Wood (USA) **The Bourne Connection**
13 **STORM LIGHTNING**, 5, b g Exceed And Excel (AUS)—All For Laura **Law Abiding Citizens**
14 **SWEET VINTAGE (IRE)**, 4, b f Singspiel (IRE)—Sauterne **Mr Derek & Mrs Marie Dean**
15 **TARO TYWOD (IRE)**, 5, br m Footstepsinthesand—Run To Jane (IRE) **Rasio Cymru Racing 1**
16 **TWO JABS**, 4, b g Teofilo (IRE)—Red Bravo (USA) **R. C. Tooth**
17 **WHIPPHOUND**, 6, b g Whipper (USA)—Golden Symbol **Mr W. M. Clare**

THREE-YEAR-OLDS

18 **MYSTICAL MAZE**, b f Multiplex—Musical Maze **Marshall Barnett / Mark Brisbourne**
19 **SARLAT**, b f Champs Elysees—Midnight Sky **The Bourne Connection**

TWO-YEAR-OLDS

20 B f 28/4 Captain Gerrard (IRE)—River Ensign (River God) (USA) **Mrs Mary Brisbourne**

Other Owners: A. J. Banton, Mr L. Barton, Mr Dennis Blagdon, Mr & Mrs Roy Broughton, D. Dean, Mrs M. Dean, Mrs C. M. Gibson, Ms K. A. Gwilliam, Mr Peter Kirk, Mr J. McGill, Mr Ray McNeil, Mr T. R. Mennell, Mr Mike Murray, Mrs C. A. Naylor, Mr J. Owen, A. Pitt, Silks Racing.

Assistant Trainer: Antony Brisbourne

Jockey (flat): Liam Jones, Tom McLaughlin, Shane Kelly. **Jockey (NH):** Liam Treadwell. **Apprentice:** Ryan Clark, Jack Duern, Matthew Hopkins. **Amateur:** Miss Becky Brisbourne.

68 **MR CLIVE BRITTAIN, Newmarket**
Postal: 'Carlburg', 49 Bury Road, Newmarket, Suffolk, CB8 7BY
Contacts: **OFFICE (01638) 664347 HOME (01638) 663739 FAX (01638) 661744
MOBILE (07785) 302121**
E-MAIL carlburgst@aol.com

1 **AFKAR (IRE)**, 6, b g Invincible Spirit (IRE)—Indienne (IRE) **C. E. Brittain**
2 **AMTHAL (IRE)**, 5, b m Dalakhani (IRE)—Al Ihtithar (IRE) **A. M. A. Al Shorafa**
3 **BOOKTHEBAND (IRE)**, 4, ch g Dubawi (IRE)—Songbook **C. E. Brittain**
4 **BUNTINGFORD (IRE)**, 4, b f Manduro (GER)—Bunting **M. Al Nabouda**
5 **JATHABAH (IRE)**, 4, b f Singspiel (IRE)—Zibet **M. Al Nabouda**
6 **MANOMINE**, 5, b g Manduro (GER)—Fascinating Hali (FR) **Mrs C. E. Brittain**
7 **MASARAH (IRE)**, 4, b f Cape Cross (IRE)—Fragrancy **M. Al Nabouda**
8 **MUDHISH (IRE)**, 9, b g Lujain (USA)—Silver Satire **C. E. Brittain**
9 **QUIXOTE**, 5, ch g Singspiel (IRE)—Rainbow Queen (FR) **C. E. Brittain**
10 **RED AGGRESSOR (IRE)**, 5, b g Red Clubs (IRE)—Snap Crackle Pop (IRE) **C. E. Brittain**

THREE-YEAR-OLDS

11 **ACCLIO (IRE)**, b f Acclamation—Hovering (IRE) **S. Manana**
12 **AQLAAM VISION**, b f Aqlaam—Dream Vision (USA) **S. Manana**
13 **AQUALUNA**, b c Aqlaam—Sirena (GER) **S. Manana**
14 **AUTOMATED**, b c Authorized (IRE)—Red Blooded Woman (USA) **S. Manana**
15 **BAHAMIAN HEIGHTS**, b c Bahamian Bounty—Tahirah **Sheikh J. Al Dalmook Maktoum**
16 **BRAZOS (IRE)**, gr c Clodovil (IRE)—Shambodia (IRE) **S. Manana**
17 **BUSH BEAUTY (IRE)**, b f Bushranger (IRE)—Scottendale **S. Manana**
18 **BUSH BRANCH (IRE)**, b f Bushranger (IRE)—Trim (IRE) **S. Manana**

MR CLIVE BRITTAIN - Continued

19 **CADEAUX POWER,** b f Major Cadeaux—Right Answer **Sheikh J. Al Dalmook Maktoum**
20 **CAPE CASTLE (IRE),** b f Cape Cross (IRE)—Kaabari (USA) **S. Manana**
21 **CAPE GOOD HOPE,** b f Cape Cross (IRE)—Fann (USA) **S. Manana**
22 **CAPELENA,** br f Cape Cross (IRE)—Roslea Lady (IRE) **S. Manana**
23 **CAPELITA,** b f Cape Cross (IRE)—Zamhrear **S. Manana**
24 **CLEARED TO GO,** b c Teofilo (IRE)—Clear Voice (USA) **S. Manana**
25 **CROWN PLEASURE (IRE),** b f Royal Applause—Tarbiyah **S. Manana**
26 **DALAKI (IRE),** b g Dalakhani (IRE)—Lunda (IRE) **S. Manana**
27 **DANCE BID,** b f Authorized (IRE)—Dancing Fire (USA) **S. Manana**
28 **DANCEALOT,** b f Lawman (FR)—Dance of Light (USA) **S. Manana**
29 **DREAM AND HOPE,** b f Royal Applause—Senta's Dream **S. Manana**
30 **FOUR CHEERS (IRE),** b c Exceed And Excel (AUS)—O Fourlunda **S. Manana**
31 **GUARACHA,** ch g Halling (USA)—Pachanga **C. E. Brittain**
32 **HALLJOY (IRE),** b f Halling (USA)—Tithcar **S. Manana**
33 **HATSAWAY (IRE),** b c Dubawi (IRE)—Scotch Bonnet (IRE) **S. Manana**
34 **IFRIKA,** ch f Iffraaj—Poyle Caitlin (IRE) **S. Manana**
35 **INTIMIDATOR (IRE),** b c Intikhab (USA)—Zither **S. Manana**
36 **KYLLACHY GLEN,** b f Kyllachy—Precious Secret (IRE) **S. Manana**
37 B f Medaglia d'oro (USA)—Love of Dubai (USA) **Mr M. Al Shafar**
38 **MEDALLERO (USA),** b c Medaglia d'oro (USA)—Rajeem **S. Manana**
39 **MEDICEAN QUEEN (IRE),** b f Medicean—Qui Moi (CAN) **S. Manana**
40 **NEW STREAM (IRE),** b c New Approach (IRE)—Shimna **S. Manana**
41 **PASTORAL WITNESS,** b f Pastoral Pursuits—Witness **S. Manana**
42 **PICCOLO MOON,** ch c Piccolo—Fleeting Moon **S. Manana**
43 **QUIZA,** b f Major Cadeaux—Quiz Show **S. Manana**
44 **REGAL SULTANA,** ch f New Approach (IRE)—Calakanga **S. Manana**
45 **RIZEENA (IRE),** b f Iffraaj—Serena's Storm (USA) **Sheikh R. D. Al Maktoum**
46 **SAMTU (IRE),** b c Teofilo (IRE)—Samdaniya **S. Manana**
47 **SLEEPING PRINCESS (IRE),** ch f Dalakhani (IRE)—Savignano **S. Ali**
48 **STEALTH MISSILE (IRE),** b f Invincible Spirit (IRE)—Wing Stealth (IRE) **S. Manana**
49 **STREET FORCE (USA),** b c Street Cry (USA)—Maskunah (IRE) **S. Manana**
50 **SURETY (IRE),** b c Cape Cross (IRE)—Guarantia **S. Manana**
51 **VIRTUAL ROSE,** ch c Virtual—Rosabee (IRE) **S. Manana**
52 **WEEKEND GETAWAY (IRE),** b f Acclamation—Week End **S. Manana**
53 **YUKON GIRL (IRE),** b f Manduro (GER)—Yukon Hope (USA) **S. Manana**

TWO-YEAR-OLDS

54 **ACCLAMARIA,** b f 18/2 Acclamation—
　　　　Grand Slam Maria (FR) (Anabaa (USA)) (16000) **Sheikh J. Al Dalmook Maktoum**
55 B c 27/3 Lope de Vega (IRE)—Atalina (FR) (Linamix (FR)) (25000) **S. Manana**
56 B f 1/3 Aqlaam—Beat As One (Medicean) (3000) **Saif Ali & Saeed H. Altayer**
57 Ch f 11/3 King's Best (USA)—Bint Doyen (Doyen (IRE)) **M. Al Nabouda**
58 B f 22/4 Teofilo (IRE)—Bronwen (IRE) (King's Best (USA)) **Mr A. S. Belhab**
59 B f 3/2 Royal Applause—Chicane (Motivator) (52000) **S. Manana**
60 Ch c 9/4 Approve (IRE)—Date Mate (USA) (Thorn Dance (USA)) (28000) **S. Manana**
61 B f 19/4 Lope de Vega (IRE)—Expectation (IRE) (Night Shift (USA)) (25000) **S. Ali**
62 B f 5/3 Sir Percy—Fin (Groom Dancer (USA)) (38000) **S. Manana**
63 **FURIOUSLY FAST (IRE),** b c 13/3 Fast Company (IRE)—
　　　　Agouti (Pennekamp (USA)) (48000) **Sheikh J. Al Dalmook Maktoum**
64 B c 2/4 Dutch Art—Half Sister (IRE) (Oratorio (IRE)) (58000) **Sheikh R. D. Al Maktoum**
65 B br f 26/3 Invincible Spirit (IRE)—Mazaaya (USA) (Cozzene (USA)) (50000) **S. Ali**
66 Gr f 14/3 Alexandros—Miss Sazanica (FR) (Zafonic (USA)) (22000) **S. Manana**
67 B f 28/4 Iffraaj—Sarmad (USA) (Dynaformer (USA)) (50000) **S. Manana**
68 Ch c 6/3 Lope de Vega (IRE)—Slap Shot (IRE) (Lycius (USA)) (35000) **S. Manana**
69 B f 4 Iffraaj—Street Star (USA) (Street Cry (USA)) (60000) **Sheikh R. D. Al Maktoum**
70 B c 14/4 Hellvelyn—Tee Cee (Lion Cavern (USA)) (32000) **S. Manana**
71 **TEOSROYAL (IRE),** br f 10/3 Teofilo (IRE)—
　　　　Fille de Joie (IRE) (Royal Academy (USA)) (60000) **Sheikh J. Al Dalmook Maktoum**
72 B f 24/4 Teofilo (IRE)—Very Nice (Daylami (IRE)) (30000) **S. Manana**
73 Ch f 13/2 Teofilo (IRE)—West Lorne (USA) (Gone West (USA)) (17000) **S. Manana**
74 B f 26/4 Iffraaj—Wink (Salse (USA)) (32000) **S. Manana**

Other Owners: S. H. Altayer.

Assistant Trainer: Mrs C. E. Brittain

69 MR MEL BRITTAIN, Warthill
Postal: **Northgate Lodge, Warthill, York, YO19 5XR**
Contacts: **PHONE (01759) 371472 FAX (01759) 372915**
E-MAIL email@melbrittain.co.uk WEBSITE www.melbrittain.co.uk

1 **AD VITAM (IRE)**, 6, ch g Ad Valorem (USA)—Love Sonnet **Mr C. J. Bennett**
2 **BALINKA**, 4, b f Bahamian Bounty—Eurolinka (IRE) **Northgate Grey**
3 **BROCKFIELD**, 8, ch g Falbrav (IRE)—Irish Light (USA) **M. A. Brittain**
4 **CARRAGOLD**, 8, b g Diktat—Shadow Roll (IRE) **M. A. Brittain**
5 **DEFENCE COUNCIL (IRE)**, 6, b g Kheleyf (USA)—Miss Gally (IRE) **R. J. Mustill**
6 **DREAM SCENARIO**, 4, b f Araafa (IRE)—Notjustaprettyface (USA) **Northgate Black**
7 **GENEROUS DREAM**, 6, ch m Generous (IRE)—First Harmony **M. A. Brittain**
8 **HUSSAR BALLAD (USA)**, 5, b g Hard Spun (USA)—Country Melody (USA) **M. A. Brittain**
9 **LEES ANTHEM**, 7, b g Mujahid (USA)—Lady Rock **Mr P. J. McMahon**
10 **LUCKY LODGE**, 4, b g Lucky Story (USA)—Melandre **M. A. Brittain**
11 **MARABOUT (IRE)**, 4, b g Haafhd—Nirvana **Koo's Racing Club**
12 **MAYFIELD GIRL (IRE)**, 4, br f One Cool Cat (USA)—Rose of Mooncoin (IRE) **M. A. Brittain**
13 **MISTER MARCASITE**, 4, gr g Verglas (IRE)—No Rehearsal (FR) **S. J. Box**
14 **STEEL STOCKHOLDER**, 8, b g Mark of Esteem (IRE)—Pompey Blue **M. A. Brittain**

THREE-YEAR-OLDS
15 **BRIDGE OF AVON**, b f Avonbridge—Out Like Magic **Northgate Yellow**
16 Ch g Sleeping Indian—Clancassie **R. Peel**
17 **DIFFERENT SCENARIO**, b f Araafa (IRE)—Racina **Northgate Orange**
18 **HOW RUDE**, b f Virtual—My Golly **The How Rude Partnership**
19 **MAYFIELD BOY**, b c Authorized (IRE)—Big Pink (IRE) **M. A. Brittain**
20 **SINGING STAR (IRE)**, b f Iffraaj—Seven Sing (USA) **M. A. Brittain**
21 **SLEEPING STAR**, ch f Sleeping Indian—Silver Purse **M. A. Brittain**
22 **SOOQAAN**, bl g Naaqoos—Dream Day (FR) **Mr D. A. Horner**
23 **WHITE ROSE RUNNER**, b f Virtual—Entrap (USA) **M. A. Brittain**
24 **WILBERFOSS (IRE)**, b g Amadeus Wolf—Pietra Dura **M. A. Brittain**

TWO-YEAR-OLDS
25 B c 22/3 Monsieur Bond (IRE)—Knavesmire (IRE) (One Cool Cat (USA)) (1523) **M. A. Brittain**
26 B c 10/4 Monsieur Bond (IRE)—Labba (Tiger Hill (IRE))
27 B c 14/3 Denounce—Lord Conyers (IRE) (Inzar (USA)) **Lord Conyers Partnership**
28 B c 23/4 Monsieur Bond (IRE)—Melandre (Lujain (USA)) (761) **M. A. Brittain**
29 B f 7/3 Holy Roman Emperor (IRE)—Noble Penny (Pennekamp (USA)) (3500)

Other Owners: Mr R T Adams, Mr J Allan, Mr Mel Brittain, Mr Paul Chambers, Mr L Chambers, Mr & Mrs N Dobbs, Mr & Mrs M Foster, Mrs F Godson, Mr J Gunn, Mr S Imeson, Mr J. Jarvis, Mr M Laws, Mr Richard Mustill, Mr G Pritchard, Mr D C Rayment, Mr H Redhead, Mr C Sim, Mr Kristian Strangeway, Mr S Taylor, Mrs Chelle Thirsk, Mr Donald B. White, Mr G Wilson, Mr N Wilson.

Head Lad: Neil Jordan

Apprentice: Kenny Corbett, Robert Dodsworth.

70 LADY BROOKE, Llandrindod Wells
Postal: **Tyn-y-Berth Farm, Dolau, Llandrindod Wells, Powys, LD1 5TW**
Contacts: **PHONE (01597) 851190 MOBILE (07977) 114834**
E-MAIL suebrooke@live.co.uk

1 **AHCOMERETOME (IRE)**, 9, ch g Oscar Schindler (IRE)—Call Me Over (IRE) **Lady Brooke**
2 **FREE WORLD (FR)**, 10, b g Lost World (IRE)—Fautine (FR) **Lady Brooke**
3 **IOUASCORE (IRE)**, 7, br g Craigsteel—Dottie Digger (IRE) **Lady Brooke**
4 **RADUIS BLEU (FR)**, 9, gr g Dadarissime (FR)—Regence Bleue (FR) **Lady Brooke**
5 **THE GENERAL LEE (IRE)**, 12, b br g Accordion—Catrionas Castle (IRE) **Lady Brooke**

Assistant Trainer: Lorna Brooke (07786) 962911

Amateur: Miss Lorna Brooke.

71 MR CHARLIE BROOKS, Chipping Norton
Postal: **Castle Barn Farm, Churchill, Chipping Norton, Oxfordshire, OX7 6RA**
Contacts: **MOBILE (07778) 476759**

1 HOPSTRINGS, 6, ch m Sulamani (IRE)—Hop Fair **Mrs S M & Mr G A Newell**
2 INSTAGRAMHER, 4, b f Beat All (USA)—Follow My Leader (IRE) **S. M. Eaton**
3 THEDRINKYMEISTER (IRE), 5, b g Heron Island (IRE)—Keel Row **Mr T. F. Lacey**

Other Owners: Mrs S. M. Newell, Mr G. A. Newell.

72 MR ROY BROTHERTON, Pershore
Postal: **Mill End Racing Stables, Netherton Road, Elmley Castle, Pershore, Worcestershire, WR10 3JF**
Contacts: **PHONE/FAX (01386) 710772 MOBILE (07973) 877280**

1 BASLE, 7, b m Trade Fair—Gibaltarik (IRE) **Mrs W. A. Brotherton**
2 DAVID'S SECRET, 4, ch g Sakhee's Secret—Mozie Cat (IRE) **Mrs W. A. Brotherton**
3 JOE BUGG (IRE), 5, b g Presenting—Four Fields (IRE) **Mr J. D. Hickman**
4 LADYDOLLY, 6, b m Kyllachy—Lady Pekan **P. S. J. Croft**
5 LOUIS VEE (IRE), 6, b br g Captain Rio—Mrs Evans (IRE) **Mrs P A Wallis & Mr M A Geobey**
6 MAXDELAS (FR), 8, ch g Sabrehill (USA)—Quendora (FR) **Mrs C. A. Newman**
7 PRINCE FREDDIE, 6, b g Red Ransom (USA)—Pitcroy **Mrs T. J. Byrne**
8 STONECRABSTOMORROW (IRE), 11, b g Fasliyev (USA)—Tordasia (IRE) **Miss N. Carroll**
9 TAWSEEF (IRE), 6, b g Monsun (GER)—Sahool **Millend Racing Club**
10 WEST COAST DREAM, 7, b g Oasis Dream—Californie (IRE) **Miss E. J. Byrd**

Other Owners: Mr Roy Brotherton, Mr M. A. Geobey, Mr T. L Martin, Mrs P. A. Wallis.

Assistant Trainer: Justin Brotherton

Jockey (flat): Tom Eaves. **Conditional:** Ryan Hatch. **Amateur:** Mr Sam Drinkwater, Mr Chris Martin.

73 MR ALAN BROWN, Malton
Postal: **Lilac Farm, Yedingham, Malton, North Yorkshire, YO17 8SS**
Contacts: **PHONE (01944) 728090 FAX (01944) 728071 MOBILE (07970) 672845**
E-MAIL ad.brownn@globaluk.net

1 BLUE SEA OF IBROX (IRE), 6, gr m Subtle Power (IRE)—Jerpoint Rose (IRE) **Rangers Racing**
2 FAIR BUNNY, 7, b m Trade Fair—Coney Hills **Mrs S. Johnson**
3 FITZOLINI, 8, b g Bertolini (USA)—Coney Hills **Mrs S. Johnson**
4 JEBEL TARA, 9, b g Diktat—Chantilly (FR) **Miss E. Johnston**
5 LADY IBROX, 4, b f Ishiguru (USA)—Last Impression **Rangers Racing**
6 LADY MARGAEUX (IRE), 4, b f Redback—Storm Lady (IRE) **A. Brown**
7 LAZARUS BELL, 4, ch g Bahamian Bounty—Snake's Head **Mr F. E. Reay**
8 MARCIANO (IRE), 4, b g Pivotal—Kitty Matcham (IRE) **Formulated Polymer Products Ltd**
9 MCMONAGLE (USA), 6, ch g Mizzen Mast (USA)—Dippers (USA) **Mr D. J. Ellis**
10 MEANDMYSHADOW, 6, ch m Tobougg (IRE)—Queen Jean **G. Morrill**
11 MISS MOHAWK (IRE), 5, ch m Hawk Wing (USA)—Karmafair (IRE) **Mrs M. A. Doherty**
12 O CROTAIGH (IRE), 10, b g Beneficial—Jerpoint Rose (IRE) **Mr D. J. Sturdy**
13 ONLY FOR YOU, 4, b f Elusive City (USA)—Enlisted (IRE) **B Selective Partnership**
14 RED SHADOW, 5, b m Royal Applause—Just A Glimmer **S. E. Pedersen**
15 REDALANI (IRE), 4, b f Redback—Zafaraya (IRE) **S. E. Pedersen**
16 RIQUET THE KING (FR), 5, b g Laveron—Brave Chartreuse (FR) **Mr D. J. Sturdy**
17 SAB LE BEAU (FR), 5, b g Sabiango (GER)—La Peliniere (FR) **Mr D. J. Sturdy**
18 SIMPLE JIM (FR), 10, b g Jimble (FR)—Stop The Wedding (USA) **Direct Racing Partnership**
19 SPIEKEROOG, 8, ch g Lomitas—Special **Mr D. J. Sturdy**

Other Owners: Mr C. Charlton, Mrs W. A. D. Craven, Mr T. P. Curry, R. Hartley, Mr S. R. H. Turner, Mr J. T. Winter.

74 **MR ANDI BROWN, Newmarket**
Postal: **Southfields Stables, Hamilton Road, Newmarket, Suffolk, CB8 7JQ**

1 **HOLLI DEYA,** 4, b f Halling (USA)—Never Say Deya **Miss L. Knocker**
2 **RED SHUTTLE,** 7, b g Starcraft (NZ)—Red Azalea **Miss L. Knocker**
3 **SUMMER ECHO,** 4, b f Echo of Light—Summer Cry (USA) **Miss L. Knocker**

THREE-YEAR-OLDS

4 Ro g Araafa (IRE)—Cape Maya **Miss L. Knocker**

75 **MR DAVID BROWN, Averham**
Postal: **The Old Stables, Averham Park, Newark, Nottinghamshire, NG23 5RU**
Contacts: **PHONE (01636) 613793 MOBILE (07889) 132931**
E-MAIL david@davidbrownracing.com

1 **AZRUR (IRE),** 4, b g Sir Percy—Tiger Spice **J. C. Fretwell**
2 **FIRE EYES,** 4, b c Exceed And Excel (AUS)—Wunders Dream (IRE) **Qatar Racing Limited**
3 **GLEN MOSS (IRE),** 5, b h Moss Vale (IRE)—Sail With The Wind **J. C. Fretwell**
4 **GUISING,** 5, ch g Manduro (GER)—Trick Or Treat **Mr P. Onslow & Mr I. Henderson**
5 **HOLLOWINA,** 4, ch f Beat Hollow—Trick Or Treat **P. Onslow**
6 **PUCKER UP,** 4, b f Royal Applause—Smooch **J. C. Fretwell**
7 **RUBY'S DAY,** 5, ch m Vital Equine (IRE)—Isabella's Best (IRE) **Mrs R. A. Archer**

THREE-YEAR-OLDS

8 **CAPTAIN MIDNIGHT (IRE),** b c Bushranger (IRE)—Beverley Macca **D. A. West**
9 **CLUMBER STREET,** ch c Compton Place—Tinnarinka **J. C. Fretwell**
10 **HUSTLE BUSTLE (IRE),** b f Elusive City (USA)—Coachhouse Lady (USA) **J. C. Fretwell**
11 **ILLUMINATING DREAM (IRE),** b f High Chaparral (IRE)—Massada **Qatar Racing Limited**
12 **MUNFALLET (IRE),** b g Royal Applause—Princess Mood (GER) **J. C. Fretwell**
13 **ROSTRUM FAREWELL,** b g Royal Applause—Acicula (IRE) **J. C. Fretwell**
14 **SAMHAIN,** b g Compton Place—Athboy Nights (IRE) **J. C. Fretwell**
15 **SIR JACK LAYDEN,** b c Sir Percy—Barawin (IRE) **Ron Hull, David Brown & Clive Watson**
16 **WIND FIRE (USA),** b f Distorted Humor (USA)—A P Dream (USA) **Qatar Racing Limited**

TWO-YEAR-OLDS

17 Ch c 9/4 Kyllachy—Alchemy (IRE) (Sadler's Wells (USA)) (38095) **J. C. Fretwell**
18 B c 2/4 Pastoral Pursuits—All The Nines (IRE) (Elusive City (USA)) (32380) **J. C. Fretwell**
19 Ch f 15/2 Kheleyf (USA)—Angry Bark (USA) (Woodman (USA)) (11428) **J. C. Fretwell**
20 Ch f 17/3 Makfi—Belle Allemande (CAN) (Royal Academy (USA)) **Mrs M. O'Sullivan**
21 B c 23/3 Acclamation—Benedicte (IRE) (Galileo (USA)) (52000) **J. C. Fretwell**
22 B c 19/5 Medicean—China (Royal Academy (USA)) (24000) **Mr D. H. Brown**
23 B f 7/3 Makfi—Common Knowledge (Rainbow Quest (USA)) **Qatar Racing Limited**
24 **GRAZED KNEES (IRE),** b c 1/4 Majestic Missile (IRE)—Carpet Lover (IRE) (Fayruz) (36190) **J. C. Fretwell**
25 Ch c 12/4 Stimulation (IRE)—Inya Lake (Whittingham (IRE)) **J. C. Fretwell**
26 B f 11/4 Kyllachy—Isis (USA) (Royal Academy (USA)) (16190) **J. C. Fretwell**
27 B c 2/4 Arcano (IRE)—Keritana (FR) (One Cool Cat (USA)) (48000) **J. C. Fretwell**
28 B c 6/5 Stimulation (IRE)—Least Said (USA) (Trempolino (USA)) (16190) **Qatar Racing Limited**
29 Ch f 5/4 Makfi—Nadeszhda (Nashwan (USA)) **Qatar Racing Limited**
30 Ch f 30/3 Dutch Art—Paquerettza (FR) (Dr Fong (USA)) **Mr L. C. Sigsworth**
31 B f 18/4 Makfi—Primo Heights (Primo Valentino (IRE)) **Qatar Racing Limited**
32 **PRINCE BONNAIRE,** b c 20/3 Kheleyf (USA)—Sparkling Clear (Efisio) (14285) **D. A. West**
33 Ch f 22/4 Dutch Art—Quadri (Polish Precedent (USA)) (17142) **J. C. Fretwell**
34 B c 12/3 Azamour (IRE)—Sioduil (IRE) (Oasis Dream) (45000) **Qatar Racing Limited**
35 C 2/3 Kheleyf (USA)—Spate Rise (Speightstown (USA)) **P. Onslow**
36 B c 26/4 Vale of York (IRE)—Strobinia (IRE) (Soviet Star (USA)) (22000) **J. C. Fretwell**
37 B c 4/3 Fastnet Rock (AUS)—Swan Wings (Bahamian Bounty) (38000) **J. C. Fretwell**
38 B c 29/4 Archipenko (USA)—Trick Or Treat (Lomitas) **P. Onslow**
39 **X RAISE (IRE),** gr f 14/3 Aussie Rules (USA)—Raise (USA) (Seattle Slew (USA)) **P. Onslow**

MR DAVID BROWN - Continued

Other Owners: Mr Adrian Archer, Mr Barry Archer, Mr D. H. Brown, Mr Graham Goforth, Mr S. Halsall, I. Henderson, Mr R. Hull, Mr G. Middlebrook, Mr Peter Onslow, Mr Ian Raeburn, Mr L C Sigsworth, Mr C. Watson.

Assistant Trainer: Dushyant Dooyea

Jockey (flat): Harry Bentley, Philip Makin, Jamie Spencer, Robert Winston. **Apprentice:** Claire Murray.

---

76 | **MR GARY BROWN, Wantage**
Postal: **50 Child Street, Lambourn, Hungerford, Berkshire, RG17 8NZ**
Contacts: **MOBILE (07545) 915253**
E-MAIL gbrownracing@hotmail.co.uk

1 HILALI (IRE), 5, b g Sakhee (USA)—Mufradat (IRE) **J. P. McManus**
2 ILEWIN KIM, 8, b g Grape Tree Road—Bridepark Rose (IRE) **T. J. Segrue**
3 O'GORMAN, 5, b g Sleeping Indian—Harryana **We Haven't Told The Wives Syndicate**
4 PETIT ECUYER (FR), 8, b g Equerry (USA)—Petite Majeste (FR) **Mr F. Michael**

THREE-YEAR-OLDS
5 DOVE MOUNTAIN (IRE), b c Danehill Dancer (IRE)—Virginia Waters (USA) **G. Brown**

Other Owners: Mr P. Curtin, Mr P. J. Fahy, Mr O. Hynes.

Jockey (flat): Liam Keniry. **Jockey (NH):** A P McCoy, Jamie Moore. **Conditional:** Joshua Moore.

---

77 | **MR REGINALD BROWN, Abergavenny**
Postal: **The Firs, Grosmont, Abergavenny, Gwent, NP7 8LY**
Contacts: **PHONE (01873) 821278**

1 KAGOUILLOT (FR), 5, gr g Kaldounevees (FR)—Espoir de Mazere (IRE) **R. L. Brown**
2 ROSES LEGEND, 9, b g Midnight Legend—Graig Hill Rose **S. R. Brown**
3 UMORISTIC (FR), 6, gr g Baroud d'honneur (FR)—Canlastou (FR) **R. L. Brown**

---

78 | **MISS MICHELLE BRYANT, Lewes**
Postal: **Bevern Bridge Farm Cottage, South Chailey, Lewes, East Sussex, BN8 4QH**
Contacts: **PHONE/FAX (01273) 400638 MOBILE (07976) 217542**

1 CORLOUGH MOUNTAIN, 10, ch g Inchinor—Two Step **Miss M. P. Bryant**
2 HAWK GOLD (IRE), 10, ch g Tendulkar (USA)—Heiress of Meath (IRE) **Miss M. P. Bryant**
3 ZUWAAR, 9, b g Nayef (USA)—Raheefa (USA) **Miss M. P. Bryant**

Amateur: Miss M. P. Bryant.

---

79 | **MRS KATE BUCKETT, Bishops Waltham**
Postal: **Woodlocks Down Farm, Upham, Bishops Waltham, Hampshire, SO32 1JN**
Contacts: **PHONE (01962) 777557**

1 BACKHOMEINDERRY (IRE), 9, b g Oscar (IRE)—Foyle Wanderer (IRE) **Mrs K. A. Buckett**
2 JOIN THE NAVY, 9, b g Sea Freedom—Join The Parade **Mrs K. A. Buckett**
3 UPHAM ATOM, 11, b g Silver Patriarch (IRE)—Upham Lady **Mrs K. A. Buckett**
4 UPHAM RUNNING (IRE), 6, b g Definite Article—Tara Brooch (IRE) **Mrs K. A. Buckett**

Jockey (NH): Mark Grant, Liam Treadwell. **Amateur:** Miss Chloe Boxall.

80 **MR BOB BUCKLER, Crewkerne**
Postal: **Higher Peckmoor, Henley, Crewkerne, Somerset, TA18 8PQ.**
As From 1st May 2014: Gibb Hill, Courtway, Spaxton, Bridgwater, Somerset, TA5 1DR
Contacts: **PHONE** (01278) 671268 **MOBILE** (07785) 773957
E-MAIL rbuckler@btconnect.com **WEBSITE** www.robertbucklerracing.co.uk

1 **BALLYEGAN (IRE),** 9, b g Saddlers' Hall (IRE)—Knapping Princess (IRE) **Ballyegan Partnership**
2 **DIGGER'S MATE,** 6, b g General Gambul—Miss Diskin (IRE) **M. J. Forrester**
3 **NEVER SAYS NEVER,** 6, b g Tamure (IRE)—Quick Exit **Mr R. Hall**
4 **SAINT PERAY (FR),** 8, b g Fragrant Mix (IRE)—Gintonique (FR) **Strictly Come Racing**
5 **SOMERSET LIAS (IRE),** 9, b g Golan (IRE)—Presenting Gayle (IRE) **P. L. Hart**
6 **THE HAPPY WARRIOR,** 6, b g Luso—Martomick **N. Elliott**
7 **TINKER TIME (IRE),** 6, b g Turtle Island (IRE)—Gypsys Girl (IRE) **Golden Cap**
8 **UGOLIN DE BEAUMONT (FR),** 6, b g Alberto Giacometti (IRE)—Okarina de Beaumont (FR) **A. J. Norman**

Other Owners: Mr R. H. Buckler, Mr D. R. Fear, Mrs Clare Lewis, Mr Nick Robinson, Mrs H. E. Shane.

Head Lad: Giles Scott (07774) 033246

Jockey (NH): Liam Heard, Sam Jones, Gerard Tumelty. **Conditional:** Giles Hawkins, Gary Derwin.

---

81 **MR MARK BUCKLEY, Stamford**
Postal: **Potters Hill Stables, Morkery Lane, Castle Bytham, Stamford, Lincolnshire, NG33 4SP**
Contacts: **OFFICE** (01780) 411158 **MOBILE** (07808) 360488
E-MAIL markbuckley215@btinternet.com

1 **LIBERTY SHIP,** 9, b g Statue of Liberty (USA)—Flag **David Lockwood & Fred Lockwood**
2 **ORIENTAL CAVALIER,** 8, ch g Ishiguru (USA)—Gurleigh (IRE) **X8 Racing Partnership 2**
3 **STEELCUT,** 10, b g Iron Mask (USA)—Apple Sauce **Potters Hill Racing**
4 **STEVIE GEE (IRE),** 10, b g Invincible Spirit (IRE)—Margaree Mary (CAN) **Livvys Racing Group**

Other Owners: M. A. Buckley, Mr P. Edwards, D. J. Lockwood, Mr F. M. Lockwood.

Assistant Trainer: Kim Buckley

---

82 **MR DAI BURCHELL, Ebbw Vale**
Postal: **Drysiog Farm, Briery Hill, Ebbw Vale, Gwent, NP23 6BU**
Contacts: **PHONE** (01495) 302551 **MOBILE** (07980) 482860

1 **CRUCHAIN (IRE),** 11, ch g Shernazar—Mack Tack (IRE) **Mr & Mrs A. J. Mutch**
2 **FLORIDA BEAT,** 4, b g Passing Glance—Florida Heart **Mr C. J. Friel**
3 **FUSE WIRE,** 7, b g Tamayaz (CAN)—Zaffaranni (IRE) **Mrs G. A. Davies**
4 **MISTER FANTASTIC,** 8, ch g Green Tune (USA)—Lomapamar **Mrs J. K. Bradley**
5 **NOTABOTHERONME (IRE),** 12, b br g Religiously (USA)—Kylogue's Delight **W. D. Burchell**
6 **ONE FOR THE BOSS (IRE),** 7, b g Garuda (IRE)—Tell Nothing (IRE) **J. E. Mutch**
7 **OUT OF NOTHING,** 11, br m Perryston View—Loves To Dare (IRE) **Mr J. Rees**
8 **RATIFY,** 10, br g Rakaposhi King—Sea Sky **Mr J. J. King**
9 **REBECCAS CHOICE (IRE),** 11, b g Religiously (USA)—Carolin Lass (IRE) **J. E. Mutch**
10 **SARAHS DOLL,** 6, b m Tatters—The Robe **Miss S. Carter**
11 **SHOMBERG,** 5, b g Bahamian Bounty—Qilin (IRE) **T. R. Pearson**
12 **SPINNING WATERS,** 8, b g Vettori (IRE)—Secret Waters **B. M. G. Group**

THREE-YEAR-OLDS

13 **SYMPHONY OF PEARLS,** b f Lucarno (USA)—Echostar **T. R. Pearson**

TWO-YEAR-OLDS

14 **SYMPHONY OF ANGELS,** b g 6/4 Sulamani (IRE)—Flying Lion (Hunting Lion (IRE)) **T. R. Pearson**
15 **SYMPHONY OF HEAVEN,** b g 13/3 Sulamani (IRE)—Echostar (Observatory (USA)) **T. R. Pearson**

Other Owners: Mr W. R. A. Davies, Mrs S. Mutch, Mr A. J. Mutch, Mr D. H. Protheroe.

Assistant Trainer: Ruth Burchell

Jockey (flat): Sam Hitchcott. **Jockey (NH):** Robert Dunne, Charlie Wallis. **Conditional:** Robert Williams. **Amateur:** Mrs Alex Dunn, Miss Sarah Lewis, Mr Nick Williams, Mr Frank Windsor Clive.

83 MR PAUL BURGOYNE, Wincanton
Postal: **Knowle Rock, Shepton Montague, Wincanton, Somerset, BA9 8JA**
Contacts: **PHONE (01963) 32138 MOBILE (07894) 081008**
E-MAIL knowlerockracing@hotmail.co.uk

1 **DARK AGES (IRE)**, 5, gr m Dark Angel (IRE)—Prosaic Star (IRE) **Mrs H. Adams**
2 **FIRE KING**, 8, b g Falbrav (IRE)—Dancing Fire (USA) **Knowle Rock Racing**
3 **FLEMISH DANCER**, 4, ch f Dutch Art—Miss Sure Bond (IRE) **Knowle Rock Racing**
4 **METROPOLITAN CHIEF**, 10, b g Compton Place—Miss Up N Go **Mrs C. E. E. Turner**
5 **ORPEN'ARRY (IRE)**, 6, b g Orpen (USA)—Closing Time (IRE) **Knowle Rock Racing**
6 **SIR LOIN**, 13, ch g Compton Place—Charnwood Queen **Mrs C. E. E. Turner**
7 **SNOWY VALLEY**, 5, ch g Three Valleys (USA)—Rasseem (IRE) **P & M Racing**
8 **TAMALETTA (IRE)**, 4, ch f Tamayuz—Annaletta **Mrs Helen Adams & Mr David Prosser**
9 **TEEN AGER (FR)**, 10, b g Invincible Spirit (IRE)—Tarwiya (IRE) **Mrs C. E. E. Turner**
10 **VICKY THE VIKING**, 4, ch f Norse Dancer (IRE)—Rasseem (IRE) **P & M Racing**
11 **WEST LEAKE**, 8, b g Acclamation—Kilshanny **Knowle Rock Racing**

TWO-YEAR-OLDS
12 **WESSEX PRINCE**, ch g 16/2 Three Valleys (USA)—Rasseem (IRE) (Fasliyev (USA)) **P & M Racing**

Other Owners: Mr M. P. Burgoyne, M. G. Hancock, Mrs P. Hancock, Mr D. Prosser.

Assistant Trainer: Mrs Corinna Leigh-Turner

Jockey (flat): Liam Keniry, Jimmy Quinn.

84 MR K. R. BURKE, Leyburn
Postal: **Spigot Lodge, Middleham, Leyburn, North Yorkshire, DL8 4TL**
Contacts: **PHONE (01969) 625088 FAX (01969) 625099 MOBILE (07778) 458777**
E-MAIL karl@karlburke.co.uk **WEBSITE** www.karlburke.co.uk

1 **ANGELS CALLING**, 4, b f Multiplex—Angel Voices (IRE) **Ontoawinner & Mrs E Burke**
2 **BARON RUN**, 4, ch g Bertolini (USA)—Bhima **Mrs E. M. Burke**
3 **BOLD MARC (IRE)**, 12, b g Bold Fact (USA)—Zara's Birthday (IRE) **Mrs E. M. Burke**
4 **BOLD PREDICTION (IRE)**, 4, b g Kodiac—Alexander Eliott (IRE) **Mrs E. M. Burke**
5 **BUZZ LAW (IRE)**, 6, b g Fasliyev (USA)—Buzz Two (IRE) **Mr Mark James & Mrs Elaine Burke**
6 **DARING PURSUIT**, 4, br f Pastoral Pursuits—Daring Destiny **Mr J Wilson & Mrs E Burke**
7 **DOYNOSAUR**, 7, b m Doyen (IRE)—Daring Destiny **Mr R Bailey & Mrs E Burke**
8 **FAIR LOCH**, 6, gr g Fair Mix (IRE)—Ardentinny **Mr B Fulton & Mrs E Burke**
9 **FRONTLINE PHANTOM (IRE)**, 7, b g Noverre (USA)—Daisy Hill **Ontoawinner & Mrs E Burke**
10 **GENERAL TIBERIUS**, 5, ch g Selkirk (USA)—Eminencia **McMahon Thoroughbreds & Mark Bates**
11 **GEORGIAN BAY (IRE)**, 4, b g Oratorio (IRE)—Jazzie (FR) **Market Avenue Racing Club & Mrs E Burke**
12 **HOT RIGHT NOW**, 4, ch f Sleeping Indian—American Rouge (IRE) **Mrs E. M. Burke**
13 **ISHIKAWA (IRE)**, 6, b g Chineur (FR)—Nautical Light **Mr T. J. Dykes**
14 **KRUPSKAYA (FR)**, 4, b f Dubai Destination (USA)—Willows World **Norton Common Farm & Mrs E Burke**
15 **LOKI'S STRIKE**, 4, ch g Firebreak—Citron **The Mount Racing Club,J O'Shea & S Hunt**
16 **MEDIA HYPE**, 7, b h Tiger Hill (IRE)—Hyperspectra **Light Valley Stud & Mrs E Burke**
17 **MIAMI GATOR (IRE)**, 7, ch g Titus Livius (FR)—Lovere **Ontoawinner & Mrs E Burke**
18 **ODELIZ (IRE)**, 4, ch f Falco (USA)—Acatama (USA) **McMahon Thoroughbreds Ltd & Mrs E Burke**
19 **REVE DE NUIT (USA)**, 8, ch g Giant's Causeway (USA)—My Dream Castles (USA) **Mrs Z. Wentworth**
20 **RIVELLINO**, 4, b g Invincible Spirit (IRE)—Brazilian Bride (IRE) **Mrs M. Bryce**
21 **STEPPING AHEAD (FR)**, 4, ch g Footstepsinthesand—Zghorta (USA) **Mr Mark James & Mrs Elaine Burke**
22 **TRIXIE MALONE**, 3, b f Ishiguru (USA)—Lady-Love **Mrs E. M. Burke**
23 **YEEOOW (IRE)**, 5, b g Holy Roman Emperor (IRE)—Taraya (IRE) **Mr R. Lee & Mrs E. Burke**
24 **YOURARTISONFIRE**, 4, ch c Dutch Art—Queens Jubilee **Mr J O'Shea,Mr W Rooney & Ontoawinner**

THREE-YEAR-OLDS
25 **ALFAAYZA (IRE)**, b f Dansili—Ayun (USA) **Mrs M. Cantillon**
26 **ARAN SKY (IRE)**, b g Arakan (USA)—Fayr Sky (IRE) **Owners For Owners: Aran Sky**
27 **BALTIC FIRE (IRE)**, b g Baltic King—Teutonic (IRE) **McKeown & Wotherspoon**
28 **BETTY BERE (FR)**, b f Peer Gynt (JPN)—Monatora (FR) **Market Avenue Racing Club & Mrs E Burke**
29 **CASCADIA (IRE)**, br f Mujadil (USA)—Tucum (IRE) **Mrs E. M. Burke**
30 **DALMARELLA DANCER**, gr f Mastercraftsman (IRE)—Ting A Greeley **Dr M E Glaze & Mr I Mcinnes**
31 B f Falco (USA)—Diamond Life (FR) **Mrs E. M. Burke**

MR K. R. BURKE - Continued

32 **EVA CLARE (IRE)**, b f Majestic Missile (IRE)—College of Arms **The Mount Racing Club & Mrs E Burke**
33 **HEAVENLY RIVER (FR)**, b f Stormy River (FR)—Aaliyah (GER) **Ontoawinner, M Hulin & E Burke**
34 **JAEGER CONNOISSEUR (IRE)**, b f Art Connoisseur (IRE)—
Nilassiba **Market Avenue Racing Club & Mrs E Burke**
35 **JAEGER TRAIN (IRE)**, b g Captain Rio—Marigold (FR) **Market Avenue Racing Club & Mrs E Burke**
36 **LILBOURNE LASS**, ch f Pastoral Pursuits—Talampaya (USA) **D. W. Armstrong**
37 **MR MATTHEWS (IRE)**, b g Diamond Green (FR)—Five Sisters **Living The Dream Partnership & Mrs Burke**
38 **RISING BREEZE (FR)**, b c Shirocco (GER)—Moon Tree (FR) **Market Avenue Racing Club Ltd**
39 **ROMANTIC BLISS (IRE)**, b f Holy Roman Emperor (IRE)—Thea di Bisanzio (IRE) **Mrs E. M. Burke**
40 **RONYA (IRE)**, b f Bushranger (IRE)—Beenablaw (IRE) **Mr H. J. Strecker**
41 **TICKING KATIE (IRE)**, b f Baltic King—Danccalli (IRE) **Ontoawinner, M Hulin & E Burke**
42 **TRUANCY (IRE)**, b c Intense Focus (USA)—Date Mate (USA) **Market Avenue Racing Club Ltd**
43 **TWO SMART (IRE)**, b f Cape Cross (IRE)—Smartest (IRE) **David & Yvonne Blunt**
44 **WE'LL SHAKE HANDS (FR)**, b g Excellent Art—Amou Daria (FR) **Market Avenue Racing Club & Mrs E Burke**
45 **WITCHY WOMAN**, b f Intikhab (USA)—Lady McBeth (IRE) **Mrs M. Bryce**

TWO-YEAR-OLDS

46 B br c 5/4 Danehill Dancer (IRE)—
Absolute Music (USA) (Consolidator (USA)) (80000) **Mr S O'Sullivan & Mrs E Burke**
47 B f 8/4 Lord Shanakill (USA)—Akarita (IRE) (Akarad (FR)) (5806)
48 Ch c 26/3 Munnings (USA)—Allure d'amour (USA) (Giant's Causeway (USA)) (37978) **Mr H. J. Strecker**
49 B f 1/3 Galileo (IRE)—Alta Anna (FR) (Anabaa (USA)) (90000) **Mr H. J. Strecker**
50 B c 15/4 Dandy Man (IRE)—Altadena Lady (IRE) (Imperial Ballet (IRE)) (14285) **D. W. Armstrong**
51 Gr ro f 25/4 Henrythenavigator (USA)—Always Auditioning (USA) (Mizzen Mast (USA)) (39146) **Mr H. J. Strecker**
52 **ARTHUR MARTINLEAKE (IRE)**, b c 27/2 Alfred Nobel (IRE)—
Golden Shine (Royal Applause) (14761) **Mr M Charge & Mrs E Burke**
53 B c 22/3 Iffraaj—Balladonia (Primo Dominie) (100000) **Mrs M. Bryce**
54 B f 14/3 Vale of York (USA)—Barbera (GER) (Night Shift (USA)) (5420)
55 B f 31/1 Nayef (USA)—Blaenavon (Cadeaux Genereux) (15000) **Mr H. J. Strecker**
56 B c 17/3 Lord Shanakill (USA)—Cannikin (IRE) (Lahib (USA)) (40000)
57 **CAPRIOR BERE (IRE)**, b c 28/3 Peer Gynt (JPN)—
Hush Hush (USA) (Horse Chestnut (SAF)) (15485) **Mrs E. M. Burke**
58 B f 6/2 Kheleyf (USA)—Daring Destiny (Daring March)
59 B f 8/3 Naaqoos—Fire Finch (Halling (USA)) (5032)
60 B f 20/2 Fast Company (IRE)—Gold Blended (IRE) (Goldmark (USA)) (14711)
61 **JOLIEVITESSE (FR)**, b c 16/2 Elusive City (USA)—
Volvoreta (Suave Dancer (USA)) (15485) **Owners For Owners: Jolievitesse**
62 B c 28/3 Equiano (FR)—Khyber Knight (IRE) (Night Shift (USA)) (38095) **D. W. Armstrong**
63 B f 18/2 Artiste Royal (IRE)—Lady Sylvester (USA) (Elusive Quality (USA)) (20131) **Mrs E. M. Burke**
64 **LIBERAL ANGEL (FR)**, b f 15/3 Librettist (USA)—Angel Voices (USA) (Tagula (IRE)) **Mrs E. M. Burke**
65 **LORD BEN STACK (IRE)**, b c 16/3 Dylan Thomas (IRE)—
Beringold (Bering) (38714) **Owners For Owners: Lord Ben Stack**
66 B f 17/3 American Post—Mercredi (FR) (Groom Dancer (USA)) (15485) **Mrs E. M. Burke**
67 Br f 11/3 Alfred Nobel (IRE)—My Girl Lisa (USA) (With Approval (CAN)) (11614)
68 B f 29/1 Excellent Art—Mystical Spirit (IRE) (Xaar) (26666) **Mr H. J. Strecker**
69 B c 29/4 Equiano (FR)—Pure Speculation (Salse (USA)) (26666) **D. W. Armstrong**
70 B f 25/2 Dylan Thomas (IRE)—Ridiforza (FR) (Starborough) (6500)
71 B c 9/2 Royal Applause—Rivalry (Medicean) **D. W. Armstrong**
72 B c 14/4 Champs Elysees—Samar Qand (Selkirk (USA)) (14711) **Mr P Dean & Mrs E Burke**
73 Ch f 29/2 Tamayuz—Sheer Glamour (IRE) (Peintre Celebre (USA)) (54200) **Mr H. J. Strecker**
74 B c 15/4 Captain Rio—The Oldladysays No (IRE) (Perugino (USA)) (16260)
75 B f 25/2 Arch (USA)—Tiz My Time (USA) (Sharp Humor (USA)) (64271) **Mr H. J. Strecker**
76 B f 16/3 Azamour (IRE)—Whos Mindin Who (IRE) (Danehill Dancer (IRE)) (2000)

Other Owners: Mr D. C. Bacon, R. Bailey, Mr M. Bates, Mr D. Blunt, Mrs Y. Blunt, Mrs T. Burns, Mr D. Capperauld, Mr M. Charge, Mr B. Dahl, Mrs A. Dahl, P. Dean, Mr A. N. Eaton, Dr C. I. Emmerson, Mr K. Flanagan, B. N. Fulton, Mr R. J. Gibbs, Dr M. E. Glaze, Mr G. W. Holden, Mr E. J. Hughes, Mr M. A. S. Hulin, Mr S. Hunt, Mr M. J. James, Mr R. Lee, I. McInnes, Mr R. C. McKeown, McMahon Thoroughbreds Ltd, Mr D. P. Meagher, Norton Common Farm Racing Ltd, N. J. O'Brien, Mr J. O'Shea, S. O'Sullivan, Mr W. Rooney, Mr D. S. Truswell, J. C. S. Wilson, Mr J. W. Wotherspoon.

Assistant Trainer: Mrs E. Burke

Jockey (flat): Martin Harley. **Apprentice:** Rob J. Fitzpatrick, Joey Haynes, Brian Treanor.

85 MR KEIRAN BURKE, Warminster
Postal: **Deverill Road, Sutton Veny, Warminster, Wiltshire, BA12 7BY**
Contacts: **PHONE (01935) 823459**

1 BUSINESSMONEY JUDI, 8, ch m Kirkwall—Cloverjay **Business Money Promotions Limited**
2 CAVITE ALPHA (IRE), 8, b g Oscar (IRE)—The Purple Penguin **Keiranwho Partnership**
3 FRUITY BUN, 4, b f Dr Fong (USA)—Little Conker **Withyslade**
4 KIRBYS GLEN (IRE), 12, b g Charente River (IRE)—Silence To Silence (IRE) **P. R. Rodford**
5 MORATAB (IRE), 5, b g Dubai Destination (USA)—Bahr **The Costermongers & A Few More**
6 SALVATOR'S LEGACY (IRE), 5, b g Scorpion (IRE)—Another Whiskey (IRE) **Keiran Burke Racing Club**
7 6, B m Tamure (IRE)—Sound Appeal
8 SPELLBOUND, 5, b m Doyen (IRE)—Kasamba **Withyslade**
9 STEEL A TUNE, 5, gr g Proclamation (IRE)—Skip 'n' Tune (IRE)
10 WELCOMETOTHEJUNGLE, 6, b m Lucky Story (USA)—Kasamba **Withyslade**
11 WHISPERING JACK, 9, b g Beat All (USA)—Ski Shot **Prestige Cars and Couriers**

THREE-YEAR-OLDS
12 B f Royal Applause—Duchcov
13 PLANET ROCK, b c Shirocco (GER)—Demand **Withyslade**

Other Owners: Mr N. Bagwell, Mrs S. L. Bender, Mr R. J. Bender, Mr David Bond, Mr K. M. F. Burke, Mr M. Holloway, Mr J. Palmer, Miss H. Pease, Mr C. P. Rudd.

86 MR HUGH BURNS, Alnwick
Postal: **Rose Cottage, Hedgeley Hall, Powburn, Alnwick, Northumberland, NE66 4HZ**

1 BUN OIR (USA), 7, b br g Seeking The Gold (USA)—Fraulein **Mr H. Burns**
2 GARTH MOUNTAIN, 7, b g Rock of Gibraltar (IRE)—One of The Family **Mr H. Burns**
3 NORTHERN WARRIOR, 6, b g Tamure (IRE)—Rail Cat **Mr H. Burns**
4 OVERPRESENTLY, 6, b m Overbury (IRE)—Coole Presence (IRE) **Mr H. Burns**
5 SOLIS, 8, b g Josr Algarhoud (IRE)—Passiflora **Mr H. Burns**
6 SUNSETTEN (IRE), 10, b g Tendulkar (USA)—Rosy Affair (IRE) **Mr H. Burns**

87 MR JOHN BUTLER, Newmarket
Postal: **The Bungalow, Charnwood Stables, Hamilton Road, Newmarket, Suffolk, CB8 7JQ**
Contacts: **MOBILE (07764) 999743**

1 BLACKTHORN STICK (IRE), 5, b g Elusive City (USA)—Hi Lyla (IRE) **Mr W. J. Dunphy**
2 LOW KEY (IRE), 7, b g Pentire—La Capilla **Mr J. Butler**
3 MINELLA FIVEO (IRE), 6, b g Westerner—Autumn Sky (IRE) **Maxilead Limited**
4 MINELLA FOR VALUE (IRE), 8, br g Old Vic—Nightngale Express (IRE) **Maxilead Limited**
5 MISLEADING PROMISE (IRE), 4, b g Refuse To Bend (IRE)—Farthing (IRE) **Mr J. Butler**
6 MONTANA BELLE (IRE), 4, b f High Chaparral (IRE)—Stiletta **Mr J. Butler**
7 NIBANI (IRE), 7, ch g Dalakhani (IRE)—Dance of The Sea (IRE) **Mr J. Butler**
8 OFFICER IN COMMAND (USA), 8, b br g Officer (USA)—Luv to Stay n Chat (USA) **Mr J. Butler**
9 STAND GUARD, 10, b g Danehill (USA)—Protectress **Maxilead Limited**
10 TIGER REIGNS, 8, b g Tiger Hill (IRE)—Showery **Wildcard Racing Syndicate**

THREE-YEAR-OLDS
11 AUTHENTICITY, b c Authorized (IRE)—Jubilee **Mrs P. Good**
12 DIAMOND LUCY (IRE), b f Diamond Green (FR)—Hi Lyla (IRE) **Mr W. J. Dunphy**

TWO-YEAR-OLDS
13 B c 31/3 Exceed And Excel (AUS)—Tamzin (Hernando (FR)) **Mrs P. Good**

Other Owners: Mr A. J. Bonarius, Mr N. J. Bonarius.

88   MR PADDY BUTLER, Lewes
Postal: **Homewood Gate Racing Stables, Novington Lane, East Chiltington, Lewes, East Sussex, BN7 3AU**
Contacts: **PHONE/FAX (01273) 890124 MOBILE (07973) 873846**
E-MAIL **homewoodgate@aol.com**

1 **ALL OR NOTHIN (IRE)**, 5, b g Majestic Missile (IRE)—Lady Peculiar (CAN) **Miss M. P. Bryant**
2 **CURRAGH DANCER (FR)**, 11, ch g Grand Lodge (USA)—Native Twine **Miss M. P. Bryant**
3 **ESTIBDAAD (IRE)**, 4, b g Haafet (USA)—Star of Siligo (USA) **Miss M. P. Bryant**
4 **GENEROUS JUNE (IRE)**, 6, ch m Generous (IRE)—Outo'theblue (IRE) **C. W. Wilson**
5 **HEADING TO FIRST**, 7, b g Sulamani (IRE)—Bahirah **Homewoodgate Racing Club**
6 **MADRINAS PRINCE (IRE)**, 5, b g Prince Arch (USA)—Madrina **Mr B. C. Rayner**
7 **QUERIDO (GER)**, 10, b g Acatenango (GER)—Quest of Fire (FR) **Homewoodgate Racing Club**
8 **SWEET PICCOLO**, 4, ch g Piccolo—Quality Street **Mr D. M. Whatmough**
9 **WHAT'S FOR TEA**, 9, b m Beat All (USA)—Come To Tea (IRE) **E Lucey-Butler,Chris Wilson,Anne Horrell**

Other Owners: Mrs A. Horrell, Mrs E. Lucey-Butler.

Assistant Trainer: Mrs E Lucey-Butler

Amateur: Miss M. Bryant.

89   MRS BARBARA BUTTERWORTH, Appleby
Postal: **Bolton Mill, Bolton, Appleby-in-Westmorland, Cumbria, CA16 6AL**
Contacts: **PHONE (01768) 361363 MOBILE (07778) 104118**

1 **BELOW THE DECK (IRE)**, 11, b m Stowaway—Clear Bid (IRE) **Mrs B. Butterworth**
2 **FRED BOJANGALS (IRE)**, 12, b g Scribano—Southern Princess **Miss E. Butterworth**
3 **KNICKERBOKERGLORY**, 8, b m Saddlers' Hall (IRE)—Cashmere Lady **Miss E. Butterworth**
4 **KNIGHT VALLIANT**, 11, gr g Dansili—Aristocratique **Mrs B. Butterworth**
5 **THE BRAVETRAVELLER (IRE)**, 11, b g Bravefoot—Morning Nurse (IRE) **Mrs B. Butterworth**
6 **WESTERN BOUND (IRE)**, 13, ch g Presenting—Mid West Girl (IRE) **Miss E. Butterworth**

Assistant Trainer: Miss Elizabeth Butterworth

Amateur: Miss Elizabeth Butterworth.

90   MR NEVILLE BYCROFT, Malton
Postal: **Beverley Farm, Highfield Road, Norton, Malton, North Yorkshire, YO17 9PT**
Contacts: **PHONE (01347) 888641 MOBILE (07802) 763227**

1 **ADIATOR**, 6, b m Needwood Blade—Retaliator **N. Bycroft**
2 **BABY MAC**, 6, b g Presidium—Nishara **N. Bycroft**
3 **DUAL MAC**, 7, br g Paris House—Carol Again **Mrs C. M. Whatley**
4 **EENY MAC (IRE)**, 7, ch g Redback—Sally Green (IRE) **Mrs J. Dickinson**
5 **EIUM MAC**, 5, b g Presidium—Efipetite
6 **FAMA MAC**, 7, b g Fraam—Umbrian Gold (IRE) **Mrs C. M. Whatley**
7 **GURU MAC**, 4, b f Ishiguru—Zacinta (USA) **N. Bycroft**
8 **MAYBEME**, 8, b m Lujain (USA)—Malvadilla (IRE) **Mrs J. Dickinson**
9 **MISU MAC**, 4, b f Misu Bond (IRE)—Umbrian Gold (IRE) **Mrs C. M. Whatley**
10 **SOMETHINGBOUTMARY**, 4, ch f Sleeping Indian—Lochleven **Wildcard Racing Syndicate**
11 **VALENTINE'S GIFT**, 4, b g Presidium—Efipetite **Hambleton Racing Partnership**
12 **WILLBEME**, 6, b m Kyllachy—Befriend (USA) **Mr P. D. Burrow**

Other Owners: Mr A. J. Bonarius, Mr N. J. Bonarius, R. C. Crawford, J. H. Hemy, Mrs E. B. Hughes.

Assistant Trainer: Seb Spencer

Jockey (flat): Jimmy Quinn, Franny Norton.

91 MISS JULIE CAMACHO, Malton

Postal: **Star Cottage, Welham Road, Norton, Malton, North Yorkshire, YO17 9QE**
Contacts: **PHONE (01653) 696205 FAX (01653) 696205 MOBILE (07779) 318135 / (07950) 356440**
E-MAIL julie@jacracing.co.uk WEBSITE www.juliecamacho.com

1 BLACK RIDER (IRE), 4, b g Elnadim (USA)—Barracade (IRE) **Mr N. Gravett**
2 DANDARRELL, 7, b g Makbul—Dress Design (IRE) **Mr J. S. De W. Waller**
3 DIESCENTRIC (USA), 7, b g Diesis—Hawzah **Axom (XVIII)**
4 DUBAI CELEBRATION, 6, b g Dubai Destination (USA)—Pretty Poppy **L Bolingbroke, N Gravett & J Camacho**
5 ILLUSTRIOUS PRINCE (IRE), 7, b g Acclamation—Sacred Love (IRE) **L. Bolingbroke & Partners**
6 KALITHEA, 4, b f Kheleyf (USA)—Baralinka (IRE) **Elite Racing Club**
7 MY SINGLE MALT (IRE), 6, b g Danehill Dancer (IRE)—Slip Dance (IRE) **Mr N. Gravett**
8 REX WHISTLER (IRE), 4, b g Tamayuz—Dangle (IRE) **Axom XXXVIII**
9 TOM SAWYER, 6, b g Dansili—Cayman Sunset (IRE) **Bolingbroke J Howard FAO MerseyR & Ptns**

THREE-YEAR-OLDS

10 GEE SHARP, b g Captain Gerrard (IRE)—Cumbrian Concerto **Axom XLIV**
11 B f U S Ranger (USA)—Hutchinson (USA) **Axom XLVII**
12 PLEASE LET ME GO, ch f Sleeping Indian—Elhida (IRE) **Mr N. Gravett**
13 WILDE INSPIRATION (IRE), ch g Dandy Man (IRE)—Wishing Chair (USA) **Mr & Mrs R. Peck**

Other Owners: Axom, Mr Lee Bolingbroke, Mr Tony Bruce, Mr S. Burrows, Miss Julie Camacho, Mrs S. L. Dale, Mr S. J. Dale, Mr Dan Downie, Mr Nigel Gravett, Mr Brian Hankey, Mr Tony Hill, Mr Graeme Howard, Ms S. M. Jamieson, Miss M. Noden, Mrs Faith O'Connor, Mr J. E. Townend.

Assistant Trainer: Mr S. Brown

Jockey (flat): Tom Eaves, Barry McHugh.

92 MR MARK CAMPION, Malton

Postal: **Whitewell House Stables, Whitewall, Malton, North Yorkshire, YO17 9EH**
Contacts: **PHONE (01653) 692729 FAX (01653) 600066 MOBILE (07973) 178311**
E-MAIL info@markcampion-racing.com WEBSITE www.markcampion-racing.com

1 ALISTORM, 8, b m Bob Back (USA)—Storm In Front (IRE) **Medbourne Racing Club**
2 CHARMING GRACE (IRE), 8, b m Flemensfirth (USA)—Lady Laureate **The Saddlers' Flyers**
3 DESERT NOVA (IRE), 12, ch g Desert King (IRE)—Assafiyah (IRE) **Whitewall Racing**
4 MINKIE MOON (IRE), 6, b g Danehill Dancer (IRE)—Minkova (IRE) **Faulkner West & Co Ltd**
5 SADDLERS' SECRET (IRE), 9, b m Saddlers' Hall (IRE)—Birdless Bush (IRE) **The Saddlers' Flyers**

TWO-YEAR-OLDS

6 COSMIC BLUE (IRE), b f 2/3 Kalanisi (IRE)—Gift of Freedom (IRE) (Presenting) **Mr J. P. Whittaker**

Other Owners: A. M. Campion, Mr V. B. Coleman, D. Hern, Mr G. Nurse, Mr I. T. Stevens.

Assistant Trainer: Mrs F. Campion

93 MS JENNIE CANDLISH, Leek

Postal: **Basford Grange Racing Stables, Basford, Leek, Staffordshire, ST13 7ET**
Contacts: **PHONE (07889) 413639 (07976) 825134 FAX (01538) 360324**
E-MAIL jenniecandlish@yahoo.co.uk WEBSITE www.jenniecandlishracing.co.uk

1 BANREENAHREENKAH (IRE), 4, b f Steppe Dancer (IRE)—Carmencita **A. J. Baxter**
2 BASFORD BEN, 6, b g Trade Fair—Moly (FR) **The Best Club In The World**
3 BASFORD BOB (IRE), 9, b g Bob's Return (IRE)—El Monica (IRE) **A. J. Baxter**
4 BEAUBOREEN (IRE), 7, b g Revoque (IRE)—Roseboreen (IRE) **Mrs R. N. C. Hall**
5 BILLY THE BANDIT (IRE), 6, b g Beneficial—Kilfane (IRE) **Mr M. M. Allen**
6 BOB'S WORLD, 5, b g Multiplex—Vocation (IRE) **Mr R. J. Cant**
7 BRYDEN BOY (IRE), 4, b g Craigsteel—Cailin Vic Mo Cri (IRE) **Alan Baxter & Brian Hall**
8 CHESTERTERN, 7, ch g Karinga Bay—My Tern (IRE) **Mr P. C. Dutton**
9 CROSS KENNON (IRE), 10, b g Craigsteel—Gaelic Million (IRE) **Mr P. & Mrs G. A. Clarke**
10 DECENT LORD (IRE), 10, b g Lord of Appeal—Otorum (IRE) **Mrs J. M. Ratcliff**
11 DETOUR AHEAD, 6, ch m Needwood Blade—My Tern (IRE) **Mr P. C. Dutton**
12 FAIRWEATHER FRIEND, 5, gr m Fair Mix (IRE)—Lucylou (IRE) **Mr P. & Mrs G. A. Clarke**

MS JENNIE CANDLISH - Continued

13 **GOLDEN CALL (IRE)**, 10, b g Goldmark (USA)—Call Me Countess (IRE) **Mr M. M. Allen**
14 6, B br h Vinnie Roe (IRE)—Grannies Pride (IRE) **M. Tucker**
15 **GRANVILLE ISLAND (IRE)**, 7, b g Flemensfirth (USA)—Fox Glen **Mr P. & Mrs G. A. Clarke**
16 **KILKENNY HAVEN (IRE)**, 5, b m Beneficial—Benbradagh Vard (IRE) **Mr M. M. Allen**
17 **LUKEYS LUCK**, 8, b g Cape Town (IRE)—Vitelucy **John Pointon & Sons**
18 **MAOI CHINN TIRE (IRE)**, 7, b g Mull of Kintyre (USA)—Primrose And Rose **A. J. Baxter**
19 **PARTY ROCK (IRE)**, 7, b g Vinnie Roe (IRE)—Garryduff Eile (IRE) **Mrs P. M. Beardmore**
20 **PRIME CONTENDER**, 12, b g Efisio—Gecko Rouge **Mrs F. M. Draper**
21 **ROCKY ISLAND (IRE)**, 6, b g Heron Island (IRE)—Loury The Louse (IRE) **Mr P. & Mrs G. A. Clarke**
22 **ROUGH KING (IRE)**, 5, b g King's Theatre (IRE)—Ringzar (IRE) **Mr P. & Mrs G. A. Clarke**
23 **SLEEPY HAVEN (IRE)**, 4, b g Indian Haven—High Society Girl (IRE) **A. J. Baxter**
24 **SNOWED IN (IRE)**, 5, gr g Dark Angel (IRE)—Spinning Gold **A. J. Baxter & David Cheetham**
25 **TERNTHEOTHERCHEEK**, 5, b m Multiplex—My Tern (IRE) **Mr P. C. Dutton**
26 **TICKET**, 5, b m Revoque—Raffles (FR) **M. Tucker**
27 **WAKE YOUR DREAMS (IRE)**, 6, b g Oscar (IRE)—Rose Karanja **Pam Beardmore & Alan Baxter**
28 **WINTERED WELL (IRE)**, 6, b g Milan—Stratosphere **Mrs K. Hunter**

Other Owners: Mr Alan Baxter, Mrs Pam Beardmore, Mr Peter Clarke, Mrs Gwenda Ann Clarke, Exors of the Late Mr R. N. C. Hall, Mrs R. N. C. Hall.

Assistant Trainer: Alan O'Keeffe

Jockey (flat): Joe Fanning, Paul Hanagan, Sean Quinlan. **Jockey (NH):** Sean Quinlan.

---

94 MR HENRY CANDY, Wantage
Postal: **Kingston Warren, Wantage, Oxfordshire, OX12 9QF**
Contacts: **PHONE (01367) 820276 / 820514 FAX (01367) 820500 MOBILE (07836) 211264**
E-MAIL henrycandy@btconnect.com

1 **ANNAWI**, 4, b f Dubawi (IRE)—Anna of Brunswick **Major M. G. Wyatt**
2 **ANNINA (IRE)**, 4, b f Singspiel—Lysandra (IRE) **The Earl Cadogan**
3 **APRICOT SKY**, 4, ch g Pastoral Pursuits—Miss Apricot **Simon Broke & Partners III**
4 **CAPE PERON**, 4, b g Beat Hollow—Free Offer **The Earl Cadogan**
5 **DINKUM DIAMOND (IRE)**, 6, b h Aussie Rules (USA)—Moving Diamonds **Eight Star Syndicate**
6 **DREAM CATCHER (FR)**, 6, gr g Della Francesca (USA)—Gallopade (FR) **Miss N. M. Haine**
7 **GREY'S ELEGY**, 4, gr g Ishiguru (USA)—Christmas Rose **Henry D. N. B. Candy**
8 **JUST CHARLIE**, 4, b g Piccolo—Siryena **Mrs A D Bourne/ Mr H Candy**
9 **LADY PIMPERNEL**, 4, ch f Sir Percy—Angeleno (IRE) **Henry Candy & Partners II**
10 **MUSIC MASTER**, 4, b c Piccolo—Twilight Mistress **G. A. Wilson**
11 **PEDRO SERRANO (IRE)**, 4, b g Footstepsinthesand—Shaiyadima (IRE) **Six Too Many**
12 **PICABO (IRE)**, 6, b m Elusive City (USA)—Gi La High **T. E. Ford**
13 **SILK ROUTE**, 4, ch f Dubai Destination (USA)—Crinolette (IRE) **D. B. Clark**
14 **SPEEDY WRITER**, 4, b g Byron—Merch Rhyd-Y-Grug **Henry D. N. B. Candy**
15 **THE CONFESSOR**, 7, b g Piccolo—Twilight Mistress **Six Too Many**
16 **TIGHT FIT**, 4, ch f Assertive—Bikini **W. M. Lidsey & H. Candy**
17 **WOOLSTON FERRY (IRE)**, 8, b g Fath (USA)—Cathy Garcia (IRE) **Ms L. Burns**
18 **ZHIGGY'S STARDUST**, 5, bg Zafeen (FR)—Lady Natilda **Henry D. N. B. Candy**

THREE-YEAR-OLDS

19 **BOROUGH BELLE**, ch f Bertolini (USA)—Sheesha (USA) **Mr F C Taylor & Mr H Candy**
20 **CHARLES MOLSON**, b g Monsieur Bond (IRE)—Arculinge **Simon Broke & Partners**
21 **CORNISH PATH**, b f Champs Elysees—Quintrell **The Cornish Path Partnership**
22 **COSETTE (IRE)**, b f Champs Elysees—Luanas Pearl (IRE) **Mr P. A. Deal/Mr H. Candy**
23 **FAURE ISLAND**, b c Myboycharlie (IRE)—Free Offer **The Earl Cadogan**
24 **GREENSIDE**, b c Dubawi (IRE)—Katrina (IRE) **Clayton, Frost, Kebell & Turner**
25 **HALF WAY**, b c Haafhd—Amhooj **Henry D. N. B. Candy**
26 **HALLBECK**, ch f Halling (USA)—Goslar **Major M. G. Wyatt**
27 **JETHOU ISLAND**, ch f Virtual—Lihou Island **Mrs F A Veasey, Mr F. C. Taylor, Mr N. Gossett**
28 **LACOCK**, b c Compton Place—Puya **Girsonfield Ltd**
29 **MARYDALE**, ch f Aqlaam—Mary Goodnight **Major M. G. Wyatt**
30 **PENNINE PANTHER**, b g Notnowcato—Kozmina (USA) **P. A. Deal & Partners**
31 **RAPUNZAL**, b f Mount Nelson—Cinnas Ransom **Port and Brandy Syndicate**

MR HENRY CANDY - Continued

32 **SCARLET SASH,** b f Sir Percy—Scarlet Buttons (IRE) **Henry Candy & Partners III**
33 **SHILLA (IRE),** b f Kodiac—Shimla (IRE) **Henry D. N. B. Candy**
34 **SPRING FLING,** b f Assertive—Twilight Mistress **Six Too Many/T A Frost/ G Wilson**
35 **STEPPE BY STEPPE,** b f Zamindar (USA)—Lixian **Andrew & Rosalind Parker-Bowles**
36 **VALONIA,** ch f Three Valleys (USA)—Descriptive (IRE) **Qatar Racing Limited**
37 **VEILED INTRIGUE,** b f Pastoral Pursuits—Verbal Intrigue (USA) **Mr D B Clark / Mr J J Byrne**
38 **WHITE RUSSIAN,** ch f Sir Percy—Danse Russe **Six Too Many**

TWO-YEAR-OLDS

39 **ALONSOA (IRE),** ch f 3/2 Raven's Pass (USA)—Alasha (IRE) (Baratheea (IRE)) **Patricia J. Burns**
40 **CAPE XENIA,** b f 4/2 Cape Cross (IRE)—Xaphania (Sakhee (USA)) (16000) **Simms, Blackburn & Candy**
41 **CHAIN OF DAISIES,** b f 8/4 Rail Link—Puya (Kris) **Girsonfield Ltd**
42 **EXOPLANET BLUE,** b f 3/5 Exceed And Excel (AUS)—Tut (IRE) (Intikhab (USA)) (25000) **Alison Ruggles**
43 **FLASHY DIVA,** ch f 26/2 Showcasing—
Dazzling View (USA) (Distant View (USA)) (9523) **The Flashy Diva Partnership**
44 **GERALD,** b g 30/4 Bahri (USA)—Gerardina (Generous (IRE)) **Henry D. N. B. Candy**
45 **GLENLYON,** b g 31/3 Thewayyouare (USA)—Helena (Helissio (FR)) **Henry D. N. B. Candy**
46 B f 17/2 Fastnet Rock (AUS)—Her Grace (IRE) (Spectrum (IRE)) **Qatar Racing Limited**
47 **ICONIC (IRE),** b f 13/3 Kodiac—Christa Maria (Alhaarth (IRE)) (30000) **First Of Many Partnership**
48 **LE TORRENT,** ch c 3/3 Sir Percy—Cinnas Ransom (Red Ransom (USA)) (47000) **First Of Many Partnership**
49 Ch f 23/2 Assertive—Level Pegging (IRE) (Common Grounds) (15238) **Lady Whent**
50 **MARAUDER,** b g 21/3 Thewayyouare (USA)—Louise d'arzens (Anabaa (USA)) **Henry D. N. B. Candy**
51 **OAT COUTURE,** b f 11/3 Kyllachy—Oat Cuisine (Mujahid (USA)) **Mrs G. Rowland-Clark**
52 **PERCEIVED,** ch f 24/2 Sir Percy—New Light (Generous (IRE)) (5000) **Candy, Pritchard & Thomas**
53 **PERESTROIKA,** b f 11/2 Sir Percy—Lekka Ding (IRE) (Raise A Grand (IRE)) (8000) **Henry D. N. B. Candy**
54 **PERSICARIA,** br f 26/4 Halling (USA)—Danae (Dansili) **Girsonfield Ltd**
55 **POSTBAG,** b f 27/2 Three Valleys (USA)—Postage Stampe (Singspiel (IRE)) **Dunchurch Lodge**
56 Ch c 18/5 First Trump—Raffelina (USA) (Carson City (USA)) **Mr G. Buck**
57 **SELDOM HEARD,** br g 20/4 Bahri (USA)—Turtle Dove (Tobougg (IRE)) **Henry D. N. B. Candy**
58 **SELFRESPECT,** b f 20/4 Thewayyouare (USA)—Self Esteem (Suave Dancer (USA)) **Henry D. N. B. Candy**
59 B c 18/2 Cape Cross (IRE)—Silent Act (USA) (Theatrical) (32000) **Mr & Mrs R. Scott**
60 **SKYMASTER,** gr c 3/4 Aussie Rules (USA)—Last Slipper (Tobougg (IRE)) (30000) **D. B. Clark**
61 **SOME SHOW,** ch f 2/3 Showcasing—
Dancing Nelly (Shareef Dancer (USA)) (15000) **The Rumble Racing Club & Mr H Candy**
62 **STOIC BOY,** ch c 14/3 Paco Boy (IRE)—Dramatic Turn (Pivotal) **Mrs David Blackburn & Mr M. Blackburn**
63 **TAP SHOES,** ch f 21/4 Equiano (FR)—Ruff Shod (USA) (Storm Boot (USA)) (15000) **D. B. Clark**
64 **TUNNEL CREEK,** b g 11/2 Tobougg (IRE)—Free Offer (Generous (IRE)) **The Earl Cadogan**
65 B c 1/4 Kyllachy—Twilight Mistress (Bin Ajwaad (IRE)) **Mr G. Wilson**
66 **UELE RIVER,** b f 20/2 Refuse To Bend (IRE)—Baddi Heights (FR) (Shirley Heights) **Alison Ruggles**
67 Ro gr f 18/3 Exceed And Excel (AUS)—Whatami (Daylami (IRE)) (20000) **Mr & Mrs David Brown**

Other Owners: Mr Alexander Acloque, Mr N. Agran, Mrs David Blackburn, Mr Simon Broke, Mr J. J. Byrne, Mr Henry Candy, Mr D. B. Clark, Mr S. Clayton, Mr W. R. Collins, Mr A. L. Deal, Mr P A. Deal, Mrs Amanda Dixon, Mr D. J. Erwin, Mr Richard Farquhar, Mr Alexander Frost, Mr T. A. F. Frost, Mr T. Gould, Mr John Inverdale, Mr J. Kebell, Mr T. J. Le Blanc-Smith, Mr W. M. Lidsey, Mr Gerry Lowe, Mr H. McNeill, Mrs Jonathan Moore, Mr D. Norris, Mrs Angela Pinder, Mrs C. M. Poland, Ms J. Ruane, Mr Michael Silver, Mrs Jenny Snowball, Mr F. C. Taylor, Mr Godfrey Wilson, Mr Richard Woods.

Assistant Trainer: David Pinder

MR GRANT CANN, Lower Hamswell
Postal: **Parkfield Farm, Hall Lane, Lower Hamswell, Bath, South Gloucestershire, BA1 9DE**
Contacts: **PHONE (01225) 891674 MOBILE (07968) 271118**

1 **ARCTIC WATCH,** 9, gr g Accondy (IRE)—Watcha (USA) **P. J. Cave**
2 **HOW'S MY FRIEND,** 9, b g Karinga Bay—Friendly Lady **J. G. Cann**
3 **I'M NOT TELLING (IRE),** 6, ch g Definite Article—Incognito (FR) **J. G. Cann**
4 **MASTER TODD (IRE),** 9, ch g Dream Well (FR)—Falika (FR) **The Borris Partnership**

Other Owners: Mr A. R. M. M. Kavanagh, Miss R. McMorrough Kavanagh.

96 **MR DON CANTILLON, Newmarket**
Postal: **10 Rous Road, Newmarket, Suffolk, CB8 8DL**
Contacts: PHONE **(01638) 668507** MOBILE **(07709) 377601**

1 AS I AM (IRE), 6, b m Old Vic—Faucon **D. E. Cantillon**
2 ELEGANT STRIDE (IRE), 4, b f One Cool Cat (USA)—Good Thought (IRE) **D. E. Cantillon**
3 GREEN TO GOLD (IRE), 9, gr g Daylami (IRE)—Alonsa (IRE) **Sir Alex Ferguson & Sotirios Hassiakos**
4 LA ESTRELLA (USA), 11, b g Theatrical—Princess Ellen **D. E. Cantillon**
5 4, B g Presenting—Nivalf **D. E. Cantillon**
6 ODIN (IRE), 6, b g Norse Dancer (IRE)—Dimelight **Mrs C. Reed**
7 OSCARS WAY (IRE), 6, b g Oscar (IRE)—Derrigra Sublime (IRE) **D. E. Cantillon**
8 POINT GUARD (IRE), 6, b g Westerner—Holly'sreturn (IRE) **D. E. Cantillon**
9 THIS IS ME, 6, b g Presenting—Shayzara (IRE) **D. E. Cantillon**
10 TRUCKERS DARLING (IRE), 7, b m Flemensfirth (USA)—Nicat's Daughter (IRE) **Mrs C. Reed**
11 WESTERN WAY (IRE), 5, b g Westerner—Faucon **D. E. Cantillon**

THREE-YEAR-OLDS

12 FAIR ADELAIDE (IRE), b f Holy Roman Emperor (IRE)—Etaaq (IRE) **Mrs C. Reed**

Other Owners: Sir A. Ferguson, S. Hassiakos.

97 **MISS CLARISSA CAROE, Thurleigh**
Postal: **Park End Farm, Robins Folly, Thurleigh, Bedfordshire, MK44 2EQ**
Contacts: PHONE **(01234) 771113** MOBILE **(07974) 483469**

1 BEST BETTE, 9, b m Bob Back (USA)—Gavotte du Cochet (FR) **Miss C. J. E. Caroe**
2 DREAM HONOURS (IRE), 11, b g City Honours (USA)—Kamstreampearl (IRE) **Miss C. J. E. Caroe**
3 HALING PARK (UAE), 8, b m Halling (USA)—Friendly (USA) **Miss C. J. E. Caroe**

98 **MRS RUTH CARR, Stillington**
Postal: **Mowbray House Farm, Easingwold Road, Stillington, York, North Yorkshire, YO61 1LT**
Contacts: PHONE **(01347) 823776 (home) (01347) 821683 (yard)** MOBILE **(07721) 926772**
E-MAIL **ruth@ruthcarrracing.co.uk** WEBSITE **www.ruthcarrracing.co.uk**

1 ABRAHAM MONRO, 4, gr g Kyllachy—Pendulum **I. M. Lynch**
2 AL ENBESS (IRE), 4, b g Kyllachy—Taghreed (IRE) **Mrs M. Chapman**
3 AL MUHEER (IRE), 9, b g Diktat—Dominion Rose (USA) **Antigua Cavaliers & Mrs R Carr**
4 AMAZING BLUE SKY, 8, b g Barathea (IRE)—Azure Lake (USA) **G Scruton, D Williamson & R Carr**
5 BECKERMET, 12, b g Second Empire (IRE)—Razida (USA) **Mrs M. Chapman**
6 CHOSEN ONE (IRE), 9, ch g Choisir (AUS)—Copious (IRE) **Bridget Houghton, Chris Jeffery & Co**
7 CONO ZUR (FR), 7, b g Anabaa (USA)—Alaskan Idol (USA) **Ruth Carr Racing**
8 DUBAI DYNAMO, 9, b g Kyllachy—Miss Mercy (IRE) **The Bottom Liners**
9 ELLAAL, 5, b g Oasis Dream—Capistrano Day (USA) **The Bottom Liners & Paul Saxton**
10 EXOTIC GUEST, 4, ch g Bahamian Bounty—Mamoura (IRE) **Mrs R. A. Carr**
11 FORT BASTION (IRE), 5, b g Lawman (FR)—French Fern (IRE) **Sprint Thoroughbred Racing Ltd**
12 GRAN MAESTRO (USA), 5, ch g Medicean—Red Slippers (USA) **Paul Saxton & The Bottom Liners**
13 HAB REEH, 6, gr g Diktat—Asian Love
14 HADAJ, 5, b g Green Desert (USA)—My Amalie (IRE) **Sprint Thoroughbred Racing Ltd**
15 HEAD SPACE (IRE), 6, b g Invincible Spirit (IRE)—Danzelline **The Bottom Liners & Mrs R. Carr**
16 KERBAAJ (USA), 4, b g Dixie Union (USA)—Mabaahej (USA) **The Bottom Liners & Mrs R. Carr**
17 KING TORUS (IRE), 6, b g Oratorio (IRE)—Dipterous (IRE) **Sprint Thoroughbred Racing Ltd**
18 KLYNCH, 8, b g Kyllachy—Inchcoonan **D. C. Renton**
19 LIGHT THE CITY (IRE), 7, b g Fantastic Light—Marine City (JPN) **Mrs R. A. Carr**
20 LOOK ON BY, 4, gr g Byron—Where's Carol **J. A. Swinburne**
21 MARCUS CAESAR (IRE), 4, b g Antonius Pius (USA)—Skyscape **A. J. Duffield**
22 MESHARDAL (GER), 4, b g Shamardal (USA)—Melody Fair (IRE) **The Hollinbridge Partnership & Ruth Carr**
23 MUTAFAAKIR (IRE), 5, b g Oasis Dream—Moon's Whisper (USA) **Michael Hill**
24 MYSTERIAL, 4, b g Invincible Spirit (IRE)—Diamond Dilemma (IRE) **Sprint Thoroughbred Racing Ltd**
25 ORPSIE BOY (IRE), 11, b g Orpen (USA)—Nordicolini (IRE) **Miss V. A. Church**
26 RED CAPE (FR), 11, b g Cape Cross (IRE)—Muirfield (FR) **Middleham Park Racing LVI**
27 SAN CASSIANO (IRE), 7, b g Bertolini (USA)—Celtic Silhouette (FR) **Mitchell, Jackson and Shaw**

MRS RUTH CARR - Continued

28 **VICTOIRE DE LYPHAR (IRE)**, 7, b g Bertolini (USA)—Victory Peak **The Beer Stalker & Mrs R Carr**
29 **WYLDFIRE (IRE)**, 4, ch g Raven's Pass (USA)—Miss Sally (IRE) **Michael Hill**

THREE-YEAR-OLDS

30 **DREAM SIKA (IRE)**, b g Elnadim (USA)—Enchantment **Michael Hill**
31 **FROSTY THE SNOWMAN (IRE)**, gr g Mastercraftsman (IRE)—
Sleeveless (USA) **Bruce Jamieson, Barbara Dean, Ruth Carr**

Other Owners: Mr S. C. Barker, T. J. E. Brereton, S. B. Clark, Mrs B. I. Dean, J. P. Hames, Miss B. J. Houlston, Mr S. R. Jackson, Mr A. B. Jamieson, Mr C. Jeffery, Mr D. R. Kelly, Dr J. C. Mitchell, Mr P. Newell, T. S. Palin, R J H Limited, P. A. Saxton, Mr G. Scruton, Mr L. D. Shaw, Mr D. J. Williamson, Mr R. W. Wilson.

Jockey (flat): P J McDonald, James Sullivan.

---

99 **MR DECLAN CARROLL, Sledmere**
Postal: **Sledmere House Stables, Sledmere, Driffield, East Yorkshire, YO25 3XG**
Contacts: **PHONE (01377) 236161 FAX (01377) 236161 MOBILE (07801) 553779**
E-MAIL **sledmereracing@hotmail.co.uk**

1 **BAILE ATHA CLIATH (IRE)**, 5, b g Barathea (IRE)—Danielli (IRE) **Dreams**
2 **CAMBRIDGE BEE**, 5, b m Doyen (IRE)—Rock Concert **Steve Ryan & James Stevens**
3 **DUKE OF YORKSHIRE**, 4, b g Duke of Marmalade (IRE)—Dame Edith (FR) **Mr M. Stewart**
4 **GLASGON**, 4, gr g Verglas (IRE)—Miss St Tropez **Mr M. J. Rozenbroek**
5 **INVINCIBLE HERO (IRE)**, 7, b g Invincible Spirit (IRE)—Bridelina (FR) **Mrs S. A. Bryan**
6 **LASTCHANCELUCAS**, 4, b g Ishiguru (USA)—Light of Aragon **C. H. Stephenson & Partners**
7 **MICK SLATES (IRE)**, 5, b g Moss Vale (IRE)—Sonic Night (IRE) **Ormskirk**
8 **MY DESTINATION (IRE)**, 5, b g Dubai Destination (USA)—Gossamer **Mrs S. A. Bryan**
9 **PROPHESY (IRE)**, 5, ch g Excellent Art—Race The Wild Wind (USA) **Mr M. Stewart**
10 **SAVE THE BEES**, 6, b g Royal Applause—Rock Concert **Mr S. P. Ryan**
11 **SOUND AMIGO (IRE)**, 6, b g Iceman—Holly Hayes (IRE) **Mr T. J. McManus**
12 **SWIFTLY DONE (IRE)**, 7, b g Whipper (USA)—Ziffany **Mr D Watts, Miss C King, J Syme & M Syme**
13 **TWO PANCAKES**, 4, b g Compton Place—Fancy Rose (USA) **Mr K. McConnell**
14 **WHOZTHECAT (IRE)**, 7, b g One Cool Cat (USA)—Intaglia (GER) **Mr S. R. Bean**

THREE-YEAR-OLDS

15 **BOUSFIELD**, b g Duke of Marmalade (IRE)—Exodia **Bousfield Boys**
16 **CLASSICAL DIVA**, b f Amadeus Wolf—America Lontana (FR) **Classical Partnership**
17 **DICKIEBIRD (IRE)**, b c Galileo (IRE)—Pieds de Plume (FR) **Mr M. Stewart**
18 **FARANG BER SONG**, b g Selkirk (USA)—Dazzle **L. C. Ibbotson & M. Rozenbroek**
19 B c Montjeu (IRE)—Inkling (USA) **Mr M. Stewart**
20 **MOSSYCOAT**, b f Footstepsinthesand—Tattercoats (FR) **Mondial Racing**
21 **PULL THE PLUG (IRE)**, b f Sleeping Indian—Babylonian **Mr C. J. Harding**
22 **SNOW PRINCE**, gr g Royal Applause—Snowdrops
23 **TWEETY PIE (IRE)**, ch f Rock of Gibraltar (IRE)—Princesse Sonia (FR) **Mr & Mrs J. G. Johnson**

TWO-YEAR-OLDS

24 B c 27/2 Monsieur Bond (IRE)—Artistic License (IRE) (Chevalier (IRE)) (8000) **Ray Flegg**
25 B g 20/4 Champs Elysees—Fairy Steps (Rainbow Quest (USA)) (12000) **Mr S. R. Bean**
26 **FLORRIE (IRE)**, b f 20/4 Baltic King—Folk Kris (Kris Kin (USA)) (774) **Mr M. C. Saunders**
27 B g 24/2 Approve (IRE)—Fruit O'the Forest (IRE) (Shinko Forest (IRE)) (11000) **Dreams**
28 B c 2/4 Hellvelyn—Mis Chicaf (IRE) (Prince Sabo) **Dreams**
29 **MRS BIGGS**, ch f 30/4 Paco Boy (IRE)—Hoh Chi Min (Efisio) (7000) **K MacKay & M. Percival**

Apprentice: Neil Farley, Jason Hart, Luke Leadbitter. **Amateur:** Mr K. Walker.

---

100 **MR TONY CARROLL, Cropthorne**
Postal: **The Cropthorne Stud, Field Barn Lane, Cropthorne, Pershore, Worcestershire, WR10 3LY**
Contacts: **PHONE (01386) 861020 FAX (01386) 861628 MOBILE (07770) 472431**
E-MAIL **a.w.carroll@btconnect.com WEBSITE www.awcarroll.co.uk**

1 **ADMIRABLE ART (IRE)**, 4, b g Excellent Art—Demi Voix **Mr D. S. G. Morgan**
2 **AKDAM (IRE)**, 4, br g Dubai Destination (USA)—Akdara (IRE) **Mr S. Louch**

MR TONY CARROLL - Continued

3 **APPYJACK**, 6, b g Royal Applause—Petrikov (IRE) **Mayden Stud**
4 **ARTE DEL CALCIO**, 5, b g Manduro (GER)—Movie Queen **K. F. Coleman**
5 **ASSERTIVE AGENT**, 4, b f Assertive—Agent Kensington **Wedgewood Estates**
6 **BOSTON BLUE**, 7, b g Halling (USA)—City of Gold (IRE) **Mr B. J. Millen**
7 **CAERWYN**, 4, ch g Pastoral Pursuits—Preference **Property Players**
8 **CANE CAT (IRE)**, 7, b br m One Cool Cat (USA)—Seven Wonders (USA) **J. W. Egan**
9 **CASPIAN PRINCE (IRE)**, 5, ch g Dylan Thomas (IRE)—Crystal Gaze (IRE) **Mr S. Louch**
10 **CHORAL RHYTHM (IRE)**, 4, b f Oratorio (IRE)—Sierra **Longview Stud & Bloodstock Ltd**
11 **DEVOTE MYSELF (IRE)**, 5, b m Kodiac—Hazarama (IRE) **Mr J. Tucker**
12 **EASYDOESIT (IRE)**, 6, b g Iffraaj—Fawaayid (USA) **T. R. Pearson**
13 **EXPANDING UNIVERSE (IRE)**, 7, b g Galileo (IRE)—Uliana (USA) **MrLB Racing**
14 **GAME MASCOT**, 4, ch g Kheleyf (USA)—Tolzey (USA) **Robert E Lee Syndicate**
15 **GHOSTWING**, 7, gr g Kheleyf (USA)—Someone's Angel (USA) **Robert E Lee Syndicate**
16 **GOT ATTITUDE (IRE)**, 11, ch g Beneficial—Ilderton Road **Three Counties Racing**
17 **GREAT LINK**, 5, b g Rail Link—The Strand **Mr C. Hodgson**
18 **HEURTEVENT (FR)**, 5, b br g Hold That Tiger (USA)—Sybilia (GER) **The Ringside Syndicate**
19 **INNOKO (FR)**, 4, gr g Carlotamix (FR)—Chalana **Mill House Racing Syndicate**
20 **JAKE THE SNAKE (IRE)**, 13, ch g Intikhab (USA)—Tilbrook (IRE) **Mr T. P. Ramsden**
21 **KING OLAV (UAE)**, 9, ch g Halling (USA)—Karamzin (USA) **Cover Point Racing**
22 **LAC SACRE (FR)**, 5, b g Bering—Lady Glorieuse (FR) **Mr S. Louch**
23 **LARAGHCON BOY (IRE)**, 5, ch g Stowaway—Hannah Mooney (IRE) **Mr M. S. Cooke**
24 **LE BACARDY (FR)**, 8, b g Bahhare (USA)—La Balagna **Mr C. Hodgson**
25 **MALANOS (IRE)**, 6, b br g Lord of England (GER)—Majorata (GER) **Mr B. J. Millen**
26 **MAYAN FLIGHT (IRE)**, 6, b g Hawk Wing—Balimaya (IRE) **Burns, Carroll, Miles & Ward**
27 **MISSIONAIRE (USA)**, 7, b br g El Corredor (USA)—Fapindy (USA) **Mr B. J. Millen**
28 **MOHAIR**, 5, b m Motivator—Cashmere **Robert E Lee Syndicate**
29 **MY LORD**, 6, br g Ishiguro (USA)—Lady Smith **Robert E Lee Syndicate**
30 **OCEAN LEGEND (IRE)**, 9, b g Night Shift (USA)—Rose of Mooncoin (IRE) **Mr W. McLuskey**
31 **OUTBID**, 4, ch f Auction House (USA)—Thicket **Mr R. Ward**
32 **PALUS SAN MARCO (IRE)**, 5, b g Holy Roman Emperor (IRE)—Kylemore (IRE) **4 Left Footers & A Blewnose**
33 **POLYDAMOS**, 5, b g Nayef—Spotlight **Mrs S. R. Keable**
34 **POUR LA VICTOIRE (IRE)**, 4, b g Antonius Pius (USA)—Lady Lucia (IRE) **Curry House Corner**
35 **RIGID**, 7, ch g Refuse To Bend (IRE)—Supersonic **Mr & Mrs J. B. Bacciochi**
36 **ROSE GARNET (IRE)**, 6, b m Invincible Spirit (IRE)—Chanterelle (IRE) **Nicholls Family**
37 **RUBY MAC (IRE)**, 6, b m Flemensfirth (USA)—Macaw-Bay (IRE) **MrLB Racing**
38 **SECRET MILLIONAIRE (IRE)**, 7, b g Kyllachy—Mithl Al Hawa **Robert E Lee Syndicate**
39 **SERENITY SPA**, 4, gr f Excellent Art—Molly Mello (GER) **Seasons Holidays**
40 **SHALAMBAR (IRE)**, 8, gr g Dalakhani (IRE)—Shalama (IRE) **Mr B. J. Millen**
41 **SMART CATCH (IRE)**, 8, b g Pivotal—Zafaraniya (IRE) **Cover Point Racing**
42 **SPIRITOFTOMINTOUL**, 5, gr g Authorized (IRE)—Diamond Line (FR) **The Sunday Players**
43 **SPRAY TAN**, 4, b f Assertive—Even Hotter **Silks Racing Partnership**
44 **SUPA SEEKER (USA)**, 8, b br g Petionville (USA)—Supamova (USA) **A. W. Carroll**
45 **TAMMUZ (IRE)**, 4, ch f Tamayuz—Favourita **Longview Stud & Bloodstock Ltd**
46 **THE RIGHT TIME**, 6, b m Val Royal (FR)—Esligier (IRE) **A. W. Carroll**
47 **THINGER LICHT (FR)**, 5, b g Clety (FR)—Family Saga (FR) **Mr C. Hodgson**
48 **TIME MEDICEAN**, 8, gr g Medicean—Ribbons And Bows (IRE) **A. W. Carroll**
49 **TIME SQUARE (FR)**, 7, b g Westerner—Sainte Parfaite (FR) **Mr M. S. Cooke**
50 **TINGLE TANGLE (USA)**, 4, b br g Mizzen Mast (USA)—Tinge (USA) **Mr Morgan, Bright & Parris**
51 **TRAVELLING**, 5, b m Dubai Destination (USA)—Attune **Longview Stud & Bloodstock Ltd**
52 **VALMINA**, 7, b g Val Royal (FR)—Minnina (IRE) **Mayden Stud**
53 **VEDANI (IRE)**, 5, b g Dalakhani (IRE)—Velandia (IRE) **Six Pack**
54 **VERTUEUX (FR)**, 9, gr g Verglas (IRE)—Shahrazad (FR) **Mr J. Rutter**
55 **WAVING**, 5, b g High Chaparral (IRE)—Pretty Davis (USA) **Mr C. Hodgson**
56 **WILD DESERT (FR)**, 9, b br g Desert Prince (IRE)—Sallivera (USA) **Whites of Coventry Limited**
57 **WILDOMAR**, 5, b g Kyllachy—Murrieta **Mr W. McLuskey**

THREE-YEAR-OLDS

58 Ch f Pastoral Pursuits—Arruhan (IRE)
59 **NOUVELLE ERE**, b c Archipenko (USA)—Sinister Ruckus (USA) **Lady Jennifer Green & Martyn C Palmer**
60 **OAKLEY DANCER**, ch f Assertive—My Dancer (IRE) **Mr B. J. Millen**
61 **SYMPHONY OF KINGS**, b c Lucarno (USA)—Flying Lion **T. R. Pearson**
62 **TIDAL BEAUTY**, gr f Verglas (IRE)—Tidal **Mrs B. Quinn**
63 **WEDGEWOOD ESTATES**, ch f Assertive—Heaven **Wedgewood Estates**

MR TONY CARROLL - Continued

Other Owners: J. T. Bacciochi, Mrs J. M. Bacciochi, M. J. Benton, Mrs S. V. Benton, Mr D. R. Blake, Mr A. D. Bright, N. A. Brimble, Mr R. Buckland, Mr P. W. Burns, Mr J. R. Daniell, Mr G. J. Davidson, J. A. Dewhurst, Mrs D. S. Dewhurst, Lady J. Green, Ms K. A. Gwilliam, Mr C. J. Jordan, Mr J. Lawrence, Mr K. Marshall, Mr T. R. Mennell, Mr S. Miles, R. J. Millen, Mr M. Nichol, Mr R. Nicholls, Mrs E. Nicholls, Mr W. G. Nixon, Mr M. C. Palmer, Mr K. J. Parris, Mr G. J. Roberts, N. Scanlan, D. T. Shorthouse, Mr J. A. Sullivan, J. White.

Jockey (NH): Lee Edwards. **Conditional:** Josh Hamer. **Apprentice:** George Downing.

---

101 **MR TONY CARSON, Newmarket**
Postal: **Main Yard, Southgate Stables, Hamilton Road, Newmarket, Suffolk, CB8 0WY**
Contacts: **PHONE (01638) 660947 MOBILE (07837) 601867**
E-MAIL topcatcarson@ymail.com

1 **DIVEA**, 5, b m Dylan Thomas (IRE)—Cumin (USA) **W. F. H. Carson**
2 **FLASH CRASH**, 5, b g Val Royal (FR)—Tessara (GER) **David J. Newman & Ross Bennett**
3 **HAIL PROMENADER (IRE)**, 8, b g Acclamation—Tribal Rite **Richard Prince**
4 **KASBHOM**, 4, b g Refuse To Bend (IRE)—Summerstrand (IRE) **Macattack, William Lea Screed & Form IT**
5 **MAY HAY**, 4, b f Dubai Destination (USA)—Trounce **W. F. H. Carson**
6 **PEACE SEEKER**, 6, b g Oasis Dream—Mina **Hugh & Mindi Byrne**
7 **SIMMI'S TIGER**, 4, b g Tiger Hill (IRE)—Simacota (GER) **W. F. H. Carson**
8 **SPIRITUAL STAR (IRE)**, 5, b g Soviet Star (USA)—Million Spirits (IRE) **Hugh and Mindi Byrne & Macattack**

THREE-YEAR-OLDS

9 **ARGOT**, b c Three Valleys (USA)—Tarot Card **Alderson Carson Francis**
10 **FINAL COUNTDOWN**, ch c Selkirk (USA)—Culture Queen **Christopher Wright & Minster Stud**
11 B c Medicean—Love Me Tender **W. F. H. Carson**
12 **PIEMAN'S GIRL**, b f Henrythenavigator (USA)—Aromatherapy **Romilla Arber & Nalin Wickremeratne**
13 B f Tiger Hill (IRE)—Trounce **W. F. H. Carson**
14 **TUCSON ARIZONA**, b c High Chaparral (IRE)—Kasakiya (IRE) **Christopher Wright & Minster Stud**

TWO-YEAR-OLDS

15 Ch f 18/2 Recharge (IRE)—Senorita Parkes (Medicean) (2095)
16 B c 13/4 Bertolini (USA)—Sister Rose (FR) (One Cool Cat (USA)) (5714) **W. F. H. Carson**

Other Owners: Mr Peter Alderson, Mrs Romilla Arber, Mr R. Bennett, Mr Hugh Byrne, Mrs Mindi Byrne, Mrs E. Carson, Mr Mike Francis, Mr William Lea, Mr T. J. McLoughlin, Mr D. J. Newman, Mr Richard Prince, Mr Nalin Wickremeratne, Mr Christopher Wright.

Assistant Trainer: Graham Carson

Jockey (flat): William Carson. **Amateur:** Mr Graham Carson.

---

102 **MR LEE CARTER, Epsom**
Postal: **The Old Yard, Clear Height Stables, Epsom, Surrey, KT18 5LB**
Contacts: **PHONE (01372) 740878 FAX (01372) 740898 MOBILE (07539) 354819**
E-MAIL leecarterracing@aol.co.uk WEBSITE www.akehurst-racing.co.uk

1 **ANY GIVEN DREAM (IRE)**, 5, b g Bahri (USA)—Anazara (USA) **Mr P. Allard**
2 **ARCHELAO (IRE)**, 6, br g Cape Cross (IRE)—Brindisi **Miss V. J. Baalham**
3 **ARTISTICAL (IRE)**, 4, b c Excellent Art—Royale Figurine (IRE) **Mr J. J. Smith**
4 **BARNET FAIR**, 6, br g Iceman—Pavement Gates **Mr D. Wheatley**
5 **BENNELONG**, 8, b g Bahamian Bounty—Bundle Up **Miss V. J. Baalham**
6 **BORN TO SURPRISE**, 5, b g Exceed And Excel (AUS)—Dubai Surprise (IRE) **Mr J. J. Smith**
7 **COMFORT AND JOY (IRE)**, 4, b f Byron—Dodona **A. D. Spence**
8 **COPPERWOOD**, 9, ch g Bahamian Bounty—Sophielu **Miss V. J. Baalham**
9 **LEGAL LEGACY**, 8, ch g Beat Hollow—Dan's Delight **Miss V. J. Baalham**
10 **LOWTHER**, 9, b g Beat All (USA)—Ever So Lonely **Mr J. J. Smith**
11 **MIDNIGHT FEAST**, 9, b g Ishiguru (USA)—Prince's Feather (IRE) **One More Bid Partnership**
12 **MUNSARIM (IRE)**, 7, b g Shamardal (USA)—Etizaaz (USA) **Mr J. J. Smith**
13 **PROPER CHARLIE**, 6, b g Cadeaux Genereux—Ring of Love **P. A. Allard**

MR LEE CARTER - Continued

14 **SEEK THE FAIR LAND**, 8, b g Noverre (USA)—Duchcov **Mr J. J. Smith**
15 **TIPPOTINA**, 4, b f Indesatchel (IRE)—Ballerina Suprema (IRE) **Miss V. J. Baalham**

THREE-YEAR-OLDS

16 **NEXT STOP**, b f Rail Link—Reaching Ahead (USA) **P. A. Allard**
17 **PERMITTED**, b f Authorized (IRE)—Discerning **Clear Racing Partnership**
18 **SYDNEY JAMES (IRE)**, b c Thousand Words—Blue Bamboo **Mr J. J. Smith**

TWO-YEAR-OLDS

19 **BLUE AMAZON (IRE)**, b f 6/5 Acclamation—
        Amazon Beauty (IRE) (Wolfhound (USA)) (5500) **Tattenham Corner Racing IV**
20 **PACT**, b f 18/4 Paco Boy (IRE)—Jade Pet (Petong) **Ewell Never Know Partnership**

Other Owners: Mr Neville Boyce, Mr P. M. Crane, Mr Gus Gordon, Mrs I. Marshall, Mr J. O'Hara, Mr Peter Oakley, Mr A. Pitt, Mrs J. Pitt.

Apprentice: Paige Bolton.

---

103 **MR BEN CASE, Banbury**
Postal: Wardington Gate Farm, Edgcote, Banbury, Oxfordshire, OX17 1AG
Contacts: PHONE (01295) 750959 FAX (01295) 758840 MOBILE (07808) 061223
E-MAIL info@bencaseracing.com WEBSITE www.bencaseracing.com

1 **ALPANCHO**, 8, ch g Alflora (IRE)—Run Tiger (IRE) **Apple Pie Partnership**
2 **BEBINN (IRE)**, 7, b m Brian Boru—Windmill Star (IRE) **The Polk Partnership**
3 **BRASS TAX (IRE)**, 8, b g Morozov (USA)—Cry Before Dawn (IRE) **Mrs C. Kendrick**
4 **BREAKING THE BANK**, 5, ch g Medicean—Russian Dance (USA) **D. C. R. Allen**
5 **CALL A TRUCE (IRE)**, 6, b g Court Cave (IRE)—No More Trouble (IRE) **Lady Jane Grosvenor**
6 **COCHINILLO (IRE)**, 5, b g Shantou (USA)—Nut Touluze (IRE) **Goodman, Hemstock, Case & Case**
7 **CROOKSTOWN (IRE)**, 7, b g Rudimentary (USA)—Millview Lass (IRE) **Case Racing Partnership**
8 **DEEP TROUBLE (IRE)**, 7, b g Shantou (USA)—Out of Trouble (IRE) **Lady Jane Grosvenor**
9 **GINGER FIZZ**, 7, ch m Haafhd—Valagalore **Itchen Valley Stud**
10 **ISLAND WHISPER (IRE)**, 7, b m Turtle Island (IRE)—Whistles Dream (IRE) **Mrs S. L. Case**
11 **KERNEL VICTOR**, 6, b g Old Vic—Noisetine (FR) **D. C. R. Allen**
12 **MAZURATI (IRE)**, 5, b g Definite Article—Mazuma (IRE) **Lady Jane Grosvenor**
13 **MIDNIGHT JAZZ**, 4, b f Midnight Legend—Ring Back (USA) **D. C. R. Allen**
14 4, B c Kayf Tara—Mille Et Une (FR) **Lady Jane Grosvenor**
15 **MOSS ON THE MILL**, 6, br g Overbury (IRE)—Mimis Bonnet (FR) **S. D. Hemstock**
16 **MR GREY (IRE)**, 6, gr g Great Palm (USA)—Presenting Shares (IRE) **D. C. R. Allen**
17 **MY RENAISSANCE**, 4, b br g Medicean—Lebenstanz **N. S. Hutley**
18 **ORANGEADAY**, 7, b g Kayf Tara—One of Those Days **D. C. R. Allen**
19 **PHARE ISLE (IRE)**, 9, b g Turtle Island (IRE)—Pharenna (IRE) **Nicholson Family Moore Moore & Kendrick**
20 **PROFIT MONITOR (IRE)**, 6, b g Court Cave (USA)—Knock Abbey Castle (IRE) **Mrs C. Kendrick**
21 **ROLLO'S REFLECTION (IRE)**, 4, b g Shantou (USA)—Lola's Reflection **Ben Case**
22 **SHANTOU RIVER (IRE)**, 6, b g Shantou (USA)—River Mousa (IRE) **Mrs L. R. Lovell**
23 **TEMPEST RIVER (IRE)**, 8, b m Old Vic—Dee-One-O-One **Fly Like The Wind Partnership**
24 **THEMANFROM MINELLA (IRE)**, 5, b g Shantou (USA)—Bobomy (IRE) **Mrs C. Kendrick**
25 **THORESBY (IRE)**, 8, b g Milan—I Remember It Well (IRE) **D. C. R. Allen**
26 **USSEE (FR)**, 6, gr m Vangelis (USA)—Duchesse Pierji (FR) **J. Wright**
27 **VESUVHILL (FR)**, 5, ch g Sabrehill (USA)—L'orchidee (FR) **Case Racing Partnership**
28 **VINEGAR HILL**, 5, b g Kayf Tara—Broughton Melody **Swanee River Partnership**
29 **WITHER YENOT (IRE)**, 7, b g Tikkanen (USA)—Acacia Bloom (IRE) **Mrs C. Kendrick**

Other Owners: Mr D. Baines, Mr N. Biggs, Mrs A. D. Bourne, Mr T. Boylan, Mrs S. Case, Mr A. P. Case, Mrs A. Charlton, Mr R. Clark, Mr C. K. Crossley Cooke, Mrs T. Curtis, Mr J. S. English, Mr A. R. Franklin, Mr E. Gladden, Mr A. Goodsik, Mr D. Green, Mrs J. Grindlay, Mr R. Hagen, Mr R. Harper, Mrs S. Harrison, Mr D. Hazlett, Mrs M. Howlett, Mrs J. Hulse, Dr C. Illsley, Mrs B. Joice, Mrs Carolyn Kendrick, Mr A. P. Liggins, Mrs H. Loggin, Mrs L. Lovell, Mr I. A. Low, Mr P. Lush, Miss A. Lush, Mr M. Matthews, Mr Wendy Moore, Mr T. W. Moore, Mr Grahame Nicholson, Mr C. Nixey, Mr J. Nowell-Smith, Mr R. Palmer, Mr & Mrs D. Payne, Mrs K. Perrem, Mrs L. Pestel, Mr John Polk, Mr James Polk, Mrs C. Ripley, Mr J. Shaw, Mr David Smith, Mrs C. Wallace.

Amateur: Mr M. J. P. Kendrick.

104 LADY JANE CECIL, Newmarket

Postal: **Warren Place, Newmarket, Suffolk, CB8 8QQ**
Contacts: **PHONE (01638) 662192 FAX (01638) 669005 MOBILE (07850) 788822**
E-MAIL henry@henrycecil.co.uk

1 **AL GUWAIR (IRE)**, 4, b g Shirocco (GER)—Katariya (IRE) **Sheikh Joaan Al Thani**
2 **EMPERICAL**, 4, b g Oasis Dream—Kalima **K. Abdullah**
3 **FLOW (USA)**, 4, b br c Medaglia d'oro (USA)—Enthused (USA) **Niarchos Family**
4 **GRASPED**, 4, ch f Zamindar (USA)—Imroz (USA) **K. Abdullah**
5 **HAMELIN (IRE)**, 4, b c Cape Cross (IRE)—Love Divine **Lordship Stud**
6 **JUST ONE KISS**, 4, b f Cape Cross (IRE)—Kissing **Lordship Stud**
7 **MAGIC OF REALITY (FR)**, 4, ch f Galileo (IRE)—Breathe (FR) **Niarchos Family**
8 **MIGHTY YAR (IRE)**, 4, gr c Teofilo (IRE)—Karaliyfa (USA) **R. A. H. Evans**
9 **NOBLE MISSION**, 5, b h Galileo (IRE)—Kind (IRE) **K. Abdullah**
10 **PERFECT SUMMER (IRE)**, 4, b f High Chaparral (IRE)—Power of Future (GER) **Mr G. Schoeningh**
11 **PHAENOMENA (IRE)**, 4, ch f Galileo (IRE)—Caumshinaun (IRE) **Niarchos Family**
12 **PHOSPHORESCENCE (IRE)**, 4, b g Sakhee (USA)—Eccentricity (USA) **Niarchos Family**
13 **RETIREMENT PLAN**, 4, b br c Monsun (GER)—Passage of Time **K. Abdullah**
14 **SAGUA LA GRANDE (IRE)**, 4, b c Teofilo (IRE)—Water Fountain **Lady J. Cecil**
15 **SEA MEETS SKY (FR)**, 4, b f Dansili—Sacred Song (USA) **Niarchos Family**

THREE-YEAR-OLDS

16 **BRIT WIT**, b f High Chaparral (IRE)—Brisk Breeze (GER) **Ennismore Racing I**
17 **BUTTON DOWN**, b f Oasis Dream—Modesta (IRE) **K. Abdullah**
18 **CHANTREA (IRE)**, br f Dansili—Celestial Lagoon (JPN) **Niarchos Family**
19 **COLOURFUL**, b f Champs Elysees—Rainbow Lake **K. Abdullah**
20 **CURVED**, br f Oasis Dream—Passage of Time **K. Abdullah**
21 **DORSET CREAM**, b f Dansili—Blend **K. Abdullah**
22 **EQUITABLE**, b c Dansili—Honest Quality (USA) **K. Abdullah**
23 **FAIR SHARE**, b c Rail Link—Quota **K. Abdullah**
24 **GALACTIC HALO**, b f Rail Link—Star Cluster **K. Abdullah**
25 **HOOP OF COLOUR (USA)**, b f Distorted Humor (USA)—Surya (USA) **Niarchos Family**
26 **JOYEUSE**, b f Oasis Dream—Kind (IRE) **K. Abdullah**
27 **LAKE ALFRED (USA)**, gr c Mizzen Mast (USA)—Brief Look **K. Abdullah**
28 **METEOROID (USA)**, b br c Dynaformer (USA)—Enthused (USA) **Niarchos Family**
29 **MORNING WATCH (IRE)**, b c Azamour (IRE)—Lady of Kildare (IRE) **De La Warr Racing**
30 Ch g Dutch Art—Nicoise (IRE) **Raymond Tooth**
31 **NICTATE (IRE)**, br f Teofilo (IRE)—Woodmaven (USA) **Niarchos Family**
32 **PERIL**, ch c Pivotal—Portodora (USA) **K. Abdullah**
33 **POSSET**, b f Oasis Dream—Midsummer **K. Abdullah**
34 **SHASTA DAISY**, b f Champs Elysees—Bouvardia **K. Abdullah**
35 **SUNRISE STAR**, b f Shamardal (USA)—Tudor Court (IRE) **Lady Bamford**
36 **SYNAESTHESIA (FR)**, b br f High Chaparral (IRE)—I'm Sensational **Niarchos Family**
37 **TACTICUS (USA)**, b c A P Indy (USA)—Visions of Clarity (IRE) **Niarchos Family**
38 **TOUCH THE SKY**, br c Sea The Stars (IRE)—Love Divine **Lordship Stud & Mr Christopher Wright**

TWO-YEAR-OLDS

39 B c 5/2 Beat Hollow—Acquisition (Dansili) **K. Abdullah**
40 B f 15/4 Rock of Gibraltar (IRE)—Ashraakat (USA) (Danzig (USA)) (10000) **Biddeston Racing**
41 B c 14/3 Oasis Dream—Bionic (Zafonic (USA)) **K. Abdullah**
42 **BURNER (IRE)**, b c 15/3 High Chaparral (IRE)—Breathe (FR) (Ocean of Wisdom (USA)) **Niarchos Family**
43 B br c 19/2 Dansili—Clepsydra (Sadler's Wells (USA)) **K. Abdullah**
44 **DECLAN**, ch c 11/2 Dylan Thomas (IRE)—Fleurissimo (Dr Fong (USA)) **Normandie Stud**
45 **DRAGON TREE**, ch c 25/4 Halling (USA)—Doggerbank (IRE) (Oasis Dream) **G Schoeningh**
46 B f 24/2 Afleet Alex (USA)—Dreamt (Oasis Dream) **K. Abdullah**
47 **EATSLEEPRACEREPEAT**, b c 6/2 Myboycharlie (IRE)—
Highland Jewel (IRE) (Azamour (IRE)) (13000) **Warren Place Syndicate**
48 B f 18/2 Champs Elysees—Market Forces (Lomitas) **K. Abdulla**
49 B c 13/4 Medicean—Marula (IRE) (Sadler's Wells (USA)) (21000) **Sisterson**
50 B f 30/3 Rail Link—Modesta (IRE) (Sadler's Wells (USA)) **K. Abdulla**
51 **MOSUO (IRE)**, b f 12/3 Oasis Dream—Light Shift (USA) (Kingmambo (USA)) **Niarchos Family**
52 **NIGEL**, b c 4/2 New Approach (IRE)—Deirdre (Azamour (IRE)) **Normandie Stud**
53 **PUDDING**, b f 30/4 Bushranger (IRE)—Kahyasi Moll (IRE) (Brief Truce (USA)) (28000) **Warren Place Syndicate**
54 Ch f 12/3 Shamardal (USA)—Purissima (USA) (Fusaichi Pegasus (USA)) **K. Abdullah**
55 B c 13/4 Shamardal (USA)—Rex Regina (IRE) (King's Best (USA)) (60000) **De La Warr Racing**

LADY JANE CECIL - Continued

56 B f 14/3 Authorized (IRE)—Shyrl (Acclamation) **Saleh Al Homaizi & Imad Al Sagar**
57 WESTERN RESERVE, b br c 30/3 Indian Charlie (USA)—Visit (Oasis Dream) **K. Abdullah**
58 YAMARHABA MALAYEEN, b c 22/4 Equiano (FR)—
Broughtons Flight (IRE) (Hawk Wing (USA)) (32000) **A A Al Shaikh**

Other Owners: Lord De La Warr, Mr J. M. O. Evans, T. F. Harris, Mrs E. A. Harris, Mr G. Schoeningh, C. N. Wright.

Assistant Trainer: George Scott

---

105 **MR PATRICK CHAMINGS, Basingstoke**
Postal: **Inhurst Farm Stables, Baughurst, Tadley, Hampshire, RG26 5JS**
Contacts: **PHONE (01189) 814494 FAX (01189) 820454 MOBILE (07831) 360970**
E-MAIL chamingsracing@talk21.com

1 AYE AYE DIGBY (IRE), 9, b g Captain Rio—Jane Digby (IRE) **Trolley Action**
2 BOLACHOIR (IRE), 12, b g Hubbly Bubbly (USA)—Boolindrum Lady (IRE) **R. V. Shaw**
3 CAPE BRETON, 8, b g Cape Cross (IRE)—Red Bouquet **Mrs A. J. Chandris**
4 CHELWOOD GATE (IRE), 4, b grg Aussie Rules (USA)—Jusoor (USA) **K. W. Tyrrell**
5 DIRECTORSHIP, 8, br g Diktat—Away To Me **Mrs R Lyon,Mrs P Hayton,Mr P R Chamings**
6 EAGER TO BOW (IRE), 8, b g Acclamation—Tullawadgeen (IRE) **Mrs J. E. L. Wright**
7 FLAVIUS VICTOR (IRE), 5, b g Holy Roman Emperor (IRE)—Teslemi (USA) **P R Chamings F T Lee**
8 FOXHAVEN, 12, ch g Unfuwain (USA)—Dancing Mirage (IRE) **The Foxford House Partnership**
9 HAIL TO PRINCESS, 4, ch f Dr Fong (USA)—Bob's Princess **P. R. Chamings**
10 HIT THE LIGHTS (IRE), 4, b g Lawman (FR)—Dawn Chorus (IRE) **Select Racing Bloodstock Limited**
11 JUST WHEN, 5, b g Dalakhani (IRE)—Cape Grace (IRE) **Inhurst Players**
12 PERFECT ROMANCE, 5, ch m Singspiel (IRE)—Flamjica (USA) **The Cadagan Partnership**
13 RONDEAU (GR), 9, ch g Harmonic Way—Areti (GR) **The Foxford House Partnership**
14 SCOTTISH GLEN, 8, ch g Kyllachy—Dance For Fun **The Foxford House Partnership**
15 TAKE A NOTE, 5, b g Singspiel (IRE)—Ela Paparouna **The Foxford House Partnership**
16 UNCLE FRED, 9, b g Royal Applause—Karla June **The Foxford House Partnership**

THREE-YEAR-OLDS

17 Ch g Iffraaj—Astuti (IRE)
18 BENTWORTH BOY, b g Archipenko (USA)—Maria di Scozia **Robinson,Wiggin,Hayward-Cole,Roberts**
19 CHURCH LEAP (IRE), gr g High Chaparral (IRE)—Alambic **Robinson,Wiggin,Hayward-Cole,Roberts**
20 DOUBLE CZECH (IRE), b g Bushranger (IRE)—Night of Joy (IRE) **K. W. Tyrrell**
21 FOXFORD, b f Clodovil (IRE)—Pulau Pinang (IRE) **The Foxford House Partnership**
22 Br f Reel Buddy (USA)—Nephetriti Way (IRE) **P. R. Chamings**
23 POETIC PRINCE, b g Byron—Bob's Princess **Mrs J. E. L. Wright**
24 SILKEN POPPY, b f Assertive—Ela Paparouna **The Berks & Hants Racing Partnership**
25 Ch g Tobougg (IRE)—Tamise (USA)
26 TOO BEND, b g Tobougg (IRE)—Benjarong **Mrs J. E. L. Wright**

TWO-YEAR-OLDS

27 REGAL MISS, b f 23/2 Royal Applause—Pretty Miss (Averti (IRE)) **Mrs J. E. L. Wright**

Other Owners: Dr S. B. Drew, N. R. R. Drew, J. R. Drew, Miss G. B. Drew, J. Glasgow, Mrs P. L. Hayton, Mrs N. Hayward-Cole, Mr S. Hill, F. T. Lee, Mrs R. Lyon, Mr R. Lyon, Mrs J. A. Newman, Mrs M. Roberts, Mr N. R. Robinson, Mr N. P. Rustad, Mr M. R. Stewart, Mrs S. A. Symonds, Mr A. J. Thomas, Mr S. R. Thomas, Mr D. P. Wiggin.

Assistant Trainer: Phillippa Chamings

---

106 **MR MICK CHANNON, West Ilsley**
Postal: **West Ilsley Stables, West Ilsley, Newbury, Berkshire, RG20 7AE**
Contacts: **PHONE (01635) 281166 FAX (01635) 281177**
E-MAIL mick@mick-channon.co.uk/susan@mick-channon.co.uk WEBSITE www.mickchannon.tv

1 AMRALAH (IRE), 4, b c Teofilo (IRE)—Sharp Mode (USA) **Prince A. A. Faisal**
2 ARNOLD LANE (IRE), 5, b h Footstepsinthesand—Capriole **Nick & Olga Dhandsa & John & Zoe Webster**
3 BALBRIGGAN (IRE), 7, gr g King's Theatre (IRE)—Halfway Home **Mrs C. M. Radford**
4 BALLYPATRICK (IRE), 8, b br g Presenting—Jewell For A King (IRE) **Martin, Jocelyn & Steve Broughton**
5 BUNGLE INTHEJUNGLE, 4, b c Exceed And Excel (AUS)—
Licence To Thrill **Christopher Wright & Miss Emily Asprey**

MR MICK CHANNON - Continued

6 **CHILWORTH ICON,** 4, b g Sixties Icon—Tamara Moon (IRE) **7RUS**
7 **CONTRADICT,** 4, b f Raven's Pass (USA)—Acts of Grace (USA) **Prince A. A. Faisal**
8 **CONVERSATIONAL (IRE),** 4, b f Thousand Words—Alpine Flair (IRE) **Mrs T. Burns**
9 **CRUCK REALTA,** 4, b f Sixties Icon—Wansdyke Lass **Anne & Steve Fisher**
10 **EFFIE B,** 4, ch f Sixties Icon—Blakeshall Rose **Mr R. W. Bastian**
11 **ELIDOR,** 4, br g Cape Cross (IRE)—Honorine (IRE) **Jon & Julia Aisbitt**
12 **FITZWILLY,** 4, b g Sixties Icon—Canadian Capers **P. Taplin**
13 **FOSTER'S ROAD,** 5, b g Imperial Dancer—Search Party **Dave & Gill Hedley**
14 **GRAPHIC GUEST,** 4, ch f Dutch Art—Makara **John Guest Racing**
15 **GREY GAZELLE,** 4, gr f Verglas (IRE)—Hampton Lucy (IRE) **M. R. Channon**
16 **HARBINGER LASS,** 4, b f Thousand Words—Penang Cry **Mrs T. Burns**
17 **HATTIE JACQUES,** 4, b f Sixties Icon—Funny Girl (IRE) **Norman Court Stud**
18 **HIGHLIFE DANCER,** 6, br g Imperial Dancer—Wrong Bride **The Highlife Racing Club**
19 **I'M SO GLAD,** 5, b m Clodovil (IRE)—Dilag (IRE) **Mr C. Wright & The Hon Mrs J.M.Corbett**
20 **INFFIRAAJ (IRE),** 5, b m Iffraaj—Incense
21 **JILLNEXTDOOR (IRE),** 4, b f Henrythenavigator (USA)—
                                        Royal Shyness **Nick & Olga Dhandsa & John & Zoe Webster**
22 **JONTLEMAN (IRE),** 4, b g Whipper (USA)—Gandia (IRE) **Mr P. D. Corbett**
23 **KNOCK HOUSE (IRE),** 5, ch g Old Vic—Lady's Gesture (IRE) **Mrs C. M. Radford**
24 **LOCH BA (IRE),** 8, b g Craigsteel—Lenmore Lisa (IRE) **Mrs C. M. Radford**
25 **MISS LAHAR,** 5, b m Clodovil (IRE)—Brigadiers Bird (IRE) **Barry Walters Catering**
26 **MONTAFF,** 8, b g Montjeu (IRE)—Meshhed (USA)
27 **PARADISE VALLEY (IRE),** 5, b g Presenting—Native Wood (IRE) **Mrs C. M. Radford**
28 **PETALUMA,** 5, b m Teofilo (IRE)—Poppo's Song (CAN) **Jon & Julia Aisbitt**
29 **PRINCESS QUEST,** 5, gr m Clodovil (IRE)—Corniche Quest (IRE) **M. R. Channon**
30 **QIBTEE (FR),** 4, b c Antonius Pius (USA)—Embers of Fame (IRE) **Mr N. C. White & Mrs C. E. White**
31 **SAVANNA DAYS (IRE),** 5, ch m Danehill Dancer (IRE)—Dominante (GER) **Jon & Julia Aisbitt**
32 **SGT RECKLESS,** 7, b g Imperial Dancer—Lakaam **Mrs C. M. Radford**
33 **SHORE STEP (IRE),** 4, br g Footstepsinthesand—Chatham Islands (USA) **Jon & Julia Aisbitt**
34 **SHRIMPTON,** 4, b f Cadeaux Genereux—Feather Boa (IRE)
35 **SOMERSBY (IRE),** 10, b g Second Empire (IRE)—Back To Roost (IRE) **Mrs C. M. Radford**
36 **SORELLA BELLA (IRE),** 4, ro f Clodovil (IRE)—Anazah (USA) **Mrs A. C. Black**
37 **STRICTLY SILCA,** 4, ch f Danehill Dancer (IRE)—Silca Chiave **Aldridge Racing Partnership**
38 **SYMBOLINE,** 4, b f Royal Applause—Ashes (IRE)
39 **TALQAA,** 4, b f Exceed And Excel (AUS)—Poppo's Song (CAN) **Sheikh M. B. K. Al Maktoum**
40 **TIDENTIME (USA),** 5, b br g Speightstown (USA)—Casting Call (USA) **Jon & Julia Aisbitt**
41 **VALLARTA (IRE),** 4, b g Footstepsinthesand—Mexican Miss (IRE) **Tails & Bargate**
42 **VIVA STEVE (IRE),** 6, b g Flemensfirth (USA)—Eluna **Mrs C. M. Radford**
43 **WARDEN HILL (IRE),** 6, br g Presenting—Moon Storm (IRE) **Mrs C. M. Radford**
44 **WASEEM FARIS (IRE),** 5, b g Exceed And Excel (AUS)—Kissing Time
45 **YOJIMBO (IRE),** 6, gr g Aussie Rules (USA)—Mythie (FR) **Jon & Julia Aisbitt**
46 **YOUMAYSEE (IRE),** 4, b f Authorized (IRE)—Purple Vision **M. R. Channon**

THREE-YEAR-OLDS

47 **AMAHORO,** b f Sixties Icon—Evanesce **Dave & Gill Hedley**
48 **ARANTES,** b c Sixties Icon—Black Opal **M. R. Channon**
49 **ARISTOCRACY,** b c Royal Applause—Pure Speculation **M. R. Channon**
50 **BERGAN (GER),** ch c Halling (USA)—Baltic Gift **S. Manana**
51 **BOY WONDER,** ch g Compton Place—Kindallachan **Dark Horse Racing Partnership 7**
52 **BRIDIE FFRENCH,** b f Bahamian Bounty—Wansdyke Lass **Anne & Steve Fisher**
53 **CHRISTMAS WISH,** b f Pastoral Pursuits—Christmas Tart (IRE) **S. Manana**
54 **CRAZEE DIAMOND,** b f Rock of Gibraltar (IRE)—Final Dynasty **Nick & Olga Dhandsa & John & Zoe Webster**
55 **DEEDS NOT WORDS (IRE),** b g Royal Applause—Wars (IRE) **G. D. P. Materna**
56 **DING DING,** ch f Winker Watson—Five Bells (IRE) **Norman Court Stud I**
57 **DIVINE (IRE),** b f Dark Angel (IRE)—Carallia (IRE) **Mr M. Al-Qatami & Mr K. M. Al-Mudhaf**
58 **EMEF DIAMOND,** b g Firebreak—On The Brink **Mrs Maragret Forsyth & MF Logistic**
59 **FINFLASH (IRE),** b c Jeremy (USA)—Sinegronto (IRE) **Insignia Racing (Coronet)**
60 **GOOD MORNING LADY,** b f Compton Place—Baldemosa (FR) **Mr A. Jaber**
61 **GRATZIE,** b f Three Valleys (USA)—La Gazzetta (IRE) **C Corbett, David Hudd, Chris Wright**
62 **GREENGAGE SUMMER,** b f Sixties Icon—Linda Green **Norman Court Stud I**
63 **GREVILLEA (IRE),** b f Admiralofthefleet (USA)—Louve Heureuse (IRE) **N. J. Hitchins**
64 **HEARTSTRINGS,** b f Invincible Spirit (IRE)—Strings **Mrs A. C. Black**
65 **HOMESTRETCH,** b c Holy Roman Emperor (IRE)—Sharp Mode (USA) **Prince A. A. Faisal**
66 **HOY HOY (IRE),** b c Iffraaj—Luxie (IRE) **Sheikh M. B. K. Al Maktoum**
67 **ISABELLA BIRD,** b f Invincible Spirit (IRE)—Meetyouthere (IRE) **Jon & Julia Aisbitt**

MR MICK CHANNON - Continued

68 JAYWALKER (IRE), b g Footstepsinthesand—Nipping (IRE) **Insignia Racing (Crest)**
69 JENNY SPARKS, b f Winker Watson—Stephanie's Mind **M. R. Channon**
70 JERSEY BROWN (IRE), br f Marju—Daniysha (IRE) **Lakedale**
71 KAIULANI (IRE), b f Danehill Dancer (IRE)—Royal Shyness **Mrs T P Radford & Tails Partnership**
72 KEEP CLOSE, b f Cape Cross (IRE)—Kelucia (IRE) **J. Abdullah**
73 KICKBOXER (IRE), gr g Clodovil (IRE)—Ajjig Dancer **Mrs T. Burns**
74 KISANJI, b c Teofilo (IRE)—Al Kamah (USA) **Box 41**
75 LINCOLN (IRE), b c Clodovil (IRE)—Gilt Linked **Mr W. G. Parish**
76 LORD BRANTWOOD, b c Sir Percy—Diddymu (IRE) **Mr & Mrs D. D. Clee**
77 LUNARIAN, ch f Bahamian Bounty—One Giant Leap (IRE) **Mrs A. C. Black**
78 MISS CAPE (IRE), b f Cape Cross (IRE)—Miss Sally (IRE) **Jon & Julia Aisbitt**
79 NANCY FROM NAIROBI, b f Sixties Icon—Madame Hoi (IRE) **Norman Court Stud**
80 NARBOROUGH, b g Winker Watson—Solmorin **Mrs E. J. Maxted**
81 NATIVE HEART, gr f Clodovil (IRE)—She's My Outsider **M. R. Channon**
82 NEEDLESS SHOUTING (IRE), b c Footstepsinthesand—
Ring The Relatives **Lord Ilsley Racing (Russell Syndicate)**
83 NUTBUSH, b f Sixties Icon—Hairy Night (IRE) **M. R. Channon**
84 PALERMA, b f Shamardal (USA)—West Lorne (USA) **Jon & Julia Aisbitt**
85 PORTEOUS, b f Sixties Icon—Fading Away **Imperial**
86 B c Tobougg (IRE)—Prairie Sun (GER)
87 RIVERBOAT SPRINGS (IRE), b c Bushranger (IRE)—Mashie **Sheikh Hamdan Bin Mohammed Al Maktoum**
88 ROUGH COURTE (IRE), b f Clodovil (IRE)—Straight Sets (IRE) **Mr W. G. Parish**
89 SHADOWS OFTHENIGHT (IRE), b f Fastnet Rock (AUS)—
Madaen (USA) **Christopher Wright & Miss Emily Asprey**
90 SHIMBA HILLS, b g Sixties Icon—Search Party **Dave & Gill Hedley**
91 STONEHAM, b f Sixties Icon—Cibenze **Norman Court Stud**
92 TAHADEE (IRE), b c Teofilo (IRE)—Queen of Lyons (USA) **Sheikh M. B. K. Al Maktoum**
93 TANOJIN (IRE), ch f Thousand Words—Indiannie Moon **Nick & Olga Dhandsa & John & Zoe Webster**
94 THE POCKET DOT, ch f Lucky Story (USA)—Daisy Do (IRE) **M. R. Channon**
95 WEE JEAN, b f Captain Gerrard (IRE)—Reeli Silli **Mr B. Robe**

TWO-YEAR-OLDS

96 B c 26/3 Bahamian Bounty—Air Maze (Dansili) (55000) **Harlequin Direct Ltd**
97 B f 23/1 Acclamation—Alexander Alliance (IRE) (Danetime (IRE)) (35000)
98 Ch f 2/3 Fast Company (IRE)—Apple Brandy (USA) (Cox's Ridge (USA)) (13000)
99 Ch f 27/1 Winker Watson—Aries (GER) (Big Shuffle (USA))
100 B f 16/4 Fast Company (IRE)—Autumn Rose (IRE) (Mujadil (USA)) (19000)
101 B c 5/4 High Chaparral (IRE)—Billet (IRE) (Danehill (USA)) (40262) **Sheikh M. B. K. Al Maktoum**
102 Ch f 22/4 Piccolo—Blakeshall Rose (Tobougg (IRE))
103 Ch c 25/4 Sixties Icon—Canadian Capers (Ballacashtal (CAN))
104 B br f 28/3 Iffraaj—Chatifa (IRE) (Titus Livius (FR)) (40000) **Sheikh M. B. K. Al Maktoum**
105 DANCING MOON (IRE), b f 3/3 Danehill Dancer (IRE)—Moon Dazzle (USA) (Kingmambo (USA)) (75000)
106 B c 12/3 Indesatchel (IRE)—Dim Ofan (Petong) (4761) **M. R. Channon**
107 B c 27/4 Equiano (FR)—Dream Vision (USA) (Distant View (USA)) (15500)
108 Gr f 3/4 Sixties Icon—Easy Red (IRE) (Hunting Lion (IRE))
109 Ch c 21/3 Captain Gerrard (IRE)—Elegant Lady (Selkirk (USA)) (43809) **M. R. Channon**
110 EMEF ROCK (IRE), b c 20/4 Acclamation—Sveva (IRE) (Danehill Dancer (USA)) (29422)
111 B f 1/2 Winker Watson—Excellent Day (IRE) (Invincible Spirit (IRE))
112 Br c 26/3 Winker Watson—Fading Away (Fraam)
113 Ch c 3/4 Sixties Icon—Five Bells (IRE) (Rock of Gibraltar (IRE))
114 FOLLOW THE FAITH, b f 11/5 Piccolo—Keeping The Faith (IRE) (Ajraas (USA))
115 B f 25/1 Winker Watson—Funny Girl (IRE) (Darshaan)
116 Ch c 25/2 Winker Watson—Hairspray (Bahamian Bounty)
117 B f 17/4 Mastercraftsman (IRE)—Hollow Hill (IRE) (Orpen (USA)) (40000)
118 Ch c 24/4 Fast Company (IRE)—Indiannie Moon (Fraam) (9291)
119 JERSEY BELLE, b f 2/2 Piccolo—Stephanie's Mind (Mind Games) **Lakedale**
120 JERSEY BULL (IRE), b c 9/4 Clodovil (IRE)—Chaguaramas (IRE) (Mujadil (USA)) (34000) **Lakedale**
121 JUST SILCA, ch f 24/3 Teofilo (IRE)—Silca Chiave (Pivotal) **Aldridge Racing Partnership**
122 Ch c 26/2 Starspangledbanner (AUS)—Licence To Thrill (Wolfhound (USA))
123 MALABAR, b f 27/3 Raven's Pass (USA)—Whirly Bird (Nashwan (USA)) (70000) **Jon & Julia Aisbitt**
124 B f 4/2 Sea The Stars (IRE)—Miss Riviera Golf (Hernando (FR)) (110000) **Jon & Julia Aisbitt**
125 B f 20/3 Sixties Icon—Mistic Magic (IRE) (Orpen (USA))
126 B c 5/3 Naaqoos (Muhtathir) (50328) **Nick & Olga Dhandsa & John & Zoe Webster**
127 B c 7/4 Winker Watson—Nadinska (Doyen (IRE))
128 Ch f 15/2 Winker Watson—Natalie Jay (Ballacashtal (CAN))

MR MICK CHANNON - Continued

129 B c 12/3 Sixties Icon—Nedwa (In The Wings)
130 B c 30/4 Acclamation—Pampas (Distant View (USA)) (52000)
131 **PENDLEBURY,** b c 6/3 Showcasing—Trinny (Rainbow Quest (USA)) (33333) **Jon & Julia Aisbitt**
132 B c 17/4 Bushranger (IRE)—Picolette (Piccolo) (16000)
133 B f 9/2 Footstepsinthesand—Piffling (Pivotal) (32000)
134 Ch f 27/3 Avonbridge—Pooka's Daughter (IRE) (Eagle Eyed (USA)) (2000)
135 **POPESWOOD (IRE),** b c 28/2 Haatef (USA)—Binfield (IRE) (Officer (USA)) **N. J. Hitchins**
136 B f 30/4 Sixties Icon—Queen of Narnia (Hunting Lion (IRE))
137 B f 10/2 Teofilo (IRE)—Queen of Stars (USA) (Green Desert (USA)) (37000) **John Guest Racing Ltd**
138 B c 7/4 Kodiac—Reality Check (IRE) (Sri Pekan (USA)) (42585) **Nick & Olga Dhandsa & John & Zoe Webster**
139 **REBEL YELL,** b c 21/4 Shamardal (USA)—Solaia (USA) (Miswaki (USA)) (90000)
140 B c 19/2 Rip Van Winkle (IRE)—Ride A Rainbow (Rainbow Quest (USA)) (75000) **G. D. P. Materna**
141 B c 25/2 Medicean—Ros The Boss (IRE) (Danehill (USA)) (72000) **John Guest Racing Ltd**
142 Gr f 28/1 Winker Watson—Rose Cheval (USA) (Johannesburg (USA))
143 Ch f 8/3 Mastercraftsman (IRE)—She Is Zen (FR) (Zieten (USA)) (55000)
144 B f 9/4 Mujadil (USA)—Sinegronto (IRE) (Kheleyf (USA)) (58071) **Nick & Olga Dhandsa & John & Zoe Webster**
145 B c 24/4 Sixties Icon—Spring Bouquet (IRE) (King's Best (USA))
146 B f 5/2 Paco Boy (IRE)—Stan's Smarty Girl (USA) (Smarty Jones (USA))
147 Ch f 11/3 Sir Percy—Sunley Shines (Komaite (USA))
148 B c 17/2 Bushranger (IRE)—Sweet Nicole (Okawango (USA)) (12000)
149 Ch f 14/4 Sixties Icon—The Screamer (IRE) (Insan (USA))
150 B c 17/4 Showcasing—Ticki Tori (IRE) (Vettori (IRE)) (22000)
151 B f 8/2 Camacho—Varnay (Machiavellian (USA)) (30971) **Jon & Julia Aisbitt**
152 B c 6/4 Fast Company (IRE)—Veronica Cooper (IRE) (Kahyasi) (30476) **Sheikh M. B. K. Al Maktoum**
153 B c 12/2 Winker Watson—Vilnius (Imperial Dancer)
154 B f 14/4 Paco Boy—Wansdyke Lass (Josr Algarhoud (IRE))
155 B c 21/3 Motivator—Yding (IRE) (Danehill (USA)) (5000) **Mr & Mrs D. D. Clee**

Other Owners: Mr F. T. Adams, J. R. Aisbitt, Mrs J. M. Aisbitt, Mrs J. M. Aisbitt, K. M. Al-Mudhaf, Mohammed Jasem Al-Qatami, E. Aldridge, Miss C. T. Aldridge, Miss E. Asprey, Sir M. F. Broughton, S. W. Broughton, D. D. Clee, Mrs J. P. Clee, The Hon Mrs C. Corbett, Dark Horse Racing Ltd, Dr N. Dhandsa, Mr T. V. Drayton, Mr S. D. Fisher, Mrs A. P. Fisher, Mrs M. Forsyth, Ms G. H. Hedley, Mr D. L. Hudd, Insignia Racing Limited, Mrs A. M. Jones, P. M. Julian, M F Logistics (UK) Ltd, Mike Channon Bloodstock Ltd, Mr M. Swallow, Mr P. Trant, Mrs T. G. Trant, Simon Trant, Mr J. Webster, Mr N. C. White, Mrs C. E. White, J. A. Williams, C. N. Wright.

---

107   MR MICHAEL CHAPMAN, Market Rasen

Postal: **Woodlands Racing Stables, Woodlands Lane, Willingham Road, Market Rasen, Lincolnshire, LN8 3RE**
Contacts: **PHONE/FAX (01673) 843663 MOBILE (07971) 940087**
E-MAIL woodlands.stables@btconnect.com WEBSITE www.woodlandsracingstables.co.uk

1 **BABY JUDGE (IRE),** 7, ch g Captain Rio—Darling Clementine **Mrs M. M. Chapman**
2 **DANCING WAVE,** 8, b m Baryshnikov (AUS)—Wavet **Mrs M. M. Chapman**
3 **EPEE CELESTE (FR),** 8, ch m Spadoun (FR)—Juste Ciel (USA) **Mrs S. M. Richards**
4 **FEELING PECKISH (USA),** 10, ch g Point Given (USA)—Sunday Bazaar (USA) **J. E. Reed**
5 **GALLEY SLAVE (IRE),** 9, b g Spartacus (IRE)—Cimeterre (IRE) **Mrs M. M. Chapman**
6 **JOYFUL MOTIVE,** 5, ch g Motivator—Triple Joy **Mrs M. M. Chapman**
7 **KATHINDI (IRE),** 7, ch g Pearl of Love (IRE)—Turfcare Flight (IRE) **Mrs M. M. Chapman**
8 **KHESKIANTO (IRE),** 8, b m Kheleyf (USA)—Gently (IRE) **F. A. Dickinson**
9 **LENDERKING (IRE),** 6, b g Sleeping Indian—Roses From Ridey (IRE) **Mrs S. M. Richards**
10 **MAZOVIAN (USA),** 6, b g E Dubai (USA)—Polish Style (USA) **Mrs M. M. Chapman**
11 **MONZINO (USA),** 6, b br g More Than Ready (USA)—Tasso's Magic Roo (USA) **Mrs M. M. Chapman**
12 **NIGHT REVELLER (IRE),** 11, b m Night Shift (USA)—Tir-An-Oir (IRE) **J. E. Reed**
13 **ORPEN WIDE (IRE),** 12, b g Orpen—Melba (IRE) **Mrs M. M. Chapman**
14 **OWLS FC (IRE),** 8, b m King's Best (USA)—Sadinga (IRE) **Mrs M. M. Chapman**
15 **PEAK SEASONS (IRE),** 11, ch g Raise A Grand (IRE)—Teresian Girl (IRE) **J. E. Reed**
16 **SANTO SUBITO (IRE),** 13, b g Presenting—Shinora (IRE) **Mrs M. M. Chapman**
17 **SIMPLIFIED,** 11, b m Lend A Hand—Houston Heiress (USA) **R. A. Gadd**
18 **SOPHIE'S BEAU (USA),** 7, b g Stormy Atlantic (USA)—Lady Buttercup (USA) **Mrs M. M. Chapman**
19 **TAYARAT (IRE),** 9, b g Noverre (USA)—Sincere (IRE) **Mrs M. M. Chapman**
20 **THE SOCIETY MAN (IRE),** 7, ch g Moscow Society (USA)—Redruth (IRE) **Mrs M. M. Chapman**
21 **TROPICAL SKY (IRE),** 6, b g Librettist (USA)—Tropical Breeze (USA) **Mrs S. M. Richards**
22 **VOGARTH,** 10, ch g Arkadian Hero (USA)—Skara Brae **Mrs M. M. Chapman**
23 **VOLCANIC JACK (IRE),** 6, b g Kodiac—Rosaria Panatta (IRE) **A. Mann**

MR MICHAEL CHAPMAN - Continued

24 **VORTEX STAR**, 5, gr g Dalakhani (IRE)—Spinning The Yarn **A. Mann**
25 **XENOPHON**, 6, b g Phoenix Reach (IRE)—Comtesse Noire (CAN) **J. M. Robinson**

THREE-YEAR-OLDS

26 **L'ES FREMANTLE (FR)**, b g Orpen (USA)—Grand Design **Quench Racing Partnership 2**

Other Owners: Mr B. Downard, Mr B. R. Harris, Mr M. Preedy, Mr R. J. Smeaton.

Assistant Trainer: Mr S. Petch

Conditional: Joe Cornwall. **Amateur:** Miss Alice Mills.

MS JANE CHAPPLE-HYAM, Newmarket
Postal: Rose Cottage, The Street, Dalham, Newmarket, Suffolk, CB8 8TF
Contacts: **PHONE (01638) 500451 FAX (01638) 661335 MOBILE (07899) 000555**
E-MAIL janechapplehyam@hotmail.co.uk

1 **ALLEGRI (IRE)**, 5, b g Key of Luck (USA)—Bermuxa (FR) **Mr Derek Iceton**
2 **APACHE (IRE)**, 6, b g Galileo (IRE)—Charroux (IRE) **Invictus**
3 **BERKELEY STREET (USA)**, 4, b g Street Cry (IRE)—Dream Ticket (USA) **Invictus**
4 **CAPTAIN BERTIE (IRE)**, 6, ch g Captain Rio—Sadika (IRE) **Invictus**
5 **JUNGLE BAY**, 7, b g Oasis Dream—Dominica **Mr S Brewster & Essex Racing Club**
6 **MULL OF KILLOUGH (IRE)**, 8, b g Mull of Kintyre (USA)—Sun Shower (IRE) **Invictus**
7 **NELSON'S VICTORY**, 4, b g Green Horizon—First Class Girl **Victory Racing**
8 **OTTAVINO (IRE)**, 5, b g Piccolo—Indian's Feather (IRE) **Ms J. F. Chapple-Hyam**
9 **SASKIA'S DREAM**, 6, b m Oasis Dream—Swynford Pleasure **Peter Bottomley & Jane Chapple-Hyam**
10 **SECRET ASSET (IRE)**, 9, gr g Clodovil (IRE)—Skerray **Simon & Mrs Jeanette Pierpoint**
11 **TOMMY'S SECRET**, 4, gr g Sakhee's Secret—La Gessa **Ms J. F. Chapple-Hyam**

THREE-YEAR-OLDS

12 **INJUN SANDS**, b c Halling (USA)—Serriera (FR) **Mrs M. D. Morriss**
13 **LARA LIPTON (IRE)**, b f Excellent Art—Dyness (USA) **Lady Susan Renouf & Jane Chapple-Hyam**

TWO-YEAR-OLDS

14 **AVENUE DES CHAMPS**, b c 27/1 Champs Elysees—Penang Cry (Barathea (IRE)) (15000) **Invictus**
15 B f 26/1 Indesatchel (IRE)—Buffy Boo (Agnes World (USA)) **Mrs Julie Martin**
16 B f 17/2 Avonbridge—Lady Berta (Bertolini (USA)) **Ms J. F. Chapple-Hyam**

Other Owners: Mr P. Bottomley, Mr S. Brewster, Mr D. A. Mccormick, Mr S. W. Pierpoint, Mrs J. T. Pierpoint, Lady S. Renouf, R. B. Root, Mrs J. P. Root, N. E. Sangster.

Assistant Trainer: Abigail Harrison

MR PETER CHAPPLE-HYAM, Newmarket
Postal: St Gatien Stables, All Saints Road, Newmarket, Suffolk, CB8 8HJ
Contacts: **PHONE (01638) 560827 FAX (01638) 561908 MOBILE (07770) 472774**
E-MAIL pchapplehyam@yahoo.com WEBSITE www.peterchapplehyam.com

1 **AGENT ALLISON**, 4, b f Dutch Art—Loquacity **Mrs F. H. Hay**
2 **BOITE (IRE)**, 4, b c Authorized (IRE)—Albiatra (USA) **Eledy SRL**
3 **BOSSA NOVA BABY (IRE)**, 4, b f High Chaparral—Attilia (GER) **P. M. Cunningham**
4 **BUCKSTAY (IRE)**, 4, b g Lawman (FR)—Stella Del Mattino (USA) **Mrs F. H. Hay**
5 **FUNKY COLD MEDINA**, 4, b f Cockney Rebel (IRE)—Monica Campbell **P. M. Cunningham**
6 **MY PROPELLER (IRE)**, 5, b m Holy Roman Emperor (IRE)—Incise **J. Barton**

THREE-YEAR-OLDS

7 **AL SENAD**, ch c Exceed And Excel (AUS)—Waafiah **Z. A. Galadari**
8 **ALPHABETIQUE**, b f Zamindar (USA)—Almamia **Miss K. Rausing**
9 **AROD (IRE)**, b c Teofilo (IRE)—My Personal Space (IRE) **Qatar Racing Limited**
10 **BATTLE COMMAND (USA)**, b br c Stormy Atlantic (USA)—Charmsil (USA) **Clipper Group Holdings Ltd**
11 **BAY OF ROSES (IRE)**, b f Pivotal—Heavenly Bay (USA) **Mrs F. H. Hay**
12 **CAPE MYSTERY**, b br f Cape Cross (IRE)—Maramba **Five Horses Ltd**

MR PETER CHAPPLE-HYAM - Continued

13 **DINO MITE**, b f Doctor Dino (FR)—Compose **P. Cunningham**
14 **DIRECT TIMES (IRE)**, b c Acclamation—Elegant Times (IRE) **Mr A. Belshaw**
15 **DOGARESSA (IRE)**, ch f Mastercraftsman (IRE)—Doregan (IRE) **Eledy SRL**
16 **ETERNITYS GATE**, b g Dutch Art—Regency Rose **Mrs F. H. Hay**
17 **FARQUHAR (IRE)**, ch c Archipenko (USA)—Pointed Arch (IRE) **Mr T Elliott & Mr P Cunningham**
18 **FEMALE STRATEGY (IRE)**, br f Holy Roman Emperor (IRE)—Strategy **Mrs F. H. Hay**
19 **GODDESS OF GLOOM**, br f Firebreak—Charcoal **Mr P. Hancock**
20 **GREEN LIGHT**, b c Authorized (IRE)—May Light **The End Of The Beginning Partnership**
21 **GROOVEJET**, b f Cockney Rebel (IRE)—Vino Veritas (USA) **P. M. Cunningham**
22 **HYDROGEN**, b c Galileo (IRE)—Funsie (FR) **Qatar Racing Limited**
23 **INCHILA**, b f Dylan Thomas (IRE)—Inchiri **Woodcote Stud Ltd**
24 **KICKING THE CAN (IRE)**, gr c Aussie Rules (USA)—Silk Meadow (IRE) **Bright Bloodstock**
25 **MAJESTIC SUN (IRE)**, b c King's Best (USA)—Shining Vale (USA) **The Horse Players Two**
26 **MASTER OF SUSPENSE**, ch c Exceed And Excel (AUS)—Ridotto **Mrs F. H. Hay**
27 **MIA SAN TRIPLE**, b f Invincible Spirit (IRE)—Atlantide (USA) **Gute Freunde Partnership**
28 **PLATINUM PEARL**, b f Shamardal (USA)—Gimasha **Z. A. Galadari**
29 **POLAR EYES**, b f Dubawi (IRE)—Everlasting Love **The Illusionists**
30 **ROCK 'N' ROLL STAR**, b c Cockney Rebel (IRE)—Sweet Afton (IRE) **P. M. Cunningham**
31 **STEELE RANGER**, b g Bushranger (IRE)—Tatora **Mr Khalifa Dasmal & Mrs Clodagh McStay**
32 **STUBBORN LOVE**, ch f New Approach (IRE)—Blue Rocket (IRE) **J. Barton**
33 **VOICE OF A LEADER (IRE)**, b c Danehill Dancer (USA)—
                                                  Thewaytosanjose (IRE) **Mrs Hay, Michael Tabor & Mrs John Magnier**

TWO-YEAR-OLDS

34 B c 24/4 Galileo (IRE)—Approach (Darshaan) (190000) **Qatar Racing Limited**
35 Ch c 24/2 Rock of Gibraltar (IRE)—Banksia (Marju (IRE)) (20905) **Mr Michael Beaumont**
36 B f 28/4 Cockney Rebel (IRE)—Compose (Anabaa (USA)) **P. M. Cunningham**
37 B c 4/5 Holy Roman Emperor (IRE)—Couverture (USA) (Lear Fan (USA)) (120000) **Mrs F. H. Hay**
38 Ch c 16/3 Footstepsinthesand—Danny's Choice (Compton Place) (50329) **Mrs F. H. Hay & Partners**
39 **ILLYA KURYAKIN**, b c 13/4 Cockney Rebel (IRE)—
                      Vino Veritas (USA) (Chief's Crown (USA)) (17142) **P. M. Cunningham**
40 B c 19/4 Holy Roman Emperor (IRE)—Indaba (IRE) (Indian Ridge) (38714) **Mr A. A. Al Shaikh**
41 B c 21/4 Fastnet Rock (AUS)—Nancy Spain (IRE) (Sadler's Wells (USA)) (81300) **Mrs F. H. Hay**
42 **NAPOLEON SOLO**, b c 23/2 Cockney Rebel (IRE)—
                      Trump Street (First Trump) (19047) **Phil Cunningham & Mr P Cunningham**
43 Br c 20/4 Kheleyf (USA)—Piverina (IRE) (Pivotal) (12380)
44 B c 17/2 Tagula (IRE)—Precipitous (IRE) (Indian Ridge) (33333) **Mr Paul Hancock & Partners**
45 B f 21/4 Makfi—Shemriyna (IRE) (King of Kings (IRE)) **Qatar Racing Limited**
46 B c 21/2 Alfred Nobel (IRE)—Van de Cappelle (IRE) (Pivotal) (19047) **Rebel Racing II**
47 B f 14/4 Aqlaam—Waafiah (Anabaa (USA)) **Z. A. Galadari**

Other Owners: A. W. Black, J. J. Brummitt, K. A. Dasmal, Mr A. R. Elliott, Mr A. Graham, Mr S. J. High, Mrs S. Magnier, Mrs C. McStay, Mr T. Muller, Mr C. Pizarro, A. H. Slone, L. G. Straszewski, M. Tabor.

---

110 MR PETER CHARALAMBOUS, Newmarket
Postal: **30 Newmarket Road, Cheveley, Newmarket, Suffolk, CB8 9EQ**
Contacts: **PHONE (01638) 730415 MOBILE (07921) 858421**
E-MAIL info@pcracing.co.uk WEBSITE www.pcracing.co.uk

1 **BOONGA ROOGETA**, 5, b m Tobougg (IRE)—Aberlady Bay (IRE) **pcracing.co.uk**
2 **COLINCA'S LAD (IRE)**, 12, b g Lahib (USA)—Real Flame **pcracing.co.uk**
3 **ELA GOOG LA MOU**, 5, b m Tobougg (IRE)—Real Flame **pcracing.co.uk**
4 **TRULEE SCRUMPTIOUS**, 5, b m Strategic Prince—Morning Rise (GER) **pcracing.co.uk**

THREE-YEAR-OLDS

5 **KALON BRAMA (IRE)**, b f Kodiac—Gilded Truffle (IRE) **pcracing.co.uk**
6 **L GE R**, b f Pastoral Pursuits—Cashbar **pcracing.co.uk**

TWO-YEAR-OLDS

7 B g 7/4 Virtual—Lady Agnes (Singspiel (IRE)) (2500) **pcracing.co.uk**
8 B f 27/3 Three Valleys (USA)—Velvet Waters (Unfuwain (USA)) (2000) **pcracing.co.uk**

111 **MR GEORGE CHARLTON, Stocksfield**
Postal: **Mickley Grange Farm, Stocksfield, Northumberland, NE43 7TB**
Contacts: **PHONE (01661) 843247 MOBILE (07808) 955029**
E-MAIL gcharlton@fsmail.net

1 BALLYVOQUE (IRE), 8, b g Revoque (IRE)—Timissa (IRE) **J. I. A. Charlton**
2 BOGSIDE (IRE), 10, ch g Commander Collins (IRE)—Miss Henrietta (IRE) **Mrs S. M. Wood**
3 KNOCKARA BEAU (IRE), 11, b g Leading Counsel (USA)—Clairabell (USA) **J. I. A. Charlton**
4 LORD USHER (IRE), 7, b g Lord Americo—Beet Five (IRE) **G. A. G. Charlton**
5 SHANKHOUSE WELLS (IRE), 6, b m Milan—Norwood Cross (IRE) **Sydney Ramsey & Partners**
6 WINSTONE (IRE), 9, b g Pierre—Cushenstown Best (IRE) **G. A. G. Charlton**

Other Owners: Mr Syd Ramsey, Mr J. T. Stobbs.

Assistant Trainer: Mr J. I. A. Charlton

Jockey (NH): Lucy Alexander, Jan Faltejsek.

112 **MR ROGER CHARLTON, Beckhampton**
Postal: **Beckhampton House, Marlborough, Wiltshire, SN8 1QR**
Contacts: **OFFICE (01672) 539533 HOME (01672) 539330 FAX (01672) 539456**
MOBILE (07710) 784511
E-MAIL r.charlton@virgin.net WEBSITE www.rogercharlton.com

1 BORDER LEGEND, 5, ch g Selkirk (USA)—Bonnie Doon (IRE) **Her Majesty The Queen**
2 CACTUS VALLEY (IRE), 5, b g Lawman (FR)—Beech Gardens **H.R.H. Sultan Ahmad Shah**
3 CAPTAIN CAT (IRE), 5, b br g Dylan Thomas (IRE)—Mother of Pearl (IRE) **Seasons Holidays**
4 CLOWANCE ESTATE (IRE), 5, b g Teofilo (IRE)—Whirly Bird **Seasons Holidays**
5 HUNTSMANS CLOSE, 4, b g Elusive Quality (USA)—Badminton **Brook House**
6 KAZAK, 4, b g Royal Applause—Kazeem **D. J. Deer**
7 MARZANTE (USA), 6, gr ro g Maria's Mon (USA)—Danzante (USA) **Beckhampton Stables Ltd**
8 QUEST FOR MORE (IRE), 4, b g Teofilo (IRE)—No Quest (IRE) **H.R.H. Sultan Ahmad Shah**
9 RANDOM SUCCESS (IRE), 4, b f Shamardal (USA)—Foreplay (IRE) **Beckhampton 2**
10 SECONDO (FR), 4, b g Sakhee's Secret—Royal Jade **D. J. Deer**
11 SO BELOVED, 4, b g Dansili—Valencia **K. Abdullah**
12 THISTLE BIRD, 6, b m Selkirk (USA)—Dolma (FR) **Lady Rothschild**
13 VALTINA (IRE), 4, b f Teofilo (IRE)—Vassiana (FR) **M J Taylor & L A Taylor**

THREE-YEAR-OLDS

14 AMBER ISLE (USA), b f First Defence (USA)—Family (USA) **K. Abdullah**
15 BE MY GAL, b f Galileo (IRE)—Longing To Dance **D. J. Deer**
16 BE MY ICON, b f Sixties Icon—Marathea (FR) **Wells House Racing**
17 BE SEEING YOU, ch g Medicean—Oshiponga **Mrs M. D. Stewart**
18 CANOVA (IRE), ch g Art Connoisseur (IRE)—Rain Dancer (IRE) **The Royal Ascot Racing Club**
19 CATADUPA, ch f Selkirk (USA)—Caribana **Miss K. Rausing**
20 CHAUVELIN, b g Sir Percy—Enforce (USA) **Mr Simon de Zoete & Partners 1**
21 CONTINENTAL DRIFT (USA), b br f Smart Strike (CAN)—Intercontinental **K. Abdullah**
22 DARK LEOPARD, b c Dubawi (IRE)—Clouded Leopard (USA) **Lady Rothschild**
23 DUMFRIES HOUSE, b g New Approach—Bonnie Doon (IRE) **Her Majesty The Queen**
24 ELITE FORCE (IRE), ch g Medicean—Amber Queen (IRE) **H.R.H. Sultan Ahmad Shah**
25 FRANGIPANNI, b br f Dansili—Frizzante **Lady Rothschild**
26 FRAY, b f Champs Elysees—Short Dance (USA) **K. Abdullah**
27 HIGH CHURCH (IRE), b g High Chaparral (IRE)—Tamso (USA) **Lady Rothschild**
28 HIKING (USA), b f First Defence (USA)—Trekking (USA) **K. Abdullah**
29 HOODED (USA), b c Empire Maker (USA)—Yashmak (USA) **K. Abdullah**
30 LADY TYNE, ch f Halling (USA)—Susun Kelapa (USA) **N. P. Hearson**
31 LAUGHARNE, b c Authorized (IRE)—Corsican Sunset (USA) **Seasons Holidays**
32 LILYFIRE, b f First Defence (USA)—Didina **K. Abdullah**
33 MAGIC SHOES (IRE), b f Manduro (GER)—Ammo (IRE) **A. E. Oppenheimer**
34 MAJOR JACK, b g Kheleyf (USA)—Azeema (IRE) **D. J. Deer**
35 MATEKA, ch f Nayef (USA)—Marakabei **Mrs J. A. M. Poulter**
36 OBSERVATIONAL, ch c Galileo (IRE)—Party (IRE) **Seasons Holidays**

MR ROGER CHARLTON - Continued

37 **OLD GUARD**, b g Notnowcato—Dolma (FR) **Lady Rothschild**
38 **PAGEANT BELLE**, ch f Bahamian Bounty—Procession **Axom XLV**
39 **PERSPICACE**, b g Sir Percy—Cassique Lady (IRE) **Paul Inglett & Partners 1**
40 **RACE TO GLORY (FR)**, b c Montjeu (IRE)—Cawett (IRE) **Team Valor LLC**
41 **ROCHAMBEAU (IRE)**, b g Sir Percy—Tableau Vivant (IRE) **Brook House**
42 **SAXON PRINCESS (IRE)**, b f Dalakhani (IRE)—Rhadegunda **A. E. Oppenheimer**
43 **SCARLET PLUM**, b f Pivotal—Scarlet Runner **N. M. H. Jones**
44 **SEA DEFENCE (USA)**, gr ro c Mizzen Mast (USA)—Palisade (USA) **K. Abdullah**
45 **SHARP LOOKOUT**, b g Shamardal (USA)—Tempting Prospect **Her Majesty The Queen**
46 **SKI BLAST**, ch g Three Valleys (USA)—Chasing Stars **K. Abdullah**
47 **SKILLED**, b g Mastercraftsman (IRE)—Treacle (USA) **Beckhampton 2**
48 **SLEEP WALK**, gr f Oasis Dream—Scuffle **K. Abdullah**
49 **STARS ABOVE ME**, b f Exceed And Excel (AUS)—Kalinova (IRE) **Elite Racing Club**
50 **STOMP**, b g Nayef (USA)—Strut **Lady Rothschild**
51 **TEMPTRESS (IRE)**, ch f Shirocco (GER)—Femme Fatale **The Pyoneers**
52 **TIDES REACH (IRE)**, ch f Mastercraftsman (IRE)—Oystermouth **D. J. Deer**
53 **WHY NOT NOW**, ch f Notnowcato—Perfect Night **Mr S. Emmet & Miss R. Emmet**
54 **WINTOUR LEAP**, b f Nayef (USA)—Mountain Leap (IRE) **D. J. Deer**

TWO-YEAR-OLDS

55 B c 11/2 Zamindar (USA)—Affluent (Oasis Dream) **K. Abdullah**
56 **ALLEZ ALAIA (IRE)**, ch f 30/3 Pivotal—Cassandra Go (Indian Ridge) **T. C. Stewart**
57 **ALLUMAGE**, b f 5/2 Montjeu (IRE)—Alaia (IRE) (Sinndar (IRE)) (100000) **M J Taylor & L A Taylor**
58 **ATAMAN (IRE)**, b c 16/2 Sholokhov (IRE)—Diora (IRE) (Dashing Blade) **M. Pescod**
59 B f 10/3 Dark Angel (IRE)—Bunditten (IRE) (Soviet Star) (40000) **Elite Racing Club**
60 B c 20/2 Oasis Dream—Clowance (Montjeu (IRE)) **Seasons Holidays**
61 B f 12/2 Rip Van Winkle (IRE)—Councilofconstance (IRE) (Footstepsinthesand) (32000) **Mr P. Inglett**
62 Ch c 9/4 Speightstown (USA)—Didina (Nashwan (USA)) **K. Abdullah**
63 Gr c 14/3 Duke of Marmalade (IRE)—Elisium (Proclamation (IRE)) (20000)
64 B f 1/3 Montjeu (IRE)—Freni (GER) (Sternkoenig (IRE)) **Seasons Holidays**
65 B f 20/2 Afleet Alex (USA)—High Walden (USA) (El Gran Senor (USA)) **K. Abdullah**
66 Ch f 24/4 Teofilo (IRE)—Home You Stroll (IRE) (Selkirk (USA)) **Mr C. M. Humber**
67 B f 24/4 Dansili—Jolie Etoile (USA) (Diesis) **K. Abdullah**
68 **JUDICIAL (IRE)**, b c 22/2 Iffraaj—Marlinka (Marju (IRE)) **Elite Racing Club**
69 B f 19/4 Dansili—Landela (Alhaarth (IRE)) (150000) **Mr C. M. Humber**
70 **LIBBARD**, ch f 20/2 Galileo (IRE)—Clouded Leopard (USA) (Danehill (USA)) **Lady Rothschild**
71 **MCCREERY**, b c 8/4 Big Bad Bob (IRE)—Dolma (FR) (Marchand de Sable (USA)) **Lady Rothschild**
72 B c 2/5 Oasis Dream—Minority (Generous (IRE)) **K. Abdullah**
73 B c 6/3 Shirocco (GER)—Missy Dancer (Shareef Dancer (USA)) (27000)
74 B f 1/4 Kheleyf (USA)—Morning After (Emperor Jones (USA)) (10000)
75 **MOUNTAIN RESCUE (IRE)**, b c 14/4 High Chaparral (IRE)—
                                    Amber Queen (IRE) (Cadeaux Genereux) (13000) **Lady Wellesley**
76 Gr c 29/2 Dubawi (IRE)—Mussoorie (IRE) (Linamix (FR)) (75000) **A. E. Oppenheimer**
77 B c 15/2 Acclamation—Obsara (Observatory (USA)) (90000) **HighclereThoroughbredRacing(Coronation)**
78 B c 11/3 Dubawi (IRE)—Passage of Time (Dansili) **K. Abdullah**
79 B f 24/1 Rail Link—Protectress (Hector Protector (USA)) **K. Abdullah**
80 B f 30/4 First Defence (USA)—Quick To Please (USA) (Danzig (USA)) **K. Abdullah**
81 **RUN BY FAITH**, b f 28/2 Sixties Icon—Sweet Pilgrim (Talkin Man (CAN)) **Mrs S. Hames**
82 Ch f 7/3 Champs Elysees—Scuffle (Daylami (IRE)) **K. Abdullah**
83 **SISTER OF MERCY (IRE)**, b f 28/2 Azamour (IRE)—Green Tambourine (Green Desert (USA)) (23228) **M. Pescod**
84 **SKATE**, gr c 4/3 Verglas (IRE)—Strut (Danehill Dancer (IRE)) **Lady Rothschild**
85 B c 28/3 Oasis Dream—Take The Hint (Montjeu (IRE)) **K. Abdullah**
86 B f 19/3 Iffraaj—Tullynally (Dansili) **A. E. Oppenheimer**

Other Owners: Axom Ltd, Mr A. Bamboye, Mr A. N. C. Bengough, Lady Bengough, Mr S. M. De Zoete, P. Dean, Mr D. Downie, Lt Cdr P. S. Emmet, Miss R. E. Emmet, The Hon H. M. Herbert, Highclere Thoroughbred Racing Ltd, Mr A. J. Hill, Mr P. J. Hopkirk, Mrs C. M. Hopkirk, Mr O. C. S. Lazenby, Ms M. Machin-Jefferies, Mr J. Makin, Miss M. Noden, Mr B. O'Brien, Mrs V. H. Pakenham, A. E. Pakenham, Mr C. D. Platel, Mr B. P. J. Spiers, Mr R. W. Stirling, Mr M. J. Taylor, Mr L. A. Taylor, Miss C. J. Wills.

Assistant Trainer: James Horton

Jockey (flat): James Doyle.

113 **MR HARRY CHISMAN, Stow-on-the-Wold**
Postal: **The Retreat Stables, Maugersbury, Stow-on-the-Wold, Gloucestershire, GL54 1HP**
Contacts: **PHONE (07787) 516723**
WEBSITE www.harrychisman.co.uk

1 **ALL RILED UP**, 6, b m Dr Massini (IRE)—Martha Reilly (IRE) **Goodall Grabham Olney Baker Sage Mesquit**
2 **AUGHCARRA (IRE)**, 9, b g High Chaparral (IRE)—Pearly Brooks **Grabham Waggott Seal Baker Byrne Bell**
3 **CAPTAIN KENDALL (IRE)**, 5, b g Clodovil (IRE)—Queen's Lace (IRE) **Goodall Kirkland Atherton Baker**
4 **GAINSBOROUGH'S ART (IRE)**, 9, ch g Desert Prince (IRE)—
Cathy Garcia (IRE) **Wood Grabham Goodall Welch Byrne Cooke**

Other Owners: Mr M. Atherton, Mr P. M. Baker, Mr Terry Bell, Mr Phillip Bueno De Mesquita, Mrs H. Byrne, Mr Harry Chisman, Mr V. R. Cooke, Mr Ray Goodall, Ms Shirley Grabham, Mr S. Kirkland, Mr M. Madden, Mr Ben Olney, Mr A. Sage, Mr B. Seal, Mr J. W. Waggott, Mr D. Welch, Mr Duncan Wood.

Jockey (NH): Tom O'Brien, Sean Quinlan, Andrew Tinkler.

114 **MRS JANE CLARK, Kelso**
Postal: **Over Roxburgh, Kelso, Roxburghshire, TD5 8LY**
Contacts: **PHONE (01573) 450271 FAX (01573) 450606 MOBILE (07977) 053634**
E-MAIL janerox@tiscali.co.uk

1 **FIDDLERS REEL**, 11, ch g Karinga Bay—Festival Fancy **Mrs M. J. Clark**

115 **MRS ANGELA CLARKE, Llangadog**
Postal: **Marlands, Llangadog, Dyfed, SA19 9EW**

1 **PANACHE**, 9, b g King's Best (USA)—Exclusive **Dr S. R. Clarke**
2 **PICOT DE SAY**, 12, b g Largesse—Facsimile **Dr S. R. Clarke**

116 **MR PATRICK CLINTON, Doveridge**
Postal: **Lordlea Farm, Marston Lane, Doveridge, Ashbourne, Derbyshire, DE6 5JS**
Contacts: **PHONE (01889) 566356 MOBILE (07815) 142642**

1 **BUSINESS BAY (USA)**, 7, b br g Salt Lake (USA)—Jeweled Lady (USA) **In The Clear Racing**
2 **IMPERIAL ROYALE (IRE)**, 13, ch g Ali-Royal (IRE)—God Speed Her **In The Clear Racing**
3 **NEZAMI (IRE)**, 9, b g Elnadim (USA)—Stands To Reason (USA) **In The Clear Racing**
4 9, B m Beat All (USA)—Salska **P. L. Clinton**
5 8, B g Beat All (USA)—Salska **In The Clear Racing**

Other Owners: G. Worrall.

Jockey (flat): Russ Kennemore.

117 **MR K. F. CLUTTERBUCK, Newmarket**
Postal: **Pond House Stables, Church Lane, Exning, Newmarket, Suffolk, CB8 7HF**
Contacts: **PHONE (01638) 577043 MOBILE (07868) 605995**

1 5, Bl m Grape Tree Road—Bayrouge (IRE) **K. F. Clutterbuck**
2 **NEVEROWNUP (IRE)**, 9, b g Quws—Cobble (IRE) **K. F. Clutterbuck**
3 **ROYAL MARSKELL**, 5, b g Multiplex—Socialise **Miss C. Y. Wootten**
4 **SAKHEE'S ALROUND**, 4, ch f Sakhee's Secret—Regal Run (USA) **The Little House Partnership**
5 **UNCLE PELDER (IRE)**, 7, b g Pelder (IRE)—Aunt Annie (IRE) **K. F. Clutterbuck**
6 **VITZNAU (IRE)**, 10, b g Val Royal (FR)—Neat Dish (CAN) **Mr D. Hazelwood**
7 **ZAFFARAN RAIN (IRE)**, 5, ch m Presenting—Borleagh Blonde (IRE) **The Chicanery Partnership**

MR K. F. CLUTTERBUCK - Continued

THREE-YEAR-OLDS
8 ZAFTUAL, b f Virtual—Zaffrani (IRE) **Mr D. Hazelwood**

Other Owners: Mr C. J. Baldwin, Mr W. A. McGregor, Mr W. I. Mckay, D. T. Norton.

---

118 **MR DENIS J. COAKLEY, West Ilsley**
Postal: **Keeper's Stables, West Ilsley, Newbury, Berkshire, RG20 7AH**
Contacts: **PHONE (01635) 281622 MOBILE (07768) 658056**
E-MAIL racing@deniscoakley.com WEBSITE www.deniscoakley.com

1 ALCANDO (IRE), 4, ch g Alhaarth (IRE)—Cantando (IRE) **The Good Mixers**
2 GABRIEL'S LAD (IRE), 5, b g Dark Angel (IRE)—Catherine Wheel **Killoran Ennis Conway**
3 HARDY PLUME, 5, ch g Manduro (GER)—Macleya (GER) **Mrs B. Coakley**
4 KASTINI, 4, b g Halling (USA)—Toucantini **West Ilsley Racing**
5 KING'S ODYSSEY (IRE), 5, b g King's Theatre (IRE)—Ma Furie (FR) **Mr J. K. Whymark**
6 MISS MARJURIE (IRE), 4, b f Marju (IRE)—Kazatzka **C. T. Van Hoorn**
7 REBECCA ROMERO, 7, b m Exceed And Excel (AUS)—Cloud Dancer **Keepers Racing II**
8 ROCKFELLA, 8, ch g Rock of Gibraltar (IRE)—Afreeta (USA) **Mr L. Raissi**

THREE-YEAR-OLDS
9 CASTAGNA GIRL, ch f Major Cadeaux—Ewenny **Finders Keepers Partnership**
10 KING CALYPSO, ch g Sir Percy—Rosa de Mi Corazon (USA) **Count Calypso Racing**
11 KUALA QUEEN (IRE), b f Kodiac—See Nuala (IRE) **Keeper's 12**
12 MON CIGAR (IRE), b c Bushranger (IRE)—Practicallyperfect (IRE) **Mr L. Raissi**
13 PRINCESS ALMALEK (IRE), ch f Dylan Thomas (IRE)—Diamond Circle **Mr L. Raissi**
14 PRINCESS HANANE (IRE), b gr f Clodovil (IRE)—Golden Ora (ITY) **Mrs B. Coakley**
15 SKANDER, b c Archipenko (USA)—Midnight Allure **Mrs B. Coakley**
16 STEPPE DAUGHTER (IRE), b f Steppe Dancer (IRE)—Carmencita **C. T. Van Hoorn**

TWO-YEAR-OLDS
17 CATAKANTA, b c 13/4 Notnowcato—Akanta (GER) (Wolfhound (USA)) (4000)
18 FANNY AGAIN, b f 12/3 Nayef (USA)—Sweet Wilhelmina (Indian Ridge) **C. T. Van Hoorn**
19 B f 6/3 Mawatheeq (USA)—Sparkling Montjeu (Montjeu (IRE)) (5500)

Other Owners: Mr A. P. Bloor, R. J. Bolam, G. Callegari, P. M. Emery, J. T. Ennis, Mr E. P. L. Faulks, Mr T. A. Killoran, J. G. Ross, R. D. Whitehead.

---

119 **MRS HEATHER COBB, Pulborough**
Postal: Kilbrannan Stud Farm, Gay Street, Pulborough, West Sussex, RH20 2HJ
Contacts: **PHONE (01798) 812541 FAX (01798) 817371 MOBILE (07764) 942854**
E-MAIL kilbrannanstud@aol.com

1 CLASSIC PEARL, 9, b m Spendent—Aun Ella **Mrs H. J. Cobb**
2 GENEROUS SPENDER, 8, b g Spendent—Molly Dreamer **Mrs H. J. Cobb**
3 MONTYS CASH, 8, b g Spendent—Satcotino (IRE) **Mrs H. J. Cobb**
4 ON THE ROB, 7, b g Spendent—Satcotino (IRE) **Mrs H. J. Cobb**

---

120 **MR PAUL COLE, Whatcombe**
Postal: Whatcombe Estate, Whatcombe, Wantage, Oxfordshire, OX12 9NW
Contacts: **PHONE (01488) 638433 FAX (01488) 638609**
E-MAIL admin@paulcole.co.uk WEBSITE www.paulcole.co.uk

1 BLUEGRASS BLUES (IRE), 4, gr g Dark Angel (IRE)—Dear Catch (IRE) **Mrs F. H. Hay**
2 CIRCUMVENT, 7, ch g Tobougg (IRE)—Seren Devious **The Fairy Story Partnership**
3 DENOTE, 4, b c Motivator—Darwinia (GER) **Mrs E. A. Bass**
4 DON LIBRE, 5, b g Librettist (USA)—Darwinia (GER) **Mrs E. A. Bass**
5 DOUBLE BILL (USA), 10, b br g Mr Greeley (USA)—Salty Perfume (USA) **P. F. I. Cole Ltd**
6 GIFTED GIRL (IRE), 5, b m Azamour (IRE)—Hoodwink (USA) **A. D. Spence**
7 KUANTAN ONE (IRE), 4, b g Strategic Prince—Starfish (IRE) **H.R.H. Sultan Ahmad Shah**

MR PAUL COLE - Continued

8 **SECRET SUCCESS**, 4, b g Exceed And Excel (AUS)—Magic Music (IRE) **P. F. I. Cole Ltd**
9 **SILVERHEELS (IRE)**, 5, gr g Verglas—Vasilia **P. F. I. Cole Ltd**
10 **ST PAUL DE VENCE (IRE)**, 4, b g Oratorio (IRE)—Ring The Relatives **Sir M Arbib, Mr C Wright & PFI Cole Ltd**
11 **STORMBOUND (IRE)**, 5, b g Galileo (IRE)—A Footstep Away (USA) **P. F. I. Cole Ltd**
12 **STRATEGIC STRIKE (IRE)**, 4, b g Strategic Prince—Puteri Wentworth **H.R.H. Sultan Ahmad Shah**

THREE-YEAR-OLDS

13 **BERKSHIRE (IRE)**, b c Mount Nelson—Kinnaird (IRE) **H.R.H. Sultan Ahmad Shah**
14 **CAFETIERE**, b f Iffraaj—Coffee Cream **A. H. Robinson**
15 **CAPE ARROW**, b g Cape Cross (IRE)—Aiming **C. Shiacolas**
16 **COMPLICIT (IRE)**, b c Captain Rio—Molomo **Mr T. R. B. T. A. Shah**
17 **DARK DAYS**, b c Black Sam Bellamy (IRE)—Darwinia (GER) **Mrs E. A. Bass**
18 **DUTCH ART DEALER**, b c Dutch Art—Lawyers Choice **R. Green**
19 **ELYSIAN PRINCE**, b c Champs Elysees—Trinkila (USA) **Mr D. S. Lee**
20 **FORT BERKELEY (IRE)**, b g Fastnet Rock (AUS)—Verbania (IRE) **Black Run Racing**
21 **GRECIAN (IRE)**, gr c Dark Angel (IRE)—Law Review (IRE) **Mrs F. H. Hay**
22 **LISAMOUR (IRE)**, b f Azamour (IRE)—Lisa de La Condra (IRE) **Mr F. P. Stella**
23 **MERITOCRACY (IRE)**, br g Kheleyf (USA)—Chiosina (IRE) **Mrs F. H. Hay**
24 **NIBBLING (IRE)**, b f Invincible Spirit (IRE)—Albarouche **Mrs F. H. Hay**
25 **NUSANTARA**, b f New Approach (IRE)—Pentatonic **Mrs F. H. Hay**
26 **POLISH BALLET**, b c Iffraaj—Madam Ninette **Mrs F. H. Hay**
27 **RUSH**, ch f Compton Place—Dorelia (IRE) **Denford Stud Limited**
28 **SKATERS WALTZ (IRE)**, gr g Verglas (IRE)—Xarzee (IRE) **Sir G Meyrick & the late Sir Dunnington-Jefferson**
29 **THATCHIT (IRE)**, b f Invincible Spirit (IRE)—Security Interest (USA) **Mr F. P. Stella**
30 **TIOGA PASS**, b f High Chaparral (IRE)—Seren Devious **The Fairy Story Partnership**
31 **TREASURE CAY (IRE)**, ch c Bahamian Bounty—Expedience (USA) **Meyrick, Dunnington-Jefferson & Wright**

TWO-YEAR-OLDS

32 **ARTHUR'S WAY (IRE)**, b c 5/2 Royal Applause—Chantilly Pearl (USA) (Smart Strike (CAN)) (31000)
33 **BRITISH ART**, b c 10/3 Iffraaj—Bush Cat (USA) (Kingmambo (USA)) (72000) **R. Green**
34 B c 9/2 Mount Nelson—Corndavon (USA) (Sheikh Albadou) (35000) **H.R.H. Sultan Ahmad Shah**
35 **DANCING ACES**, ch c 16/4 Shamardal (USA)—Rainbow Dancing (Rainbow Quest (USA)) (50329) **Mr D. Ali**
36 **DUSTY BLUE**, ch f 1/4 Medicean—Jazz Jam (Pivotal) **Denford Stud Limited**
37 **DUTCH PORTRAIT**, b c 4/4 Dutch Art—Silken Promise (USA) (Pulpit (USA)) (52000) **R. Green**
38 **FALMOUTH HARBOUR**, b c 22/4 Champs Elysees—Divina Mia (Dowsing (USA)) (4000)
39 **FAST ROMANCE (USA)**, b f 6/3 Fastnet Rock (AUS)—Satulagi (USA) (Officer (USA)) **Mrs F. H. Hay**
40 **GIPSY DOLL**, b f 17/4 Dansili—Gipsy Moth (Efisio) (85000) **Mrs M. Bryce**
41 **IMPERIAL LINK**, b f 12/2 Rail Link—Imperia (GER) (Tertullian (USA)) **Mrs E. A. Bass**
42 **JASMINE BLUE (IRE)**, b f 14/2 Galileo (IRE)—Impressionist Art (USA) (Giant's Causeway (USA)) **Mrs F. H. Hay**
43 **KIPUKA**, b f 24/2 Authorized (IRE)—Rakata (USA) (Quiet American (USA)) **A. H. Robinson**
44 B c 6/2 Danehill Dancer (IRE)—Kirkinola (Selkirk (USA)) (49000) **C. Shiacolas**
45 B c 7/5 Rip Van Winkle (IRE)—
                        Muskoka Dawn (USA) (Miswaki (USA)) (30000) **Pavel Erochkine & Camilla Rizayeva**
46 Ch c 19/2 Starspangledbanner (AUS)—Pivotalia (IRE) (Pivotal) (40000) **H.R.H. Sultan Ahmad Shah**
47 B c 27/2 Teofilo (IRE)—Quixotic (Pivotal) (178086) **Mrs F. H. Hay**
48 **SCIMITARRA**, gr f 10/5 Motivator—Scrupulous (Dansili) **Mrs E. A. Bass**
49 **SECRET FANTASIES**, b f 29/3 Fastnet Rock (AUS)—Trinkila (USA) (Cat Thief (USA)) **Mr D. S. Lee**
50 B c 28/2 Rock of Gibraltar (IRE)—Skehana (IRE) (Mukaddamah (USA)) (34000)
51 Gr c 20/3 Paco Boy (IRE)—Snowdrops (Gulch (USA)) (40262) **H.R.H. Sultan Ahmad Shah**
52 **SPEED MACHINE (IRE)**, b c 7/4 Naaqoos—Copernica (Galileo (IRE)) **Lane Racing Ltd**
53 B br c 28/1 Aussie Rules (USA)—
                        Why Worry (FR) (Cadeaux Genereux) (34843) **Pavel Erochkine & Camilla Rizayeva**

Other Owners: M. Arbib, T. M. Bird, Mrs V. Cole, Exors of the Late Sir Mervyn Dunnington-Jefferson, Mr P Erochkine, E. R. Goodwin, Ms I. Korolitcki, Sir George Meyrick, Mrs K. Rizayeva, Miss C. S. Scott-Balls, C. N. Wright.

Assistant Trainer: Oliver Cole

MR TOBIAS B. P. COLES, Newmarket
Postal: The Cottage, Phantom House, Fordham Road, Newmarket, Suffolk, CB8 7AA
Contacts: **MOBILE (07904) 779222**

1 **CAMELOPARDALIS**, 5, b m Tobougg (IRE)—Bonne Etoile
2 **DEAR MAURICE**, 10, b g Indian Ridge—Shamaiel (IRE)

MR TOBIAS B. P. COLES - Continued

3 **NELSON'S MUSE**, 4, b f Mount Nelson—French Quartet (IRE)
4 **WATCHABLE**, 4, ch g Pivotal—Irresistible

THREE-YEAR-OLDS

5 **APTITUDE**, ch f With Approval (CAN)—Moi Aussi (USA)
6 **COMPANY INK**, b f Authorized (IRE)—Priti Fabulous (IRE)
7 **EPSOM HILL (SWE)**, b c Homme d'honneur (FR)—Energiya Sacc (SWE)
8 **LA GRASSETTA (GER)**, b f Nayef (USA)—La Reine Noir (GER)
9 **MINLEY**, b g Acclamation—Fatal Attraction
10 **NABLUS (GER)**, b g Dai Jin—Nouvelle Princesse (GER)
11 B f Lemon Drop Kid—Nafisah (IRE)
12 **ORANGE GROVE**, ch c Hernando (FR)—Ryella (USA)
13 **RESIST**, b f Rock of Gibraltar (IRE)—Cecily
14 **ROCKED THE BOAT**, b c Mizzen Mast (USA)—Jazz Jam
15 **WAY WITH WORDS**, b g Intikhab (USA)—Winsa (USA)
16 **WINTER PICNIC (IRE)**, b f Oratorio (IRE)—Salpiglossis (GER)
17 **WULFTHRYTH**, b f Champs Elysees—Bolsena (USA)

TWO-YEAR-OLDS

18 **LITTLEMISSBLAKENEY**, b f 2/2 Sir Percy—Littlemisssunshine (IRE) (Oasis Dream)
19 B f 6/3 Sir Percy—Miss Prism (Niniski) (USA) (6194)
20 Br f 29/4 Sakhee's Secret—Pain Perdu (IRE) (Waajib)
21 B f 22/4 Fastnet Rock (AUS)—Scotch Bonnet (FR) (Montjeu (IRE)) (10000)
22 B f 16/2 Fastnet Rock (AUS)—Speak Softly To Me (USA) (Ogygian (USA)) (47619)
23 **UNNOTICED**, b c 6/4 Observatory (USA)—Celestial Empire (USA) (Empire Maker (USA))

Owners: P.Bamford, A. W. Black, Mrs J. E. Black, C. M. Budgett, Chasemore Farm LLP, Mr T. B. P. Coles, Mrs M. S. Coles, Denford Stud Limited, Dr S. Eversfield, The Far Yard Racing Club, Miss D. F. Fleming, Mrs Sarah Hamilton, Mr M. J. McStay, Mr S. L. Parker, Qatar Racing Limited, Miss K. Rausing, Mr J. H. Richmond Watson, Mr C. G. Rowles Nicholson, Mr T. Saito, Gestut Am Schlossgarten.

---

122 **MR STUART COLTHERD, Selkirk**
Postal: **Clarilawmuir Farm, Selkirk, Selkirkshire, TD7 4QA**
Contacts: **PHONE** (01750) 21251 **FAX** (01750) 21251 **MOBILE** (07801) 398199
E-MAIL wscoltherd@clarilawmuir.wanadoo.co.uk

1 **AMETHYST ROSE (IRE)**, 7, ch m Beneficial—Cap The Rose (IRE) **Whyte Binnie Macdonald Coltherd**
2 **CLOVERHILL LAD (IRE)**, 10, b g New Frontier (IRE)—Flat Dutch (IRE) **Coltherd Turnbull**
3 **DARSI DANCER (IRE)**, 6, b g Darsi (FR)—Jaystara (IRE) **W. S. Coltherd**
4 **DOUBLEDSDOUBLEDAT (IRE)**, 7, ch g Vinnie Roe (IRE)—Castle Graigue (IRE)
5 **FOL HOLLOW (IRE)**, 9, b g Monashee Mountain (USA)—Constance Do **Mr A. Gunning**
6 **FOZY MOSS**, 8, b g And Beyond (IRE)—Peggy Sioux (IRE) **J. Hogg**
7 **GUNNER LINDLEY (IRE)**, 7, ch g Medicean—Lasso **Mr A. Gunning**
8 **HOTGROVE BOY**, 7, b g Tobougg (IRE)—Tanwir **Coltherd Cawkwell**
9 **LACHLAN MOR**, 5, b g Josr Algarhoud (IRE)—Miss Campanella **Harelaw Racing**
10 **SHAN VALLEY (IRE)**, 8, ch m Shantou (USA)—Statim **Coltherd, Jeffrey & Hall**
11 **SHARNEY SIKE**, 8, ch g And Beyond (IRE)—Squeeze Box (USA) **J. Hogg**
12 **SUPRISE VENDOR (IRE)**, 8, ch g Fath (USA)—Dispol Jazz **Mr A. Gunning**
13 **TALKIN SENCE (IRE)**, 9, b g Heron Island (IRE)—Catatonia (IRE) **Gunning, Conchar, Hancock**
14 **TARTAN SNOW**, 14, b g Valseur (USA)—Whitemoss Leader (IRE) **R. V. Westwood**
15 **THATSMYLOT (IRE)**, 5, ch g Rudimentary (USA)—Yellow Soil Star (IRE) **Trevaskis Coltherd**

Other Owners: Mr R. A. Binnie, Mr S. F. Cawkwell, Mr T. Conchar, Mr R. M. Cox, Mr I. Hall, Mr N. Hancock, J. B. Jeffrey, R. MacDonald, Mr P. H. Pitchford, Mrs A. Trevaskis, Mr A. Turnbull, Mr A. G. Whyte.

Jockey (NH): Richie McGrath, Henry Brooke, Brian Harding. **Apprentice:** Gary Rutherford.

---

123 **MR ALAN COOGAN, Ely**
Postal: **31 Hasse Road, Soham, Ely, Cambridgeshire, CB7 5UW**
Contacts: **PHONE** (01353) 721673 **FAX** (01353) 721117

1 **ABANOAS (USA)**, 4, b br f Proud Citizen (USA)—Alabaq (USA) **A. B. Coogan**

MR ALAN COOGAN - Continued

2 **GRANDAD MAC**, 6, b g Invincible Spirit (IRE)—No Rehearsal (FR) **A. B. Coogan**
3 **SUNNY BANK**, 5, b g Notnowcato—Sweet Mandolin **A. B. Coogan**

124 **MR JOHN COOMBE, Weymouth**
Postal: **Sea Barn Farm, Fleet, Weymouth, Dorset, DT3 4ED**
Contacts: **PHONE (01305) 761745 (0780) 3752831 FAX (01305) 775396 MOBILE (07796) 990760**
E-MAIL wib@seabarnracing.com WEBSITE www.seabarnracing.com

1 **CHESIL BEACH BOY**, 11, b g Commanche Run—Eatons **M. J. Coombe**
2 **DAIS RETURN (IRE)**, 10, b g Lahib (USA)—Bayazida **J. D. Roberts**
3 **JUST WATCH OLLIE (IRE)**, 8, b g Indian Danehill (IRE)—Westgate Run **M. J. Coombe**
4 **SAN MARINO (FR)**, 11, ch g Bering—Sienne (FR) **M. J. Coombe**
5 **SHANNONS BOY (IRE)**, 12, b g Anshan—Dusky Lady **M. J. Coombe**
6 , B m Arkadian Hero (USA)—Zambran Calypso

Assistant Trainer: Mr John Roberts

Amateur: Mrs M. Roberts.

125 **MRS SUSAN CORBETT, Otterburn**
Postal: **Girsonfield, Otterburn, Newcastle upon Tyne, Tyne and Wear, NE19 1NT**
Contacts: **PHONE (01830) 520771 FAX (01830) 520771 MOBILE (07713) 651215**
E-MAIL girsonfield@outlook.com WEBSITE www.girsonfield.co.uk

1 **BALLYREESODE (IRE)**, 9, b g Waveney (UAE)—Sineads Joy (IRE) **Enright, Goodfellow, Corbett**
2 **BRACING**, 5, ch m Alflora (IRE)—Sports Express **Bissett Racing**
3 **DEFINITE APPEAL (IRE)**, 11, ch g Definite Article—Marian's Wish (IRE) **Mr W. F. Corbett**
4 **FIVE RIVERS (IRE)**, 8, ch g Accordion—Native Country (IRE) **Mr J. Goodfellow**
5 **HARLEYS MAX**, 5, b g Winged Love (IRE)—Researcher (IRE) **Mr W. F. Corbett**
6 **JORDANS DAY**, 9, gr m Baryshnikov (AUS)—Magical Day **Mrs J. L. Corbett**
7 **MARY MAY**, 6, b m Ferrule (IRE)—Leighton Lass (IRE) **Ms R. Enright**
8 **MASTER SPIDER (IRE)**, 5, b g Scorpion—Penteli **Mr W. F. Corbett**
9 **RIPONIAN**, 4, ch g Trade Fair—Dispol Katie **Mr W. F. Corbett**
10 **SAMANDY**, 5, ch m Septieme Ciel (USA)—Magical Day **Mr W. F. Corbett**
11 **SUPER COLLIDER**, 7, b g Montjeu (IRE)—Astorg (USA) **Mrs J. L. Corbett**
12 **TOARMANDOWITHLOVE (IRE)**, 6, ch m Choisir (AUS)—Deadly Buzz (IRE) **Ms R. Enright**

Other Owners: A. A. Bissett, Mrs J. Bissett.

Assistant Trainer: Mr W.F. Corbett

Conditional: James Corbett.

126 **MR LIAM CORCORAN, Castle Cary**
Postal: **Lovington Racing Stables, Ashview Farm, Lovington, Castle Cary, Somerset, BA7 7PU**
Contacts: **MOBILE (07789) 368234**
E-MAIL corcoranracing@aol.co.uk

1 **ADVANCEMENT**, 11, b g Second Empire (IRE)—Lambast **Mr M. J. Lethbridge**
2 **BARON'S BEST**, 4, gr g Lucky Story (USA)—Dispol Isle (IRE) **Mrs V. A. P. Antell**
3 **CUTE COURT (IRE)**, 7, b g Court Cave (IRE)—Cute Play **Mrs V. A. P. Antell**
4 **DBANKS (IRE)**, 11, ch g Blueprint (IRE)—Smiles Again (IRE) **Miss C. L. Bowles**
5 **DO MORE BUSINESS (IRE)**, 7, b g Dubai Destination (USA)—Tokyo Song (USA) **Mr R. Prince**
6 **FLASHY LAD (IRE)**, 7, ch g Blueprint (IRE)—Flashy Pearl (IRE) **A. J. Norman**
7 **GAIR LEAT (IRE)**, 10, ch g Oscar Schindler (IRE)—Valsdaughter (IRE) **Mr R. B. Antell**
8 **GIREVOLE**, 6, b g Tiger Hill (IRE)—Taranto **Mr R. B. Antell**
9 **ICE COOL BREEZE (IRE)**, 7, b m Kris Kin (USA)—Klipperstreet (IRE) **Miss C. L. Bowles**
10 4, ch f Devil's Jump—Lady Grenville
11 4, ch f Franklins Gardens—Launceston
12 **MICHAELA'S CHOICE (IRE)**, 6, b m Heron Island (IRE)—Rock On Susie (IRE) **Mr N. A. Eggleton**
13 **MURCAR**, 9, ch g Medicean—In Luck **Mr R. B. Antell**
14 **OH SO HIGH (IRE)**, 5, ch m Mountain High (IRE)—Oh So Breezy (IRE) **Mr N. A. Eggleton**

MR LIAM CORCORAN - Continued

15 **STERLING GENT (IRE)**, 7, gr g Cloudings (IRE)—Company Credit (IRE) **Mr R. B. Antell**
16 **SULA TWO**, 7, b m Sulamani (IRE)—There's Two (IRE) **Mr R. Prince**
17 **UNCLE BUNGE (IRE)**, 8, b g Rock of Gibraltar (IRE)—Ouija's Sister **Mr N. A. Eggleton**

---

127 | **MR JOHN CORNWALL, Melton Mowbray**
Postal: **April Cottage, Pasture Lane, Hose, Melton Mowbray, Leicestershire, LE14 4LB**
Contacts: **PHONE (01664) 444453 FAX (01664) 444754 MOBILE (07939) 557091**
E-MAIL johncornwall7@gmail.com

1 **FIFTYONEFIFTYONE (IRE)**, 10, b g Oscar (IRE)—Great Dante (IRE) **J. R. Cornwall**
2 **FLICHITY (IRE)**, 9, br g Turtle Island (IRE)—Chancy Gal **J. R. Cornwall**
3 **MAD PROFESSOR (IRE)**, 11, b g Mull of Kintyre (USA)—Fancy Theory (USA) **J. R. Cornwall**
4 **NEXT EXIT (IRE)**, 9, b g Exit To Nowhere (USA)—Pilgrim Star (IRE) **J. R. Cornwall**
5 **PHOENIX DES MOTTES (FR)**, 11, b g Useful (FR)—Camille des Mottes (FR) **J. R. Cornwall**
6 **RADSOC DE SIVOLA (FR)**, 9, bl g Video Rock (FR)—Kerrana (FR) **J. R. Cornwall**
7 **THAT'S THE DEAL (IRE)**, 10, b br g Turtle Island (IRE)—Sister Swing **J. R. Cornwall**

Conditional: Joe Cornwall.

---

128 | **MR ROBERT COWELL, Newmarket**
Postal: **Bottisham Heath Stud, Six Mile Bottom, Newmarket, Suffolk, CB8 0TT**
Contacts: **PHONE (01638) 570330 FAX (01638) 570330 MOBILE (07785) 512463**
E-MAIL robert@robertcowellracing.co.uk WEBSITE www.robertcowellracing.co.uk

1 **ANGEL'S PURSUIT (IRE)**, 7, ch g Pastoral Pursuits—Midnight Angel **Malih L. Al Basti**
2 **ARCTIC LYNX (IRE)**, 7, b g One Cool Cat (USA)—Baldemara (FR) **Heading For The Rocks Partnership**
3 **DARK DIAMOND (IRE)**, 4, b g Dark Angel (IRE)—Moon Diamond **Mr Khalifa Dasmal & Bottisham Heath Stud**
4 **DUKE OF FIRENZE**, 5, ch h Pivotal—Nannina **Cheveley Park Stud Limited**
5 **GOLDREAM**, 5, br g Oasis Dream—Clizia (IRE) **Mr J Sargeant & Mrs J Morley**
6 **IFFRANESIA (FR)**, 4, ch f Iffraaj—Farnesina (FR) **C. Humphris**
7 **INDIAN TINKER**, 5, b g Sleeping Indian—Breakfast Creek **Mr J. Sargeant**
8 **INTRINSIC**, 4, b c Oasis Dream—Infallible **Bottisham Heath Stud**
9 **JIROFT (ITY)**, 7, b g Blu Air Force (IRE)—Dexia (ITY) **Thomas Morley & Speedlic Racing**
10 **KINGSGATE NATIVE (IRE)**, 9, b g Mujadil (USA)—Native Force (IRE) **Cheveley Park Stud Limited**
11 **MAGLIETTA FINA (IRE)**, 5, gr m Verglas (IRE)—Whipped Queen (USA) **Scuderia Archi Romani**
12 **MARCH**, 4, b f Dutch Art—Royal Pardon **Al Asayl Bloodstock Ltd**
13 **NORMAL EQUILIBRIUM**, 4, b g Elnadim (USA)—Acicula (IRE) **T W Morley & Mrs J Morley**
14 **PEARL ACCLAIM (IRE)**, 4, b c Acclamation—With Colour **Pearl Bloodstock Limited**
15 **PROHIBIT**, 9, b g Oasis Dream—Well Warned **Dasmal, Rix, Barr, Morley, Mrs Penney**
16 **R WOODY**, 7, ch g Ishiguru (USA)—Yarrita **Quintessential Thoroughbreds & Partner**
17 **ROYAL ACQUISITION**, 4, b c Royal Applause—Flavian **Mr J. Sargeant**
18 **SILKEN EXPRESS (IRE)**, 5, ch m Speightstown (USA)—Laureldean Express **Malih L. Al Basti**
19 **SIR PEDRO**, 5, b g Acclamation—Milly-M **T. W. Morley**
20 **SUEHAIL**, 5, b g Cadeaux Genereux—Why Dubai (USA) **Malih L. Al Basti**
21 **UBETTERBEGOOD (ARG)**, 6, b g Distorted Humor (USA)—Movie Star (BRZ) **Malih L. Al Basti**
22 **VICTORY LAUREL (IRE)**, 4, b c Holy Roman Emperor (IRE)—Special Cause (IRE) **Qatar Racing Limited**

THREE-YEAR-OLDS

23 **COPPER CAVALIER**, ch c Haafhd—Elle Crystal **Mrs D Rix, Mr J Partridge & Partner**
24 **FEBRAYER STAR**, br c Majestic Missile (IRE)—Ginger Not Blonde (USA) **Mr A. Gzema**
25 B g Kyllachy—Fondled **Malih L. Al Basti**
26 **HOT AMBER (USA)**, ch f Langfuhr (CAN)—Tres Chaud (USA) **Mr T W Morley & Speedlic Racing**
27 B f U S Ranger (USA)—My Little Dragon (IRE) **Speedlic Racing**
28 **NAIVASHA**, b f Captain Gerrard (IRE)—Netta (IRE) **Lowther Racing**
29 Ch c Teofilo (IRE)—Neat Shilling (IRE) **Malih L. Al Basti**
30 **OASIS MIRAGE**, b f Oasis Dream—Canda (USA) **Cheveley Park Stud Limited**
31 **SKINNY LOVE**, b f Holy Roman Emperor (IRE)—Lady Mickataine (USA) **Mr T W Morley & Mr J Barton**
32 **SPEED HAWK (USA)**, b br c Henny Hughes (USA)—Cosmic Wing **K. A. Dasmal**
33 **VIED (USA)**, b f Elusive Quality (USA)—Unacloud (USA) **Muhammed Nadeem & Yasmin Khan**

MR ROBERT COWELL - Continued

TWO-YEAR-OLDS

34 B c 22/3 Showcasing—Excello (Exceed And Excel (AUS)) **Bottisham Heath Stud**
35 B c 13/2 Sakhee's Secret—Greenfly (Green Desert (USA)) (35000)
36 IL ZENDER (FR), gr c 20/3 Namid—Pearl Argyle (FR) (Oasis Dream) (17034) **Qatar Racing Limited**
37 B f 20/1 Arcano (IRE)—Lyca Ballerina (Marju (IRE)) (55238) **Mr Abdulla Al Mansoori**
38 B f 26/4 Stimulation (IRE)—Sontime (Son Pardo) (9523) **Mr A. Goode**
39 B c 30/3 Vale of York (IRE)—Sweet Home Alabama (IRE) (Desert Prince (IRE)) **Mr Sultan Ali**
40 Ch f 5/3 Notwowcato—Two Step (Mujtahid (USA)) **Bottisham Heath Stud**
41 B f 26/3 Acclamation—Upperville (IRE) (Selkirk (USA)) (50000) **Mr Abdulla Al Mansoori**

Other Owners: Mr Paolo Agostini, Mrs Emma Agostini, Al Asayl Bloodstock Ltd, Malih Al Basti, Mr Sultan Ali, Mr Federico Barberini, Mr F. G. Barr, Mr Joseph Barton, Cheveley Park Stud, Mr Khalifa Dasmal, Mr A. Goode, Miss S. Hoare, Mr C. Humphris, Mr Muhammad Nadeem Khan, Mrs Yasmin Reana Nadeem Khan, Countess of Lonsdale, Manor Farm Stud (Rutland), Mr Abdulla Al Mansoori, Mr T. W. Morley, Mrs J. Morley, Mr Christopher Newing, Newsells Park Stud, Mr Malcolm Norman, Mr J. Partridge, Pearl Bloodstock, Mrs J. M. Penney, Qatar Racing, Mr Leo Quinn, Mr Peppe Quintale, Mr Allen Rix, Mrs Diana Rix, Mr J. Sargeant, Mr S. J. Whelan.

Assistant Trainer: Miss Claire Short

---

129 **MR PAUL COWLEY, Banbury**
Postal: **Lodge Farm Barn, Culworth, Banbury, Oxfordshire, OX17 2HL**
Contacts: **PHONE (01295) 768998 MOBILE (07775) 943346**
E-MAIL paulcowleyequine@yahoo.co.uk

1 BILL THE LAD (IRE), 7, b g Classic Cliche (IRE)—Quilty's Rose Bud (IRE) **S. G. West**
2 4, B f Definite Article—Campannello
3 GRAND ARTICLE (IRE), 10, ch g Definite Article—Grand Morning (IRE) **S. G. West**
4 HARRIS GARDEN (IRE), 7, b g Pilsudski (IRE)—Bay Pearl (FR) **Mrs A. Cowley**
5 SEAS OF GREEN, 7, ch m Karinga Bay—Emerald Project (IRE) **Mrs R. M. Wilkinson**

Other Owners: Mr R. Batchelor, Mr L. A. Garfield, Mr J. Leadbetter, Mr C. Smyth-Osborne, Mr D. Wilson.

---

130 **MR CLIVE COX, Hungerford**
Postal: **Beechdown Farm, Sheepdrove Road, Lambourn, Hungerford, Berkshire, RG17 7UN**
Contacts: **OFFICE (01488) 73072 FAX (01488) 73500 MOBILE (07740) 630521**
E-MAIL clive@clivecox.com WEBSITE www.clivecox.com

1 AINT GOT A SCOOBY (IRE), 4, br g Red Clubs (IRE)—La Bataille (USA) **Mrs O. A. Shaw**
2 AQUATINTA (GER), 4, b f Samum (GER)—Arpista (GER) **Mr P. W. Harris**
3 DANCE EXPRESS (IRE), 5, b m Rail Link—Swingsky (IRE) **Mrs T. L. Cox**
4 ES QUE LOVE (IRE), 5, br h Clodovil (IRE)—Es Que **Crone Stud Farms Ltd**
5 GREYLAMI (IRE), 9, gr g Daylami (IRE)—Silent Crystal (USA) **Mr J Humphreys & Mr B Ecclestone**
6 HASSLE (IRE), 5, b g Montjeu (IRE)—Canterbury Lace (USA) **A. D. Spence**
7 HE'S NO ANGEL (IRE), 5, ch g Excellent Art—Gentle Night **Mr B Ecclestone & Mr J Humphreys**
8 HIGHLAND DUKE (IRE), 5, b g Dansili—House In Wood (FR) **Highland Thoroughbred Ltd**
9 JIMMY STYLES, 10, ch g Inchinor—Inya Lake **Gwyn Powell & Peter Ridgers**
10 MALILLA (IRE), 4, b f Red Clubs (IRE)—Maleha (IRE) **Mrs T. L. Cox**
11 MILLY'S GIFT, 4, b f Trade Fair—Milly's Lass **Ken Lock Racing**
12 PERFECT CRACKER, 6, ch g Dubai Destination (USA)—Perfect Story (IRE) **Mildmay Racing**
13 PERFECT HAVEN, 4, gr f Singspiel (IRE)—Night Haven **Hants & Herts**
14 PERFECT MUSE, 4, b f Oasis Dream—Perfect Echo **R. J. Vines**
15 PERFECT VENTURE, 4, b f Bahamian Bounty—Perfect Cover (IRE) **Mildmay Racing**
16 POET, 9, b g Pivotal—Hyabella **Mrs T. L. Cox**
17 RED TO AMBER (IRE), 4, b c Redback—Amber's Bluff **Mrs O. A. Shaw**
18 SANDAURA (IRE), 4, b f Footstepsinthesand—Stratosmere **Mrs T. L. Cox**
19 SEEKING MAGIC, 6, b g Haafhd—Atnab (USA) **The Seekers**
20 SHADES OF GREY, 7, gr m Dr Fong (USA)—Twosixtythreewest (FR) **Dr & Mrs John Merrington**

THREE-YEAR-OLDS

21 Ch c Pivotal—Abandon (USA) **Qatar Racing Limited**
22 ADVANCE (FR), b c Aqlaam—Rabeera **Al Asayl Bloodstock Ltd**
23 ANDROID (IRE), ch g Dandy Man (IRE)—Noble View (USA) **Al Asayl Bloodstock Ltd**

MR CLIVE COX - Continued

24 **ASHKARI (IRE)**, ch c Dutch Art—Frivolity **Al Asayl Bloodstock Ltd**
25 **BATUTA**, b f New Approach (IRE)—Nantyglo **Wood Hall Stud**
26 **BELDALE MEMORY (IRE)**, b f Camacho—Hartstown House (IRE) **Qatar Racing Limited**
27 **BOWBERRY**, b f Cockney Rebel (IRE)—Blaeberry **Lady Bland**
28 **BRIGHT CECILY (IRE)**, b f Excellent Art—Roman Love (IRE) **Old Peartree Stud**
29 **CAPE ICON**, b c Mount Nelson—Cape Merino **Mondial Racing & Robert Haim**
30 **DEBIT**, b g Pivotal—Silver Kestrel (USA) **Mr D. J. Burke & Mr Peter Alderson**
31 **DESERT ACE (IRE)**, ch c Kheleyf (USA)—Champion Place **Arabian Knights**
32 **DO WAH DIDDY DIDDY**, b c Teofilo (IRE)—Quite Elusive (USA) **A. D. Spence**
33 **DUTCH S**, ch f Dutch Art—Park Law (IRE) **Mondial Racing & Robert Haim**
34 **FEAR OR FAVOUR (IRE)**, b c Haatef (USA)—Insaaf **A. G. Craddock**
35 **GOLDEN JOURNEY (IRE)**, ch c Nayef (USA)—Beatrix Potter (IRE) **P. N. Ridgers**
36 **HIGHLAND STARDUST**, b f Sakhee (USA)—Highland Starlight (USA) **Highland Thoroughbred Ltd**
37 **JACOB BLACK**, b c Amadeus Wolf—First Eclipse (IRE) **Redgate Bloodstock Ltd**
38 **KENDAL MINT**, b f Kyllachy—Windermere Island **Hot To Trot Racing Club & Mrs J Scott**
39 **LACAN (IRE)**, b c New Approach (IRE)—Invincible Isle (IRE) **Al Asayl Bloodstock Ltd**
40 **LE MAITRE CHAT (USA)**, b g Tale of The Cat (USA)—Bedside Story **M. H. Watt**
41 **MARMARUS**, b g Duke of Marmalade (IRE)—Polly Perkins (IRE) **Ms G. F. Khosla**
42 **MY MAJOR (IRE)**, b g Holy Roman Emperor (IRE)—Greek Easter (USA) **Mr P. W. Harris**
43 **PENDLEY LEGACY**, b f Leporello (IRE)—Albavilla **Mr P. W. Harris**
44 **PERFECT BLESSINGS (IRE)**, b f Kheleyf (USA)—Yxenery (IRE) **Mr John Drew & Mr Ian M Brown**
45 **PERFECT PURSUIT**, b f Pastoral Pursuits—Perfect Cover (IRE) **Mr J Drew & Mr D H Caslon**
46 **PROCKS GIRL**, gr f Proclamation (IRE)—Sashay **Calne Engineering Ltd**
47 **RAISE YOUR GAZE**, gr g Mastercraftsman (IRE)—Regal Magic (IRE) **Miss J. Deadman & Mr S. Barrow**
48 **REDINHA**, b f Dansili—So Squally (GER) **Mr P. W. Harris**
49 **SHANKLY**, br c Monsun (GER)—Miracle Seeker **Qatar Racing Ltd & Mr D J Burke**
50 **SPIRIT OF FANTASY**, b f Manduro (GER)—Aline (GER) **Mrs M. Campbell-Andenaes**
51 **STEREO LOVE (FR)**, b c Champs Elysees—My Heart's Deelite (USA) **Al Asayl Bloodstock Ltd**
52 **STRATEGIC FORCE (IRE)**, b g Strategic Prince—Mooching Along (IRE) **P. N. Ridgers**
53 **TRILLIAN ASTRA (IRE)**, b f Bahamian Bounty—Ms Sophie Eleanor (USA) **Mr A. B. S. Webb**
54 **TUBEANIE (IRE)**, ch f Intense Focus (IRE)—Ryalahna (IRE) **A. Butler**
55 **UNBRIDLED JOY (IRE)**, b f Acclamation—Unlock (IRE) **B Allen, G Hill & N Wagland**
56 **UNFORGING MINUTE**, b c Cape Cross (IRE)—Ada River **Mr P. W. Harris**
57 **VOYAGEOFDISCOVERY (USA)**, b br c Henrythenavigator (USA)—Look Out Lorie (USA) **The Navigators**
58 **WESTERN BELLA**, b f High Chaparral (IRE)—Sindarbella **Theakston Stud**
59 **WHAT A SCORCHER**, b f Authorized (IRE)—Street Fire (IRE) **Mr & Mrs P Hargreaves & Mr A D Spence**
60 **WINTER SPICE (IRE)**, gr g Verglas (IRE)—Summer Spice (IRE) **Spice Traders**

TWO-YEAR-OLDS

61 B c 26/4 Major Cadeaux—Alexander Ballet (Mind Games) (40000) **Mr & Mrs P. Hargreaves**
62 Ch c 23/3 Shamardal (USA)—Anse Victorin (USA) (Mt Livermore (USA)) (57142) **C. G. Cox**
63 Ch f 12/2 Leporello (IRE)—Baileys Honour (Mark of Esteem (IRE)) (4000) **C. G. Cox**
64 B f 4/3 Camacho—Belle of The Blues (IRE) (Blues Traveller (IRE)) (30971) **Qatar Racing Limited**
65 **BRAZEN SPIRIT**, gr c 17/2 Zebedee—Never Say Deya (Dansili) (19047) **Mr T. H. S. Fox**
66 Ch f 9/2 Siyouni (FR)—Crozon (Peintre Celebre (USA)) (476) **Mrs J Maitland-Jones**
67 Ch f 23/2 Pivotal—Dea Caelestis (FR) (Dream Well (FR)) **Mr David W. Armstrong**
68 B c 1/5 Paco Boy (IRE)—Fairy Contessa (IRE) (Fairy King (USA) (20000) **Tony Perkins**
69 FINIAL, ch f 13/3 Dutch Art—Rotunda (Pivotal) **Cheveley Park Stud**
70 Br c 8/4 Kodiac—Hawattef (IRE) (Mujtahid (USA)) (62000) **Mrs O. A. Shaw**
71 **LADY D'S ROCK (IRE)**, gr f 5/4 Aussie Rules (USA)—Za Za (Barathea (IRE)) (26325) **Mrs A. M. Dawes**
72 **LAIDBACK ROMEO**, br c 15/3 Kodiac—Belmora (USA) (Scrimshaw (USA)) (24777) **Mr R. P. Craddock**
73 **LITTLE PALAVER**, b c 16/4 Showcasing—Little Nymph (Emperor Fountain) (1428) **Mr T. H. S. Fox**
74 **LOUIE DE PALMA**, b c 22/4 Pastoral Pursuits—Tahirah (Green Desert (USA)) (46000) **P. N. Ridgers**
75 B c 15/4 Makfi—Marika (Marju (IRE)) (50000) **Qatar Racing Limited**
76 B f 21/3 High Chaparral (IRE)—Millestan (IRE) (Invincible Spirit (IRE)) (36000) **Mr D J Burke**
77 Gr c 30/4 Aussie Rules (USA)—My American Beauty (Wolfhound (USA)) (20905) **New Syndicate**
78 Ch f 29/3 Equiano (FR)—Mystic Love (Pivotal) **Mr David W. Armstrong**
79 Ch f 27/2 Sakhee's Secret—Naayla (IRE) (Invincible Spirit (IRE)) (26666) **New Syndicate**
80 Ch f 8/3 Bahamian Bounty—Perfect Cover (IRE) (Royal Applause) **Mildmay Racing**
81 Ch f 14/3 Equiano (FR)—Perfect Story (IRE) (Desert Story (IRE)) (46000) **Mildmay Racing & D. H. Caslon**
82 **POLAR VORTEX**, ch f 24/4 Pastoral Pursuits—Valandraud (IRE) (College Chapel) (24761) **A. G. Craddock**
83 **PRESSURE**, ch c 6/3 Equiano (FR)—Classical Dancer (Dr Fong (USA)) (85000) **A. D. Spence**
84 **PROFITABLE**, b c 16/2 Invincible Spirit (IRE)—Dani Ridge (IRE) (Indian Ridge) (95000) **A. D. Spence**
85 **QUINTUS CERIALIS**, b c 12/4 Vale of York (IRE)—Red Fox (IRE) (Spectrum (IRE)) (40000) **Brighthelm Racing**

MR CLIVE COX - Continued

86 **SHALIMAH (IRE)**, br c 10/2 Dark Angel (IRE)—Jemima's Art (Fantastic Light (USA)) (27000) **Mrs C. A. Craddock**
87 B c 12/4 Cockney Rebel (IRE)—Smart Red (Bachelor Duke (USA)) (8000) **Mr P Bamford & Mr D Barnes**
88 B c 21/4 Arch (USA)—Sneak Preview (Monsieur Bond (IRE)) (42000) **Inner Circle Thoroughbreds - Lavery**
89 B c 5/2 Duke of Marmalade (IRE)—Splendid (IRE) (Mujtahid (USA)) (29422) **New Syndicate**
90 **ST GEORGES ROCK (IRE)**, b c 18/2 Camacho—Radio Wave (Dalakhani (IRE)) (100000) **Mrs A. M. Dawes**
91 **TARLETON**, b c 17/3 Invincible Spirit (IRE)—Aguinaga (IRE) (Machiavellian (USA)) (61942) **D. W. Armstrong**
92 **TICKS THE BOXES (IRE)**, ch c 5/3 Fast Company (IRE)—
                                           Swan Sea (USA) (Sea Hero (USA)) (38095) **Miss J. Deadman & Mr S. Barrow**
93 Ch c 20/4 Dutch Art—Valentina Guest (IRE) (Be My Guest (USA)) (90000) **D. W. Armstrong**

Other Owners: P. S. Alderson, Miss B. Allen, S. W. Barrow, J. Bernstein, Mrs N. M. Booth, I. M. Brown, D. J. Burke, D. H. Caslon, Miss J. Deadman, Dr S. B. Drew, J. R. Drew, Mr B. C. Ecclestone, G. W. Elphick, Mr T. Elphick, Mr D. C. Flynn, Miss E. Foley, Miss C. A. Green, R. Haim, Mrs R. J. Hargreaves, Mr P. K. Hargreaves, Mr J. Hetherington, Mr S. Hill, Mr G. I. Hill, Mr R. S. Hoskins, J. Humphreys, Inner Circle Thoroughbreds Limited, Ms D. S. Jones, L. Lillington, Mrs R. F. Lowe, Mr J. C. McGrath, Mr A. McIntyre, Miss C. McIntyre, Dr J. Merrington, Mrs U. Merrington, G. E. Powell, Mrs J. M. M. Scott, Mr N. Wagland.

Jockey (flat): John Fahy, Adam Kirby. **Apprentice:** Ryan Tate.

---

131 MR TONY COYLE, Norton
Postal: **Long Row Stables, Beverley Road, Norton, Malton, North Yorkshire, YO17 9PJ**
Contacts: **MOBILE (07976) 621425**
E-MAIL **tonycoyleracing@hotmail.co.uk**

1 **BILLY CUCKOO (IRE)**, 8, b g Alderbrook—First Battle (IRE) **Gary Dewhurst & Tony Coyle**
2 **CHECKPOINT**, 5, ch g Zamindar (USA)—Kalima **24-7 Recruitment & Brian Dunn**
3 **DAYLAN (IRE)**, 6, b g Darsi (FR)—Mrs McClintock (IRE) **Twenty Four Seven Recruitment Services Ltd**
4 **DYNASTIC**, 5, b g Dynaformer (USA)—Demure **M. A. O'Donnell**
5 **FLICKA WILLIAMS (IRE)**, 7, b g Broadway Flyer (USA)—
                                           Millies Girl (IRE) **Twenty Four Seven Recruitment Services Ltd**
6 **ITS A STING (IRE)**, 5, b g Scorpion (IRE)—Wyndham Sweetmarie (IRE) **Mrs A. M. O'Sullivan**
7 **KEEP IT DARK**, 5, b g Invincible Spirit (IRE)—Tarneem (USA) **N. Hetherton**
8 **LANDMARQUE**, 5, b g Milan—M N L Lady **C. E. Whiteley**
9 **LOST IN PARIS (IRE)**, 8, b g Elusive City (USA)—Brazilia **Mr A. C. Coyle**
10 **LUCKY LANDING (IRE)**, 8, b br g Well Chosen—Melville Rose (IRE) **Gary Dewhurst & Tony Coyle**
11 **MAD JAZZ**, 4, b f Sir Percy—Gwen John (USA) **Brian Kerr & Chris Green & Tony Coyle**
12 **NOWDORO**, 5, ch g Notnowcato—Salydora (FR) **Wentdale Limited**
13 **PIPER HILL (IRE)**, 6, b g Hawk Wing (USA)—Mini Dane (IRE) **Twenty Four Seven Recruitment Services Ltd**
14 **PROBABLY SORRY**, 5, ch g Osorio (GER)—Twist The Facts (IRE)
15 **QOUBILAI (FR)**, 10, b g Passing Sale (FR)—Varcady (FR) **Mr B. Kerr**
16 **RIVER DRAGON (IRE)**, 9, b g Sadler's Wells (USA)—Diarshana (GER) **Brian Kerr & Tony Coyle**
17 **SHILLITO**, 4, b g Kyllachy—Kiss Me Kate **Mr A. C. Coyle**
18 **SILVER DRAGON**, 6, gr g Silver Patriarch (IRE)—Gotogeton **Twenty Four Seven Recruitment Services Ltd**
19 **SON OF FLICKA**, 10, b g Groom Dancer (USA)—Calendula **Twenty Four Seven Recruitment Services Ltd**
20 **SURGING SEAS (IRE)**, 5, b g Tiger Hill (IRE)—Musardiere **Mr A. C. Coyle**
21 **THATCHERITE (IRE)**, 6, gr g Verglas—Damiana (IRE) **Mr B. Kerr**
22 **TWO MOONS**, 4, b g Echo of Light—Forever Loved **Mr A. C. Coyle**
23 **TY'N Y WERN**, 5, b g Dylan Thomas (IRE)—Silk (IRE) **Mr A. C. Coyle**

THREE-YEAR-OLDS

24 **BARBARA ELIZABETH**, b f Sir Percy—Fair View (GER) **Michael O'Donnell & I Milburn & N Kench**
25 B c Three Valleys (USA)—Bollin Rita
26 **FLOWER POWER**, b f Bollin Eric—Floral Rhapsody **Ms M. H. Matheson**
27 **IRONDALE EXPRESS**, b f Myboycharlie (IRE)—Olindera (GER) **W. P. Flynn**
28 **KIRKSTALL ABBEY (IRE)**, b f Bushranger (IRE)—Spanish Falls **Morecool Racing & Gary Dewhurst**
29 **LENDAL BRIDGE**, ch g Avonbridge—Dunloe (IRE) **Will Dawson, R Stenton, V C Sugden**
30 **LILY RULES (IRE)**, br f Aussie Rules—Causeway Charm (USA) **C. E. Whiteley**
31 **MAYSVILLE (IRE)**, b f Lawman (FR)—Morality
32 **NEWGATE QUEEN**, gr f Phoenix Reach (IRE)—Arctic Queen **W. P. S. Johnson**
33 **TANCRED (IRE)**, b g Oratorio (IRE)—Mythologie (FR) **The End Of The Beginning Partnership**

TWO-YEAR-OLDS

34 **BINKY BLUE (IRE)**, b f 1/3 Approve (IRE)—Sabander Bay (USA) (Lear Fan (USA)) (10065) **B. Dunn**
35 **JUST NO RULES**, gr f 13/4 Aussie Rules (USA)—Grand Lucre (Grand Slam (USA)) (5000) **Mr G. Dewhurst**

MR TONY COYLE - Continued

36 B f 11/3 Kyllachy—Lady McBeth (IRE) (Avonbridge) (7619) **Morecool Racing**
37 B f 20/3 Bushranger (IRE)—Lady Thyne (IRE) (Mujadil (USA)) (3619)
38 **LUCILLA AURELIUS (IRE),** b f 14/4 Holy Roman Emperor (IRE)—
Spiritual Air (Royal Applause) (9523) **The Birrafun Partnership**
39 **MAUREB (IRE),** br f 28/3 Excellent Art—
Almost Blue (USA) (Mr Greeley (USA)) (11614) **Gap Personnel & Craig Buckingham**
40 Ch f 15/2 Sir Percy—Misplace (IRE) (Green Desert (USA)) (10000)
41 **MOLLY APPROVE (IRE),** b f 18/3 Approve (IRE)—Kathleen Rafferty (IRE) (Marju (IRE)) (4761) **Kerr's Cronies**
42 B f 14/3 Jeremy—Prakara (IRE) (Indian Ridge) (11614)
43 **PRINCESS BLUE,** b f 9/3 Bushranger (IRE)—Nevada Princess (IRE) (Desert Prince (IRE)) (3000) **B. Dunn**
44 B f 5/3 Baltic King—Red Trance (IRE) (Soviet Star (USA)) (6000)
45 B f 1/3 Multiplex—Romping Home (IRE) (Rock Hopper) **Mr G. Dewhurst**
46 Gr f 15/4 Zebedee—Rublevka Star (USA) (Elusive Quality (USA)) (9000)
47 **SIR KELTIC BLUE,** b g 4/4 Sir Percy—
Bougainvilia (IRE) (Bahamian Bounty) (37000) **Brian Dunn & Michael Beaumont**
48 B f 18/1 Sakhee's Secret—Snow Moccasin (USA) (Oasis Dream) (1500)

Other Owners: Mr M. Beaumont, Mr S. Bland, J. J. Brummitt, Mr C. Buckingham, Mr B. J. Connolly, Mr W. R. J. Dawson, Gap Personnel Franchises Limited, C. R. Green, Mr N. M. Kench, Mr I. Milburn, A. H. Slone, Mr R. Stenton, L. G. Straszewski, Mr M. C. P. Suddards, Mrs V. C. Sugden, Mr M. Sykes, Mr A. Wilson.

Assistant Trainer: Jaimie Kerr

Jockey (flat): Stephen Craine, Barry McHugh. **Amateur:** Miss Harriet Dukes.

---

132 **MR RAY CRAGGS, Sedgefield**
Postal: **East Close Farm, Sedgefield, Stockton-On-Tees, Cleveland, TS21 3HW**
Contacts: **PHONE (01740) 620239 FAX (01740) 623476**

1 **FLEURTILLE,** 5, b m Tillerman—Miss Fleurie **R. Craggs**
2 **NEEDWOOD PARK,** 6, br g Needwood Blade—Waterpark **R. Craggs**
3 **SHOWMEHOW,** 6, b m Grape Tree Road—Rasin Luck **R. Craggs**

THREE-YEAR-OLDS

4 **TAKE A BREAK,** b f Josr Algarhoud (IRE)—Waterpark **R. Craggs**

Assistant Trainer: Miss J N Craggs

---

133 **MR PETER CRATE, Newdigate**
Postal: **Springfield Farm, Parkgate Road, Newdigate, Dorking, Surrey, RH5 5DZ**
Contacts: **MOBILE (07775) 821560**
E-MAIL peterdcrate@jandjfranks.com

1 **ELUSIVITY (IRE),** 6, b g Elusive City (USA)—Tough Chic (IRE) **P. D. Crate**
2 **LIONHEART,** 4, ch g Zamindar (USA)—Victoire Celebre (USA) **P. D. Crate**
3 **LUJEANIE,** 8, br g Lujain (USA)—Ivory's Joy **Peter Crate & Gallagher Equine Ltd**
4 **PICANSORT,** 7, b g Piccolo—Running Glimpse (IRE) **P. D. Crate**
5 **SANDFRANKSKIPSGO,** 5, ch g Piccolo—Alhufoof (USA) **P. D. Crate**
6 **TAAJUB (IRE),** 7, b g Exceed And Excel (AUS)—Purple Tiger (IRE) **P. D. Crate**
7 **TOP OFFER,** 5, b g Dansili—Zante **P. D. Crate**

Other Owners: Gallagher Equine Ltd.

Jockey (flat): Shane Kelly, Adam Kirby. **Amateur:** Mr George Crate.

---

134 **MR EDWARD CREIGHTON, Sittingbourne**
Postal: **Eyehorn Farm, Oad Street, Munsgore Lane, Borden, Sittingbourne, Kent, ME9 8JU**
Contacts: **PHONE (01795) 842455 MOBILE (07772) 760442**
E-MAIL edwardcreighton@btinternet.com WEBSITE www.eyehornfarm.co.uk

1 **BIG WHISKEY (IRE),** 4, ch g Ad Valorem (USA)—El Opera (IRE) **Mr N. Dyshaev**
2 **BOLD RING,** 8, ch m Bold Edge—Floppie Disk **Miss C. L. Harper**

MR EDWARD CREIGHTON - Continued

3 **CHUNCK**, 7, ch g Alflora (IRE)—Gaye Fame **Mrs K. Douglas**
4 **GIRL AT THE SANDS (IRE)**, 4, gr f Clodovil (IRE)—Invincible Woman (IRE) **Mr P. Dewey**
5 **GREEK ISLANDS (IRE)**, 6, b g Oasis Dream—Serisia (FR) **Mr P. Dewey**
6 **MIA'S VIC (IRE)**, 9, b g Old Vic—Mill Lane Flyer (IRE) **Mr P. Dewey**
7 **PRINCESS SPIRIT**, 5, b m Invincible Spirit (IRE)—Habariya (IRE) **Mr N. Dyshaev**
8 **SALLY BRUCE**, 4, b f Byron—Show Trial (IRE) **Ripple Racing**
9 **TARTARIA**, 8, b m Oasis Dream—Habariya (IRE) **Mr N. Dyshaev**

THREE-YEAR-OLDS

10 **BLACK SCEPTRE (IRE)**, br c Diamond Green (FR)—Salford Princess (IRE) **Mr D. A. Creighton**
11 Ch g Tobougg (IRE)—Brogue Lanterns (IRE) **Mr D. A. Creighton**

TWO-YEAR-OLDS

12 Ch f 11/4 Dutch Art—Flawless Diamond (IRE) (Indian Haven) **Mr J. Griffin**
13 B f 12/2 Azamour (IRE)—Galileo's Star (IRE) (Galileo (IRE)) (25000) **Miss C. L. Harper**
14 Bc 4/4 Vale of York (IRE)—Lady Van Gogh (Dubai Destination (USA)) (24761) **Mr N. Dyshaev**
15 Ch c 1/5 Mount Nelson—Lolita's Gold (USA) (Royal Academy (USA)) **Mr N. Dyshaev**
16 B c 13/2 Mawatheeq (USA)—Muwakaba (USA) (Elusive Quality (USA)) (7742) **Mr N. Dyshaev**
17 B c 19/4 Fast Company (IRE)—Salty Air (IRE) (Singspiel (IRE)) **Mr N. Dyshaev**
18 **VERULAMIUM**, b f 17/3 Myboycharlie (IRE)—Actionplatinum (IRE) (Act One) **Mr J. Schwartz**

Other Owners: Miss K. M. Ferguson, Mrs Janys Ferguson.

---

135 **MR ANDREW CROOK, Leyburn**
Postal: **Ashgill Stables (Yard 2), Tupgill Park, Coverham, Middleham, North Yorkshire, DL8 4TJ**
Contacts: **PHONE (01969) 640303 MOBILE (07764) 158899**
E-MAIL andycrookracing@fsmail.net WEBSITE www.andrewcrookracing.co.uk

1 **AGESILAS (FR)**, 6, gr g Ultimately Lucky (IRE)—Aimessa du Berlais (FR) **R. P. E. Berry**
2 **AIR CHIEF**, 9, ch g Dr Fong (USA)—Fly For Fame **Lucky Catch Partnership**
3 **ALONG CAME THEO (IRE)**, 4, b g Vertical Speed (FR)—Kachina (IRE) **Mr G. Heap**
4 **BOCAMIX (FR)**, 8, gr g Linamix (FR)—Bocanegra (FR) **Mrs H. Sinclair**
5 **CABAL**, 7, br m Kyllachy—Secret Flame **Leeds Plywood & Doors Ltd**
6 **CORNISH CASTLE (USA)**, 8, ch g Mizzen Mast (USA)—Rouwaki (USA) **Mrs D. S. Wilkinson**
7 **JIMMIE BROWN (USA)**, 6, b g Street Cry (IRE)—Vid Kid (CAN) **The 100 Club**
8 **LORD AVONBROOK**, 4, b g Avonbridge—Miss Brookie **Lucky Catch Partnership**
9 **MATMATA DE TENDRON (FR)**, 14, gr g Badolato (USA)—Cora des Tamarix (FR) **Lucky Catch Partnership**
10 **MUTANAWWER**, 5, br g Red Ransom (USA)—Nasheed (USA) **RA Syndicate**
11 **PHILCHEZSKI (IRE)**, 7, ch g Pilsudski (IRE)—Springfield Gilda (IRE)
12 **PINK MISCHIEF**, 4, gr f Holy Roman Emperor (IRE)—Feather (USA) **Lucky Catch Partnership**
13 **RED JOKER (IRE)**, 4, br g Red Clubs (IRE)—Lady Singspiel (IRE) **D. C. Young**
14 **REMEDIO (IRE)**, 4, b g Ramonti (FR)—Cant Hurry Love
15 **REVERBERATE**, 5, b m Echo of Light—Niseem (USA) **Lucky Catch Partnership**
16 **RORY BOY (USA)**, 9, b g Aldebaran (USA)—Purr Pleasure (USA) **J. D. Gordon**
17 **SAVILLE ROW (IRE)**, 9, b g Snurge—Designer Lady **Lucky Catch Partnership**
18 **SEA CLIFF (IRE)**, 10, b g Golan (IRE)—Prosaic Star (USA) **Mrs D. S. Wilkinson**
19 **SHEILAS LADY**, 6, b m Tamure (IRE)—Ladies From Leeds **Mr T. E. England**
20 **SOHCAHTOA (IRE)**, 8, b g Val Royal (FR)—Stroke of Six (IRE) **John Sinclair (Haulage) Ltd**
21 **STRATHAIRD (IRE)**, 10, b g Medicean—Heed My Warning (IRE) **Mrs K. M. Savage**
22 **TWO OSCARS (IRE)**, 8, b g Oscar (IRE)—Coumeenoole Lady **Lucky Catch Partnership**
23 **YOUNG JAY**, 4, b g Josr Algarhoud (IRE)—Young Sue **Adamson Etheridge Henderson Evans**
24 **ZAZAMIX (FR)**, 9, b g Sagamix (FR)—Ombre Bleue (FR) **Mrs C. Hopper**

THREE-YEAR-OLDS

25 B f Alflora (IRE)—Fairlie

TWO-YEAR-OLDS

26 **FOUR BUCKS**, b g 15/3 Virtual—Jontys'lass (Tamure (IRE))

MR ANDREW CROOK - Continued

Other Owners: Mr G. G. Adamson, Mr M. Bland, Mr G. P. Clarkson, A. Crook, Mr Gary Etheridge, Mr S. N. Evans, Miss S. R. Haynes, Mr W. Henderson, Mr J. A. Saxby.

Jockey (flat): Robert Havlin, Franny Norton. **Jockey (NH):** Dougie Costello, Ryan Mania. **Conditional:** Johnny England. **Amateur:** Mr Darren Costello.

---

136 MISS JO CROWLEY, Whitcombe
Postal: Whitcombe Monymusk Racing Stables, Whitcombe, Dorchester, Dorset, DT2 8NY
Contacts: **PHONE (01305) 265300 FAX (01305) 265499 MOBILE (07918) 735219**
E-MAIL jocrowley61@hotmail.co.uk

1 5, B m Cockney Rebel (IRE)—Bianca Sforza **Mrs J. A. Cornwell**
2 **CAPTAIN STARLIGHT (IRE),** 4, b g Captain Marvelous (IRE)—Jewell In The Sky (IRE) **Kilstone Ltd**
3 **COMADOIR (IRE),** 8, ch g Medecis—Hymn of The Dawn (USA) **Mrs E. A. M. Nelson**
4 **EMPEROR JULIUS (IRE),** 4, b g Antonius Pius (USA)—Queen's Victory **Kilstone Ltd**
5 4, B g Haatef (USA)—Fantastic Account **Mrs J. A. Cornwell**
6 **MUSIC MAN (IRE),** 4, b g Oratorio (IRE)—Chanter **Kilstone Ltd**
7 **MYSTICAL SAPPHIRE,** 4, b f Sakhee's Secret—Nadyma (IRE) **Mrs E. A. M. Nelson**
8 **PATAVIUM PRINCE (IRE),** 11, ch g Titus Livius (FR)—Hoyland Common (IRE) **Mrs E. A. M. Nelson**
9 **PRINCESS ICICLE,** 6, b m Iceman—Sarabah (IRE) **Kilstone Ltd**
10 **SWEET MARWELL (IRE),** 4, b f Excellent Art—Bee Eater (IRE) **Mrs E. A. M. Nelson**
11 **THE HOLYMAN (IRE),** 6, ch g Footstepsinthesand—Sunset (IRE) **Kilstone Ltd**
12 **THRASOS (IRE),** 5, b g Invincible Spirit (IRE)—Plymsole (USA) **Kilstone Ltd**
13 **WILFRED PICKLES (IRE),** 8, ch g Cadeaux Genereux—Living Daylights (IRE) **Kilstone Ltd**

THREE-YEAR-OLDS

14 **DREAM BIG (IRE),** b f Echo of Light—Lovely Dream (IRE) **Pinehurst Stud**
15 **DREAM RULER,** b g Holy Roman Emperor (IRE)—Whatcameoverme (USA) **Mrs E. A. M. Nelson**
16 **PERRYDOT (IRE),** b f Footstepsinthesand—Titoli di Coda (IRE) **Mrs E. A. M. Nelson**
17 **ROSARINA,** ch f Rock of Gibraltar (IRE)—Spring Fashion (IRE) **Mrs J. A. Cornwell**
18 Ch f Compton Place—Starfleet **Mrs J. A. Cornwell**

TWO-YEAR-OLDS

19 **SHAVAUGHN,** b f 24/2 Kheleyf (USA)—Shannon Falls (FR) (Turgeon (USA)) **Mrs E. A. M. Nelson**
20 B f 21/2 Paco Boy (IRE)—Takarna (IRE) (Mark of Esteem (IRE)) **Mrs J. A. Cornwell**
21 **TANZINA,** b f 9/4 Equiano (IRE)—Pilcomayo (IRE) (Rahy (USA)) **Mrs E. A. M. Nelson**

Other Owners: Mr M. Pou, Mr T. J. Roberts.

Assistant Trainer: Anthony Clark

Jockey (flat): Dane O'Neill, Fergus Sweeney.

---

137 MR LUCA CUMANI, Newmarket
Postal: Bedford House Stables, Bury Road, Newmarket, Suffolk, CB8 7BX
Contacts: **PHONE (01638) 665432 FAX (01638) 667160 MOBILE (07801) 225300**
E-MAIL luca@lucacumani.com WEBSITE www.lucacumani.com

1 **AFSARE,** 7, b g Dubawi (IRE)—Jumaireyah **Sheikh Mohammed Obaid Al Maktoum**
2 **AJMAN BRIDGE,** 4, ch c Dubawi (IRE)—Rice Mother (IRE) **Sheikh Mohammed Obaid Al Maktoum**
3 **AJMANY (IRE),** 4, b g Kheleyf (USA)—Passarelle (USA) **Sheikh Mohammed Obaid Al Maktoum**
4 **AMELIORATE (IRE),** 4, b f Galileo (IRE)—Arkadina (IRE) **Merry Fox Stud Limited**
5 **AYAAR (IRE),** 4, b br c Rock of Gibraltar (IRE)—Teide Lady **H.E. Sheikh J. B. H. B. K. Al Thani**
6 **BONANZA CREEK (IRE),** 4, b r Anabaa (USA)—Bright Moon (USA) **Wildenstein Stables Limited**
7 **BOUCLIER (IRE),** 4, ch c Zamindar (USA)—Bastet (USA) **Wildenstein Stables Limited**
8 **DANADANA (IRE),** 6, b h Dubawi (IRE)—Zeeba (IRE) **Sheikh Mohammed Obaid Al Maktoum**
9 **ELHAAME (IRE),** 4, b g Acclamation—Gold Hush (USA) **Sheikh Mohammed Obaid Al Maktoum**
10 **ENDLESS CREDIT (IRE),** 4, b br g High Chaparral (IRE)—Pay The Bank **L. Marinopoulos**
11 **HAVANA COOLER (IRE),** 4, ch c Hurricane Run (IRE)—Unquenchable (USA) **L. Marinopoulos**
12 **JAZZ MASTER,** 4, b c Singspiel (IRE)—Turn of A Century **Castle Down Racing**
13 **KHIONE,** 5, b m Dalakhani (IRE)—Sularina (IRE) **Aston House Stud**
14 **KIKONGA,** 4, b f Danehill Dancer (IRE)—Kibara **Fittocks Stud**
15 **KINDU,** 4, b f Pivotal—Kithanga (IRE) **Fittocks Stud**

MR LUCA CUMANI - Continued

16 **KIRTHILL (IRE)**, 6, b g Danehill Dancer (IRE)—Kirtle **L. Marinopoulos**
17 **MAKAFEH**, 4, br g Elusive Quality (USA)—Demisemiquaver **Sheikh Mohammed Obaid Al Maktoum**
18 **MALLORY HEIGHTS (IRE)**, 4, gr c Dalakhani (IRE)—My Dark Rosaleen **Merry Fox Stud Limited**
19 **MISSION APPROVED**, 4, b g Dansili—Moon Search **H.E. Sheikh J. B. H. B. K. Al Thani**
20 **MOUNT MACEDON**, 4, b c Hernando (FR)—White Palace **Mr S. A. Stuckey**
21 **NELSON'S HILL**, 4, b g Mount Nelson—Regal Step **L. Marinopoulos**
22 **NORWAY CROSS**, 4, b f Cape Cross (IRE)—Queen of Norway (USA) **Bartisan Racing**
23 **PASSING PARADE**, 4, b f Cape Cross (IRE)—Model Queen (USA) **Merry Fox Stud Limited**
24 **PLEASURE BENT**, 4, b c Dansili—Nitya (FR) **C. Bennett**
25 **SAIGON CITY**, 4, b g Mount Nelson—Hoh Chi Min **L. Marinopoulos**
26 **SEMEEN**, 5, b g Dubawi (IRE)—Zeeba (IRE) **Sheikh Mohammed Obaid Al Maktoum**
27 **SEUSSICAL (IRE)**, 4, b br c Galileo (IRE)—Danehill Music (IRE) **O.T.I. Racing**
28 **SILK SARI**, 4, b f Dalakhani (IRE)—So Silk **Fittocks Stud & Andrew Bengough**
29 **SIR MIKE**, 5, ch g Haafhd—Tara Moon **H.E. Sheikh J. B. H. B. K. Al Thani**
30 **SIR WALTER SCOTT (IRE)**, 4, b c Galileo (IRE)—Flamingo Sea (USA) **O.T.I. Racing**
31 **VELOX**, 4, b g Zamindar (USA)—Victoire Finale **Mr S. A. Stuckey**
32 **VERMONT (IRE)**, 4, b g Muhtathir—Venetian Beauty **Wildenstein Stables Limited**

THREE-YEAR-OLDS

33 **ALISIOS (GR)**, b c Iaysos (GR)—Macanuda (IRE) **L. Marinopoulos**
34 **ALKETIOS (GR)**, b c Kavafi (IRE)—Mazea (IRE) **L. Marinopoulos**
35 **BACK TO BUXTED (IRE)**, b c Aqlaam—Incoming Call (USA) **Buxted Partnership**
36 **BLUE WALTZ**, b f Pivotal—Blue Symphony **Fittocks Stud & Andrew Bengough**
37 **BRACKEN**, ro c Dubawi (IRE)—Belle Reine **Sheikh Mohammed Obaid Al Maktoum**
38 **COMEDY KING (IRE)**, b br c Dansili—Comic (IRE) **Sheikh Mohammed Obaid Al Maktoum**
39 **CONNECTICUT**, b c New Approach (IRE)—Craigmill **Sheikh Mohammed Obaid Al Maktoum**
40 **CROSS COUNTRY (IRE)**, b c Cape Cross (IRE)—Altruiste (USA) **Sheikh Mohammed Obaid Al Maktoum**
41 **DON'T**, b f Invincible Spirit (IRE)—Frigid **Fittocks Stud**
42 **GALUPPI**, b c Galileo (IRE)—La Leuze (IRE) **Bartisan Racing Ltd**
43 **JORDAN PRINCESS**, b f Cape Cross (IRE)—Princess Nada **Sheikh Mohammed Obaid Al Maktoum**
44 **JOYS OF SPRING (IRE)**, b f Invincible Spirit (IRE)—Sonachan (IRE) **Sheikh Mohammed Obaid Al Maktoum**
45 **KINSHASA**, b c Pivotal—Kibara **Fittocks Stud**
46 **KLEO (GR)**, b f Kavafi (IRE)—Selfish **L. Marinopoulos**
47 **LAWYER (IRE)**, b c Acclamation—Charaig **Sheikh Mohammed Obaid Al Maktoum**
48 **LUNASEA (IRE)**, b c Sea The Stars (IRE)—Musical Treat (IRE) **Mr J. S. Kelly**
49 **MADAME CLOUSEAU (IRE)**, b f Galileo (IRE)—Healing Music (FR) **Mr J. S. Kelly**
50 **MIZZOU (IRE)**, b c Galileo (IRE)—Moments of Joy **Mr J. S. Kelly**
51 **MOUNT LOGAN (IRE)**, ch c New Approach (IRE)—Vistaria (USA) **Sheikh Mohammed Obaid Al Maktoum**
52 **PAST FORGETTING (IRE)**, b f Pivotal—Brigitta (IRE) **Mr S. A. Stuckey**
53 **PATTERNED**, b f Dansili—Paisley **Fittocks Stud**
54 **PETTICOAT LANE**, b f High Chaparral (IRE)—Barter **Fittocks Stud**
55 **PICK POCKETT**, b c Dansili—Quelle Vitesse **Mr J. S. Kelly**
56 **PLEASANT VALLEY (IRE)**, b f Shamardal (USA)—Poughkeepsie (IRE) **Wildenstein Stables Limited**
57 **POSTPONED (IRE)**, b c Dubawi (IRE)—Ever Rigg **Sheikh Mohammed Obaid Al Maktoum**
58 **RIJM**, b c New Approach (IRE)—Astorg (USA) **H.E. Sheikh J. B. H. B. K. Al Thani**
59 **ROSEBURG (IRE)**, ch c Tamayuz—Raydaniya (IRE) **Sheikh Mohammed Obaid Al Maktoum**
60 **SECOND STEP (IRE)**, b g Dalakhani (IRE)—My Dark Rosaleen **Merry Fox Stud Limited**
61 **SEEK A STAR (USA)**, ch f Smart Strike (CAN)—Queen of the Night **Mr M Tabor, Mrs J Magnier & Mr D Smith**
62 **TAP YOUR TOES (IRE)**, b c Danehill Dancer (IRE)—Sharplaw Star **Mr J. S. Kelly**
63 **TOLMIAS (GR)**, br c Iaysos (GR)—Shikasta (IRE) **L. Marinopoulos**
64 **UP THE JUNCTION**, b c New Approach (IRE)—Hyabella **Castle Down Racing**
65 **VOLUME**, b f Mount Nelson—Victoire Finale **Mr S. A. Stuckey**
66 **WENGEN**, b c Montjeu (IRE)—High Reserve **Castle Down Racing**
67 **WILLOW VIEW (USA)**, b f Lemon Drop Kid (USA)—Time Control **Merry Fox Stud Limited**
68 **WISTAR**, b c Dubawi (IRE)—Vallota **Sheikh Mohammed Obaid Al Maktoum**
69 **ZAKYAH**, b f Exceed And Excel (AUS)—Suba (USA) **Sheikh Mohammed Obaid Al Maktoum**
70 **ZAWIYAH**, b f Invincible Spirit (IRE)—Marika **Mr S. A. Stuckey**

TWO-YEAR-OLDS

71 **AL**, b c 23/3 Halling (USA)—Incarnation (IRE) (Samum (GER)) (44000) **Hunter, Moulton, Ramsden**
72 **ARANKA**, ch f 12/4 Iffraaj—Vallota (Polish Precedent (USA)) **L. Marinopoulos**
73 **ARCHERY PEAK**, b c 23/3 Arch (USA)—
Come Touch The Sun (IRE) (Fusaichi Pegasus (USA)) (235000) **Mr J. S. Kelly**
74 **BARSANTI (IRE)**, b c 14/2 Champs Elysees—
Silver Star (Zafonic (USA)) (170000) **Sheikh Mohammed Obaid Al Maktoum**

MR LUCA CUMANI - Continued

75 **BARTHOLOMEW FAIR,** b c 9/4 Dansili—
Rebecca Sharp (Machiavellian (USA)) (525000) **Sheikh Mohammed Obaid Al Maktoum**
76 Ch f 19/3 Motivator—Basque Beauty (Nayef (USA)) **Rachel Countess of Coventry**
77 **BERMONDSEY,** b c 24/3 Galileo (IRE)—Barter (Daylami (IRE)) (150000) **Fittocks Stud**
78 B c 9/2 Acclamation—Dixie Eyes Blazing (USA) (Gone West (USA)) (63491) **L. Marinopoulos**
79 **DREAMLIKE,** b f 9/4 Oasis Dream—So Silk (Rainbow Quest (USA)) **Fittocks Stud**
80 **DUFFEL,** ch c 28/5 Shamardal (USA)—Paisley (Pivotal)
81 **FIESOLE,** b c 13/3 Montjeu (IRE)—Forgotten Dreams (IRE) (Olden Times) (575000) **Fittocks Stud**
82 **FRANCOPHILE,** ch c 9/5 Sea The Stars (IRE)—Empress of France (USA) (Storm Cat (USA)) (123886)
83 **GRAND SPIRIT (IRE),** b c 9/3 Lord Shanakill (USA)—
Spirit Watch (IRE) (Invincible Spirit (IRE)) (35000) **Mr Bruce Corman**
84 **HANDBELL (IRE),** b f 9/3 Acclamation—
Dulcian (IRE) (Shamardal (USA)) (135500) **Sheikh Mohammed Obaid Al Maktoum**
85 **IRISH HAWKE (IRE),** b c 2/4 Montjeu (IRE)—Ahdaab (USA) (Rahy (USA)) (216801) **Mr J. S. Kelly**
86 B f 11/5 Oasis Dream—Kibara (Sadler's Wells (USA)) **Fittocks Stud**
87 **KING BOLETE (IRE),** b c 28/2 Cape Cross (IRE)—
Chanterelle (FR) (Trempolino (USA)) (174216) **Sheikh Mohammed Obaid Al Maktoum**
88 **KOORA,** b f 8/3 Pivotal—Kithanga (IRE) (Darshaan) **Fittocks Stud**
89 **LA BOHEME (GER),** b f 9/4 Montjeu (IRE)—La Reine Noir (GER) (Rainbow Quest (USA)) (201316) **Mr J. S. Kelly**
90 **LADY OF DUBAI,** b f 19/2 Dubawi (IRE)—
Lady of Everest (IRE) (Montjeu (IRE)) (450000) **Sheikh Mohammed Obaid Al Maktoum**
91 **LAURENCE,** b c 26/5 Dubawi (IRE)—
Victoire Celebre (USA) (Stravinsky (USA)) **Fittocks Stud & Andrew Bengough**
92 B f 7/4 Yeats (IRE)—Librettista (AUS) (Elusive Quality (USA)) **Mr S. A. Stuckey**
93 **LILIAN BAYLIS (IRE),** b f 27/3 Shamardal (USA)—
Kiyra Wells (IRE) (Sadler's Wells (USA)) (178086) **Sheikh Mohammed Obaid Al Maktoum**
94 **METAVOS (GR),** b c 15/2 Ialysos (GR)—Polyxeni (Nayef (USA)) **L Marinopoulos**
95 **MONOTYPE (IRE),** b c 4/5 Makfi—
Mill Guineas (USA) (Salse (USA)) (300000) **Sheikh Mohammed Obaid Al Maktoum**
96 B f 17/3 Montjeu (IRE)—O' Bella Ballerina (USA) (Fusaichi Pegasus (USA)) (105000) **Mr S. A. Stuckey**
97 B f 4/2 Duke of Marmalade (IRE)—Palanca (Inchinor) (92914) **Highclere Thoroughbred Racing (Albany)**
98 **PARNASIA (GR),** b f 17/2 Ialysos (GR)—Mazea (IRE) (Montjeu (IRE)) **L. Marinopoulos**
99 B f 6/4 New Approach (IRE)—Patacake Patacake (USA) (Bahri (USA)) (450000) **H.E. Sheikh J. B. H. B. K. Al Thani**
100 **PAXAMOS (GR),** b c 13/1 Kavafi (IRE)—Boukia (GR) (Filandros (GR)) **L. Marinopoulos**
101 **RAGGETY ANN (IRE),** b f 17/4 Galileo (IRE)—Sassenach (IRE) (Night Shift (USA)) (450000) **Mrs J. S. Kelly**
102 Ch f 9/2 Galileo (IRE)—Ramruma (USA) (Diesis) **Coolmore**
103 **RICHARD OF YORKE,** b c 13/2 Oasis Dream—Cascata (IRE) (Montjeu (IRE)) **Mr S. A. Stuckey**
104 B f 14/3 Beat Hollow—Rivara (Red Ransom (USA)) **Sarah J Leigh**
105 **SHAKOPEE,** b c 12/5 High Chaparral (IRE)—Tentpole (USA) (Rainbow Quest (USA)) **Fittocks Stud**
106 **SPIRITING (IRE),** b c 14/2 Invincible Spirit (IRE)—
Gold Bubbles (USA) (Street Cry (IRE)) (450000) **Sheikh Mohammed Obaid Al Maktoum**
107 **STARS AND STRIPES,** ch c 26/1 Selkirk (USA)—
Capannina (Grand Lodge (USA)) (100658) **Sheikh Mohammed Obaid Al Maktoum**
108 **WHITE LAKE,** b c 24/2 Pivotal—
White Palace (Shirley Heights) (240000) **Sheikh Mohammed Obaid Al Maktoum**
109 B c 30/3 Rip Van Winkle (IRE)—Wind Surf (USA) (Lil's Lad (USA)) (130000) **Mr Nagy El Azar**
110 **WINTERVAL,** b c 27/2 Dubawi (IRE)—
Festivale (IRE) (Invincible Spirit (IRE)) (90000) **Sheikh Mohammed Obaid Al Maktoum**

Other Owners: Mr A. N. C. Bengough, Mr Daniel Boorer, Mr P. Booth, Mrs Luca Cumani, Mr H. S. Ellingsen, Fittocks Stud, Mr Jim Hanifin, Mr T. Henderson, Mrs John Magnier, Mr Paul Moulton, Mr S. O'Donnell, Mr Andrew Patey, Mrs J. Ruthven, Mr Paul G. S. Silver, Mrs Angie Silver, Mr Derrick Smith, Mr M. Tabor, Mr M. Weinfeld.

Assistant Trainer: Matthew Cumani

138	**MR SEAN CURRAN, Upper Lambourn** Postal: **Frenchmans Lodge Stables, Upper Lambourn, Hungerford, Berkshire, RG17 8QW** Contacts: **PHONE (01488) 72095 FAX (01488) 72095 MOBILE (07774) 146169** E-MAIL seancurran99@hotmail.co.uk

1 **ANGLO PADDY (IRE),** 5, ch m Mountain High (IRE)—
Hazel Sylph (IRE) **Janet Kirk, Michael Lowry & Keith Adams**
2 **BAY KNIGHT (IRE),** 8, b g Johannesburg (USA)—Sabeline (IRE) **Scuderia Vita Bella**
3 **BYRON AGAIN,** 4, b g Byron—Kiss Me Again (IRE) **Mr P. Cranney**

MR SEAN CURRAN - Continued

4 **CLASSIC CASE (IRE)**, 7, b g Classic Cliche (IRE)—Rashie (IRE) **The Three Graces**
5 **DOUGALSTAR (FR)**, 5, b g Layman (USA)—Concert House (IRE) **A. J. White**
6 **GREENFORDGIRL (IRE)**, 4, b f Diamond Green (FR)—Cappadoce (IRE) **Mrs B. Hardiman**
7 **HIGHWAY UNITED (IRE)**, 4, ch f Arakan (USA)—Luscinia **Mr P. M. Mannion**
8 **INTERIM LODGE (IRE)**, 5, b m King's Theatre (IRE)—Brownlow Castle (IRE) **Mr R. K. Adams**
9 **JAY BEE BLUE (IRE)**, 5, b g Kyllachy—Czarna Roza **Scuderia Vita Bella**
10 **JUST GETS BETTER (IRE)**, 5, gr g Bertolini (USA)—Fun Loving (IRE) **Mr Liam O'Kane**
11 **KING'S CIEL (IRE)**, 5, ch g Septieme Ciel (USA)—King's Jewel **Bob Cooper & Val Dean**
12 **OPERA BUFF (IRE)**, 5, b g Oratorio (IRE)—Opera Glass **Bob Cooper & Val Dean**
13 **OURNIAMHEEN (IRE)**, 4, b f Papal Bull—Still As Sweet (IRE)
14 **PLETTENBURG BAY (IRE)**, 9, b g Oscar Schindler (IRE)—Fairyfort Queen (IRE) **Mr P. M. Mannion**
15 **POLAR KITE (IRE)**, 6, b g Marju (IRE)—Irina (IRE) **Mr R. K. Adams**
16 **TINY HAVEN (IRE)**, 5, b g Beat All (USA)—Flower Haven **A. J. White**
17 **WEBBSWOOD (IRE)**, 5, b g Catcher In The Rye (IRE)—Victory Run (IRE) **H. J. M. Webb**
18 **ZELOS DIKTATOR (IRE)**, 8, br g Diktat—Chanterelle (IRE) **A. J. White**

THREE-YEAR-OLDS

19 **BOLD RUNNER**, ch g Mount Nelson—Music In Exile (USA) **Bob Cooper & Val Dean**
20 **MISSTEMPER (IRE)**, b f Diamond Green (FR)—Legnani **Bob Cooper & Val Dean**
21 **SAKHEE'SSQUIRREL**, ch f Sakhee's Secret—China Cherub **Dukes Head Racing**

Other Owners: J. L. Collins, Mr R. Cooper, Mr P. G. Dalton, Miss V. Dean, Mr L. Graffato, Mr T. A. Killoran, Mrs J. Kirk, Mr P. J. Legros, Mr M. J. Lowry, Mr J. Norman, Mr P. Thwaites.

---

139 MISS REBECCA CURTIS, Newport
Postal: Fforest Farm, Newport, Pembrokeshire, SA42 0UG
Contacts: **PHONE** (01348) 811489 **MOBILE** (07970) 710690
E-MAIL rebcurtis@hotmail.com

1 **ACES OVER KINGS (IRE)**, 7, b g Overbury (IRE)—Aces Royale (IRE) **Mr M. A. Sherwood**
2 **ASHES HOUSE (IRE)**, 8, b g Dushyantor (USA)—Cailinclover (IRE) **Diamond Racing Ltd**
3 **AT FISHERS CROSS (IRE)**, 7, b g Oscar (IRE)—Fermoy Supreme (IRE) **J. P. McManus**
4 **AUDACIOUS PLAN (IRE)**, 5, b g Old Vic—North Star Poly (IRE) **Mr A. McIver**
5 **BALLYHOLLOW**, 7, ch m Beat Hollow—Ballet-K **Miss S. R. Gallagher**
6 **BINGE DRINKER (IRE)**, 5, b g Spadoun (FR)—Our Honey (IRE) **Miss R. Curtis**
7 5, B m Kayf Tara—Blueberry Bramble (IRE) **Miss R. Curtis**
8 **BOB FORD (IRE)**, 7, b g Vinnie Roe (IRE)—Polar Lamb (IRE) **The Bob Ford Partnership**
9 **BOB KEOWN (IRE)**, 6, b g Indian Danehill (IRE)—Arteea Princess (IRE) **C. R. Trembath**
10 **BOYFROMNOWHERE (IRE)**, 7, br g Old Vic—Eist Do Gale (IRE) **Mr A J Rhead & Mr G B Williams**
11 **CARNINGLI (IRE)**, 5, b g Old Vic—Name For Fame (USA) **The Newport Partnership**
12 **CHAMPAGNE RIAN (IRE)**, 6, b g Dr Massini (IRE)—Vul Gale **Mr C. S. Hinchy**
13 **CHURCHTOWN LOVE (IRE)**, 6, b m Beneficial—Katie Murphy (IRE) **Mr A. J. Rhead**
14 **CLANCY'S CROSS (IRE)**, 5, b g Oscar (IRE)—Murphy's Lady (IRE) **Mr C. S. Hinchy**
15 **CLOUD BROOK (IRE)**, 6, b g Cloudings (IRE)—Stoney Brook (IRE) **Mr R. J. H. Geffen**
16 **CROWD CONTROL (IRE)**, 5, b g Oscar (IRE)—Apollo Lady **A. Longman**
17 **DOING FINE (IRE)**, 6, b g Presenting—Howaya Pet (IRE) **Mr C. S. Hinchy**
18 **EL MACCA (IRE)**, 5, ch g Old Vic—Cluain-Ard (IRE) **J. P. McManus**
19 **FISHOUTOFWATER (IRE)**, 10, ch g Old Vic—Frost Bound **J. P. McManus**
20 **FORYOURINFORMATION**, 5, b g Kayf Tara—Sleepless Eye **Mr C. S. Hinchy**
21 **FOXTAIL HILL (IRE)**, 5, b g Dr Massini (IRE)—Flynn's Girl (IRE) **Options O Syndicate**
22 **GATE PLEASE (IRE)**, 9, b g Rashar (USA)—Linda Babe (IRE) **Diamond Racing Ltd**
23 **GOLDEN MILAN (IRE)**, 6, b g Milan—Belle Provence (FR) **G. Costelloe**
24 **GUS MACRAE (IRE)**, 10, b g Accordion—Full of Surprises (IRE) **Quicksilver Racing Partnership**
25 **IMAGINE THE CHAT**, 5, b g Kayf Tara—Be My Bird **J. P. McManus**
26 **IRISH CAVALIER (IRE)**, 5, gr ro g Aussie Rules (USA)—Tracker **Mr A. McIver**
27 **KEEP PRESENTING (IRE)**, 5, b g Presenting—Keep The Change (IRE) **Mr C. S. Hinchy**
28 **LOOKSLIKERAINTED (IRE)**, 7, b g Milan—Kilcrea Gale (IRE) **G. Costelloe**
29 **MASTER BUTCHER (IRE)**, 7, b g Court Cave (IRE)—Carleen Gold **The Sophomores**
30 **MINELLA ON LINE (IRE)**, 5, b g King's Theatre (IRE)—Bally Bolshoi (IRE) **AHB Racing Partnership**
31 **MINELLA RECEPTION (IRE)**, 8, b g King's Theatre (IRE)—Cadourova (FR) **Options O Syndicate**
32 **MONKEY KINGDOM**, 6, b g King's Theatre (IRE)—Blast Freeze (IRE) **Mr C. S. Hinchy**
33 **MONTE CAVALLO (SAF)**, 9, b g Saumarez—Mufski (SAF) **G. Costelloe**
34 **MYORAN OSCAR (IRE)**, 6, b g Oscar (IRE)—Miss Bertaine (IRE) **G. Costelloe**

MISS REBECCA CURTIS - Continued

35 O'FAOLAINS BOY (IRE), 7, b g Oscar (IRE)—Lisa's Storm (IRE) **Trembath, Hyde, Outhart & Hill**
36 ONE TERM (IRE), 7, b g Beneficial—One Edge (IRE) **Miss L Reid & Mr G Costelloe**
37 PECKHAMECHO (IRE), 8, b g Beneficial—Nolans Pride (IRE) **C. R. Trembath**
38 POTTERS CROSS, 7, b g Alflora (IRE)—Teeno Nell **Conyers, O'Reilly, Roddis, Zeffman**
39 RED DEVIL LADS (IRE), 5, b g Beneficial—Welsh Sitara (IRE) **Mr A. McIver**
40 RELENTLESS DREAMER (IRE), 5, br g Kayf Tara—Full of Elegance (FR) **Mr N. D. Morris**
41 RENDL BEACH (IRE), 7, b g Milan—Erins Emblem (IRE) **The O'Connor Duffy Racing Partnership**
42 SOUTHSEA ISLAND (IRE), 6, b g Heron Island (IRE)—Southsea Lady (IRE) **Miss R. Curtis**
43 SWNYMOR (IRE), 5, b g Dylan Thomas (IRE)—Propaganda (IRE) **Mr C. S. Hinchy**
44 TARA ROAD, 6, b g Kayf Tara—Sparkling Jewel **Mr N. D. Morris**
45 TEAFORTHREE (IRE), 10, b g Oscar (IRE)—Ethel's Bay (IRE) **Conyers, O'Reilly, Roddis, Zeffman**
46 THE BEAR TRAP (IRE), 7, b g Westerner—Calendula **J. P. McManus**
47 THE ROMFORD PELE (IRE), 7, b g Accordion—
                          Back And Fore (IRE) **C. Trembath, M. Hill, T. Outhart, N. Fletcher**

Other Owners: Mr J. Conyers, D. P. Duffy, Mr J. Flannery, Mr N. Fletcher, Mr T. M. Hailstone, Mr J. C. I. Heilbron, M. Hill, Mr J. R. Holmes, Mr R. Hyde, Mr E. M. O'Connor, Mr J. P. O'Reilly, A. J. Outhart, Miss L. Reid, Mr D. A. Robinson, Mr N. M. Roddis, Mr G. Sturgeon, Mr S. G. Wignall, Mr G. B. Williams, D. C. Zeffman.

Assistant Trainer: Paul Sheldrake

---

140 | **MR ROGER CURTIS, Lambourn**
Postal: Delamere Stables, Baydon Road, Lambourn, Hungerford, Berkshire, RG17 8NT
Contacts: **PHONE** (01488) 73007 **FAX** (01488) 73909 **MOBILE** (07836) 320690
E-MAIL rcurtislambourn@aol.com **WEBSITE** www.rogercurtis.com

1 BADB CATHA (IRE), 8, b m Flemensfirth (USA)—Beann Ard (IRE) **The Racing 4 Fun Partnership**
2 BALLY GUNNER, 9, br g Needle Gun (IRE)—Rich Pickings **The Bally Gunners**
3 CLAUDE GREENWOOD, 4, b g Lucky Story (USA)—Greenmeadow **Mr R. Dean**
4 COLLODI (GER), 5, b g Konigstiger (GER)—Codera (GER) **Stocky And Gunny**
5 ELEGANT OLIVE, 11, b m Alflora (IRE)—Strong Cloth (IRE) **Collective Dreamers**
6 GYPSY RIDER, 5, b g Ishiguru (USA)—Spaniola (IRE) **The Racing 4 Fun Partnership**
7 LADY CLICHE, 5, b m Kirkwall—Madam Cliche **The Maderson Blue Partnership**
8 MACCABEES, 5, b g Motivator—Takarna (IRE) **Mrs F. J. Dean**
9 ROMNEY MARSH, 13, br m Glacial Storm (USA)—Mirador **The Romney Marsh Partnership**

Other Owners: Miss A. Atkin, Ms L. M. Barton, R. Curtis, Mrs D. S. Gibbs, Mrs P. McCluskey, B. Newman, Mr S. Stockdale, Dr P. G. Walker.

Assistant Trainer: Dawn Gibbs

Jockey (flat): Dane O'Neill, James Doyle. **Jockey (NH):** Dave Crosse, Hadden Frost. **Amateur:** Mr Freddy Tett.

---

141 | **MR THOMAS CUTHBERT, Brampton**
Postal: Woodlands, Cowranbridge, How Mill, Brampton, Cumbria, CA8 9LH
Contacts: **PHONE** (01228) 560822 **FAX** (01228) 560822 **MOBILE** (07747) 843344
E-MAIL cuthbertracing@fsmail.net

1 EDAS, 12, b g Celtic Swing—Eden (IRE) **Mrs J. Cuthbert**
2 LANDESHERR (GER), 7, b g Black Sam Bellamy (IRE)—Lutte Marie (GER) **T. A. K. Cuthbert**

Assistant Trainer: Helen Cuthbert

Amateur: Miss H. Cuthbert.

---

142 | **MR PAUL D'ARCY, Newmarket**
Postal: Charnwood Stables, Hamilton Road, Newmarket, Suffolk, CB8 7JQ
Contacts: **PHONE** (01638) 662000 **FAX** (01638) 661100 **MOBILE** (07768) 807653
E-MAIL pauldarcy@fsmail.net **WEBSITE** www.pauldarcyracing.com

1 COME ON BLUE CHIP (IRE), 5, b g Holy Roman Emperor (IRE)—Rapid Action (USA) **Blue Chip Feed Ltd**
2 DARNATHEAN, 5, b g Librettist (USA)—Meddle **Mr K. Snell**
3 DELGANY DEVIL, 4, b g Kayf Tara—Little Twig (IRE) **C. M. Wilson**

MR PAUL D'ARCY - Continued

4 **FAST FINIAN (IRE)**, 5, gr g Clodovil (IRE)—Delphie Queen (IRE) **Mr J. W. Kennedy**
5 **GLOBAL LEADER (IRE)**, 4, b c Dark Angel (IRE)—Headborough Lass (IRE) **Dr J. S. Kinnear**
6 **MAGICAL ROSE (IRE)**, 4, b f Elusive City (USA)—Xarzee (IRE) **Mr K. Snell**
7 **MCBIRNEY (USA)**, 7, b g Danehill Dancer (IRE)—Dear Girl (IRE) **Mrs S. I. D'Arcy**
8 **SMART EIGHTEEN**, 4, b g Exceed And Excel (AUS)—Papabile (USA) **Champion Bloodstock Limited**
9 **TEIDE PEAK (IRE)**, 5, b g Cape Cross (IRE)—Teide Lady **C. M. Wilson**
10 **TRUE SPIRIT**, 4, b g Shamardal (USA)—Petonellajill **P. W. D'Arcy**

THREE-YEAR-OLDS

11 **BIKINI CLUB**, br f Pastoral Pursuits—Black Sea Pearl **Mrs J. Harris**
12 **RELATION ALEXANDER (IRE)**, ch f Dandy Man (IRE)—Elshamms **Mr K. Snell**

TWO-YEAR-OLDS

13 B c 14/4 Intense Focus (USA)—Biasca (Erhaab (USA)) (77000) **Champion Bloodstock Limited**
14 Br f 23/2 Kyllachy—Meddle (Diktat) (50000) **Mr K. Snell**
15 **SPRING LOADED (IRE)**, b gr c 2/3 Zebedee—Nisriyna (IRE) (Intikhab (USA)) (19047) **Rowley Racing**

Other Owners: Mr Paul D'Arcy, Mrs Sue D'Arcy, Mr W P Drew, Mr R Ford, Mr M Hyson.

Assistant Trainer: Sue D'Arcy

Apprentice: Stacey Kidd. **Amateur:** Mrs Rachel Wilson.

---

143 **MR LUKE DACE, Billingshurst**
Postal: **Copped Hall Farm, Okehurst Lane, Billingshurst, West Sussex, RH14 9HR**
Contacts: **OFFICE (01403) 780889 FAX (01403) 780889 MOBILE (07949) 401085**
E-MAIL lukedace@yahoo.co.uk WEBSITE www.lukedace.co.uk

1 **ACER DIAMONDS (IRE)**, 5, b g Red Clubs (IRE)—Tree House (USA) **Grabupenn Racing**
2 **ALNOOMAAS (IRE)**, 5, b g Oasis Dream—Remarkable Story **M. J. Benton**
3 **AMERICAN SPIN**, 10, ch g Groom Dancer (USA)—Sea Vixen **Mr G Collacott & Mr R Gadd**
4 **AUTUMN DAY (IRE)**, 9, b g Milan—Alice Freyne (IRE) **Copped Hall Farm & Stud**
5 **BARACHIEL**, 6, b g Pivotal—Coveted **Mr Peter Gray & Mr John Buchanan**
6 **DRAWNFROMTHEPAST (IRE)**, 9, ch g Tagula (IRE)—Ball Cat (FR) **M. J. Benton**
7 **ECHO BRAVA**, 4, gr g Proclamation (IRE)—Snake Skin **M. J. Benton**
8 **EMMAN BEE**, 5, gr m Dark Angel (IRE)—Two Sets To Love (IRE) **M. J. Benton**
9 **ESTATES RECOVERY (IRE)**, 9, b g Luso—Jendam (IRE) **M. J. Benton**
10 **LASCAUX**, 5, ch m Pivotal—Tora Bora **M. J. Benton**
11 **TRACK STAR (IRE)**, 9, b g Sadler's Wells (USA)—Angelica Tree (CAN) **Copped Hall Farm & Stud**

THREE-YEAR-OLDS

12 **BOBBY BENTON (IRE)**, b c Invincible Spirit (IRE)—Remarkable Story **M. J. Benton**
13 **DAWNFROMTHEPAST (IRE)**, b g Tagula (IRE)—Ball Cat (FR) **M. J. Benton**
14 **DEBT SETTLER (IRE)**, b c Art Connoisseur (IRE)—Musical Dancer **M. J. Benton**
15 B g Tagula (IRE)—Henrietta Mews **M. J. Benton**
16 **OFFICER DRIVEL (IRE)**, b g Captain Rio—Spiritville (IRE) **M. J. Benton**
17 **SHIRLEY VANESSA (IRE)**, b f Camacho—Mas A Fuera (IRE) **M. J. Benton**

Other Owners: Mr J. C. Buchanan, L. A. Dace, Mrs L. J. Dace, R. A. Gadd, Mr P. J. Gray, Mr G. Gray, Mr A. N. Penn.

Assistant Trainer: Mrs L Dace

---

144 **MR KEITH DALGLEISH, Carluke**
Postal: **Belstane Racing Stables, Carluke, Lanarkshire, ML8 5HN**
Contacts: **PHONE (01555) 773335**

1 **ACT YOUR SHOE SIZE**, 5, b m Librettist (USA)—Howards Heroine (IRE) **G. McDowall**
2 **ARGAKI (IRE)**, 4, ch g Strategic Prince—Amathusia **D. G. Savala**
3 **ARR' KID (USA)**, 4, b c Medaglia d'oro (USA)—Viaduct (USA) **Weldspec Glasgow Limited**
4 **BELLOROPHON (IRE)**, 5, ch g Beneficial—Mrs Kick (IRE) **Straightline Construction Ltd**
5 **CHIRON (IRE)**, 5, b g Celtic Swing—Jane Digby (IRE) **Alison Walker Sarah Cousins**
6 **CHOOKIE ROYALE**, 6, ch g Monsieur Bond (IRE)—Lady of Windsor (IRE) **Raeburn Brick Limited**
7 **CIRCUITOUS**, 6, b g Fasliyev (USA)—Seren Devious **Alison Walker Sarah Cousins**

MR KEITH DALGLEISH - Continued

8 **CORTON LAD**, 4, b g Refuse To Bend (IRE)—Kelucia (IRE) **Mr J. J. Hutton**
9 **FABLED CITY (USA)**, 5, ch g Johannesburg (USA)—Fabulous Fairy (USA) **John Kelly & Kevin Mowatt**
10 **FORT BELVEDERE**, 6, ch g King's Best (USA)—Sweet Folly (IRE) **Straightline Construction Ltd**
11 **GILBERT'S GAMBLE (IRE)**, 5, b g Brian Boru—Sister Anna **Straightline Construction Ltd**
12 **GOODLUKIN LUCY**, 7, ch m Supreme Sound—Suka Ramai **Evergreen Racing**
13 **HANALEI BAY (IRE)**, 4, b c Tamayuz—Genial Jenny (IRE) **Mrs F. E. Mitchell**
14 **HURRICANE HOLLOW**, 4, b g Beat Hollow—Veenwouden **Straightline Construction Ltd**
15 **JEANNIE GALLOWAY (IRE)**, 7, b m Bahamian Bounty—Housekeeper (IRE) **Mr D. Renwick**
16 **KINGZINNI (IRE)**, 5, b g King's Theatre (IRE)—Daizinni **Equus Syndicate**
17 **LIVE DANGEROUSLY**, 4, b g Zamindar (USA)—Desert Lynx (IRE) **Lamont Racing**
18 **LOVER MAN (IRE)**, 5, b g Lawman (FR)—Seltitude (IRE) **Straightline Construction Ltd**
19 **LUCTOR EMERGO (IRE)**, 5, b g Amadeus Wolf—Batilde (IRE) **Straightline Construction Ltd**
20 **MILLERS REEF (IRE)**, 8, b g Bob Back (USA)—Silent Supreme (IRE) **M. C. MacKenzie**
21 **NADEMA ROSE (IRE)**, 5, b m Elnadim (USA)—Noctilucent (JPN) **Mr G. R. Leckie**
22 **NATURES LAW (IRE)**, 4, b f Lawman (FR)—Misaayef (USA) **Prestige Thoroughbred Racing**
23 **NEXIUS (IRE)**, 5, b g Catcher In The Rye (IRE)—Nicolaia (GER) **Straightline Construction Ltd**
24 5, bl m Flemensfirth (USA)—Pechaubar (FR) **Equus Syndicate**
25 **ROYAL SUPREME (IRE)**, 4, br g Royal Anthem (USA)—Supreme Baloo (IRE) **Straightline Construction Ltd**
26 **SALVATORE FURY (IRE)**, 4, b c g Strategic Prince—Nocturnal (FR) **Prestige Thoroughbred Racing**
27 **SANTEFISIO**, 8, b g Efisio—Impulsive Decision (IRE) **Weldspec Glasgow Limited**
28 **SEASIDE ROCK (IRE)**, 4, b g Oratorio (IRE)—Miss Sacha (IRE) **Sharron & Robert Colvin**
29 **SECRET ADVICE**, 4, ch f Sakhee's Secret—Flylowflylong (IRE) **A. R. M Galbraith**
30 **SOUND ADVICE**, 5, b g Echo of Light—Flylowflylong (IRE) **G L S Partnership**
31 **STONEFIELD FLYER**, 5, b h Kheleyf (USA)—Majestic Diva (IRE) **Mr G. R. Leckie**
32 **TARA MAC**, 5, b m Kayf Tara—Macklette (IRE) **Equus Syndicate**
33 **TECTONIC (IRE)**, 5, b g Dylan Thomas (IRE)—Pine Chip (USA) **Mrs L. A. Ogilvie**
34 **WAYWARD GLANCE**, 6, b g Sadler's Wells (USA)—Daring Aim **Straightline Construction Ltd**
35 **WEST LEAKE DIMAN (IRE)**, 5, b g Namid—Roselyn **Lamont Racing**
36 **WINDSOR SECRET**, 4, ch f Sakhee's Secret—Lady of Windsor (IRE) **Raeburn Brick Limited**

THREE-YEAR-OLDS

37 **BALTIC SPIRIT (IRE)**, b f Baltic King—Beau Petite **Prestige Thoroughbred Racing**
38 **BEAUTIFUL STRANGER (IRE)**, b c Iffraaj—Monarchy (IRE) **Weldspec Glasgow Limited**
39 B f Bushranger (IRE)—Blu Spirit (IRE)
40 **BOOGANGOO (IRE)**, b f Acclamation—Spice World (IRE) **Middleham Park Racing II**
41 **CHOOKIE'S LASS**, ch f Compton Place—Lady of Windsor (IRE) **Raeburn Brick Limited**
42 B c Archipenko (USA)—Flylowflylong (IRE) **G L S Partnership**
43 **FRANKTHETANK (IRE)**, ch c Captain Gerrard (IRE)—Mi Amor (IRE) **Straightline Construction Ltd**
44 **HAYHAR Z**, b f Striking Ambition—Segretezza (IRE) **Mrs F. E. Mitchell**
45 B c Orpen (USA)—Impulsive Decision (IRE) **Weldspec Glasgow Limited**
46 **INCURS FOUR FAULTS**, b c Halling (USA)—Rapsgate (IRE) **J. S. Morrison**
47 **KIRTLING BELLE**, br f Pastoral Pursuits—Twenty Seven (IRE) **Redgate Bloodstock**
48 **LES GAR GAN (IRE)**, b f Iffraaj—Story **Middleham Park Racing XLIII**
49 **LOMOND LASSIE**, ch f Sakhee's Secret—Numanthia (IRE) **Straightline Construction Ltd**
50 **NEUF DES COEURS**, b f Champs Elysees—Intervene **Mr C. J. Colgan**
51 **PAL ELLA**, ch f Byron—Bridge Pal **Miss E. G. MacGregor**
52 **PORTHOS DU VALLON**, b g Jeremy—Princess Caraboo (IRE) **Lamont Racing**
53 **SANDRA'S DIAMOND (IRE)**, b f Footstepsinthesand—Lucky Us (IRE) **Prestige Thoroughbred Racing**
54 **SCOTS LAW (IRE)**, b f Lawman (FR)—Misaayef (USA) **Prestige Thoroughbred Racing**
55 **SCURR MIST (IRE)**, gr g Aussie Rules (USA)—Stratospheric **Lamont Racing**
56 **SLEEPING SHADOW**, ch f Sleeping Indian—Short Shadow (USA) **Straightline Construction Ltd**
57 **STONEY QUINE (IRE)**, b f Royal Applause—Shauna's Honey (IRE) **Middleham Park Racing XXII**
58 B f Milk It Mick—Suka Ramai **Mr S. J. Baird**
59 **THE POETS NEPHEW (IRE)**, b c Invincible Spirit (IRE)—Chatifa (IRE) **Straightline Construction Ltd**
60 **THIS CHARMING MAN (IRE)**, b g Diamond Green (FR)—Incendio **Middleham Park Racing XLIII**
61 **VOSNE ROMANEE**, ch g Arakan (USA)—Vento Del Oreno (FR) **Straightline Construction Ltd**
62 **WEE FRANKIE (IRE)**, ch c Heliostatic (IRE)—Kimono (IRE) **Lamont Racing**

TWO-YEAR-OLDS

63 B f 25/3 Kodiac—Annus Iucundus (IRE) (Desert King (IRE)) (13162) **Straightline Construction Ltd**
64 B f 10/3 Paco Boy (IRE)—Brilliance (Cadeaux Genereux) (8571)
65 **DOC CHARM**, b c 23/4 Hellvelyn—Songsheet (Dominion) (7619) **Prestige Thoroughbred Racing II**
66 Ch g 20/3 Zebedee—Hapipi (Bertolini (USA)) (523) **Lamont Racing**
67 B f 29/1 Royal Applause—Katina (USA) (Danzig (USA)) (12380)

MR KEITH DALGLEISH - Continued

68 **LADY DESIRE (IRE)**, b f 6/4 Lookin At Lucky (USA)—
Princess Desire (IRE) (Danehill (USA)) (20905) **Mr G. Brogan**
69 B f 28/3 Mount Nelson—Manila Selection (USA) (Manila (USA)) (4000)
70 B f 5/3 Intikhab (USA)—Mi Rubina (IRE) (Rock of Gibraltar (IRE)) (6968) **Lamont Racing**
71 B c 24/4 Arabian Gleam—Milli Can Can (Supreme Sound)
72 B f 10/4 Captain Gerrard (IRE)—Mondello (IRE) (Tagula (IRE)) (4000)
73 B f 26/3 Kodiac—Silver Cache (USA) (Silver Hawk (USA)) (11428)
74 **SIR LANCELOTT**, b c 8/3 Piccolo—Selkirk Rose (IRE) (Pips Pride) (15238) **Mr G. Brogan**
75 B c 5/5 Arabian Gleam—Suka Ramai (Nashwan (USA))
76 Gr c 12/1 Zebedee—Tomintoul Singer (IRE) (Johannesburg (USA)) (24761) **Straightline Construction Ltd**
77 **TOMMY DOCC (IRE)**, b c 16/3 Thewayyouare (USA)—
Liturgy (IRE) (Catcher In The Rye (IRE)) (9523) **Mr R. Docherty**

Other Owners: Mr W. Burke, R. Colvin, Mrs S. Colvin, Miss S. M. Cousins, Mr D. C. Flynn, Miss E. Foley, Mr R. P. Gilbert, Mr J. Kelly, Mrs E. McClymont, Mr D. McClymont, J. Millican, Mr K. Mowatt, T. S. Palin, M. Prince, Mrs S. C. Reay, Mr R. Renwick, P. P. Thorman, Miss A. Walker.

Assistant Trainer: Kevin Dalgleish

---

145 MR HENRY DALY, Ludlow
Postal: **Downton Hall Stables, Ludlow, Shropshire, SY8 3DX**
Contacts: **OFFICE (01584) 873688 FAX (01584) 873525 MOBILE (07720) 074544**
E-MAIL henry@henrydaly.co.uk WEBSITE www.henrydaly.co.uk

1 **ANSHANTOR (IRE)**, 8, ch g Anshan—Ephony Lady (IRE) **Severn River Racing**
2 **ARCTIC BEN (IRE)**, 10, gr g Beneficial—Hurst Flyer **Mrs A. W. Timpson**
3 **BOTSWANA**, 6, ch m Alflora (IRE)—Sister's Choice **Mrs B. Clarke**
4 **BRAVE BUCK**, 6, b g Bollin Eric—Silken Pearls **P. E. Truscott**
5 **BRIERY BELLE**, 5, b m King's Theatre (IRE)—Briery Ann **Mrs H Plumbly J Trafford K Deane S Holme**
6 **BRIGHT INTERVALS (IRE)**, 6, b m Flemensfirth (USA)—Sail By The Stars **T. F. F. Nixon**
7 **CALL ME KATE**, 4, b f Kalanisi (IRE)—Last of Her Line **T. F. F. Nixon**
8 **CANTONY**, 5, b m Fantastic Spain (USA)—Lancaige (IRE) **Ms H. V. Rowley Davies**
9 **CASTLE CONFLICT (IRE)**, 9, b g Close Conflict (USA)—Renty (IRE) **Strachan, Clarke, Gabb, Corbett & Salwey**
10 **CHICORIA (IRE)**, 5, ch g Presenting—Coco Girl **T. J. Hemmings**
11 **CYRIEN STAR**, 7, b g Bollin Eric—Sainte Etoile (FR) **Puteus Profundus**
12 **GO WEST YOUNG MAN (IRE)**, 6, b g Westerner—Last of Her Line **T. F. F. Nixon**
13 **GOOHAR (IRE)**, 5, b g Street Cry (IRE)—Reem Three **R. J. Brereton**
14 **GROVE PRIDE**, 9, b g Double Trigger (IRE)—Dara's Pride (IRE) **T. J. Hemmings**
15 **HERONSHAW (IRE)**, 7, b g Heron Island (IRE)—
Cool Merenda (IRE) **Strachan, Stoddart, Griffith, Barlow & Harf'd**
16 **KAYFLEUR**, 5, b m Kayf Tara—Combe Florey **B. G. Hellyer**
17 **KESHI PEARL**, 6, b m Kayf Tara—Pearly-B (IRE) **The Wadeley Partnership**
18 **KINGSMERE**, 9, b g King's Theatre (IRE)—Lady Emily **E. R. Hanbury**
19 **L STIG**, 4, b g Striking Ambition—Look Here's May **Strachan, Thompson, Inkin, Graham & Lewis**
20 **LORD GRANTHAM (IRE)**, 7, b g Definite Article—Last of Her Line **T. F. F. Nixon**
21 **MICKIE**, 6, gr m Kayf Tara—Island Mist **Ludlow Racing Partnership**
22 **MIGHTY MINNIE**, 5, b m Sir Harry Lewis (USA)—Vanina II (FR) **E. R. Hanbury**
23 **NIGHTLINE**, 4, b g Midnight Legend—Whichway Girl **Mrs D. P. G. Flory**
24 **NO DUFFER**, 7, ch g Karinga Bay—Dolly Duff **Mr D. C. Robey**
25 **NORDIC NYMPH**, 5, b m Norse Dancer (IRE)—Silken Pearls **P. E. Truscott**
26 **OYSTER SHELL**, 7, br g Bollin Eric—Pearly-B (IRE) **The Glazeley Partnership 2**
27 **PEARLYSTEPS**, 11, ch g Alflora (IRE)—Pearly-B (IRE) **The Glazeley Partnership**
28 **PICKAMUS (FR)**, 4, gr g April Night (FR)—Duchesse du Cochet (FR) **Neville Statham & Family**
29 **POSSOL (FR)**, 11, b g Robin des Pres (FR)—Alberade (FR) **Neville Statham & Family**
30 **QUEEN SPUD**, 5, b m Multiplex—Hurtebise (FR) **Barlow, Brindley, Hanley & Russell**
31 **QUENTIN COLLONGES (FR)**, 10, gr g Dom Alco (FR)—Grace Collonges (FR) **Neville Statham & Family**
32 **ROCKITEER (IRE)**, 11, b g Rudimentary (USA)—Party Woman (IRE) **Michael O'Flynn & John Nesbitt**
33 **SAFRAN DE COTTE (FR)**, 8, gr g Dom Alco (FR)—Vanille de Cotte (FR) **Mrs A. W. Timpson**
34 **SIRTOSKI**, 5, b h Kayf Tara—Miss Toski **Mrs D. P. G. Flory**
35 **SURE THING (FR)**, 8, b g Ragmar (FR)—Harpe (FR) **Henry Daly**
36 **TARA MIST**, 5, gr m Kayf Tara—Island Mist **Strachan, Mangnall, Gabb, Griffith, Graham**
37 **TIMPO (FR)**, 11, ch g Baby Turk—Faensa (FR) **Mrs A. W. Timpson**
38 **TOP TOTTI**, 6, b m Sir Harry Lewis (USA)—Jannina (FR) **Hamer & Hawkes**
39 **UPBEAT COBBLER (FR)**, 6, gr m Brier Creek (USA)—Jade de Chalamont (FR) **Mrs A. W. Timpson**

MR HENRY DALY - Continued

40 **VICE ET VERTU (FR)**, 5, b g Network (GER)—Duchesse du Cochet (FR) **Neville Statham & Family**
41 **WESSEX KING (IRE)**, 10, b g Second Empire (IRE)—Winchester Queen (IRE) **Mrs D. P. G. Flory**
42 **WINDS AND WAVES (IRE)**, 8, b g Aflflora (IRE)—Sail By The Stars **T. F. F. Nixon**

Other Owners: Sir John K. Barlow, Mr M Barlow, Mr John Brindley, Mrs S. T. Clarke, Mrs Belinda Clarke, Mrs P. Corbett, Mrs Henry Daly, Mr Henry Daly, Lord Daresbury, Mrs K. Deane, Mr G. C. L. Everall, Mrs Roger Gabb, Mrs Douglas Graham, Mrs J. G. Griffith, Mr C. M. Hamer, Mr John Hanley, Mr M. Hawkes, Mrs Jane Hearn, Mrs S. Holme, Mr Peter Holt, Mr W. Jenks, Mr W Jenks, Mrs D Lewis, Mrs Richard Mangnall, Mr Richard Mapp, Mrs Helen Plumbly, Mr R. Russell, Mr H. Salwey, Mr Neville Statham, Mrs P. Statham, Mr M Stoddart, Mr Richard Strachan, Mrs Jane Trafford.

Assistant Trainer: Alastair Ralph

Jockey (NH): Richard Johnson. **Conditional:** Jake Greenall. **Amateur:** Mr Paul John.

---

146 **MR PHILIP DANDO, Peterston-Super-Ely**
Postal: **Springfield Court, Peterston-Super-Ely, Cardiff, South Glamorgan, CF5 6LG**
Contacts: **PHONE (01446) 760012 MOBILE (07872) 965395**

1 **AUTUMN HAZE**, 9, b g Chaddleworth (IRE)—Kristal Haze **Mr Phillip Dando & Mr Anthony Brown**
Other Owners: Mr H. A. Brown, P. C. Dando.
Assistant Trainer: Miss Rebecca Dando

---

147 **MR VICTOR DARTNALL, Barnstaple**
Postal: **Higher Shutscombe Farm, Charles, Brayford, Barnstaple, Devon, EX32 7PU**
Contacts: **PHONE (01598) 710280 FAX (01598) 710708 MOBILE (07974) 374272**
E-MAIL victor@victordartnallracing.com WEBSITE www.victordartnallracing.com

1 **AMBION WOOD (IRE)**, 8, b g Oscar (IRE)—Dorans Grove **Mr O. C. R. Wynne & Mrs S. J. Wynne**
2 **DARLOA (IRE)**, 5, br g Darsi (FR)—Lady Lola (IRE) **Mr S. W. Campbell**
3 **EXMOOR MIST**, 6, gr g Kayf Tara—Chita's Flora **Exmoor Mist Partnership**
4 **HENRY KING (IRE)**, 10, gr g Great Palm (USA)—Presenting Shares (IRE) **Mrs C. M. Barber**
5 **KNOW MORE OATS (IRE)**, 6, b g Sanglamore (USA)—Greenacre Mandalay (IRE) **Mrs D. J. Fleming**
6 **LETMESPEAK (IRE)**, 9, b g Tikkanen (USA)—Ithastobesaid (IRE) **Mrs C. M. Barber**
7 **MIC'S DELIGHT (IRE)**, 10, b g Witness Box (USA)—Warrior Princess (IRE) **The Higos Hopefuls**
8 **MOLESKIN (IRE)**, 11, b g Saddlers' Hall (IRE)—Magic Gale (IRE) **Mrs C. M. Barber**
9 **OVERCLEAR**, 12, b g Overbury (IRE)—Callope (USA) **Exe Valley Racing**
10 **REGAL PRESENCE (IRE)**, 7, ch g Presenting—Lucy Lodge (IRE) **Fine Wine & Bubbly**
11 **REQUIN (FR)**, 9, b br g Video Rock (FR)—Funkia (FR) **Mrs S. De Wilde**
12 **RICHARD'S SUNDANCE (IRE)**, 12, b g Saddlers' Hall (IRE)—
                                         Celestial Rose (IRE) **Mrs Lucy Barlow & Mrs Sarah Vernon**
13 **ROUDOUDOU VILLE (IRE)**, 9, b br g Winning Smile (FR)—Jadoudy Ville (FR) **Mrs S. De Wilde**
14 **RUGGED JACK (FR)**, 7, b g Bonbon Rose (FR)—A Plus Ma Puce (FR) **G. D. Hake**
15 **SEEBRIGHT**, 7, b g Milan—Aranga (IRE) **Mrs D. J. Fleming**
16 **SHAMMICK BOY (IRE)**, 9, b g Craigsteel—Dulcet Music (IRE) **First Brayford Partnership**
17 **SILVER COMMANDER**, 7, gr g Silver Patriarch (IRE)—New Dawn **Exe Valley Racing**
18 **SLEEPING CITY (FR)**, 7, b br g Sleeping Car (FR)—City Prospect (FR) **The Whacko Partnership**
19 **TARTAK (FR)**, 11, b g Akhdari (USA)—Tartamuda (FR) **Power Panels Electrical Systems Ltd**
20 4, B c Scorpion (IRE)—Thrilling Prospect (IRE) **Mrs S. J. Wynne**
21 **TOLKEINS TANGO (IRE)**, 6, ch g Beneficial—Aule (USA) **Mrs S. M. Hall**
22 **TRESOR DE LA VIE (FR)**, 7, gr g Epalo (GER)—Joie de La Vie (FR) **Edge Of Exmoor**
23 **UN BLEU A L'AAM (FR)**, 6, b g Shaanmer (USA)—Bleu Perle (FR) **F. R. Williamson**
24 **UNEFILLE DE GUYE (FR)**, 6, b br m Voix du Nord (FR)—
                                         Mascotte de Guye (FR) **The Second Brayford Partnership**
25 **UT MAJEUR AULMES (FR)**, 6, ch g Northern Park (USA)—My Wish Aulmes (FR) **Mrs S. De Wilde**

THREE-YEAR-OLDS

26 B br f Fair Mix (IRE)—Manque Pas d'air (FR) **Mrs L. M. Northover**

MR VICTOR DARTNALL - Continued

Other Owners: Mrs L. Barlow, Mrs Jean Browning, Mrs Paula Cunliffe, Mr V. R. A. Dartnall, Mr G. A. Dartnall, Mr Jeffery Edelman, Mrs Mary Fletcher, Mr I. F. Gosden, Mr B. Greening, Mr N. P. Haley, Mr Colston Herbert, Mr G. Kennington, Mr G. Leatherbarrow, Mr M. W. Richards, Mr Mike Rowe, Mr T. Saye, Mrs Sara Vernon, Mr R. Watts, Mr C. R. Wilde, Mr David Willis, Mrs S. J. Wynne, Mr O. C. R. Wynne.

Assistant Trainer: G A Dartnall

Jockey (NH): Jack Doyle. **Conditional:** Giles Hawkins. **Amateur:** Mr Matt Hampton.

---

148 **MR TOM DASCOMBE, Malpas**
Postal: **Manor House Stables, Shay Lane, Hampton, Malpas, Cheshire, SY14 8AD**
Contacts: **PHONE** (01948) 820485 **FAX** (01948) 820495 **MOBILE** (07973) 511664
E-MAIL tom@manorhousestables.com **WEBSITE** www.manorhousestables.com

1 **ALDWICK BAY (IRE)**, 6, b g Danehill Dancer (IRE)—Josie Doocey (IRE) **C. E. R. Greenway**
2 **ANACONDA (FR)**, 5, b g Anabaa (USA)—Porretta (IRE) **The MHS 8X8 Partnership**
3 **BALLISTA (IRE)**, 6, b g Majestic Missile (IRE)—Ancient Secret **Well Done Top Man Partnership**
4 **BARRACUDA BOY (IRE)**, 4, b g Bahamian Bounty—Madame Boulangere **L. A. Bellman**
5 **BEAR BEHIND (IRE)**, 5, b g Kodiac—Gerobies Girl (USA) **Bellman Black Marantelli Owen**
6 **BROCKWELL**, 5, b g Singspiel (IRE)—Noble Plum (IRE) **South Wind Racing 3**
7 **BROWN PANTHER**, 6, b h Shirocco (GER)—Treble Heights (IRE) **Mr A. Black & Owen Promotions Limited**
8 **CAPO ROSSO (IRE)**, 4, b g Red Clubs (IRE)—Satin Cape (IRE) **Deva Racing Red Clubs Partnership**
9 **CHEWOREE**, 5, b m Milk It Mick—Jodrell Bank (IRE) **S Stoneham,E Van Cutsem,A Hoctor-Duncan**
10 **CHOSEN CHARACTER (IRE)**, 6, b g Choisir (AUS)—Out of Thanks (IRE) **Aykroyd & Sons Limited**
11 **COOL RUNNINGS (IRE)**, 4, gr g Dalakhani (IRE)—Aguinaga (IRE) **Siwan & Ward Ward Jnr**
12 **DARING INDIAN**, 6, ch g Zamindar (USA)—Anasazi (IRE) **Denarius Consulting Ltd**
13 **DEAUVILLE PRINCE (FR)**, 4, b g Holy Roman Emperor (IRE)—
                    Queen of Deauville (FR) **N & S Mather, C Ledigo, L Basran**
14 **DOUBLE DISCOUNT (IRE)**, 4, b g Invincible Spirit (IRE)—Bryanstown Girl (IRE) **L. A. Bellman**
15 **ELECTRIC QATAR**, 5, b g Pastoral Pursuits—Valandraud (IRE) **Mr A. Black & Owen Promotions Limited**
16 **FAT GARY**, 4, ch g Dutch Art—Suzuki (IRE) **Manor House Racing Club**
17 **ICE PIE**, 4, b f Mount Nelson—Statua (IRE) **Mr A. Black & Owen Promotions Limited**
18 **KENNY POWERS**, 5, b g Vital Equine (IRE)—Alexander Ballet **First Manor**
19 **MENELIK (IRE)**, 5, b g Oasis Dream—Chica Roca (USA) **L. A. Bellman**
20 **MISS AVONBRIDGE (IRE)**, 4, b f Avonbridge—Red Planet **Deva Racing Avonbridge Partnership**
21 **MONTJESS (IRE)**, 4, b f Montjeu (IRE)—Wing Stealth (IRE) **The Tipperary Partners**
22 **TRINITYELITEDOTCOM (IRE)**, 4, b g Elusive City (USA)—Beal Ban (IRE) **Manor House Racing Club**

THREE-YEAR-OLDS

23 **ALL REDDY**, ch g Compton Place—Raphaela (FR) **L. A. Bellman**
24 **ART OF WAR (IRE)**, b g Invincible Spirit (IRE)—Chica Roca (USA) **David Ward & Laurence Bellman**
25 **BETTY THE THIEF (IRE)**, b f Teofilo (IRE)—Siphon Melody (USA) **Mr D. Ward**
26 **BOB MASNICKEN**, b g Dandy Man—Twilight Belle (IRE) **Chasemore Farm LLP**
27 **CAPTAIN WHOOSH (IRE)**, gr g Dandy Man—Caerella (IRE) **Mr D. Ward**
28 **CONCOCT (IRE)**, b f Aqlaam—Jinskys Gift (IRE) **De La Warr Racing**
29 **CROWLEY'S LAW**, b f Dubawi (IRE)—Logic **Paul Crowley & Co**
30 **DREAMS OF REALITY**, b f Bushranger (IRE)—No Nightmare (USA) **J. A. Duffy**
31 **DRIFTER (IRE)**, b g Footstepsinthesand—Bright Bank (IRE) **L Bellman, D Lowe, K Trowbridge**
32 **ELOQUENCE**, b f Oratorio (IRE)—Noble Plum (IRE) **South Wind Racing 3**
33 **FINE 'N DANDY (IRE)**, ch g Dandy Man—Pearly Brooks **Mr R. Ng**
34 **GHOSTING (IRE)**, ro c Invincible Spirit (IRE)—Exclusive Approval (USA) **The United Rocks**
35 **HIGH LOVE (IRE)**, b f High Chaparral (IRE)—All Embracing (IRE) **Laurence Bellman & David Lowe**
36 **HOT COFFEE (IRE)**, b f Haatef (USA)—Cafe Creme (IRE) **The MHS 2013 Partnership**
37 **LADY RED OAK**, ch f Medicean—Nuit Sans Fin (FR) **Mr D. R. Passant**
38 **LARSEN BAY (IRE)**, b c Kodiac—Teem (IRE) **T. G. Dascombe**
39 **NOTHING SPECIAL**, gr f Verglas (IRE)—Barathiki **The Boys From Cluj**
40 **PARKHILL STAR**, b f Araafa (IRE)—Runaway Star **Mr M. P. Cooper**
41 **PASSIONATE AFFAIR (IRE)**, ch g Broken Vow (USA)—Charmgoer (USA) **The Passionate Partnership**
42 **QUANTUM DOT (IRE)**, ch g Exceed And Excel (AUS)—Jeed (IRE) **Mrs Y. Fleet**
43 **QUINCEL**, b g Exceed And Excel (AUS)—Quinzey's Best (IRE) **Deva Racing Exceed And Excel Partnership**
44 **ROCKSEE (IRE)**, ch f Rock of Gibraltar (IRE)—Sightseer (USA) **Deva Racing Classic Partnership**
45 **SITTING PRITTY (IRE)**, b f Compton Place—Queen Bodicea (IRE) **N & S Mather,Owen Promotions,I Flanagan**
46 **STEPPING OUT (IRE)**, b f Tagula (IRE)—Teodora (IRE) **Attenborough Bellman Ingram Lowe**
47 **THATABOY (IRE)**, b g Green Desert (USA)—Hawas **David Lowe & Laurence Bellman**

MR TOM DASCOMBE - Continued

48 THE KID, b g High Chaparral (IRE)—Shine Like A Star **Mr D. Ward**
49 UJAGAR (IRE), gr g Dalakhani (IRE)—No Secrets (USA) **Denarius Consulting Ltd**
50 WAR OF ART (IRE), b c Tamayuz—Lucky Clio (IRE) **Mr N. A. Jackson**

TWO-YEAR-OLDS

51 Br f 20/3 Excellent Art—Afra Tsitsi (FR) (Belong To Me (USA)) (40263) **Bellman Lowe O'Halloran Trowbridge**
52 B f 20/1 Approve (IRE)—Bellacoola (GER) (Lomitas) (29422)
53 B f 15/2 Holy Roman Emperor (IRE)—Campbellite (Desert Prince (IRE)) (33333) **De La Warr Racing**
54 CAPTAIN REVELATION, ch c 19/2 Captain Rio—Agony Aunt (Formidable (USA)) (23809) **Cheshire Racing**
55 Ch f 6/3 Paco Boy (IRE)—Clever Millie (IRE) (Cape Canaveral (USA)) (52000)
56 B br c 13/2 Henrythenavigator (USA)—Damini (USA) (Seeking The Gold (USA)) (19357)
57 DAWN'S EARLY LIGHT (IRE), gr c 5/3 Starspangledbanner (AUS)—
                                    Sky Red (Night Shift (USA)) (57142) **Empire State Racing Partnership**
58 DIATOMIC (IRE), b c 31/3 Bushranger (IRE)—
                                    Gilded Truffle (IRE) (Peintre Celebre (USA)) (11614) **Mr J. D. Brown**
59 Gr c 10/5 Dark Angel (IRE)—Dictatrice (FR) (Anabaa (USA)) (38714)
60 B c 14/4 Dark Angel (IRE)—Divine Design (IRE) (Barathea (IRE)) (40262)
61 B f 5/3 Exceed And Excel (AUS)—Don't Tell Mary (IRE) (Starcraft (NZ)) **K. P. Trowbridge**
62 B c 30/3 Kodiac—Eau Rouge (Grand Lodge (USA)) (33333) **Manor House Stables LLP**
63 Gr c 1/5 Big Bad Bob (IRE)—
                                    Exclusive Approval (USA) (With Approval (CAN)) (50000) **Doak Garner Mather Owen**
64 Ch f 10/4 Strategic Prince—Fikrah (Medicean)
65 B c 14/4 Strategic Prince—First Bank (IRE) (Anabaa (USA)) (18095)
66 GAMESTERS LAD, b c 26/3 Firebreak—Gamesters Lady (Almushtarak (IRE)) (952) **Gamesters Partnership**
67 B c 14/3 Majestic Missile (IRE)—
                                    Harvest Joy (IRE) (Daggers Drawn (USA)) (29000) **Coxon Dascombe Lowe Pritchard**
68 B f 19/3 Tagula (IRE)—Key Girl (IRE) (Key of Luck (USA)) (24761) **Attenborough Bellman Ingram Lowe**
69 B f 4/3 Equiano (FR)—La Tintoretta (IRE) (Desert Prince (IRE)) (27100) **Galloways Bakers Ltd**
70 B c 15/4 Showcasing—Lalectra (King Charlemagne (USA)) (50000)
71 Ch c 29/1 Nayef (USA)—Looby Loo (Kyllachy) **Chasemore Farm LLP**
72 B c 17/4 Rip Van Winkle (IRE)—Mania (IRE) (Danehill (USA)) (38714)
73 Ch f 25/4 Lope de Vega (IRE)—Neutrina (IRE) (Hector Protector (USA)) (37165)
74 NEWERA, ch c 18/3 Makfi—Coming Home (Vettori (IRE)) (48000) **Mr D. R. Passant**
75 Gr c 11/4 Dandy Man (IRE)—On Thin Ice (IRE) (Verglas (IRE)) (30971)
76 B f 22/3 Zamindar (USA)—Park Acclaim (IRE) (Clodovil (IRE)) (4761) **Chasemore Farm LLP**
77 B br c 12/3 Starspangledbanner (AUS)—Pascali (Compton Place) (70000)
78 PASSIONATE SPIRIT (IRE), gr c 31/3 Zebedee—
                                    El Morocco (USA) (El Prado (IRE)) (20131) **The Passionate Partnership 2**
79 B c 9/4 Duke of Marmalade (IRE)—Primissima (GER) (Second Set (IRE)) (52380) **Manor House Stables LLP**
80 B c 6/3 Kodiac—Refuse To Give Up (IRE) (Refuse To Bend (IRE)) (42585)
81 Ch c 28/4 Zebedee—Road To Reality (IRE) (Indian Danehill (IRE)) (47619)
82 B c 9/3 Alfred Nobel (IRE)—Sandbox Two (IRE) (Foxhound (USA)) (46457)
83 B f 18/4 Winker Watson—Shawhill (Dr Fong (USA)) **Chasemore Farm LLP**
84 B c 28/1 Acclamation—Society Gal (IRE) (Galileo (IRE)) (46457)
85 B c 3/2 Kodiac—Somersault (Pivotal) (47000)
86 B c 29/3 Bushranger (IRE)—Start The Music (IRE) (King's Best (USA)) (24761)
87 Ch c 1/4 Panis—Teia Tephi (Elnadim (USA)) (3871) **Chasemore Farm LLP**
88 B c 11/4 Shirocco (GER)—Treble Heights (IRE) (Unfuwain (USA)) **Owen Promotions Limited**
89 B f 24/1 Rock Hard Ten (USA)—Veiled Beauty (IRE) (Royal Academy (USA)) **Chasemore Farm LLP**
90 WAR PAINT (IRE), br f 8/4 Excellent Art—Stairway To Glory (IRE) (Kalanisi (IRE)) (82000) **Mr D. Ward**
91 B c 2/3 Fast Company (IRE)—Winnifred (Green Desert (USA)) (60000)

Other Owners: Mr D. Athorn, N. B. Attenborough, A. M. Basing, Mr L. S. Basran MBE, A. W. Black, Mrs J. E. Black, Mrs M. Coxon, Mrs A. E. Dascombe, B. Dascombe, Lord De La Warr, Countess De La Warr, Mr J. Doak, Mr I. R. Flanagan, M. D. Foster, Mrs J. Foster, Mr N. R. Garner, Mr A.C. Hoctor-Duncan, Mrs C. L. Ingram, Mr T. D. Jones, Mr C. Ledigo, Mr C. Lindley, Mr D. J. Lowe, Mr D. I. Lubert, Mr B. Marantelli, Mr N. P. Mather, Mrs S. E. Mather, Mr S. N. Mound, Mrs A. C. Mound, Mr P. Naviede, Mr G. Nicholas, A. F. O'Callaghan, Mr M. O'Halloran, Mr M. Owen, Mr C. D. Pritchard, Mr C. R. Pugh, Mrs B. M. Richmond, Mr G. Shepherd, Mrs S. J. Stoneham, Mr E. B. C. Van Cutsem, Ms S. A. Ward, Mr D. A. Ward, Mr D. V. Williams.

Assistant Trainer: Colin Gorman

Jockey (flat): Richard Kingscote.

149 MR TRISTAN DAVIDSON, Carlisle
Postal: Bellmount, Laversdale, Irthington, Carlisle, Cumbria, CA6 4PS

1 GREY AREA (IRE), 9, gr g Portrait Gallery (IRE)—Queen's Run (IRE) **G. E. Davidson**
2 LIFES A RISK, 5, b m Erhaab (USA)—Rhyming Moppet **J. T. Davidson**
3 SILVER STORM, 6, gr m Tikkanen (USA)—Ifni du Luc (FR) **G. E. Davidson**
4 THOUVA (FR), 7, ro g Ragmar (FR)—Lady Thou (FR) **G. E. Davidson**

150 MR JOHN DAVIES, Darlington
Postal: Denton Grange, Piercebridge, Darlington, Co. Durham, DL2 3TZ
Contacts: PHONE (01325) 374366 MOBILE (07746) 292782
E-MAIL johndavieshorses@live.co.uk WEBSITE www.johndaviesracing.com

1 DOYENTHEDECENTHING, 6, gr m Doyen (IRE)—Nearly Decent **Mr P. Taylor**
2 MILLKWOOD, 4, b g Millkom—Wedgewood Star **K. Kirkup**
3 NOOSA SOUND, 4, ch f Halling (USA)—Crimson Topaz **Mr P. Taylor**
4 THE OSTEOPATH (IRE), 11, ch g Danehill Dancer (IRE)—Miss Margate (IRE) **K. Kirkup**
5 WENDY'SGREYHORSE, 8, gr m Beneficial—Nearly Decent **Mrs W. Taylor**

THREE-YEAR-OLDS
6 HANK SCHRADER, b g Avonbridge—Swift Baba (USA) **Mr C. W. Davies**
7 B g Dapper—Lonely One **J. J. Davies**
8 MOXEY, ch g Nayef (USA)—Emily Blake (IRE) **Mr & Mrs R. Scott**
9 QUEENS PARK (FR), b f King's Best (USA)—Anna Deesse (FR) **Mr & Mrs R. Scott**
10 WOLFWOOD, b g Ferrule (IRE)—Wedgewood Star **K. Kirkup**

Other Owners: R. Scott, Mrs P. M. Scott.

Jockey (flat): P. J. McDonald.

151 MR PAUL DAVIES, Bromyard
Postal: 20 Hatton Park, Bromyard, Herefordshire, HR7 4EY

1 EMMA SODA, 9, b m Milan—Ms Trude (IRE) **Mr P. S. Davies**
2 MY DIBABA (IRE), 7, b m Pierre—Toulon Toulouse (IRE) **Mr P. S. Davies**

152 MISS SARAH-JAYNE DAVIES, Leominster
Postal: The Upper Withers, Hundred Lane, Kimbolton, Leominster, Herefordshire, HR6 0HZ
Contacts: PHONE (01584) 711780 MOBILE (07779) 797079
E-MAIL sjdracing@live.co.uk

1 ACCESSALLAREAS (IRE), 9, ch g Swift Gulliver (IRE)—Arushgold (IRE) **Miss S. J. Davies**
2 BIG JOHN CANNON (IRE), 4, b g High Chaparral (IRE)—Bakiya (USA) **Miss S. J. Davies**
3 CAPISCI (IRE), 9, br g Tikkanen (USA)—Dolce Notte (IRE) **Miss S. J. Davies**
4 CHANKILLO, 5, ch g Observatory (USA)—Seasonal Blossom (IRE) **Mr A. J. Gough**
5 COMMERCIAL (IRE), 6, br g Kodiac—Call Collect (IRE) **Miss S. J. Davies**
6 DAZINSKI, 8, ch g Sulamani (IRE)—Shuheb **Mr D. M. J. Lloyd**
7 DR THISTLE (IRE), 7, b g Dr Massini (IRE)—Thistle Thyne (IRE) **Mrs S. M. Davies**
8 DREAM'S PARK, 4, b f Fictional—Monty's Dream VII
9 DRESDEN (IRE), 6, b g Diamond Green (FR)—So Precious (IRE) **Mr D. M. J. Lloyd**
10 DRUMGOOLAND (IRE), 7, b g Tikkanen (USA)—Credora Storm (IRE) **Mr J. H. M. Mahot**
11 FLORABURY, 5, b m Alflora (IRE)—Emerald Reign (IRE) **W. S. Layton**
12 GLACIAL ROES (IRE), 6, ch m Vinnie Roe (IRE)—Glacial Field (IRE) **Mrs S. M. Davies**
13 HERR LARRY HEWIS, 6, b g Sir Harry Lewis (USA)—Avenches (GER) **Mr R. A. Skidmore**
14 KANDARI (FR), 10, b g Kahyasi—Nee Brune (FR) **Miss S. J. Davies**
15 MISS DIMPLES, 5, gr m Tikkanen (USA)—Scolboa House (IRE) **Ms H. Taylor**
16 PAINTED GOLD, 8, ch m Central Park (IRE)—Iron Pyrites **Mr C. Thomson**
17 PASSING FIESTA, 5, b m Passing Glance—Clarice Starling **Mr A. J. Gough**

MISS SARAH-JAYNE DAVIES - Continued

18 PEMBROKE HOUSE, 7, gr g Terimon—Bon Coeur **Mr A. Mortimer**
19 PERFECT SHOT (IRE), 8, b g High Chaparral (IRE)—Zoom Lens (IRE) **Mrs C. Kerr**
20 SHALAMIYR (FR), 9, gr g Linamix (FR)—Shamanara (IRE) **Miss S. J. Davies**
21 SUPARI, 5, b g Beat All (USA)—Susie Bury **Good Evans Racing Partnership**
22 TWIN BARRELS, 7, ch g Double Trigger (IRE)—Caballe (USA) **K. E. Stait**

Other Owners: Mr M. Evans, Mr D. Richardson.

Assistant Trainer: Jeremy Mahot

Jockey (NH): Will Kennedy, Liam Treadwell. **Amateur:** Miss Sarah-Jayne Davies, Mr Jeremy Mahot.

---

153 MR WILLIAM DAVIES, Tenbury Wells
Postal: **Arceye House, Kyre, Tenbury Wells, Worcestershire, WR15 8RW**

1 SUMNER (IRE), 10, b g Xaar—Black Jack Girl (IRE) **W. Davies**

---

154 MISS JOANNA DAVIS, East Garston
Postal: **South Cottage, Pounds Farm, East Garston, Hungerford, Berkshire, RG17 7HU**
Contacts: **PHONE (01488) 649977 FAX (01488) 649977 MOBILE (07879) 811535**
E-MAIL davisjo_007@hotmail.com WEBSITE www.jodavisracing.com

1 BRIGHT DECISION, 8, b g Thowra (FR)—Bright Spangle (IRE) **Miss J. S. Davis**
2 CAPTAIN FLASH, 5, b br g Indian River (FR)—Westgate Run **Mr R. K. Allsop**
3 ELIXIR DU LAC, 7, gr m Fair Mix (IRE)—Hutcel Loch **V. R. Bedley**
4 GO ANNIE, 6, gr m Proclamation (IRE)—Bright Spangle (IRE) **Lockstone Business Services Ltd**
5 INDIEFRONT, 5, b m Indesatchel (IRE)—Jonchee (FR) **Mr R. K. Allsop**
6 LEEROAR (IRE), 6, b g Let The Lion Roar—Leane (IRE) **The Hard Hat Gang**
7 LYMM GREY, 5, gr m Fair Mix (IRE)—Ellie Bee **D. Clayton**
8 MR FITZROY (IRE), 4, ch g Kyllachy—Reputable **Dr P. J. Brown**
9 NATAANI (IRE), 11, br g Presenting—Clahada Rose (IRE) **Mr T. Worth**
10 PASSATO (GER), 10, b g Lando (GER)—Passata (FR) **Mr R. K. Allsop**
11 RED LILAC (IRE), 5, b m Red Clubs (IRE)—Let's Pretend **Mrs P. M. Brown**
12 ROSE OF THE WORLD (IRE), 6, ch m Vinnie Roe (IRE)—Frankly Native (IRE) **Oakhedge Racing**
13 THE IRON MAIDEN, 5, gr m Proclamation (IRE)—Bright Spangle (IRE) **Lockstone Business Services Ltd**
14 WAS MY VALENTINE, 7, b m Best of The Bests (IRE)—Eleonor Sympson **Oakhedge Racing**

THREE-YEAR-OLDS

15 B f Rainbow High—Bright Spangle (IRE) **Miss J. Davis**
16 DARK MUSIC, br f Misu Bond (IRE)—Tender Moments **Mrs P. M. Brown**
17 POCKET WARRIOR, b g Tobougg (IRE)—Navene (IRE) **Mrs B. M. Cuthbert**

Other Owners: Mr A. D. Hutchinson, Mrs J. P. Hutchinson, Mr M. Morgan, Mrs Mary Tobin.

Conditional: Jack Savage.

---

155 MISS ZOE DAVISON, East Grinstead
Postal: **Shovelstrode Racing Stables, Shovelstrode Lane, Ashurstwood, East Grinstead, West Sussex, RH19 3PN**
Contacts: **FAX (01342) 323153 MOBILE (07970) 839357 & (07812) 007554**
E-MAIL andy01031976@yahoo.co.uk WEBSITE www.shovelstroderacing.co.uk

1 AIREDALE LAD (IRE), 13, b g Charnwood Forest (IRE)—Tamarsiya (USA) **Mrs S. E. Colville**
2 ASKER (IRE), 6, b g High Chaparral (IRE)—Pay The Bank **The Secret Circle**
3 ATMANNA, 5, br m Manduro (GER)—Samdaniya **A. J. Irvine**
4 BEGGERS BELIEF, 6, ch g Bertolini (USA)—Dropitlikeit's Hot (IRE) **African Sky**
5 BOSSY JANE, 4, b f Assertive—Jane's Payoff (IRE) **Mr K. C. Bennett**
6 BREEZEALONG RILEY, 5, br m Arkadian Hero (USA)—Mountain Magic **Miss Z. C. Davison**
7 CUT'N'SHUT, 7, b g Motivator—Millennium Dash **Mrs J. A. Irvine**
8 DERRYOGUE (IRE), 9, b g Tikkanen (USA)—Snugville Sally **The Secret Circle**

MISS ZOE DAVISON - Continued

9 **DOLLY COLMAN (IRE)**, 6, br gr m Diamond Green (FR)—Absolutely Cool (IRE) **Mr K. Corke**
10 **FAULT**, 8, b g Bahamian Bounty—Trundley Wood **Mrs S. E. Colville**
11 **FRANK N FAIR**, 6, br m Trade Fair—Frankfurt (GER) **Shovelstrode Racing Club**
12 **GILBERT**, 7, b g Pasternak—Regal's Last **A. J. Irvine**
13 **HOUSEPARTY**, 6, b g Invincible Spirit (IRE)—Amusing Time (IRE) **Sussex Racing**
14 **HUBOOD**, 6, b m Refuse To Bend (IRE)—Shuheb **Mrs J. A. Irvine**
15 **INDIAN VIOLET (IRE)**, 8, b g Indian Ridge—Violet Spring (IRE) **Macable Partnership**
16 **JOHN'S GEM**, 9, ch g Silver Patriarch—Hollow Legs **Golfguard Limited**
17 **JUMEIRAH LIBERTY**, 6, ch g Proclamation (IRE)—Gleam of Light (IRE) **The Secret Circle**
18 **JUST BEWARE**, 12, b m Makbul—Bewails (IRE) **The Secret Circle**
19 **LINDSAY'S DREAM**, 8, b m Montjeu (IRE)—Lady Lindsay (IRE) **Mr S. P. O'Loughlin**
20 **LITTLETON LAD (IRE)**, 6, b b rg Close Conflict (USA)—Knockraha Star (IRE) **Miss Z. C. Davison**
21 **MAC'S GREY (IRE)**, 7, gr g Great Palm (USA)—Gypsy Kelly (IRE) **Macable Partnership**
22 **MISTY MORNIN**, 6, gr m Central Park (IRE)—Belle Rose (IRE) **Macable Partnership**
23 **MY SCAT DADDY (USA)**, 5, b g Scat Daddy (USA)—Will Be A Bates (USA) **Sussex Racing**
24 **NOZIC (FR)**, 13, b g Port Lyautey (FR)—Grizilh (FR) **The Lump O'Clock Syndicate**
25 **PIAZZA SAN PIETRO**, 8, ch g Compton Place—Rainbow Spectrum (FR) **Mr K. Corke**
26 **ROGER BEANTOWN (IRE)**, 9, b g Indian Danehill (IRE)—Best Wait (IRE) **The Sophisticated Seven**
27 **SHERJAWY (IRE)**, 10, b g Diktat—Arruhan (IRE) **A. J. Irvine**
28 **SPYMISTRESS**, 4, ch f Sakhee's Secret—Martha (IRE) **Sussex Racing**
29 **STANDING STRONG (IRE)**, 6, b g Green Desert (USA)—Alexander Three D (IRE) **Sussex Racing**
30 **TCHANG GOON (FR)**, 10, b g Marathon (USA)—Royal Hostess (IRE) **J. E. Belsey**
31 **THELORDBEWITHYOU (IRE)**, 10, b g Turtle Island (IRE)—Georgic **A. J. Irvine**

THREE-YEAR-OLDS

32 **BOLD MAX**, b g Assertive—Jane's Payoff (IRE) **Mr K. C. Bennett**
33 **SKINNY LOVE**, b f Holy Roman Emperor (IRE)—Lady Mickataine (USA) **Sussex Racing**

Other Owners: S. J. Clare, Mrs E. Fry, Mr W. G. Fry, Mr S. Mackintosh, Mr F. W. Mackintosh, Mr S. J. Moll, A. N. Waters.

Assistant Trainer: A. Irvine

Jockey (flat): Sam Hitchcott. **Conditional:** Gemma Gracey-Davison.

156
MR ANTHONY DAY, Hinckley
Postal: **Wolvey Fields Farm, Coalpit Lane, Wolvey, Hinckley, Leicestershire, LE10 3HD**
Contacts: **PHONE (01455) 220225 MOBILE (07928) 835330**
E-MAIL kathy197@btinternet.com

1 **CHARMING LAD (IRE)**, 9, b g Dushyantor (USA)—Glens Lady (IRE) **Mrs K. D. Day**
2 **COOL FUSION**, 5, b m Beat All (USA)—Fusion of Tunes **Mrs K. D. Day**
3 **OHMS LAW**, 9, b g Overbury (IRE)—Polly Live Wire **Mrs K. D. Day**
4 **POLLY LIGHTFOOT**, 5, b m Dalby Walks—Polly Live Wire
5 **SECRET ISLAND**, 5, b m Alflora (IRE)—Precious Island **Mrs K. D. Day**
6 **SHESLIKETHEWIND**, 6, b m Central Park (IRE)—Velvet Leaf **Mrs K. D. Day**
7 **STARLIT EVE**, 6, br m Samraan (USA)—Kissed By Moonlite **Mrs K. D. Day**
8 5, B m Central Park (IRE)—Velvet Leaf

Assistant Trainer: Mrs K. D. Day (07546) 593485

Amateur: Mr Jon Day.

157
MISS LISA DAY, Pontypool
Postal: **Well Cottage, Penyhroel, Pontypool, Gwent**

1 **BABE HEFFRON (IRE)**, 13, ch g Topanoora—Yellow Ochre (IRE) **Miss L. Day**
2 **DI'PHILLY'S DREAM**, 6, b m Gentleman's Deal (IRE)—Mia's Moll (IRE) **Miss L. Day**
3 **EDGEVINE**, 10, b m Grape Tree Road—Vieille Russie **W. J. Day**
4 **FORCE TO SPEND**, 7, b m Reset (AUS)—Mon Petit Diamant **Miss L. Day**
5 **STRAND LINE (IRE)**, 14, b g Supreme Leader—Good Credentials **Miss L. Day**

158 **MR WILLIAM DE BEST-TURNER, Calne**
Postal: **8 North End, Calne, Wiltshire, SN11 9DQ**
Contacts: **PHONE (01249) 811944 HOME (07977) 910779 FAX (01249) 811955 MOBILE (07977) 910779**
E-MAIL calnevets@btconnect.com

1 CHICAGO SOCKS, 4, b c Catcher In The Rye (IRE)—Sachiko **W. de Best-Turner**
2 FOOLSANDORSES (IRE), 6, b g Beneficial—All Honey (IRE) **De Best Racing**
3 4, B f Catcher In The Rye (IRE)—Maylan (IRE) **W. de Best-Turner**
4 SPARTACULOUS, 6, b m Spartacus (IRE)—Sachiko **De Best Racing**

TWO-YEAR-OLDS

5 Ch c 10/3 Schiaparelli (GER)—Maylan (IRE) (Lashkari) **W. de Best-Turner**
6 B c 4/4 Bertolini (USA)—Sachiko (Celtic Swing) **W. de Best-Turner**

Other Owners: Miss S J Slade.

Assistant Trainer: Heidi Sweeting

159 **MR ED DE GILES, Ledbury**
Postal: **Lilly Hall Farm, Little Marcle, Ledbury, Herefordshire, HR8 2LD**
Contacts: **PHONE (01531) 637369 MOBILE (07811) 388345**
E-MAIL ed@eddegilesracing.com WEBSITE www.eddegilesracing.com

1 AL MUKHDAM, 4, b g Exceed And Excel (AUS)—Sakhya (IRE) **T. Gould**
2 CATHEDRAL, 5, b g Invincible Spirit (IRE)—Capades Dancer (USA) **Mr C. Bowles**
3 CRAVAT, 5, b g Dubai Destination (USA)—Crinolette (IRE) **T. Gould**
4 CROQUEMBOUCHE (IRE), 5, b g Acclamation—Wedding Cake (IRE) **Mr P. J. Manser**
5 4, B f Ishiguro (USA)—Cute **E. B. de Giles**
6 DIAMONDHEAD (IRE), 5, b g Kyllachy—Hammrah **T. Gould**
7 JINKER NOBLE, 5, b g Green Desert (USA)—Depressed **Mr A. P. Ridgers**
8 KINGSGATE CHOICE (IRE), 7, b g Choisir (AUS)—Kenema (IRE) **Tight Lines Partnership**
9 LIVING IT LARGE (FR), 7, ch g Bertolini (USA)—Dilag (IRE) **T. Gould**
10 MAHADEE (IRE), 9, br g Cape Cross (IRE)—Rafiya **2 1/2 - 3 1/2 Club**
11 MEN DON'T CRY (IRE), 5, b g Street Cry (IRE)—Naissance Royale (IRE) **Clarke, King & Lewis**
12 PRINCE OF DREAMS, 7, b g Sadler's Wells (USA)—Questina (FR) **Jennifer & Alex Viall**
13 SPRINGINMYSTEP (IRE), 5, b g Footstepsinthesand—Joyful (IRE) **T. Gould**
14 TIJUCA (IRE), 5, b m Captain Rio—Some Forest **E. B. de Giles**
15 TWENTY ONE CHOICE (IRE), 5, ch g Choisir (AUS)—Midnight Lace **Penna Racing**
16 WHISKEY N STOUT (IRE), 4, b g Amadeus Wolf—Yasmin Satine (IRE) **B. T. McDonald**

THREE-YEAR-OLDS

17 BAZOOKA (IRE), b c Camacho—Janadam (IRE) **T. Gould**
18 HOSTILE FIRE (IRE), b g Iffraaj—Royal Esteem **Mr A. Mortazavi**
19 KASHMIRI SUNSET, b c Tiger Hill (IRE)—Sagamartha **Jennifer & Alex Viall**
20 KOPENHAGEN (IRE), ch c Captain Rio—Quizzical Lady **Mr A. Mortazavi**
21 MARENGO, gr c Verglas (IRE)—Cloudchaser (IRE) **Mrs S. Smith**
22 QUINTA FEIRA (IRE), gr g Medicean—Bunditten (IRE) **Mr S. Treacher**
23 SMIDGEN (IRE), b c Bahamian Bounty—Brazilian Style **Boardman, Golder, Sercombe & Viall**
24 WEEKENDATBERNIES (IRE), b g War Chant (USA)—Morena Park **Alex Ridgers & Robert Jones**
25 ZUGZWANG (IRE), b c Kodiac—Kris's Bank **Mr S. Treacher**

Other Owners: Mr R. J. Boardman, Mr D. Clarke, Mr M. J. Gibbons, Mr J. C. Golder, Mr R. S. Jones, C. J. King, Mrs E. V. Lewis, Mr M. C. Penna, Mr P. R. Sercombe, A. J. Viall.

160 **MR BEN DE HAAN, Lambourn**
Postal: **Fair View, Long Hedge, Lambourn, Newbury, Berkshire, RG17 8NA**
Contacts: **PHONE (01488) 72163 FAX (01488) 71306 MOBILE (07831) 104574**
E-MAIL bendehaanracing@aol.com WEBSITE www.bendehaanracing.com

1 BILIDN, 6, b m Tiger Hill (IRE)—Brightest Star **Mrs D. Vaughan**
2 DECIDING MOMENT (IRE), 8, b g Zagreb (USA)—Fontaine Jewel (IRE) **W. A. Tyrer**
3 GENERALYSE, 5, b g Cadeaux Genereux—Dance To The Blues (IRE) **Mrs D. Vaughan**

MR BEN DE HAAN - Continued

4 **LONDON SILVER,** 5, b g Zafeen (FR)—Princess Londis **J. Simms**
5 **LOOKS LIKE SLIM,** 7, b g Passing Glance—Slims Lady **Mr M. Butler**
6 **NATIVE GALLERY (IRE),** 9, gr g Portrait Gallery (IRE)—Native Bev (IRE) **W. A. Tyrer**
7 **NOM DE GUERRE (IRE),** 12, b g Presenting—Asklynn (IRE) **Mr N. Tatman & Exors of the Late Mrs E. Tatman**

THREE-YEAR-OLDS

8 **BYRON'S GOLD,** ch f Byron—Dance To The Blues (IRE) **Mrs D. Vaughan**

Other Owners: N. A. Tatman, Exors of the Late Mrs E. Tatman.

Jockey (flat): Adam Kirby. Jockey (NH): Noel Fehily, Daryl Jacob.

---

161 **MR GEOFFREY DEACON, Compton**
Postal: Hamilton Stables, Hockham Road, Compton, Newbury, Berkshire, RG20 6QJ
Contacts: MOBILE (07967) 626757
E-MAIL geoffdeacon@aol.com WEBSITE www.geoffreydeacontraining.com

1 **AFFILIATE,** 6, ch m Nayef (USA)—Allied Cause **Woodhall, Nicol & Co**
2 **BANKS ROAD (IRE),** 9, b g Beneficial—Cecelia's Charm (IRE) **Mr C. W. Duckett**
3 **BERTIE MOON,** 4, b g Bertolini (USA)—Fleeting Moon **Mr J. J. Kelly**
4 **DAWN CATCHER,** 4, ch f Bertolini (USA)—First Dawn **Mayden Stud & Associates**
5 4, B c Sleeping Indian—Elderberry **Mr G. Deacon**
6 **ERNIE,** 7, ch g Reset (AUS)—Bonita Bee **P. D. Cundell**
7 **ESEEJ (USA),** 9, ch g Aljabr (USA)—Jinaan (USA) **Miss S. J. Duckett**
8 **GLASTONBERRY,** 6, gr m Piccolo—Elderberry **Mr G. Deacon**
9 **HAVING A BALL,** 10, b g Mark of Esteem (IRE)—All Smiles **P. D. Cundell**
10 **IZZY PICCOLINA (IRE),** 6, b m Morozov (USA)—Chloara (IRE) **C. O. King**
11 **KOVOLINI,** 4, ch f Bertolini (USA)—Petrikov (IRE) **J. A. Dewhurst**
12 5, B g Overbury (IRE)—Maiden Aunt (IRE)
13 **MCDELTA,** 4, b g Delta Dancer—McNairobi **P. D. Cundell**
14 **MOON TRIP,** 5, b g Cape Cross (IRE)—Fading Light **Mr G. Deacon**
15 **PICC OF BURGAU,** 4, b f Piccolo—Rosein **The Outta Lunch Partnership**
16 **RYEDALE LASS,** 6, b m Val Royal (FR)—First Dawn **Mayden Stud & Associates**
17 **SOUBRETTE,** 4, ch f Zafeen (FR)—Nihal (IRE) **White Star Racing Syndicate**
18 **SPRINGHILL LAD,** 7, b g Kayf Tara—Anouska **J. Davies**
19 **TAKITWO,** 11, b g Delta Dancer—Tiama (IRE) **P. D. Cundell**
20 **TRAFORDS HERO,** 6, b g Parthian Springs—Be My Shuile (IRE) **Mrs A. M. O'Sullivan**
21 **VERMEYEN,** 5, b g Dutch Art—Madame Maxine (USA) **Miss S. J. Duckett**
22 **VICTORIAN NUMBER (FR),** 6, ch g Numerous (USA)—Malaisia (FR) **Mr A. R. Pittman**
23 **YAIR HILL (IRE),** 6, b g Selkirk (USA)—Conspiracy **Mr G. Deacon**

Other Owners: Mrs D. S. Dewhurst, Mr D. Greaney, Mr R. Lim, Mrs A. Nicol, Mrs H. C. L. Woodhall, D. M. Woodhall.

Assistant Trainer: Sally Duckett

---

162 **MR DAVID DENNIS, Hanley Swan**
Postal: Tyre Hill Racing Stables, Hanley Swan, Worcester, Worcestershire, WR8 0EQ
Contacts: PHONE (01684) 565310 MOBILE 07867 974880
E-MAIL david@daviddennistrainer.co.uk WEBSITE www.ddracing.co.uk

1 **A KEEN SENSE (GER),** 5, b g Sholokhov (IRE)—All Our Luck (GER) **Superdream Creative Limited**
2 **ANGUS GLENS,** 4, gr g Dalakhani (IRE)—Clara Bow (IRE) **Corbett Stud**
3 **BALLYBOUGH PAT (IRE),** 7, b g Waky Nao—Princess Ruth (IRE) **Favourites Racing Ltd**
4 **FINAL NUDGE (IRE),** 5, b g Kayf Tara—Another Shot (IRE) **Corbett Stud**
5 **FLORIDA QUAYS (IRE),** 6, b g Craigsteel—Florida Bay (IRE) **Favourites Racing Ltd**
6 **HELL'S SPIRIT (IRE),** 6, b g Oscar (IRE)—Last Century (IRE) **Favourites Racing Ltd**
7 **KEY TO THE WEST (IRE),** 7, b g Westerner—Monte Solaro (IRE) **Favourites Racing Ltd**
8 **KING'S SONG (FR),** 4, b g King's Theatre (IRE)—Chanson Indienne (FR) **Corbett Stud**
9 **MALLER TREE,** 7, b g Karinga Bay—Annaberg (IRE) **Favourites Racing Ltd**
10 **MARJU'S QUEST (IRE),** 4, b g Marju (IRE)—Queen's Quest **Favourites Racing Ltd**
11 **NETHER STREAM (IRE),** 10, b g Blueprint (IRE)—Shuil Ub **James Berryman & Partner**
12 **PRINCESS CAETANI (IRE),** 5, b m Dylan Thomas (IRE)—Caladira (IRE) **Favourites Racing Ltd**
13 **QUEENSWOOD BAY,** 8, b m Karinga Bay—Forest Maze **W. R. Gaskins**

MR DAVID DENNIS - Continued

14 **ROMAN FLIGHT (IRE)**, 6, b g Antonius Pius (USA)—Flight Sequence **Favourites Racing Ltd**
15 **STEEL SUMMIT (IRE)**, 5, b g Craigsteel—B Greenhill **Favourites Racing Ltd**
16 **UN ANJOU (FR)**, 6, b br g Panoramic—Idee d'estruval (FR) **Superdream Creative Limited**

THREE-YEAR-OLDS

17 **EXCEED POLICY**, ch g Exceed And Excel (AUS)—Policy Setter (USA) **Corbett Stud**
18 **SPIN FOR A HARP (IRE)**, b g Bushranger (IRE)—Shining Desert (IRE) **Corbett Stud**

Other Owners: Mr J. D. Berryman, Mr M. J. S. Cockburn, C. Lysaght, Mrs J. Rees.

---

163   **MR TIM DENNIS, Bude**
Postal: **Thorne Farm, Bude, Cornwall, EX23 0LU**
Contacts: **PHONE (01288) 352849 MOBILE (07855) 785781**
E-MAIL **trainertwdennis@gmail.com**

1 **ASK THE BOSS**, 9, b g Deploy—Fermoy Lady (IRE) **Mrs J. E. Dennis**
2 **ITS A LONG ROAD**, 6, b g Grape Tree Road—Blue Shannon (IRE) **Mrs J. E. Dennis**
3 **VALLEY ROAD**, 6, b m Grape Tree Road—Vallingale (IRE) **Mrs J. E. Dennis**
4 **WISHES AND STARS (IRE)**, 8, b m Old Vic—She's No Trouble (IRE) **Mrs J. E. Dennis**

---

164   **MR ROBIN DICKIN, Alcester**
Postal: **Hill Farm, Park Lane, Great Alne, Alcester, Warwickshire, B49 6HS**
Contacts: **PHONE (01789) 488148 (01789) 488249 MOBILE (07979) 518593 / (07979) 518594**
E-MAIL **robin@robindickinracing.org.uk** WEBSITE **www.robindickinracing.org.uk**

1 **AUTUMN SPIRIT**, 10, ch m Kadastrof (FR)—Dickies Girl **The Lordy Racing Partnership**
2 **BADGERS COVE (IRE)**, 10, b g Witness Box (USA)—Celestial Rose (IRE) **E. R. C. Beech & B. Wilkinson**
3 **BALLY LAGAN (IRE)**, 6, gr g Kalanisi (IRE)—Rose Palma (FR) **Park Lane Partnership**
4 **BALLYHOOLEY BOY (IRE)**, 7, b g Oscar (IRE)—Nivalf **The Tricksters**
5 **BE MY WITNESS (IRE)**, 5, b m Witness Box (USA)—Smokey Firth (IRE) **Mrs A. L. Merry**
6 **CORNISH ICE**, 10, b g Dolpour—Icelandic Poppy **R. G. Whitehead**
7 **DAN'S QUEST**, 4, b g Kalanisi (IRE)—Piedmont (UAE) **Mark James Bloodstock**
8 **DANCE FOR LIVVY (IRE)**, 6, br m Kodiac—Dancing Steps **Mark James Bloodstock**
9 **DANCING DAFFODIL**, 9, ch m Kadastrof (FR)—Whistling Song **Mr & Mrs Cooper and Mrs C Dickin**
10 **ENTERTAIN ME**, 10, b m Kadastrof (FR)—Just The Ticket (IRE) **Mrs A. L. Merry**
11 **GARRAHALISH (IRE)**, 6, b g Presenting—Savu Sea (IRE) **Just 4 Fun**
12 **GRAYLYN AMBER**, 9, b m Nomadic Way (USA)—State Lady (IRE) **Graham & Lynn Knight**
13 **GRAYLYN RUBY (FR)**, 9, b g Limnos (JPN)—Nandi (IRE) **Graham & Lynn Knight**
14 **KAWA (FR)**, 8, gr g Kouroun (FR)—Kulitch **Mrs C. M. Dickin**
15 **KAYF TIGER**, 5, b g Kayf Tara—La Marette **Natalie Jameson**
16 **KITEGEN (IRE)**, 8, b g Milan—Keen Gale (IRE) **R. G. Whitehead**
17 **LAIDBACK LEO**, 6, ch g Golden Snake (USA)—Rockstine (USA) **The Jameson & Elbro Partnership**
18 **LAKE LEGEND**, 10, b g Midnight Legend—Lac Marmot (FR) **Paul Wilson**
19 **MINNIE MILAN (IRE)**, 5, b m Milan—Shiminnie (IRE) **Nic Allen**
20 **MISS MORN (IRE)**, 8, b m Loup Sauvage (USA)—Frosty Morn **Mrs C. M. Dickin**
21 4, B f Kalanisi (IRE)—Montanara (IRE) **Nic Allen**
22 **NICKS POWER (IRE)**, 8, b g Luso—Shii-Take's Girl **J. F. R. Stainer**
23 **PACCO (FR)**, 11, b g Assessor (IRE)—Uguette IV (FR) **Ray & Marian Elbro**
24 **PLAYING WITH FIRE (IRE)**, 10, gr m Witness Box (USA)—Smokey Path (IRE) **Mrs A. L. Merry**
25 **POINT OF ATTACK (IRE)**, 5, ch g Beneficial—Aimees Princess (IRE) **Mrs C. M. Dickin**
26 **PRESENTING PADDY (IRE)**, 6, b g Presenting—Bula Beag (IRE) **The Bonnie Tyler Partnership**
27 5, Br m Kayf Tara—Princess Timon **Mark James Bloodstock**
28 **RESTLESS HARRY**, 10, b g Sir Harry Lewis (USA)—Restless Native (IRE) **R. G. Whitehead**
29 **RUSSIAN ROMANCE (IRE)**, 9, b m Moscow Society (USA)—My Romance **Mrs A. L. Merry**
30 **SCARLETT O'TARA**, 8, b m Kayf Tara—Lynoso **J. F. R. Stainer**
31 4, B g Norse Dancer (IRE)—Small Amount **Mrs C. M. Dickin**
32 4, B f King's Theatre (IRE)—Supreme du Casse (FR) **Nic Allen**
33 **THE ABSENT MARE**, 6, gr m Fair Mix (IRE)—Precious Lucy (FR) **Mr J. C. Clemmow**
34 **THE DE THAIX (FR)**, 7, b g Polish Summer—Etoile de Thaix (FR) **John Priday**
35 **THOMAS CRAPPER**, 7, b g Tamure (IRE)—Mollycarrs Gambul **Apis.uk.com**
36 **TILT DU CHATELIER (FR)**, 7, ch g Arnaqueur (USA)—Une Du Chatelier (FR) **Avante (UK) Limited**

MR ROBIN DICKIN - Continued

37 **TOM O'TARA**, 10, b g Kayf Tara—Mrs May **Knight, Ward & Marriot**
38 **TROYAN (IRE)**, 7, b g King's Theatre (IRE)—Talk The Talk **John Priday**
39 **UNFORGETTABLE (IRE)**, 11, b g Norwich—Miss Lulu (IRE) **John Rogers**
40 **VALRENE**, 8, b m Grape Tree Road—Across The Water **John Priday**
41 **YOUNG LOU**, 5, b m Kadastrof (FR)—Wanna Shout **E. R. C. Beech & B. Wilkinson**

THREE-YEAR-OLDS

42 B g Midnight Legend—Simple Glory (IRE) **E. R. C. Beech & B. Wilkinson**

TWO-YEAR-OLDS

43 B c 28/4 Black Sam Bellamy (IRE)—Simple Glory (IRE) (Simply Great (FR)) **E. R. C. Beech & B. Wilkinson**
44 **STORMING HARRY**, ch g 29/4 Assertive—Miss Pebbles (IRE) (Lake Coniston (IRE)) **N. K. Thick**

Other Owners: Mr E. R. Clifford Beech, Mr Hugh Brown, Ms Joanne Clark, Mr J. R. Cooper, Mrs M. A. Cooper, Mr C. J. Dickin, Mrs C. M. Dickin, Mrs Marian Elbro, Mr Ray Elbro, Mrs Jan Gibson, Mr S. Kirby, Mr G. Knight, Mrs L. C. Knight, Mr John Porter, Mr P. Venvell, Mr B. Wilkinson, Mr Brian Wilson.

Assistant Trainer: Claire Dickin

Jockey (flat): Luke Morris. **Jockey (NH):** Charlie Poste, Wayne Kavanagh. **Conditional:** Joseph Palmowski.
Amateur: Miss Paige Jeffrey, Mr Toby Wheeler.

---

165 **MR JOHN DIXON, Carlisle**
Postal: **Moorend, Thursby, Carlisle, Cumbria, CA5 6QP**
Contacts: **PHONE (01228) 711019**

1 **CIRCUS STAR (USA)**, 6, b g Borrego (USA)—Picadilly Circus (USA) **Mrs S. F. Dixon**
2 **CROFTON ARCH**, 14, b g Jumbo Hirt (USA)—Joyful Imp **Mrs E. M. Dixon**
3 **CROFTON LANE**, 8, b g And Beyond (IRE)—Joyful Imp **Mrs S. F. Dixon**
4 **DANIEL'S DREAM**, 14, b g Prince Daniel (USA)—Amber Holly **Mrs E. M. Dixon**
5 **JOYFUL BE**, 9, ch m And Beyond (IRE)—Joyful Imp **Mrs E. M. Dixon**

Amateur: Mr J. J. Dixon.

---

166 **MR SCOTT DIXON, Retford**
Postal: **Haygarth House Stud, Haygarth House, Babworth, Retford, Nottinghamshire, DN22 8ES**
Contacts: **PHONE (01777) 869300 (01777) 869079/701818 FAX (01777) 869326**
MOBILE (07976) 267019
E-MAIL scottdixon1987@hotmail.com / mrsyvettedixon@gmail.com
WEBSITE www.scottdixonracing.com

1 **ASKAUD (IRE)**, 6, b m Iffraaj—Tarabaya (IRE) **The Doncaster Racing Club**
2 **BURNHOPE**, 5, b g Choisir (AUS)—Isengard (USA) **Ontoawinner 4**
3 **CADEAUX PEARL**, 6, b g Acclamation—Anneliina **P. J. Dixon**
4 **DALDINI**, 12, b g Josr Algarhoud (IRE)—Arianna Aldini **P. J. Dixon**
5 **DOCOFTHEBAY (IRE)**, 10, ch g Docksider (USA)—Baize **P. J. Dixon**
6 **DR RED EYE**, 6, ch g Dr Fong (USA)—Camp Fire (IRE) **The Red Eye Partnership**
7 **EVEN STEVENS**, 6, br g Ishiguru (USA)—Promised (IRE) **P. J. Dixon**
8 **FELICE (IRE)**, 4, b f Papal Bull—Tarabaya (IRE) **Gen. Sir G Howlett Paul Nolan & Partners**
9 **GABRIAL'S GIFT (IRE)**, 5, gr g Verglas (IRE)—Sahara Lady (IRE) **The Friday Follies**
10 **INCOMPARABLE**, 9, ch g Compton Place—Indian Silk (IRE) **P. J. Dixon**
11 **JILLYWINKS**, 4, b f Milk It Mick—Thunderous Days **Jilly Cooper & Friends**
12 **JIMINY**, 4, b g Acclamation—Grasshoppergreen (IRE) **Jeremy Gompertz & Paul Dixon**
13 **KING OF KUDOS (IRE)**, 4, b g Acclamation—Perugina (FR) **The Achievers**
14 **LUCKY MOUNTAIN**, 4, ch c Mount Nelson—Wild Clover **P J Dixon & Partners**
15 **MASKED DANCE (IRE)**, 7, gr g Captain Rio—Brooks Masquerade **The Doncaster Racing Club**
16 **MONNOYER**, 5, ch g Dutch Art—Ellebanna **P J Dixon & Partners**
17 **PASTUREYES**, 4, ch f Milk It Mick—Veils of Salome **Paul J Dixon & Mrs Jayne Jackson**
18 **PEARL NOIR**, 4, b g Milk It Mick—Cora Pearl (IRE) **P J Dixon & Partners**
19 **PICENO (IRE)**, 6, b g Camacho—Ascoli **Ontoawinner 4**
20 **ROBYN**, 4, b f Byron—Discoed **P J Dixon & Partners**
21 **SACROSANCTUS**, 6, ch g Sakhee (USA)—Catalonia (IRE) **P. J. Dixon**
22 **SIR GEOFFREY (IRE)**, 8, b g Captain Rio—Disarm (IRE) **General Sir G. H. W. Howlett**

MR SCOTT DIXON - Continued

23 **SIX WIVES,** 7, b m Kingsalsa (USA)—Regina **Sexy Six Partnership**
24 **SPOWARTICUS,** 5, ch g Shamardal (USA)—Helen Bradley (IRE) **P. J. Dixon**
25 **THERAPEUTIC,** 4, b f Milk It Mick—Theoretical **P J Dixon & Partners**
26 **THREES GRAND,** 4, b f Milk It Mick—Ginger Cookie **Paul J Dixon & Mrs Jayne Jackson**

THREE-YEAR-OLDS

27 **ARMELLE (FR),** b f Milk It Mick—Park Ave Princess (IRE) **The Friday Follies**
28 **BISCUITEER,** ch f Byron—Ginger Cookie **P J Dixon & Partners**
29 **LA PAIVA (FR),** b f Milk It Mick—Cora Pearl (IRE) **The Achievers**
30 **LE LAITIER (FR),** b g Milk It Mick—La Brigitte **P. J. Dixon**
31 **MINISTER OF FUN,** b c Pastoral Pursuits—Diane's Choice **P. J. Dixon**
32 **PENNINE WARRIOR,** b c Lucky Story (USA)—Discoed
33 **SLANDEROUS,** b f Sleeping Indian—Honesty Pays **P J Dixon & Partners**
34 **WIMBOLDSLEY,** ch g Milk It Mick—Chrystal Venture (IRE) **Paul J Dixon & The Chrystal Maze Ptn**

Other Owners: Mr A. D. Baker, Mrs J. Cooper, Mrs Y. Dixon, A. J. J. Gompertz, Mrs J. Jackson, Mr R. Jackson, J. S. Kennerley, Mr P. Nolan, N. J. O'Brien, Mr A. C. Timms.

Assistant Trainer: Mr K. Locking (07835 360125)

Apprentice: Matthew Hopkins. **Amateur:** Mr Kevin Locking.

---

167 MRS ROSE DOBBIN, Alnwick
Postal: **South Hazelrigg Farm, Chatton, Alnwick, Northumberland, NE66 5RZ**
Contacts: **PHONE** (01668) 215395 (office) (01668) 215151 (house) **FAX** (01668) 215114
MOBILE (07969) 993563
E-MAIL hazelriggracing1@btconnect.com **WEBSITE** www.rosedobbinracing.co.uk

1 **ANOTHER DIMENSION (IRE),** 8, b g Overbury (IRE)—Freshwater (IRE) **Carole Jones & Rose Dobbin**
2 **BE MY PRESENT,** 7, b m Presenting—Simply Divine (IRE) **Straightline Construction Ltd**
3 **CAERLAVEROCK (IRE),** 9, br g Statue of Liberty (USA)—Dazivra (IRE) **Mr & Mrs Duncan Davidson**
4 4, B g Kalanisi (IRE)—Dangerous Dolly (IRE) **Mr & Mrs A. Dobbin**
5 **DOKTOR GLAZ (FR),** 4, b g Mount Nelson—Deviolina (IRE) **Mrs R. Dobbin**
6 **FLAWLESS FILLY (IRE),** 4, gr f Clodovil (IRE)—Min Asl Wafi (USA) **Mr & Mrs Duncan Davidson**
7 **FLING ME (IRE),** 7, b g Definite Article—Seductive Dance **The Friday Lions**
8 **HONOURABLE GENT,** 6, b g Gentleman's Deal (IRE)—Gudasmum **Mr & Mrs Duncan Davidson**
9 **MARKEM (IRE),** 7, ch g Beneficial—Dummy Run (IRE) **Mr & Mrs Duncan Davidson**
10 **MARRAKECH TRADER (NZ),** 7, ch g Pentire—Eastern Bazzaar (NZ) **Tom Jenks**
11 **ON THE BUCKLE,** 6, b g Overbury (IRE)—Arctic Revel **Mr J Filmer-Wilson & Mrs D Davidson**
12 **POLITENESS (FR),** 5, b g Poliglote—Martiniquaise (FR) **Mr & Mrs Duncan Davidson**
13 5, B g Beneficial—Porter Tastes Nice (IRE) **Mr & Mrs A. Dobbin**
14 **PRINT SHIRAZ (IRE),** 6, b g Bahri (USA)—Cherry Hills (IRE) **Major-Gen C. A. Ramsay**
15 **PURCELL'S BRIDGE (FR),** 7, b g Trempolino (USA)—Theatrical Lady (USA) **Mr J. A. F. Filmer-Wilson**
16 **PYJAMA GAME (IRE),** 8, b g Hernando (FR)—Princess Claudia (IRE) **Straightline Construction Ltd**
17 5, B g Beneficial—Railstown Lady (IRE) **Mr & Mrs A. Dobbin**
18 **ROBIN'S COMMAND (IRE),** 7, gr g Tikkanen (USA)—Marian's Wish (IRE) **M Hunter, J Matterson & R Jacobs**
19 **ROCKING BLUES (FR),** 9, b g Lavirco (GER)—Herbe de La Roque (FR) **Mr J Filmer-Wilson & Mrs D Davidson**
20 **ROS CASTLE (IRE),** 8, ch g Flemensfirth (USA)—Castlehaven (IRE) **Mr & Mrs Duncan Davidson**
21 **SHADY SADIE (IRE),** 7, b m Dushyantor (USA)—Beltane Queen (IRE) **Mrs M. C. Coltman**
22 **SPITZ (FR),** 6, b g Enrique—Spezzia (FR) **Mr R. A. Jacobs**
23 **STITCHED IN TIME (IRE),** 7, b g Needle Gun (IRE)—Broken Pockets (IRE) **Mr & Mrs Duncan Davidson**
24 **TWEEDO PARADISO (NZ),** 7, br g Golan (IRE)—Buzz (NZ) **Mr J. L. Dickson**
25 **UTOPIAN,** 5, b g Rock of Gibraltar (IRE)—Idealistic (IRE) **Mr Ronald Barber & Mr Duncan Davidson**
26 **VINNY GAMBINI (IRE),** 7, b g Vinnie Roe (IRE)—Red Velvet **Mr & Mrs Duncan Davidson**

Other Owners: Mr R. H. T. Barber, Mr R. G. W. Brown, Mr D. Davidson, Mrs D. Davidson, Mrs Rose Dobbin, Mr James Filmer-Wilson, Mr Mark Hunter, Mr R. Jacobs, Mr J. R. Jeffreys, Mr Tom Percival Jenks, Miss C. L. Jones, Miss Jean Matterson.

Assistant Trainer: Tony Dobbin (07775) 680894

Jockey (NH): Wilson Renwick. **Conditional:** Shaun Dobbin. **Amateur:** Miss Holly Harper.

168 **MR ASHLEY DODGSON, Thirsk**
Postal: **Southerby House, Catton, Thirsk, North Yorkshire, YO7 4SQ**

1 **WITCH ONE,** 11, b m Silver Patriarch (IRE)—Catton Lady **Mr A. C. Dodgson**
2 **WITCH WAY,** 9, gr m Silver Patriarch (IRE)—Catton Lady **Mr A. C. Dodgson**

169 **MR MICHAEL DODS, Darlington**
Postal: **Denton Hall Farm, Piercebridge, Darlington, Co. Durham, DL2 3TY**
Contacts: **PHONE (01325) 374270 FAX (01325) 374020**
MOBILE (07860) 411590/ (07773) 290830 C Dods
E-MAIL dods@michaeldodsracing.co.uk WEBSITE www.michaeldodsracing.co.uk

1 **BARNEY MCGREW (IRE),** 11, b g Mark of Esteem (IRE)—Success Story **N. A. Riddell**
2 **BEAT THE TIDE,** 4, b g Black Sam Bellamy (IRE)—Sablonne (USA) **J A Wynn-Williams & D Neale**
3 **BONNIE ECHO,** 7, b m Overbury (IRE)—Sunday News'n'echo (USA) **D. C. Batey**
4 **CARA'S REQUEST (AUS),** 9, gr g Urgent Request (IRE)—Carahill (AUS) **Mr S. Aitken**
5 **CHEATING TIGER (IRE),** 6, b g Tiger Hill (IRE)—Chita Rivera
6 **ESCAPE TO GLORY (USA),** 6, b g Bernstein (USA)—Escape To Victory **Pearson, Lamb, Wynn Williams**
7 **HAKUNA MATATA,** 7, b g Dubai Destination (USA)—Green Song (FR) **Sekura Trade Frames Ltd**
8 **HALF A BILLION (IRE),** 5, b g Acclamation—Amankila (IRE) **I.Galletley, B.Stenson, S.Lowthian**
9 **KIWI BAY,** 9, b g Mujahid (USA)—Bay of Plenty (FR)
10 **KOLONEL KIRKUP,** 4, b g Dr Fong (USA)—Strawberry Lolly **K. Kirkup**
11 **LE CHAT D'OR,** 6, b g One Cool Cat (USA)—Oh So Well (IRE) **Dr A. J. F. Gillespie**
12 **MASH POTATO (IRE),** 4, b g Whipper (USA)—Salva **Bennett Potatoes & Banister**
13 **MASS RALLY (IRE),** 7, b g Kheleyf (USA)—Reunion (IRE) **Business Development Consultants Limited**
14 **MUHARRER,** 5, b g Shamardal (USA)—Shawahid (USA) **Mr W. A. Tinkler**
15 **MY NAME IS RIO (IRE),** 4, ch g Captain Rio—Walk In My Shadow (IRE) **Mr K Kirkup & Mrs T Galletley**
16 **ODDYSEY (IRE),** 5, b m Acclamation—Darling Smile (IRE) **Pearson & Lowthian**
17 **ORBIT THE MOON (IRE),** 6, b g Oratorio (IRE)—Catch The Moon (IRE) **Appleton - Davison - Spinks**
18 **OSTEOPATHIC REMEDY (IRE),** 10, ch g Inchinor—Dolce Vita **K. Kirkup**
19 **ROCKTHERUNWAY (IRE),** 5, ch g Nayef (USA)—Femme Fatale **Sedgewick,Dods,Sunley Racing Partnership**

THREE-YEAR-OLDS

20 **BELTOR,** b g Authorized (IRE)—Carahill (AUS) **Mr S. Aitken**
21 **BROOKES BOY (IRE),** b g Tagula (IRE)—Satan's Sister **Sekura Trade Frames Ltd**
22 **CAMATINI (IRE),** b f Camacho—Trentini (IRE)
23 **KOMMANDER KIRKUP,** ch g Assertive—Bikini **K. Kirkup**
24 **MECCA'S ANGEL (IRE),** gr f Dark Angel (IRE)—Folga (FR) **D. T. J. Metcalfe**
25 **ONE BOY (IRE),** ch g Captain Gerrard (IRE)—Paris Song (IRE) **Sekura Trade Frames Ltd**
26 **RUNNING WOLF (IRE),** b g Amadeus Wolf—Monet's Lady (IRE) **M. J. K. Dods**
27 **TRINITY STAR (IRE),** gr g Kheleyf (USA)—Zamiyla (IRE) **Trinity Racing**

TWO-YEAR-OLDS

28 **ALANS PRIDE (IRE),** ch g 28/4 Footstepsinthesand—
  True Crystal (IRE) (Sadler's Wells (USA)) (6000) **Alan Henderson & Alan Bolton**
29 B c 9/4 Hernando (FR)—Alba Stella (Nashwan (USA)) (24000) **D. C. Batey**
30 Ch g 4/4 Captain Rio—Be My Lover (Pursuit of Love) (3251) **Denton Hall Racing Ltd**
31 B g 30/3 Major Cadeaux—Bikini (Trans Island) (11000) **K. Kirkup**
32 **BLACKFOOT BRAVE (IRE),** ch c 29/1 Iffraaj—Beatrice Potter (IRE) (Cadeaux Genereux) (40000) **D. R. Graham**
33 B f 10/4 Urgent Request (IRE)—Carahill (AUS) (Danehill (USA)) **Mr S. Aitken**
34 **COLLOSIUM (IRE),** b g 29/4 Showcasing—
  Ragsta (IRE) (Key of Luck (USA)) (15485) **Business Development Consultants Limited**
35 Ch f 25/4 Footstepsinthesand—Dangle (IRE) (Desert Style (IRE)) (6500) **D. T. J. Metcalfe**
36 B g 12/3 Authorized (IRE)—Desert Royalty (IRE) (Alhaarth (IRE)) (29000) **Mr M. J. Sedgewick**
37 **DRAGON KING (IRE),** ch c 13/4 Dylan Thomas (IRE)—
  Alexander Queen (IRE) (King's Best (USA)) (26325) **Mr & Mrs Paul Gaffney**
38 **FAIR VENTURE (IRE),** b g 3/3 Intikhab (USA)—Aqua Vitae (IRE) (Camacho) (16260) **Mrs C. M. Hewitson**
39 Ch c 25/3 Windsor Knot (IRE)—Genuinely (IRE) (Entrepreneur) (8517) **D. Neale**
40 Gr c 27/2 Aussie Rules (USA)—Heaven's Vault (Hernando (FR)) (12775) **D. Neale**
41 Br f 31/3 Arcano (IRE)—Jinsiyah (USA) (Housebuster (USA)) (21680) **Mrs C. E. Dods**
42 **OCEAN SHERIDAN (IRE),** b c 18/4 Starspangledbanner (AUS)—
  Endless Night (GER) (Tiger Hill (IRE)) (15000) **Mr J Blackburn & Mr A Turton**

MR MICHAEL DODS - Continued

43 B c 27/3 Makfi—Pizzicato (Statoblest) **Mrs C. E. Dods**
44 **PUNK ROCKER (IRE),** b f 26/3 Fastnet Rock (AUS)—
Cape Vintage (IRE) (Cape Cross (IRE)) (52651) **Mr & Mrs Paul Gaffney**
45 B gr f 10/5 Fast Company (IRE)—Rectify (IRE) (Mujadil (USA)) (5806) **Denton Hall Racing Ltd**
46 **REET PETITE (IRE),** b f 18/4 Fast Company (IRE)—
Damjanich (IRE) (Mull of Kintyre (USA)) (6666) **J. A. Wynn-Williams**
47 B c 1/3 Amadeus Wolf—Rose de France (IRE) (Diktat) (41811) **Mr & Mrs Paul Gaffney**
48 **SEKURAS GIRL (IRE),** b f 18/2 Approve (IRE)—Alinda (IRE) (Revoque (IRE)) (20000) **Sekura Trade Frames Ltd**
49 **SMART STEPPER (IRE),** b g 9/2 Acclamation—
Miss Smilla (Red Ransom (USA)) (18000) **Appleton, Davison, Thompson**
50 Ch c 2/3 Sakhee's Secret—Suzie Quw (Bahamian Bounty) (17142) **Dunham Trading Ltd**
51 B f 19/2 Notnowcato—True Vision (IRE) (Pulpit (USA)) **D. V. Roper**

Other Owners: Mr P. Appleton, Mr C. Banister, Bennett Potatoes Ltd, J. N. Blackburn, Mr A. Bolton, Mr J. Cockcroft, Mr R. Cockcroft, Mr W. Cockcroft, Mr S. Cockcroft, R. Davison, Mr P. Gaffney, Mrs J. Gaffney, Mr I. Galletley, Mrs J. M. T. Galletley, A. J. Henderson, W. S. D. Lamb, S. R. Lowthian, Mr M. D. Pearson, V. J. Spinks, J. W. Stenson, Mr G. C. Thompson, Mr A. Turton, F. Watson.

Assistant Trainer: C Dods, Steve Alderson (07533) 401887

Jockey (flat): Tom Eaves, Paul Mulrennan. **Apprentice:** Connor Beasley.

170	**MR DESMOND DONOVAN, Newmarket**

Postal: **The Beeches, London Road, Newmarket, Suffolk, CB8 0TR**
Contacts: **PHONE (01638) 578494 FAX (01638) 578494 MOBILE (07761) 841285**
E-MAIL hareparkbloodstock@yahoo.co.uk WEBSITE www.desdonovan.co.uk

1 **EYE OF THE TIGER (GER),** 9, b g Tiger Hill (IRE)—Evening Breeze (GER) **River Racing**
2 **GIANT SEQUOIA (USA),** 10, ch g Giant's Causeway (USA)—
Beware of the Cat (USA) **Exors of the Late Mr P. A. Byrne**
3 **INDUS VALLEY (IRE),** 7, ch g Indian Ridge—Gloriously Bright (USA) **River Racing**
4 **RECWAY LASS,** 6, ch m Doyen (IRE)—Zarma (FR) **W. P. Flynn**
5 **SAVARONOLA (USA),** 9, ch g Pulpit (USA)—Running Debate (USA) **River Racing**
6 **TEVEZ,** 9, b g Sakhee (USA)—Sosumi **River Racing**

Other Owners: Mr J. D. Donovan, P. P. Mclaughlin.

171	**MR CONOR DORE, Frampton Fen**

Postal: **Barford Farm, Swineshead Road, Frampton Fen, Boston, Lincolnshire, PE20 1SG**
Contacts: PHONE (01775) 822747 MOBILE (07984) 609170
E-MAIL dores@supanet.com

1 **A LITTLE BIT DUSTY,** 6, ch g Needwood Blade—Dusty Dazzler (IRE) **Mr David Baldwin & Mr Chris Marsh**
2 **ABOVE THE STARS,** 6, b m Piccolo—Swindling **Mrs J. R. Marsh**
3 **BELLE DE FONTENAY (FR),** 9, b m Spadoun (FR)—Friendly Hostess **Boston Park Racing Club**
4 **CLOCKMAKER (IRE),** 8, b g Danetime (IRE)—Lady Ingabelle (IRE) **CHP Consulting Limited**
5 **DESERT STRIKE,** 8, b g Bertolini—Mary Jane **A. N. Page**
6 **EFISTORM,** 13, b g Efisio—Abundance
7 **EXCEEDEXPECTATIONS (IRE),** 5, b g Intikhab (USA)—Jazan (IRE) **Mrs L. J. Marsh**
8 **GEORGE FENTON,** 5, ch g Piccolo—Mashmoum **Mrs L. J. Marsh**
9 **GREENSWARD,** 8, b g Green Desert (USA)—Frizzante **Chris McHugh Chris Eliades**
10 **JOHNNYS LEGACY (IRE),** 7, b g Ecton Park (USA)—Lexy May (USA) **Mr D. N. Baldwin**
11 **LASTKINGOFSCOTLAND (IRE),** 8, b g Danehill Dancer (IRE)—Arcade **Mrs J. R. Marsh**
12 **STANDPOINT,** 8, b g Oasis Dream—Waki Music (USA) **Mrs J. R. Marsh**
13 **YASIR (USA),** 6, b g Dynaformer (USA)—Khazayin (USA) **Mrs L. J. Marsh**

Other Owners: Mr C. T. Eliades, Mr M. Fitzsimons, C. D. Marsh, C. J. McHugh.

172 MR FRANCOIS DOUMEN, Bouce

Postal: **Le Gue, 61570 Bouce, France**
Contacts: PHONE **(0033) 2 33 67 11 59** FAX **(0033) 2 33 67 82 37** MOBILE **(0033) 6 07 42 33 58**
E-MAIL **doumenecouves@orange.fr** WEBSITE **www.francoisdoumenracing.com**

1 **ARAMARA (IRE),** 4, b f Marju (IRE)—Atalina (FR)
2 **CABARETUNE (FR),** 9, b g Green Tune (USA)—Cabaret Club (FR)
3 **CELTIC CELEB (IRE),** 7, ch g Peintre Celebre (USA)—Gaelic Bird (FR)
4 **DIABLE DE JIM (FR),** 8, b g Diableneyev (USA)—Jolie Jim (FR)
5 **FAST FLIGHT (FR),** 5, b g Anabaa (USA)—Flight Night
6 **FIERE (FR),** 4, b f Authorized (IRE)—Dan's Pride (USA)
7 **GOLDIE JOLIE (FR),** 5, b m Gold Away (FR)—Jolie Jim (FR)
8 **GREEN BANANAS (FR),** 8, b m Green Tune (USA)—Anabaa Republic (FR)
9 **JOLIE NOCE (FR),** 6, b m Muhtathir (USA)—Jolie Jim (FR)
10 **KAPSTADT (FR),** 4, b g Country Reel (USA)—King's Parody (IRE)
11 **PHIL MAN (IRE),** 5, b h Manduro (GER)—Fureau (GER)
12 **RAGEUR (FR),** 6, b g Iffraaj—Ethelinda
13 **TOP TRIP,** 5, b h Dubai Destination (USA)—Topka (FR)
14 **XPO UNIVERSEL (FR),** 5, b g Poliglote—Xanadu Bliss (FR)

THREE-YEAR-OLDS

15 **BAMBOUZLE (FR),** b f Forestier (FR)—Quibble (FR)
16 **BLYDE RIVER (IRE),** b c Shamardal (USA)—Bunting (USA)
17 **CRAZY CAT (FR),** b g Hold That Tiger (USA)—Folle Dingue (FR)
18 **DAUPHINE DOREE,** b f Archange d'or (IRE)—Dauphine (SAF)
19 **ENERGIVORE (FR),** b g Layman (USA)—The Trollop (FR)
20 **GREAT SILENCE (FR),** gr c Great Journey (JPN)—Henrietta (FR)
21 **KINGSMAN (FR),** b c Elusive City (USA)—Topka (FR)
22 **MAPLE GROVE (FR),** gr f Sinndar (IRE)—Tarkwa
23 **MARGOT MACHANCE,** b f Creachadoir (IRE)—Margot Mine (IRE)
24 **NANIA (FR),** b f Namid—Gigana (FR)
25 **PINK CHALICE,** b f Authorized (IRE)—Flamingo Flower (USA)
26 **PRETZELLE (FR),** b f Zamindar (USA)—Pretty As Can Be
27 **UNDER THE RADAR (FR),** b c Footstepsinthesand—Fast Lane Lili
28 **VAMOSALAPLAYA (FR),** ch g Footstepsinthesand—Marital Bliss (FR)
29 **XCELLENCE (FR),** b f Champs Elysees—Xanadu Bliss (FR)

TWO-YEAR-OLDS

30 B f 23/2 Equiano (FR)—Azlaa (Dubawi (IRE)) (17034)
31 Gr f 15/3 Mastercraftsman (IRE)—Be My Lady (GER) (Be My Guest (USA)) (63492)
32 **BLISS IN THE CITY (FR),** b c 19/4 Elusive City (USA)—Marital Bliss (FR) (Double Bed (FR))
33 Gr g 18/3 Footstepsinthesand—Cheyrac (FR) (Smadoun (FR)) (54200)
34 Ch f 28/3 Motivator—Dauphine (SAF) (Rich Man's Gold (USA))
35 B c 23/5 Siyouni (FR)—Heaven's Help (USA) (Royal Academy (USA)) (34843)
36 c 10/4 Authorized (IRE)—Margot Mine (IRE) (Choisir (AUS))
37 **REALLY TONIC (FR),** b f 11/2 Country Reel (USA)—Hertzienne (FR) (Hernando (FR))
38 B c 24/1 Bahamian Bounty—Sign of Life (Haafhd) (17808)
39 **SILVER BULLET (FR),** gr f 21/3 Silver Frost (IRE)—Folle Dingue (FR) (Golan (IRE))
40 **SWING STATE (FR),** b c 22/4 Siyouni (FR)—Fast Lane Lili (Fasliyev (USA))
41 B f 23/5 King's Best (USA)—Topka (FR) (Kahyasi)
42 B f 2/4 Slickly (FR)—Turfontein (FR) (Kahyasi)
43 **XHALE (FR),** b c 10/4 Halling (USA)—Xanadu Bliss (FR) (Xaar)

Owners: Mr Dermot Cantillon, Mr Xavier Doumen, Gold and Blue Ltd, Haras D'Ecouves, Marquise de Moratalla, Conte Henri de Pracomtal, Mr Eric Puerari, Mr J. B. Robinson, Mr Anthony Smurfit, Mr Michael Somerset-Leeke, Mr Joerg Vasicek, Mr Hans Peter Vogt.

Jockey (flat): Cristian Demuro, Gerald Mosse.

172a MR SIMON DOW, Epsom

Postal: **Clear Height Stables, Derby Stables Road, Epsom, Surrey, KT18 5LB**
Contacts: **PHONE (01372) 721490 FAX (01372) 748099 MOBILE (07860) 800109**
E-MAIL simon@simondow.co.uk Office: mary@simondow.co.uk WEBSITE www.simondow.co.uk
Twitter: @SimonDowRacing

1 **BROCKLEBANK (IRE)**, 5, b g Diamond Green (FR)—La Stellina (IRE) **C. G. J. Chua**
2 **CLAUDE MONET (BRZ)**, 5, ch g Vettori (IRE)—Femme Fatale (BRZ) **T. G. Parker**
3 **CLEAR PRAISE (USA)**, 7, b g Songandaprayer (USA)—Pretty Clear **Racing Clear Partnership**
4 **DAWN ROCK**, 4, b f Rock of Gibraltar (IRE)—Ommadawn (IRE) **Malcolm & Alicia Aldis**
5 **DIAMOND CHARLIE (IRE)**, 6, br g Diamond Green (FR)—Rosy Lydgate **David & Stanley Adams**
6 **FAIR VALUE (IRE)**, 6, b m Compton Place—Intriguing Glimpse **Don & Val Churston**
7 **FIDUCIA**, 4, b f Lawman (FR)—Silca Key **P. G. Jacobs**
8 **FORCEFUL APPEAL (USA)**, 6, b b g Successful Appeal (USA)—Kinetic Force (USA) **Mr S. A. Caunce**
9 **GOLDEN DESERT (IRE)**, 10, b g Desert Prince (IRE)—Jules (IRE) **T. G. Parker**
10 **KEEP KICKING (IRE)**, 7, b g Tiger Hill (IRE)—Dalannda (IRE) **P. McCarthy**
11 **LITMUS (USA)**, 5, ch m Latent Heat (USA)—Fairy Glade (USA) **T. G. Parker**
12 **MALAYSIAN BOLEH**, 4, ch c Compton Place—Orlena (USA) **JCG Chua & CK Ong**
13 **MARJONG**, 4, b f Mount Nelson—Vermilliann (IRE) **Mr J. L. Marsden**
14 **NOEL'S HOPE**, 4, b g Anabaa (USA)—Sourire **Mr M. McAllister**
15 **NORTHERN SPY (USA)**, 10, b g War Chant (USA)—Sunray Superstar **S. L. Dow**
16 **PRESUMIDO (IRE)**, 4, b g Iffraaj—Miss Megs (IRE) **R. Moss & J. Page**
17 **SPRING TONIC**, 5, b g Fantastic View (USA)—Nukhbah (USA) **Robinson,Butler,Parker & Scandrett**

THREE-YEAR-OLDS

18 **ROSINA JAY (IRE)**, b f Art Connoisseur (IRE)—Noora (IRE) **P. G. Jacobs**
19 **SIXTIES LOVE**, b f Sixties Icon—Love Always **T. Staplehurst**

TWO-YEAR-OLDS

20 **AUTUMN TONIC (IRE)**, b c 9/4 Approve (IRE)—Trempjane (Lujain (USA)) (18000) **K. F. Butler**
21 **EL CAMPEON**, b br c 18/4 Multiplex—Villabella (FR) (Hernando (FR)) (20000) **Mr R. J. Moss**
22 **GALINTHIAS**, b c 10/5 Sixties Icon—
                    Tidie France (USA) (Cape Town (USA)) (3200) **Taylor, Meadows, Snell, Taylor & Wright**
23 **TANGRAMM**, b c 2/3 Sakhee's Secret—Tripti (IRE) (Sesaro (USA)) (3000) **Mr J. L. Marsden**

Other Owners: Mr D. Adams, Mr S. J. Adams, Mrs A. Aldis, Mr M. S. Aldis, D. G. Churston, Mrs V. Churston, Mr R. I. Goalen, Mrs S. P Meadows, Mr R. Moore, Mr F. Ong, Mr J. W. Page, Ms E. Robinson, N. S. Scandrett, Ms S. A. Snell, Miss J. E. Taylor, Mr W. J. Taylor, Mrs L. A. Wright.

Assistant Trainer: Daniel Hutchison

173 MR CHRIS DOWN, Cullompton

Postal: **Upton, Cullompton, Devon, EX15 1RA**
Contacts: **PHONE (01884) 33097 FAX (01884) 33097 MOBILE (07828) 021232**
E-MAIL cjdownracing@gmail.com

1 **AROSEFOROSCAR**, 5, b m Oscar (IRE)—Made For A King **The Red White & Blue Partnership**
2 **ARTISTS BOY**, 7, ch g Thank Heavens—Night Bloomer (USA) **C. J. Down**
3 **BILLY DUTTON**, 8, ch g Sir Harry Lewis (USA)—Tinoforty (FR) **W. A. Bromley**
4 **BILLY MY BOY**, 5, b g Volochine (IRE)—Key West (FR) **Mr J. B. Radford**
5 **CRAIGANEE (IRE)**, 7, b g Craigsteel—Hows She Going (IRE) **P Holland,JT Measures,MA Kerr,V Holland**
6 **CURLEW (IRE)**, 8, b g Cape Cross (IRE)—Billbill (USA) **F. G. Hollis**
7 **DRAGON'S DEN (IRE)**, 7, b g Antonius Pius (USA)—Tallassee **G. R. Waterman**
8 **EXTREMELY SO**, 8, ch m Kyllachy—Antigua **Mrs M. Trueman**
9 **FROZEN OVER**, 6, b g Iceman—Pearly River **Down, Capps, Jones, Di-Vincenzo**
10 **HOT PEPPER**, 6, gr g Tikkanen (USA)—Copper Valley **Mrs G. H. Leeves**
11 **INCOGNITA**, 4, ch f Sakhee's Secret—Angel Sprints **Ms V. M. Halloran**
12 **JAMBOBO**, 5, b g Acclamation—Hovering (IRE) **Mrs M. Trueman**
13 **KEY TO MILAN**, 4, b g Milan—Key West (FR) **M. R. Lavis & C. J. Down**
14 **KINGS FLAGSHIP**, 9, b g Lahib (USA)—Queen's Flagship (IRE) **Mrs G. H. Leeves**
15 **LADIES DANCING**, 8, b g Royal Applause—Queen of Dance (IRE) **Upton Racing**
16 **LEGION D'HONNEUR (UAE)**, 9, b g Halling (USA)—Renowned (IRE) **Mrs F. Down**
17 **LILY POTTS**, 5, gr m Proclamation (IRE)—Jucinda **C. J. Down**
18 **LOYAUTE (FR)**, 7, ch m Green Tune (USA)—Iles Marquises (IRE) **Upton Racing 2**

MR CHRIS DOWN - Continued

19 MISTER SNOWBALL (FR), 7, ch g Ballingarry (IRE)—
No Coincidence (IRE) **P Holland,JT Measures,MA Kerr,V Holland**
20 MONIQUES GIFT, 6, b m Grape Tree Road—Dalticia (FR) **C. J. Down**
21 NEW CHRISTMAS (USA), 7, gr ro g Smoke Glacken (USA)—Occhi Verdi (IRE) **Dr M. J. Dixon**
22 6, Ch m Generosity—No Nort **Mrs G. H. Leeves**
23 NOTHING IS FOREVER (IRE), 10, b g Daylami (IRE)—Bequeath (USA) **The Globe Partnership**
24 ORDENSRITTER (GER), 6, ch g Samum (GER)—Dramraire Mist **Red Baron Racing**
25 REVEREND GREEN (IRE), 8, b g Tagula (IRE)—Red Letter **C. J. Down**
26 RUSSIE WITH LOVE, 8, b m Alflora (IRE)—Vieille Russie **Howzat Partnership**
27 SERAPHIEL, 5, b h Royal Applause—Angel Sprints **Ms V. M. Halloran**
28 SOME SECRET, 9, b m Fleetwood (IRE)—Secret Dance **Mrs G. H. Leeves**
29 SUNSHINE BUDDY, 7, b m Reel Buddy (USA)—Bullion **No Illusions Partnership**
30 THEDEBOFTHEYEAR, 10, b m Sir Harry Lewis (USA)—Juste Belle (FR) **Culm Valley Racing**
31 UPTON WOOD, 8, ch g Fleetwood (IRE)—Miss Counsel **C. J. Down & C. B. Stevens**

Other Owners: Mr M. G. Capps, Mrs S. J. Cork, Mr M. Di-Vincenzo, Mr P. A. Edwards, Mrs P. H. Edwards, Mr A. D. Hill, P. D. Holland, Mrs V. Holland, Mr N. S. Jones, Ms M. A. Kerr, M. R. Lavis, Mr J. T. Measures, Mrs S. E. Norman, Mr J. A. G. Norman, Mrs D. M. Philpott, Mr M. J. Philpott, Mr B. Stamp, Mr C. B. Stevens, K. W. Tyrrell.

Jockey (flat): Jemma Marshall. **Jockey (NH):** James Davies, Richard Johnson, Tom Scudamore.
Conditional: Giles Hawkins.

---

174 **MR RICHARD DRAKE, Guiseley**
Postal: **Manor Farm, Old Hollings Hill, Guiseley, Leeds, West Yorkshire, LS20 8EW**

1 ANOTHER TIPPLE, 4, b g Kayf Tara—Devon Peasant **Mrs J. E. Drake**
2 DEAL DONE (FR), 10, b g Vertical Speed (FR)—Five Rivers (FR) **Mrs J. E. Drake**
3 DEVIL AT MIDNIGHT (IRE), 6, b g Midnight Legend—Obligee de Sivola (FR) **Mrs J. E. Drake**
4 KEEVERFIELD (IRE), 13, b g Lord Americo—Quayfield **Mrs J. E. Drake**
5 VARDAS SUPREME (IRE), 11, b g Beneficial—Mrs Supreme (IRE) **Mrs J. E. Drake**

---

175 **MR CLIVE DREW, Rampton**
Postal: **Fox End Stables, 83 King Street, Rampton, Cambridgeshire, CB24 8QD**
Contacts: **PHONE/FAX (01954) 250772 MOBILE (07917) 718127**

1 MAISON BRILLET (IRE), 7, b g Pyrus (USA)—Stormchaser (IRE) **C. Drew**
2 MY SILVER LILLY, 7, b m Silver Patriarch (IRE)—Myumi **Miss P. Drew**
3 MYTARA, 9, br m Kayf Tara—Myumi **M. Brown, J. Burt, C. Drew & J. Paull**

TWO-YEAR-OLDS

4 Br f 24/4 Halling (USA)—Maziona (Dansili) (3000) **C. Drew**
5 B br f 28/3 Pastoral Pursuits—Nursling (IRE) (Kahyasi) (2500) **C. Drew & A. D. Plumb**

Other Owners: Mrs J. Bland, Mr M. M. Brown, Mrs J. K. Burt, Mr J. D. Paull, Mr A. D. Plumb.

Assistant Trainer: Miss Polly Drew

---

176 **MISS JACKIE DU PLESSIS, Saltash**
Postal: **Burell Farm, Longlands, Saltash, Cornwall, PL12 4QH**
Contacts: **PHONE (01752) 842362 MOBILE (07970) 871505**
E-MAIL ziggerson@aol.com

1 ABSOLUTELY BYGONES (IRE), 6, b g Alderbrook—Majella (IRE) **Du Plessis Treleaven Martin Waterman**
2 ARMENIAN BOY (FR), 11, b g Simon du Desert (FR)—Jade d'eau (IRE) **Miss J. M. du Plessis**
3 COOL GEORGE, 8, b g Pastoral Pursuits—Magic Valentine **R. J. Reip, M. Stevenson**
4 DIDDYPURPTOON, 8, b m Lucky Story (USA)—Dafne **Miss J. M. du Plessis**
5 DINARIUS, 9, b g Bertolini (USA)—Ambassadress (USA) **Mr S. A. Al Helaissi**
6 FEAR GLIC (IRE), 8, b g Dr Massini (IRE)—Graineuaile (IRE) **Du Plessis Treleaven Martin Waterman**
7 5, B m Blueprint (IRE)—Graineuaile (IRE) **Miss J. M. du Plessis**
8 LANDULPH LASS, 7, b m Thank Heavens—Easter Again **Miss J. M. du Plessis**

MISS JACKIE DU PLESSIS - Continued

9 **LONG JOHN**, 7, gr g Silver Patriarch (IRE)—Magic Valentine **R. J. Reip, M. Stevenson**
10 **RAY DIAMOND**, 9, ch g Medicean—Musical Twist (USA) **Miss J. M. du Plessis**
11 **ST DOMINICK (IRE)**, 7, b g Oscar (IRE)—Kilcrea Breeze (IRE) **Miss J. M. du Plessis**
12 **TESS DE WODELAND**, 7, b m Bandmaster (USA)—Kingsmill Quay **Miss J. M. du Plessis**
13 **WINNING SPARK (USA)**, 7, b g Theatrical—Spark Sept (FR) **Miss J. M. du Plessis**
14 **WISE HAWK**, 9, b g Hawk Wing—Dombeya (IRE) **G. R. Waterman**
15 **ZIGGERSON HILL**, 7, ch m Kadastrof (FR)—Tregale **Miss J. M. du Plessis**

Other Owners: Mr T. J. G. Martin, Mr R. J. Reip, Mr M. F. Stevenson, Mrs A. A. Treleaven.

---

177 MRS ANN DUFFIELD, Leyburn
Postal: **Sun Hill Racing Stables, Sun Hill Farm, Constable Burton, Leyburn, North Yorkshire, DL8 5RL**
Contacts: PHONE **(01677) 450303** FAX **(01677) 450993** MOBILE **(07802) 496332**
E-MAIL **ann@annduffield.co.uk** WEBSITE **www.annduffield.co.uk**

1 **CHANT (IRE)**, 4, b g Oratorio (IRE)—Akarita (IRE) **Mrs A. Starkie & Mrs I. Starkie**
2 **HEIDI'S DELIGHT (IRE)**, 5, b m Red Clubs (IRE)—Alexander Confranc (IRE) **David & Carole McMahon**
3 **RED CHARMER (IRE)**, 4, b g Red Clubs (IRE)—Golden Charm (IRE) **Mr I. Farrington & Mr R. Chapman**
4 **RUST (IRE)**, 4, b c Elnadim (USA)—Reddening **The Duchess of Sutherland**

THREE-YEAR-OLDS

5 **BEARSKIN (IRE)**, br g Kodiac—Dark Arts (USA) **Evelyn, Duchess of Sutherland**
6 B f Major Cadeaux—Eloquent Isle (IRE) **Mrs D. Addison**
7 **GREENBURY (IRE)**, b g Jeremy (USA)—Truly Genuine (IRE) **Mr David K. Barker**
8 **HELLO BEAUTIFUL (IRE)**, ch f Captain Rio—Tekhania (IRE) **Mr Nick Allenby**
9 **IN VINO VERITAS (IRE)**, b c Art Connoisseur (IRE)—Robin **Mr Jimmy Kay**
10 **LA HAVRESE (FR)**, ch f Le Havre (IRE)—La Buena (IRE) **Mr Jimmy Kay**
11 **LADY JAMESWAY (IRE)**, b f Acclamation—Baltic Dip (IRE) **James Pak & Middleham Park Racing**
12 **LADY MONTENEGRO**, b f Milk It Mick—Floral Spark **Ison, Smith & Duffield**
13 **MASTER CLOCKMAKER (IRE)**, gr c Mastercraftsman (IRE)—Mairead Anne (USA) **Mrs Juliet Thompson**
14 **MILLY'S SECRET (IRE)**, ch f Sakhee's Secret—Swan Sea (USA) **Mr Jimmy Kay**
15 **MISTER UNO (IRE)**, b c Tamayuz—Starlight Smile (USA) **Mr John Gatenby**
16 **PADDY'S ROCK (IRE)**, b c Whipper (USA)—Hedera (USA) **Mr Jimmy Kay**
17 **PETITE MADAME (IRE)**, b f Champs Elysees—Seeking The Fun (USA) **Mr Nick Saint**
18 **QATAR PRINCESS (IRE)**, b f Marju (IRE)—Bridal Dance (IRE) **Easton Park Stud**
19 **TOBOGGAN STAR**, b g Lucky Story (USA)—Toboggan Lady **Mr T. P. McMahon & Mr D. McMahon**

TWO-YEAR-OLDS

20 **DOPPLER EFFECT**, ch c 12/4 Monsieur Bond (IRE)—Scarlet Oak (Zamindar (USA)) (16190) **Mr Lee Bond**
21 B f 27/3 Alfred Nobel (IRE)—Fashion Guide (IRE) (Bluebird (USA)) (18000)
22 **GEORGE DRYDEN (IRE)**, b c 24/3 Zebedee—Key To Fortune (GER) (Big Shuffle (USA)) (11000) **Mr S. Bradley**
23 B f 30/1 Equiano (FR)—Impressible (Oasis Dream) (29523) **Qatar Racing Limited**
24 B f 11/2 Zebedee—Louvolite (IRE) (Fayruz) (16190) **Easton Park Stud & Mrs A. Starkie**
25 **MR COOL CASH**, b c 1/3 Firebreak—Cashleen (USA) (Lemon Drop Kid) (10000) **Mr I. Lawson**
26 **NOTNOWDEAR**, ch c 12/4 Notnowcato—Cup of Love (USA) (Behrens (USA)) **Girls On Top**
27 Ch f 22/2 Arcano (IRE)—Ossiana (IRE) (Polish Precedent (USA)) (14285)
28 **PARLIAMENT (IRE)**, b c 24/2 Fast Company (IRE)—
Yaselda (Green Desert (USA)) (19047) **Mrs A. Starkie & Easton Park Stud**
29 Ch f 23/3 Avonbridge—Sareb (FR) (Indian Ridge) (4000) **Grange Park Racing**
30 B f 22/4 Dylan Thomas (IRE)—Se La Vie (FR) (Highest Honor (FR)) (16000)
31 Ch c 27/4 Lord Shanakill (USA)—Sharp Diversion (USA) (Diesis) (11500)
32 **SPIRITUAL JOURNEY (IRE)**, b f 23/2 Zebedee—
Daneville (IRE) (Danetime (IRE)) (17000) **Easton Park Stud & Mr I. Farrington**
33 **TOBOGGAN'S GIFT**, b f 27/1 Major Cadeaux—
Toboggan Lady (Tobougg (IRE)) (3333) **Mr T. P. McMahon & Mr D. McMahon**

Other Owners: Mr R. P. Chapman, Mrs Ann Duffield, Mr I. J. Farrington, Mr T. Ison, Mr A. J. Livingston, Mr D. McMahon, Mrs C. A. McMahon, Mr T. P. McMahon, Mr J. Pak, T. S. Palin, Mr S. T. Slack, Mr Basil Smith, Mrs A. Starkie, Mrs I. L. A. Starkie, Mr C. P. Watson, Mr Peter Watson.

Assistant Trainer: G Duffield **Jockey (flat):** P. J. McDonald. **Apprentice:** Rowan Scott.

178 MR BRENDAN W. DUKE, Curragh
Postal: **Fenway House, Pollardstown, Curragh, Co. Kildare, Ireland**
Contacts: **PHONE (00353) 045 521104 FAX (00353) 45 521104 MOBILE (00353) 85 8189724**

1 CRUINNEAS (IRE), 5, b m Westerner—Grinneas (IRE) **Mr Brian O'Connor**
2 5, B g Kutub (IRE)—Davis Rock **Mr Brendan Duke Jnr**
3 5, Ch m Trans Island—Hayward's Heath **Mrs Angela Duke**
4 I'M SHEIKRA (IRE), 5, b m Captain Rio—Gentle Peace (IRE) **Near Buy Friends Syndicate**
5 MISTER BENEDICTINE, 11, b g Mister Baileys—Cultural Role **Kennedy Transport**
6 OLD PHOBIE (IRE), 7, b m Catcher In The Rye (IRE)—Blackchurch Mist (IRE) **Mr Patrick Brennan**
7 R U SIRIUS (IRE), 4, b f Soviet Star—Emlach Star (IRE) **Mr Joseph Duke**
8 SCEILG (IRE), 4, b f Rock Hard Ten (USA)—Intriguing Humor (CAN) **Mrs Jackie Bolger**
9 4, B f Scorpion (IRE)—Square Up (IRE) **Mr Joseph Duke**
10 5, B g Tiger Hill (GER)—Taca d'oli (FR) **Mrs Angela Duke**
11 TEODOLITE (IRE), 5, ch m Teofilo (IRE)—Tamra Delight (USA) **Mrs Jackie Bolger**
12 WELSH NAYBER, 5, ch g Nayef (USA)—Aberdovey **Mr Mark MacDonagh**
13 WILLOWING (USA), 4, b f Hard Spun (USA)—Sweet Arizona (USA) **Mrs Jackie Bolger**

THREE-YEAR-OLDS
14 FOCUSSED (IRE), b g Intense Focus (USA)—Tus Maith (IRE) **Mrs Jackie Bolger**
15 PUNCH BAG (IRE), ch g Teofilo (IRE)—Heir Today (IRE) **Mrs Jackie Bolger**

TWO-YEAR-OLDS
16 BEHIND THE BUSH (IRE), b f 24/4 Bushranger (IRE)—Ellen's Girl (IRE) (Desert Prince (IRE)) **Mrs Angela Duke**
17 B f 25/3 Cape Cross (IRE)—Fashion Trade (Dansili) (6194) **Mr Cristy Leonard**
18 VERBAL STILETTO (IRE), b c 31/5 Vocalised (USA)—Ceirseach (IRE) (Don't Forget Me) **Mrs Jackie Bolger**
19 VOCAL HEIR (IRE), b f 11/5 Vocalised (USA)—Heir Today (IRE) (Princely Heir (IRE)) **Mrs Jackie Bolger**
20 VOCAL WARM UP (IRE), b f 20/4 Vocalised (USA)—Faoileoir (USA) (Dehere (USA)) **Mrs Jackie Bolger**

Other Owners: Britton International, Mr Peter & Di Cave, Mr & Mrs John Davidson, Mr Tom Fletcher, Mr Brian Goldswain, Mr & Mrs Peter Telling, Ms Ruth Tupper.

Jockey (flat): Roary Cleary, K. J. Manning. Jockey (NH): David Crosse, Conor Brassil. Apprentice: Conor King, Rhonan Whelan.

179 MR IAN DUNCAN, Coylton
Postal: **Sandhill Farm, Coylton, Ayr, Ayrshire, KA6 6HE**
Contacts: **PHONE (01292) 571118 FAX (01292) 571118 MOBILE (07731) 473668**

1 BALLYCOLIN, 11, ch g Alflora (IRE)—Shift Changeover **Michael Kearney, Stephen Sinclair, Ian Duncan**
2 DEMETRIUS (IRE), 6, gr g Antonius Pius (USA)—Innocentines (FR) **Dr S. Sinclair**
3 DODGEY DREAM, 12, ch g Zaffaran (USA)—Dinnys Dream (IRE)
4 FINAGHY AYR (IRE), 6, ch g Lahib (USA)—Ali Ankah (IRE) **Mr A. J. R. Lilley**
5 GOLDEN SPARKLE (IRE), 8, ch m Samraan (USA)—Bye For Now **Miss H. A. Cross**
6 KNOCKCAIRN (IRE), 7, ch m Lahib (USA)—Knockcairn Express (IRE) **Miss H. A. Cross**
7 SPRING OVER (IRE), 8, ch m Samraan (USA)—Superswap (IRE) **I. A. Duncan**

Other Owners: Mr M. Kearney.

180 MR ED DUNLOP, Newmarket
Postal: **La Grange Stables, Fordham Road, Newmarket, Suffolk, CB8 7AA**
Contacts: **PHONE (01638) 661998 FAX (01638) 667394 MOBILE (07785) 328537**
E-MAIL edunlop@eddunlopracing.co.uk WEBSITE www.eddunlop.com

1 AUCTION (IRE), 4, b f Mr Greeley (USA)—Exhibit One (USA) **Highclere Thoroughbred Racing - Coventry**
2 BANTAM (IRE), 4, b f Teofilo (IRE)—Firecrest (IRE) **Brooke Kelly Partnership**
3 BURWAAZ, 5, b h Exceed And Excel (AUS)—Nidhaal (IRE) **Hamdan Al Maktoum**
4 CONTRIBUTER (IRE), 4, b c High Chaparral (IRE)—Serisia (FR) **Mr G. B. Bolton**
5 GWORN, 4, b c Aussie Rules (USA)—Crochet (IRE) **Mr N. Martin**
6 HOMERIC (IRE), 5, b g Montjeu (IRE)—Al Saqiya (USA) **Highclere Thoroughbred Racing - Jackson**
7 JOSHUA TREE (IRE), 7, b h Montjeu (IRE)—Madeira Mist (IRE) **Mr K K Al Nabooda & Mr K Albahou**

MR ED DUNLOP - Continued

8 **MAN OF PLENTY**, 5, ch g Manduro (GER)—Credit-A-Plenty **Bluehills Racing Limited**
9 **MUBARAZA (IRE)**, 5, ch g Dalakhani (IRE)—Mokaraba **Hamdan Al Maktoum**
10 **NAAZ (IRE)**, 4, ch c Tamayuz—Naazeq **Mr R. Ng**
11 **RED AVENGER (USA)**, 4, b br c War Front (USA)—Emotional Rescue (USA) **The Hon R. J. Arculli**
12 **RED CADEAUX**, 8, ch g Cadeaux Genereux—Artisia (IRE) **The Hon R. J. Arculli**
13 **RED RUNAWAY**, 4, ch g Medicean—Gretna **The Hon R. J. Arculli**
14 **ROMEO MONTAGUE**, 6, b g Montjeu (IRE)—Issa **Mrs G. A. Rupert**
15 **TIMES UP**, 8, b g Olden Times—Princess Genista **Mrs I. H. Stewart-Brown & Mr M. J. Meacock**
16 **WHITE NILE (IRE)**, 5, b h Galileo (IRE)—Super Gift (IRE) **Sir R. Ogden C.B.E., LLD**

THREE-YEAR-OLDS

17 **AMAZING MARIA (IRE)**, gr f Mastercraftsman (IRE)—Messias da Silva (USA) **Sir R. Ogden C.B.E., LLD**
18 **AURORA BOREALIS (IRE)**, b f Montjeu (IRE)—Elaflaak (USA) **Sir R. Ogden C.B.E., LLD**
19 **BIG BONED (USA)**, b f Street Sense (USA)—Lizzy Cool (USA) **Qatar Racing Limited**
20 **CAPE SUMMIT**, ch c Tamayuz—Peace Summit **Thurloe Thoroughbreds XXXI**
21 **COUNTRY DRIVE (USA)**, ch f Shirocco (GER)—Call Mariah (USA) **Mr G. B. Bolton**
22 **CRADLE OF LIFE (IRE)**, ch f Notnowcato—Pursuit of Life **Chasemore Farm LLP**
23 B f Nayef (USA)—Cruinn A Bhord **Lord Derby**
24 **DALAROSSO**, b c Dalakhani (IRE)—Jamboretta (IRE) **The Hon R. J. Arculli & Mr Robert Ng**
25 **FIRE SPINNER**, ch f Galileo (IRE)—Mubkera (IRE) **Mrs G. A. Rupert**
26 **GIFT OF RAIN (IRE)**, b f Galileo (IRE)—La Sylvia (IRE) **Mrs G. A. Rupert**
27 **GOD WILLING**, b c Arch (USA)—Bourbon Ball (USA) **Qatar Racing & Essafinaat**
28 **HANNO (USA)**, b c Henrythenavigator (USA)—Archstone (USA) **Mrs P. Moseley**
29 **ISLAND REMEDE**, b f Medicean—Island Odyssey **Mrs Janice Quy**
30 **KAAB (IRE)**, b c Kheleyf (USA)—Ms Victoria (IRE) **Hamdan Al Maktoum**
31 **LIBERTY RED (GER)**, b c Dubawi (IRE)—Late Night (GER) **The Hon R. J. Arculli**
32 **LIFEJACKET (IRE)**, ch g Notnowcato—My American Beauty **Miltil Consortium**
33 **LIGHT OF ASIA (IRE)**, b c Oratorio (IRE)—Lucy Cavendish (USA) **The Hon R. J. Arculli & Mr Robert Ng**
34 **LOCH MA NAIRE (IRE)**, gr f Galileo (IRE)—Hotelgenie Dot Com **St Albans Bloodstock LLP**
35 **MAGHAANEM (IRE)**, b c Acclamation—Shishangaan (IRE) **Hamdan Al Maktoum**
36 **MIRROR (IRE)**, b f Dandy Man (IRE)—Fields of Joy (GER) **Highclere Thoroughbred Racing-Queen Mary**
37 **MIYACHIKU**, ch g Pivotal—First Bloom (USA) **Mrs S. M. Roy**
38 **MORE BEAU (USA)**, b br c More Than Ready (USA)—Frontier Beauty (USA) **Mr R. Ng**
39 **MUSALAHA (IRE)**, b f Nayef (USA)—Gilded (IRE) **Hamdan Al Maktoum**
40 **OASIS FANTASY (IRE)**, br c Oasis Dream—Cara Fantasy (IRE) **Windflower Overseas & J L Dunlop OBE**
41 **PALACE PRINCESS (FR)**, ch f Dubawi (IRE)—Queen of Norway (USA) **Palace House Racing**
42 **QUIKSTEP**, b f Fastnet Rock (AUS)—Waltz (IRE) **Alec and Leanne Leopold**
43 **RAWOOF (IRE)**, b f Nayef (USA)—Tanaghum **Hamdan Al Maktoum**
44 **RED GALILEO**, b c Dubawi (IRE)—Ivory Gala (FR) **The Hon R. J. Arculli**
45 **REHANAAT (USA)**, b f Daaher (CAN)—Sultana (USA) **Hamdan Al Maktoum**
46 **SHAF (IRE)**, b c Medaglia d'oro (USA)—Jaish (USA) **Hamdan Al Maktoum**
47 **TAQNEEN (IRE)**, b c Cape Cross (IRE)—Badee'a (IRE) **Hamdan Al Maktoum**
48 **TED'S SECRET**, b g Sakhee's Secret—Sinduda **The Hon R. J. Arculli & Mr Robert Ng**
49 **TELEGRAPHY (USA)**, gr f Giant's Causeway (USA)—Cable (USA) **Cliveden Stud**
50 **TRIP TO PARIS (IRE)**, b c Champs Elysees—La Grande Zoa (IRE) **La Grange Partnership**
51 **ZAAWIA (IRE)**, ch f Elnadim (USA)—Nidhaal (USA) **Hamdan Al Maktoum**
52 **ZARWAAN**, b c Dutch Art—Develyn **Hamdan Al Maktoum**
53 **ZILBER (GER)**, b c High Chaparral (IRE)—Zephyrine (IRE) **Dr Marwan Koukash**

TWO-YEAR-OLDS

54 B f 22/3 Rip Van Winkle (IRE)—Acquifer (Oasis Dream) (17500) **Ed Dunlop Racing**
55 B f 22/4 Footstepsinthesand—Beautiful Hill (IRE) (Danehill (USA)) (31000) **Smythe, Kilroy, Milmo & Gompertz**
56 B f 29/2 Acclamation—Blue Beacon (Fantastic Light (USA)) (65000) **Lady Derby Partnership**
57 B f 7/2 Dalakhani (IRE)—Clarietta (Shamardal (USA)) (30000) **Lavington Stud**
58 B c 23/1 Hurricane Run (IRE)—Cross Current (Sakhee (USA)) (40263) **Mr B. Andersson**
59 **DARK RED (IRE)**, b c 28/3 Dark Angel (IRE)—
                    Essexford (IRE) (Spinning World (USA)) (82000) **The Hon R. J. Arculli**
60 Ch f 20/5 Summer Bird (USA)—Dispute (USA) (Danzig (USA)) (14607) **Mrs Susan Roy**
61 **EJBAAR**, br c 24/2 Oasis Dream—Habaayib (Royal Applause) **Hamdan Al Maktoum**
62 **ERTIDAAD (IRE)**, b c 6/3 Kodiac—Little Scotland (Acclamation) (76190) **Hamdan Al Maktoum**
63 **EUROPA (GER)**, b f 28/3 Arcano (IRE)—Easy Sunshine (IRE) (Sadler's Wells (USA)) (7742) **Hamdan Al Maktoum**
64 B br c 21/3 High Chaparral (IRE)—Final Legacy (USA) (Boston Harbor (USA)) (92000) **Qatar Racing Limited**
65 **HAYDAR (IRE)**, b c 23/3 Makfi—Waveband (Exceed And Excel (AUS)) (104761) **Hamdan Al Maktoum**

MR ED DUNLOP - Continued

66 B f 22/4 Authorized (IRE)—Island Odyssey (Dansili) (3000) **Mr I Quy**
67 **LAKE CHAMPLAIN (IRE),** b c 14/5 Manduro (GER)—
Fantasy Girl (IRE) (Marju (IRE)) **Windflower Overseas Holdings Inc**
68 B f 29/3 Royal Applause—Love Roi (ITY) (Roi Danzig (USA)) (34000) **Mr C. Murfitt**
69 B c 14/3 Pastoral Pursuits—Luminda (IRE) (Danehill (USA)) (50000) **Deal, Deal, Kilroy & Sieff**
70 **MACHIAVELIAN STORM (IRE),** gr f 20/3 Dark Angel (IRE)—
Terri's Charmer (USA) (Silver Charm (USA)) (13162) **Mr J Strauss & Sir Anthony Pagewood**
71 **MAHSOOBA (USA),** b f 13/2 Hard Spun (USA)—Ishraak (USA) (Sahm (USA)) **Hamdan Al Maktoum**
72 **NAADY,** b br f 5/2 Mawatheeq (USA)—Al Tamooh (IRE) (Dalakhani (IRE)) **Hamdan Al Maktoum**
73 **NAIZAH (IRE),** b f 23/2 Tamayuz—Etizaaz (USA) (Diesis) **Hamdan Al Maktoum**
74 Gr c 12/4 Fast Company (IRE)—Park Approach (IRE) (Indian Ridge) (32000) **Mr Mohammed Jaber**
75 **PRINCE GAGARIN (IRE),** b c 29/4 Dubawi (IRE)—
Cara Fantasy (IRE) (Sadler's Wells (USA)) **Windflower Overseas Holdings Inc**
76 **RAFEEQ (FR),** ch c 14/2 Raven's Pass (USA)—Alzaroof (USA) (Kingmambo (USA)) **Hamdan Al Maktoum**
77 Br gr f 1/3 Aqlaam—Reason To Dance (Damister (USA)) (30000) **Mrs G. A. Rupert**
78 **RED TYCOON (IRE),** b c 8/2 Acclamation—Rugged Up (IRE) (Marju (IRE)) (100000) **The Hon R. J. Arculli**
79 Ch c 31/1 Bahamian Bounty—Reeling N' Rocking (IRE) (Mr Greeley (USA)) (25714) **Mr M. Mitchell**
80 B f 10/4 Lawman (FR)—Saga Celebre (FR) (Peintre Celebre (USA)) (20000) **Mrs Gurdon & Patrick Milmo**
81 B c 18/2 Dansili—Sagacious (IRE) (Dalakhani (IRE)) (100000) **Mr George Bolton**
82 **SAMEEH (IRE),** b c 17/2 Acclamation—Varenka (IRE) (Fasliyev (USA)) (175000) **Hamdan Al Maktoum**
83 **SEAWORTHY (IRE),** b f 6/4 Sea The Stars (IRE)—Night Fairy (IRE) (Danehill (USA)) (92914) **Airlie Stud**
84 B f 16/4 Montjeu (IRE)—Sharplaw Star (Xaar) (50000) **Mr Paul Shanahan**
85 **SHURFAH (IRE),** ch f 18/5 Sea The Stars (IRE)—Cap Coz (IRE) (Indian Ridge) (400000) **Hamdan Al Maktoum**
86 **SPORTING PRINCE,** b c 18/2 Pastoral Pursuits—
Queen of Iceni (Erhaab) (IRE) **Mrs I Stewart-Brown & M Meacock**
87 **TAJATHUB,** gr ro c 31/3 Bahamian Bounty—Galapagar (USA) (Miswaki (USA)) (150000) **Hamdan Al Maktoum**
88 **THANAAYA (IRE),** b f 6/2 Haatef (USA)—Mejala (IRE) (Red Ransom (USA)) **Hamdan Al Maktoum**
89 **TOCORORO (IRE),** b f 20/4 Teofilo (IRE)—Firecrest (IRE) (Darshaan) (38000) **Brooke Kelly Partnership**

Other Owners: Mr K. Albahou, The Hon R J Arculli, The Countess of Derby, Mr J. L. Dunlop, Mrs Edward Dunlop, Mr E. A. L. Dunlop, Mr Jeremy Gompertz, Mr Jon Haseler, The Hon H. Herbert, Highclere Thoroughbred Racing Ltd, Mr Khalid Khalifa Al Nabooda, Mrs Mandy Koukash, Mr Patrick Milmo, Mr Robert Ng, Mr O. J. W. Pawle, Mr J. A. B. Stafford, Mr Andrew Stone, Mrs M. F. Stone, Countess of Wessex, Windflower Overseas Holdings Inc, Zaro Srl.

Assistant Trainer: Tom Brideoake

---

181 **MR HARRY DUNLOP, Lambourn**
Postal: **Windsor House Stables, Crowle Road, Lambourn, Hungerford, Berkshire, RG17 8NR**
Contacts: **PHONE** (01488) 73584 **FAX** (01488) 674172 **MOBILE** (07880) 791895
E-MAIL info@harrydunlopracing.com **WEBSITE** www.harrydunlopracing.com

1 **MISS TIGER LILY,** 4, b f Tiger Hill (IRE)—Waitingonacloud **Mr & Mrs D. Hearson**
2 **MOMBASA,** 4, b g Dubawi (IRE)—Limuru **Wis Green Partners**
3 **POITIN,** 4, b f Kheleyf (USA)—Port Providence **David & Paul Hearson**
4 **SOLITAIRE GIRL,** b m 5 Loup Solitaire (USA)—Aphrodisias (FR) **Glanvilles Stud Partners**
5 **VIKING STORM,** 6, b g Hurricane Run (IRE)—Danehill's Dream (IRE) **Be Hopeful Partnership**

THREE-YEAR-OLDS

6 **ARTWOLF (IRE),** b c Peintre Celebre (USA)—Steno (USA) **The Hungry Wolves**
7 **BLACK LABEL,** b g Medicean—Black Belt Shopper (IRE) **Black Label**
8 **CADMIUM,** b f Major Cadeaux—Miss Mirasol **Susan Abbott Racing**
9 **CINNAMON SPICE,** b br g High Chaparral (USA)—Hot And Spicy **Be Hopeful (2)**
10 **EARLY MORNING (IRE),** gr c New Approach (IRE)—Summer's Eve **Early Risers**
11 **ENCORE ENCORE (FR),** b f Royal Applause—Angel Rose (IRE) **Pam & Peter Deal & Jeni & David Sieff**
12 **HAVANA GIRL (IRE),** ch f Teofilo (IRE)—Future Flight **Sir Eric Parker & Mary Anne Parker**
13 **MACNAMARA (IRE),** b f Dylan Thomas (IRE)—Portrait of A Lady (IRE) **Sir Eric Parker & Mary Anne Parker**
14 **PEARLOFTHEQUARTER,** b f Rock of Gibraltar (IRE)—Run for Lassie (IRE) **Biddestone Racing Club**
15 **SMILE FOR ME (IRE),** b f Elnadim (USA)—Pershaan (IRE) **Windflower Overseas Holdings Inc**
16 **SPACE WALKER (IRE),** b g Astronomer Royal (USA)—
Hot Property (USA) **Carter, Craig-Wood, Drake, Gehring, Lewis**
17 **STAR ANISE (FR),** b f Astronomer Royal (USA)—Sasicha (IRE) **The Astronomers 2**

MR HARRY DUNLOP - Continued

TWO-YEAR-OLDS

18 B f 16/3 Amadeus Wolf—Alexander Wonder (IRE) (Redback) (6500) **Windsor House Stables Partnership**
19 **ANNA DOLCE (FR),** b f 30/3 Areion (GER)—
Anna Spectra (IRE) (Spectrum (IRE)) (15485) **Bennett, Macauliffe, Nutting, Ranganath & Partners**
20 B f 28/3 Multiplex—Border Ballet (IRE) (Noverre (USA)) **Glanville Stud Partners**
21 **BRITTLETON,** b c 8/2 Aqlaam—
Fairy Dance (IRE) (Zafonic (USA)) (20000) **Sir Philip Wroughton & Mrs James Blyth Currie**
22 **DON'T TARRY (IRE),** b c 12/4 Elnadim (USA)—Bobbie Soxer (IRE) (Pivotal) **Windflower Overseas Holdings Inc**
23 **EDMUND HALLEY,** b c 15/3 Astronomer Royal (USA)—
Lazy Afternoon (IRE) (Hawk Wing (USA)) (3097) **Lowe, Silver, Deal**
24 Ch g 5/3 Dr Fong (USA)—
Encircle (USA) (Spinning World (USA)) (26325) **Blockley, Cross, Johnson, Whitaker, Woodley**
25 **ESTOURNEL,** b f 13/3 Danehill Dancer (IRE)—Estephe (IRE) (Sadler's Wells (USA)) **J. Gompertz & P. H. Milmo**
26 Ch f 13/4 Duke of Marmalade (IRE)—Fastback (IRE) (Singspiel (IRE)) **Brightwalton Stud**
27 **LULANI (IRE),** b f 24/1 Royal Applause—Louverissa (IRE) (Verglas (IRE)) (8571) **Mr & Mrs James Blyth Currie**
28 B c 25/3 Teofilo (IRE)—Mary Pekan (IRE) (Sri Pekan (USA)) (12000) **The Blue Bar Partnership**
29 **MEMORIES GALORE (IRE),** b c 1/2 Invincible Spirit (IRE)—
Persian Memories (IRE) (Indian Ridge) **Windflower Overseas Holdings Inc**
30 **MISTER ARDEN (FR),** b c 10/2 Desert Style (IRE)—
Katie Arden (IRE) (Barathea (IRE)) (10840) **Mary-Anne Parker**
31 **PACO'S DREAM,** b f 24/3 Paco Boy (IRE)—Isle of Flame (Shirley Heights) (10952) **Bermuda & Berrow Racing**
32 **PALOMA DANCER,** b f 3/2 Refuse to Bend (IRE)—
Anapola (GER) (Polish Precedent (USA)) (7000) **Bedford, Dixon-Smith, Dobie, Evans, Lewis, De Zoete**
33 **RUM SWIZZLE,** b f 25/4 Mawatheeq (USA)—Port Providence (Red Ransom (USA)) (3000) **Mr Nicholas Pascall**
34 B f 16/3 Kheleyf—Sanjuna (Tiger Hill (IRE)) (3333) **Mr Allan McWilliam**
35 **SKYE MORNING,** b f 6/4 Invincible Spirit (IRE)—
Bright Morning (USA) (Storm Cat (USA)) (80000) **Mr Paul Hearson**
36 **STORM ROCK,** b c 1/2 Rock of Gibraltar (IRE)—
Seasonal Cross (Cape Cross (IRE)) (6666) **Malcolm & Alicia Aldis**
37 **SUNDAY ROYAL (FR),** b g 4/5 Sunday Break (JPN)—
Princess d'orange (FR) (Anabaa (USA)) (36391) **Mr & Mrs T O'Donohoe**

Other Owners: Mrs Harry Dunlop, Mrs E. J. Gregson-Williams, Dr G. W. Guy, Mrs S. E. Lakin, Mr Barry Marsden, Mr C. M. Parker, Mr W. D. Procter, Mr L. C. Reed, Mrs V. J. Thrower.

---

182   MRS ALEXANDRA DUNN, Wellington
Postal: **Georges Farm, Cutsey, Trull, Taunton, Somerset, TA3 7NY**
Contacts: **MOBILE (07738) 512924**
WEBSITE www.alexandradunnracing.com

1 **ARRAYAN,** 9, b g Catcher In The Rye (IRE)—Ganga (IRE) **Dunn Racing**
2 **BLACKDOWN BABE,** 6, b m Weld—Blackdown Beauty **M. J. Coate**
3 **COME ON ANNIE,** 8, b m Karinga Bay—Irish Ferry **Mrs E. V. A. Trotman**
4 **DIDO,** 4, b g Killer Instinct—Bowdlane Barb **Mr R. H. Fox**
5 **DOUBLE MEAD,** 12, b m Double Trigger (IRE)—Normead Lass **Mrs K. R. Smith-Maxwell**
6 **HELIUM (FR),** 9, b g Dream Well (FR)—Sure Harbour (SWI) **Dunn Racing**
7 **HOLY VEIL,** 5, b m Kayf Tara—Holy Smoke **Dunn Racing**
8 **LION ON THE PROWL (IRE),** 10, b g Sadler's Wells (USA)—Ballerina (IRE) **Mrs K. R. Smith-Maxwell**
9 **MISS GLORIOSO,** 5, b m Helissio (FR)—Miss Glory Be **Mr D. N. Gladwin**
10 **NATIVE BRIAN (IRE),** 8, b g Brian Boru—Gentle Native (IRE) **Miss S. J. Lock**
11 **PICAROON,** 10, b g Jade Robbery (USA)—Anaam **Mrs K. R. Smith-Maxwell**
12 **THE SNEEZER (IRE),** 11, br g Topanoora—Bel Azur (IRE) **Mr T. H. Dunn**

Other Owners: Mr Thomas Dunn.

---

183   MRS CHRISTINE DUNNETT, Norwich
Postal: **College Farm, Hingham, Norwich, Norfolk, NR9 4PP**
Contacts: **PHONE (01953) 850596 FAX (01953) 851364 MOBILE (07775) 793523**
E-MAIL christine@christinedunnett.com WEBSITE www.christinedunnett.com

1 **COACH MONTANA (IRE),** 5, b g Proud Citizen (USA)—Market Day **Mr C. R. Moore**
2 **COLLEGE DOLL,** 5, ch m Piccolo—Southwarknewsflash **P D West, A S Machin & C A Dunnett**

MRS CHRISTINE DUNNETT - Continued

3 **DANZOE (IRE)**, 7, br g Kheleyf (USA)—Fiaba **One For All**
4 **FLAMINGO BEAT**, 4, ch g Beat Hollow—Flamingo Flower (USA) **Mr P. D. West**
5 **GIVE US A BELLE (IRE)**, 5, b g Kheleyf (USA)—Bajan Belle (IRE) **Mr F Butler & Mrs C Dunnett**
6 **IRISH BOY (IRE)**, 6, b g Desert Millennium (IRE)—Shone Island (IRE) **Annwell Inn Syndicate**
7 **JALUSIVE (IRE)**, 5, br g Elusive City (USA)—Jaldini (IRE) **West, Price & Dunnett**
8 **PERSEVERENT PETE (USA)**, 4, b br g Johannesburg (USA)—Indian Halloween (USA) **Mr P. D. West**
9 **SPEEDYFIX**, 7, b g Chineur (FR)—Zonnebeke **Annwell Inn Syndicate**

THREE-YEAR-OLDS

10 **CLASSIC HART**, ch g Dutch Art—Tata Naka **Mrs Mary Benjafield**
11 **ELLINGHAM (IRE)**, b f Bushranger (IRE)—No Way (IRE) **One For All**
12 **GIVE IT A WHIRL**, br f Pastoral Pursuits—Life's A Whirl **Mr A. Machin & Mrs C. Dunnett**
13 **HAPPYDOINGNOTHING**, b g Avonbridge—Neferura **Mr P. D. West**
14 B g Phoenix Reach (IRE)—Southwarknewsflash

Other Owners: Mrs M. A. Benjafield, G. Bromley, Mr D. G. Burt, F. Butler, Mrs C. A. Dunnett, Mr A. S. Machin, G. R. Price, Mr M. Skellett, Mr E. N. Sparkes, Mr P. D. West.

184

MR SEAMUS DURACK, Upper Lambourn
Postal: **The Croft Stables, Upper Lambourn, Hungerford, Berkshire, RG17 8QH**
Contacts: **PHONE (01488) 71941 MOBILE (07770) 537971**
E-MAIL **sd.111@btinternet.com**

1 **BOHEMIAN RHAPSODY (IRE)**, 5, b g Galileo (IRE)—Quiet Mouse (USA) **Mr A. A. Byrne**
2 **BRECCBENNACH**, 4, b g Oasis Dream—Next **Mrs A. Cowley**
3 **BUGSY**, 4, br g Dansili—Maroussie (FR) **Mr Peter Deal & Grandpa's**
4 **DERFENNA ART (IRE)**, 5, b g Excellent Art—Cordelia **Mrs A. Cowley**
5 **EIGHTFOLD**, 5, b g Cadeaux Genereux—Nirvana **Miss S. J. Beddoes**
6 **KELPIE BLITZ (IRE)**, 5, gr g Verglas (IRE)—Summer Spice (IRE) **Mrs A. Cowley**
7 **LITIGANT**, 6, b g Sinndar (IRE)—Jomana (IRE) **Mr A. A. Byrne**
8 **OGARITMO**, 5, ch m Manduro (GER)—Querida **Mrs O. Carlini Cozzi**
9 **PEACHEZ**, 6, ch m Observatory (USA)—Streccia **Mrs S. J. Doyle**
10 **REYES MAGOS (IRE)**, 8, b g Indian Danehill (IRE)—Cincuenta (IRE) **A. A. Bynne & Miss S. J. Beddoes**
11 **SCOTTISH BOOGIE (IRE)**, 7, b g Tobougg (IRE)—Scottish Spice **Mr A. A. Byrne**
12 **SHAOLIN (IRE)**, 4, b g Footstepsinthesand—Baboosh (IRE) **P. A. Deal & Mr A. A. Byrne**
13 **SHIRAZZ**, 5, b m Shirocco (GER)—Streccia **Mrs S. J. Doyle**
14 **SNAPCHAT (IRE)**, 7, b g Shantou (USA)—Kelly's Native (IRE) **Mr S. J. P. O'Farrell**

THREE-YEAR-OLDS

15 **FOR AYMAN**, b c Bertolini (USA)—Saharan Song (IRE) **Mr A. A. Byrne**
16 B f Shirocco (GER)—Night Symphonie **Hot to Trot Racing Club**

TWO-YEAR-OLDS

17 Ch c 17/4 Footstepsinthesand—Pivka (Pivotal) (17034) **Ardent Tide Ltd**
18 B c 23/1 Street Cry (IRE)—Touch My Soul (FR) (Tiger Hill (IRE)) (17034) **Mr A. A. Byrne**
19 Ch c 20/4 Arcano (IRE)—Western Sky (Barathea (IRE)) (100000) **S. P. Tucker**
20 B c 6/4 Dark Angel (IRE)—Winesong (IRE) (Giant's Causeway (USA)) (140000) **S. P. Tucker**

Other Owners: Miss Sam Beddoes, Mr A. A. Byrne, Mr P. A. Deal.

Assistant Trainer: Faye Bramley

Jockey (flat): George Baker, Micky Fenton. **Jockey (NH):** Conor O'Farrell.

185

MRS NERYS DUTFIELD, Seaton
Postal: **Crabhayne Farm, Axmouth, Seaton, Devon, EX12 4BW**
Contacts: **PHONE (01297) 553560 FAX (01297) 551185**
E-MAIL **nerys.dutfield@tiscali.co.uk WEBSITE www.nerysdutfield.com**

1 **PRESENT ACCEPTED**, 7, b g Presenting—Kwaheri **S. J. Dutfield**

186 MR CHRIS DWYER, Newmarket
Postal: **Grooms Cottage, Brickfield Stud, Exning Road, Newmarket, Suffolk, CB8 7JH**
Contacts: **PHONE (01638) 570074 FAX (01638) 570074 MOBILE (07831) 579844**
E-MAIL getadwyer@aol.com

1 BALATINA, 4, ch f Byron—Primavera **Mrs I. L. Sneath**
2 COMMANCHE, 5, ch g Sleeping Indian—Happy Memories (IRE) **M. M. Foulger**
3 FOIE GRAS, 4, b g Kyllachy—Bint Zamayem (IRE) **Mrs S. Dwyer**
4 HANNAHS TURN, 4, b f Dubai Destination (USA)—Fontaine House **Mrs I. L. Sneath**
5 MIA'S BOY, 10, b g Pivotal—Bint Zamayem (IRE) **Mrs S. Dwyer**
6 PATRIOTIC (IRE), 6, b g Pivotal—Pescara (IRE) **M. M. Foulger**
7 SARAH BERRY, 5, b m First Trump—Dolly Coughdrop (IRE) **Mrs S. Dwyer**
8 TATTING, 5, ch g Street Cry (IRE)—Needlecraft (IRE) **Mrs I. L. Sneath**

THREE-YEAR-OLDS
9 APPELLEZ BAILEYS (FR), b c Halling (USA)—Bitza Baileys (IRE) **G. R. Bailey Ltd**
10 BACK ON BAILEYS, b f Kyllachy—Baileys Gleam **G. R. Bailey Ltd**
11 BASIL BERRY, b g Tobougg (IRE)—Dolly Coughdrop (IRE) **Strawberry Fields Stud**
12 NORMAN'S STAR, b g Tiger Hill (IRE)—Canis Star **D. L. Bowkett**
13 STAGE GIRL, b f Tiger Hill (IRE)—Primavera **Mrs I. L. Sneath**
14 TREFNANT (IRE), ch f Bahamian Bounty—Miss Trish (IRE) **R. S. G. Jones**

TWO-YEAR-OLDS
15 B c 25/2 Equiano (FR)—Dream Day (Oasis Dream) **Mrs S. Dwyer**
16 Ch f 5/3 Pastoral Pursuits—Royal Mistress (Fasliyev (USA)) **G. R. Bailey Ltd**

Other Owners: G. F. L. Robinson, F. B. B. White, Mrs A. L. J. White.

Assistant Trainer: Shelley Dwyer

Apprentice: Josh Crane.

187 MISS CLAIRE DYSON, Evesham
Postal: **Froglands Stud Farm, Froglands Lane, Cleeve Prior, Evesham, Worcestershire, WR11 8LB**
Contacts: **PHONE (07803) 720183 (01789) 774000 FAX (01789) 774000**
E-MAIL cdyson@live.co.uk WEBSITE www.clairedysonracing.co.uk

1 BOOMTOWN, 9, b g Fantastic Light (USA)—Ville d'amore (USA) **FSF Racing**
2 BURNTHILL (IRE), 9, b g Winged Love (IRE)—Kilcorig (IRE) **FSF Racing**
3 CHADFORD, 6, b g Trade Fair—Quiz Time **B & S Vaughan, Lisa Rogers & Partner**
4 CHEAT THE CHEATER (IRE), 7, b g Flemensfirth (USA)—Ballyclough Gale **Guy Sainsbury & John Dyson**
5 4, B g Scorpion (IRE)—Classic Fantasy
6 ECHO FOXTROT, 5, b g Echo of Light—April Lee (USA) **Mr K. Elvins**
7 EL INDIO (IRE), 7, b g Flemensfirth (USA)—Final Bond (IRE)
8 GIVEITACHANCE (IRE), 7, b g Clerkenwell—Native Lisa (IRE) **FSF Racing**
9 ICANMOTOR, 7, b m Midnight Legend—Lochnagold **Mr K. Elvins**
10 KHAZIUM (IRE), 5, br g Kheleyf (USA)—Hazium (IRE) **Mr Tim Wixted & Mr Tony Anderson**
11 KILFLORA, 11, b g Alflora (IRE)—Stac-Pollaidh **Lisa Rogers, B & S Vaughan & Partner**
12 MANY MOONS (FR), 5, b m Sleeping Car (IRE)—Ishka Baha (IRE) **Mr G. E. P. Dudfield**
13 MR JAY DEE (IRE), 9, b g Lord Americo—Emmas Flyer (IRE) **B & S Vaughan & Partner**
14 MUSICAL WEDGE, 10, ch g Sir Harry Lewis (USA)—Wedge Musical **D. J. Dyson**
15 MYSULA, 7, b m Sulamani (IRE)—Air of Affection **Miss R. J. Rowland**
16 NELTARA, 10, b g Kayf Tara—Lucia Forte **D. J. Dyson**
17 OVER MY HEAD, 6, gr g Overbury (IRE)—Altesse de Sou (FR) **Ms I. Heritage**
18 4, Ch c Midnight Legend—Owlesbury Dream (IRE)
19 5, B m Kayf Tara—Pearly Bay
20 PEQENO DIABLO (IRE), 9, br g Alexius (IRE)—Miss Huro (IRE) **FSF Racing**
21 POETIC POWER (IRE), 5, b g Dylan Thomas (IRE)—Chalice Wells **Miss C. Dyson**
22 QUAYSIDE COURT (IRE), 10, ch g Anshan—Rustic Court (IRE) **Guy Sainsbury & Carl Mason**
23 THARAYA, 9, b m Choisir (AUS)—Karlaska **Miss R. J. Rowland**
24 WHEELAVHER, 8, br m Fair Mix (IRE)—True Rose **FSF Racing**
25 WHEELAVIM, 6, b g Beat All (USA)—Plus Tu Mets (FR) **D. J. Dyson**
26 WHEELAVIT (IRE), 11, b g Elnadim (USA)—Storm River (USA) **Miss C. Dyson**
27 WYCHWOODS MIST, 7, b m Umistim—Blackchurch Lass (IRE) **Kevin & Anne Glastonbury**

MISS CLAIRE DYSON - Continued

Other Owners: Mr Tony Anderson, Miss C. Dyson, Mr D. J. Dyson, Mr Kevin Glastonbury, Mrs Anne Glastonbury, Mr Carl Mason, Miss L. Rogers, Mr Guy Sainsbury, Mr B. Vaughan, Mrs S. Vaughan, Mr Tim Wixted.

Assistant Trainer: Becky Rowland

Jockey (NH): Jamie Moore, Nick Scholfield. **Conditional:** Gerald Quinn. **Amateur:** Miss Gina Swan.

---

188 **MR SIMON EARLE, Warminster**
Postal: Little Croft, Tytherington, Warminster, Wiltshire, BA12 7AD
Contacts: **PHONE** (01985) 840450 **FAX** (01985) 840450 **MOBILE** (07850) 350116
E-MAIL simon@simonearleracing.com **WEBSITE** www.simonearleracing.com

1 ALREADY BASKING (CAN), 6, ch g More Than Ready (USA)—Basking (USA) **Mrs G. C. Goldsmith**
2 GET BACK TO ME (IRE), 7, br g Presenting—My Name's Not Bin (IRE) **R. L. Dacombe**
3 HEADLY'S BRIDGE (IRE), 8, b g Tillerman—Brockton Flame **Mrs P. L. Bridel**
4 HOMER RUN (IRE), 7, b g Classic Cliche (IRE)—Suir Native (IRE) **EPDS Racing Partnership 3**
5 LOXLEY MEZILE, 5, br m Strategic Prince—Haiti Dancer **EPDS Racing Partnership 2**
6 MONEY MAID (IRE), 6, ch m Blueprint (IRE)—Maid of Music (IRE) **EPDS Racing Partnership 5**
7 RED NOT BLUE (IRE), 11, b g Blueprint (IRE)—Silent Valley **The Plum Merchants**
8 ROYAL SIGNALLER, 4, b g Dylan Thomas (IRE)—Whirly Bird **Mr Archibald Hargie & Mr Brian Hargie**
9 SHANADERRY KIN (IRE), 5, b g Kris Kin (USA)—Sweet Innocence (IRE) **Mr John Powell**
10 WATER RAIL, 5, b g Manipulator—Madame Mozaik (USA)
11 ZAKATAL, 8, gr g Kalanisi (IRE)—Zankara (FR) **David Furman & John Sugarman**

Other Owners: Mr A. C. Clift, Mr David Furman, Mr John Powell, Mr T. M. Santry, Miss T. Sloan, Mr John Sugarman.

Jockey (flat): George Baker. **Jockey (NH):** Andrew Thornton, Gerard Tumelty. **Amateur:** Miss Alice Mills.

---

189 **MR MICHAEL EASTERBY, Sheriff Hutton**
Postal: New House Farm, Sheriff Hutton, York, North Yorkshire, YO60 6TN
Contacts: **PHONE** (01347) 878368 **FAX** (01347) 878204 **MOBILE** (07831) 347481
E-MAIL enquiries@mickeasterby-racing.co.uk **WEBSITE** www.mickeasterby-racing.co.uk

1 ABOVE STANDARD (IRE), 6, ch g Shamardal (USA)—Prealpina (IRE) **Mr A Saha, Mr M Cox & Mr E Grant**
2 AETNA, 4, b f Indesatchel (IRE)—On The Brink **Mr B. Padgett**
3 ALLURING STAR, 6, b m Gentleman's Deal (IRE)—Alustar **Jeff Hamer & Bernard Bargh**
4 AMAZING EIGHT, 5, b g Erhaab (USA)—Harry's Bride **Mr Nick Bannister**
5 ANCIENT CROSS, 10, b g Machiavellian (USA)—Magna Graecia (IRE) **P Bown, S Chappell, R Fiddes & S Hull**
6 BARREN BROOK, 7, b g Beat Hollow—Carinthia (IRE) **Mr D Scott, Mrs E Wright & Mr J Clark**
7 BE LUCKY, 4, ch f Kyllachy—Spritzeria **The Sangster Family & M W Easterby**
8 BLACK ANNIS BOWER, 6, gr m Proclamation (IRE)—Bow Bridge **Mrs A. Jarvis**
9 BLACKSMITHS ARMS, 4, b g Multiplex—Kingsfold Blaze **M. W. Easterby**
10 BORIS GRIGORIEV (IRE), 5, b br g Excellent Art—Strategy **Mrs L. M. Ward**
11 CAN YOU CONGA, 4, b g Piccolo—Takes Two To Tango **M Cox, E Grant, S Chappell & S Hull**
12 CITY GROUND (USA), 7, b br g Orientate (USA)—Magnet (USA) **S. Hull**
13 CLOCK ON TOM, 4, b g Trade Fair—Night Owl **Mr A Simpson & Mr J Rooney**
14 COTTAM MAYBEL, 5, b m Doyen (IRE)—Northern Bird **Peter Easterby**
15 CRAZY CHESTER (IRE), 5, b g Golan (IRE)—Nosey Oscar (IRE) **Lord Daresbury**
16 DAY OF THE EAGLE (IRE), 8, b g Danehill Dancer (IRE)—Puck's Castle **S Hull, S Hollings & D Fielding**
17 FAME AGAIN, 6, b g Gentleman's Deal (IRE)—Ballet Fame (USA) **Mrs C. E. Mason**
18 HERNANDO TORRES, 6, b g Iffraaj—Espana **R. F. H. Partnership 1**
19 HOOF IT, 7, b g Monsieur Bond (IRE)—Forever Bond **Mr A. Chandler & Mr L. Westwood**
20 HOOFALONG, 4, b g Pastoral Pursuits—Baymist **A Chandler, L Westwood, D & Y Blunt**
21 HOOFITRITA, 4, b f Shirocco (GER)—Aunt Rita (IRE)
22 HOT SPICE, 6, b g Kodiac—Harlestone Lady **Steve Hull & David Swales**
23 ICEBLAST, 6, b g Iceman—Medici Princess **Mr B. Padgett**
24 IGGY, 4, ch g Lucarno (USA)—Fujakka (USA) **Dewhirst, Moore, Rooney, Simpson & Hull**
25 ITLAAQ, 6, b g Alhaarth (IRE)—Hathrah (IRE) **Mr L. J. Turpin**
26 IVESTAR, 9, b g Fraam—Hazardous **Mrs K. R. Brown**
27 JEER (IRE), 10, ch g Selkirk (USA)—Purring (USA) **Mr L. J. Turpin**
28 KALK BAY (IRE), 7, b g Hawk Wing (USA)—Politesse (USA) **Mr L. J. Turpin**
29 LE DELUGE (FR), 4, b g Oratorio (IRE)—Princess Sofia (UAE) **Mrs L. J. Turpin**

MR MICHAEL EASTERBY - Continued

30 **LIGHTENING ROD**, 9, b g Storming Home—Bolero **N. W. A. Bannister**
31 **MAJESTIC DREAM (IRE)**, 6, b g Exceed And Excel (AUS)—Tallassee **Mr A Simpson, B Hoggarth & S Hull**
32 **NAMEITWHATYOULIKE**, 5, b g Trade Fair—Emma Peel **Mr S Hollings, Mr S Hull & S. Chappell**
33 **NARCISSIST (IRE)**, 5, b g Dylan Thomas (IRE)—Gabare (FR) **The Friday Club**
34 **NETWORK STORY**, 4, b f Pastoral Pursuits—Ballet Fame (USA) **Mick Cox, Eliot Grant & Christine Mason**
35 **OIL STRIKE**, 7, b g Lucky Story (USA)—Willisa **Mr A. Saha**
36 **OLD MAN CLEGG**, 4, b g Pastoral Pursuits—Stolen Melody **Irkroy Racing & Steve Hull**
37 **ON THE HOOF**, 5, gr g Monsieur Bond (IRE)—Smart Hostess **Andrew Chandler & Lee Westwood**
38 **PERFECT PASTURE**, 4, b g Pastoral Pursuits—Word Perfect **Mrs L. J. Turpin**
39 **PERTEMPS NETWORKS**, 10, b g Golden Snake (USA)—Society Girl **E. A. Brook**
40 **PIVOTMAN**, 6, ch g Pivotal—Grandalea **Mrs L. J. Turpin**
41 **POLITBUREAU**, 7, b g Red Ransom (USA)—Tereshkova (USA) **W. H. & Mrs J. A. Tinning**
42 **REAR ADMIRAL (IRE)**, 8, b g Dushyantor (USA)—Ciaras Charm (IRE) **Mr S Hollings & Mr J Bryan**
43 **SAINTS AND SINNERS (IRE)**, 6, b g Gold Well—How Provincial (IRE) **Mr P Deal & Mr N Wrigley**
44 **SHADOWS LENGTHEN**, 8, b g Dansili—Bay Shade (USA) **T. A. F. Frost**
45 **SINGZAK**, 6, ch g Singspiel (IRE)—Zakuska **Clark Industrial Services Partnership**
46 **SPACE WAR**, 7, b g Elusive City (USA)—Princess Luna (GER) **R. F. H. Partnership & Brian Padgett**
47 **SPENCERS LAD**, 4, b c Sixties Icon—Black Opal **Dave Standing & Eric Brook**
48 **STRONG MAN**, 6, b g Gentleman's Deal (IRE)—Strong Hand **Mrs L. J. Turpin**
49 **TAPIS LIBRE**, 6, b g Librettist (USA)—Stella Manuela (FR) **Mrs S. E. Mason**
50 **TOWBEE**, 5, b g Doyen (IRE)—Bow Bridge **Mrs A. Jarvis**
51 **UNEX MICHELANGELO (IRE)**, 5, b g Dansili—Chenchikova (IRE) **Mrs L. J. Turpin**
52 **UP TEN DOWN TWO (IRE)**, 5, b g Hurricane Run (IRE)—
Darabela (IRE) **B Delaney, A Duke & Backup Technology**
53 **WARLU WAY**, 7, b h Sakhee (USA)—Conspiracy **Mr B Hoggarth & Mr S Hollings**
54 **WE'LL DEAL AGAIN**, 7, b g Gentleman's Deal (IRE)—Emma Amour **K. Wreglesworth**

THREE-YEAR-OLDS

55 **ALDRETH**, b g Champs Elysees—Rowan Flower (IRE) **M Cox, E Grant & A Stott**
56 **BAJAN REBEL**, ch f Bahamian Bounty—Silca Key **Julian Rooney Steve Hull Simon Chappell**
57 **BON CHANCE**, b g Byron—Stolen Melody **The SB Club**
58 **CAPTAIN JOE**, ch g Captain Gerrard (IRE)—Bond Shakira **Mr D Fielding & Mr S Chappell**
59 **HOOF'S SO LUCKY**, ch f Compton Place—Lucky Dip **A Chandler, L Westwood, M Cox & E Grant**
60 **KRAKA GYM (IRE)**, b g Clodovil (IRE)—Accounting **Clark Industrial Service & Mr S Hollings**
61 **LADY BUBBLES**, b f Distant Peak (IRE)—Mount Hillaby (IRE) **Mr S Hull, Mr D Swales & Mr M Metcalfe**
62 **NETWORK PERFECTION**, ch c Distant Peak (IRE)—Word Perfect **M Cox, E Grant, B Padgett & S Hull**
63 **SLINGSBY**, b g Dutch Art—Ballet Fame (USA) **Mr S Hull, Mr B Hoggarth & Mrs C Mason**
64 **SYROS (IRE)**, ch g Kheleyf (USA)—Starring (FR) **Mr S. Chappell**
65 **TAANIF**, b g Aqlaam—Firebelly **Mr S. Chappell & Mr S. Hull**
66 **TAMAYUZ MAGIC (IRE)**, b g Tamayuz—Anne Tudor (IRE) **W. H. & Mrs J. A. Tinning**
67 **VADARA**, b g Aqlaam—Hufflepuff (IRE) **Mr D. M. Standring**

TWO-YEAR-OLDS

68 B c 13/3 Monsieur Bond (IRE)—Bow Bridge (Bertolini (USA)) **Mrs A. Jarvis**
69 **DEBT FREE DAME**, ch f 20/1 Arcano (IRE)—
Runkerry Point (USA) (Giant's Causeway (USA)) (5000) **Mr B. Sangster & A R Legal Collections Limited**
70 B f 22/3 Stimulation (IRE)—Goes A Treat (IRE) (Common Grounds) (5714) **Mr E. Brook**
71 B c 14/4 Monsieur Bond (IRE)—Ice Girl (Iceman) (9523) **Mr B. Padgett**
72 B c 20/3 Hellvelyn—Jane Jubilee (IRE) (Mister Baileys) (8571) **Mr E. Brook**
73 **LEAVE IT TO ARNO**, ch c 17/4 Paco Boy (IRE)—
Presto Vento (Air Express (IRE)) (5000) **A R Legal Collections Limited**
74 B f 3/3 Myboycharlie (IRE)—On The Brink (Mind Games) (15238) **Mr B. Padgett**
75 **PERFECT PEAK**, ch f 2/5 Distant Peak (IRE)—Word Perfect (Diktat) (15238) **Mrs L. J. Turpin**
76 **RECKLESS HUNTER**, ch f 12/2 Bahamian Bounty—
Frambroise (Diesis) (5238) **Mr Keith Hollinrake, Mr Kevin Hollinrake, Mr Peter Gilleard & Mr S. Hull**
77 Ch c 31/3 Monsieur Bond (IRE)—Royal Distant (USA) (Distant View (USA)) **Mr T. Dewhirst & Mr J. R. Moore**
78 Ch c 21/3 Major Cadeaux—Smooth As Silk (IRE) (Danehill Dancer (IRE)) (6666) **Mr & Mrs B. Buckley**
79 Ch c 5/4 Stimulation (IRE)—Splicing (Sharpo) (19047) **Spence,Hull,Cox,Grant,Chandler,Westwood**
80 B c 22/1 Acclamation—Strawberry Moon (IRE) (Alhaarth (IRE)) (42000) **Mr A. Saha**
81 B c 14/3 Poseidon Adventure (IRE)—Upton Seas (Josr Algarhoud (IRE)) **Mr E. Brook**
82 B f 2/4 Monsieur Bond (IRE)—Villa Del Sol (Tagula (USA)) (2666) **Mr K. Wreglesworth**

Other Owners: Mr Bernard Bargh, Mrs A. Blanchard, Mr David Blunt, Mrs Y. Blunt, Mr S. Bowett, Mr P. J. Bown, Mr E. A. Brook, Mr John Bryan, Mr Andrew Chandler, Mr S. Chappell, Mr Jim Clark, Mr A. W. Clark, Mr M. Cox, Lord Daresbury, Mr P. A. Deal, Mr Bill Delaney, Mr T. C. Dewhirst, Mr A. Duke, Mr M. W. Easterby, Mr Ritchie Fiddes, Mr Dean Fielding, Mr E.

MR MICHAEL EASTERBY - Continued

Grant, Mrs Catherine Hesketh, Mr Bernard Hoggarth, Mr S. A. Hollings, Mr Steve Hull, Mrs C. E. Mason, Mr Mark W. Metcalfe, Mr J. R. Moore, Mr A. Morse, Mr B. Padgett, Mr Julian Rooney, Mr A. Saha, Mr B. V. Sangster, Mr G. E. Sangster, Mr David Scott, Mr Nick Sharp, Mr Andrew Simpson, Stittenham Racing, Mr A. F. Stott, Mr D. Swales, Mrs J. A. Tinning, Mr W. H. Tinning, Mr Lee Westwood, Mrs E. Wright, Mr N. H. T. Wrigley.

Assistant Trainer: D. M. Easterby

Jockey (flat): Graham Gibbons, Paul Mulrennan, James Sullivan. **Conditional:** Jake Greenall. **Apprentice:** Danielle Mooney. **Amateur:** Mr H. Bannister, Miss S. Brotherton, Miss J. Coward, Miss Anna Hesketh, Miss Joanna Mason.

---

190 MR TIM EASTERBY, Malton
Postal: **Habton Grange, Great Habton, Malton, North Yorkshire, YO17 6TY**
Contacts: **PHONE (01653) 668566 FAX (01653) 668621**

1 ANOTHER CITIZEN (IRE), 6, b g Byron—Royal Rival (IRE) **Middleham Park Racing V & Partners**
2 ARC LIGHT (IRE), 6, b g Shamardal (USA)—Banakill (FR) **Mr J. R. Beamson**
3 ARDLUI (IRE), 6, b g Galileo (IRE)—Epping **C. H. Stevens**
4 ATTENTION SEAKER, 4, b f Bollin Eric—Pay Attention **Ryedale Partners No 6**
5 BACHOTHEQUE (IRE), 4, b g Chineur (FR)—Bacchanalia (IRE) **R. Taylor & Mr P. Hebdon**
6 BANDERITOS, 5, b g Revoque (IRE)—Orchid **Habton Farms**
7 BELANNA, 5, b m Bollin Eric—Bollin Annabel **Habton Farms**
8 BODY AND SOUL (IRE), 4, b f Captain Rio—Goodwood March **C. H. Stevens**
9 BOLLIN GRETA, 9, b br m Mtoto—Bollin Zola **Habton Farms**
10 BURREN VIEW LADY (IRE), 4, br f Dansili—Westerly Gale (USA) **Habton Farms**
11 CAPTAIN DUNNE (IRE), 9, b g Captain Rio—Queen Bodicea (IRE) **Middleham Park Racing XV & Partners**
12 CARRYONREGARDLESS (IRE), 6, b g Presenting—Lady Apprentice (IRE) **T. J. Hemmings**
13 CHEERS FOR THEA (IRE), 9, gr m Distant Music (USA)—Popiplu (USA) **R. A. George**
14 CHOISAN (IRE), 5, b g Choisir (AUS)—Attanagh (IRE) **Croft, Taylor & Hebdon**
15 CRACKENTORP, 9, b g Generous (IRE)—Raspberry Sauce **C. H. Stevens**
16 DANCE KING, 4, ch g Danehill Dancer (IRE)—One So Wonderful **A. R. Turnbull**
17 DARK DUNE (IRE), 6, b g Diamond Green (FR)—Panpipes (USA) **Habton Farms**
18 DARK EROS (IRE), 4, b f Dark Angel (IRE)—Capetown Girl
19 DEEPSAND (IRE), 5, br g Footstepsinthesand—Sinamay (USA) **T. J. Hemmings**
20 DENNIS, 4, b g Mind Games—Hetti Lewis **The Mutineers & Habton Farms**
21 FAST SHOT, 6, b g Fasliyev (USA)—Final Pursuit **Ontoawinner & Partners**
22 GETABUZZ, 6, b g Beat Hollow—Ailincala (IRE) **Langham Hall Stud Three**
23 GRISSOM (IRE), 8, b g Desert Prince (IRE)—Misty Peak (IRE) **Jim & Helen Bowers**
24 HAMISH MCGONAGALL, 9, b g Namid—Anatase **Reality Partnerships I**
25 HAWK HIGH (IRE), 4, b g High Chaparral (IRE)—Septembers Hawk (IRE) **T. J. Hemmings**
26 HAYEK, 7, b g Royal Applause—Salagama (IRE) **Habton Farms**
27 HAZELRIGG (IRE), 9, b g Namid—Emma's Star (ITY) **The Senators**
28 HOLY ANGEL (IRE), 5, b g Dark Angel (IRE)—Bakewell Tart (IRE) **Three Jolly Farmers**
29 JANAAB (IRE), 4, ch g Nayef (USA)—Mood Indigo (IRE) **Numac Engineering Ltd**
30 KING OF THE CELTS (IRE), 6, b g Celtic Swing—Flamands (IRE) **Mrs B. Oughtred**
31 LAFFAN (IRE), 5, b g Dark Angel (IRE)—Lady Corduff (IRE) **Middleham Park Racing XI & Partners**
32 LEBANNA, 4, br f Bollin Eric—Bollin Annabel **C. H. Stevens**
33 LILAC LACE (IRE), 4, b f Captain Marvelous (IRE)—Lilac Mist **S. A. Heley**
34 LOUKOUMI, 6, b m Iffraaj—Odalisque (USA) **Habton Farms**
35 MAPPIN TIME (IRE), 6, b g Orientate (USA)—Different Story (USA) **P. Baillie**
36 MAVEN, 6, b m Doyen (IRE)—Bollin Jeannie **Mrs J. E. Pallister**
37 MAYBEAGREY, 5, b m Shamardal (USA)—Grey Again **Habton Farms**
38 MEDICI TIME, 9, gr g Medicean—Pendulum **Mrs C. A. Hodgetts**
39 MOJOLIKA, 6, ch g Motivator—Kalandika **Mr A. Brannon & Habton Farms**
40 MONITA BONITA, 5, b m King's Theatre (IRE)—Monita des Bois (FR) **C. H. Stevens**
41 NO POPPY (IRE), 6, b m Chineur (FR)—Capetown Girl **J. Musgrave**
42 NONOTNOW, 4, ch g Notnowcato—Get Jealous (IRE) **Mr P S Cook & Mr A Parker**
43 OFF ART, 4, ch c Dutch Art—Off Camera **D. B. Lamplough**
44 PENNY GARCIA, 4, b f Indesatchel (IRE)—Katie Boo (IRE) **Jim & Helen Bowers**
45 PRINTMAKER (IRE), 6, b g Shamardal (USA)—Marie Laurencin **Mr J. R. Beamson**
46 RED COBRA (IRE), 4, b g Redback—Queen Cobra (IRE) **J & P Baillie & C & G Baillie**
47 RELIGHT MY FIRE, 4, ch g Firebreak—Making Music **J. Gill**
48 RIVER BOLLIN, 4, b g Bollin Eric—Bollin Roberta **C. H. Stevens**
49 RIVER RHYTHM, 5, b m Bollin Eric—Cumbria Rhapsody **Habton Farms**

MR TIM EASTERBY - Continued

50 **ROYAL COMPOSER (IRE)**, 11, b g Mozart (IRE)—Susun Kelapa (USA) **Mrs B. Oughtred**
51 **ROYAL RASCAL**, 4, b f Lucky Story (USA)—Royal Punch **C. H. Stevens**
52 **RUN RUCTIONS RUN (IRE)**, 5, b m Westerner—Perfect Prospect (IRE) **T. E. Ford**
53 **SEE CLEARLY**, 5, b m Bertolini (USA)—True Vision (IRE) **Ryedale Partners No 4**
54 **SILVERY MOON (IRE)**, 7, gr g Verglas (IRE)—Starry Night **C. H. Stevens**
55 **SURROUND SOUND**, 4, b g Multiplex—Tintera (IRE) **Mr C. Wilson**
56 **TIPTOEAWAY (IRE)**, 9, b g Insan (USA)—My Blackbird (IRE) **T. J. Hemmings**
57 **TRUSTAN TIMES (IRE)**, 8, b g Heron Island (IRE)—
                                Ballytrustan Maid (IRE) **Mrs M E Armitage & Mr Peter Armitage**

THREE-YEAR-OLDS

58 **ALPINE FLOWER (IRE)**, b f Intense Focus (USA)—Wine House (IRE) **Miss B. C. Duxbury**
59 **ANOTHER ROYAL**, b f Byron—Royal Punch **C. H. Stevens**
60 **AZAGAL (IRE)**, b f Azamour (IRE)—Brave Madam (IRE) **R. Sidebottom**
61 **BAR SHY**, b g Dutch Art—Notable Lady (IRE) **Habton Farms**
62 **BLUE TALISMAN (IRE)**, ch g Alhaarth (IRE)—Amaniy (USA) **A. R. Turnbull**
63 **BREAKABLE**, ch f Firebreak—Magic Myth (IRE) **Ryedale Partners No 9**
64 **CHIVERS (IRE)**, b c Duke of Marmalade (IRE)—Thara (USA) **C. H. Stevens**
65 **COLOUR OF THE WIND**, gr f Dylan Thomas (IRE)—Makhsusah (IRE) **S. A. Heley**
66 B f Monsieur Bond (IRE)—Damelza (IRE) **Habton Farms**
67 **DANZIG IN THE DARK (IRE)**, b f Mastercraftsman (IRE)—Cape Jasmine (IRE) **Mr & Mrs J. D. Cotton**
68 **DUTCH BREEZE**, ch c Dutch Art—Oasis Breeze **Mr & Mrs J. D. Cotton**
69 **ELECTION NIGHT**, b f Mount Nelson—Psychic (IRE) **J. Shack**
70 **HEROIQUE (IRE)**, b f Acclamation—Gay Heroine **Mr K. Nicholson**
71 **KENNY THE CAPTAIN (IRE)**, ch c Captain Rio—Kelso Magic (USA) **Reality Partnerships V**
72 **LITTLE BRUV (IRE)**, b g Observatory (USA)—Ailincala (IRE) **Langham Hall Stud Three**
73 **MAVREE (IRE)**, b f Captain Marvelous (IRE)—Hemasree (IRE) **Habton Farms**
74 B c Halling (USA)—Murielle **Mrs J. M. MacPherson**
75 **NOTAPRAYER**, b g Notnowcato—Punch Drunk **Allan Kerr & Peter McGivney**
76 **OSCURO**, b g Manduro (GER)—Jabbara (IRE) **P. H. Milmo**
77 **PONTY PURSUIT**, b f Pastoral Pursuits—Spring Clean (FR) **Mr M. O'Neill**
78 **RIOBLANCO (IRE)**, ch f Captain Rio—Salva **A. R. Turnbull**
79 **ROOMIE**, b f Pastoral Pursuits—Pomponette (USA) **Mrs J. Boxcer**
80 **SAYTHATAGAIN (IRE)**, b f Echo of Light—The Oldladysays No (IRE) **T. E. Ford**
81 **SEE THE SUN**, ch g Assertive—Cocabana **C. H. Stevens**
82 **SOUL ARTIST (IRE)**, b f Bushranger—Itsanothergirl **Clipper Group Holdings Ltd**
83 **SOUL BROTHER (IRE)**, b c Captain Rio—Goodwood March **C. H. Stevens**
84 **STORYLINE (IRE)**, b f Kodiac—Petite Histoire (IRE) **Miss Y. M. G. Jacques**
85 **STREET BOSS (IRE)**, gr g Verglas (IRE)—Gladstone Street (IRE) **Habton Farms**
86 **SUPA U**, b f Authorized (IRE)—Supa Sal **R. A. Pegum**
87 **TEARS AND RAIN (IRE)**, b f Iffraaj—Massalia (IRE) **Mr B Guerin & Habton Farms**
88 **THE HOODED CLAW (IRE)**, ch g Dandy Man (IRE)—Changari (USA) **April Fools**
89 **TO BEGIN**, b g Tobougg (IRE)—Sagina **Habton Farms**
90 **TRADITIONELLE**, b f Indesatchel (IRE)—Mookhlesa **Lovely Bubbly Racing**
91 **TWO B'S**, b g Bollin Eric—Bollin Nellie **Habton Farms**
92 **VALE MENTOR (IRE)**, b c Moss Vale (IRE)—Sinamay (USA) **T. J. Hemmings**
93 **VENTURA MIST**, ch f Pastoral Pursuits—Kerry's Dream **Middleham Park Racing XXIV**
94 **WHITE FLAG**, b f Sakhee's Secret—Rainbow Spectrum (FR) **Habton Farms**

TWO-YEAR-OLDS

95 **AGREEABLE LADY (IRE)**, b f 5/4 Approve (IRE)—
                    Spirit of Hope (Danehill Dancer (IRE)) (5032) **A. R. Turnbull**
96 B f 11/4 Equiano (FR)—Alhufoof (USA) (Dayjur (USA)) (11000) **Reality Partnerships II**
97 **ARRACOURT**, b c 6/5 Multiplex—Retaliator (Rudimentary (USA)) **W. H. Ponsonby**
98 **ARTISTIC DANCER**, b f 2/3 Dutch Art—Self Expression (Dansili) (14285) **D. A. West**
99 **CISCO BOY**, b c 27/2 Paco Boy (IRE)—Miss Wells (IRE) (Sadler's Wells (USA)) (25714) **Ryedale Partners No 7**
100 B c 8/4 Major Cadeaux—Dancing Loma (FR) (Danehill Dancer (IRE)) (2857) **Habton Farms**
101 B c 16/2 Bushranger (IRE)—Emma Dora (IRE) (Medaglia d'oro (USA)) (25714) **Habton Farms**
102 **FATHER BERTIE**, b c 5/3 Firebreak—Magical Music (Fraam) (4761) **Mr J. R. Saville**
103 B c 28/2 Hellvelyn—Flying Highest (Spectrum (IRE)) (4761) **Grange Park Racing VI**
104 **HONEYSUCKLE LIL (IRE)**, b f 18/4 Alfred Nobel (IRE)—Twinberry (IRE) (Tagula (IRE)) (5420) **A. R. Turnbull**
105 B c 6/3 Indesatchel (IRE)—Katie Boo (IRE) (Namid) **J. F. Bowers**
106 **LLYN**, ch f 5/5 Dutch Art—Makara (Lion Cavern (USA)) (65000) **Mr A. Gray**

MR TIM EASTERBY - Continued

107 **MAID IN ROME (IRE)**, b f 26/4 Holy Roman Emperor (IRE)—
Kashra (IRE) (Dancing Dissident (USA)) (8095) **D. B. Lamplough**
108 **MIDNIGHT MOJITO**, b f 6/2 Azamour (IRE)—Shaken And Stirred (Cadeaux Genereux) (21904) **D. A. West**
109 B f 28/3 Paco Boy (IRE)—Mint Royale (IRE) (Cadeaux Genereux) (14285) **Rio Grande Partnership**
110 B f 30/3 Captain Rio—Miss Donovan (Royal Applause) (11614) **Reality Partnerships III**
111 **MOCKINGBIRD HILL**, b c 24/2 Cockney Rebel (IRE)—Claws (Marju (IRE)) (8571) **N. A. Jackson**
112 **MYSTIC MIRAAJ**, ch c 1/4 Iffraaj—Salsa Brava (IRE) (Almutawakel) (23809) **R. Taylor & Mr P. Hebdon**
113 B f 16/3 Paco Boy (IRE)—Orange Pip (Bold Edge) (25714) **D. B. Lamplough**
114 **PERFECT GIRL (IRE)**, b f 18/4 Iffraaj—Chatline (IRE) (One Cool Cat (USA)) (16260) **P. C. J. Bourke**
115 **PIXEY PUNK**, gr f 4/2 Mount Nelson—Mosquera (GER) (Acatenango (GER)) (15238) **Mr J. R. Saville**
116 **PONTY GRIGIO (IRE)**, b c 17/3 Acclamation—
Inishtearaght (IRE) (Verglas (IRE)) (20000) **Calvert, O'Neill & Partner**
117 **PONTY ROSSO**, ch c 20/3 Paco Boy (IRE)—Amazed (Clantime) (15000) **Calvert, O'Neill & Partner**
118 **SIGN OF THE TIMES**, b f 11/3 Medicean—Still Small Voice (Polish Precedent) (15000) **J. Shack**
119 B c 9/2 Sakhee's Secret—Sofia Royale (Royal Applause) (5032) **Ontoawinner, M Hulin & Partner**
120 **SPARKLE GIRL**, ch f 24/2 Stimulation (IRE)—Seren Teg (Timeless Times) (3047) **Mr J. R. Saville**
121 B c 10/4 Myboycharlie (IRE)—Whatcameoverme (USA) (Aldebaran (USA)) (4761) **G. Horsford**
122 B c 5/2 Bushranger (IRE)—Zafaraya (IRE) (Ashkalani (IRE)) (9000) **Ryedale Partners No 8**
123 **ZEELA (IRE)**, b f 23/1 Zebedee—Vintage Allure (Barathea (IRE)) (12380) **Mrs J. P. Connew**
124 B c 14/3 Assertive—Zonta Zitkala (Daylami (IRE)) (13333) **Reality Partnerships IV**

Other Owners: Mrs M. E. Armitage, P. Armitage, Mr G. M. Baillie, Mr P. M. Baillie, G. M. Barnard, P. J. W. Botham, Mrs H. M. Bowers, Mr A. Brannon, Mr P. S. Cook, J. D. Cotton, Mrs B. Cotton, Mrs P. D. Croft, A. D. Crombie, T. D. Easterby, M. H. Easterby, Mr B. M. P. R. Guerin, Mr P. F. Hebdon, Mr M. A. S. Hulin, Mr A. Kerr, Mr M. J. Lewendon, Mrs J. Magnier, Mr P. McGivney, Mr J. Mounsey, Mr P. E. Nodding, N. J. O'Brien, Dr M. J. O'Brien, T. S. Palin, Mr A. R. Parker, Mr M. Pearson, Mr D. Pearson, Mr J. Preston, M. Prince, A. H. Raby, A. Rhodes, R. B. Rosenberg, Mr G. Sunley, Mr E. Surr, R. Taylor, Miss S. J. Turner, D. E. Wilsdon.

---

191 **MR BRIAN ECKLEY, Brecon**
Postal: **Closcedi Farm, Llanspyddid, Brecon, Powys, LD3 8NS**
Contacts: **PHONE (01874) 622422 MOBILE (07891) 445409**
E-MAIL brian.eckley@live.co.uk

1 **CLOUDY SMITH**, 5, b m Cloudings (IRE)—Poppy Smith **B. J. Eckley**
2 **JAUNTY INFLIGHT**, 5, b g Busy Flight—Jaunty Walk **B. J. Eckley**
3 4, B g Norse Dancer (IRE)—Jaunty Walk **B. J. Eckley**
4 **LUCKY PRINCE**, 7, b g Lucky Owners (NZ)—Sun Bonnet **B. J. Eckley**
5 4, B f Desert King (IRE)—Sun Bonnet **B. J. Eckley**
6 **SUNSATIONAL GIRL**, 5, ch m Byron—Sun Bonnet **B. J. Eckley**
7 **TIMEFORAGIN**, 7, b m Pasternak—Little Time **B. J. Eckley**

---

192 **MR PAT EDDERY, Nether Winchendon**
Postal: **Musk Hill Stud, Nether Winchendon, Aylesbury, Buckinghamshire, HP18 0EB**
Contacts: **RACING OFFICE: (01844) 296153 FAX (01844) 290282 MOBILE (07718) 984799**
E-MAIL info@patedderyracing.com WEBSITE www.patedderyracing.com

1 **BARNACLE**, 5, b g Compton Place—Bombalarina (IRE) **P. J. J. Eddery**
2 **EZETIGER**, 4, b g Tiger Hill (IRE)—Guilty Secret (IRE) **P. J. J. Eddery**
3 **GEORDIE MAN**, 4, b c Manduro (GER)—Opening Ceremony (USA) **Mr L. F. Daly**
4 **HINTON ADMIRAL**, 10, b g Spectrum (IRE)—Shawanni **P. J. J. Eddery**
5 **HOONOSE**, 5, ch g Cadeaux Genereux—Roodeye **Miss E. L. Owen**
6 **KAAHEN**, 4, b br g Jazil (USA)—Khassah **Miss E. L. Owen**
7 **LUTINE CHARLIE (IRE)**, 7, b g Kheleyf (USA)—Silvery Halo (USA) **Miss E. L. Owen**
8 **MISTS OF TIME (IRE)**, 4, b f Excellent Art—Capriole **Pat Eddery Racing (Excellent Art)**
9 **NEPALESE PEARL**, 4, b f Tiger Hill (IRE)—Grey Pearl **Pat Eddery Racing (Tiger Hill)**
10 **PASHAN GARH**, 5, b g Anabaa (USA)—Mimisel **Miss E. L. Owen**
11 **RAPID WATER**, 8, b g Anabaa (USA)—Lochsong **Miss E. L. Owen**
12 **SOMERTON STAR**, 4, b c Avonbridge—Leaping Flame (USA) **P. Dean**
13 **STORM HAWK (IRE)**, 7, b g Hawk Wing (USA)—Stormy Larissa (USA) **Miss E. L. Owen**
14 **SWEET POSSESSION (USA)**, 8, b m Belong To Me (USA)—Bingo Meeting (USA) **Miss E. L. Owen**
15 **THENOBLEPRANKSTER (IRE)**, 5, b g Dynaformer (USA)—Aqaarid (USA) **Miss E. L. Owen**

MR PAT EDDERY - Continued

16 **TWILIGHT ANGEL**, 6, ch m Compton Place—Leaping Flame (USA) **P. J. J. Eddery**
17 **WRENINGHAM**, 9, br g Diktat—Slave To The Rythm (IRE) **Miss E. L. Owen**

THREE-YEAR-OLDS

18 **BLACK WIDOW**, b f Bertolini (USA)—Malvadilla (IRE) **P. J. J. Eddery**
19 **INCA DRUM (USA)**, b c Empire Maker—Around **K. Abdullah**
20 **REIMPOSE (USA)**, b f First Defence (USA)—Rougeur (USA) **K. Abdullah**
21 **VERA LOU (IRE)**, ch f Manduro (GER)—Baltica (IRE) **Mr L. F. Daly**

Assistant Trainer: Miss Emma L. Owen (07718984799) **Jockey (flat):** Luke Morris, Cathy Gannon, Joe Fanning.

193 **MR ROBERT EDDERY, Newmarket**
Postal: **Robert Eddery Racing, Heyward Place Stables, Hamilton Road, Newmarket, Suffolk, CB8 7JQ**
Contacts: **PHONE (01638) 428001 MOBILE (07938) 898455**
E-MAIL info@roberteddery racing.com WEBSITE www.robberteddery racing.com

1 **BEAU SELECT (IRE)**, 4, b g Lucky Story (USA)—Practicallyperfect (IRE) **Ms T. Keane**
2 **FRONT PAGE NEWS**, 4, ch f Assertive—Branston Berry (IRE) **Gurnett, Rayment & Anderson**
3 **QUADRIGA (IRE)**, 4, b g Acclamation—Turning Light (GER) **Mr C. R. Eddery**
4 **SPESSARTINE (IRE)**, 4, b g Duke of Marmalade (IRE)—Lasting Chance (USA) **E. S. Phillips**

THREE-YEAR-OLDS

5 **BUSH WARRIOR (IRE)**, b c Bushranger (IRE)—Lady Corduff (IRE) **Ian Anderson**
6 **CRAFTSMANSHIP (FR)**, ch c Mastercraftsman (IRE)—Jennie Jerome (IRE) **Trisha Keane & Julia Rayment**
7 **DONNCHA (IRE)**, br c Captain Marvelous—Seasonal Style (IRE) **Mr D. Bannon**
8 **EASTER TIME**, b f Myboycharlie (IRE)—Alectrona (FR) **Mr O. O'Brien**
9 **GAELIC O'REAGAN**, b c Refuse to Bend (IRE)—Gaelic Roulette (IRE) **Graham & Lynn Knight**
10 **HONEY MEADOW**, ch f Avonbridge—All The Nines (IRE) **G & L Knight, J Mitchell & N Donaldson**
11 **ISABELLA LIBERTY (FR)**, b f Soldier of Fortune (IRE)—Samsa (FR) **Mr E Phillips & Mrs M Matthews**
12 **OLYMNIA**, b f Teofilo (IRE)—Diotima **E. S. Phillips**
13 **RED OASIS**, b g Captain Gerrard (IRE)—Sahara Silk (IRE) **Mr C. R. Eddery**
14 **RUDI FIVE ONE (FR)**, b c American Post—Dansia (GER) **Anderson, Mathews & Kerve**
15 **SHREWD BOB (IRE)**, b c Whipper (USA)—Cheyenne Spirit **E. S. Phillips**
16 **SOLENT LAD (USA)**, ch c English Channel (USA)—Ting A Folie (ARG) **P Shrives, J Rayment & M Mathews**
17 **TYRSAL (IRE)**, b g Jeremy (USA)—Blanchelande (IRE) **Phillips, Fullerton & Riesebieter**

Other Owners: Mr I Anderson, Mrs N. Donaldson, Mrs G. Fullerton, Mr C. Gurnett, M. E. Kerve, G. Knight, Mrs L. C. Knight, Mrs M. Mathews, Mr J. Mitchell, Mrs J. M. Rayment, Mr E. H. Riesebieter, Mr P. Shrives.

Jockey (flat): Andrea Atzeni.

194 **MR GORDON EDWARDS, Minehead**
Postal: **Summering, Wheddon Cross, Minehead, Somerset, TA24 7AT**
Contacts: **PHONE (01643) 831549 FAX (01643) 831549 MOBILE (07970) 059297**
E-MAIL angela@edwards3212.fsnet.co.uk

1 **BRIEFCASE (IRE)**, 9, b g Witness Box (USA)—Another Tycoon (IRE) **G. F. Edwards**
2 **CONSULATE (IRE)**, 10, b g Rock of Gibraltar (IRE)—Soha (USA) **G. F. Edwards**
3 **SHANANN STAR (IRE)**, 8, br m Anshan—Baile An Droichid (IRE) **G. F. Edwards**

Amateur: Mr D. Edwards.

195 **MR CHARLES EGERTON, Upper Lambourn**
Postal: **Uplands, Upper Lambourn, Hungerford, Berkshire, RG17 8QH**
Contacts: **OFFICE (01488) 73164 FAX (01488) 73133 MOBILE (07795) 220630**
E-MAIL charles@charlesegerton.co.uk WEBSITE www.charlesegerton.co.uk

1 **ACT OF SUPREMACY (IRE)**, 4, b g Presenting—Supreme Touch (IRE) **Equis**
2 **CAPELLINI (IRE)**, 7, b g Cape Cross (IRE)—Red Stella (FR) **Bruce Pomford & Malcolm Frost**
3 **CARRIBS LEAP (IRE)**, 9, b g Old Vic—Majister Ludi (IRE) **Equis**

MR CHARLES EGERTON - Continued

  4 **DR LIVINGSTONE (IRE)**, 9, b g Dr Fong (USA)—Radhwa (FR) **C. R. Egerton**
  5 **EASY BEESY**, 6, b g Kalanisi (IRE)—Queen of The Bees (IRE) **Mrs S. A. Roe**
  6 **GEE HI (IRE)**, 8, b g Milan—Curzon Street **Equis**
  7 4, B g Milan—Nonnetia (FR) **Equis**
  8 **SEEDLING**, 5, b g Cockney Rebel (IRE)—Unseeded **Equis & Christopher Spence**
  9 **SEEDSMAN**, 7, ch g Sulamani (IRE)—Unseeded **Christopher Spence & Partners**
10 **VIA VOLUPTA**, 4, b f Kayf Tara—Via Ferrata (FR) **Equis**

Other Owners: Mr & Mrs B. Allan, Mr Ian Barratt, Mr C. Bull, Mr J. Cavanagh, Mr M. Davidson, Mr D. J. Erwin, Mr J. Floyd, Mr R. Glasspool, Mr M. J. Graham, Mr A. Jones, Mr M. B. J. Kimmins, Mr M. Kirby, Mr P. Knapman, Mr A. Livermore, Mr S. Malone, Mr P. Nicholls, Mr B. Parker, Mr J. Ritblat, Mr Kieran P. Ryan, Mr J. Strachan, Mr J. Straker, Mr C. Taylor, Mr D. Thomas.

Assistant Trainer: David Plunkett (07778) 379341

Jockey (NH): A. P. McCoy (w/a), Sam Twiston-Davies (w/a). **Conditional:** Gavin Sheehan (w/a).

---

196 **MR BRIAN ELLISON, Malton**
Postal: Spring Cottage Stables, Langton Road, Norton, Malton, North Yorkshire, YO17 9PY
Contacts: OFFICE (01653) 690004 FAX (01653) 690008 MOBILE (07785) 747426
E-MAIL ellisonracing@aol.com WEBSITE www.brianellisonracing.co.uk

  1 **ADILI (IRE)**, 5, ch g Dubai Destination (USA)—Adirika (IRE) **Brian Ellison & Chris Lowther**
  2 **ADMIRAL HAWKE (IRE)**, 8, b g Stowaway—Classical Rachel (IRE) **Prism Bloodstock**
  3 **ALL THAT REMAINS (IRE)**, 9, b g King's Theatre (IRE)—Morning Breeze (IRE) **Mrs J. A. Martin**
  4 **AMAZE**, 6, ch g Pivotal—Dazzle **A Farrell, A Williamson, H Lynn**
  5 **ANDREO BAMBALEO**, 10, ch g Silver Patriarch (IRE)—Time And A Place (IRE) **Brian Ellison**
  6 **APTERIX (IRE)**, 4, b g Day Flight—Ohe Les Aulmes (FR) **P. J. Martin**
  7 **AUTUN (USA)**, 4, b c Empire Maker (USA)—Sense of Joy **P. J. Martin**
  8 **BALTY BOYS (IRE)**, 5, b g Cape Cross (IRE)—Chatham Islands (USA) **Koo's Racing Club, Carr & Jacobs**
  9 **BARAWEEZ (IRE)**, 4, b g Cape Cross (IRE)—Aquarelle Bleue **A. R. Barnes**
10 **BEN CEE PEE M (IRE)**, 9, ch g Beneficial—Supreme Magical **CPM Group Limited**
11 **BEST TRIP (IRE)**, 7, b g Whipper (USA)—Tereed Elhawa **Koo's Racing Club**
12 **BISHOP'S CASTLE (USA)**, 5, b g Distorted Humor (USA)—Miss Caerleona (IRE) **Koo's Racing Club & Lee Keys**
13 **CAPE EXPLORER**, 5, b g Cape Cross (IRE)—Eve **Mr M Grayson & Mr I P O'Brien**
14 **CAPELLANUS (IRE)**, 8, b g Montjeu (IRE)—Secret Dream (IRE) **Mrs C. L. Ellison**
15 **CLARENCE BEEKS (IRE)**, 4, gr g Vergias (IRE)—Dazzling Dancer **Mr L. S. Keys**
16 **D'ARGENT CLOUD**, 6, gr g Tikkanen (USA)—Sounds Familiar (IRE) **CPM Group Limited**
17 **DESTINY BLUE (IRE)**, 7, b g Danehill Dancer (IRE)—Arpege (IRE) **Elliott Brothers And Peacock**
18 **DISCOVERY BAY**, 6, b g Dansili—Rainbow's Edge **Ms F. Devaney**
19 **DIZZY RIVER (IRE)**, 9, ch g Flemensfirth (USA)—Dizzy Dealer **Mr D. R. Gilbert**
20 **DODINA (IRE)**, 4, b f Acclamation—Etica (IRE) **Ontoawinner & Brian Ellison**
21 **DOLPHIN ROCK**, 7, b g Mark of Esteem (IRE)—Lark In The Park (IRE) **Mia Racing**
22 **DREAM WALKER (FR)**, 5, gr g Gold Away (IRE)—Minnie's Mystery (FR) **Mr K. Brown**
23 **DUSKY BOB (IRE)**, 9, br g Bob Back (USA)—Sunsets Girl (IRE) **Mr D. R. Gilbert**
24 **EL MASSIVO (IRE)**, 4, b g Authorized (IRE)—Umthoulah (IRE) **D Gilbert, M Lawrence, A Bruce**
25 **EVER FORTUNE (USA)**, 5, ch g El Corredor (USA)—Beyond Price (USA) **D Gilbert, M Lawrence, A Bruce**
26 **FILM DIRECTOR (IRE)**, 6, b g Tiger Hill (IRE)—Stage Manner **P. J. Martin**
27 **FIVE IN A ROW (IRE)**, 6, ch g Blueprint (IRE)—Ela Plaisir (IRE) **P. J. Martin**
28 **FLEET DAWN**, 8, b g Polish Precedent (USA)—Wychnor Dawn (IRE) **Prism Bloodstock**
29 **FLORAL PATCHES**, 9, ch m Alflora (IRE)—Island Gift **William Bethell & Jim Beaumont**
30 **FUJIN DANCER (FR)**, 9, ch g Storming Home—Badaayer (USA) **W. A. Bethell**
31 **GLOBAL VILLAGE (IRE)**, 9, b g Dubai Destination (USA)—
                                            Zelding (IRE) **Kevin Corcoran Aaron Pierce Chris Weare**
32 **GONE FOREVER**, 4, b g Quest For Fame—Erudite **P. J. Martin**
33 **GRAND JIPECK (IRE)**, 4, b g Soviet Star (USA)—Inourthoughts (IRE) **Mrs I. Woolfitt**
34 **GRANDILOQUENT**, 5, b g Rail Link—High Praise (USA) **Mrs J. Bownes**
35 **HARD CORE DEBT**, 4, b g Muhtathir—Al Durrah (USA) **Koo's Racing Club**
36 **INOOGOO (IRE)**, 9, b g Great Palm—Ballindante (IRE) **EBB Racing**
37 **INVESTMENT EXPERT (IRE)**, 4, b g Tamayuz—Kindling **Coopers Yard**
38 **IT'S A MANS WORLD**, 8, b g Kyllachy—Exhibitor (USA) **David Foster & Brian Ellison**
39 **JOYFUL SOUND (IRE)**, 6, b g Acclamation—Eman's Joy **Mr & Mrs E. J. Dolan-Abrahams**
40 **KAYFROU**, 9, b g Kayf Tara—Roufontaine **Dan Gilbert & Kristian Strangeway**
41 **KNIGHTLY ESCAPADE**, 6, ch g Sakhee (USA)—Queen of Iceni **Mrs J. A. Martin**
42 **LAIKA**, 5, b m Rail Link—Space Quest **M Khan X2**

MR BRIAN ELLISON - Continued

43 **LIFETIME (IRE)**, 6, b g Shamardal (USA)—La Vita E Bella (IRE) **Koo's Racing Club**
44 **LLANARMON LAD (IRE)**, 5, b g Red Clubs (IRE)—Blue Crystal (IRE) **Middleham Park Racing XLIII & Partner**
45 **LOCHNELL (IRE)**, 5, b m Winged Love (IRE)—Nothing For Ever (IRE) **J. D. Macgregor**
46 **LUCKY CODY (IRE)**, 5, b g Blueprint (IRE)—Ware Vic (IRE) **Mike & Eileen Newbould**
47 **MAGIC SKYLINE (IRE)**, 4, b f Refuse To Bend (IRE)—Grecian Air (FR) **Mike & Eileen Newbould**
48 **MASHAARI (IRE)**, 5, b g Monsun (GER)—Thakafaat (IRE) **P. J. Martin**
49 **MASIRANN (IRE)**, 6, b g Tiger Hill (GER)—Masilia (IRE) **Mike & Eileen Newbould**
50 **MEMORY CLOTH**, 7, b g Cape Cross (IRE)—Gossamer **Racing Management & Training Ltd**
51 **MISS TWIGGY**, 6, b m Alflora (IRE)—Gee Tee Supermodel **Antonio Marucci & Brian Ellison**
52 **MIXED MESSAGE (IRE)**, 4, b f Kodiac—Berenica (IRE) **W. I. Bloomfield**
53 **MON BRAV**, 7, b g Sampower Star—Danehill Princess (IRE) **Koo's Racing Club**
54 **MONTEFELTRO**, 6, ch g Medicean—Bustling **D Gilbert, M Lawrence, A Bruce**
55 **MOYODE WOOD**, 9, b g Overbury (IRE)—Country Choice (IRE) **Mr D. Foster**
56 **MUBROOK (USA)**, 9, b g Alhaarth (IRE)—Zomaradah **Mrs C. L. Ellison**
57 **NAJEEB**, 4, b g Sakhee (USA)—Forest Fire (SWE) **Brian Ellison**
58 **NEPTUNE EQUESTER**, 11, b g Sovereign Water (FR)—All Things Nice **Koo's Racing Club**
59 **OCEAN CLUB**, 7, ch g Storming Home—Strictly Cool (USA) **Westbourne Racing Club & Brian Ellison**
60 **PACIFIC HEIGHTS (IRE)**, 5, b g Galileo (IRE)—Song to Remember (USA) **A. R. Barnes**
61 **PALAZZO BIANCO**, 6, b g Shirocco (GER)—White Palace **The Palazzo Bianco Partnership**
62 **PALOS CONTI (FR)**, 11, ch g Robin des Champs (FR)—Dona Mirande (FR) **C. N. Barnes**
63 **PELMANISM**, 7, b g Piccolo—Card Games **Koo's Racing Club**
64 **PHASE SHIFT**, 6, b m Iceman—Silent Waters **Mr D. R. Gilbert**
65 **PLATINUM PROOF (USA)**, 4, b br g Smart Strike (CAN)—Keeper Hill (USA) **The Golden Years Partnership**
66 **POWERFUL AMBITION (IRE)**, 8, b g Bob Back (USA)—Native Shore (IRE) **Koo's Racing Club**
67 **PRESENTED (IRE)**, 7, ch g Presenting—Rustic Court (IRE) **Miss C. A. Carr**
68 **RACING EUROPE (IRE)**, 5, b g Kayf Tara—Titanic Quarter (IRE) **P. J. Martin**
69 **RACY**, 7, b g Medicean—Soar **Koo's Racing Club**
70 **RED INCA**, 6, ch g Pivotal—Magicalmysterykate (USA) **D Gilbert, M Lawrence, A Bruce**
71 **SAPTAPADI (IRE)**, 8, ch g Indian Ridge—Olympienne (IRE) **Koo's Racing Club**
72 **SERENITY NOW (IRE)**, 6, b g Key of Luck (USA)—Imdina (IRE) **Mr J. M. Basquill**
73 **SHERMAN MCCOY**, 8, ch g Reset (AUS)—Naomi Wildman (USA) **Koo's Racing Club**
74 **SPIN CAST**, 6, b g Marju (IRE)—Some Diva **W. A. Bethell**
75 **STORMY WEATHER (FR)**, 8, gr g Highest Honor (FR)—
                              Stormy Moud (USA) **Mr S. L. Catchpole & Mr K. Hanson**
76 **STREETS OF NEWYORK**, 7, b g Dalakhani (IRE)—Minute Waltz **Brian Ellison**
77 **TEEATREIDS (IRE)**, 6, ch m Royal Anthem (USA)—Orchard Lass **Racing Management & Training Ltd**
78 4, Ch f Mount Nelson—Tetravella (IRE) **Brian Ellison**
79 **THE TRACEY SHUFFLE**, 8, br g Kapgarde (FR)—Gaspaisie (FR) **J. D. Macgregor**
80 **THREE WHITE SOCKS (IRE)**, 7, b g Whipper (USA)—Halesia (USA) **Racing Management & Training Ltd**
81 **TOP NOTCH TONTO (IRE)**, 4, ch g Thousand Words—Elite Hope (USA) **Mr K. Brown**
82 **TOTALIZE**, 5, b g Authorized (IRE)—You Too **D Gilbert, M Lawrence, A Bruce**
83 **TRAVIS COUNTY (IRE)**, 5, b g Jeremy (USA)—Manchaca (FR) **D Gilbert, M Lawrence, A Bruce**
84 **TRUE THAT (IRE)**, 4, b g Captain Marvelous (IRE)—Bratislava **Ann-Marie McManus & Finola Devaney**
85 **TWELVE STRINGS (IRE)**, 5, b g Iffraaj—Favoritely (USA) **M Khan X2**
86 **TY GWR**, 5, b g Echo of Light—House Maiden (IRE) **Kevin Corcoran Aaron Pierce Chris Weare**
87 **ULTIMATE**, 8, b g Anabaa (USA)—Nirvana **Mr D. R. Gilbert**
88 **VIVA COLONIA (IRE)**, 9, ch g Traditionally (USA)—Ansariya (USA) **Bolingbroke Racing, Mersey Racing**
89 **WAR POET**, 9, b g Singspiel (IRE)—Summer Sonnet **Mr M. Kirby**
90 **WITCH WAY WENT**, 4, b f Royal Applause—Celestial Princess **Mr K. Brown**
91 **YESYOUCAN (IRE)**, 9, b g Beneficial—Except Alice (IRE) **Prism Bloodstock**
92 **YORKIST (IRE)**, 6, ch g Urban Ocean (FR)—Kilbarry Demon (IRE) **Mike & Eileen Newbould**
93 **ZEUS MAGIC**, 4, b g Zamindar (USA)—Milly of The Vally **Koo's Racing Club**

THREE-YEAR-OLDS

94 **ASPIRANT**, b g Rail Link—Affluent **Koo's Racing Club**
95 **BAYTOWN KESTREL**, b f Captain Gerrard (IRE)—Litewska (IRE) **The Acorn Partnership**
96 **COME ON SUNSHINE**, b c Authorized (IRE)—Tagula Sunrise (IRE) **M Khan X2**
97 **FULL DAY**, ch f Champs Elysees—Capistrano Day (USA) **Prism Bloodstock**
98 B f Tagula (IRE)—Gutter Press (IRE) **Brian Ellison**
99 B f Captain Gerrard (IRE)—Hillside Heather (IRE) **Mr K. Brown**
100 **JIMMY CRACKLE (IRE)**, b g Intense Focus (USA)—Slieve **Mrs J. A. Martin**
101 **LIVIA DRUSILLA (IRE)**, b f Holy Roman Emperor (IRE)—Shaiyadima (IRE) **Mrs C. L. Ellison**
102 **MADEMOISELLE LILY**, b f Monsieur Bond (IRE)—Lily Lenor (IRE) **Brian Ellison**
103 **MISS ACCLAIMED (IRE)**, gr f Acclamation—Miss Shaan (FR) **Market Avenue Racing, Acorn Partnership**

MR BRIAN ELLISON - Continued

104 MUSICAL MOLLY (IRE), gr f Mastercraftsman (IRE)—Park Approach (IRE) **Mrs J. A. Martin**
105 OFELIA (IRE), b f Teofilo (IRE)—Rose Bourbon (USA) **Mr D. R. Gilbert**
106 ORIENTAL MAID, b f Sakhee's Secret—Julia Domna **Mr K. Brown**
107 PENINA (IRE), b f Lawman (FR)—Poussiere d'or (IRE) **Antonio Marucci & Brian Ellison**
108 RESONATED (USA), b g Pleasant Tap (USA)—Third Times Better (USA)

TWO-YEAR-OLDS

109 Gr f 13/3 Sir Percy—Brave Mave (Daylami (IRE)) (11428) **Brian Ellison**
110 B f 28/4 Acclamation—Daqtora (Dr Devious (IRE)) (22857) **P. J. Martin**
111 B f 26/2 Azamour (IRE)—Fringe (In The Wings) (3871) **Brian Ellison**
112 B f 15/3 Sir Percy—Grain Only (Machiavellian (USA)) (18582) **Brian Ellison**
113 B c 27/2 Kheleyf (USA)—Kool Acclaim (Royal Applause) (22857) **Brian Ellison**
114 B c 30/1 Duke of Marmalade (IRE)—Pharapache (USA) (Lyphard (USA)) (15485) **P. J. Martin**
115 B f 22/4 Thewayyouare (USA)—Pointing North (USA) (Orientate (USA)) (3619) **The Acorn Partnership**
116 B c 11/3 Bushranger (IRE)—Queen Cobra (IRE) (Indian Rocket) (20952) **Mrs J. A. Martin**
117 Gr c 14/3 Verglas (IRE)—Tullawadgeen (IRE) (Sinndar (IRE)) (20131) **P. J. Martin**
118 B c 21/4 Approve (IRE)—Umlani (IRE) (Great Commotion (USA)) (16190) **Mrs J. A. Martin**

Other Owners: Mr B. M. J. Allan, J. J. Beaumont, L. A. Bolingbroke, H. A. Brydon, S. Cannon, A. Carr, Mr S. L. Catchpole, K. J. Corcoran, Mr D. R. Crossman, Mrs P. E. Dolan-Abrahams, E. J. Dolan-Abrahams, J. M. Elliott, C. R. Elliott, Mr Gary Etheridge, Mr A. S. Farrell, Mr N. Gravett, Mr M. Grayson, Mr D. P. Grundy, Mr K. Hanson, Mrs F. K. Hathorn, J. J. Hathorn, Mrs M. C. Jacobs, Mr M. Jones, Mr R. Jones, M. Khan, M. Khan, Mr M. Lawrence, Mr K. Leggett, C. P. Lowther, Mr H. J. Lynn, Mr R. G. Makin, Market Avenue Racing Club Ltd, A. Marucci, Mrs A. M. Mcmanus, J. M. Newbould, Mrs E. E. Newbould, N. J. O'Brien, Mr I. P. O'Brien, S. P. Oldroyd, T. S. Palin, Mr T. W. Parker, Mr A. T. Pierce, M. Prince, Mrs A. Sellers, Mr J. Strangeway, M. A. Tickle, Mrs I. M. Tickle, A. Tickle, Mr M. W. G. Trounce, Mr M. R. Turner, Mr C. E. Weare, Westbourne Consultants Ltd, A. S. Williamson.

Assistant Trainer: Mrs Claire Ellison, Mobile (07979) 570652

Jockey (flat): Tom Eaves, Paul Pickard, Dale Swift. **Jockey (NH):** Danny Cook. **Conditional:** Garry Lavery.
Amateur: Miss Harriet Bethell, Mr Declan Levey.

---

197 MR DAVID ELSWORTH, Newmarket
Postal: **Kings Yard, Egerton House Stables, Cambridge Road, Newmarket, Suffolk, CB8 0TH**
Contacts: **PHONE (01638) 665511 FAX (01638) 665310 MOBILE (07771) 804828**
E-MAIL david.elsworth@virgin.net

1 EMERGING, 4, b c Mount Nelson—Pan Galactic (USA) **Mr B. C. M. Wong**
2 ENGROSSING, 5, b g Tiger Hill (IRE)—Pan Galactic (USA) **D. R. C. Elsworth**
3 FLASHYFRANK, 5, b g Franklins Gardens—White Flash **D. R. C. Elsworth**
4 FLEMISH SCHOOL, 4, ch f Dutch Art—Rosewood Belle (USA) **Mrs B. M. Keller**
5 HIGHLAND CASTLE, 6, b g Halling (USA)—Reciprocal (IRE) **W. A. Harrison-Allan**
6 KINGSTON EUCALYPT, 4, b f Halling (USA)—Derartu (AUS) **Mr R. C. Hains**
7 MAID A MILLION, 4, b f Kyllachy—Poldhu **K. A. Dasmal**
8 REVISE (IRE), 4, b g Dansili—Niner's Home (USA) **D. R. C. Elsworth**
9 SALFORD PRINCE (IRE), 6, b g Invincible Spirit (IRE)—Bring Plenty (USA) **D. R. C. Elsworth**
10 SENATOR BONG, 4, ch c Dutch Art—Sunley Gift **J. Dwyer**
11 SOLAR SKY, 6, ch g Galileo (IRE)—La Sky (IRE) **Lordship Stud**
12 SONG LIGHT, 4, b g Echo of Light—Blue Lullaby (IRE) **D & C Bloodstock I**
13 THEREDBALLOON, 8, ch g Sulamani (IRE)—Sovana (FR) **Miss V. L. Allan**
14 UPAVON, 4, b g Avonbridge—Blaina **McPabb Racing**
15 ZAIN EAGLE, 4, b c Dylan Thomas (IRE)—Pearl City (USA) **Mr A. Al Banwan**

THREE-YEAR-OLDS

16 DASHING PRINCE, b g Nayef (USA)—Dashiba **J. C. Smith**
17 JUSTICE DAY (IRE), b c Acclamation—Rock Exhibition **Mr R. Ng**
18 MASTER THE WORLD (IRE), gr c Mastercraftsman (IRE)—Zadalla **K. Quinn/ C. Benham/ I. Saunders**
19 Ch f Hurricane Run (IRE)—Muschana
20 SLEEPY SIOUX, b f Sleeping Indian—Bella Chica (IRE) **D. R. C. Elsworth**
21 SPECULATIVE BID (IRE), b c Excellent Art—Barzah (IRE) **K. Quinn/ C. Benham/ I. Saunders**

MR DAVID ELSWORTH - Continued

22 **SWISS LAIT,** b f Milk It Mick—Matilda Peace **Hodge & Elsworth**
23 **WATER DANCER (IRE),** ch c Ad Valorem (USA)—River Patrol **J. C. Smith**

TWO-YEAR-OLDS

24 B f 23/2 Dubawi (IRE)—Barshiba (IRE) (Barathea (IRE)) **J. C. Smith**
25 Ch c 29/1 Sir Percy—Cartoon (Danehill Dancer (IRE)) (26000)
26 Gr c 31/1 Dark Angel (IRE)—Disco Lights (Spectrum (IRE)) (45000)
27 B f 11/4 Cape Cross (IRE)—Gower Song (Singspiel (IRE)) (45000) **D. R. C. Elsworth**
28 Ch f 9/3 Paco Boy (IRE)—Haiyfoona (Zafonic (USA)) (2380) **D. R. C. Elsworth**
29 Ch c 17/2 Paco Boy (IRE)—Jodrell Bank (IRE) (Observatory (USA)) (47000) **D. R. C. Elsworth**
30 **KINGSTON SASSAFRAS,** b c 3/3 Halling (USA)—Kingston Acacia (King of Roses (AUS)) **Mr R. C. Hains**
31 **MARK HOPKINS,** b c 22/3 Mount Nelson—Halska (Unfuwain (USA)) (15000) **R. J. McCreery**
32 Ch f 12/4 Sir Percy—May West (Act One) (10452) **D. R. C. Elsworth**
33 B f 24/2 Halling (USA)—Optimistic (Reprimand) (5000) **D. R. C. Elsworth**
34 Ch c 26/3 Winker Watson—Peintre d'argent (IRE) (Peintre Celebre (USA))
35 B c 26/2 Halling (USA)—Porthcawl (Singspiel (IRE)) (20000) **Mr R. Ng**
36 Ch c 14/3 Cockney Rebel (IRE)—Prairie Oyster (Emperor Jones (USA)) (3000) **D. R. C. Elsworth**
37 B c 12/3 Acclamation—Qui Moi (CAN) (Swain (IRE)) (65000) **Mr R. Ng**
38 B c 28/3 Vale of York (IRE)—Rock Exhibition (Rock of Gibraltar (IRE)) (34842) **D. R. C. Elsworth**
39 B c 14/2 Acclamation—Siren's Gift (Cadeaux Genereux) **J. C. Smith**
40 B c 8/5 Amadeus Wolf—Summer Spice (IRE) (Key of Luck (USA)) (4645) **D. R. C. Elsworth**
41 B c 24/3 Clodovil (IRE)—Two Marks (USA) (Woodman (USA)) (6000) **D. R. C. Elsworth**
42 Ch c 20/2 Champs Elysees—Vivianna (Indian Ridge) (24777)

Other Owners: Mr C. F. Benham, T. F. Harris, Mrs E. A. Harris, D. A. Hodge, Mr D. S. G. Morgan, Mr K. J. Parris, K. J. Quinn, Mr I. N. Saunders, D. Sutherland, C. Wilson.

Assistant Trainer: Mr Paul Holley

---

198 **MR GERRY ENRIGHT, Lewes**
Postal: **The Oaks, Old Lewes Racecourse, Lewes, East Sussex, BN7 1UR**
Contacts: **PHONE/FAX (01273) 479183 MOBILE (07922) 085875**
E-MAIL enright@btinternet.com

1 **BONNIE MAJOR,** 4, ch f Apple Tree (FR)—Carly Bay **A. O. Ashford**
2 **MAKE A FUSS,** 5, gr m Proclamation (IRE)—Fustaan (IRE) **Homebred Racing**

Other Owners: C. M. Wall, Mrs S. Wall.

Assistant Trainer: Mrs M Enright

Jockey (NH): Robert Thornton.

---

199 **MR TIM ETHERINGTON, Malton**
Postal: **Wold House Stables, Langton Road, Norton, Malton, North Yorkshire, YO17 9QG**
Contacts: **OFFICE (01653) 692842 HOME (01653) 693049**

1 **ABSOLUTE BEARING (IRE),** 5, b g Majestic Missile (IRE)—Garnock Academy (USA) **T. J. Etherington**
2 **BURNING THREAD (IRE),** 7, b g Captain Rio—Desert Rose **T. J. Etherington**
3 **CLASSIC PUNCH (IRE),** 11, b g Mozart (IRE)—Rum Cay (USA) **Mrs Brown's Boys**
4 **HOW FORTUNATE,** 6, b m Haafhd—However (IRE) **Mrs T. A. Foreman**
5 **SUNNY REAGH,** 9, ch m Presidium—Ownenreagh (IRE) **J. H. Hewitt**
6 **TANAWAR (IRE),** 4, b g Elusive City (USA)—Parakopi (IRE) **JB & MD**
7 **TOUCHING HISTORY (IRE),** 5, b g Titus Livius (FR)—Lady Naryana (IRE) **T. J. Etherington**

THREE-YEAR-OLDS

8 **CONNEXION FRANCAIS,** b f Lucarno (USA)—Sainte Gig (FR) **World Wide Racing Partners**

Other Owners: Mrs J. Brown, Mr P. N. Dowding, Mrs N. Dowding, J. Dwyer, Miss J. A. Tait.

200 | MR JAMES EUSTACE, Newmarket

Postal: **Park Lodge Stables, Park Lane, Newmarket, Suffolk, CB8 8AX**
Contacts: **PHONE (01638) 664277 FAX (01638) 664156 MOBILE (07802) 243764**
E-MAIL jameseustace@tiscali.co.uk WEBSITE www.jameseustace.com

1 AVIATOR (GER), 6, br g Motivator—Amore (GER) **The MacDougall Two**
2 BAAN (USA), 11, ch g Diesis—Madaen (USA) **Mrs G. R. Eustace**
3 IRON BUTTERFLY, 5, b m Shirocco (GER)—Coh Sho No **H. D. Nass**
4 LONDON SKOLAR, 4, b g Tobougg (IRE)—Coh Sho No **H. D. Nass**
5 PRECINCT, 4, b f Refuse To Bend (IRE)—Preceder **Major M. G. Wyatt**
6 SCOTTISH STAR, 6, gr g Kirkwall—Child Star (FR) **Mr I. L. Rushby**
7 SPA'S DANCER (IRE), 7, b g Danehill Dancer (IRE)—Spa **The MacDougall Two**
8 TIGHT LIPPED (IRE), 5, gr g Dark Angel (IRE)—Kayoko (IRE) **Blue Peter Racing 11**
9 WILY FOX, 7, ch g Observatory (USA)—Kamkova (USA) **Blue Peter Racing 10**

THREE-YEAR-OLDS

10 DANCING ANGEL, ch f Norse Dancer (IRE)—Indian Angel **J. C. Smith**
11 GREEN MUSIC, b f Oratorio (IRE)—Loch Verdi **J. C. Smith**
12 ICE SLICE (IRE), b g Dark Angel (IRE)—Ice Rock (IRE) **The MacDougall Two**
13 MAJOR CRISPIES, b g Pastoral Pursuits—Nellie Melba **G. N. Carstairs**
14 NIMBLE KIMBLE, ch f Kirkwall—Lovely Lyca **Mr I. L. Rushby**
15 SANDY COVE, br g Oasis Dream—Maganda (IRE) **Blue Peter Racing 12**

TWO-YEAR-OLDS

16 Ch f 20/3 Bahamian Bounty—Blue Siren (Bluebird (USA)) **J. C. Smith**
17 B c 27/2 Norse Dancer (IRE)—Indian Angel (Indian Ridge) **J. C. Smith**
18 PENCIL, b f 18/1 Excellent Art—Penelewey (Groom Dancer (USA)) **Major M. G. Wyatt**
19 Ch c 22/3 Avonbridge—Rosy Outlook (USA) (Trempolino (USA)) **J. C. Smith**
20 WIND PLACE AND SHO, br g 5/2 Shirocco (GER)—Coh Sho No (Old Vic) **H. D. Nass**

Other Owners: Mr R. P. Abel, Mr D. F. Ballheimer, T. H. Barma, Mr B. M. Cimmering, C. Z. Curtis, Mr T. E. Dyke, Mr A. C. Frost, Mr R. J. Hagen, Mrs L. R. Lawson, R. J. McCreery, Mrs K. A. McGladdery, Mr R. J. Uzupris.

201 | MR DAVID EVANS, Abergavenny

Postal: **Ty Derlwyn Farm, Pandy, Abergavenny, Monmouthshire, NP7 8DR**
Contacts: **PHONE (01873) 890837 (07834) 834775 E. Evans FAX (01873) 890837**
MOBILE (07860) 668499
E-MAIL info@pdevansracing.co.uk / pdevansracing@btinternet.com
WEBSITE www.pdevansracing.co.uk

1 AL'S MEMORY (IRE), 5, b g Red Clubs (IRE)—Consensus (IRE) **Mr W. R. J. Dawson**
2 ANNALUNA (IRE), 5, b m Whipper (USA)—Annaletta **N. Shutts**
3 BLACK DAVE (IRE), 4, b g Excellent Art—Miss Latina (IRE) **Mrs E Evans & Mr J Smith**
4 BUSSA, 6, b g Iceman—Maid To Dance **Mrs E. Evans**
5 CABUCHON (GER), 7, b g Fantastic Light (USA)—Catella (GER) **Mrs E. Evans**
6 DARK LANE, 8, b g Namid—Corps de Ballet (IRE) **Mrs E. Evans**
7 DECISION BY ONE, 5, ch g Bahamian Bounty—Intellibet One **Mrs I. M. Folkes**
8 DELIGHTFUL SLEEP, 6, b g Sulamani (IRE)—Naemi (GER) **Mrs E. Evans**
9 ECHOES OF JOY, 5, b g Echo of Light—Lambadora **N. Shutts**
10 ELUSIVE HAWK (IRE), 10, b g Noverre (USA)—Two Clubs **Mrs I. M. Folkes**
11 ESHTYAAQ, 7, b g Mark of Esteem (IRE)—Fleet Hill (IRE) **T. H. Gallienne**
12 FLEETWOODSANDS (IRE), 7, b g Footstepsinthesand—Litchfield Hills (USA) **E. R. Griffiths**
13 FOREST EDGE (IRE), 5, b g Amadeus Wolf—Compass Light (USA) **P & K Swinnerton**
14 HAADEETH, 7, b g Oasis Dream—Musical Key **Mrs I. M. Folkes**
15 HOMEBOY (IRE), 6, b g Camacho—Berenica (IRE) **Mrs E. Evans**
16 HONEY OF A KITTEN (USA), 6, b g Kitten's Joy (USA)—Sweet Baby Jane (USA) **Mrs E. Evans**
17 KIMBALI (IRE), 5, b g Clodovil (IRE)—Winnifred **Mr J. A. Wilcox**
18 LAGER TIME (IRE), 4, b g Tagula (IRE)—Polish Belle **Mrs E. Evans**
19 LAPIS BLUE (IRE), 4, b f Invincible Spirit (IRE)—Triple Try (IRE) **Mr P. F. O'Callaghan**
20 LUCKSTER, 4, b g Lucky Story (USA)—Bisaat (USA) **Miss E. Tanner**
21 MISS TILLY OSCAR (IRE), 8, b m Oscar (IRE)—Whisky Chaser **Mr B. J. Mould**
22 ONE WAY OR ANOTHER (AUS), 11, b g Carnegie (IRE)—True Blonde (AUS) **Mrs E. Evans**
23 PRINCE OF BURMA (IRE), 6, b h Mujadil (USA)—Spinning Ruby **E. R. Griffiths**
24 QUEEN AGGIE (IRE), 4, b f Elnadim (USA)—Catfoot Lane **Shropshire Wolves 4**

MR DAVID EVANS - Continued

25 **RUN IT TWICE (IRE)**, 4, b g Dark Angel (IRE)—Alinda (IRE) **Shropshire Wolves 4**
26 **SCOTSBROOK CLOUD**, 9, gr g Cloudings (IRE)—Angie Marinie **Mrs E. Evans**
27 **SCRIBE (IRE)**, 6, b g Montjeu (IRE)—Crafty Example (USA) **Shropshire Wolves/John Wilcox**
28 **SECRET BEAU**, 4, gr g Sakhee's Secret—Belle Reine **T. Reffell**
29 **SILENT MISSION**, 5, b m Overbury (IRE)—Peg's Permission
30 **SOMMERSTURM (GER)**, 10, b g Tiger Hill (IRE)—Sommernacht (GER) **Ms S. A. Howell**
31 **SURE FIRE (GER)**, 9, b g Monsun (GER)—Suivez (FR) **Mrs E. Evans**
32 **THE MONGOOSE**, 6, b g Montjeu (IRE)—Angara **Mr G Evans & Mr P D Evans**
33 **VERSE OF LOVE**, 5, b g Byron—Lovellian **H. M. W. Clifford**

THREE-YEAR-OLDS

34 **BIG KENNY**, b g Multiplex—Jezadil (IRE) **P. D. Evans**
35 Ch f Observatory (USA)—Composition **Mr K. M. Pinfield**
36 **EALAIN AIBREAN (IRE)**, b f Excellent Art—April (IRE) **Mrs E Evans & C W Racing**
37 **INTENSE FEELING (IRE)**, br f Intense Focus (USA)—Titania **Mrs E. Evans**
38 **INTERMATH (IRE)**, br g Camacho—Royal Interlude (IRE) **H. M. W. Clifford**
39 **JAZZY LADY (IRE)**, b f Intikhab (USA)—Lock's Heath (CAN) **Mr W. R. J. Dawson**
40 **KHEE SOCIETY**, b g Sakhee (USA)—Society Rose **H. M. W. Clifford**
41 **KNOW YOUR NAME**, ch g Halling (USA)—Lady Agnes **David Lockwood & Fred Lockwood**
42 **KODAFINE (IRE)**, br f Kodiac—Zafine **Mr J. A. Wilcox & P. D. Evans**
43 **LIMEGROVE**, b f Captain Gerrard (IRE)—Cherry Belle (IRE) **J. E. Abbey**
44 **LONE WARRIOR (IRE)**, b g Oratorio (IRE)—Warrior Wings **H. M. W. Clifford**
45 **MAHON FALLS**, ch f Dandy Man (IRE)—Saphire **Mrs E. Evans**
46 **NEEDS THE RUN**, b g Ivan Denisovich (IRE)—Maydew **Mr K. M. Pinfield**
47 **ORMER**, b f Kyllachy—Authoritative **T. H. Gallienne**
48 **SHAMARDYH (IRE)**, b f Shamardal (USA)—State Secret **Mr P. F. O'Callaghan**
49 **SLEEPING ANGEL**, ch f Sleeping Indian—Ellopassoff **E. R. Griffiths**
50 **SOLO HUNTER**, b g Sleeping Indian—Night Owl **H. M. W. Clifford**
51 **THREE D ALEXANDER (IRE)**, ch f Aqlaam—Pivotal's Princess (IRE) **Mr N. I. O'Callaghan**
52 **VODKA TIME (IRE)**, b c Indian Haven—Cappuccino (IRE) **Mrs E. Evans**

TWO-YEAR-OLDS

53 **AS A DREAM (IRE)**, b f 22/3 Azamour (IRE)—
    Wedding Dream (Oasis Dream) (3000) **Mr A Morgans & Mrs E Evans**
54 B f 1/5 Multiplex—Cashel Dancer (Bishop of Cashel) **R. Kent**
55 B f 5/5 Bushranger (IRE)—
    Dolphin Stamp (IRE) (Dolphin Street (FR)) (7742) **Exors of the Late Mrs S. E. Edwards**
56 **GO WHITE LIGHTNING (IRE)**, br f 11/2 Lord Shanakill (USA)—
    Ghurra (USA) (War Chant (USA)) (15000) **Miss E. Tanner**
57 B c 7/2 Paco Boy (IRE)—Helen Sharp (Pivotal) (26000) **T. H. Gallienne**
58 **MADAME ASCENSION**, ch f 17/5 Captain Gerrard (IRE)—
    Madame Jones (IRE) (Lycius (USA)) (3333) **D. J. Lockwood**
59 B f 27/2 Kodiac—Meaon (IRE) (Oratorio (IRE)) (16260) **Mrs E. Evans**
60 Ch f 5/5 Stimulation (IRE)—Minette (Bishop of Cashel) (6000) **T. Reffell**
61 B f 23/2 Approve (IRE)—Preach (IRE) (Danehill Dancer (IRE)) (6194) **Mrs E. P. Ambrose**
62 B f 20/4 Zebedee—River Style (IRE) (Desert Style (IRE)) (3097) **A. F. O'Callaghan**
63 **SMUGGLERS LANE (IRE)**, b c 7/2 Bushranger (IRE)—Finty (IRE) (Entrepreneur) **Mr T Earle & Mr P D Evans**
64 B f 20/2 Kodiac—Star Profile (IRE) (Sadler's Wells (USA)) (65000) **Mr N. I. O'Callaghan**
65 B f 25/3 Hellvelyn—Sweet Sorrow (IRE) (Lahib (USA)) (2857) **Mr J. A. Wilcox**
66 B c 13/1 Bushranger (IRE)—Tipperary Boutique (IRE) (Danehill Dancer (IRE)) (7619) **N. Shutts**
67 **VERCHILD LAD (IRE)**, gr c 17/3 Verglas (IRE)—
    Confidentiality (IRE) (Desert Style (IRE)) (5420) **Mr T Earle & Mr P D Evans**
68 B f 31/3 Multiplex—Vita Mia (Central Park (IRE))
69 B c 26/2 Captain Gerrard (IRE)—Waterline Twenty (IRE) (Indian Danehill (IRE)) (8517) **R. Kent**

Other Owners: Mr J. Babb, Mr P. A. P. Clays, Mr T. H. Earle, Mr G. G. Evans, Mr F. M. Lockwood, E. A. R. Morgans, Mr D. Percival, R. Simpson, Mr J. E. Smith, Mr P. B. Swinnerton, Mr K. F. Swinnerton.

Assistant Trainer: Mrs Emma Evans

Jockey (flat): Cathy Gannon, Adam Kirby. **Apprentice:** Eoin Walsh, Declan Bates, Hollie Doyle.

202 | MR HYWEL EVANS, Kidwelly
Postal: **Llwynpiod Farm, Llangyndeyrn, Kidwelly, Carmarthenshire, SA17 5HD**

1 **TOM BACH (IRE)**, 10, ch g Bach (IRE)—Fiovefontaine (IRE) **Mr H. G. Evans**

203 | MR JAMES EVANS, Worcester
Postal: **Stone Farm, Broadwas, Worcester, Worcestershire, WR6 5NE**
Contacts: **MOBILE (07813) 166430**
E-MAIL herbie_evans@hotmail.com WEBSITE www.hjamesevans.co.uk

1 **BOLDWOOD**, 5, b g September Storm (GER)—Christie **Enigma Racing**
2 **BUCKONTUPENCE (IRE)**, 6, b g Brian Boru—Miss Od (IRE) **The Prince Of Darkness Partnership**
3 **CALDERCRUIX (USA)**, 7, ch g Rahy (USA)—Al Theraab (USA) **Mr D. C. Mantle**
4 **FRIENDSHIP BAY**, 10, b g Midnight Legend—Friendly Fairy **Mrs J. Evans**
5 **GLIMPSE OF MAGIC**, 5, b m Passing Glance—Friendly Fairy **Mrs J. Evans**
6 **IT'S OSCAR (IRE)**, 7, b g Oscar (IRE)—Lady Bramble (IRE) **Miss S. Troughton**
7 **JAMMY (IRE)**, 5, b g Oscar (IRE)—Tabachines (FR) **Miss S. Troughton**
8 **LATERAL THINKING (IRE)**, 4, b g Excellent Art—Sumingasefa **Mr B. W. Preece**
9 **MIDNIGHT CHOICE**, 9, b g Midnight Legend—Pearl's Choice (IRE) **Mrs O. H. Stewart**
10 **NEIGHBOURHOOD (USA)**, 6, b br g Street Cry (IRE)—Miznah (IRE) **James Evans Racing & Alan Kaplan**
11 **PETRUS DE SORMAIN (FR)**, 11, b g Milford Track (IRE)—Bialystok (FR) **Mrs J. Evans**
12 **PHOENIX FLIGHT (IRE)**, 9, b g Hawk Wing (USA)—Firecrest (IRE) **Mrs J. Evans**
13 **RAGING BEAR (USA)**, 4, b g Leroidesanimaux (BRZ)—Gliding Light (USA) **Mr P. Wright-Bevans**
14 **ROC DE GUYE (FR)**, 9, b g Video Rock (FR)—Kasibelle de Guye (FR) **S. Crawley, T. Crawley**
15 **SHAKESPEARE DANCER**, 5, b m Norse Dancer (IRE)—Sharbasia **Mrs J. Evans**
16 **SOFTSONG (FR)**, 6, b g Singspiel (IRE)—Soft Gold (USA) **Mr Andrew Cohen & Mr Alan Kaplan**
17 **STONEYLEY MINSTREL**, 5, br g Thethingaboutitis—Typaz Lady **Mr Roger Brooke**
18 **TANNER HILL (IRE)**, 6, b g Milan—Carlingford Leader (IRE) **Paul Wright-Bevans & Steve Matner**
19 **TRACKMATE**, 8, b g Muhtarram (USA)—Cruz Santa **Preece Hamilton Porter Deni**

THREE-YEAR-OLDS
20 **MIDNIGHT BROWNIE**, b c Midnight Legend—Friendly Fairy **Mrs J. Evans**

Other Owners: A. L. Cohen, Mrs S. E. Crawley, Mr T. P. M. Crawley, Mr H. J. Evans, Mrs J. Evans, Mr M. S. Hamilton, Miss D. Harper Adams, Alan Kaplan, Mr R. S. Matner, Miss T. L. Porter, Mr B. Preece, Mr S. M. Smith, Mrs L. A. Smith, Mr Paul Wright-Bevans.

Assistant Trainer: Mrs Jane Evans

204 | MRS MARY EVANS, Haverfordwest
Postal: **Hengoed, Clarbeston Road, Haverfordwest, Pembrokeshire, SA63 4QL**
Contacts: **PHONE (01437) 731336**

1 **MAIZY MISSILE (IRE)**, 12, b m Executive Perk—Landsker Missile **Mary & Billy Evans**
2 **MOUNTAIN OF ANGELS**, 5, b m Midnight Legend—Landsker Missile **Unregistered Partnership**
3 **PRU**, 6, br m Weld—Floranz **W. J. Evans**

Other Owners: Mrs M. Evans.

Assistant Trainer: W J Evans

205 | MRS NIKKI EVANS, Abergavenny
Postal: **Penbiddle Farm, Penbidwal, Pandy, Abergavenny, Gwent, NP7 8EA**
Contacts: **(01873) 890957 FAX (01873) 890957 MOBILE (07977) 753437**
E-MAIL nikki@penbiddle.fsnet.co.uk WEBSITE www.nikki-evans-racing.co.uk

1 **ARABOUGG**, 4, b g Tobougg (IRE)—Arabellas Homer **Mr J. Berry**
2 **4**, Ch g Dreams End—Atlantic Lady (GER) **Mrs N. S. Evans**
3 **BOGEY HOLE (IRE)**, 5, gr m Aussie Rules (USA)—Sticky Green **Cheshire Charlies**
4 **BUAITEOIR (FR)**, 8, b g Mineshaft (USA)—Witching Hour (FR) **Mr M. Farr**

MRS NIKKI EVANS - Continued

5 **CYPRUSORMILAN**, 7, b g Milan—Persrolla **Hanford's Chemist Ltd**
6 **FICELLE (IRE)**, 5, b m Chineur (FR)—Petite Boulangere (IRE) **Mr J. Berry**
7 **FINAL FLYER (IRE)**, 10, br g Beneficial—Highways Daughter (IRE) **Running Dragon Racing 2**
8 **FOILED**, 4, b g Dutch Art—Isengard (USA) **P. T. Evans**
9 **HECTOR'S HOUSE**, 8, b g Tobougg (IRE)—Thrasher **Iwantaracehorse.Com**
10 **ILLEGALE (IRE)**, 8, b m Poliglote—Pinkai (IRE) **Hanford's Chemist Ltd**
11 **JUST LEWIS**, 7, ch g Sir Harry Lewis (USA)—McMahon's River
12 **MAYTHETENTH (IRE)**, 8, b m Dr Massini (IRE)—Maythefifth **Mrs M. E. Gittings-Watts**
13 **STEEL RAIN**, 6, b g Striking Ambition—Concentration **Mr J. Berry**
14 **SUMMER IN FEBRUARY**, 4, b f Sixties Icon—Endless Love (IRE) **Mrs M. E. Gittings-Watts**
15 **TUNNEL VISION (IRE)**, 7, b br g Craigsteel—Mill Top Lady (IRE) **Penbiddle Racing**

THREE-YEAR-OLDS

16 **PREMIER JACK'S**, b c Tobougg (IRE)—Arabellas Homer **Mr R. J. E. Evans**
17 **SAKURAMACHI**, b f Sixties Icon—Queen of Narnia **Hanford's Chemists Ltd/ John Berry**
18 **THRTYPOINTSTOTHREE (IRE)**, b g Kodiac—Miss Taken (IRE) **Hanford's Chemists Ltd/ John Berry**

Other Owners: Mrs D. J. Babbage, Mr M. Llewelyn, Mrs H. Llewelyn, Mr L. W. Merrick.

Assistant Trainer: Mr P. T. Evans

---

206 MR JAMES EWART, Langholm
Postal: **James Ewart Racing Limited, Craig Farm, Westerkirk, Langholm, Dumfriesshire, DG13 0NZ**
Contacts: **PHONE (01387) 370707 FAX (01387) 370733 MOBILE (07786) 995073**
E-MAIL office@jeracing.co.uk WEBSITE www.jamesewartracing.com

1 **AIKMAN (IRE)**, 10, b g Rudimentary (USA)—Omas Lady (IRE) **J. D. Gordon**
2 **ALANOS (IRE)**, 5, b g Choisir (AUS)—Pickwick Papers **M S Borders Racing Club 1**
3 **ARGENTIX (FR)**, 4, gr g Fragrant Mix (IRE)—Fleche Noir II (FR) **Miss A. Bramall**
4 **ARISTO DU PLESSIS (FR)**, 4, b g Voix du Nord (FR)—J'aime (FR) **Mrs J. E. Dodd**
5 **AVIDITY**, 5, b g Passing Glance—Epicurean **Leeds Plywood & Doors Ltd**
6 **CA LE FERRA (FR)**, 4, b g Turgeon (USA)—Branceilles (FR) **Southhayrigg Partnership, Friel, Wilson**
7 **CIVIL UNREST**, 8, ch g Blueprint—Yore (IRE) **The Ancrum Pointer 1**
8 **DREAMISI (IRE)**, 5, b g Kalanisi (IRE)—Marvellous Dream (FR) **The Dreamisi Team**
9 **GILNOCKIE**, 6, b g Kayf Tara—Eloquent Lawyer **Mr N M L Ewart & Rocket & Stan Racing**
10 **HARRY THE LEMMON (IRE)**, 8, br g Milan—
Na Habair Tada (IRE) **Kay Boyce Payne Henderson Panther4FatBellies**
11 **HERON'S MILL (IRE)**, 6, b g Heron Island (IRE)—Princess Vic (IRE) **Jump Racing Up North**
12 6, Ch g Waky Nao—Highland May (IRE)
13 **HUEHUECOYTLE**, 4, br g Turgeon (USA)—Azturk (IRE) **N. M. L. Ewart**
14 **LEADING SCORE (IRE)**, 4, b g Scorpion (IRE)—Leading Rank (IRE) **Ewart, Drew, Sperling**
15 **LORD WISHES (IRE)**, 7, b g Milan—Strong Wishes (IRE) **Leeds Plywood & Doors Ltd**
16 **LYBOWLER**, 4, b g Lyphento (USA)—Bowling On **W. H. Whitley**
17 **MANDARIN SUNSET (IRE)**, 7, ch g Presenting—Danatello (FR) **The Sunsets**
18 **PREMIER GRAND CRU (FR)**, 8, b g Kaldounevees (FR)—Last Harvest (FR) **Leeds Plywood & Doors Ltd**
19 **QUICUYO (GER)**, 11, ch g Acatenango (GER)—Quila (IRE) **D Coppola J Ewart**
20 **ROC DE PRINCE**, 5, b g Shirocco (GER)—Louella (USA) **Ewart, Humbert, Kesson**
21 **ROCKAWANGO (FR)**, 8, b g Okawango (USA)—Janou La Belle (FR) **Mr M. J. Tedham**
22 **SA SUFFIT (FR)**, 11, b g Dolpour—Branceilles (FR) **J. Ewart**
23 **SACRE TOI (FR)**, 8, b g Network (GER)—Magicielle (FR) **Miss A. Bramall**
24 **SCORPIONS STING (IRE)**, 5, b g Scorpion (IRE)—
Strong Wishes (IRE) **Dodd Carruthers Kesson Murrills Palmer Ewart**
25 **SLEEP IN FIRST (FR)**, 8, b br g Sleeping Car (FR)—First Union (FR) **The First Sleepers Union**
26 **SNUKER**, 7, b g Snurge—Briar Rose (IRE) **Mrs Percy, Mr Down & Mr Boyd**
27 **SON DU SILENCE (IRE)**, 5, b br g Elusive City (USA)—Fez **The Craig Farm Syndicate**
28 **TAX BENEFIT (IRE)**, 9, b g Beneficial—Sweedy (IRE) **Miss A. Bramall**
29 **TEO VIVO (FR)**, 7, gr g Great Pretender (IRE)—Ifranne (FR) **It's a Bargain Syndicate**
30 **THORLAK (FR)**, 7, b h Caballo Raptor (CAN)—Temara (FR) **J. D. Gordon**
31 **TOUCH OF STEEL (IRE)**, 5, b g Craigsteel—Tourmaline Girl (IRE) **Mrs Hugh Fraser**
32 **TRESOR DE L'ISLE (FR)**, 7, br g Dark Moondancer—Ad Vitam Eternam (FR) **Miss A. Bramall**
33 **UEUETEOTL (FR)**, 6, gr g Tikkanen (USA)—Azturk (IRE) **Going Grey**
34 **UN GUET APENS (FR)**, 6, b g Enrique—Belisama (FR) **Drew, Sperling, Graham, Carruthers**
35 **UNEX CANALETTO**, 5, b g Motivator—Logic **The Craig Farm Syndicate**
36 **VARENE DE VAUZELLE (FR)**, 5, b g Assessor (IRE)—Laureine (FR) **Mr Colin Gray & Mr Nhi Tran**

MR JAMES EWART - Continued

37 **VERNI (FR)**, 5, ch g Sabrehill (USA)—Nobless d'aron (FR) **N. M. L. Ewart**
38 **WILDE PASTURES (IRE)**, 9, gr g Oscar (IRE)—Kingsfield Clover **Border Pastures**
39 **ZARU (FR)**, 8, b br g Laveron—Zianini (FR) **Mrs Humbert, Drew**

THREE-YEAR-OLDS

40 **FLIXX**, b f Multiplex—Playful Lady **Mrs Hugh Fraser**

Other Owners: Mr J. D. Allen, Mr J. Boyce, Mr R. M. Boyd, Mr R. Carruthers, Mr A. C. Cartner, Mr G. Chamberlain, Mr D. J. Coppola, Mr M. T. Cowen, Mr D. Down, Mrs L. J. Drew, Mrs R. L. Elliot, Mrs V. A. Ewart, Mrs E. M. Fairbairn, Exors of the Late Mr G. B. Fairbairn, Mr N. J. Fortune, Mr M. Friel, Mr R. Galashan, Mr D. Graham, W. Graham, Mr C. Gray, Mrs M. J. Hales, Mrs D. A. Henderson, Miss R. K. Hill, Mrs A. G. Humbert, Mr J. A. Kay, Dr C. M. Kesson, Mr S. McKenzie, Mr S. A. Murrills, Mr P. M. Ogilvie, Dr R. A. Palmer, Panther Racing Limited, Mr D. Paterson, Mr J. Payne, Mrs J. D. Percy, Postracing Limited, Mr D. I. Rolinson, Mr R. E. Smith, Mr N. A. Sperling, Mrs J. Sperling, Mr D. R. Stanhope, Mr G. Taitt, Mr G. Taylor, Mr A. I. D. Todd, Mr N. Tran, Ms H. K. Walker, James Westoll, Mr K. A. Wilson, Mr S. Wood.

Assistant Trainer: Briony Ewart

Jockey (NH): Brian Hughes. **Conditional:** Dale Irving. **Amateur:** Mr R. Lindsay.

---

207 **MR RICHARD FAHEY, Malton**
Postal: **RF Racing Ltd, Mews House, Musley Bank, Malton, North Yorkshire, YO17 6TD**
Contacts: **PHONE (01653) 698915 FAX (01653) 699735 MOBILE (07713) 478079**
E-MAIL enquiries@richardfahey.com WEBSITE www.richardfahey.com

1 **ALBEN STAR (IRE)**, 6, b g Clodovil (IRE)—Secret Circle **Mr J. K. Shannon & Mr M. A. Scaife**
2 **ALLNECESSARYFORCE (FR)**, 4, gr g Verglas (IRE)—Kosmic View (USA) **Mr P. F. O'Callaghan**
3 **ARCTIC FEELING (IRE)**, 6, ch g Camacho—Polar Lady **Percy / Green Racing 2**
4 **BALLESTEROS**, 5, ch g Tomba—Flamenco Dancer **Dr M. B. Q. S. Koukash**
5 **BAYAN KASIRGA (IRE)**, 4, b f Aussie Rules (USA)—Gwyllion (USA) **Mr S. Humphreys**
6 **CHISWICK BEY (IRE)**, 6, b g Elusive City (USA)—Victoria Lodge **Leeds Contracts Limited**
7 **CLONALIG HOUSE (IRE)**, 4, b g Rakti—Balakera (FR) **G. Devlin**
8 **COSMIC HALO**, 5, ch m Halling (USA)—Cosmic Case **The Cosmic Cases**
9 **DAKOTA CANYON (IRE)**, 5, b g Rock of Gibraltar (IRE)—Dakota Sioux (USA) **Mrs U. Towell**
10 **DIAMOND BLUE**, 6, ch m Namid—Petra Nova **Mrs J. E. Newett**
11 **DOLPHIN VILLAGE (IRE)**, 4, b g Cape Cross (IRE)—Reform Act (USA) **Mr Y. M. Nasib**
12 **DUSKY QUEEN (IRE)**, 4, b f Shamardal (USA)—Sanna Bay (IRE) **Mrs H. Steel**
13 **EL VIENTO (FR)**, 6, ch g Compton Place—Blue Sirocco **John Nicholls Ltd/David Kilburn**
14 **EXTRATERRESTRIAL**, 10, b g Mind Games—Expectation (IRE) **G. J. Paver**
15 **FARLOW (IRE)**, 6, ch g Exceed And Excel (AUS)—Emly Express (IRE) **Red Sky Partnership 1**
16 **FLIGHTY CLARETS (IRE)**, 4, ch f Bahamian Bounty—Flying Clarets (IRE) **The Matthewman One Partnership**
17 **FLYMAN**, 4, b g Pastoral Pursuits—Satin Bell **G. Murray**
18 **GARSWOOD**, 4, b c Dutch Art—Penchant **Mr D W Armstrong & Cheveley Park Stud**
19 **GATEPOST (IRE)**, 5, br g Footstepsinthesand—Mandama (IRE) **Dr M. B. Q. S. Koukash**
20 **GLEN'S DIAMOND**, 6, b g Intikhab (USA)—Posta Vecchia (USA) **S & G Clayton**
21 **HEAVEN'S GUEST (IRE)**, 4, b g Dark Angel (IRE)—Bakewell Tart (IRE) **Mr J. K. Shannon & Mr M. A. Scaife**
22 **HI THERE (IRE)**, 5, b g Dark Angel (IRE)—Ornellaia (USA) **Market Avenue Racing Club Ltd**
23 **INGLEBY SPIRIT**, 7, b g Avonbridge—Encore du Cristal (USA) **Percy/Green Racing**
24 **INGLEBY SYMPHONY (IRE)**, 4, b f Oratorio (IRE)—Alizaya (IRE) **Percy Green Racing 4 & Partner**
25 **IT'S MY TIME**, 5, b m Green Desert (USA)—Soviet Terms **Mrs D. M. Swinburn**
26 **JUSTONEFORTHEROAD**, 8, b g Domedriver (IRE)—Lavinia's Grace (USA) **Middleham Park Racing LXV**
27 **KHELMAN (IRE)**, 4, b g Kheleyf (USA)—Mandolin (IRE) **S & G Clayton**
28 **KIAMA BAY (IRE)**, 8, b g Fraam—La Panthere (USA) **Dr M. B. Q. S. Koukash**
29 **KYLLACHY STAR**, 8, b g Kyllachy—Jaljuli **Dr M. B. Q. S. Koukash**
30 **LAS VERGLAS STAR (IRE)**, 6, gr g Verglas (IRE)—Magnificent Bell (USA) **CBWS Partnership**
31 **LAUDATE DOMINUM (IRE)**, 4, b f Oratorio (IRE)—
                                    Feeling Wonderful (IRE) **Inner Circle Thoroughbreds - Ab Ovo**
32 **LAYLA'S OASIS**, 4, b f Oasis Dream—Kirk **Dr M. B. Q. S. Koukash**
33 **LEXINGTON BAY (IRE)**, 6, b g High Chaparral (USA)—
                                    Schust Madame (IRE) **Mr Keith Denham & Mr Tony Denham**
34 **LORD AERYN (IRE)**, 7, b g Antonius Pius (USA)—White Paper (IRE) **Mrs H. Steel**
35 **MAJESTIC MOON (IRE)**, 4, b g Majestic Missile (IRE)—Gala Style (IRE) **Mr J. Gaffney**
36 **MAJESTIC MYLES (IRE)**, 6, b g Majestic Missile (IRE)—Gala Style (IRE) **Mr J. Gaffney**
37 **MANCHESTAR**, 4, b g Elusive City (USA)—Grande Terre (IRE) **Mr & Mrs G. Calder**
38 **MARBLE STATUETTE (USA)**, 4, gr ro f Mizzen Mast (USA)—Offbeat Fashion (IRE) **Mrs K. Devlin**

MR RICHARD FAHEY - Continued

39 **MICA MIKA (IRE)**, 6, ch g Needwood Blade—Happy Talk (IRE) **Mrs U. Towell**
40 **MYSTERY BET (IRE)**, 4, b f Kheleyf (USA)—Dancing Prize (IRE) **Mrs H. Steel**
41 **PERSONAL TOUCH**, 5, ch g Pivotal—Validate **Nicholas Wrigley & Kevin Hart**
42 **POLSKI MAX**, 4, b g Kyllachy—Quadrophenia **Market Avenue Racing & Tremousser**
43 **RENE MATHIS (GER)**, 4, ch g Monsieur Bond (IRE)—Remina (GER) **Dr M. B. Q. S. Koukash**
44 **ROMANTIC SETTINGS**, 4, ch f Mount Nelson—Lacework **Mr Mel Roberts & Ms Nicola Meese 1**
45 **SIMPLY SHINING (IRE)**, 4, ch f Rock of Gibraltar (IRE)—Bright Smile (IRE) **Mrs H. Steel**
46 **SIR REGINALD**, 6, b g Compton Place—Clincher Club **Mr J. C. McGrath**
47 **SPIRIT OF THE LAW (IRE)**, 5, b g Lawman (FR)—Passion Bleue **The Matthewman One Partnership**
48 **TALES OF GRIMM (USA)**, 5, b h Distorted Humor (USA)—Stupendous Miss (USA) **Sir R. Ogden C.B.E., LLD**
49 **TATLISU (IRE)**, 4, b g Red Clubs (IRE)—Zwadi (IRE) **Middleham Park Racing LIV**
50 **TIME AND PLACE**, 4, ch g Compton Place—Forthefirsttime **Mr Mel Roberts & Ms Nicola Meese 1**

THREE-YEAR-OLDS

51 **ANGEL FLORES (IRE)**, b f Art Connoisseur (IRE)—Emmas Princess (IRE) **R. A. Fahey**
52 **BAHAMIAN C**, b g Bahamian Bounty—Amandian (IRE) **S & G Clayton**
53 **BALLYHURST (IRE)**, b g High Chaparral (IRE)—Billet (IRE) **Mrs H. Steel**
54 **BRETHERTON**, ch c Exceed And Excel (AUS)—Cliche **D. W. Armstrong**
55 **CANYARI (IRE)**, b c Dandy Man (IRE)—Morna's Fan (FR) **M A Leatham & G H Leatham**
56 **COCOA'S PRINCESS**, b f Kyllachy—Princess Cocoa (IRE) **Mr & Mrs P. Ashton**
57 **CRISIS AVERTED (IRE)**, ch c Compton Place—Luxuria (IRE)
58 **DISCO DALE**, gr g Verglas (IRE)—Artisia (IRE) **Richard Fahey**
59 **EASTERN IMPACT (IRE)**, b g Bahamian Bounty—Kate The Great **D. W. Barker**
60 **EMERAHLDZ (IRE)**, b f Excellent Art—Sancia (IRE) **Mrs H. Steel**
61 **FAIR FLUTTER (IRE)**, b g Manduro (GER)—Polish Affair **Mr & Mrs J. D. Cotton**
62 **FLYCATCHER (IRE)**, ro f Medicean—Night Haven **Mrs P. B. E. P. Farr**
63 **FOXY CLARETS (IRE)**, ch g Camacho—Muscari **Hazel Tattersall & Mr G. Hyde**
64 **HESKETH BANK**, b g Aqlaam—Wendylina (IRE) **D. W. Armstrong**
65 **HIGHLAND REBEL (IRE)**, b g Dandy Man (IRE)—Dancing Tempo **Mrs H. Steel**
66 **IMSHIVALLA (IRE)**, b f Acclamation—Subtle Affair (IRE) **Pow Partnership**
67 **IXELLES DIAMOND (IRE)**, br f Diamond Green (FR)—Silk Point (IRE) **Miss L. Tillett**
68 **JAN VAN HOOF (IRE)**, b g Dutch Art—Cosenza **Mr G. H. Leatham & Mr M. A. Leatham**
69 **KALAHARI KINGDOM (IRE)**, b g Footstepsinthesand—Visite Royale (USA) **Mrs H. Steel**
70 **KHALICE**, b f Bahamian Bounty—Siena Gold **The G-Guck Group**
71 **LATENIGHTREQUEST**, b f Major Cadeaux—Love Quest **Middleham Park Racing XVI & Partner**
72 **LAYLA'S RED DEVIL (IRE)**, b f Dalakhani (IRE)—Brazilian Samba (IRE) **Dr M. B. Q. S. Koukash**
73 **LORD CLYDE**, ch g Sakhee's Secret—Sabina **City Vaults Racing**
74 **MAIDEN APPROACH**, b f New Approach (IRE)—Ivowen (USA) **Middleham Park Racing LXVII**
75 **MALRAAJ**, b g Iffraaj—Lafontaine Bleu **The Cosmic Cases**
76 **MCCARTHY MOR (IRE)**, b g Bushranger (IRE)—Alexander Anapolis (IRE) **M. A. Scaife**
77 **MENDELITA**, ch f Archipenko (USA)—Dame de Noche **The G-Guck Group**
78 **MFIFTYTHREEDOTCOM (IRE)**, ch g Tamayuz—Pearl Trader (IRE) **M53 Motors Ltd T/A M53 Ford**
79 **MIAPLACIDUS (IRE)**, b f Shamardal (USA)—Nandy's Cavern **Mrs H. Steel**
80 **MISS LUCY JANE**, ch f Aqlaam—Ocean View (USA) **Mr R. J. Bown**
81 **MY BOY BOB**, b g Myboycharlie (IRE)—Empress Jain **P. D. Smith Holdings Ltd**
82 **NEIGHBOTHER**, b g Invincible Spirit (IRE)—Aravonian **Mrs H. Steel**
83 **NEW STREET (IRE)**, gr c Acclamation—New Deal **D. W. Armstrong**
84 **OAK BLUFFS (IRE)**, b g Royal Applause—Key Stage (IRE) **Mrs U. Towell**
85 **OUR GABRIAL (IRE)**, b g Rock of Gibraltar (IRE)—Jojeema **Dr M. B. Q. S. Koukash**
86 **PARBOLD (IRE)**, b c Dandy Man (IRE)—Gala Style (IRE) **Mr D W Armstrong & Cheveley Park Stud**
87 **PICCADILLY JIM (IRE)**, gr g Royal Applause—Silver Dip **Frank Lenny Financial Services Limited**
88 **PRINCESS PHEENY (IRE)**, b f Tagula (IRE)—Carmona **Middleham Park Racing XXI & Partner**
89 **QUEEN OF ARTS**, ch f Dutch Art—Grande Terre (IRE) **Mr & Mrs G. Calder**
90 **QUEST OF COLOUR (IRE)**, b f Iffraaj—With Colour **Havelock Racing 2**
91 **REGIMENT**, ch c Major Cadeaux—My First Romance **Mr T. G. & Mrs M. E. Holdcroft**
92 **ROACHDALE HOUSE (IRE)**, b c Mastercraftsman (IRE)—Golden Legacy (IRE) **G. Devlin**
93 **ROYAL CONNOISSEUR (IRE)**, b g Art Connoisseur (IRE)—Valferno **Skeltools Ltd**
94 **RUFFORD (IRE)**, b c Invincible Spirit (IRE)—Speedy Sonata (USA) **Mr D W Armstrong & Cheveley Park Stud**
95 **SAAKHEN (IRE)**, b c Invincible Spirit (IRE)—Upperville (IRE) **Middleham Park Racing LXXI & Partner**
96 **SANDIVA (IRE)**, ch f Footstepsinthesand—Miss Corinne **H.E. Sheikh J. B. H. B. K. Al Thani**
97 **SHOT IN THE SUN (IRE)**, b f Kodiac—Summer Sunshine **Middleham Park Racing XXX & C Tasker**
98 **SKYE'S THE LIMIT**, ch g Pastoral Pursuits—Sound of Sleat **The Fairweather Foursome**
99 **SPICEUPYOURLIFE (IRE)**, b f Sakhee's Secret—Tiger Spice **Diamond Racing Ltd**
100 **SUPPLICANT**, b c Kyllachy—Pious **Cheveley Park Stud Limited**

MR RICHARD FAHEY - Continued

101 **THE GRUMPY GNOME (IRE)**, b g Dandy Man (IRE)—Certain Charm (USA) **The Black Sheep Partnership**
102 **TIGER TWENTY TWO**, b g Authorized (IRE)—Collette's Choice **P. D. Smith Holdings Ltd**
103 **TWO SHADES OF GREY (IRE)**, gr g Oratorio (IRE)—Elitista (FR) **Mr J. K. Shannon & Mr M. A. Scaife**
104 **UPHOLLAND**, b c Dutch Art—Never Away **D. W. Armstrong**
105 **VENTURA REEF (IRE)**, b c Excellent Art—Run To Jane (IRE) **Middleham Park Racing LXI & Partner**
106 **WEALTH (IRE)**, b c Invincible Spirit (IRE)—Whisp (GER) **Mrs A. G. Kavanagh**
107 **WESTERN SANDS (IRE)**, ch f Footstepsinthesand—West One **Manor House Farm Bloodstock**
108 **WITHERNSEA (IRE)**, b g Dark Angel (IRE)—Charlene Lacy (IRE) **City Vaults Racing 1**
109 **WOODLAND GIRL**, ch f Kyllachy—Locharia **P. Timmins**

TWO-YEAR-OLDS

Trainer did not supply details of his two-year-olds.

Other Owners: A. Rhodes Haulage Ltd, Mr David W. Armstrong, Mr P. Ashton, Mrs P. Ashton, Mr S. G. Barnes, Mr Mike J. Beadle, Mr Andy Bonarius, Mr D. Bowen, Mr Stuart Brown, Mr I. T. Buchanan, Mr Neil Burns, Mr G. Calder, Mrs J. Calder, Mr J. P. Carr, Mr M. Channon, Cheveley Park Stud, Mr A. Clark, Mr Steven Clayton, Mrs G. A. Clayton, Mr James Clayton, Mr John Clydesdale, Mr N. Collins, Mr A. E. Corbett, Mr S. C. Corbett, Mr J. D. Cotton, Mrs B. Cotton, Mr K. A. Dean, Mr Keith Denham, Mr Sam Ellis, Mr R. A. Fahey, Mr I. Farley, Mr K. J. Farrer, Mr Mark Fowler, Mr Brian W. Goodall, Mr Jeff Goodall, Mr J. D. Gordon, Mr David A. Green, Mr P. L. Harrison, Mr Kevin Hart, Mr George G. Hillen, Mr Christopher A. Hood, Mr G. R. Hunnam, Mr G. Hyde, Inner Circle Thoroughbreds Limited, Mr R. H. Jennings, Mr D. R. John, John Nicholls (Trading) Ltd, Mr R. F. Johnson, Mr D. Kilburn, Mrs Christine Lally, Mr G. H. Leatham, Mr Mark A. Leatham, Mrs J Malcolmson, Market Avenue Racing Club Ltd, Mr Bill Martin (Fife), Mr Jim McGrath, Mr D. J. P. McWilliams, Mr T. M. McKain, Ms Nicola Meese, Mrs Margaret Nelson, Mr John R. Owen, Mr T. S. Palin, Mr G. J. Paver, Mr Mel Roberts, Mr Michael Ryan (Bradford), Mr M. A. Scaife, Mr Dave Scott, Mr J. K. Shannon, Mr D. W. E. Sowden, Mr A. Tattersall, Mrs Hazel Tattersall, Mr Steven Taylor, Mr D. M. Tempest, Mr Peter Timmins, Mr P. M. Watson, Mr G. Weaver, Mr John Wicks, Mr N. H. T. Wrigley.

Assistant Trainer: Robin O'Ryan

Jockey (flat): Tony Hamilton, Paul Hanagan, Barry McHugh, Lee Topliss. **Jockey (NH):** Brian Hughes.
Apprentice: George Chaloner, Samantha Bell, Josh Quinn. **Amateur:** Miss Alyson Deniel.

---

208 | **MR CHRIS FAIRHURST, Middleham**
Postal: **Glasgow House, Middleham, Leyburn, North Yorkshire, DL8 4QG**
Contacts: **PHONE/FAX (01969) 622039 MOBILE (07889) 410840**
E-MAIL cfairhurst@tiscali.co.uk WEBSITE www.chrisfairhurstracing.com

1 **DISTRICT ATTORNEY (IRE)**, 5, b g Lawman (FR)—Mood Indigo (IRE) **The PQD Partnership**
2 **JENNY TWIGG**, 4, b f Paris House—Yorke's Folly (USA) **Mrs A. M. Leggett**
3 **MAGICAL MISCHIEF**, 4, b f Rob Roy (USA)—Magical Flute **Mrs C. Arnold**
4 **MOOTABAR (IRE)**, 7, gr g Verglas (IRE)—Melanzane **Mrs A. M. Leggett**
5 **SHIRLS SON SAM**, 6, b g Rambling Bear—Shirl **Mrs C. Arnold**
6 **SPRUZZO**, 8, b g Emperor Fountain—Ryewater Dream **980 Racing**
7 **THACKERAY**, 7, b g Fasliyev (USA)—Chinon (FR) **Mrs C. Arnold**
8 **WHO'S SHIRL**, 8, b m Shinko Forest (IRE)—Shirl **Mrs S. France**

TWO-YEAR-OLDS

9 **DANZELLA**, b f 17/3 Desideratum—Danzatrice (Tamure (IRE)) **980 Racing**
10 **ELLERINA**, b f 5/3 Stimulation (IRE)—Dream Quest (Rainbow Quest (USA)) (7000) **Mr A. Davies**

Other Owners: Mr T. Bryson, Mr J. M. Tozer, Mr M. D. Tozer.

---

209 | **MR JAMES FANSHAWE, Newmarket**
Postal: **Pegasus Stables, Snailwell Road, Newmarket, Suffolk, CB8 7DJ**
Contacts: **PHONE (01638) 664525 / 660153 FAX (01638) 664523**
E-MAIL james@jamesfanshawe.com WEBSITE www.jamesfanshawe.com

1 **AOMEN ROCK**, 4, b g Rock of Gibraltar (IRE)—Siren Sound **Dragon Gate**
2 **ARAGOSTA**, 4, ch f Pivotal—Langoustine (AUS) **Lord Vestey**
3 **BOMBARDIER**, 4, ch g Manduro (GER)—Lady Stardust **Mrs Martin Armstrong**

MR JAMES FANSHAWE - Continued

4 COSSETED, 4, b f Pivotal—Fondled Cheveley Park Stud
5 DON'T STARE, 4, b g Zamindar (USA)—Joshua's Princess Mr Guy A.A.C. Gredley
6 EMULATING (IRE), 4, ch g Duke of Marmalade (IRE)—Ascendancy Mr Ben C. M. Wong
7 GONE DUTCH, 4, ch g Dutch Art—Ice Palace The Ice Syndicate
8 GREEN MONKEY, 4, b g Green Desert (USA)—Firenze Mr & Mrs P Hopper, Mr & Mrs M Morris
9 HALLELUJAH, 6, b m Avonbridge—My Golly CLS (Chippenham) Limited
10 HIGH JINX (IRE), 6, b h High Chaparral (IRE)—Leonara (GER) Mr & Mrs W. J. Williams
11 KNIGHT OWL, 4, b g Rock of Gibraltar (IRE)—Miss Ivanhoe (IRE) Miss Annabelle Condon
12 KOALA BEAR, 4, b f Oasis Dream—Birthday Suit (IRE) Lady Halifax
13 MAC'S SUPERSTAR (FR), 4, b g Elusive City (USA)—Diamond Light (USA) Mr Michael McDonnell
14 MAGIC HURRICANE (IRE), 4, b g Hurricane Run (IRE)—Close Regards (IRE) Dragon Gate
15 NOVIRAK (IRE), 6, gr g Noverre (USA)—Manchaca (FR) Mr Norman Brunskill
16 OKAVANGO, 4, ch f Nayef (USA)—Ivory Gala (FR) Mr T. R. G. Vestey
17 RIBBONS, 4, ch f Manduro (GER)—Sister Act Elite Racing Club
18 ROBERTSON, 4, b g Duke of Marmalade (IRE)—Mythologie (FR) Mr & Mrs W. J. Williams
19 SEAL OF APPROVAL, 5, b m Authorized (IRE)—Hannda Mr T. R. G. Vestey
20 SHWAIMAN (IRE), 4, br c Authorized (IRE)—Blue Lightning Mr Mohamed Obaida
21 WALL STREET BOSS (USA), 4, b g Street Boss (USA)—Pad The Wallet (USA) Axom XXXIV
22 WEDDING SPEECH (IRE), 4, b f Acclamation—Wedding Cake (IRE) Mr G & Mrs L J Marney

THREE-YEAR-OLDS

23 AUF WIEDERSEHEN, b g Byron—Buena Notte (IRE) Mr Malcolm C. Denmark
24 BAYNUNAH (USA), br f Medaglia d'oro (USA)—Damaniyat Girl (USA) Mr Mohamed Obaida
25 CAPTAIN GEORGE (IRE), b g Bushranger (IRE)—High Society Girl (IRE) Mr P Tarrant & Mr A L R Morton
26 CELESTIAL KNIGHT, b g Compton Place—Garter Star Carivalis, Eady, Papworth & Swinburn
27 DUBIAN TO (IRE), ch f Sea The Stars (IRE)—Mrs Lindsay (USA) Mr Mohamed Obaida
28 ELIZONA, b f Pastoral Pursuits—Morning After Mrs Alice Cherry
29 ENCOUNTERING (IRE), b g Duke of Marmalade (IRE)—Naval Affair (IRE) Mr Ben C. M. Wong
30 ENSURING, br c New Approach (IRE)—Dynacam (USA) Mr Ben C. M. Wong
31 B g Peintre Celebre (USA)—Flying Finish (FR) Dragon Gate
32 FRESH KINGDOM (IRE), ch g Dubawi (IRE)—Polyquest (IRE) Mr Cheng Wai Too
33 GALE FORCE, b f Shirocco (GER)—Hannda (IRE) Mr T. R. G. Vestey
34 HE'S MY BOY (IRE), gr g Dark Angel (IRE)—Rose of Battle Mr P. S. Ryan
35 HORS DE COMBAT, ch c Mount Nelson—Maid For Winning (USA) Mr Chris van Hoorn
36 INCREDIBLE FRESH (IRE), b g Bushranger (IRE)—Red Fox (IRE) Mr Cheng Wai Too
37 INVASOR LUCK (USA), b c Invasor (ARG)—Lonely Ahead (USA) Mr Mohamed Obaida
38 INVINCIBLE FRESH (IRE), b g Footstepsinthesand—Princess Serena (USA) Mr Cheng Wai Too
39 IT'S A YES FROM ME, b g Bahamian Bounty—Valjarv (IRE) The Foncey Syndicate
40 MALORY TOWERS, b f Giant's Causeway (USA)—Dalisay (IRE) Mr Philip Newton
41 PANATELLA, b f Medicean—Panna Lord Halifax
42 SAAB ALMANAL, b c Dubawi (IRE)—Caribbean Pearl (USA) Mr Mohamed Obaida
43 SEALED WITH A KISS, b f Authorized (IRE)—Always On My Mind Mascalls Stud
44 SHE'S GORGEOUS (IRE), b f Acclamation—Acquiesced (IRE) Johnstone Partnership
45 SHINING GLITTER (IRE), b f Shamardal (USA)—Lune Rose Dragon Gate
46 SPIRIT RAISER (IRE), b f Invincible Spirit (IRE)—Macadamia (IRE) Lord Vestey
47 B f Jeremy (USA)—Startarette (USA) Clipper Logistics
48 SWORDBEARER, ch g Selkirk (USA)—Isis (USA) Dr Catherine Wills
49 TAHCHEE, ch g Sleeping Indian—Neyraan Mr Chris van Hoorn
50 WROOD (USA), b br f Invasor (ARG)—Ras Shaikh (USA) Mohamed Obaida
51 ZMAN AWAL (IRE), ch f Dubawi (IRE)—Pivotal Lady Mohamed Obaida

TWO-YEAR-OLDS

52 ACQUITTAL, b f 15/3 Lawman (FR)—Zamid (FR) (Namid) (46457) Cheveley Park Stud
53 B c 22/3 Danehill Dancer (IRE)—Althea Rose (IRE) (Green Desert (USA)) (90000) The Dabsters
54 ANGEL DELIGHT (IRE), b f 24/3 Dark Angel (IRE)—
Roof Fiddle (USA) (Cat Thief (USA)) (21680) Andrew & Julia Turner
55 AUMERLE, b c 11/5 Authorized (IRE)—Succinct (Hector Protector (USA)) Dr Catherine Wills
56 CELESTIAL FRESH, b f 14/2 Medicean—Celeste (Green Desert (USA)) Cheveley Park Stud
57 COLLIDER, ch g 28/2 Cockney Rebel (IRE)—Moidart (Electric) Dr Catherine Wills
58 B f 10/2 Shamardal (USA)—Dash To The Front (Diktat) Helena Springfield Ltd
59 ELGIN, b c 12/3 Duke of Marmalade (IRE)—China Tea (USA) (High Chaparral (IRE)) Elite Racing Club
60 ESTEEMABLE, ch f 18/2 Nayef (USA)—Ring of Esteem (Mark of Esteem (IRE)) Mrs C. R. Philipson
61 Br f 28/2 Halling (USA)—First Fantasy (Be My Chief (USA)) Nigel & Caroline Elwes
62 FULL OF SPEED (USA), ch c 3/2 Raven's Pass (USA)—
Knock Twice (USA) (Two Punch (USA)) (52000) Tom Mohan & Michael McDonnell

MR JAMES FANSHAWE - Continued

63 B c 22/4 Dutch Art—Lady Hen (Efisio) **Andrew Coombs & RASL**
64 **LANDWADE LAD,** b c 21/2 Dansili—Sell Out (Act One) (72000) **Mr Simon Gibson**
65 B c 22/2 Clodovil (IRE)—Majestic Night (IRE) (Mujadil (USA)) (16000) **Mr Mohamed Obaida**
66 B f 19/3 Zamindar (USA)—Match Point (Unfuwain (USA)) (8500) **Helena Springfield Ltd**
67 **MATRON,** ch f 5/2 Bahamian Bounty—Prescription (Pivotal) **Cheveley Park Stud**
68 B f 8/2 Makfi—Meetyouthere (IRE) (Sadler's Wells (USA)) (52000) **Mr Salem bel Obaida**
69 **MIRO (IRE),** b c 7/2 Rock of Gibraltar (IRE)—Mission Secrete (IRE) (Galileo (IRE)) (65000) **Mrs Alison Swinburn**
70 B f 20/2 Makfi—Miss Delila (USA) (Malibu Moon (USA)) (38000) **Mr Saeed bel Obaida**
71 **MR PICKWICK,** b c 22/2 Mount Nelson—Never Lose (Diktat) (18000) **Johnstone Partnership**
72 **OSIPOVA,** b f 11/2 Makfi—Barynya (Pivotal) **Cheveley Park Stud**
73 **PECKING ORDER (IRE),** b f 21/4 Fastnet Rock (AUS)—Shemaya (Dixie) (Darshaan) **Merry Fox Stud Limited**
74 **PRESTO BOY,** b c 26/1 Compton Place—
                                          Presto Levanter (Rock of Gibraltar (IRE)) (38000) **Fred Archer Racing - Silvio**
75 **REGAL FLAME,** b f 17/4 Pivotal—Regal Rose (Danehill (USA)) **Cheveley Park Stud**
76 B c 19/2 Sea The Stars (IRE)—Sayyedati Storm (USA) (Storm Cat (USA)) **Mr Mohamed Obaida**
77 Ch c 22/4 Makfi—Sinduda (Anabaa (USA)) (40000) **Mr Mohamed Obaida**
78 B c 25/3 Mastercraftsman (IRE)—Splash Mountain (IRE) (Peintre Celebre (USA)) (200000) **Mr Ben C. M. Wong**
79 Ch f 21/2 Makfi—Spotlight (Dr Fong (USA)) (20000) **Mr Mohamed Obaida**
80 B c 11/3 Makfi—Starstone (Diktat) (40000) **Mr Saeed bel Obaida**
81 B c 17/3 Teofilo (IRE)—Storming Sioux (Storming Home) **Mr Mohamed Obaida**
82 **THAI NOON (IRE),** b f 21/1 Dansili—Alsace Lorraine (IRE) (Giant's Causeway (USA)) **Merry Fox Stud Limited**
83 **THE TIN MAN,** b c 19/2 Equiano (FR)—Persario (Bishop of Cashel) (80000) **Fred Archer Racing - Ormonde**
84 B f 6/2 Makfi—Whispering Blues (IRE) (Sadler's Wells (USA)) (22000) **Mr Mohamed Obaida**

Assistant Trainer: Alison Harper

---

210 **MR JOHNNY FARRELLY, Bridgwater**
Postal: **Smocombe Racing Stables, Enmore, Bridgwater, Somerset, TA5 2EB**
Contacts: **PHONE (01278) 671782**

1 **AMANTIUS,** 5, b g Multiplex—Ghana (GER) **H. M. W. Clifford**
2 **BATHWICK BRAVE (IRE),** 7, b g Westerner—Dorans Grove **H. M. W. Clifford**
3 **BATTLE GROUP,** 9, b g Beat Hollow—Cantanta **Jolly Boys Outing**
4 **BEDOUIN BAY,** 7, b g Dubai Destination (USA)—Sahara Sonnet (USA) **Hanham Boys Racing Partnership**
5 **DIMITAR (USA),** 5, b g Mizzen Mast (USA)—Peace And Love (IRE) **P. M. Tosh**
6 **KAZLIAN (FR),** 6, b g Sinndar (IRE)—Quiet Splendor (USA) **Twelve Pipers Piping**
7 **LANSDOWNE PRINCESS,** 12, b m Cloudings (IRE)—Premier Princess **The Lansdowners**
8 **LEAVE IT BE (IRE),** 7, gr g High-Rise (IRE)—Farh Quest (IRE) **Hanham Boys Racing Partnership**
9 **OSCAR JANE (IRE),** 7, b m Oscar (IRE)—Turrill House **P. M. Tosh**
10 **PERFECT TIMING,** 6, b g Shantou (USA)—Winnetka Gal (IRE) **Hanham Boys Racing Partnership**
11 **SPORTING BOY (IRE),** 6, b g Barathea (IRE)—Sportsticketing (IRE) **H. M. W. Clifford**
12 **TARABELA,** 11, b m Kayf Tara—Rocky Revival **G2 Recruitment Solutions Ltd**

Other Owners: J. F. Baldwin, Mr S. J. Dew, Mr M. J. Fitzpatrick, Mr J. Gwyther, Mr J. G. Mogg, R. T. Wilkins.

---

211 **MISS JULIA FEILDEN, Newmarket**
Postal: **Harraton Stud, Laceys Lane, Exning, Newmarket, Suffolk, CB8 7HW**
Contacts: **PHONE (01638) 577470 FAX (01638) 578628 MOBILE (07974) 817694**
E-MAIL hoofbeatstours@aol.com WEBSITE www.juliafeildenracing.com

1 **AMELIA GEORGE,** 4, b f Avonbridge—Tamara **John Ford**
2 **ATTAIN,** 5, b g Dansili—Achieve **Miss J. D. Feilden**
3 **AUTOMOTIVE,** 6, b g Beat Hollow—Bina Ridge **Stowstowquickquickstow Partnership**
4 **AVIDLY,** b f Beat Hollow—Balmy **Mr & Mrs George Bhatti**
5 **BETHAN,** 5, b m Nayef (USA)—Elizabethan Age (FR) **Ms H. C. Ranner**
6 **CANDESTA (USA),** 4, b c First Defence (USA)—Wandesta **Mr & Mrs George Bhatti**
7 **HAMBLE,** 5, b g Librettist (USA)—Time For Tea (IRE) **Hoofbeats Racing Club**
8 **HANDHELD,** 7, ch g Observatory (USA)—Kid Gloves **Hoofbeats Racing Club**
9 **HONEYMOON EXPRESS (IRE),** 4, br f Mujadil (USA)—Royal Jelly **Hoofbeats Racing Club**
10 **LUHAIF,** 4, b c Cape Cross (IRE)—Hot And Spicy **R. J. Creese, R. Birkett, Miss J. Feilden**
11 **MEDDLING,** 4, ch f Halling (USA)—Piffling **Good Company Partnership 2**

MISS JULIA FEILDEN - Continued

12 **NO SUCH NUMBER,** 6, b g King's Best (USA)—Return (USA) **Good Company Partnership**
13 **OMEGA OMEGA,** 5, b m Halling (USA)—In Luck **Mr John W. Ford**
14 **SHEILA'S HEART,** 4, ch g Dubai Destination (USA)—Sefemm **Peter Foster**
15 **SILVER ALLIANCE,** 6, gr g Proclamation (IRE)—Aimee Vibert **In It To Win Partnership**
16 **THE DUCKING STOOL,** 7, ch m Where Or When (IRE)—Dance Sequel **Hoofbeats Racing Club**
17 **TIGER'S HOME,** 4, b f Tiger Hill (IRE)—Homeward **Miss J. D. Feilden**
18 **VASTLY (USA),** 5, gr ro g Mizzen Mast (USA)—Valentine Band **The Sultans of Speed**
19 **VEERAYA,** 4, b g Rail Link—Follow Flanders **Mr A. R. Farook**

THREE-YEAR-OLDS

20 **BUSHY GLADE (IRE),** b f Bushranger (IRE)—Cladantom (IRE) **R. J. Creese**
21 **OPUS TOO (IRE),** b g Lawman (FR)—Jerez (IRE) **Mr A. Dee & G. Smith-Bernal**
22 **PREVIOUS ACCLAIM (IRE),** b f Acclamation—Erstwhile (FR) **Miss J. Feilden**
23 **TOLLY MCGUINESS,** ch c Araafa (IRE)—Golden Flyer (FR) **Miss J. D. Feilden**

TWO-YEAR-OLDS

24 **CAPTAIN NAVARRE,** b c 9/4 Excellent Art—
                          Quantum (IRE) (Alhaarth (IRE)) (11000) **Mr Graham & Mrs Vivianne Johnson**
25 **CELESTINE ABBEY,** b f 15/4 Authorized (IRE)—Billie Jean (Bertolini (USA)) **Mr A. Dee & G. Smith-Bernal**
26 **DUKE OF DIAMONDS,** gr c 6/3 Duke of Marmalade (IRE)—
                          Diamond Line (FR) (Linamix (FR)) (12000) **Carol Bushnell & Partners**
27 **ITALIA,** ch f 16/4 Zebedee—Italian Affair (Fumo di Londra (IRE)) (3200) **R. J. Creese**
28 **MERCY ME,** b f 11/2 Mawatheeq (USA)—Fantastic Santanyi (Fantastic Light (USA)) **G Smith-Bernal**

Other Owners: Mr George Bhatti, Mrs Caroline Bhatti, Mr R. Birkett, Miss S. E. Elsdon, Miss J. Feilden, Mr John W. Ford, Mr Graham Johnson, Mrs Vivianne Johnson, Mr Chris Page, Exors of the Late Mr P. J. Trivass, Mr R. Wright.

Assistant Trainer: John Birkett

Jockey (flat): Adam Beschizza. **Apprentice:** Shelley Birkett. **Amateur:** Mr R. Birkett.

---

212 **MR CHARLIE FELLOWES,** Newmarket
Postal: Saffron House Stables, Hamilton Road, Newmarket, Suffolk, CB8 0NY
Contacts: **MOBILE (07968) 499596**
E-MAIL charlie@charliefellowesracing.co.uk WEBSITE www.charliefellowesracing.co.uk

1 **ACCESSION (IRE),** 5, b g Acclamation—Pivotal's Princess (IRE) **Lady de Ramsey**
2 **BUCKLAND (IRE),** 6, b g Oratorio (IRE)—Dollar Bird (IRE) **Mr P. S. McNally**
3 **ORDERS FROM ROME (IRE),** 5, b g Holy Roman Emperor (IRE)—
                          Fatat Alarab (USA) **Saffron House Stables Partnership**
4 **PEARL ICE,** 6, b g Iffraaj—Jezebel **Lady de Ramsey**

THREE-YEAR-OLDS

5 **BARBARY (IRE),** b g Rock of Gibraltar (IRE)—Silver Cache (USA) **Mr G. Mills**
6 **BUCKLAND BEAU,** b g Rock of Gibraltar (IRE)—Heavenly Whisper (IRE) **Mr P. S. McNally**
7 **GUESSHOWMUCHILOVEU (IRE),** b c Cape Cross (IRE)—Overruled (IRE) **Harriet Loder**
8 **THIS IS THE DAY,** b f Footstepsinthesand—Miss Pinkerton **A. E. Oppenheimer**

TWO-YEAR-OLDS

9 B c 23/2 Henrythenavigator (USA)—
                          Aljawza (USA) (Riverman (USA)) (30971) **Saffron House Stables Partnership**
10 **BOARDING PARTY (USA),** ch c 22/3 More Than Ready (USA)—
                          Oceans Apart (Desert Prince (IRE)) **Elite Racing Club**
11 **BOMBAY MIX,** gr f 25/2 Sleeping Indian—Mix It Up (Linamix (FR)) **Lady de Ramsey**
12 Ch c 7/5 Makfi—Dolydille (IRE) (Dolphin Street (FR)) (45000) **Mohamed Obaida**
13 Ch c 15/4 Makfi—Midnight Shift (IRE) (Night Shift (USA)) (6000) **Mohamed Obaida**
14 B c 10/5 Makfi—Misty Waters (IRE) (Caerleon (USA)) (22000) **Salem bel Obaida**
15 B c 23/4 Makfi—Night Club (Mozart (IRE)) (10000) **Salem bel Obaida**

MR CHARLIE FELLOWES - Continued

16 Ch f 24/3 Lope de Vega (IRE)—Polly Floyer (Halling (USA)) **Barton Stud**
17 Ch f 14/4 Mount Nelson—Tropical Barth (IRE) (Peintre Celebre (USA)) (5000) **Salem bel Obaida**
18 Ch f 19/4 Makfi—You Too (Monsun (GER)) (10000) **Saeed bel Obaida**

---

213 **MR PHILIP FENTON, Carrick-On-Suir**
Postal: **Glenbower Stables Ltd., Garryduff, South Lodge, Carrick-On-Suir, Co. Tipperary, Ireland**
Contacts: **PHONE (00 353) 51 647901 FAX (00 353) 51 647901 MOBILE (00 353) 87 2581048**
E-MAIL glenbowerstables@gmail.com WEBSITE www.glenbowerstables.com

1 **AINTREE MY DREAM (FR)**, 4, b br g Saint des Saints (FR)—Pretty Melodie (FR) **Philip Fenton**
2 **AKITO (FR)**, 4, b g Network (GER)—Quimea (FR) **James Moran**
3 **ANGE D'OR JAVILEX (FR)**, 4, b g Puit d'or (IRE)—Ixia de Menil (FR) **Thomas Coleman**
4 4, B g Saint des Saints (FR)—Aulne River (FR) **Pan European Partnership**
5 **BADGERFORT (IRE)**, 5, b g Fruits of Love (USA)—Ding Dong Belle **J. P. McManus**
6 **BAND OF BLOOD (IRE)**, 6, b g King's Theatre (IRE)—Cherry Falls (IRE) **Gigginstown House Stud**
7 **BENTELIMAR (IRE)**, 5, ch g Beneficial—Montel Girl (IRE) **J. Ryan**
8 **CAIM HILL (IRE)**, 11, b g Deploy—Glen's Gale (IRE) **M. Dempsey**
9 **CASINO MARKETS (IRE)**, 6, br g Fruits of Love (USA)—Vals Dream (IRE) **Pan European Partnership**
10 **DESERT ROE (IRE)**, 5, b g Vinnie Roe (IRE)—Kingspice (IRE) **D. Gray**
11 **DESERTMORE STREAM (IRE)**, 6, b g Celtic Swing—Another Cross (FR) **Gigginstown House Stud**
12 **DR ZOOM (IRE)**, 5, b g Milan—Dante Gale (IRE) **Kaizen Syndicate**
13 **DRON ON LOCKY (IRE)**, 7, b g Milan—Husyans Beauty (IRE) **Keep on Dreaming Syndicate**
14 **DUNGUIB (IRE)**, 11, b g Presenting—Edermine Berry (IRE) **Mrs E. Lawlor**
15 **LADY GERONIMO (IRE)**, 5, b br m Hawk Wing (USA)—Birthday (IRE) **M. Daly Jnr**
16 **LAST INSTALMENT (IRE)**, 9, ch g Anshan—Final Instalment (IRE) **Gigginstown House Stud**
17 **ON MY OWN (IRE)**, 10, b g Shernazar—Bloomfield (IRE) **John Sayers**
18 **PATSIO (IRE)**, 6, b g Moscow Society (USA)—Supreme Favour (IRE) **Colm Herron & Philip Fenton**
19 **REAL STEEL (IRE)**, 6, br b g Old Vic—Grangeclare Dancer (IRE) **Gigginstown House Stud**
20 **ROBBER BARON (IRE)**, 7, b g Goldmark (USA)—Geraldine's Girl (IRE) **E. Lyons**
21 **ROBIN DU FAU (FR)**, 5, b g Robin des Champs (FR)—Isaba (FR) **Gigginstown House Stud**
22 **ROBYN'S ROSE (IRE)**, 5, ch m Golan (IRE)—Rose of Inchiquin (IRE) **J. McDonald**
23 **ROE YOUR OWN BOAT (IRE)**, 5, ch g Vinnie Roe (IRE)—Wire Lady (IRE) **John Sayers**
24 **SAGE MONKEY (IRE)**, 5, br g Craigsteel—Braw Lass **Cregg Resources Ltd**
25 **TEN SIXTY (IRE)**, 4, br g Presenting—Senora Snoopy (IRE) **Pan European Partnership**
26 **THE TULLOW TANK (IRE)**, 6, b g Oscar (IRE)—Bobbing Back (IRE) **Barry Connell**
27 **VALUE AT RISK**, 5, b g Kayf Tara—Miss Orchestra (IRE) **Marc Huglin**
28 **VOLUPTUEUX (FR)**, 6, b g Enrique—Orphee de Vonnas (FR) **Voluptueux Syndicate**
29 **VOLVALIEN (FR)**, 5, b g Network (GER)—Josvalie (FR) **Barry Connell**
30 **WHISPER ROCK (IRE)**, 6, br m Presenting—Loch Na Mona (IRE) **John Power**

Jockey (NH): Brian O'Connell. **Amateur:** Mr R. J. Kiely.

---

214 **MR JOHN FERGUSON, Cowlinge**
Postal: **Bloomfields, Cowlinge, Newmarket, Suffolk, CB8 9HN**
Contacts: **PHONE (01638) 500423 FAX (01638) 500387**

1 **AALIM**, 4, b g Nayef (USA)—Anna Palariva (IRE) **Bloomfields**
2 **AQALIM**, 4, b g Raven's Pass (USA)—Aviacion (BRZ) **Bloomfields**
3 **BORDONI (USA)**, 5, b g Bernardini (USA)—Argentina (IRE) **Bloomfields**
4 **BROUGHTON (GER)**, 4, b g Teofilo (IRE)—Boccassini (GER) **Bloomfields**
5 **BUSHEL (USA)**, 4, b g Street Cry (IRE)—Melhor Ainda (USA) **Bloomfields**
6 **BUTHELEZI (IRE)**, 6, b br g Dynaformer (USA)—Ntombi (USA) **Bloomfields**
7 **CAYMAN ISLANDS**, 6, b g Shirocco (GER)—Barbuda **Bloomfields**
8 **CERTIFICATION (IRE)**, 4, b g Authorized (IRE)—Most Charming (FR) **Bloomfields**
9 **CHAT ROOM**, 6, ch g Dubawi (IRE)—Contradictive (USA) **Bloomfields**
10 **COLONEL IAIN**, 8, gr g Alflora (IRE)—Cheeky Mare **Bloomfields**
11 **COMMISSIONED (IRE)**, 4, b g Authorized (IRE)—Zelda (IRE) **Bloomfields**
12 **COTTON MILL**, 7, b g Tiger Hill (IRE)—Mill Line **Bloomfields**
13 **DREAMY GEORGE (IRE)**, 8, b g Goldmark (USA)—Killenard (IRE) **Bloomfields**

MR JOHN FERGUSON - Continued

14 **DUBAI PRINCE (IRE)**, 6, b g Shamardal (USA)—Desert Frolic (IRE) **Bloomfields**
15 **EARTH DREAM (IRE)**, 11, b g Old Vic—Barbaras Mews (IRE) **Mr J. P. Ferguson**
16 **EL NAMOOSE (IRE)**, 5, b g Authorized (IRE)—Hashimiya (USA) **Bloomfields**
17 **FATHER EDWARD (IRE)**, 5, b g Flemensfirth (USA)—Native Side (IRE) **Bloomfields**
18 **FENNELL BAY (IRE)**, 5, b g Dubawi (IRE)—Woodrising **Bloomfields**
19 **HAWKER**, 4, ch g Street Cry (IRE)—Dunnes River (USA) **Bloomfields**
20 **HONOUR SYSTEM (IRE)**, 7, ch g King's Best (USA)—Rawabi **Bloomfields**
21 **ITTIRAD (USA)**, 6, b g Dubai Destination (USA)—Noushkey **Bloomfields**
22 **JOE FARRELL (IRE)**, 5, b g Presenting—Luck of The Deise (IRE) **Bloomfields**
23 **MAGISTRAL**, 4, b g Manduro (GER)—Tamalain (USA) **Bloomfields**
24 **MAHICAN (IRE)**, 4, b g Cape Cross (IRE)—Dark Indian (IRE) **Bloomfields**
25 **MEMORABILIA**, 6, b g Dansili—Sentimental Value (USA) **Bloomfields**
26 **MIJHAAR**, 6, b g Shirocco (GER)—Jathaabeh **Bloomfields**
27 **MUHTARIS (IRE)**, 4, b g Teofilo (IRE)—Fann (USA) **Bloomfields**
28 **NEW YEAR'S EVE**, 6, b g Motivator—Midnight Angel (GER) **Bloomfields**
29 **PRINCE SIEGFRIED (FR)**, 8, b g Royal Applause—Intrum Morshaan (IRE) **Bloomfields**
30 **PURPLE BAY (IRE)**, 5, b g Dubawi (IRE)—Velvet Lady **Bloomfields**
31 **RAINBOW PEAK (IRE)**, 8, b g Hernando (FR)—Celtic Fling **Bloomfields**
32 **RETRIEVE (AUS)**, 7, b g Rahy (USA)—Hold To Ransom (USA) **Bloomfields**
33 **RONNIE LAWSON (IRE)**, 5, b g King's Theatre (IRE)—Sarahs Quay (IRE) **Bloomfields**
34 **ROYAL SKIES (IRE)**, 4, b g Dubawi (IRE)—Kalana (FR) **Bloomfields**
35 **RUACANA**, 5, b g Cape Cross (IRE)—Farrfesheena (USA) **Bloomfields**
36 **SEA LORD (IRE)**, 7, b g Cape Cross (IRE)—First Fleet (USA) **Bloomfields**
37 **SHREWD**, 4, b g Street Sense (USA)—Cala (FR) **Bloomfields**
38 **SHUBAAT**, 7, ch g Monsun (GER)—Zaynaat **Bloomfields**
39 **SPRING OF FAME (USA)**, 8, b g Grand Slam (USA)—Bloomy (USA) **Bloomfields**
40 **THEMILANHORSE (IRE)**, 8, b g Milan—Sports Leader (IRE) **Bloomfields**
41 **THREE KINGDOMS (IRE)**, 5, ch g Street Cry (IRE)—Chan Tong (BRZ) **Bloomfields**
42 **TOMMY O'DWYER (IRE)**, 5, b g Milan—Always Present (IRE) **Bloomfields**
43 **WHISPERING GALLERY**, 8, b g Daylami (USA)—Echoes In Eternity (IRE) **Bloomfields**
44 **ZUIDER ZEE (GER)**, 7, b g Sakhee (USA)—Zephyrine (IRE) **Bloomfields**

Other Owners: Mrs F. E. Ferguson.

215

MR DOMINIC FFRENCH DAVIS, Lambourn
Postal: **College House, 3 Oxford Street, Lambourn, Hungerford, Berkshire, RG17 8XP**
Contacts: YARD **(01488) 73675** FAX **(01488) 72342** FAX **(01488) 73675** MOBILE **(07831) 118764**
E-MAIL ffrenchdavis@btinternet.com WEBSITE www.ffrenchdavis.com

1 **ADMIRABLE DUQUE (IRE)**, 8, b g Selkirk (USA)—Stunning (USA) **Mrs J. E. Taylor**
2 **BALADY (IRE)**, 5, b m Zamindar (USA)—Faydah (USA) **Marchwood Aggregates**
3 **BRANDYWELL BOY (IRE)**, 11, b g Danetime (IRE)—Alexander Eliott (IRE) **D. J. S. ffrench Davis**
4 **CANDYMAN CAN (IRE)**, 4, b g Holy Roman Emperor (IRE)—Palwina (FR) **Miss Alison Jones**
5 **CHILL IN THE WOOD**, 5, br m Desert King (IRE)—Zaffaranni (IRE) **Mr D. G. Cramm**
6 **GAELIC WIZARD (IRE)**, 6, b g Fasliyev (USA)—Fife (IRE) **D. J. S. ffrench Davis**
7 6, B g Westerner—Gold Air
8 **IF I WERE A BOY (IRE)**, 7, b m Invincible Spirit (IRE)—Attymon Lill (IRE) **Mr R. F. Haynes**
9 **JUSTCALLMEHANDSOME**, 12, ch g Handsome Ridge—Pearl Dawn (IRE) **Mrs J. E. Taylor**
10 5, Br g Arcadio (GER)—Phar From Men (IRE) **D. J. S. ffrench Davis**
11 **PLAY THE BLUES (IRE)**, 7, gr m Refuse To Bend (IRE)—Paldouna (IRE) **The Cool Blue Partnership**
12 **WINDPFEIL (IRE)**, 8, bl g Indian Ridge—Flying Kiss (IRE) **Miss J. A. Ewell**

THREE-YEAR-OLDS

13 B f Moss Vale (IRE)—Attymon Lill (IRE) **Mr R. F. Haynes**
14 **ROLLING DICE**, b c Rail Link—Breathing Space (USA) **Miss Alison Jones**

TWO-YEAR-OLDS

15 B f 13/3 Rail Link—Sailing Days (Kris) (1800) **Mrs E. Morris**

Other Owners: Mr M. A. Allen, Mrs C. J. Lowman. **Assistant Trainer:** Avery Ffrench Davis

Jockey (flat): James Doyle. **Jockey (NH):** Mark Grant.

216 **MR GIUSEPPE FIERRO, Hednesford**
Postal: **Bentley Brook House, Rawnsley Road, Hednesford, Cannock, Staffordshire, WS12 1RB**
Contacts: **HOME/YARD (01543) 879611 MOBILE (07976) 321468**

1 FRANKIE FALCO, 8, br h Bollin Eric—Marsh Marigold **G. Fierro**
2 JUST LIKE BETH, 6, b m Proclamation (IRE)—Just Beth **G. Fierro**
3 LITTLE DOTTY, 5, br m Erhaab (USA)—Marsh Marigold **G. Fierro**
4 PEHERA BOY, 7, b g Fleetwood (IRE)—Abbiejo (IRE) **G. Fierro**
5 RED HOTT ROBBIE, 5, b g Revoque (IRE)—Abbiejo (IRE) **G. Fierro**
6 SUNDANCE BOY, 5, gr g Proclamation (IRE)—Just Beth **G. Fierro**

Assistant Trainer: M Fierro

217 **MRS MARJORIE FIFE, Stillington**
Postal: **White Thorn Farm, Stillington, Easingwold, York, YO61 1LT**
Contacts: **PHONE (01347) 822012 MOBILE (07890) 075217**
E-MAIL wfife10416@aol.com

1 AMTIRED, 8, gr g Beauchamp King—Rising Talisker **Mr G. Smith**
2 BELLE INTRIGUE, 4, ch f Sakhee's Secret—Belle Bellino (FR) **Mr & Mrs D. C. Coates**
3 CAMEROONEY, 11, b g Sugarfoot—Enkindle **Mrs J. Stapleton**
4 CROOKED ARROW (IRE), 6, b g Galileo (IRE)—Mythologie (FR) **Market Avenue Racing Club Ltd**
5 JUST THE TONIC, 7, ch m Medicean—Goodwood Blizzard **R. W. Fife**
6 MANDALAY NAB (IRE), 9, b g King's Best (USA)—Mahamuni (IRE) **R. W. Fife**
7 PERFECT WORDS (IRE), 4, ch g Thousand Words—Zilayah (USA) **Green Lane**
8 ROYAL HOLIDAY (IRE), 7, ch g Captain Rio—Sunny Slope **Mrs M. Turner**
9 SIMMPLY SAM, 7, b m Nomadic Way (USA)—Priceless Sam
10 TIMBER KING, 5, b g Desideratum—Chanteuse **P. Allison**
11 YORKSTERS PRINCE (IRE), 7, b g Beat Hollow—Odalisque (IRE) **Mrs M. Turner**

THREE-YEAR-OLDS

12 SARTORI, b c Elnadim (USA)—Little Caroline (IRE) **Chris Tremewan, Mike Saini, Tom Fife**
13 SHERRY FOR NANNY (IRE), b f Amadeus Wolf—Sugars for Nanny (USA) **Mr & Mrs D. C. Coates**
14 THORNABY PRINCESS, b f Camacho—Ingleby Princess **Mr D. Scott**

Other Owners: Mrs A. Coates, Mr D. C. Coates, Mr T. W. Fife, Mr C. R. Piercy, Mr M. Saini, C. Tremewan.

218 **MR TIM FITZGERALD, Malton**
Postal: **Norton Grange, Norton, Malton, North Yorkshire, YO17 9EA**
Contacts: **OFFICE (01653) 692718 FAX (01653) 600214 MOBILE (07950) 356437**
E-MAIL fitzgeraldracing@hotmail.com

1 ACRAI RUA (IRE), 11, ch g Rock Hopper—Dontbelieveaword (IRE) **Grange Park Racing**
2 COMERAGH KING, 10, b g Kayf Tara—Velcro Girl (IRE) **Grange Park Racing**
3 KASTELA STARI, 7, b m Beat Hollow—Campaspe **Mr Paul Coulter & Mr T J Fitzgerald**
4 MR SYNTAX (IRE), 10, b g King's Theatre (IRE)—Smile Awhile (USA) **Regalmist Associates Ltd**
5 ROCK ON BOLLINSKI, 4, b g Bollin Eric—Bred For Pleasure **Mr E. J. Worrell**
6 SEDANO (FR), 8, b br g Dark Moondancer—Kadalville (FR) **N. P. Ender**

Other Owners: Mr P. Coulter, A. D. Crombie, T. J. Fitzgerald, Mr E. Surr.

219 **MR JEREMIAH FITZPATRICK, Cork**
Postal: **Deruna, Curragh, Kanturk, Co Cork, Ireland**
Contacts: **PHONE (00 353) 29 50125 MOBILE (00 353) 86 3101931**

1 SANFORIZED (IRE), 8, b m Catcher In The Rye (IRE)—Native Magic **Mrs W. M. Fitzpatrick**

220 MR PAUL FITZSIMONS, Upper Lambourn
Postal: **Saxon Gate Stables, Malt Shovel Lane, Lambourn, Berkshire, RG17 8QH**
Contacts: **PHONE (01488) 72712 FAX (01488) 72716 MOBILE (07795) 566359**
E-MAIL paulfitzsimons@saxon-gate.com WEBSITE www.saxon-gate.com

1 **BEAUCHAMP BELLA,** 4, b f Manduro (GER)—Baharah (USA) **E. Penser**
2 **BEAUCHAMP SUNSET,** 4, b g Tiger Hill (IRE)—Orange Sunset (IRE) **E. Penser**
3 **COMPTON BIRD,** 5, b m Motivator—Noble Peregrine **E. Penser**
4 **COMPTON SILVER,** 4, ch g Haafhd—Anna Oleanda (IRE) **E. Penser**
5 **TREE OF LIFE,** 4, ch f Medicean—Antebellum (FR) **Miss H. Moller**

THREE-YEAR-OLDS

6 **BEAUCHAMP KITE,** b g Compton Admiral—Orange Sunset (IRE) **E. Penser**
7 **BEAUCHAMP MELBA,** b f Compton Admiral—Ashford Castle (USA) **E. Penser**
8 **CLAPPERBOARD,** b f Royal Applause—Roseum **Mr C. W. Wan**
9 **COMPTON REX,** br g Mount Nelson—Jane Austen (IRE) **E. Penser**
10 **FRAMED MASTERPIECE,** ch g Dutch Art—Photographie (USA) **Saxon Gate Bloodstock (Helene Moller)**
11 **LUPARA,** ch f Double Trigger (IRE)—Pooka's Daughter (IRE) **Saxon Gate Bloodstock (Helene Moller)**

TWO-YEAR-OLDS

12 **BEAUCHAMP ACE,** b c 15/4 Compton Admiral—Aquarelle (Kenmare (FR)) **E. Penser**
13 **BEAUCHAMP DIAMOND,** b f 6/4 Compton Admiral—Orange Sunset (IRE) (Roanoke (USA)) **E. Penser**
14 **BEAUCHAMP EAGLE,** ch c 27/4 Compton Admiral—Ashford Castle (USA) (Bates Motel (USA)) **E. Penser**
15 **BEAUCHAMP FIRE,** b c 11/3 Compton Admiral—Bestemor (Selkirk (USA)) **E. Penser**
16 **BEAUCHAMP RUBY,** b f 7/5 Cockney Rebel (IRE)—Beauchamp Utopia (Compton Admiral) **E. Penser**

Other Owners: P. Fitzsimons.

Assistant Trainer: Chris Martin

221 MR JOHN FLINT, Bridgend
Postal: **Cherry Tree, 71 Woodlands Park, Kenfig Hill, Bridgend, Mid-Glamorgan, CF33 6EB**
Contacts: **PHONE (01656) 744347 FAX (01656) 744347 MOBILE (07581) 428173**
E-MAIL john@johnflintracing.com WEBSITE www.johnflintracing.com

1 **GRAMS AND OUNCES,** 7, b g Royal Applause—Ashdown Princess (IRE) **Mr R. C. Williams**
2 **KAYF MOSS,** 6, b g Kayf Tara—Madam Mosso **Mr L. H. & Mrs T. Evans**
3 **LASTCHANCEFORLISA (IRE),** 8, b m Old Vic—Montelisa (IRE) **J. L. Flint**
4 **LEAHNOR (IRE),** 5, gr m Flemensfirth (USA)—Silver Pursuit **Mr P. Conway**
5 **ROWLESTONE LAD,** 7, b g Sulamani (IRE)—Charmante Femme **Mr R. C. Williams**
6 **SHAKEN NOT STIRRED,** 4, b f Monsieur Bond (IRE)—Kanisfluh **E. R. Griffiths**
7 **SILVA MINX,** 5, gr m Fair Mix (IRE)—Senna da Silva **J. L. Flint**

THREE-YEAR-OLDS

8 Gr f Dr Massini (IRE)—Senna da Silva

Other Owners: Mr L. H. Evans, Mrs T. Evans.

Assistant Trainer: Mrs Martine Louise Flint (07968) 044487

Jockey (NH): Rhys Flint.

222 MR DAVID FLOOD, Chiseldon
Postal: **15 High Street, Chiseldon, Swindon, Wiltshire, SN4 0NG**
Contacts: **PHONE (07919) 340619**
E-MAIL davidflood1@hotmail.co.uk

1 **TAPPANAPPA (IRE),** 7, b g High Chaparral (IRE)—Itsibitsi (IRE) **Mr N. Ahmad**
2 **TRADER JACK,** 5, b g Trade Fair—Azeema (IRE) **Mr N. Ahmad**

THREE-YEAR-OLDS

3 Br f Pastoral Pursuits—Cape Wood

223 MR TONY FORBES, Uttoxeter
Postal: **Hill House Farm, Poppits Lane, Stramshall, Uttoxeter, Staffordshire, ST14 5EX**
Contacts: **PHONE (01889) 569568 MOBILE (07967) 246571**
E-MAIL tony@thimble.net

1 **EXCELLENT NEWS (IRE)**, 5, ch m Excellent Art—Subito **Mr A. L. Forbes**
2 **HOLLINS**, 10, b g Lost Soldier (USA)—Cutting Reef (IRE) **Mr A. L. Forbes**
3 **NOLECCE**, 7, ch g Reset (AUS)—Ghassanah **Mr A. L. Forbes**

Assistant Trainer: Mr Tim Eley

224 MRS PAM FORD, Hereford
Postal: **Stone House Stables, Preston Wynne, Hereford, Herefordshire, HR1 3PB**
Contacts: **HOME/FAX (01432) 820604 MOBILE (07733) 152051**
E-MAIL pam_ford@hotmail.co.uk

1 **ANNIE CONFIDENTIAL (IRE)**, 11, b m Turtle Island (IRE)—Black Ivor (USA) **Ms S. Yeomans**
2 9, B gr m M'bebe—Candy Copper
3 7, B m Erhaab (USA)—Candy Copper
4 **CAPTAIN OATS (IRE)**, 11, b g Bahhare (USA)—Adarika **R. S. Herbert**
5 6, B g Tikkanen (USA)—Dara's Course (IRE)
6 6, B h Grape Tree Road—Zajira (IRE) **K. R. Ford**

Assistant Trainer: Mr K Ford

Jockey (flat): Hayley Turner, Royston Ffrench. **Jockey (NH):** J. Davies.

225 MR RICHARD FORD, Garstang
Postal: **The Paddocks, Strickens Lane, Barnacre, Garstang, Lancashire, PR3 1UD**
Contacts: **PHONE (01995) 605790 (07802) 764094 MOBILE (07976) 522768**
E-MAIL clarksonhorses@barnacre.fsbusiness.co.uk
WEBSITE www.lancashireracingstables.co.uk

1 **DEBT TO SOCIETY (IRE)**, 7, ch g Moscow Society (USA)—Nobody's Darling (IRE) **Mr & Mrs G. E. Pickering**
2 **DOESLESSTHANME (IRE)**, 10, ch g Definite Article—Damemill (IRE) **Mr R. J. Hewitt**
3 **ELLIES IMAGE**, 7, b m Lucky Story (USA)—Crown City (USA) **Mr J. H. Chrimes**
4 **GET READY TO GO (IRE)**, 10, b g Turtle Island (IRE)—Buckalong (IRE) **The Hexham Handicappers**
5 4, B g Byron—Hasty Lady **Sports 360**
6 **INSOLENCEOFOFFICE (IRE)**, 6, b g Kodiac—Sharp Diversion (USA) **CCCNLP**
7 **KYLE OF BUTE**, 8, ch g Kyllachy—Blinding Mission (IRE) **Mr J.H.Chrimes & Mr & Mrs G.W.Hannam**
8 **MAKELLYS BLACKPOOL**, 5, b m Sir Harry Lewis (USA)—Pondimari (FR) **Miss R. M. Kelly**
9 **MARK OF MEYDAN**, 9, ch g Mark of Esteem (IRE)—Rose Bounty **The Bounty Hunters**
10 **MEGLIO ANCORA**, 7, ch g Best of The Bests (IRE)—May Fox **Sports 360**
11 **MIDNIGHT RETURN (IRE)**, 8, b m Midnight Legend—By Return (IRE) **Harpers Brook Racing**
12 **NANI JANI**, 5, ch m Halling (USA)—Betty's Pride **Betty's Brigade**
13 4, B f Proclamation (IRE)—No Comebacks **Lancashire Racing Stables Limited**
14 **NOBLE JACK (IRE)**, 8, b g Elusive City (USA)—Begine (IRE) **Mrs S. E. Barclay**
15 **RECKLESS ROMEO (IRE)**, 5, b g Heliostatic (IRE)—Ballerina Babe (IRE) **Winks Racing**
16 4, B g Tiger Hill (IRE)—Rose Bounty **Mrs S. E. Barclay**
17 **SEAMSTER**, 7, ch g Pivotal—Needles And Pins (IRE) **Mr P. Bamford**
18 **SILVER STEEL (FR)**, 11, b g Robin des Pres (FR)—Oliver's Queen (FR) **Mrs Julie Gordon & Mr Keith Hesketh**
19 **SWALEDALE LAD (IRE)**, 7, b g Arakan (USA)—Tadjnama (USA) **Mr W. D. Challoner**

THREE-YEAR-OLDS

20 **CAPTAIN T**, b g Captain Gerrard (IRE)—Royaltea **Exors Of The Late Mr S. Hamilton**
21 B g Proclamation (IRE)—Monica Geller **The Most Wanted Partnership**
22 **THE BROCKSTER**, ch g Proclamation (IRE)—Synergie (IRE) **Mr B. Hartley**

TWO-YEAR-OLDS

23 B g 10/4 Bertolini (USA)—Betty's Pride (Lion Cavern (USA)) **Mrs S. E. Barclay**
24 B g 12/5 Bertolini (USA)—Monica Geller (Komaite (USA)) **Mrs S. E. Barclay**
25 **TOWN ORATOR**, gr g 3/3 Proclamation (IRE)—Town House (Paris House) **Mr J. H. Chrimes**

MR RICHARD FORD - Continued

Other Owners: Mrs Leslie Buckley, Mr John Calderbank, Mr Andrew Calderbank, Mr W. R. Chudley, Mr Paul Clarkson, Mr Keith Hesketh, Mr Martin James, Mr Paul Kelly, Paul & Gemma Mann, Mr Richard Mattinson, Miss N. C. Taylor, Mr Thomas R. Vaughan, Mr Matt Watkinson.

Assistant Trainer: Stella Barclay

Jockey (flat): Graham Lee. **Jockey (NH):** Lucy Alexander, Richie McGrath. **Conditional:** Harry Challoner. **Apprentice:** Josh Baudains. **Amateur:** Mr Thomas Greenwood.

---

226 MRS RICHENDA FORD, Dorchester
Postal: **Cross Farm, Brockhampton, Buckland Newton, Dorchester, Dorset, DT2 7DJ**

1 **ABAYAAN**, 8, gr g Sadler's Wells (USA)—Showdown **K. B. Snook**
2 **BALL HOPPER (IRE)**, 10, ch g Rock Hopper—Lady Vic (IRE) **K. B. Snook**
3 **SOMERBY (IRE)**, 11, b g Sadler's Wells (USA)—Oriental Mystique **K. B. Snook**
4 **THE CAT'S AWAY (IRE)**, 6, ch g Alderbrook—Mrs Jack Russell (IRE) **K. B. Snook**

---

227 MR BRIAN FORSEY, Taunton
Postal: **Three Oaks, Ash Priors, Taunton, Somerset, TA4 3NQ**
Contacts: **PHONE (01823) 433914 MOBILE (07747) 392760**
E-MAIL forsey2001@yahoo.com

1 **AUREATE**, 10, ch g Jade Robbery (USA)—Anne d'autriche (IRE) **B. Forsey**
2 **BARISTA (IRE)**, 6, b g Titus Livius (FR)—Cappuccino (IRE) **Mr K. C. Jago**
3 **FOLLOW THE MASTER**, 8, b g Afflora (IRE)—Daisy May **Mrs P. M. Bosley**
4 **SIR LEXINGTON (IRE)**, 5, b g Desert Style (IRE)—Shulammite Woman (IRE) **Mr D. R. Arthur**
5 **VIVA VETTORI**, 10, ch g Vettori (IRE)—Cruinn A Bhord **B. Forsey**

Assistant Trainer: Susan Forsey

---

228 MISS SANDY FORSTER, Kelso
Postal: **Halterburn Head, Yetholm, Kelso, Roxburghshire, TD5 8PP**
Contacts: **PHONE/FAX (01573) 420615 FAX (01573) 420615**
MOBILE (07880) 727877 or (07976) 587315
E-MAIL clivestorey@btinternet.com

1 **BARNEVELDER (IRE)**, 9, ch g Old Vic—Cluain-Ard (IRE) **Mr J. M. Crichton & Miss H. M. Crichton**
2 **CHERRY'S BAY**, 8, b m Helissio (FR)—Buck Comtess (USA) **Mr N Wrigley**
3 **DARKAN ROAD**, 9, b br g Beat All (USA)—Sister Seven (IRE) **Miss S. E. Forster**
4 **HIGH FAIR**, 8, b m Grape Tree Road—Miss Tango **Mr D. Simpson**
5 **SEE THE LEGEND**, 9, b m Midnight Legend—Amys Delight **The Border Racers**
6 5, B br g Overbury (IRE)—Sister Seven (IRE)
7 **SOUL ANGEL**, 10, ch g Tipsy Creek (USA)—Over Keen **Soul Searchers**

Other Owners: Mr J. M. Crichton, Miss Hazel Crichton, Miss Sandra Forster, Mr A. J. Howarth, Mr D. Skeldon, Mr C. Storey.

Assistant Trainer: C. Storey

Jockey (NH): Adrian Lane.

---

229 MISS JOANNE FOSTER, Ilkley
Postal: **Brookleigh Farm, Burley Road, Menston, Ilkley, West Yorkshire, LS29 6NS**
Contacts: **PHONE (07980) 301808 MOBILE (07980) 301808**
E-MAIL info@jofosterracing.co.uk WEBSITE www.jofosterracing.co.uk

1 **ANNIE'S ACT**, 5, b m Act One—Nite Fox (IRE) **Mrs S. Whitney**
2 **CARA COURT (IRE)**, 8, b g Court Cave (IRE)—Tarasandy (IRE) **Miss J. E. Foster**
3 **ESCAPE TO THE WEST**, 6, b g Westerner—Makeabreak (IRE) **Eshwin Racing & Partners**

MISS JOANNE FOSTER - Continued

4 FORCE OF HABIT, 8, gr g Dalakhani (IRE)—Bedside Story **Grange Park Racing V**
5 PINDAR (GER), 10, b g Tertullian (USA)—Pierette (GER) **The Golden Syndicate**
6 WINGED FARASI, 10, b g Desert Style (IRE)—Clara Vale (IRE) **Miss J. E. Foster**

Other Owners: A. D. Crombie, P. Foster, Mr G. Pickersgill, Mr E. Surr, Mr D. Taylor.

Assistant Trainer: P. Foster **Conditional:** Sam Drake.

---

230 **MRS LORNA FOWLER, Summerhill**
Postal: **Rahinston, Summerhill, Co. Meath, Ireland**
Contacts: PHONE (00353) 46 955 7014 MOBILE (00353) 87 126 7433
E-MAIL lorna-fowler@me.com WEBSITE www.rahinston.com

1 GOOD EGG (IRE), 11, b g Exit To Nowhere (USA)—Full of Surprises (IRE) **Mrs A. Frost & Mr H. Fowler**
2 JUMBO JOHN (IRE), 8, b g Presenting—Hazel's Glory (IRE) **Mrs A. Frost & Mr H. Fowler**
3 LORD VALENTINE, 6, b g Overbury (IRE)—Lady Fleur **The Lady Fleur Partnership**
4 STATION CLOSED (IRE), 6, b m Kutub (IRE)—Laser Supreme (IRE) **M. Keogh**

---

231 **MR JIMMY FOX, Marlborough**
Postal: **Highlands Farm Stables, Herridge, Collingbourne Ducis, Marlborough, Wiltshire, SN8 3EG**
Contacts: PHONE (01264) 850218 (07931) 724358 MOBILE (07702) 880010
E-MAIL jcfoxtrainer@aol.com

1 ANNES ROCKET (IRE), 9, b h Fasliyev (USA)—Aguilas Perla (IRE) **Claire Underwood, Fay Thomas & S-J Fox**
2 DREAMING AGAIN, 4, b g Young Ern—Maedance **The Dancing Partners**
3 GRACIOUS GEORGE (IRE), 4, b c Oratorio (IRE)—Little Miss Gracie **Mrs B. A. Fuller**
4 NEWTOWN CROSS (IRE), 4, ch c Kheleyf (USA)—Sacred Pearl (IRE) **Mrs A. M. Coughlan**
5 THE WEE CHIEF (IRE), 8, ch g King Charlemagne (USA)—La Belle Clare (IRE) **R. E. Kavanagh**

THREE-YEAR-OLDS

6 HENRY GRACE (IRE), b c Oratorio (IRE)—Little Miss Gracie **Mrs B. A. Fuller**

Other Owners: G. B. Balding, Mrs E. Estall, Mrs S. J. Fox, Miss F. L. Thomas, Mrs C. C. Underwood.

Assistant Trainer: Sarah-Jane Fox

Jockey (flat): Pat Dobbs.

---

232 **MISS SUZZANNE FRANCE, Norton on Derwent**
Postal: **Cheesecake Hill House, Highfield, Beverley Road, Norton on Derwent, North Yorkshire, YO17 9PJ**
Contacts: PHONE (01653) 691947 FAX (01653) 691947 MOBILE (07904) 117531
E-MAIL suzzannemunchie@talk21.com

1 BACHELOR KNIGHT (IRE), 6, b g Bachelor Duke (USA)—Labetera **Newstart Partnership**
2 BOND BLADE, 6, ch g Needwood Blade—Bond Cat (IRE) **Newstart Partnership**
3 SIR GEORGE (IRE), 9, b g Mujadil (USA)—Torrmana (IRE) **Newstart Partnership**
4 STAMP DUTY (IRE), 6, b g Ad Valorem (USA)—Lothian Lass (IRE) **Newstart Partnership**

Other Owners: Mrs P. France, Mr P. R. France.

Amateur: Mr Aaron James.

---

233 **MR DEREK FRANKLAND, Brackley**
Postal: **Springfields, Mixbury, Brackley, Northamptonshire, NN13 5RR**
Contacts: FAX (01280) 847334 MOBILE (07763) 020406
E-MAIL dsfrankland@aol.com

1 HOWLETT (IRE), 6, b g Ishiguru (USA)—Royal Show (IRE) **D. S. Frankland & D. J. Trott**
2 MULAAZEM, 11, b g King's Best (USA)—Harayir (USA) **D. S. Frankland & D. J. Trott**

MR DEREK FRANKLAND - Continued

  3 **ORIGINAL STAR (IRE)**, 9, b g Rashar (USA)—Hogan Stand **D. S. Frankland & D. J. Trott**
  4 **REBEL HIGH (IRE)**, 10, ch g Hymns On High—Celia's Fountain (IRE) **D. S. Frankland & D. J. Trott**

Other Owners: D. S. Frankland, Mr D. J. Trott.

Jockey (NH): David Bass, Harry Skelton, Liam Treadwell.

234

MR JAMES FROST, Buckfastleigh
Postal: **Hawson Stables, Buckfastleigh, Devon, TQ11 0HP**
Contacts: **YARD (01364) 642267 HOME (01364) 642332 FAX (01364) 643182
MOBILE (07860) 220229**

  1 **BRACKENWOOD**, 8, b g Morpeth—Sarena Pride (IRE) **J. D. Frost**
  2 **CHASE GATE**, 9, ch g Arkadian Hero (USA)—Carlingford Lass (IRE) **Mrs J. Bury**
  3 **KILDERRY DEAN (IRE)**, 7, b g Croco Rouge (IRE)—Perkalette (IRE) **Miss M. D. Wheaton**
  4 **MASTER WELLS (IRE)**, 13, b g Sadler's Wells (USA)—Eljazzi **J. D. Frost**
  5 **MORE TRICKS**, 6, b m Morpeth—Supreme Daughter **J. D. Frost**
  6 **NORTH LONDON**, 7, b g Morpeth—Miss Grace **Mr T. G. Russell**
  7 **RAILWAY VIC (IRE)**, 7, b g Old Vic—Penny Apples (IRE) **J. D. Frost**
  8 **RUSTY NAIL (IRE)**, 9, b g Tikkanen (USA)—Aoki (IRE) **J. D. Frost**
  9 **SARENICE (FR)**, 8, gr g April Night (FR)—Delice du Soleil (FR) **Mrs J. Bury**
10 **UNION SAINT (FR)**, 6, b g Saint des Saints (FR)—Us Et Coutumes (FR) **P. M. Tosh**
11 **WANSBECK**, 6, b g Morpeth—Adalie **Mr & Mrs Barnett, Mr B. Keays & Mr Balding**

Other Owners: Mr G. B. Balding, Mr G. R. Barnett, Mrs P. R. Barnett, Mr J. D. Frost, Mr Geoff Martin, Mrs J. McCormack.

Assistant Trainer: G. Frost

Jockey (NH): Hadden Frost, Tom O'Connor. **Amateur:** Miss Bryony Frost.

235

MR KEVIN FROST, Alcester
Postal: **Red Hill Farmyard, Red Hill, Alcester, Warwickshire, B49 6NQ**
Contacts: **PHONE (07748) 873092 (07919) 370081
E-MAIL info@kevinfrostracing.co.uk WEBSITE www.kevinfrostracing.co.uk**

  1 **CATCHING ZEDS**, 7, b m Lucky Story (USA)—Perfect Poppy **The Ferandlin Peaches**
  2 **FINE MOMENT**, 6, b m Pivotal—Evasive Quality (FR) **The Ferandlin Peaches**
  3 **ILE DE RE (FR)**, 8, gr g Linamix (FR)—Ile Mamou (IRE) **Mr D. Mead**
  4 **LIGHT THE WORLD (FR)**, 6, b g Layman (USA)—Lignite (IRE) **Miss J. L. Lloyd**
  5 **PIDDIE'S POWER**, 7, ch m Starcraft (NZ)—Telori **Mr D. Mead**
  6 **RUBRICS (IRE)**, 5, gr g High Chaparral (IRE)—Inner Strength (FR) **David & Jan Mead**
  7 **SURF AND TURF (IRE)**, 8, ch g Beneficial—Clear Top Waltz (IRE) **Mr K. Frost**
  8 **SWITCHED OFF**, 9, b g Catcher In The Rye (IRE)—Button Hole Flower (IRE) **Mr P Nicholls & Mr D Mead**
  9 **THE KICKING LORD**, 5, b g Avonbridge—Lady Killer (IRE) **Mr K. Frost**
10 **TORNADO FORCE (IRE)**, 6, ch g Shamardal (USA)—Pharma West (USA) **Playboy Kennels Partnership**

Other Owners: P. V. Harris, Ms R. J. Harris, Mrs J. A. Mead, Mr D. Mead, Mr P. R. Nicholls, Playboy Kennels Partnership.

Jockey (NH): Dougie Costello, Brian Hughes.

236

MR HARRY FRY, Seaborough
Postal: **Flat 1, Manor Farm, Seaborough, Beaminster, Dorset, DT8 3QY**
Contacts: **PHONE (01308) 868192 FAX (01308) 867512
E-MAIL info@harryfryracing.com WEBSITE www.harryfryracing.com**

  1 **ACTIVIAL (FR)**, 4, gr ro g Lord du Sud (FR)—Kissmirial (FR) **Potensis Limited**
  2 **ASSAM BLACK (IRE)**, 6, b g Oscar (IRE)—Contrasting Lady **The Tea Party Syndicate**
  3 **BILLY MERRIOTT (IRE)**, 8, b g Dr Massini (IRE)—Hurricane Bella (IRE) **G. D. Taylor**
  4 **BITOFAPUZZLE**, 6, b m Tamure (IRE)—Gaelic Gold (IRE) **R. Barber**
  5 **BLUE BUTTONS (IRE)**, 6, b m King's Theatre (IRE)—Babet (IRE) **R. Barber**
  6 **BOLD CHIEF (IRE)**, 9, br g Oscar (IRE)—Cottage Girl (IRE) **The Eyre Family**
  7 **CHEMISTRY MASTER**, 6, b g Doyen (IRE)—Elemental **Trebles Holford & Simon Cullum**
  8 **DANCINGTILMIDNIGHT**, 7, ch m Midnight Legend—Solo Dancer **Mrs S. J. Maltby**

MR HARRY FRY - Continued

9 **DASHING OSCAR (IRE)**, 4, b g Oscar (IRE)—Be My Leader (IRE) **Andy & Sharon Measham**
10 **DON POOLEONI (IRE)**, 9, b g Catcher In The Rye (IRE)—Liss Rua (IRE) **The Dons**
11 **FAIR DREAMER**, 6, gr g Fair Mix (IRE)—Emma's Dream **J. P. Blakeney**
12 **FLETCHERS FLYER (IRE)**, 6, b g Winged Love (IRE)—Crystal Chord (IRE) **Masterson Holdings Limited**
13 **GARTON STAR (IRE)**, 5, bl g Presenting—Suir Decision (IRE) **Trailer Resources Ltd**
14 **HANDSOME RANSOM**, 5, b g Red Ransom (USA)—Maid For The Hills **Normandie Stud Ltd**
15 **HENRYVILLE**, 6, b g Generous (IRE)—Aquavita **R P B Michaelson & E M Thornton**
16 **HIGHLAND RETREAT**, 7, b m Exit To Nowhere (USA)—St Kilda **R. Barber**
17 **JOLLY'S CRACKED IT (FR)**, 5, b g Astarabad (USA)—Jolly Harbour **GDM Partnership**
18 **KARINGA DANCER**, 8, b g Karinga Bay—Miss Flora **H. B. Geddes**
19 **KING'S ENCORE (IRE)**, 4, b g King's Theatre (IRE)—Royal Nora (IRE) **The Jago Family Partnership**
20 **LADY OF LAMANVER**, 4, b f Lucarno (USA)—Lamanver Homerun **Dr D. Christensen**
21 **MENDIP EXPRESS (IRE)**, 8, b br g King's Theatre (IRE)—Mulberry (IRE) **The Mendip Syndicate**
22 **OPENING BATSMAN (IRE)**, 8, b g Morozov (USA)—Jolly Signal (IRE) **The Twelfth Man Partnership**
23 **OSCARSLAD (IRE)**, 8, b g Oscar (IRE)—Velvet Huxley (IRE) **Mr J. M. Dare**
24 **POLAMCO (IRE)**, 5, b g Old Vic—Shanesia (IRE) **Mr A. D. Polson**
25 **POPULAR OPINION (IRE)**, 4, b f Oscar (IRE)—Jeu de Dame
26 **PRESENTING ARMS (IRE)**, 7, b g Presenting—Banningham Blaze **Mr J. M. Dare**
27 **PRESENTING THE WAY**, 7, ch g Presenting—Euphorie (GER) **MKG Racing**
28 **RENE'S GIRL (IRE)**, 4, b f Presenting—Brogella (IRE) **Andy & Sharon Measham**
29 **ROCK ON RUBY (IRE)**, 9, b g Oscar (IRE)—Stony View (IRE) **The Festival Goers**
30 **SIR IVAN**, 4, b g Midnight Legend—Tisho **The Eyre Family**
31 **THOMAS BROWN**, 5, b g Sir Harry Lewis (USA)—Tentsmuir **The Corse Lawners**
32 **TRIANGULAR (USA)**, 9, b g Diesis—Salchow (USA) **GDM Partnership**
33 **VAUBAN DU SEUIL (FR)**, 5, b g Epalo (GER)—Parika du Seuil (FR) **The Lost In France Partnership**
34 **VIOLIN DAVIS (FR)**, 8, b m Turgeon (USA)—Trumpet Davis (FR) **Mr A. D. Polson**
35 **VUKOVAR (FR)**, 5, b g Voix du Nord (FR)—Noraland (USA) **GDM Partnership**
36 **ZULU OSCAR**, 5, b g Oscar (IRE)—Loxhill Lady **Caroline Fry & Susie Dilhorne**

THREE-YEAR-OLDS

37 **BIM BAM BOUM (FR)**, b g Crossharbour—Quobalt (FR)

Other Owners: J. R. Barber, P. K. Barber, Mrs S. Barber, Mr C. Blackburn, P. H. Boss, G. Calder, Mrs J. Calder, G. Charlesworth, D. Charlesworth, Mr S. Cullum, Miss P. J. Dare, Viscountess S. J. Dilhorne, E. J. Dolan-Abrahams, Mrs P. E. Dolan-Abrahams, Mrs C. A. Eyre, Mr H. Eyre, Miss R. E. Eyre, Mr C. G. S. Eyre, Dr C. E. Fry, R. A. Fry, Mrs F. Jackson, Mr P. J. A. Jago, Miss M. L. A. Jago, Mrs J. L. Jago, Mr F. C. A. Jago, Mr R. F. Magrath, Mr R. McCarthy, Mr A. R. Measham, Mrs S. M. Measham, R. P. B. Michaelson, Mr M. Powell, A. G. Sim, Mr M. Smith, E. M. Thornton, Trebles Holford Thoroughbreds, P. M. Warren.

Assistant Trainer: Ciara O'Connor

Jockey (NH): Ryan Mahon, Noel Fehily, Nick Scholfield. **Conditional:** Martin McIntyre, Gary Derwin.
Amateur: Mr Will Biddick.

---

237   MISS CAROLINE FRYER, Wymondham
Postal: **Browick Hall Cottage, Browick Road, Wymondham, Norfolk, NR18 9RB**
Contacts: PHONE **(01953) 601257** MOBILE **(07768) 056076**
E-MAIL **caroline@carolinefryerracing.co.uk** WEBSITE **www.carolinefryerracing.co.uk**

1 **COUNTY ZEN (FR)**, 11, b br g Lost World (IRE)—Fair County (FR) **Miss C. Fryer**
2 **IDE NO IDEA (IRE)**, 10, b g Anshan—Gales Wager **Mrs S. Fryer**
3 **POLLY WIGGLE**, 5, ch m Generous (IRE)—Single Handed **Mr J. D. Ward**
4 **RIDDLESTOWN (IRE)**, 7, b g Cloudings (IRE)—Gandi's Dream (IRE) **Mr J. D. Ward**
5 **STORM TO PASS**, 6, b g Overbury (IRE)—Silver Peak (FR) **Miss C. Fryer**
6 **VOLCAN SURPRISE (FR)**, 6, b g Dom Alco (FR)—Invitee Surprise (FR) **Mrs S. Fryer**
7 **WESTERN DOLLY**, 5, b m Westerner—Dolly Sparks (IRE) **Peter Wales & Matthew Bartram**

Other Owners: Mr M. Bartram, Mr P. R. Wales.

238 MR JOHN GALLAGHER, Moreton-In-Marsh
Postal: Grove Farm, Chastleton, Moreton-In-Marsh, Gloucestershire, GL56 0SZ
Contacts: PHONE/FAX (01608) 674492 MOBILE (07780) 972663
E-MAIL gallagherracing@phonecoop.coop WEBSITE www.gallagherracing.com

1 ADDICTIVE NATURE (IRE), 4, b g Acclamation—Movie Queen **Caveat Emptor Partnership**
2 ALPHA DELTA WHISKY, 6, ch g Intikhab (USA)—Chispa **Adweb Ltd**
3 CELESTIAL ISLAND, 7, gr m Silver Patriarch (IRE)—Celtic Island **Mr R. W. Brown**
4 FINALEE, 4, b f Cockney Rebel (IRE)—Celtic Island **Mr R. W. Brown**
5 HEARTSONG (IRE), 5, b m Kheleyf (USA)—Semiquaver (IRE) **C. Rashbrook**
6 LADWEB, 4, ch g Bertolini (USA)—Adweb **Adweb Ltd & Mr Andrew Bell**
7 OSTRALEGUS, 4, b g Choisir (AUS)—Midnight Pearl (USA) **The Oystercatcher Racing Syndicate**
8 SOUNDBYTE, 9, b g Beat All (USA)—Gloaming **John Gallagher**

THREE-YEAR-OLDS
9 ISEEMIST (IRE), gr f Verglas (IRE)—Krasivaya (IRE) **J-P Lim & Mr Keith Marsden**
10 PRINCESS FLORENTIA, b f Misu Bond (IRE)—Medici Princess **Ms A. Clifford**
11 PUSEY STREET VALE, b f Moss Vale (IRE)—Pusey Street Girl **C. R. Marks (Banbury)**

TWO-YEAR-OLDS
12 AMBER CRYSTAL, b f 11/3 Multiplex—Glitz (IRE) (Hawk Wing (USA)) **R. Biggs**
13 Ch f 23/4 Piccolo—Endear (Pivotal)
14 MAJOR PUSEY, ch c 26/3 Major Cadeaux—Pusey Street Lady (Averti (IRE))
15 ONE MORE PUSEY, b f 8/4 Hellvelyn—Pusey Street Girl (Gildoran) (11428)
16 VIRTUALISE, ch c 26/3 Virtual—Snake Skin (Golden Snake (USA)) **Adweb Ltd**

Other Owners: Mr D. Abraham, Mr A. Bell, Mr Arthur Brown, Mr M. W. Goodall, Mr J. P. Lim, J. F. Long, Mrs B. A. Long, K. Marsden, Mr P. P. Richou.

Assistant Trainer: Mrs R. Gallagher

Jockey (flat): Neil Callan, Jamie Spencer, Chris Catlin, Martin Lane.

239 MRS ILKA GANSERA-LEVEQUE, Newmarket
Postal: Saffron House Stables, Hamilton Rd, Newmarket, CB8 7DH
Contacts: PHONE (01638) 665504 MOBILE (07855) 532072
E-MAIL ilkagansera@gmail.com WEBSITE www.gansera-leveque.com

1 DUKE OF GRAZEON (IRE), 4, b g Duke of Marmalade (IRE)—Rambler **J. R. Rowbottom**
2 TOSCA (GER), 4, b f Amadeus Wolf—Tamarita (GER) **Mrs I. Gansera-Leveque**

THREE-YEAR-OLDS
3 GODIVA'S PRIDE, b g Byron—Lambeth Belle (USA) **Mrs I. Gansera-Leveque**
4 HONEY BADGER, b br g Pastoral Pursuits—Taminoula (IRE) **Mrs D. J. Black**

TWO-YEAR-OLDS
5 B f 8/4 Aussie Rules (USA)—All On Sugar (GER) (Red Ransom (USA))
6 IONIAN LIBRETTA (AUT), b f 26/2 Librettist (USA)—Ionia (IRE) (Montjeu (IRE))
7 Gr ro f 15/3 Zebedee—Ma Nikitia (IRE) (Camacho) (5500)

Jockey (flat): Mickael Barzalona, Raul Da Silva, Martin Lane.

240 MRS SUSAN GARDNER, Exeter
Postal: Woodhayes Farm, Longdown, Exeter, Devon, EX6 7SB
Contacts: PHONE/FAX (01392) 811213 MOBILE (07971) 097936
E-MAIL woodhayesstudfarm@btinternet.com

1 BRAVE ENCOUNTER (IRE), 6, br g Indian Danehill (IRE)—Dartmeet (IRE) **Mr D V Gardner & Mrs B Russell**
2 BREDON HILL LAD, 7, ch g Kirkwall—Persian Clover **R. W. Mitchell**
3 BREDON HILL POPPY, 5, b m Kayf Tara—Persian Clover **R. W. Mitchell**
4 CLEAR MIX, 6, b m Fair Mix (IRE)—Nortonthorpe-Rose **Clear Racing 1**

MRS SUSAN GARDNER - Continued

5 **FLYING AWARD (IRE)**, 10, br g Oscar (IRE)—Kates Machine (IRE) **Mr & Mrs P George & Mrs B Russell**
6 **HERE'S HERBIE**, 6, b g Classic Cliche (IRE)—Tyre Hill Lilly **D. V. Gardner**
7 **LOOK FOR LOVE**, 6, b g Pursuit of Love—Look Here's May **D. V. Gardner**
8 **MISS SAFFRON**, 11, br m Access Ski—Saffron Lake **P. A. Tylor**
9 **RAFAFIE**, 6, b g Kayf Tara—Florie **D. V. Gardner**
10 **RIVER DU NORD (FR)**, 7, b m Voix du Nord (FR)—Palala River **Mr J. Mercier**
11 **SALUT L'AS (FR)**, 8, ch g Kaldou Star—Kayas (FR) **D. V. Gardner**
12 **SOUTHWAY QUEEN**, 10, b m Morpeth—Nearly A Score **Clear Racing**
13 **STORM ALERT**, 7, ch g Karinga Bay—Rash-Gale (IRE) **D. V. Gardner**
14 **TREVAYLOR BOY (IRE)**, 7, b g Lahib (USA)—Blue Glass **G. N. Noye**

Other Owners: Mr D. V. Gardner, Mrs P. George, Mr P. George, Mr B. Greening, Mrs M. M. Greening, Mrs Brenda Russell, Mr T. R. Watts.

Assistant Trainer: D. V. Gardner

Jockey (NH): Aidan Coleman, Sam Thomas. **Conditional:** Micheal Nolan. **Amateur:** Miss L. Gardner.

---

241 | **MR JEREMY GASK, Warminster**
Postal: The Beeches, Deverill Road, Sutton Veny, Warminster, Wiltshire, BA12 7BY
Contacts: **PHONE** (01985) 841166 **FAX** (01985) 840474 **MOBILE** (07507) 555303
E-MAIL info@horsesfirstracing.com **WEBSITE** www.horsesfirstracing.com

1 **ARC LIGHTER (USA)**, 5, b g Street Cry (IRE)—Flamelet (USA)
2 **BAINNE (IRE)**, 4, b f Strategic Prince—Laemeen (IRE) **Philip Bamford & Guy Carstairs**
3 **COMPTON ALBION (IRE)**, 4, ch f Compton Place—Yomalo (IRE) **Mr A. G. Bloom**
4 **DALAKLEAR (IRE)**, 4, b c Dalakhani (IRE)—Clear Vision **The Kathryn Stud Limited**
5 **DASHING STORM**, 4, b f Milk It Mick—Salalah **Mr S. Y. Sun**
6 **DOMINIUM (USA)**, 7, b g E Dubai (USA)—Sudenlylastsummer (USA) **Horses First Racing Ltd**
7 **EXKALIBER**, 5, b g Exceed And Excel (AUS)—Kalindi **The Exkaliber Partnership**
8 **GABBIANO**, 5, b g Zafeen (FR)—Hollybell **Mr A. G. Bloom**
9 **GREEN MILLIONAIRE**, 4, b g Green Desert (USA)—Millyant **Mr A. G. Bloom**
10 **KARITZA (FR)**, 4, b f Barathea (IRE)—Kritzia **The Kathryn Stud Limited**
11 **LASER BLAZER**, 6, b g Zafeen (FR)—Sashay **Calne Engineering Ltd**
12 **LIGHT ROSE (IRE)**, 4, b f Cape Cross (IRE)—Laureldean Lady (IRE) **Jamie & Lucy Hart**
13 **MEDICEAN MAN**, 8, ch g Medicean—Kalindi **Mr Stuart Dobb & Miss Kate Dobb**
14 **NELSON QUAY (IRE)**, 4, b g Holy Roman Emperor (IRE)—Frippet (IRE) **S. T. Brankin**
15 **NEVER A QUARREL (IRE)**, 4, b f Acclamation—Welsh Mist **Coral Champions Club**
16 4, B c Oasis Dream—Pinacotheque (IRE) **R. G. & T. E. Levin**
17 **PRECISION FIVE**, 5, b m Proclamation (IRE)—Sashay **Calne Engineering Ltd**
18 **SENATOR MATT**, 4, b c Joe Bear (IRE)—Anytime Anywhere **Mrs M. Lethbridge-Brown**
19 **STREET POWER (USA)**, 9, b br g Street Cry (IRE)—Javana (USA) **Horses First Racing & Ownaracehorse**
20 **SULIS MINERVA (IRE)**, 7, b m Arakan (USA)—Lacinia **R. L. Page**
21 **TOGA TIGER (IRE)**, 7, b g Antonius Pius (USA)—Minerva (GER) **For Sale**
22 **TRENDING (IRE)**, 5, gr g Dark Angel (IRE)—Call Later (USA) **The Twitterati**

THREE-YEAR-OLDS

23 **CAMINEL (IRE)**, b f Kyllachy—Jalissa **Mr M. Allen**
24 **FLYING BEAR (IRE)**, b c Kodiac—Marinebird (IRE) **Flying Bear Partnership**
25 **GOLLY MISS MOLLY**, b f Exceed And Excel (AUS)—Amicable Terms **Amelco UK Ltd**
26 **KINGS CHAPEL (USA)**, b g Elusive Quality (USA)—Ladyecho (USA) **Jamie & Lucy Hart**
27 Gr f Sinndar (IRE)—Kritzia **The Kathryn Stud Limited**
28 **PETITE FILLE**, ch f Sleeping Indian—Ravenna **R. L. Page**
29 **SUTTON SIOUX**, b f Sleeping Indian—Once Removed **The Sutton Veny Syndicate**

Other Owners: Mr P. Bamford, Mr Tony Bloom, Mr G. Carstairs, Mr S. J. Clare, Miss K. M. Dobb, Mr Jamie Hart, Mrs Lucy Hart,. Horses First Racing Limited, Mr J. A. Knight, Mr Richard Levin, Mrs T. E. Levin, Ownaracehorse Ltd (ownaracehorse.co.uk), Mr A. C. Pickford, Mr Eamonn Wilmott, Mrs Oriana Wilmott.

Assistant Trainer: Mr. David Stratton (07960 874489)

Apprentice: David Parkes.

242 **MRS ROSEMARY GASSON, Banbury**
Postal: **Alkerton Grounds, Balscote, Banbury, Oxfordshire, OX15 6JS**
Contacts: PHONE **(01295) 730248** MOBILE **(07769) 798430**
E-MAIL **arb@aqf.myzen.co.uk**

1 **ADIOS ALONSO (IRE)**, 8, b g Saffron Walden (FR)—Rosy Rockford (IRE) **Mrs R. Gasson**
2 **ALWAYSLOOKBACK (IRE)**, 5, b g Trans Island—Malachy's Attic (IRE) **Mrs R. Gasson**
3 **CROCO MISTER (IRE)**, 7, ch g Croco Rouge (IRE)—Nimrods Dream (IRE) **Mrs R. Gasson**
4 **ELITE BENEFICIAL (IRE)**, 9, ch g Beneficial—A Fine Romance (IRE) **Mrs R. Gasson**
5 4, B g Gamut (IRE)—Fairytaleofnewyork (IRE) **Mrs R. Gasson**
6 **GENTLEMAN ANSHAN (IRE)**, 10, b g Anshan—Second Violin (IRE) **Mrs R. Gasson**
7 **JOLLY BOYS OUTING (IRE)**, 11, b g Glacial Storm (IRE)—St Carol (IRE) **Mrs R. Gasson**
8 **KILCASCAN**, 10, b g Alflora (IRE)—Peasedown Tofana **Mrs R. Gasson**
9 **SCUTSISLAND (IRE)**, 5, br g Heron Island (IRE)—Soviet Princess (IRE) **Mrs R. Gasson**

Conditional: Ben Poste.

243 **MR MICHAEL GATES, Stratford-Upon-Avon**
Postal: **Comfort Park Stud, Campden Road, Clifford Chambers, Stratford-Upon-Avon**
Contacts: MOBILE **(07581) 246070**
E-MAIL **comfortparkstud@hotmail.co.uk**

1 **CARN ROCK**, 6, b g Tamure (IRE)—Solent Sunbeam **M. Gates**
2 **COLLINGBOURNEDUCIS (IRE)**, 4, b g Bahamian Bounty—Quickstyx **M. Gates**
3 **FULL OV BEANS**, 10, ch g Midnight Legend—Scarlet Baroness **M. Gates**
4 **HANDSOME BUDDY (IRE)**, 7, br g Presenting—Moya's Magic (IRE) **M. Gates**
5 **KILLEGNEY**, 10, bl b m Tel Quel (FR)—The Distaff Spy **M. Gates**
6 **MEZARAT (ITY)**, 9, ch g Dream Well (FR)—Dayara (GER) **M. Gates**

244 **MR JONATHAN GEAKE, Marlborough**
Postal: **Harestone House, East Kennett, Marlborough, Wiltshire, SN8 4EY**
Contacts: PHONE **(01672) 861784** MOBILE **(07768) 350738**
E-MAIL **jageake@yahoo.co.uk**

1 **ABBEY DORE (IRE)**, 11, ch g Alderbrook—Bone of Contention (IRE) **Mrs A. Leftley**
2 **AT FIRST LIGHT**, 5, b m Echo of Light—Bisaat (USA) **Miss E. Tanner**
3 **BALLYMAN (IRE)**, 13, gr g Accordion—Sliabhin Rose **Mrs A. Leftley**
4 **BEWARE CHALK PIT (IRE)**, 10, b g Anshan—Rakiura (IRE) **Mrs A. Leftley**
5 **BONDI MIST (IRE)**, 5, gr m Aussie Rules (USA)—Akoya (IRE) **Double Kings Partnership**
6 **DANCE WITH ME (IRE)**, 5, b g Danehill Dancer (IRE)—Perpetual Time **A. J. Geake**
7 **GLENS WOBBLY**, 6, ch g Kier Park (IRE)—Wobbly **Mr R. G. Symes**
8 **HEEZARARITY**, 6, b g Librettist (USA)—Extremely Rare (IRE) **Miss E. Tanner**
9 **MICQUUS (IRE)**, 5, b g High Chaparral (IRE)—My Potters (USA) **Mrs A. Leftley**
10 **SACRAMENTO KING (IRE)**, 5, gr g Desert King—Kindle Ball (FR) **Mrs P. D. Gulliver**
11 **SHOT IN THE DARK (IRE)**, 5, ch g Dr Fong (USA)—Highland Shot **Mrs P. D. Gulliver**

THREE-YEAR-OLDS

12 **A LASTING JOY**, b f Refuse To Bend (IRE)—Sir Kyffin's Folly **Mrs A. Leftley**
13 **THEA'S DANCE**, b f Delta Dancer—Tagula Song (IRE) **Mrs S. A. Geake**

Other Owners: Mrs S. A. Geake, Mrs Margaret Geake.

Assistant Trainer: Mrs S. A. Geake **Pupil Assistant:** Mr Sam Geake

Jockey (NH): Mark Grant, Gerald Tumelty. **Apprentice:** Ryan Tate.

245 MISS KAREN GEORGE, Crediton

Postal: **Higher Eastington Stables, Lapford, Crediton, Devon, EX17 6NE**
Contacts: **PHONE (01363) 83092 FAX (01363) 83092 MOBILE (07917) 007892**
E-MAIL eastington1@yahoo.com WEBSITE www.eastingtonracing.co.uk

1 4, B g Tobougg (IRE)—Aquavita
2 **BELLE PARK**, 7, b m Hamairi (IRE)—Cape Siren
3 **GIZZIT (IRE)**, 8, b g Son of Sharp Shot (IRE)—Suez Canal (FR) **Miss K. M. George**
4 **GOOD AUTHORITY (IRE)**, 7, b g Chineur (FR)—Lady Alexander (IRE) **Karen George & Adrian Parr**
5 **JEZZA**, 8, br g Pentire—Lara (GER) **Mrs J. Scrivens**
6 **MR HICHENS**, 9, b g'Makbul—Lake Melody **Miss K. M. George**
7 **NOTHING PERSONAL**, 7, b g Double Trigger (IRE)—Nothings Forever **Miss K. M. George**

THREE-YEAR-OLDS

8 Gr f Proclamation (IRE)—Dubai Marina

Other Owners: Sheikh Imran Ahmad, Mr R. E. Basterille, Mr R. Bimson, Miss Karen George, Mr A. B. Parr, Mr Athole Still, Mrs J. V. Wilkinson.

Assistant Trainer: Mr P. George, Mr R. E. Baskerville **Jockey (NH):** Andrew Thornton.

246 MR TOM GEORGE, Slad

Postal: **Down Farm, Slad, Stroud, Gloucestershire, GL6 7QE**
Contacts: **PHONE (01452) 814267 MOBILE (07850) 793483**
E-MAIL tom@trgeorge.com WEBSITE www.tomgeorgeracing.co.uk

1 **ABSOLUTE RETURN**, 5, b g Kayf Tara—Kitty Wong (IRE) **Mr & Mrs R. E. R. Rumboll**
2 **ARTHUR'S PASS**, 10, b g Midnight Legend—Bella Coola **Vicki Robinson & James Williams**
3 **AT YOUR PEARL (IRE)**, 5, ch g Blueprint (IRE)—Normandy Girl (IRE) **Sharon C. Nelson & Dermot O'Donohoe**
4 **BALLINVARRIG (IRE)**, 7, b g Beneficial—Leos Holiday (IRE) **Lady Hilda Clarke & Simon W Clarke**
5 **BALLYALLIA MAN (IRE)**, 9, b g Flemensfirth (USA)—
                        Hatch Away (IRE) **H S Smith, R & M Gabbertas P Deal P Gough**
6 **BE DEFINITE (IRE)**, 10, b g Definite Article—Etoile Margot (FR) **Simon W Clarke & Vicki Robinson**
7 **BIG FELLA THANKS**, 12, b g Primitive Rising (USA)—Nunsdream **Crossed Fingers Partnership**
8 **BIG SOCIETY (IRE)**, 8, b g Flemensfirth (USA)—Choice of Kings (IRE) **Simon Clarke & David Thorpe**
9 **CALL ME VIC (IRE)**, 7, b g Old Vic—Call Me Dara (IRE) **C. B. Compton**
10 **CHARTREUX (FR)**, 9, gr g Colonel Collins (USA)—Ruaha River (FR) **R. S. Brookhouse**
11 **DARE TO ENDEAVOUR**, 7, b g Alflora (IRE)—Miss Chinchilla **Nationwide Acquisitions PLC**
12 **DEFINITELY BETTER (IRE)**, 6, ch m Definite Article—Chevet Girl (IRE) **Mrs E. A. Fletcher**
13 **DESPERATE DEX (IRE)**, 14, b g Un Desperado—Too Sharp **Crossed Fingers Partnership**
14 **DOUBLE KRIS (IRE)**, 4, b br g My Risk (FR)—Roots Sleeping (FR) **Crossed Fingers Partnership**
15 **EGYPT MILL SPIRIT (IRE)**, 8, b g Overbury (IRE)—Miss Tickill (IRE) **Mr S. R. Webb**
16 **FIT THE BRIEF**, 4, b f Kayf Tara—Tulipa (POL) **Mrs S. C. Nelson**
17 **FORGOTTEN GOLD (IRE)**, 8, b g Dr Massini (IRE)—Ardnataggle (IRE) **Mr & Mrs R. Cornock**
18 **FORMIDABLE (FR)**, 4, b g Sageburg (IRE)—Forcat (FR) **McNeill Family Ltd**
19 **GOD'S OWN (IRE)**, 6, b g Oscar (IRE)—Dantes Term (IRE) **Crossed Fingers Partnership**
20 **GOOD ORDER**, 9, b g Alflora (IRE)—Twinnings Grove (IRE) **Sharon C. Nelson & Dermot O'Donohoe**
21 **GORSKY ISLAND**, 6, b g Turtle Island (IRE)—Belle Magello (FR) **Mrs Robin Birley**
22 **HALLEY (FR)**, 7, b g Loup Solitaire (USA)—Moon Glow (FR) **PJL Racing & Mr T R George**
23 **HENRI DE BOISTRON (FR)**, 4, b g Enrique—Highness Royale (FR) **H Stephen Smith & The Gabbertas Family**
24 **IFYOUSAYSO (IRE)**, 7, ch g Definite Article—Rosato (IRE) **The Joaly Partnership**
25 **IN BY MIDNIGHT**, 6, ch m Midnight Legend—Moyliscar **Silkword Racing Partnership**
26 **IRONIC (FR)**, 6, b g Califet (FR)—Iron Lassie (USA) **St Albans Bloodstock LLP**
27 **KILBREE KID (IRE)**, 7, b g Cloudings (IRE)—Bustingoutallover (USA) **Five Valleys Racing Partnership**
28 **KING'S WARRIOR (FR)**, 7, b g King's Best (USA)—Save Me The Waltz (FR) **Mr P. Hancock**
29 **LORDOFTHEHOUSE (IRE)**, 6, ch g Danehill Dancer (IRE)—Bordighera (USA) **St Albans Bloodstock LLP**
30 **MAIL DE BIEVRE (FR)**, 9, b g Cadoudal (FR)—Coyote Davis (IRE) **P. E. Atkinson**
31 **MAJALA (FR)**, 8, b g Lavirco (GER)—Majae (FR) **Sharon Nelson Jayne Taylor Darren Taylor**
32 **MASTER CYNK**, 7, ch g Diableneyev (USA)—Model View (USA) **Barlow, Nelson, O'Donohoe & Stratford**
33 **MODULE (IRE)**, 7, b g Panoramic—Before Royale (FR) **Mr S. W. Clarke**
34 **MONSIEUR CADOU (FR)**, 9, b g Cadoudal (FR)—
                        Dame De Trefles (FR) **C Trembath ECD Ltd D Obree T & J McGill**
35 **MOONLIGHT MAGGIE**, 7, b m Pasternak—Moyliscar **Capt & Mrs J. A. George**
36 **MORGAN'S BAY**, 9, b g Karinga Bay—Dubai Dolly (IRE) **Mr S. W. Clarke**

MR TOM GEORGE - Continued

37 **NOCHE DE REYES (FR)**, 5, b br g Early March—Cochinchine (IRE) **Mr D. W. Fox**
38 **NODEBATEABOUTIT**, 9, b g Alflora (IRE)—Mystere (IRE) **Sharon C. Nelson & Dermot O'Donohoe**
39 **OLOFI (FR)**, 8, gr g Slickly (FR)—Dona Bella (FR) **McNeill Family Ltd**
40 **ON THE CASE**, 6, ch g Generous (IRE)—Tulipa (POL) **Mrs S. C. Nelson**
41 **OVERNIGHT FAME (IRE)**, 10, b m Kayf Tara—Best of The Girls (IRE) **Mr & Mrs R. Cornock**
42 **PARSNIP PETE**, 8, b g Pasternak—Bella Coola **The Parsnips**
43 **RING BO REE (IRE)**, 11, b g Topanoora—La Ronde **T. George**
44 **ROC D'APSIS (FR)**, 5, gr g Apsis—Rocapina (FR) **Mr M. N. Khan**
45 **RODY (FR)**, 9, ch g Colonel Collins (USA)—Hamelie II (FR) **R A Dalton & J C E Laing**
46 **SEVEN WOODS (IRE)**, 8, b g Milan—Charlotte's Moss **M. K. George**
47 **SHANENDOU (IRE)**, 5, br m Turtle Island (IRE)—Portobello Sunrise (IRE) **ECD Ltd, Mike George & Anne Elliott**
48 **SID'S TOPPER (IRE)**, 4, b br g Anabaa Blue—Last Sicyos (FR) **Chemipetro Limited**
49 **SIR VALENTINO (FR)**, 5, b g Early March—Valentine (FR) **Doone Hulse Susie Saunders & Lady Cobham**
50 **SIVOLA DE SIVOLA (FR)**, 8, gr g Martaline—Kerrana (FR) **D O'Donohoe, S & P Nelson & D Silvester**
51 **SONG SAA**, 4, b f Midnight Legend—Mystere (IRE) **Mrs S. C. Nelson**
52 **STELLAR NOTION (IRE)**, 6, b br g Presenting—Green Star (FR) **R. S. Brookhouse**
53 **STORMING STRUMPET**, 4, b f Kayf Tara—Rosita Bay **PJL Racing**
54 **TIRE LARIGOT (FR)**, 7, b g Muhtathir—Rhaetia (IRE) **Thoroughbred Ladies**
55 **TRIBU D'ESTRUVAL (FR)**, 7, b br m Sleeping Car (FR)—
        Mome d'estruval (FR) **Simon W Clarke & Vicki Robinson**
56 **TRUCKERS STEEL (IRE)**, 6, b g Craigsteel—Frantesa **Crossed Fingers Partnership**
57 **VAGNER (FR)**, 5, b g Voix du Nord (FR)—Evane (FR) **Mrs Robin Birley**
58 **VALSEUR DU GRANVAL (FR)**, 5, b g Della Francesca (USA)—La Grande Vallee (FR) **Mr S. W. Clarke**
59 **VEYRANNO (FR)**, 5, b br g Anzillero (GER)—Nheyranne (FR) **Miss J. A. Hoskins**
60 **VIACOMETTI (FR)**, 5, gr g Alberto Giacometti (IRE)—L'epi (FR) **S Nelson S O'Donohoe J C Taylor D Taylor**
61 **WHATS HAPPENING (IRE)**, 7, b g Lahib (USA)—Rebeccas Star (IRE) **David Rea, Mike George, ECD Ltd**
62 **WUFF (IRE)**, 6, b g Beneficial—Dummy Run (IRE) **R. S. Brookhouse**

Other Owners: Mr George Baker, Mrs D. M. Barker, Mr M. H. D. Barlow, Mrs C. D. Chamberlain, Lady Clarke, Mr Simon W. Clarke, Lady Cobham, Mr R. Cornock, Mrs Michele Cornock, Mr R. A. Dalton, Mr P. A. Deal, Mrs Anne Elliott, Express Contract Drying Ltd, Mr J. M. Fawbert, Mr Mark Gabbertas, Mr R. K. Gabbertas, Mrs S. Gabbertas, Mr T. R. George, Mrs C. M. George, Capt. J. A. George, Mrs S. P. George, Mr M. K. George, Mrs Petra Gough, Mrs Doone Hulse, Miss Jennifer Laing, Mr John B. Lawson, Mr L. Lugg, Mrs J. Massey, Mr C. D. Massey, Mr A. G. McGill, Mr Joseph McGill, Mrs Sharon C. Nelson, Mr D. J. O'Donohoe, Mr David Obree, Mr Nick Rieger, Ms Vicki Robinson, Mrs C. Rollings, Mrs Robin Rumboll, Mr R. E. R. Rumboll, Mrs Susie Saunders, Mr H. Stephen Smith, Mr A. E. Smith & Co, Mrs A. Sproson, Mr P. Sproson, Mr Andrew Stone, Mrs M. F. Stone, Mr Mike Stratford, Mr Jeremy Taylor, Mr Darren Taylor, Mr D. A. Thorpe, Mr C. R. Trembath, Mr R. F. Tromans, Mr James S. Williams, Mr Nicholas Williamson.

Jockey (NH): Paddy Brennan, Alain Cawley, Aodhagan Conlon. **Amateur:** Mr Freddie Tett.

---

247   MR THOMAS GIBNEY, Kells
Postal: Ballyhist, Carnaross, Kells, Co Meath, Ireland
Contacts: **MOBILE (00353) 87 7499778**
E-MAIL gibneyracing@gmail.com WEBSITE www.gibneyracing.com

1 **BALNAGON BOY (IRE)**, 6, ch g Hernando (FR)—Taormina (IRE) **Tom, Mick & Pat Syndicate**
2 6, B g Norwich—Beglawella **Anne Keane**
3 **BETWEEN ME AND YOU (IRE)**, 10, br g Norwich—Sealthedeal **Heidi Gibney**
4 **CHICKEN CHASER (IRE)**, 8, b g Mull of Kintyre (USA)—Sweet Lass **Fergus Grimes**
5 **CIRCE'S ISLAND (IRE)**, 4, b f Kodiac—Circe's Melody (IRE) **Meath & Co Syndicate**
6 **CROCON SI (IRE)**, 10, gr g Great Palm (USA)—Belle Dame (IRE) **Heidi Gibney**
7 5, Gr m Zagreb (USA)—Curracloe Rose (IRE) **Noeleen Gaughran**
8 6, B g Kutub (IRE)—Devon Cherry (IRE) **Frank Daly**
9 **FURZE FLYER (IRE)**, 7, b g Dr Massini (IRE)—Dereenavurrig (IRE)
10 **GRANNYS GARDEN (IRE)**, 8, b m Sayarshan (FR)—The Top Road (IRE) **Lorna Groarke**
11 **IVANOR BOY (IRE)**, 9, b g Craigsteel—Legal Lady (IRE) **Ivan Maxwell**
12 **LION NA BEARNAI (IRE)**, 12, b g New Frontier (USA)—Polly Plum (IRE) **The Lock Syndicate**
13 **MAISIE MC (IRE)**, 7, ch m Exit To Nowhere (USA)—Lerichi (IRE) **Daniel McCarten**
14 **NATIVE PALM (IRE)**, 8, gr g Great Palm (USA)—Neath Native Sky (IRE) **Palm Tree Syndicate**
15 5, Ch m Raintrap—Ninevah (IRE) **Larry Green**
16 **ORPHEUS VALLEY (IRE)**, 11, ch g Beneficial—Native Mo (IRE) **No Horse Box Syndicate**
17 7, B h Expelled (USA)—Passion Killer (IRE) **Nicholas Brown**
18 **SHAHRAFI (IRE)**, 8, b g Barathea (IRE)—Sharamana (IRE) **Shahrafi Syndicate**
19 **TO CHOOSE (IRE)**, 5, b g Choisir (AUS)—Jannadav (IRE) **Lennard Kinsella**

248 **MRS THERESA GIBSON, Hexham**
Postal: **Embley, Steel, Hexham, Northumberland, NE47 0HW**
Contacts: **PHONE (01434) 673334**
E-MAIL theresagibson356@btinternet.com

1 **GOLD CYGNET (IRE),** 9, b g Beneficial—Windy Bee (IRE) **Mrs T. M. Gibson**
2 **ITS NOT FAIR (IRE),** 6, b g Darsi (FR)—Choice Annie (IRE) **Mrs T. M. Gibson**

249 **MR NICK GIFFORD, Findon**
Postal: **The Downs, Stable Lane, Findon, West Sussex, BN14 0RT**
Contacts: **OFFICE (01903) 872226 FAX (01903) 877232 MOBILE (07940) 518077**
E-MAIL downs.stables@btconnect.com WEBSITE www.nickgiffordracing.co.uk

1 **A HARE BREATH (IRE),** 6, b g Alkaadhem—Lady Willmurt (IRE) **Mrs S. N. J. Embiricos**
2 **BALLYBACH (IRE),** 10, b g Bach (IRE)—Croom River (IRE) **Mr M. K. O'Shea**
3 **BIT OF A CLOWN (IRE),** 8, b g Anshan—Dead Right Too (IRE) **Mr D. P. Foulkes**
4 **BRANDON THOMAS (IRE),** 8, br g Norwich—Last Sunrise (IRE) **S. L. Rodwell**
5 **CATCHER STAR (IRE),** 6, b g Catcher In The Rye (IRE)—Drumdeels Star (IRE) **Exors of the Late Mr P. A. Byrne**
6 **CHRISTOPHER WREN (USA),** 7, ch g D'wildcat (USA)—Ashley's Coy (USA) **J. P. McManus**
7 **COVE (IRE),** 7, b m Westerner—Phillis Hill **Nick Gifford Racing Club**
8 **DIGGER GETS LUCKY (IRE),** 12, b g Lord Americo—Exclusive View (IRE) **The Chanctonbury Ring**
9 **DOLLAR BILL,** 5, ch g Medicean—Jardin **Mrs C. L. Kyle**
10 **FAIRY RATH (IRE),** 8, ch g Accordion—Killoughey Fairy (IRE) **Mrs C. L. Kyle**
11 **GENEROUS RANSOM (IRE),** 6, ch g Generous (IRE)—Pennyrose Bay **Sir Christopher Wates**
12 **GEORGE ARTHUR,** 6, ch g Croco Rouge (IRE)—Belmarita (IRE) **S. L. Rodwell**
13 5, B g Milan—Just Stunning (IRE)
14 **KIKILI,** 6, b g Cotation—Dawn Frolics **Mr H. T. Pelham**
15 **KUILSRIVER (IRE),** 7, b g Cape Cross (IRE)—Ripple of Pride (IRE) **Mrs T. J. Stone-Brown**
16 **ON TREND (IRE),** 8, b g Jammaal—Comrun (IRE) **Ham Manor Farms Ltd**
17 **PETERBROWN (IRE),** 6, b g Shantou (USA)—Grove Juliet (IRE) **P. H. Betts**
18 **PROUTS PUB (IRE),** 5, b g Catcher In The Rye (IRE)—A Woman In Love **Nick Gifford Racing Club**
19 **SECRET STING (IRE),** 4, b g Scorpion (IRE)—Roxtown **B. Noakes & Baroness S. Noakes**
20 **SPECIALAGENT ALFIE,** 8, b g Alflora (IRE)—Oso Special **Mr M. K. O'Shea**
21 **STARS ROYALE (IRE),** 5, b g King's Best (USA)—Open Your Heart (IRE) **Jeremy Kyle & Friends**
22 **TOOHIGHFORME (IRE),** 5, b g Mountain High (IRE)—Summertime Girl (IRE)
23 **TULLAMORE DEW (IRE),** 12, ch g Pistolet Bleu (IRE)—Heather Point **Give Every Man His Due**
24 **UNSIST (FR),** 6, b br g Shaanmer (IRE)—Nigita (FR) **Mrs R. E. Gifford**
25 **VINNIE THE POOH (IRE),** 6, b g Vinnie Roe (IRE)—Ministerial Model (IRE) **Mrs R. E. Gifford**

Other Owners: G. H. L. Bird, D. H. C. Booth, Mr A. Bradley, Mrs S. Cotty, S. N. Embiricos, Mr L. Horvath, Mr J. Kyle, Baroness S. Noakes, C. B. Noakes, Mr M. J. Tracey.

Jockey (NH): Tom Cannon, Liam Treadwell.

250 **MR MARK GILLARD, Sherborne**
Postal: **Elm Tree Stud, Holwell, Sherborne, Dorset, DT9 5LL**
Contacts: **PHONE (01963) 23026 FAX (01963) 23297 MOBILE (07970) 700605**
E-MAIL Mark@thegillards.co.uk WEBSITE markgillardracing.com

1 **ADVISOR (FR),** 8, gr g Anabaa (USA)—Armilina (FR) **Ms T. Conner**
2 **BOBTAIL,** 4, b g Nomadic Way (USA)—Rabbit **Mr M. E. Harris**
3 **BRAVO BRAVO,** 7, b g Sadler's Wells (USA)—Top Table **Davies & Price**
4 **COMICAL RED,** 6, ch g Sulamani (IRE)—Sellette (IRE) **N. J. McMullan**
5 **DONT CALL ME OSCAR (IRE),** 7, b g Oscar (IRE)—Coolrua (IRE) **Davies & Price**
6 **DREAM DESTINY,** 5, b m King's Theatre (IRE)—Queen's Banquet **Mr D. M. G. Fitch-Peyton**
7 **ENCHANTING SMILE (FR),** 7, b m Rakti—A Thousand Smiles (IRE) **N. J. McMullan**
8 **KARL MARX (IRE),** 4, b g Red Clubs (IRE)—Brillano (FR) **Mrs P. M. R. Grace**
9 **LADY BRIDGET,** 6, b m Hawk Wing (USA)—Change Partners (IRE) **Mr B. R. Rudman**
10 **LAMB'S CROSS,** 8, b g Rainbow High—Angie Marinie **Out Of Bounds Racing Club**
11 **LANDENSTOWN STAR (IRE),** 9, ch g Bob's Return (IRE)—Slieve Bernagh (IRE) **Mr B Jones & Mr N Wright**
12 **MEDAL OF VALOUR (JPN),** 6, b g Medaglia d'oro (USA)—Tres Tres Joli (USA) **Bloomfields**
13 **NO NO CARDINAL (IRE),** 5, ch g Touch of Land (FR)—Four Moons (IRE) **R. A. Bracken**

MR MARK GILLARD - Continued

14 **OVER THE BRIDGE**, 4, b g Multiplex—Do It On Dani **Mr A. G. Price**
15 **REVAADER**, 6, b m Revoque (IRE)—Wave Rider **Miss Kay Russell**
16 5, B m Flemensfirth (USA)—Rowlands Dream (IRE) **Pippa Grace**
17 **TENBY JEWEL (IRE)**, 9, ch g Pilsudski (IRE)—Supreme Delight (IRE)
18 **THE NAME IS FRANK**, 9, b g Lujain (USA)—Zaragossa **Don Hazzard**
19 **WICKLEWOOD**, 8, b g Mujahid (USA)—Pinini **Mr W. A. Thomas**

Other Owners: Mr R. A. Davies, Mr John P. Ferguson, Mrs John Ferguson, Mr Michael Harris, Mr Brian Jones, Mr A. G. Price, Mr C. Winter, Mr N. W. Wright.

Assistant Trainer: Pippa Grace

Jockey (NH): Tommy Phelan.

251

MR PATRICK GILLIGAN, Newmarket
Postal: **Sackville House, Sackville Street, Newmarket, Suffolk, CB8 8DX**
Contacts: PHONE **(01638) 669151** MOBILE **(07881) 796612**
E-MAIL gilliganmax@aol.com WEBSITE www.patrickgilligan.org

1 **NICE 'N' SLEAZY (IRE)**, 7, ch g Arakan (USA)—Coulisse (IRE) **Miss C. Elbrow**
2 **SHAHRAZAD (IRE)**, 5, b m Cape Cross (IRE)—Khulasah (IRE) **Mr L. J. Doolan**
3 **STRANGELITTLEGIRL**, 6, b m Shirocco (GER)—Cephalonia **Miss C. Elbrow**

THREE-YEAR-OLDS

4 **FOOTSIEONEHUNDRED**, b f Footstepsinthesand—Zapping (IRE) **Mrs M. Roche**

TWO-YEAR-OLDS

5 Ch c 21/3 Duke of Marmalade (IRE)—Zapping (IRE) (Lycius (USA)) (10840) **Mrs M. Roche**

Other Owners: Mr P. J. Crowe.

Apprentice: Jack Gilligan.

252

MR JAMES GIVEN, Willoughton
Postal: **Mount House Stables, Long Lane, Willoughton, Gainsborough, Lincolnshire, DN21 5SQ**
Contacts: PHONE **(01427) 667618** FAX **(01427) 667734** MOBILE **(07801) 100496**
E-MAIL james@jamesgivenracing.com WEBSITE www.jamesgivenracing.com

1 **ARTFUL PRINCE**, 4, ch g Dutch Art—Royal Nashkova **Ingram Racing**
2 **DISSENT (IRE)**, 5, b g Dansili—Centifolia (FR) **P. Swann**
3 **GLENRIDDING**, 10, b g Averti (IRE)—Appelone **Tremousser Partnership**
4 **GOLDMADCHEN (GER)**, 6, b m Ivan Denisovich (IRE)—Goldkatze (GER) **Mr A. Clarke**
5 **GRAND LIAISON**, 5, b m Sir Percy—Dancinginthedark (IRE) **Barrie Catchpole & Michael Meaney**
6 **KUNG HEI FAT CHOY (USA)**, 5, b g Elusive Quality (USA)—Lady Succeed (JPN) **The Cool Silk Partnership**
7 **NO DOMINION (IRE)**, 5, b g Dylan Thomas (IRE)—Boast **Mr J. A. Barson**
8 **RETURNTOBRECONGILL**, 4, ch g Pastoral Pursuits—Turn Back **The Cool Silk Partnership**
9 **ROYAL BAJAN (USA)**, 6, gr ro g Speightstown (USA)—Crown You (USA) **The Cool Silk Partnership**
10 5, Ch g Selkirk (USA)—Woodnook **Mr & Mrs W. J. Williams**
11 **WOODY BAY**, 4, b g New Approach (IRE)—Dublino (USA) **Mr J. A. Barson**

THREE-YEAR-OLDS

12 **BAILEYS FOREVER**, ch f Mount Nelson—Forever Fine (USA) **G. R. Bailey Ltd**
13 **CHEEKY PETA'S**, b f Compton Place—Cheeky Girl **P. Swann**
14 **GALACTIC HEROINE**, b f Galileo (IRE)—Thermopylae **Biddestone Racing Club**
15 **INYORDREAMS**, b f Teofilo (IRE)—Wunders Dream (IRE) **Bolton Grange**
16 **MASTER DAN**, b c Mastercraftsman (IRE)—Danella (IRE) **The Cool Silk Partnership**
17 **ODEON**, b c Galileo (IRE)—Kite Mark **Mr A. Owen**
18 **ORIENTAL RELATION (IRE)**, gr g Tagula (IRE)—Rofan (USA) **The Cool Silk Partnership**
19 **QUEENIE'S HOME**, gr f Shamardal (USA)—Nolas Lolly (IRE) **The Cool Silk Partnership**
20 **REBEL CODE (USA)**, b c City Zip (USA)—Confederate Lady (USA) **The Cool Silk Partnership**

MR JAMES GIVEN - Continued

21 **SANDSMAN'S GIRL (IRE),** b f Kodiac—Inter Madera (IRE) **P. Swann**
22 **SHADES OF SILK,** b f Bahamian Bounty—Terentia **The Cool Silk Partnership**
23 **SPEEDBIRD ONE,** ch f Mount Nelson—Good Girl (IRE) **Miss S. J. Ballinger**
24 **SWEET ANGELICA,** ch f Pastoral Pursuits—Glencal **The Cool Silk Partnership**
25 **WILFUL MINX (FR),** b f Le Havre (IRE)—Miskina **Mrs S. Oliver**

TWO-YEAR-OLDS

26 Ch c 19/1 Naaqoos—Aalya (IRE) (Peintre Celebre (USA)) (9523) **Play Nicely Syndicate**
27 Br c 19/3 Hellvelyn—Aimee's Delight (Robellino (USA)) (10840) **Trickledown Stud**
28 **DARK WAR (IRE),** b c 23/3 Dark Angel (IRE)—
    Waroonga (IRE) (Brief Truce (USA)) (55238) **The Cool Silk Partnership**
29 **DARK WONDER (IRE),** b c 27/3 Dark Angel (IRE)—
    Wondrous Story (USA) (Royal Academy (USA)) (50000) **The Cool Silk Partnership**
30 B c 5/5 Naaqoos—Exhibitor (USA) (Royal Academy (USA)) (5420) **G. R. Bailey Ltd**
31 **LOPITO DE VEGA (IRE),** ch c 23/4 Lope de Vega (IRE)—
    Athenian Way (IRE) (Barathea (IRE)) (40000) **Mr D Poulton & Mr N Hildred**
32 **MAGIC FLORENCE (IRE),** ch f 12/3 Zebedee—
    Lady Shanghai (IRE) (Alhaarth (IRE)) (53333) **The Cool Silk Partnership**
33 **PASTORAL GIRL,** b f 2/2 Pastoral Pursuits—
    Talampaya (USA) (Elusive Quality (USA)) (76190) **The Cool Silk Partnership**
34 **RUSSIAN PUNCH,** b f 9/2 Archipenko—Punch Drunk (Beat Hollow) **Lovely Bubbly Racing**
35 B f 21/4 Captain Rio—Salingers Star (IRE) (Catcher In The Rye (IRE)) **Mr D. Gibbons & Mrs T. Gaunt**
36 **SANDS CHORUS,** b c 28/2 Footstepsinthesand—
    Wood Chorus (Singspiel) (55000) **The Cool Silk Partnership**
37 **SILKY SANDS,** b c 13/2 Kyllachy—Choosey Girl (IRE) (Choisir (AUS)) (52380) **The Cool Silk Partnership**

Other Owners: Mr Mike J. Beadle, Mr Neil Hildred, Mr R. H. Jennings, Mr David Poulton, Mr Peter Swann, Mrs B. E. Wilkinson.

---

253 **MR J. L. GLEDSON, Hexham**
Postal: **Buteland Farm, Bellingham, Hexham, Northumberland, NE48 2EX**

1 **CLONEA POWER (IRE),** 7, ch g Subtle Power (IRE)—Clonea Taipan (IRE) **J. L. Gledson**
2 **FAIRLEE GREY,** 5, gr g Fair Mix (IRE)—Halo Flora **J. L. Gledson**
3 **NEVILLE WOODS,** 7, b g Alflora (IRE)—Angie Marinie **J. L. Gledson**
4 **THEREVEREND CLOVER,** 5, b g Revoque (IRE)—Ring of Clover **J. L. Gledson**

---

254 **MR JIM GOLDIE, Glasgow**
Postal: **Libo Hill Farm, Uplawmoor, Glasgow, Lanarkshire, G78 4BA**
Contacts: **PHONE (01505) 850212 MOBILE (07778) 241522**
WEBSITE www.jimgoldieracing.com

1 **ALEKSANDAR,** 5, ch g Medicean—Alexander Celebre (IRE) **Mrs M. Craig**
2 **ANOTHER FOR JOE,** 6, b g Lomitas—Anna Kalinka (GER) **Mr A. D. Dick**
3 **ARCTIC COURT (IRE),** 10, b g Arctic Lord—Polls Joy **Mr & Mrs Raymond Anderson Green**
4 **CALEDONIA,** 7, b g Sulamani (IRE)—Vanessa Bell (IRE) **Johnnie Delta Racing**
5 **DHAULAR DHAR (IRE),** 12, b g Indian Ridge—Pescara (IRE) **Johnnie Delta Racing**
6 **GO GO GREEN (IRE),** 8, b g Acclamation—Preponderance (IRE) **Johnnie Delta Racing**
7 **HAWKEYETHENOO (IRE),** 8, b g Hawk Wing (USA)—Stardance (USA) **Johnnie Delta Racing**
8 **HERO'S STORY,** 4, b g Mount Nelson—Red Roses Story (FR) **Mr J. S. Morrison**
9 **HIGGS BOSON,** 9, b g Overbury (IRE)—Evening Splash (IRE) **J. S. Goldie**
10 **I GOT SUNSHINE,** 6, b g Grape Tree Road—I Got Rhythm **J. S. Goldie**
11 **INNISCASTLE BOY,** 5, b g Sir Percy—Galapazue (USA) **Johnnie Delta Racing**
12 **JACK DEXTER,** 5, b br g Orientor—Glenhurich (IRE) **Johnnie Delta Racing**
13 **JONNY DELTA,** 7, ch g Sulamani (IRE)—Send Me An Angel (IRE) **Johnnie Delta Racing**
14 **KALANESSA,** 5, br m Kalanisi (IRE)—Vanessa Bell (IRE) **Lorimer Racing**
15 **LATIN REBEL (IRE),** 7, b g Spartacus—Dance To The Beat **Mr R. W. C. McLachlan**
16 **LILLIOFTHEBALLET (IRE),** 7, b m Rakti—Lillibits (USA) **The Dregs Of Humanity**
17 **LOS NADIS (GER),** 10, ch g Hernando (FR)—La Estrella (GER) **I. G. M. Dalgleish**
18 **MERCHANT OF DUBAI,** 9, b g Dubai Destination (USA)—Chameleon **Highland Racing 2**

MR JIM GOLDIE - Continued

19 **MOLLY MILAN**, 6, b m Milan—Dolly Sparks (IRE) **Barraston Racing**
20 **MOWHOOB**, 4, b g Medicean—Pappas Ruby (USA) **Johnnie Delta Racing**
21 **NANTON (USA)**, 12, gr ro g Spinning World (USA)—Grab The Green (USA) **J. S. Goldie**
22 **NEVER FOREVER**, 5, ch g Sir Percy—Codename **Whitestonecliffe Racing Partnership**
23 **PLUS JAMAIS (FR)**, 7, b g Caballo Raptor (CAN)—Branceilles (FR) **Alba-Eire Syndicate**
24 **RASAMAN (IRE)**, 10, b g Namid—Rasana **P. Moulton**
25 **RONALD GEE (IRE)**, 7, ch g Garuda (IRE)—Panache Lady (IRE) **J. S. Goldie**
26 **ROTHESAY CHANCER**, 6, ch g Monsieur Bond (IRE)—Rhinefield Beauty (IRE)
27 **SIOUXSIE GEE**, 4, ch f Sleeping Indian—Annie Gee **Johnnie Delta Racing**
28 **SOMEONE'S DARLING**, 4, b f Jeremy (USA)—Green Sensazione **The McMaster Springford Partnership**
29 **SPIRIT OF A NATION (IRE)**, 9, b g Invincible Spirit (IRE)—Fabulous Pet **Mr & Mrs Gordon Grant**
30 **STORMIN EXIT (IRE)**, 11, b g Exit To Nowhere (USA)—Stormin Norma (IRE) **Thomson & Fyffe Racing**
31 **TESTA ROSSA (IRE)**, 4, b c Oratorio (IRE)—Red Rita (IRE) **Mr J. S. Morrison**
32 **TIGER JIM**, 4, b g Tiger Hill (IRE)—Quintrell **Barry Macdonald**
33 **TITUS BOLT (IRE)**, 5, b g Titus Livius (FR)—Megan's Bay **I. G. M. Dalgleish**
34 **TOO COOL TO FOOL (IRE)**, 11, b g Bob Back (USA)—Mandysway (IRE) **Johnnie Delta Racing**
35 **TURTLE WATCH**, 6, b g Where Or When (USA)—Cita Verda (FR) **Mr & Mrs Raymond Anderson Green**
36 **YOURLOOKINATHIM (IRE)**, 8, b g Flemensfirth (USA)—Christmas River (IRE) **Johnnie Delta Racing**

THREE-YEAR-OLDS

37 SLEEPER CLASS, b f Sleeping Indian—Class Wan **F. Brady**

Other Owners: Mr R. M. S. Allison, Mrs Sue Armstrong, Mr E. N. Barber, Mr T. Cobain, Mr Forbes Connor, Mr Gerry Davidson, Mr J. Doherty, Mr J. Frew, Mr Maurice Friel, Mr S. Fyffe, Mr J. Fyffe, Mr J. S. Goldie, Mr Gordon Grant, Mrs C. H. Grant, Mr Raymond Anderson Green, Mrs Anita Green, Mr Alan Guthrie, Mr P. Hampshire, Mr E. W. Hyslop, Mr Matthew Hyslop, Mr Barry MacDonald, Mr Alan MacDonald, Mr A. Manson, Mrs Wendy McGrandles, Mr A. McManus, Mr Brown McMaster, Mrs Jean McMaster, Mr William A. Powrie, Mr Billy Robinson, Mr N. Springford, Mrs Dorothy Springford, Mr G. Thomson.

Assistant Trainers: James & George Goldie

Jockey (flat): Graham Lee. **Jockey (NH):** Lucy Alexander, Henry Brooke, Ryan Mania, Denis O'Regan.
Amateur: Mrs Carol Bartley, Mrs I. Goldie.

---

255 **MR ROBERT GOLDIE, Kilmarnock**
Postal: **Harpercroft, Old Loans Road, Dundonald, Kilmarnock, Ayrshire, KA2 9DD**
Contacts: **PHONE (01292) 317222 FAX (01292) 313585 MOBILE (07801) 922552**

1 **ALEXANDER OATS**, 11, b g Insan (USA)—Easter Oats **R. H. Goldie**
2 **ALFRED OATS**, 10, b g Alflora (IRE)—Easter Oats **R. H. Goldie**
3 **EASTER QUEEN**, 12, b m Rakaposhi King—Easter Oats **R. H. Goldie**
4 **EASTER VIC**, 13, b m Old Vic—Easter Oats **R. H. Goldie**

Assistant Trainer: Mrs R H Goldie

---

256 **MR KEITH GOLDSWORTHY, Kilgetty**
Postal: **Grumbly Bush Farm, Yerbeston, Kilgetty, Pembrokeshire, SA68 0NS**
Contacts: **PHONE/FAX (01834) 891343 MOBILE (07796) 497733**
E-MAIL grumbly@supanet.com WEBSITE www.keithgoldsworthyracing.co.uk

1 **CALDEY**, 5, b m Overbury (IRE)—Barfleur (IRE) **S. F. Barlow**
2 **HILLS OF ARAN**, 12, b g Sadler's Wells (USA)—Danefair
3 **SIR BENFRO**, 8, b g Runyon (IRE)—Dunrowan **Mr R. J. Barrack**
4 **WILLIAM HOGARTH**, 9, b g High Chaparral (IRE)—Mountain Holly **ROL Plant Hire Ltd**

TWO-YEAR-OLDS

5 B c 13/4 Dr Massini (IRE)—Prescelli (IRE) (Snurge) **S. F. Barlow**

Other Owners: M. Duthie, Greenacre Racing Partnership Ltd, Mrs F. V. Miller.

Assistant Trainer: Mrs L. A. Goldsworthy **Amateur:** Miss Charlotte Evans.

257 **MR STEVE GOLLINGS, Louth**
Postal: **Highfield House, Scamblesby, Louth, Lincolnshire, LN11 9XT**
Contacts: **YARD** (01507) 343204 **HOME/FAX** (01507) 343213 **MOBILE** (07860) 218910
E-MAIL stevegollings@aol.com **WEBSITE** www.stevegollings.com

1 **ALLIED ANSWER,** 6, gr g Danehill Dancer (IRE)—Hotelgenie Dot Com **P. J. Martin**
2 **BALINDERRY (IRE),** 7, b g Flemensfirth (USA)—Erins Love (IRE) **BDS Pointers**
3 **BAR DE LIGNE (FR),** 8, b g Martaline—Treekle Toffee (FR) **P. J. Martin**
4 **CONQUISTO,** 9, ch g Hernando (FR)—Seal Indigo (IRE) **P. J. Martin**
5 **DEFICIT (IRE),** 4, gr g Dalakhani (IRE)—Venturi **I. S. Naylor**
6 **DEFINITLY RED (IRE),** 5, ch g Definite Article—The Red Wench (IRE) **P. J. Martin**
7 **DUNLUCE CASTLE (IRE),** 6, br g Secret Singer (FR)—Royale Laguna (FR) **P. J. Martin**
8 **HANDIWORK,** 4, ch g Motivator—Spinning Top **Mr C. A. Johnstone**
9 **HONEST JOHN,** 10, b g Alzao (USA)—Tintera (IRE) **P. J. Martin**
10 **JAC THE LEGEND,** 5, b g Midnight Legend—Sky Burst **P. J. Martin**
11 **KYLLADDIE,** 7, ch g Kyllachy—Chance For Romance **Mrs Jayne M. Gollings**
12 **LOCAL HERO (GER),** 7, b g Lomitas—Lolli Pop (GER) **P. J. Martin**
13 **LOOKING ON,** 6, b g Observatory (USA)—Dove Tree (FR) **I. S. Naylor**
14 **MAKE ME A FORTUNE (IRE),** 6, b br g Heron Island (IRE)—Biora Queen (IRE) **P. J. Martin**
15 **POWERSTOWN DREAMS (IRE),** 5, b g Brian Boru—Our Idol (IRE) **P. J. Martin**
16 **RELIC ROCK (IRE),** 6, b g Bienamado (USA)—Nighty Bless (IRE) **P. J. Martin**
17 **RESPONSE,** 4, ch g New Approach (IRE)—Spotlight **I. S. Naylor**
18 **RICARDO'S GIRL (IRE),** 5, b m Westerner—Precious Lady **Richard Atterby & Christine Atterby**
19 **ROCKWEILLER,** 7, b h Rock of Gibraltar (IRE)—Ballerina Suprema (IRE) **P. Whinham**
20 **RUSSIAN GEORGE (IRE),** 8, ch g Sendawar (IRE)—Mannsara (IRE) **Mr P. S. Walter**
21 **SOUDAIN (FR),** 8, ch g Dom Alco (FR)—Ebene d'avril (FR) **P. J. Martin**
22 **THE GREY TAYLOR (IRE),** 5, gr g Royal Anthem (USA)—Penny Tan (IRE) **P. J. Martin**
23 **THEOLOGY,** 7, b g Galileo (IRE)—Biographie **P. J. Martin**
24 **TROOPINGTHECOLOUR,** 8, b g Nayef (USA)—Hyperspectra **I. S. Naylor**
25 **WALKABOUT CREEK (IRE),** 7, b g Alderbrook—La Mouette (USA) **P. J. Martin**
26 **ZAMOYSKI,** 4, ch g Dutch Art—Speech **I. S. Naylor**

THREE-YEAR-OLDS

27 **SIR WALTER BENGAL,** b g Tiger Hill (IRE)—Lady Darayna **Mr P. S. Walter**

Other Owners: Mr R. J. Atterby, Mrs C. A. Atterby, Mr R. A. Carter, Mrs S. A. Daubney, Mr D. M. Evans.

Assistant Trainer: Mrs J M Gollings

Jockey (flat): Darryll Holland, Jamie Spencer. **Jockey (NH):** Keith Mercer, Brian Hughes, Timmy Murphy, A. P. McCoy, Tom Scudamore. **Conditional:** Paul Bohan.

258 **MR CHRIS GORDON, Winchester**
Postal: **Morestead Farm Stables, Morestead, Winchester, Hampshire, SO21 1JD**
Contacts: **PHONE** (01962) 712774 **FAX** (01962) 712774 **MOBILE** (07713) 082392
E-MAIL chrisgordon68@hotmail.co.uk **WEBSITE** www.chrisgordonracing.com

1 **ABSOLUTE SHAMBLES,** 10, b g Shambo—Brass Castle (IRE) **Chris Gordon Racing Club**
2 **BENNY THE SWINGER (IRE),** 9, b g Beneficial—The Olde Swinger (IRE) **L. Gilbert**
3 **BLAZING KNIGHT (IRE),** 4, b g Red Clubs (IRE)—Johar Jamal (IRE) **C. E. Gordon**
4 **CHILWORTH SCREAMER,** 6, b m Imperial Dancer—The Screamer (IRE) **L. Gilbert**
5 **COMEONGINGER (IRE),** 7, b g King's Theatre (IRE)—Miss Poutine (FR) **Mr & Mrs Michael Coates**
6 **CURTAIN RAZER (IRE),** 8, b g Old Vic—Echo Creek (IRE) **Fontwellians**
7 **FAMILY MOTTO,** 5, b g Tobougg (IRE)—Be My Mot (IRE) **Chris Gordon Racing Club**
8 **JAEGER BOMBER,** 5, b m Zafeen (FR)—Glenpine (IRE) **Mr S. C. Hobbs**
9 **JUICY LEGEND,** 7, b g Midnight Legend—Juicy Lucy **Mrs J. M. Butler**
10 **KAKI ISLAND (IRE),** 6, b g Heron Island (IRE)—Arctic Banner (IRE) **Mr M. Matthews**
11 **KERRY MAUR,** 5, b g Kayf Tara—Eau de Vie **Mr G. Sturt**
12 **KING EDMUND,** 11, b g Roi de Rome (USA)—Cadbury Castle **A. C. Ward-Thomas**
13 **LIGHTENTERTAINMENT (IRE),** 6, b g King's Theatre (IRE)—
Dochas Supreme (IRE) **The Not Over Big Partnership**
14 **MARIE DEJA LA (FR),** 8, b m Daliapour (IRE)—Comedie Divine (FR) **Chris Gordon Racing Club**
15 **NOBLE FRIEND (IRE),** 6, b g Presenting—Laragh (IRE) **Mrs K. Digweed**
16 **OSMOSIA (FR),** 9, b m Mansonnien (FR)—Osmose (FR) **Mr G. Sturt**
17 **PETTOCHSIDE,** 5, b g Refuse To Bend (IRE)—Clear Impression (IRE) **C. E. Gordon**

MR CHRIS GORDON - Continued

18 **PRINCELY HERO (IRE)**, 10, b g Royal Applause—Dalu (IRE) **L. Gilbert**
19 **PROMISED WINGS (GER)**, 7, ch g Monsun (GER)—
Panagia (USA) **Mr & Mrs Mr Roger Alwen Mrs Heather Alwen**
20 **SEAS THE MOMENT (IRE)**, 5, b m Westerner—Meursault (IRE) **Mr A. W. Spooner**
21 **SUPERCILIARY**, 5, b g Dansili—Supereva (IRE) **Mr D. F. Henery**
22 **SUTTON SID**, 4, ch g Dutch Art—Drastic Measure **Mrs K. Digweed**
23 **SWEET BOY VIC (IRE)**, 6, b g Old Vic—Sweet Second (IRE) **Mr F. H. Ramsahoye**
24 **TARA BRIDGE**, 6, b g Kayf Tara—Annie Greenlaw **B. J. Champion**
25 **THE MASTER REMOVER (IRE)**, 5, ch g Royal Anthem (USA)—Kit Kat Kate (IRE) **A. C. Ward-Thomas**
26 **THE SELECTOR**, 5, b m Crosspeace (IRE)—Lojo **The Select Syndicate**
27 **YES CHEF**, 7, ch g Best of The Bests (IRE)—Lady Chef **Mr & Mrs Mr Roger Alwen Mrs Heather Alwen**

Other Owners: Mr R. N. Alwen, Mrs H. J. Alwen, Mrs Sarah Bullen, Mrs C. Burnyeat, M. O. Coates, Mrs F. A. Coates, Mr A. B. Kelly, P J. H. Rowe, R. M. Venn.

Assistant Trainer: Jenny Gordon

Conditional: Tom Cannon. **Amateur:** Miss M. R. Trainor.

---

259 MR J. T. GORMAN, Curragh
Postal: **Maddenstown Lodge Stables, Maddenstown, Curragh, Co. Kildare, Ireland**
Contacts: **PHONE (00353) 45 441404 FAX (00353) 45 441404 MOBILE (00353) 872 599603**
E-MAIL jtgorman1@hotmail.com

1 **C'EST MA SOUER (IRE)**, 4, b f Oratorio (IRE)—Gilded Edge **W. Foley**
2 **CEST NOTRE GRIS (IRE)**, 4, gr g Verglas (IRE)—Alikhlas **W. Foley**
3 **CONAN'S ROCK**, 5, b g Shamardal (USA)—Reeling N' Rocking (IRE) **W. Foley**
4 **EAST LODGE (IRE)**, 7, b g Intikhab (USA)—Adelaide Road **Mc McWey**
5 **ELUSIVE GENT (IRE)**, 7, b g Elusive City (USA)—Satin Cape (IRE) **J. Gorman**
6 **GOLDEN SHOE (IRE)**, 6, br g Footstepsinthesand—Goldilocks (IRE) **W. Foley**
7 **HISTORY (IRE)**, 7, b g Milan—Foxtail (IRE) **W. Foley**
8 **I FOUGHT THE LAW (IRE)**, 5, b g Lawman (FR)—Indian Express **W. Foley**
9 **JERCOVA (IRE)**, 5, b m Jeremy (USA)—Nemcova (USA) **The Andrews Syndicate**
10 **KEEP STRAIGHT (IRE)**, 4, b f Kheleyf (USA)—Silkie Smooth (IRE) **The Andrews Syndicate**
11 **KINGDOMFORTHEBRIDE (IRE)**, 5, b m Titus Livius (FR)—Desert Bride (USA) **M. McWey**
12 **LIBERTY TO ROCK (IRE)**, 8, b g Statue of Liberty (USA)—Polynesian Goddess (IRE) **W. Foley**
13 **LOVEINASANDDUNE**, 6, b g Oasis Dream—Windy Gulch (USA) **W. Foley**
14 **PIERRE D'OR (IRE)**, 5, ch g Rock of Gibraltar (IRE)—Gilded Edge **W. Foley**
15 **RELAY**, 4, b f Clodovil (USA)—Figlette **M. McWey**
16 **RIGID ROCK (IRE)**, 7, b g Refuse To Bend (IRE)—Delia (IRE) **W. Foley**
17 **ROCKIN N REELIN (USA)**, 7, b g Forest Camp (USA)—Dusti's Tune (USA) **W. Foley**
18 **WELL HELLO (IRE)**, 5, b m Manduro (GER)—Road Harbour (USA) **The Andrews Syndicate**
19 **WREKIN ROCK (IRE)**, 6, br g Statue of Liberty (USA)—Orpendonna (IRE) **W. Foley**

THREE-YEAR-OLDS

20 **CHASE THE CHALLIS (IRE)**, b g War Chant (USA)—Estimation **W. Foley**
21 **LE TROISIEME GRIS (IRE)**, gr g Verglas (IRE)—Suailce (IRE) **W. Foley**
22 **MISS SPELLT (IRE)**, b f Diamond Green (FR)—Eastern Spell (IRE) **The Tylery Syndicate**
23 **PENNYS ANGEL (IRE)**, b g Dark Angel (IRE)—The Good Life (IRE) **W. Foley**
24 **SNAP CLICK (IRE)**, b g Kodiac—Happy Hour (GER) **P. Reilly**

TWO-YEAR-OLDS

25 Ch f 8/4 Lawman (FR)—Billys Dream (Dubai Destination (USA)) **W. Foley**
26 Br c 17/3 Excellent Art—Dancing With Stars (IRE) (Where Or When (IRE)) (7742) **P. Reilly**
27 B f 29/2 Kodiac—Ufallya (IRE) (Statue of Liberty (USA)) (7742) **W. Foley**

Jockey (flat): Kevin Manning, C. D. Hayes, D. McDonagh. **Jockey (NH):** B. Dalton.

260 **MR JOHN GOSDEN, Newmarket**
Postal: **Clarehaven, Bury Road, Newmarket, Suffolk, CB8 7BY**
Contacts: **PHONE (01638) 565400 FAX (01638) 565401**
E-MAIL jhmg@johngosden.com

1 **BRASS RING**, 4, b g Rail Link—Moraine
2 **CAMBORNE**, 6, b g Doyen (IRE)—Dumnoni
3 **CAUCUS**, 7, b g Cape Cross (IRE)—Maid To Perfection
4 **FENCING (USA)**, 5, ch g Street Cry (IRE)—Latice (IRE)
5 **FLYING OFFICER (USA)**, 4, b g Dynaformer (USA)—Vignette (USA)
6 **FREEDOM'S LIGHT**, 4, b f Galileo (IRE)—Aricia (IRE)
7 **GATEWOOD**, 6, b h Galileo (IRE)—Felicity (IRE)
8 **GREGORIAN (IRE)**, 5, gr h Clodovil (IRE)—Three Days In May
9 **HANSEATIC**, 5, b h Galileo (IRE)—Insinuate (USA)
10 **LAHAAG**, 5, b g Marju (IRE)—Chater
11 **NABUCCO**, 5, b h Dansili—Cape Verdi (IRE)
12 **POMOLOGY (USA)**, 4, b br f Arch (USA)—Sharp Apple (USA)
13 **REMOTE**, 4, b c Dansili—Zenda
14 **SULTANINA**, 4, ch f New Approach (IRE)—Soft Centre
15 **THE FUGUE**, 5, b br m Dansili—Twyla Tharp (IRE)
16 **TOAST OF THE TOWN (IRE)**, 4, b f Duke of Marmalade (IRE)—Boast
17 **WILLOW BECK**, 5, b m Shamardal (USA)—Woodbeck
18 **WOODLAND ARIA**, 4, b f Singspiel (IRE)—Magic Tree (UAE)

THREE-YEAR-OLDS
19 **ALLEGRIA (IRE)**, gr f Dalakhani (IRE)—Drifting (IRE)
20 **ANGELIC AIR**, b f Oasis Dream—Innocent Air
21 **ANGLO IRISH**, b c Dansili—Tebee
22 **AWARD (IRE)**, b f Tamayuz—Fantastic Account
23 **BAHA**, b c Dubawi (IRE)—Anamato (AUS)
24 **BELLE D'OR (USA)**, b f Medaglia d'oro (USA)—Glatisant
25 **BETIMES**, ch f New Approach (IRE)—See You Later
26 **BILLOWING**, ch f Candy Ride (ARG)—Cloudspin (USA)
27 **BILLY BLUE (IRE)**, b g High Chaparral (IRE)—Silk Dress (IRE)
28 **BRIMFUL (IRE)**, b f Invincible Spirit (IRE)—Alsharq (IRE)
29 **CAMLANN (IRE)**, b c Cape Cross (IRE)—Elle Galante (GER)
30 **CLOUDSCAPE (IRE)**, b c Dansili—Set The Scene (IRE)
31 **CRITERIA (IRE)**, b f Galileo (IRE)—Aleagueoftheirown (IRE)
32 **D'AVIGNON (USA)**, b br c Smart Strike (CAN)—No Matter What (USA)
33 **DEUCE AGAIN**, b f Dubawi (IRE)—Match Point
34 **DIVISIONAL**, ch c Medicean—Peppermint Green
35 **DOROTHY B (IRE)**, b f Fastnet Rock (AUS)—Slow Sand (USA)
36 **DUBAI STAR (IRE)**, b c Dubawi (IRE)—Tango Tonic (IRE)
37 **DYNAGLOW (USA)**, b f Dynaformer (USA)—Lantern Glow (USA)
38 **EAGLE TOP**, ch c Pivotal—Gull Wing (IRE)
39 **EASTERN BELLE**, b f Champs Elysees—Fleche d'or
40 **ENRAPTURED (IRE)**, b f Oasis Dream—Arty Crafty (USA)
41 **FALLEN IN LINE (IRE)**, b c Pivotal—Fallen Star
42 **FINE TUNE (IRE)**, b c Medicean—Phillippa (IRE)
43 **FOREVER NOW**, b c Galileo (IRE)—All's Forgotten (USA)
44 **GAY MARRIAGE (IRE)**, b f New Approach (IRE)—Doctrine
45 **GHARAANEEJ (IRE)**, br f Pivotal—Neverletme Go (IRE)
46 **GILBEY'S MATE**, b g Medicean—Al Joudha (FR)
47 **GM HOPKINS**, b c Dubawi (IRE)—Varsity
48 **GOLD STRUCK**, br c Raven's Pass (USA)—Love The Rain
49 **GRANDEST**, b c Dansili—Angara
50 **HER HONOUR (IRE)**, b f Shamardal (USA)—Hazarayna
51 **HOLBERG SUITE**, b f Azamour (IRE)—Humouresque
52 **JOYFUL FRIEND**, b f Dubawi (IRE)—Cheerleader
53 **KINGMAN**, b c Invincible Spirit (IRE)—Zenda
54 **LIKELIHOOD (USA)**, gr f Mizzen Mast (USA)—Light Jig
55 **LISANOR**, b f Raven's Pass (USA)—Arthur's Girl
56 **LONG CROSS**, b c Cape Cross (IRE)—Majestic Roi (USA)
57 **LOVING HOME**, b c Shamardal (USA)—Fallen In Love

MR JOHN GOSDEN - Continued

58 **MAHSOOB**, b c Dansili—Mooakada (IRE)
59 **MARZOCCO (USA)**, b br c Kitten's Joy (USA)—Dynamia (USA)
60 **MATALLEB (USA)**, b g Elusive Quality (USA)—Our Rite of Spring (USA)
61 **MAVERICK WAVE (USA)**, ch c Elusive Quality (USA)—Misty Ocean (USA)
62 **MR SMITH**, gr c Galileo (IRE)—Intrigued
63 **MUCH PROMISE**, b f Invincible Spirit (IRE)—Prowess (IRE)
64 **MUNJAZ**, ch c Sea The Stars (IRE)—Qurrah (IRE)
65 **MUWAARY**, b br c Oasis Dream—Wissal (USA)
66 **NEVER TO BE (USA)**, b c Thewayyouare (USA)—Kitty Foille (USA)
67 **NIGHT FEVER (IRE)**, b f Galileo (IRE)—Ask For The Moon (FR)
68 **NIGHT SONG**, b f Oasis Dream—All For Laura
69 **NONNO GIULIO (IRE)**, ch c Halling (USA)—Contrary (IRE)
70 **OH STAR (USA)**, b br f Tale of The Cat (USA)—Sleepytime (IRE)
71 **ORION'S BOW**, ch c Pivotal—Heavenly Ray (USA)
72 **PRINCE OF STARS**, b c Sea The Stars (IRE)—Queen's Logic (IRE)
73 **PROVIDENT SPIRIT**, b c Invincible Spirit (IRE)—Port Providence
74 **PSILOVEYOU**, ch f Sea The Stars (IRE)—Soinlovewithyou (USA)
75 **RECTITUDE**, b f Virtual—Evasive Quality (FR)
76 **REWAAYA (IRE)**, b f Authorized (IRE)—Sulaalah (IRE)
77 **ROMSDAL**, ch c Halling (USA)—Pure Song
78 **SAARREM (USA)**, b c Dynaformer (USA)—Effectual (USA)
79 **SACRED ACT**, b c Oasis Dream—Stage Presence (IRE)
80 **SAINT LUCY**, b f Selkirk (USA)—Sister Maria (USA)
81 **SEAGULL (IRE)**, b f Sea The Stars (IRE)—Caumshinaun (IRE)
82 **SEJEL (IRE)**, b f Cape Cross (IRE)—Wajaha (IRE)
83 **SEMBLANCE**, b f Pivotal—Illusion
84 **SIMPLE MAGIC (IRE)**, b f Invincible Spirit (IRE)—Cephalonie (USA)
85 **SKI LIFT**, ch f Pivotal—Morzine
86 **SOLAR MAGIC**, ch f Pivotal—Moon Goddess
87 **SONA**, b f Dansili—Neartica (FR)
88 **SPIRIT OF WINNING**, b f Invincible Spirit (IRE)—Crossmolina (IRE)
89 **STELLA BELLISSIMA (IRE)**, b f Sea The Stars (IRE)—Dolores
90 **SWIFT CAMPAIGN (IRE)**, b f Intikhab (USA)—Indolente (USA)
91 **SWISS KISS**, br f Dansili—Swiss Lake (USA)
92 **TAGHROODA**, b f Sea The Stars (IRE)—Ezima (IRE)
93 **TAWTEEN (USA)**, b f Street Sense (USA)—Wid (USA)
94 **TERHAAB (USA)**, b f Elusive Quality (USA)—Star of Paris (USA)
95 **THE THIRD MAN**, gr c Dalakhani (IRE)—Spinning Queen
96 **TOO THE STARS (IRE)**, ch f Sea The Stars (IRE)—Finsceal Beo (IRE)
97 **TRUST THE WIND**, b f Dansili—Hypnology (USA)
98 **TWIN POINT**, br c Invincible Spirit (IRE)—Gemini Joan
99 **VENTUROUS SPIRIT (IRE)**, b f Invincible Spirit (IRE)—Venturi
100 **VOTARY (IRE)**, b c Authorized (IRE)—So Admirable
101 **WANNABE YOURS (IRE)**, b c Dubawi (IRE)—Wannabe Posh (IRE)
102 **WATER HOLE (IRE)**, b f Oasis Dream—Arosa (IRE)
103 **WESTERN HYMN**, b c High Chaparral (IRE)—Blue Rhapsody
104 **WESTMINSTER (IRE)**, b c Exceed And Excel (AUS)—Pivka
105 **WESTWOOD HOE**, b c Oasis Dream—Disco Volante
106 **WINDLASS (IRE)**, b f Teofilo (IRE)—Emerald Peace (IRE)
107 **ZERFAAL**, b c Dubawi (IRE)—Dhelaal

TWO-YEAR-OLDS

108 B f 25/1 Oasis Dream—Arabesque (Zafonic (USA))
109 **CALIFORNIA (IRE)**, b f 19/2 Azamour (IRE)—Maskaya (IRE) (Machiavellian (USA)) (75000)
110 B c 28/4 Acclamation—Champion Place (Compton Place) (154858)
111 Ch c 7/4 New Approach (IRE)—Colorado Dawn (Fantastic Light (USA)) (240000)
112 B f 6/2 Invincible Spirit (IRE)—Dance Troupe (Rainbow Quest (USA)) (280000)
113 Gr f 1/3 Iffraaj—Do The Honours (IRE) (Highest Honor (FR)) (54200)
114 **EMMANUEL**, b c 27/2 Exceed And Excel (AUS)—Agnus (IRE) (In The Wings)
115 **EXCEEDINGLY**, b f 16/3 Exceed And Excel (AUS)—Miss Rochester (IRE) (Montjeu (IRE))
116 **FALLEN FOR A STAR**, b c 5/3 Sea The Stars (IRE)—Fallen Star (Brief Truce (USA))
117 B f 31/3 War Front (USA)—Fanzine (USA) (Cozzene (USA))
118 **FAYDHAN (USA)**, b br c 24/2 War Front (USA)—Agreeable Miss (USA) (Speightstown (USA)) (292141)
119 **GHAYAHEEB**, b c 7/2 Dansili—Eshaadeh (USA) (Storm Cat (USA))

MR JOHN GOSDEN - Continued

120 B f 7/4 Bernardini (USA)—Glatisant (Rainbow Quest (USA))
121 Br c 29/3 Sea The Stars (IRE)—Global World (GER) (Big Shuffle (USA)) (460000)
122 GOLDEN HORN, b c 27/3 Cape Cross (IRE)—Fleche d'or (Dubai Destination (USA)) (190000)
123 GRETCHEN, ch f 9/3 Galileo (IRE)—Dolores (Danehill (USA))
124 Ch c 11/3 Medicean—Hazy Dancer (Oasis Dream) (65000)
125 B c 24/2 Rip Van Winkle (IRE)—Hespera (Danehill (USA))
126 B f 29/1 Vale of York (IRE)—High Days (Hennessy (USA))
127 Br f 25/4 Dansili—Innocent Air (Galileo (IRE))
128 JARNES BARNES (IRE), b c 15/2 Acclamation—Mahalia (IRE) (Danehill (USA)) (240030)
129 KASB (IRE), ch c 6/4 Arcano (IRE)—Cape Columbine (Diktat)
130 B c 14/4 Lucarno (USA)—Las Flores (IRE) (Sadler's Wells (USA))
131 LASHKAAL, b f 9/2 Teofilo (IRE)—Mudaaraah (Cape Cross (USA))
132 Ch c 24/1 Giant's Causeway (USA)—Latice (IRE) (Inchinor)
133 Br f 8/4 Iffraaj—Leopoldine (Desert Prince (IRE)) (40000)
134 Br gr c 19/2 Exceed And Excel (AUS)—Likeable (Dalakhani (IRE))
135 LOVE BALLAD (IRE), b f 5/2 Teofilo (IRE)—O Fourlunda (Halling (USA)) (60000)
136 B f 24/3 Galileo (IRE)—Love The Rain (Rainbow Quest (USA))
137 LOVING THINGS, b f 11/4 Pivotal—Fallen In Love (Galileo (IRE))
138 MAKTABA (IRE), b f 3/2 Dansili—Ezima (Sadler's Wells (USA))
139 MALAF (USA), b c 26/1 Elusive Quality (USA)—Holy Wish (USA) (Lord At War (ARG)) (175284)
140 MARMION, b c 17/4 Cape Cross (IRE)—Margarula (IRE) (Doyoun)
141 MARTLET, b f 15/1 Dansili—Marywell (Selkirk (USA))
142 MAYNOOTH, b f 4/3 Tamayuz—Dublino (USA) (Lear Fan (USA))
143 MELBOURNE SHUFFLE (USA), b br f 3/2 Street Cry (IRE)—Liffey Dancer (IRE) (Sadler's Wells (USA))
144 B c 18/3 Paco Boy (IRE)—Miss Queen (USA) (Miswaki (USA))
145 B f 16/3 Dubawi (IRE)—Montare (IRE) (Montjeu (IRE))
146 B c 6/5 Dansili—Mountain Chain (USA) (Royal Academy (USA))
147 MY REVERIE, ch f 10/3 Selkirk (USA)—Follow My Dream (Kyllachy)
148 B c 17/3 Iffraaj—Najmati (Green Desert (USA)) (15000)
149 PERSIAN BREEZE, b f 27/2 Pivotal—Persian Jasmine (Dynaformer (USA))
150 POLITICO, ch f 3/3 Medicean—Tafawut (Nayef (USA)) (31000)
151 B f 6/2 Azamour (IRE)—Princess Aurora (USA) (Mr Greeley (USA))
152 B f 15/3 Teofilo (IRE)—Rafting (IRE) (Darshaan) (37000)
153 REELTOP (USA), b f 31/3 Quality Road (USA)—Light Jig (Danehill (USA))
154 B c 5/3 First Defence (USA)—Rio Carnival (USA) (Storm Cat (USA))
155 ROCK KRISTAL (IRE), b f 16/4 Fastnet Rock (AUS)—Pellinore (USA) (Giant's Causeway (USA)) (130000)
156 B c 18/1 Danehill Dancer (IRE)—Rose Cut (USA) (Montjeu (IRE)) (100000)
157 SNOANO, b c 3/3 Nayef (USA)—White Dress (IRE) (Pivotal)
158 Gr ro f 22/1 Mizzen Mast (USA)—Summer Shower (Sadler's Wells (USA))
159 B c 2/3 Halling (USA)—Swain's Gold (USA) (Swain (IRE)) (60000)
160 TARTOOR (GER), br c 18/3 Oasis Dream—Templerin (GER) (Acatenango (GER)) (69686)
161 B c 13/4 Shamardal (USA)—Twyla Tharp (IRE) (Sadler's Wells (USA)) (290000)
162 B c 14/1 Teofilo (IRE)—Vadazing (FR) (Spinning World (USA)) (58072)
163 Ch f 24/4 New Approach (IRE)—Waldmark (GER) (Mark of Esteem (IRE))
164 WANNABE SPECIAL, b f 16/2 Galileo (IRE)—Wannabe Posh (IRE) (Grand Lodge (USA))
165 WEALD OF KENT (USA), b br c 2/4 Successful Appeal (USA)—Apple of Kent (USA) (Kris S (USA))
166 WILLOUGHBY (IRE), b f 24/4 Oasis Dream—Magnificient Style (USA) (Silver Hawk (USA))
167 B c 11/3 Oasis Dream—Winter Sunrise (Pivotal)
168 B f 2/5 Dansili—Zenda (Zamindar (USA))

Jockey (flat): William Buick, Robert Havlin, Nicky Mackay, Marc Halford.

MRS HARRIET GRAHAM, Jedburgh
Postal: **Brundeanlaws Cottage, Camptown, Jedburgh, Roxburghshire, TD8 6NW**
Contacts: PHONE **(01835) 840354** MOBILE **(07843) 380401**
E-MAIL **hgrahamracing@aol.com**

1 AZERODEGREE (IRE), 5, b g Azamour (IRE)—Fairy (USA) **H G Racing**
2 BE WISE (IRE), 7, gr g Cloudings (IRE)—Crashtown Lucy **Mrs H. O. Graham**
3 MACGILLYCUDDY, 5, b g And Beyond (IRE)—Tofino Swell **Mrs H. O. Graham**
4 MAGGIE BLUE (IRE), 6, b m Beneficial—Top Ar Aghaidh (IRE) **R. S. Hamilton**
5 PRINCE TAM, 10, gr g Terimon—Princess Maxine (IRE) **Miss G. Joughin**

MRS HARRIET GRAHAM - Continued

  6 SCOTSWELL, 8, b g Endoli (USA)—Tofino Swell **H G Racing**
  7 SOUL MAGIC (IRE), 12, b g Flemensfirth (USA)—Indian Legend (IRE) **H G Racing**

Other Owners: R. D. Graham.

Assistant Trainer: R D Graham

Jockey (NH): James Reveley.

---

262   **MR CHRIS GRANT**, Billingham
Postal: **Low Burntoft Farm, Wolviston, Billingham, Cleveland, TS22 5PD**
Contacts: **PHONE/FAX (01740) 644054 MOBILE (07860) 577998**
E-MAIL chrisgrantracing@gmail.com WEBSITE www.chrisgrantracing.co.uk

  1 AFICIONADO, 4, ch g Halling (USA)—Prithee **Straightline Construction Ltd**
  2 ALAPLEE, 6, b g Alflora (IRE)—Cloudy Pearl **Miss A. P. Lee**
  3 ALLEGED VANITY (IRE), 8, ch g Flemensfirth (USA)—Vanity Jane (IRE) **C. Grant**
  4 ALPHA ONE (IRE), 8, b g Fruits of Love (USA)—Dunedin Lass (IRE) **J. Wade**
  5 AMOUR COLLONGES (FR), 4, b g Lavirco (GER)—Kapucine Collonges (FR) **Elliott Brothers And Peacock**
  6 BACKWORTH SHANDY (IRE), 6, b m Trans Island—Executive Ellie (IRE) **D&D Armstrong Limited**
  7 BEAU DANDY (IRE), 9, b br g Exit To Nowhere (USA)—
                                          Northern Dandy **D Lofthouse E Lofthouse Mrs M Nicholas**
  8 BLUE BELLINI, 6, b m Blueprint (IRE)—Knysna Belle **G. F. White**
  9 BROADWAY BELLE, 4, b f Lucarno (USA)—Theatre Belle **Division Bell Partnership**
10 BROKETHEGATE, 9, b g Presenting—Briery Ann **C. Grant**
11 CINNOMHOR, 6, b m Grape Tree Road—Brass Buckle (IRE) **Miss A. P. Lee**
12 CLASSIC STATEMENT, 6, ch g Rashar (USA)—Bank On Inland **D&D Armstrong Limited**
13 DERMO'S DILEMMA, 4, b g Multiplex—Gertrude Webb **C. Grant**
14 DONNA'S DIAMOND (IRE), 5, gr g Cloudings (IRE)—Inish Bofin (IRE) **D&D Armstrong Limited**
15 DOWNTOWN BOY (IRE), 6, br g Kheleyf (USA)—Uptown (IRE) **R. Craggs**
16 GENEROUS CHIEF (IRE), 6, b g Generous (IRE)—Yosna (FR) **Mrs S. Sunter**
17 IL TESTONE (FR), 5, b g Laveron—Gaelic Music (FR) **N. E. M. Jones**
18 JEU DE ROSEAU (IRE), 10, b g Montjeu (IRE)—Roseau **W. Raw**
19 LYSINO (GER), 5, ch g Medicean—Lysuna (GER) **Straightline Construction Ltd**
20 MA CRANKY (IRE), 6, b m Flemensfirth (USA)—Northern Mill (IRE) **D&D Armstrong Limited**
21 MARLBOROUGH HOUSE, 4, b g Dylan Thomas (IRE)—
                                          Eurolink Raindance (IRE) **D&D Armstrong Ltd,I Henderson,R Oliver**
22 MICRO MISSION (IRE), 8, b m Flemensfirth (USA)—Micro Villa (IRE) **D&D Armstrong Limited**
23 MISTER STICKLER (IRE), 10, b g Alflora (IRE)—Almost Trumps **T. J. Hemmings**
24 NOTONEBUTTWO (IRE), 7, b g Dushyantor (USA)—Daiquiri (IRE) **D&D Armstrong Limited**
25 OCARITO (GER), 13, b g Auenadler (GER)—Okkasion **Skip Racing Limited**
26 OLLIE G, 8, b g Denounce—Silver Rosa **D&D Armstrong Limited**
27 PATTERNING, 7, b g Pivotal—Historian (IRE) **Elliott Brothers And Peacock**
28 PRESIDENTIAL LADY (IRE), 5, b m Hurricane Run (IRE)—Sheer Glamour (IRE) **D&D Armstrong Limited**
29 RIDE THE RANGE (IRE), 5, br g High Chaparral (IRE)—Jade River (FR) **D&D Armstrong Limited**
30 ROCK RELIEF (IRE), 8, gr g Daylami (IRE)—Sheer Bliss (IRE) **D&D Armstrong Limited**
31 SWINGBRIDGE (IRE), 6, b g Milan—Creative Approach (IRE) **T. J. Hemmings**
32 TEARS FROM HEAVEN (USA), 8, b br g Street Cry (IRE)—Heavenly Aura (USA) **Mrs S. Sunter**
33 THATILDEE (IRE), 6, b g Heron Island (IRE)—Good Thyne Mary (IRE) **Peacock Boys Partnership**
34 TOUGH TRADE, 5, b g Trade Fair—Cesana (IRE) **D & D Armstrong Ltd & Nigel E M Jones**
35 TRYNWYN, 4, b f Grape Tree Road—Brass Buckle (IRE) **Miss A. P. Lee**
36 VOLO MIO, 7, b g Endoli (USA)—Carol's Flight **G. F. White**
37 WAR ON (IRE), 7, br g Presenting—Alannico **D&D Armstrong Limited**

THREE-YEAR-OLDS

38 THEATRE ACT, ch f Act One—Theatre Belle **Division Bell Partnership**

Other Owners: T. Cunningham, J. M. Elliott, C. R. Elliott, Mr J. Henderson, Mr I. F. Henderson, Mr D. A. Lofthouse, A. Meale, Mrs M. Nicholas, Mr R. W. Oliver, Mr R. Poole, A. D. Wright.

Assistant Trainer: Mrs S. Grant

Jockey (NH): Denis O'Regan, Wilson Renwick. **Conditional:** Diarmuid O'Regan.

263 MR LIAM GRASSICK, Cheltenham
Postal: **Postlip Racing Stables, Winchcombe, Cheltenham, Gloucestershire, GL54 5AQ**
Contacts: PHONE **(01242) 603124** YARD **(01242) 603919** MOBILE **(07816) 930423**
E-MAIL **mark.grassick@btopenworld.com**

1 **CLEEVE CLOUD (IRE)**, 8, b g Noverre (USA)—La Galeisa (IRE) **L. P. Grassick**
2 **KALLINA (IRE)**, 6, b m Kalanisi (IRE)—Ballerina Babe (IRE) **S. J. Bryan**
3 **LATE REG**, 15, br m Chaddleworth (IRE)—Prominent Princess **C. M. Rutledge**

Assistant Trainer: Mark Grassick

264 MR M. C. GRASSICK, Curragh
Postal: **Fenpark House, Pollardstown, Curragh, Co. Kildare, Ireland**
Contacts: MOBILE **(00353) 86 364 8829**
E-MAIL **mcgrassick@hotmail.com** WEBSITE **www.michaelcgrassick.com**

1 **ACTING TALENT (USA)**, 4, b f Bernstein (USA)—Soaring Emotions (USA) **M. C. Grassick**
2 **DARBREE (IRE)**, 5, b g Vinnie Roe (IRE)—Dariyba (IRE) **Mrs M T Crowley**
3 **ELUSIVE IN PARIS (IRE)**, 5, b g Elusive City (USA)—Bradwell (IRE) **Joseph E. Keeling**
4 **KING OF ARAN (IRE)**, 7, b br g Val Royal (FR)—Innishmore (IRE) **Dont Tell The Missus Syndicate**
5 **LAUREL CREEK (IRE)**, 9, b g Sakura Laurel (JPN)—Eastern Sky (AUS) **Mr Patrick McKeon**
6 **ONLY EXCEPTION (IRE)**, 5, b m Jeremy (USA)—Misaayef (USA) **A. Goonan**

THREE-YEAR-OLDS

7 **ALANNA BHEAG (IRE)**, b f Kodiac—Strina (IRE) **J. Keeling**
8 **BLUEBERRY GAL (IRE)**, b f Bushranger (IRE)—Mythie (FR) **J. Keeling**
9 **OAMARU (IRE)**, b f High Chaparral (IRE)—Virgin Hawk (USA) **J. Higgins**
10 **RO ALAINN (IRE)**, b f Westerner—Tordasia (IRE) **Roisin Grassick**
11 **TEXAS ROCK (IRE)**, b c Rock of Gibraltar (IRE)—Vestavia (IRE) **T. Geary**

TWO-YEAR-OLDS

12 **MIZPAH (IRE)**, b f 4/3 Excellent Art—Philosophers Guest (IRE) (Desert Prince (IRE)) **M. C. Grassick**
13 **RIVER INDIAN (IRE)**, b c 18/3 Sleeping Indian—River Pearl (GER) (Turfkonig (GER)) (13333) **Fenpark Syndicate**
14 **SCRIPTURIENT (IRE)**, ch g 20/4 Arakan (USA)—
Kelso Magic (USA) (Distant View (USA)) (8571) **Fenpark Syndicate**
15 B f 25/4 Flemensfirth (USA)—Tordasia (IRE) (Dr Devious (IRE)) **Roisin Grassick**

Assistant Trainer: Dave Flynn

Jockey (flat): Niall McCullagh. **Apprentice:** Stephen Kelly.

265 MR CARROLL GRAY, Bridgwater
Postal: **Horlake, Moorland, Bridgwater, Somerset, TA7 0AT**
Contacts: HOME **(01278) 691359** MOBILE **(07989) 768163**

1 **ALL BUT GREY**, 8, ro g Baryshnikov (AUS)—Butleigh Rose **Mr R. J. Napper and Mr N. P. Searle**
2 **CONVERTI**, 10, b g Averti (IRE)—Conquestadora **Mrs E. A. Heal**
3 **GINGERS REFLECTION**, 8, ch g Alflora (IRE)—Trassey Bridge **The Dr Gadian Partnership**
4 **LAMBLORD (IRE)**, 7, b g Brian Boru—Princess Symphony (USA) **The Lamb Inn - Pethy**
5 **LEVICHE**, 4, ch g Shirocco (GER)—Alla Prima (IRE) **Riverdance Consortium 2**
6 **MON CHEVALIER (IRE)**, 11, b g Montjeu (IRE)—Kumta (IRE) **S. C. Botham**
7 **SAINT BREIZ (FR)**, 8, b br g Saint des Saints (FR)—Balladina (FR) **Riverdance Consortium 2**
8 **VOLIO VINCENTE (FR)**, 7, b br g Corri Piano (FR)—Vollore (FR) **optimumracing.co.uk**

Other Owners: Mr R. G. Botham, Mr M. J. Colenutt, Mr Richard Flenk, Dr D. S. Gadian, Mrs Christine Gray, Mrs A. Johnson, Mr Andrew Lowrie, Mrs J. Lowrie, Mr R. Napper, Mr N. P. Searle, Mr R. L. Squire.

Assistant Trainer: Mrs C M L Gray

Jockey (NH): Micheal Nolan. **Amateur:** Mr R. Hawker.

266 MR PETER GRAYSON, Formby
Postal: Apartment 7, The Sandwarren, 21 Victoria Road, Formby
Contacts: PHONE (01704) 830668 FAX (01704) 830668
E-MAIL info@pgr.uk.com WEBSITE www.pgr.uk.com

1 AVONVALLEY, 7, b m Avonbridge—Piper's Ash (USA) R. S. Teatum
2 DINGAAN (IRE), 11, b g Tagula (IRE)—Boughtbyphone R. S. Teatum
3 EVENS AND ODDS (IRE), 10, ch g Johannesburg (USA)—Coeur de La Mer (IRE) R. S. Teatum
4 FLOW CHART (IRE), 7, b g Acclamation—Free Flow Mr E. Grayson
5 ISHETOO, 10, b g Ishiguru (USA)—Ticcatoo (IRE) R. S. Teatum
6 MID YORKSHIRE GOLF, 5, b m Doyen (IRE)—Jodeeka R. S. Teatum
7 RAJEH, 11, b g Key of Luck (USA)—Saramacca (IRE) Mr E. Grayson
8 RIGHTCAR, 7, b g Bertolini (USA)—Loblolly Bay R. S. Teatum
9 5, B m Echo of Light—Seeking Utopia
10 SONG OF PARKES, 7, b m Fantastic Light (USA)—My Melody Parkes Mr E. Grayson
11 STONEACRE BRIGITTE (IRE), 5, b h Refuse To Bend (IRE)—Kaveri (USA) R. S. Teatum
12 STONEACRE HULL (IRE), 5, b m Bachelor Duke (USA)—Amount R. S. Teatum
13 STONEACRE LAD (IRE), 11, b h Bluebird (USA)—Jay And-A (IRE) R. S. Teatum
14 STONEACRE OSKAR, 5, b m Echo of Light—Keidas (FR) R. S. Teatum
15 STONEACRE THIRSK (IRE), 5, br m Red Clubs (IRE)—Alexander Eliott (IRE) R. S. Teatum
16 STONEACRE TILLY, 5, b h Tiger Hill (IRE)—B Beautiful (IRE) R. S. Teatum
17 VHUJON (IRE), 9, b g Mujadil (USA)—Livius Lady (IRE) R. S. Teatum

Assistant Trainer: Mrs S. Grayson

267 MR WARREN GREATREX, Upper Lambourn
Postal: Uplands, Upper Lambourn, Hungerford, Berkshire, RG17 8QH
Contacts: PHONE (01488) 670279 FAX (01488) 670279 MOBILE (07920) 039114
E-MAIL info@wgreatrexracing.com WEBSITE www.wgreatrexracing.com

1 4, B g Kalanisi (IRE)—A And Bs Gift (IRE) Mr W. J. Greatrex
2 ANDI'AMU (FR), 4, b g Walk In The Park (IRE)—Sainte Parfaite (FR) The Pheasant Inn Racing Club
3 BABY MIX (FR), 6, gr g Al Namix (FR)—Douchka (FR) GDM Partnership
4 BALLYCULLA (IRE), 7, b g Westerner—Someone Told Me (IRE) No Dramas Partnership
5 BARLOW (IRE), 7, br g Beneficial—Carrigeen Kerria (IRE) GDM Partnership
6 4, B br g Indian River (FR)—Beechill Dancer (IRE) Mr W. J. Greatrex
7 BERKELEY AVENUE, 5, ch g Needwood Blade—Dropitlikeit's Hot (IRE) Uplanders Partnership
8 CAITYS JOY (GER), 4, b f Malinas (GER)—Cassilera (GER) Mr W. J. Greatrex
9 CARPIES BOY, 5, b g Dreams End—Bungar Belle (IRE) Mr G. Davies
10 CHALK IT DOWN (IRE), 5, b g Milan—Feedthegoodmare (IRE) J. P. McManus
11 CHASE THE WIND (IRE), 5, ch g Spadoun (FR)—Asfreeasthewind (IRE) Mrs Jill Eynon & Mr Robin Eynon
12 COLE HARDEN (IRE), 5, b g Westerner—Nosie Betty (IRE) Mrs Jill Eynon & Mr Robin Eynon
13 CON FORZA, 5, b g Milan—Classic Track Fawley House Stud
14 DOLATULO (IRE), 7, ch g Le Fou (IRE)—La Perspective (FR) Chasemore Farm LLP
15 ELLNANDO QUEEN, 6, b m Hernando (FR)—Queen of Spades (IRE) Mrs R. I. Vaughan
16 FLICK THROUGH (IRE), 5, ch g Publisher (USA)—Maple River (IRE) Mrs T. Greatrex & Mr Paul Syson
17 GOOD OF LUCK, 5, b g Authorized (IRE)—Oops Pettie Mr & Mrs Bernard Panton
18 HAND ON BACH (IRE), 6, b g Bach (IRE)—Deise Blues (IRE) Outdoor Five
19 HANNAH'S PRINCESS (IRE), 5, b m Kalanisi (IRE)—Donna's Princess (IRE) The Swanee River Partnership
20 HEAD RUSH, 6, b g Exit To Nowhere (USA)—Petale de Rose (IRE) Mrs T. J. Stone-Brown
21 HIGH KITE (IRE), 8, b br g High-Rise (IRE)—Sister Rose (IRE) The High Kites
22 HORSTED VALLEY, 4, gr g Fair Mix (IRE)—Kullu Valley The Broadwell Fox Partnership
23 KETTLEWELL, 5, ch g Auction House (USA)—Angel Chimes Mark Duthie Partnership
24 4, B g Kayf Tara—La Dame Brune (FR)
25 MA DU FOU (FR), 4, b br g Le Fou (IRE)—Belle du Ma (FR) Lee Bolingbroke & Graeme Howard
26 MADNESS LIGHT (FR), 5, b g Satri (IRE)—Majestic Lady (FR) Mrs T. J. Stone-Brown
27 MASQUERADE (IRE), 5, b g Fruits of Love (USA)—Beechill Dancer (IRE) Mrs S. Griffiths
28 MISS ESTELA (IRE), 4, b f Tobougg (IRE)—Simply Divine (IRE) Mrs L. Suenson-Taylor
29 MIXOLOGIST, 7, gr g Fair Mix (IRE)—Matchboard Again (IRE) Mrs T. J. Stone-Brown
30 ONE TRACK MIND (IRE), 4, b g Flemensfirth (USA)—Lady Petit (IRE) Mr Andy Weller
31 OSCAR PRAIRIE (IRE), 9, b g Oscar (IRE)—Silver Prairie (IRE) Mr W. J. Greatrex
32 SILENT KNIGHT (IRE), 5, b g Pierre—Aristocracy Lass (IRE) GDM Partnership
33 SKY WATCH (IRE), 7, b g Flemensfirth (USA)—The Shining Force (IRE) Bolingbroke, Lewis, Meggs & Horgan
34 STAGE KING, 8, b g King's Theatre (IRE)—Blue Dante (IRE) Fallon Family Partnership

MR WARREN GREATREX - Continued

35 TEOCHEW (IRE), 6, b m Shantou (USA)—Papal Princess (IRE) **Hooch & Hooves Partnership**
36 TOP DANCER (FR), 7, b g Dark Moondancer—Latitude (FR) **The Lone Star Partnership**
37 TRANQUIL SEA (IRE), 12, b g Sea Raven (IRE)—Silver Valley (IRE) **No Dramas Partnership 1**
38 TSAR ALEXANDRE (FR), 7, b g Robin des Champs (FR)—Bertrange (FR) **Mr W. J. Greatrex**
39 WESTWARD POINT, 7, ch g Karinga Bay—Hottentot **Mr J. F. F. White**
40 WOJCIECH, 4, b f Lucarno (USA)—Pondimari (FR) **Uplands Ladies**

Other Owners: Mr A. Black, Mrs J. E. Black, Mr Lee Bolingbroke, Mr Gregory Charlesworth, Mr Daniel Charlesworth, Mrs Wendy Coles, Mr M. Duthie, Mrs J. M. Eynon, Mr R. A. F. Eynon, Mrs Padraic Fallon, Mr S. Fisher, Mr Rupert Fowler, Mrs D. S. Gillborn, Mr Warren Greatrex, Mrs Tessa Greatrex, Mr M. W. Gregory, Ms Ginny Hambly, Mr John Horgan, Mr Graeme Howard, Mr Darren Johns, Mrs Michael Lambert, Mr Christopher Lewis, Mrs Anne Meggs, Mrs Hugh Murphy, Mr E. R. Newnham, Mr Bernard Panton, Mrs Jane Panton, Miss C. Shipp, Mr Michael Smith, Mr Charles Sutton, Mr T. D. J. Syder, Mr Paul Syson.

Head Lad: Graham Baines, **Racing Secretary:** Oriana-Jane Young

Jockey (NH): Noel Fehily. **Conditional:** William Featherstone, Gavin Sheehan.

---

268 **MR PAUL GREEN**, Lydiate
Postal: **Oak Lea, Southport Road, Lydiate, Liverpool, Merseyside, L31 4HH**
Contacts: **PHONE (0151) 526 0093 FAX (0151) 520 0299 MOBILE (07748) 630685**
E-MAIL paulgreen@mitchell-james.com

1 BALTIC PRINCE (IRE), 4, b c Baltic King—Brunswick **Mr A. Mills**
2 BEAU MISTRAL (IRE), 5, ch m Windsor Knot (IRE)—Carpet Lover (IRE) **The Winsor Not Group**
3 DUBARA REEF (IRE), 7, ch g Dubawi (IRE)—Mamara Reef **Oaklea Aces**
4 FERDY (IRE), 5, b h Antonius Pius (USA)—Trinity Fair **Men Behaving Badly Two**
5 HOLLYDANFAYE, 4, b f Avonbridge—Canina **Mr I. Furlong**
6 LUCKY DAN (IRE), 8, b g Danetime (IRE)—Katherine Gorge (USA) **P. Green**
7 M J WOODWARD, 5, b h Needwood Blade—Canina **P. Green**
8 REFUSE COLETTE (IRE), 5, ch m Refuse To Bend (IRE)—Roclette (USA) **Mr D. Kearns**
9 RUSTY ROCKET (IRE), 5, ch h Majestic Missile (IRE)—Sweet Compliance **Seven Stars Racing**
10 WORLD RECORD (IRE), 4, b c Choisir (AUS)—Dancing Debut **Mr C. S. Hinchy**

THREE-YEAR-OLDS

11 DE REPENTE, b f Captain Rio—Suddenly **M. F. Nolan**
12 EVIE JAY (IRE), ch f Windsor Knot (IRE)—Carpet Lover (IRE) **The Winsor Not Group 2**
13 B f Myboycharlie (IRE)—Jilly Why (IRE)
14 PAPARIMA (IRE), b f Elnadim (USA)—Daily Double (FR) **Gary Williams & Ged Barton**
15 ROCKIE ROAD (IRE), b c Footstepsinthesand—Roclette (USA) **Mr D. Kearns**
16 SUNI DANCER, b f Captain Gerrard (IRE)—Sunisa (IRE) **Mr I. Furlong**
17 YNWA, b c Myboycharlie (IRE)—Sudden Impact (IRE) **G. Williams**

TWO-YEAR-OLDS

18 CITISONSMITH (IRE), b c 21/4 Amadeus Wolf—Ink Pot (USA) (Green Dancer (USA)) (3871) **Mr A. Mills**
19 B c 22/4 Bushranger (IRE)—Dress Up (IRE) (Noverre (USA)) (4645)
20 B f 4/3 Bushranger (IRE)—Hazium (IRE) (In The Wings) (6194) **M. F. Nolan**
21 B f 16/3 Dark Angel (IRE)—Roclette (USA) (Rock of Gibraltar (IRE)) **Mr C. S. Hinchy**

Other Owners: Mr G. Barton, P. Lavin, I. P. Mason.

Assistant Trainer: Fiona Ford

---

269 **MR TOM GRETTON**, Inkberrow
Postal: **C/o Gretton & Co Ltd, Middle Bouts Farm, Bouts Lane, Inkberrow, Worcester, WR7 4HP**
Contacts: **PHONE (01386) 792240 FAX (01386) 792472 MOBILE (07866) 116928**
E-MAIL tomgretton@hotmail.co.uk WEBSITE www.tomgrettonracing.com

1 ARMEDANDBEAUTIFUL, 6, b m Oscar (IRE)—Grey Mistral **Not The Peloton Partnership**
2 ARMEDANDDANGEROUS (IRE), 9, b g Kris Kin (USA)—Lucky Fountain (IRE) **Not The Peloton Partnership**
3 CLARA PEGGOTTY, 7, b m Beat All (USA)—Clair Valley **Geoffrey Price & Edward Gretton**
4 CRAZY JANE (IRE), 5, br m Definite Article—Blue Romance (IRE) **Mr E. M. O'Connor**

MR TOM GRETTON - Continued

5 **FINE JEWELLERY,** 5, b g Epalo (GER)—Lola Lolita (FR) **Ms A. S. Potze**
6 **JACKTHEJOURNEYMAN (IRE),** 5, b g Beneficial—Maslam (IRE) **The Delaynomore Group**
7 **LITTLE JIMMY,** 7, br g Passing Glance—Sementina (USA) **Pip Walter & M Khan X2**
8 **LL COOL HORSE,** 5, b g Lavirco (GER)—Jaxelle (FR) **Mr J W & Mrs J S Dale & Mr M G Vivian**
9 **LORDSHIP (IRE),** 10, b g King's Best (USA)—Rahika Rose **G1 Racing Club Ltd**
10 **SANDANSKI (IRE),** 6, b g Definite Article—Castle Hope (IRE) **The O'Connor Duffy Racing Partnership**
11 **SWING STATE,** 9, b g Overbury (IRE)—Peg's Permission **G1 Racing Club Ltd**
12 **THATS BEN (IRE),** 9, b g Beneficial—Classy Dancer (IRE) **G1 Racing Club Ltd**

Other Owners: Mr J. W. Dale, Mrs J. S. Dale, D. P. Duffy, T. R. Gretton, Mr E. P. Gretton, Mr J. R. Hynes, M. Khan, Mustafa Khan, Mr E. O'Connor, Mr G. H. E. Price, Mr M. G. Vivian, Mr P. J. Walter.

Assistant Trainer: Laura Gretton (07789) 754806

Jockey (NH): Dougie Costello, Felix De Giles.

---

270 MR PATRICK GRIFFIN, Co Dublin
Postal: Killeen House, Oldtown, Co. Dublin, Ireland
Contacts: **MOBILE (00353) 871301719**
E-MAIL pggriffin@live.ie

1 **INCA KOLA,** 6, gr g Verglas (IRE)—Palm Reef (USA) **Mr M. Deren & Mr J. A. Griffin**
2 5, Br m Beneficial—Kigali (IRE) **B. Griffin**
3 **LISBON (IRE),** 6, b g Cape Cross (IRE)—Caraiyma (IRE) **Mr M. Deren**
4 **MAGGIO (FR),** 9, b g Trempolino (USA)—La Musardiere (FR) **Mr M. Deren**
5 4, B g Poliglote—Place d'armes (IRE) **Maggio Racing**
6 9, Ch m Definite Article—Smash N Lass **Mrs F. Griffin**
7 **SORROW (FR),** 4, b g Early March—Cochinchine (IRE) **Maggio Racing**
8 **SUDSKI STAR (IRE),** 6, b g Pilsudski (IRE)—Mogen's Star (IRE) **Mr M. D. Fitzpatrick**
9 **TWENTYPOUNDLUCK (IRE),** 9, ch g Beneficial—Guitane Lady (IRE) **Mr M. Deren**
10 **ZAMBEZI TIGER (IRE),** 5, b g Tiger Hill (IRE)—Johannesburg Cat (USA) **Mr M. Deren**

THREE-YEAR-OLDS
11 **GRAND TOUR,** b f Rail Link—Cordoba **Maggio Racing**

Other Owners: Clarricien Syndicate, G. Davies, J. Dillon, R. T. Griffin, Ms S. J. Hardie, L. Heron, A. Hulme, JAG Bloodstock, J. Lawless, Maggio Bloodstock, P. Scholes, C. White.

Assistant Trainer: James Griffin

Jockey (NH): James Reveley, Brian Hughes. **Conditional:** D. R. Fox.

---

271 MR DAVID C. GRIFFITHS, Bawtry
Postal: Martin Hall, Martin Common, Bawtry, Doncaster, South Yorkshire, DN10 6DA
Contacts: **PHONE (01302) 714247 MOBILE (07816) 924621**
E-MAIL davidgriffiths250@hotmail.com WEBSITE www.dcgracing.co.uk

1 **CYFLYMDER (IRE),** 8, b g Mujadil (USA)—Nashwan Star (IRE) **Eros Bloodstock**
2 **MUNAAWIB,** 6, b g Haafhd—Mouwadh (USA) **W. McKay**
3 **WHISKY BRAVO,** 5, b g Byron—Dress Design (IRE) **Dallas Racing & Owen Robinson**
4 **WILD HILL BOY,** 4, b g Tiger Hill (IRE)—Kalamansi (IRE) **Norcroft Park Stud**
5 **YUNGABURRA (IRE),** 10, b g Fath (USA)—Nordic Living (IRE) **Mr D. W. Noble**

THREE-YEAR-OLDS
6 **ASHA,** ch f Dutch Art—Golden Asha **Norcroft Park Stud**
7 **BRITAIN (IRE),** b f Manduro (GER)—Unreal Morton Racing
8 **MAMBO FEVER,** b f Footstepsinthesand—Mambo's Melody **Norcroft Park Stud**
9 **RED HOUSE,** b g Auction House (USA)—Highest Dream (IRE) **Mr Shaun Humphries & Mr D Griffiths**
10 **ST PAUL'S (IRE),** b c Bushranger (IRE)—Regina Ballerina (IRE) **R P B Michaelson, R Crowe & S Griffiths**

MR DAVID C. GRIFFITHS - Continued

TWO-YEAR-OLDS

11 B f 14/4 Captain Gerrard (IRE)—Branston Jewel (IRE) (Prince Sabo) (10065) **Gee Gee Racing**
12 B f 31/3 Kodiac—Campiglia (IRE) (Fairy King (USA)) (6968)
13 B f 9/3 Lawman (FR)—Enchanting Muse (USA) (Fusaichi Pegasus (USA)) (774)
14 Ch f 16/2 Captain Gerrard (IRE)—Lady Duxyana (Most Welcome) (8095) **Mickley Stud & D C Griffiths**
15 STORM PRINCESS, ch f 17/3 Zamindar (USA)—Tarandot (IRE) (Singspiel (IRE)) **Norcroft Park Stud**

Other Owners: R. L. Crowe, A. D. Gee, Mr R. G. Gee, Mr M. A. Glassett, Mrs S. Griffiths, D. C. Griffiths, A. J. Hollis, Mr D. M. Hollis, Mr S. Humphries, R. Kent, R. P. B. Michaelson, Mrs S. Noble, Norton Common Farm Racing Ltd, Mr O. Robinson.

Assistant Trainer: Mrs S. E. Griffiths

Apprentice: Ali Rawlinson.

272
MR SIMON GRIFFITHS, Easingwold
Postal: **Hazel Hill Farm, Blackwoods, Easingwold, York, North Yorkshire, YO61 3ER**
Contacts: **PHONE (01347) 811770 MOBILE (07967) 039208**
E-MAIL elizabeth.grant@longbridgeuk.co.uk

1 CHARLES PARNELL (IRE), 11, b g Elnadim (USA)—Titania **Mr S. P. Griffiths**
2 HARPERS RUBY, 4, b f Byron—La Belle Katherine (USA) **Mr S. P. Griffiths**
3 PHOENIX JOY, 6, b m Presidium—Miss Ceylon **Mr S. P. Griffiths**
4 TENDER CARE, 6, b g Gentleman's Deal (IRE)—Intavac Girl **Mr S. P. Griffiths**

Assistant Trainer: Elizabeth Grant

273
MRS DIANA GRISSELL, Robertsbridge
Postal: **Brightling Park, Robertsbridge, East Sussex, TN32 5HH**
Contacts: **PHONE (01424) 838241 MOBILE (07950) 312610**
E-MAIL digrissell@aol.com WEBSITE www.grissellracing.co.uk

1 ARBEO (IRE), 8, b g Brian Boru—Don't Waste It (IRE) **Nigel & Barbara Collison**
2 BISKY BAR, 6, b m Nomadic Way (USA)—Deeprivie **Ms C. A. Lacey**
3 BLUE BEAR (IRE), 5, b g Blueprint (IRE)—In For It (IRE) **Ms J. A. Lambert**
4 BOY OF BORU (IRE), 7, b g Brian Boru—Don't Waste It (IRE) **The Wasteinit Partnership**
5 HERE I AM (IRE), 7, br g Presenting—The Last Bank (IRE) **Nigel & Barbara Collison**
6 IMPERIAL CRU, 6, b g Imperial Dancer—Miss Fizz **Mrs D. M. Grissell**
7 OSCAR BABY (IRE), 8, b m Oscar (IRE)—Snowbaby (IRE) **Mr R. E. Halley**
8 ROPARTA AVENUE, 7, b g Nomadic Way (USA)—Miss Fizz **Mrs D. M. Grissell**
9 TORERO, 5, b g Hernando (FR)—After You **Mr E. S. Hicks**
10 WUNFURLEZ, 6, b g Kayf Tara—Fairlead **Nigel & Barbara Collison**

Other Owners: Mr N. Collison, Mrs B. Collison, Mr M. Cutler.

Jockey (NH): Marc Goldstein, Sam Thomas.

274
MR JOHN BYRAN GROUCOTT, Much Wenlock
Postal: **11 Bourton Cottages, Much Wenlock, Shropshire, TF13 6QF**
Contacts: **PHONE (01746) 785603 FAX (01746) 785603 MOBILE (07866) 480830**
E-MAIL lisajmwillis@aol.com

1 BOOSHA, 9, ch m Sir Harry Lewis (USA)—Musical Vocation (IRE) **Mr P Price & Mr P Williams**
2 HONOUR THE KING (IRE), 8, b br g Insan (USA)—Cassies Girl (IRE) **Paternosters Racing**
3 LORD GALE (IRE), 8, ch g Bach (IRE)—Wire Lady (IRE) **Ms L. J. M. Willis**
4 ONE MORE DINAR, 11, b g Kayf Tara—One More Dime (IRE) **Mrs A. V. Winwood**
5 PRET A THOU (FR), 11, ch g Funny Baby (FR)—Va Thou Line (FR) **C. J. Tipton**
6 WAYWOOD PRINCESS, 9, b m Sir Harry Lewis (USA)—First Bee **Mr P Price & Mr P Williams**

Other Owners: T. P. Cain, D. M. Hughes, Mr P. Price, P. J. D. Williams.

275　**MR BRIAN GUBBY, Bagshot**
Postal: **Dukes Wood, Bracknell Road, Bagshot, Surrey, GU19 5HX**
Contacts: OFFICE **(01276) 850513** MOBILE **(07768) 867368**

1 **AL AQABAH (IRE)**, 9, ch m Redback—Snow Eagle (IRE) **B. Gubby**
2 **KINGLAMI**, 5, b g Kingsalsa (USA)—Red Japonica **B. Gubby**
3 **PAL OF THE CAT**, 4, ch g Choisir (AUS)—Evenstorm (USA) **B. Gubby**

Assistant Trainer: Larry Wilkins

276　**MR RAE GUEST, Newmarket**
Postal: **Chestnut Tree Stables, Hamilton Road, Newmarket, Suffolk, CB8 0NY**
Contacts: PHONE **(01638) 661508** FAX **(01638) 667317** MOBILE **(07711) 301095**
E-MAIL raeguest@raeguest.com WEBSITE www.raeguest.com

1 **ARCHIVE**, 4, b f Dansili—Modesta (IRE) **C. J. Murfitt**
2 **CALM ATTITUDE (IRE)**, 4, ch f Dutch Art—Turban Heights (IRE) **The Calm Again Partnership**
3 **CARDI CAVALIER**, 4, b g Bertolini (USA)—Bonnie Belle **Mr D. H. L. Jones**
4 **FIRST CLASS**, 6, b g Oasis Dream—Break Point **Mr B. Cooper & Miss E. Reffo**
5 **KICKINGTHELILLY**, 5, ch m Byron—Teller (ARG) **Homecroft Wealth Racing**
6 **MILIIKA**, 5, b m Green Desert (USA)—Miss Anabaa **Bradmill Meats Ltd**
7 **MILLION FACES**, 5, ch m Exceed And Excel (AUS)—Millyant **C. J. Mills**
8 **MIRZA**, 7, b g Oasis Dream—Millyant **C. J. Mills**
9 **ROSIE REBEL**, 4, ch f Cockney Rebel (IRE)—Meandering Rose (USA) **P. W. Saunders, R. Guest & O. Lury**
10 **RUFFLED**, 4, b f Harlan's Holiday (USA)—Mirabilis (USA) **C. J. Murfitt**

THREE-YEAR-OLDS

11 **ARCHDUCHESS**, b f Archipenko (USA)—Eminencia **Miss K. Rausing**
12 **CHESS VALLEY**, b f Shamardal (USA)—Grecian Air (FR) **The Boot Sarratt Racing Syndicate**
13 **DISTANT HIGH**, b f High Chaparral (IRE)—Distant Dreamer (USA) **Mrs Paula Smith & Mr Rae Guest**
14 **FIRST EXPERIENCE**, b f Tamayuz—Lolla's Spirit (IRE) **Fitorfat Racing & Guy Carstairs**
15 **FLYING BY**, b f Byron—Flyfisher (USA) **Joseph, Smart & Guest**
16 **GOD'S SPEED (IRE)**, b c Oratorio (IRE)—Guilia **The Hornets**
17 **MINISKIRT**, b f Naaqoos—Minnola **C. J. Mills**
18 **MINK COAT**, b f Amadeus Wolf—Grand Slam Anabaa (IRE) **C. J. Mills**
19 **MISS BUCKSHOT (IRE)**, b f Tamayuz—Miss Bellbird (IRE) **Buckhurst Chevaliers**
20 B f Ad Valorem (USA)—Riva Royale **Mr D. H. L. Jones**
21 **SOUND OF LIFE (IRE)**, b f Cape Cross (IRE)—Stylist (IRE) **Purple & Yellow**
22 B f Dubawi (IRE)—Still Small Voice **Mrs M. Bryce**
23 **STRAWBERRIESNCREAM (IRE)**, b f Teofilo (IRE)—Jellett (IRE) **Ballymore Downunder Syndicate**
24 **STRIKE A LIGHT**, gr f Dutch Art—Bridal Path **Mr T. J. Benton**
25 **STROLL ON (IRE)**, ch f Exceed And Excel (USA)—Violet (IRE) **Mr T. J. Benton**
26 **TORREON (IRE)**, b c High Chaparral (IRE)—Teide Lady **E. P. Duggan**
27 **WORLD OF GOLD (IRE)**, b f High Chaparral (IRE)—Twyla (AUS) **Mr J. M. Camilleri**

TWO-YEAR-OLDS

28 Ch c 20/3 Rock of Gibraltar (IRE)—Amicable Terms (Royal Applause) **The Storm Again Syndicate**
29 **DALAMAR**, b f 1/3 Montjeu (IRE)—Dalasyla (IRE) (Marju (IRE)) (120000) **R. Guest**
30 Ch f 2/2 Captain Rio—Dancing Jest (IRE) (Averti (IRE)) **O. T. Lury**
31 Gr f 23/3 Zebedee—Dixie Jazz (Mtoto) (8903) **B. Stewart**
32 **DREAM APPROACH (IRE)**, b f 8/4 New Approach (IRE)—
　　　　　　　　Witch of Fife (USA) (Lear Fan (USA)) (60000) **Fishdance Ltd**
33 **DUCHESSOFMARMALADE**, b f 7/4 Duke of Marmalade (IRE)—
　　　　　　　　Helena Molony (IRE) (Sadler's Wells (USA)) (62000) **Fishdance Ltd**
34 **ELLA'S HONOUR**, b f 2/4 Makfi—Danella (FR) (Highest Honor (FR))
35 B f 2/5 Makfi—Entre Nous (IRE) (Sadler's Wells (USA)) (27000) **R. Guest**
36 B f 15/3 Azamour (IRE)—Guilia (Galileo (IRE)) **The Hornets**
37 **MONT FEU (IRE)**, b f 20/4 Montjeu (IRE)—I'm In Love (USA) (Zafonic (USA)) **Fishdance Ltd**
38 B f 25/3 Acclamation—Pearl Trader (IRE) (Dubai Destination (USA)) (22000)
39 B f 15/1 Exceed And Excel (AUS)—Reflected Image (USA) (Refuse To Bend (IRE)) (100000) **Mr F. L. Li**
40 **SATIN AND LACE (IRE)**, b f 6/3 Mawatheeq (USA)—Katayeb (USA) (Machiavellian (USA)) (14000) **D. J. Willis**
41 **SECRET PALACE**, ch f 16/2 Pastoral Pursuits—
　　　　　　　　Some Sunny Day (Where Or When (IRE)) (18000) **We'll Meet Again Partnership**

MR RAE GUEST - Continued

42 B c 16/3 Royal Applause—Silver Rhapsody (USA) (Silver Hawk (USA)) (3000) **Mr Trevor Benton & Mr Rae Guest**
43 B f 3/3 Intense Focus (USA)—Timber Tops (UAE) (Timber Country (USA)) (10000)

Other Owners: G. N. Carstairs, B. A. Cooper, A. P. Davies, Mr M. K. Duggan, B. J. Flahive, J. W. Fullick, R. T. Goodes, T. Hirschfeld, Mrs G. A. Jennings, Mr C. S. Joseph, Mr R. P. Legh, Mr M. D. Moroney, S. J. Piper, Mr N. Pogmore, D. G. Raffel, Ms E. M. B. A. Reffo, P. A. Sakal, P. W. Saunders, G. W. Smart, Mrs P. Smith.

Assistant Trainer: Nicholas McKee **Head Lad:** Steve Lodge

Jockey (flat): Chris Catlin.

---

 277 **MR RICHARD GUEST, Ingmanthorpe**
Postal: **Ingmanthorpe Racing Stables, Ingmanthorpe Grange Farm, Ingmanthorpe, Wetherby, West Yorkshire, LS22 5HL**
Contacts: **PHONE (01937) 587552 (07715) 516072 / (07715) 516073 FAX (01937) 587552 MOBILE (07715) 516071**
E-MAIL enquiries@richardguestracing.co.uk WEBSITE www.richardguestracing.co.uk

1 ALPHA TAURI (USA), 8, b g Aldebaran (USA)—Seven Moons (JPN) **Mrs A. L. Guest**
2 AMBITIOUS ICARUS, 5, b g Striking Ambition—Nesting Box **ABS Metals & Waste**
3 BALINROAB (IRE), 7, b g Milan—Gentle Eyre (IRE) **Miss C. Fordham**
4 BLAZEOFENCHANTMENT (USA), 4, b g Officer (USA)—Willow Rush (USA) **Mrs A. L. Guest**
5 CAPTAIN SCOOBY, 8, b g Captain Rio—Scooby Dooby Do **Resdev Ltd**
6 CHAPELLERIE (IRE), 5, b m Acclamation—Castellane (FR) **Mrs A. L. Guest**
7 CHARLEMAGNE DIVA, 4, b f Holy Roman Emperor (IRE)—Opera Ridge (FR) **Mr C. J. Penney**
8 DI'S GIFT, 5, b g Generous (IRE)—Di's Dilemma **Mr & Mrs T. W. Readett-Bayley**
9 FRENCH CANADIAN (FR), 8, b g Spadoun (FR)—Floresca (FR) **Mr G. Hibbert**
10 HAZZA THE JAZZA, 4, br g Jeremy (USA)—Zagaleta **Mr D. A. Aarons**
11 HYDRANT, 8, b g Haafhd—Spring **Mr C. Hatch**
12 JOHNNY CAVAGIN, 5, b g Superior Premium—Beyond The Rainbow **Mr A. Bell**
13 KHAWATIM, 6, b g Intikhab (USA)—Don't Tell Mum (IRE) **Mrs A. L. Guest**
14 LORD BUFFHEAD, 5, br g Iceman—Royal Pardon **Mrs A. L. Guest**
15 MISS BELLA ROSE, 7, gr m Silver Patriarch (IRE)—City Rose **Mr G. Hibbert**
16 ORATORY (IRE), 8, b g Danehill Dancer (IRE)—Gentle Night **Mrs A. L. Guest**
17 OUTLAW TORN (IRE), 5, ch g Iffraaj—Touch And Love (IRE) **J. S. Kennerley**
18 POLAR FOREST, 4, br g Kyllachy—Woodbeck **Maze Rattan Limited**
19 PRECISION STRIKE, 4, b g Multiplex—Dockside Strike **Resdev Ltd**
20 QUALITY ART (USA), 6, b g Elusive Quality (USA)—Katherine Seymour **Mrs A. L. Guest**
21 ROBIN THE RICH (IRE), 4, b g Robin des Pres (FR)—Maid of Music (IRE) **Miss C. Fordham**
22 RYLEE MOOCH, 6, grey g Choisir (AUS)—Negligee **Katie Hughes, Sheila White, Julie McCarlie**
23 SKY KHAN, 5, b g Cape Cross (IRE)—Starlit Sky **The Unique Partnership**
24 STOREY HILL (USA), 9, b br g Richter Scale (USA)—Crafty Nan (USA) **Mrs A. L. Guest**
25 TED'S BROTHER (IRE), 6, b g Fath—Estertide (IRE) **Ontoawinner & Bob McCoy**

THREE-YEAR-OLDS

26 EDDIEMAURICE, ch g Captain Rio—Annals **Mrs A. L. Guest**
27 GENAX (IRE), b f Green Desert (USA)—Steam Cuisine **Mrs A. L. Guest**
28 IT'S ALL A GAME, ch g Sleeping Indian—St Edith (IRE) **Viscount Environmental Ltd**
29 PAINT IT RED (IRE), ch f Papal Bull—Skerries (IRE) **Mrs A. L. Guest**
30 SAKHALIN STAR (IRE), ch g Footstepsinthesand—Quela (GER) **Bamboozelem**
31 TORTOISE, b f Multiplex—Wonderful Island (GER) **Mrs A. L. Guest**

TWO-YEAR-OLDS

32 B g 2/4 Captain Rio—Alchimie (IRE) (Sri Pekan (USA)) (3871) **Mrs A. L. Guest**
33 ERIC THE VIKING, b g 28/3 Monsieur Bond (IRE)—
Whatdo You Want (IRE) (Spectrum (IRE)) (1523) **Ann & Eric Lumley**
34 B f 13/5 Cockney Rebel (IRE)—Hill Tribe (Tiger Hill (IRE)) (761) **Mrs A. L. Guest**
35 Gr g 27/2 Aussie Rules (USA)—Krasotka (IRE) (Soviet Star (USA)) (6194) **Resdev Ltd**
36 Ch f 2/3 Captain Gerrard (IRE)—Mindfulness (Primo Dominie) (2857)
37 B g 24/2 Multiplex—No Page (IRE) (Statue of Liberty (USA)) (5714)
38 B f 15/5 Assertive—Princess Almora (Pivotal) (2095) **Mr C. J. Penney**
39 B g 29/4 Dandy Man—Shewillifshewants (IRE) (Alzao (USA)) (19357)
40 B g 29/3 Stimulation (IRE)—Shining Oasis (IRE) (Mujtahid (USA)) (2857)

MR RICHARD GUEST - Continued

Other Owners: Mrs S. Aldam, Mr A. Bullock-Smith, Mr A. R. Findlay, Mrs G. Findlay, Mrs Alison Guest, Mr Eric Lumley, Mrs Ann Lumley, M. J. Mahony, Mr R. McCoy, N. J. O'Brien, Mr T. W. Readett-Bayley, Mrs T. W. Readett-Bayley, M. E. White, Mrs S. White.

Jockey (flat): Billy Cray, Robbie Fitzpatrick. **Jockey (NH):** Denis O'Regan, Jack Quinlan.
Apprentice: Melissa Thompson. **Amateur:** Mr R. Asquith, Mr S. Bushby.

---

278 MISS POLLY GUNDRY, Ottery St Mary
Postal: Holcombe Brook, Holcombe Lane, Ottery St Mary, Devon, EX11 1PH
Contacts: PHONE (01404) 811181 MOBILE (07932) 780621
E-MAIL pollygundrytraining@live.co.uk

1 5, B m Windsor Heights—Alderley Girl **Mrs Diana Shepherd**
2 CHABLAIS (FR), 9, b g Saint des Saints (FR)—Malandra **Mr & Mrs R. G. Kelvin Hughes**
3 DAWSON CITY, 5, b g Midnight Legend—Running For Annie **Ian Payne and Kim Franklin**
4 GLADSTONE (IRE), 6, b g Dansili—Rockerlong **G. N. Carstairs**
5 HARRY'S FAREWELL, 7, b g Sir Harry Lewis (USA)—Golden Mile (IRE) **Mr J. P. Selby**
6 LADY ANNABEL (IRE), 4, br f Robin des Pres (FR)—Zaffie Parson (IRE) **Miss P. Gundry**
7 MR GARDNER (IRE), 11, b g Deploy—Lady Padivor (IRE) **Mr & Mrs R. G. Kelvin Hughes**
8 PROPER JOB, 6, b g Rainbow High—Merlin Cider **T. R. Oliver**

Other Owners: Miss Polly Gundry, Mr R. Kelvin-Hughes, Mrs R. Kelvin-Hughes.

Assistant Trainer: Edward Walker

Jockey (flat): Liam Keniry. **Jockey (NH):** James Best, Tom O'Brien. **Amateur:** Mr Ed Barrett, Mr Robbie Henderson.

---

279 MR WILLIAM HAGGAS, Newmarket
Postal: Somerville Lodge, Fordham Road, Newmarket, Suffolk, CB8 7AA
Contacts: PHONE (01638) 667013 FAX (01638) 660534 MOBILE (07860) 282281
E-MAIL william@somerville-lodge.co.uk

1 BATTALION (IRE), 4, b c Authorized (IRE)—Zigarra **Sheikh Juma Dalmook Al Maktoum**
2 CAPE CLASSIC (IRE), 6, b g Cape Cross (IRE)—Politesse (USA) **Mr B. Kantor**
3 CONDUCT (IRE), 7, gr g Selkirk (USA)—Coventina (IRE) **Highclere T'bred Racing Royal Palace**
4 DARE TO ACHIEVE, 4, b g Galileo (IRE)—Mussoorie (FR) **B. Kantor & M. Jooste**
5 EMPRESS ADELAIDE, 4, ch f Pivotal—Emperice (USA) **Cheveley Park Stud**
6 EPIC BATTLE (IRE), 4, b g Acclamation—Wrong Key (IRE) **Saleh Al Homaizi & Imad Al Sagar**
7 FAST OR FREE, 5, ch g Notnowcato—Ewenny **Ian & Christine Beard**
8 FURY, 6, gr g Invincible Spirit (IRE)—Courting **Cheveley Park Stud**
9 GRAPHIC (IRE), 5, ch g Excellent Art—Follow My Lead **The Royal Ascot Racing Club**
10 HARRIS TWEED, 7, b g Hernando (FR)—Frog **Mr B. Haggas**
11 HEERAAT (IRE), 5, b h Dark Angel (IRE)—Thawrah (IRE) **Hamdan Al Maktoum**
12 HOMAGE (IRE), 4, b g Acclamation—Night Sphere (IRE) **Highclere Thoroughbred Racing - Dalmeny**
13 LEITRIM PASS (USA), 4, ch g Raven's Pass (USA)—Santolina **Gallagher Equine Ltd**
14 MUKHADRAM, 5, b h Shamardal (USA)—Magic Tree (UAE) **Hamdan Al Maktoum**
15 MUTHMIR (IRE), 4, b g Invincible Spirit (IRE)—Fairy of The Night (IRE) **Hamdan Al Maktoum**
16 OUR OBSESSION (IRE), 4, ch f Shamardal (USA)—Hidden Hope **A. E. Oppenheimer**
17 QUEENSBERRY RULES (IRE), 4, b g Teofilo (IRE)—Fantastic Spring (USA) **L. Sheridan**
18 REX IMPERATOR, 5, b g Royal Applause—Elidore **Mr G. D. Turner**
19 ROCK CHOIR, 4, b f Pivotal—Choir Mistress **Cheveley Park Stud**
20 STENCIVE, 5, b h Dansili—Madeira Mist (IRE) **B. Kantor & M. Jooste**
21 TWEED, 4, b f Sakhee (USA)—Frog **Mr B. Haggas**
22 WELL PAINTED (IRE), 5, ch g Excellent Art—Aoife (IRE) **Options O Syndicate**

THREE-YEAR-OLDS

23 ALSHADHIA (IRE), b f Marju—Wijdan (USA) **Hamdan Al Maktoum**
24 APPROACHING STAR (FR), ch f New Approach (IRE)—Madame Arcati (IRE) **Sheikh Juma Dalmook Al Maktoum**
25 ARABIAN COMET (IRE), b f Dubawi (IRE)—Aviacion (BRZ) **Abdulla Al Mansoori**
26 AUTHORIZED TOO, b g Authorized (IRE)—Audaz **Abdulla Al Mansoori**
27 B f Cape Cross (IRE)—Avila **Saeed Manana**
28 BELAHODOOD, b c New Approach (IRE)—Broken Peace (USA) **Sultan Ali**
29 BILIMBI (IRE), b g Duke of Marmalade (IRE)—Starship (IRE) **Scott / Magnier / Piggott**

MR WILLIAM HAGGAS - Continued

30 **BROWN EYED HONEY**, b f Elusive City (USA)—Tiger Mist (IRE) **M S Bloodstock Ltd**
31 **BUREDYMA**, ch f Dutch Art—Petong's Pet **Saleh Al Homaizi & Imad Al Sagar**
32 **CLOUD LINE**, b f Danehill Dancer (IRE)—Superstar Leo (IRE) **Lael Stable**
33 **CUSTER (IRE)**, b c Invincible Spirit (IRE)—Red Feather (IRE) **Highclere T'Bred Racing & Lady O'Reilly**
34 **DANEHILL REVIVAL**, b f Pivotal—Danehill Destiny **Cheveley Park Stud**
35 **DAYDREAMER**, b g Duke of Marmalade (IRE)—Storyland (USA) **Mr & Mrs R. Scott**
36 **DREAM SPIRIT (IRE)**, b g Invincible Spirit (IRE)—
Dream Valley (IRE) **Roberts, Green, Whittall-Williams, Savidge**
37 **EHTIFAAL (IRE)**, b g Teofilo (IRE)—Kashoof **Hamdan Al Maktoum**
38 **ELHAAM (IRE)**, b f Shamardal (USA)—Loulwa (IRE) **Saleh Al Homaizi & Imad Al Sagar**
39 **ERTIJAAL (IRE)**, b c Oasis Dream—Shabiba (USA) **Hamdan Al Maktoum**
40 **ETAAB (USA)**, b f Street Cry (IRE)—Ethaara **Hamdan Al Maktoum**
41 **EXAMINER (IRE)**, ch g Excellent Art—Therry Girl (IRE) **Ian & Christine Beard**
42 **FAWN**, ch f Selkirk (USA)—Blue Dream (IRE) **Mr B. Haggas**
43 **FLIPPANT (IRE)**, ch f Pivotal—Moon Dazzle (USA) **Mr B. Kantor**
44 **GHANY (IRE)**, b f Lawman (FR)—Broken Spectre **Hamdan Al Maktoum**
45 **GOLD APPROACH**, ch f New Approach (IRE)—Samira Gold (FR) **Jaber Abdullah**
46 **JACOB'S PILLOW**, b c Oasis Dream—Enticing (IRE) **Lael Stable**
47 **KHAAWY (USA)**, b br f Arch (USA)—Jaleela (USA) **Hamdan Al Maktoum**
48 **LAW KEEPER (IRE)**, b f Lawman (IRE)—Lisieux Orchid (IRE) **Mr Saif Ali**
49 **LILLY JUNIOR**, b f Cape Cross (IRE)—Sweet Lilly **Jaber Abdullah**
50 **MANGE ALL**, b g Zamindar (USA)—Blancmange **Mr B. Haggas**
51 **MITRAAD (IRE)**, b g Aqlaam—Badweia (USA) **Hamdan Al Maktoum**
52 **MUTAKAYYEF**, ch c Sea The Stars (IRE)—Infallible **Hamdan Al Maktoum**
53 **NEZAR (IRE)**, ch g Mastercraftsman (IRE)—Teddy Bears Picnic **Saleh Al Homaizi & Imad Al Sagar**
54 **NOTEBOOK**, b c Invincible Spirit (IRE)—Love Everlasting **Highclere Thoroughbred Racing - Brunel**
55 **OSARUVEETIL (IRE)**, b c Teofilo (IRE)—Caraiyma (IRE) **Sheikh Mohammed Bin Khalifa Al Maktoum**
56 **OUR CHANNEL (USA)**, ch c English Channel (USA)—Raw Gold (USA) **Abdulla Al Mansoori**
57 **OXSANA**, b f Dubawi (IRE)—Turning Leaf (IRE) **Sultan Ali**
58 **PENNY DROPS**, b f Invincible Spirit (IRE)—Penny Cross **Mr & Mrs G. Middlebrook**
59 **PERFECT LIGHT (IRE)**, ch f Galileo (IRE)—Beauty Bright (IRE) **L. Sheridan**
60 **PURPLE SPECTRUM**, gr g Verglas (IRE)—Rainbow's Edge **Her Majesty The Queen**
61 **QUEEN OF ICE**, ch f Selkirk (USA)—Ice Palace **Cheveley Park Stud**
62 **REDKIRK**, b g Notnowcato—Flag **Scotney/Symonds/Fisher Partnership**
63 **ROYAL MEZYAN (IRE)**, b g Royal Applause—Rice Mother (IRE) **Sheikh Juma Dalmook Al Maktoum**
64 **SAAYERR**, b c Acclamation—Adorn **Sheikh Ahmed Al Maktoum**
65 **SATELLITE (IRE)**, b c Danehill Dancer (IRE)—Perihelion (IRE) **Highclere Thoroughbred Racing - Distinction**
66 **SCRUTINY**, b g Aqlaam—Aunty Mary **Highclere Thoroughbred Racing - Lake Coniston**
67 **SEAGULL STAR**, b c Sea The Stars (IRE)—Dash To The Top **Mr A. G. Bloom**
68 **SURVIVED**, b f Kyllachy—Regina **Cheveley Park Stud**
69 **TELMEYD**, b c Dutch Art—Blithe **Sheikh Ahmed Al Maktoum**
70 **TOKEN OF LOVE**, b f Cape Cross (IRE)—Nyarhini **A. E. Oppenheimer**
71 **TREPIDATION**, ch g Danehill Dancer (IRE)—Trianon **Her Majesty The Queen**
72 **UNAUTHORIZE**, b c Authorized (IRE)—Cross Current **Sheikh Juma Dalmook Al Maktoum**
73 **UNDRESS (IRE)**, ch f Dalakhani (IRE)—Dress Uniform (USA) **Mr B. Haggas**
74 **WATER QUEEN**, b f Shamardal (USA)—Central Force **Mohammed Jaber**
75 **WOJHA (IRE)**, ch f Pivotal—Hureya (USA) **Hamdan Al Maktoum**
76 **WONDERSTRUCK (IRE)**, b f Sea The Stars (IRE)—Bordighera (USA) **Lael Stable**
77 **WRANGLER**, b c High Chaparral (IRE)—Tipsy Me **Highclere Thoroughbred Racing - Ashes**
78 **YENHAAB (IRE)**, b c Cape Cross (IRE)—Skiphall **Essafinaat & Qatar Racing**
79 **YUFTEN (IRE)**, b c Invincible Spirit (IRE)—Majestic Sakeena (IRE) **Saleh Al Homaizi & Imad Al Sagar**
80 **ZARAEE (IRE)**, b c Dubawi (IRE)—Camaret (IRE) **Hamdan Al Maktoum**
81 **ZEE ZEELY**, ch c Champs Elysees—Zee Zee Gee **Mr B. Kantor**

TWO-YEAR-OLDS

82 B f 24/1 Vale of York (IRE)—Ahla Wasahl (Dubai Destination (USA)) (150000) **Sultan Ali**
83 **ALASAAL (USA)**, b br c 29/3 War Front (USA)—
A P Investment (USA) (A P Indy (USA)) (321355) **Hamdan Al Maktoum**
84 **ALGHAAZ**, b c 14/2 Dansili—Thakafaat (IRE) (Unfuwain (USA)) **Hamdan Al Maktoum**
85 B f 24/3 Zebedee—Amber's Bluff (Mind Games) (19047) **The Super Sprinters**
86 **BIN NARAIN**, br c 7/3 Arcano (IRE)—Badweia (USA) (Kingmambo (USA)) **Hamdan Al Maktoum**
87 B f 15/5 Sea The Stars (IRE)—Bitooh (Diktat) (96786) **Sheikh Juma Dalmook Al Maktoum**
88 Ch f 4/2 Iffraaj—Camp Riverside (USA) (Forest Camp (USA)) (30476) **Abdulla Al Mansoori**
89 B c 17/2 Firebreak—Charlie Girl (Puissance) (47619) **Sheikh Juma Dalmook Al Maktoum**
90 B f 5/3 Vale of York (IRE)—Crystal Moments (Haafhd) **Mohammed Jaber**

MR WILLIAM HAGGAS - Continued

91 Br gr c 13/4 Galileo (IRE)—Crystal Swan (IRE) (Dalakhani (IRE)) **Saleh Al Homaizi & Imad Al Sagar**
92 B c 1/2 Rip Van Winkle (IRE)—Dancing Eclipse (IRE) (Danehill Dancer (IRE)) **Mr D I Scott & Mr M Kerr-Dineen**
93 B f 17/3 Authorized (IRE)—Dancing Fire (USA) (Dayjur (USA)) (32000) **Sheikh Juma Dalmook Al Maktoum**
94 **DAWN MISSILE,** b c 3/3 Nayef (USA)—Ommadawn (IRE) (Montjeu (IRE)) (12500) **Somerville Lodge Limited**
95 B f 5/2 Authorized (IRE)—Dhan Dhana (IRE) (Dubawi (IRE)) **Mohammed Jaber**
96 B f 25/2 Iffraaj—Diam Queen (GER) (Lando (GER)) **Jaber Abdullah**
97 Ch f 24/1 Shamardal (USA)—Dubai Surprise (IRE) (King's Best (USA)) (140000) **Dr Ali Ridha**
98 **DUTCH ROSEBUD,** b f 27/2 Dutch Art—Regency Rose (Danehill (USA)) **Cheveley Park Stud**
99 B c 15/2 Acclamation—Easter Heroine (IRE) (Exactly Sharp (USA)) (46457) **Abdulla Al Mansoori**
100 **EASTERN ROMANCE,** b f 13/3 Duke of Marmalade (IRE)—Dance East (Shamardal (USA)) **Cheveley Park Stud**
101 **EFFUSIVE,** ch f 7/2 Starspangledbanner (AUS)—Thrill (Pivotal) **Cheveley Park Stud**
102 B f 20/3 Oasis Dream—Enticing (IRE) (Pivotal) **Lael Stable**
103 B c 22/2 Dutch Art—Faldal (Falbrav (IRE)) (68000) **Mr R. Cooper**
104 **FARSAKH,** b f 4/2 Smart Strike (CAN)—Ethaara (Green Desert (USA)) **Hamdan Al Maktoum**
105 **FLAMME FANTASTIQUE (GER),** b f 15/2 Nayef (USA)—
                Flames To Dust (GER) (Oasis Dream) (178087) **Hamdan Al Maktoum**
106 **FLYING FANTASY,** b c 7/3 Oasis Dream—Disco Volante (Sadler's Wells (USA)) **A. E. Oppenheimer**
107 B c 1/2 Danehill Dancer (IRE)—
                Gilded Vanity (IRE) (Indian Ridge) (155000) **Highclere Thoroughbred Racing (Queen Anne)**
108 **HEAD COACH,** ch c 13/3 Medicean—Lilli Marlane (USA) (Sri Pekan (USA)) (67000) **Mrs C. A. Cyzer**
109 **HEARTBREAK HERO,** b c 27/2 Exceed And Excel (AUS)—Artistic Blue (USA) (Diesis) (50000) **J. C. Smith**
110 B f 15/2 Dansili—Hidden Hope (Daylami (USA)) **A. E. Oppenheimer**
111 Ch c 6/2 Halling (USA)—Italian Connection (Cadeaux Genereux) (40000) **Sheikh Ahmed Al Maktoum**
112 **ITS GONNA BE ME (IRE),** b c 14/1 Zebedee—
                Dorn Hill (Lujain (USA)) (47619) **Sheikh Hamdan Bin Maktoum Al Maktoum**
113 **JAMM (IRE),** b f 24/3 Duke of Marmalade (IRE)—Starship (IRE) (Galileo (IRE)) **The Starship Partnership**
114 B f 4/4 Shamardal (USA)—Karmifira (FR) (Always Fair (USA)) (120000) **Mr D. Blunt**
115 **KHALAAS,** b c 13/2 Iffraaj—Bahia Breeze (Mister Baileys) (150000) **Hamdan Al Maktoum**
116 B f 8/4 Big Bad Bob (IRE)—Lamanka Lass (USA) (Woodman (USA)) **Hot To Trot Racing Club**
117 B f 8/3 Invincible Spirit (IRE)—
                Lethal Quality (USA) (Elusive Quality (USA)) (290360) **Saleh Al Homaizi & Imad Al Sagar**
118 B c 7/2 Dandy Man (IRE)—Light Sea (IRE) (King's Best (USA)) (55000) **Sheikh Rashid Bin Dalmook Al Maktoum**
119 B c 31/3 Oasis Dream—Longing To Dance (Danehill Dancer (IRE)) (160000) **Clipper Logistics**
120 B c 7/4 Sea The Stars (IRE)—Love Me Only (IRE) (Sadler's Wells (USA)) **Sheikh Juma Dalmook Al Maktoum**
121 Ch f 9/3 Dubawi (IRE)—Majestic Roi (IRE) (Street Cry (IRE)) **Jaber Abdullah**
122 B c 8/4 Invincible Spirit (IRE)—Manoeuvre (IRE) (Galileo (IRE)) (220000) **St Albans Bloodstock LLP**
123 **MAWJOOD,** b c 1/2 Dubawi (IRE)—Gile Na Greine (IRE) (Galileo (IRE)) **Hamdan Al Maktoum**
124 **MUBTAGHAA (IRE),** b c 7/4 Acclamation—Mabalane (IRE) (Danehill (USA)) (76190) **Hamdan Al Maktoum**
125 **MUFFRI'HA (IRE),** b f 28/3 Iffraaj—Grecian Dancer (Dansili) (85000) **Sheikh Juma Dalmook Al Maktoum**
126 **MUHTADIM (IRE),** b c 13/5 Dubawi (IRE)—Dhelaal (Green Desert (USA)) **Hamdan Al Maktoum**
127 Ch f 2/4 Kyllachy—My Girl Jode (Haafhd) (11428) **The Super Sprinters**
128 **NOBLEST,** ch f 9/4 Pivotal—Noble One (Primo Dominie) **Cheveley Park Stud**
129 **NOZHAR (IRE),** b f 28/3 Iffraaj—Give A Whistle (IRE) (Mujadil (USA)) (387146) **Hamdan Al Maktoum**
130 **PILLAR BOX (IRE),** ch c 6/3 Sakhee's Secret—Red Red Rose (Piccolo) (22857) **The Super Sprinters**
131 B br c 5/3 Hat Trick (JPN)—
                Plaisir Des Yeux (FR) (Funambule (USA)) (26292) **Roberts, Green, Whittall-Williams, Savidge**
132 **QUAKE,** b f 1/5 Dubawi (IRE)—Politesse (USA) (Barathea (IRE)) (260000) **Mr B. Kantor**
133 B f 21/4 Holy Roman Emperor (IRE)—
                Queen Padme (IRE) (Halling (USA)) (42857) **Chris Humber & Amanda Brudenell**
134 B f 3/5 Oasis Dream—Queen's Logic (IRE) (Grand Lodge (USA)) **Jaber Abdullah**
135 **RIVE GAUCHE,** b f 15/4 Fastnet Rock (AUS)—Raysiza (IRE) (Alzao (USA)) (193573) **Mr C. M. Humber**
136 B c 11/3 Zebedee—Romany Princess (AUS) (Viking Ruler (AUS)) (90000) **Sheikh Ahmed Al Maktoum**
137 **ROXY STAR (IRE),** b f 9/3 Fastnet Rock (AUS)—
                Sweet Dreams Baby (IRE) (Montjeu (IRE)) (38714) **Mrs D. J. James**
138 **SARAHA,** b f 9/3 Dansili—Kareemah (IRE) (Peintre Celebre (USA)) **Hamdan Al Maktoum**
139 B c 6/3 Exceed And Excel (AUS)—Sensible (Almutawakel) (110000) **Sheikh Ahmed Al Maktoum**
140 **SHAKSHOUKA (IRE),** b f 14/3 Dark Angel (IRE)—
                Tropical Moment (IRE) (Cape Cross (IRE)) (24761) **Abdulla Al Mansoori**
141 **SHARQEYIH,** br f 27/3 Shamardal (USA)—Shabiba (USA) (Seeking The Gold (USA)) **Hamdan Al Maktoum**
142 **SKYLIGHT (IRE),** b f 17/3 Acclamation—Swingsky (IRE) (Indian Ridge) (82000) **Cheveley Park Stud**
143 B c 30/4 Sea The Stars (IRE)—Speed Song (Fasliyev (USA)) (115000) **Clipper Logistics**
144 B f 16/2 War Front (USA)—Stroll By (USA) (Stroll (USA)) (99328) **Sheikh Rashid Dalmook Al Maktoum**
145 **SUN ODYSSEY,** b f 27/1 Mastercraftsman (IRE)—Penolva (IRE) (Galileo (IRE)) (36000) **Mrs C. A. Cyzer**
146 B br c 28/3 Dansili—Superstar Leo (IRE) (College Chapel) **Lael Stables**
147 **TADPOLE,** b f 3/4 Sir Percy—Frog (Akarad (FR)) **Mr B. Haggas**

MR WILLIAM HAGGAS - Continued

148 **TADQEEQ**, b c 4/2 Makfi—Perfect Spirit (IRE) (Invincible Spirit (IRE)) **Hamdan Al Maktoum**
149 B c 19/3 Acclamation—Tatiana Romanova (USA) (Mr Greeley (USA)) (90000) **Sheikh Ahmed Al Maktoum**
150 **TEMPTING**, ch f 10/3 Pivotal—Entrap (USA) (Phone Trick (USA)) **Cheveley Park Stud**
151 **TERHAAL (IRE)**, b c 6/2 Raven's Pass (USA)—Silk Trail (Dubai Destination (USA)) **Hamdan Al Maktoum**
152 **THAMES PAGEANT**, b f 22/2 Dansili—Golden Stream (IRE) (Sadler's Wells (USA)) **Her Majesty The Queen**
153 B c 17/3 Danehill Dancer (IRE)—
                        Toolentidhaar (USA) (Swain (IRE)) (77429) **Highclere Thoroughbred Racing (Gold Cup)**
154 **TOWN CRIER (IRE)**, b c 2/4 Acclamation—Miss Dela (IRE) (King's Best (USA)) (80000) **Cheveley Park Stud**
155 B c 18/2 Paco Boy (IRE)—Wilaya (USA) (Bernardini (USA)) (100000) **Mr Masamichi Hayashi**
156 B br f 17/3 Rock Hard Ten (USA)—
                        Wild Forest (USA) (Forest Wildcat (USA)) (58428) **Sheikh Rashid Dalmook Al Maktoum**
157 B f 18/1 Galileo (IRE)—Winds of Time (IRE) (Danehill (USA)) (55000) **Mr & Mrs R. Scott**
158 B c 2/3 Halling (USA)—Wonder Why (GER) (Tiger Hill (IRE)) **Jaber Abdullah**
159 **ZAANEH (IRE)**, br f 17/5 Aqlaam—Intishaar (IRE) (Dubai Millennium) **Hamdan Al Maktoum**
160 Ch c 10/3 Approve (IRE)—Zabadani (Zafonic (USA)) (80000) **Sheikh Ahmed Al Maktoum**
161 B c 26/3 Iffraaj—Zahour Al Yasmeen (Cadeaux Genereux) **Jaber Abdullah**

Other Owners: Mr Imad Al-Sagar, Mr Ian Beard, Mrs Christine Beard, Mrs A. J. Brudenell, Mr M. C. Fisher, Mr J. Flannery, F. M. Green, Mr D. Hearson, Mrs David Hearson, The Hon H. Herbert, Highclere Thoroughbred Racing Ltd, Mr Saleh Al Homaizi, Mr R. Jackson, Mrs G. S. Jackson, Mr M. J. Jooste, Bernard Kantor, M. Kerr-Dineen, L. K. Piggott Ltd, Mrs John Magnier, Mr G. Middlebrook, Mrs L. Middlebrook, Lady O'Reilly, Qatar Racing Limited, G. A. Roberts, Mr M. G. Savidge, Mrs A. Scotney, Mr D. I. Scott, Mrs P. M. Scott, Mr Robert Scott, Somerville Lodge Ltd, Mr Andrew Stone, Mrs M. F. Stone, Mr A. Symonds, Mr M. Tabor, Mr E. B. Whittal-Williams, Mr S. Wignall.

Assistant Trainers: Archie Watson & Jason Favell

Apprentice: Nathan Allison, Stephanie Joannides.

280
MR ALEX HALES, Edgecote
Postal: **Trafford Bridge Stables, Edgecote, Banbury**
Contacts: **PHONE (01295) 660131 FAX (01295) 660128 MOBILE (07771) 511652**
E-MAIL alex@alexhalesracing.co.uk **WEBSITE** www.alexhalesracing.co.uk

1 **BOBBISOX (IRE)**, 9, ch m Bob Back (USA)—Swift Approach (IRE) **Tony & the late Mrs D. Lousada**
2 **BRIGINDO**, 4, b f Kayf Tara—Lac Marmot (FR) **S. P. Bloodstock**
3 **CAUSEWAY KING (USA)**, 8, ch g Giant's Causeway (USA)—A P Petal (USA) **A. M. Hales**
4 **CELEBRIAN**, 7, b m Fasliyev (USA)—Triplemoon (USA) **D. Taylor**
5 **COME ON HARRIET**, 5, b m Kayf Tara—Royal Musical **Mr R. E. Frost**
6 **CRAFTY ROBERTO**, 6, ch g Intikhab (USA)—Mowazana (IRE) **S Brown H Steele D Fitzgerald**
7 **FIDELOR (IRE)**, 8, b g Sagacity (FR)—Fille Fidele (FR) **Edging Ahead**
8 **GILZEAN (IRE)**, 8, b g Flemensfirth (USA)—Sheknowso **Edging Ahead**
9 **GOODTIME BOY (IRE)**, 6, b g Catcher In The Rye (IRE)—Tour At Dawn (IRE) **Edging Ahead**
10 **GUMBRILLS'S GEORGE**, 6, b g Revoque (IRE)—Chilly Squaw (IRE) **Gumbrills Racing Partnership**
11 **LILAC BELLE**, 8, b m Robellino (USA)—Lilac Dreams **The Of-Ten Racing Partnership**
12 **LORD KENNEDY (IRE)**, 9, b g Saddlers' Hall (IRE)—Minstrel Madame (IRE) **The Patient Partnership**
13 **MIDNIGHT CHORISTER**, 6, b g Midnight Legend—Royal Musical **The Choristers**
14 **MINELLAFORLEISURE (IRE)**, 6, br g King's Theatre (IRE)—Dame Foraine (FR) **The Patient Partnership**
15 **PERIQUEST**, 5, b g Overbury (IRE)—Rippling Brook **The Fortune Hunters**
16 **RIF (FR)**, 9, b g Byzantium (FR)—Isabellita (FR) **The Patient Partnership**
17 **ROSENEATH (IRE)**, 10, b g Saddlers' Hall (IRE)—Vital Approach (IRE) **The Strathclyders**
18 **ROYAUME BLEU (FR)**, 9, ch g Kapgarde (FR)—Dear Blue (FR) **The Royaume Bleu Racing Partnership**
19 **SALUT HONORE (FR)**, 8, b g Lost World (IRE)—Kadalkote (FR) **The Hexagon Racing Partnership**
20 **SARANDO**, 9, b g Hernando (FR)—Dansara **Mrs D. W. James**
21 **SCOOTER BOY**, 6, b g Revoque (IRE)—Always Forgiving **The Scooter Boy Partnership**
22 **SHINOOKI (IRE)**, 7, br g Blueprint (IRE)—Rapid Response (IRE) **D. C. R. Allen**
23 **TAKE TWO**, 5, b g Act One—Lac Marmot (FR) **S. P. Bloodstock**
24 **ULTIMATUM DU ROY (FR)**, 6, b g Brier Creek (USA)—La Fleur du Roy (FR) **D. C. R. Allen**
25 **VAILLANT CREEK (FR)**, 5, b g Brier Creek (USA)—Ker Marie (FR) **D. C. R. Allen**

THREE-YEAR-OLDS

26 **COME ON LILA**, b f Dutch Art—Exchanging Glances **Mr R. E. Frost**

Other Owners: Mrs L. Barlow, Mr S. Brown, Miss S. Burnell, Mr J. Cleary, J. S. C. Fry, Mrs K. A. Fry, Mr A. F. Lousada, Exors of the Late Mrs D. A. Lousada, R. E. Morris-Adams, Mr R. E. Partridge, Mrs H. Steele, Mrs C. Taylor, Mr S. T. Wallace, Mrs P. S. Wallace, Mrs J. Wood.

281 MR MICHAEL HALFORD, Kildare
Postal: **Copper Beech Stables, Doneaney, Kildangan Road, Kildare Town, Co. Kildare, Ireland**
Contacts: **PHONE (00 353) 45 526119 FAX (00 353) 45 526157 MOBILE (00 353) 87 2579204**
E-MAIL info@michaelhalford.com WEBSITE www.michaelhalford.com

1 **ALVAR (USA)**, 6, ch g Forest Danger (USA)—Diameter (USA) **Mr Paul Rooney**
2 **BANNA BOIRCHE (IRE)**, 8, b g Lucky Owners (NZ)—Ziet d'alsace (FR) **Mr Paul Rooney**
3 **BOSSTIME (IRE)**, 4, b g Clodovil (IRE)—Smoken Rosa (USA) **Mr John Dewberry**
4 **CASTLE GUEST (IRE)**, 5, b g Rock of Gibraltar (IRE)—Castelletto **Mr Paul Rooney**
5 **CEBUANO**, 9, ch g Fraam—Ideal Figure **Mr Paul McMahon**
6 **CERTERACH (IRE)**, 6, b g Halling (USA)—Chartres (IRE) **Mr Paul Rooney**
7 **DABADIYAN (IRE)**, 4, b c Zamindar (USA)—Dabista (IRE) **HH Aga Khan**
8 **DRIFTING MIST (IRE)**, 4, gr f Muhtathir—Fenella's Link **Mrs A. Kavanagh**
9 **EASTERN RULES (IRE)**, 6, b g Golden Snake (USA)—Eastern Ember **Simon Hales**
10 **EBADANI (IRE)**, 4, ch g Halling (USA)—Ebatana (IRE) **Mr Fergus Healey**
11 **GUESTOFTHENATION (USA)**, 8, b br g Gulch (USA)—French Flag **Louise Halford**
12 **LA FEMME (IRE)**, 4, b f Cape Cross (IRE)—Nick's Nikita (IRE) **Mr Nicky Hartery**
13 **MIZZAVA (IRE)**, 4, b br f Cape Cross (IRE)—Flamanda **Mr Jed O'Leary**
14 **ONDEAFEARS (IRE)**, 7, b m Chineur (FR)—Irma La Douce (IRE) **Mrs Caroline Roper**
15 **PADDY THE CELEB (IRE)**, 8, ch g Peintre Celebre (USA)—On The Razz (USA) **Mr Paul McMahon**
16 **RED LASER (IRE)**, 5, br g Red Clubs (IRE)—Prancing **Mr Mark Phelan**
17 **REGULATION (IRE)**, 5, br g Danehill Dancer (IRE)—Source of Life (IRE) **Barouche Stud**
18 **RUMMAGING (IRE)**, 6, ch g Chineur (FR)—Roundabout Girl (IRE) **Evan Newell**
19 **RUSSIAN SOUL (IRE)**, 6, b g Invincible Spirit (IRE)—Russian Hill **Mrs A. Kavanagh**
20 **SENDMYLOVETOROSE**, 4, b f Bahamian Bounty—Windy Gulch (USA) **Mr Michael Enright**
21 **SENYUMAN (IRE)**, 4, ch f Shirocco (GER)—Skerries (IRE) **George Tay**
22 **SETTLE FOR RED (IRE)**, 4, ch g Redback—Balmy Choice (IRE) **Evan Newell**
23 **SHADAGANN (IRE)**, 4, b c Invincible Spirit (IRE)—Shamadara (IRE) **Mr Paul Rooney**
24 **SLIPPER ORCHID (IRE)**, 5, b m Verglas (IRE)—Lahiba (IRE) **Mrs Caroline Roper**
25 **SWITCHER (IRE)**, 5, b m Whipper (USA)—Bahamamia **Eddie & Wendy O'Leary**
26 **VICTOR'S BEACH (IRE)**, 4, b g Footstepsinthesand—Your Village (IRE) **Dr Keith Swanick**
27 **VILETTA (GER)**, 4, b f Doyen (IRE)—Vallauris (GER) **Mrs A. Kavanagh**
28 **WON DIAMOND**, 4, b g Mount Nelson—Read Federica **Mr Paul Rooney**

THREE-YEAR-OLDS

29 **ADELANA (IRE)**, ch f Manduro (GER)—Adelfia (IRE) **HH Aga Khan**
30 **ASBURY BOSS (IRE)**, b br c Dalakhani (IRE)—Nick's Nikita (IRE) **Mr Nicky Hartery**
31 **BLAMELESS (IRE)**, b f Authorized (IRE)—Crystal House (CHI) **Darley Stud Management Co Ltd**
32 **BLEEDING HEARTS (IRE)**, ch c Peintre Celebre (USA)—Society Gal (IRE) **Michael O'Leary**
33 **CALLISTAN (IRE)**, gr f Galileo (IRE)—Alabastrine **Mr Michael Enright**
34 **CAMAKASI (IRE)**, b c Camacho—Innocence **Michael Halford**
35 **DABASAN (IRE)**, b c Rock of Gibraltar (IRE)—Dabista (IRE) **HH Aga Khan**
36 **DARK ALLIANCE (IRE)**, b g Dark Angel (IRE)—Alinda (IRE) **Mr Paul McMahon**
37 **DIYLAWA (IRE)**, b f Mastercraftsman (IRE)—Dibiya (IRE) **HH Aga Khan**
38 **GLASSATURA (IRE)**, gr f Verglas (IRE)—Dunbrody (FR) **Mr Michael Enright**
39 **HAZLEDOC (IRE)**, b f Azamour (IRE)—Grand Oir (USA) **John Dewberry & John Kennedy**
40 **IONTAS (IRE)**, b f Invincible Spirit (IRE)—Poetry In Motion (IRE) **Brenda Cooney**
41 **KERNOFF (IRE)**, b g Excellent Art—Daganya (IRE) **J. D. Claque**
42 **KINGS RYKER (IRE)**, b c Bushranger (IRE)—Mia Mambo (USA) **Eric Koh**
43 **MEZOGIORNO (IRE)**, b f Zamindar (USA)—Midpoint (USA) **Mrs A. Kavanagh**
44 **PIT STOP (IRE)**, b c Iffraaj—Journey's End (IRE) **Darley Stud Management Co Ltd**
45 **PRETTY ANGEL (IRE)**, gr f Dark Angel (IRE)—Colleville **George Tay**
46 **PRINCESS PEARLITA (IRE)**, b f Manduro (GER)—Pearlats Passion (IRE) **Mr Michael Enright**
47 **RIAZAN (IRE)**, ch g Sinndar (IRE)—Ramzia (IRE) **HH Aga Khan**
48 **SANDY SMILE (IRE)**, b f Footstepsinthesand—Shy Smile (IRE) **Eddie Hanagan**
49 **SEA COAST (IRE)**, b f Rock of Gibraltar (IRE)—Varna **Mrs A. Kavanagh**
50 **SEA THE LION (IRE)**, b c Sea The Stars (IRE)—Ramona **John Connaughton**
51 **TEMASEK STAR (IRE)**, b g Soviet Star (USA)—Crazy About You (IRE) **George Tay**
52 **VELESINI (IRE)**, b c Rock of Gibraltar (IRE)—Velandia (IRE) **HH Aga Khan**
53 **WARBIRD**, b c Royal Applause—Air Biscuit (IRE) **Darley Stud Management Co Ltd**
54 **WAVEBREAK**, b f Tiger Hill (IRE)—Neptune's Bride (USA) **Darley Stud Management Co Ltd**
55 **WESTPIESER (IRE)**, b f Azamour (IRE)—Khibraat **Mrs A. Kavanagh**
56 **ZAIMAN (IRE)**, gr g Oratorio (IRE)—Zaziyra (IRE) **HH Aga Khan**
57 **ZAINDERA (IRE)**, b f Acclamation (IRE)—Zalaiyma (FR) **HH Aga Khan**
58 **ZARIB (IRE)**, b c Azamour (IRE)—Zariziyna (IRE) **HH Aga Khan**

MR MICHAEL HALFORD - Continued

TWO-YEAR-OLDS
59 B c 12/4 Kyllachy—Ablida (Cape Cross) (IRE) (15000) **Michael Halford**
60 B f 9/5 Nayef (USA)—Adelfia (IRE) (Sinndar (IRE)) **HH Aga Khan**
61 B c 28/3 Nayef (USA)—Adjaliya (IRE) (Sinndar (IRE)) **HH Aga Khan**
62 **ALAMGYIR (IRE)**, b c 23/3 Desert Style—Alaiyma (IRE) (Refuse to Bend (IRE)) **HH Aga Khan**
63 **DALEWARI (IRE)**, b c 15/4 Desert Style—Dalataya (IRE) (Sadler's Wells (USA)) **HH Aga Khan**
64 **DARRAM (IRE)**, b c 28/2 Desert Style—Daravika (IRE) (Soviet Star (USA)) **HH Aga Khan**
65 B c 13/3 Lord Shanakill (USA)—Enchanted Empress (IRE) (Holy Roman Emperor (IRE)) (21000) **Michael Halford**
66 B f 14/3 Oratorio (IRE)—Erdiyna (IRE) (Selkirk (USA)) **HH Aga Khan**
67 B c 10/2 Teofilo (IRE)—Galley (Zamindar (USA)) **Darley Stud Management Co Ltd**
68 **HALIKAYA (IRE)**, ch f 14/2 Teofilo (IRE)—Halawanda (IRE) (Ashkalani (IRE)) **HH Aga Khan**
69 B c 26/4 Excellent Art—Love In The Mist (USA) (Silver Hawk (USA)) (2477) **Michael Halford**
70 **MAIRA (IRE)**, b f 27/2 Zamindar (USA)—Masiyma (IRE) (Dalakhani (IRE)) **HH Aga Khan**
71 B c 7/5 Rock of Gibraltar (IRE)—Manda Hill (GER) (Tiger Hill (IRE)) (16260) **George Tay**
72 B f 13/2 Excellent Art—Meek Appeal (USA) (Woodman (USA)) (80000) **Mr Michael Enright**
73 B c 10/3 Shamardal (USA)—Paimpolaise (IRE) (Priolo (USA)) **Mr Michael Enright**
74 B c 25/4 Lope de Vega (IRE)—Pearlitas Passion (IRE) (High Chaparral (IRE)) **Mr Michael Enright**
75 B f 6/3 Galileo (IRE)—Piste Noire (USA) (Diesis) (170343) **Mr Michael Enright**
76 B f 16/3 Pivotal—Portal (Hernando (FR)) (180000) **Mr Michael Enright**
77 **RASHAAN (IRE)**, ch c 20/3 Manduro (GER)—Rayyana (IRE) (Rainbow Quest (USA)) **HH Aga Khan**
78 B br f 9/2 Rock of Gibraltar (IRE)—Raydiya (IRE) (Marju (IRE)) **HH Aga Khan**
79 **SHAMASH (IRE)**, b c 7/2 Oasis Dream—Shareen (IRE) (Bahri (USA)) **HH Aga Khan**
80 Ch c 9/5 Medicean—Siniyya (IRE) (Grand Lodge (USA)) **HH Aga Khan**
81 B c 20/3 Cape Cross (IRE)—Snippets (IRE) (Be My Guest (USA)) (123886) **Darley Stud Management Co Ltd**
82 B br c 24/2 Raven's Pass (USA)—Superfonic (FR) (Zafonic (USA)) **Darley Stud Management Co Ltd**
83 **TAMAZAN (USA)**, ch c 16/2 City Zip (USA)—Tawaria (FR) (Sendawar (IRE)) **HH Aga Khan**
84 B c 12/5 Shamardal (USA)—Tuzla (FR) (Panoramic) **Darley Stud Management Co Ltd**
85 B c 12/4 Mastercraftsman (IRE)—Velandia (IRE) (Sadler's Wells (USA)) **HH Aga Khan**

Assistant Trainer: Louise Halford

Jockey (flat): Shane Foley. **Jockey (NH):** Robbie Power. **Apprentice:** Conor Hoban, Sean Corby, Shane B Kelly, Damien Melia. **Amateur:** Mr J. Heavey.

---

282 **MISS SALLY HALL, Middleham**
Postal: **Brecongill, Coverham, Leyburn, North Yorkshire, DL8 4TJ**
Contacts: **PHONE (01969) 640223 FAX (0800) 066 4274**
E-MAIL sally@brecongill.co.uk

1 4, Ch g Central Park (IRE)—Lucinda Lamb **Miss S. E. Hall**
2 **MAGIC HAZE**, 8, b g Makbul—Turn Back **Miss S. E. Hall**
3 **OAKWELL (IRE)**, 6, b g Antonius Pius (USA)—Cindy's Star (IRE) **Colin Platts**
4 **ROCK A DOODLE DOO (IRE)**, 7, b g Oratorio (IRE)—Nousaiyra (IRE) **Colin Platts**

Assistant Trainer: Colin Platts **Jockey (NH):** Richard Johnson. **Amateur:** Mrs D.S. Wilkinson.

---

283 **MRS MARY HAMBRO, Cheltenham**
Postal: **Cotswold Stud, Sezincote, Moreton-In-Marsh, Gloucestershire, GL56 9TB**
Contacts: **PHONE (01386) 700700 FAX (01386) 700701 MOBILE (07860) 632990**
E-MAIL maryhambro@mac.com

1 **DOVER'S HILL**, 12, b g Pistolet Bleu (IRE)—Classic Beauty (IRE) **Mrs M. C. Hambro**
2 **HAZEL BROOK**, 5, b m High Chaparral (IRE)—Didbrook **Mrs M. C. Hambro**
3 **SQUIRREL WOOD (IRE)**, 6, b m Sadler's Wells (USA)—Didbrook **Mrs M. C. Hambro**

284 MRS DEBRA HAMER, Carmarthen
Postal: **Bryngors Uchaf Stables, Nantycaws, Carmarthen, Dyfed, SA32 8EY**
Contacts: **HOME (01267) 234585 MOBILE (07980) 665274**
E-MAIL **hamerracing@hotmail.co.uk**

1 ARGUIDOS (IRE), 10, b g Winged Love (IRE)—Open Meeting (IRE) **Mr J. Rees**
2 BENDANT, 9, b g Beat All (USA)—Rendita (IRE) **T. L. Cooper**
3 BRILLIANT (GER), 11, ch g Risk Me (FR)—Belle Orfana (GER) **W. J. Cole**
4 CELTIC FELLA (IRE), 7, gr b g Kahtan—Mens Business (IRE) **Mr T M & Mrs S M Morse**
5 LOOKS LIKE POWER (IRE), 4, ch g Spadoun (FR)—Martovic (IRE) **Mr C. A. Hanbury**
6 MICHIGAN ASSASSIN (IRE), 12, b g King's Theatre (IRE)—Shuil Ar Aghaidh **Mr C. A. Hanbury**
7 PENNANT DANCER, 7, b g Grape Tree Road—Pennant Princess **Mr P. J. Woolley**
8 WHO AM I, 8, b br g Tamayaz (CAN)—Short Fuse **W. J. Cole**
9 WYNN DARWI (IRE), 9, b br g Anshan—Noughtynova **Mr D. W. Davies**

Other Owners: Mr T. M. Morse, Mrs S. M. Morse.

Assistant Trainer: Mr M P Hamer

285 MRS ALISON HAMILTON, Denholm
Postal: **The Dykes, Denholm, Roxburghshire, TD9 8TB**
Contacts: **PHONE (01450) 870323 MOBILE (07885) 477349**
E-MAIL **Alisonhamilton53@yahoo.com**

1 AGGIE'S LAD (IRE), 12, b g Saddlers' Hall (IRE)—Grangemills **J P G Hamilton & I Lothian**
2 BOW SCHOOL (IRE), 13, b g New Frontier (IRE)—Sallaghan (IRE) **J. P. G. Hamilton**
3 DAMASCUS STEEL (IRE), 6, gr g Definite Article—Diamarouna (FR) **J. P. G. Hamilton**
4 DANEHILLS WELL (IRE), 6, b g Indian Danehill (IRE)—Collatrim Choice (IRE) **J. P. G. Hamilton**
5 GRANARUID (IRE), 11, br g Alderbrook—Lady Lorraine (IRE) **J. P. G. Hamilton**
6 LENEY COTTAGE (IRE), 7, b g Witness Box (USA)—Fleur de Tal **P Hegarty & P Gaffney**
7 SOME LAD (IRE), 9, b g Beneficial—Some News (IRE) **J. P. G. Hamilton**

Other Owners: Mr P. M. J. Gaffney, Mr P. J. Hegarty, Mr I. W. Lothian.

Assistant Trainer: Mr G. Hamilton

286 MRS ANN HAMILTON, Newcastle Upon Tyne
Postal: **Claywalls Farm, Capheaton, Newcastle Upon Tyne, NE19 2BP**
Contacts: **PHONE (01830) 530219**
E-MAIL **annhamilton1952@hotmail.com**

1 EDMUND (IRE), 7, b g Indian River (FR)—Awomansdream (IRE) **I. Hamilton**
2 FARM PIXIE (IRE), 8, b g Snurge—Blue Bobby (IRE) **I. Hamilton**
3 4, B f Great Palm (USA)—Miss Royello **I. Hamilton**
4 PROUD JACK, 6, br g Generous (IRE)—Miss Royello **I. Hamilton**
5 ROLECARR (IRE), 11, b g Tragic Role (USA)—Nuit d'ete (USA) **I. Hamilton**
6 RUNSWICK ROYAL (IRE), 5, ch g Excellent Art—Renada **I. Hamilton**
7 TRUST THOMAS, 6, ch g Erhaab (USA)—Yota (FR) **I. Hamilton**

THREE-YEAR-OLDS

8 Gr g Great Palm (USA)—Miss Royello **I. Hamilton**

Assistant Trainer: Ian Hamilton

287 MR B. R. HAMILTON, Co. Down
Postal: **100 Ballynoe Road, Downpatrick, Co. Down, Northern Ireland**
Contacts: **PHONE (004428) 44842843 MOBILE (07779) 591970**
E-MAIL **brianhamilton70@yahoo.co.uk**

1 BOBBINA (IRE), 7, br m Bob Back (USA)—Twinkle Sunset **Mrs B. Cunningham**
2 CORDELIA BELLE (IRE), 7, b m Accordion—Unfaithful Thought **Johnnie Flanagan**
3 HONEY BACH (IRE), 7, b m Bach (IRE)—Lough Lein Leader (IRE) **Stick To The Cows Syndicate**

MR B. R. HAMILTON - Continued

4 **JOHNNYOFCOURSE (IRE)**, 10, b g Saddlers' Hall (IRE)—Zafilly **Mr B. Turley**
5 **MOSCOW MANNON (IRE)**, 8, b g Moscow Society (USA)—Unfaithful Thought **Johnnie Flanagan**
6 **WARNE (IRE)**, 10, b g Bob Back (USA)—Dusky Diva (IRE) **Mrs C. Magill**

Assistant Trainer: B. A. Hamilton

Jockey (NH): D. Lavery. **Amateur:** Mr P. E. Turley.

---

288 **MR MICKY HAMMOND, Middleham**
Postal: **Oakwood Stables, East Witton Road, Middleham, Leyburn, North Yorkshire, DL8 4PT**
Contacts: PHONE **(01969) 625223** MOBILE **(07808) 572777**
E-MAIL **mdhammondracing@tiscali.co.uk** WEBSITE **www.mickyhammondracing.co.uk**

1 **ALDERBROOK LAD (IRE)**, 8, ch g Alderbrook—Alone Tabankulu (IRE) **Masters Of The Hall**
2 **AMIR PASHA (UAE)**, 9, br g Halling (USA)—Clarinda (IRE) **M.H.O.G.**
3 **CORREGGIO**, 4, ch g Bertolini (USA)—Arian Da **Forty Forty Twenty**
4 **DANCEINTOTHELIGHT**, 7, gr g Dansili—Kali **Maybe The Last Time**
5 **DARK CASTLE**, 5, b g Dark Angel (IRE)—True Magic **Mr J Cox & Mr E Tasker**
6 **DIDDY ERIC**, 4, b g Oratorio (IRE)—Amber Queen (IRE) **Mrs R. Butler**
7 **DREAM ALLY (IRE)**, 4, b g Oasis Dream—Alexander Alliance (IRE) **M. D. Hammond**
8 **EASTLANDS LAD (IRE)**, 5, b br g Strategic Prince—Uisce Tine (IRE) **Mr J. F. Wilson**
9 **FRANK THE SLINK**, 8, b g Central Park (IRE)—Kadari **M.H.O.G.**
10 **HEAD OF STEAM (USA)**, 7, ch g Mizzen Mast (USA)—Summer Mist (USA) **Mr R. M. Howard**
11 **KATHLATINO**, 7, b m Danbird (AUS)—Silver Rhythm **50/50 Racing Club**
12 **KHELAC**, 4, b g Kheleyf (USA)—Miss Lacey (IRE) **Half Cut Glass Partnership**
13 **MASTER OF THE HALL (IRE)**, 10, b g Saddlers' Hall (IRE)—
Frankly Native (IRE) **Mr N Rust Mr J Carthy Mr J Pettit**
14 **MERCHANT OF MEDICI**, 7, b g Medicean—Regal Rose **Mr J. F. Wilson**
15 **MORNIN' GORGEOUS**, 4, ch f Motivator—Sentimental Value (USA) **M. D. Hammond**
16 **ONE KOOL DUDE**, 5, ch g Iceman—Hiraeth **M. D. Hammond**
17 **ONLY ORSENFOOLSIES**, 5, b g Trade Fair—Desert Gold (IRE) **This Time Next Year Partnership**
18 **PERTUIS (IRE)**, 8, gr g Verglas (IRE)—Lady Killeen (IRE) **M.H.O.G.**
19 **RALEIGH QUAY (IRE)**, 7, b g Bachelor Duke (USA)—Speedbird (USA) **M. D. Hammond**
20 **RAYADOUR (IRE)**, 5, b g Azamour (IRE)—Rayyana (IRE) **Straightline Construction Ltd**
21 **ROSAIRLIE (IRE)**, 6, ch m Halling (USA)—Mrs Mason (IRE) **The Late Night Drinkers & Wishful Thinkers**
22 **SAMTHEMAN**, 9, b g Dancing Spree (USA)—Sisterly **The Rat Pack Racing Club**
23 **SHAHDAROBA (IRE)**, 4, b g Haafet (USA)—Gold Script (FR) **Barlow Racing Partnership**
24 **STICKLEBACK**, 5, ch m Manduro (GER)—The Stick **N. J. Rust**
25 **SUMMERLEA (IRE)**, 8, ch g Alhaarth (IRE)—Verbania (IRE) **Straightline Construction Ltd**
26 **THE PEAKY BLINDER**, 4, b g Manduro (GER)—White Star (IRE) **The Dress Fine & Walk The Line Syndicate**
27 **THE RAMBLIN KID**, 6, b g Westerner—Disallowed (IRE) **J. Buzzeo**

THREE-YEAR-OLDS

28 **LACERTA**, b g Astronomer Royal (USA)—Rubber (IRE) **M. D. Hammond**
29 **SKINNY LATTE**, ch c Piccolo—Coffee Ice **M. D. Hammond**

TWO-YEAR-OLDS

30 Gr f 21/3 Equiano (FR)—Dansa Queen (Dansili) (28000) **Mrs G. Hogg**

Other Owners: Mr J. Carthy, Mr S. J. M. Cobb, Mr J. W. Cox, Mr R. Green, Mr D. A. Harrison, Mr D. Hartley, Mr J. A. Hill, N. H. B. Ingham, Mr J. Pettit, Mr E. Price, Mr T. Rodney, Mr A. Smith, Mr A. E. Tasker, Mr K. Ward, O. R. Weeks, Mr P. Wyslych.

Assistant Trainer: Mrs. G. Hogg (07809) 428117

Conditional: Joe Colliver. **Apprentice:** Katie Dowson. **Amateur:** Miss R. Smith.

289 **MR MIKE HAMMOND, Abberley**
Postal: **Cherry Ash, Bank Lane, Abberley, Worcester, Worcestershire, WR6 6BQ**
Contacts: **PHONE** (01299) 896057 **MOBILE** 07894 050183
E-MAIL mphatwellcottage@aol.com **WEBSITE** www.hammondracing.co.uk

1 **ASHBURY (IRE)**, 7, b m Catcher In The Rye (IRE)—The Real Athlete (IRE) **Mr M. P. Hammond**
2 5, B g Gold Well—Bondi Babe (IRE) **B. Hawkins**
3 **LILY MARIE**, 5, b m Overbury (IRE)—Rose Marie (IRE) **D Pain & Sons**

Other Owners: Mr P. R. Pain, Mr A. Pain, Mrs S. Pain, Mrs P. R. Pain, Mrs A. S. Taylor.

Assistant Trainer: Zoe Hammond

290 **MR JOHN JOSEPH HANLON, Co. Carlow**
Postal: **Fennis Court, Bagenalstown, Co. Carlow, Ireland**
Contacts: **PHONE** (00353) 59 9721443 **FAX** (00353) 59 9723613 **MOBILE** (00353) 87 6924831
E-MAIL johnjhanlon@hotmail.com **WEBSITE** www.johnhanlon.ie

1 **ABOLITIONIST (IRE)**, 6, b g Flemensfirth (USA)—All The Roses (IRE) **Mr P. Holden**
2 **ARAKU VALLEY (IRE)**, 7, b g Indian Danehill (IRE)—Bobazure (IRE) **Mrs A. F. Mee**
3 **BALLYGUR LADY (IRE)**, 6, b m Stowaway—Miss Electric (IRE) **Mr W. Hanlon**
4 **BIRZALI (FR)**, 7, gr g Kalanisi (IRE)—Bernimixa (FR) **Silver Chain Syndicate**
5 **CALL THE DETECTIVE (IRE)**, 5, b g Winged Love (IRE)—Aneeza (IRE) **Forever Never Syndicate**
6 **CLONDAW FARMER (IRE)**, 5, b g Scorpion (IRE)—Accordian Lady (IRE) **Mrs A. F. Mee**
7 4, B g Oscar (IRE)—Coming Home (FR) **Mr S. Hehir**
8 **COOL IDEAS (IRE)**, 5, b g Artan (IRE)—Toview (IRE) **Miss R. O'Neill**
9 4, B g Stowaway—Cooleycall (IRE) **Miss R. O'Neill**
10 **DANESFORT**, 6, gr g Fair Mix (IRE)—Dutch Czarina **Forever Never Syndicate**
11 4, B g Mountain High (IRE)—Dear Money (IRE) **Forever Never Syndicate**
12 **DENOMINATOR (IRE)**, 5, b g Diamond Green (FR)—Molomo **Barry Connell**
13 **DOWN TIME (USA)**, 4, b g Harlan's Holiday (USA)—Frappay (USA) **Miss R. O'Neill**
14 , Ch g Beneficial—Drama Chick **Mr W. Hanlon**
15 **FENNIS MOLL (IRE)**, 5, b m Presenting—No Moore Bills **Miss P. Twiss**
16 **GEORGE FERNBECK**, 6, ch g Java Gold (USA)—Burmese Days **Mr P. Holden**
17 **HEAD OF THE CLASS (IRE)**, 5, ch g Flemensfirth (USA)—Dinner At One (IRE) **Miss R. O'Neill**
18 **HIDDEN CYCLONE (IRE)**, 9, b g Stowaway—Hurricane Debbie (IRE) **Mrs A. F. Mee & David Mee**
19 4, Ch g Stowaway—Honey Mustard (IRE) **Mr P. McMahon**
20 **IT'S ALL AN ACT (IRE)**, 6, br g Presenting—Royal Lucy (IRE) **Mrs A. F. Mee**
21 4, Br gr g Act One—Kaydee Queen (IRE) **Mr P. McMahon**
22 4, B g Beneficial—Latin Mistress **Miss R. O'Neill**
23 **LUSKA LAD (IRE)**, 10, ch g Flemensfirth (USA)—Notsophar (IRE) **Barry Connell**
24 **LUSO'S WAY (IRE)**, 6, b m Stowaway—Coccinella (IRE) **Mrs N. Wheatley**
25 **MARCH SEVENTEENTH (IRE)**, 6, br g Flemensfirth (USA)—Palesa Accord (IRE) **Mr D. P. Kelly**
26 **NEAREST THE PIN (IRE)**, 9, b g Court Cave (IRE)—Carnbelle (IRE)
27 **OBVIATE**, 5, b g Rail Link—Maritima **Forever Never Syndicate**
28 **OLD KILCASH (IRE)**, 6, ch g Urban Ocean (FR)—Brierfield Lady (IRE) **Barry Connell**
29 **OLD STORM (IRE)**, 5, b g Old Vic—Sissinghurst Storm (IRE) **Mrs A. F. Mee**
30 **ON THE TANGLE (IRE)**, 6, b g Exit To Nowhere (USA)—Navaro (IRE) **SW Partnership**
31 **ON VACATION (IRE)**, 6, b g Kahyasi—Lurane (FR) **G. Mullins**
32 **ONE COOL BOY (IRE)**, 5, b br g One Cool Cat (USA)—Pipewell (IRE) **D. Hannigan**
33 **ONE SHOT DAVY (IRE)**, 8, b g Classic Cliche (IRE)—Call Catherine (IRE) **Mr P. Kelly**
34 4, B g Beat All (USA)—Osocool **Mrs A. N. Durkan**
35 **RARE LEGEND (IRE)**, 7, b g Stowaway—Shambala (IRE) **Mr N. Eager**
36 **REFUSED A NAME**, 7, b g Montjeu (IRE)—Dixielake (IRE) **Brendain Long**
37 4, B g Scorpion (IRE)—Sabbatical (IRE) **Miss R. O'Neill**
38 **STOWAWAY SHARK (IRE)**, 5, b g Stowaway—Anno Mundi (USA) **Barry Connell**
39 **THE REBEL PANTHER (IRE)**, 6, ch g Stowaway—Nooradeen (IRE) **Mr K. Murray**
40 **WESTERN LEADER (IRE)**, 10, b g Stowaway—Western Whisper (IRE) **Barry Connell**
41 **WITHOUT ICE (IRE)**, 5, br g Artan (IRE)—Woodbank Sue (IRE) **Miss R. O'Neill**

Jockey (NH): Sean McDermott, Andrew J. McNamara, Danny Mullins. **Conditional:** Brian Hayes, Chris Timmons.
Amateur: Miss Rachael Blackmore, Mr J. T. Carroll, Mr W. Thompson.

291 MR RICHARD HANNON, Marlborough

Postal: East Everleigh Stables, Everleigh, Marlborough, Wiltshire, SN8 3EY
Contacts: PHONE (01264) 850254 FAX (01264) 850076
E-MAIL richard.hannon@btinternet.com WEBSITE www.richardhannonracing.co.uk

1 **AGAINST THE TIDE (IRE)**, 4, ch f Teofilo (IRE)—Hundred Year Flood (USA) **S. Manana**
2 **BEEDEE**, 4, b c Beat Hollow—Dawnus (IRE) **Mr & Mrs D. D. Clee**
3 **BROADWAY DUCHESS (IRE)**, 4, ch f New Approach (IRE)—Annee Lumiere (IRE) **M. Pescod**
4 **BROWNSEA BRINK**, 4, b c Cadeaux Genereux—Valiantly **The Heffer Syndicate**
5 **EMELL**, 4, ch c Medicean—Londonnetdotcom (IRE) **Mr & Mrs D. D. Clee**
6 **LORD OFTHE SHADOWS (IRE)**, 5, ch g Kyllachy—Golden Shadow (IRE) **Richard Hitchcock Alan King**
7 **MAGIC CITY (IRE)**, 5, b g Elusive City (USA)—
Annmarie's Magic (IRE) **Barker, Ferguson, Mason, Hassiakos, Done**
8 **MAUREEN (IRE)**, 4, b f Holy Roman Emperor (IRE)—Exotic Mix (FR) **Mr A. A. Alkhallafi**
9 **MONTIRIDGE (IRE)**, 4, b c Ramonti (FR)—Elegant Ridge (IRE) **M. Abdullah**
10 **MUTAZAMEN**, 4, ch g Sakhee's Secret—Disco Lights **Hamdan Al Maktoum**
11 **NINJAGO**, 4, b c Mount Nelson—Fidelio's Miracle (USA) **J Palmer-Brown & Potensis Ltd**
12 **OLYMPIC GLORY (IRE)**, 4, b c Choisir (AUS)—Acidanthera **H.E. Sheikh J. B. H. B. K. Al Thani**
13 **PETHER'S MOON (IRE)**, 4, b c Dylan Thomas (IRE)—Softly Tread (IRE) **J. D. Manley**
14 **PRINCE'S TRUST (IRE)**, 4, b g Invincible Spirit (IRE)—Lost In Wonder (USA) **Her Majesty The Queen**
15 **PRODUCER**, 5, ch h Dutch Art—River Saint (USA) **J. Palmer-Brown**
16 **SEA SHANTY (USA)**, 4, b g Elusive Quality (USA)—Medley **Her Majesty The Queen**
17 **SKY LANTERN (IRE)**, 4, gr ro f Red Clubs (IRE)—Shawanni **Mr B. W. Keswick**
18 **TOBACCO ROAD (IRE)**, 4, b g Westerner—Virginias Best **Noodles Racing**
19 **TORONADO (IRE)**, 4, b c High Chaparral (IRE)—Wana Doo (USA) **H.E. Sheikh J. B. H. B. K. Al Thani**
20 **TRUMPET MAJOR (IRE)**, 5, b h Arakan (USA)—Ashford Cross **J. D. Manley**
21 **VIEWPOINT (IRE)**, 5, b g Exceed And Excel (AUS)—Lady's View (USA) **The Heffer Syndicate**
22 **WENTWORTH (IRE)**, 4, b c Acclamation—Miss Corinne **Mrs J Magnier, Mr M Tabor & Mr D Smith**
23 **ZURIGHA (IRE)**, 4, b f Cape Cross (IRE)—Noyelles (IRE) **S. H. Altayer**

THREE-YEAR-OLDS

24 **ABYAAT (IRE)**, b c Halling (USA)—Why Dubai (USA) **Malih L. Al Basti**
25 **AL HANYORA**, b f Teofilo (IRE)—Chrysalis **S. H. Altayer**
26 **AMONTILLADO (IRE)**, b f Pastoral Pursuits—Almost Amber (USA) **Shark Bay Racing Syndicate**
27 **ART OFFICIAL (IRE)**, b c Excellent Art—Dama'a (IRE) **Chris Giles,Potensis Ltd,J Palmer-Brown**
28 **BANAADEER (IRE)**, ch c Tamayuz—Loose Julie (IRE) **Hamdan Al Maktoum**
29 **BARLEY MOW (IRE)**, b c Zamindar (USA)—Harvest Queen **Lady Rothschild**
30 **BLACK CAESAR (IRE)**, b c Bushranger (IRE)—Evictress (IRE) **Carmichael Humber**
31 **BOLD SPIRIT**, b g Invincible Spirit (IRE)—Far Shores (USA) **Her Majesty The Queen**
32 **BON VOYAGE**, b c Kyllachy—Coming Home **Sheikh J. Al Dalmook Maktoum**
33 **BROADWAY MUSICAL (IRE)**, b f Exceed And Excel (AUS)—Broadway Hit **Saif Ali & Saeed H. Altayer**
34 **BROWN GLAZE (USA)**, b f War Front (USA)—Easy To Cope (USA) **Qatar Racing Limited**
35 **BROWN SUGAR (IRE)**, b c Tamayuz—Lady Livius (IRE) **De La Warr Racing**
36 **BUNKER (IRE)**, br c Hurricane Run (IRE)—
Endure (IRE) **Sheikh Joaan Al Thani, Morecombe, Anderson, Hughes**
37 **CAMEO TIARA (IRE)**, b f High Chaparral (IRE)—Cuilaphuca (IRE) **Mrs J. Wood**
38 **CAPE WRATH**, b gr c Verglas—Capades Dancer **Lady Rothschild**
39 **CARTHAGE (IRE)**, b c Mastercraftsman—Pitrizzia **M. Pescod**
40 **CAY DANCER**, gr f Danehill Dancer—White Cay **R. Barnett**
41 **CHAMPAGNE SYDNEY (IRE)**, ch c Iffraaj—Special Touch (IRE) **The Sydney Arms Racing Club**
42 **CHAMPIONSHIP (IRE)**, ch c Exceed And Excel (AUS)—Aljafliyah **Mrs J. Wood**
43 **CHIEF BARKER (IRE)**, b c Azamour (IRE)—Millay **Middleham Park Racing XXIII**
44 **CONSTANTINE**, b g Holy Roman Emperor (IRE)—Whatami **The Royal Ascot Racing Club**
45 **COULSTY (IRE)**, b c Kodiac—Hazium (IRE) **Lord Vestey**
46 **CRICKLEWOOD GREEN (USA)**, ch g Bob And John (USA)—
B Berry Brandy (USA) **Mr Chris Wright & Mr Andy Macdonald**
47 **CRYSTAL NYMPH (IRE)**, ch f Rock of Gibraltar (IRE)—Flower of Kent (USA) **Mrs E. C. Roberts**
48 **DANSANTE**, b f Champs Elysees—Danseuse du Soir (IRE) **Woodcote Stud Ltd**
49 **DAY OF CONQUEST**, ch c Major Cadeaux—Dayville (USA) **Mr M. Sultan**
50 **ESTIDRAAJ (USA)**, b f Medaglia d'oro (USA)—Bsharpsonata (USA) **Hamdan Al Maktoum**
51 **EXPERT (IRE)**, gr c Mastercraftsman (IRE)—Raphimix (FR) **Mrs J. Wood**
52 **HABDAB**, ch f Halling (USA)—Dawnus (IRE) **Mr & Mrs D. D. Clee**
53 **HERE FOR GOOD (IRE)**, b c Aqlaam—North East Bay (USA) **Middleham Park Racing LXXII**
54 **HOUSE CAPTAIN**, ch c Captain Gerrard (IRE)—Dalmunzie (IRE) **Mrs J. Wood**

MR RICHARD HANNON - Continued

55 **HYMENAIOS (IRE)**, ch c Danehill Dancer (IRE)—
　　　　　　　　　　Wedding Morn (IRE) **H.H. Sheikh Mohammed bin Khalifa Al-Thani**
56 **JOYBRINGER (IRE)**, b f Acclamation—Pina Colada **Mrs J. Wood**
57 **KAMALAYA**, b c Teofilo (IRE)—Saint Ann (USA) **J Palmer-Brown,Potensis Ltd,Chris Giles**
58 **KANTARA CASTLE (IRE)**, b c Baltic King—Arbitration (IRE) **Middleham Park Racing XXV**
59 **KARRAAR**, b c Dubawi (IRE)—Maghya (IRE) **Hamdan Al Maktoum**
60 **KINLOSS**, ch f Kheleyf (USA)—Celtic Cross **Her Majesty The Queen**
61 **LA NAPOULE**, ch f Piccolo—Peggy Spencer **Exors of the Late Mr G. Reed**
62 **LADY DAY**, b f Selkirk (USA)—Lady Links **M. Pescod**
63 **LINDART (ITY)**, ch c Dutch Art—Linda Surena (ARG) **Potensis Limited & Mr Chris Giles**
64 **LOOKSLIKEANANGEL**, b f Holy Roman Emperor (IRE)—Valiantly **Carmel Stud**
65 **MAGNUS MAXIMUS**, b c Holy Roman Emperor (IRE)—Chanrossa (IRE) **Carmichael Humber**
66 **MALACHIM MIST (IRE)**, gr g Dark Angel (IRE)—Sixfields Flyer (IRE) **Mr M. Daniels**
67 **MANDERLEY (IRE)**, gr f Clodovil (IRE)—Three Days In May **Mrs J. Wood**
68 **MANOR WAY (IRE)**, b c Holy Roman Emperor (IRE)—Cannikin (IRE) **Mrs A. Williams**
69 **MIDNITE ANGEL (IRE)**, gr f Dark Angel (IRE)—Two Sets To Love (IRE) **H.E. Sheikh J. B. H. B. K. Al Thani**
70 **MISS BRAZIL (IRE)**, ch f Exceed And Excel (AUS)—Amazon Beauty (IRE) **S. Manana**
71 **MONSEA (IRE)**, gr c Manduro (GER)—Sea Drift (FR) **S. Manana**
72 **MUMTAZA**, b f Nayef (USA)—Natagora (FR) **Hamdan Al Maktoum**
73 **MUNJALLY**, b g Acclamation—Parabola **Hamdan Al Maktoum**
74 **MUSICAL COMEDY**, b g Royal Applause—Spinning Top **Her Majesty The Queen**
75 **MUTAWATHEA**, b c Exceed And Excel (AUS)—Esteemed Lady (IRE) **Hamdan Al Maktoum**
76 B f Street Sense (USA)—Nasheej (USA) **Malih L. Al Basti**
77 **NIGHT OF THUNDER (IRE)**, ch c Dubawi (IRE)—Forest Storm **S. Manana**
78 **ORAYDA (IRE)**, ch f New Approach (IRE)—Wadaat **H.E. Sheikh J. B. H. B. K. Al Thani**
79 **PASSING BY**, b f Raven's Pass (USA)—Miss Anabaa **S. Manana**
80 **PEAK ROYALE**, b g Royal Applause—Mountain Law (USA) **Malih L. Al Basti**
81 **POTENTATE (IRE)**, b c Acclamation—Wish List (IRE) **Saleh Al Homaizi & Imad Al Sagar**
82 **PRETTY FLEMINGO (IRE)**, b f Danehill Dancer (IRE)—Kicking Bird (FR) **Thurloe Thoroughbreds XXXIII**
83 **PROTECTED**, b c Exceed And Excel (AUS)—Pink Stone (FR) **S. Ali**
84 **PUPIL (IRE)**, b c Mastercraftsman (IRE)—Blue Iris **Mr W. A. Tinkler**
85 **REMEMBER**, b f Selkirk (USA)—Forgotten Dreams (IRE) **S. Manana**
86 **SAND DANCER (IRE)**, b f Footstepsinthesand—Annacloy Pearl (IRE) **Mr Michael Pescod & Mr Justin Dowley**
87 **SEBASTIAN BEACH (IRE)**, b c Yeats (IRE)—Night Club **Mr Justin Dowley & Mr Michael Pescod**
88 **SELWAAN (IRE)**, b c Invincible Spirit (IRE)—Lia (IRE) **H.E. Sheikh J. B. H. B. K. Al Thani**
89 **SHAFRAH (IRE)**, b c Acclamation—Rosy Dudley (IRE) **Hamdan Al Maktoum**
90 **SHAMSHON (IRE)**, b c Invincible Spirit (IRE)—Greenisland (IRE) **H.E. Sheikh J. B. H. B. K. Al Thani**
91 **SHIFTING POWER**, ch c Compton Place—Profit Alert (IRE) **Ms Elaine Chivers & Potensis Ltd**
92 **SHOWPIECE**, b c Kyllachy—Striving (IRE) **Cheveley Park Stud Limited**
93 **SLEMY**, b c Raven's Pass (USA)—Wolf Cleugh (IRE) **H.E. Sheikh J. B. H. B. K. Al Thani**
94 **STAR CODE**, b c Kodiac—Mira (IRE) **Sheikh R. D. Al Maktoum**
95 **STARS ALIGNED (IRE)**, b f Sea The Stars (IRE)—Senora Galilei (IRE) **Mrs J. Wood**
96 **STORM RIDER (IRE)**, b c Fastnet Rock (AUS)—On The Nile (IRE) **Carmichael Humber**
97 **STORM TROOPER (IRE)**, b c Acclamation—Maid To Order (IRE) **Mr M Tabor, Mr D Smith & Mrs J Magnier**
98 **STRAIT RUN (IRE)**, ch c Rock of Gibraltar (IRE)—Gentlemen's Guest (USA) **Noodles Racing**
99 **SWANWICK SHORE (IRE)**, b c Tagula (IRE)—Cinzia Vegas (IRE) **Mrs J. Wood**
100 **TABREEK (USA)**, ch c Distorted Humor (USA)—Blushing (USA) **Hamdan Al Maktoum**
101 **TANQEYA (IRE)**, b c Intense Focus (USA)—Spinning Well (IRE) **Hamdan Al Maktoum**
102 **TARAP (IRE)**, b f Myboycharlie (IRE)—Tanzania (IRE) **H.H. Sheikh Mohammed bin Khalifa Al-Thani**
103 **TEA IN TRANSVAAL (IRE)**, b f Teofilo (IRE)—Mpumalanga **Sheikh J. Al Dalmook Maktoum**
104 **TOORMORE (IRE)**, b c Arakan (USA)—Danetime Out (IRE) **Middleham Park Racing IX & James Pak**
105 **TOUZR**, b c Invincible Spirit (IRE)—Carrig Girl **H.E. Sheikh J. B. H. B. K. Al Thani**
106 **TREE OF GRACE (FR)**, ch c Gold Away (IRE)—Three Times (SWE) **H.E. Sheikh J. B. H. B. K. Al Thani**
107 **TRUTH OR DARE**, b c Invincible Spirit (IRE)—Unreachable Star **Carmel Stud**
108 **UNSCRIPTED (IRE)**, b c Oratorio—Fancy Intense **Mr B. Dolan**
109 **VIRILE (IRE)**, ch c Exceed And Excel (AUS)—Winding (USA) **Mrs J. Wood**
110 **WASHAAR (IRE)**, b c Kodiac—Dabtiyra (IRE) **Hamdan Al Maktoum**
111 **WINDSHEAR**, b c Hurricane Run (IRE)—Portal **Mr M. Daniels**
112 B f Oratorio (IRE)—Wolumla (IRE) **Glebe Farm Stud**

TWO-YEAR-OLDS

113 **ABAQ**, b f 5/3 Oasis Dream—Indian Ink (IRE) (Indian Ridge) **Hamdan Al Maktoum**
114 Br c 23/3 Jeremy (USA)—Absolutely Cool (IRE) (Indian Ridge) (38095) **R. Hannon**
115 Ch c 29/3 Arcano (IRE)—Acatama (USA) (Efisio) (30971) **Byerley Thoroughbred & Anna Doyle**
116 **ACCLIMATISATION (IRE)**, b f 6/3 Acclamation—Tahara (IRE) (Caerleon (USA)) (110000) **Denford Stud Limited**

MR RICHARD HANNON - Continued

117 B c 24/2 Galileo (IRE)—Akdarena (Hernando (FR)) (193573) **H.E. Sheikh J. B. H. B. K. Al Thani**
118 **AL BANDAR (IRE),** b c 8/2 Monsieur Bond (IRE)—Midnight Mystique (IRE) (Noverre (USA)) (55000) **A. Al Shaikh**
119 **AMONG ANGELS,** b c 18/2 Acclamation—Love Action (IRE) (Motivator) (25000) **The Pineapple Stud**
120 B f 17/3 Acclamation—Art Work (Zafonic (USA)) (66666) **Malih L. Al Basti**
121 Ch c 14/3 Giant's Causeway (USA)—
            Astrologie (FR) (Polish Precedent (USA)) (232288) **H.E. Sheikh J. B. H. B. K. Al Thani**
122 **AZMAAM (IRE),** gr c 13/2 Dark Angel (IRE)—Miss Indigo (Indian Ridge) (260000) **Hamdan Al Maktoum**
123 **BARONESSA (IRE),** b f 19/3 Royal Applause—All Embracing (IRE) (Night Shift (USA)) (24761) **Mr S. A. Lootah**
124 **BASATEEN (IRE),** ch c 5/3 Teofilo (IRE)—
            Tasha's Dream (USA) (Woodman (USA)) (250000) **Hamdan Al Maktoum**
125 B c 15/3 Rock of Gibraltar (IRE)—Bean Uasal (IRE) (Oasis Dream) (61942) **The Royal Ascot Racing Club**
126 B c 1/3 Myboycharlie (IRE)—Becuille (IRE) (Redback) (82000) **J Palmer-Brown, J Sullivan, Mrs Ensor**
127 B c 17/3 Proclamation (IRE)—Bella Bertolini (Bertolini (USA)) (8571) **Middleham Park Racing LXXIX**
128 B c 15/2 Paco Boy (IRE)—Bisaat (USA) (Bahri (USA)) (20000)
129 **BLACK CHERRY,** b f 29/3 Mount Nelson—Arctic Char (Polar Falcon (USA)) (50000) **Mrs E. C. Roberts**
130 **BLUESBREAKER (IRE),** b c 16/5 Fastnet Rock (AUS)—Jalisco (IRE) (Machiavellian (USA)) (53333) **M. Pescod**
131 B c 7/2 Tamayuz—Carioca (IRE) (Rakti) (100000) **Michael Kerr-Dineen & Martin Hughes**
132 B c 28/1 Kodiac—Cassava (IRE) (Vettori (IRE)) (140000) **Qatar Racing Limited**
133 B c 20/3 Big Bad Bob (IRE)—Chica Roca (USA) (Woodman (USA)) (48005)
134 B f 17/2 Camacho—Cinnamon Tree (IRE) (Barathea (IRE)) **Mrs A. J. Brudenell**
135 B f 7/4 Rip Van Winkle (IRE)—Cland di San Jore (IRE) (Lando) (46457) **Thurloe Thoroughbreds XXXV**
136 B c 20/4 Rip Van Winkle (IRE)—Cold Cold Woman (Machiavellian (USA)) (54200)
137 B c 8/2 Tagula (IRE)—Come April (Singspiel (IRE)) (39047) **P. G. Jacobs**
138 Ch c 9/4 Compton Place—Corryvreckan (IRE) (Night Shift (USA)) (46457) **Potensis Limited**
139 Ch c 30/3 Sakhee's Secret—Corton Charlemagne (IRE) (King Charlemagne (USA)) (36190) **Mr M. S. Al Shahi**
140 **CRYSTAL MALT (IRE),** b f 17/4 Intikhab (USA)—Elegantly Filly (Rock of Gibraltar (IRE)) (36000) **D. Boocock**
141 B c 16/1 Acclamation—Cursory (Hurricane Run (IRE)) (130000) **Carmichael Jennings**
142 **DAME LIBERTY (IRE),** ch f 20/2 Tamayuz—
            Elizabeth Swann (Bahamian Bounty) (55000) **Mr Michael Cohen & Mr Adam Victor**
143 B c 14/3 Teofilo (IRE)—Dance Club (IRE) (Fasliyev (USA)) **H.E. Sheikh J. B. H. B. K. Al Thani**
144 B f 19/4 High Chaparral (IRE)—
            Danehill's Dream (IRE) (Danehill) (143243) **H.E. Sheikh J. B. H. B. K. Al Thani**
145 **DANGEROUS MOONLITE (IRE),** b f 28/2 Acclamation—Light It Up (IRE) (Elusive City (USA)) **Mrs J. Wood**
146 **DECISIVE (IRE),** ch f 28/3 Iffraaj—Guarantia (Selkirk (USA)) (80000) **Cheveley Park Stud Limited**
147 **DELUXE,** b c 30/1 Acclamation—Ainia (Alhaarth (IRE)) **Mrs J. Wood**
148 **DENWAY PARK,** b c 7/3 Paco Boy (IRE)—Bolshaya (Cadeaux Genereux) (28000)
149 **DHARWA,** b f 10/4 Kyllachy (IRE)—Stoneacre Sarah (Cadeaux Genereux) (105000) **Hamdan Al Maktoum**
150 **DIAMOND RIDGE (IRE),** gr c 4/3 Zebedee—
            Porky Pie (IRE) (Grand Lodge (USA)) (28571) **R Ambrose W Reilly N Williams 4SGroup MS**
151 **DITTANDER,** b f 24/1 Exceed And Excel (AUS)—Penny's Gift (Tobougg (IRE)) **Mr B. W. Keswick**
152 **DOUGAL (IRE),** b c 28/2 Zebedee—Liscoa (IRE) (Foxhound (USA)) **Mrs J. Wood**
153 **DR NO,** gr c 2/2 Aussie Rules (USA)—Annalina (USA) (Cozzene (USA)) **Denford Stud Limited**
154 B f 11/3 Motivator—Elegant Beauty (Olden Times) (320000) **H.E. Sheikh J. B. H. B. K. Al Thani**
155 B c 6/2 Zebedee—Elizabelle (IRE) (Westerner) **Mr M. S. Al Shahi**
156 **EMPERORS WARRIOR (IRE),** ch c 11/4 Thewayyouare (USA)—
            World Sprint (GER) (Waky Nao) (13333) **Shark Bay Racing Syndicate II**
157 **ESTIDHKAAR (IRE),** b c 15/3 Dark Angel (IRE)—
            Danetime Out (IRE) (Danetime (IRE)) (190476) **Hamdan Al Maktoum**
158 B f 28/2 Shamardal (USA)—First Fleet (USA) (Woodman (USA)) (154858) **H.E. Sheikh J. B. H. B. K. Al Thani**
159 **FORRES (IRE),** b f 7/4 Fastnet Rock (AUS)—Slieve (Selkirk (USA)) (70000) **Mrs A. Wigan**
160 B f 17/2 Acclamation—Galistic (IRE) (Galileo (IRE)) (449089) **H.E. Sheikh J. B. H. B. K. Al Thani**
161 B c 19/3 High Chaparral (IRE)—Gallivant (Danehill (USA)) (150000) **H.E. Sheikh J. B. H. B. K. Al Thani**
162 **GIBEON (IRE),** b c 1/3 Cape Cross (IRE)—Gravitation (Galileo (IRE)) **Lady G. De Walden**
163 **HAIL CLODIUS (IRE),** b c 22/3 Clodovil (IRE)—Dhairkana (IRE) (Soviet Star (USA)) (33333) **R. Hannon**
164 B c 9/3 Lawman (FR)—Halicardia (Halling (USA)) (40262) **Mr M. S. Al Shahi**
165 **HARBOUR PATROL (IRE),** b c 23/3 Acclamation—
            Traou Mad (IRE) (Barathea (IRE)) (60000) **The Heffer Syndicate**
166 B c 18/3 Rip Van Winkle (IRE)—Have Faith (IRE) (Machiavellian (USA)) (170000)
167 B c 22/4 Sir Percy—Heat of The Night (Lear Fan (USA)) (40262) **Brook Farm Bloodstock**
168 **HOLLAND PARK,** b c 2/4 More Than Ready (USA)—
            B Berry Brandy (USA) (Event of The Year (USA)) (150000) **Macdonald, Wright, Creed & Jiggins**
169 **I KNOW,** ch f 7/4 Archipenko (USA)—I Do (Selkirk (USA)) **Miss K. Rausing**
170 B c 21/2 Sakhee's Secret—Icing (Polar Falcon (USA)) (70000) **M Hughes & M Kerr-Dineen**
171 B f 3/4 Invincible Spirit (IRE)—Idilic Calm (IRE) (Indian Ridge) (247773) **H.E. Sheikh J. B. H. B. K. Al Thani**
172 B f 9/4 Acclamation—Idonea (CAN) (Swain (IRE)) (50000)

MR RICHARD HANNON - Continued

173 B c 7/4 Exceed And Excel (AUS)—
    Imperial Quest (Rainbow Quest (USA)) (90000) **H.H. Sheikh Mohammed bin Khalifa Al-Thani**
174 Gr c 16/3 Dutch Art—Jillolini (Bertolini (USA)) (40000) **Des Anderson & Ben Keswick**
175 **JUNE (IRE),** b f 28/2 High Chaparral (IRE)—Aguilas Perla (IRE) (Indian Ridge) **Mrs J. Wood**
176 B c 12/2 Zebedee—Keenes Royale (Red Ransom (USA)) (220000) **Carmichael Jennings**
177 B c 15/1 Paco Boy (IRE)—Key Light (IRE) (Acclamation) (49523) **Highclere Thoroughbred Racing (Albany)**
178 **KEY TO THE HIGHWAY (GER),** b c 16/3 Dashing Blade—Key To Win (FR) (Halling) (18583) **R. Hannon**
179 Ch c 11/4 Compton Place—Lady Darayna (Polish Precedent (USA)) (45714) **Mr M. S. Al Shahi**
180 B c 3/3 Lope de Vega (IRE)—Lady Livius (IRE) (Titus Livius (FR)) (60000) **De La Warr Racing**
181 **LADY MASCOT (IRE),** ch f 27/3 Zebedee—
    Tradmagic (Traditionally (USA)) (26666) **Mason Brown Partnership**
182 B c 13/3 Dylan Thomas (IRE)—Lady Taufan (IRE) (Taufan (USA)) (50000) **Mr B. C. M. Wong**
183 **LAHAYEB,** b f 11/4 High Chaparral (IRE)—Tea Break (Daylami (IRE)) (30000) **Mr M. S. Al Shahi**
184 Gr c 4/4 Mastercraftsman (IRE)—Lake Ladoga (Green Desert (USA)) (17034)
185 Ch f 12/4 Dutch Art—Lambadora (Suave Dancer (USA)) (40000) **K. T. Ivory**
186 B c 29/1 Acclamation—Lanark Belle (Selkirk (USA)) **H.E. Sheikh J. B. H. B. K. Al Thani**
187 **LEXINGTON TIMES (IRE),** b c 3/2 Paco Boy (IRE)—Fuaigh Mor (IRE) (Dubai Destination (USA)) (46457)
188 B c 9/3 Montjeu (IRE)—Madeira Mist (IRE) (Grand Lodge (USA)) (600000) **H.E. Sheikh J. B. H. B. K. Al Thani**
189 **MAFTOON (IRE),** b c 15/3 Dark Angel (IRE)—Chincoteague (IRE) (Daylami (IRE)) (85000) **Hamdan Al Maktoum**
190 **MAGICAL ROUNDABOUT (IRE),** gr c 10/2 Zebedee—Chimere (FR) (Soviet Lad (USA)) **Mrs J. Wood**
191 B c 5/4 Equiano (IRE)—Mail The Desert (IRE) (Desert Prince (USA)) (140000) **Malih L. Al Basti**
192 B c 25/2 Kyllachy—Mamounia (IRE) (Green Desert (USA)) (36190) **R. Hannon**
193 **MANDARIN GIRL,** b f 8/5 Paco Boy (IRE)—Cake (IRE) (Acclamation) **Mr D. J. Anderson**
194 Ch f 16/4 Champs Elysees—Marla (GER) (Pentire) (69686) **S. Manana**
195 B c 24/1 Kyllachy—Marliana (IRE) (Mtoto) (57142) **Mr A. A. Alkhallafi**
196 **MARSH HAWK,** b f 26/2 Invincible Spirit (IRE)—Asaawir (Royal Applause) **Rockcliffe Stud**
197 Ch f 29/3 Raven's Pass (USA)—Mauri Moon (Green Desert (USA)) (30000) **S. Manana**
198 B f 31/3 Danehill Dancer (IRE)—Mennetou (IRE) (Entrepreneur) (220000) **H.E. Sheikh J. B. H. B. K. Al Thani**
199 Ch c 11/2 Dubawi (IRE)—Mise (IRE) (Indian Ridge) (774293) **H.E. Sheikh J. B. H. B. K. Al Thani**
200 B f 10/5 Fastnet Rock (AUS)—Miss Beabea (IRE) (Catrail (USA))
201 B c 22/3 Royal Applause—Miss Sophisticat (Alhaarth (IRE)) (29000)
202 **MISTERIOSO (IRE),** b c 13/2 Iffraaj—Roystonea (Polish Precedent (USA)) (130000) **M. Pescod**
203 **MONTIDEUX (IRE),** b c 22/2 Acclamation—
    Pearls of Wisdom (Kyllachy) (70000) **Martin Clarke & James Jeffries**
204 B f 26/3 Dansili—Mrs Marsh (Marju (IRE))
205 B f 22/3 Raven's Pass (USA)—
    Multicolour Wave (IRE) (Rainbow Quest (USA)) (80000) **Mrs Boocock, Mrs Doyle, Mr Barry**
206 **MUMFORD,** b c 30/1 Stimulation (IRE)—Noble Nova (Fraam) (110000) **Mr W. A. Tinkler**
207 **MUTASAYYID,** ch c 25/3 Bahamian Bounty—
    Clear Voice (USA) (Cryptoclearance (USA)) (75000) **Hamdan Al Maktoum**
208 B f 15/4 Acclamation—My (King's Best (USA)) **M. Abdullah**
209 B f 29/2 Zebedee—Night of Joy (IRE) (King's Best (USA)) (77428) **H.H. Sheikh Mohammed bin Khalifa Al-Thani**
210 B f 13/2 Naaqoos—Nikolenka (IRE) (Indian Ridge) (23228)
211 Ch c 4/3 Lord Shanakill (USA)—No Greater Love (USA) (Stravinsky (USA)) (47619) **R. Hannon**
212 **NUFOOTH (IRE),** b f 14/2 Elnadim (USA)—Sahaayeb (IRE) (Indian Haven) **Hamdan Al Maktoum**
213 Ch c 14/1 Raven's Pass (USA)—Olympic Medal (Nayef (USA)) (250000) **H.E. Sheikh J. B. H. B. K. Al Thani**
214 **ON A WHIM,** b f 3/2 Tamayuz—Love Me Tender (Green Desert (USA)) (27000) **T. Hyde**
215 **ON HIGH,** b f 23/4 Exceed And Excel (AUS)—Kirk (Selkirk (USA)) **P. T. Tellwright**
216 B c 8/3 Lawman (FR)—On My Kness (FR) (Fasliyev (USA)) (170000) **H.E. Sheikh J. B. H. B. K. Al Thani**
217 B f 18/2 High Chaparral (IRE)—Onereuse (Sanglamore (USA)) **H.E. Sheikh J. B. H. B. K. Al Thani**
218 B c 14/2 Paco Boy (IRE)—Oshiponga (Barathea (IRE)) (35000) **Highclere T'Bred Racing(St James's Palace)**
219 **PACK TOGETHER,** b f 8/2 Paco Boy (IRE)—New Assembly (IRE) (Machiavellian) (55000) **Her Majesty The Queen**
220 B c 19/2 Raven's Pass (USA)—Palatial (Green Desert (USA)) (525000) **H.E. Sheikh J. B. H. B. K. Al Thani**
221 **PAPIER,** b f 27/2 Paco Boy (IRE)—Angus Newz (Compton Place) (55000) **Mrs A. Turner**
222 **PARSLEY (IRE),** br f 6/3 Zebedee—Montefino (IRE) (Shamardal (USA)) (16190) **De La Warr Racing**
223 **PEACOCK,** b c 11/3 Paco Boy (IRE)—Rainbow's Edge (Rainbow Quest (USA)) **Her Majesty The Queen**
224 B f 3/3 Zebedee—Penny Rouge (IRE) (Pennekamp (USA)) **Mrs J. Wood**
225 **PIPING DREAM (IRE),** b f 24/4 Approve (IRE)—French Fern (IRE) (Royal Applause) (34285) **R. Hannon**
226 **PORT,** b c 22/3 Hurricane Run (IRE)—Captain's Paradise (IRE) (Rock of Gibraltar (IRE)) **Mrs J. Wood**
227 B c 8/2 Rock of Gibraltar (IRE)—Powder Blue (Daylami (IRE)) (45000) **Mr M. S. Al Shahi**
228 Br f 18/4 Hurricane Run (IRE)—Precautionary (Green Desert (USA)) (13937) **Mr J. N. Reus**
229 **PRESCIENCE (IRE),** b c 20/3 Kyllachy—Clear Vision (Observatory (USA)) **Mrs J. Wood**
230 B f 8/3 Invincible Spirit (IRE)—
    Propaganda (IRE) (Sadler's Wells (USA)) (216801) **H.E. Sheikh J. B. H. B. K. Al Thani**
231 **PROPOSED,** b c 29/2 Invincible Spirit (IRE)—On A Soapbox (USA) (Mi Cielo (USA)) (58000) **Mrs J. Wood**

MR RICHARD HANNON - Continued

232 B c 11/4 Elusive Quality (USA)—
Pure Incentive (USA) (Fusaichi Pegasus (USA)) (50000) **Hughes, Morecombe, Anderson**
233 QAARIB (IRE), b c 23/3 Exceed And Excel (AUS)—
No Complaining (IRE) (Alhaarth (IRE)) (82000) **Hamdan Al Maktoum**
234 QUAE SUPRA, b c 19/4 Exceed And Excel (AUS)—
Noodle Soup (USA) (Alphabet Soup (USA)) (22000) **Mrs A. Williams**
235 REFLATION, b c 6/2 Stimulation (IRE)—Miss Poppy (Averti (IRE)) (40000) **Mr A. G. Smith**
236 REMBRANDT, b c 13/2 Dutch Art—Authoritative (Diktat) **Mrs J. Wood**
237 RENAISSANT, ch f 30/3 Dutch Art—Sofonisba (Rock of Gibraltar (IRE)) (36000) **Cheveley Park Stud Limited**
238 Ch c 22/2 Teofilo (IRE)—Ribot's Guest (IRE) (Be My Guest (USA)) (170000) **H.E. Sheikh J. B. H. B. K. Al Thani**
239 ROYAL TOAST (IRE), b c 4/2 Duke of Marmalade (IRE)—Ripalong (IRE) (Revoque (IRE)) (40000) **G. P. Triefus**
240 C c 11/3 Rip Van Winkle (IRE)—Rozella (IRE) (Anabaa (USA)) (185830) **H.E. Sheikh J. B. H. B. K. Al Thani**
241 Ch c 27/2 Selkirk (USA)—Ryella (USA) (Cozzene (USA)) (88000) **Morecombe, Anderson, Hughes**
242 SAWAAHEL, b c 14/4 Pastoral Pursuits—Sheer Indulgence (FR) (Pivotal) (95238) **Hamdan Al Maktoum**
243 Ch f 24/2 Equiano (FR)—Scottish Exile (IRE) (Ashkalani (IRE)) (10476) **Mr K. McMullen**
244 B c 8/3 Big Bad Bob (IRE)—Scrumptious (Sakhee (USA)) (210000) **Sir A. Ferguson**
245 B f 9/4 Whipper (USA)—Selkis (FR) (Darshaan) (43360) **Hey You**
246 SHADOW ROCK (IRE), gr c 1/2 Verglas (IRE)—Ice Rock (IRE) (Rock of Gibraltar (IRE)) (77428) **Mr M. Daniels**
247 B f 28/2 Acclamation—
Shady Nook (USA) (Key of Luck (USA)) (50000) **HighclereThoroughbredRacing(Jersey Lily)**
248 SHELL BAY (USA), b c 7/4 Hard Spun (USA)—
Rebel Account (USA) (Dixieland Band (USA)) (62000) **Mr H. R. Heffer**
249 SILVER QUAY (IRE), gr c 28/3 Dark Angel (IRE)—She Runs (FR) (Sheyrann) (70000) **Mr H. R. Heffer**
250 SIXTY (IRE), b c 9/2 Iffraaj—Follow My Lead (Night Shift (USA)) **Mrs J. Wood**
251 SKI SLOPE, b f 17/3 Three Valleys (USA)—Danehurst (Danehill (USA)) **Cheveley Park Stud Limited**
252 SOLDIER SAM (IRE), gr c 23/4 Zebedee—Fey Rouge (Fayruz) (55000) **Mrs J. Wood**
253 B c 7/4 Paco Boy (IRE)—Solola (GER) (Black Sam Bellamy (IRE)) (147115) **H.E. Sheikh J. B. H. B. K. Al Thani**
254 B c 24/3 Intikhab (USA)—Song of Passion (IRE) (Orpen (USA)) (70000)
255 SPIRIT OF XIAN (IRE), b f 6/4 Kodiac—Gold Again (USA) (Touch Gold (USA)) (89042) **Mr B. W. Keswick**
256 B c 7/4 Majestic Missile (IRE)—Starisa (IRE) (College Chapel) (30971) **Ladyswood Stud**
257 STATE OF THE UNION (IRE), ch c 31/1 Approve (IRE)—First Lady (IRE) (Indian Ridge) (33333) **Mrs J. Wood**
258 STEAL THE SCENE (IRE), ch c 8/2 Lord Shanakill (USA)—
Namoos (USA) (Sahm (USA)) (47619) **Ms Elaine Chivers & Potensis Ltd**
259 STEP TO THE SHEARS, ch c 6/4 Footstepsinthesand—Rockie Bright (Rock of Gibraltar (IRE)) (23809)
260 SUNSET SAIL (IRE), b c 17/4 Arcano (IRE)—Mythologie (FR) (Bering) (55000) **Mr H. R. Heffer**
261 B f 9/4 Holy Roman Emperor (IRE)—Sweet Namibia (IRE) (Namid) (16190) **H.E. Sheikh J. B. H. B. K. Al Thani**
262 SYDNEY RUFFDIAMOND, c 6/5 Equiano (FR)—
Pirouetting (Pivotal) (38000) **The Sydney Arms Racing Club II**
263 SYMBOLIST, b f 23/3 Yeats (IRE)—Pescia (IRE) (Darshaan) **Mrs J. Wood**
264 B c 19/2 Fast Company (IRE)—Tawaafur (Fantastic Light (USA)) (200000) **H.E. Sheikh J. B. H. B. K. Al Thani**
265 Ch f 3/2 Dutch Art—The Fairies Did It (USA) (Elusive Quality (USA)) (123886) **Saleh Al Homaizi & Imad Al Sagar**
266 B c 10/2 Sea The Stars (IRE)—Three Moons (IRE) (Montjeu (IRE)) (380000) **H.E. Sheikh J. B. H. B. K. Al Thani**
267 THREE ROBINS, b f 27/3 Cape Cross (IRE)—Three Wrens (IRE) (Second Empire (IRE)) **Mrs A. Wigan**
268 B c 9/2 Camacho—Tides (Bahamian Bounty) (66666) **Carmichael Jennings**
269 TIGGY WIGGY (IRE), b f 7/3 Kodiac—
Kheleyf's Silver (USA) (Kheleyf (USA)) (39047) **Potensis Ltd & Ms Elaine Chivers**
270 TOM HARK (FR), ch c 21/1 Makfi—Raisonable (USA) (El Prado (IRE)) (89043) **J. D. Manley**
271 B f 22/1 Lope de Vega (IRE)—Truth Beauty (IRE) (Dubai Destination (USA)) (81300) **Qatar Racing Limited**
272 TYPHOON SEASON, b c 19/3 Kyllachy—Alovera (IRE) (King's Best (USA)) **Rockcliffe Stud**
273 VELOCITER (IRE), ch c 28/3 Zebedee—Polly Jones (USA) (Lear Fan (USA)) (27100)
274 VESNINA, b f 15/2 Sea The Stars (IRE)—Safina (Pivotal) **Cheveley Park Stud Limited**
275 Ch f 31/3 Elusive Quality (USA)—What A Treasure (IRE) (Cadeaux Genereux) **M. Abdullah**
276 WHEN WILL IT END (IRE), b c 15/4 Kodiac—
Alexander Duchess (IRE) (Desert Prince (IRE)) (35238) **M. A. C. Buckley**
277 WHO DARES WINS (IRE), b c 6/5 Jeremy (USA)—Savignano (Polish Precedent (USA)) (30000) **W. H. Ponsonby**
278 WILD TOBACCO, br c 8/2 More Than Ready (USA)—Princess Janie (USA) (Elusive Quality (USA)) **Rockcliffe Stud**
279 B c 19/3 Lawman (FR)—Zuniga's Date (USA) (Diesis) (204761) **Carmichael Jennings**

Other Owners: Mrs R. Ablett, Mr M. J. Ablett, I. J. Al-Sagar, Mr D. T. W. Altham, Mr R. D. Ambrose, Ms C. S. Antell, Axom Ltd, D. J. Barry, Mrs C. B. Barry, Mr C. Bloor, Mrs K. C. Boocock, Mr M. P. Brewer, Mr D. P. N. Brown, Mr S. Brown, B. Bull, Byerley Racing Limited, Mrs F. J. Carmichael, Mr M. Carver, Ms E. C. Chivers, Ms L. D. Chivers, Miss C. I. Chivers, Mr M. Clarke, D. D. Clee, Mrs J. P. Clee, Mr P. Coates, Mr M. L. Cohen, Mr V. A. Coutin, J. M. Curtis, Mr G. Davison, Lord De La Warr, Countess De La Warr, Mr D. L. Dixon, Mr P. E. Done, Mr L. J. Dowley, Mr D. Downie, Mrs A. M. Doyle, Mrs R. A. Duggan, Mr S. Ensor, Mr S. Fielden, Mr J. Fiyaz, Mr R. J. Fowler, Mr C. M. Giles, A. J. J. Gompertz, J. K. Grimes, Mrs F. M. Hallett, Mr R. Hannon, S. Hassiakos, Mr R. P. Heffer, The Hon H. M. Herbert, Highclere Thoroughbred Racing Ltd, Mr A. J. Hill, R. G. Hitchcock, Saleh Al Homaizi, Mr R. S. Hoskins, Mr M. B. Hughes, Mr C. M. Humber, Mr J.

MR RICHARD HANNON - Continued

Jeffries, Mr I. Jennings, Ms S. J. Johnson, M. Kerr-Dineen, Mr M. J. Kershaw, Mr S. L. Keswick, A. E. King, Mr A. T. Macdonald, Mrs S. Magnier, G. A. Mason, Mr A. Mason, R. L. Maynard, P. H. Milmo, R. H. W. Morecombe, P. H. Morgan, Mrs M. E. Morgan, Mr J. Pak, T. S. Palin, O. J. W. Pawle, M. Prince, Mr T. J. Ramsden, Mr W. J. Reilly, Mr N. M. S. Rich, N. J. F. Robinson, Mr A. R. Skeites, Mr K. P. Skeites, Mr John Smith, D. Smith, Mr J. A. B. Stafford, Mr J. R. F. Stunt, Mr J. Sullivan, The Sydney Arms Racing Club Ltd, M. Tabor, Mr S. E. Tiffin, S. P. Tindall, Mr R. Valiant, Mr A. Victor, Mr M. K. Webb, Mr N. A. Williams, Mrs J. Williamson, Mr T. Withers, C. N. Wright.

Jockey (flat): Richard Hughes, Pat Dobbs, Sean Levey, Ryan Moore, Dane O'Neill, Kieran O'Neill. **Apprentice:** Cameron Hardie, John Keating, Stephen King, Gary Mahon.

---

292 MR GEOFFREY HARKER, Thirsk
Postal: **Stockhill Green, York Rd, Thirkelby, Thirsk, North Yorkshire, YO7 3AS**
Contacts: **PHONE (01845) 501117 FAX (01845) 501614 MOBILE (07803) 116412/(07930) 125544**
E-MAIL gandjhome@aol.com

1 **BLING KING**, 5, b g Haafhd—Bling Bling (IRE) **P. I. Harker**
2 **BRANSTON JUBILEE**, 4, ch f Assertive—Branston Jewel (IRE) **G. A. Harker**
3 **CONJOLA**, 7, b m Grape Tree Road—Conchita **Miss R. G. Brewis**
4 **DIALOGUE**, 8, b g Singspiel (IRE)—Zonda **P. I. Harker**
5 **EIJAAZ (IRE)**, 13, b g Green Desert (USA)—Kismah **A. S. Ward**
6 **FAVOURABLE FELLOW (IRE)**, 5, b g Beneficial—Magic Moonbeam (IRE) **A. S. Ward**
7 **FIRESIDE DREAMS**, 5, b g Boogie Street—Champagne N Dreams **Mrs J. L. Harker**
8 **FIRST SARGEANT**, 4, gr c Dutch Art—Princess Raya **Rothmere Racing Limited**
9 **FREE ART**, 6, b g Iffraaj—Possessive Artiste **A. S. Ward**
10 **GINGER JACK**, 7, ch g Refuse To Bend (IRE)—Coretta (IRE) **C. H. McGhie**
11 **I CONFESS**, 9, br g Fantastic Light (USA)—Vadsagreya (FR) **Mr B. Harker**
12 **JACARANDA STAR**, 6, b g Grape Tree Road—Chantilly Rose **Miss R. G. Brewis**
13 **JUDICIOUS**, 7, ch g Pivotal—Virtuous **Mr M. Reay**
14 **MASTER ROONEY (IRE)**, 8, b br g Cape Cross (IRE)—Wimple (USA) **A. Turton, P. Langford & S. Brown**
15 **MISTY EYES**, 5, b m Byron—Wax Eloquent **Haven Stud Partnership**
16 **MOCCASIN (FR)**, 5, b g Green Tune (USA)—Museum Piece **Mr & Mrs Rattonsey & Mr Nensey**
17 **TARTAN GIGHA (IRE)**, 9, b g Green Desert (USA)—High Standard **A. S. Ward**
18 **WANNABE KING**, 8, b g King's Best (USA)—Wannabe Grand (IRE) **Mr & Mrs H Nensey, Saif Nensey**
19 **ZIGGY LEE**, 8, b g Lujain (USA)—Mary O'grady (USA) **Rothmere Racing Limited**

THREE-YEAR-OLDS

20 **MY GIRL RIO (IRE)**, ch f Captain Rio—Pinewoods Lily (IRE) **Mr M. Reay**

Other Owners: Mr S. W. Brown, Mr G. Burgess, Mrs P. L. Burgess, Mr P. M. Langford, Mr H. S. A. Nensey, Mr S. Nensey, Mrs N. Nensey, Mr Z. F. Rattonsey, Mrs R. Rattonsey, Mr A. Turton.

Assistant Trainer: Jenny Harker

Jockey (NH): W. T. Kennedy. **Apprentice:** Jordan Nason.

---

293 MR W. HARNEY, Co. Tipperary
Postal: **Manna Cottage, Templemore, Co. Tipperary, Ireland**
Contacts: **PHONE (00353) 504 31534 FAX (00353) 504 31534 MOBILE (00353) 86 2498836**
E-MAIL harneyvet@eircom.net

1 **BONZO BING (IRE)**, 6, b g Gold Well—She's A Dreamer (IRE) **Patrick Harney**
2 **FISCAL NOMAD (IRE)**, 7, b g Flemensfirth (USA)—Tradaree (IRE) **Patrick Harney**
3 4, b g Indian River (FR)—French Class **Mrs W. Harney**
4 **JOHNSTON'S BEST (IRE)**, 7, b m King's Theatre (IRE)—Johnston's Crest (IRE) **Mr F. McKevitt**
5 **JOXER (IRE)**, 7, b g Gold Well—Tender Return (IRE) **Mrs W. Harney**
6 **KAKAGH (IRE)**, 10, b g Tel Quel (FR)—Pheisty **Liam Breslin**
7 **KILLTILANE ROSE (IRE)**, 9, ch m Flemensfirth (USA)—Miss Rose (IRE) **Mrs W. Harney**
8 **LADY BOULEA (IRE)**, 9, b m Windsor Castle—Manna Fairy (IRE) **Michael Barrett**
9 4, Br f Robin des Champs (FR)—Sorrentina (IRE) **Mrs W. Harney**
10 **THE CONKER CLUB (IRE)**, 8, ch m Beneficial—Puff of Magic (IRE) **Old Port Syndicate**

Assistant Trainer: Rachel Harney. **Jockey (NH):** Bryan J. Cooper. **Conditional:** D. E. Splaine. **Amateur:** Mr J. J. King.

294 MR RICHARD HARPER, Banbury

Postal: **Home Farm, Kings Sutton, Banbury, Oxfordshire, OX17 3RS**
Contacts: **PHONE (01295) 810997 FAX (01295) 812787 MOBILE (07970) 223481**
E-MAIL rharper@freeuk.com

1 **CHAPEL HOUSE**, 11, b g Beneficial—My Moona **R. C. Harper**
2 **SPIKE MAC (IRE)**, 9, b g Glacial Storm (USA)—Edionda (IRE) **R. C. Harper**
3 **TOP BENEFIT (IRE)**, 12, gr g Beneficial—Cottage Lass (IRE) **R. C. Harper**

Assistant Trainer: C. Harper

295 MRS JESSICA HARRINGTON, Kildare

Postal: **Commonstown Racing Stables Ltd., Moone, Co. Kildare, Ireland**
Contacts: PHONE (00353) 5986 24153 FAX (00353) 5986 24292 MOBILE (00353) 8725 66129
E-MAIL jessica@jessicaharringtonracing.com WEBSITE www.jessicaharringtonracing.com

1 **ANNIE OAKLEY (IRE)**, 6, br b m Westerner—Gaye Artiste (IRE) **Mrs Gina Galvin**
2 **BANKER BURKE (IRE)**, 4, br g Big Bad Bob (IRE)—Ski For Gold **Anamoine Ltd**
3 **BULLOCK HARBOUR (IRE)**, 10, b g Second Empire (USA)—Coteri Run **Mr Barry Connell**
4 **BURN AND TURN (IRE)**, 8, b m Flemensfirth (USA)—Pescetto Lady (IRE) **Mr Joe O'Flaherty**
5 **CAILIN ANNAMH (IRE)**, 6, b m Definite Article—Prairie Bell (IRE) **Flyers Syndicate**
6 4, Ch f Robin des Champs (FR)—Callherwhatulike (IRE) **Mr John Harrington**
7 4, Br g Arcadio (GER)—Carryonharriet (IRE) **Full Moone Syndicate**
8 **DIRECTOR'S FORUM (IRE)**, 6, ch g Pivotal—Stage Struck (IRE) **Mr Barry Connell**
9 **FIRE DAWN (IRE)**, 5, b m Kayf Tara—Fire Queen (IRE) **Mr John Harrington**
10 **FRESH BY NATURE (IRE)**, 7, b m Flemensfirth (USA)—Star Alert (IRE) **Fresh By Nature Syndicate**
11 **GAMBLING GIRL (IRE)**, 5, ch m Hawk Wing (USA)—Gambling Spirit **River Racing Partnership**
12 **GIMLI'S ROCK (IRE)**, 8, b g Rock of Gibraltar (IRE)—Beltisaal (FR) **Mr Geoffrey Ruddock**
13 **GIMLI'S VOYAGE (IRE)**, 4, b g Stowaway—Rathturtin Brief (IRE) **Mr Geoffrey Ruddock**
14 5, B g Mountain High (IRE)—Great Cullen (IRE) **Full Moone Syndicate**
15 **HURRICANE RIDGE (IRE)**, 5, b g Hurricane Run (IRE)—Warrior Wings **Lakeside Syndicate**
16 **JETSON (IRE)**, 9, b g Oscar (IRE)—La Noire (IRE) **Mr Gerard McGrath**
17 **JEZKI (IRE)**, 6, b g Milan—La Noire (IRE) **Mr J. P. McManus**
18 5, Ch g Hernando (FR)—Joleah (IRE) **Mr Ron Wood**
19 **KNIGHTSONE (IRE)**, 5, b g Chevalier—Delivered (IRE) **Half Full Syndicate**
20 **LILLY OF THE MOOR (IRE)**, 6, b m Flemensfirth (USA)—Serenique **Mr Steve Hemstock**
21 **LOUGH LASS (IRE)**, 5, b m Kayf Tara—Gazza's Girl (IRE) **Mr Arthur McCooey**
22 **MACNICHOLSON (IRE)**, 5, b g Definite Article—Heroic Performer (IRE) **Mr Joe O'Flaherty**
23 **MASTEROFDECEPTION (IRE)**, 6, b g Darsi (FR)—Sherberry (IRE) **Mr John Harrington**
24 **MORE OF THE SAME (IRE)**, 4, b f Kyllachy—Inchberry **Mr J. P. McManus**
25 **MOSCOW MAGIC (IRE)**, 6, b g Moscow Society (USA)—
See More Tricks **Mr Hugh Williams & Mr William Jenks**
26 **MR FIFTYONE (IRE)**, 5, b g Jeremy (USA)—Maka (USA) **Mr David Bobbett**
27 5, B m Kalanisi (IRE)—Mrs Woman (IRE) **Mrs Kathleen Quinn**
28 **NEWBERRY HILL (IRE)**, 4, ch g Kheleyf (USA)—Zonic **Rathmoyle Exports**
29 4, B g Celtic Swing—Noble Choice **Full Moone Syndicate**
30 **ONE FINE DAY (IRE)**, 5, b m Choisir (AUS)—Night Eyes (IRE) **Mr John Harrington**
31 **OPERATING (IRE)**, 7, b g Milan—Seymourswift **Mr Michael Buckley**
32 **ORBITING (IRE)**, 5, b m Oscar (IRE)—Seymourswift **Mr George Hartigan**
33 **OSCARS WELL (IRE)**, 9, b br g Oscar (IRE)—Placid Willow (IRE) **Molly Malone Syndicate**
34 **OVERCALL (IRE)**, 5, b g Choisir (AUS)—My Darling Dodo (IRE) **Mr Barry Connell**
35 **PAINTED LADY (IRE)**, 5, b m Presenting—Amathea (FR) **Mr Steve Hemstock**
36 **PEGGY'S LEG (USA)**, 4, b f Henrythenavigator (USA)—Audit (USA) **Mrs Sue Ann Foley**
37 **PLAY THE MARKET (IRE)**, 7, b g King's Theatre (IRE)—Market Lass (IRE) **Mrs Judy Wilson**
38 **POLISHED ROCK (IRE)**, 4, ch g Rock of Gibraltar (IRE)—Where We Left Off **Mr Robert Ryan**
39 **PROTESTANT (IRE)**, 4, b g Papal Bull—Vintage Escape (IRE) **Mrs P. K. Cooper**
40 **RAE'S CREEK (IRE)**, 4, ch g New Approach (IRE)—Allort's Forgotten (USA) **Mr J. P. McManus**
41 **ROCK ON THE MOOR (IRE)**, 6, b m Flemensfirth (USA)—Home At Last (IRE) **Mr Steve Hemstock**
42 **ROCK THE WORLD (IRE)**, 6, b g Orpen (USA)—Sue N Win (IRE) **Mr Michael Buckley & Mr Justin Carthy**
43 4, B g Scorpion (IRE)—Shandora (IRE) **Buckley, Carthy, Nicoll, Reid Scott**
44 **SIN MIEDO (IRE)**, 4, br g Intikhab (USA)—Xaviera (IRE) **Mr John Harrington**
45 **STEPS TO FREEDOM (IRE)**, 8, b g Statue of Liberty (USA)—Dhakhirah (IRE) **Mrs Elizabeth Hussey**
46 5, Ch g Exit To Nowhere (USA)—Tahaddi Hall (IRE) **Mr Eugene McCooey**
47 4, B f Whipper (USA)—Tertia (IRE) **Mr John Harrington**

MRS JESSICA HARRINGTON - Continued

48 **TRACK THE PLAGUE (IRE)**, 6, b g Oscar (IRE)—Madmoiselle Etoile (IRE) **Mr David Bobbett**
49 **TRI NA CEILE (IRE)**, 4, ch f Galileo (IRE)—Pescia (IRE) **Mr J. P. McManus**
50 **TTEBBOB (IRE)**, 5, b g Milan—Our Dream (IRE) **Mr David Bobbett**
51 **VOICE OF A CURLEW (IRE)**, 4, b f Duke of Marmalade (IRE)—Zaafran **A Blessing In Disguise Partnership**
52 **WEATHER WATCH (IRE)**, 4, b c Hurricane Run (IRE)—Caravan of Dreams (IRE) **Mrs P. K. Cooper**
53 4, B f Zamindar (USA)—Zariliya (IRE) **Mr Des Donegan**

THREE-YEAR-OLDS

54 **BEATIFY (IRE)**, b f Big Bad Bob (IRE)—Convent Girl (IRE) **Anamoine Ltd**
55 **BENNY BLANCO (IRE)**, b g Big Bad Bob (IRE)—Dona Alba (IRE) **Anamoine Ltd**
56 **BILLBOARD (IRE)**, b g Big Bad Bob (IRE)—Lamanka Lass (USA) **Mrs P. K. Cooper**
57 **BRIBE THE BOUNCER (IRE)**, b g Big Bad Bob (IRE)—Nouvelle Nova (IRE) **Anamoine Ltd**
58 **BUTTERFLY DANCER (IRE)**, b f Teofilo (IRE)—Azolla **Commonstown Stables**
59 **HOMERIC HYMN (FR)**, b f Acclamation—Mary Arnold (IRE) **Flaxman Stables Ireland Ltd**
60 **KABJOY (IRE)**, b f Intikhab (USA)—Lunar Love (IRE) **Favourites Racing Ltd**
61 **KOMITOE (IRE)**, b f Nayef (USA)—Bobbie Soxer (IRE) **Anamoine Ltd**
62 B f Jeremy (USA)—Krynica (USA) **Mr John Harrington**
63 **LAKE SUPERIOR (IRE)**, b g Dalakhani (IRE)—Lakatoi **Mr Mark Dixon**
64 **NEVERUSHACON (IRE)**, b g Echo of Light—Lily Beth (IRE) **Mr Gerry Byrne**
65 **ODE TO PSYCHE (IRE)**, b f Dansili—Quan Yin (IRE) **Flaxman Stables Ireland Ltd**
66 **PAR THREE (IRE)**, b br g Azamour (IRE)—Little Whisper (IRE) **Mr Peter Winkworth**
67 **PERSIAN CALIPH (IRE)**, ch g Intikhab (USA)—Persian Memories (IRE) **Anamoine Ltd**
68 **PORT MERRION (IRE)**, b g Intense Focus (USA)—Aminata **Mr John Harrington**
69 **PRINCESS ALOOF (IRE)**, b f Big Bad Bob (IRE)—Little Miss Diva (IRE) **Mr John Harrington**
70 **SILENT LADY (IRE)**, b f Big Bad Bob (IRE)—Desert Trail (IRE) **Mr John Harrington**

TWO-YEAR-OLDS

71 B f 27/1 Intikhab (USA)—Babberina (IRE) (Danehill Dancer (IRE)) **Mrs P. K. Cooper & Mr R. Galway**
72 **BARNACLE BILL (IRE)**, gr c 19/4 Big Bad Bob (IRE)—Katch Me Katie (Danehill (USA)) (69685) **Millhouse LLC**
73 **BOCCA BACIATA (IRE)**, b br f 8/4 Big Bad Bob (IRE)—
                        Sovana (IRE) (Desert King (IRE)) (178086) **Flaxman Stables Ireland Ltd**
74 B f 8/3 Rip Van Winkle (IRE)—Celeste (FR) (Muhtathir) (27100) **Commonstown Racing Stables**
75 B f 2/5 Holy Roman Emperor (IRE)—
                        Crazy About You (IRE) (Montjeu)) **Mrs Yvonne Nicoll & David Reid Scott**
76 B f 24/4 Excellent Art—Greenisland (IRE) (Fasliyev (USA)) **Stonethorn Stud Farm Ltd**
77 **JACK NAYLOR**, b f 22/4 Champs Elysees—Fashionable (Nashwan (USA)) (8129) **Mr Gerry Byrne**
78 **JEANNE GIRL (IRE)**, b f 15/3 Rip Van Winkle (IRE)—
                        Sister Golightly (Mtoto) (20131) **Commonstown Racing Stables**
79 B f 13/2 Excellent Art—La Quinta (IRE) (Indian Ridge) **Flaxman Stables Ireland Ltd**
80 B c 15/2 Big Bad Bob (IRE)—Magpie (USA) (Woodman (USA)) (30971) **Commonstown Racing Stables**
81 B c 11/5 Big Bad Bob (IRE)—Meduse Bleu (Medicean) **Mr John Harrington**
82 B f 5/3 Equiano (FR)—Polly Perkins (IRE) (Pivotal) (18582) **Commonstown Racing Stables**
83 B c 17/4 Echo of Light—Tucum (IRE) (Diktat) **Mr John Wholey**

Assistant Trainers: Mrs Emma Galway, Mr Eamonn Leigh

Jockey (flat): Fran Berry. **Jockey (NH):** Robert Power, Andrew Leigh, Mark Bolger, Tommy Treacy.
Conditional: Kevin Sexton. **Apprentice:** Charlie Elliott. **Amateur:** Mr Mark Fahey, Miss Kate Harrington.

---

296 MR RONALD HARRIS, Chepstow
Postal: **Ridge House Stables, Earlswood, Chepstow, Monmouthshire, NP16 6AN**
Contacts: **PHONE (01291) 641689 FAX (01291) 641258 MOBILE (07831) 770899**
E-MAIL ridgehousestables.ltd@btinternet.com WEBSITE www.ronharrisracing.co.uk

1 **ALHABAN (IRE)**, 8, gr g Verglas (IRE)—Anne Tudor (IRE) **Ridge House Stables Ltd**
2 **APRIL CIEL**, 5, b g Septieme Ciel (USA)—By Definition (IRE) **Paul & Ann de Weck**
3 **BELLE BAYARDO (IRE)**, 6, b g Le Vie Dei Colori—Heres The Plan (IRE) **William Jones Lisa Harrington**
4 **CHELSEA GREY (IRE)**, 4, gr f Verglas (IRE)—Kapera (FR) **Mr L. Scadding**
5 **CORPORAL MADDOX**, 7, b g Royal Applause—Noble View (USA) **Robert & Nina Bailey**
6 **DIAMOND VINE (IRE)**, 6, b g Diamond Green (FR)—Glasnas Giant **Ridge House Stables Ltd**
7 **FAITHFUL RULER (USA)**, 10, b br g Elusive Quality—Fancy Ruler (USA) **Ridge House Stables Ltd**
8 **GLAMOROUS SISTER (IRE)**, 4, b f Jeremy (USA)—Glamorous Air (IRE) **Robert & Nina Bailey**
9 **HILL FORT**, 4, ch c Pivotal—Cairns (UAE) **Ridge House Stables Ltd**
10 **HYPNOTISM**, 4, ch g Pivotal—Hypnotize **Unique Sports Racing & Partner**

MR RONALD HARRIS - Continued

11 **ISHISOBA**, 4, ch f Ishiguru (USA)—Bundle Up (USA) **Mr M. M. Cox**
12 **ITALIAN TOM (IRE)**, 7, b h Le Vie Dei Colori—Brave Cat (IRE) **S. & A. Mares**
13 **JUDGE 'N JURY**, 10, ch g Pivotal—Cyclone Connie **Robert & Nina Bailey**
14 **KEPT**, 5, ch g Pivotal—Possessed **Robert & Nina Bailey**
15 **LADY MANGO (IRE)**, 6, ch m Bahamian Bounty—Opera **Mr L. Scadding**
16 **LIGHT FROM MARS**, 9, gr g Fantastic Light (USA)—Hylandra (USA) **Mrs N. Macauley**
17 **MOBLEY CHAOS**, 4, b g Darnay—Emmarander **Mrs Lynn Cullimore**
18 **NIGHT TRADE (IRE)**, 7, b m Trade Fair—Compton Girl **Alan & Adam Darlow, A Darlow Productions**
19 **OFFBEAT SAFARIS (IRE)**, 6, b g Le Vie Dei Colori—Baywood **Mrs J. E. F. Adams**
20 **POWERFUL WIND (IRE)**, 5, ch g Titus Livius (FR)—Queen of Fools (IRE) **Mr A. D. Cooke**
21 **SIR DYLAN**, 5, b g Dylan Thomas (IRE)—Monteleone (IRE) **Ridge House Stables Ltd**
22 **SPINNING RIDGE (IRE)**, 9, ch g Spinning World (USA)—Summer Style (IRE) **Ridge House Stables Ltd**
23 **STARLIGHT ANGEL (IRE)**, 4, gr f Dark Angel (IRE)—King of All (IRE) **Mrs A. Mares**
24 **TOP COP**, 5, b g Acclamation—Speed Cop **Ridge House Stables Ltd**
25 **VERGALITY RIDGE (IRE)**, 4, gr g Verglas (IRE)—Phoenix Factor (IRE) **Ridge House Stables Ltd**
26 **VINCENTTI (IRE)**, 4, b g Invincible Spirit (IRE)—Bint Al Balad (IRE) **Robert & Nina Bailey**
27 **XCLUSIVE**, 4, b g Pivotal—Dance A Daydream **Monmouthshire Racing Club**

THREE-YEAR-OLDS

28 **CLASSIC PURSUIT**, b c Pastoral Pursuits—Snake's Head **David & Gwyn Joseph**
29 **DANDYS PERIER (IRE)**, br c Dandy Man (IRE)—Casual Remark (IRE) **Farley, Mares & Ridge House Stables**
30 **FANTASY JUSTIFIER (IRE)**, b c Arakan (USA)—Grandel **Farley, Fantasy Fellowship & RHS**
31 **FLICKSTA (IRE)**, b c Hard Spun (USA)—Sindy Jacobson (USA) **Ridge House Stables Ltd**
32 **GO GLAMOROUS (IRE)**, b f Elnadim (USA)—Glamorous Air (IRE) **Robert & Nina Bailey**
33 **GOWER PRINCESS**, ch f Footstepsinthesand—Hollow Quaill (IRE) **David & Gwyn Joseph**
34 **MR DANDY MAN (IRE)**, ch c Dandy Man (IRE)—Boudica (IRE) **S. & A. Mares**
35 **PENSAX LAD (IRE)**, gr c Verglas (IRE)—Betelgeuse **S. & A. Mares**
36 **SEVERNWIND (IRE)**, b g Diamond Green (FR)—Zeena **Mr A. D. Cooke**
37 **SUPERSTA**, ch c Pivotal—Resort **Serrell, Salthouse & Ridge House Stables**
38 **TRIGGER PARK (IRE)**, ch c Tagula (IRE)—Raazi **Mr J. Hatherell & Ridge House Stables**
39 **ZAFRAAJ**, b c Iffraaj—Woodbury **Mrs J. Jarrett**

TWO-YEAR-OLDS

40 Br c 20/3 Zebedee—Cruise Line (Rainbow Quest (USA)) (13809) **David & Gwyn Joseph**
41 B c 30/3 Zebedee—Dubai Princess (IRE) (Dubai Destination (USA)) (24761) **Mrs R. M. Serrell**
42 B f 20/4 Bertolini (USA)—Frisson (Slip Anchor) (2666)
43 Ch c 2/3 Pivotal—Invitee (Medicean) (17808) **Ridge House Stables Ltd**
44 B f 9/4 Camacho—Lamassu (IRE) (Entrepreneur) (2167) **Ridge House Stables Ltd**
45 B c 17/4 Vale of York (IRE)—State Secret (Green Desert (USA)) (3483) **Ridge House Stables Ltd**
46 **UNION ROSE**, b c 8/3 Stimulation (IRE)—Dot Hill (Refuse To Bend (IRE)) (6666) **Mr D. A. Evans**
47 B c 25/3 Majestic Missile (IRE)—Xena (Mull of Kintyre (USA)) (42585) **Ridge House Stables Ltd**

Other Owners: Fantasy Fellowship, Mr Robert Bailey, Mrs Nina Bailey, Mr A. M. Blewitt, Mr J. C. G. Chua, Mr Ken Clarke, Mr Peter Coll, Mr John Colley, Mr Antony Cooke, Mr Merv Cox, Mrs Lynn Cullimore, Mr Alan Darlow, Mr Adam Darlow, Mrs Ann E. de Weck, Drag Star On Swan, Mr Adrian Evans, Mr I. Farley, Ms Lisa Harrington, Mr John Hatherell, Mr Brian Hicks, Mrs Jarrett, Mr William Jones, Mr D. M. Joseph, Mr D. G. Joseph, Mr S. Mares, Mrs A. Mares, Monmouthshire Racing club, Mr Paul Moultan, Mr Peter Nurcombe, Mrs Sue Nurcombe, Mr Terry Reffell, Ridge House Stables Ltd, Mr W. J. Salthouse, Mr Les Scadding, Mrs Ruth M. Serrell, Mrs Ruth Severell, Mr M. C. Watts, Mr Mike Watts, Mr R. D. Willis, Mr Paul de Weck.

Jockey (flat): Liam Jones, Luke Morris, Robert Winston. **Apprentice:** Daryl Byrne, Abie Knowles.

---

297   MR SHAUN HARRIS, Worksop
Postal: Pinewood Stables, Carburton, Worksop, Nottinghamshire, S80 3BT
Contacts: **PHONE** (01909) 470936 **FAX** (01909) 470936 **MOBILE** (07768) 950460
E-MAIL shaunharris.racing@hotmail.co.uk **WEBSITE** www.shaunharrisracing.co.uk

1 **BETTY BOO (IRE)**, 4, ch f Thousand Words—Poker Dice **Mr A. K. Elton**
2 **BLUE CLUMBER**, 4, b f Sleeping Indian—Blue Nile (IRE) **Miss G. H. Ward**
3 **BOTANIST**, 7, b g Selkirk (USA)—Red Camellia **N Blencowe, R Booth, D Cooper, M Lenton**
4 **EL BRAVO**, 8, ch g Falbrav (IRE)—Alessandra **www.nottinghamshireracing.co.uk (2)**
5 **FATHER SHINE (IRE)**, 11, b br g Supreme Leader—Shean Hill (IRE) **Mrs A. Kenny**
6 **FATHOM FIVE**, 10, b g Fath (USA)—Ambria (ITY) **Nottinghamshire Racing**
7 **HELLBENDER (IRE)**, 8, ch g Exceed And Excel (AUS)—Desert Rose **Southwell Racecourse Owners Group**

MR SHAUN HARRIS - Continued

   8 **LORD FOX (IRE)**, 7, b g Alflora (IRE)—Foxfire **Miss G. H. Ward**
   9 **MAJOR MUSCARI (IRE)**, 6, ch g Exceed And Excel (AUS)—Muscari **J. Morris**
10 **MEDAM**, 5, b m Medicean—Mamounia (IRE) **Burton Agnes Bloodstock**
11 **MYJESTIC MELODY (IRE)**, 6, b m Majestic Missile (IRE)—Bucaramanga (IRE) **Mrs S. L. Robinson**
12 4, Ch g Phoenix Reach (IRE)—Rainbows Guest (IRE) **Mr C. Harris**
13 **REALITY SHOW (IRE)**, 7, b g Cape Cross (IRE)—Really (IRE) **Miss G. H. Ward**
14 **RED STAR LADY (IRE)**, 4, b f Redback—Vigorous (IRE) **Nottinghamshire Racing**
15 **RICHO**, 8, ch g Bertolini (USA)—Noble Water (FR) **Miss G. H. Ward**
16 **RISE TO GLORY (IRE)**, 6, b h King's Best (USA)—Lady At War **N Blencowe,J Sunderland,M Lenton,CHarris**
17 **ROY'S LEGACY**, 5, b h Phoenix Reach (IRE)—Chocolada **K Blackwell Steve Mohammed & Stew Rowley**
18 **RUMPLETEAZER (IRE)**, 6, b g Oscar (IRE)—Fleeting Arrow (IRE) **N Blencowe, M Lenton & J Sunderland**
19 **TOM WADE (IRE)**, 7, b g Rakti—Plutonia **Mr P. Tonks**
20 **VIKING WARRIOR (IRE)**, 7, ch g Halling (USA)—Powder Paint **Wilf Hobson & Ciaran Harris**

THREE-YEAR-OLDS

21 **BEARING KISSES (IRE)**, gr f Clodovil (IRE)—Masakira (IRE) **Paul Birley & Wilf Hobson**
22 **COME ON LULU**, ch f Calcutta—Flashing Floozie **Mrs A. Kenny**
23 **NOTTS SO BLUE**, b f Pastoral Pursuits—Blue Nile (IRE) **www.nottinghamshireracing.co.uk (2)**
24 **THAT BE GRAND**, b f Firebreak—Manila Selection (USA) **Mr C. Harris**
25 B f Indesatchel (IRE)—Zaville **J. Morris**

TWO-YEAR-OLDS

26 B f 19/3 Multiplex—Agooda (Rainbow Quest (USA))
27 **PHOENIX PHIL**, ch c 11/2 Phoenix Reach (IRE)—
                                           Pearl's Girl (King's Best (USA)) (761) **Lime Tree Avenue Racing**

Other Owners: Mr P. Birley, Mr K. Blackwell, Mr N. J. Blencowe, Mr R. Booth, Mrs M. C. Coltman, Mr D. Cooper, The Hon Mrs E. S. Cunliffe-Lister, S. A. Harris, Mr W. Hobson, Mr M. Lenton, Mr S. Mohammed, Mr S. Rowley, Mr R. J. Shearing, Mr J. J. Sunderland.

298	**MR GARY HARRISON, Newmarket** Postal: **Cadland Cottage, Moulton Road, Newmarket, Suffolk, CB8 8DU** Contacts: **PHONE (01558) 824685 MOBILE (07813) 846899** E-MAIL gary.harrison@live.co.uk

   1 **AL RAQEEB (IRE)**, 4, b g Lawman (FR)—Caerlina (IRE) **Franconson Partners**
   2 **COALBURN**, 6, ch g Captain Rio—Pusey Street Girl **W. G. Harrison**
   3 **ELLEN MAY**, 4, b f Rock of Gibraltar (IRE)—Triskel **Franconson Partners**
   4 **ENRICHING (USA)**, 6, ch g Lemon Drop Kid (USA)—Popozinha (USA) **Franconson Partners**
   5 **FORWARD MARCH**, 4, b g Beat Hollow—Cantanta **Franconson Partners**
   6 5, B g Atraf—Gaoth Na Mara (IRE)
   7 **HAZZAAT (IRE)**, 4, ch g Iffraaj—Hurricane Irene (IRE) **Franconson Partners**
   8 **MERIDIUS (IRE)**, 4, b g Invincible Spirit (IRE)—Eliza Acton **Franconson Partners**
   9 **NOT RIGG (USA)**, 4, b g Henrythenavigator (USA)—St Helens Shadow (USA) **Franconson Partners**

THREE-YEAR-OLDS

10 **BORN TO FLY (IRE)**, b f Kodiac—Cayambe (IRE) **Franconson Partners**
11 **EMPORIUM**, b f Exceed And Excel (AUS)—Australian Dreams **Franconson Partners, Maze Rattan Ltd**
12 **OHIO (IRE)**, b f Teofilo (IRE)—Royals Special (IRE) **Franconson Partners, Maze Rattan Ltd**
13 **OYSTER (IRE)**, br f Diamond Green (FR)—Lost Icon (IRE) **Franconson Partners**
14 **REMY**, b f Oratorio (IRE)—Kristina **Franconson Partners**
15 **SEVEN LUCKY SEVEN**, b c Avonbridge—Moon Bird **Franconson Partners**
16 **THREE QUID (IRE)**, b f Clodovil (IRE)—Justice System (USA) **Franconson Partners**
17 **WILL**, ch c Kyllachy—Stormy Monday **Franconson Partners**

Other Owners: Mrs D. Curran, D. Curran, Maze Rattan Limited.

Assistant Trainer: Stephanie A Williams 07581 319284

Jockey (flat): Mark Lawson.

299 MISS LISA HARRISON, Wigton
Postal: **Cobble Hall, Aldoth, Nr Silloth, Cumbria, CA7 4NE**
Contacts: PHONE **(01697) 361753** FAX **(01697) 342250** MOBILE **(07725) 535554**
E-MAIL **lisa@daharrison.co.uk**

1 5, B h Double Trigger (IRE)—Double Flight **David A. Harrison**
2 **SOLWAY BAY,** 12, b g Cloudings (IRE)—No Problem Jac **David A. Harrison**
3 **SOLWAY DANDY,** 7, b g Danroad (AUS)—Solway Rose **David A. Harrison**
4 5, B m Double Trigger (IRE)—Solway Donal (IRE) **David A. Harrison**
5 **SOLWAY DORNAL,** 9, b g Alflora (IRE)—Solway Donal (IRE) **David A. Harrison**
6 **SOLWAY LEGEND,** 7, ch g And Beyond (IRE)—Spicey Cut **David A. Harrison**
7 5, Ch h Double Trigger (IRE)—Solway Rose **David A. Harrison**
8 **SOLWAY SAM,** 11, b g Double Trigger (IRE)—Some Gale **David A. Harrison**
9 **SOLWAY SILVER,** 8, gr g Silver Patriarch (IRE)—Solway Rose **David A. Harrison**
10 **SOLWAY STAR,** 11, ch g Zaha (CAN)—Cuddle Bunny (IRE) **David A. Harrison**
11 **VIVONA HILL,** 10, b g Overbury (IRE)—Lets Go Dutch **Mrs F. Crone & Mrs V. Birnie**

Other Owners: Mrs V. A. Birnie, Mrs F. H. Crone.

300 MR BEN HASLAM, Middleham
Postal: **Castle Barn Cottage, Castle Hill, Middleham, Leyburn, North Yorkshire, DL8 4QW**
Contacts: PHONE **(01969) 624351** FAX **(01969) 624463** MOBILE **(07764) 411660**
E-MAIL **office@benhaslamracing.com** WEBSITE **www.benhaslamracing.com**

1 **ABBOTSFIELD (IRE),** 4, ch f Sakhee's Secret—May Day Queen (IRE) **Middleham Park Racing I**
2 **AZZURRA DU CAPRIO (IRE),** 6, ch m Captain Rio—Dunbrody (FR) **Blue Lion Racing IX**
3 **DANCE FOR GEORGIE,** 5, ch m Motivator—Chetwynd (IRE) **Mr M. J. James**
4 **DIAKTOROS (IRE),** 4, b g Red Clubs (IRE)—Rinneen (IRE) **Mr S Hassiakos & Sir Alex Ferguson**
5 **DREAMING OF RUBIES,** 5, b m Oasis Dream—Rubies From Burma (USA) **Middleham Park Racing XXVII**
6 **EXECUTIVE'S HALL (IRE),** 10, b g Saddlers' Hall (IRE)—Overtime (IRE) **Mrs C. Barclay**
7 **HI CANDY (IRE),** 4, b f Diamond Green (FR)—Dancing Steps **Go Alfresco Racing**
8 **HI DANCER,** 11, b g Medicean—Sea Music **Mr R. Tocher**
9 **JEWEL IN THE SUN (IRE),** 9, b g Milan—Savanagh (IRE) **Mr John P. McManus**
10 **LILIARGH (IRE),** 5, b m Acclamation—Discover Roma (IRE) **Middleham Park Racing XXVII**
11 **OPERATEUR (IRE),** 6, b g Oratorio (IRE)—Kassariya (IRE) **Mrs Alison Royston & Mrs C Barclay**
12 **PINK CADILLAC (IRE),** 4, b f Clodovil (IRE)—Green Life **Go Alfresco Racing**
13 **POETIC STAR,** 4, b g Byron—Balwarah (IRE) **Go Alfresco Racing**
14 **SHESNOTFORTURNING (IRE),** 4, b f Refuse To Bend (IRE)—Diplomats Daughter **Mrs C. Barclay**
15 **WOODLEY WONDER (IRE),** 4, b g Byron—City Maiden (USA) **Go Alfresco Racing**

THREE-YEAR-OLDS

16 **CAMANCHE GREY (IRE),** gr c Camacho—Sense of Greeting (IRE) **Mr L. Ashmore**
17 **EASTERN DYNASTY,** b g Exceed And Excel (AUS)—Agooda **Middleham Park Racing I**
18 **MOON OVER RIO (IRE),** b f Captain Rio—Moonchild (GER) **Blue Lion Racing IX**

TWO-YEAR-OLDS

19 B f 8/5 Holy Roman Emperor (IRE)—Banba (IRE) (Docksider (USA)) (7742) **Mr B. M. R. Haslam**
20 B f 13/2 Champs Elysees—One Zero (USA) (Theatrical) (5420) **Mr B. M. R. Haslam**

Other Owners: Mrs C. Barclay, Mr M. T. Buckley, Sir Alex Ferguson, Mr B. M. R. Haslam, Mr S. Hassiakos, Mr T. S. Palin, Mr M. Prince, Mrs Alison Royston, Mr R. Young.

Assistant Trainer: Louise Black

Conditional: Ryan D. Clark.

301 MR P. J. HASSETT, Quin
Postal: **Parkview House, Moyriesk, Quin, Co. Clare, Ireland**
Contacts: PHONE **(00353) 65 6840555 (00353) 65 6825621** FAX **(00353) 65 6825621**

1 **A NEW DAWN (IRE),** 8, b g Old Vic—Andros Dawn (IRE) **Summer Sun Syndicate**
2 **BOURGELAT (IRE),** 7, b g Flemensfirth (USA)—Sister Cinnamon **Look At Me Syndicate**

MR P. J. HASSETT - Continued

3 5, Br g Kaieteur (USA)—Bridgeville Queen (IRE) **P. J. Hassett**
4 MIYAJIMA, 14, b g Polar Prince (IRE)—Patina **BallyC Syndicate**
5 STOP N STARE (IRE), 8, b g Danetime (IRE)—Ballina Belle **P. M. Hassett**
6 7, B m Revoque (IRE)—Swing The Lead (IRE) **P. J. Hassett**
7 WIN FOR US (IRE), 9, ch g Rossini (USA)—Noble Flame (IRE) **BallyC Syndicate**

Assistant Trainer: G. Hassett

Amateur: Mr P. J. O'Neill.

---

302 **MRS FLEUR HAWES, Diss**
Postal: **Hill Farm Barn, High Rd, Bressingham, Diss, Norfolk, IP22 2AT**
Contacts: **MOBILE (07775) 795805**
E-MAIL fleur@fleurhawesracingltd.co.uk WEBSITE www.fleurhawesracing.co.uk

1 BANTRY BERE (IRE), 10, b g Distant Music (USA)—Tirana (USA) **Mrs F. Hawes**
2 CAPPIELOW PARK, 5, b g Exceed And Excel (AUS)—Barakat **Wing & A Prayer**
3 FLAMING GORGE (IRE), 9, ch g Alderbrook—Solmus (IRE) **A Fool & His Money**

Other Owners: Mr J. Edwards, Mrs E. Kenward.

---

303 **MR NIGEL HAWKE, Tiverton**
Postal: **Thorne Farm, Stoodleigh, Tiverton, Devon, EX16 9QG**
Contacts: **MOBILE (07899) 922827**
E-MAIL nigel@thornefarmracing.co.uk

1 ANAY TURGE (FR), 9, gr g Turgeon (USA)—Anayette (FR) **Ms K. Mead**
2 BIG NIGHT OUT, 8, b m Midnight Legend—Big Decision **Exors of the Late Mr D. E. F. Bloomfield**
3 CAUGHT INTHE LIGHT, 9, b g Old Vic—Webb Find (IRE) **Ms K. Mead**
4 GREYBOUGG, 5, gr g Tobougg (IRE)—Kildee Lass **Thorne Farm Racing Partnership**
5 KADALKIN (FR), 8, b g Robin des Champs (FR)—Kadalma (FR) **D. R. Mead**
6 LE PERGOLESE (FR), 8, b g Sagacity (FR)—Rasinixa (FR) **Thorne Farm Racing Partnership**
7 MASTER NEO (FR), 8, gr g Turgeon (USA)—Really Royale (FR) **W E Donohue J M Donohue**
8 MISTER WISEMAN, 12, gr g Bal Harbour—Genie Spirit **Thorne Farm Racing Partnership**
9 NAIL 'M (IRE), 6, b g Milan—Honor Kicks (FR) **Mr David Mitchell & D R Mead**
10 PAGHAM BELLE, 6, b m Brian Boru—Sambara (IRE) **N. J. McMullan & S. H. Bryant**
11 PIRANS CAR, 8, b g Sleeping Car (FR)—Karolina (FR) **R. J. & Mrs J. A. Peake**
12 SAMINGARRY (FR), 7, ch g Ballingarry (IRE)—Samansonnienne (FR) **Pearce Bros 1**
13 SEDGEMOOR CLASSACT (IRE), 6, b m Exit To Nowhere (USA)—Kim Fontenail (FR) **Junction 24 Ltd**
14 SEDGEMOOR EXPRESS (IRE), 6, b br g Presenting—Pretty Native (IRE) **Pearce Bros 2**
15 SEDGEMOOR TOP BID (IRE), 6, b g Marignan (USA)—Hazy Fiddler (IRE) **Thorne Farm Racing Partnership**
16 THE DODGY DEALER, 5, gr g With Approval (CAN)—Annishirani **Mr J. A. Vowles**
17 TOKYO JAVILEX (FR), 7, b g Sleeping Car (FR)—Etoile du Lion (FR) **D. R. Mead**

Other Owners: Mrs K. M. Brain, S. H. Bryant, W. E. Donohue, Mrs J. M. Donohue, N. J. McMullan, Mr D. Mitchell, R. J. Peake, Mrs J. A. Peake, Mr S. R. Pearce, Mr W. J. Simms, Mrs D. E. Smith.

Assistant Trainer: David Judd

---

304 **MR RICHARD HAWKER, Frome**
Postal: **Rode Farm, Rode, Bath, Somerset, BA11 6QQ**
Contacts: **PHONE (01373) 831479**

1 MINI ISLAND (IRE), 5, b m Heron Island (IRE)—Our Prima Donna (IRE)
2 MONDERON (FR), 7, b br g Laveron—Lomonde (FR) **Mrs G. Morgan**

305 MR DEREK HAYDN JONES, Pontypridd
Postal: **Garth Paddocks, Efail Isaf, Pontypridd, Mid-Glamorgan, CF38 1SN**
Contacts: **PHONE (01443) 202515 FAX (01443) 201877 MOBILE (07967) 680012**

1 **CATFLAP (IRE)**, 5, b m One Cool Cat (USA)—Consignia (IRE) **Llewelyn Newman & Runeckles**
2 **FIRST POST (IRE)**, 7, b g Celtic Swing—Consignia (IRE) **Llewelyn, Runeckles**
3 **MOLLY JONES**, 5, b m Three Valleys (USA)—And Toto Too **Mrs E. M. Haydn Jones**
4 **MONTY FAY (IRE)**, 5, b br g Iffraaj—Blast (USA) **R & M Williams Limited**
5 **SCHOTTISCHE**, 4, ch f Pastoral Pursuits—Calligraphy **Mrs E. M. Haydn Jones**
6 **SLIP OF THE TONGUE**, 4, ch g Zamindar—Kiswahili **G. I. D. Llewelyn**
7 **TENBRIDGE**, 5, b m Avonbridge—Tenebrae (IRE) **Mrs E. M. Haydn Jones**
8 **TINSHU (IRE)**, 8, ch m Fantastic Light (USA)—Ring of Esteem **Llewelyn, Runeckles**

THREE-YEAR-OLDS
9 **JESSY MAE**, b f Oratorio (IRE)—Welsh Valley (USA) **North Cheshire Trading & Storage Ltd**
10 **LLYRICAL**, b g Firebreak—One of The Family **Llewelyn Yardley Runeckles**
11 **VERSIGNIA (IRE)**, gr f Verglas (IRE)—Consignia (IRE) **Llewelyn, Runeckles**

TWO-YEAR-OLDS
12 **FUJIANO**, b f 18/2 Equiano (FR)—The Fugative (Nicholas (USA)) (16000) **G. I. D. Llewelyn**

Other Owners: Mr I. Dodds-Smith, Mrs M. L. Parry, J. F. Runeckles, B. Sheppard.

Assistant Trainer: Mrs E. M. Haydn Jones

---

306 MR JONATHAN HAYNES, Brampton
Postal: **Cleugh Head, Low Row, Brampton, Cumbria, CA8 2JB**
Contacts: **PHONE (01697) 746253 MOBILE (07771) 511471**

1 **BERTIELICIOUS**, 6, b g And Beyond (IRE)—Pennepoint **J. C. Haynes**
2 **BEYONDTEMPTATION**, 6, ch m And Beyond (IRE)—Tempted (IRE) **J. C. Haynes**
3 **MRS GRASS**, 7, ch m And Beyond (IRE)—Tempted (IRE) **J. C. Haynes**
4 **PANTHERS RUN**, 14, b g Jendali (USA)—Dorado Beach **J. C. Haynes**

---

307 MR TED HAYNES, Highworth
Postal: **Red Down Farm, Highworth, Wiltshire, SN6 7SH**
Contacts: **PHONE/FAX (01793) 762437 FAX (01793) 762437 MOBILE (07704) 707728**
E-MAIL reddownracing@aol.com

1 **BLUES BUDDY**, 7, b m Dubai Destination (USA)—Swift Spring (FR) **Mr K. T. Coxhead**
2 **EBONY STORM**, 7, b g Zafeen (FR)—Stormworthy Miss (IRE) **Miss S. R. Haynes**
3 **MR TED**, 7, b g Kayf Tara—Fly Home **Miss S. R. Haynes**
4 5, B g Kier Park (IRE)—Rupert's Princess (IRE)
5 **STANWELL**, 6, ch g Kier Park (IRE)—Magical Dancer (IRE) **The Reddown High Explosive Partnership**
6 **THE NAMES HARRY**, 9, b g Sir Harry Lewis (USA)—Fly Home **Miss S. R. Haynes**

TWO-YEAR-OLDS
7 B c 30/4 Crosspeace (IRE)—Fly Home (Skyliner)

Other Owners: H. E. Haynes, Mrs H. E. Haynes.

Assistant Trainer: Sally R Haynes (07711) 488341

---

308 MRS C. HEAD-MAAREK, Chantilly
Postal: **32 Avenue du General Leclerc, 60500 Chantilly, France**
Contacts: **PHONE (0033) 3445 70101 FAX (0033) 3445 85333 MOBILE (0033) 6073 10505**
E-MAIL christiane.head@wanadoo.fr

1 **ALEXANDRE D'OR (FR)**, 5, b h Gold Away (IRE)—Reine Annicka (FR)
2 **ASSEZ CLAIR (USA)**, 4, b c Pleasant Tap (USA)—Pretty Clear (USA)
3 **BARLOVENTO (FR)**, 8, gr g Tobougg (IRE)—Tempete Tropicale (FR)

MRS C. HEAD-MAAREK - Continued

4 **DIKTABAMA (FR)**, 7, b m Diktat—Miss Alabama (FR)
5 **GOLF JUAN (USA)**, 5, b g Invasor (ARG)—Great Buy (USA)
6 **LEMON PEARL**, 4, ch f Singspiel (IRE)—Basemah (FR)
7 6, B g Iron Mask (USA)—Padina (GER)
8 **SEXY (FR)**, 4, B F Sinndar (IRE)—Seacleef (FR)
9 **TARTARIN (IRE)**, 7, b g Statue of Liberty (USA)—Tigresse Africaine (FR)
10 **TREVE (FR)**, 4, b f Motivator—Trevise (FR)
11 **WHY AREEB (IRE)**, 4, B C Galileo (IRE)—Piquetnol (USA)

THREE-YEAR-OLDS

12 **AFRICAN PLAINS**, b f Oasis Dream—African Rose
13 **ALTAIRA**, b c Dubawi (IRE)—Peach Pearl
14 **ARTISTE LADY (FR)**, b f Artiste Royal (IRE)—Fantasy Lady (USA)
15 **BRUXELLOISE (FR)**, ch f Sevres Rose (IRE)—Baleare (FR)
16 **COMBINATION (FR)**, b f Dashing Blade—Nicol's Girl
17 **FAIRWATER (USA)**, b f Empire Maker (USA)—Jazz Drummer (USA)
18 **FOREST KING (FR)**, b c Whipper (USA)—Queensalsa (FR)
19 **GLORIEUX (FR)**, b c Dunkerque (FR)—Grenade (FR)
20 **GREENSTREET**, b c Mr Sidney (USA)—Treasure Queen (USA)
21 **INFANTRY**, b c Rail Link—Zorleni
22 **LISTRIA (IRE)**, b br f Footstepsinthesand—Perugina (FR)
23 **MS MONIQUE (FR)**, b f Mr Sidney (USA)—Ares Choix
24 **PIEDRA (IRE)**, b f Lawman (FR)—Albisola (IRE)
25 **PROCUREMENT**, b f Zamindar (USA)—Acquisition
26 **QUICK SUCCESSION (USA)**, b c Successful Appeal (USA)—Chaffinch (USA)
27 **ROCHEFORT (FR)**, b g Mr Sidney (USA)—Roanne (FR)
28 **SEIGNEUR (FR)**, b g Sevres Rose (IRE)—Spenderella (FR)
29 **SILVAPLANA (FR)**, b f Montmartre (FR)—Silvery Bay (FR)
30 **TEA BLOSSOM**, b f Rail Link—Snow Blossom
31 **TELEX (USA)**, gr ro c Empire Maker (USA)—Kinetic Force (USA)
32 **TERRE BRULEE (FR)**, ch f Dream Well (FR)—Une Majeste (FR)
33 **TSARDOM (USA)**, b f Empire Maker (USA)—Shoogle (USA)

TWO-YEAR-OLDS

34 B f 8/5 Exceed And Excel (AUS)—Bimini (Sadler's Wells (USA))
35 **DENTELLE (FR)**, b f 30/3 Mr Sidney (USA)—Dalna (FR) (Anabaa (USA))
36 **DESTIN (FR)**, b c 3/2 Mr Sidney (USA)—Dissertation (FR) (Sillery (USA)) (30971)
37 **DIHNA (FR)**, b f 26/3 Fuisse (FR)—Dame Blanche (USA) (Cherokee Run (USA))
38 B f 19/2 Dansili—Etoile Montante (USA) (Miswaki (USA))
39 **FULL (FR)**, b c 28/1 Mr Sidney (USA)—Funny Feerie (FR) (Sillery (USA)) (77429)
40 **FUTURISTIC (FR)**, ch c 24/3 Mr Sidney (USA)—Modern Rose (USA) (Dixieland Band (USA))
41 **GALLICE (IRE)**, b f 20/3 Fuisse (FR)—Gout de Terroir (USA) (Lemon Drop Kid (USA))
42 **GALLIUM (FR)**, b c 25/3 Mr Sidney (USA)—Golden Life (USA) (Coronado's Quest (USA))
43 **GARANTIE (FR)**, b f 19/4 Motivator—Great News (FR) (Bering)
44 B c 22/2 Oasis Dream—Kilo Alpha (King's Best (USA))
45 B f 28/2 Youmzain (IRE)—Louis' Lover (FR) (Anabaa (USA))
46 **MAGISTRATE (FR)**, b f 16/4 Motivator—Matanilla (FR) (Anabaa (USA))
47 B f 12/3 Dunkerque (FR)—Malaisie (USA) (Bering)
48 B c 18/4 Oasis Dream—Phantom Wind (USA) (Storm Cat (USA))
49 **REALISATOR (FR)**, b c 9/5 Mr Sidney (USA)—Rouge (FR) (Red Ransom (USA))
50 B c 7/3 Youmzain (IRE)—Rosa Mundi (Alhaarth (IRE))
51 **SAINTES (FR)**, ch f 7/4 Kentucky Dynamite (USA)—Soierie (FR) (Bering)
52 **SALOME (FR)**, b f 1/1 Fuisse (FR)—Silverqueen (FR) (Alydar (USA))
53 **SOUVERAINE (FR)**, b f 16/4 Fuisse (FR)—Silvery Bay (FR) (Numerous (USA))
54 Gr ro f 28/1 Tapit (USA)—Special Duty (Hennessy (USA))
55 **SPLASHING (FR)**, ch g 9/2 Fuisse (FR)—Spirale d'or (FR) (High Yield (USA))
56 **TORIDE (FR)**, b f 1/1 Fuisse (FR)—Trevise (FR) (Anabaa (USA))
57 B f 22/2 Mr Sidney (USA)—Treasure (FR) (Anabaa (USA)) (69686)
58 **VAGA (FR)**, b f 1/1 Gold Away (IRE)—Vassia (USA) (Machiavellian (USA))
59 **VISTA (FR)**, b f 1/5 Mr Sidney (USA)—Villadolide (FR) (Anabaa (USA))
60 B c 13/2 Zamindar (USA)—Winter Silence (Dansili)
61 B c 9/5 Mizzen Mast (USA)—Yashmak (USA) (Danzig (USA))

Assistant Trainer: C. Rossi

309 MR PETER HEDGER, Eastergate
Postal: Melcroft, Eastergate Lane, Eastergate, Chichester, West Sussex, PO20 3SJ
Contacts: PHONE (01243) 543863 FAX (01243) 543913 MOBILE (07860) 209448
E-MAIL hedgerlaura@hotmail.com

1 AFRO, 4, b f Araafa (IRE)—Largo (IRE) **P C F Racing Ltd**
2 BARNMORE, 6, b g Royal Applause—Veronica Franco **P C F Racing Ltd**
3 BIG DUKE (IRE), 4, b g Duke of Marmalade (IRE)—Liscune (IRE) **P C F Racing Ltd**
4 BRIDGE BUILDER, 4, b g Avonbridge—Amazing Dream (IRE) **P C F Racing Ltd**
5 CONTINUUM, 5, b br g Dansili—Clepsydra **P C F Racing Ltd**
6 FRANCO IS MY NAME, 8, b g Namid—Veronica Franco **P C F Racing Ltd**
7 HARLESTONE WOOD, 5, b g Olden Times—Harlestone Lady **P C F Racing Ltd**
8 KAAFEL (IRE), 5, b g Nayef (USA)—Tafaani (IRE) **P C F Racing Ltd**
9 LISAHANE BOG, 7, b g Royal Applause—Veronica Franco **P C F Racing Ltd**
10 LUCKY DI, 4, br f Araafa (IRE)—Lucky Date (IRE) **P C F Racing Ltd**
11 PUTMEINTHESWINDLE, 4, ch g Monsieur Bond (IRE)—Birthday Belle **P C F Racing Ltd**
12 RUZEIZ (USA), 5, b h Muhtathir—Saraama (USA) **P C F Racing Ltd**
13 SILVER DIXIE (USA), 4, br c Dixie Union (USA)—More Silver (USA) **P C F Racing Ltd**
14 SISTER GURU, 5, b m Ishiguru (USA)—Ulysses Daughter (IRE) **Mr J. F. McHale**
15 SLIP SLIDING AWAY (IRE), 7, b g Whipper (USA)—Sandy Lady (IRE) **Mr S. R. Holt**
16 TRANQUIL BAY (IRE), 5, ch g Medecis—Tranquil Sky **P C F Racing Ltd**
17 VERONICA'S PURSUIT, 4, b f Pastoral Pursuits—Veronica Franco **P C F Racing Ltd**
18 WHIPCRACKAWAY (IRE), 5, b g Whipper (USA)—Former Drama (USA) **P. R. Hedger**

THREE-YEAR-OLDS
19 FRANCO'S SECRET, b g Sakhee's Secret—Veronica Franco **P C F Racing Ltd**

Other Owners: Prof D. B. A. Silk.

Assistant Trainer: John Swallow

Jockey (flat): Dane O'Neill. **Jockey (NH):** Leighton Aspell.

310 MR NICKY HENDERSON, Lambourn
Postal: Seven Barrows, Lambourn, Hungerford, Berkshire, RG17 8UH
Contacts: PHONE (01488) 72259 FAX (01488) 72596 MOBILE (07774) 608168
E-MAIL nj.henderson@virgin.net

1 ABBEY COURT (IRE), 6, b g Wareed (IRE)—North Kerry Rose (IRE) **M. A. C. Buckley**
2 ACCORDINGTOJODIE (IRE), 8, b g Accordion—La Fiamma (FR) **Sir Peter & Lady Gibbings**
3 ACT ALONE, 5, b g Act One—Figlette **S W Group Logistics Limited**
4 ACT FOUR (IRE), 6, b g Old Vic—Quadrennial (IRE) **Triermore Stud**
5 ADEUPAS D'YCY (FR), 4, gr g Al Namix (FR)—Jacady (FR) **Mr Simon Munir & Mr Isaac Souede**
6 ADMIRAL MILLER, 4, b g Multiplex—Millers Action **W. H. Ponsonby**
7 ALEXANDRE SIX (FR), 5, b g Robin des Champs (FR)—Karmiva (FR) **S. E. Munir**
8 ALTIOR (IRE), 4, b g High Chaparral (IRE)—Monte Solaro (IRE) **Mrs P. J. Pugh**
9 ANQUETTA (IRE), 10, b g Anshan—Quetta (IRE) **R. B. Waley-Cohen**
10 AREA FIFTY ONE, 6, b g Green Desert (USA)—Secret History (USA) **Middleham Park Racing III**
11 BEAR'S AFFAIR (IRE), 8, br g Presenting—Gladtogetit **G. B. Barlow**
12 BEAT THAT (IRE), 6, b g Milan—Knotted Midge (IRE) **M. A. C. Buckley**
13 BIG HANDS HARRY, 5, b g Multiplex—Harristown Lady **A. D. Spence**
14 BLUE FASHION (IRE), 5, b g Scorpion (IRE)—Moon Glow (FR) **Mr & Mrs J. D. Cotton**
15 BOBS WORTH (IRE), 9, b g Bob Back (USA)—Fashionista (IRE) **The Not Afraid Partnership**
16 BRINGITHOMEMINTY, 5, gr g Presenting—Rosie Redman (IRE) **Walters Plant Hire Ltd**
17 CALL THE COPS (IRE), 5, b g Presenting—Ballygill Heights (IRE) **Matt & Lauren Morgan**
18 CAPE EXPRESS (IRE), 9, b g Cape Cross (IRE)—Lilissa (IRE) **A. D. Spence**
19 CAPTAIN CONAN (FR), 7, b g Kingsalsa (USA)—Lavandou **Triermore Stud**
20 CAPTAIN CUTTER (IRE), 7, b g Westerner—Hollygrove Samba (IRE) **J. P. McManus**
21 CARACCI APACHE (IRE), 4, b g High Chaparral (IRE)—Campanella (GER) **W. H. Ponsonby**
22 CARNIVAL FLAG (FR), 5, ch m Ballingarry (IRE)—Run For Laborie (FR) **The Perfect Day Partnership**
23 CASH AND GO (IRE), 7, b g Sulamani (GER)—Calcida (GER) **Mr R. J. H. Geffen**
24 CLONDAW BANKER (IRE), 5, b g Court Cave (IRE)—Freya Alex **A. D. Spence**
25 CLOSE TOUCH, 6, ch g Generous (IRE)—Romantic Dream **Her Majesty The Queen**
26 COCKTAILS AT DAWN, 6, b g Fair Mix (IRE)—Fond Farewell (IRE) **R J H Geffen & Sir John Ritblat**
27 COOL MACAVITY (IRE), 6, b g One Cool Cat (USA)—Cause Celebre (IRE) **Triermore Stud**

MR NICKY HENDERSON - Continued

28 **COURTESY CALL (IRE)**, 5, br g Manduro (GER)—Three Wrens (IRE) **A. D. Spence**
29 **CUP FINAL (IRE)**, 5, ch g Presenting—Asian Maze (IRE) **J. P. McManus**
30 **DAWALAN (FR)**, 4, gr g Azamour (IRE)—Daltawa (IRE) **Mr Simon Munir & Mr Isaac Souede**
31 **DEFINITE RUBY (IRE)**, 6, b m Definite Article—Sunset Queen (IRE) **Trevor & Linda Marlow**
32 **EARTH AMBER**, 5, ch m Hurricane Run (IRE)—Too Marvelous (IRE) **Pump & Plant Services Ltd**
33 **ELECTROLYSER (IRE)**, 9, gr g Daylami (IRE)—Iviza (IRE) **Mr & Mrs P. Hargreaves**
34 **ERICHT (IRE)**, 8, b g Alderbrook—Lady Orla (IRE) **Mrs B. A. Hanbury**
35 **FABRIKA**, 6, b m Presenting—Daprika (FR) **Mr & Mrs R. G. Kelvin-Hughes**
36 **FIRST IN THE QUEUE (IRE)**, 7, b g Azamour (IRE)—Irina (IRE) **L. Breslin**
37 **FOREVER PRESENT (IRE)**, 7, br m Presenting—Sidalcea (IRE) **M. W. Lightbody**
38 **FORGOTTEN VOICE (IRE)**, 9, b g Danehill Dancer (IRE)—Asnieres (USA) **Mrs S. M. Roy**
39 **FOURTH ESTATE (IRE)**, 8, b g Fantastic Light (USA)—Papering (IRE) **Out The Box Racing**
40 **FREE THINKING**, 6, b m Hernando (FR)—Liberthine (FR) **R. B. Waley-Cohen**
41 **FRENCH OPERA**, 11, b g Bering—On Fair Stage (IRE) **Mrs Judy Wilson & Martin Landau**
42 **FULL SHIFT (FR)**, 5, b g Ballingarry (IRE)—Dansia (GER) **J. P. McManus**
43 **GAITWAY**, 4, b g Medicean—Milliegait **Mrs J. K. Powell**
44 **GIBB RIVER (IRE)**, 8, ch g Mr Greeley (USA)—Laurentine (USA) **Corbett Stud**
45 **GIORGIO QUERCUS (FR)**, 9, b g Starborough—Winter Breeze (FR) **Seasons Holidays**
46 **GOLDEN HOOF (IRE)**, 6, b g Oscar (IRE)—Nuovo Style (IRE) **The Hoof Partnership**
47 **GRANDOUET (FR)**, 7, b br g Al Namix (FR)—Virginia River (FR) **S. E. Munir**
48 **GREY BLUE (IRE)**, 4, gr g Verglas (IRE)—Zut Alors (IRE) **A. D. Spence**
49 **HADRIAN'S APPROACH (IRE)**, 7, b g High Chaparral (IRE)—

Gifted Approach (IRE) **Mr & Mrs R. G. Kelvin-Hughes**
50 **HERONRY (IRE)**, 6, b g Heron Island (IRE)—In A Tizzy **The Ten From Seven**
51 **HUNT BALL (IRE)**, 9, b g Winged Love (IRE)—La Fandango (IRE) **Atlantic Equine**
52 **HUNTERS HOOF (IRE)**, 5, b g Flemensfirth (USA)—Madgehil (IRE) **London Bridge Racing Partnership**
53 **IN FAIRNESS (IRE)**, 5, b g Oscar (IRE)—Dix Huit Brumaire (FR) **Mr Simon Munir & Mr Isaac Souede**
54 **JOSSES HILL (IRE)**, 6, b g Winged Love (IRE)—Credora Storm **A. D. Spence**
55 **KARAZHAN**, 6, b g Dr Fong (USA)—Karasta (IRE) **Pump & Plant Services Ltd**
56 **KENTUCKY HYDEN (IRE)**, 4, ch g Kentucky Dynamite (USA)—

Cap Serena (FR) **Mr Simon Munir & Mr Isaac Souede**
57 **KID CASSIDY (IRE)**, 8, b g Beneficial—Shuil Na Lee (IRE) **J. P. McManus**
58 **KINGS LODGE**, 8, b g King's Theatre (IRE)—Mardello **W. H. Ponsonby**
59 5, B g Milan—Lady Lamb (IRE) **Seven Barrows Limited**
60 **LADY OF PROVENCE**, 5, gr m Fair Mix (FR)—Rosa Canina **W. H. Ponsonby**
61 **LAUDATORY**, 8, b g Royal Applause—Copy-Cat **Mr E. R. Newnham**
62 **LAURIUM**, 4, ch g Gold Away (IRE)—Silver Peak (FR) **The Ten From Seven**
63 **LESSONS IN MILAN (IRE)**, 6, b g Milan—Lessons Lass (IRE) **T. J. Hemmings**
64 **LIEUTENANT MILLER**, 8, b g Beat All (USA)—Still Runs Deep **W. H. Ponsonby**
65 **LONG RUN (FR)**, 9, b br g Cadoudal (FR)—Libertina (FR) **R. B. Waley-Cohen**
66 **LYVIUS**, 6, b g Paolini (GER)—Lysuna (GER) **T. J. Hemmings**
67 **MA FILLEULE (FR)**, 6, gr m Turgeon (USA)—Kadaina (FR) **S. E. Munir**
68 **MAD ABOUT THE BOY**, 4, b g Robin des Pres (FR)—Dalamine (FR) **M. A. C. Buckley**
69 **MADAME DE GUISE (FR)**, 5, b m Le Balafre (FR)—Paradana (FR) **Million in Mind Partnership**
70 **MAESTRO ROYAL**, 5, b g Doyen (IRE)—Close Harmony **Mrs R. H. Brown**
71 **MAGNA CARTOR**, 4, b g Motivator—Hora **Mr & Mrs R. G. Kelvin-Hughes**
72 **MAKARI**, 7, b g Makbul—Seraphim (FR) **Matt & Lauren Morgan**
73 **MALT MASTER (IRE)**, 7, b g Milan—Dantes Profit (IRE) **J. P. McManus**
74 **MASTER OF THE GAME (IRE)**, 8, ch g Bob's Return (IRE)—

Lady Monilousha (IRE) **Mr & Mrs R. G. Kelvin-Hughes**
75 **MAYFAIR MUSIC (IRE)**, 5, br m Presenting—Native Bid (IRE) **Mrs E. C. Roberts**
76 **MEDIEVAL CHAPEL (FR)**, 6, gr g Ballingarry (IRE)—Best Ever (FR) **R. A. Bartlett**
77 **MEGALYPOS (FR)**, 5, b br g Limnos (JPN)—Bourbonnaise (FR) **Mr Simon Munir & Mr Isaac Souede**
78 **MIGHT DO**, 6, b m Alflora (IRE)—Always Hope **The Turf Club & David Ford**
79 **MINELLA FORFITNESS (IRE)**, 7, b g Westerner—Ring of Water (USA) **M. A. C. Buckley**
80 **MISS BALLANTYNE**, 7, br m Definite Article—Gardana (FR) **Mr & Mrs R. G. Kelvin-Hughes**
81 **MISTER CHAIRMAN (IRE)**, 6, b g Shantou (USA)—Out of Trouble (IRE) **Lady Tennant**
82 **MISTER DILLON**, 7, b g Sulamani (IRE)—Kabayil **Elite Racing Club**
83 **MOEL FAMAU**, 5, b m Flemensfirth (USA)—Daprika (FR) **Racegoers Club Owners Group**
84 **MY TENT OR YOURS (IRE)**, 7, b g Desert Prince (IRE)—Spartan Girl (IRE) **J. P. McManus**
85 **MY WIGWAM OR YOURS (IRE)**, 5, b g Beneficial—Midnight Pond (IRE) **The Happy Campers**
86 **NADIYA DE LA VEGA (FR)**, 8, b br m Lost Word (IRE)—Shinobie (FR) **J. P. McManus**
87 **NELSON'S BRIDGE (IRE)**, 7, b g Oscar (IRE)—High Park Lady (IRE) **J. P. McManus**
88 **NESTERENKO (GER)**, 5, b g Doyen (IRE)—Nordwahl (GER) **Mr J. Meyer**
89 **NEW HORIZONS (IRE)**, 4, b g Presenting—Namloc (IRE) **Lady Tennant**

MR NICKY HENDERSON - Continued

90 **NO PUSHOVER**, 5, b m Scorpion (IRE)—Poussetiere Deux (FR) **The Perfect Day Partnership**
91 **NORDIC QUEST (IRE)**, 5, b g Montjeu (IRE)—Nordtanzerin (GER) **A. D. Spence**
92 **NOW BEN (IRE)**, 6, ch g Beneficial—Bannow Beach (IRE) **Mr & Mrs Sandy Orr**
93 **ONE CONEMARA (IRE)**, 6, b g Milan—Rose of Kerry (IRE) **Triermore Stud**
94 **ONE LUCKY LADY**, 6, b m Lucky Story (USA)—One For Philip **S W Group Logistics Limited**
95 **OPEN HEARTED**, 7, b g Generous (IRE)—Romantic Dream **Her Majesty The Queen**
96 **OSCAR HOOF (IRE)**, 6, b g Oscar (IRE)—New Legislation (IRE) **The Hoof Partnership**
97 **OSCAR WHISKY (IRE)**, 9, b g Oscar (IRE)—Ash Baloo (IRE) **Walters Plant Hire Ltd**
98 **PETIT ROBIN (FR)**, 11, b g Robin des Pres (FR)—Joie de Cotte (FR) **S W Group Logistics Limited**
99 **PIPPA GREENE**, 10, b g Galileo (IRE)—Funny Girl (IRE) **R. A. H. Evans**
100 **PLAYHARA (IRE)**, 5, b m King's Theatre (IRE)—Harringay **Mrs R. I. Vaughan**
101 **POLLY PEACHUM (IRE)**, 6, b m Shantou (USA)—Miss Denman (IRE) **Lady Tennant**
102 **PREMIER BOND**, 4, b g Kayf Tara—Celtic Native (IRE) **Middleham Park Racing XI**
103 **PRINCE OF PIRATES (IRE)**, 9, b g Milan—Call Kate (IRE) **J. P. McManus**
104 **PROFIT COMMISSION (IRE)**, 4, b g Presenting—Silver Pursuit **Vasek Insurance Services Ltd**
105 **RAJDHANI EXPRESS**, 7, br g Presenting—Violet Express (FR) **R. B. Waley-Cohen**
106 **RALLY**, 5, b g Rail Link—Waki Music (USA) **Walters Plant Hire Ltd**
107 **REVERB**, 5, b g Tiger Hill (IRE)—Gemini Gold (IRE) **Elite Racing Club**
108 **RIVER MAIGUE (IRE)**, 7, b g Zagreb (USA)—Minor Tantrum (IRE) **M. A. C. Buckley**
109 **RIVERSIDE THEATRE**, 10, b g King's Theatre (IRE)—Disallowed (IRE) **Jimmy Nesbitt Partnership**
110 **ROBERTO GOLDBACK (IRE)**, 12, b g Bob Back (USA)—Mandysway (IRE) **S. E. Munir**
111 **ROBINS REEF (IRE)**, 4, br f Robin des Champs (FR)—Tropical Ocean (IRE) **Meikle Ben Stables Limited**
112 **ROLLING STAR (FR)**, 5, b g Smadoun (FR)—Lyli Rose (FR) **Michael Buckley & The Vestey Family**
113 **ROSIE PROBERT (IRE)**, 5, b m Dylan Thomas (IRE)—Corsican Sunset (USA) **Seasons Holidays**
114 **ROYAL BOY (FR)**, 7, b br g Lavirco (GER)—Quintanilla (FR) **M. A. C. Buckley**
115 **ROYAL IRISH HUSSAR (IRE)**, 4, b c Galileo (IRE)—Adjalisa (IRE) **Triermore Stud**
116 **RYDE BY KNIGHT**, 6, b g Grape Tree Road—Knight Ryde **Mrs N. S. Tregaskes**
117 **SCOLBOAQUEEN (IRE)**, 6, br m Lahib (USA)—Ladyrosaro (IRE) **Scolboaqueen Partnership**
118 **SEAHAM HALL**, 6, ch m Peintre Celebre (USA)—Freni (GER) **Seasons Holidays**
119 **SHAKALAKABOOMBOOM (IRE)**, 10, b g Anshan—Tia Maria (IRE) **L. Breslin**
120 **SIDE STEP**, 5, b m Norse Dancer (IRE)—Magic Score **Her Majesty The Queen**
121 **SIGN OF A VICTORY (IRE)**, 5, b g Kayf Tara—Irish Wedding (IRE) **Matt & Lauren Morgan**
122 **SIMONSIG**, 8, gr g Fair Mix (IRE)—Dusty Too **R. A. Bartlett**
123 **SNAKE EYES (IRE)**, 6, b g Oscar (IRE)—Be My Belle (IRE) **J. P. McManus**
124 **SPARTAN ANGEL (IRE)**, 6, b m Beneficial—Greek Melody (IRE) **Sir Eric Parker & Mary Anne Parker**
125 **SPECIAL AGENT**, 5, b g Invincible Spirit (IRE)—Flight of Fancy **Her Majesty The Queen**
126 **SPEEDY TUNES (IRE)**, 7, b g Heron Island (IRE)—Art Lover (IRE) **Jimmy Hack Racing Partners**
127 **SPRINGINHERSTEP (IRE)**, 7, b m Saddlers' Hall (IRE)—Lady Lamb (IRE) **Turf Club 2012**
128 **SPRINTER SACRE (FR)**, 8, b br g Network (GER)—Fatima III (FR) **Mrs C. M. Mould**
129 **STAND TO REASON (IRE)**, 6, ch g Danehill Dancer (IRE)—Ho Hi The Moon (IRE) **Seasons Holidays**
130 **SUGAR BARON (IRE)**, 4, b g Presenting—Shuil Oilean (IRE) **Anthony Speelman**
131 **SUHAILI**, 6, b g Shirocco (GER)—Mezzogiorno **B. E. Nielsen**
132 **SWEET DEAL (IRE)**, 4, gr g Verglas (IRE)—Compromise (FR) **Mrs S. M. Roy**
133 **TAKE A BOW**, 5, b g Norse Dancer (IRE)—Madame Illusion (FR) **M. A. C. Buckley**
134 **TANKS FOR THAT (IRE)**, 11, br g Beneficial—Lady Jurado (IRE) **Mrs B. A. Hanbury**
135 **TAYLOR (IRE)**, 5, b m Presenting—Britway Lady (IRE) **Mr Simon Munir & Mr Isaac Souede**
136 **TETLAMI (IRE)**, 8, ch g Daylami (IRE)—Tetou (IRE) **Mrs S. M. Roy**
137 **THANKS FOR COMING**, 8, b g Helissio (FR)—Kylc Rhea **J. Whittle**
138 **TILLER BELLE**, 6, b m Revoque (IRE)—Farmer's Pet **W. H. Ponsonby**
139 **TISTORY (FR)**, 7, ch g Epalo (GER)—History (FR) **Mrs J. Wilson**
140 **TOP OF THE RANGE (IRE)**, 7, be g Presenting—Brenny's Pearl (IRE) **Walters Plant Hire Ltd**
141 **TOWERING (IRE)**, 5, b g Catcher In The Rye (IRE)—Bobs Article (IRE) **Middleham Park Racing LIX**
142 **TRADEWINDS (IRE)**, 6, b g Kapgarde (FR)—Royale Floriane (FR) **M. A. C. Buckley**
143 **TRIOLO D'ALENE (FR)**, 7, ch g Epalo (GER)—Joliette d'alene (FR) **Mr & Mrs Sandy Orr**
144 **UNE ARTISTE (FR)**, 6, b m Alberto Giacometti (IRE)—Castagnette III (FR) **S. E. Munir**
145 **UNION DU CHENET (FR)**, 6, b g Kahyasi—Tchela (FR) **The After Party**
146 **UTOPIE DES BORDES (FR)**, 6, b m Antarctique (IRE)—Miss Berry (FR) **Mr Simon Munir & Mr Isaac Souede**
147 **VANITEUX (FR)**, 5, b g Voix du Nord (FR)—Expoville (FR) **Mr & Mrs R. G. Kelvin-Hughes**
148 **VASCO DU RONCERAY (FR)**, 5, gr g Al Namix (FR)—
                                    Landza de Ronceray (FR) **Mr Simon Munir & Mr Isaac Souede**
149 **VODKA 'N TONIC (IRE)**, 5, b g Presenting—Ballagh Dawn (IRE) **Bradley Partnership**
150 **VOLNAY DE THAIX (FR)**, 5, ch g Secret Singer (FR)—Mange de Thaix (FR) **Mrs J. Wilson**
151 **VYTA DU ROC (FR)**, 5, gr g Lion Noir—Dolce Vyta (FR) **Mr Simon Munir & Mr Isaac Souede**
152 **WEST WIZARD (FR)**, 5, b br g King's Theatre (IRE)—Queen's Diamond (GER) **Walters Plant Hire Ltd**
153 **WHISPER (FR)**, 6, b g Astarabad (USA)—Belle Yepa (FR) **Walters Plant Hire Ltd**

MR NICKY HENDERSON - Continued

154 WHO'S CROSS (IRE), 6, b g Runyon (IRE)—Mystery Escort **Mr D. Donohoe**
155 WILLIAM HENRY (IRE), 4, b g King's Theatre (IRE)—Cincuenta (IRE) **Walters Plant Hire Ltd**
156 WILLPOWER (IRE), 5, b g Montjeu (IRE)—Noble Pearl (GER) **A. D. Spence**
157 WOODBANK, 7, br g Needwood Blade—Potter's Gale (IRE) **James & Jean Potter**

Other Owners: Mr R. B. Antell, Mrs V. A. P. Antell, Mr R. Berridge, Mr D. Bickerton, Mrs D. C. Broad, A. R. Bromley, B. G. Brown, Mr S. W. Buckley, Mr B. J. Bull, E. Burke, Miss A. J. Burr, Mr M. J. Butt, Mr J. G. Camping, Mr N. J. Carter, Mr A. Chandler, Mr D. Clegg, Mr P. R. Clinton, Mr M. J. S. Cockburn, A. K. Collins, Mrs J. F. Collins, Mr S. F. Coton, J. D. Cotton, Mrs B. Cotton, Mr J. P. Craft, R. Cressey, Mr C. T. Cromwell, G. M. Davies, K. H. M. Doyle, A. T. Eggleton, Mr R. Fisher, Mr D. G. Ford, Mr T. K. Frame, Sir Peter Gibbings, The Hon Lady Gibbings, G. F. Goode, C. O. P. Hanbury, R. V. Harding, Mrs R. J. Hargreaves, Mr P. K. Hargreaves, Mr S. Harris, Mr K. A. Harris, N. J. Henderson, Mr A. J. Hill, J. Hornsey, Mr E. J. Hughes, D. Humphreys, Mr R. A. Jacobs, J. F. Jarvis, R. G. Kelvin-Hughes, Mrs E. A. Kelvin-Hughes, Mr M. B. J. Kimmins, Mrs A. M. Kirk, Mrs M. E. Kirk, Mrs S. D. Knipe, Miss E. A. Lake, M. R. Landau, K. F. J. Loads, Mr J. Lomas, Dr C. V. MacPhail, Mr T. G. Marlow, Mrs L. E. Marlow, Miss N. Martin, Mr C. McGinn, Mr D. M. Menzies, Mr I. D. Miller, P. J. Mills, W. D. C. Minton, Mr J. Monaghan, M. Moorgan, Mrs L. K. Morgan, Mr R. K. Munn, Mr W. J. Nesbitt, Mrs D. C. Nicholson, Miss M. Noden, Mr L. D. Nunn, Mr J. O'Keefe, Mrs C. R. Orr, Mr J. A. M. Orr, M. A. Osborne, T. S. Palin, Sir Eric Parker, Mrs M. Parker, Mr R. Pathak, S. R. C. Philip, Mrs J. Plumptre, S. I. Pollard, J. E. Potter, Mrs M. J. Potter, Brig C. K. Price, Mr S. P. Price, M. Prince, Mr P. Quinn, Mrs J. Rees, Mr A. Reid, Mr W. A. Rice, Sir J. H. Ritblat, Miss P. A. Ross, U. E. Schwarzenbach, Mr H. S. Sharpstone, W. G. C. Shaw, Mr G. A. Sheppard, Mr J. Simpson, Mr I. Souede, B. T. Stewart-Brown Esq, D. F. Sumpter, Mrs N. J. G. Thorbek-Hooper, Lord Vestey, The Hon W. G. Vestey, The Hon A. G. Vestey, Mr L. J. Westwood, Miss S. Wilde, Mr S. T. Williams-Thomas, Mr M. J. F. T. Wilson, Miss M. E. Woodd.

Jockey (NH): Barry Geraghty, A. P. McCoy, Andrew Tinkler, David Bass.
Conditional: Jeremiah McGrath, Peter Carberry, Nico De Boinville. **Amateur:** Mr F. Mitchell.

---

311 MR PAUL HENDERSON, Whitsbury
Postal: **1 Manor Farm Cottage, Whitsbury, Fordingbridge, Hampshire, SP6 3QP**
Contacts: **PHONE (01725) 518113 FAX (01725) 518113 MOBILE (07958) 482213**
E-MAIL phendersonracing@gmail.com

1 ADMIRAL BOOM (IRE), 8, b g Beneficial—Gleann Na Smaointe (IRE) **The Admiral Boom Partnership**
2 AMAURY DE LUSIGNAN (IRE), 8, b g Dushyantor (USA)—Celtic Sails (IRE) **D. S. Dennis**
3 BACK IN JUNE, 6, b g Bach (IRE)—Bathwick June (IRE) **Mrs D. H. Potter**
4 BALLYHILTY BRIDGE, 8, b g Exit To Nowhere (USA)—Gemolly (IRE) **J. H. W. Finch**
5 CAPTAIN OCANA (IRE), 9, b g Karinga Bay—Jaystara (IRE) **Mr N. D. G. Brown**
6 CHASERS CHANCE (IRE), 11, ch g Shernazar—Lucy Walters (IRE) **D. S. Dennis**
7 CNOC SEODA (IRE), 9, b m Dr Massini—Hill Diamond (IRE) **Mr R. B. Antell**
8 DOHENY BAR (IRE), 11, b g Freddie's Star—Old Fontaine (IRE) **The Rockbourne Partnership**
9 DUSHY VALLEY (IRE), 7, b g Dushyantor (USA)—Mum's Miracle (IRE) **The Moore Family & Friends**
10 FASHION FAUX PAS (IRE), 7, b m Beneficial—Supreme Designer (IRE) **Antell, Coles & Finch**
11 FLASHY STAR, 5, ch m Mr Greeley (USA)—Galileo's Star (IRE) **The Affordable (3) Partnership**
12 GARDE FOU (FR), 8, b g Kapgarde (FR)—Harpyes (FR) **Mr R. B. Antell**
13 HIGHBURY HIGH (IRE), 7, gr g Salford Express (IRE)—Betseale (IRE) **The Affordable Partnership**
14 LIFE OF A LUSO (IRE), 10, b g Luso—Life of A Lady (IRE) **Mareildar Racing Part 1**
15 MINELLA GATHERING (IRE), 5, b g Old Vic—A Plus Ma Puce (FR) **The Rockbourne Partnership**
16 MINELLA RANGER (IRE), 8, ch g Beneficial—Minella Lass (IRE) **Mr R. B. Antell**
17 MINELLA SPECIAL (IRE), 8, b g King's Theatre (IRE)—Della Wee (IRE) **Mr R. B. Antell**
18 MOUNT VESUVIUS (IRE), 6, b g Spartacus—Parker's Cove (USA) **The Ray Of Hope Partnership**
19 NEXT OASIS (IRE), 8, b g Classic Cliche (IRE)—Clearwater Glen **The Ray Of Hope Partnership**
20 PADDY THE STOUT (IRE), 9, b g Oscar Schindler (IRE)—Misty Silks **Mr R. B. Antell**
21 PULLMEN, 6, gr g Silver Patriarch (IRE)—Moon Spinner **The Affordable (3) Partnership**
22 RIOR (IRE), 7, b g King's Theatre (IRE)—Sara's Gold (IRE) **The Paul Henderson Racing Club**
23 ROYAL RIPPLE (IRE), 6, ch g Royal Anthem (USA)—Sparkling Opera **The Affordable Partnership**
24 RULE OF THUMB, 6, b g Tobougg (IRE)—Carreamia **GLR Racing**
25 SEE MORE POWER (IRE), 9, ch g Fleetwood (IRE)—Joan of Arc **Antell & Coles Families Partnership**
26 SHANNON SPIRIT (IRE), 9, b g Snurge—Spirit of The Nile (FR) **D. S. Dennis**
27 TWO MILE BRIDGE (IRE), 8, b m Dushyantor (USA)—Serengeti Plains (IRE) **The Rockbourne Partnership**
28 ZELKOVA ISLAND (IRE), 9, gr g Rashar (USA)—Island Diva (IRE) **Mr R. B. Antell**

Other Owners: Mrs V. A. P. Antell, Mr S. Clegg, D. J. Coles, Mr R. J. Galpin, Mr R. B. Griffin, P. F. Henderson, Mr D. L. Lacey, Mr P. D. Moore, Miss J. Patten.

312 LADY HERRIES, Littlehampton
Postal: **Angmering Park, Littlehampton, West Sussex, BN16 4EX**
Contacts: **YARD (01903) 871605 HOME (01903) 871421 FAX (01903) 871609**
MOBILE (07785) 282996
E-MAIL **angparkstables@btconnect.com**

1 **BARWICK**, 6, b g Beat Hollow—Tenpence **Seymour Bloodstock (UK) Ltd**
2 **BEAUFORT TWELVE**, 5, b g Hurricane Run (IRE)—Violette **Lady Herries**
3 **BOUGGATTI**, 6, b g Tobougg (IRE)—Western Sal **Lady Sarah Clutton**
4 **COTTON KING**, 7, b g Dubawi (IRE)—Spinning The Yarn **Lady Mary Mumford**
5 **DUMBFOUNDED (FR)**, 6, b br g Vettori (IRE)—Take The Light (FR) **Lady Sarah Clutton**
6 **JUST ARCHIE (USA)**, 6, b g Arch (USA)—Copper Rose (USA) **Lady Sarah Clutton**
7 **MUSICAL MOON**, 4, b g Piccolo—Lunasa (IRE) **Angmering Park**
8 **PEARL RANSOM (IRE)**, 4, b g Intikhab (USA)—Massada **Seymour Bloodstock (UK) Ltd**
9 **SWIFT BLADE (IRE)**, 6, ch g Exceed And Excel (AUS)—Gold Strike (IRE) **Angmering Park**

THREE-YEAR-OLDS

10 **DEAUVILLE DANCER (IRE)**, b g Tamayuz—Mathool (IRE) **Suffolk Bloodstock**

Other Owners: P. Bamford, Mr D. R. Mann.

313 MR MICHAEL HERRINGTON, Thirsk
Postal: **Garbutt Farm, Cold Kirby, Thirsk, North Yorkshire, YO7 2HJ**
Contacts: **PHONE (01845) 597793 MOBILE (07792) 604405**
E-MAIL **hlloyd19@gmail.com** WEBSITE **www.michaelherringtonracing.co.uk**

1 **CHEYENNE RED (IRE)**, 8, br g Namid—Red Leggings **Mr J. S. Herrington**
2 **CLOUDS OF GLORY**, 5, b m Resplendent Glory (IRE)—Rosewings **Miss Vivian Pratt**
3 **EASTWARD HO**, 6, ch g Resplendent Glory (IRE)—Mofeyda (IRE) **Miss Vivian Pratt**
4 **GLADSOME**, 6, b m Resplendent Glory (IRE)—Christening (IRE) **Miss Vivian Pratt**
5 4, Ch g Trade Fair—Khandala (IRE) **Mr J. S. Herrington**
6 **KUWAIT STAR**, 5, ch g Resplendent Glory (IRE)—Mofeyda (IRE) **Miss Vivian Pratt**
7 **MISHAAL (IRE)**, 4, ch g Kheleyf (USA)—My Dubai (IRE) **Kelvyn Gracie & Lawrence McCaughey**
8 **MORNA'S GLORY**, 5, b m Resplendent Glory (IRE)—Tipsy Cake **Miss Vivian Pratt**
9 **PETER'S FRIEND**, 5, b g Gentleman's Deal (IRE)—Giffoine **Mr J. S. Herrington**
10 **ROMANTICIZE**, 8, b m Kyllachy—Romancing **Miss Vivian Pratt**
11 **TAXIFORMISSBYRON**, 4, b f Byron—Miss Respect **H. M. Hurst**
12 5, Br m Resplendent Glory (IRE)—Tip The Spirit **Miss Vivian Pratt**

THREE-YEAR-OLDS

13 B g Piccolo—Dolphin Dancer **D. G. Clayton**
14 Bl f Authorized (IRE)—Miss Respect **H. M. Hurst**
15 **WORCHARLIE'SLASS**, b f Myboycharlie (IRE)—Angry Bark (USA) **H. M. Hurst**

TWO-YEAR-OLDS

16 Ch f 11/3 Medicean—Opening Ceremony (USA) (Quest For Fame) (17142) **H.M. Hurst**

Assistant Trainer: Helen Lloyd-Herrington

314 MR PETER HIATT, Banbury
Postal: **Six Ash Farm, Hook Norton, Banbury, Oxfordshire, OX15 5DB**
Contacts: **PHONE (01608) 737255 FAX (01608) 730641 MOBILE (07973) 751115**

1 **ANOTHER SQUEEZE**, 6, gr m Proclamation (IRE)—Tight Squeeze **Burt Gibbs Harrisons**
2 **DONTPAYTHEFERRYMAN (USA)**, 9, ch g Wiseman's Ferry (USA)—Expletive Deleted (USA) **P. W. Hiatt**
3 **FLAG OF GLORY**, 7, b g Trade Fair—Rainbow Sky **N. D. Edden**
4 **GEEAITCH**, 5, ch g Cockney Rebel (IRE)—Grand Rebecca (IRE) **P. J. R. Gardner**
5 **LAMBERT PEN (USA)**, 4, ch g Johannesburg (USA)—Whiletheiron'shot (USA) **P. W. Hiatt**
6 **MAZIJ**, 6, b m Haafhd—Salim Toto **P. Kelly**

MR PETER HIATT - Continued

7 RHINESTONE REBEL (IRE), 8, ch g Rashar (USA)—Flute Opera (IRE) **P. Porter**
8 ROXY LANE, 5, b m Byron—Comme Ca **Mr R G Robinson & Mr R D Robinson**
9 SHIRATAKI (IRE), 6, b g Cape Cross (IRE)—Noodle Soup (USA) **Mr C. Demczak**
10 SINGS POET, 4, ch g Singspiel (IRE)—Royale Rose (FR) **R. N. Coles**
11 THEWESTWALIAN (USA), 6, b br g Stormy Atlantic (USA)—Skies Of Blue (USA) **P. W. Hiatt**
12 TUXEDO, 9, ch g Cadeaux Genereux—Serengeti Bride (USA) **P. Kelly**
13 WAAHEJ, 8, b g Haafhd—Madam Ninette **P. W. Hiatt**

THREE-YEAR-OLDS

14 MONARCH MAID, b f Captain Gerrard (IRE)—Orange Lily **Mr C. Demczak**

Other Owners: Mr Anthony Harrison, Mrs C. E. Harrison, Mr Ivor Potter, Mr R. Robinson, Mr R. D. Robinson.

Assistant Trainer: Mrs E. Hiatt

Jockey (flat): William Carson, Chris Catlin. **Apprentice:** Ryan Clark. **Amateur:** Miss M. Edden.

---

315 **MR PHILIP HIDE, Findon**
Postal: **Cissbury Stables, Findon, Worthing, West Sussex, BN14 0SR**
Contacts: **MOBILE (07768) 233324**

1 ISKRABOB, 4, ch g Tobougg (IRE)—Honour Bolton **Mr P. E. Hide**
2 PEMBROKE PRIDE, 4, b f Indesatchel (IRE)—Elegia Prima **C. V. Cruden**
3 TIMOTHY T, 6, bl g Pastoral Pursuits—Point Perfect **Mr W. E. Mocatta**
4 URAMAZIN (IRE), 8, ch g Danehill Dancer (IRE)—Uriah (GER) **S. P. C. Woods**

THREE-YEAR-OLDS

5 MASTER DANCER, gr c Mastercraftsman (IRE)—Isabella Glyn (IRE) **S. P. C. Woods**
6 PENARA, b f Archipenko (USA)—Takegawa **Mr P. E. Hide**
7 SILENT PURSUIT, br f Pastoral Pursuits—Lay A Whisper **Mr W. F. N. Davis**
8 SLEIPNIR, ch g Medicean—Resistance Heroine **S. P. C. Woods**
9 SNOW CONDITIONS, b f Aussie Rules (USA)—Snow Gonal (FR) **P. Turner, J. Davies & The Hides**
10 TOPOFTHEDROPS (IRE), b g High Chaparral (IRE)—Basin Street Blues (IRE)
11 ZAMBEASY, b c Zamindar (USA)—Hanella (IRE) **Heart Of The South Racing**

TWO-YEAR-OLDS

12 Gr f 21/4 Dark Angel (IRE)—Ballroom Dancer (IRE) (Danehill Dancer (IRE))
13 B f 20/3 Indesatchel (IRE)—Hope Chest (Kris) **C. V. Cruden**
14 B c 2/2 Iffraaj—Miss Lacey (IRE) (Diktat) (100000) **Mr P. E. Hide**
15 B c 8/2 Authorized (IRE)—Sablonne (USA) (Silver Hawk (USA)) (80000)
16 Ch c 3/3 Rock of Gibraltar (IRE)—Takegawa (Giant's Causeway (USA))

Other Owners: J. Davies, Mr A. G. Hide, J. R. Penny, Miss E. Penny, Mr P. Turner.

---

316 **MRS LAWNEY HILL, Aston Rowant**
Postal: **Woodway Farm, Aston Rowant, Watlington, Oxford, OX49 5SJ**
Contacts: PHONE **(01844) 353051** FAX **(01844) 354751** MOBILE **(07769) 862648**
E-MAIL **lawney@lawneyhill.co.uk** WEBSITE **www.lawneyhill.co.uk**

1 BILLY TWYFORD (IRE), 7, b g Brian Boru—The Distaff Spy **Mr A. J. Weller**
2 CHAPOLIMOSS (FR), 10, ch g Trempolino (USA)—Chamoss (FR) **A. Barr, J. Basquill, A. Hill, H. Mullineux**
3 COME ON LAURIE (IRE), 6, b g Oscar (IRE)—Megan's Magic **Mr P. Mellett**
4 COOL CASCADE, 8, b m Alderbrook—Miss Pout **Miss F. A. Molle**
5 COOLKING, 7, b g King's Theatre (IRE)—Osocool **Sir Peter & Lady Forwood**
6 DIVINE FOLLY (GER), 9, b g Kotashaan (FR)—Jennys Grove (IRE) **Mrs H. C. Mullineux**
7 DOUBLE HANDFUL (GER), 8, bl g Pentire—Durania (GER) **Les Cross & Alan Hill**
8 FROSTY LAD (IRE), 10, b g Moscow Society (USA)—Johnston's Crest (IRE) **A. Hill, S. Florey, H. Webb**
9 JAMMY (IRE), 5, b g Oscar (IRE)—Tabachines (FR) **Mrs W. P. Cohen**
10 KING OZZY (IRE), 10, b g King Charlemagne (USA)—Kingpin Delight **The Sunday Night Partnership**
11 MIGHTY MAMBO, 7, b g Fantastic Light (USA)—Mambo's Melody **Fortnum Racing**

MRS LAWNEY HILL - Continued

12 **MISS MAYFAIR (IRE),** 7, b m Indian Danehill (IRE)—Cocktail Party (USA) **A. Hill**
13 **ROYAL ETIQUETTE (IRE),** 7, b g Royal Applause—Alpine Gold (IRE) **A. Hill**
14 **SAFE INVESTMENT (USA),** 10, b g Gone West (USA)—Fully Invested (USA) **A. Hill**
15 **SASKOMPLIQ (FR),** 8, b g Sleeping Car (FR)—Royale Laguna (FR) **Mrs D. M. Caudwell**
16 **SO OSCAR (IRE),** 6, b g Oscar (IRE)—So Proper (IRE) **Mrs K. G. Exall & R. Lee**
17 **TORRAN SOUND,** 7, b g Tobougg (IRE)—Velvet Waters **Mrs D. Clark**
18 **WHAT'S UP DOC (IRE),** 13, b g Dr Massini (IRE)—Surprise Treat (IRE) **A. Hill**

Other Owners: Mr Andrew Barr, Mr J. M. Basquill, Mr Les Cross, Mr Simon Florey, Sir Peter Forwood, Lady Forwood, Mrs T. Hill, Mr Alan Hill, Mr Brian Hiskey, Mrs Helen Mullineux, Mr D. F. Sumpter, Mr H. J. M. Webb.

Jockey (flat): Dane O'Neill. **Jockey (NH):** David Bass, Aidan Coleman. **Amateur:** Mr Joe Hill.

---

317 **MR MARTIN HILL, Totnes**
Postal: **The Barn, Knaves Ash Stables, Nr Redpost, Littlehempston, Totnes, Devon, TQ9 6NG**
Contacts: **PHONE (01803) 813102 MOBILE (07980) 490220**
E-MAIL info@martinhillracing.co.uk WEBSITE www.martinhillracing.co.uk

1 **BEAT THE BOUNDS,** 5, b g Beat All (USA)—Regally **The Village People**
2 **BOLD PERK (IRE),** 12, ch g Executive Perk—Mugazine **D. Luscombe & M. Hill**
3 **DETROIT RED,** 8, b m Hamairi (IRE)—Kingston Black **The Detroit Reds**
4 **EASILY PLEASED (IRE),** 8, b g Beneficial—Bro Ella (IRE) **Roger Oliver & Claire Harding**
5 **ERNEST SPEAK (IRE),** 5, b g Jeremy (USA)—Mijouter (IRE) **The Lucky Fifteen**
6 **FLAMENCO LAD,** 4, b g Tamure (IRE)—Monda **Mrs H. M. Luscombe**
7 **KIM TIAN ROAD (IRE),** 8, b m King's Theatre (IRE)—Shaunies Lady (IRE) **The Kimonos**
8 **LUCKY GAL,** 4, b f Overbury (IRE)—Lucky Arrow **M. E. Hill**
9 **RYDON PYNES,** 6, b g Beat All (USA)—Persian Smoke **The Rydon Pynes Partnership**
10 **SHERIFF HUTTON (IRE),** 11, b g Rudimentary (USA)—Will She What (IRE) **Mr R. G. Dennis**
11 **SHIVSINGH,** 5, b g Montjeu (IRE)—Vistaria (USA) **F. A. Clegg**
12 **THE RATTLER OBRIEN (IRE),** 8, b g Beneficial—Clonea Lady (IRE) **Spirit Of Devon**
13 **TZORA,** 9, b g Sakhee (USA)—Lucky Arrow **Tzora Partners**
14 **WATCOMBE HEIGHTS,** 4, b g Scorpion (IRE)—Golden Bay **The R C Partnership**
15 **WHATWILLWEDONEXT (IRE),** 8, b g Brian Boru—Pigeon Rock (IRE) **M. E. Hill**
16 **Y A BON (IRE),** 6, b g Black Sam Bellamy (IRE)—Tarte Fine (FR) **The Lucky Fifteen**

THREE-YEAR-OLDS

17 **MIKEY MISS DAISY,** ch f Champs Elysees—Savoy Street **Mr M. Leach**

Other Owners: Mr J. L. Coombs, Mrs Claire Harding, Mr Jon Hearne, Mr Martin Hill, Mr M. Leach, Mr R. Lester, Mr David Luscombe, Ms Sarah Mascall, Mr Neil. C. Matthews, Mr R. O. Oliver, Mr Keith Pook, Mr Peter Serjeant, Mr M. Z. Tarlowski, Mr R. Thomasson, Mrs C. D. Tibbetts, Mr D. R. Tribe, Mrs P. A. Wolfenden.

Assistant Trainer: Rachel Williams

Jockey (flat): Luke Morris. **Jockey (NH):** Hadden Frost. **Conditional:** Jeremiah McGrath. **Amateur:** Miss Alice Mills.

---

318 **MR CHARLES HILLS, Lambourn**
Postal: **Wetherdown House, Lambourn, Hungerford, Berkshire, RG17 8UB**
Contacts: **PHONE (01488) 71548 FAX (01488) 72823**
E-MAIL info@charleshills.co.uk WEBSITE www.charleshills.com

1 **ENGLISHMAN,** 4, b c Royal Applause—Tesary **Qatar Racing Limited & Mr P Winkworth**
2 **FORGOTTEN HERO (IRE),** 5, b br g High Chaparral (IRE)—Sundown **Mrs Julie Martin & David R. Martin**
3 **GLENARD,** 4, b g Arch (USA)—Olaya (USA) **Highclere T'Bred Racing & John C Grant**
4 **JUST THE JUDGE (IRE),** 4, b f Lawman (FR)—Faraday Light (IRE) **Qatar Racing Limited & Sangster Family**
5 **LOVE EXCEL,** 4, b c Exceed And Excel (AUS)—Navajo Love Song (IRE) **Mr Robert Ng**
6 **LUCKY BEGGAR (IRE),** 4, gr c Verglas (IRE)—Lucky Clio (IRE) **Hon Mrs Corbett, C Wright, Mrs B W Hills**
7 **OGBOURNE DOWNS,** 4, b c Royal Applause—Helen Sharp **S W Group Logistics Limited**
8 **ONE WORD MORE (IRE),** 4, b c Thousand Words—Somoushe **Tony Wechsler & Ann Plummer**
9 **RED INVADER (IRE),** 4, b c Red Clubs (IRE)—Tifariti (USA) **The Hon R. J. Arculli**
10 **REGAL DAN (IRE),** 4, b c Dark Angel (IRE)—
Charlene Lacy (IRE) **N N Browne, Paul McNamara, Hon Mrs Napier**

MR CHARLES HILLS - Continued

11 SHROPSHIRE (IRE), 6, gr g Shamardal (USA)—Shawanni **The Hon Mrs J. M. Corbett & Mr C. Wright**
12 STORM (IRE), 4, b f Excellent Art—Bali Breeze (IRE) **R Morecombe, M E Sangster, E O'Leary**

THREE-YEAR-OLDS

13 A GREAT BEAUTY, b f Acclamation—Regatta (USA) **Mrs E. O'Leary**
14 ABATIS (USA), b br f Aptitude (USA)—Rouwaki (USA) **Mr K. Abdullah**
15 ALMUHALAB, b br c Dansili—Ghanaati (USA) **Mr Hamdan Al Maktoum**
16 ALZAMMAAR (USA), b c Birdstone (USA)—Alma Mater **Mr Hamdan Al Maktoum**
17 AMOOD (IRE), ch c Elnadim (USA)—Amanah (USA) **Mr Hamdan Al Maktoum**
18 ARABLE, ch c Three Valleys (USA)—Cut Corn **Mr K. Abdullah**
19 BROADWAY RANGER (IRE), b c Bushranger (IRE)—Broadways Millie (IRE) **John C Grant & Ray Harper**
20 BROWN DIAMOND (IRE), b f Fastnet Rock (AUS)—Adjalisa (IRE) **Triermore Stud**
21 CABLE BAY (IRE), b c Invincible Spirit (IRE)—Rose de France (IRE) **Julie Martin & David R. Martin & Partner**
22 CAMBRIDGE, b f Rail Link—Alumni **Mr K. Abdullah**
23 CAPE KARLI (IRE), br f Cape Cross (IRE)—Karliysha (IRE) **Jim & Susan Hill**
24 CAPTAIN BOB (IRE), b g Dark Angel (IRE)—Birthday Present **Mr A. L. R. Morton**
25 Gr f High Chaparral (IRE)—Cause Celebre (IRE) **Triermore Stud**
26 COLUMBIAN ROULETTE (IRE), b c Bushranger (IRE)—Rainbow Lyrics (IRE) **Mr Stewart Jones**
27 COMPUTER (USA), ch c Mizzen Mast (USA)—Tolerance (USA) **Mr K. Abdullah**
28 CORAL MIST, ch f Bahamian Bounty—Treasure Trove (USA) **Triermore Stud & Mr R A Scarborough**
29 DESPOT (IRE), gr c Verglas (IRE)—Ms Bossy Boots (USA) **Hon Mrs Corbett, C Wright, Mrs B W Hills**
30 DREAM AND SEARCH (GER), b c Raven's Pass (USA)—Diamond Eyes (GER) **Qatar Racing Limited**
31 DUTCH ROMANCE, ch f Dutch Art—Endless Love (IRE) **Mrs Susan Roy**
32 ERMINE RUBY, b f Cape Cross (IRE)—Ruby Rocket (IRE) **Sir Peter Vela & The Hon Mrs P Stanley**
33 EXCELLENT ROYALE (IRE), b c Excellent Art—Farbenspiel (IRE) **Jim & Susan Hill**
34 GLASGOW CENTRAL, b c Rail Link—Musical Key **Mrs J. K. Powell**
35 GOWN (IRE), b f Excellent Art—Chehalis Sunset **Mrs J. K. Powell**
36 GREEB, b br c Oasis Dream—Shamtari (IRE) **Mr Hamdan Al Maktoum**
37 IFTAAR (IRE), b c Bushranger (IRE)—Kheleyf's Silver (IRE) **Mr Hamdan Al Maktoum**
38 INTERJECT (USA), b br f Empire Maker (USA)—Introducing (USA) **Mr K. Abdullah**
39 JAZZ (IRE), b c Danehill Dancer (IRE)—Jazz Baby (IRE) **N Browne, P McNamara, J Napier, J Powell**
40 KISS OF SPRING (IRE), br f Dansili—In The Light **Mr Michael Buckley**
41 KIYOSHI, b f Dubawi (IRE)—Mocca (IRE) **Qatar Racing Limited**
42 LATE NIGHT MARK (IRE), b c Marju (IRE)—Khatela (IRE) **Jim & Susan Hill**
43 LIMOUSINE, ch f Beat Hollow—Market Forces **Mr K. Abdullah**
44 LOVELOCKS (IRE), b f High Chaparral (IRE)—Civility Cat (USA) **Triermore Stud & Mr R A Scarborough**
45 MAAYAAT (USA), b f Jazil (USA)—Wasnah (USA) **Mr Hamdan Al Maktoum**
46 MARMOOM, ch c Dutch Art—Cosmic Song **Mr Hamdan Al Maktoum**
47 MARTINETTE (USA), b br f Mizzen Mast (USA)—Faraway Flower (USA) **Mr K. Abdullah**
48 MISS CRYSTAL (IRE), b f Montjeu (IRE)—Crystal Curling (IRE) **Triermore Stud**
49 MOONTOWN, ch c Sea The Stars (IRE)—Eva's Request (IRE) **Lady Bamford**
50 MY PAINTER (IRE), b f Jeremy (USA)—Last Cry (FR) **Jim & Susan Hill**
51 NATHR (USA), br c Dixie Union (USA)—Sweet Rider (USA) **Mr Hamdan Al Maktoum**
52 PASSING STAR, b c Royal Applause—Passing Hour (USA) **Mr John C. Grant**
53 QAWAASEM (USA), b f Shamardal (USA)—Misdaqeya **Mr Hamdan Al Maktoum**
54 QUEEN CATRINE (IRE), b f Acclamation—Kahira (IRE) **QRL/Sheikh Suhaim Al Thani/M Al Kubaisi**
55 RANDWICK (IRE), b c High Chaparral (IRE)—Subito **Mr John C. Grant**
56 RIVER GODDESS (IRE), b f Marju (IRE)—Talwin (IRE) **Mrs G Galvin, J Gompertz, B V Sangster**
57 ROCK OF DREAMS (IRE), b g Rock of Gibraltar (IRE)—
Manhattan Dream (USA) **Marston Stud & Mr Arthur Mitchell**
58 ROSEHILL ARTIST (IRE), b f Excellent Art—Conference (IRE) **Mr John C. Grant**
59 SAHRA AL KHADRA, b c Green Desert (USA)—Maimoona (IRE) **Sheikh Hamdan Bin Maktoum Al Maktoum**
60 SCILLONIAN SUNSET (IRE), ch f Teofilo (IRE)—Hundred Year Flood (USA) **John C Grant & Ray Harper**
61 SO SATISFIED, b c Aqlaam—Pirouetting **Mrs B. W. Hills**
62 SOCIAL RISER (IRE), b f High Chaparral (IRE)—Parvenue (FR) **Jim & Susan Hill**
63 TANZEEL (IRE), ch c Elusive City (USA)—Royal Fizz (IRE) **Mr Hamdan Al Maktoum**
64 THREE PEAKS, ch c Three Valleys (USA)—Coming Back **Mr K. Abdullah**
65 TUDDENHAM (USA), b br g Latent Heat (USA)—Storming On (USA) **Mr K. Abdullah**
66 WILD AFFAIRE (IRE), b f High Chaparral (IRE)—En Garde (IRE) **Mr R A Scarborough & Triermore Stud**
67 YEAH BABY (IRE), b f Danehill Dancer (IRE)—Street Shaana (FR) **Mr Tony Elliott & Mr Jeff King**

TWO-YEAR-OLDS

68 Ch f 12/3 Giant's Causeway (USA)—A Mind of Her Own (IRE) (Danehill Dancer (IRE)) (100658)
69 ABHAJAT (IRE), b f 12/4 Lope de Vega (IRE)—Starry Messenger (Galileo (IRE)) (400000)
70 B f 7/5 Fastnet Rock (AUS)—Adjalisa (IRE) (Darshaan)

MR CHARLES HILLS - Continued

71 **ALAKHTAL (IRE)**, br c 18/2 Lord Shanakill (USA)—Definite Opinion (IRE) (Kheleyf (USA)) (100000)
72 **ALJAAZYA (USA)**, b f 10/2 Speightstown (USA)—Matiya (IRE) (Alzao (USA))
73 Br f 7/3 Equiano (FR)—All Quiet (Piccolo) (28571)
74 **ALNASHAMA**, b br c 24/2 Dubawi (IRE)—Ghanaati (USA) (Giant's Causeway (USA))
75 B c 15/3 Fastnet Rock (AUS)—Amethyst (IRE) (Sadler's Wells (USA)) (61942)
76 B f 27/2 Galileo (IRE)—Artful (IRE) (Green Desert (USA)) (135000)
77 **BEIJING STAR**, ch c 11/4 Dylan Thomas (IRE)—Signella (Selkirk (USA)) (45000)
78 **BIG CHILL**, b c 29/3 Acclamation—Royal Consort (IRE) (Green Desert (USA))
79 **CALIMA BREEZE**, b f 6/2 Oasis Dream—Paris Winds (IRE) (Galileo (IRE)) (100000)
80 **CARPE VITA (IRE)**, b f 23/4 Montjeu (IRE)—Dance Parade (USA) (Gone West (USA))
81 Ch ro c 3/3 Piccolo—Cherrycombe-Row (Classic Cliche (IRE)) (54200)
82 Ch c 28/1 Exceed And Excel (AUS)—Continua (USA) (Elusive Quality (USA)) (75000)
83 B f 31/3 Rock Hard Ten (USA)—Costume (Danehill (USA))
84 B f 20/4 Fastnet Rock (AUS)—Crinolette (IRE) (Sadler's Wells (USA)) (105000)
85 B f 28/1 Henrythenavigator (USA)—Crystal Crossing (IRE) (Royal Academy (USA))
86 B f 10/3 Galileo (IRE)—Crystal Valkyrie (IRE) (Danehill (USA)) (228416)
87 B c 26/4 Zamindar (USA)—Daring Miss (Sadler's Wells (USA))
88 **DARK PROFIT (IRE)**, gr c 4/5 Dark Angel (IRE)—Goldthroat (IRE) (Zafonic (USA)) (240030)
89 B f 8/3 Fastnet Rock (AUS)—Dream Time (Rainbow Quest (USA)) (45682)
90 Ch c 6/4 Dutch Art—Endless Love (IRE) (Dubai Destination (USA))
91 B f 27/2 Oasis Dream—Enora (GER) (Noverre (USA))
92 **ESPECIALLY MADE (IRE)**, b c 13/3 Moss Vale (IRE)—Maid To Order (USA) (Zafonic (USA)) (28571)
93 B f 1/3 Equiano (FR)—Fabine (Danehill Dancer (IRE))
94 B f 14/2 Mastercraftsman (IRE)—Fact (American Post) (55238)
95 B f 17/2 Acclamation—Favoritely (USA) (Favorite Trick (USA)) (38095)
96 Ch c 22/1 Iffraaj—Geesala (IRE) (Barathea (IRE)) (60000)
97 B f 25/3 Iffraaj—Gift of Spring (Gilded Time (USA)) (100000)
98 **CORZETTI (FR)**, Ch c 23/4 Linngari (IRE)—Green Maid (USA) (Green Dancer (USA)) (23228)
99 **HAKAM (USA)**, b br c 22/2 War Front (USA)—Lauren Byrd (USA) (Arch (USA)) (262927)
100 **HEATSTROKE (IRE)**, b c 20/2 Galileo (IRE)—Walklikeanegyptian (IRE) (Danehill (USA))
101 B f 19/3 Dansili—High Praise (USA) (Quest For Fame)
102 **HUNDI (IRE)**, b f 13/5 Fastnet Rock (AUS)—Hypoteneuse (IRE) (Warning) (270000)
103 B f 12/3 Kyllachy—Hurricane Harriet (Bertolini (USA)) (21904)
104 B c 7/4 Oasis Dream—Hypoteneuse (IRE) (Sadler's Wells (USA))
105 B f 1/2 Motivator—Israar (Machiavellian (USA)) (185829)
106 B c 24/4 First Defence (USA)—Jazz Drummer (USA) (Dixieland Band (USA))
107 B c 26/2 Approve (IRE)—Kelsey Rose (Most Welcome) (46457)
108 **KHAREER (IRE)**, b c 16/5 Acclamation—Fantastic Account (Fantastic Light (USA)) (150000)
109 **LAMYAA**, ch f 11/3 Arcano (IRE)—Divine Grace (IRE) (Definite Article)
110 B f 6/3 Henrythenavigator (USA)—Madamascus (USA) (Sheikh Albadou) (32135)
111 **MAGICAL MEMORY (IRE)**, gr c 17/4 Zebedee—Marasem (Cadeaux Genereux) (27100)
112 **MARY MCPHEE**, ch f 3/3 Makfi—Aunty Mary (Common Grounds) (147619)
113 B f 18/3 Zebedee—Masai Queen (IRE) (Mujadil (USA)) (23228)
114 B f 1/3 Duke of Marmalade (IRE)—Ms Sophie Eleanor (USA) (Grand Slam (USA)) (25163)
115 **MUHAAFIZ (IRE)**, br g 3/4 Lord Shanakill (USA)—Yasmin Satine (IRE) (Key of Luck (USA)) (100000)
116 **MUHAARAR**, b c 25/2 Oasis Dream—Tahrir (IRE) (Linamix (FR))
117 **MURTASSIM (IRE)**, b c 8/2 Tamayuz—Meanya (IRE) (Revoque (IRE)) (47619)
118 **NAWAASY (USA)**, ch f 29/1 Distorted Humor (USA)—Stormin Maggy (USA) (Storm Cat (USA)) (277534)
119 Ch f 12/4 Equiano (FR)—Never A Doubt (Night Shift (USA))
120 Ch gr f 4/2 Zebedee—Occhi Verdi (IRE) (Mujtahid (USA)) (10840)
121 Gr c 9/2 Beat Hollow—Onemix (Fair Mix (IRE))
122 B f 3/2 Kodiac—Operissimo (Singspiel (IRE)) (100000)
123 **RENAISSANCE RED**, ch c 4/3 Medicean—Special Moment (IRE) (Sadler's Wells (USA)) (35000)
124 B f 8/5 Duke of Marmalade (IRE)—Reprise (Darshaan) (50328)
125 Ch c 26/2 Zamindar (USA)—Revered (Oasis Dream)
126 Ch f 27/2 Bahamian Bounty—Reveuse de Jour (IRE) (Sadler's Wells (USA)) (170000)
127 B c 21/3 Fast Company (USA)—Right Ted (IRE) (Mujadil (USA)) (28000)
128 **RISE UP LOTUS (IRE)**, gr f 25/1 Zebedee—Face The Storm (IRE) (Barathea (IRE)) (71428)
129 **ROCKING THE BOAT (IRE)**, b f 14/4 Zebedee—Rocking (Oasis Dream) (90000)
130 **ROSSLARE (IRE)**, b f 26/4 Fastnet Rock (AUS)—Waterways (IRE) (Alhaarth (IRE)) (65000)
131 **SAGUNA (FR)**, b f 27/1 Le Havre (IRE)—Sandy Winner (FR) (Priolo (USA)) (23228)
132 **SALT ISLAND**, b c 26/3 Exceed And Excel (AUS)—Tiana (Diktat) (55000)
133 Ch c 19/1 Iffraaj—Smartest (IRE) (Exceed And Excel (AUS)) (72000)
134 B c 10/4 Kyllachy—Something Blue (Petong) (110000)
135 Ch f 16/2 Galileo (IRE)—Song of My Heart (IRE) (Footstepsinthesand)

MR CHARLES HILLS - Continued

136 Ch f 16/4 Halling (USA)—Sospira (Cape Cross (IRE))
137 B c 16/4 Dark Angel (IRE)—Spring View (Fantastic Light (USA)) (69685)
138 B f 10/4 Dark Angel (IRE)—Startarette (USA) (Dixieland Band (USA)) (116143)
139 STINKY SOCKS (IRE), b f 12/2 Footstepsinthesand—City of Cities (IRE) (In The Wings) (65814)
140 SYDNEY HEIGHTS (IRE), ch c 21/3 Lord Shanakill (USA)—Ashdali (IRE) (Grand Lodge (USA)) (63491)
141 TAKAFOL (IRE), b c 27/2 Fast Company (IRE)—Jamary (IRE) (Grand Reward (USA)) (80000)
142 TAQNEYYA (IRE), b f 20/2 Raven's Pass (USA)—Misdaqeya (Red Ransom (USA))
143 Br f 23/2 Dark Angel (IRE)—The Hermitage (IRE) (Kheleyf (USA)) (162600)
144 THE TWISLER, b c 2/4 Motivator—Panna (Polish Precedent (USA)) (10000)
145 B br f 25/3 Rock Hard Ten (USA)—Tinge (USA) (Kingmambo (USA))
146 Ch c 10/4 Lord Shanakill (USA)—Titian Queen (Tobougg (IRE)) (50328)
147 B c 17/3 Lawman (FR)—Truly Magnificent (USA) (Elusive Quality (USA)) (65814)
148 TWISTAWAY (IRE), b f 28/2 Teofilo (IRE)—River Mountain (Reset (AUS)) (50000)
149 UNION SPIRIT (IRE), ch f 22/4 Mastercraftsman (IRE)—Valentine Hill (IRE) (Mujadil (USA)) (15485)
150 VIXEN HILL, b f 6/4 Acclamation—Heckle (In The Wings) (80000)
151 B br f 13/2 Arch (USA)—Youcan'ttakeme (USA) (He's Tops (USA)) (160677)

Other Owners: Ahmad Abdulla Al Shaikh & Co, Sheikh Juma Dalmook Al Maktoum, Mr Des Anderson, Mr R Barnes, Black Gold Partnership, Mrs E. Carson, Mr C. Conroy, Mr E Farquhar, Mr Alex Frost, Mr Berkeley Greenwood, Major Christopher Hanbury, Mrs Christopher Hanbury, Mr John Harrington, Mrs Fitri Hay, Mrs Philippa Hills, Mr C. B. Hills, Mrs V Hubbard, Mr D M James, Mrs Barbara Keller, Kennet Valley Thoroughbreds VIII, Kennet Valley Thoroughbreds I, Mr Kenneth Lau, Livingstone Syndicate, Mr Alexander Lloyd-Baker, Mr Brandon Lui, Mr F Ma, Mr M V Magnier, Mrs John Magnier, Mrs Clodagh McStay, Mr S. Munir, Mr A. V. Nicoll, Mr Thomas O'Donohoe, Mr Eloise O'Donohoe, Sir Robert Ogden, Mr R A Pegum, Mr David Reid Scott, Mrs E. Roberts, Mr S. E. Sangster, Mrs B V Sangster, Mr G. E. Sangster, Mr Urs E. Schwarzenbach, Mrs Paul Shanahan, Mr Peter Shepherd, Mr Isaac Souede, Mr P J Vela, Lady Richard Wellesley, Lady Whent, Ms A A Yap.

Assistant Trainers: Kevin Mooney, Joe Herbert

Apprentice: James Merrett, Callum Shepherd, Jack Budge.

---

319 **MR J. W. HILLS, Lambourn**
Postal: **Kingwood Stud, Lambourn, Berkshire, RG17 7RS**
Contacts: **PHONE (01488) 73144 FAX (01488) 73099 MOBILE (07836) 283091**
E-MAIL john@johnhills.com TWITTER @HillsJW WEBSITE www.johnhills.com

Horses owned by Hamdan Al Maktoum are based at the adjacent Kingwood House Stables under the supervision of B. W. Hills.

1 ARMS (IRE), 4, b c Excellent Art—Enchanting Way **Mr M. H. Lui**
2 B FIFTY TWO (IRE), 5, br g Dark Angel (IRE)—Petite Maxine **Gary & Linnet Woodward**
3 BLACKDOWN HILLS, 4, b f Presenting—Lady Prunella (IRE) **Mr J. M. Cole**
4 BOOMERANG BOB (IRE), 5, b h Aussie Rules (USA)—Cozzene's Pride (USA) **R. J. Tufft**
5 DANGEROUS AGE, 4, br f Sleeping Indian—Rye (IRE) **R Hunter, D Klein, M Hoodless**
6 DUCHESS OF HYGROVE, 4, b f Duke of Marmalade (IRE)—Elegant Pride **Mr D.H. Francis**
7 ECO WARRIOR, 4, b g Echo of Light—Kryssa **D. J. Deer**
8 GAMBOL (FR), 4, ch g New Approach (IRE)—Guardia (GER) **Hamdan Al Maktoum**
9 KEENE'S POINTE, 4, br g Avonbridge—Belle's Edge **Mrs D. Abberley**
10 MARIA MONTEZ, 5, b m Piccolo—Easy Feeling (IRE) **Mr J. M. Cole**
11 MAZAAHER, 4, b c Elnadim (USA)—Elutrah **Hamdan Al Maktoum**
12 SOUL INTENT (IRE), 4, b c Galileo (IRE)—Flamingo Guitar (USA) **Andy Weller & Gary Styles**
13 XINBAMA (IRE), 5, b h Baltic King—Persian Empress (IRE) **Tony Waspe Partnership**

THREE-YEAR-OLDS

14 ADHWAA, br f Oasis Dream—Hammiya (IRE) **Hamdan Al Maktoum**
15 ARTISTIC MUSE (IRE), b f Excellent Art—Course de Diamante (IRE) **Miss E. Asprey & C. W. Wright**
16 HONITON LACE, ch f Tobougg (IRE)—Mellifluous (IRE) **Mrs P. de W. Johnson**
17 JOLLY RED JEANZ (IRE), ch f Intense Focus (USA)—Sovienne (USA) **MMIMM Racing**
18 KATJA, b f Sleeping Indian—Toffee Vodka (IRE) **Gary & Linnet Woodward**
19 MAKRUMA, b f Dubawi (IRE)—Qelaan (USA) **Hamdan Al Maktoum**
20 MAWASEEL, ch c Sea The Stars (IRE)—Kareemah (IRE) **Hamdan Al Maktoum**
21 MUSTADRIK (USA), b c Jazil (USA)—Uroobah (USA) **Hamdan Al Maktoum**
22 RASAMEEL (USA), ch c Jazil (USA)—Positioning (USA) **Hamdan Al Maktoum**
23 SEAT OF MARS (IRE), b g Yeats (IRE)—Haraplata (GER) **Mr P. A. Abberley**

MR J. W. HILLS - Continued

24 **SECURE CLOUD (IRE)**, b g High Chaparral (IRE)—Cabo (FR) **Prolinx Limited**
25 **SYNONYM (ITY)**, ch f Haatef (USA)—Shatarah **G. P. Troeller**

TWO-YEAR-OLDS

26 Ch c 7/5 Mastercraftsman (IRE)—Al Amlah (USA) (Riverman (USA)) **Gary And Linnet Woodward**
27 B c 25/2 Henrythenavigator (USA)—Alegendinmyownmind (Cape Cross (IRE)) (60000)
28 **ALGAITH (USA)**, b c 27/3 Dubawi (IRE)—Atayeb (Rahy (USA)) **Hamdan Al Maktoum**
29 **BAYLAY (USA)**, b c 8/3 Blame (USA)—Rock Candy (Mineshaft (USA)) (175284) **Hamdan Al Maktoum**
30 B f 3/3 Mawatheeq (USA)—Efisio's Star (Efisio) **Mr Khalil Al Sayegh**
31 Gr f 14/4 Starspangledbanner (AUS)—Enchanting Way (Linamix (FR)) (9523)
32 **FADHAYYIL (IRE)**, b f 8/2 Tamayuz—Ziria (IRE) (Danehill Dancer (IRE)) (220000) **Hamdan Al Maktoum**
33 B c 31/3 Montjeu (IRE)—Janoubi (Dansili) (22000)
34 **KAFAALA (IRE)**, b f 28/4 Shamardal (USA)—Hammiya (IRE) (Darshaan) **Hamdan Al Maktoum**
35 **KIBAAR**, b c 27/3 Pastoral Pursuits—Ashes (IRE) (General Monash (USA)) (95238) **Hamdan Al Maktoum**
36 **LYFKA**, ch f 30/3 Kheleyf (USA)—Tarkamara (IRE) (Medicean) **A. H. Robinson**
37 **MARKAZ (IRE)**, gr c 26/3 Dark Angel (IRE)—Folga (Atraf) (190476) **Hamdan Al Maktoum**
38 **MOHATEM (USA)**, ch c 26/3 Distorted Humor (USA)—
    Soul Search (USA) (A P Indy (USA)) (350569) **Hamdan Al Maktoum**
39 **MOONADEE (USA)**, gr c 14/4 Haatef (USA)—
    Again Royale (IRE) (Royal Academy (USA)) (85171) **Hamdan Al Maktoum**
40 **MUFFARREH (USA)**, b c 21/2 First Samurai (USA)—Sarayir (USA) (Mr Prospector (USA)) **Hamdan Al Maktoum**
41 **MUGHARRED**, b c 23/4 Bernardini (USA)—Wid (USA) (Elusive Quality (USA)) **Hamdan Al Maktoum**
42 **MUZARKASH**, b c 14/2 Kyllachy—Quinzey's Best (IRE) (King's Best (USA)) (59047) **Hamdan Al Maktoum**
43 **NAFAQA (IRE)**, b c 14/3 Sir Percy—Maghya (IRE) (Mujahid (USA)) **Hamdan Al Maktoum**
44 **SAHAAFY (USA)**, b c 1/2 Kitten's Joy (USA)—
    Queen's Causeway (USA) (Giant's Causeway (USA)) (151913) **Hamdan Al Maktoum**
45 **SARHAAN**, b c 3/5 New Approach (IRE)—Coveted (Sinndar (IRE)) (120000) **Hamdan Al Maktoum**
46 B f 27/2 Vale of York (IRE)—Silvertine (IRE) (Alzao (USA)) (19357)
47 **SIRDAAB (USA)**, b c 20/2 City Zip (USA)—
    Stormy Union (USA) (Dixie Union (USA)) (81799) **Hamdan Al Maktoum**
48 **TAFAHOM (IRE)**, b c 8/4 Acclamation—Dance Set (Selkirk (USA)) (110000) **Hamdan Al Maktoum**
49 **TANSFEEQ**, b c 6/4 Aqlaam—Qelaan (USA) (Dynaformer (USA)) **Hamdan Al Maktoum**
50 **TEDHKAAR (IRE)**, b f 30/4 Teofilo (IRE)—Merayaat (IRE) (Darshaan) **Hamdan Al Maktoum**
51 Br f 7/3 Pastoral Pursuits—Toffee Vodka (IRE) (Danehill Dancer (IRE)) (19047) **Gary & Linnet Woodward**

Other Owners: Asia VIP Club Ltd, Mr Michael Baxter, Mr Robert Benton, Mr Duncan Carmichael-Jack, Mr Nick Clark, Mr Michael Constantinidi, Mr Chris Davis, Mrs Gill Flanagan, Mr D. Fulford, Mr Andy Geary, Mr Paul Gold, Mr Jim Hackett, Mrs Susanna Heinemann, Mr Martin Hough, Mr Mark Hough, Mr Neil Ledger, Lord Lloyd Webber, Mrs J. Magnier, Mr John Marshall, Mr Pat McDonagh, Mr Ian Morris, Mr Alan Prince, Mr Maurice Randall, Mrs Eve Scott, Mr P. Shanahan, Mr Peter Shearlock, Mr Peter Stopp, Mrs Patsy Todd, Mr Luke Tofts, Mr Peter Vanderborgh, Mr T. Waspe, Mr Eddie Wong, Mr Cy Woodward.

Apprentice: Tyler Saunders.

---

320 | **MR MARK HOAD, Lewes**
Postal: **Windmill Lodge Stables, Spital Road, Lewes, East Sussex, BN7 1LS**
Contacts: PHONE **(01273) 477124/(01273) 480691 FAX (01273) 477124 MOBILE (07742) 446168**
E-MAIL markhoad@aol.com

1 **ALFIE ALEXANDER (IRE)**, 6, b g Indian Danehill (IRE)—Bella Galiana (ITY) **Mrs L. Bangs**
2 **DOCTOR HILARY**, 12, b g Mujahid (USA)—Agony Aunt **J. Baden White**
3 **MAFI (IRE)**, 6, b g Modigliani (USA)—Yulara (IRE) **Mrs J. E. Taylor**
4 **TAX REFORM (IRE)**, 4, b g Namid—Happy Flight (IRE) **Mr M. R. Baldry**
5 **TIROL LIVIT (IRE)**, 11, ch g Titus Livius (FR)—Orange Royale (IRE) **Baldry/Sharp Racing**
6 **TOTAL OBSESSION**, 7, b m Mujahid (USA)—Buon Amici **Miss H. S. Matthews**

THREE-YEAR-OLDS

7 **SEBS SENSEI (IRE)**, ch c Art Connoisseur (IRE)—Capetown Girl **Mr M. J. Huxley**

Other Owners: P. J. Sharp.

321 MR PHILIP HOBBS, Minehead

Postal: Sandhill, Bilbrook, Minehead, Somerset, TA24 6HA
Contacts: PHONE (01984) 640366 FAX (01984) 641124 MOBILE (07860) 729795
E-MAIL pjhobbs@pjhobbs.com WEBSITE www.pjhobbs.com

1 ACCORDING TO SARAH (IRE), 6, ch m Golan (IRE)—Miss Accordion (IRE) P. J. Hobbs
2 AL ALFA, 7, ch g Alflora (IRE)—Two For Joy (IRE) The Hon J. R. Drummond
3 ALLTHEKINGSHORSES (IRE), 8, b g King's Theatre (IRE)—Penny Brae (IRE) R Triple H
4 AUGUST HILL (IRE), 6, b m Presenting—Nuit des Chartreux (FR) Mrs Caren Walsh & Mrs Kathleen Quinn
5 BALLYGARVEY (FR), 8, b g Laveron—Vollore (FR) The Dark Horse Syndicate
6 BALLYTOBER, 8, b g Kahyasi—Full of Birds (FR) Mrs D. L. Whateley
7 BALTHAZAR KING (IRE), 10, b g King's Theatre (IRE)—Afdala (IRE) The Brushmakers
8 BERKELEY BARRON (IRE), 6, b g Subtle Power (IRE)—Roseabel (GER) Mrs E. A. Prowting
9 BERTIE BORU (IRE), 7, b g Brian Boru—Sleeven Lady Unity Farm Holiday Centre Ltd
10 BIG EASY (GER), 7, b g Ransom O'war (USA)—Basilea Gold (GER) J. T. Warner
11 BILBROOK BLAZE, 4, b g Kayf Tara—Za Beau (IRE) Owners For Owners: Bilbrook Blaze
12 BINCOMBE, 8, gr g Indian Danehill (IRE)—Siroyalta (FR) M. Short
13 4, B g Midnight Legend—Bobbie Dee Louisville Syndicate II
14 BREAN PLAY PERCY, 4, b g Tobougg (IRE)—Jenny From Brean Unity Farm Holiday Centre Ltd
15 BROTHER TEDD, 5, gr g Kayf Tara—Neltina Scrase Farms
16 CALUSA STAR, 5, b g Multiplex—Pugnacious Lady P. Luff
17 CAPTAIN CHRIS (IRE), 10, b g King's Theatre (IRE)—Function Dream (IRE) Mrs D. L. Whateley
18 CARRIGMORNA KING (IRE), 8, b g King's Theatre (IRE)—Carrigmorna Flyer (IRE) R. & Mrs J. E. Gibbs
19 CHAMPAGNE WEST (IRE), 6, b g Westerner—Wyndham Sweetmarie (IRE) R. S. Brookhouse
20 CHANCE DU ROY (FR), 10, ch g Morespeed—La Chance Au Roy (FR) Miss I. D. Du Pre
21 CHELTENIAN (FR), 8, b g Astarabad (USA)—Salamaite (FR) R. S. Brookhouse
22 CLOUD CREEPER (IRE), 7, b g Cloudings (IRE)—First of April (IRE) Mick Fitzgerald Racing Club
23 COLOUR SQUADRON (IRE), 8, b g Old Vic—That's The Goose (IRE) J. P. McManus
24 DANANDY (IRE), 7, b g Cloudings (IRE)—Tower Princess (IRE) Ms M. Ryan
25 5, Br m Presenting—Dara's Pride (IRE) P. J. Hobbs
26 DE LA BECH, 7, ch g Karinga Bay—Vallis Vale B. K. Peppiatt
27 DOCTOR FOXTROT (IRE), 9, b g Milan—French Life (IRE) Dr V. M. G. Ferguson
28 DREAMS AND SONGS, 6, ch m Presenting—Karello Bay D. J. Burke
29 DUKE OF LUCCA (IRE), 9, b g Milan—Derravaragh Native (IRE) Mrs L. H. Field
30 DUNRAVEN STORM (IRE), 9, br g Presenting—Foxfire Mrs K. V. Vann
31 FILBERT (IRE), 8, b g Oscar (IRE)—Coca's Well (IRE) R Triple H
32 FINGAL BAY (IRE), 8, b g King's Theatre (IRE)—Lady Marguerrite Mrs C. Skan
33 FREE OF CHARGE (IRE), 5, ch g Stowaway—Sweetasanu (IRE) A. P. Staple
34 GARDE LA VICTOIRE (FR), 5, b g Kapgarde (FR)—Next Victory (FR) Mrs D. L. Whateley
35 GAS LINE BOY (IRE), 8, b g Blueprint (IRE)—Jervia Mick Fitzgerald Racing Club
36 GAUVAIN (GER), 12, b g Sternkoenig (IRE)—Gamina (GER) The Spoofers
37 GEORGIE LAD (IRE), 6, b g Gold Well—Top Step (IRE) D R Peppiatt & Partners (Georgie Lad)
38 HELLO GEORGE (IRE), 5, b g Westerner—Top Ar Aghaidh (IRE) M. St Quinton/ C. Hellyer/ M. Strong
39 HORIZONTAL SPEED (IRE), 6, b g Vertical Speed (FR)—Rockababy (IRE) Favourites Racing Ltd
40 IF IN DOUBT (IRE), 6, b g Heron Island (IRE)—Catchers Day (IRE) J. P. McManus
41 IMPERIAL CIRCUS (IRE), 8, b g Beneficial—Aunty Dawn (IRE) R. A. S. Offer
42 4, Ch g Shirocco (GER)—Impudent (IRE) Mrs D. L. Whateley
43 IRISH BUCCANEER (IRE), 7, b g Milan—Supreme Serenade (IRE) J. P. McManus
44 JAYANDBEE (IRE), 7, b g Presenting—Christines Gale (IRE) J & B Gibbs & Sons Ltd
45 KARTANIAN (IRE), 8, br g Kalanisi (IRE)—Katiykha (IRE) Louisville Syndicate III
46 KUBLAI (FR), 4, b g Laveron—Java Dawn (IRE) Mr D. W. Hill
47 LADY CHARISMA, 5, b m Presenting—Lady Cad (FR) Owners For Owners: Lady Charisma
48 LAMB OR COD (IRE), 7, ch g Old Vic—Princess Lizzie J. T. Warner
49 LORD LESCRIBAA (FR), 11, b g Ungaro (GER)—Manon Lescribaa (FR) Mrs S. Hobbs
50 LORD PROTECTOR (IRE), 7, b g Oscar (IRE)—Warts And All (IRE) Louisville Syndicate
51 MEETMEATTHEMOON (IRE), 5, gr m Flemensfirth (USA)—Valleya (FR) Mrs C. J. Walsh
52 MEIRIG'S DREAM (IRE), 8, b g Golan (IRE)—Women In Love (IRE) Miss V. Dunn & Mr H. Davies
53 MENORAH (IRE), 9, b g King's Theatre (IRE)—Maid For Adventure (IRE) Mrs D. L. Whateley
54 MIGHTY MOBB (IRE), 7, b g Accordion—Dusty Lane (IRE) T. J. Hemmings
55 MILOSAM (IRE), 7, b g Milan—Lady Sam (IRE) R. J. Croker
56 MOORLANDS MIST, 7, gr g Fair Mix (IRE)—Sandford Springs (USA) J. T. Warner
57 MOUNTAIN KING, 5, b g Definite Article—Belle Magello (FR) Mrs D. L. Whateley
58 NEVILLE, 6, b g Revoque (IRE)—Dudeen (IRE) Mr M. Pendarves
59 NO LIKEY (IRE), 7, b g Helissio (FR)—Money Galore (IRE) The Country Side
60 ONENIGHTINVIENNA (IRE), 5, b g Oscar (IRE)—Be My Granny P. Luff
61 ORABORA, 8, b g Alflora (IRE)—Magic Orb Dr V. M. G. Ferguson

MR PHILIP HOBBS - Continued

62 **PATEESE (FR)**, 9, b g Priolo (USA)—Flyer (FR) **The Test Valley Partnership**
63 4, Br g Presenting—Paumafi (IRE) **P. J. Hobbs**
64 **PERSIAN SNOW (IRE)**, 8, b g Anshan—Alpine Message **D. R. Peppiatt**
65 **PISTOL (IRE)**, 5, b g High Chaparral (IRE)—Alinea (USA) **Clark, Devlin, Knox & Wells & Monroe**
66 **PLANET OF SOUND**, 12, b g Kayf Tara—Herald The Dawn **Mr C. G. M. Lloyd-Baker**
67 **POWERFUL ACTION (IRE)**, 6, b g Tau Ceti—Abbey The Leader (IRE) **Miss I. D. Du Pre**
68 **PRINCELY PLAYER (IRE)**, 7, b g King's Theatre (IRE)—Temptation (FR) **Thurloe 52**
69 **QUADRILLER (FR)**, 7, b g Lando (GER)—Tabachines (FR) **Ms M. Ryan**
70 **QUICK DECISSON (IRE)**, 6, b g Azamour (IRE)—Fleet River (USA) **Owners For Owners: Quick Decisson**
71 **QUINZ (FR)**, 10, b g Robin des Champs (FR)—Altesse du Mou (FR) **A. L. Cohen**
72 **RETURN SPRING (IRE)**, 7, b g Vinnie Roe (IRE)—Bettys Daughter (IRE) **D. J. Jones**
73 4, B f Beneficial—Returning **P. J. Hobbs**
74 **RIVER DEEP (IRE)**, 5, ch g Mountain High (IRE)—Testaway (IRE) **Bradley Partnership**
75 **ROALCO DE FARGES (FR)**, 9, gr g Dom Alco (FR)—Vonaria (FR) **The Brushmakers**
76 **ROB CONTI (FR)**, 9, b br g Network (GER)—Initiale Royale (FR) **D. Maxwell**
77 **ROLL THE DICE (IRE)**, 8, b g Oscar (IRE)—Sallowglen Gale (IRE) **The Kingpins**
78 **ROYAL PLAYER**, 5, b g King's Theatre (IRE)—Kaydee Queen (IRE) **Mrs D. L. Whateley**
79 **ROYAL REGATTA (IRE)**, 6, b g King's Theatre (IRE)—Friendly Craic (IRE) **Mr J C Murphy & Mrs L Field**
80 **SADDLERS ENCORE (IRE)**, 5, br g Presenting—Saddlers Leader (IRE) **R. & Mrs J. E. Gibbs**
81 **SAUSALITO SUNRISE (IRE)**, 6, b g Gold Well—Villaflor (IRE) **Mrs D. L. Whateley**
82 **SO FINE (IRE)**, 8, b br g Definite Article—Not So Green (IRE) **Mrs L. R. Lovell**
83 **STATE DEPARTMENT**, 7, b g Doyen (IRE)—Time For Tea (IRE) **P. J. Hobbs**
84 **TALKONTHESTREET (IRE)**, 7, b g Milan—Super Size (IRE) **Mrs D. L. Whateley**
85 **THE DISENGAGER (IRE)**, 10, b g Snurge—The Doctors Wife (IRE) **Govier & Brown**
86 **THE SKYFARMER**, 6, br g Presenting—Koral Bay (FR) **Mrs J. J. Peppiatt**
87 **THOMAS WILD**, 9, ch g Muhtarram (USA)—Bisque **C L T**
88 **THUNDERSTORM (IRE)**, 9, b g Milan—Elizabeth Tudor (IRE) **Mr J. P. McManus**
89 **TIQRIS**, 6, ch g Midnight Legend—Calamintha **R. S. Brookhouse**
90 **TONY STAR (FR)**, 7, b g Lone Bid (FR)—Effet de Star (FR) **Thurloe 51**
91 **TOOWOOMBA (IRE)**, 6, b g Milan—Lillies Bordello (IRE) **Michael Watt, J A McGrath, The Anzacs**
92 **TRICKAWAY (IRE)**, 6, b g Stowaway—Rosie's Trix (IRE) **The Mount Fawcus Partnership**
93 **TRIGGERMAN**, 12, b g Double Trigger (IRE)—Carrikins **M. G. St Quinton**
94 **UNCLE JIMMY (IRE)**, 7, b br g Alderbrook—Carrabawn **Mr A. R. E. Ash**
95 **VAL D'ARC (FR)**, 5, b g Le Balafre (FR)—Lextrienne (FR) **Thurloe 54**
96 **VILLAGE VIC (IRE)**, 7, b g Old Vic—Etoile Margot (FR) **A. E. Peterson**
97 **VODKAONTHEROCKS (IRE)**, 6, b g Oscar (IRE)—My Native (IRE) **Walters Plant Hire Ltd**
98 **WALTER WHITE (IRE)**, 4, b g Dark Angel (IRE)—Fun Time **Walter White Partnership**
99 **WESTERN JO (IRE)**, 6, b g Westerner—Jenny's Jewel (IRE) **T. J. Hemmings**
100 **WESTERN MOVIE**, 6, b g Westerner—Fortune's Girl **M. H. Watt**
101 **WHO'S JEFF (IRE)**, 6, b g Westerner—Kitty Maher (IRE) **Coalville Glass & Glazing Ltd**
102 **WISHFULL THINKING**, 11, ch g Alflora (IRE)—Poussetiere Deux (FR) **Mrs D. L. Whateley**
103 **WOODFORD COUNTY**, 7, b g Sonus (IRE)—Moylena **E & A England and A & A Heywood**
104 4, B g King's Theatre (IRE)—Wyndham Sweetmarie (IRE)

Other Owners: Mr R. B. Antell, Mr D. J. Baker, Mr J. A. Barnes, G. S. Brown, P. C. Browne, J. Burley, C. J. Butler, Mr A. J. Chapman, Mr G. P. A. Clark, Mrs C. A. Clarke, Mr J. P. Cooper, H. J. Davies, Mr C. J. Dendy, R. W. Devlin, Miss V. C. Dunn, Mr T. J. Dykes, Mr A. D. England, Mrs E. England, Mr J. Fairrie, Mrs M. W. Fawcus, Mr S. S. Fawcus, H. R. Gibbs, Mrs J. E. Gibbs, Mrs C. F. Godsall, Mr M. G. Godsall, Mr P. Govier, Mr P. F. Govier, Mr R. H. M. Grant, Mr T. M. Hailstone, J. R. Hall, S. R. Harman, C. G. Hellyer, Mr A. H. Heywood, Mr A. S. Heywood, Mr J. R. Holmes, Mr E. J. Hughes, Mr B. R. Ingram, Mr S. Kidston, Knox & Wells Limited, Mr D. Lockwood, Mr A. P. Maddox, Mr T. J. Malone, Miss N. Martin, J. A. McGrath, Mr J. R. Monroe, J. C. Murphy, Mr I. A. Nunn, Mr T. E. Olver, O. J. W. Pawle, N. D. Peppiatt, Mr A. C. Phillips, Miss J. Pimblett, Mrs K. Quinn, D. A. Rees, Mr M. C. Sargent, N. C. Savery, Mrs J. E. Scrase, Mr J. M. Scrase, Mr N. D. Scrase, Mr J. Simpson, Mr J. A. B. Stafford, M. A. Strong, M. A. Swift, C. J. M. Walker, Mrs J. C. P. Walter, T. C. Wheeler, Mrs T. S. Wheeler, Mr R. M. E. Wright.

Assistant Trainer: Richard White

Jockey (NH): Richard Johnson, Tom O'Brien. **Conditional:** James Best, Tom Cheesman, Chris Davies, Micheal Nolan. **Amateur:** Mr Ciaran Gethings, Mr Conor Smith.

MR RICHARD HOBSON, Barnstaple
Postal: Higher Shutscombe, Charles, Brayford, Barnstaple, Devon, EX32 7PU

1 **SAMBULANDO (FR)**, 11, gr g Kouroun (FR)—Somnambula (IRE) **Mr R. H. Hobson**

323 | MR RON HODGES, Somerton
Postal: **Bull Brook Stables, West Charlton, Charlton Mackrell, Somerton, Somerset, TA11 7AL**
Contacts: **PHONE (01458) 223922 FAX (01458) 223969 MOBILE (07770) 625846**
E-MAIL mandyhodges@btconnect.com

1 **ACTONETAKETWO**, 4, b f Act One—Temple Dancer **Miss R. J. Dobson**
2 **ALFIE JOE**, 5, b g Bandmaster (USA)—The Grey Bam Bam **Mrs C. P. Taylor**
3 **CANTABILLY (IRE)**, 11, b g Distant Music (USA)—Cantaloupe **R. J. Hodges**
4 **DREAMS OF GLORY**, 6, ch h Resplendent Glory (IRE)—Pip's Dream **P. E. Axon**
5 **MILES OF SUNSHINE**, 9, b g Thowra (FR)—Rainbow Nation **The Gardens Entertainments Ltd**
6 **MISS TENACIOUS**, 7, b m Refuse To Bend (IRE)—Very Speed (USA) **John Frampton & Paul Frampton**
7 **MISTER MUSICMASTER**, 5, b g Amadeus Wolf—Misty Eyed (IRE) **Mrs L. Sharpe & Mrs S. G. Clapp**
8 **ONE LAST DREAM**, 5, ch g Resplendent Glory (IRE)—Pip's Dream **Mrs L. Sharpe & Mrs S. G. Clapp**
9 **PEARL (IRE)**, 10, b m Daylami (IRE)—Briery (IRE) **R. G. Andrews**
10 **TAMMIS**, 4, b f Whipper (USA)—Tamise (USA) **Miss R. J. Dobson**
11 **THE QUARTERJACK**, 5, b g Haafhd—Caressed **P. E. Axon**

THREE-YEAR-OLDS

12 **MY SECRET DREAM (FR)**, b f Stormy River (FR)—Aventure Secrete (FR) **P. E. Axon**
13 **THE FRENCH GREY (FR)**, gr f Stormy River (FR)—Khaliyna (IRE) **P. E. Axon**

Other Owners: Mrs S. G. Clapp, Mr J. L. Frampton, Mr Paul S. Frampton, Mr R. J. Hodges, Mrs L. Sharpe.

324 | MR SIMON HODGSON, Yeovil
Postal: **Queen Camel House Stables, Queen Camel, Yeovil, Somerset, BA22 7NF**
Contacts: **PHONE (01935) 851152**

1 **ATHWAAB**, 7, b m Cadeaux Genereux—Ahdaaf (USA) **Mrs L. M. Clarke**
2 **BASINGSTOKE (IRE)**, 5, b g Elusive City (USA)—Ryninch (IRE)
3 **BRIDGETOWN**, 6, gr g Beat All (USA)—Moon Magic **Mr M Truan & Miss Juliet E Reed**
4 7, B gr g Baryshnikov (AUS)—Jessinca **P. T. Newell**
5 **MICK DUGGAN**, 4, ch g Pivotal—Poppy Carew (IRE) **Mr M. A. Muddiman**
6 **NESTON GRACE**, 6, b m Kayf Tara—Politely **Dr N. J. Knott**
7 **NORPHIN**, 4, b c Norse Dancer (IRE)—Orphina (IRE) **Mr J. A. Mould**
8 **PONTE DI ROSA**, 6, b m Avonbridge—Ridgewood Ruby (IRE) **Reed, Mould, Gorley & Spershott**
9 **SNOW RIDGE**, 6, b g Iceman—Confetti **The Villains**
10 **STRONG CONVICTION**, 4, ch g Piccolo—Keeping The Faith (IRE) **George Materna & Mark Barrett**
11 **VEXILLUM (IRE)**, 5, br g Mujadil (USA)—Common Cause **J. Heaney**

THREE-YEAR-OLDS

12 **QUEEN CEE**, b f Royal Applause—Tee Cee **Simon Hodgson Racing Partnership 1**

TWO-YEAR-OLDS

13 **BROTHER NORPHIN**, b c 1/4 Norse Dancer (IRE)—Orphina (IRE) (Orpen (USA)) **Mr J. A. Mould**

Other Owners: M. Barrett, Mr A. A. Gorley, G. D. P. Materna, Mr S. A. J. Penny, Miss J. E. Reed, Mr D. G. Spershott, Mr M. R. Truan, L. R. Turland.

325 | MR EAMONN M. HOGAN, Roscam
Postal: **Rosshill, Roscam, Galway, Co. Galway. Ireland**
Contacts: **PHONE (00353) 91756899 MOBILE (00353) 879175175**
E-MAIL rosshillfarm@eircom.net

1 **ALL THE ACES (IRE)**, 9, b g Spartacus (IRE)—Lili Cup (FR) **E. M. Hogan**
2 **ASTEROID BELT (IRE)**, 5, ch g Heliostatic (IRE)—Affaire Royale (IRE) **D.M. Greally**
3 4, B g Oscar (IRE)—Back To Bavaria (IRE) **B. M. Hogan**
4 **MONTOYA'S SON (IRE)**, 9, ch g Flemensfirth (USA)—Over The Grand (IRE) **Mary Hogan**

THREE-YEAR-OLDS

5 B g Olden Times—Tokay **D. M. Greally**

Jockey (flat): Fran Berry.

326 **MR HENRY HOGARTH, Stillington**
Postal: **New Grange Farm, Stillington, York, YO61 1LR**
Contacts: **PHONE (01347) 811168 FAX (01347) 811168 MOBILE (07788) 777044**
E-MAIL harryhogarth@gmail.com

1 DENY, 6, ch g Mr Greeley (USA)—Sulk (IRE) **Hogarth Racing**
2 DUNDEE BLUE (IRE), 6, gr g Cloudings (IRE)—Eurolucy (IRE) **Hogarth Racing**
3 ENCORE UN FOIS, 6, br g Val Royal (FR)—Factice (USA) **Hogarth Racing**
4 IFANDBUTWHY (IRE), 12, b g Raise A Grand (USA)—Cockney Ground (IRE) **Hogarth Racing**
5 LAKEFIELD REBEL (IRE), 8, b br g Presenting—River Mousa (IRE) **Hogarth Racing**
6 MASTER CONOR (IRE), 8, b g Classic Cliche (IRE)—Shuil Iontach (IRE) **Hogarth Racing**
7 OVER AND ABOVE (IRE), 8, b g Overbury (IRE)—Rose Gold (IRE) **Hogarth Racing**
8 PAMAK D'AIRY (FR), 11, b g Cadoubel (FR)—Gamaska d'airy (FR) **Hogarth Racing**
9 PIERRERS BOUNTY (IRE), 7, b g Pierre—Willow Stream (IRE) **Hogarth Racing**
10 ROJO VIVO, 8, b g Deploy—Shareef Walk **Hogarth Racing**
11 ROZENER (IRE), 8, b g Moscow Society (USA)—David's Lass (IRE) **Hogarth Racing**
12 WELL RELATED, 7, ch g Prince Daniel (USA)—Wynyard Lady **Hogarth Racing**

Other Owners: Mr H. P. Hogarth, Mr P. H. Hogarth, Mr J. Hogarth, Mr J. L. Hogarth.

Jockey (NH): Ritchie McGrath. **Conditional:** Tony Kelly.

---

327 **MR ALAN HOLLINGSWORTH, Feckenham**
Postal: **Lanket House, Crofts Lane, Feckenham, Redditch, Worcestershire, B96 6PU**
Contacts: **PHONE (01527) 68644/892054 FAX (01527) 60310 MOBILE (07775) 670644**
E-MAIL kombined@btconnect.com

1 AGITATION, 10, b g Cloudings (IRE)—Shadowgraff
2 8, B m Alflora (IRE)—An Bothar Dubh
3 5, B m Kayf Tara—An Bothar Dubh
4 BEE BUMBLE, 9, b g Alflora (IRE)—Shadowgraff
5 CLEETONS TURN, 7, b g Alflora (IRE)—Indyana Run
6 RIN TIN TIN, 7, br g Alflora (IRE)—Celtic Tore (IRE)

Assistant Trainer: Sharon Smith

Jockey (NH): James Davies, Nick Scholfield.

---

328 **MR ANDREW HOLLINSHEAD, Upper Longdon**
Postal: **Lodge Farm, Upper Longdon, Rugeley, Staffordshire, WS15 1QF**
Contacts: **PHONE (01543) 490298**

1 AMBITIOUS BOY, 5, bl g Striking Ambition—Cherished Love (IRE) **Mr C. W. Wardle & Mrs J. E. Wardle**
2 ASTONISHED HARRY (GER), 5, b g Dubai Destination (USA)—Aijala (FR) **D. Coppenhall**
3 AUREOLIN GULF, 5, b g Proclamation (IRE)—Vermilion Creek **M. A. N. Johnson**
4 BILASH, 7, gr g Choisir (AUS)—Goldeva **Pyle & Hollinshead**
5 BOLLIN ACROSS, 6, b m Bollin Eric—Miss Lacroix **Mrs N. S. Harris**
6 CADMIUM LOCH, 6, b g Needwood Blade—Vermilion Creek **M. A. N. Johnson**
7 CLOUDY SPIRIT, 9, gr m Silver Patriarch (IRE)—Miss Lacroix **Mrs N. S. Harris**
8 DANGER IN THE PARK, 5, ch g Central Park (IRE)—Danger Bird (IRE) **Mrs J. M. Rowe**
9 DHA CHARA (IRE), 4, b g Ramonti (FR)—Campiglia (IRE) **Mr N. S. Sweeney**
10 EASTERN MAGIC, 7, b g Observatory (USA)—Inchtina **Mrs C. A. Stevenson**
11 EYELINE, 4, b g Needwood Blade—Waterline Twenty (IRE) **X8 Racing Partnership 1**
12 FOURSQUARE FUNTIME, 5, b g Common World (USA)—Farina (IRE) **T. Kelly**
13 LACEY, 5, b g Rail Link—Shamana (USA) **Mr N. S. Sweeney**
14 LADY FAYE, 5, b m Multiplex—Rebel County (IRE) **Mr S. A. Ewart**
15 LINEMAN, 4, b g Rail Link—Shamana (USA) **The HRH Trio**
16 LORD PAGET, 5, b g Three Valleys (USA)—Appelone **Exors of the Late Mr R. Hollinshead**
17 MADAME ELIZABETH, 4, b f Multiplex—Madame Jones (IRE) **David Lockwood & Fred Lockwood**
18 MATERIANA (IRE), 6, b br m Presenting—Jay Lo (IRE) **David Lockwood & Fred Lockwood**
19 MOORWAY (IRE), 4, b g Dylan Thomas (IRE)—Cordelia **Moores Metals Ltd**
20 MOUNT HOLLOW, 9, b g Beat Hollow—Lady Lindsay (IRE) **Mr P. A. Shaw**
21 NATALIA, 5, ch m Dutch Art—Pintle **Robert Heathcote**
22 ONE SCOOP OR TWO, 8, b g Needwood Blade—Rebel County (IRE) **Mr S. A. Ewart**

MR ANDREW HOLLINSHEAD - Continued

23 **RAPID HEAT LAD (IRE)**, 5, b g Aussie Rules (USA)—Alwiyda (USA) **Graham Brothers Racing Partnership**
24 **SCARLET STRAND**, 4, b f Pastoral Pursuits—Vermilion Creek **M. A. N. Johnson**
25 **SEWN UP**, 4, ch c Compton Place—Broughton Bounty **J. L. Marriott**
26 **SNOWY DAWN**, 4, gr g Notnowcato—Tereyna **Mrs C. A. Stevenson**
27 **SPANISH PLUME**, 6, b g Ishiguru (USA)—Miss Up N Go **The Three R's**
28 **STRAVERSJOY**, 7, b m Kayf Tara—Stravsea **Miss S. A. Hollinshead**
29 **STRIKING ECHO**, 4, b g Striking Ambition—Sunderland Echo (IRE) **Mr G. Lloyd**
30 **TEPMOKEA (IRE)**, 8, ch g Noverre (USA)—Eroica (GER) **Hollinshead Chapman & Evitt**
31 **UNCLE BERNIE (IRE)**, 4, gr g Aussie Rules (USA)—Alwiyda (USA) **Graham Brothers Racing Partnership**
32 **WELL OWD MON**, 4, b g Vitus—Farina (IRE) **The Giddy Gang**
33 **ZENAFIRE**, 5, b h Firebreak—Zen Garden **E Coquelin R Moseley**

THREE-YEAR-OLDS

34 **ESSANAR**, br g Notnowcato—Spirito Libro (USA) **Mr Paul Shaw & Mr Mark Round**
35 **FLYING CAPE (IRE)**, b g Cape Cross (IRE)—Reine Zao (FR) **J. L. Marriott**
36 **WHITBY HIGH LIGHT**, b g Halling (USA)—Ballroom Dancer (IRE) **N. Chapman**

TWO-YEAR-OLDS

37 B g 24/2 Notnowcato—Gilah (IRE) (Saddlers' Hall (IRE)) (23228)
38 B f 8/2 Jeremy (USA)—Mawaared (Machiavellian (USA)) (10840) **J. L. Marriott**
39 B g 15/2 Azamour (IRE)—Snowpalm (Halling (USA)) (13162) **J. L. Marriott**

Other Owners: Mrs E. M. Coquelin, Mr P. Edwards, Mr J. P. Evitt, Mr A. M. Graham, Mr M. P. Graham, D. R. Horne, Mr A. Lawrence, Mr E. T. D. Leadbeater, D. J. Lockwood, Mr F. M. Lockwood, A. L. Marriott, Mr R. J. R. Moseley, M. J. F. Pyle, Mrs T. P. Pyle, R. Robinson, Mr M. D. Round, C. W. Wardle, Mrs J. E. Wardle.

---

329 MRS STEPH HOLLINSHEAD, Rugeley

Postal: **Deva House, Bardy Lane, Longdon, Rugeley, Staffordshire, WS15 4LJ**
Contacts: **PHONE (01543) 493656 MOBILE (07791) 385335**
E-MAIL steph@schracing.co.uk

1 **HIDDEN TALENT**, 4, b g Kyllachy—Creative Mind (IRE) **Brownhills Barmy Army Partnership**
2 **LINDEN ROSE**, 5, b m Striking Ambition—Inchtina **Mrs L. A. Hollinshead**
3 **LOULOU VUITTON**, 4, ch f Needwood Blade—Shepherds Warning (IRE) **Mr M. F. Hamblett**
4 **MIDNIGHT MEMORIES**, 4, ch f Midnight Legend—Bajan Blue **No More Excuses**
5 **MY MATE MAX**, 9, b g Fraam—Victory Flip (IRE)

TWO-YEAR-OLDS

6 **HAZEL'S SONG**, b f 3/3 Orpen (USA)—Songbook (Singspiel (IRE))
7 B f 2/4 Multiplex—Song of The Desert (Desert Sun) (761)
8 Ro f 6/4 Hellvelyn—Tharwa (IRE) (Last Tycoon) (9523)
9 B f 17/3 Pastoral Pursuits—Vermilion Creek (Makbul)

Other Owners: Mr M. Evans, Mr S. Hamblett, Mrs S. C. Hawkins, Mrs C. A. Stevenson, Dr H. J. F. Why, Mrs J. A. Why.

Assistant Trainer: Adam Hawkins

---

330 MR PATRICK HOLMES, Middleham

Postal: **Little Spigot, Coverham, Middleham, Leyburn, North Yorkshire, DL8 4TL**
Contacts: **PHONE (01347) 889008 MOBILE (07740) 589857**
E-MAIL patrick@foulriceparkracing.com WEBSITE www.foulriceparkracing.com

1 **BEAR ISLAND FLINT**, 6, br g Overbury (IRE)—Chippewa (FR) **Mrs C M Clarke, Foulrice Park Racing Ltd**
2 **BOW FIDDLE (IRE)**, 8, br m Anshan—Elite Racing **Mrs A. M. Stirling**
3 **COAX**, 6, b g Red Ransom (USA)—True Glory (IRE) **Foulrice Park Racing Limited**
4 **DORLESH WAY (IRE)**, 7, ch g Rakti—Patalavaca (GER) **Di Midwinter Foulrice Park Racing Ltd**
5 **FOOT THE BILL**, 9, b g Generous (IRE)—Proudfoot (IRE) **Mr C. R. Stirling**
6 **GOLDEN GROOM**, 11, b g Groom Dancer (USA)—Reine de Thebes (FR) **Mr C. R. Stirling**
7 **IMPERATOR AUGUSTUS (IRE)**, 6, b g Holy Roman Emperor (IRE)—Coralita (IRE) **Foulrice Park Racing Limited**
8 **LIL SOPHELLA (IRE)**, 5, ch m Indian Haven—Discotheque (USA) **Foulrice Park Racing Limited**
9 **MAILLOT JAUNE (IRE)**, 4, b f Ramonti (FR)—Roclette (USA) **FPR Syndicate 1**
10 **MRS GORSKY**, 4, b f Duke of Marmalade (IRE)—Dowager **Foulrice Park Racing Limited**

MR PATRICK HOLMES - Continued

11 **NEWBURY STREET**, 7, b g Namid—Cautious Joe **Foulrice Park Racing Limited**
12 **REX ROMANORUM (IRE)**, 6, b g Holy Roman Emperor (IRE)—Willowbridge (IRE) **Foulrice Park Racing Limited**
13 **SLIP OF A GIRL (IRE)**, 4, b f Strategic Prince—Fig Leaf (FR) **FPR Syndicate 2**
14 **TIME OF MY LIFE (IRE)**, 5, b g Galileo (IRE)—In My Life (IRE) **Mrs C M Clarke, Foulrice Park Racing Ltd**
15 **VOICE FROM ABOVE (IRE)**, 5, b m Strategic Prince—Basin Street Blues (IRE) **Grange Park Racing**
16 **YOURHOLIDAYISOVER (IRE)**, 7, ch g Sulamani (IRE)—Whitehaven **Foulrice Park Racing Limited**

THREE-YEAR-OLDS

17 **PROSTATE AWARENESS (IRE)**, b c Camacho—Genuinely (IRE) **Mr C. Peach**

Other Owners: Mrs C. M. Clarke, A. D. Crombie, Miss D. Midwinter, Mr E. Surr.

---

331 **MR JOHN HOLT, Peckleton**
Postal: Hall Farm, Church Road, Peckleton, Leicester
Contacts: PHONE/FAX (01455) 821972 MOBILE (07850) 321059
E-MAIL hallfarmracing@btconnect.com WEBSITE www.hallfarmracing.co.uk

1 **EMPERATRIZ**, 4, b f Holy Roman Emperor (IRE)—Fairmont (IRE) **Mr E. Boumans**
2 **IZZA DIVA**, 6, b m Nomadic Way (USA)—Pebbles Moonlight (IRE) **Mr P. R. Burgess**
3 **METAL MICKY**, 7, ch g First Trump—Luvvie One (IRE)
4 **MINI'S DESTINATION**, 6, b m Dubai Destination (USA)—Heather Mix **J. R. Holt**
5 **NOMADIC WARRIOR**, 9, b g Nomadic Way (USA)—Jesmund **Ms C. A. Lacey**
6 **NUMBER THEORY**, 6, b g Halling (USA)—Numanthia (IRE) **Mr M. S. Fonseka**
7 **RAZERA (IRE)**, 4, b g Dylan Thomas (IRE)—Rahila (IRE) **J. R. Holt**

THREE-YEAR-OLDS

8 **DUTCH LADY**, ch f Dutch Art—Tattling **David Botterill & John Guest**
9 **FLAMING STAR**, b f Firebreak—Day Star
10 **FOXTROT PEARL (IRE)**, b f Bahamian Bounty—Nina Blini **J. R. Holt**
11 **GOADBY**, gr f Kodiac—Gone Sailing **Cleartherm Glass Sealed Units Ltd**
12 **MARY'S PRAYER**, b f Champs Elysees—Phi Phi (IRE) **Get Fresh Investments Ltd**
13 **SWEET SUMMER**, ch f Sakhee (USA)—Sweet Reply **Mrs P. Y. Page**

TWO-YEAR-OLDS

14 **CHANSON DE MARINS (FR)**, b f 12/2 Le Havre (IRE)—Easy To Sing (Johannesburg (USA)) **M. Bass & R. Smith**

Other Owners: M. P. Bass, D. R. Botterill, Mr J. J. Guest, Mr R. L. Smith.

Assistant Trainer: Jessica Holt

---

332 **MR ANTHONY HONEYBALL, Beaminster**
Postal: Potwell Farm, Mosterton, Beaminster, Dorset, DT8 3HG
Contacts: PHONE (01308) 867452 MOBILE (07815) 898569
E-MAIL a.honeyballracing@btinternet.com WEBSITE www.ajhoneyballracing.co.uk

1 **ANDA DE GRISSAY**, 4, b f Network (GER)—Karima II (FR) **The Deauville Connection**
2 **AS DE FER (FR)**, 8, b g Passing Sale (FR)—Miss Hollywood (FR) **Midd Shire Racing**
3 **CHANTARA ROSE**, 5, br m Kayf Tara—Fragrant Rose **Steve & Jackie Fleetham**
4 **CHILL FACTOR (IRE)**, 5, b g Oscar (IRE)—Glacial Princess (IRE) **Potwell Partners**
5 **CITY SUPREME (IRE)**, 4, b g Milan—Run Supreme (IRE) **San Siro Six**
6 4, B f Midnight Legend—Cresswell Willow (IRE) **A. Honeyball**
7 **DANIMIX (IRE)**, 9, b g Dr Massini (IRE)—Spring Blend (IRE) **Steve & Jackie Fleetham**
8 **DESERT QUEEN**, 6, b m Desert King (IRE)—Priscilla **H. T. Cole**
9 **DORSET NAGA**, 8, b g Alflora (IRE)—Tellicherry **Steve & Jackie Fleetham**
10 **DOUBLE ACCORD**, 4, ch f Double Trigger (IRE)—Got Tune (IRE) **R W Huggins & Atlantic Racing**
11 **FOUNTAINS FLYPAST**, 10, b g Broadway Flyer (USA)—Miss Flower Girl **The Fountains Partnership**
12 **FOUNTAINS MARY**, 6, gr m Midnight Legend—Carswell Mayfly VII **Mrs M. H. Bowden**
13 **GOLAN SILK**, 4, b g Golan (IRE)—Silk Daisy **R W Huggins & Atlantic Racing**
14 **HORACE HAZEL**, 5, b g Sir Harry Lewis (USA)—Kaream **T. C. Frost**
15 **JACKIES SOLITAIRE**, 5, ch m Generous (IRE)—Bond Solitaire **Steve & Jackie Fleetham**
16 **JAJA DE JAU**, 5, br m Sakhee (USA)—Jadidh **Anthony Honeyball Racing Club Ltd**
17 **JULLY LES BUXY**, 4, b f Black Sam Bellamy (IRE)—Jadidh **Mr A. F. G. Brimble**

MR ANTHONY HONEYBALL - Continued

18 **LILY WAUGH (IRE)**, 7, b m King's Theatre (IRE)—Killultagh Dawn (IRE) **Go To War**
19 **MAN OF LEISURE**, 10, b g Karinga Bay—Girl of Pleasure (IRE) **Anthony Honeyball Racing Club Ltd**
20 **MARIE DES ANGES (FR)**, 6, b m Ballingarry (IRE)—No Coincidence (IRE) **Atlantic Racing & R. W. Huggins**
21 **MIDNIGHT MINX**, 7, b m Midnight Legend—Phar Breeze (IRE) **Mrs J. M. E. Mann**
22 **ON THE MOVE**, 6, b m Sir Harry Lewis (USA)—What A Mover **John & Heather Snook**
23 **OSCARTEEA (IRE)**, 5, b g Oscar (IRE)—Miss Arteea (IRE) **Steve & Jackie Fleetham**
24 **REGAL ENCORE (IRE)**, 6, b g King's Theatre (IRE)—Go On Eileen (IRE) **J. P. McManus**
25 **ROUQUINE SAUVAGE**, 6, ch m Loup Sauvage (USA)—No Need For Alarm **J. P. McManus**
26 **ROYAL NATIVE (IRE)**, 6, b g King's Theatre (IRE)—Hollygrove Native (IRE) **Michael & Angela Bone**
27 **ROYAL SALUTE**, 4, br g Flemensfirth (USA)—Loxhill Lady **Distillery Stud**
28 **ROYAL SWAIN (IRE)**, 8, b g Val Royal (FR)—Targhyb (IRE) **Steve & Jackie Fleetham**
29 **ROYALE'S LEGACY**, 5, bl g Fair Mix (IRE)—Royale De Vassy (FR) **Len, Davies, Downes, Hewlett, Smith, Booth**
30 **SOLSTICE SON**, 5, b g Haafhd—Karasta (IRE) **The Summer Solstice**
31 **SOLSTICE STAR**, 4, b g Kayf Tara—Clover Green (IRE) **Mr J. Pike & Mr G. Pike**
32 **STEADY GIRLFRIEND**, 9, ch m Classic Cliche (IRE)—Dame Fonteyn **Barrow Hill**
33 **SWINCOMBE STONE**, 7, ch g Best of The Bests (IRE)—Soloism **Yeo Racing Partnership**
34 **TARADREWE**, 7, b m Kayf Tara—Kaream **Frosties Friends II**
35 **THE GEEGEEZ GEEGEE (IRE)**, 5, b g Beneficial—Shanann Lady (IRE) **Geegeez.co.uk PA**
36 **VELATOR**, 7, b g Old Vic—Jupiter's Message **Steve & Jackie Fleetham**
37 **VICATOR**, 6, b g Old Vic—Jupiter's Message **Anthony Honeyball Racing Club Ltd**
38 **VICTORS SERENADE (IRE)**, 9, b g Old Vic—Dantes Serenade (IRE) **Michael & Angela Bone**
39 **WILDE OAK (IRE)**, 4, b g Oscar (IRE)—Tree Oaks (IRE) **Owners For Owners: Wilde Oak**

Other Owners: Atlantic Racing Limited, G. T. Birks, Mr M. Bisogno, Mrs A. P Bone, Mr M. J. Bone, Dr M. Booth, D. F. Briers, J. D. Brownrigg, J. Burley, Mr J. Cannon, Mr I. Dickson, Mr T. J. Dykes, Mrs C. A. Eyre, Mr J. Fairrie, Mr S. Fleetham, Mrs J. Fleetham, Mrs S. Green, R. W. Huggins, Mr E. J. Hughes, L. J. Jakeman, N. J. McMullan, B. G. Middleton, K. B. W. Parkhouse, Mr J. M. Pike, Mr G. E. Pike, R. Robinson, Mrs Margaret Robinson, M. W. Rowe, A. J. Shire, J. W. Snook, Mrs H. A. Snook, Mrs S. L. Tizzard, R. G. Tizzard, Mr N. C. Vowles, Mrs K. D. Yeo.

Assistant Trainer: Rachael Green **Jockey (NH):** Aidan Coleman, Rachael Green, Sam Thomas.

---

333 MR MICHAEL HOURIGAN, Limerick
Postal: Lisaleen, Patrickswell, Co. Limerick, Ireland
Contacts: PHONE (00353) 6139 6603 FAX (00353) 6139 6812 MOBILE (00353) 8682 26655
E-MAIL info@mhourigan.ie WEBSITE www.mhourigan.ie

1 **A FINE YOUNG MAN (IRE)**, 9, b g Snurge—Miss Platinum (IRE) **Doran Bros (London) Ltd**
2 **AERLITE SUPREME (IRE)**, 7, b g Gold Well—Supreme Evening (IRE) **J. Murphy & G. Walsh**
3 **AWKWARD MOMENT (IRE)**, 10, ch g Deploy—True Blade **Anne Hourigan**
4 **CLEAR HILLS (IRE)**, 7, b g Marju (IRE)—Rainbows For All (IRE) **Doran Bros (London) Ltd**
5 **DAWERANN (IRE)**, 5, b g Medicean—Dawera (IRE) **T. Morrisson**
6 **DOESHEEVERSTOP (IRE)**, 6, b g Turtle Island (IRE)—Mary Connors (IRE) **Cairde Chiarrai Syndicate**
7 **DRUMACOO (IRE)**, 5, b g Oscar (IRE)—My Native (IRE) **Robin Birley**
8 **DUSHYBEAG (IRE)**, 7, b g Dushyantor (USA)—Bula Beag (IRE) **Donal O'Connor**
9 **ENCHANTED FOREST (IRE)**, 6, b h Galileo (IRE)—Halland Park Lass (IRE) **Francis Campbell**
10 **FALSE ECONOMY (IRE)**, 9, b g Orpen (USA)—Ashanti Dancer (IRE) **Mrs Miriam Murphy**
11 **GILLIAMSTOWN (IRE)**, 5, br g Whitmore's Conn (USA)—Dis Phar (IRE) **David Morton**
12 **GIVE ME A BREAK (IRE)**, 5, br m Scorpion (IRE)—Love And Porter (IRE) **Mr J. P. McManus**
13 **GOING BACK (IRE)**, 5, b g Bach (IRE)—Going For A Song (IRE) **Michael Hourigan**
14 **HANS CRESCENT (FR)**, 9, b g Dansili—Embroider (IRE) **S.Lucey / Mrs Mary Curtin**
15 **HASH BROWN (IRE)**, 5, ch g Vinnie Roe (IRE)—Keralba (USA) **Catherine Magnier**
16 **HOLEINTHEWALL BAR (IRE)**, 6, b g Westerner—Cockpit Lady (IRE) **S. Fahy**
17 **MAGICAL MOON**, 5, b g Dansili—Sheppard's Watch **Burrow Syndicate**
18 **MILAN ELITE (IRE)**, 5, b g Milan—Lady Elite (IRE) **Donal O'Connor**
19 **MOORES ROAD (IRE)**, 5, ch g Vertical Speed (FR)—Lady Quesada (IRE)
20 **RUN WITH THE WIND (IRE)**, 8, b g Sadler's Wells (USA)—Race The Wild Wind (USA) **John B. O'Hagan**
21 **SHOW ME THE MONKEY**, 5, ch m Old Vic—Ashnaya (FR) **Kay Hourigan**
22 **THE CRAFTY BUTCHER (IRE)**, 7, b g Vinnie Roe (IRE)—Ivy Queen (IRE) **Cairde Chiarrai Syndicate**
23 **THE JOB IS RIGHT**, 6, gr g With Approval (CAN)—Common Request (USA) **Mrs Mary Devine**
24 **TROPICAL THREE (IRE)**, 6, gr m Portrait Gallery (IRE)—
Tropical Ocean (IRE) **Mary Curtin / S. Lucey / M. Hourigan**
25 **UNDRESSED (FR)**, 6, b g Lost World (IRE)—Latitude (FR) **Christy White**

Jockey (NH): A. P. Heskin.

334 MR STUART HOWE, Tiverton
Postal: **Ringstone Stables, Oakford, Tiverton, Devon, EX16 9EU**
Contacts: PHONE **(01398) 351224** MOBILE **(07802) 506344**
E-MAIL **hshowe@stuarthoweracing.co.uk**

1 **ASHKALARA**, 7, b m Footstepsinthesand—Asheyana (IRE) **C R Hollands Cutting Tools Company Ltd**
2 5, Br m Lahib (USA)—Clifton Mist
3 **ETOILE DE VIE**, 4, ch f Lucarno (USA)—Spark of Life **A. Etheridge**
4 **KAYF CHARMER**, 4, b f Kayf Tara—Silver Charmer **B. P. & V. W. Jones**
5 **MY LEGAL LADY**, 9, b m Sir Harry Lewis (USA)—Clifton Mist **H. S. Howe**
6 **PARTY PALACE**, 10, b m Auction House (USA)—Lady-Love **B. P. Jones**

THREE-YEAR-OLDS
7 Ch f Tobougg (IRE)—Uig **B. P. Jones & H. S. Howe**

Other Owners: Mrs V. W. Jones, Mr B. P. Jones.

Jockey (NH): Tom Scudamore. **Conditional:** Giles Hawkins.

335 MR D. T. HUGHES, Kildare
Postal: **Osborne Lodge, Kildare, Co. Kildare, Ireland**
Contacts: PHONE **(00353) 4552 1490** FAX **(00353) 4552 1643** MOBILE **(00353) 8625 34098**
E-MAIL **dthughes1@eircom.net**

1 **AFTERCLASS (IRE)**, 6, b g Stowaway—Afsana (IRE) **Three Locks Syndicate**
2 **ALL HELL LET LOOSE (IRE)**, 5, b g Shantou (USA)—Gan Ainm (IRE) **Gigginstown House Stud**
3 **APACHE JACK (IRE)**, 6, b br g Oscar (IRE)—Cailin Supreme (IRE) **Mrs P. Sloane**
4 **ARDGLEN (IRE)**, 10, b br g Bach (IRE)—Royal Toombeola (IRE) **Ardglen Partnership**
5 **ART OF LOGISTICS (IRE)**, 6, b g Exit To Nowhere (USA)—Sanadja (IRE) **Munnelly Support Services Ltd.**
6 **ART OF PAYROLL (GER)**, 5, b g Shirocco (GER)—Anna Maria (GER) **Bishopsgate Syndicate**
7 **BACK BEFORE DAWN (IRE)**, 5, b m Oscar (IRE)—Back To Bavaria (IRE) **Us Of Pieland Syndicate**
8 **BOB'S CALL (IRE)**, 5, b g Scorpion (IRE)—Whizz **Lyreen Syndicate**
9 **BOLD CONQUEST (IRE)**, 6, b g Oscar (IRE)—Massappeal Supreme (IRE) **P. Gleeson**
10 **BOLD OPTIMIST (IRE)**, 8, b g Oscar (IRE)—Massappeal Supreme (IRE) **P. Gleeson**
11 **BRIGHT NEW DAWN (IRE)**, 7, br g Presenting—Shuil Dorcha (IRE) **Gigginstown House Stud**
12 **CAHERONAUN (IRE)**, 8, b m Milan—Fair Present (IRE) **Dan Corry**
13 **CANALY (IRE)**, 9, b g Bob Back (USA)—Starry Lady (IRE) **Michael Moore**
14 **CAPTAIN ARCEUS (IRE)**, 8, b g Captain Rio—Siana Springs (IRE) **T. O'Driscoll**
15 **CITY CALLING (IRE)**, 5, b g Exit To Nowhere (USA)—Zenith **London Calling Syndicate**
16 4, B g Kayf Tara—Coldabri (IRE) **Mr Noel Hayes**
17 **COUSIN BILL (IRE)**, 6, b g Gamut (IRE)—Sister Sebastien (IRE) **Mr Donald King**
18 **DAYDREAM ISLAND (IRE)**, 4, b g Trans Island—Ring Hill **Mrs Sarah Gleeson**
19 **DIXON'S FANCY (IRE)**, 5, b g Germany (USA)—Noon Performance **Mr. Michael Dixon**
20 **EL FONTAN (FR)**, 9, gr g Verglas (IRE)—Valeriane (FR) **Mrs P. Sloane**
21 **EMPEROR OF EXMOOR (IRE)**, 7, b g Montjeu (IRE)—Shamriyna (IRE) **D. T. Hughes**
22 **EVERYTHING ZAIN (IRE)**, 5, b g Cape Cross (IRE)—Chamela Bay (IRE) **D. T. Hughes**
23 **FATHER JACK (IRE)**, 7, b g Beneficial—Mrs Paddy Jack (IRE) **Mrs M. Roche**
24 **FLIGHT PLAN (IRE)**, 4, ch g Strategic Prince—Nans Lady (IRE) **D. T. Hughes**
25 **GIANTOFAMAN (IRE)**, 6, b g Stowaway—Anno Mundi (USA) **Mrs A. Durkan**
26 **GLOBALIZED (IRE)**, 8, b g Alhaarth (IRE)—Piacenza (IRE) **D. T. Hughes**
27 4, B f Kalanisi (IRE)—Grangeclare Lark (IRE) **Mr Phil Munnelley**
28 **GUITAR PETE (IRE)**, 4, br g Dark Angel (IRE)—Innishmore (IRE) **Mrs P. Sloan**
29 **HUNTING PARTY (IRE)**, 8, b g City Honours (USA)—Highland May (IRE) **Lyreen Syndicate**
30 **HURLER AND FARMER (IRE)**, 5, b g Red Clubs (IRE)—Undercover Glamour (USA) **Mr Glen Devlin**
31 **INDIAN ICON (FR)**, 4, b c Indian Rocket—Playing Star (FR) **Mr J. P. Dunne**
32 4, B g High Chaparral—Irish Wedding (IRE) **Munnelley Support Service**
33 **KIND OFFER (IRE)**, 6, b m Old Vic—Jemima Jay (IRE) **D. T. Hughes**
34 **LIEUTENANT COLONEL**, 5, br g Kayf Tara—Agnese **Gigginstown House Stud**
35 **LIPINSKI (IRE)**, 5, b m Germany (USA)—Dancing On Ice (IRE) **D. T. Hughes**
36 **LITTLE ROCKY**, 6, b h Cadeaux Genereux—Tahirah **Barry Connell**
37 **LYREEN LEGEND (IRE)**, 7, b g Saint des Saints (FR)—Bint Bladi (FR) **Lyreen Syndicate**
38 **MACKEYS FORGE (IRE)**, 10, b g Mr Combustible (IRE)—Lucy Walters (IRE) **Seven To Eleven Syndicate**
39 **MINSK (IRE)**, 6, b g Dalakhani (IRE)—Penza **Barry Connell**
40 **MONTANA BREEZE (IRE)**, 5, gr g Alflora (IRE)—Pearlsforthegirls **D. T. Hughes**

MR D. T. HUGHES - Continued

41 **MORNEY WING (IRE)**, 5, b g Antonius Pius (USA)—Tillan Fuwain (FR) **Mr S. Bell**
42 **NEARLY NAMA'D (IRE)**, 6, b g Millenary—Coca's Well (IRE) **J. P. McManus**
43 4, Br f Oscar (IRE)—O Mio My (IRE) **Three Locks Syndicate**
44 **OFF THE CHARTS (IRE)**, 5, b g Beneficial—Coppenagh Lady (IRE) **J. P. McManus**
45 **OUR CONOR (IRE)**, 5, b g Jeremy (USA)—Flamands (IRE) **Mr B. Connell**
46 **PAUPLEWEL (FR)**, 4, b g Kaldounevees (FR)—Miss Irish (FR) **Mr Tim O'Driscoll**
47 4, B f Presenting—Peripheral Vision (IRE) **Mrs P. Doyle**
48 **PHIL'S MAGIC (IRE)**, 4, b br g Fruits of Love (USA)—Inch Rose (IRE) **Lyreen Syndicate**
49 **PINK COAT**, 7, gr g Alhaarth (IRE)—In The Pink (IRE) **Always Optimist Syndicate**
50 **POETIC LORD**, 5, b g Byron—Jumairah Sun (IRE) **Mrs J. Lee**
51 **RARE BOB (IRE)**, 12, b br g Bob Back (USA)—Cut Ahead **D. A. Syndicate**
52 **RAZ DE MAREE (FR)**, 9, ch g Shaanner (IRE)—Diyala III (FR) **J. J. Swan**
53 **REDUNDANT MAN**, 6, b g Kayf Tara—Lady Emily **Mrs A. N. Durkan**
54 **RIVAGE D'OR (FR)**, 9, b g Visionary (FR)—Deesse d'allier (FR) **Gigginstown House Stud**
55 **ROCK'S FIELD (IRE)**, 5, ch m Presenting—Elphis (IRE) **Ms A. M. Ryan & Willie Aird**
56 **ROSS NA RIGH (IRE)**, 10, b br g Presenting—Gladys May (IRE) **Mr D O'Keefe**
57 **RUDOLF (IRE)**, 6, b g Oscar (IRE)—Stormweather Girl (IRE) **Horseplay Syndicate**
58 **RUNDELL**, a, b c Notnowcato—Shardette (IRE) **J. P. McManus**
59 **SEEFOOD (IRE)**, 7, b g Kahyasi—Anne Theatre **Lyreen Syndicate**
60 **SI C'ETAIT VRAI (FR)**, 8, b g Robin des Champs (FR)—Bleu Perle (FR) **Gigginstown House Stud**
61 **SOME TIKKET (IRE)**, 7, b g Tikkanen (USA)—Ally Rose (IRE) **Mr Ken Jones**
62 **SOMETHINGWONDERFUL (IRE)**, 6, b br g Viking Ruler (AUS)—Innishmore (IRE) **Gigginstown House Stud**
63 5, B m Presenting—Star of Arcady (IRE) **Mr J. O'Dwyer**
64 4, B f King's Theatre (IRE)—Steel Grey Lady (IRE) **D. T. Hughes**
65 **STONEY**, 7, b g Stowaway—Classical Rachel (IRE) **Slaneyville Syndicate**
66 **SUB LIEUTENANT (IRE)**, 5, b g Brian Boru—Satellite Dancer (IRE) **Gigginstown House Stud**
67 **SUGAR BULLET (IRE)**, 10, b m Witness Box (USA)—Deep Inthought (IRE) **Just Friends Syndicate**
68 **THE TABSTER (IRE)**, 5, b m Intikhab (USA)—Istibshar (USA) **Mrs P. Sloane**
69 **THUNDER AND ROSES (IRE)**, 6, b br g Presenting—Glen Empress (IRE) **Gigginstown House Stud**
70 **TIGER TREK (IRE)**, 5, b g Tiger Hill (IRE)—Zayana (IRE) **Lyreen Syndicate**
71 **TWO ROSES (IRE)**, 7, b m Vinnie Roe (IRE)—Istibshar (USA) **Mrs P. Sloane**
72 **WHITE STAR LINE (IRE)**, 10, b g Saddlers' Hall (IRE)—Fairly Deep **Exors of the Late Patsy Byrnes**
73 **WRATH OF TITANS (IRE)**, 5, b g Oscar (IRE)—Glen Empress (IRE) **Gigginstown House Stud**

THREE-YEAR-OLDS

74 **OUR KIERAN (IRE)**, b g Majestic Missile (IRE)—Forbidden Pleasure **Man About Town Syndicate**
75 **SILKEN THOMAS (IRE)**, br c Dark Angel (IRE)—Innishmore (IRE) **Munnelley Support Service**

TWO-YEAR-OLDS

76 B c 10/4 Jeremy (USA)—Kimberely Bay (IRE) (Trade Fair) (12000) **D. T. Hughes**

---

336   MRS JO HUGHES, Lambourn
Postal: **Hill House Stables, Folly Road, Lambourn, Hungerford, Berkshire, RG17 8QE**
Contacts: PHONE **(01488) 71444** FAX **(01488) 71103** MOBILE **(07900) 680189**
E-MAIL **johughes3@aol.co.uk** WEBSITE **www.johughesracing.co.uk**

1 **ANWYL HOUSE**, 4, gr g Auction House (USA)—Amwell Star (USA) **Chester Racing Club Ltd**
2 **BEACHWOOD BAY**, 6, b g Tobougg (IRE)—The Terrier **Lynn Hayward & Jo Hughes**
3 **CALEDONIA LADY**, 5, b m Firebreak—Granuaile O'malley (IRE) **Isla & Colin Cage**
4 **CANDELITA**, 7, b m Trade Fair—Gramada (IRE) **Paul & David Bedford**
5 **CHESTER'SLITTLEGEM (IRE)**, 5, b m Atraf—Ceylon Round (FR) **Chester Racing Club Ltd**
6 **CHIEF EXECUTIVE (IRE)**, 4, gr g Dalakhani (IRE)—Lucky (IRE) **Eastwind Racing Ltd & Martha Trussell**
7 **EXZACHARY**, 4, b g Multiplex—Icky Woo **J. Smith**
8 **FLYING GIANT (IRE)**, 4, ch g Danroad (AUS)—Our Emmy Lou **Champion Bloodstock Limited**
9 **JAT PUNJABI**, 10, b g Karinga Bay—Balmoral Princess **Mr H. S. Maan**
10 **JOSIE'S DREAM (IRE)**, 6, b g Tau Ceti—Gallery Breeze **J. Smith**
11 **JUST A POUND (IRE)**, 4, b g Ad Valorem (USA)—Gallery Breeze **J. Smith**
12 **LONDON BRIDGE (USA)**, 4, b c Arch (USA)—Kindness **Eastwind Racing Ltd & Martha Trussell**
13 **PARADISE SEA (USA)**, 5, b m Stormy Atlantic (USA)—
        Paradise River (USA) **Eastwind Racing Ltd & Martha Trussell**
14 **PENSNETT BAY**, 9, ch g Karinga Bay—Balmoral Princess **Mr H. S. Maan**
15 **SOLL**, 9, ch g Presenting—Montefolene (IRE) **D. Mossop**

MRS JO HUGHES - Continued

THREE-YEAR-OLDS

16 **BOGNOR (USA)**, b g Hard Spun (USA)—Ms Blue Blood (USA) **21C Telecom.co.uk**
17 **BUY OUT BOY**, gr g Medicean—Tiger's Gene (GER) **21C Telecom.co.uk**
18 **CALEDONIA LAIRD**, b c Firebreak—Granuaile O'malley (IRE) **Isla & Colin Cage**
19 **CITIZEN KAINE (IRE)**, ch g Manduro (GER)—Precious Citizen (USA) **Chester Racing, J Henderson, I Phillips**
20 **COMPANY SECRETARY (USA)**, gr c Awesome Again (CAN)—Maria Elena (USA) **Mrs C. C. Regalado-Gonzalez**
21 **DIAMOND LADY**, b f Multiplex—Ellen Mooney **B Bedford P Hanly D Bird D Bedford**
22 **EFFECT (IRE)**, b c Bahri (USA)—Wana Doo (USA) **Mrs J. F. Hughes**
23 **ELITE FREEDOM (IRE)**, b f Acclamation—Jebel Musa (IRE) **21C Telecom.co.uk**
24 **HIDDEN POWER**, b g Elusive Quality (USA)—Northern Mischief (USA) **James Henderson & Jo Hughes**
25 **HOT STOCK (FR)**, b g Elusive City (USA)—Hermance **Mrs C. C. Regalado-Gonzalez**
26 **KATE KELLY (IRE)**, b f Bushranger (IRE)—Tranquil Sky **Mrs J. F. Hughes**
27 **LYNNGALE**, b f Myboycharlie (IRE)—Belle Annie (USA) **Lynn Hayward & Jo Hughes**
28 **NICK THE ODDS (IRE)**, b g Diamond Green (FR)—Impressive Act (IRE) **James Henderson & Jo Hughes**
29 **PICKS PINTA**, b g Piccolo—Past 'n' Present **Chester Racing Club Ltd**
30 **SMART LIFE**, b g Multiplex—Vita Mia **Champion Bloodstock Limited**

TWO-YEAR-OLDS

31 **AMADEITY (IRE)**, b c 10/4 Amadeus Wolf—
　　　　　　　　　　　　Magadar (USA) (Lujain (USA)) **Chester Racing Club Ltd & Jo Hughes**
32 **CHESTER BOUND**, gr f 28/2 Equiano (FR)—
　　　　　　　　　　　　Varanasi (High Chaparral (IRE)) (10000) **Chester Racing Club Ltd & Jo Hughes**
33 **CHESTER DEAL**, b c 31/3 Multiplex—Elusive Deal (USA) (Elusive Quality (USA)) **Chester Racing Club Ltd**
34 B f 28/1 Archipenko (USA)—Kelang (Kris) (12388) **James Henderson & Jo Hughes**
35 Ch c 8/3 Archipenko (USA)—Lady Le Quesne (IRE) (Alhaarth (IRE)) **Mrs J. Kersey & Jo Hughes**
36 B c 29/4 Excellent Art—Looker (Barathea (IRE)) (8095) **Looker Partnership**
37 **MONSART (IRE)**, b c 1/4 Echo of Light—
　　　　　　　　　　　　Monet's Lady (IRE) (Daylami (USA)) **Chester Racing Club Ltd & Jo Hughes**
38 B c 7/4 Notnowcato—Tashkiya (FR) (Alzao (USA)) (2857) **Miss J. L. Tucker**

Other Owners: Mr B. W. Bedford, Mr David Bedford, Mr Paul Bedford, Mr D. G. Bird, Mrs I. Cage, Mr C. J. Cage, Chester Racing Club Ltd, Mr H. Downs, East Wind Racing Ltd, Mr P. J. Hanly, Mrs Lynn Hayward, Mr Joseph Hearne, Mr J. Henderson, Mrs Joanna Hughes, Mr R. A. Hunt, Mrs Nicola Hunt, Mr I. J. Phillips, Mr B. E. V. Thomas, Mrs Robert B. Trussell.

Assistant Trainer: Paul Blockley (07778 318295)

Jockey (flat): Paul Hanagan. Jockey (NH): Mark Grant. Apprentice: Harry Burns, Josephine Gordon.
Amateur: Mr James Hughes.

337　**MR STEPHEN HUGHES, Gilfach Goch**
Postal: **Dusty Forge, 2 Oak Street, Gilfach Goch, Porth, Mid-Glamorgan, CF39 8UG**
Contacts: PHONE **(07823) 334300 (07943) 396083 FAX (01443) 672110 MOBILE (07823) 334282**
E-MAIL **maggiekidner2@gmail.com**

1 **NOT YET HARTLEY**, 8, b g Relief Pitcher—Beinn Mohr **S. A. Hughes**
2 **ROYAL OPERA**, 6, b g Acclamation—Desert Gold (IRE) **S. A. Hughes**
3 **TIGER'S TILEAH**, 7, ch m Presenting—Aunt Rita (IRE) **S. A. Hughes**

Assistant Trainer: Maggie Kidner Hughes

338　**MS N. M. HUGO, Kelsall**
Postal: **Yewtree House, 1 Brasseys Contract Road, Edge, Malpas, Cheshire, SY14 8LB**
Contacts: PHONE **(01829) 782020 (01948) 820649 FAX (01829) 782020 MOBILE (07736) 360550**
E-MAIL **nicky.hugo@btconnect.com**

1 **MANILA MAN**, 9, b g Commanche Run—Double Chimes **Ms N. M. Hugo**
2 5, B m Fruits of Love (USA)—Mill Thyme **Ms N. M. Hugo**
3 **MY MATE PADDY**, 7, b g Deploy—City Times (IRE) **Mr J. R. Barnett**
4 **SIGNORE MOMENTO (IRE)**, 8, b g Captain Rio—Gitchee Gumee Rose (IRE)
5 **SILENT CLICHE (IRE)**, 10, b g Classic Cliche (IRE)—Mini Moo Min **K. Rowlands**

339 MRS SARAH HUMPHREY, West Wratting
Postal: Yen Hall Farm, West Wratting, Cambridge, Cambridgeshire, CB21 5LP
Contacts: PHONE (01223) 291445 FAX (01223) 291451 MOBILE (07798) 702484
E-MAIL sarah@yenhallfarm.com WEBSITE www.sarahhumphrey.co.uk

1 ARFUR DIDIT (IRE), 6, b g Blueprint (IRE)—Authentic Creature (IRE) **Yen Hall Farm Racing**
2 BALLY RONE (IRE), 6, br g Fruits of Love (USA)—Presenting Marble (IRE) **Dr R. Britton & Mrs S. Humphrey**
3 BIG MIKE (IRE), 6, b g Flemensfirth (USA)—Minoras Return (IRE) **Mrs S. Humphrey**
4 CALL HIM SOMETHING (IRE), 6, b g Heron Island (IRE)—
                                          Stoned Immaculate (IRE) **A Whyte, D Nott & J Custerson**
5 CARPINCHO (FR), 10, b br g Jimble (FR)—La Rapaille (IRE) **Mr J. B. Waterfall**
6 CHENDIRY (FR), 5, gr g Red Ransom (USA)—Cherryxma (FR) **Mrs S. Humphrey**
7 FLEMI TWO TOES (IRE), 8, b g Flemensfirth (USA)—Silva Venture (IRE) **A Whyte, J Custerson, D Nott**
8 HODGSON (IRE), 9, gr g Oscar (IRE)—Gairha Grey (IRE) **Yen Hall Farm Racing**
9 I'M A JOKER, 5, ch g Erhaab (USA)—Yota (FR) **Mrs S. Humphrey**
10 INDIAN DAUDAIE (FR), 7, ch g Nicobar—Aldounia (FR) **Yen Hall Farm Racing**
11 LANDENSTOWN PEARL (IRE), 8, b m Definite Article—Golden Moment (IRE) **Mr A. A. Whyte**
12 LANGHAM LILY (USA), 5, b br m Badge of Silver (USA)—Silver Frau (USA) **Mr M. Howard**
13 LARTETA (FR), 5, b g Enrique—Ariel (IRE) **Mrs S. Humphrey**
14 LITTLE BIT LIVELY (IRE), 5, gr g Flemensfirth (USA)—Miranda's Lace (IRE) **Mrs S. Humphrey**
15 MINELLA HERO (IRE), 6, b g Old Vic—Shannon Rose (IRE) **P. Chapman**
16 MOYALIFF (IRE), 7, b g King's Theatre (IRE)—Instant Queen (IRE) **P. Chapman**
17 4, B g Midnight Legend—Pentasilea **Mrs S. Humphrey**
18 TORNADE D'ESTRUVAL (FR), 7, b m Network (GER)—Onde d'estruval (FR) **Mrs J. A. Bowen**
19 VASCO D'YCY (FR), 5, b g Equerry (USA)—Ingrid des Mottes (FR) **P. Chapman**

Other Owners: Mr & Mrs C. Bearman, Dr R. Britton, Miss J. M. Custerson, Mr R. Fuller, Mr A. R. Humphrey, Mrs S. J. Humphrey, Mrs S. Lintott, Mr D. F. Nott, Mr G. Thomas, Mr A. A. Whyte.

Assistant Trainer: Mr W. Degnan

Conditional: Mikey Ennis, Jack Quinlan.

340 MR KEVIN HUNTER, Natland
Postal: Larkrigg, Natland, Cumbria, LA9 7QS
Contacts: PHONE (01539) 560245

1 MILAN ROYALE, 9, b g Milan—Siroyalta (FR) **J. K. Hunter**

341 MISS LAURA HURLEY, Kineton
Postal: Kineton Grange Farm, Kineton, Warwick, Warwickshire, CV35 0EE
Contacts: PHONE (01926) 640380

1 GAME DORABELLA, 6, ch m Avonbridge—Ground Game **Mrs R. Hurley**
2 MOSCOW MULE, 11, b g Moscow Society—Madam Advocate **Mrs R. Hurley**
3 ORANG OUTAN (FR), 12, b g Baby Turk—Ellapampa (FR) **Mrs R. Hurley**
4 TUROYAL (FR), 6, gr g Turgeon (USA)—Quelle Est Belle (FR) **Mrs R. Hurley**

342 MISS ALISON HUTCHINSON, Newmarket
Postal: 116 Parkers Walk, Studlands, Newmarket, Suffolk, CB8 7AP
Contacts: PHONE (01638) 482180 MOBILE (07960) 630204
E-MAIL alison.hutchinson1@hotmail.co.uk
WEBSITE www.alisonhutchinsonhorseracing.weebly.com

1 BIG WAVE (IRE), 6, b m Choisir (AUS)—Mystery Solved (USA) **Miss A. L. Hutchinson**
2 HELAMIS, 4, b f Shirocco (GER)—Alnoor (USA) **Mr J. T. Mangan**
3 ICEMAN GEORGE, 10, b g Beat Hollow—Diebiedale (IRE) **Mr J. T. Mangan**
4 IZZY TOO, 4, b f Oratorio (IRE)—Quiet Counsel (IRE) **Mr J. T. Mangan**
5 MAYA DE VENTURA, 4, b f Tiger Hill (IRE)—Sharp Dresser (USA) **Mr I. R. Hatton**
6 MUCKY MOLLY, 6, ch m Bahamian Bounty—Indian Flag (IRE) **Miss A. L. Hutchinson**

MISS ALISON HUTCHINSON - Continued

7 **SALBATORE**, 6, ch g Chineur (FR)—Au Contraire **Mr J. T. Mangan**
8 **STRIKE FORCE**, 10, b g Dansili—Miswaki Belle (USA) **Miss A. L. Hutchinson**

THREE-YEAR-OLDS

9 Ch f Poseidon Adventure (IRE)—Walt Mc Don (IRE) **worldracing.network**

Jockey (flat): Natasha Eaton, Tom Eaves, Robert Havlin. **Jockey (NH):** Dougie Costello.
Amateur: Miss A. L. Hutchinson.

343

MR ROGER INGRAM, Epsom
Postal: **Wendover Stables, Burgh Heath Road, Epsom, Surrey, KT17 4LX**
Contacts: **PHONE (01372) 748505 or (01372) 749157 FAX (01372) 748505**
MOBILE (0777) 3665980
E-MAIL **roger.ingram.racing@virgin.net** WEBSITE **www.rogeringramracing.com**

1 **BUXTON**, 10, b g Auction House (USA)—Dam Certain (IRE) **Mr P. J. Burton**
2 **ENCAPSULATED**, 4, b g Zamindar (USA)—Star Cluster **Mrs E. N. Nield**
3 **FONTERUTOLI (IRE)**, 7, gr g Verglas (IRE)—
Goldendale (IRE) **Mrs Cathy Hallam, Martyn Cruse & Sarah Maxwell**
4 **GABRIAL'S WAWA**, 4, b g Dubai Destination (USA)—Celestial Welcome **Jerry Murphy & Viktoriia Virych**
5 **GEBAYL**, 4, b f Compton Place—Glimpse **Mr A. C. D. Main**
6 **JACKIE LOVE (IRE)**, 6, b m Tobougg (IRE)—Gutter Press (IRE) **Miss O. Maylam**
7 **SILVER MARIZAH (IRE)**, 5, b m Manduro (GER)—Maharani (USA) **Mrs C. E. Hallam**
8 **TRIPLE CHOCOLATE**, 4, b g Danehill Dancer (IRE)—Enticing (IRE) **Mr F. Al Dabbous**

THREE-YEAR-OLDS

9 **HANNAH LOUISE (IRE)**, b f Iffraaj—Answer Do **Mr A. C. D. Main**
10 **IL GRAN CAPO (IRE)**, b c Cape Cross (IRE)—Rambler **Mr F. Al Dabbous**
11 **ROSIE PROSPECTS**, b f Byron—Sea Jade (IRE) **T. H. Barma**
12 B f Byron—Sunny Times (IRE) **T. H. Barma**

Other Owners: Mr M. F. Cruse, Miss Sarah Maxwell, Mr J. Murphy, Miss V. Virych.

Assistant Trainer: Sharon Ingram

Apprentice: Tommy Harrigan. **Amateur:** Miss Rhiain Ingram.

344

MR DEAN IVORY, Radlett
Postal: **Harper Lodge Farm, Harper Lane, Radlett, Hertfordshire, WD7 7HU**
Contacts: **PHONE (01923) 855337 FAX (01923) 852470 MOBILE (07785) 118658**
E-MAIL **dean.ivory@virgin.net** WEBSITE **www.deanivoryracing.co.uk**

1 **ADA LOVELACE**, 4, b f Byron—Satin Braid **Mr D. A. Clark**
2 **AYE AYE SKIPPER (IRE)**, 4, b g Captain Marvelous (IRE)—Queenfisher **Heather Yarrow & Lesley Ivory**
3 **BATCHWORTH LADY**, 4, b f Pastoral Pursuits—Batchworth Belle **Mrs D. T. M. S. Price**
4 **BELINSKY (IRE)**, 7, b g Compton Place—Westwood (FR) **Wentdale Limited**
5 **CHILTERN SECRET**, 4, ch f Sakhee's Secret—Regal Curtsy **Solario Racing (Latimer)**
6 **DUCHESS OF GAZELEY (IRE)**, 4, ch f Halling (USA)—Flying Finish (FR) **Heather & Michael Yarrow**
7 **EL MIRAGE (IRE)**, 4, b f Elusive Quality (USA)—Hucking Hot **Mrs H. Yarrow**
8 **ELEGANT OPHELIA**, 5, ch m Osorio (GER)—Ela's Giant **World Freight Consultants Ltd**
9 **FOSSA**, 4, b g Dubai Destination (USA)—Gayanula (USA) **Mr G. M. Copp**
10 **GUARDI (IRE)**, 5, gr g Dalakhani (IRE)—Grizel **Heather Yarrow & Lesley Ivory**
11 **GUNNING FOR GLORY**, 4, b g Indesatchel (IRE)—Today's The Day **Solario Racing (Amersham)**
12 **HIGH TONE**, 4, b f Bertolini (USA)—High Finale
13 **HILL OF DREAMS (IRE)**, 5, b m Indian Danehill (IRE)—Shaunas Vision (IRE) **Mr I Gethin & Mr R Gethin**
14 **JOYOUS**, 4, b f Assertive—Ivory's Joy **K. T. Young**
15 **LANCELOT DU LAC (ITY)**, 4, b c Shamardal (USA)—Dodie Mae (USA) **Mr M. J. Yarrow**
16 **LINKS DRIVE LADY**, 6, br m Striking Ambition—Miskina **It's Your Lucky Day**
17 **MALICHO**, 5, ch g Manduro (GER)—Shane (GER) **Mr K. B. Taylor**
18 **MIDNIGHT BAHIA (IRE)**, 5, b m Refuse To Bend (IRE)—Midnight Partner (IRE) **Mr K. B. Taylor**
19 **MOSMAN**, 4, b g Haafhd—Last Dream (IRE) **Mrs Elaine White William Harris P Blows**
20 **RUSSIAN ICE**, 6, ch m Iceman—Dark Eyed Lady (IRE) **Mr R. Beadle**
21 **SHAUNAS SPIRIT (IRE)**, 6, b m Antonius Pius (USA)—Shaunas Vision (IRE) **Cynthia Smith & Dean Ivory**

MR DEAN IVORY - Continued

22 **SIRIUS PROSPECT (USA)**, 6, b br g Gone West (USA)—Stella Blue (FR) **Miss N. I. Yarrow**
23 **SNOW TROOPER**, 6, ch g Iceman—Snow Shoes **Mr K. B. Taylor**
24 **SOARING SPIRITS (IRE)**, 4, ch g Tamayuz—Follow My Lead **Mrs D. A. Carter**
25 **TAGULA NIGHT (IRE)**, 8, ch g Tagula (IRE)—Carpet Lady (IRE) **Hufford & Papworth**
26 **TOP SHOW**, 5, b g Sakhee (USA)—Rose Show **Mr R. Beadle**
27 **TROPICS (USA)**, 6, ch g Speightstown—Taj Aire (USA) **D. K. Ivory**
28 **VALID REASON**, 7, b g Observatory (USA)—Real Trust (USA) **Mr M. J. Yarrow**
29 **ZAEEM**, 5, b g Echo of Light—Across (ARG) **Richard Lewis & Steve Farmer**

THREE-YEAR-OLDS

30 **AMADIVA (IRE)**, b f Amadeus Wolf—Divine Quest **Solario Racing (Chorleywood)**
31 **CRYSTALIZED (IRE)**, ch f Rock of Gibraltar (IRE)—Magnificent Bell (IRE) **Mr T. Glynn**
32 **GOLDEN AMBER (IRE)**, b f Holy Roman Emperor (IRE)—Time of Gold (USA) **Heather & Michael Yarrow**
33 **GREY ODYSSEY**, gr g Verglas (IRE)—Reading Habit (USA) **Miss N. I. Yarrow**
34 **SPEED THE PLOUGH**, b g Kyllachy—Danceatdusk **John Waterfall & K T Ivory**

TWO-YEAR-OLDS

35 B g 30/3 Iffraaj—Its On The Air (IRE) (King's Theatre (IRE)) (18000) **Mr G. M. Copp**
36 Ch g 12/2 Thewayyouare (USA)—Major Minor (IRE) (Desert Prince (IRE)) (17142)
37 **O DEE**, ch c 24/1 Iffraaj—Queen's Grace (Bahamian Bounty) (55000) **Mr G. M. Copp**

Other Owners: Mr S. K. I. Double, Mr S. Farmer, Mr J. Foley, Mr I. R. Gethin, Mr R. Gethin, Mr W. H. Harris, Mr J. Hufford, Mrs L. A. Ivory, Mr R. A. Lewis, Mr J. R. Neville, G. Papworth, Mrs C. Smith, Mr K. W. Smith, Mr J. B. Waterfall, Mrs E. M. White.

Assistant Trainer: Chris Scally

Apprentice: Paul Booth.

---

345 **MISS TINA JACKSON, Loftus**
Postal: Tick Hill Farm, Liverton, Loftus, Saltburn, Cleveland, TS13 4TG
Contacts: **PHONE (01287) 644952 MOBILE (07774) 106906**

1 **BORIS THE BLADE**, 12, gr g Cloudings (IRE)—Cherry Lane **Simon Bodsworth & Howard Thompson**
2 **FLEDERMAUS (IRE)**, 4, br g Jeremy (USA)—Khayrat (IRE) **H. L. Thompson**
3 **HITMAN HARRY**, 6, b g Sir Harry Lewis (USA)—Bonnie Buttons **Mrs P. A. Cowey**
4 **JAN DE HEEM**, 4, ch g Dutch Art—Shasta **H. L. Thompson**
5 **JOSEPH MERCER (IRE)**, 7, b g Court Cave (IRE)—Vikki's Dream (IRE) **H. L. Thompson**
6 **MANYSHADESOFBLACK (IRE)**, 6, b m Tikkanen (USA)—Wynyard Dancer **Mrs P. A. Cowey**
7 **MISS SUNFLOWER**, 12, ch m Keen—Ellfiedick **H. L. Thompson**
8 **PURPLE HARRY**, 6, gr g Sir Harry Lewis (USA)—Ellfiedick **H. L. Thompson**
9 **ROSY RYAN (IRE)**, 4, b f Tagula (IRE)—Khaydariya (IRE) **H. L. Thompson**
10 **SIR POSEALOT**, 7, gr g Clerkenwell (USA)—Ellfiedick **H. L. Thompson**
11 **SPEEDY STAR (IRE)**, 5, b g Authorized (IRE)—North Sea (IRE) **H. L. Thompson**

Other Owners: Mr S. Bodsworth.

---

346 **MRS VALERIE JACKSON, Newcastle Upon Tyne**
Postal: Edge House, Belsay, Newcastle Upon Tyne, Tyne and Wear, NE20 0HH
Contacts: **PHONE (01830) 530218 MOBILE (07808) 812213**

1 **CAST IRON CASEY (IRE)**, 12, ch g Carroll House—Ashie's Friend (IRE) **Mrs V. S. Jackson**
2 **SPORTS MODEL (IRE)**, 8, ch g Presenting—Belmarita (IRE) **Mrs V. S. Jackson**
3 **WAVE POWER (IRE)**, 10, ch g Definite Article—Romany Rose (IRE) **Mrs V. S. Jackson**
4 **WHEYAYE**, 12, ch m Midnight Legend—Sayin Nowt **Mrs V. S. Jackson**

347 **MR LEE JAMES, Malton**
Postal: **Cheesecake Hill Stables, Beverley Road, Norton, Malton, North Yorkshire, YO17 8PJ**
Contacts: **PHONE (01653) 699466 FAX (01653) 699581 MOBILE (07732) 556322**

1 4, B c Echo of Light—Alisdanza
2 **FREEDOM FLYING,** 11, b m Kalanisi (IRE)—Free Spirit (IRE)
3 4, B f Dubai Destination (USA)—Palisandra (USA)
4 **SHADOW OF THE DAY,** 7, b g Sugarfoot—She Who Dares Wins
5 **STRIKEMASTER (IRE),** 8, b g Xaar—Mas A Fuera (IRE)
6 **ZOOM IN,** 6, b g Indesatchel (IRE)—Korolieva (IRE)

Assistant Trainer: Carol James

Jockey (NH): Kyle James. **Amateur:** Mr Aaron James.

348 **MR IAIN JARDINE, Hawick**
Postal: **Paradise Cottage, Gatehousecote, Bonchester Bridge, Hawick, Roxburghshire, TD9 8JD**
Contacts: **PHONE (01450) 860718 MOBILE (07738) 351232**
E-MAIL iainjardineracing@hotmail.co.uk

1 **CARTERS REST,** 11, gr g Rock City—Yemaail (IRE) **Mr A. Dawson & Mrs K. Campbell**
2 **CLASSY CHASSIS (IRE),** 6, br m Heron Island (IRE)—Marika's King (IRE) **Mrs L. J. McLeod**
3 **DOUBLE WHAMMY,** 8, b g Systematic—Honor Rouge (IRE) **Alex & Janet Card**
4 **GALLEONS WAY,** 5, gr g Generous (IRE)—Yemaail (IRE) **Mr A. Dawson & Mrs K. Campbell**
5 **I AM WHO I AM,** 4, b f Notnowcato—Elusive Kitty (USA) **Tapas Partnership**
6 **JUST POPPY (IRE),** 5, ch m Ad Valorem (USA)—Nebulae (IRE) **A M Brown & D N Jeffrey**
7 **LA BACOUETTEUSE (FR),** 9, b g Miesque's Son (USA)—Toryka **The Gold Cup In Mind**
8 **PUSH ME (IRE),** 7, gr m Verglas (IRE)—Gilda Lilly (USA) **Alex & Janet Card**
9 **RUBERSLAW,** 8, b g Beat All (USA)—Plus Tu Mets (FR) **Rule Valley Racing Club**

THREE-YEAR-OLDS

10 **NAKEETA,** b g Sixties Icon—Easy Red (IRE) **Alex & Janet Card**

Other Owners: Mrs S. M. Barker, Mrs K. I. J. Brown, Mr A. M. Brown, R. S. Brown, Mrs K. Campbell, Mr A. M. Card, Mrs J. A. Card, A. Dawson, Mr D. N. Jeffrey, Mrs H. Macfarlane, Mr I. McAllan, Mr A. T. Murphy, Mr D. Reddihough, A. Walmsley.

Jockey (flat): David Allan. **Jockey (NH):** Adrian Lane.

349 **MR ALAN JARVIS, Twyford**
Postal: **Twyford Mill, Mill Lane, Twyford, Buckingham, Buckinghamshire, MK18 4HA**
Contacts: **PHONE (01296) 730707 FAX (01296) 733572 MOBILE (07770) 785551**
E-MAIL alan@alanjarvis.co.uk WEBSITE www.alanjarvis.co.uk

1 **ALBONNY (IRE),** 5, b g Aussie Rules (USA)—Silk Law (IRE) **M&J Partnership**
2 **ANOTHER TRY (IRE),** 9, b g Spinning World (USA)—Mad Annie (USA) **The Twyford Partnership**
3 **FAITHER,** 4, b g Bertolini (USA)—Hawait Al Barr **Mac Asphalt Ltd**
4 **LADY GIBRALTAR,** 5, b m Rock of Gibraltar (IRE)—Lady Adnil (IRE) **Buckingham Flooring**
5 **MARTINAS DELIGHT (USA),** 4, b f Johannesburg (USA)—Lerici (USA) **T&J Partnership**
6 **NAVAJO CHIEF,** 7, b g King's Best (USA)—Navajo Rainbow **Mr G. S. Bishop**
7 **OETZI,** 6, ch g Iceman—Mad Annie (USA) **Allen B. Pope & Jarvis Associates**
8 **PRINCE REGAL,** 4, ch g Cockney Rebel (IRE)—Wachiwi (IRE) **T&J Partnership**
9 **STAR OF MAYFAIR (USA),** 4, ch g Tale of The Cat (USA)—Kinsale Lass (USA) **Cedars Partnership**
10 **SUBSTANTIVO (IRE),** 4, b g Duke of Marmalade (IRE)—Damson (IRE) **Jarvis Associates**

THREE-YEAR-OLDS

11 **ABOVE THE REST (IRE),** b c Excellent Art—Aspasias Tizzy (USA) **Cedars Two**
12 **ALWAYS RESOLUTE,** b c Refuse To Bend (IRE)—Mad Annie (USA) **Market Avenue Racing Club & Partners**
13 **BAARS CAUSEWAY (IRE),** ch f Intense Focus (USA)—Barbera (GER) **Brian Goldswain & Jarvis Associates**
14 **CALRISSIAN (IRE),** ch c Lando (GER)—Dallaah **Cedars Two**
15 **CANARY LAD (IRE),** ch c Iffraaj—Sweet Myrtle (USA) **Market Avenue Racing Club & Partners**
16 Ch f Peintre Celebre (USA)—Cream Tease **Market Avenue Racing Club Ltd**
17 **DANCING JUICE,** b c Major Cadeaux—Mancunian Way **Market Avenue Racing Club Ltd**

MR ALAN JARVIS - Continued

18 **DIAMOND SOLITAIRE (IRE),** br f Diamond Green (FR)—Eastern Blue (IRE) **Market Avenue Racing Club Ltd**
19 **DIVINE WARRIOR (IRE),** b c High Chaparral (IRE)—Lady of Talent (USA) **Cedars Two**
20 **I AM NOT HERE (IRE),** b c Amadeus Wolf—Newgate Lodge (IRE) **Jarvis Associates**
21 **INTENSE TANGO,** b f Mastercraftsman (IRE)—Cover Look (SAF) **Cedars Two**
22 **LADY LARA (IRE),** b f Excellent Art—Shanty **Cedars Two**
23 **LAVENDAR FIELDS (IRE),** b f High Chaparral (IRE)—Rose Parade **Cedars Two**
24 **LUNA SUNRISE,** b f Virtual—Moon Crystal **Mr G. S. Bishop**
25 **RIVER PEARL (IRE),** b f High Chaparral (IRE)—Gassal **Mrs S. E. Simmons**
26 **ROBYNELLE,** b f Royal Applause—Chicita Banana **Mac Asphalt Ltd**
27 **ROGUE WAVE (IRE),** b c Iffraaj—Lady Naomi (USA) **Market Avenue Racing Club & Partners**
28 **SAVANNA SPRING (IRE),** b f Bushranger (IRE)—Brogan's Well (IRE) **Market Avenue Racing Club & Partners**
29 **SILVER DUKE (IRE),** b gr c Papal Bull—Dumaani's Dream (USA) **Mac Asphalt Ltd**
30 **SPRING LADY,** b f Refuse To Bend (IRE)—Spring Goddess (IRE) **Jarvis Associates**
31 **TOP OF THE GLAS (IRE),** gr c Verglas (IRE)—Fury Dance (USA) **Market Avenue Racing Club Ltd**
32 **YOU'RE FIRED (IRE),** b c Firebreak—My Sweet Georgia (IRE) **Market Avenue Racing Club & Partners**

TWO-YEAR-OLDS

33 **SABHA (IRE),** b f 7/2 Thewayyouare (USA)—Genipabu (IRE) (Danetime (IRE))
34 B c 11/5 Refuse To Bend (IRE)—Spring Goddess (IRE) (Daggers Drawn (USA)) **Grant & Bowman Limited**

Other Owners: B. H. Goldswain, Mr T. O. Jarvis, A. B. Pope, Mr G. J. Reboul, Mrs H. Reboul.

Assistant Trainer: M. A. Jarvis, S. E. Simmons, T. O. Jarvis

---

350 **MR WILLIAM JARVIS, Newmarket**
Postal: **Phantom House, Fordham Road, Newmarket, Suffolk, CB8 7AA**
Contacts: **OFFICE (01638) 669873 HOME (01638) 662677 FAX (01638) 667328**
E-MAIL mail@williamjarvis.com WEBSITE www.williamjarvis.com

1 **ARGENT KNIGHT,** 4, gr g Sir Percy—Tussah **Dr J. Walker**
2 **CLERK'S CHOICE (IRE),** 8, b g Bachelor Duke (USA)—Credit Crunch (IRE) **M. C. Banks**
3 **DIXIE'S DREAM (IRE),** 5, b g Hawk Wing (USA)—Hams (USA) **The Dream Team Partnership**
4 **EMBANKMENT,** 5, b g Zamindar (USA)—Esplanade **Canisbay Bloodstock**
5 **JODIES JEM,** 4, br g Kheleyf (USA)—First Approval **Mrs M. C. Banks**
6 **NIGHT'S WATCH,** 4, b c Authorized (IRE)—Nachtigall (GER) **Dr J. Walker**
7 6, B g Cadeaux Genereux—Orlena (USA) **Mrs S. J. Davis**
8 **PERSIAN PATRIOT,** 4, ch f Bahamian Bounty—Persian Lass (IRE) **Miss J. D. Margossian**
9 **RASKOVA (USA),** 4, b f Henrythenavigator (USA)—Diamond Necklace (USA) **Mr K. J. Hickman**

THREE-YEAR-OLDS

10 **AMETRINE (IRE),** b f Fastnet Rock (AUS)—Amethyst (IRE) **Mr K. J. Hickman**
11 **BEAKERS N NUM NUMS (IRE),** b c Iffraaj—Ivy League Star (IRE) **The Willie Robertson Partnership**
12 **BISHAN BEDI (IRE),** b c Intikhab (USA)—Knockatotaun **Dr J. Walker**
13 **BLURRED VISION,** b c Royal Applause—Sparkling Eyes **Clive Washbourn**
14 **FIRST EMBRACE,** b f Dubawi (IRE)—Bronwen (IRE) **Mr A. S. Belhab**
15 **HALLAGA,** ch f Halling (USA)—Gayanula (USA) **G. B. Turnbull Ltd**
16 **NEW ROW,** b f Teofilo (IRE)—Memo **The New Row Partnership**
17 **SILVER MOUNTAIN,** gr c Sir Percy—Pearl Bright (FR) **Ms W. Dio**

TWO-YEAR-OLDS

18 Gr ro c 21/3 Compton Place—Dictatrix (Diktat) (38095)
19 B f 19/4 Holy Roman Emperor (IRE)—Dolce Dovo (Medicean) **Mr Paul Shanahan**
20 B f 25/3 Monsieur Bond (IRE)—Katy O'hara (Komaite (USA)) (3333) **Miss S. E. Hall**
21 **L'ADDITION,** b f 17/3 Exceed And Excel (AUS)—La Adelita (IRE) (Anabaa (USA)) (25000) **Mr C. A. Washbourn**
22 B c 4/4 Royal Applause—Making Waves (IRE) (Danehill (USA)) (40000) **Tony Foster & Partners**
23 **MISS OLIVE (IRE),** b f 19/2 Rip Van Winkle (IRE)—
Desert Darling (Green Desert (USA)) (34000) **Mr K. J. Hickman**
24 **MUST HAVE (FR),** ch c 26/2 Le Havre (IRE)—Belle Et Brave (FR) (Falbrav (IRE)) (36391) **Dr J. Walker**
25 B c 28/1 Sir Percy—Nicola Bella (IRE) (Sadler's Wells (USA)) **Mr & Mrs A. E. Pakenham**
26 **NUNO TRISTAN (USA),** b c 1/3 Henrythenavigator (USA)—
Saintly Speech (USA) (Southern Halo (USA)) (115000) **Mr C. A. Washbourn**
27 **PERCY'S DREAM,** b f 8/2 Sir Percy—Monaco Dream (IRE) (Hawk Wing (USA)) **Mr Tony Verrier & Partners**
28 B c 22/4 Azamour (IRE)—Sadie Thompson (IRE) (King's Best (USA)) (15000)

MR WILLIAM JARVIS - Continued

29 B c 24/2 Medicean—Seasonal Blossom (IRE) (Fairy King (USA)) (70000) **A. Foster**
30 SILK KNIGHT, ch c 21/2 Sir Percy—Tussah (Daylami (IRE)) **Dr J. Walker**
31 Gr c 18/2 Zebedee—Sinead (USA) (Irish River (FR)) (28571) **A Partnership**
32 SOLSTALLA, b f 2/3 Halling (USA)—Solstice (Dubawi (IRE)) **G. B. Turnbull Ltd**
33 YAT DING YAU, b f 1/3 Air Chief Marshal (IRE)—The Jostler (Dansili) (17034) **Dr J. Walker**

Other Owners: Mr James Bowditch, Norman Collins, Mr Paul Cousins, Mr N. J. Donald, John Dowman, Mr Nigel T. Gadsby, Mrs P.J. George, Miss M Greenwood, Mr William Jarvis, Roger Kilby, Mr Peter Maybury, Mr A M Mitchell, Mr A. E. Pakenham, Mrs Victoria Pakenham, Mr Asa Pamplin, Mr Robert G Percival, Edward Randall, Mr Nigel Rich, Mo Stopher, Mr Neil Warnock, Mr Clive Washbourn.

---

351 MR MALCOLM JEFFERSON, Malton
Postal: **Newstead Cottage Stables, Norton, Malton, North Yorkshire, YO17 9PJ**
Contacts: PHONE **(01653) 697225** MOBILE **(07710) 502044**
E-MAIL **newsteadracing@btconnect.com** WEBSITE **www.malcolmjefferson.co.uk**

1 ANEYEFORANEYE (IRE), 8, ch m Definite Article—Resolute Approach (IRE) **Mrs J. U. Hales**
2 ANNE'S VALENTINO, 4, b f Primo Valentino (IRE)—Annie's Gift (IRE) **The Magic Circle**
3 ATTAGLANCE, 8, b g Passing Glance—Our Ethel **H Young, G Eifert, R Snyder**
4 CAPE TRIBULATION, 10, b g Hernando (FR)—Gay Fantastic **J. D. Abell**
5 CLASSIC RALLY (IRE), 8, b g Zagreb—Classic Material **T. J. Hemmings**
6 COOZAN GEORGE, 5, b g Bollin Eric—Pasja (IRE) **A. N. Barrett**
7 CROXTON KERRIAL, 5, b g Doyen (IRE)—Julatten (IRE) **J. D. Abell**
8 CRUSHED ICE, 8, gr g Silver Patriarch (IRE)—Altogether Now (IRE) **Mrs M. M. Jagger**
9 DANBY'S LEGEND, 7, b g Midnight Legend—Miss Danbys **D. T. Todd**
10 DOUBLE W'S (IRE), 4, ch g Fruits of Love (USA)—Zaffre (IRE) **Wharton & Wilson**
11 DREAMERS OF DREAMS (IRE), 9, b g Flemensfirth (USA)—
　　　　　　　　　　　　　　　　　　　　Cushogan (IRE) **Dean Bostock & Raymond Bostock**
12 ENCHANTED GARDEN, 6, ch g Sulamani (IRE)—Calachuchi **Mrs D. W. Davenport**
13 ETERNAL VINE, 5, gr m Grape Tree Road—Altogether Now (IRE) **RAPS Partnership**
14 FIRTH OF THE CLYDE, 9, b g Flemensfirth (USA)—Miss Nel **R. H. Goldie**
15 HENRY JENKINS, 7, gr g Fair Mix (IRE)—Altogether Now (IRE) **Mrs K. M. Richardson**
16 HERECOMESTROUBLE, 7, b g Gentleman's Deal (IRE)—Owenreagh (IRE) **Mr J.H. Hewitt**
17 HI GEORGE, 6, b g Doyen (IRE)—Our Ethel **Mr & Mrs H Young**
18 KING OF THE NIGHT (GER), 10, b g Lomitas—Kaiserlerche (GER) **Mr & Mrs G. Calder**
19 KING OF THE WOLDS (IRE), 7, b g Presenting—Azaban (IRE) **Mr & Mrs G. Calder**
20 LUA DE ITAPOAN, 9, gr m Silver Patriarch (IRE)—Gotogeton **Mr T. A. Pearcy**
21 MAGIC PRESENT, 7, b g Presenting—Magic Bloom **P. Nelson**
22 MAJOR IVAN (IRE), 8, b g Fruits of Love (USA)—Martinstown Queen (IRE) **Mrs I C Straker & Steven Key**
23 MCMURROUGH (IRE), 10, b g Spectrum (IRE)—Sensitive (IRE) **Mrs D. W. Davenport**
24 NAUTICAL TWILIGHT, 4, gr f Proclamation (IRE)—Anabranch **Capt M. S. Bagley**
25 OLEOHNEH (IRE), 6, b m Flemensfirth (USA)—Dewasentah (IRE) **Mr T. A. Stephenson & Mrs S. Jefferson**
26 OSCAR ROCK (IRE), 6, b g Oscar (IRE)—Cash And New (IRE) **Mr & Mrs G. Calder**
27 OUR BOY BEN, 5, b g Revoque (IRE)—Magic Bloom **P. Nelson**
28 PAIR OF JACKS (IRE), 6, ch g Presenting—Halona **Mrs R. Williams**
29 QUITE THE MAN (IRE), 9, b g Zagreb—Ballinard Lizzie (IRE) **Boundary Garage (Bury) Limited**
30 RENOYR (FR), 9, b g Kalmoss (FR)—Idee de Valeur (FR) **Mr M. L. Harvey**
31 RETRIEVE THE STICK, 5, b m Revoque (IRE)—Anabranch **Newstead Racing Partnership**
32 SECRETE STREAM (IRE), 5, ch g Fruits of Love (USA)—Bonny River (IRE) **Mrs M. E. Dixon**
33 SUN CLOUD (IRE), 7, b g Cloudings (IRE)—Miss Melrose **Boundary Garage (Bury) Limited**
34 THE MAGIC BISHOP, 9, b g Bishop of Cashel—Magic Bloom **P. Nelson**
35 THE PANAMA KID (IRE), 10, b g Gentleman's Deal (IRE)—Mrs Jodi **Mrs D. W. Davenport**
36 TORRINGTON DEAL, 6, b m Gentleman's Deal (IRE)—Miss Danbys **D. T. Todd**
37 UNCLE BRIT, 8, b g Efisio—Tarneem (USA) **J. M. Jefferson**
38 UPPINGHAM, 5, ch g Doyen (IRE)—Karakul (IRE) **J. D. Abell**
39 URBAN HYMN (FR), 6, b g Robin des Champs (FR)—Betty Brune (FR) **Mr & Mrs G. Calder**

Other Owners: Mr J. R. Bostock, Mr Dean Graham Bostock, Mr G. Calder, Mrs J. Calder, Mr G. Eifert, Mrs J. U. Hales, Mrs S. Jefferson, Mrs L. M. Joicey, Mr P. Nelson, Mr R. Synder Jnr, Mr N. J. Taylor, Mr R. Wharton, Mr J. H. Wilson, Mrs Sandra Windross, Mr H. Young, Mrs E. A. Young.

Assistant Trainer: Ruth Jefferson

Jockey (NH): Harry Haynes, Brian Hughes. **Conditional:** Jack Jordan. **Amateur:** Mr J. Teal.

352 MR J. R. JENKINS, Royston

Postal: Kings Ride, Baldock Road, Royston, Hertfordshire, SG8 9NN
Contacts: PHONE (01763) 241141 HOME (01763) 246611 FAX (01763) 248223
MOBILE Car: (07802) 750855
E-MAIL john@johnjenkinsracing.co.uk WEBSITE www.johnjenkinsracing.co.uk

1 **AMOSITE**, 8, b m Central Park (IRE)—Waterline Dancer (IRE) **Mrs C. Goddard**
2 **ATHLETIC**, 5, b g Doyen (IRE)—Gentle Irony
3 **AUDEN (USA)**, 6, b g Librettist (USA)—Moyesii (USA) **Ms A. Juskaite**
4 **BILLY RED**, 10, ch g Dr Fong (USA)—Liberty Bound **Mrs I. C. Hampson**
5 **BLADEWOOD GIRL**, 6, b m Needwood Blade—Willmar (IRE) **Byron Boys**
6 **BOW BELLE**, 4, ch f Cockney Rebel (IRE)—Miss Ippolita **D. J. P. Bryans**
7 **BUBBLY BAILEY**, 4, b g Byron—Night Gypsy **Mrs S. Bowmer**
8 **CARAMELITA**, 7, b m Deportivo—Apple of My Eye **La Senoritas**
9 **CLOSEST FRIEND**, 5, b g Kayf Tara—Princess of War **Lottie Parsons & Sue Raymond**
10 **DORCEUS**, 7, b g Doyen (IRE)—Jawwala (USA) **P. J. Kirkpatrick**
11 **DORKAS**, 5, b m Doyen (IRE)—Jawwala (USA) **P. J. Kirkpatrick**
12 **FROSTY FRIDAY**, 6, b m Storming Home—Seasonal Blossom (IRE) **Mr A. J. Turner**
13 **GO AMWELL**, 11, b g Kayf Tara—Daarat Alayaam (IRE) **Mr R. Stevens**
14 **GREAT EXPECTATIONS**, 6, b g Storming Home—Fresh Fruit Daily **The Great Expectations Partnership**
15 **HI TIDE (IRE)**, 10, br g Idris (IRE)—High Glider **Mrs W. A. Jenkins**
16 **KARAM ALBAARI (IRE)**, 6, b h King's Best (USA)—Lilakiya (IRE) **Mr M. D. Goldstein**
17 **LITTLE INDIAN**, 4, b c Sleeping Indian—Once Removed **Two Little Indians**
18 **MAGIC BY BELL**, 5, ch m Reel Buddy—Bella Beguine **Mr M. Turner**
19 **MAWAAKEF (IRE)**, 6, b g Azamour (IRE)—Al Euro (FR) **The Three Honest Men**
20 **MEDITERRANEAN SEA (IRE)**, 8, b m Medecis—High Glider **Mrs W. A. Jenkins**
21 **MISHRIF (USA)**, 8, b br g Arch (USA)—Peppy Priscilla (USA) **Mrs W. A. Jenkins**
22 **MONSIEUR JAMIE**, 6, b g Monsieur Bond (IRE)—Primula Bairn **Mr M. D. Goldstein**
23 **MY MANEKINEKO**, 5, b g Authorized (IRE)—Echo River (USA) **Bond Street General Services Ltd**
24 **MYBOYALFIE (USA)**, 7, b g Johannesburg (USA)—Scotchbonnetpepper (USA) **D. Badham**
25 **NOT TIL MONDAY (IRE)**, 8, b g Spartacus (IRE)—Halomix **B. Silkman**
26 **ONLY TEN PER CENT (IRE)**, 6, b g Kheleyf (USA)—Cory Everson (IRE) **B. Silkman**
27 **OSCARS JOURNEY**, 4, ch g Dubai Destination (USA)—Fruit of Glory **Exors of the Late Mr R. B. Hill**
28 **PINK LIPS**, 6, b m Noverre (USA)—Primrose Queen **Mr & Mrs J. Sales**
29 **PRETTY BUBBLES**, 5, b m Sleeping Indian—Willmar (IRE) **Mr M. D. Goldstein**
30 **PROM DRESS**, 4, b f Mount Nelson—Dress Code (IRE) **Mrs W. A. Jenkins**
31 **RAMBO WILL**, 6, b g Danbird (AUS)—Opera Belle **Mrs S. Bambridge**
32 **RAY OF JOY**, 8, b m Tobougg (IRE)—Once Removed **Mr R. Stevens**
33 **SAKASH**, 4, b c Sakhee (USA)—Ashwell Rose **Mr & Mrs C. Schwick**
34 **SPITFIRE**, 9, b g Mujahid (USA)—Fresh Fruit Daily **Mrs W. A. Jenkins**
35 **SWEET SUGAR (FR)**, 8, ch g Loup Solitaire (USA)—Violette d'avril (FR) **Sweet Sugar Racing Club**
36 **TAMING THE TWEET**, 4, b f Act One—Pants **Mrs W. A. Jenkins**
37 **TIRADIA (FR)**, 7, b br g Without Connexion (IRE)—Jimanji (FR) **B. S. P. Dowling**

THREE-YEAR-OLDS

38 **DIODATI**, b g Byron—Apple of My Eye **Exors of the Late Mr R. B. Hill**
39 **MEEBO (IRE)**, b f Captain Rio—Abbeyleix Lady (IRE) **Ms A. Juskaite**
40 **PERSPICACITY**, ch f Sir Percy—Sakhacity **David Bryans & Philippa Casey**
41 **RUBY LOOKER**, b c Bertolini (USA)—Ellcon (IRE) **Mr M. Turner**
42 **TEMPLAR BOY**, br g Myboycharlie (IRE)—Zagala **Mrs C. Goddard**
43 **WHO SPLASHED ME**, ch f Medicean—Cavallo da Corsa **Bookmakers Index Ltd**

Other Owners: D. Abrey, R. Bradbury, S. J. Brewer, Mr S. M. Bullock, Mr G. J. Burchell, Mr I. J. Callaway, Miss P. Casey, Mrs C. A. Hill, Mrs C. L. Parsons, G. J. Pascoe, Mr A. M. Phillips, Mrs A. S. C. Raymond, Mr J. Sales, Mrs K. Sales, C. Schwick, Mrs C. V. Schwick, Mr P. Trotter.

Apprentice: Danny Brock. **Amateur:** Mr Ray Barrett.

353 MR ALAN JESSOP, Chelmsford

Postal: Flemings Farm, Warren Road, South Hanningfield, Chelmsford, Essex, CM3 8HU
Contacts: PHONE (01268) 710210 MOBILE (07718) 736482

1 **CHORAL BEE**, 5, b m Oratorio (IRE)—Chief Bee **Mrs G. Jessop**
2 **MAHAB EL SHAMAAL**, 6, b g Motivator—Soliza (IRE) **Mrs G. Jessop**

MR ALAN JESSOP - Continued

3 **MAJY D'AUTEUIL (FR),** 12, b g Discover d'auteuil (FR)—Majestic Dancer (FR) **Mrs G. Jessop**
4 **STEEPLEOFCOPPER (IRE),** 8, ch g Classic Cliche (IRE)—Tanya Thyne (IRE) **Mrs G. Jessop**
5 **STICKERS,** 7, b g Generous (IRE)—Dunsfold Duchess (IRE) **Mrs G. Jessop**

---

354 MRS LINDA JEWELL, Maidstone
Postal: **Southfield Stables, South Lane, Sutton Valence, Maidstone, Kent, ME17 3AZ**
Contacts: **PHONE (01622) 842788 FAX (01622) 842943 MOBILE (07856) 686657**
E-MAIL lindajewell@hotmail.com WEBSITE www.lindajewellracing.co.uk

1 **CELESTIAL RAY,** 5, ch g Pivotal—Heavenly Ray (USA) **K. Johnson & K. Jessop**
2 **CLONUSKER (IRE),** 6, b g Fasliyev (USA)—Tamburello (IRE) **Valence Racing**
3 **FLEETING INDIAN (IRE),** 5, b g Sleeping Indian—Glebe Garden **Mr M. J. Boutcher**
4 **ITOLDYOU (IRE),** 8, ch g Salford Express (IRE)—Adisadel (IRE) **Valence Racing**
5 **KAYFLIN (FR),** 6, b m Kayf Tara—Flinders **Leith Hill Chasers**
6 **KINGSCOMBE (USA),** 5, gr ro g Mizzen Mast (USA)—Gombeen (USA) **P. A. Oppenheimer**
7 **RED ANCHOR (IRE),** 10, ch g Snurge—Clonartic (IRE) **Mrs S. M. Stanier**
8 **REDINGA,** 8, ch m Karinga Bay—Medway Queen **Mrs S. M. Stanier**
9 **ROWE PARK,** 11, b g Dancing Spree (USA)—Magic Legs **Mrs S. M. Ashdown**
10 **SPIRIT OF XAAR (IRE),** 8, b g Xaar—Jet Cat (IRE) **K. Johnson, K. Jessop**
11 **STRATEGIC ACTION (IRE),** 5, ch g Strategic Prince—Ruby Cairo (IRE) **Mr M. J. Boutcher**

THREE-YEAR-OLDS

12 **ALICE KINGSLEY (IRE),** b f Invincible Spirit (IRE)—Art Eyes (USA) **L. Jewell**
13 **I'M LUCY (IRE),** b f Papal Bull—Melaaya (USA) **Mrs R. V. Watson**
14 **LENA PLAYER (SWE),** ch f Honeysuckle Player (SWE)—Russian Rhapsody (SWE) **Reverend C. F. Arvidsson**

Other Owners: Mr K. Jessup, Mrs Linda Jewell, Mr K. Johnson, Mr N. F. Maltby, Mr A. May, Mr R. I. B. Young.

Assistant Trainer: Karen Jewell

Jockey (flat): Steve Drowne, Robert Havlin, Liam Keniry. **Jockey (NH):** Andrew Thornton, Gerard Tumelty.
Apprentice: Daniel Cremin. **Amateur:** Mr F. Mitchell.

---

355 MR BRETT JOHNSON, Epsom
Postal: **The Durdans Stables, Chalk Lane, Epsom, Surrey, KT18 7AX**
Contacts: **MOBILE (07768) 697141**
E-MAIL thedurdansstables@googlemail.com WEBSITE www.brjohnsonracing.co.uk

1 **ABIGAILS ANGEL,** 7, br m Olden Times—Make Ready **B R Johnson & Omni Colour Presentations**
2 **ASSIST,** 4, b g Zamindar (USA)—Cochin (USA) **Tann Racing**
3 **BOBBY TWO SHOES,** 4, b g Byron—Taminoula (IRE) **Mrs A. M. Upsdell**
4 **CAYUGA,** 5, b g Montjeu (IRE)—Ithaca (USA) **J. Daniels**
5 **FIRMDECISIONS (IRE),** 4, b g Captain Rio—Luna Crescente (USA) **White Bear Racing**
6 **KAYLEE,** 5, b m Selkirk (USA)—Mrs Brown **Mr D. Phelan**
7 **PERSEPOLIS (IRE),** 4, gr g Dansili—La Persiana **J. Daniels**
8 **THE DANCING LORD,** 5, br g Imperial Dancer—Miss Brookie **Mr D. Phelan**
9 **TORRES DEL PAINE,** 7, b g Compton Place—Noble Story **Tann Racing**

THREE-YEAR-OLDS

10 **CRAFTYBIRD,** ch f Mastercraftsman (IRE)—Tobaranama (IRE) **Sir Eric Parker**
11 **DANCING SAL (IRE),** b f Azamour (IRE)—Miss Tango Hotel **P. Naughton**
12 **HAINES,** ch g Shirocco (GER)—Spring Dream (IRE) **Bow River Racing**
13 **SATCHVILLE FLYER,** ch g Compton Place—Palinisa (FR) **Mr N Jarvis, Mr T Broke-Smith, Mr G Tann**
14 B c Oratorio (IRE)—Whassup (FR) **Mrs A. M. Upsdell**

Other Owners: Mr S. T. J. Broderick, Mr T. W. Broke-Smith, C. Conroy, Miss N. J. Hood, Mr N. A. Jarvis, B. R. Johnson, Omni Colour Presentations Ltd, G. Tann, Mrs E. Tann, Ms L. Thompson.

Assistant Trainer: Vanessa Johnson

356
MR ROBERT JOHNSON, Newcastle Upon Tyne
Postal: **Johnson Racing Ltd, Grange Farm, Newburn, Newcastle Upon Tyne**
Contacts: PHONE **(01912) 674464** FAX **(01912) 674464** MOBILE **(07774) 131133**
E-MAIL **rjohnsonracing@talktalk.net** WEBSITE **www.rwjohnsonracing.co.uk**

1 **ALMOND COURT (IRE)**, 11, ch m Accordion—Glencairn Fox (IRE) **Mr A. V. W. Kidd**
2 **BELLINGO**, 7, b m Danroad (AUS)—Rasin Luck **R. Craggs**
3 **BYGONES FOR COINS (IRE)**, 6, ch m Danroad (AUS)—Reservation (IRE) **R. W. Johnson**
4 **KING VAHE (IRE)**, 5, b g One Cool Cat (USA)—Tethkar **R. W. Johnson**
5 **LIBERAL LADY**, 6, b m Statue of Liberty (USA)—Noble Story **J. L. Armstrong**
6 **LORD BRENDY**, 6, gr g Portrait Gallery (IRE)—Hervey Bay **T L A & R A Robson**
7 **LORDENSHAWS (IRE)**, 7, b ro g Cloudings (IRE)—Slaney Rose (IRE) **Sarah Fenwick & Derek Milburn**
8 **MOHEEBB (IRE)**, 10, b g Machiavellian (USA)—Rockerlong **Miss N. Morris**
9 **POLITELYSED**, 8, ch m Courteous—Allegedly Red **Mr Robert Johnson & Mr J. Lund**
10 **ROSQUERO (FR)**, 9, ch g Blushing Flame (USA)—Kingsgirl (FR) **Alan Kidd Dave Bamlet Racing R Johnson**
11 **SUNRISE DANCE**, 5, ch m Monsieur Bond (IRE)—Wachiwi (IRE) **Mr M. Saunders**
12 **VALNAMIXE DU MEE (FR)**, 5, b g Al Namix (FR)—Kateline du Mee (FR) **TLA & RA Robson & Mrs L Gander**
13 **VODKA RED (IRE)**, 6, b g Ivan Denisovich (IRE)—Begine (IRE) **Ontoawinner, R Johnson, Carter Thomson**
14 **WAVE BREAKER (IRE)**, 7, b g Moscow Society (USA)—Lily Langtry (IRE) **Robert C Whitelock R Johnson**
15 **YUKON DELTA (IRE)**, 7, ch g Old Vic—Red Fern (IRE) **Magpie Racing**

THREE-YEAR-OLDS

16 **HIGH MEADOW JENNY**, b f Boogie Street—High Meadow Rose **G. Graham**

Other Owners: Mr D. Bamlet, Mr I. M. Blacklock, Mr A. Carter, Mrs S. D. Fenwick, Mrs L. R. Gander, Mr N. N. Kane, Mr J. Lund, Mr D. L. Milburn, N. J. O'Brien, T. L. A. Robson, Mrs R. A. Robson, Mr S. Thompson, R. C. Whitelock.

Jockey (NH): Kenny Johnson. **Amateur:** Mr P. Johnson, Mr T. Speke.

357
MRS SUSAN JOHNSON, Madley
Postal: **Carwardine Farm, Madley, Hereford**
Contacts: PHONE **(01981) 250214** FAX **(01981) 251538**

1 **HOME GIRL (IRE)**, 6, br m Milan—Homebird (IRE) **I. K. Johnson**
2 **I'M SO SPECIAL (IRE)**, 8, b m Milan—Hudson Hope (IRE) **I. K. Johnson**
3 **THE LAST BRIDGE**, 7, b g Milan—Celtic Bridge **I. K. Johnson**

Jockey (NH): Richard Johnson.

357a
MISS EVE JOHNSON HOUGHTON, Blewbury
Postal: **Woodway, Blewbury, Didcot, Oxfordshire, OX11 9EZ**
Contacts: PHONE **(01235) 850480 (01235) 850500 (Home)** FAX **(01235) 851045**
MOBILE **(07721) 622700**
E-MAIL **Eve@JohnsonHoughton.com** WEBSITE **www.JohnsonHoughton.com**

1 **AMULET**, 4, gr f Ishiguru (USA)—Loveofmylife **Mrs V. D. Neale**
2 **NEW RICH**, 4, b g Bahamian Bounty—Bling Bling (IRE) **Eden Racing Club**
3 **PANTHER PATROL (IRE)**, 4, b g Tagula (IRE)—Quivala (USA) **G. C. Stevens**
4 **PEACE TREATY**, 4, b g Lucky Story (USA)—Peace Lily **Mrs F. M. Johnson Houghton**
5 **STARLIGHT SYMPHONY (IRE)**, 4, b f Oratorio (IRE)—
                                          Phillippa (IRE) **Brian & Liam McNamee, Les & Ian Dawson**

THREE-YEAR-OLDS

6 **AJIG**, ch f Bahamian Bounty—Atwirl **Eden Racing Club**
7 **ALUTIQ (IRE)**, b f Kodiac—Marasem **Qatar Racing Limited**
8 **BOLD ARIAL**, b f Authorized (IRE)—No Frills (IRE) **Dr P. J. Brown**
9 **CHARLIE WELLS (IRE)**, b g High Chaparral (IRE)—Numbers Game **Eden Racing**
10 **COOL BAHAMIAN (IRE)**, b g Bahamian Bounty—Keritana (FR) **Mr L R Godfrey & Mr R F Johnson Houghton**
11 **DIGGIN' FOR GOLD (IRE)**, b f Tamayuz—Arabian Coral (IRE) **Exors of the Late Mr G. Ward**
12 **DRIVE ON (IRE)**, b g Tagula (IRE)—Thelma Louise (IRE) **J. H. Widdows**
13 **GANYMEDE**, b c Oasis Dream—Gaze **Ganymede Partnership**
14 **KHUTZE (GER)**, b g Duke of Marmalade (IRE)—Kalahari Dancer **The Picnic Partnership**
15 **PEACEMAKER (IRE)**, b f High Chaparral (IRE)—Sauterne **Mr R L Maynard & Mr B McNamee**

MISS EVE JOHNSON HOUGHTON - Continued

16 **PERSIAN BOLT (USA)**, b f U S Ranger (USA)—Silent Cat (USA) **B Larizadeh P Wollaston**
17 **PICANIGHT**, b f Piccolo—Midnight Fling **Mr S. Emmet & Miss R. Emmet**
18 **PINK DIAMOND**, b f Champs Elysees—Fairy Dance (IRE)
19 **SATIN WATERS**, b f Halling (USA)—Velvet Waters **Mr R. E. Crutchley**
20 **SPARKLING ICE (IRE)**, gr f Verglas (IRE)—Sand Crystal (IRE) **Mrs E Rice & Mrs R F Johnson Houghton**
21 **SQUAW KING**, b g Sleeping Indian—Change Partners (IRE) **Lord Astor,Lady Lewinton,R Morgan-Jones**
22 **STARLIT CANTATA**, b f Oratorio (IRE)—Starlit Sky **Mrs H. B. Raw**
23 **WHAT ABOUT CARLO (FR)**, b c Creachadoir (IRE)—Boccatenera (GER) **A. J. Pye-Jeary**

TWO-YEAR-OLDS

24 **AEVALON**, b f 21/3 Avonbridge—Blaina (Compton Place) **Mill House Partnership**
25 **BEEKY**, ch c 30/3 Haafhd—Vive La Chasse (IRE) (Mull of Kintyre (USA)) (476) **R. F. Johnson Houghton**
26 B c 21/5 Paco Boy (IRE)—Blandish (USA) (Wild Again (USA)) (32520) **Qatar Racing Limited**
27 **BRITISH EMBASSY (IRE)**, b c 17/4 Clodovil (IRE)—Embassy Belle (IRE) (Marju (IRE)) (17500) **Eden Racing IV**
28 B f 28/4 Kodiac—Danccalli (IRE) (Traditionally (USA)) (10452) **Miss E. A. Johnson Houghton**
29 Ch f 5/2 Bahamian Bounty—Deep Bleu (Kyllachy) (10000) **Mrs B Green & Mr H Marsh**
30 B c 22/4 Areion (GER)—Globuli (GER) (Surako (GER)) (35000) **G. C. Stevens**
31 **GOLDEN WEDDING (IRE)**, b c 14/3 Archipenko (USA)—Peace Lily (Dansili) **Mrs F. M. Johnson Houghton**
32 B c 6/2 Cape Cross (IRE)—Gretna (Groom Dancer (USA)) (6000) **Miss E. A. Johnson Houghton**
33 B c 17/1 Invincible Spirit (IRE)—Hammrah (Danehill (USA)) (40000) **G. C. Stevens**
34 B f 29/1 Zamindar (USA)—Luminous Gold (Fantastic Light (USA)) **Dr P. J. Brown**
35 **MISTAMEL (IRE)**, b c 29/1 Rip Van Winkle (IRE)—
                              Without Precedent (FR) (Polish Precedent (USA)) (21680) **A. J. Pye-Jeary**
36 **PLYMOUTH SOUND**, b c 28/4 Fastnet Rock (AUS)—Shardette (IRE) (Darshaan) (16000)
37 **POMME DE GUERRE (IRE)**, b c 28/2 Kodiac—
                              Lucky Apple (Key of Luck (USA)) (17142) **Mr L. R. A. Godfrey**
38 **ROOM KEY**, ch c 24/2 Mount Nelson—Saturday Girl (Peintre Celebre (USA)) (12000) **The Picnic Partnership**
39 B f 12/4 Azamour (IRE)—Sauterne (Rainbow Quest (USA)) (6580) **Mr P Wollaston & Mr R F Johnson Houghton**
40 Ch f 8/3 Tagula (IRE)—Support Fund (IRE) (Intikhab (USA)) (2857) **The Ascot Colts & Fillies Club**

Other Owners: Viscount Astor, Mr N. B. Bentley, Mr L. W. Dawson, Mr I. W. Dawson, Lt Cdr P. S. Emmet, Miss R. E. Emmet, Mrs P. J. Green, Mr B. Larizadeh, Lady Lewinton, Fiona Marner, Mr P. H. Marsh, R. L. Maynard, B. P. McNamee, Mr L. P. McNamee, Mrs J. A. McWilliam, R. J. Morgan-Jones, Mrs E. R. Rice, J. R. Wallis, Major-Gen G. H. Watkins, Mr P. R. Wollaston.

Assistant Trainer: R. F. Johnson Houghton

---

358 **MR MARK JOHNSTON, Middleham**
Postal: **Kingsley House Racing Stables, Middleham, Leyburn, North Yorkshire, DL8 4PH**
Contacts: **PHONE (01969) 622237 FAX (01969) 622484**
E-MAIL mark@markjohnstonracing.com WEBSITE www.markjohnstonracing.com

1 **ALTA LILEA (IRE)**, 4, b f Galileo (IRE)—In My Life (IRE) **Mrs S Bianco & Ms J Bianco**
2 **ARYAL**, 4, gr g Singspiel (IRE)—Majoune (FR) **Sheikh Hamdan Bin Mohammed Al Maktoum**
3 **BEYLERBEY (USA)**, 4, b br f Street Cry (USA)—
                              Connie Belle (USA) **Sheikh Hamdan Bin Mohammed Al Maktoum**
4 **BLUE IS THE COLOUR (IRE)**, 4, b c Dalakhani (IRE)—Coyote **A. D. Spence**
5 **BLUE WAVE (IRE)**, 4, b g Raven's Pass (USA)—
                              Million Waves (IRE) **Sheikh Hamdan Bin Mohammed Al Maktoum**
6 **BOUND COPY (USA)**, 4, b f Street Cry (IRE)—In A Bound (AUS) **Sheikh Hamdan Bin Mohammed Al Maktoum**
7 **BUGLER'S DREAM (USA)**, 6, b br g Medaglia d'oro (USA)—
                              Marquet Rent (USA) **Sheikh Hamdan Bin Mohammed Al Maktoum**
8 **BUSATTO (USA)**, 4, b br c Bernardini (USA)—
                              Lyphard's Delta (USA) **Sheikh Hamdan Bin Mohammed Al Maktoum**
9 **CLOVERDALE**, 4, ch f Pivotal—Lane County (USA) **Sheikh Hamdan Bin Mohammed Al Maktoum**
10 **CORSARO (IRE)**, 4, b c Invincible Spirit (IRE)—Urgele (FR) **Sheikh Hamdan Bin Mohammed Al Maktoum**
11 **DOLDRUMS**, 4, b f Bernardini (USA)—
                              Appealing Storm (USA) **Sheikh Hamdan Bin Mohammed Al Maktoum**
12 **ETON DORNEY (USA)**, 5, b g Medaglia d'oro (USA)—
                              Sweet and Firm (USA) **Sheikh Hamdan Bin Mohammed Al Maktoum**
13 **EVERMORE (IRE)**, 4, b f Dansili—Reunite (IRE) **Sheikh Hamdan Bin Mohammed Al Maktoum**

MR MARK JOHNSTON - Continued

14 **FAVOURITE TREAT (USA)**, 4, b g Hard Spun (USA)—
                                   Truart (USA) **Sheikh Hamdan Bin Mohammed Al Maktoum**
15 **FIRST MOVE**, 4, b c New Approach (IRE)—
                            Loving Kindness (USA) **Sheikh Hamdan Bin Mohammed Al Maktoum**
16 **GREELEYS LOVE (USA)**, 4, ch c Mr Greeley (USA)—Aunt Winnie (IRE) **Crone Stud Farms Ltd**
17 **HAJRAS (IRE)**, 5, b g Dubai Destination (USA)—Nufoos **Hamdan Al Maktoum**
18 **HEAVY METAL**, 4, b g Exceed And Excel (AUS)—
                                  Rock Opera (SAF) **Sheikh Hamdan Bin Mohammed Al Maktoum**
19 **HENRY THE AVIATOR (USA)**, 4, b g Henrythenavigator (USA)—Fashion Star (USA) **Crone Stud Farms Ltd**
20 **HUNTING GROUND (USA)**, 4, b g Street Cry (IRE)—
                                  Panty Raid (USA) **Sheikh Hamdan Bin Mohammed Al Maktoum**
21 **HURRICANE HIGGINS (IRE)**, 6, br g Hurricane Run (IRE)—Mare Aux Fees **A. D. Spence**
22 **ITTIJAH (USA)**, 4, ch f Pivotal—Rahiyah (USA) **Sheikh Hamdan Bin Mohammed Al Maktoum**
23 **IZZY BOY (USA)**, 4, b g Elusive Quality (USA)—Michele Royale (USA) **Mr F. Bird**
24 **KOSIKA (USA)**, 4, b f Hard Spun (USA)—Song of Africa (USA) **Sheikh Hamdan Bin Mohammed Al Maktoum**
25 **LAYL (USA)**, 4, b br c Street Cry (IRE)—Cymbal (IRE) **Sheikh Hamdan Bin Mohammed Al Maktoum**
26 **LICENCE TO TILL (USA)**, 7, b g War Chant (USA)—With A Wink (USA) **The Vine Accord**
27 **LIFE AND TIMES (USA)**, 6, b br g Medaglia d'oro (USA)—
                                Sur Ma Vie (USA) **Sheikh Hamdan Bin Mohammed Al Maktoum**
28 **LILAC TREE**, 4, b c Dubawi (IRE)—Kalidasa (USA) **Sheikh Hamdan Bin Mohammed Al Maktoum**
29 **LOUD**, 4, ch g Dutch Art—Applauding (IRE) **Sheikh Hamdan Bin Mohammed Al Maktoum**
30 **MARSHGATE LANE (USA)**, 5, b h Medaglia d'oro (USA)—
                                Louvain (IRE) **Sheikh Hamdan Bin Mohammed Al Maktoum**
31 **MONDLICHT (USA)**, 4, b g Malibu Moon (USA)—
                                Moonlight Cruise (USA) **Sheikh Hamdan Bin Mohammed Al Maktoum**
32 **MU'AJIZA**, 4, ch f Pivotal—Siyasa (USA) **Sheikh Hamdan Bin Mohammed Al Maktoum**
33 **MY HISTORY (IRE)**, 4, b c Dubawi (IRE)—Reine Zao (FR) **Sheikh Hamdan Bin Mohammed Al Maktoum**
34 **NEWSREADER (IRE)**, 4, b g New Approach (IRE)—Headline **Sheikh Hamdan Bin Mohammed Al Maktoum**
35 **PARTY LINE**, 5, b m Montjeu (IRE)—Party (IRE) **S. R. Counsell**
36 **PARTY ROYAL**, 4, b g Royal Applause—Voliere **D & G Mercer 1**
37 **PENNY STOCK (IRE)**, 4, b f Dansili—Beta **Sheikh Hamdan Bin Mohammed Al Maktoum**
38 **PERIVALE (USA)**, 4, b f Street Cry (IRE)—Windsharp (USA) **Sheikh Hamdan Bin Mohammed Al Maktoum**
39 **PILATES (IRE)**, 4, b f Shamardal (USA)—Caribbean Escape **Sheikh Hamdan Bin Mohammed Al Maktoum**
40 **PRINCE OF ORANGE (IRE)**, 5, b g Shamardal (USA)—
                                Cox Orange (USA) **Sheikh Hamdan Bin Mohammed Al Maktoum**
41 **PUPPET THEATRE (IRE)**, 4, ch f Pivotal—Eilean Ban (USA) **Sheikh Hamdan Bin Mohammed Al Maktoum**
42 **SALUTATION (IRE)**, 4, b g Iffraaj—Totally Yours (USA) **Sheikh Hamdan Bin Mohammed Al Maktoum**
43 **SENNOCKIAN STAR**, 4, ch g Rock of Gibraltar (IRE)—Chorist **The Vine Accord**
44 **SILENT MOVIE (IRE)**, 4, gr c Cape Cross (IRE)—
                                Screen Star (USA) **Sheikh Hamdan Bin Mohammed Al Maktoum**
45 **SIR FRANK MORGAN (IRE)**, 4, b g Montjeu (IRE)—Woodland Orchid (IRE) **Mark Johnston Racing Ltd**
46 **SIR GRAHAM WADE (IRE)**, 5, gr g Dalakhani (IRE)—Needwood Epic **P. Dean**
47 **SKYTRAIN**, 4, ch g Exceed And Excel (AUS)—Viola da Braccio (IRE) **Ready To Run Partnership**
48 **SPIN ARTIST (USA)**, 4, b g Hard Spun (USA)—Miss Cap (USA) **Sheikh Hamdan Bin Mohammed Al Maktoum**
49 **STAFFHOSS**, 4, b g Lucky Story (USA)—Jerre Jo Glanville **Emjayaarrghh Syndicate**
50 **SUMMER SCHOOL (IRE)**, 4, b f Street Cry (IRE)—
                                Measured Tempo **Sheikh Hamdan Bin Mohammed Al Maktoum**
51 **SUMMERFREE (IRE)**, 4, b br g Medaglia d'oro (USA)—
                                Summer Flash (USA) **Sheikh Hamdan Bin Mohammed Al Maktoum**
52 **TALENTED KID**, 5, b g Teofilo (IRE)—See You Later **Sheikh Hamdan Bin Mohammed Al Maktoum**
53 **TARTAN JURA**, 6, b g Green Desert (USA)—On A Soapbox (USA) **Mr F. Bird**
54 **THATCHMASTER (USA)**, 4, br g Street Cry (IRE)—Michita (USA) **Sheikh Hamdan Bin Mohammed Al Maktoum**
55 **THOROUGHFARE (IRE)**, 4, b c Teofilo (IRE)—Passageway (USA) **Sheikh Hamdan Bin Mohammed Al Maktoum**
56 **TRAIN HARD**, 4, b g Rail Link—Melpomene **Mrs C. E. Budden**
57 **TRAVEL (USA)**, 4, ch f Street Cry (IRE)—Away (USA) **Sheikh Hamdan Bin Mohammed Al Maktoum**
58 **TURNBUCKLE**, 4, ch c Teofilo (IRE)—Forest Pearl (USA) **Sheikh Hamdan Bin Mohammed Al Maktoum**
59 **UNIVERSAL (IRE)**, 5, ch h Dubawi (IRE)—Winesong (IRE) **Mr A. Al Mansoori**
60 **WADACRE SARKO**, 4, b c Oratorio (IRE)—Saxon Maid **Wadacre Stud**

THREE-YEAR-OLDS

61 **ALEX MY BOY (IRE)**, b c Dalakhani (IRE)—Alexandrova (IRE) **J. Abdullah**
62 **ALMARGO (IRE)**, b c Invincible Spirit (IRE)—
                                Alexander Youth (IRE) **Sheikh Hamdan Bin Mohammed Al Maktoum**
63 **ATLANTIC AFFAIR (IRE)**, gr f Clodovil (IRE)—Adultress (IRE) **Mrs R. Broadbent**

MR MARK JOHNSTON - Continued

64 **BAILEYS PARTYTIME,** b f Aqlaam—Third Party **G. R. Bailey Ltd**
65 **BE RELEASED (IRE),** b f Three Valleys (USA)—Boa Estrela (IRE) **D & G Mercer 1**
66 **BOW CREEK (IRE),** b c Shamardal (USA)—Beneventa **Sheikh Hamdan Bin Mohammed Al Maktoum**
67 **BRANSTON DE SOTO,** b g Hernando (FR)—Julatten (IRE) **J. D. Abell**
68 **BROWNSVILLE (USA),** b c Bernstein (USA)—Net Worth (USA) **Sheikh M. B. M. Al Maktoum**
69 **BUREAU (IRE),** ch f Halling (USA)—Embassy **Sheikh Hamdan Bin Mohammed Al Maktoum**
70 B g Josr Algarhoud (IRE)—Caysue **C. H. Greensit & W. A. Greensit**
71 **CHERIKA (IRE),** b f Cape Cross (IRE)—Charita (IRE) **Sheikh Hamdan Bin Mohammed Al Maktoum**
72 **COSQUILLAS (IRE),** b f Selkirk (USA)—Crystany (IRE) **Haras D'Etreham**
73 **CRAFTED (IRE),** b g Shamardal (USA)—Designed **Sheikh Hamdan Bin Mohammed Al Maktoum**
74 **CRAFTY SPELL,** ro f Mastercraftsman (IRE)—Isle of Flame **Mr S Richards,Mr N Browne,Mrs R Frosell**
75 **CROWDMANIA,** ch g Shamardal (USA)—Riotous Applause **Sheikh Hamdan Bin Mohammed Al Maktoum**
76 **DOUBLE BLUFF (IRE),** b c Azamour (IRE)—Damask Rose (IRE) **R. W. Huggins**
77 **DRY YOUR EYES (IRE),** b f Shamardal (USA)—Kindling **D & G Mercer 1**
78 **EMAAD (USA),** b c Arch (USA)—Red Dot (USA) **Hamdan Al Maktoum**
79 **ENQUIRING,** b c Cape Cross (IRE)—Questina (FR) **Sheikh Hamdan Bin Mohammed Al Maktoum**
80 **EVERY HONOUR,** ch c Duke of Marmalade (IRE)—Time Honoured **R. Barnett**
81 **FILAMENT OF GOLD (USA),** b g Street Cry (IRE)—
    Raw Silk (USA) **Sheikh Hamdan Bin Mohammed Al Maktoum**
82 **FINE VINTAGE (FR),** b g Montjeu (IRE)—Viking's Cove (USA) **A. D. Spence**
83 **FIRE FIGHTING (IRE),** b g Soldier of Fortune (IRE)—Savoie (IRE) **A. D. Spence**
84 **FIRE MARSHAL (IRE),** b c Shamardal (USA)—Flamelet (USA) **Sheikh Hamdan Bin Mohammed Al Maktoum**
85 B f Acclamation—Fritta Mista (IRE) **Mark Johnston Racing Ltd**
86 **GLACE (IRE),** gr f Verglas (IRE)—Swynford Lady (IRE) **Lady C. J. O'Reilly**
87 **HANDWOVEN (IRE),** b g Shamardal (USA)—Seamstress (IRE) **Sheikh Hamdan Bin Mohammed Al Maktoum**
88 **HARTNELL,** b c Authorized (IRE)—Debonnaire **Sheikh Hamdan Bin Mohammed Al Maktoum**
89 **IFWECAN,** b g Exceed And Excel (AUS)—Kirk **D. C. Livingston**
90 **INEVITABLE,** b g Dubawi (IRE)—Come What May **Sheikh Hamdan Bin Mohammed Al Maktoum**
91 **INSAANY,** b c Shamardal (USA)—Mother of Pearl (IRE) **Hamdan Al Maktoum**
92 **JALINGO (IRE),** b c Cape Cross (IRE)—Just Special **Sheikh Hamdan Bin Mohammed Al Maktoum**
93 **KING OF MACEDON (IRE),** b g Invincible Spirit (IRE)—Allexina **Sheikh Hamdan Bin Mohammed Al Maktoum**
94 **LADY FRANCES,** b f Exceed And Excel (AUS)—Lady Catherine **Sheikh Hamdan Bin Mohammed Al Maktoum**
95 **LANARK (IRE),** b c Cape Cross (IRE)—Amenixa (IRE) **Sheikh Hamdan Bin Mohammed Al Maktoum**
96 **LATE SHIPMENT,** b g Authorized (IRE)—Time Over **R. Barnett**
97 **LITTLE SHAMBLES,** ch f Shamardal (USA)—Meiosis (USA) **Sheikh Hamdan Bin Mohammed Al Maktoum**
98 B c Fastnet Rock (AUS)—Littlepacepaddocks (IRE) **Mrs J. Keaney**
99 **LOVE D'ORO (USA),** b f Medaglia d'oro (USA)—Unbridled Belle (USA) **Crone Stud Farms Ltd**
100 **LYN VALLEY,** b c Shamardal (USA)—Demisemiquaver **Mr J. A. Barson**
101 **MAID IN RIO (IRE),** ch f Captain Rio—Silver Whale (FR) **The New Fairyhouse Partnership**
102 **MAMBO RHYTHM,** b f Authorized (IRE)—Mambo Halo **Around The World Partnership**
103 **MARACUJA,** b f Medicean—Blinking **The Duke of Roxburghe & The Duke of Devonshire**
104 **MASTER OF FINANCE (IRE),** ch c Mastercraftsman (IRE)—
    Cheal Rose (IRE) **Mr J David Abell & Mr Markus Graff**
105 **MAXIE T,** b g Dalakhani (IRE)—Ballet Ballon (USA) **Mr C. Johnston**
106 **MBHALI (IRE),** b c Cape Cross (IRE)—Ma Paloma (IRE) **Sheikh Hamdan Bin Mohammed Al Maktoum**
107 **MITCHELTON (FR),** b f High Chaparral (IRE)—Fortunately **Mr Gerry Ryan**
108 **MOUNT GLENN,** b c Mount Nelson—Glen Rosie (IRE) **Newsells Park Stud Limited**
109 **MUTEELA,** b f Dansili—Nufoos **Hamdan Al Maktoum**
110 **NAGAMBIE (IRE),** b f Duke of Marmalade (IRE)—Sina Cova (IRE) **Mr Gerry Ryan**
111 **NOTARISED,** b c Authorized (IRE)—Caribbean Dancer (USA) **Mr H. C. Hart**
112 **OPERA FAN (FR),** b f Cape Cross (IRE)—Persian Belle **Sheikh M. B. M. Al Maktoum**
113 **OUTBACKER (IRE),** gr f Aussie Rules (USA)—Naomh Geileis (USA) **Mrs C. E. Budden**
114 **PACQUITA,** b f Dubawi (IRE)—Pryka (ARG) **Sheikh Hamdan Bin Mohammed Al Maktoum**
115 **PEMBROKESHIRE,** b c Shamardal (USA)—Solva **Sheikh Hamdan Bin Mohammed Al Maktoum**
116 **PETERKIN (IRE),** b c Invincible Spirit (IRE)—Alizes (NZ) **Sheikh Hamdan Bin Mohammed Al Maktoum**
117 **PIGEON PIE,** b f Bahamian Bounty—Pixie Ring **Ready To Run Partnership**
118 **PITON,** b g Archipenko (USA)—Scandalette **T T Bloodstocks**
119 **POTENT EMBRACE (USA),** b f Street Cry (IRE)—
    Karen's Caper (USA) **Sheikh Hamdan Bin Mohammed Al Maktoum**
120 **POWER UP,** b f Rail Link—Melpomene **Mrs C. E. Budden**
121 **QUICKASWECAN,** b c Shamardal (USA)—Arctic Air **D. C. Livingston**
122 **RIGHT OF APPEAL,** b g Dubawi (IRE)—Easy To Love (USA) **Sheikh Hamdan Bin Mohammed Al Maktoum**
123 **ROOKERY (IRE),** b c Raven's Pass (USA)—Zacheta **Sheikh Hamdan Bin Mohammed Al Maktoum**
124 **SHERSTON,** b g Shamardal (USA)—Shersha (IRE) **Sheikh Hamdan Bin Mohammed Al Maktoum**
125 **SIR CHARLIE KUNZ,** gr c Dalakhani (IRE)—Darrfonah (IRE) **P. Dean**

MR MARK JOHNSTON - Continued

126 SIR GUY PORTEOUS (IRE), ch g Shamardal (USA)—Ermine And Velvet **P. Dean**
127 SOMEWHAT (USA), b c Dynaformer (USA)—Sometime (IRE) **Sheikh M. B. M. Al Maktoum**
128 SPECIAL FIGHTER (IRE), ch c Teofilo (IRE)—Susu **Sheikh Hamdan Bin Mohammed Al Maktoum**
129 STETCHWORTH (IRE), ch c New Approach (IRE)—
Hallowed Park (IRE) **Sheikh Hamdan Bin Mohammed Al Maktoum**
130 STOUT CORTEZ, b g Hernando (FR)—Zooming (IRE) **J. D. Abell**
131 SWIVEL, ch c Shirocco (GER)—Pivotal Drive (IRE) **Sheikh Hamdan Bin Mohammed Al Maktoum**
132 TANSEEB, b g Royal Applause—Perfect Story (IRE) **Hamdan Al Maktoum**
133 TARRAFAL (IRE), b c Shamardal (USA)—Cape Verdi (IRE) **Sheikh Hamdan Bin Mohammed Al Maktoum**
134 TESTING (FR), gr f New Approach (IRE)—Testama (FR) **A. D. Spence**
135 B c Oratorio (IRE)—The Spirit of Pace (IRE) **Mrs J. Keaney**
136 TIZLOVE REGARDLESS (USA), b c Tiznow (USA)—Dianehill (IRE) **Crone Stud Farms Ltd**
137 TORCHLIGHTER (IRE), ch c Shamardal (USA)—Ever Love (BRZ) **Sheikh Hamdan Bin Mohammed Al Maktoum**
138 TORNADO CHALLENGE (USA), b c War Chant (USA)—Princess Kris **J. Abdullah**
139 TORRIDON, b c Bahamian Bounty—Intellibet One **Dr R. Holleyhead**
140 TRAFALGAR ROCK, b c Mount Nelson—Helter Helter (USA) **The New Fairyhouse Partnership**
141 WATERLORD, b c Cape Cross (IRE)—Shell Garland (USA) **Sheikh Hamdan Bin Mohammed Al Maktoum**
142 WATERSMEET, gr c Dansili—Under The Rainbow **Mr J. A. Barson**
143 ZANOUSKA (USA), b f Bernardini (USA)—Zanoubia (USA) **N. Mourad**
144 ZUMURUDAH (FR), b f Dubawi (IRE)—Brianza (USA) **J. Abdullah**

TWO-YEAR-OLDS

145 B c 5/3 Duke of Marmalade (IRE)—
Act of The Pace (IRE) (King's Theatre (IRE)) (15485) **Mark Johnston Racing Ltd**
146 Ch c 17/1 Iffraaj—
Alexander Youth (IRE) (Exceed And Excel (AUS)) (110000) **Sheikh Hamdan Bin Mohammed Al Maktoum**
147 B c 9/3 Raven's Pass (USA)—All's Forgotten (USA) (Darshaan) (15000) **Mrs J. E. Newett**
148 Ch f 1/2 Bahamian Bounty—Astrodonna (Carnival Dancer) (7619) **J. Abdullah**
149 BLACK N BLUE, ch c 14/4 Galileo (IRE)—Coyote (Indian Ridge) (190000) **A. D. Spence**
150 B f 14/3 Shamardal (USA)—Bright Morning (Dubai Millennium) **Sheikh Hamdan Bin Mohammed Al Maktoum**
151 B c 31/3 Bushranger (IRE)—Cakestown Lady (Petorius) (7742) **The New Fairyhouse Partnership**
152 B f 2/4 Halling (USA)—Caribbean Dancer (USA) (Theatrical) **Mr H. C. Hart**
153 CASILA (IRE), b f 9/2 High Chaparral (IRE)—Miletrian (IRE) (Marju (IRE)) (23228) **M. Wormald**
154 B c 17/2 Echo of Light—Concordia (Pivotal) **Sheikh Hamdan Bin Mohammed Al Maktoum**
155 B f 26/4 Shamardal (USA)—Crossover (Cape Cross (IRE)) **Sheikh Hamdan Bin Mohammed Al Maktoum**
156 B c 11/4 Rock of Gibraltar (IRE)—Cruel Sea (USA) (Mizzen Mast (USA)) (15000) **Mark Johnston Racing Ltd**
157 B f 8/5 Danehill Dancer (IRE)—Crystal Bull (USA) (Holy Bull (USA)) (24777) **Mark Johnston Racing Ltd**
158 B c 3/5 Street Cry (IRE)—Danelagh (AUS) (Danehill (USA)) **Sheikh Hamdan Bin Mohammed Al Maktoum**
159 B c 25/5 Pivotal—Danse Arabe (IRE) (Seeking The Gold (USA)) **Sheikh Hamdan Bin Mohammed Al Maktoum**
160 DIAZ (IRE), b c 7/2 Azamour (IRE)—New Girlfriend (IRE) (Diesis) (20905) **Mr J. S. Dean**
161 B c 15/5 Shamardal (USA)—
Discreet Brief (IRE) (Darshaan) (150000) **Sheikh Hamdan Bin Mohammed Al Maktoum**
162 DONNA GRACIOSA (GER), b f 24/4 Samum (GER)—
Donna Alicia (GER) (Highland Chieftain) (15485) **Mr A. Al Mansoori**
163 B c 4/2 Shamardal (USA)—
Dubai Opera (IRE) (Dubai Millennium) **Sheikh Hamdan Bin Mohammed Al Maktoum**
164 B f 6/4 Shamardal (USA)—Dunnes River (USA) (Danzig) (USA)) **Sheikh Hamdan Bin Mohammed Al Maktoum**
165 B c 20/5 Shamardal (USA)—Flamelet (USA) (Theatrical) **Sheikh Hamdan Bin Mohammed Al Maktoum**
166 Ch f 24/2 Teofilo (IRE)—Fragrancy (IRE) (Singspiel (IRE)) (100000) **A. D. Spence**
167 FREIGHT TRAIN (IRE), b c 20/2 Manduro (GER)—Sigonella (IRE) (Priolo (USA)) (54200) **A. D. Spence**
168 B c 20/2 Echo of Light—Hawsa (USA) (Rahy (USA)) **Sheikh Hamdan Bin Mohammed Al Maktoum**
169 KIFAAYA, b c 14/2 Intikhab (USA)—Juniper Girl (IRE) (Revoque (IRE)) (80000) **Hamdan Al Maktoum**
170 B c 4/7 Jalil (USA)—Laughsome (Be My Guest (USA)) **Sheikh Hamdan Bin Mohammed Al Maktoum**
171 B f 18/1 Mastercraftsman (IRE)—Linorova (USA) (Trempolino (USA)) (23228) **A. D. Spence**
172 B c 2/4 Excellent Art—Mac Melody (IRE) (Entrepreneur) (3871) **Mrs R. Broadbent**
173 MACSHEESH (IRE), b c 25/1 Azamour (IRE)—
Princess Roseburg (USA) (Johannesburg (USA)) (7742) **M. C. MacKenzie**
174 B f 3/3 Makfi—Mambo Halo (USA) (Southern Halo (USA)) (38000) **Around The World Partnership**
175 MANSHAA (IRE), ch c 18/3 Dubawi (IRE)—Ghizlaan (USA) (Seeking The Gold (USA)) **Hamdan Al Maktoum**
176 MARTINIQUAISE, b f 8/2 Mawatheeq (USA)—Maria di Scozia (Selkirk (USA)) **Miss K. Rausing**
177 Ch f 11/4 Three Valleys (USA)—Melpomene (Peintre Celebre (USA)) **Mrs C. E. Budden**
178 B c 5/4 Iffraaj—Mike's Wildcat (USA) (Forest Wildcat (USA)) **Sheikh Hamdan Bin Mohammed Al Maktoum**
179 B c 19/3 Shamardal (USA)—Mille (Dubai Millennium) **Sheikh Hamdan Bin Mohammed Al Maktoum**
180 B c 29/3 Cape Cross (IRE)—
Mirina (FR) (Pursuit of Love) (108401) **Sheikh Hamdan Bin Mohammed Al Maktoum**

MR MARK JOHNSTON - Continued

181 **MISS EXCELLENCE,** b f 3/4 Exceed And Excel (AUS)—
   Hunter's Fortune (USA) (Charismatic (USA)) (20000) **Greenland Park Stud**
182 Br c 13/4 Cape Cross (IRE)—Miss Ivanhoe (IRE) (Selkirk (USA)) (70000) **Mr A. Al Mansoori**
183 B f 1/4 Aqlaam—Missisipi Star (IRE) (Mujahid (USA)) (42586) **G. R. Bailey Ltd**
184 **MISTRESS MAKFI (IRE),** ch f 17/2 Makfi—
   Rapid Ransom (USA) (Red Ransom (USA)) (23228) **Mrs S Bianco & Ms J Bianco**
185 **MONT D'ARGENT,** gr c 3/2 Montjeu (IRE)—Ayla (IRE) (Daylami (IRE)) (90000) **Mrs J. E. Newett**
186 **MUKHMAL (IRE),** ch c 11/4 Bahamian Bounty—
   May Day Queen (IRE) (Danetime (IRE)) (57142) **Hamdan Al Maktoum**
187 **MUTAFARREJ,** b c 4/2 Paco Boy (IRE)—Crinkle (IRE) (Distant Relative) (123809) **Hamdan Al Maktoum**
188 B c 29/2 Pivotal—Mysterial (USA) (Alleged (USA)) **Sheikh Hamdan Bin Mohammed Al Maktoum**
189 **MYTHICAL CITY (IRE),** b f 16/3 Rock of Gibraltar (IRE)—
   Rainbow City (IRE) (Rainbow Quest (USA)) (9291) **Miss E Asprey, Mr C Wright, Mr W Carson**
190 B f 12/3 Holy Roman Emperor (IRE)—Naomh Geileis (USA) (Grand Slam (USA)) **Mrs C. E. Budden**
191 Ro c 5/3 Dalakhani (IRE)—Noble Galileo (IRE) (Galileo (IRE)) (3500) **Mark Johnston Racing Ltd**
192 **NOMENKLATURA,** b f 8/2 Archipenko (USA)—Ninotchka (USA) (Nijinsky (CAN)) **Miss K. Rausing**
193 Br c 3/5 Danehill Dancer (IRE)—Obsessive (USA) (Seeking The Gold (USA)) (50328) **Mrs J. E. Newett**
194 B c 12/4 Shamardal (USA)—
   Ocean Silk (USA) (Dynaformer (USA)) **Sheikh Hamdan Bin Mohammed Al Maktoum**
195 **OREGON GIFT,** b c 11/2 Major Cadeaux—Dayville (USA) (Dayjur (USA)) (22000) **N. N. Browne**
196 B c 18/4 Invincible Spirit (IRE)—
   Persian Secret (FR) (Persian Heights) **Sheikh Hamdan Bin Mohammed Al Maktoum**
197 B f 13/3 Thewayyouare (USA)—Prima Volta (Primo Dominie) (5420) **Mark Johnston Racing Ltd**
198 Br f 9/5 Jeremy (USA)—Princess Atoosa (USA) (Gone West (USA)) (17034) **Mrs R. Broadbent**
199 B c 30/4 Pivotal—Punctilious (Danehill (USA)) **Sheikh Hamdan Bin Mohammed Al Maktoum**
200 Ch f 8/2 Raven's Pass (USA)—Rasana (Royal Academy (USA)) (17034) **J. Abdullah**
201 **REGAL WAYS (IRE),** b br f 22/3 Royal Applause—
   Step This Way (USA) (Giant's Causeway (USA)) (19047) **S. R. Counsell**
202 B f 7/2 Archipenko (USA)—Roses From Ridey (IRE) (Petorius) (5420) **The New Fairyhouse Partnership**
203 Bc 17/2 Dark Angel (IRE)—Scarlet O'hara (IRE) (Sadler's Wells) (24777) **J. Abdullah**
204 B gr c 22/3 Iffraaj—Screen Star (IRE) (Tobougg (IRE)) **Sheikh Hamdan Bin Mohammed Al Maktoum**
205 B f 1/5 Equiano (FR)—Shersha (IRE) (Priolo (USA)) (15000) **Mark Johnston Racing Ltd**
206 B c 13/3 Shamardal (USA)—
   Shinko Hermes (IRE) (Sadler's Wells) **Sheikh Hamdan Bin Mohammed Al Maktoum**
207 B c 5/5 Bellamy Road (USA)—Sometime (IRE) (Royal Academy (USA)) (58428) **Sheikh M. B. M. Al Maktoum**
208 B c 31/3 Invincible Spirit (IRE)—
   Subtle Charm (Machiavellian (USA)) **Sheikh Hamdan Bin Mohammed Al Maktoum**
209 B c 24/3 Mount Nelson—Sunley Gift (Cadeaux Genereux) (50000) **Newsells Park Stud Limited**
210 **SUREWECAN,** b c 21/4 Royal Applause—Edge of Light (Xaar) (30000) **D. C. Livingston**
211 **TADARROK,** ch c 6/2 Elusive Quality (USA)—
   Don't Forget Faith (Victory Gallop (CAN)) (75000) **Hamdan Al Maktoum**
212 B f 13/3 Makfi—Terentia (Diktat) (26000) **Mark Johnston Racing Ltd**
213 **THINK SNOW (USA),** ch f 10/3 Giant's Causeway (USA)—
   Snow Forest (USA) (Woodman (USA)) (40899) **Mr Christopher Wright & Vicky Snook**
214 Ch c 11/2 Bahamian Bounty—Touching (IRE) (Kheleyf (USA)) (100000) **Mr A. Al Mansoori**
215 **VIVE MA FILLE (GER),** b f 2/4 Doyen (IRE)—
   Vive Madame (GER) (Big Shuffle (USA)) (13162) **Atlantic Racing & R W Huggins**
216 **YORKIDDING,** b f 24/3 Dalakhani (IRE)—Claxon (Caerleon (USA)) (140000) **Mr P. R. York**
217 **YORKIE TALKIE (IRE),** bc 13/2 Paco Boy (IRE) Ultra Finesse (Rahy (USA)) (42000) **Mr P. R. York**
218 **YORKSHIRE SPIRIT,** b f 5/4 Sea The Stars (IRE)—Paracel (USA) (Gone West (USA)) (90000) **Mr P. R. York**
219 B c 24/3 Bahri—Young Sue (Local Suitor (USA)) **C. H. Greensit & W. A. Greensit**

Other Owners: Miss E. Asprey, Mr B. Bennett, Mrs S. Bianco, Ms J. F. Bianco, E. Brierley, M. Budden, M. Budden, Mr A. J. Burke, W. F. H. Carson, Mrs E. Carson, Mr N. De Chambure, Mr Eric De Chambure, The Duke of Devonshire, Mrs S. P. B. Frosell, M. W. Graff, A. Greenhalgh, C. H. Greensit, W. A. Greensit, Mr T. Heywood, Mr R. B. Huckerby, J. R. Kennedy, Exors of the Late Mrs Y. J. Kennedy, Mrs J. E. Knight, Mr A. A. Larnach, Mr M. R. Lonsdorfer, Mrs J. Matthews-Griffiths, Mr D. C. Mercer, G. Mercer, Mr C. Norton, Mr S. J. Richards, Mrs D. L. K. Richards, The Duke Of Roxburghe, Mrs V. M. Snook, C. Wachter, J. Wachter, C. N. Wright.

Assistant Trainers: Deirdre Johnston & Jock Bennett

Jockey (flat): Silvestre De Sousa, Joe Fanning.

359 **MR ALAN JONES, Minehead**
Postal: **East Harwood Farm, Timberscombe, Minehead, Somerset, TA24 7UE**
Contacts: **FAX 01633 680232 MOBILE (07901) 505064**
E-MAIL heritageracing@btconnect.com WEBSITE www.alanjonesracing.co.uk

1 ARCAS (IRE), 5, br g Shamardal (USA)—Callisto (IRE) **G. Doel**
2 BROGEEN BOY (IRE), 6, br g Golan (IRE)—Brogeen Lady (IRE) **Mr T. S. M. S. Riley-Smith**
3 BULL MARKET (IRE), 11, b g Danehill (USA)—Paper Moon (IRE) **Burnham Plastering & Drylining Ltd**
4 GUEST BOOK (IRE), 7, b g Green Desert (USA)—Your Welcome **Mr T. S. M. S. Riley-Smith**
5 HIDDENSEE (USA), 12, b g Cozzene (USA)—Zarani Sidi Anna (USA) **Mr T. S. M. S. Riley-Smith**
6 HUMBEL BEN (IRE), 11, br g Humbel (USA)—Donegans Daughter **Burnham Plastering & Drylining Ltd**
7 LETS GET CRACKING (FR), 10, gr g Anabaa Blue—Queenhood (FR) **Mr T. S. M. S. Riley-Smith**
8 MA'IRE RUA (IRE), 7, ch g Presenting—Long Acre **Mr T. S. M. S. Riley-Smith**
9 NORISAN, 10, ch g Inchinor—Dream On Deya (IRE) **Burnham Plastering & Drylining Ltd**
10 QUINCY DES PICTONS (FR), 10, b g Kadalko (FR)—
Izabel des Pictons (FR) **Burnham Plastering & Drylining Ltd**
11 REST AND BE (IRE), 7, b br m Vinnie Roe (IRE)—Bobs Star (IRE) **Mr T. S. M. S. Riley-Smith**
12 SECRET DANCER (IRE), 9, b g Sadler's Wells (USA)—Discreet Brief (IRE) **Burnham Plastering & Drylining Ltd**
13 SUPERNOVERRE (IRE), 8, b g Noverre (USA)—Caviare **Mr T. S. M. S. Riley-Smith**
14 SUTES, 6, b g Kahyasi—Misleain (USA) **Mr T. S. M. S. Riley-Smith**
15 TIQUER (FR), 6, b g Equerry (USA)—Tirenna (FR) **Burnham Plastering & Drylining Ltd**
16 WITH HINDSIGHT (IRE), 6, ch g Ad Valorem (USA)—Lady From Limerick (IRE) **Mr T. S. M. S. Riley-Smith**

THREE-YEAR-OLDS
17 SONG OF ROWLAND (IRE), b g Holy Roman Emperor (IRE)—Makarova (IRE) **Mr T. S. M. S. Riley-Smith**

Assistant Trainer: Miss A. Bartelink

Jockey (NH): Richard Johnson, Paddy Brennan, Tom O' Brien. **Amateur:** Mr O. Greenall.

360 **MR GEORGE JONES, Tenbury Wells**
Postal: **13 Market Square, Tenbury Wells, Worcestershire, WR15 8BL**

1 ALMOWJ, 11, b g Fasliyev (USA)—Tiriana **Mrs A. M. McCartney**
2 MI MAN SAM (IRE), 9, ch g Exit To Nowhere (USA)—Brinawa (IRE)
Other Owners: G. H. Jones.

361 **MS LUCY JONES, Kilgetty**
Postal: **2 South Row, Cresselly, Kilgetty, Pembrokeshire, SA68 0SR**
Contacts: **MOBILE (07973) 689040**
E-MAIL info@cleddauracing.co.uk WEBSITE www.cleddauracing.co.uk

1 ANNIMATION (IRE), 10, b m Accordion—Euro Breeze (IRE) **S. Jones**
2 GENUINE ART, 7, b m Generosity—Impulsive Bid (IRE) **Mr A. A. Palmer**
3 IFYOUTHINKSO, 7, b g Hernando (FR)—Evriza (FR) **Mrs J. M. Edmonds**
4 PRINCE PIPPIN (IRE), 8, b g King Charlemagne (USA)—Staploy **Mr H. D. R. Harrison-Allen**
5 RAVING RENEE, 6, b m Overbury (IRE)—Chartridge Hill **S. Jones**
6 SUPREME BOB (IRE), 8, b g Bob's Return—Suprememories (IRE) **Mrs J. M. Edmonds**
7 TOE TO TOE (IRE), 6, br g Presenting—Tavildara (IRE) **Palms Landscaping Limited**

362 **MRS VIOLET M. JORDAN, Moreton Morrell**
Postal: **Far Westfields Farm, Moreton Morrell, Warwick, Warwickshire, CV35 9DB**
Contacts: **MOBILE (07831) 101632**
E-MAIL jordyracer29@hotmail.co.uk

1 ALACCORDION, 9, br g Alflora (IRE)—Song For Jess (IRE) **Farmers & Cricketers Partnership**
2 ALL THE FASHION (IRE), 10, br m Alflora (IRE)—Fashion Day **Mrs Violet M. Jordan**
3 CLOUDY START, 8, b g Oasis Dream—Set Fair (USA) **A. Cocum**
4 FORMEDABLE (IRE), 12, ch g Moonax (IRE)—Castle Flame (IRE) **Farmers & Cricketers Partnership**

MRS VIOLET M. JORDAN - Continued

5 **KILFINICHEN BAY (IRE)**, 6, b g Westerner—Cailin Deas (IRE) **Cracker Syndicate**
6 **KILLFINNAN CASTLE (IRE)**, 11, br g Arctic Lord—Golden Seekers **Mrs Violet M. Jordan**
7 **LITTLE CARMELA**, 10, gr m Beat Hollow—Carmela Owen **Near & Far Racing**
8 **MON REVE**, 6, br m Fair Mix (IRE)—Song For Jess (IRE) **Mrs Violet M. Jordan**
9 **WOLF HALL (IRE)**, 7, br g Presenting—Water Rock **Mrs Violet M. Jordan**

THREE-YEAR-OLDS

10 **MEESON**, gr g Fair Mix (IRE)—Premiere Foulee (FR)

Other Owners: Mr S. Aspinall, R. K. Betts, Mr N. S. Pearse, Mr D. J. Pearson, D. M. Thornton, Mrs J. G. Williams.

Assistant Trainer: Gaye Williams

---

363   MR TOM KEDDY, Newmarket
Postal: **246 Exning Road, Newmarket, Suffolk, CB8 0AN**
Contacts: **PHONE** (01638) 561498 **FAX** (01638) 561498 **MOBILE** (07542) 036544/(07745) 238018
E-MAIL tkracing1@hotmail.co.uk

1 **ARCHIE RICE (USA)**, 8, b g Arch (USA)—Gold Bowl (USA) **Mrs H. E. Keddy**
2 **GREYFRIARSCHORISTA**, 7, ch g King's Best (USA)—Misty Heights **Hayley Keddy, Lynn Lambert, Val Beeson**
3 **PISCEAN (USA)**, 9, b br g Stravinsky (USA)—Navasha (USA) **A. J. Duffield**

Other Owners: Mrs V. M. Beeson, Mrs L. M. Lambert.

Assistant Trainer: Hayley Keddy

Jockey (NH): Jack Quinlan. **Apprentice:** Ryan Clark.

---

364   MRS CAROLINE KEEVIL, Motcombe
Postal: **Larkinglass Farm, Motcombe, Shaftesbury, Dorset, SP7 9HY**
Contacts: **PHONE** (07768) 867424 **FAX** (01761) 463927 **MOBILE** (07768) 867424
E-MAIL carolinekeevil@yahoo.co.uk

1 **BALLY LEGEND**, 9, b g Midnight Legend—Bally Lira **B. A. Derrick**
2 **CANARBINO GIRL**, 7, b m Beat All (USA)—Peasedown Tofana **Lady Sutton**
3 **CINEVATOR (IRE)**, 7, b g Dr Massini (IRE)—Hurricane Bella (IRE) **The Optimist & Pessimist Partnership**
4 **CLOUDY LADY**, 6, gr m Alflora (IRE)—Cirrious **P. L. Hart**
5 **COOL FANTASY (IRE)**, 5, b g One Cool Cat (USA)—Regal Fantasy (IRE) **Mrs C. Keevil**
6 **DARKESTBEFOREDAWN (IRE)**, 7, br g Dr Massini (IRE)—Camden Dolphin (IRE) **The Jago Family Partnership**
7 **GENERAL GIRLING**, 7, b g General Gambul—Gold Charm **The Yeovilton Flyers**
8 **JACK BY THE HEDGE**, 5, b g Overbury (IRE)—Bluebell Path **Mrs Sara Biggins & Mrs Celia Djivanovic**
9 **JUDGE DAVIS**, 7, b g Alflora (IRE)—Minimum **Gale Force Three**
10 **KNIGHT OFTHE REALM**, 5, b g Kayf Tara—Flow **Mrs H. R. Dunn**
11 **LA MADONNINA (IRE)**, 6, b m Milan—Supreme Nova **Mrs H. R. Dunn**
12 **LARKS RISING**, 6, b g Relief Pitcher—Black A Brook (IRE) **Mrs L. R. Lovell**
13 **LARKS WING (IRE)**, 6, b g Desert King (IRE)—Thyne Square (IRE) **The Optimist & Pessimist Partnership**
14 **MATAKO (FR)**, 11, b g Nikos—Verabatim (FR) **P. M. Bryant**
15 **MIDNIGHT LIRA**, 7, ch m Midnight Legend—Bally Lira **B. A. Derrick**
16 **MOORLAND SUNSET**, 7, b g Pasternak—Lady Harriet Luis **Moorland Sunset Partnership**
17 **MRS WINCHESTER (IRE)**, 5, b m Scorpion (IRE)—Supreme Nova **Mrs H. R. Dunn**
18 **MUTASHABEK (USA)**, 4, b g Arch (USA)—Siyadah (USA) **Hamdan Al Maktoum**
19 **POD**, 6, b g Tikkanen—Opal'lou (FR) **Mrs H. R. Dunn**
20 **PUSH TO EXIT**, 6, b g Exit To Nowhere (USA)—Shiny Thing (USA) **The Deep Pockets Partnership**
21 **REGAL FLOW**, 7, b g Erhaab (USA)—Flow **Mrs H. R. Dunn**
22 **SHADDAII (FR)**, 8, gr g April Night (FR)—Gypsie d'artois (FR) **Mrs C. E. Davies**
23 **SOUTHFIELD BELLE (IRE)**, 5, b m Presenting—Laureldean Belle (IRE) **Mrs A. B. Yeoman**
24 **STRAWBERRY HILL (IRE)**, 8, b g Winged Love (IRE)—Icydora (IRE) **K S B Bloodstock**
25 **SYLVAN LEGEND**, 6, b g Midnight Legend—Sylvan Warbler (USA) **B. A. Derrick**
26 **TAMIRA**, 7, b m Tamure—Welsh Lustre (IRE) **Mrs L. R. Lovell**
27 **TIME DO (FR)**, 7, ch g Grand Tresor (FR)—Demoiselle Do (FR) **Mrs L. R. Lovell**
28 **WHAT LARKS (IRE)**, 6, b g Pierre—Bint Rosie **Mrs C. Keevil**

MRS CAROLINE KEEVIL - Continued

Other Owners: Mr T. R. A. Bartlett, Mr K. W. Biggins, Mrs S. J. Biggins, Mr P. D. Biss, Mrs J. L. Biss, Mr W. R. Bougourd, Mrs S. S. Cole, Mrs C. J. Djivanovic, Mr M. Doughty, Mr A. P. Gale, Mrs A. J. Girling, Mr A. Girling, Mr P. J. A. Jago, Mrs J. L. Jago, Miss M. L. A. Jago, Mr F. C. A. Jago, P. F. Popham, Mrs M. E. Stirratt.

Jockey (NH): Will Kennedy, Tom O'Brien, Ian Popham.

---

365 MR MARTIN KEIGHLEY, Cheltenham
Postal: **Condicote Stables, Luckley, Moreton-In-Marsh, Gloucestershire, GL56 0RD**
Contacts: **MOBILE (07767) 472547**
E-MAIL info@martinkeighleyracing.com WEBSITE www.martinkeighleyracing.com

1 **ALTESSE DE GUYE (FR)**, 4, ch f Dom Alco (FR)—Mascotte de Guye (FR) **Daydream Believers**
2 **ALWAYS BOLD (IRE)**, 9, ch g King's Best (USA)—Tarakana (USA) **Mrs B. J. Keighley**
3 **ANNACOTTY (IRE)**, 6, b g Beneficial—Mini Moo Min **Mrs E. A. Prowting**
4 **ANY CURRENCY (IRE)**, 11, b g Moscow Society (USA)—Native Bavard (IRE) **Cash Is King**
5 **BENBANE HEAD (USA)**, 10, ch g Giant's Causeway (USA)—Prospectress (USA) **Mrs L. Jones**
6 **BOLD TARA**, 7, b m Kayf Tara—Bruley **Mrs Anne Lee-Warner**
7 **CASTLE CHEETAH (IRE)**, 6, br g Presenting—Castle Crystal (IRE) **Mr B. Eccles**
8 **CHAMPION COURT (IRE)**, 9, b g Court Cave (IRE)—Mooneys Hill (IRE) **M. Boothright**
9 **COURT IN SESSION (IRE)**, 9, b g Court Cave (IRE)—Dangerous Dolly (IRE) **The Figjam Partnership**
10 **COYABA**, 4, b g Midnight Legend—Peel Me A Grape **Mrs E. A. Prowting**
11 **CREEPY (IRE)**, 6, b g Westerner—Prowler (IRE) **M. Boothright, T. Hanlon, S. Harman**
12 **DIVINE INTAVENTION (IRE)**, 10, b g Exit To Nowhere (USA)—Merrill Gaye (IRE) **Mr H. E. L. Wilson**
13 **EPIC STORM (IRE)**, 6, b g Montjeu (IRE)—Jaya (USA) **Mr T. J. F. Exell**
14 **FAULTLESS FEELINGS (IRE)**, 8, b g Milan—Duchess of Cork (IRE) **Mrs E. A. Prowting**
15 **FLEMENTIME (IRE)**, 6, ch m Flemensfirth (USA)—Funny Times **Figjam II**
16 **GEORGIAN KING**, 11, b g Overbury (IRE)—Roslin **R. Allsop**
17 **HAIL TIBERIUS**, 7, b g Iktibas—Untidy Daughter **Mr T. J. F. Exell**
18 **HAVINGOTASCOOBYDO (IRE)**, 9, b g Witness Box (USA)
    In Blue (IRE) **D Bishop C Bowkley M Parker D Wilson**
19 **JEANS LADY**, 5, b m Milan—Indian Miss **D. G. Robinson**
20 **JOHNNY OG**, 5, b g Flemensfirth (USA)—Mrs Roberts **T.Hanlon M.Boothright S.Hanlon N.Martin**
21 **KYLES FAITH (IRE)**, 6, b g Court Cave (IRE)—Littleton Liberty **Mrs B. J. Keighley**
22 **MAURICETHEATHLETE (IRE)**, 11, b g Sayarshan (FR)—Ardagh Princess **Mr A. G. Slatter**
23 **MERLIN'S WISH**, 9, gr g Terimon—Sendai **Miss R. Toppin**
24 **MONTY'S REVENGE (IRE)**, 9, b g Bob's Return (IRE)—Native Bavard (IRE) **The Red Socks**
25 **MORTLESTOWN (IRE)**, 6, b g Milan—Pima (IRE) **M. Boothright**
26 **PRIMO CAPITANO (IRE)**, 6, b g Milan—Miss Mayberry (IRE) **Owners For Owners: Primo Capitano**
27 **PYLEIGH LASS**, 8, gr m Silver Patriarch (IRE)—Lady Callernish **F. D. Popham**
28 **RIGHT ON ROY**, 4, b g Double Trigger (IRE)—One Wild Night **Mr R. E. Bailey**
29 **SEQUOIA FOREST**, 5, gr g Proclamation (IRE)—Armada Grove **Mrs K. J Foster-Smith**
30 **SEYMOUR ERIC**, 9, b g Bollin Eric—Seymour Chance **Mrs C J Black & Ten Out Of Ten Racing**
31 **THE KVILLEKEN**, 6, b g Fair Mix (IRE)—Wannaplantatree **M. Boothright**
32 **THE WEXFORDIAN (IRE)**, 5, b g Shantou (USA)—Going My Way
33 **TYPHON DE GUYE (FR)**, 7, ch g Dom Alco (FR)—Mascotte de Guye (FR) **Daydream Believers**
34 **UP IN FLAMES (IRE)**, 5, b g Red Clubs (IRE)—Flames **M. Boothright**
35 **VIKING MISTRESS**, 6, b m Bollin Eric—Mistress Caramore (IRE) **Mrs S. L. Richardson**
36 **WESTERLY BREEZE (IRE)**, 6, b g Westerner—Sup A Whiskey (IRE) **P. R. Armour**

THREE-YEAR-OLDS
37 **MORNING HERALD**, br f Lucky Story (USA)—Wakeful

Other Owners: Mr N. Bannister, Mr S. Bannister, D. Bishop, Mrs C. J. Black, Mr C. Bowkley, Mr P. K. Davis, Mr T. J. Dykes, Mr G. Ellis, Mr T. Hanlon, S. R. Harman, Mr E. J. Hughes, Mr M. Johnson, M. H. Keighley, Dr M. M. Ogilvy, Mr M. D. Parker, Mr P. R. Thomas, G. M. Thornton, Mr P. H. Watts, Mr D. A. Wilson.

Assistant Trainer: Mrs Belinda Keighley

Jockey (NH): Alain Cawley, Ian Popham. **Conditional:** Daniel Hiskett.

366 MR CHRISTOPHER KELLETT, Swadlincote
Postal: **Jubilee Racing Stables, Snarestone Road, Appleby Magna, Swadlincote, Derbyshire, DE12 7AJ**
Contacts: **PHONE (01530) 515395 FAX (01530) 515395 MOBILE (07966) 097989**
E-MAIL christopherkellett@btinternet.com WEBSITE www.chriskellettracing.co.uk

1 AMAZINGREYCE, 9, gr m Rainbow High—Lightning Belle **Miss S. L. Bailey**
2 BELLA BIJOU, 4, br f Multiplex—Madam Bijou **Miss S. L. Walley**
3 BRYTER LAYTER, 4, b g Deportivo—Bahhmirage (IRE) **Miss S. L. Walley**
4 CASH IN HAND (IRE), 14, b g Charente River (IRE)—Fern Fields (IRE) **Miss S. L. Bailey**
5 DIAMOND PRO (IRE), 5, b g Diamond Green (FR)—Speedbird (USA) **J. E. Titley**
6 MR SQUIRREL (IRE), 7, gr g Great Palm (USA)—
                                    Patsy Donnellan (IRE) **D. H. Muir & Exors of the Late Mrs R. E. Muir**
7 NEXT TO NOWHERE (IRE), 9, ch g Exit To Nowhere (USA)—
                                    Zarote (IRE) **D. H. Muir & Exors of the Late Mrs R. E. Muir**
8 NORTHWOLD, 10, b g Cloudings (IRE)—Briery Gale **D. H. Muir & Exors of the Late Mrs R. E. Muir**
9 PRAVDA STREET, 9, ch g Soviet Star (USA)—Sari **The Edwardsons**
10 SING ALONE, 8, ch g Band On The Run—Remalone **T. E. Wardall**
11 SPACECRAFT (IRE), 7, b g Starcraft (NZ)—Brazilian Samba (IRE) **The Edwardsons**
12 SPANISH TRAIL, 5, b m Rail Link—La Coruna **G. C. Chipman**
13 UPPER LAMBOURN (IRE), 6, b g Exceed And Excel (AUS)—In The Fashion (IRE) **The Edwardsons**
14 WESTON LODGE (IRE), 8, b g Aahsaylad—Slip Me Fippence **D. H. Muir & Exors of the Late Mrs R. E. Muir**

Other Owners: Mr K. W. Edwardson, Mrs J. L. Edwardson, D. H. Muir, Exors of the Late Mrs R. E. Muir.

367 MISS GAY KELLEWAY, Newmarket
Postal: **Queen Alexandra Stables, 2 Chapel Street, Exning, Newmarket, Suffolk, CB8 7HA**
Contacts: **PHONE (01638) 577778 MOBILE (07974) 948768**
E-MAIL gaykellewayracing@hotmail.co.uk WEBSITE www.gaykellewayracing.com

1 CONDUCTING, 6, b g Oratorio (IRE)—Aiming **John Farley & Ben Parish**
2 DESTINY HIGHWAY (FR), 4, b g Sir Percy—Grace Bankes **Miss G. M. Kelleway**
3 KNIGHT CHARM, 4, b g Haafhd—Enchanted Princess **Ben Parish & Gay Kelleway**
4 LAYLINE (IRE), 7, b g King's Best (USA)—Belle Reine **J Cranwell, B Smith & N Scandrett**
5 MUNGO PARK, 6, b g Selkirk (USA)—Key Academy **M. M. Foulger**
6 PIXILATED, 4, b g Phoenix Reach (IRE)—Chocolada **Patricia Crook & Francis Aspin**
7 ROYAL ALCOR (IRE), 7, b g Chevalier (IRE)—Arundhati **A MacLennan, G Kelleway & P Kerridge**
8 SMILESWITHHEREYES (USA), 4, ch f Mr Greeley (USA)—Russian Lullaby (IRE) **Matt Bartram & Gay Kelleway**
9 SWING ALONE (IRE), 5, b g Celtic Swing—Groupetime (USA) **Whatley, Stanbrook, Brown & Kelleway**
10 UPHOLD, 7, b g Oasis Dream—Allegro Viva (USA) **Miss G. M. Kelleway**
11 YOJOJO (IRE), 5, ch m Windsor Knot (IRE)—Belle of The Blues (IRE) **Winterbeck Manor Stud Ltd**

THREE-YEAR-OLDS

12 ACT OF CHARITY (IRE), b c Royal Applause—Kay Es Jay (FR) **Mr Y. C. Wong**
13 AUSTERIAN, ro c Mastercraftsman (IRE)—Singed **Mr R. Ng**
14 BERTIE BABY, b f Bertolini (USA)—Los Organos (IRE) **Mrs S. Bailey**
15 BLACK TIE DANCER (IRE), gr g Mastercraftsman (IRE)—Opera Star (IRE) **Paul Kerridge & Ben Parish**
16 CHANCEUSE, b f Lucky Story (USA)—Miss Madame (IRE) **Mr B. M. Parish**
17 DANZKI (IRE), b c Bushranger (IRE)—Miniver (IRE) **Mr R. Ng**
18 DOMINANDROS (FR), b c Teofilo (IRE)—Afya **Winterbeck Manor Stud & Partners**
19 LUCKY VISIONE, b g Lucky Story (USA)—Maid For Running **Hodson, Tyler, Bartram & McLean**
20 MIZZENI (FR), gr c Verglas (IRE)—Bashful (IRE) **Mr R. Ng**
21 SEALED (USA), b br c Speightstown (USA)—Sinister Sister (USA) **Mr R. Ng**
22 SOUL OF MOTION, b c Phoenix Reach (IRE)—Chocolada **Matt Bartram, Gay Kelleway & Adrian Parr**
23 STOSUR (IRE), b f Mount Nelson—Jules (IRE) **B. C. Oakley**
24 SUNNINGDALE ROSE (IRE), b f Art Connoisseur (IRE)—Eloquent Rose (IRE) **Mr B. M. Parish**
25 VALUE (IRE), gr f Clodovil (IRE)—Shalev (GER) **Mr A. G. MacLennan**

TWO-YEAR-OLDS

26 NEW ABBEY DANCER (IRE), b f 15/2 Thewayyouare (USA)—
                                Brave Cat (IRE) (Catrail (USA)) (6000) **Mr A. G. MacLennan**
27 Ch c 28/4 Lookin At Lucky (USA)—Rose of Zollern (IRE) (Seattle Dancer (USA)) (36000) **Mr Y. C. Wong**
28 B c 13/4 Mastercraftsman (IRE)—Thats Your Opinion (Last Tycoon) (32000) **Mr Y. C. Wong**

MISS GAY KELLEWAY - Continued

Other Owners: Mr F. E. Aspin, Mr M. Bartram, D. A. Brown, Mr J. T. Cranwell, Miss P. F. Crook, Mr J. W. Farley, Mr T. Hawthorne, Mr G. A. Hodson, Mr P. B. Kerridge, Mrs J. B. M. Mathieson, A. B. Parr, N. S. Scandrett, R. W. Smith, Mrs L. C. Stanbrook, Mr P. R. Tyler, M. C. Whatley.

Head Girl: Liz Mullin

Jockey (NH): Jamie Moore. **Apprentice:** Lauren Hunter.

368
MISS LYNSEY KENDALL, Carlisle
Postal: **The Stables, Lambley Bank, Scotby, Carlisle, Cumbria, CA4 8BX**
Contacts: **PHONE (01228) 513069 MOBILE (07818) 487227**
E-MAIL **lynseykendall@hotmail.co.uk**

1 **GRIMWITH**, 7, b g Doyen (IRE)—Poyle Caitlin (IRE) **Mr & Mrs R. S. Kendall**

Other Owners: Mr R. S. Kendall, Mrs M. E. Kendall.

369
MR NICK KENT, Brigg
Postal: **Newstead House, Newstead Priory, Cadney Road, Brigg, Lincolnshire, DN20 9HP**
Contacts: **PHONE (01652) 650628 MOBILE (07710) 644428**
E-MAIL **nick@nickkent.co.uk** WEBSITE **www.nickkent.co.uk**

1 **AROUND A POUND (IRE)**, 9, b g Old Vic—Mary Ellen Best (IRE) **Nick Kent Racing Club**
2 **BOWIE (IRE)**, 7, br g Pelder (IRE)—La Fenice (IRE) **Cynthia Commons, Marina Kent, Nick Kent**
3 **CELTIC SIXPENCE (IRE)**, 6, b m Celtic Swing—Penny Ha'penny **Cynthia Commons, Nick Kent**
4 **COMBUSTIBLE KATE (IRE)**, 8, b m Mr Combustible (IRE)—Aussie Hope **Nick Kent Racing Club II**
5 5, Ch g Pelder (IRE)—Concinna (FR) **J. N. Kent**
6 **DOTING**, 5, b g Pursuit of Love—Star Sign **G. N. Parker**
7 5, B g Grape Tree Road—Dutch Czarina
8 4, Ch f Primo Valentino (IRE)—Farmer's Pet **J. N. Kent**
9 **GONALSTON CLOUD (IRE)**, 7, gr g Cloudings (IRE)—Roseoengus (IRE) **R. J. Jackson**
10 **IVANS BACK (IRE)**, 9, b g Soviet Star (USA)—Better Back Off (IRE) **Ms V. M. Cottingham**
11 **KELLSLODGE (IRE)**, 7, b g Masterful (USA)—Connaught Lace **Nick Kent Racing Club**
12 **LOST IN NEWYORK (IRE)**, 7, b g Arakan (USA)—Lace Flower **Timbercare Racing Partnership**
13 **PALMARRICK (IRE)**, 7, b g Great Palm (USA)—Lynrick Lady (IRE) **Mr A. R. P. Parkin**
14 **SKYFIRE**, 7, ch g Storm Cat (USA)—Sunray Superstar **Cynthia Commons, Nick Kent**

THREE-YEAR-OLDS
15 B gr f Great Palm (USA)—Millquista d'or **Liz Horn**
16 **WEISSE GIRL**, b f Halling (USA)—White Turf (GER) **J. N. Kent**

Other Owners: Mr Ray Boot, Mr Ken Boot, Miss C. Commons, Mr Nick Kent, Mrs Marina Kent, Ms Vivienne Mitchell, Mrs Wendy Wesley.

Assistant Trainer: Mrs Jane Kent

Jockey (flat): Michael Stainton. **Jockey (NH):** Harry Haynes. **Conditional:** Charlie Deutsch.
Apprentice: Shelley Birkett. **Amateur:** Miss Alice Mills.

370
MISS SARAH KERSWELL, Kingsbridge
Postal: **Bearscombe Farm, Kingsbridge, Devon, TQ7 2DW**
Contacts: PHONE (01548) 853614

1 **ROMANCE DANCE**, 11, b m Terimon—Run On Stirling **Miss S. L. Kerswell**

Other Owners: R. H. Kerswell.

Jockey (NH): Ryan Mahon, Brendan Powell.

371 MR ALAN KING, Barbury Castle

Postal: **Barbury Castle Stables, Wroughton, Wiltshire, SN4 0QZ**
Contacts: **PHONE (01793) 815009 FAX (01793) 845080 MOBILE (07973) 461233**
E-MAIL alanking.racing@virgin.net WEBSITE www.alankingracing.co.uk

1 **ALI BABA**, 8, ch g Nayef (USA)—Alligram (USA) **Alan King**
2 **ARALDUR (FR)**, 10, ch g Spadoun (FR)—Aimessa (FR) **Mr D. J. S. Sewell**
3 **AVISPA**, 5, b m Kayf Tara—Ladylliat (FR) **The Wasp Partnership**
4 **BALDER SUCCES (FR)**, 6, b g Goldneyev (USA)—Frija Eria (FR) **Masterson Holdings Limited**
5 **BATONNIER (FR)**, 8, ch g Spadoun (FR)—La Bazine (FR) **H. R. Mould**
6 **BELLE DE LONDRES (IRE)**, 4, b f King's Theatre (IRE)—J'y Reste (FR)
7 **BILLY BISCUIT (IRE)**, 6, b g Presenting—Native Novel (IRE) **Miss J. M. Bodycote**
8 **BLESS THE WINGS (IRE)**, 9, b g Winged Love (IRE)—Silva Venture (IRE) **Mrs L. H. Field**
9 **BULL AND BUSH (IRE)**, 5, br m Presenting—Sound of The Crowd (IRE) **W. A. Harrison-Allan**
10 **CARRAIG MOR (IRE)**, 6, b g Old Vic—Lynrick Lady (IRE) **Masterson Holdings Limited**
11 **CHOCALA (IRE)**, 4, b g Rock of Gibraltar (IRE)—Arbella **High 5**
12 **DALAVAR (IRE)**, 6, b g Dalakhani (IRE)—Giant's Way (IRE) **N. S. G. Bunter**
13 **DESERT JOE (IRE)**, 8, b g Anshan—Wide Country (IRE) **Mrs E. A. Prowting**
14 **DESERT ROBE**, 6, b g Desert King (IRE)—Hot 'n Saucy **Alan King**
15 **DEVIL TO PAY**, 8, b g Red Ransom (USA)—My Way (IRE) **Horace 5**
16 **DUNDEE**, 6, ch g Definite Article—Gardana (FR) **T. J. Hemmings**
17 **DUROBLE MAN**, 4, b g Manduro (GER)—Jalousie (GER) **McNeill Family Ltd**
18 **FIGHTER JET**, 6, b g Oasis Dream—Totality **Ladas**
19 **FINE WORDS**, 6, b g Alflora (IRE)—Gospel (IRE) **Mrs S. C. Welch**
20 **FIRE FIGHTER (IRE)**, 6, b g Tiger Hill (IRE)—Firecrest (USA) **Masterson Holdings Limited**
21 **FIRST MOHICAN**, 6, ch g Tobougg (IRE)—Mohican Girl **W. H. Ponsonby**
22 **FORRESTERS FOLLY**, 8, b g Bollin Eric—Miss Wyandotte **Mr E. T. D. Leadbeater**
23 **FRED LE MACON (FR)**, 5, b g Passing Sale (FR)—Princess Leyla **Alan King & Niall Farrell**
24 **FRIZZO (FR)**, 7, ch g Ballingarry (FR)—Floridene (FR) **Jerry Wright, Stewart Rogers & John Webb**
25 **GABRIELLA ROSE**, 4, b f Kayf Tara—Elaine Tully (IRE)
26 **GENSTONE TRAIL**, 8, b m Generous (IRE)—Stoney Path **Mickleton Racing Club**
27 **GODSMEJUDGE (IRE)**, 8, b g Witness Box (USA)—Eliza Everett (IRE) **Favourites Racing Ltd**
28 **GOLD INGOT**, 7, ch g Best of The Bests (IRE)—Realms of Gold (USA) **Mrs Sue Welch & Ms Caroline Rowland**
29 **GONE TOO FAR**, 6, b g Kayf Tara—Major Hoolihan **J. P. McManus**
30 **GRUMETI**, 6, b g Sakhee (USA)—Tetravella (IRE) **McNeill Family Ltd**
31 **HANDAZAN (IRE)**, 5, b g Nayef (USA)—Handaza (IRE) **McNeill Family Ltd**
32 **HEROD THE GREAT**, 4, ch g Sakhee's Secret—Pella **Mr S M Smith & Mr D Minton**
33 **HINDON ROAD (IRE)**, 7, b g Antonius Pius (USA)—Filoli Gardens **A. J. Viall**
34 **HOLLOW PENNY**, 6, b g Beat Hollow—Lomapamar **Mr D. J. S. Sewell**
35 **HOWWRONGCANYOUBE**, 5, b g Kayf Tara—Diva
36 **HUNG PARLIAMENT (FR)**, 6, b g Numerous (USA)—Sensational Mover (USA) **The Tipperary Partners**
37 **HURRICANE VIC**, 4, b g Mount Nelson—Fountains Abbey (USA) **The Trouble Partnership**
38 **INNER DRIVE (IRE)**, 6, b g Heron Island—Hingis (IRE) **McNeill Family Ltd**
39 **INVICTUS (IRE)**, 8, b g Flemensfirth (USA)—Clashwilliam Girl (IRE) **Mr & Mrs R. G. Kelvin-Hughes**
40 **JETNOVA (IRE)**, 9, b g Luso—Yamashina (IRE) **Mr D. J. S. Sewell**
41 **JOJABEAN (IRE)**, 7, b g Milan—Garden City (IRE) **The Dunkley & Reilly Partnership**
42 4, B g Robin des Pres (FR)—Kick And Run (IRE) **Ian Payne & Kim Franklin**
43 **KINGS BAYONET**, 7, ch g Needwood Blade—Retaliator **W. H. Ponsonby**
44 **KOTKIRI (FR)**, 5, b g Ballingarry (FR)—Kakira (FR) **Walters Plant Hire Ltd**
45 **KUDA HURAA (IRE)**, 6, b g Montjeu (IRE)—Healing Music (FR) **Thurloe 53**
46 **KUMBESHWAR**, 7, b g Doyen (IRE)—Camp Fire (IRE) **McNeill Family & Mr Nigel Bunter**
47 **L'AMIRAL DAVID (FR)**, 4, b br g My Risk (FR)—Mme La Vicomtesse (FR) **Mr D. J. S. Sewell**
48 **L'UNIQUE (FR)**, 5, b m Reefscape—Sans Tune (FR) **D. J. Barry**
49 **LASER BLAZER**, 6, b g Zafeen (FR)—Sashay **Calne Engineering Ltd**
50 **LETSBY AVENUE**, 6, b g Tikkanen (USA)—Peel Me A Grape **Mrs E. A. Prowting**
51 **LIDAR (IRE)**, 9, ch g Take Risks (FR)—Light Wave (FR) **High 5**
52 **LORD OF SCOTLAND**, 5, gr g Lord du Sud—Etoile Rose (IRE) **S. E. Munir**
53 **LOTUS POND (IRE)**, 6, b g Beneficial—Capard Lady (IRE) **T. J. Hemmings**
54 **LOVCEN (GER)**, 9, b g Tiger Hill (IRE)—Lady Hawk (GER) **The Barbury Apes**
55 **MALDIVIAN REEF (IRE)**, 6, ch g Reefscape—Spirited Soul **Alan King**
56 **MANYRIVERSTOCROSS (IRE)**, 9, b g Cape Cross (IRE)—Alexandra S (IRE) **Mrs M. C. Sweeney**
57 5, B g Heron Island—Marikala (IRE) **Mr & Mrs R. Scott**
58 **MCVICAR**, 5, b g Tobougg (IRE)—Aries (GER) **Mr & Mrs R. Scott**
59 **MEDERMIT (FR)**, 10, gr g Medaaly—Miss d'hermite (FR) **The Dunkley & Reilly Partnership**
60 **MEDINAS (FR)**, 7, b br g Malinas (GER)—Medicis (FR) **Mr & Mrs F. D. Bell**
61 **MEISTER ECKHART (IRE)**, 8, b br g Flemensfirth (USA)—Carrabawn **Atlantic Equine**

MR ALAN KING - Continued

62 **MEMBEROF (FR)**, 4, b br g Khalkevi (IRE)—Former Member (USA) **Mr Simon Munir & Mr Isaac Souede**
63 **MIDNIGHT APPEAL**, 9, b g Midnight Legend—Lac Marmot (FR) **Mr D. J. S. Sewell**
64 **MIDNIGHT CATARIA**, 5, b m Midnight Legend—Calamintha **Mrs K. Holmes**
65 **MIDNIGHT PRAYER**, 9, b g Midnight Legend—Onawing Andaprayer **The Legends Partnership**
66 **MIDNIGHT SAIL**, 11, b g Midnight Legend—Mayina **Mr A. R. W. Marsh**
67 **MILES TO MEMPHIS (IRE)**, 5, b g Old Vic—Phillis Hill **Mrs Lesley Field & Mr Jules Sigler**
68 **MINX OF THE LAMP**, 5, br gr m Fair Mix (IRE)—Lamp's Return **A. P. Racing**
69 **MIRKAT**, 4, b g Kalanisi (IRE)—Miracle **Bellamy, Burke, Hannigan & Harding**
70 **MONEY FOR NOTHING**, 5, b g Kayf Tara—Top of The Dee **Mrs M. C. Sweeney**
71 **MONKSGOLD (IRE)**, 6, b g Gold Well—Opium **The Dreamers**
72 **MONTBAZON (FR)**, 7, b br g Alberto Giacometti (IRE)—Duchesse Pierji (FR) **Mr D. J. S. Sewell**
73 **MYSTERY DRAMA**, 4, b f Hernando (FR)—Mystery Lot (IRE) **Incipe Partnership**
74 **NED STARK (IRE)**, 6, b g Wolfe Tone (IRE)—Last Moon (IRE) **The Dunkley & Reilly Partnership**
75 **NO SUBSTITUTE (IRE)**, 9, b g Definite Article—Kindly Light (IRE) **Mr J. R. Hales**
76 **OH CRICK (FR)**, 11, ch g Nikos—Other Crik (FR) **Mr D. J. S. Sewell**
77 **ORDO AB CHAO (IRE)**, 5, b g Heron Island (IRE)—Houldyurwhist (IRE) **Mr A. R. W. Marsh**
78 **OUR PHYLLI VERA (IRE)**, 5, b m Motivator—With Colour **Let's Live Racing**
79 **OUR POLLYANNA (IRE)**, 7, b m Flemensfirth (USA)—Polly Anthus **The Dunkley & Reilly Partnership**
80 **PANTXOA (FR)**, 7, b g Daliapour (IRE)—Palmeria (FR) **Mrs J. A. Watts**
81 **PIRATES CAY**, 7, b g Black Sam Bellamy (IRE)—Mistic World **Mr D. J. S. Sewell**
82 **POUVOIR (FR)**, 11, gr g Verglas (IRE)—Policia (FR) **Mr R. Scott**
83 **PRETTYASAPICTURE**, 5, b m King's Theatre (IRE)—Fortune's Girl **Let's Live Racing**
84 **PRIDE IN BATTLE (IRE)**, 9, b g Chevalier (IRE)—Afasara (IRE) **Mrs E. Pearce**
85 **RAYA STAR (IRE)**, 8, b g Milan—Garden City (IRE) **S. E. Munir**
86 **ROBERTO PEGASUS (USA)**, 8, b br g Fusaichi Pegasus (USA)—
　　　　　　　　　　　　　　　　　　　　Louju (USA) **Mrs P Andrews, I Payne & Ms K Franklin**
87 **RONALDINHO (IRE)**, 4, b g Jeremy (USA)—Spring Glory **The Ronaldinho Partnership**
88 **SALMANAZAR**, 6, b g Classic Cliche (IRE)—Leroy's Sister (FR) **Top Brass Partnership**
89 **SAY WHEN**, 6, b g Fair Mix (IRE)—Miss Wyandotte **Alan King**
90 **SEA TIGER**, 4, b g Tiger Hill (IRE)—Possessive Artiste **Mrs D. M. Swinburn**
91 **SECRET EDGE**, 6, b g Tobougg (IRE)—Burton Ash **Nigel Bunter & David Anderson**
92 **SEGO SUCCESS (IRE)**, 6, b g Beneficial—The West Road (IRE) **Mr E. T. D. Leadbeater**
93 **SEVENTH SIGN**, 5, b g Pivotal—Rahayeb **Masterson Holdings Limited**
94 **SHADY LANE**, 7, b m Alflora (IRE)—Stoney Path **Ms C Rowland,Mrs Welch & R Fitzgerald**
95 **SIMPLY A LEGEND**, 5, b g Midnight Legend—Disco Danehill (IRE) **Mrs E. A. Prowting**
96 **SMAD PLACE (FR)**, 7, gr g Smadoun (FR)—Bienna Star (FR) **Mrs P. Andrews**
97 **SMART MOTIVE**, 4, b g Motivator—Santana Lady (IRE) **Mrs C. Skan**
98 **SPRINGBOKS (IRE)**, 4, b g Flemensfirth (USA)—Roaming (IRE) **Mr & Mrs R. G. Kelvin-Hughes**
99 **STONEY'S TREASURE**, 10, ch g Silver Patriarch (IRE)—Stoney Path **Mrs S. C. Welch**
100 **SUBURBAN BAY**, 9, ch g Karinga Bay—Orchid House **S. Bullimore**
101 **SUPER LUNAR (IRE)**, 5, b g Super Celebre (FR)—Kapricia Speed (FR) **Million in Mind Partnership**
102 **TAFFY DARE (IRE)**, 5, b m Court Cave (IRE)—Three More (USA) **A. P. Racing**
103 **TANTE SISSI (FR)**, 5, b m Lesotho (USA)—Kadjara (FR) **Thurloe 51**
104 **THE MUMPER (IRE)**, 7, br g Craigsteel—Na Moilltear (IRE) **The Weighed In Partnership**
105 **THE PIRATE'S QUEEN (IRE)**, 5, b m King's Theatre (IRE)—Shivermetimber (IRE) **Mr & Mrs C. Harris**
106 **TICKITY BLEUE**, 6, gr m Tikkanen (USA)—Cerise Bleue (FR) **Let's Live Racing**
107 **TIGER CLIFF (IRE)**, 5, b g Tiger Hill (IRE)—Verbania (IRE) **W. H. Ponsonby**
108 **TIGER FEAT**, 4, b g Tiger Hill (IRE)—Hannah's Dream (IRE) **ROA Racing Partnership V**
109 **TOMOCHICHI (IRE)**, 4, b g Indian River (FR)—Polar Lamb (IRE) **Mr D. J. S. Sewell**
110 **TRIGGER THE LIGHT**, 13, ch g Double Trigger (IRE)—Lamper's Light **Mrs D. Shutes**
111 **TURN OVER SIVOLA (FR)**, 7, b g Assessor (IRE)—Notting Hill (FR) **International Plywood (Importers) Ltd**
112 **TWO ROCKERS (IRE)**, 7, b g Milan—Foxhall Blue (IRE) **Masterson Holdings Limited**
113 **ULZANA'S RAID (IRE)**, 5, ch g Bach (IRE)—Peace Time Beauty (IRE) **T. Barr**
114 **UNKNOWN LEGEND (IRE)**, 7, b g Heron Island (IRE)—Late Call (IRE) **Boretech, Dolan & Sadler**
115 **URIAH HEEP (FR)**, 5, b g Danehill Dancer (IRE)—Canasita **G Keirle, J Holmes, R Levitt & A King**
116 **UXIZANDRE (FR)**, 6, ch g Fragrant Mix (IRE)—Jolisandre (FR) **J. P. McManus**
117 **VALDEZ**, 7, b g Doyen (IRE)—Skew **Riverdee Stable**
118 **VENDOR (FR)**, 6, gr g Kendor (FR)—Village Rainbow (FR) **Thurloe 52**
119 **WALKON (FR)**, 9, gr g Take Risks (FR)—La Tirana (FR) **McNeill Family Ltd**
120 **WEST END ROCKER (IRE)**, 12, b br g Grand Plaisir (IRE)—
　　　　　　　　　　　　　　　Slyguff Lord (IRE) **Mr Barry Winfield & Mr Tim Leadbeater**
121 **WILDE BLUE YONDER (IRE)**, 5, b g Oscar (IRE)—Blue Gallery (IRE) **Maybe Only Fools Have Horses**
122 **WILLOUGHBY HEDGE**, 7, b g King's Theatre (IRE)—Mini Mandy **T. J. Hemmings**
123 **WOOLY BULLY**, 4, b g Sixties Icon—Baycliffe Rose **W. A. Harrison-Allan**

MR ALAN KING - Continued

124 YANWORTH, 4, ch g Norse Dancer (IRE)—Yota (FR) **Alan King**
125 ZIGA BOY (FR), 5, gr g Califet (FR)—Our Ziga (FR) **Axom LI**

THREE-YEAR-OLDS

126 CHATEZ (IRE), b g Dandy Man (IRE)—Glory Days (GER) **Mrs P. Andrews**
127 GIMME FIVE, b g Champs Elysees—Waitingonacloud **McNeill Family Ltd**
128 NYANZA (GER), b f Dai Jin—Nouvelle Fortune (IRE) **Hunscote Stud**
129 Ch g Champs Elysees—Starparty (USA) **Mr & Mrs R. Scott**
130 TOO FAR GONE (IRE), br g Jeremy (USA)—Rockahoolababy (IRE) **N. S. G. Bunter**

Other Owners: Mr D. J. Anderson, Mrs V. A. P. Antell, Mr R. B. Antell, Axom Ltd, Ms C. A. Bailey Tait, M. Ball, Mr F. C. Barber, Mrs H. L. Bell, Mr F. D. Bell, D. Bellamy, Mr R. J. Benton, Mr R. A. Bevan, Mrs A. Blackwell, Boretech Limited, A. R. Bromley, D. J. Burke, Mr J. Burn, Mr R. J. Caddick, Ms C. L. Calver, Mr N. J. Carter, Mrs D. C. Casey-McCarthy, Mr M. L. Cheesmer, Mr J. H. Chester, Mr S. Clancy, J. L. Clarke, Mr N. Clyne, Mr J. A. Cover, J. R. Creed, Mr D. Crossley, J. M. Curtis, Mr B. H. Dolan, Mr D. Downie, P. J. Dunkley, A. T. Eggleton, Mrs S. Evans, N. Farrell, Mr R. J. N. Fitzgerald, S. F. Frampton, Miss K. M. Franklin, S. G. Friend, G. F. Goode, Mr M. Grier, Mr A. J. Hannigan, P. R. Harding, Mr C. I. K. Harris, Mrs C. A. Harris, Mr S. Harris, Mr L. A. Harvey, Mr D. A. Heffer, D. F. Hill, Mr A. J. Hill, J. Holmes, Mr A. Horne, Mr A. Humphreys, D. Humphreys, Mr R. A. Jacobs, Lady J. A. Kay, G. F. Keirle, R. G. Kelvin-Hughes, Mrs E. A. Kelvin-Hughes, Miss E. A. Lake, Mr W. P. Ledward, R. M. Levitt, Mr A. T. Macdonald, Mrs S. M. Maine, Mr G. T. Mann, Mrs A. S. Mayhew, Mr I. D. Miller, W. D. C. Minton, Mr C. Mullin, Mrs M. T. Mullin, Mr J. J. Murray, Mr G. Nicholas, Mrs D. C. Nicholson, Mr P. J. O'Neill, Mr P. Patel, O. J. W. Pawle, Mr I. T. Payne, Mr R. M. Potter, Mr S. P. Price, Mr C. R. Pugh, D. F. Reilly, J. P. L. Reynolds, Paul Robson, Mr S. J. Rogers, Ms C. C. Rowland, Mr A. Sadler, R. Scott, Mrs P. M. Scott, J. Sigler, Prof D. B. A. Silk, S. M. Smith, Mrs L. A. Smith, Mr I. Souede, Mr J. A. B. Stafford, Mr J. A. Tabet, Mrs M. G. Thomas, A. J. Thompson, Mrs C. Townroe, Mrs K. J. Tudor, Mr B. Wallis, J. B. Webb, Mr J. Wilton, B. Winfield, Mr T. Withers, J. Wright.

Assistant Trainers: Oliver Wardle, Dan Horsford

Jockey (NH): Wayne Hutchinson, Steven O'Donovan, Robert Thornton, Gerard Tumelty.
Amateur: Mr Josh Newman, Mr Harry Teal.

---

372 MR NEIL KING, Newmarket

Postal: **St Gatien Racing Ltd, St Gatien Cottage, Vicarage Road, Newmarket, Suffolk, CB8 8HP**
Contacts: **PHONE/FAX (01638) 666150 FAX (01638) 666150 MOBILE (07880) 702325**
E-MAIL neil@neil-king.co.uk WEBSITE www.neil-king.co.uk

1 A LITTLE SWIFTER (IRE), 8, ch m Noverre (USA)—Swiftur **Dr Clive Layton & Ken Lawrence**
2 ASTRUM, 4, gr g Haafhd—Vax Star **Sarah & Wayne Dale**
3 ATTWAAL (IRE), 5, b g Teofilo (IRE)—Qasirah (IRE) **Dr & Mrs Clive Layton**
4 BALLYVONEEN (IRE), 9, b g Stowaway—Miss Ita Zarad (IRE) **Across The Pond Partnership**
5 BRASS MONKEY (IRE), 7, b g Craigsteel—Saltee Great (IRE) **The St Gatien Racing For Fun Partnership**
6 DELGANY DEMON, 6, b g Kayf Tara—Little Twig (IRE) **C. M. Wilson**
7 DOCTOR'S ORDERS (IRE), 4, b g Mountain High (IRE)—Ballinaroone Girl (IRE) **Dr & Mrs Clive Layton**
8 FOCAIL MAITH, 6, b g Oratorio (IRE)—Glittering Image (IRE) **Ken Lawrence, Bob Smith, Michael Gibbons**
9 JOLLY VALENTINE, 6, b g Sakhee (USA)—Violet (IRE) **Mrs P. I. Veenbaas**
10 KAYSERSBERG (FR), 7, b g Khalkevi (IRE)—Alliance Royale (FR) **Mrs Julien Turner & Mr Andrew Merriam**
11 KELTIC RHYTHM (IRE), 7, b g Milan—Ballinaroone Girl (IRE) **Stephen Lower Insurance Services Limited**
12 LOOKS LIKE MAGIC, 5, gr g Fair Mix (IRE)—Cirrious **Mark & Tracy Harrod**
13 MERCERS COURT (IRE), 6, b g Court Cave (IRE)—
                                              Vikki's Dream (IRE) **David Nott, Ken Lawrence, Tim Messom**
14 MILANSBAR (IRE), 7, b g Milan—Ardenbar **R. N. Bothway**
15 NAFAATH (IRE), 8, ch g Nayef (USA)—Alshakr **Sarah & Wayne Dale**
16 NINFEA (IRE), 6, b m Le Vie Dei Colori—Attymon Lill (IRE) **The St Gatien Racing For Fun Partnership**
17 QUINCY MAGOO (IRE), 5, ch g Mountain High (IRE)—Vicky's Lodge (IRE) **Mark & Tracy Harrod**
18 ROJA DOVE (IRE), 5, b m Jeremy (USA)—Knight's Place (IRE) **Barry Williams & Donald Caldwell**
19 SAFFRON WELLS (IRE), 6, b g Saffron Walden (FR)—Angel's Folly **Mark Harrod & Peter Beadles**
20 SINGAPORE STORY (FR), 5, b br g Sagacity (FR)—Vettorina (FR) **Mark Harrod & Peter Beadles**
21 THE RED LAIRD, 11, b g Kayf Tara—Sekhmet **The Red Laird Partnership**
22 TOWN MOUSE, 4, ch g Sakhee (USA)—Megdale (IRE) **Mr Brian Bell & Mr John Smith**
23 UNBUCKLED (IRE), 4, b f Presenting—Una Kasala (GER) **Mrs H. M. Buckle**
24 VANDROSS (IRE), 4, b g Iffraaj—Mrs Kanning **Mr D. S. Lee**
25 WOM, 6, b g Tiger Hill (IRE)—Vayavaig **Mark & Tracy Harrod**
26 ZEROESHADESOFGREY (IRE), 5, gr g Portrait Gallery (IRE)—Hazy Rose (IRE) **Mrs H. M. Buckle**

Other Owners: Mr P. M. H. Beadles, Mrs P. B. E. Beaton, Mr I. J. Beaton, Mr B. Bell, Mr D. R. Caldwell, Mr N. J. Catterwell, Mrs S. J. Dale, Mr W. R. Dale, Mr M. H. Gibbons, Mr M. Harrod, Mrs T. Harrod, N. King, Mr K. Lawrence, Dr C.

MR NEIL KING - Continued

A. Layton, Mrs H. M. Layton, A. W. K. Merriam, Mr T. J. Messom, D. F. Nott, R. W. Smith, Mr J. H. Smith, Mrs N. C. Turner, Mr B. M. V. Williams.

Head Girl: Marie Parker

Jockey (flat): Seb Sanders, Martin Lane, Hayley Turner. **Jockey (NH):** Leighton Aspell, Dougie Costello, Richard Johnson, Jamie Moore. **Conditional:** Trevor Whelan. **Amateur:** Miss Bridgett Andrews, Mr Connor Smith.

---

373 MR RICHARD KING, Dorchester
Postal: **The Lanches, East Farm, Tolpuddle, Dorchester, Dorset, DT2 7EP**
Contacts: **PHONE (01305) 848592 FAX (01305) 849134 MOBILE (07779) 991356**
E-MAIL sherilyn.king@yahoo.co.uk

1 HERBERT PERCY, 7, b g Morpeth—Cold Feet **Mrs S. King**
2 MADAM NOSO, 10, ch m Riverwise (USA)—Lady Noso **Mrs S. King**
3 MOREBUTWHEN, 7, b m Morpeth—Lady Noso **Mrs S. King**

---

374 MR WILLIAM KINSEY, Ashton
Postal: **R Kinsey Partnership, Peel Hall, Gongar Lane, Ashton, Chester**
Contacts: **PHONE (01829) 751230 MOBILE (07803) 753719**
E-MAIL kinsey.peelhall@tiscali.co.uk

1 ALLBARNONE, 6, b g Alflora (IRE)—What A Gem **Mr W. R. Kinsey**
2 ALPHA VICTOR (IRE), 9, b g Old Vic—Harvest View (IRE) **Denton, Kinsey, Osborne Hse, Wesley-Yates**
3 BLAZING DESERT, 10, b g Beat All (USA)—Kingsfold Blaze **Mr W. R. Kinsey**
4 DUNCOMPLAINING (IRE), 5, b g Milan—Notcomplainingbut (IRE) **D. Wesley-Yates**
5 EDDISBURY HILL, 6, b g Needwood Blade—Veni Vici (IRE) **Mr W. R. Kinsey**
6 FIDDLEESTICKS (IRE), 6, b g Heron Island (IRE)—Dawn Native (IRE) **Manley Steeplechasing**
7 GWLADYS STREET (IRE), 7, b g Portrait Gallery (IRE)—Native Ocean (IRE) **The Missing Link**
8 HARRIS (IRE), 7, b g Beneficial—Porter Tastes Nice (IRE) **Harris Syndicate**
9 KYKATE, 8, b m Hamas (IRE)—Coleham **David Bithell Racing**
10 MISS DUFFY, 6, ch m Sir Harry Lewis (USA)—Dolly Duff **PeelerDealers**
11 SHOULDAVBOUGHTGOLD (IRE), 7, b g Classic Cliche (IRE)—Sancta Miria (IRE) **The Missing Link**
12 TEA IN MARRAKECH (IRE), 6, b g Spadoun (FR)—Bagatelle (IRE) **Mr P. A. Eaton & Mr W. R. Kinsey**

Other Owners: D. P. Bithell, Mr C. B. Denton, Mr T. B. Denton, Mr P. A. Eaton, Mrs J. Kinsey, Mr J. H. Martin, Osborne House Ltd, Mr M. C. Plumridge, Mr T. F. Sharratt.

---

375 MR PHILIP KIRBY, Middleham
Postal: **Sharp Hill Farm, Park Lane, Middleham, Leyburn, North Yorkshire, DL8 4QY**
Contacts: **PHONE (01969) 624400 MOBILE (07984) 403558**
E-MAIL wakingned1@hotmail.com WEBSITE www.philipkirbyracing.co.uk

1 AGGLESTONE ROCK, 9, b g Josr Algarhoud (IRE)—Royalty (IRE) **Geoff Kirby & Pam Kirby & Brian Cobbett**
2 ANCIENT TIMES (USA), 7, b br g Smart Strike (CAN)—Histoire Sainte (FR) **L & D Interiors Ltd**
3 BEDALE LANE (IRE), 5, b m Kayf Tara—Misleain (IRE) **Mr R. N. Ellerbeck**
4 BLONDINABAR, 5, b m Beat All (USA)—Kissinthepeach **Mr D. Hopper**
5 BOB'S TICKET (IRE), 9, ch g Bob's Return (IRE)—Some Ticket (IRE) **The Kwick Syndicate**
6 BRIGADOON, 7, b g Compton Place—Briggsmaid **Mr R. Oliver**
7 BRUNELLO, 6, b g Leporello (IRE)—Lydia Maria **Ownaracehorse Ltd**
8 BURNS NIGHT, 8, ch g Selkirk (USA)—Night Frolic **The Kwick Syndicate**
9 CALL IT ON (IRE), 8, ch g Raise A Grand (IRE)—Birthday Present **The Wiggins Family**
10 CAVALIERI (IRE), 4, b g Oratorio (IRE)—Always Attractive (IRE) **The Cavalieri Partnership**
11 CHLOE'S IMAGE, 4, b f Lucky Story—Iwunder (IRE)
12 CLEVE COTTAGE, 6, ch g Presenting—Reverse Swing **G Fawcett & D Phillips**
13 COOL OPERATOR, 11, b g Kahyasi—Gardana (FR) **The Gathering & Alderclad**
14 COURTOWN OSCAR (IRE), 5, b g Oscar (IRE)—Courtown Bowe VII **Boretech, Dolan & Sadler**
15 DANEHILL FLYER (IRE), 4, b c Danehill Dancer (IRE)—Zagreb Flyer **Mrs J. Sivills**
16 DEVOTION TO DUTY (IRE), 8, b g Montjeu (IRE)—Charmante (USA) **Racing Management & Training Ltd**
17 DR IRV, 5, ch g Dr Fong (USA)—Grateful **I. M. Lynch**
18 ELSPETH'S BOY (USA), 7, b br g Tiznow (USA)—Miss Waki Club (USA) **Preesall Garage**

MR PHILIP KIRBY - Continued

19 **EMBSAY CRAG**, 8, b g Elmaamul (USA)—Wigman Lady (IRE) **Grange Park Racing IV & Partner**
20 **ENZAAL (USA)**, 4, b c Invasor (ARG)—Ekleel (IRE) **C B Construction (Cleveland) Limited**
21 **EVERAARD (USA)**, 8, ch g Lion Heart (USA)—Via Gras (USA) **Tennant, Sharpe & Boston**
22 **FACTOR FIFTY (IRE)**, 5, b g Definite Article—Sun Screen **The Topspec Partnership**
23 **FULL SPEED (GER)**, 9, b g Sholokhov (IRE)—Flagny (FR) **L & D Interiors Ltd**
24 **GLOSHEN (IRE)**, 8, b h Fath—Olivia Jane (IRE) **Mr P. F. Gleeson**
25 **GOLD RULES**, 7, ch g Gold Away (IRE)—Raphaela (FR)
26 **GREY COMMAND (USA)**, 9, gr g Daylami (IRE)—Shmoose (IRE) **The Shades of Grey Partnership**
27 **HAIL THE BRAVE (IRE)**, 5, ch g Lahib—Parverb (IRE) **Junco P'Tners Ontoawinner Foster Bocking**
28 **IKTIVIEW**, 6, ch g Iktibas—Eastview Princess **Eastview Thoroughbreds**
29 **JASPER MASSINI (IRE)**, 9, b g Dr Massini (IRE)—Graigue Lass (IRE) **Billy & Philip Platts**
30 **JAWAAB (IRE)**, 10, ch g King's Best (USA)—Canis Star **L & D Interiors Ltd**
31 **JUST CAMERON (IRE)**, 4, b g Kayf Tara—Miss Fencote **Mr & Mrs P. Chapman**
32 **JUST PAUL (IRE)**, 4, b g Clodovil (IRE)—Tatamagouche (IRE) **Mr & Mrs P. Chapman**
33 **KIWAJU**, 5, b g Medicean—Kibara **Mrs J. Sivills**
34 **LADY BUTTONS**, 4, b f Beneficial—Lady Chapp (IRE) **Mrs J. Sivills**
35 **LIBBY MAE (IRE)**, 4, b f High Chaparral (IRE)—Empty Pocket **Mr & Mrs P. Chapman**
36 **LOWCARR MOTION**, 4, ch c Rainbow High—Royalty (IRE) **I. M. Lynch**
37 **MARMOT BAY (IRE)**, 4, b f Kodiac—Tides **Mr G. McCrann**
38 **MATTHEW RILEY (IRE)**, 7, b g Dr Massini (IRE)—Helorhiwater (IRE) **Mr & Mrs P. Chapman**
39 **MOSCOW PRESENTS (IRE)**, 6, b g Presenting—Moscow Madame (IRE) **Boretech & Tony Sadler**
40 **MRS EFF**, 8, b m Tamure (IRE)—Roman Uproar **Ingham Racing Syndicate**
41 **MUSIKHANI**, 4, b f Dalakhani (IRE)—Musicanna **Mrs K. Holmes**
42 **MYSTERIOUS WONDER**, 4, b g Oasis Dream—Raskutani **Mr P. Kirby**
43 **NEXT EDITION (IRE)**, 6, b g Antonius Pius (USA)—Starfish (IRE) **The Dibble Bridge Partnership**
44 **NOIR GIRL**, 5, b m Beat All (USA)—Forever Shineing **The McBar Partnership**
45 **OR D'OUDAIRIES (IRE)**, 12, b g April Night (FR)—Belle Truval (FR) **Gay & Peter Hartley**
46 **OSCAR O'SCAR (IRE)**, 6, b g Oscar (IRE)—Shining Lights (IRE) **Newroc 1**
47 **PASS MUSTER**, 7, b g Theatrical—Morning Pride (IRE) **C B Construction (Cleveland) Limited**
48 **PERENNIAL**, 5, ch g Motivator—Arum Lily (USA) **The Gathering & The Gathered**
49 **PICKS MILAN (IRE)**, 8, b g Milan—Butchies Girl (IRE) **Mr H. J. Pickersgill**
50 **PLATINUM (IRE)**, 7, b g Azamour (IRE)—Dazzling Park (IRE) **Mrs P. R. Kirby**
51 **RIO COBOLO (IRE)**, 8, b g Captain Rio—Sofistication (IRE) **Mr C. M. Grech**
52 **RUMBLE OF THUNDER (IRE)**, 8, b g Fath (USA)—Honey Storm (IRE) **The Well Oiled Partnership**
53 4, B g Trans Island—Shady's Wish (IRE) **Mrs K. Walton**
54 **STOPPED OUT**, 9, gr g Montjoy (USA)—Kiomi **The Well Oiled Partnership**
55 **STORMY MORNING**, 8, ch g Nayef (USA)—Sokoa (USA) **Ownaracehorse Ltd**
56 **TAXI DES OBEAUX (FR)**, 7, b br g Maresca Sorrento (FR)—Madrilene (FR) **Sharp Hill 2**
57 **TOOLA BOOLA**, 4, b f Tobougg (IRE)—Forsythia
58 **TRANSIENT BAY (IRE)**, 4, b g Trans Island—Boarding Pass (IRE) **The Waking Ned Partnership**
59 **TRIPLE EIGHT (IRE)**, 6, b g Royal Applause—Hidden Charm (IRE) **RedHotGardogs**
60 **UP THE BEES**, 4, b g Kayf Tara—West River (USA) **Mr C. L. W. German**
61 **WAR LORD (IRE)**, 4, b g Aussie Rules (USA)—Carn Lady (IRE) **Mr & Mrs G. Turnbull**
62 **WESTERN TRIGGER (IRE)**, 5, b g Westerner—Single Trigger (USA) **Yarm Racing Partnership**
63 **WOODPOLE ACADEMY (IRE)**, 7, b g Beneficial—Midday Caller (IRE) **Boretech Limited**

THREE-YEAR-OLDS

64 **BACK BABY PARIS (IRE)**, b f Flemensfirth (USA)—Babygotback (IRE) **Exors of the Late Mrs J. Haughton**
65 **LADY HEIDI**, b f High Chaparral (IRE)—Water Feature **Hardisty Rolls II**
66 **MONEY TEAM (IRE)**, b c Kodiac—Coral Dawn (IRE) **Hardisty Rolls II**
67 **OLY'ROCCS (IRE)**, b c Tagula (IRE)—Orpendonna **Mr C. M. Grech**
68 **SELLINGALLTHETIME (IRE)**, ch c Tamayuz—Anthyllis (GER) **Mr R. Oliver**
69 **WARRIOR JACK (IRE)**, b g Coroner (IRE)—On The Up (IRE) **Exors of the Late Mrs J. Haughton**

TWO-YEAR-OLDS

70 **ESK VALLEY LADY**, b f 2/3 Three Valleys (USA)—
Glory Oatway (IRE) (Desert Prince (IRE)) (857) **Oakley Walls Partnership**
71 **FORGIVING GLANCE**, gr f 25/3 Passing Glance—Giving (Generous (IRE)) **Mrs K. Holmes**

Other Owners: Miss L. Adams, Alderclad Ltd, T. Alderson, Mr J. A. Barber, Mr J. K. Bell, Mr A. D. Bingham, Mr S. Bocking, R. A. Brown, R. G. Capstick, Mr P. W. Chapman, Mrs J. Chapman, Mr E. L. Coates, Mr B. A. G. Cobbett, Mr D. G. Colledge, A. D. Crombie, Mr A. C. Davies, Mr B. H. Dolan, Mr G. Fawcett, K. L. Foster, Mr R. Hamilton, Mr J. D. Hanson, P. A. H. Hartley, Mrs R. C. Hartley, Mr P. A. Helm, Mr M. P. Helm, Mr G. K. Henderson, Mr T. S. Ingham, Mrs P. S. Kirby, Mr G. S. Kirby, Mr G. W. Lonsdale, J. H. Madden, Mr D. G. Marshall, Mr P. McMartin, Mr G. Newton, T. I. Nicol, Mr A. Norrington, N. J. O'Brien, G. R. Orchard, Mr M. D. Parker, Mr D. J. Phillips, Mr W. N. Platts, Mr P. Platts, Hugh T. Redhead, Mr P. Rolls,

MR PHILIP KIRBY - Continued

Mrs J. Rolls, Mr A. Sadler, C. M. Sharpe, R. Standring, Mr J. G. R. Stent, J. E. Tennant, Mr G. Turnbull, Mrs S. E. Turnbull, Mr L. Underwood, Mr L. C. Wiggins, Mrs C. Wiggins, Mr S. A. Wiggins, Mr S. J. Wyatt.

Assistant Trainer: Simon Olley

Jockey (NH): James Reveley, Richie McGrath. **Conditional:** Kyle James.

---

376 MR SYLVESTER KIRK, Upper Lambourn
Postal: Cedar Lodge Stables, Upper Lambourn, Hungerford, Berkshire, RG17 8QT
Contacts: **PHONE** (01488) 73215 **FAX** (01488) 670012 **MOBILE** (07768) 855261
E-MAIL info@sylvesterkirkracing.co.uk **WEBSITE** www.sylvesterkirkracing.co.uk

1 **BERWIN (IRE)**, 5, b m Lawman (FR)—Topiary (IRE)
2 **CAPETOWN KID**, 4, gr g Cape Town (IRE)—Doris Souter (IRE) **Mr P. D. Merritt**
3 **CELESTIAL BAY**, 5, b m Septieme Ciel (USA)—Snowy Mantle **Homebred Racing**
4 **CHARLES CAMOIN (IRE)**, 6, b g Peintre Celebre (USA)—
　　　　　　　　　　　　　　　　　　　　　　Birthday (IRE) **Mr C. Wright & The Hon Mrs J.M.Corbett**
5 **DELAGOA BAY (IRE)**, 6, b m Encosta de Lago (AUS)—Amory (GER) **Homebred Racing**
6 **GLENNTEN**, 5, b g Ishiguro (USA)—Uplifting **Mr D. Potter**
7 **LAST MINUTE LISA (IRE)**, 4, b f Strategic Prince—Bradwell (IRE) **Mr G. Dolan**
8 **MOJO BEAR**, 4, b f Indesatchel (IRE)—Four Legs Good (IRE) **S. A. Kirk**
9 **SEE AND BE SEEN**, 4, b g Sakhee's Secret—Anthea **T. K. Pearson**
10 **THE NOBLE ORD**, 5, b g Indesatchel (IRE)—Four Legs Good (IRE)

THREE-YEAR-OLDS

11 **ARISTOCRATIC DUTY**, b f Zamindar (USA)—Duty Paid (IRE) **J. C. Smith**
12 **ASSOLUTA (IRE)**, ch f Danehill Dancer (IRE)—A P Easy (USA) **M. Nicolson, G. Doran, A. Wilson**
13 **BAKER MAN (IRE)**, b g Dandy Man (IRE)—Anne Bonney **P. D. Rogers**
14 **BELLETRISTE (FR)**, gr f Literato (FR)—Mulled Wine (FR) **The Hon Mrs J. M. Corbett & Mr C. Wright**
15 **CROSSHARE**, b c Crosspeace (IRE)—Perecapa (IRE) **Miss P. Stutchbury**
16 **DUCHESSOFALDERMOOR**, b f Paris House—Naval Dispatch **Mr B. Selfe, Ms M. Timpson & Mrs C. Vickery**
17 **FOREST GLEN (IRE)**, b f Camacho—Lisfannon **Sapphire Racing Partnership**
18 B c Duke of Marmalade (IRE)—Green Room (FR) **Mr S. McKay & Mr D. Potter**
19 **GROUNDWORKER (IRE)**, b c Tagula (IRE)—Notepad **Deauville Daze Partnership**
20 **HEINRICH (USA)**, gr ro g Henrythenavigator (USA)—C'est La Cat (USA) **Verano Quartet**
21 **INIS AIRC (IRE)**, b f Footstepsinthesand—Inis Boffin **Ms C. Cleary**
22 **INSPECTOR NORSE**, b c Norse Dancer (IRE)—Indiana Blues **J. C. Smith**
23 **KANTO (GER)**, b c Sholokhov (IRE)—Kristin's Charm (USA) **Mr T. Cummins & Mr E. King**
24 **LEAD A MERRY DANCE**, b f Bertolini (USA)—Green Supreme **Mrs M. A. & Miss A. M. Rawding**
25 **LITTLE BIG MAN**, b g Sleeping Indian—Doris Souter (IRE) **Mr N. Simpson & Mr S. Kirk**
26 **MAYMYO (IRE)**, b c Invincible Spirit (IRE)—Lady Windermere (IRE) **Mr H. Balasuriya**
27 **MISS SKYFALL (IRE)**, ch f Tagula (IRE)—Full of Nature **Mrs C. Cleary**
28 **MY ANCHOR**, b g Mount Nelson—War Shanty **R. Hannon**
29 **NORSE STAR (IRE)**, b c Norse Dancer (IRE)—Spot Prize (USA) **J. C. Smith**
30 **PENNY'S BOY**, ch g Firebreak—Sunderland Echo (IRE) **Mr Malcolm Brown & Mrs Penny Brown**
31 **PICNIC IN THE GLEN**, b f Piccolo—True Magic **Mr T. Lock**
32 **SCARIFF HORNET (IRE)**, b f Tagula (IRE)—Housa Dancer (IRE) **Denis, Kieran & Andy Bugler**
33 **SIMMA (IRE)**, gr f Dark Angel (IRE)—Staylily (IRE) **Mr N. Simpson**
34 **TRAVIS BICKLE (IRE)**, b g Sky Mesa (USA)—Out of Woods (USA) **Sir A. Ferguson, S. Hassiakos & M. Clarke**

TWO-YEAR-OLDS

35 **CARRY ON DERYCK**, b c 26/3 Halling (USA)—Mullein (Oasis Dream) (30000) **Mr C. Hartwell & Mr D. Walters**
36 **DIAMOND SAM**, ch c 2/3 Compton Place—Kurtanella (Pastoral Pursuits) **Mrs J. I. Snow**
37 B f 1/1 Sakhee's Secret—Dimelight (Fantastic Light (USA)) **J. C. Smith**
38 B c 12/4 Kodiac—Dreamalot (Falbrav (IRE)) (30000) **Mr D. Kavanagh & Mr D. Murphy**
39 B c 1/3 Norse Dancer (IRE)—Indiana Blues (Indian Ridge) **J. C. Smith**
40 B c 2/3 Thewayyouare (USA)—Jolie Clara (FR) (Kahyasi) (29000) **Dr Barbara Matalon & Mr Ian Wight**
41 B f 17/4 Rip Van Winkle (IRE)—Knockatotaun (Spectrum (IRE)) (19000) **Malih L. Al Basti**
42 **NOBLE MASTER**, b c 13/2 Sir Percy—Eurolinka (IRE) (Tirol) (19000) **R. A. Gander**
43 **OAKLING**, b f 7/4 High Chaparral (IRE)—
　　　　　　　　　　Lambroza (IRE) (Grand Lodge (USA)) (4000) **D. O'Loughlin & Mrs P. Shanahan**
44 **PERCY VEER**, ch c 22/4 Sir Percy—Fandangerina (Hernando (FR)) (13937) **Mr & Mrs M Crow**
45 **PINK RIBBON (IRE)**, b c 13/3 Dark Angel (IRE)—
　　　　　　　　　　My Funny Valentine (IRE) (Mukaddamah (USA)) (75000) **Mrs M. Cousins**

MR SYLVESTER KIRK - Continued

46 B f 25/1 Showcasing—Poulaine Bleue (Bertolini (USA)) (7500)
47 B c 4/3 Nayef (USA)—Premier Prize (Selkirk (USA)) **J. C. Smith**
48 B c 25/2 Bushranger (IRE)—She's A Softie (IRE) (Invincible Spirit (IRE)) (9523) **Thurloe Thoroughbreds XX**
49 B f 19/4 Kyllachy—Tinnarinka (Observatory (IRE)) (16000) **Mr R. Hannon**

Other Owners: Mr R. J. Brennan, Mr M. J. Brown, Mrs P. A. Brown, Mr D. Bugler, Mr K. Bugler, Mr A. Bugler, Mr M. Clarke, The Hon Mrs C. Corbett, Ms G. F. Doran, Mr M. East, Sir A. Ferguson, R. Hannon, S. Hassiakos, Mr M. V. Hill, Mr Sylvester Kirk, Mrs K. J. Morton, Mr D. P. Moss, M. M. Nicolson, Mr D. O'Loughlin, Mr Neil Simpson, Miss B. A. Snow, Mr J. A. B. Stafford, Mr J. S. Threadwell, Mr C. M. Wall, Mrs S. Wall, Mr A. D. Wilson, Mrs J. Wiltshire, C. N. Wright.

Assistant Trainer: Fanny Kirk

Jockey (flat): James Doyle, Liam Keniry. **Apprentice:** Josh Baudains. **Amateur:** Miss C. Boxall.

---

377 MR STUART KITTOW, Cullompton
Postal: **Hayneld Farm, Blackborough, Cullompton, Devon, EX15 2JD**
Contacts: **HOME (01823) 680183 FAX (01823) 680601 MOBILE (07714) 218921**
E-MAIL stuartkittowracing@hotmail.com WEBSITE stuartkittowracing.com

1 DILGURA, 4, b f Ishiguru (USA)—Dilys **S. Kittow, R. Perry, B. Hopkins**
2 FLIPPING, 7, br g Kheleyf (USA)—Felona **R. S. E. Gifford**
3 GUILDED SPIRIT, 4, b g Ishiguru (USA)—Soft Touch (IRE) **The Racing Guild**
4 ICE NELLY (IRE), 6, b m Iceman—Dancing Nelly **Lady Hardy**
5 KILK, 6, b m Striking Ambition—Bathwick Alice **Mr G Jewell & Mr D Stevens**
6 KLEITOMACHOS (IRE), 6, b g Barathea (IRE)—Theben (GER) **E. J. S. Gadsden**
7 MACDILLON, 8, b g Acclamation—Dilys **Boswell,Pillans,Harris,Urquhart & Kittow**
8 MAY BE SOME TIME, 6, ch g Iceman—Let Alone **Dr G. S. Plastow**
9 NOBLE PROTECTOR, 4, b f Haafhd—All Glory **The Black Type Partnership III**
10 ON STAGE, 5, ch m Act One—In The Stocks **E. J. S. Gadsden**
11 OUR FOLLY, 6, b g Sakhee (USA)—Regent's Folly (IRE) **Midd Shire Racing**
12 RESURGE (IRE), 9, b g Danehill Dancer (IRE)—Resurgence **Chris & David Stam**
13 RUSSIAN ROYALE, 4, b f Royal Applause—Russian Ruby (FR) **P. A. & M. J. Reditt**
14 SIGNIFICANT MOVE, 7, b g Motivator—Strike Lightly **Midd Shire Racing**
15 WEAPON OF CHOICE (IRE), 6, b g Iffraaj—Tullawadgeen (IRE) **Chris & David Stam**

THREE-YEAR-OLDS
16 Ch f Tobougg (IRE)—Let Alone **Dr G. S. Plastow**
17 MAD ENDEAVOUR, b g Muhtathir—Capelly **R. S. E. Gifford**
18 MONTE VISO, b g Piccolo—Mrs Snaffles (IRE) **The Monte Viso Partners**
19 PLAUSEABELLA, b f Royal Applause—Ellablue **Midd Shire Racing**

TWO-YEAR-OLDS
20 Ch f 16/3 Kyllachy—Enrapture (USA) (Lear Fan (USA)) (33333)
21 B f 29/1 Halling (USA)—Extreme Pleasure (IRE) (High Chaparral (IRE)) (6666)
22 B f 11/3 Alhaarth (IRE)—Kahalah (IRE) (Darshaan)
23 B c 7/5 Sleeping Indian—Our Piccadilly (IRE) (Piccolo) (5714)
24 B c 24/4 Pastoral Pursuits—There's Two (IRE) (Ashkalani (IRE)) (11428) **Mr G. D. C. Jewell**
25 UPPISH, ch g 23/3 Compton Place—Uplifting (Magic Ring (IRE)) **H. A. Cushing**

Other Owners: Mrs S. G. Arnesen, D. W. Arnesen, John Boswell, Andrew Bull, Mr A. J. Cottrell, R. Eagle, M. E. Harris, Mr N. Harvey, Mr B. S. Hopkins, Mr A. R. Ingham, W. S. Kittow, B. G. Middleton, Mr R. N. Olsen, The Hon Mrs R. Pease, Mrs R. J. M. Perry, Mr M. D. Pillans, Mrs P. A. Reditt, M. J. Reditt, A. J. Shire, Mr D. B. Stam, Dr C. Stam, Mr D. J. Stevens, Ms W. A. Stoker, R. A. Stoker, D. R. Tucker, Mr J. R. Urquhart.

Assistant Trainer: Mrs Judy Kittow **Jockey (flat):** Fergus Sweeney. **Jockey (NH):** Tom Scudamore.

---

378 MR WILLIAM KNIGHT, Angmering
Postal: **Lower Coombe Racing Stables, Angmering Park, Littlehampton, West Sussex, BN16 4EX**
Contacts: **PHONE (01903) 871188 FAX (01903) 871184 MOBILE (07770) 720828**
E-MAIL william@wknightracing.co.uk WEBSITE www.wknightracing.co.uk

1 AEOLIAN BLUE, 4, ch f Bahamian Bounty—Blue Mistral (IRE) **Mrs S. M. Mitchell**
2 AUSSIE REIGNS (IRE), 4, b g Aussie Rules (USA)—Rohain (IRE) **The Old Brokers**

MR WILLIAM KNIGHT - Continued

3 **BEACON LADY**, 5, ch m Haafhd—Oriental Lady (IRE) **The Pro-Claimers**
4 **BLOODSWEATANDTEARS**, 6, b g Barathea (IRE)—Celestial Princess **Canisbay Bloodstock**
5 **FIRE SHIP**, 5, b g Firebreak—Mays Dream **IGP Partnership & P. Winkworth**
6 **JACOB CATS**, 5, b g Dutch Art—Ballet **Canisbay Bloodstock**
7 **KEEP THE SECRET**, 4, ch f Sakhee's Secret—Starfleet **Mr & Mrs N. Welby**
8 **MAVERIK**, 6, ch g Iceman—Nouvelle Lune **Mr A. L. Brooks**
9 **MODERNSTONE**, 4, b f Duke of Marmalade (IRE)—Post Modern (USA) **Biddestone Racing Club**
10 **NASSAU STORM**, 5, b g Bahamian Bounty—Got To Go **The Oil Men Partnership**
11 **NOBLE GIFT**, 4, ch g Cadeaux Genereux—Noble Penny **Gail Brown Racing (V)**
12 **OBLITEREIGHT (IRE)**, 5, ch g Bertolini (USA)—Doctrine **The Oil Men Partnership**
13 **PALACE MOON**, 9, b g Fantastic Light (USA)—Palace Street (USA) **Canisbay Bloodstock**
14 **PIRA PALACE (IRE)**, 4, b f Acclamation—Takrice **Miss T. Walters**
15 **ROWAN RIDGE**, 6, ch g Compton Place—Lemon Tree (USA) **Mr & Mrs N. Welby**
16 **SECRET ART (IRE)**, 4, ch g Excellent Art—Ivy Queen (IRE) **Circuit Racing**
17 **STORY WRITER**, 5, b g Sakhee (USA)—Celestial Princess **The Pheasant Rew Partnership**
18 **SWEET MARTONI**, 4, b f Dubawi (IRE)—Sweetness Herself **Grainger Lavell**
19 **WHIPPER SNAPPER (IRE)**, 4, b g Whipper (USA)—Topiary (IRE) **The Oil Merchants**

THREE-YEAR-OLDS

20 **ALLERGIC REACTION (IRE)**, b g Kyllachy—Wood Chorus **Four Men & A Dream Partnership**
21 **BEACH BAR (IRE)**, b c Azamour (IRE)—Toasted Special (USA) **P. Winkworth & Mrs Bex Seabrook**
22 **BLACK MARY**, b f Bushranger (IRE)—Corps de Ballet (IRE) **Mr T. G. Roddick**
23 **CAPMONDE (IRE)**, b f Cape Cross (IRE)—Esclarmonde (IRE) **Mrs F. Ashfield**
24 **CRAFTY EXIT**, gr c Mastercraftsman (IRE)—Demerger (USA) **Brooks, Cavanagh, Tracey**
25 **EXALTED (IRE)**, b g Acclamation—Eman's Joy **The Old Brokers**
26 **GAVLAR**, b g Gentlewave (IRE)—Shawhill **Chasemore Farm LLP**
27 **GOODWOOD STORM**, ch f Shamardal (USA)—Artifice **Goodwood Racehorse Owners Group (20) Ltd**
28 **HURRICANE HARRY**, b g Royal Applause—Stormy Weather **Brooks, Cavanagh, Tracey**
29 **LOCHALSH (IRE)**, ch g Duke of Marmalade (IRE)—Kylemore (IRE) **Mrs M. Bryce**
30 **PERCYBELLE**, ch f Sir Percy—Chelsea (USA) **Jon & Julia Aisbitt**
31 **SOUNDTRACK (IRE)**, br g Excellent Art—Annthoulah (IRE) **Wardley Bloodstock**
32 **SWEETHEART ABBEY**, b f Dancing Spree (USA)—Hinton Pearl **Miss S. Bannatyne**
33 **TIPTREE LACE**, b f Duke of Marmalade (IRE)—Crinolette (IRE) **Mr & Mrs N. Welby**
34 **TULLIA (IRE)**, b f Footstepsinthesand—Whipped Queen (USA) **P. L. Winkworth**
35 **TUNNEL TIGER (IRE)**, b f Dylan Thomas (IRE)—Nakiska **The Pro-Claimers**

TWO-YEAR-OLDS

36 **ASHAPURNA (IRE)**, ch f 24/1 Tamayuz—Bond Deal (IRE) (Pivotal) **Jon & Julia Aisbitt**
37 B c 18/4 Duke of Marmalade (IRE)—Bintalreef (USA) (Diesis) (40000)
38 B f 21/4 Azamour (IRE)—Esclarmonde (IRE) (In The Wings) (12000) **Mr & Mrs N. Welby**
39 **GOODWOOD MOONLIGHT**, b c 22/2 Azamour (IRE)—
                 Corrine (IRE) (Spectrum (IRE)) (36000) **Goodwood Racehorse Owners Group (21) Ltd**
40 Ch f 24/3 Lope de Vega (IRE)—Isabella Glyn (IRE) (Sadler's Wells (USA)) (35000) **G. Roddick**
41 Ch f 10/3 Mastercraftsman (IRE)—Koniya (IRE) (Doyoun) (9000) **G. Roddick**
42 B f 24/4 Royal Applause—Rapsgate (IRE) (Mozart (IRE)) (13000) **Mrs Sheila Mitchell**
43 **SKY ROSE**, b f 6/2 Sakhee (USA)—Intersky High (USA) (Royal Anthem (USA)) **Jane Keir & Christine Sandall**
44 **SOLAR FLAIR**, b c 1/2 Equiano (FR)—
                 Air Biscuit (IRE) (Galileo (IRE)) (18095) **Circuit Racing & The Kimber Family**

Other Owners: Mr Jon Aisbitt, Mrs Julia Aisbitt, Mr Tareq Al-Mazeedi, Mr A. Black, Mrs J. E. Black, Mr Tim Bostwick, Mr A. Brooks, Mr R. G. W. Brown, Mr G. J. Burchell, Mr I. J. Callaway, Mr J. Cavanagh, Mrs H. G. Clinch, Mr D. Ellis, Mr G. H. Galazka, Mr Laurence Grainger, Mr P. J. Gregg, Mr Rupert Gregson-Williams, Mrs E. Gregson-Williams, Mr R. F. Kilby, Mr W. J. Knight, Mrs Margaret Lavell, Mr Nick Peacock, Mr N. J. Roach, Mr Mike Rudd, Mr J. Seabrook, Mr M. Stone, Miss Maureen Stopher, Mr Mark Tracey, Mr N. Welby, Mrs N. Welby, Mr P. Winkworth.

Assistant Trainer: Matthew Darling

Jockey (flat): Jim Crowley.

379 MR DANIEL KUBLER, Whitsbury
Postal: **2 Warditch Cottages, Whitsbury, Fordingbridge, Hampshire, SP6 3QH**
Contacts: PHONE **(01725) 518690 MOBILE (07984) 287254**
E-MAIL **daniel@kublerracing.com** WEBSITE **www.kublerracing.com**

1 **CRIUS (IRE)**, 5, b h Heliostatic (IRE)—Fearless Flyer (IRE) **Titan Assets**
2 **EMINENTLY**, 4, b f Exceed And Excel (AUS)—Imperial Bailiwick (IRE) **Mr & Mrs G. Middlebrook**
3 **FIREBACK**, 7, b g Firebreak—So Discreet
4 **MONT SIGNAL**, 4, ch g Pivotal—Anse Victorin (USA) **Mr & Mrs G. Middlebrook**
5 **SHAMIANA**, 4, b br f Manduro (GER)—Camp Riverside (USA) **Mrs F. Denniff**

THREE-YEAR-OLDS

6 **BAILIWICK**, b c Oratorio (IRE)—Imperial Bailiwick (IRE) **Mr & Mrs G. Middlebrook**
7 **CRUCIBLE**, b c Danehill Dancer (IRE)—Baize **Mr & Mrs G. Middlebrook**
8 **MARMANDE (IRE)**, ch f Duke of Marmalade (IRE)—Roselyn **Mr & Mrs G. Middlebrook**
9 **NORSE LEGEND**, b c Norse Dancer (IRE)—Methodical **Woodhaven Racing Syndicate**
10 **SHOCK**, b g Kheleyf (USA)—Montcalm (IRE) **Mrs C. E. Kubler**

TWO-YEAR-OLDS

11 B f 25/3 Duke of Marmalade (IRE)—Albertine Rose (Namid) **Mr & Mrs G. Middlebrook**
12 B f 25/4 Teofilo (IRE)—Asinara (GER) (Big Shuffle (USA)) (31000) **Capture The Moment II**
13 **CHICA RAPIDA**, ch f 30/4 Paco Boy (IRE)—Tora Bora (Grand Lodge (USA)) (22000) **Who Dares Wins**
14 **COVENANT**, b c 15/4 Raven's Pass (USA)—Love Everlasting (Pursuit of Love) (68000) **Mr & Mrs G. Middlebrook**
15 **LADY FIONA**, b f 26/3 Royal Applause—Perfect Echo (Lycius (USA)) (26000) **Mrs F. C. Shepherd**
16 Ch c 23/4 Exceed And Excel (AUS)—Ludynosa (USA) (Cadeaux Genereux) (80000) **Kubler Racing Ltd**
17 **PICCADILLO**, b f 8/4 Piccolo—Dahshah (Mujtahid (USA)) (14285) **Diskovery Partnership II**
18 **THEWAYTHEWINDBLOWS (IRE)**, gr c 8/2 Thewayyouare (USA)—
Bali Breeze (IRE) (Common Grounds) (30476) **Who Dares Wins**
19 **VIVA MADIBA (IRE)**, b f 22/1 Kodiac—Degree of Honor (FR) (Highest Honor (FR)) (12775)
20 **WHO'STHEDADDY**, b c 4/3 Avonbridge—Lisathedaddy (Darnay) **Mrs P. S. Wilson**

Other Owners: Mr S. G. Lake, C. A. Leafe, G. Middlebrook, Mrs L. A. Middlebrook, Mrs M. O'Sullivan, Miss J. E. Reed.

Assistant Trainer: Claire Kubler

Jockey (flat): Mickael Barzalona, Martin Dwyer, Richard Kingscote.

---

380 MR CARLOS LAFFON-PARIAS, Chantilly
Postal: **38, Avenue du General Leclerc, 60500 Chantilly, France**
Contacts: PHONE **(0033) 344 575375 FAX (0033) 680 182909**
E-MAIL **ecuries.laffon.parias@wanadoo.fr**

1 **AGUAFRIA (USA)**, 4, b f More Than Ready (USA)—Briviesca **Sarl Darpat France**
2 **ALAJAR (IRE)**, 4, b f Galileo (IRE)—Arazena (USA) **Sarl Darpat France**
3 **CANTABRICO**, 4, ch g Sakhee (USA)—Sakha **Felipe Hinojosa**
4 **ESLES (FR)**, 6, b g Motivator—Resquilleuse (USA)
5 **FEREVIA (IRE)**, 4, b f Motivator—Frynia (USA) **H.H. Sheikh Mohammed Bin Khalifa Al Thani**
6 **LYKASTOS (IRE)**, 4, b g Holy Roman Emperor (IRE)—Granadilla **Stilvi Compania Financiera**
7 **MENEAS (FR)**, 4, b c American Post—Okalea (IRE) **Stilvi Compania Financiera**
8 **NIKODAMOS (GR)**, 4, b c Clodovil (IRE)—Shikasta (IRE) **Stilvi Compania Financiera**
9 **PINK ANEMONE**, 4, b f Dansili—Crystal Reef **W. McAlpin**
10 **SINGING (IRE)**, 4, b c Singspiel (IRE)—Ring Beaune (USA) **Wertheimer Et Frere**
11 **SPIN A SPELL (USA)**, 4, b f Empire Maker (USA)—Arabian Spell (USA) **W. McAlpin**
12 **TOPAZE BLANCHE (IRE)**, 4, b f Zamindar (USA)—
Pearl Earrine (FR) **H.H. Sheikh Mohammed Bin Khalifa Al Thani**

THREE-YEAR-OLDS

13 **AIMANTE (FR)**, b f Dansili—Acago (USA) **Wertheimer Et Frere**
14 **BAWINA (IRE)**, b f Dubawi (IRE)—Esneh (IRE) **Wertheimer Et Frere**
15 **CHANT DE SABLE (IRE)**, b f Oasis Dream—Akhla (USA) **Stilvi Compania Financiera**
16 **CHASINA (IRE)**, b f Medaglia d'oro (USA)—Lindelaan (USA) **Mr P. Fudge**
17 **COSCA (FR)**, b f Kavafi (IRE)—Vytinna (FR) **Stilvi Compania Financiera**
18 **DHUMA**, b br f Falco (USA)—Tender Morn (USA) **Wertheimer Et Frere**
19 **DREAM GIRL**, b f Oasis Dream—Iron Lips **Wertheimer Et Frere**

MR CARLOS LAFFON-PARIAS - Continued

20 **EMPREINTE (USA)**, ch f Footstepsinthesand—Zagzig **Wertheimer Et Frere**
21 **ERIAS (FR)**, ch c Gold Away (IRE)—Betwixt (IRE) **Stilvi Compania Financiera**
22 **FARADAN (FR)**, ch f King's Best (USA)—Eriza **Stilvi Compania Financiera**
23 **FESTIAS**, b g Pivotal—Loxandra **Stilvi Compania Financiera**
24 **FLAMBEUSE**, b f Cape Cross (IRE)—Flamenba **Wertheimer Et Frere**
25 **HUELIN**, b c Arch (USA)—Briviesca **Sarl Darpat France**
26 **ICARIUM (FR)**, ch c Medicean—Delfinia (FR) **Stilvi Compania Financiera**
27 **ICELIDE (IRE)**, gr f Verglas (IRE)—Arrivee (FR) **Wertheimer Et Frere**
28 **IQUEST (FR)**, b f Falco (USA)—Dynalosca (USA) **Wertheimer Et Frere**
29 **KARACTERIEL**, b g Dalakhani (IRE)—Spring Star (FR) **Wertheimer Et Frere**
30 **KILAVA (FR)**, b f Invincible Spirit (IRE)—Agiel (FR) **Stilvi Compania Financiera**
31 **MEDEO (FR)**, b g Elusive City (USA)—Oceanique (USA) **Wertheimer Et Frere**
32 **MENANDORE (FR)**, b f Invincible Spirit (IRE)—Kezia (FR) **Stilvi Compania Financiera**
33 **NO MOOD**, ch c Monsun (GER)—Impressionnante **Wertheimer Et Frere**
34 **NOLOHAY (IRE)**, ch c Dubawi (IRE)—Antioquia **Felipe Hinojosa**
35 **ORSOVIA**, ch f Shamardal (USA)—Alyzea (IRE) **Stilvi Compania Financiera**
36 **PLANETAIRE**, b c Galileo (IRE)—Occupandiste (IRE) **Wertheimer Et Frere**
37 **PRIVATE**, b c Pivotal—Icelips (USA) **Wertheimer Et Frere**
38 **QUALIDA (FR)**, b f Falco (USA)—Queen's Conquer **Wertheimer Et Frere**
39 **RAINBOW LOLLIPOP**, b f Dubawi (IRE)—Cross Section (USA) **W. McAlpin**
40 **RAREMENT (IRE)**, ch f Monsun (GER)—Fidelite (IRE) **Wertheimer Et Frere**
41 **REDING (FR)**, b c Pivotal—Alfaguara (USA) **Sarl Darpat France**
42 **RENTIER (IRE)**, b g Elusive City (USA)—Reverie Solitaire (IRE) **Stilvi Compania Financiera**
43 **SOSIA (GER)**, b f Shamardal (USA)—Sahel (GER) **Wertheimer Et Frere**
44 **SPIRITUEUX (IRE)**, b c Invincible Spirit (IRE)—Stormina (USA) **Wertheimer Et Frere**
45 **TELMIOS (IRE)**, gr c Mastercraftsman (IRE)—Drosia (IRE) **Stilvi Compania Financiera**
46 **VILLANUEVA (IRE)**, b f Whipper (USA)—Mabalane (IRE) **Sarl Darpat France**
47 **VRISSA (FR)**, gr f Duke of Marmalade (IRE)—Pearl Earrine (FR) **Stilvi Compania Financiera**
48 **WADIRUM (IRE)**, b c Dashing Blade—Dubai (IRE) **Wertheimer Et Frere**
49 **WISIGO (GER)**, b c Tiger Hill (IRE)—Wild Star (IRE) **Wertheimer Et Frere**
50 **ZAKAYLA**, b f Aqlaam—Zarkavean **Mr P. Fudge**
51 **ZAMARRILA**, b f High Chaparral (IRE)—Highphar (FR) **Sarl Darpat France**

TWO-YEAR-OLDS

52 **ALARCOS (FR)**, b c 27/3 Mr Sidney (USA)—Alfaguara (USA) (Red Ransom (USA)) **Montojo**
53 **ALCAUCIN (FR)**, b c 6/5 Siyouni (FR)—Trylko (USA) (Diesis) (26325) **Sarl Darpat France**
54   f 1/1 Zamindar (USA)—Alyzea (IRE) (King Charlemagne (USA)) **Stilvi Compania Financiera**
55 **ANASTER (FR)**, b c 5/2 Footstepsinthesand—Arikaria (IRE) (Sri Pekan (USA)) **Stilvi Compania Financiera**
56 **ANDARIST (IRE)**, ch c 27/2 Halling (USA)—Alfreda (Unfuwain (USA)) **Stilvi Compania Financiera**
57 **ARCENFETE (FR)**, b c 24/3 Arch (USA)—Soft Pleasure (USA) (Diesis) **Wertheimer Et Frere**
58 **ARTIFICIER (USA)**, ch c 26/3 Lemon Drop Kid (USA)—
                                  Quiet Royal (USA) (Royal Academy (USA)) **Wertheimer Et Frere**
59 **ARVIOS**, ch c 27/3 Medicean—Akrivi (IRE) (Tobougg (IRE)) **Stilvi Compania Financiera**
60 **BILISSIE**, b f 2/3 Dansili—Balladeuse (FR) (Singspiel (IRE)) **Wertheimer Et Frere**
61 **CLARMINA (IRE)**, b f 25/3 Cape Cross (IRE)—Stormina (Gulch (USA)) **Wertheimer Et Frere**
62 **COLDSTONE (FR)**, ch c 15/2 Gold Away (IRE)—Vraona (Fantastic Light (USA)) **Stilvi Compania Financiera**
63 **DAUGHTER DAWN (IRE)**, ch f 25/3 New Approach (IRE)—
                                  Light Quest (USA) (Quest For Fame (USA)) **Stilvi Compania Financiera**
64 **DESMIOS (FR)**, b c 26/1 Hold That Tiger (USA)—
                                  Sapfo (FR) (Peintre Celebre (USA)) **Stilvi Compania Financiera**
65 **DIALECTIC (IRE)**, b c 21/3 Monsun (GER)—Wandering Spirit (GER) (Dashing Blade) **Wertheimer Et Frere**
66   B f 16/3 Duke of Marmalade (IRE)—Frynia (USA) (Cat Thief (USA)) **Stilvi Compania Financiera**
67 **GIBRALFARO (IRE)**, b c 4/4 Dalakhani (IRE)—Ronda (Bluebird (USA)) (9291) **Sarl Darpat France**
68 **INCENDIUM (IRE)**, ch c 12/2 Ialysos (GER)—Polyegos (IRE) (Hawk Wing (USA)) **Stilvi Compania Financiera**
69 **INSTAGRAM (FR)**, b c 1/1 Falco (USA)—Trumbaka (IRE) (In The Wings) **Wertheimer Et Frere**
70 **JETON (IRE)**, b c 13/3 Montjeu (IRE)—Red Stella (FR) (Rainbow Quest (USA)) **Wertheimer Et Frere**
71 **JUBRIQUE (IRE)**, ch c 19/5 Zamindar (USA)—Agapimou (IRE) (Spectrum (IRE)) **Felipe Hinojosa**
72 **KADLA (FR)**, b f 3/3 Falco (USA)—Kalisia (King's Best (USA)) **Stilvi Compania Financiera**
73 **MYRLA (FR)**, b f 19/5 Elusive City (USA)—Agiel (FR) (Bering) **Stilvi Compania Financiera**
74   B f 23/1 Orpen (USA)—Okalea (IRE) (Dalakhani (IRE)) **Stilvi Compania Financiera**
75 **OLANTHIA (IRE)**, b f 30/1 Zamindar (USA)—Olvia (IRE) (Giant's Causeway (USA)) **Stilvi Compania Financiera**
76 **PALE PEARL (IRE)**, ch f 26/4 King's Best (USA)—
                                  Pearl Earrine (FR) (Kaldounevees (FR)) **Stilvi Compania Financiera**
77 **PICKAWAY (IRE)**, b f 6/4 Pivotal—Danzigaway (USA) (Danehill (USA)) **Wertheimer Et Frere**
78 **PITAMORE (USA)**, b f 29/3 More Than Ready (USA)—Pitamakan (USA) (Danzig (USA)) **Wertheimer Et Frere**

MR CARLOS LAFFON-PARIAS - Continued

79 **PRIMLY (FR)**, b f 22/4 King's Best (USA)—Eriza (Distant Relative) **Stilvi Compania Financiera**
80 **RAVAGE**, gr f 8/3 Verglas (IRE)—Arrivee (FR) (Anabaa (USA)) **Wertheimer Et Frere**
81 **REPRINT (IRE)**, b f 16/4 Nayef (USA)—Desertiste (Green Desert (USA)) **Wertheimer Et Frere**
82 **RIVEN LIGHT (IRE)**, b c 27/2 Raven's Pass (USA)—Vivacity (Trempolino (USA)) **Stilvi Compania Financiera**
83 **SEASONAL (IRE)**, ch c 4/4 Samum (GER)—Never Green (IRE) (Halling (USA)) **Wertheimer Et Frere**
84 **SERENDY (USA)**, ch f 5/4 Pleasantly Perfect (USA)—Ydillique (IRE) (Sadler's Wells (USA)) **Wertheimer Et Frere**
85 **SPONDE (FR)**, b f 10/2 Three Valleys (USA)—Iasia (GR) (One Cool Cat (USA)) **Stilvi Compania Financiera**
86 **SQUARE SET (IRE)**, b c 2/5 Country Reel (USA)—Delfinia (FR) (Drastikos (GR)) **Stilvi Compania Financiera**
87 **SYNDROMOS (FR)**, b c 24/3 Muhtathir—Dexandra (GR) (Evippos (GR)) **Stilvi Compania Financiera**
88 **TOLOX (FR)**, c 5/5 Zamindar (USA)—Briviesca (Peintre Celebre (USA)) **Sarl Darpat France**
89 **WHIPPETTE (FR)**, b f 26/4 Whipper (USA)—Betwixt (IRE) (Sinndar (IRE)) **Stilvi Compania Financiera**

Assistant Trainer: Charles Peck

---

381 **MR NICK LAMPARD, Marlborough**
Postal: **South Cottage, 2 The Crossroads, Clatford, Marlborough, Wiltshire, SN8 4EA**
Contacts: **PHONE (01672) 861420**

1 **GOOCHYPOOCHYPRADER**, 7, ch m Karinga Bay—Mrs Ritchie **The Outside Chance Racing Club**
2 **HEATHYARDS FLYER**, 11, b g Beat All (USA)—Heathyards Gem **Mr I. M. Scaramanga**
3 **JUST SATISFACTION**, 5, b m Trade Fair—Bathwick Fancy (IRE) **The Outside Chance Racing Club**
4 **PUR DE SIVOLA (FR)**, 11, b g Robin des Champs (FR)—Gamine d'ici (FR) **The Outside Chance Racing Club**

Other Owners: Miss A. E. A. Solomon, Mr H. Spooner.

---

382 **MR DAVID LANIGAN, Upper Lambourn**
Postal: **Kingsdown Stables, Upper Lambourn, Hungerford, Berkshire, RG17 8QX**
Contacts: **PHONE (01488) 71786 FAX (01488) 674148**
E-MAIL david@laniganracing.co.uk WEBSITE www.laniganracing.co.uk

1 **BIOGRAPHER**, 5, b h Montjeu (IRE)—Reflective (USA)
2 **DAWN SKY**, 10, b g Fantastic Light (USA)—Zacheta
3 **DUKES DELIGHT (IRE)**, 4, b f Duke of Marmalade (IRE)—Fashion Model
4 **FOOTSTEPSINTHERAIN (IRE)**, 4, b g Footstepsinthesand—Champagne Toni (IRE)
5 **FOR WHAT (USA)**, 6, ch h Mingun (USA)—Cuanto Es (USA)
6 **INTERCEPTION (IRE)**, 4, ch f Raven's Pass (USA)—Badee'a (IRE)
7 **LEONARD THOMAS**, 4, b g Singspiel (IRE)—Monawara (USA)
8 **NUR JAHAN (IRE)**, 4, b f Selkirk (USA)—Have Faith (IRE)
9 **PLUTOCRACY (IRE)**, 4, b c Dansili—Private Life (FR)
10 **TINGHIR (IRE)**, 4, b c Dansili—Palmeraie (USA)
11 **TYPHON (USA)**, 4, b g Proud Citizen (USA)—Seven Moons (JPN)
12 **ZETEAH**, 4, b f Passing Glance—Ajeebah (USA)

THREE-YEAR-OLDS

13 **ALIGHIERI (IRE)**, b c Sea The Stars (IRF)—Ange Bleu (USA)
14 **ALLEGATION (FR)**, b f Lawman (FR)—Anja (IRE)
15 **BABUR (IRE)**, ch g Pivotal—Bright Morning (USA)
16 **BOLD LASS (IRE)**, b f Sea The Stars (IRE)—My Branch
17 B f Dalakhani (IRE)—Crystal Music (USA)
18 **HIGHPLAINS DRIFTER (IRE)**, b g High Chaparral (IRE)—Qhazeenah
19 **HOIST THE COLOURS (IRE)**, b c Sea The Stars (IRE)—Multicolour Wave (IRE)
20 **ILE FLOTTANTE**, b f Duke of Marmalade (IRE)—Aqaarid (USA)
21 **LOLA MONTEZ (IRE)**, b f Duke of Marmalade (IRE)—Fille de Joie (IRE)
22 **PLACIDIA (IRE)**, b f Sea The Stars (IRE)—Palmeraie (USA)
23 **POLYBIUS**, b g Oasis Dream—Freedonia
24 **RAGGED ROBBIN (FR)**, ch g Speightstown (USA)—Ikat (IRE)
25 **REMBRANDT VAN RIJN (IRE)**, b c Peintre Celebre (USA)—Private Life (FR)
26 **SALMON SUSHI**, ch g Dalakhani (IRE)—Salsa Steps (USA)
27 **SEQUESTER**, ch f Selkirk (USA)—Al Theraab (USA)
28 **SINGING HINNIE**, b f Halling (USA)—Tawny Way
29 **WARRIOR OF LIGHT (IRE)**, b c High Chaparral (IRE)—Strawberry Fledge (USA)
30 **WOWEE**, b g Archipenko (USA)—Katya Kabanova

MR DAVID LANIGAN - Continued

TWO-YEAR-OLDS

31 B c 13/2 Galileo (IRE)—Alexander Goldrun (IRE) (Gold Away (IRE)) (400000)
32 Ch f 15/5 Galileo (IRE)—Ange Bleu (USA) (Alleged (USA))
33 B f 10/3 Lawman (FR)—Chervil (Dansili) (55000)
34 B f 24/4 Dansili—Cut Short (USA) (Diesis) (160000)
35 B c 6/2 Paco Boy (IRE)—Dont Dili Dali (Dansili) (46000)
36 B c 7/2 Zamindar (USA)—Femme de Fer (Hamas (IRE))
37 B c 11/3 Dubawi (IRE)—Geminiani (IRE) (King of Kings (IRE))
38 HELIOSPHERE (USA), b f 25/2 Medaglia d'oro (USA)—Flying Passage (USA) (A P Indy (USA)) (876424)
39 B br f 8/5 Galileo (IRE)—Hoity Toity (Darshaan) (300000)
40 HUMAN (USA), b f 16/2 Blame (USA)—Angel In My Heart (FR) (Rainbow Quest (USA))
41 B c 21/2 Mawatheeq (USA)—Katya Kabanova (Sadler's Wells (USA))
42 B f 19/4 Halling (USA)—Kisses (Sakhee (USA))
43 B c 13/1 Sea The Stars (IRE)—Melodramatic (IRE) (Sadler's Wells (USA))
44 B f 6/4 Oasis Dream—Palmeraie (USA) (Lear Fan (USA))
45 B f 14/2 Dynaformer (USA)—Reflective (USA) (Seeking The Gold (USA))
46 Gr ro f 7/3 Smart Strike (CAN)—Rose Diamond (IRE) (Daylami (IRE))
47 SNEAKING BUDGE, b c 13/3 Nayef (USA)—Ikat (IRE) (Pivotal)
48 SYNODIC (USA), b br c 19/2 Henrythenavigator (USA)—Seven Moons (JPN) (Sunday Silence (USA))
49 Ch c 10/3 Danehill Dancer (IRE)—Thinking Positive (Rainbow Quest (USA)) (45000)
50 B f 8/3 Medaglia d'oro (USA)—Trepidation (USA) (Seeking The Gold (USA)) (198656)

Owners: Ben & Sir Martyn Arbib, Mrs Emma Capon, Chelston Ireland, Favourites Racing, Flaxman Stables Ireland Ltd, Mrs Z. E. Hade, Ms E. A. Judd, Mr Bob Lanigan, Mrs David Lanigan, Lord Lloyd-Webber, Mrs John Magnier & Partner, Niarchos Family, B. E. Nielsen, Orpendale, J. A. Reed, Wedgewood Estates.

---

383 MISS EMMA LAVELLE, Andover

Postal: **Cottage Stables, Hatherden, Andover, Hampshire, SP11 0HY**
Contacts: PHONE **(01264) 735509** OFFICE **(01264) 735412** FAX **(01264) 735529**
MOBILE **(07774) 993998**
E-MAIL **emma@elavelle.freeserve.co.uk** WEBSITE **www.emmalavelle.com**

1 ABITOFBOB, 5, b g Enrique—My World (FR) **Mrs N. Turner, Mrs P. Tozer & Miss C. Schicht**
2 ALBERT BRIDGE, 6, gr g Hernando (FR)—Alvarita **The Cheyne Walkers**
3 ANDY KELLY (IRE), 5, ch g Flemensfirth (USA)—Fae Taylor (IRE) **The Optimists**
4 BLOWN COVER, 5, b g Kayf Tara—Cullen Bay (IRE) **Roger Hetherington & Colin Bothway**
5 BOUGGLER, 9, b g Tobougg (IRE)—Rush Hour (IRE) **Axom (XXI)**
6 BRANTINGHAM BREEZE, 6, gr m Tamure (IRE)—Absalom's Lady **Cottage Stables Racing Club**
7 CAPTAIN SUNSHINE, 8, b g Oscar (IRE)—Gaye Fame **Mrs N. C. Turner**
8 CAULFIELDS VENTURE (IRE), 8, b g Catcher In The Rye (IRE)—Saddlers' Venture (IRE) **C. F. Colquhoun**
9 CLARET CLOAK (IRE), 7, b g Vinnie Roe (IRE)—Bewildered (USA) **Hawksmoor Partnership**
10 CLOSING CEREMONY (IRE), 5, b g Flemensfirth (USA)—
Supreme Von Pres (IRE) **The High Altitude Partnership**
11 CLYFFE DANCER, 6, b m Grape Tree Road—Chandni (IRE) **Mrs C. F. E. Hall**
12 COMPASSION, 6, b m Tiger Hill (GER)—Windmill **Mrs S. Metcalfe**
13 COOLE RIVER (IRE), 10, ch g Carroll House—Kyle Cailin **Queens' Prices Syndicate**
14 COURT BY SURPRISE (IRE), 9, b g Beneficial—Garryduff Princess (IRE) **N. Mustoe**
15 COURT IN MOTION (IRE), 9, br g Fruits of Love (USA)—Peace Time Girl (IRE) **N. Mustoe**
16 COURT VICTORY (IRE), 9, b g Old Vic—Sarah's Smile **N. Mustoe**
17 DAYMAR BAY (IRE), 8, b g Oscar (IRE)—Sunset View (IRE) **The Hawk Inn Syndicate 2**
18 DAYS GONE BY, 6, b g Kayf Tara—Nuzzle **Swanbridge Bloodstock Limited**
19 DEMOGRAPHIC (USA), 5, b g Aptitude (USA)—Private Line (USA) **Mrs A. C. Lavelle**
20 EASTER DANCER, 7, ch m Karinga Bay—Easter Comet **Mr & Mrs S. C. Willes**
21 EASTER METEOR, 8, b g Midnight Legend—Easter Comet **Mr & Mrs S. C. Willes**
22 4, B g Oscar (IRE)—Fine Fortune (IRE) **The George Inn Racing Syndicate**
23 FIX IT RIGHT (IRE), 6, br g Vinnie Roe (IRE)—Rock Cottage Lady (IRE) **The Hawk Inn Syndicate**
24 FOX APPEAL (IRE), 7, b g Brian Boru—Lady Appeal (IRE) **The Hawk Inn Syndicate 3**
25 FURTHER MORE (IRE), 7, gr g Hasten To Add (USA)—Cottage Lass (IRE) **Frisky Fillies 4**
26 GLEANN EAGAS (IRE), 7, b g Gold Well—Glen Princess (IRE) **R. J. Lavelle**
27 GLOBAL WARMING (IRE), 10, b g King's Theatre (IRE)—
Croi Na Greine (IRE) **The Older But No Wiser Syndicate**
28 GREY WULFF (IRE), 9, gr g Oscar (IRE)—Only A Rose **Mrs S. V. M. Stevens**
29 GULLINBURSTI (IRE), 8, b g Milan—D'ygrande (IRE) **N. Mustoe**

MISS EMMA LAVELLE - Continued

30 **HATTON BANK**, 5, ch m Flemensfirth (USA)—Persian Walk (FR) **Mr G. P. MacIntosh**
31 **HIGHLAND LODGE (IRE)**, 8, b g Flemensfirth (USA)—Supreme Von Pres (IRE) **The Unusual Suspects**
32 **JUNCTION FOURTEEN (IRE)**, 5, b g King's Theatre (IRE)—Chevet Girl (IRE) **M. St Quinton & T. Syder**
33 **JUST GOT LUCKY**, 6, ch m Definite Article—Single Handed **Swanbridge Bloodstock Limited**
34 **KANGAROO COURT (IRE)**, 10, b g Lahib (USA)—Tombazaan (IRE) **N. Mustoe**
35 **KENTFORD GREY LADY**, 8, gr m Silver Patriarch (IRE)—Kentford Grebe **D. I. Bare**
36 **KIND OF EASY (IRE)**, 8, b g Kalanisi (IRE)—Specifiedrisk (IRE) **Mr T. D. J. Syder & Mr N. Mustoe**
37 **KINDLY NOTE**, 7, ch m Generous (USA)—Vent d'aout (IRE) **Elite Racing Club**
38 **KING BORU (IRE)**, 6, b g Brian Boru—Final Instalment (IRE) **Lavelle Wallis Farrington**
39 **LE BEC (FR)**, 6, ch g Smadoun (FR)—La Pelode (FR) **T. D. J. Syder**
40 **MAXILIAN (IRE)**, 5, b g Milan—Super Size (IRE) **Mrs Julien Turner & Mr Andrew Merriam**
41 **MILANESE (IRE)**, 6, b g Milan—Elma Joyce (IRE) **The C H F Partnership**
42 **MOSSPARK (IRE)**, 6, b g Flemensfirth (USA)—Patio Rose **N. Mustoe & T. Syder**
43 **OCEANA GOLD**, 10, ch g Primo Valentino (IRE)—Silken Dalliance **The C H F Partnership**
44 **OFF THE GROUND (IRE)**, 8, b g Oscar (IRE)—Kaysel (IRE) **Axom (XXVI)**
45 **ONDERUN (IRE)**, 5, b g Flemensfirth (USA)—Warts And All (IRE) **R. J. Lavelle**
46 **OUT OF THE MIST (IRE)**, 5, b m Flemensfirth (USA)—Mistinguett (IRE) **Swanbridge Bloodstock Limited**
47 **PADRE TITO (IRE)**, 6, b g Milan—Augusta Brook (IRE) **T. D. J. Syder**
48 **PARISH BUSINESS (IRE)**, 6, b br g Fruits of Love (USA)—Parkality (IRE) **N. Mustoe**
49 **PASKALIS**, 5, b g Kayf Tara—Easter Comet **Mr & Mrs S. C. Willes**
50 4, B f Kayf Tara—Prophets Honor (FR) **N. Mustoe**
51 **QIANSHAN LEADER (IRE)**, 10, b g Anshan—Gaelic Leader (IRE) **The Pick 'N' Mix Partnership**
52 **RED ROCK (FR)**, 9, b g Saint Cyrien (FR)—Ariloba de Brize (FR) **Mrs S. V. M. Stevens**
53 **SHOTGUN PADDY (IRE)**, 7, b g Brian Boru—Awesome Miracle (IRE) **Axom (XXXVI)**
54 **STAIGUE FORT**, 6, b g Kirkwall—Mulberry Wine **Lady Bland**
55 **STARLIGHT SONATA**, 4, b f Tagula (IRE)—Starlight Express (FR) **D. M. Bell**
56 **SWALLOWSHIDE**, 5, b g Hernando (FR)—Kentford Grebe **D. I. Bare**
57 **THE LAST NIGHT (FR)**, 7, ch g April Night (FR)—La Pelode (FR) **T. D. J. Syder**
58 **THE POTTING SHED (IRE)**, 7, br g Presenting—Barracree Rose (IRE) **N. Mustoe & T. Syder**
59 **TIME IS MONEY**, 5, b m Presenting—No More Money **Cottage Stables Racing Club**
60 **TIMESREMEMBERED (IRE)**, 6, b br g Akbar (IRE)—Native Hope (IRE) **Tim Syder & Sarah Prior**
61 **TOCCA FERRO (FR)**, 9, gr g April Night (FR)—La Pelode (FR) **T. D. J. Syder**
62 **VAGRANT EMPEROR (IRE)**, 11, b g Oscar (IRE)—Dragonmist (IRE) **Mrs A. C. Lavelle**
63 **VENDREDI TROIS (FR)**, 5, b g Shaanmer (IRE)—Legende Sacree (FR) **Awdry, Gemmell, Pomford & Williams**
64 **WATER WAGTAIL**, 7, b g Kahyasi—Kentford Grebe **D. I. Bare**
65 **WELL CONNECTED**, 5, b m Presenting—Lisa du Chenet (FR) **P. G. Jacobs**
66 **WELL REGARDED (IRE)**, 9, b g Dr Massini (IRE)—Glenelly Valley (IRE) **The Unusual Suspects**
67 **WELL REWARDED (IRE)**, 4, b g Beneficial—Lady Fancy (IRE) **Andy & The Frisky Fillies**
68 **WOODLAND WALK**, 6, ch m Generous (USA)—Duchess of Kinsale (IRE) **Cottage Stables Racing Club**
69 **YABADABADOO**, 6, b g Doyen (IRE)—Kabayil **Elite Racing Club**

THREE-YEAR-OLDS

70 Gr g Sagamix (FR)—Folie Dancer

Other Owners: Mr C. V. Awdry, Axom Ltd, Mr C. H. Bothway, Mr D. Downie, Mr W. T. Farrington, K. H. Fischer, C. H. Fischer, Mr R. J. Fowler, Mr A. Gemmell, Mrs N. J. Haigh, C. G. Hellyer, Mrs S. C. Hepworth, Mr R. R. Hetherington, Mr A. J. Hill, J. R. Hulme, J. R. Lavelle, Mr J. J. P. McNeile, A. W. K. Merriam, P. B. Mitford-Slade, Mr P. Nicholls, Miss M. Noden, B. G. Pomford, G. R. Pooley, Mrs S. K. Prior, Mr J. W. Randall, K. P. Ryan, Mr O. F. Ryan, Miss C. Schicht, Sir David Sieff, M. St Quinton, Mrs K. M. Taylor, Mrs P. Tozer, Mr J. W. Turner, Mrs J. C. Verity, J. R. Wallis, Mr P. R. Weston, Mr A. G. Weston, Mr S. C. Willes, Mrs M. Willes, Mrs P. H. Williams.

Assistant Trainer: Barry Fenton

---

384 MR BARRY LEAVY, Stoke-on-Trent
Postal: **Saverley House Farm, Saverley Green, Stoke-on-Trent, ST11 9QX**
Contacts: **HOME/FAX (01782) 398591 MOBILE (07540) 806915**
E-MAIL **lauraleavy@hotmail.co.uk** WEBSITE **www.leavyracing.co.uk**

1 **DANCING DUDE (IRE)**, 7, ch g Danehill Dancer (IRE)—Wadud **Cops & Robbers**
2 **DI KAPRIO (FR)**, 8, b g Kapgarde (FR)—Miss Nousha (FR) **Cops & Robbers**
3 **FLOBURY**, 6, b m Overbury (IRE)—Miss Flora **Mr J. K. S. Cresswell**
4 **GHAABESH (IRE)**, 7, b g Alhaarth (IRE)—Alyakkh (IRE) **B. Leavy**
5 **KING ZEAL (IRE)**, 10, b g King's Best (USA)—Manureva (USA) **Deborah Hart & Alan Jackson**
6 **LEAN BURN (USA)**, 8, b g Johannesburg (USA)—Anthelion (USA) **N. Heath**

MR BARRY LEAVY - Continued

7 **MATERIAL BOY**, 7, b g Karinga Bay—Material Girl **You Can Be Sure**
8 **MISS TWIGGS**, 5, b m Helissio (FR)—Seviot **Miss S. M. Thomas**
9 **MOHI RAHRERE (IRE)**, 11, b g New Frontier (IRE)—Collinstown Lady (IRE) **Mrs S D Ashford & Mr J G Williams**

Other Owners: Mrs S. D. Ashford, Mr Frank Dronzek, Mrs Deborah Hart, Mr Alan Jackson, Mr Brendan Jones, Mr Barry Leavy, Mr Chris Nightingale, Mr D. Rowlinson, Mr J. G. Williams.

Assistant Trainer: Mrs L Leavy

Jockey (NH): Liam Heard. **Conditional:** Harry Challoner. **Apprentice:** Ryan Holmes.

---

385   MR RICHARD LEE, Presteigne
Postal: **The Bell House, Byton, Presteigne, LD8 2HS**
Contacts: **PHONE (01544) 267672 FAX (01544) 260247 MOBILE (07836) 537145**
E-MAIL rleeracing@btinternet.com WEBSITE www.rleeracing.com

1 **BARNEY RUBBLE**, 5, b g Medicean—Jade Chequer **J. D. Cound**
2 **BIG NEWS**, 8, ch g Karinga Bay—Welcome News **Mrs Caroline Shaw & Mrs Christine Graves**
3 **BLACK IS BEAUTIFUL (FR)**, 6, b g Black Sam Bellamy (IRE)—Queen's Theatre (FR) **B Bailey & K Edwards**
4 **CARAMACK**, 4, ch g Danehill Dancer (IRE)—Oshiponga **D. E. Edwards**
5 **DARDANELLA**, 7, b m Alflora (IRE)—Ella Falls (IRE) **R. Bailey**
6 **DROPZONE (USA)**, 5, b g Smart Strike (CAN)—Dalisay (IRE) **R. A. Lee**
7 **GASSIN GOLF**, 5, b g Montjeu (IRE)—Miss Riviera Golf **W. Roseff**
8 **GOODTOKNOW**, 6, b g Presenting—Atlantic Jane **Burling Daresbury MacEchern Nolan Potter**
9 **GREY EARL**, 7, gr g Karinga Bay—Forever Grey (IRE) **Mr E. P. Parkes**
10 **GREY GOLD (IRE)**, 9, gr g Strategic Choice (USA)—Grouse-N-Heather **Mrs M. A. Boden**
11 **HECTOR'S CHOICE (FR)**, 10, b br g Grey Risk (FR)—The Voice (FR) **James & Jean Potter**
12 **HIGHWAY CODE (USA)**, 8, b g Street Cry (IRE)—Fairy Heights (IRE) **D. E. Edwards**
13 **INCENTIVISE (IRE)**, 11, ch g Snurge—
Festive Isle (IRE) **Ron Bartlett, Jeff Hulston & Exors of the Late F J Ayres**
14 **KNOCK A HAND (IRE)**, 9, br g Lend A Hand—Knockcross (IRE) **D. A. Halsall**
15 **KRIS SPIN (IRE)**, 6, br g Kris Kin (USA)—Auditing Empress (IRE) **Six To Five Against**
16 **MILO MILAN (IRE)**, 9, b g Milan—Simply Divine (IRE) **Mrs Caroline Shaw & Mrs Christine Graves**
17 **MOUNTAINOUS (IRE)**, 9, b g Milan—Mullaghcloga (IRE) **Walters Plant Hire & James & Jean Potter**
18 **MR BACHSTER (IRE)**, 9, b g Bach (IRE)—Warrior Princess (IRE) **R. A. Lee**
19 **RAVENS BROOK (IRE)**, 8, br g Alderbrook—Triple Triumph (IRE) **R. A. Lee**
20 **RIFLEMAN (IRE)**, 14, ch g Starborough—En Garde (USA) **J. M. Jackson**
21 **RUSSE BLANC (FR)**, 7, wh g Machiavellian Tsar (FR)—Fleur de Mad (FR) **Mr M. R. H. Jackson**
22 **SCALES (IRE)**, 8, b g Bob Back (USA)—Mrs Avery (IRE) **A Beard B Beard S Ripley**
23 **SIMPLY WINGS (IRE)**, 10, b g Winged Love (IRE)—Simply Deep (IRE) **Exors of the Late G. D. Thorp**
24 **THE CHAZER (IRE)**, 9, gr g Witness Box (USA)—Saffron Holly (IRE) **Mr & Mrs C. R. Elliott**
25 **TRESOR DE BONTEE (FR)**, 7, b g Grand Seigneur (FR)—Bontee (FR) **Glass Half Full**

Other Owners: Exors of the Late Mr F. J. Ayres, Mr Barry J. Bailey, Mr R. L Baker, Mr Ron Bartlett, Mr Alan Beard, Mr B. Beard, Mr Patrick Burling, Mrs Roslyn Burling, Lord Daresbury, Mr Ken Edwards, Mr C. R. Elliott, Mrs J. A. Elliott, Mrs Christine Graves, Mr R. L. C. Hartley, Mr Jeff Hulston, Mr Richard Lee, Mr Gavin MacEchern, Mr Paul B. Nolan, Mr J. E. Potter, Mrs J. E. Potter, Lady Susan Ripley, Mr Will Roseff, Mrs Caroline Shaw, Walters Plant Hire Ltd.

Assistant Trainer: Kerry Lewis

Jockey (NH): Richard Johnson, Charlie Poste. **Conditional:** Micheal Nolan.

---

386   MRS SOPHIE LEECH, Westbury-on-Severn
Postal: **T/A Leech Racing Limited, Tudor Racing Stables, Elton Road, Elton, Newnham, Gloucestershire, GL14 1JN**
Contacts: **PHONE (01452) 760691 MOBILE (07775) 874630**
E-MAIL info@leechracing.co.uk WEBSITE www.leechracing.co.uk

1 **ANTEROS (IRE)**, 6, b g Milan—Sovereign Star (IRE) **K. W. Bell**
2 **BANYAN TREE (IRE)**, 7, b g Danehill Dancer (IRE)—User Friendly **C. J. Leech**
3 **BLOWING A HOOLIE (IRE)**, 6, b m Val Royal (FR)—Moly **Bluebirds Racing & C J Leech**
4 **COOLAGAD WONDER (IRE)**, 9, ch g Fath (USA)—Wonder Bell (IRE) **C. J. Leech**
5 **GOD'S COUNTY (FR)**, 9, gr g Verglas (IRE)—Toujours Elle (USA) **G. Doel & C. J. Leech**
6 **GREY SOLDIER (IRE)**, 9, gr g Galileo (IRE)—Crusch Alva (FR) **J. O'Brien & C. J. Leech**

MRS SOPHIE LEECH - Continued

7 IS IT ME (USA), 11, ch g Sky Classic (CAN)—Thea (GER) **Cheltenham Racing Club**
8 KAPRICORNE (FR), 7, b g Kapgarde (FR)—Colombe Royale (FR) **Cheltenham Racing Club**
9 KASSIODOR (GER), 7, b g Tiger Hill (IRE)—Kitcat (GER) **C. J. Leech**
10 KELTIC CRISIS (IRE), 10, b g Needle Gun (IRE)—Catch Ball **Cheltenham Racing Club**
11 LE GRAND CHENE (FR), 8, b g Turgeon (USA)—Faitiche d'aubry (FR) **T. Westmacott & C. J. Leech**
12 MOSTLY BOB (IRE), 11, b g Bob Back (USA)—Town Gossip (IRE) **Bluebirds Racing, A French & C J Leech**
13 NELLIE FORBUSH, 4, b f Phoenix Reach (IRE)—Santa Isobel **C. J. Leech**
14 NICENE CREED, 9, b g Hernando (FR)—First Fantasy **C. J. Leech**
15 NOMADIC DREAMER, 11, ch g Nomadic Way (USA)—Nunsdream **C. J. Leech**
16 OLD MAGIC (IRE), 9, b g Old Vic—Maeve's Magic (IRE) **Cheltenham Racing Club**
17 OLYMPIAN BOY (IRE), 10, b g Flemensfirth (USA)—Notanissue (IRE) **J. Cocks & C. J. Leech**
18 OWEN GLENDOWER (IRE), 9, br g Anshan—Native Success (IRE) **C. J. Leech**
19 PETARA BAY (IRE), 10, b g Peintre Celebre (USA)—Magnificient Style (USA) **C. J. Leech**
20 PIANO CONCERTO (USA), 7, b g Red Ransom (USA)—Storm Song (USA) **J. Cocks & C. J. Leech**
21 RADMORES REVENGE, 11, b g Overbury (IRE)—Harvey's Sister **CJ Leech & RS Liddington**
22 RIVER D'OR (FR), 9, b g Saint Preuil (FR)—Une Pomme d'or (FR) **Frame, Lawton, Mitchell, O'Brien & Leech**
23 ROLLING DOUGH (IRE), 6, b m Indian Danehill (IRE)—High Dough (IRE) **C. J. Leech**
24 SEASIDE SHUFFLE (IRE), 9, b br g Wizard King—Leaden Sky (IRE) **Cheltenham Racing Club**
25 SEVEN SUMMITS (IRE), 7, b g Danehill Dancer (IRE)—Mandavilla (IRE) **C. J. Leech**
26 SILMI, 10, gr g Daylami (IRE)—Intimaa (IRE) **J. O'Brien & C. J. Leech**
27 SLEEPY (FR), 8, b g Sleeping Car (FR)—Haida IV (FR) **Cheltenham Racing Club**
28 TAKE OF SHOC'S (IRE), 10, ch g Beneficial—Dear Dunleer (IRE) **C. J. Leech**
29 TAKEROC (FR), 11, gr g Take Risks (FR)—Rochambelle (FR) **C. J. Leech**
30 TAMARILLO GROVE (IRE), 7, b g Cape Cross (IRE)—Tamarillo **G. Doel & C. J. Leech**
31 WINSTON CHURCHILL (IRE), 8, b g Presenting—Star Councel (IRE) **G. D. Thompson**
32 WOODY WALLER, 9, ch g Lomitas—Reamzafonic **C J Leech & A French**

Other Owners: Mr J. J. Cocks, G. Doel, B. H. Downs, Mr K. A. Frame, Mr A. I. French, Mr C J Hodgson, Mr D. W. Lawton, Mr R. S. Liddington, Mr D. Mitchell, J. O'Brien, Mr C. Parkin, Mr I. P. Phillips, Mr T. Westmacott.

Assistant Trainer: Christian Leech (07880) 788464

Jockey (NH): Paul Moloney.

---

387 MR ALASTAIR LIDDERDALE, Lambourn
Postal: **Lidderdale Racing LLP, Felstead Court Stables, Folly Road, Lambourn, Hungerford, Berkshire, RG17 8QE**
Contacts: **PHONE** (01488) 670443 **FAX** (01488) 670443 **MOBILE** (07785) 785375
E-MAIL alastair@lidderdaleracing.co.uk **WEBSITE** www.lidderdaleracing.co.uk

1 ALBERTO, 4, b g Bertolini (USA)—Al Awaalah **M Salaman,C Hill,T Tinson,G Else,S Green**
2 ALDO, 7, b g Lucky Owners (NZ)—Chaperone **Entertainments Committee**
3 ASIAN PRINCE (IRE), 5, b g Strategic Prince—Asian Alliance (IRE) **Lidderdale Racing LLP**
4 CANDY KITTEN, 4, b f Assertive—Birthday Venture **Mr A. J. Weller**
5 CHELLA THRILLER (SPA), 5, b m Chevalier (IRE)—Arundhati (IRE) **The Saucy Horse Partnership**
6 FREE FALLING, 8, ch m Selkirk (USA)—Free Flying **A.C. Entertainment Technologies Limited**
7 HANNAH JUST HANNAH, 5, gr m Proclamation (IRE)—Evaporate **The New Kennet Connection**
8 KIJIVU, 9, gr m Erhaab (USA)—Alsiba **KMC Partnership Three**
9 KILBURN, 10, b g Grand Lodge (USA)—Lady Lahar **Lidderdale Racing LLP**
10 KNOW NO FEAR, 9, b g Primo Valentino—Alustar **Bolingbroke Gravett Howard O'Connor**
11 MAJESTIC ZAFEEN, 5, b m Zafeen (FR)—Arasong **Lambourn Valley Racing II**
12 MICHAEL'S NOOK, 7, b g Intikhab (USA)—Mysterious Plans (IRE) **Lidderdale Racing LLP**
13 MOLLY WANNAKRACKER, 5, b m Multiplex—Kingsfold Blaze **White Diamond Racing**
14 NORTH CAPE (USA), 8, b g Action This Day (USA)—Cape (USA) **Mr A. McIver**
15 OVERRIDER, 4, b g Cockney Rebel (IRE)—Fustaan (IRE) **The Jersey Royals**
16 ROYAL MIZAR (SPA), 4, b g What A Caper (IRE)—Zahaadid (FR) **J. P. Duffy**
17 SIMMONS, 6, b m Spartacus (IRE)—One For Me **Miss R. Greenaway**
18 SSAFA, 6, b m Motivator—Orange Sunset (IRE) **Mr A. J. Weller**
19 TALLULAH MAI, 7, b m Kayf Tara—Al Awaalah **M. A. Salaman**

THREE-YEAR-OLDS

20 CAPERS ROYAL STAR (FR), b c What A Caper (IRE)—Arundhati (IRE) **Royal Windsor Racing Club**
21 KALLIGRAPHY, ch g Bertolini (USA)—Bold Byzantium **The Singleton Park**
22 KUBEBA (IRE), b c Kodiac—Brillano (FR) **The Kubeba Partnership**

MR ALASTAIR LIDDERDALE - Continued

23 **MADAME MIME ARTIST,** b f Dutch Art—Silent Waters **Bolingbroke Gravett Howard O'Connor**
24 **PENDO,** b g Denounce—Abundant **Mr B. K. Hopson**

Other Owners: Mr D. Barrett, Mrs D. M. Barrett, L. A. Bolingbroke, Mr K. B. Brant, Mr J. M. Duncan, Mr G. Else, Mr M. J. Foxton-Duffy, Mr N. Gravett, Ms S. Green, Mr C. R. Hill, W. R. Hinge, G. P. Howard, A. J. D. Lidderdale, K. P. McCarthy, D. J. Muir, Mrs A. Muir, Mrs F. A. O'Connor, Ms J. M. Smith, Miss A. E. A. Solomon, Mr T. P. Tinson.

Business & Racing Manager: Kevin McCarthy

Amateur: Miss Zoe Lilly.

---

388   **MR CLIFFORD LINES, Exning**
Postal: **Hethersett House, Church House, Exning, Newmarket, Suffolk, CB8 7EH**
Contacts: **PHONE (01638) 608016 FAX (01638) 608016 MOBILE (07980) 120157**
E-MAIL hethersetthouse@gmail.com

1 **PROUD CHIEFTAIN,** 6, b g Sleeping Indian—Skimra **Prima Racing Partnership**

THREE-YEAR-OLDS
2 B c Prince Arch (USA)—Ball Gown **Prima Racing Partnership**

Other Owners: Ms S. Cawthorn, C. V. Lines.

---

389   **MR NICK LITTMODEN, Newmarket**
Postal: **Brook Farm, Dullingham Ley, Dullingham, Newmarket, Suffolk, CB8 9XG**
Contacts: **PHONE (01638) 508491 FAX (01638) 508491 MOBILE (07770) 964865**
E-MAIL nicklittmoden@btinternet.com WEBSITE www.nicklittmoden.com

1 **BARNABY BROOK (CAN),** 4, b g North Light (IRE)—Mascara (USA) **A. A. Goodman**
2 **CASH IS KING,** 4, b g Bahamian Bounty—Age of Chivalry (IRE) **A. A. Goodman**
3 **EX EX,** 4, b g Exceed And Excel (AUS)—Temple of Thebes (IRE) **N. P. Littmoden**
4 **KINDLELIGHT STORM (USA),** 4, b g Stormy Atlantic (USA)—
　　　　　　　　　　　　　　　　Rose of Zollern (IRE) **Kindlelight Ltd, N Shields & N Littmoden**
5 4, Br g Anabaa (USA)—Lanciana (IRE)
6 **LIVING LEADER,** 5, b g Oasis Dream—Royal Jade **N. R. Shields**
7 **PENBRYN (USA),** 7, b g Pivotal—Brocatelle **Mrs K Graham, N Littmoden, A Highfield**
8 **THE STIG (FR),** 6, b g Panoramic—Statyra (FR) **A. A. Goodman**
9 **UN JOUR D ETE (FR),** 6, b m Dano-Mast—Hasta Manana (FR) **A. A. Goodman**

THREE-YEAR-OLDS
10 **DEAVIN,** b c Mind Games—So Discreet **Mr P. M. Deavin**
11 **HARRY'S SUMMER (USA),** b br g Roman Ruler (USA)—Magnificent Lady (USA) **G. F. Chesneaux**
12 **MIGHTY FORCE (IRE),** b c Acclamation—Ikan (IRE) **Mrs L. M. Francis**
13 **POETIC CHOICE,** b f Byron—Ennobling **A A Goodman, L Stratton, N Littmoden**
14 B br g Elusive City (USA)—Rock Harmonie (FR)
15 **SPREADABLE (IRE),** br g Duke of Marmalade (IRE)—Spring View **G. F. Chesneaux**

TWO-YEAR-OLDS
16 **RED HARRY (IRE),** ch c 16/3 Manduro (GER)—Iktidar (Green Desert (USA)) (19047) **Mr D. P. Harrison**

Other Owners: Ms P. Ferguson, Mrs K. B. Graham, Mr A. J. Highfield, Kindlelight Ltd, L. J. Stratton.

---

390   **MR BERNARD LLEWELLYN, Bargoed**
Postal: **Ffynonau Duon Farm, Pentwyn, Fochriw, Bargoed, Mid-Glamorgan, CF81 9NP**
Contacts: **PHONE (01685) 841924 FAX (01685) 843838 MOBILE (07971) 233473/(07960) 151083**
E-MAIL bernard.llewellyn@btopenworld.com

1 **ARTY CAMPBELL (IRE),** 4, b g Dylan Thomas (IRE)—Kincob (USA) **B. J. Llewellyn**
2 **BAZART,** 12, b g Highest Honor (FR)—Summer Exhibition **B. J. Llewellyn**
3 **CAPTAIN SHARPE,** 6, ch g Tobougg (IRE)—Helen Sharp **B. J. Llewellyn**
4 **DRUMMOND,** 5, b g Zamindar (USA)—Alrisha (IRE) **Mr A. James**

MR BERNARD LLEWELLYN - Continued

5 **FILATORE (IRE)**, 5, ch g Teofilo (IRE)—Dragnet (IRE) **Mr A. James**
6 **GOING NOWHERE FAST (IRE)**, 9, b g Exit To Nowhere (USA)—Sister Gabrielle (IRE) **A. J. Williams**
7 **HANSUPFORDETROIT (IRE)**, 9, b g Zagreb (USA)—Golden Needle (IRE) **Mr A. James**
8 **HENDRY TRIGGER (IRE)**, 5, ch g Double Trigger (IRE)—Denise Best (IRE) **T. Reffell**
9 **JAMES POLLARD (IRE)**, 9, ch g Indian Ridge—Manuetti (IRE) **B. J. Llewellyn**
10 **JAZZ THYME (IRE)**, 5, b m Helissio (FR)—Thyne Square (IRE) **Mr G. I. Isaac**
11 **KOZMINA BAY**, 5, b m Notnowcato—Kozmina (IRE) **Mr G. Anstee**
12 **L FRANK BAUM (IRE)**, 7, b g Sinndar (IRE)—Rainbow City (IRE) **Mr A. James**
13 **LIGHTS FAST OF BROADWAY (IRE)**, 8, b m Broadway Flyer (USA)—Supreme Call (USA) **B. W. Parren**
14 **SCRIPTURIST**, 5, b g Oratorio (IRE)—Lambroza (IRE) **B. J. Llewellyn**
15 **STAG HILL (IRE)**, 5, ch g Redback—Counting Blessings **B. W. Parren**
16 **TASTE THE WINE (IRE)**, 8, gr g Verglas (IRE)—Azia (IRE) **A. J. Williams**
17 **TIJORI (IRE)**, 6, b g Kyllachy—Polish Belle **B. J. Llewellyn**

Assistant Trainer: J L Llewellyn

Jockey (flat): Robert Havlin, David Probert. **Jockey (NH):** Mark Quinlan. **Conditional:** Robert Williams.
Apprentice: Robert Williams. **Amateur:** Mr Chris West.

---

391 **MISS NATALIE LLOYD-BEAVIS, East Garston**
Postal: **2 Parsonage Cottages, Newbury Road, East Garston, Hungerford, Berkshire, RG17 7ER**
Contacts: **PHONE (07768) 117656 MOBILE (07768) 117656**
E-MAIL nlbracing@gmail.com

1 4, B f Beat All (USA)—Champagne Lou Lou **Mr Y. Mustafa**
2 **EVERGREEN FOREST (IRE)**, 6, ch g Haafhd—Inaaq **Mr T. Suttle**
3 **FIACHRA (IRE)**, 4, b g Elnadim (USA)—Nesaah's Princess **Lloyd-Beavis, Eagle & Tulloch**
4 **FLOWERBUD**, 9, b m Fantastic Light (USA)—Maidment **M. J. Hills**
5 **HIGHEST RED**, 5, ch g Byron—Honor Rouge (IRE) **Mr T. Suttle**
6 **LEYLAND (IRE)**, 5, b g Peintre Celebre (USA)—Lasting Chance (USA) **Mr Y. Mustafa**
7 **MUNICH (IRE)**, 10, b g Noverre (USA)—Mayara (IRE) **Miss N. A. Lloyd-Beavis**
8 **PEINTRE DU ROI (USA)**, 10, ch g El Prado (USA)—Peinture Bleue (USA) **Mr S. Lloyd-Beavis**
9 **STRAVITA**, 10, b m Weet-A-Minute (IRE)—Stravsea **M. J. Hills**
10 **UNTIL THE MAN (IRE)**, 7, b g Tillerman—Canoe Cove (IRE) **M. J. Hills**
11 **WITCHRY**, 12, gr g Green Desert (USA)—Indian Skimmer (USA) **Miss N. A. Lloyd-Beavis**

Other Owners: R. Eagle, Mr F. W. Tulloch.

Assistant Trainer: Hywel Davies

Jockey (NH): James Davies. **Apprentice:** Ryan Clark.

---

392 **MR ALAN LOCKWOOD, Malton**
Postal: **Fleet Cross Farm, Brawby, Malton, North Yorkshire, YO17 6QA**
Contacts: **PHONE (01751) 431796 MOBILE (07747) 002535**

1 **PORT VIEW (IRE)**, 8, b g Classic Cliche (IRE)—Francie's Treble **A. J. Lockwood**
2 **SAXBY (IRE)**, 7, ch g Pastoral Pursuits—Madam Waajib (IRE) **A. J. Lockwood**

---

393 **MR JOHN E. LONG, Woldingham**
Postal: **Main Yard, Tillingdowns, Woldingham, Caterham, Surrey, CR3 7JA**
Contacts: **PHONE (01883) 340730 MOBILE (07958) 296945/(07815) 186085**
E-MAIL winalot@aol.com

1 **BE A REBEL**, 4, b f Cockney Rebel (IRE)—Star Apple **Mr & Mrs K. G. Newland**
2 **BERMACHA**, 9, ch m Bertolini (USA)—Machaara **M. J. Gibbs**
3 **CATIVO CAVALLINO**, 11, ch g Bertolini (USA)—Sea Isle **M. J. Gibbs**
4 **CHANDRAYAAN**, 7, ch g Bertolini (USA)—Muffled **R. D. John**
5 **CUSTOM HOUSE (IRE)**, 6, b g Tale of The Cat (USA)—L'acajou (CAN) **Mr B C Oakley & Mr H Robin Heffer**
6 **ENTRAPPING**, 4, b g Tiger Hill (USA)—Meddle **M Fernandes E Cooper V Fox F Collyer**
7 **FOR LIFE (IRE)**, 12, b g Bachir (IRE)—Zest (USA) **B. C. Oakley**
8 **GRACEFUL WILLOW**, 4, b f Phoenix Reach (IRE)—Opera Belle **Mr T H Bambridge T/As The Willow Stud**

MR JOHN E. LONG - Continued

9 **ICE APPLE**, 6, b m Iceman—Star Apple **Mr & Mrs K. G. Newland**
10 **MICROLIGHT**, 6, b g Sleeping Indian—Skytrial (USA) **R. D. John**
11 **PRINCESS WILLOW**, 6, b m Phoenix Reach (IRE)—Highland Hannah (IRE) **Mrs S. Bambridge**
12 **RED WILLOW**, 8, ch m Noverre (USA)—Chelsea Blue (ITY) **J. King**
13 **TRUST ME BOY**, 6, gr g Avonbridge—Eastern Lyric **R. Pearson & J. Pearson**

Other Owners: Miss M. B. Fernandes, Mrs V. J. Fox, Mr H. R. Heffer, Mr K. G. Newland, Mrs J. E. Newland, Mr R. J. Pearson, Miss J. L. Pearson.

Assistant Trainer: Miss S Cassidy

Jockey (flat): Natalia Gemelova, Richard Thomas.

394

MR CHARLIE LONGSDON, Chipping Norton
Postal: **Hull Farm Stables, Stratford Road, Chipping Norton, Oxfordshire, OX7 5QF**
Contacts: **PHONE (08450) 525264 FAX (08450) 525265 MOBILE (07775) 993263**
E-MAIL charlie@charlielongsdonracing.com WEBSITE www.charlielongsdonracing.com

1 **A VOS GARDES (FR)**, 4, br g Kapgarde (FR)—Miscia Nera (FR) **The Rollright Stones**
2 **AZURE FLY (IRE)**, 6, br g Blueprint (IRE)—Lady Delight (IRE) **Girls Allowed**
3 **BATTLE BORN**, 5, b g Kayf Tara—Realms of Gold (USA) **D. A. Halsall**
4 **BRIEF MARK (IRE)**, 9, b g Revoque (IRE)—Queens Mark (IRE) **R. Jenner & J. Green**
5 **CADOUDOFF (FR)**, 4, gr g Davidoff (GER)—Hera du Berlais (FR) **The Four Kings**
6 **CHAIN OF BEACONS**, 5, b g Midnight Legend—Millennium Girl **Mrs A. E. Lee**
7 **CREDIT FOR LIFE (IRE)**, 7, b g Zagreb (USA)—Nero's Game
8 **CROSS OF HONOUR (IRE)**, 7, ch g Publisher (USA)—
                            Browneyed Daughter (IRE) **C Booth, J Hughes, M Ogilvy, R Perkins**
9 **DABINETT MOON**, 6, b m Midnight Legend—Miss Crabapple **Apple Bobbers**
10 **DOM LUKKA (FR)**, 6, b br g Dom Alco (FR)—Orlamonde Queen (FR) **R. D. J. Swinburne**
11 **DOMINO KING**, 4, br g Overbury (IRE)—Parlour Game **Mrs T. H. Barclay/Mrs F. D. McInnes Skinner**
12 **DONT TAKE ME ALIVE**, 5, b g Araafa (IRE)—Up At Dawn **Biddestone Racing Club**
13 **DROP OUT JOE**, 6, ch g Generous (IRE)—La Feuillarde (FR) **The Jesters**
14 **ELY BROWN (IRE)**, 9, b g Sunshine Street (USA)—
                            Browneyed Daughter (IRE) **Countrywide Vehicle Rentals Limited**
15 **FRAMPTON (IRE)**, 5, b g Presenting—Drumavish Lass (IRE) **Mr R. D. H. Brindle**
16 **GERMANY CALLING (IRE)**, 5, b g Germany (USA)—Markir (IRE) **Mr T. Hanlon**
17 **GLOWINGINTHEDARK (IRE)**, 6, b g Dr Massini (IRE)—Autumn Beauty (IRE) **D. A. Halsall**
18 **GRANDADS HORSE**, 8, br br g Bollin Eric—Solid Land (FR) **Whites of Coventry Limited**
19 **GREEN BANK (IRE)**, 8, b g Morozov (USA)—Queen Polly (IRE) **C. Longsdon**
20 **GREENLAW**, 8, b g Helissio (FR)—Juris Prudence (IRE) **Mr & Mrs Simon and June Cadzow**
21 **HANNIBAL THE GREAT (IRE)**, 6, b g Milan—Town Gossip (IRE) **The Pantechnicons**
22 **HARRISTOWN**, 4, ch g Bering—New Abbey **Kyuna Memories**
23 **HAYJACK**, 9, b g Karinga Bay—Celtic Native (IRE) **James Hayman-Joyce & HJ Racing**
24 **HAZY TOM (IRE)**, 8, b g Heron Island (IRE)—The Wounded Cook (IRE) **D. A. Halsall**
25 **ICE 'N' EASY (IRE)**, 8, b g Dushyantor (USA)—Glacial Valley (IRE) **R. Jenner & J. Green**
26 **IN THE GATE (IRE)**, 6, b g King's Theatre (IRE)—The Distaff Spy **OE Racing NH Partnership**
27 **INVESTISSEMENT**, 8, b g Singspiel (IRE)—Underwater (USA) **Countrywide Vehicle Rentals Limited**
28 **JAVA ROSE**, 5, b m Ishiguru (USA)—Mighty Splash **Mildmay Racing & Mark E Smith**
29 **KAUTO RELKO (FR)**, 10, b g With The Flow (USA)—Kauto Relka (FR) **Countrywide Vehicle Rentals Limited**
30 **KILCOOLEY (IRE)**, 5, b g Stowaway—Bealaha Essie (IRE) **J. H. & S. M. Wall**
31 **KILLALA QUAY**, 7, b g Karinga Bay—Madam Bijou **Mr Richard & Mrs Susan Perkins**
32 **LEITH HILL LEGASI**, 5, b m Kahyasi—Leith Hill Star **Mr & Mrs N. F. Maltby**
33 **LITTLE CHIP (IRE)**, 7, b g Dushyantor (USA)—Aunt Chris (IRE) **L. Dens (Shipbrokers) Limited**
34 **LONG LUNCH**, 5, b g Kayf Tara—Royal Keel **Battersby, Birchall, Halsall & Vestey**
35 **LONG WAVE (IRE)**, 7, b g Milan—Mrs Avery (IRE) **Neysauteur Partnership**
36 **LOOSE CHIPS**, 8, b g Sir Harry Lewis (USA)—Worlaby Rose **Barrels Of Courage**
37 **MAGNIFIQUE ETOILE**, 7, b g Kayf Tara—Star Diva (IRE) **Magnifique Etoile Partnership**
38 **MANOR BROOK (IRE)**, 6, b m Westerner—Fey Macha (IRE) **C. Longsdon**
39 **MEXICAN MICK**, 5, ch g Atraf—Artic Bliss **First Chance Racing**
40 **MILES AWAY (IRE)**, 5, ch g Generous (IRE)—Mazillara (IRE) **Home Farm Racing & Aidan Gunning**
41 **MUNSAAB (IRE)**, 8, b g Alhaarth (IRE)—Claustra (IRE) **Countrywide Vehicle Rentals Limited**
42 **MY MISS LUCY**, 8, b m Alflora (IRE)—Corn Lily **Mrs S. McDonald**
43 **NO NO BINGO (IRE)**, 8, b g Craigsteel—Little Anna (IRE) **R. Jenner & J. Green**
44 **NO NO MAC (IRE)**, 5, b g Oscar (IRE)—Whatdoyouthinkmac (IRE) **R. Jenner & J. Green**

MR CHARLIE LONGSDON - Continued

45 **NO NO ROMEO (IRE)**, 5, b g Scorpion (IRE)—Penny Brae (IRE) **R. Jenner & J. Green**
46 **ORANGE NASSAU (FR)**, 8, gr g Martaline—Vilaya (FR) **The Ferandlin Peaches**
47 **OSTLAND (GER)**, 9, b g Lando (GER)—Ost Tycoon (GER) **Mr Richard & Mrs Susan Perkins**
48 **OUR KAEMPFER (IRE)**, 5, b g Oscar (IRE)—Gra-Bri (IRE) **Swanee River Partnership**
49 **PENDRA (IRE)**, 6, ch g Old Vic—Mariah Rollins (IRE) **J. P. McManus**
50 **PETE THE FEAT (IRE)**, 10, b g King's Theatre (IRE)—Tourist Attraction (IRE) **Mr G. J. Larby & Mr P. J. Smith**
51 **PIED DU ROI (IRE)**, 4, b g Robin des Pres (FR)—Long Acre **The Pantechnicons II**
52 **PRESENT TREND (IRE)**, 5, br m Presenting—Trendy Attire (IRE) **Foxtrot NH Racing Partnership IV**
53 **PROMANCO**, 5, b m Kayf Tara—Shelayly (IRE) **C. Longsdon**
54 **READY TOKEN (IRE)**, 6, gr g Flemensfirth (USA)—Ceol Tire (IRE) **Mr C. S. Horton**
55 **RUSSETT STAR**, 6, ch m Midnight Legend—Apple Anthem **Apple Bobbers**
56 **SACROBLEU (FR)**, 4, gr g Sacro Saint (FR)—Harpyes (FR) **E. M. G. Roberts**
57 **SASSANOVA (IRE)**, 4, b f Sassanian (USA)—Anglaise (IRE) **C. Longsdon**
58 **SERGEANT MATTIE (IRE)**, 6, b g Naheez (USA)—Glyde Lady (IRE) **Swanee River Partnership**
59 **SHANTOU MAGIC (IRE)**, 7, b g Shantou (USA)—Supreme Magical **Owners For Owners: Shantou Magic**
60 **SHEAR ROCK (IRE)**, 4, b g Spadoun (FR)—Sleeping Diva (FR) **Jones, Smith & Walsh**
61 **SPANISH ARCH (IRE)**, 7, b g Westerner—Piepowder **Tunnel Vision**
62 **SPIRIT OF SHANKLY (IRE)**, 6, ch g Sulamani (IRE)—Lago d'oro **D. A. Halsall**
63 **SUKIYAKI (IRE)**, 5, b g Dubawi (IRE)—Sukeena (IRE) **C. Longsdon**
64 **SUPERIOR FIRE (IRE)**, 4, b g Arcadio (GER)—Take Aim **The Stewkley Shindiggers Partnership**
65 **SUPERIOR QUALITY (IRE)**, 9, br g Winged Love (IRE)—
Unknown Quality **The Stewkley Shindiggers Partnership**
66 **THEATRELANDS**, 6, ch g Beat Hollow—Dance Dress (USA) **Mr N Davies & Mr S Crowley**
67 **TIDAL WAY (IRE)**, 5, gr g Red Clubs (IRE)—Taatof (USA) **Harold Peachey & Saddleworth Players**
68 **TOPAZE COLLONGES (FR)**, 7, gr g Dom Alco (FR)—Flicka Collonges (FR) **No Boys Allowed**
69 **UP TO SOMETHING (FR)**, 6, b g Brier Creek (USA)—Evane (FR) **E. M. G. Roberts**
70 **VENCEREMOS**, 7, b m Generous (IRE)—Miss Orchestra (IRE) **D. M. Huglin**
71 **VULCANITE (IRE)**, 7, b g Dubawi (IRE)—Daraliya (IRE) **J. P. McManus**
72 **WADSWICK COURT (IRE)**, 6, b g Court Cave (IRE)—Tarasandy (IRE) **The Chosen Few**
73 **WHISPERING BOB (IRE)**, 7, b g Presenting—Baden's Queen (IRE) **Mr G. P. Bone**
74 **YES I WILL**, 5, b g Kahyasi—Flinders **Leith Hill Chasers**

Other Owners: Mr D. Abraham, Mr R. J. Aplin, H. R. F. Arthur, G. H. S. Bailey, Mrs J. Barclay, Mr J. G. Bell, Mr N. M. Birch, Mr T. J. Boniface, Mr C. J. Booth, T. P. Bostwick, Miss C. Bovill, Mr T. E. Boylan, I. M. Brown, J. C. F. Burke, J. Burley, Mr R. T. Burns, Mr R. Byron-Scott, Mr S. R. Cadzow, Mrs J. Cadzow, Mr S. J. Corcoran, Mr C. K. Crossley Cooke, Mr S. Crowley, Mr N. Davies, Mrs R. J. Doel, Dr S. B. Drew, J. R. Drew, Mr T. J. Dykes, H. H. J. Fentum, Mr N. M. Finegold, Mrs A. J. Green, Mr M. W. Gregory, Mr J. D. Halsall, Mr B. Halsall, P. V. Harris, Ms R. J. Harris, R. D. Hawkins, Mrs C. A. M. Hayman-Joyce, Mr J. L. Hayman-Joyce, Mr S. Hill, Mrs H. J. Hoffman, Home Farm Racing Limited, Mr E. J. Hughes, Ms R. A. Jenner, Mr C. Jones, Mrs L. King, G. J. Larby, Mrs S. J. Lavan, Mr C. O. A. Liverton, Mr J. K. Llewellyn, Mrs S. Longsdon, Mrs J. Maltby, Mr N. F. Maltby, C. J. W. Marriott, Mrs A. May, Mrs F. D. McInnes Skinner, R. D. Nicholas, Dr M. M. Ogilvy, Mr H. E. Peachey, Miss N. J. C. Pearson, R. A. H. Perkins, Mrs R. S. Perkins, Mrs P. A. Perriss, Mr B. P. Roberts, Mr J. Roddan, Mr M. J. Savage, W. G. C. Shaw, P. J. Smith, Mr M. E. Smith, Mr S. Spencer-Jones, Mrs S. Spencer-Jones, R. D. Stainer, Mrs R. Steel, Mr P. A. E. Tuson, Mr J. H. Wall, Mrs S. M. Wall, Mrs C. J. Walsh, Mr R. C. Wilkin, Mr F. Wintle.

Jockey (NH): Noel Fehily. **Conditional:** Charlie Deutsch, Kielan Woods. **Amateur:** Miss Claire Hart.

---

395 **MR DANIEL MARK LOUGHNANE, Butterton**
Postal: **Butterton Racing Stables, Park Road, Butterton, Newcastle, Staffordshire, ST5 4DZ**
Contacts: **MOBILE (07805) 531021**

1 **CENTRAL SCHOOL**, 4, ch c Central Park (IRE)—Floral Dance (IRE) **Mr R. M. Brilley**
2 **COILLTE CAILIN (IRE)**, 4, b f Oratorio (IRE)—Forest Walk (IRE) **Mr P. Moran**
3 **COMBUSTIBLE (IRE)**, 4, b f Halling (USA)—Jazz Baby (IRE) **Mrs C. M. Loughnane**
4 **DISCO DAVE (IRE)**, 6, ch g Dalakhani (IRE)—Amoureux (USA) **Mrs C. M. Loughnane**
5 **FIRST IN COMMAND (IRE)**, 9, b g Captain Rio—Queen Sigi (USA) **Mrs C. M. Loughnane**
6 **FOR SHIA AND LULA (IRE)**, 5, b g Majestic Missile (IRE)—
Jack-N-Jilly (IRE) **Loughnane, Fletcher, Ward & Ebanks-Blake**
7 **GOLDEN SANDSTORM (IRE)**, 5, ch g Golden Tornado (IRE)—Killoughey Fairy (IRE) **Mr R. M. Brilley**
8 **HONEST STRIKE (USA)**, 7, b g Smart Strike (CAN)—Honest Lady (USA) **Mrs C. M. Loughnane**
9 **JUST FOR MARY**, 10, b g Groom Dancer (USA)—Summer Dance **Mrs C. M. Loughnane**
10 **LARGHETTO (USA)**, 6, b m Giant's Causeway (USA)—Marquetessa (USA) **B. Kirby**

MR DANIEL MARK LOUGHNANE - Continued

11 **LOGANS LAD (IRE)**, 4, b g Baltic King—Lulu Island **Mr Ian O'Connor**
12 **MATRAASH (USA)**, 8, b h Elusive Quality (USA)—Min Alhawa (USA) **Over The Moon Racing**
13 **NAFA (IRE)**, 6, br m Shamardal (USA)—Champs Elysees (USA) **Mr Ian O'Connor**
14 **PRIME EXHIBIT**, 9, b g Selkirk (USA)—First Exhibit **Mr R. M. Brilley**
15 **SAHARIA (IRE)**, 7, b g Oratorio (IRE)—Inchiri **Over The Moon Racing**
16 **STANLOW**, 4, b g Invincible Spirit (IRE)—Ghazal (USA) **Ms A. Quinn**
17 **VERUS DELICIA (IRE)**, 5, b m Chineur (FR)—Ribbon Glade (UAE) **Mr R. M. Brilley**
18 **YOURINTHEWILL (USA)**, 6, ch g Aragorn (IRE)—Lenarue (USA) **Over The Moon Racing**

THREE-YEAR-OLDS

19 B c Myboycharlie (IRE)—Akhira **Mr Ian O'Connor**
20 **AUSSIE SKY (IRE)**, b f Aussie Rules (USA)—Skyscape (USA) **Mr Ian O'Connor**
21 **CHENNAI WIND**, ch g Piccolo—Madrasee **Mr D. S. Allan**
22 Gr f Paris House—Floods of Tears **B. Kirby**
23 B c Saville Road—Lauren Eria
24 **MANNERIST**, br c Excellent Art—Atienza (USA) **Brooklands Racing**
25 **OUR OLD FELLA**, gr g Misu Bond (IRE)—Kilmovee **Mr P. Moran**
26 **SHANNON HAVEN (IRE)**, b g Oratorio (IRE)—Red Shoe **Mr J. J. McGarry**
27 **SPEEDY RIO (IRE)**, ch g Captain Rio—Love Sonnet **Mr Raymond Yeung**
28 Ch f Manduro (GER)—Sunray Superstar
29 **UP HILL BATTLE'S**, b f Tiger Hill (IRE)—Nasij (USA) **Mr Ian O'Connor**
30 **UTMOST REGARDS**, b c Green Desert (USA)—Utmost (IRE) **Ms A. Quinn**

TWO-YEAR-OLDS

31 B f 30/3 Starspangledbanner (AUS)—Dromod Mour (IRE) (Azamour (IRE)) (11614)

Other Owners: M. H. Bates, Mr S. Ebanks-Blake, Mr S. Fletcher, S. P. Hackney, D. S. Lovatt, Mrs A. M. Mercs, Mr S. Ward.

---

396 **MR SHAUN LYCETT, Cheltenham**
Postal: **1 Aston Farm Cottages, Bourton-On-The-Water, Cheltenham, Gloucestershire, GL54 3BZ**
Contacts: **PHONE (01451) 824143 MOBILE (07788) 100894**
E-MAIL trainer@bourtonhillracing.co.uk WEBSITE www.bourtonhillracing.co.uk

1 **ALL THE WINDS (GER)**, 9, ch g Samum (GER)—All Our Luck (GER) **Nicholls Family**
2 **DARROUN (IRE)**, 6, gr g Dalakhani (IRE)—Darayka (FR) **Mr P. Grocott**
3 **EXCELLENT PUCK (IRE)**, 4, b c Excellent Art—Puck's Castle **Mr P. Grocott**
4 **FADE TO GREY (IRE)**, 10, gr g Aljabr (USA)—Aly McBear (USA) **Worcester Racing Club**
5 **HACKETT (IRE)**, 6, b h Hawk Wing (USA)—Khudud **S. Lycett**
6 **HARVEST MIST (IRE)**, 6, ch m Captain Rio—Thaw **Mr C. C. Buckingham**
7 **KALAMILL (IRE)**, 7, b g Kalanisi (IRE)—Desert Pageant (IRE) **R. Davies**
8 **MALLUSK (IRE)**, 9, b g Exit To Nowhere (USA)—Saucy Nun (IRE) **Worcester Racing Club**
9 **MASTER EDDY**, 14, b g Alflora (IRE)—Mistress Star **The Atkin Partnership**
10 **OUR GOLDEN GIRL**, 4, ch f Dutch Art—Nemorosa **The Golden Boys Partnership**
11 **SCOTSBROOK LEGEND**, 6, b m Midnight Legend—Scots Brook Terror **A. E. J. Price**
12 **THE WINGED ASSASIN (USA)**, 8, b g Fusaichi Pegasus (USA)—Gran Dama (USA) **Mr A. R. James**
13 5, Br h Alflora (IRE)—Tia Marnie **S. Lycett**
14 **TRAM EXPRESS (FR)**, 10, ch g Trempolino (USA)—Molly Dance (FR) **S. Lycett**
15 **WEAPON OF WAR (IRE)**, 10, ro g Alderbrook—Nagillah (IRE) **Nicholls Family**
16 **WINNEYS BOY**, 6, b g Mr Kalandi (IRE)—Winneys Folly **N. E. Powell**

TWO-YEAR-OLDS

17 B f 8/4 Kheleyf (USA)—Kyleene (Kyllachy)

Other Owners: T. J. Atkin, J. A. Atkin, M. P. Hill, Mr M. Lovett, Mrs E. Lycett, Mr R. Nicholls, Mrs E. Nicholls, Mr M. White.

397 MR GER LYONS, Dunsany

Postal: **Glenburnie Stables, Kiltale, Dunsany, Co. Meath, Ireland**
Contacts: **PHONE (00353) 46 9025666 FAX (00353) 46 9026364 MOBILE (00353) 86 8502439**
E-MAIL office@gerlyons.ie WEBSITE www.gerlyons.ie

1 BRENDAN BRACKAN (IRE), 5, b g Big Bad Bob (IRE)—Abeyr **Anamoine Ltd**
2 BURN THE BOATS (IRE), 5, br g Big Bad Bob (IRE)—Forever Phoenix **Mr D. T. Spratt**
3 CHAPTER SEVEN, 5, ch g Excellent Art—My First Romance **Pearl Bloodstock Ltd**
4 GREEK CANYON (IRE), 5, gr g Moss Vale (IRE)—Lazaretta (IRE) **S. Jones**
5 MACHETE MARK (IRE), 4, b g Indian Haven—Beziers (IRE) **Mr D. T. Spratt**
6 PIRI WANGO (IRE), 5, ch g Choisir (AUS)—Zoldan **Mr D. T. Spratt**
7 TENNESSEE WILDCAT (IRE), 4, b g Kheleyf (USA)—Windbeneathmywings (IRE) **S. Jones**
8 TOCCATA BLUE (IRE), 4, gr g Verglas (IRE)—Jinxy Jill **Nolan & Lyons**

THREE-YEAR-OLDS

9 B g Sinndar (IRE)—Aliyshan (IRE) **Mrs Ann Marshall**
10 ANGEL OF JOY (IRE), gr g Dark Angel (IRE)—Moy Joy (IRE) **Mr John Quinn**
11 APACHE TROOPER (IRE), b g Oratorio (IRE)—Mandaraka (FR) **S. Jones**
12 ARTISTIC INTEGRITY, b g Dutch Art—Valley of The Moon (IRE) **S. Jones**
13 AZURITE (IRE), b g Azamour (IRE)—High Lite **S. Jones**
14 BAD NEWS BEAR (IRE), b g Big Bad Bob (IRE)—Cosmic Speed Queen (USA) **Anamoine Ltd**
15 BELTS AND BRACES (IRE), b f Big Bad Bob (IRE)—Soviet Belle (IRE) **Anamoine Ltd**
16 BILDERBERG (IRE), b f Big Bad Bob (IRE)—Ski For Me (IRE) **Anamoine Ltd**
17 BILLY SPARKS (IRE), b g Azamour (IRE)—Fez **S. Jones**
18 BODY BEAUTIFUL (IRE), b f Big Bad Bob (IRE)—Forever Phoenix **Anamoine Ltd**
19 BONJOUR BOB (IRE), b g Big Bad Bob (IRE)—Petite Cherie (IRE) **Mrs P. K. Cooper**
20 CAPTAIN TEEMO (IRE), b g Oratorio (IRE)—Bluebell Park (USA) **S. Jones**
21 CHOCOLATE DIAMOND (IRE), ch g Intense Focus (USA)—Sagemacca (IRE) **RMS Syndicate**
22 CRISTAL FASHION (IRE), b f Jeremy (USA)—Mango Groove (IRE) **Jim McDonald**
23 FOG OF WAR, b c Azamour (IRE)—Cut Short (USA) **Qatar Racing Limited**
24 FUINNIMH (IRE), b f King's Best (USA)—Strudel (IRE) **Mrs Ann Marshall**
25 INFLATION RISK, b g Compton Place—Small Fortune **S. Jones**
26 KAMINARI (IRE), b f Sea The Stars (IRE)—Karmifira (FR) **Qatar Racing Limited**
27 MAGNOLIA BEACH (IRE), b c Footstepsinthesand—Misskinta (IRE) **Qatar Racing Limited**
28 MANSURI, ch g Piccolo—Antonia's Choice **S. Jones**
29 MONTELLO, b f Cape Cross (IRE)—Mount Elbrus **Sheikh Mohammed**
30 OBLITERATOR (IRE), br c Oratorio (IRE)—Faraday Light (IRE) **Qatar Racing Limited**
31 PHANTOM NAVIGATOR (USA), gr g Henrythenavigator (USA)—Minicolony (USA) **S. Jones**
32 RELENTLESS PURSUIT (IRE), b g Kodiac—Dancing Debut **Mr Vincent Gaul**
33 ROHERYN (IRE), b f Galileo (IRE)—La Chunga (USA) **Qatar Racing Limited**
34 SNOWMANE (IRE), b c Galileo (IRE)—Tree Tops **Qatar Racing Limited**
35 SYSTEM OVERLOAD (IRE), gr g Verglas (IRE)—Candelabra **S. Jones**
36 THIRD DIMENSION, b g Dubawi (IRE)—Round The Cape **S. Jones**
37 THIRTEEN DIAMONDS (IRE), b g Diamond Green (FR)—Latin Lace **Mr Declan Landy**
38 UNREQUITED (IRE), b c Authorized (IRE)—Superfonic (FR) **Tess Mahon**
39 UNUSUALLY HOT (IRE), b f Unusual Heat (USA)—That's Hot (IRE) **Mr John Burke**
40 VECTOR FORCE (IRE), b g Kodiac—Summer Magic (IRE) **Mr Vincent Gaul**

TWO-YEAR-OLDS

41 B c 18/2 Clodovil (IRE)—Abysse (Gulch (USA)) (20952) **S. Jones**
42 B f 21/2 Invincible Spirit (IRE)—Allannah Abu (Dubawi (IRE)) (110000) **Airlie & Ennistown Studs**
43 B f 21/2 Camacho—Amber Tide (IRE) (Pursuit of Love) (100658) **Qatar Racing Limited**
44 B c 30/4 Cape Cross (IRE)—Aqraan (In The Wings) (38714) **S. Jones**
45 B f 22/4 Zebedee—Blusienka (IRE) (Blues Traveller (IRE)) (10840) **RMS Syndicate**
46 Gr c 24/4 Dark Angel (IRE)—Cape Cod (IRE) (Unfuwain (USA)) (23228) **S. Jones**
47 B c 21/2 Piccolo—Cape Wood (Cape Cross (IRE)) (38714) **S. Jones**
48 B c 25/4 Dandy Man (IRE)—Cockaleekie (USA) (Alphabet Soup (USA)) **S. Jones**
49 B c 26/1 Vale of York (IRE)—Condilessa (IRE) (Key of Luck (USA)) (35000) **S. Jones**
50 B c 2/4 Iffraaj—Dance of Light (USA) (Sadler's Wells) (40262) **S. Jones**
51 Gr c 29/3 Silver Frost (IRE)—Desert Nights (IRE) (Desert Style (IRE)) (21680) **Mr Vincent Gaul**
52 B br c 2/3 Zebedee—Double Precedent (Polish Precedent (USA)) (30000) **S. Jones**
53 B c 27/4 Iffraaj—Elutrah (Darshaan) (44761) **S. Jones**
54 B c 5/4 Azamour (IRE)—Folly Lodge (Grand Lodge (USA)) (15000) **Mr Sean Jones & Mr David Spratt**
55 B c 18/2 Iffraaj—Go Lovely Rose (Pivotal) (83809) **Qatar Racing Limited**
56 B c 14/4 Intikhab (USA)—Golden Rose (GER) (Winged Love (IRE)) (30971) **S. Jones**

MR GER LYONS - Continued

57 B c 30/4 Approve (IRE)—Headborough Lass (IRE) (Invincible Spirit (IRE)) (15485) **S. Jones**
58 B f 8/4 Dark Angel (IRE)—Hemasree (IRE) (Exceed And Excel (AUS)) (11614) **Mrs Lynne Lyons**
59 B c 5/5 Makfi—Jalousie (IRE) (Barathea (IRE)) **Qatar Racing Limited**
60 Gr c 25/4 Dark Angel (IRE)—Kayoko (IRE) (Shalford (IRE)) (42585) **S. Jones**
61 B f 14/3 Dark Angel (IRE)—Line Ahead (IRE) (Sadler's Wells (USA)) (27874) **Mrs Clodagh Mitchell**
62 B c 14/3 Showcasing—Madam President (Royal Applause) (25000) **S. Jones**
63 B f 2/3 Approve (IRE)—Miss Corinne (Mark of Esteem (IRE)) (74285) **Qatar Racing Limited**
64 B c 31/3 Dark Angel (IRE)—Moy Joy (IRE) (Orpen (USA)) **Mr John Quinn**
65 B c 16/3 Arch (USA)—Proudeyes (GER) (Dashing Blade) (87642) **Qatar Racing Limited**
66 B c 10/3 Kodiac—Risk A Look (Observatory (USA)) (30476) **S. Jones**
67 B c 24/4 Holy Roman Emperor (IRE)—Souffle (Zafonic (USA)) (92914) **Mr Edmond Lee**
68 Gr c 1/3 Verglas—Staylily (IRE) (Grand Lodge (USA)) (17142) **Mr Damian Nolan**
69 B c 30/4 Kyllachy—Stellar Brilliant (USA) (Kris S (USA)) (45000) **Qatar Racing Limited**
70 B c 26/3 Fast Company (IRE)—Valluga (IRE) (Ashkalani (IRE)) (27619) **Mr Sean Jones & Mr David Spratt**
71 B f 15/4 Layman (USA)—Yazmin (IRE) (Green Desert (USA)) **Mrs Ann Marshall**
72 B c 10/2 Cape Cross (IRE)—Zahoo (IRE) (Nayef (USA)) (24777) **Mr Vincent Gaul**

Jockey (flat): Gary Carroll, Colin Keane, Emmet McNamara.

---

398 | MR GUILLAUME MACAIRE, Les Mathes
Postal: **Hippodrome de la Palmyre, 17570 Les Mathes, France**
Contacts: **PHONE (0033) 5462 36254 FAX (0033) 5462 25438 MOBILE (0033) 6076 54992**
E-MAIL entrainement-g.macaire@wanadoo.fr

1 AINSIQUE DE L'ISLE (FR), 4, b g Lavirco (GER)—Naiade de l'isle (FR) **Mr Terry Amos**
2 ALAPARO (FR), 4, b g Saint des Saints (FR)—Messine (FR) **Mr Francois Parreau**
3 ALTO DE LA ROQUE (FR), 4, b g Kapgarde (FR)—Louve de La Roque (FR) **Mr Robert Mongin**
4 AMOUR DE LA ROQUE (FR), 4, b c Laveron—La Orotava (FR) **Mr Robert Mongin**
5 ANCOLIE DE COTTE (FR), 4, ch f Dom Alco (FR)—Pensee de Cotte (FR) **Mr Terry Amos**
6 ANGE DE LA ROQUE (FR), 4, b g Kapgarde (FR)—Nacelle de La Roque (FR) **Mr Robert Mongin**
7 ART MAJEUR (FR), 4, b g Panoramic—Magenta (FR) **Mr Jacques Detre**
8 ASTARTE (FR), 4, b f Apsis—Ellapampa (FR) **Mr Pierre de Maleissye**
9 AUPALIM (FR), 4, b g Martaline—Mayence (FR) **Ecurie Sagara**
10 BEBE STAR (FR), 4, b g Poliglote—Benefique (FR) **Mr Stephane Szwarc**
11 BEUVRON (FR), 4, b g Martaline—Virginia River (FR) **Mr Robert Fougedoire**
12 CLASSIC DIVA (GER), 5, b m Sholokhov (IRE)—Classic Cara (GER) **Ecurie Jaeckin**
13 COELHO (FR), 6, ch g Kapgarde (FR)—Exela (FR) **Miss Patricia Le Tellier**
14 FLOGASORTE (FR), 4, b g Marshall (FR)—Rosala (FR) **Mr Francis Fernandes**
15 GABO (FR), 4, ch g Forestier (FR)—Merciki (FR) **Mme Patrick Papot**
16 GILLO (FR), 4, b g Balko—Syva (FR) **Mr Gilles Baratoux**
17 GORVELLO (FR), 5, b g Poliglote—Rolandale (FR) **Mme Patrick Papot**
18 GRANDISSIME (FR), 4, b g Saint des Saints (FR)—Vie de Reine (FR) **Mr Jean-Claude Audry**
19 GUERLINA (FR), 4, gr f Martaline—Incorrigible (FR) **Cheval Etoile**
20 HOLY VIRGIN (FR), 4, bl f Saint des Saints (FR)—Topira (FR) **Mme Patrick Papot**
21 LADY KOKO (FR), 4, b f Kapgarde (FR)—Aconit (FR) **Mr Francis Picoulet**
22 MILLION (FR), 5, ber g Motivator—Miss Alabama (FR) **Mr Gerard Laboureau**
23 MON NICKSON (FR), 4, b g Nickname (FR)—Linaving (FR) **Mr Edouard Coirre**
24 MY ALCO (FR), 4, ch f Dom Alco (FR)—My Asadore (FR) **Mr Jacques Detre**
25 SANTA GIRL (FR), 4, b f Saint des Saints (FR)—Bumble (FR) **Mr Jacques Detre**
26 SKELLIG MICHAEL (FR), 4, b g Saint des Saints (FR)—Skellig Mist (FR) **Mr John Cotton**
27 STORM OF SAINTLY (FR), 5, b g Saint des Saints (FR)—The Storm (FR) **Mr Jeannot Andt**
28 SUERTE PARA TODOS (FR), 5, ch g Kapgarde (FR)—Hever Rose (GER) **Mr Pierre de Maleissye**
29 SUNDRIVER (FR), 4, b g Poliglote—Myrthe (GER) **Ecurie Sagara**
30 SYSTEMIQUE (FR), 4, b g Saint des Saints (FR)—Gavotte de Brejoux (FR) **Mr Jacques Detre**
31 UNITED PARK (FR), 6, b g Antarctique (IRE)—Goldoulyssa (FR) **Mr Terry Amos**
32 URZEIT, 4, b f Sholokhov (IRE)—Ustilla (GER) **Mr Jeannot Andt**
33 VAGUE D'ESTRUVAL (FR), 5, b m Khalkevi (FR)—Kob d'estruval (FR) **Mme Bernard Le Gentil**
34 VANILLA CRUSH (FR), 5, b g Martaline—Latitude (FR) **Mme Patrick Papot**
35 VAUDAIRE (FR), 5, b m Astarabad (USA)—Miss Academy (FR) **Mme Joseph Shalam**
36 VERKAP (FR), 4, b g Kapgarde (FR)—Hever Rose (GER) **Mr Pierre de Maleissye**
37 VISTA D'ESTRUVAL (FR), 5, b m Network (GER)—Nouvelle d'estruval (FR) **Mme Bernard Le Gentil**
38 VIZIR D'ESTRUVAL (FR), 5, b g Cachet Noir (USA)—Heure d'estruval (FR) **Mme Bernard Le Gentil**
39 VOEUX D'ESTRUVAL (FR), 5, b g Daliapour (IRE)—Perle d'estruval (FR) **Mr Simon Munir**
40 VOTEZ POUR MOI (FR), 5, gr g Sacro Saint (FR)—Biblique (FR) **Haras De St Voir**

MR GUILLAUME MACAIRE - Continued

THREE-YEAR-OLDS

41 **A LA LUNA (FR)**, b f Califet (FR)—Aubane (FR) **Ecurie Sagara**
42 **AMERICAN CREEK (FR)**, b f Califet (FR)—Loin de Moi (FR) **Mr R. A. Green**
43 **AUENWIRBEL (GER)**, b c Sholokhov (IRE)—Auentime (GER) **Mr Jeremie Bossert**
44 **BEAU SOLEIL (FR)**, b g Lauro (GER)—Hallucinante (FR) **Ecurie Jaeckin**
45 **BEGUIN D'ESTIVAUX (FR)**, b g Saint Des Saints—Noces D'or A Estivaux **Mr Charles de Chaisemartin**
46 **BIEN PLACEE (FR)**, gr f Irish Wells (FR)—Euil Eagle (FR) **Mme Patrick Papot**
47 **BOGADOR (FR)**, b g Kapgarde (FR)—Newgador (FR) **Mr Jean-Pierre Masselin**
48 **BON CHEVAL (FR)**, b g Laverock (IRE)—Pail Mel (FR) **Haras de Saint Voir**
49 **BONBON AU MIEL (FR)**, b g Khalkevi (IRE)—Friandise II (FR) **Mme Patrick Papot**
50 **BONNE MAMAN (FR)**, ch f Coastal Path—Line Saj (FR) **Haras de Saint Voir**
51 **BRANLE BAS (FR)**, b g Saint des Saints (FR)—Formosa (FR) **Haras de Saint Voir**
52 **BRICE CANYON (FR)**, b g Kapgarde (FR)—Fille Formidable (USA) **Mme Patrick Papot**
53 **BUCHE DE NOEL (FR)**, ch f Coastal Path—Kyrie (FR) **Haras de Saint Voir**
54 **CARDLINE (FR)**, gr f Martaline—Powder Card (FR) **Mr Jacques Bisson**
55 **CORSCIA (FR)**, b f Nickname (FR)—Cardamine (FR) **Mr Michel Tessier**
56 **DINE (SPA)**, ch f Dutch Art—Masakala (IRE) **Mr Gerard Laboureau**
57 **DUC LAGRANGE (FR)**, b g Sholokhov (IRE)—Princesse Lagrange (FR) **Mme Patrick Papot**
58 **EL CALIFE (FR)**, b g Califet (FR)—Ecaline (FR) **Mr Jeannot Andt**
59 **FIRSTY (IRE)**, b g Flemensfirth (USA)—Loughaderra Dame (IRE) **Mme Benoit Gabeur**
60 **FLEUR DEFENDUE (FR)**, b f Walk In The Park (IRE)—Lucena (FR) **Mme Elisabeth Laboureau**
61 **FLOGAPA (FR)**, ch g Marshall (FR)—Rosala (FR) **Mr Francis Fernandes**
62 **GOLDMANTIS (FR)**, ch g Full of Gold (FR)—Mante Jolie (FR) **Mr Patrice Detre**
63 **HINDOU (FR)**, b g Califet (FR)—Pluie d'or (IRE) **Mme Patrick Papot**
64 **INVINCIBLE FIGHTER (FR)**, b g Nickname (FR)—Bahama Pearl (FR) **Mr Gilbert Conesa**
65 **JEU ST ELOI (FR)**, b c Saint des Saints (FR)—Ottolina (FR) **Mr Jacques Detre**
66 **JONCSAINT (FR)**, b c Saint des Saints (FR)—Fleur d'ajonc (FR) **Mr Alain Benaroch**
67 **KALKIR (FR)**, b g Montmartre (FR)—Kakira (FR) **Mme Marie-Therese Dubuc-Grassa**
68 **KOBROUK (FR)**, b g Saint des Saints (FR)—Kotkira (FR) **Mr John-Dowson Cotton**
69 **L'EXPLORATEUR (FR)**, ch g Passing Sale (FR)—Lally Turk (FR) **Miss Aline Masselin**
70 **LADY POLIGLOTE (FR)**, b f Poliglote—Madison Road (IRE) **Mr Donald Galt**
71 **LE BARON NOIR (FR)**, b g Limnos (JPN)—Lishmer (FR) **Ecurie Sagara**
72 **LE COSTAUD (FR)**, ch g Forestier (FR)—Loya Lescribaa (FR) **Mr Terry Amos**
73 **MANGENIE (FR)**, b f Irish Wells (FR)—Aubisquinette (FR) **Mme Patrick Papot**
74 **MISS BAILLY (FR)**, b f Kapgarde (FR)—Move Again (FR) **Ecurie Sagara**
75 **MISS PIERJI (FR)**, gr f Martaline—Paola Pierji (FR) **Mr R. A. Green**
76 **MON SUCCESSEUR (FR)**, ch g Forestier (FR)—Sainte Lea (FR) **Mr Pierre de Maleissye**
77 **ONSAIJAMAIS (FR)**, b g Kap Rock (FR)—Romantique Cotte (FR) **Mr Terry Amos**
78 **ORBASA (FR)**, b g Full of Gold (FR)—Ierbasa de Kerpaul (FR) **Mr Claude Patfoort**
79 **PAS COUSQUET (FR)**, b f Cadoubel (FR)—Pic Saint Loup (FR) **Mr Jean-Paul Wattelle**
80 **PER SALDO (GER)**, b g Sholokhov (IRE)—Perima (GER) **Mr Jacques Bisson**
81 **PERSEPOLIA (FR)**, b f Poliglote—Darae (FR) **Mr Francis Picoulet**
82 **PISTOLETTO (SPA)**, b g Green Tune (USA)—Ishi Adiva **Mr Gerard Laboureau**
83 **PRINCE SUMITAS (FR)**, b g Sumitas (GER)—Princesse Irena (FR) **Mr Claude Patfoort**
84 **RIBAMBELLE (FR)**, b f Martaline—Royale Majesty (FR) **Ecurie Rib**
85 **STAR DES VALOIS (FR)**, b f Poliglote—Bara Bahau (FR) **Mr Regis Maurice**
86 **SYMPATHIQUE (FR)**, b g Saint des Saints (FR)—Ty Mat (FR) **Mme Patrick Papot**
87 **THE BARBER (FR)**, gr g Martaline—Vie de Reine (FR) **Mme Myriam Montauban**
88 **TOP NOTCH (FR)**, b g Poliglote—Topira (FR) **Mme Marie Tyssandier**
89 **VIENS CHERCHER (IRE)**, b g Milan—La Zingarella (FR) **Mme Patrick Papot**
90 **WALK MOON (FR)**, b f Robin des Champs (FR)—De Loose Mongoose (IRE) **Mme Marie Tyssandier**
91 **WELLS DE LUNE (FR)**, b g Irish Wells (FR)—Pepite de Lune (FR) **Mr Francis Picoulet**

Jockey (NH): Vincent Cheminaud, Arnaud Duchene, Jan Faltejsek. **Conditional:** Kevin Aubree, Simon Cibot, Lewis Conan, Jeremie Rougier.

---

399 **MR JOHN MACKIE, Church Broughton**
Postal: **The Bungalow, Barton Blount, Church Broughton, Derby, Derbyshire, DE65 5AN**
Contacts: **PHONE** (01283) 585604/585603 **FAX** (01283) 585603 **MOBILE** (07799) 145283
E-MAIL jmackie@bartonblount.freeserve.co.uk **WEBSITE** www.johnmackieracing.co.uk

1 **ARIZONA JOHN (IRE)**, 9, b g Rahy (USA)—Preseli (IRE) **Derbyshire Racing**
2 **AVAILABLE (IRE)**, 5, b m Moss Vale (IRE)—Divert (IRE) **Derbyshire Racing V**

MR JOHN MACKIE - Continued

3 **FARMER'S FRIEND,** 5, b g Passing Glance—Flawspar **Mr N. J. Sessions**
4 **HALLSTATT (IRE),** 8, ch g Halling (USA)—Last Resort **Mrs J. Mackie**
5 **HISPANIA (IRE),** 4, b f Teofilo (IRE)—Badalona **R. Kent**
6 **HURRY HOME POPPA (IRE),** 4, b g Holy Roman Emperor (IRE)—My Renee (USA) **Mr D. Ward**
7 **ILLUSTRIOUS FOREST,** 6, ch g Shinko Forest (IRE)—Illustre Inconnue (USA) **Derbyshire Racing VII**
8 **IMPECCABILITY,** 4, b f Lucky Story (USA)—Impeccable Guest (IRE) **Derbyshire Racing IV**
9 **INANDOVER,** 9, b g Dover Patrol (IRE)—Inspirational (IRE) **Mrs K. L. Oliver**
10 **KEEP CALM,** 4, b c War Chant (USA)—Mayaar (USA) **Derbyshire Racing VIII**
11 **KNIGHT IN PURPLE,** 10, b g Sir Harry Lewis (USA)—Cerise Bleue (FR) **A J Wall, G Hicks & N Hooper**
12 **MARMAS,** 5, ch g Sir Percy—Kitabaat (IRE) **Mr G. R. Shelton**
13 **OFF THE PULSE,** 4, b g Araafa (IRE)—Off By Heart **G. B. Maher**
14 **RIVER PURPLE,** 7, b g Bollin Eric—Cerise Bleue (FR) **Sotby Farming Company Limited**
15 **ROCK SONG,** 5, b g Rock of Gibraltar (IRE)—Jackie's Opera (FR) **Sotby Farming Company Limited**
16 **SAINT THOMAS (IRE),** 7, b g Alhaarth (IRE)—Aguilas Perla (IRE) **P. Riley**
17 **SIR HARRY HOTSPUR,** 6, gr g Tikkanen (USA)—Harry's Bride **A. J. Wall**

THREE-YEAR-OLDS

18 **SPARTAN BELLE,** ch f Black Sam Bellamy (IRE)—Dolly Spartan **G. B. Maher**
19 **STREAM OF LIGHT,** b f Multiplex—Flawspar **Mr N. J. Sessions**

Other Owners: Mr Gary Hicks, Mr Neil Hooper, Mr A. Larkin, Mrs J. Mackie, Mr David Penman, Mr G. Pickering, Mr Gary Shelton, Mr A. J. Wall, Mr C. J. Wall.

---

400 **MR ALAN MACTAGGART, Hawick**
Postal: **Wells, Denholm, Hawick, Roxburghshire, TD9 8TD**
Contacts: **PHONE (01450) 870060 MOBILE (07711) 200445**

1 **ROYAL MACKINTOSH,** 13, b g Sovereign Water (FR)—Quick Quote **Mrs A. H. Mactaggart**

Assistant Trainer: Mrs M. A. Mactaggart

---

401 **MR BRUCE MACTAGGART, Hawick**
Postal: **Greendale, Hawick, Roxburghshire, TD9 7LH**
Contacts: **PHONE/FAX (01450) 372086 MOBILE (07764) 159852/(07718) 920072**
E-MAIL brucemact@btinternet.com

1 **QUEENS REGATTA,** 5, b m King's Theatre (IRE)—Friendly Craic (IRE) **Greendale Racing Syndicate**
2 **RED TANBER (IRE),** 11, ch g Karinga Bay—Dreamy Desire **Mrs F. Godson & Mrs H. MacTaggart**
3 4, B f Flemensfirth (USA)—Water Stratford (IRE) **Greendale Racing Syndicate**

TWO-YEAR-OLDS

4 B f 12/3 Robin des Champs (FR)—Buffy (Classic Cliche (IRE)) **Mr K. Rennie**
5 B f 22/3 King's Theatre (IRE)—Daisies Adventure (IRE) (Flemensfirth (USA)) **Mr B. MacTaggart**
6 B f 28/3 King's Theatre (IRE)—Water Stratford (IRE) (Jurado (USA)) **Mrs F. Godson**

Other Owners: Mrs Hilary Mactaggart, Mr Hugh T. Redhead.

Assistant Trainer: Mrs H. Mactaggart

---

402 **MR MICHAEL MADGWICK, Denmead**
Postal: **Forest Farm, Forest Road, Denmead, Waterlooville, Hampshire, PO7 6UA**
Contacts: **PHONE/FAX (02392) 258313 MOBILE (07835) 964969**

1 **BALLY BROADWELL,** 4, b f Kayf Tara—Ballyhoo (IRE) **I. M. McGready**
2 **COMEDY HOUSE,** 6, b g Auction House (USA)—Kyle Akin **Los Leader**
3 **CTAPPERS,** 5, b g Imperial Dancer—Stride Home **Mr P. Taplin**
4 **GOLD WEIGHT,** 4, ch g Denounce—Jewel (IRE) **Mrs L. N. Harmes**
5 **MONEY TALKS,** 4, br g Motivator—Movie Mogul **Recycled Products Limited**
6 **MULTITASK,** 4, b g Multiplex—Attlongglast **Mrs L. N. Harmes**
7 **SHANTOU BREEZE (IRE),** 7, b m Shantou—Homersmare (IRE) **I. M. McGready**
8 **SUPERSTICION,** 5, b m Red Ransom (USA)—Go Supersonic **Thrills & Spills**

MR MICHAEL MADGWICK - Continued

    9 WARBOND, 6, ch g Monsieur Bond (IRE)—Pick A Nice Name **M. J. Madgwick**
  10 WHERE'S SUSIE, 9, ch m Where Or When (IRE)—Linda's Schoolgirl (IRE) **Recycled Products Limited**

TWO-YEAR-OLDS

  11 B g 13/2 Royal Applause—Movie Mogul (Sakhee (USA)) **Recycled Products Limited**
  12 B f 26/2 Halling (USA)—Steel Free (IRE) (Danehill Dancer (IRE)) **Recycled Products Limited**

Other Owners: Mr M. Madgwick, Mr Robert Oliver, Mr T. Smith, Mr Alfred Walls.

Assistant Trainer: David Madgwick

Jockey (flat): George Baker, Adam Kirby. **Jockey (NH):** Marc Goldstein.

403

MRS HEATHER MAIN, Wantage
Postal: **Kingston Common Farm, Kingston Lisle, Wantage, Oxfordshire, OX12 9QT**
Contacts: **PHONE (01367) 820124 FAX (01367) 820125**
E-MAIL heather.main@hotmail.com WEBSITE www.heathermainracing.com

  1 ACHALAS (IRE), 6, b g Statue of Liberty (USA)—Princess of Iona (IRE) **Mr & Mrs D. R. Guest**
  2 BYRONESS, 4, b f Byron—Parting Gift **Byroness Les Chevaliers**
  3 CODY WYOMING, 8, b g Passing Glance—Tenderfoot **Highnote Thoroughbreds**
  4 COOLBEG (IRE), 8, b g Oscar (IRE)—Dianeme **R. P. Foden**
  5 HAPPY FAMILIES, 4, b f Singspiel (IRE)—One of The Family **K Mercer & Wetumpka Racing**
  6 HECTOR'S CHANCE, 5, ch g Byron—Fleur A Lay (USA) **Mr M. Scott Russell**
  7 LAURA SECORD (CAN), 4, b f Henny Hughes (USA)—Heart Lake (CAN) **Les Trois Mousquetaires**
  8 MAM RATAGAN, 13, b g Mtoto—Nika Nesgoda **Highnote Thoroughbreds**
  9 SOUTH KENTER (USA), 5, ch g Silver Deputy (CAN)—Crystal Downs (USA) **Les Chevaliers**
 10 TICINESE, 4, b g Lucarno (USA)—Maidwell **R P Foden & Colin Waugh**
 11 TOKYO BROWN (USA), 5, b g Marquetry (USA)—Miasma (USA) **Wetumpka Racing**

THREE-YEAR-OLDS

 12 Ch g Shirocco (GER)—Affirmed Native (USA)
 13 CHILDESPLAY, ch f Byron—Parting Gift **Les Chevaliers**
 14 POKER GOLD (FR), b c Gold Away (IRE)—Becquarette (FR) **Mr & Mrs D. R. Guest**

Other Owners: Mr D. Grenier, Mr D. R. Guest, R. B. Kolien, Mrs H. S. Main, J. P. M. Main, K. J. Mercer, Mr C. M. Waugh.

404

MR PETER MAKIN, Marlborough
Postal: **Bonita Racing Stables, Ogbourne Maisey, Marlborough, Wiltshire, SN8 1RY**
Contacts: **PHONE (01672) 512973 FAX (01672) 514166 MOBILE (07836) 217825**
E-MAIL hq@petermakin-racing.com WEBSITE www.petermakin-racing.com

  1 JUST ISLA, 4, ch f Halling (USA)—Island Rapture **D. A. Poole**
  2 KOHARU, 4, b gr f Ishiguru (USA)—Vellena **Keith & Brian Brackpool**
  3 MORACHE MUSIC, 6, b g Sleeping Indian—Enchanted Princess **R P Marchant D M Ahier Mrs E Lee**
  4 SIR TYTO (IRE), 6, b g Fruits of Love (USA)—Sophie May **Mr WH & Mrs Jennifer Simpson**
  5 UNISON (IRE), 4, b g Jeremy (USA)—Easter Song (USA) **Mr J. P. Carrington**
  6 WORDISMYBOND, 5, b g Monsieur Bond (IRE)—La Gessa **T. W. Wellard & Partners**

THREE-YEAR-OLDS

  7 CAPTAIN RYAN, b g Captain Gerrard (IRE)—Ryan's Quest (IRE) **Og Partnership**
  8 DARK PHANTOM (IRE), b g Dark Angel (IRE)—Stoneware **Mrs J. I. Simpson**
  9 DREAM IMPOSSIBLE (IRE), b f Iffraaj—Romea **Mrs J. N. Humphreys**
 10 FINDHORN MAGIC, b f Kyllachy—Enchanted Princess **Mr R. P. Marchant**
 11 SONG OF NORWAY, b f Halling (USA)—Amarullah **RA Henley RP Marchant JP Carrington**
 12 SPIDER LILY, b f Sleeping Indian—Scarlett Ribbon **Ten Of Hearts**
 13 SUITSUS, b g Virtual—Point Perfect **M Holland H Davies D Allen S Woods F Everleigh**
 14 TOUCHE DE ROUGE (IRE), b f Sholokhov (IRE)—Chaguaramas (IRE) **Mr B. Mortimer & Partners 1**

MR PETER MAKIN - Continued

TWO-YEAR-OLDS

15 B f 8/4 Fast Company (IRE)—Akariyda (IRE) (Salse (USA)) (23000) **Gerry Moss & Partners**
16 B c 26/2 Mawatheeq (USA)—
     Amarullah (FR) (Daylami (IRE)) (18000) **J P Carrington, Stewart Marchant, R P Marchant**
17 B f 16/4 Royal Applause—Milly Fleur (Primo Dominie) (20000) **Gerry Moss & Partners**
18 **MISS MITTENS**, b f 22/4 Shirocco (GER)—
     River of Silence (IRE) (Sadler's Wells (USA)) (6500) **Mrs Jennifer Simpson**
19 B g 16/4 Captain Gerrard (IRE)—Nigella (Band On The Run) (10000) **W. H. Simpson & Andy Lomax**
20 B f 8/4 Excellent Art—Royal Bounty (IRE) (Generous (IRE)) **J. P. Carrington**
21 Ch f 21/3 Assertive—Shustraya (Dansili) **Mrs P. J. Makin**
22 B c 12/2 Champs Elysees—Trick of Ace (USA) (Clever Trick (USA)) (44000) **R. P. Marchant & Partners**

Other Owners: D. M. Ahier, B. A. W. Brackpool, K. Brackpool, Mr J P Carrington, Mr K. A. Carter, H. J. W. Davies, Mr R A Henley, M. H. Holland, R. Kent, Mr P. A. Lee, Mr A. R. A. Lomax, Countess of Lonsdale, Mrs P J Makin, Mr P J Makin, Mr R P Marchant, Mr B. Mortimer, Mr W. H. Simpson, Mrs Jennifer Simpson, T. W. Wellard.

Jockey (flat): Steve Drowne, Seb Sanders.

---

405 **MRS ALYSON MALZARD, Jersey**
Postal: **Les Etabl'yes, Grosnez Farm, St Ouen, Jersey, JE3 2AD**
Contacts: **PHONE (01534) 483773 MOBILE (07797) 738128**
E-MAIL malzardracing@gmail.com

1 **AZARIA (FR)**, 8, b m Miesque's Son (USA)—Polar Return (FR) **Macwin Racing**
2 **COPPER FALLS**, 5, b m Trade Fair—Strat's Quest **Phil Banfield & John Hackett**
3 **COUNTRY BLUE (FR)**, 5, b g Country Reel (USA)—Exica (FR) **Mr A. Taylor**
4 **JACKPOT**, 4, b f Avonbridge—Strat's Quest **Phil Banfield & John Hackett**
5 **KERSIVAY**, 8, b g Royal Applause—Lochmaddy **Fast & Furious Racing**
6 **NEUILLY**, 7, b m Nayef (USA)—Narasimha (USA) **Sheik A Leg Racing**
7 **PAS D'ACTION**, 6, ch g Noverre (USA)—Bright Vision **Jim Jamouneau**
8 **REACH OUT**, 6, ch g Phoenix Reach (IRE)—Cocorica (IRE) **Malzard Racing**
9 **ROCQUAINE (IRE)**, 5, b m Oratorio (IRE)—Watch The Clock **Trevor & Pat Gallienne**
10 **SISSI GUIHEN (FR)**, 8, ch m Lord of Men—Assermara (FR) **P. A. Guiton & Y. Stead**
11 **SPANISH BOUNTY**, 9, b g Bahamian Bounty—Spanish Gold **Malzard Racing**

Assistant Trainer: Karl Kukk

Jockey (flat): Jemma Marshall. **Jockey (NH):** Mattie Batchelor. **Conditional:** Tom Garner.

---

406 **MR JAMES JOSEPH MANGAN, Mallow**
Postal: **Curraheen, Conna, Mallow, Co. Cork, Ireland**
Contacts: **PHONE (00353) 585 9116 FAX (00353) 585 9116 MOBILE (00353) 8726 84611**

1 **ANNACARTON (IRE)**, 10, b g Oscar (IRE)—Gallica (IRE) **Mrs Mary Mangan**
2 **CARRIES DARLING**, 7, b m Flemensfirth (USA)—Knock Down (IRE) **Mr W. M. Mangan**
3 **CASTLE WINGS (IRE)**, 9, b g Winged Love (IRE)—Mrs Hegarty **The Kings Syndicate**
4 **CYPRUSORMILAN**, 7, b g Milan—Persrolla **Handford Chemists Ltd**
5 **DONT TELL PA (IRE)**, 7, b g Oscar (IRE)—Glacial Snowboard (IRE) **Mrs Mary Mangan**
6 **FAIR DILEMMA (IRE)**, 9, b g Dr Massini (IRE)—Midnight Dilemma (IRE) **Patrick Furey**
7 **KILCREA (IRE)**, 7, b g Definite Article—Lightly Dreaming (FR) **Mr M. I. O'Driscoll**
8 **MONTYS MEADOW (IRE)**, 6, b g Oscar (IRE)—Montys Miss (IRE) **Hanford's Chemist Ltd**
9 **NORAS FANCY (IRE)**, 8, b m Brian Boru—Verney Bird (IRE) **Mr M. I. Dixon**
10 **OSCAR DELTA (IRE)**, 11, b g Oscar (IRE)—Timerry (IRE) **Miss Karen O'Driscoll**
11 **OSCAR TOWN (IRE)**, 7, b m Oscar (IRE)—Meadstown Miss (IRE) **John J. Bermingham**
12 **QUARRYVALE (IRE)**, 10, b m Beneficial—Miss McCormick (IRE) **Thomas O'Flynn**
13 **SMALL IS BEAUTIFUL (IRE)**, 6, b m Beneficial—Cherry Black (IRE) **Mrs Mary Mangan**
14 **THE FLYING DOC (IRE)**, 6, b m Dr Massini (IRE)—Meadstown Miss (IRE) **Mrs Rita Keating**
15 **TIPP ON AIR (IRE)**, 6, b m Indian River (FR)—Air Affair **After Ten Syndicate**
16 **WHATSTHECRACK JACK (IRE)**, 7, b g Croco Rouge (IRE)—Glebe Melody (IRE) **Conor Lannen**

Assistant Trainer: Mary Mangan

407 **MR CHARLIE MANN, Upper Lambourn**
Postal: Neardown, Upper Lambourn, Hungerford, Berkshire, RG17 8QP
Contacts: PHONE (01488) 71717 / 73118 FAX (01488) 73223 MOBILE (07721) 888333
E-MAIL charlie@charliemann.info WEBSITE www.charliemannracing.com

1 AIRMEN'S FRIEND (IRE), 8, b g Craigsteel—High Academy (IRE) **Prolinx Limited**
2 ALMOST GEMINI (IRE), 5, gr g Dylan Thomas (IRE)—Streetcar (IRE) **C. J. Mann**
3 ALWAYS SMILING (IRE), 7, b m Dushyantor (USA)—Aherlabeag (IRE) **Mrs J. Bannister**
4 AREA ACCESS (IRE), 6, b g Oscar (IRE)—Lady Bramble (IRE) **Edwyn Good & Bryan Beacham**
5 ATTIMO (GER), 5, ch g Nayef (USA)—Alanda (GER) **The Neardown VI**
6 CHAMPAGNE N CAVIAR (IRE), 6, b g Tiger Hill (IRE)—Leukippids (IRE) **N. W. A. Bannister**
7 DRAGON CITY, 4, b c Elusive City (USA)—Oulianovsk (IRE) **C. J. Mann**
8 DUKE OF MONMOUTH (IRE), 7, b g Presenting—Hayley Cometh (IRE) **Bryan & Philippa Burrough**
9 ELMORE BACK (IRE), 5, b g Wareed (IRE)—Katie Buckers (IRE) **Mr A Stone, Mr B Brindle & Mrs C Hill**
10 FINE PARCHMENT (IRE), 11, b g Presenting—Run For Cover (IRE) **N. W. A. Bannister**
11 GREYFRIARS DRUMMER, 6, ch g Where Or When (IRE)—Loveleaves **Amity Finance and The Drummers**
12 LATELO, 6, b g Shirocco (GER)—Laurencia **C. J. Mann**
13 LORD OF HOUSE (GER), 6, ch g Lord Of England (GER)—Lake House (IRE) **Good Lord Partnership**
14 LOW GALES (IRE), 8, b g Dr Massini (IRE)—Glorious Gale (IRE) **The Low Gales Partnership**
15 MURRAY MOUNT (IRE), 4, b g Trans Island—Ash **C. J. Mann**
16 PLUM STONE, 5, b m Loup Sauvage (USA)—Stoney Path **The Top Cats II**
17 PORTMONARCH (IRE), 4, b g Galileo (IRE)—Egyptian Queen (USA) **Mr J. Heron**
18 SANDS COVE (IRE), 7, b g Flemensfirth (USA)—

    Lillies Bordello (IRE) **Stapleton,Walsh,Thorneloe & Windsor-Clive**
19 SEVENTH SKY (GER), 7, b g King's Best (USA)—Sacarina **Mr J. Heron**
20 SHOCKINGTIMES (IRE), 7, b g Wareed (IRE)—Jolly Lady (IRE) **S.Beccle,J.Maynard,Lady Hart,Boscobel EL**
21 4, B g Duke of Marmalade (IRE)—Stylist (IRE) **C. J. Mann**
22 SURENESS (IRE), 4, ch f Hurricane Run (IRE)—Silk Dress (IRE) **C. J. Mann**
23 VERANO (GER), 5, ch g Lord of England (GER)—Vive La Vie (GER) **The Hennessy Five Syndicate**
24 VICTOR LEUDORUM (IRE), 7, b g Wareed (IRE)—Rock Garden (IRE) **R. Curry, C. Leuchars & R. Tompkins**
25 WESTERN KING (IRE), 7, b g Definite Article—Western Road (GER) **The Western King Partnership**
26 WHO OWNS ME (IRE), 8, b g Milan—Top Lassie (IRE) **Fromthestables.com Racing**

Other Owners: Amity Finance Ltd, Mr N. W. A. Bannister, Mr David Batten, Mr Bryan Beacham, Mr S. Beccle, Boscobel Estates Limited, Mr W. Brindle, Mr B. R. H. Burrough, Mrs Philippa Burrough, Mr N. A. Coster, Mr R. M. F. Curry, Mr Robert Frosell, Mr Edwyn Good, Lady Hart, Mrs C. Hill, Mrs A. Holt, Mrs Caroline Hunter, Miss D. Jones, Mr N. J. Kempner, Mr Charlie Mann, Mr I. G. Martin, Mrs Judy Maynard, Mr R. P. B. Michaelson, Mr J. Robinson, Mr T. Simmons, Mr Tony Stapleton, Mr Andy Stone, Mrs L. C. Taylor, Major J. G. Thorneloe, Mr R. J. Tompkins, Mrs P. J. Walsh, Mrs S. C. Welch, Mr Andy Weller, The Hon D. J. Windsor-Clive, Mrs Penny Zarbafi.

Secretary: Rose Osborn

Jockey (NH): Noel Fehily. **Conditional:** Gavin Sheehan.

408 **MR GEORGE MARGARSON, Newmarket**
Postal: Graham Lodge, Birdcage Walk, Newmarket, Suffolk, CB8 0NE
Contacts: HOME/FAX (01638) 668043 MOBILE (07860) 198303
E-MAIL george@georgemargarson.co.uk WEBSITE www.georgemargarson.co.uk

1 ARTFUL LADY (IRE), 5, br m Excellent Art—Fear And Greed (IRE) **Graham Lodge Partnership**
2 ENTHUSIASTIC, 6, b g Galileo (IRE)—Que Puntual (ARG) **Mr M. Keller**
3 EXCELLENT ANN, 7, b g Exceed And Excel (AUS)—Snugfit Annie **Graham Lodge Partnership II**
4 EXCELLENT GUEST, 7, b g Exceed And Excel (AUS)—Princess Speedfit (FR) **John Guest Racing Ltd**
5 IMAGINARY DIVA, 8, b m Lend A Hand—Distant Diva **Graham Lodge Partnership II**
6 JAMMY GUEST (IRE), 4, b g Duke of Marmalade (IRE)—Ardbrae Lady **John Guest Racing Ltd**
7 MAGICAL SPEEDFIT (IRE), 9, ch g Bold Fact (USA)—Magical Peace (IRE) **Graham Lodge Partnership II**
8 NOGUCHI (IRE), 9, ch g Pivotal—Tuscania (USA) **Mrs F Shaw**
9 POYLE VINNIE, 4, b g Piccolo—Poyle Dee Dee **Cecil and Miss Alison Wiggins**
10 REBELLIOUS GUEST, 5, b g Cockney Rebel (IRE)—Marisa (GER) **John Guest Racing Ltd**
11 RED CATKIN, 4, b f Notnowcato—Red Salvia **Graham Lodge Partnership**
12 STORM RUNNER (IRE), 6, b g Rakti—Saibhreas (IRE) **Graham Lodge Partnership II**
13 TAMAYUZ STAR (IRE), 4, ch c Tamayuz—Magical Peace (IRE) **Mr A. Al Mansoori**
14 UPRISE, 5, b g Pivotal—Soar **Pitfield Partnership**
15 WOOLFALL SOVEREIGN (IRE), 8, b g Noverre (USA)—

    Mandragore (USA) **Wildcard Racing Syndicate & Partners**

MR GEORGE MARGARSON - Continued

THREE-YEAR-OLDS

16 **BOUNTIFUL SIN,** ch g Sinndar (IRE)—Tropical Barth (IRE) **Maxwell Morrison**
17 **ELUSIVE GUEST (FR),** b c Elusive City (USA)—Mansoura (IRE) **John Guest Racing Ltd**
18 **EXCEED AND EXCEED,** b c Exceed And Excel (AUS)—Gandini **Mr A. Al Mansoori**
19 **HAAFFA SOVEREIGN,** ch g Haafhd—Royal Nashkova **G. Wilson**
20 **JAY GEE SPEEDFIT (IRE),** b c Bushranger (IRE)—Prodigal Daughter **John Guest Racing Ltd**
21 **LUCKY KRISTALE,** b f Lucky Story (USA)—Pikaboo **Graham Lodge Partnership**
22 **SHYRON,** b g Byron—Coconut Shy **Mr & Mrs F. Butler**

TWO-YEAR-OLDS

23 B f 28/3 Showcasing—Clincher Club (Polish Patriot (USA)) (110000) **Mr S. Rashid**
24 Ch c 6/2 Exceed And Excel (AUS)—Dearest Daisy (Forzando) (200000)
25 Ch c 14/3 Raven's Pass (USA)—Generous Lady (Generous (IRE)) (300000)
26 B c 2/4 Kodiac—Golden Shadow (IRE) (Selkirk (USA)) (47619) **John Guest Racing Ltd**
27 Gr c 26/4 Aussie Rules (USA)—Jusoor (USA) (El Prado (IRE)) (29000) **John Guest Racing Ltd**
28 B f 24/2 Intikhab (USA)—Literacy (USA) (Diesis) (34842) **Mr A. Al Mansoori**
29 B f 12/2 Lawman (FR)—Lunduv (IRE) (Pivotal) (95000) **Mr S. Rashid**
30 B c 25/4 Kodiac—Mirwara (IRE) (Darshaan) (27100) **Mr A. Al Mansoori**
31 B f 20/3 Kyllachy—Miss Otis (Danetime (IRE)) (35000) **Graham Lodge Partnership**
32 B f 9/3 Iffraaj—Princess Speedfit (FR) (Desert Prince (IRE)) (150000) **John Guest Racing Ltd**

Assistant Trainer: Katie Margarson

MR A. J. MARTIN, Summerhill
Postal: **Arodstown, Moynalvey, Summerhill, Co. Meath, Ireland**
Contacts: **PHONE (00353) 46 955 8633 FAX (00353) 46 955 8632 MOBILE (00353) 86 276 0835**
E-MAIL arodstown@eircom.net

1 **BENEFFICIENT (IRE),** 8, ch g Beneficial—Supreme Breda (IRE) **A Shiels/Niall Reilly**
2 **BLAIR PERRONE (IRE),** 5, b g Rudimentary (USA)—Stonehallqueen (IRE) **John Breslin**
3 **BOG WARRIOR (IRE),** 10, b g Strategic Choice (USA)—Kilmac Princess (IRE) **Gigginstown House Stud**
4 **CAPTAIN HOX (IRE),** 5, b g Danehill Dancer (USA)—Shangri La (IRE) **Mrs Siobhan Ryan**
5 **CASSELLS ROCK (IRE),** 4, br g Rock of Gibraltar (IRE)—Se La Vie (IRE) **Donal Houlihan**
6 **DEDIGOUT (IRE),** 8, b g Bob Back (USA)—Dainty Daisy (IRE) **Gigginstown House Stud**
7 **EASY VIC (IRE),** 10, ch g Old Vic—Anotherfling (IRE) **J. Duff**
8 **ELISHPOUR (IRE),** 4, b g Oasis Dream—Elbasana (IRE) **Barry Connell**
9 **FERNHURST LAD (IRE),** 9, b g Aahsaylad—Devils Lady (IRE) **SCR Syndicate**
10 **FILL YOUR HANDS (IRE),** 5, b g Milan—Cailin's Perk (IRE) **Gigginstown House Stud**
11 **GALLANT OSCAR (IRE),** 8, b g Oscar (IRE)—Park Wave (IRE) **Mr G. Kelly**
12 **GARDELITO (FR),** 7, b br g Al Namix (FR)—Sweet Magic (FR) **Peter William Partnership**
13 **GIFT OF DGAB (IRE),** 10, b g Winged Love (IRE)—Creative Princess (IRE) **Gigginstown House Stud**
14 **GLADIATOR KING (IRE),** 5, b g Dylan Thomas (IRE)—Sheer Bliss (IRE) **Tony Martin / Seamus Fitzpatrick**
15 **GOLANTILLA (IRE),** 6, br g Golan (IRE)—Scintilla **B. Connell**
16 **GOLDEN FIRTH (IRE),** 7, b m Flemensfirth (USA)—Golden Flower (GER) **R. W. Donaldson**
17 **GREATNESS (IRE),** 4, gr g Dalakhani (IRE)—Dancing Diva (FR) **Newtown Anner Stud Farms Ltd**
18 **HEATHFIELD (IRE),** 7, ch g Definite Article—Famous Lady (IRE) **P. J. McGee / Jos Kirwan**
19 **KING OF THE REFS (IRE),** 9, b g Zagreb (USA)—Regal Pursuit (IRE) **Mr E. Waters**
20 **LASTOFTHELEADERS (IRE),** 11, b g Supreme Leader—
                                        Heather Breeze (IRE) **Desmond Doherty & Declan Gannon**
21 **LIVING NEXT DOOR (IRE),** 8, b g Beneficial—Except Alice (IRE) **John Breslin**
22 **MATSUKAZE (IRE),** 7, b g Norwich—The Bowlers Boreen **Tom McGoldrick**
23 **MOYVIC (IRE),** 5, b g Old Vic—Moydrum Castle (IRE) **Ms Siobhan Gallagher**
24 **MULLEADY (IRE),** 6, ch m Definite Article—Brief Sentiment (IRE) **Hard Hat Syndicate**
25 **MYDOR (FR),** 4, ch g Stormy River (FR)—Fabulousday (USA) **Mulvany's Bar Syndicate**
26 **NARCOTIC NORA (IRE),** 6, b m Hawk Wing (USA)—Winning Sally (IRE) **D. J. Reddan**
27 **PIRES,** 10, br g Generous (IRE)—Kaydee Queen (IRE) **Lily Lawlor**
28 **QUICK JACK (IRE),** 5, ch g Footstepsinthesand—Miss Polaris **John Breslin**
29 **QUICKPICK VIC (IRE),** 7, b g Old Vic—Anotherfling (IRE) **J. Duff**
30 **SARWISTAN (IRE),** 4, b g Nayef (USA)—Seraya (FR) **John Breslin / Tony Martin**
31 **SAVELLO (IRE),** 8, ch g Anshan—Fontaine Frances (FR) **Gigginstown House Stud**
32 **SHEMSHAL (FR),** 6, b g Dalakhani (IRE)—Shemala (IRE) **Tony Martin / Mrs Sheila Moffett**
33 **SPACIOUS SKY (USA),** 5, b g North Light (IRE)—Ratings (USA) **P. Reilly**
34 **SRAID PADRAIG (IRE),** 8, b g Revoque (IRE)—Loughaneala (IRE) **B. Connell**

409

MR A. J. MARTIN - Continued

35 **TED VEALE (IRE)**, 7, b g Revoque (IRE)—Rose Tanner (IRE) **John Breslin**
36 **THE PLAN MAN (IRE)**, 4, b g Jeremy (USA)—Sanfrancullinan (IRE) **Gigginstown House Stables**
37 **UNDERTHEBOARDWALK (IRE)**, 8, b g Dr Massini (IRE)—Bernyhostess (IRE) **Independent Syndicate**
38 **VELVET MAKER (FR)**, 5, b g Policy Maker (IRE)—Evasion de L'orne (FR) **B. Connell**
39 **VICTRIX GALE (IRE)**, 8, b m Presenting—Ballyclough Gale **Badgers Syndicate**
40 **WINGTIPS (FR)**, 6, gr g High Chaparral (IRE)—Without Shoes (FR) **Ms Sheila Moffett**
41 **WRONG TURN (IRE)**, 8, b g Well Chosen—Friendly Spirit **John Breslin**

Other Owners: Alzo the Great Syndicate, City Gunners Syndicate, Adrian Collins, Stephen Curran, Neil Curtin, Timothy Fitzgerald, Seamus Fitzpatrick, Irish Shamrock Syndicate, Dermot Kilmurray, J. A. McCarthy, John P. McManus, Mr Tayto Partnership, Alan Murray, Newgrange Partnership, Peter William Partnership, Thomas Steele, George Swan, Ultimate Dreams Syndicate.

Jockey (flat): F. Berry, John Brennan, S. Heffernan, Colin Keane, W. Lordan, J. P. Murtagh, Shane Shortall.
Jockey (NH): P. Carberry, R. C. Colgan, Bryan Cooper, Barry Geraghty, R. M. Power, D. N. Russell, P. Townend, R. Walsh.
Conditional: John Brennan, Shane Shortall. **Amateur:** Mr S. Clements, Mr J. J. Codd, Mr C. W. Fennessy, Mr D. J. Hand, Mr M. J. P. O'Connor, Mr D. O'Connor, Mr E. M. O'Sullivan, Miss Maxine O'Sullivan.

410

MR ANDREW J. MARTIN, Chipping Norton
Postal: **Yew Tree Barn, Hook Norton Road, Swerford, Chipping Norton, Oxfordshire, OX7 4BF**
Contacts: **PHONE (01608) 737288**

1 **FITZ VOLONTE**, 7, br g Passing Glance—Swordella **A. J. Martin**
2 **GONEINAGLANCE**, 5, b m Passing Glance—It's Missy Imp **A. J. Martin**
3 **MIDNIGHT MUSTANG**, 7, b g Midnight Legend—Mustang Molly **A. J. Martin**
4 **MINNIE MUSTANG**, 6, b m Midnight Legend—Mustang Molly **A. J. Martin**
5 **ORANGER (FR)**, 12, b g Antarctique (IRE)—True Beauty **A. J. Martin**
6 **SONIC WELD**, 5, b m Zafeen (FR)—Jamadast Roma **A. J. Martin**
7 **SUNNY LEDGEND**, 9, b g Midnight Legend—Swordella **A. J. Martin**
8 **TRACKING TIME**, 7, b g Central Park (IRE)—E Minor (IRE) **A. J. Martin**
9 **TRIFOLLET**, 9, b m Kirkwall—St Doughla's (IRE) **A. J. Martin**

411

MR CHRISTOPHER MASON, Caerwent
Postal: **Whitehall Barn, Five Lanes, Caerwent, Monmouthshire**
Contacts: **PHONE (01291) 422172 FAX (01633) 666690 MOBILE (07767) 808082**
E-MAIL cjmason@tiscali.co.uk

1 **ARTHUR'S EDGE**, 10, b g Diktat—Bright Edge **Mr & Mrs C. J. Mason**
2 **EDGED OUT**, 4, b f Piccolo—Edge of Light **Mr & Mrs C. J. Mason**
3 **SUPERIOR EDGE**, 7, b m Exceed And Excel (AUS)—Beveled Edge **Mr & Mrs C. J. Mason**

THREE-YEAR-OLDS

4 **HEAVENS EDGE**, b f Royal Applause—Elidore **Mr & Mrs C. J. Mason**

Other Owners: C. J. Mason, Mrs A. L. Mason. **Assistant Trainer:** Annabelle Mason.

412

MRS JENNIFER MASON, Cirencester
Postal: **Manor Farm, Ablington, Bibury, Cirencester, Gloucestershire, GL7 5NY**
Contacts: **PHONE (01285) 740445 MOBILE (07974) 262438**
E-MAIL pwmason2002@yahoo.co.uk WEBSITE www.jennifermasonracing.com

1 **CATCHAROSE (IRE)**, 4, b f Catcher In The Rye (IRE)—Persian Flower **The If At First Partnership**
2 **GALWAY VIEW (IRE)**, 7, br g Pilsudski (IRE)—Laurens Pride (IRE) **Mrs J. S. Mason**
3 **MIC AUBIN (FR)**, 11, b g Broadway Flyer (USA)—Patney (FR) **C. M. Clarke**
4 **TOMORROW NIGHT**, 4, b f Kayf Tara—Whizz Back (IRE) **Mrs J. S. Mason**

Other Owners: Mrs R. D. Greenwood, Mrs M. E. Slocock.

Assistant Trainer: Mr Peter W. Mason

Jockey (NH): Felix De Giles, Timmy Murphy. **Amateur:** Mr Peter Mason.

413 **MR ROBIN MATHEW, Burford**
Postal: **Church Farm, Little Barrington, Burford, Oxfordshire, OX18 4TE**
Contacts: **PHONE (01451) 844311 MOBILE (07960) 990037**

1 BALLY SANDS (IRE), 10, b g Luso—Sandwell Old Rose (IRE) **R. Mathew**
2 BRAVO RIQUET (FR), 8, br g Laveron—Jeroline (FR) **R. Mathew**
3 EMPEROR COMMODOS, 7, b g Midnight Legend—Theme Arena **R. Mathew**
4 ERGO SUM, 7, bl g Fair Mix (IRE)—Idiot's Lady **R. Mathew**

Jockey (NH): Lee Edwards. **Conditional:** Ed Cookson, Robbie Dunne.

414 **MR G. C. MAUNDRELL, Marlborough**
Postal: **Ogbourne Down, Ogbourne St Andrew, Marlborough, Wilts**
Contacts: **PHONE (01672) 841202**

1 DELINEATE (IRE), 5, b m Definite Article—New Line (IRE) **G. C. Maundrell**
2 DREAM PERFORMANCE (IRE), 9, b m Oscar (IRE)—Pharlen's Dream (IRE) **G. C. Maundrell**
3 MINOR CHORD, 8, b m Alflora (IRE)—Minimum **G. C. Maundrell**

Jockey (NH): G. Tumelty.

415 **MR KEVIN MCAULIFFE, Faringdon**
Postal: **Fernham Farm, Fernham, Faringdon, Oxfordshire, SN7 7NX**
Contacts: **PHONE (01367) 820236 FAX (01367) 820110 E-MAIL kevin@fernhamfarm.com**

1 RIBBON ROYALE, 4, b f Royal Applause—Ribbonwood (USA)

THREE-YEAR-OLDS

2 Ch c Pastoral Pursuits—Lady Le Quesne (IRE) **Mrs J. Kersey**

416 **MR PHILIP MCBRIDE, Newmarket**
Postal: **Exeter House Stables, 33 Exeter Road, Newmarket, Suffolk, CB8 0NY**
Contacts: **PHONE/FAX (01638) 667841 MOBILE (07929) 265711**

1 KEENE, 4, b g Cockney Rebel (IRE)—Lumpini Park **Four Winds Racing Partnership**

THREE-YEAR-OLDS

2 BLUE OYSTER, b f Medicean—Bluebelle **C. M. Budgett**
3 CHOICE OF DESTINY, ch f Haafhd—Lumpini Park **Four Winds Racing Partnership**
4 OLD TOWN BOY, b c Myboycharlie (IRE)—Native Ring (FR) **Mr R. Wilson**
5 RITE TO REIGN, b g Tiger Hill (IRE)—Magical Cliche (USA) **Maelor Racing**
6 WALK WITH AN ANGEL, b f Myboycharlie (IRE)—Broughtons Revival **P. J. McBride**

Other Owners: Miss A. M. Farrier, Mr D. L. Jackson, S. J. Mear, Mrs E. A. Mear.

417 **MR ALAN MCCABE, Averham**
Postal: **Cheveral Barn, Averham, Newark, Nottinghamshire, NG23 5RU**
Contacts: **PHONE (01636) 701668 FAX (01636) 706579 MOBILE (07766) 302092**
E-MAIL ajmacc@tiscali.co.uk

1 AMETHYST DAWN (IRE), 8, gr m Act One—A L'aube (IRE) **Craig and Maureen Buckingham**
2 ANSAAB, 6, b g Cape Cross (IRE)—Dawn Raid (IRE) **Craig and Maureen Buckingham**
3 AUBRIETIA, 5, b m Dutch Art—Petong's Pet **Shropshire Wolves 4**
4 BEDLOE'S ISLAND (IRE), 9, b g Statue of Liberty (USA)—Scenaria (IRE) **Mr M. E. Timms**
5 CORNUS, 12, ch g Inchinor—Demerger (USA) **Triple A Partnership**
6 ELUSIVE WARRIOR (USA), 11, b g Elusive Quality (USA)—Love To Fight (CAN) **Mrs M. J. McCabe**
7 ENJOYMENT, 7, b m Dansili—Have Fun **A. J. McCabe**
8 FRATELLINO, 7, ch h Auction House (USA)—Vida (IRE) **Sale Of The Century**

MR ALAN MCCABE - Continued

9 **KAI**, 5, b g Kyllachy—Belle Ile (USA) **Mr J. R. Atherton**
10 **MARIA'S CHOICE (IRE)**, 5, b g Oratorio (IRE)—Amathusia **Craig and Maureen Buckingham**
11 **MASTERFUL ACT (USA)**, 7, ch g Pleasantly Perfect (USA)—Catnip (USA) **Universal Recycling Company**
12 **MOUSIE**, 5, b m Auction House (USA)—Goes A Treat (IRE) **Lucky Heather**
13 **NAABEGHA**, 7, ch g Muhtathir—Hawafiz **Mrs M. J. McCabe**
14 **SHOWBOATING (IRE)**, 6, b g Shamardal (USA)—Sadinga (IRE) **Mr M&Mrs L Cooke Mr A Pierce Mr A McCabe**
15 **TASRIH (USA)**, 5, b g Hard Spun (USA)—Rare Gift (USA) **Craig and Maureen Buckingham**
16 **THE ART OF RACING (IRE)**, 4, b g Acclamation—Divert (IRE) **Craig and Maureen Buckingham**
17 **THE GREAT GABRIAL**, 5, b g Oasis Dream—Quiff **Mr T. Al Nisf**
18 **TRUE TO FORM (IRE)**, 7, b g Rock of Gibraltar (IRE)—Truly Yours (IRE) **Craig and Maureen Buckingham**
19 **UNA BELLA COSA**, 4, b f Dubai Destination (USA)—Blinding Mission (IRE) **Averham Racing Syndicates 1**

THREE-YEAR-OLDS

20 **CLEVER MISS**, b f Mount Nelson—Clever Millie (USA) **K. A. Dasmal**
21 **GALAXY (IRE)**, b g Oratorio (IRE)—Gravitation **Craig and Maureen Buckingham**
22 **LOMA MOR**, b f Auction House (USA)—Dancing Loma (FR) **Lucky Heather**
23 **MOLLY AHOY**, b f Captain Gerrard (IRE)—Demolition Molly **Mrs J. A. Bowen**
24 **RAZIN' HELL**, b g Byron—Loose Caboose (IRE) **Timms, Timms, McCabe & Warke**
25 **RED BIBA (IRE)**, ch f Intense Focus (USA)—Vital Laser (USA) **Craig and Maureen Buckingham**
26 **RED PRIMO (IRE)**, b c Iffraaj—Testa Unica (ITY) **Craig and Maureen Buckingham**
27 **RED TIDE (IRE)**, gr g Tamayuz—Rectify (IRE) **Craig and Maureen Buckingham**
28 **RED WIFEY (IRE)**, b f High Chaparral (USA)—Raspberry Beret (IRE) **The Ladies' Rioja Collective**
29 **ROCKY HILL RIDGE**, b g Auction House (USA)—Amwell Star **Lucky Heather**
30 **ROYAL WARRIOR**, b g Royal Applause—Tiana **A. J. McCabe**
31 **SPIRIT O GOODCHILD**, b g Sleeping Indian—Well of Echoes **Mr M. G. Warke**
32 **VOLODINA (IRE)**, ch f Soviet Star (USA)—Why Now **Mr T. Al Nisf**

TWO-YEAR-OLDS

33 **GO COMPLAIN**, b f 11/4 Mount Nelson—Trounce (Barathea (IRE)) (30000) **Craig and Maureen Buckingham**
34 **MONSIEUR ROUGE (IRE)**, b c 25/1 Monsieur Bond (IRE)—
                              Brosna Time (Danetime (IRE)) (22857) **Craig and Maureen Buckingham**
35 B f 17/3 Stimulation (IRE)—Moon Bird (Primo Dominie) (5904) **The Michaelmas Daisy Partnership**
36 **RED CONNECT**, b c 10/3 Aqlaam—Close Knit (USA) (Hennessy (USA)) (9523) **Craig and Maureen Buckingham**
37 **RED FLUTE**, ch c 13/4 Piccolo—
                              Fee Fum Fum (IRE) (Great Commotion (USA)) (25714) **Craig and Maureen Buckingham**
38 **RED UNICO (IRE)**, b c 19/4 Vale of York (IRE)—
                              Testa Unica (ITY) (Nordance (USA)) (23000) **Craig and Maureen Buckingham**
39 **THE OTHER LADY**, b f 13/2 Peintre Celebre (USA)—
                              Tamalain (USA) (Royal Academy (USA)) (15000) **Craig and Maureen Buckingham**

Other Owners: Mr J. Babb, Mr A. D. Baker, Mr C. Buckingham, Mrs M. Buckingham, Miss H. P. Chellingworth, Mr M. Cooke, Mr J. Cooke, R. Simpson, Mr P. Smith, Mr A. C. Timms.

Jockey (flat): Shane Kelly, Seb Sanders, Robert Winston.

---

418 **MR DONALD MCCAIN, Cholmondeley**
Postal: **Bankhouse, Cholmondeley, Malpas, Cheshire, SY14 8AL**
Contacts: **PHONE (01829) 720352/720351 FAX (01829) 720475 MOBILE (07903) 066194**
E-MAIL info@donaldmccain.co.uk WEBSITE www.donaldmccain.co.uk

1 **ABBEY STORM (IRE)**, 8, br g Presenting—Bobbies Storm (IRE) **Mr & Mrs Paul Rooney**
2 **ABSINTHE (IRE)**, 8, b g King's Best—Triple Try (IRE) **Mr & Mrs Paul Rooney**
3 **ACROSS THE BAY (IRE)**, 10, b g Bob's Return (IRE)—The Southern (IRE) **Scotch Piper Syndicate**
4 **AGENT ARCHIE (USA)**, 7, b g Smart Strike (CAN)—Dans La Ville (CHI) **D. M. Gorton**
5 **ALDERLEY ROVER (IRE)**, 10, gr g Beneficial—St Anne's Lady (IRE) **A. Craig & A. Dick**
6 **ANY GIVEN DAY (IRE)**, 9, gr g Clodovil (IRE)—Five of Wands **T. G. Leslie**
7 **APOLLO ELEVEN (IRE)**, 5, b g Manduro (GER)—Arlesienne (IRE) **Mr F. McAleavy**
8 **ASKAMORE DARSI (IRE)**, 5, b g Darsi (FR)—Galamear **Deva Racing Darsi Partnership**
9 **ATLANTA FALCON (IRE)**, 9, b g Winged Love (IRE)—Oneofmegirls (IRE)
10 **BALLYBRIGGAN (IRE)**, 10, b g Flemensfirth (USA)—Shean Hill (IRE) **Stewart Andrew & Jim Shaw**
11 **BEEVES (IRE)**, 7, b g Portrait Gallery (IRE)—Camas North (IRE) **Mr & Mrs Paul Rooney**
12 **BENZANNO (IRE)**, 5, b g Refuse To Bend (IRE)—Crossanza (IRE) **T. G. Leslie**
13 **BILLFROMTHEBAR (IRE)**, 7, b g Morozov (USA)—Eden Breeze (IRE) **Mr M. W. Sanders**
14 **BIT OF A JIG (IRE)**, 7, ch g Alderbrook—Ardower (IRE) **Let's Live Racing**

MR DONALD McCAIN - Continued

15 **BLACKWATER KING (IRE)**, 6, b br g Beneficial—Accordian Lady (IRE) **Mr & Mrs Paul Rooney**
16 **BOURNE**, 8, gr g Linamix (FR)—L'affaire Monique **M. J. Taylor**
17 **BRADY (IRE)**, 8, ch g Albano (IRE)—Quiet Sovereign **Luxham Racing**
18 **CALCON (IRE)**, 7, ch g Presenting—Cordal Dream (IRE)
19 4, B g Gamut (IRE)—Calendula
20 **CINDERS AND ASHES**, 7, b g Beat Hollow—Moon Search **Dermot Hanafin & Phil Cunningham**
21 **CLASSIC MOVE (IRE)**, 5, b g Flying Legend (USA)—Jennylee (IRE) **T. G. Leslie**
22 **CLONDAW DRAFT (IRE)**, 6, b g Shantou (USA)—Glen Ten (IRE) **T. G. Leslie**
23 **CLONDAW HERO (IRE)**, 6, b g Milan—Rose of Winter (IRE)
24 **CLONDAW KAEMPFER (IRE)**, 6, b g Oscar (IRE)—Gra-Bri (IRE) **T Leslie & D Gorton**
25 **CLOUDANTE (IRE)**, 6, b m Cloudings (IRE)—Carrig Lucy (IRE) **Thomson & Fyffe Racing**
26 **CLOUDY JOKER (IRE)**, 6, gr g Cloudings (IRE)—Rosa View (IRE)
27 **COOL SKY**, 5, b g Millkom—Intersky High (USA) **Norte Sur Partnership**
28 **CORRIN WOOD (IRE)**, 7, gr g Garuda (IRE)—Allstar Rose (IRE) **Mr D. Hanafin**
29 **DARLINGTON COUNTY (IRE)**, 6, b g Oscar (IRE)—Laura's Native (IRE) **Brendan Richardson & Jon Glews**
30 **DEEP MARGIN (IRE)**, 5, b g Scorpion (IRE)—Deep Supreme (IRE) **T. J. Hemmings**
31 **DEGOOCH (IRE)**, 5, ch g Gamut (IRE)—Blonde Ambition (IRE) **Mr & Mrs Paul Rooney**
32 **DEISE DYNAMO (IRE)**, 6, br g Zagreb (USA)—Magical Mist (IRE) **Mr D. Hanafin**
33 **DESERT CRY (IRE)**, 8, b br g Desert Prince (IRE)—Hataana (USA) **N.Y.P.D Racing**
34 **DESOTO COUNTY**, 5, gr g Hernando (FR)—Kaldounya **Mr & Mrs Paul Rooney**
35 **DIAMOND KING (IRE)**, 6, b g King's Theatre (IRE)—Georgia On My Mind (IRE) **Mrs D. L. Whateley**
36 **DILIGENT**, 6, b m Generous (IRE)—Diletia **Chasing Gold Racing Club**
37 **DIOCLES (IRE)**, 8, b g Bob Back (USA)—Ardrina **L. G. M. Racing**
38 **DISPOUR (IRE)**, 4, ch g Monsun (GER)—Dalataya (IRE) **Mr & Mrs Paul Rooney**
39 **DIVERS (FR)**, 10, gr g Highest Honor (FR)—Divination (FR) **Let's Live Racing**
40 **DIVINE HONOUR (IRE)**, 4, b g Kalanisi (IRE)—Hazel Honey (IRE) **D. Reilly & Mrs C. Reilly**
41 **DJ MILAN (IRE)**, 8, b g Milan—Cafe Matisse (IRE)
42 **DOYLY CARTE**, 6, b m Doyen (IRE)—Generous Diana **Elite Racing Club**
43 **DREAMS OF MILAN (IRE)**, 6, b g Milan—Joe's Dream Catch (IRE) **Axom XXXVII**
44 **DUNGEEL (IRE)**, 8, b g Moscow Society (USA)—Mis Fortune (IRE) **Mr M. R. Kemp**
45 **DUNOWEN POINT (IRE)**, 8, b g Old Vic—Esbeggi **T. G. Leslie**
46 **FAIR MONEY**, 5, gr g Fair Mix (IRE)—Mrs Moneypenny **Deva Racing Fair Mix Partnership**
47 **FEARLESS TUNES (IRE)**, 6, b g Shantou (USA)—Miss Snapdragon (IRE) **Mr & Mrs Paul Rooney**
48 4, B g Mahler—Flushtown Vale (IRE) **Mr D. Owens**
49 **FRANCISCAN**, 6, b g Medicean—Frangy **T. G. Leslie**
50 **FRECKLETON (IRE)**, 6, b g Milan—Chancy Lass (IRE) **David Barlow & John A Raybone**
51 **GABRIAL THE GREAT (IRE)**, 5, b g Montjeu (IRE)—Bayourida (USA) **Mr & Mrs Paul Rooney**
52 **GLACED OVER**, 9, br m Overbury (IRE)—Brun Bess (IRE) **The Room 1.01 Syndicate**
53 **GREENSALT (IRE)**, 6, b g Milan—Garden City (IRE) **T. J. Hemmings**
54 **GROUSE LODGE (IRE)**, 8, b g Well Chosen—Arctic Jane (IRE) **Mr F. McAleavy**
55 **GULF PUNCH**, 7, b m Dubawi (IRE)—Fruit Punch (IRE) **Mr R. J. Gwynne**
56 **HALO MOON**, 6, br g Kayf Tara—Fragrant Rose **Level Par Racing**
57 **HELLORBOSTON (IRE)**, 6, b g Court Cave (IRE)—Helorhiwater (IRE) **Thomson & Fyffe Racing**
58 **HILLS OF DUBAI (IRE)**, 5, ch g Dubai Destination (USA)—Mowazana (IRE) **T. G. Leslie**
59 **HOLLOW TREE**, 6, b g Beat Hollow—Hesperia **Brannon Dick Holden**
60 **HOWABOUTNEVER (IRE)**, 6, b g Shantou (USA)—Sarah's Cottage (IRE) **Brannon, Dick, Hernon & Holden**
61 **HOWABOUTNOW (IRE)**, 7, ch g Shantou (USA)—Sarah's Cottage (IRE) **Brannon, Dick, Hernon & Holden**
62 **I NEED GOLD (IRE)**, 5, b g Gold Well—Coola Cross (IRE) **Deva Racing Golden Partnership**
63 **I TOLD YOU SO (IRE)**, 5, b g m Oscar (IRE)—My Twist (IRE)
64 **I'M A ROCKER (IRE)**, 5, b g Gold Well—Over Slyguff (IRE) **General Men Racing Club I**
65 **INDIAN CASTLE (IRE)**, 6, b g Dr Massini (IRE)—Indian Legend (IRE) **Askew Dick Hernon Reynard**
66 **IT'S OSCAR (IRE)**, 7, b g Oscar (IRE)—Lady Bramble (IRE) **Leach, Viney & Wilson**
67 **JELLIED EEL JACK (IRE)**, 5, b g Scorpion (IRE)—Melodic Tune (IRE) **Mr T. Perkins**
68 **JUMBO SUPREME (IRE)**, 8, gr g Portrait Gallery (IRE)—Supreme Caution (IRE) **Lucky Bin Racing**
69 **KATACHENKO (IRE)**, 7, b g Kutub (IRE)—Karalee (IRE) **T. J. Hemmings**
70 **KEENELAND (IRE)**, 7, b g Westerner—Delphinium (IRE) **Mr & Mrs Paul Rooney**
71 **KIE (IRE)**, 6, b g Old Vic—Asura (GER) **A. Stennett**
72 **KING'S GRACE**, 8, b g King's Theatre (IRE)—Beauchamp Grace **T. G. Leslie**
73 **KINGS BANDIT (IRE)**, 6, b g King's Theatre (IRE)—Gentle Lady (IRE) **Mrs D. L. Whateley**
74 **KITCHAPOLY (FR)**, 4, b g Poliglote—Kotkicha (FR) **Mr & Mrs Paul Rooney**
75 **KNOCKGRAFFON KING (IRE)**, 9, ch g Beneficial—Kilternan Gale **Hollyville Partnership**
76 **KOUP DE KANON (FR)**, 8, b g Robin des Pres (FR)—Coup de Sabre (FR) **M. J. Taylor**
77 **KRUZHLININ (GER)**, 7, ch g Sholokhov (IRE)—Karuma (GER) **Mr & Mrs Paul Rooney**
78 **LAIRD OF MONKSFORD (IRE)**, 5, b g Shantou (USA)—Back Log (IRE) **Mr & Mrs Paul Rooney**
79 **LEXI'S BOY (IRE)**, 6, gr g Verglas (IRE)—Jazan (IRE) **T. G. Leslie**

MR DONALD MCCAIN - Continued

80 **LIFE AND SOUL (IRE)**, 7, b g Azamour (IRE)—Way For Life (GER) **M. J. Taylor**
81 **LIVELY BARON (IRE)**, 9, b g Presenting—Greavesfind **T. J. Hemmings**
82 **LYRIC STREET (IRE)**, 6, b g Hurricane Run (IRE)—Elle Danzig (GER) **M. J. Taylor**
83 **MAJOR PARKES**, 4, gr g Fair Mix (IRE)—My Melody Parkes **J. Heler**
84 **MANSONIEN L'AS (FR)**, 8, b g Mansonnien (FR)—Star des As (FR) **Let's Live Racing**
85 **MASTER DEE (IRE)**, 5, b g King's Theatre (IRE)—Miss Lauren Dee (IRE) **Mr & Mrs Paul Rooney**
86 **MASTER RED (IRE)**, 5, b g Red Clubs (IRE)—Glory Days (GER) **Mr & Mrs Paul Rooney**
87 **MAWAQEET (USA)**, 5, b g Dynaformer (USA)—Lady Ilsley (USA) **Mr I. McAleavy**
88 **MOSS CLOUD (IRE)**, 7, b g Cloudings (IRE)—Adare Moss (IRE) **T. J. Hemmings**
89 **MR CHIPPY (IRE)**, 10, b g Laveron—Lady Denel (IRE) **Mr P. Holden**
90 **MR HOPEFUL (IRE)**, 5, b g Helissio (FR)—Lisadian Lady (IRE) **Essential Racing 3**
91 **MR SATCO (IRE)**, 6, b g Mr Combustible—Satlin (IRE)
92 **MULLIGAN'S MAN (IRE)**, 7, b g Morozov (USA)—Rashmulligan (IRE) **Deva Racing Fair Mix Partnership**
93 **NODFORM RICHARD**, 8, b g Groom Dancer (USA)—Shayzara (IRE) **D. M. Gorton**
94 **ORLITTLEBYLITTLE**, 8, b g Bollin Eric—Davana Blue (FR) **Deva Racing Bollin Eric Partnership**
95 **ORTOLAN (GER)**, 9, ch g Next Desert (IRE)—Optik (GER) **A. Stennett**
96 **OSCATARA (IRE)**, 7, b br g Oscar (IRE)—Nethertara **T. G. Leslie**
97 **OUR MICK**, 8, gr g Karinga Bay—Dawn's Della **K. Benson & Mrs E. Benson**
98 **OVERTURN (IRE)**, 10, b g Barathea (IRE)—Kristal Bridge **T. G. Leslie**
99 **PALERMO DON**, 4, b g Beat Hollow—Kristal Bridge **T. G. Leslie**
100 **PAMPANITO**, 8, b g Bollin Eric—Seamill (IRE) **Tim & Miranda Johnson**
101 **PEDDLERS CROSS (IRE)**, 9, b g Oscar (IRE)—Patscilla **T. G. Leslie**
102 **PLAN AGAIN (IRE)**, 7, b g Gamut (IRE)—Niamh's Leader (IRE) **Mr & Mrs Paul Rooney**
103 **POLARBROOK (IRE)**, 7, br g Alderbrook—Frozen Cello (IRE) **Lucky Bin Racing**
104 **PRINCE KHURRAM**, 4, b c Nayef (USA)—Saree (USA)
105 **RADIO NOWHERE (IRE)**, 6, b g Beneficial—Creidim (IRE) **Mr J. M. Glews**
106 **RAILWAY DILLON (IRE)**, 9, b g Witness Box (USA)—Laura's Native (IRE) **T W Johnson & G Maxwell**
107 **RAISE A SPARK**, 4, b g Multiplex—Reem Two **Mr R Pattison & Mr R Kent**
108 **REAL MILAN (IRE)**, 9, b g Milan—The Real Athlete (IRE) **Mrs D. L. Whateley**
109 **RED MERLIN (IRE)**, 9, ch g Soviet Star (USA)—Truly Bewitched (USA) **M. J. Taylor**
110 **RIGHT TO RULE (IRE)**, 5, b g Rock of Gibraltar (IRE)—Epistoliere (IRE) **Mr F. McAleavy**
111 **RIGUEZ DANCER**, 10, b g Dansili—Tricoteuse **Let's Live Racing**
112 **ROCKY STONE (IRE)**, 6, b g Cloudings (IRE)—Crandon Park **Penketh & Sankey Jech Racing Club**
113 **SACRED SQUARE (GER)**, 4, ch g Peintre Celebre (USA)—Square The Circle **Mr A. G. Bloom**
114 **SALTO CHISCO (IRE)**, 6, b g Presenting—Dato Fairy **Mrs D. L. Whateley**
115 4, Ch g Shantou (USA)—Sarah's Cottage (IRE) **Brannon Dick Hernon Matthewman**
116 **SEALOUS SCOUT (IRE)**, 6, b g Old Vic—Hirayna **T. G. Leslie**
117 **SHANTOU TIGER (IRE)**, 5, b g Shantou (USA)—Opus One **Deva Racing Shantou Partnership**
118 **SHE RANKS ME (IRE)**, 7, gr m Golan (IRE)—Rosealainn (IRE) **Roger O'Byrne**
119 **SHORT TAKES (USA)**, 6, ch g Lemon Drop Kid (USA)—Gabriellina Giof **Mr T. P. McMahon & Mr D. McMahon**
120 **SIGN MANUAL**, 9, b g Motivator—New Assembly (IRE) **Graham & Carole Worsley**
121 **SIR MANGAN (IRE)**, 6, b g Darsi (FR)—Lady Pep (IRE) **Mr F. McAleavy**
122 **SMADYNIUM (IRE)**, 6, gr g Smadoun (FR)—Sea Music (FR) **The Vacuum Pouch Company Limited**
123 **SPITFIRE ACE (IRE)**, 6, b g Zagreb (USA)—Coolafancy (IRE) **D & G Mercer**
124 **STAR IN FLIGHT**, 7, b g Mtoto—Star Entry **Lucky Bin Racing**
125 **STONEBROOK (IRE)**, 6, b g Flemensfirth (USA)—Boberelle (IRE) **Mr J. P. McManus**
126 **STORMING GALE (IRE)**, 8, b g Revoque (IRE)—Dikler Gale (IRE) **T. G. Leslie**
127 **SUD PACIFIQUE (IRE)**, 6, b g Montjeu (IRE)—Anestasia (IRE) **Mr A. G. Bloom**
128 **SUPER DUTY (IRE)**, 8, b g Shantou (USA)—Sarah's Cottage (IRE) **Brannon, Dick, Hernon & Holden**
129 **SUPREME ASSET (IRE)**, 6, b g Beneficial—Hollygrove Supreme (IRE) **Lucky Bin Racing**
130 **SWATOW TYPHOON (IRE)**, 7, b g Shantou (USA)—Oscar Leader (IRE) **Mr G. Fitzpatrick**
131 **SWIFT ARROW (IRE)**, 8, b g Overbury (IRE)—Clover Run (IRE) **Mrs A. E. Strang Steel**
132 **SYDNEY PAGET (IRE)**, 7, b g Flemensfirth (USA)—Shuil Aoibhinn (IRE) **Roger O'Byrne**
133 **TAKE THE CASH (IRE)**, 5, b g Cloudings (IRE)—Taking My Time (IRE) **T. J. Hemmings**
134 **TARLAN (IRE)**, 8, b g Milan—Nethertara **T. G. Leslie**
135 **THE BACKUP PLAN (IRE)**, 5, ch g Presenting—Jay Lo (IRE) **N.Y.P.D Racing**
136 **THE FLYING COLUMN (IRE)**, 8, b g Dr Massini (IRE)—Annie Cares (IRE) **Brannon, Dick, Hernon & Holden**
137 **THE LAST SAMURI (IRE)**, 6, ch g Flemensfirth (USA)—Howaboutthis (IRE) **Mr & Mrs Paul Rooney**
138 **THE WEATHERMAN (IRE)**, 7, b g Definite Article—Stateable Case (IRE) **Clwydian Connections**
139 **THEATRICAL STYLE (IRE)**, 5, b g Alhaarth (IRE)—Little Theatre (IRE) **Deva Racing Palladium Partnership**
140 **THIMAAR (USA)**, 6, b br g Dynaformer (USA)—Jinaan (USA) **Jon Glews, David Lockwood, Fred Lockwood**
141 **THREE FACES WEST (IRE)**, 6, b g Dr Massini (IRE)—Ardnataggle (IRE) **Mr & Mrs Paul Rooney**
142 **TONVADOSA**, 6, b m Flemensfirth (USA)—Sleepless Eye **T Meehan & D J Burke**
143 **TORNADO BOB (IRE)**, 9, b br g Bob Back (USA)—Double Glazed (IRE) **Mrs D. L. Whateley**
144 **TOUR D'ARGENT (FR)**, 7, b g Martaline—Keep Well (FR) **Mr & Mrs Paul Rooney**

MR DONALD MCCAIN - Continued

145 **TREND IS MY FRIEND (USA)**, 5, b br g Lemon Drop Kid (USA)—Silva (FR) **T Leslie & D Gorton**
146 **UBALTIQUE (FR)**, 6, b g Balko (FR)—Ode Antique (FR) **T. G. Leslie**
147 **UNCLE MONTY (IRE)**, 5, b g Milan—She's A Gamble (IRE) **Clwydian International**
148 **UP AND GO (FR)**, 6, ch g Martaline—Santoria (FR) **T. G. Leslie**
149 **UPPERCUT DE L'ORNE (FR)**, 6, ch g Kapgarde (FR)—Murcie (FR) **Mr & Mrs Paul Rooney**
150 **UPPERTOWN CAVE (IRE)**, 5, b g Court Cave (IRE)—Newtown Charlie (IRE) **Mr & Mrs Paul Rooney**
151 **VALLEYOFMILAN (IRE)**, 7, b g Milan—Ikdam Valley (IRE) **Tim & Miranda Johnson**
152 **VASCO PIERJI (FR)**, 5, b g Sleeping Car (FR)—Angelina (FR) **Tim Johnson & Donald McCain**
153 **VELOCE (IRE)**, 6, b g Hurricane Run (IRE)—Kiftsgate Rose (FR) **Axom XL**
154 **VERDASCO (FR)**, 5, b g Sassanian (USA)—Babolna (FR) **Deva Racing Festival Partnership**
155 **VINSTAR (FR)**, 5, b g Charming Groom (FR)—Kali Star (FR) **T. G. Leslie**
156 **VOLCANIC (FR)**, 5, b br g Al Namix (FR)—Queen of Rock (FR) **Elite Racing Club**
157 **WELSH BARD (IRE)**, 5, ch g Dylan Thomas (IRE)—Delphinium (IRE) **George Tobitt & Richard Gurney**
158 **WHISKEY CHASER (IRE)**, 6, br g Flemensfirth (USA)—
                                    Cregane Lass (IRE) **Deva Racing Flemensfirth Partnership**
159 **WILCOS MO CHARA (IRE)**, 6, b g Oscar (IRE)—She's A Venture (IRE) **A&K Ecofilm Ltd**
160 **WILD CARD**, 7, b g First Trump—Vanina II (FR) **Mr J. C. Heron**
161 **WITNESS IN COURT (IRE)**, 7, b g Witness Box (USA)—Inter Alia (IRE) **T. G. Leslie**
162 **ZIGGIE (IRE)**, 7, b g Dilshaan—Like A Caterpillar (IRE) **Mr M. W. Sanders**
163 **ZIP WIRE (IRE)**, 5, b g Oratorio (IRE)—Jaya (USA) **M. J. Taylor**

Other Owners: Mr J. E. Abbey, Mr Stewart Andrew, Axom, Mr M. Ball, Mr Andrew Barr, Mr J. M. Basquill, Mr M. Basquill, Mr K. Benson, Mrs E. Benson, Mr Andrew Brannon, Mr D. J. Burke, Mr Mick Burrowes, Mr P. A. Cafferty, Mr G. Caine, Mr Michael J. Campbell, Mr Anthony Coyne, Mr K. Coyne, Mr Alec Craig, Mr Phil Cunningham, Mr Andrew Dick, Mr Dan Downie, Mr W. A. Eastup, Mr M. Foster, Mrs J. Foster, Mr L. R. Frampton, Mr J. Fyffe, Mr Jon Glews, Mr D. Gorton, Mr Julian Gouder, Mr Dermot Hanafin, Mr Tony Hill, Mr Philip Holden, Mr Tim Johnson, Mrs Miranda Johnson, Mr G. L. Joynson, Mr S. A. Kaznowski, Mrs Kay Kent, Mr R. Kent, Mr Steve Kent, Mr T. G. Leslie, Mr Brendan Madden, Mr George Maxwell, Mr Ian McAleavy, Mr D. McCain Jnr, Mr Stewart McDonald, Mr D. McMahon, Mr T. P. McMahon, Mr Tony Meehan, Mr D. C. Mercer, Mr Grant Mercer, Mr D. Moyes, Miss M. Noden, Mr Ray Pattison, Mr David Reilly, Mrs Candice Reilly, Mr John Reynard, Mr Brendan Richardson, Mr B. Robbins, Mr P. A. Rooney, Mrs C. Rooney, Mr J. Shaw, Mrs Lynne Stuart, Mr Matthew Taylor, Mr G. Thomson, Mr Damian Tiernan, Mr F. Towey, Mr K. Towey, Mr S. Trevor, Mr Ken Viney, Mr Neil Watt, Mr G. Wills, Mr S. Wilson, Mr Graham Worsley, Mrs Carole Worsley.

Assistant Trainer: Adrian Lane

Jockey (NH): Jason Maguire, Henry Brooke, Adrian Lane. **Conditional:** James Cowley, Nick Slatter.

---

419 **MR TIM MCCARTHY, Godstone**
Postal: **Nags Hall Farm, Oxted Road, Godstone, Surrey, RH9 8DB**
Contacts: **PHONE (01883) 740379 FAX (01883) 740381 MOBILE (07887) 763062**

1 **CAVALRY GUARD (USA)**, 10, ch g Officer (USA)—Leeward City (USA) **Surrey Racing Club**
2 **GHOST TRAIN (IRE)**, 5, b g Holy Roman Emperor (IRE)—Adrastea (IRE) **Surrey Racing Club**
3 **JIMMY RYAN (IRE)**, 13, b g Orpen (USA)—Kaysama (FR) **Mrs C. V. McCarthy**
4 **RUN RABBIT RUN**, 6, b g Hurricane Run (IRE)—Triple Gold (IRE) **A. D. Spence**
5 **UNDERSTORY (USA)**, 7, b g Forestry (USA)—Sha Tha (USA) **Homecroft Wealth Racing**

THREE-YEAR-OLDS
6 **RUN FOR HOME**, bl g Kheleyf (USA)—Dodona **A. D. Spence**

Other Owners: T. D. McCarthy, S. J. Piper, Mr N. Pogmore.

Assistant Trainer: Mrs C.V. McCarthy

---

420 **MISS DANIELLE MCCORMICK, Westhead**
Postal: **Brookfields, Charity Lane, Westhead, Ormskirk, Lancashire, L40 6LG**
Contacts: **PHONE (01695) 579334 MOBILE (07590) 513752**
E-MAIL danielle-mccormick@hotmail.co.uk

1 **AMELIA JAY**, 4, b f Avonbridge—Rainbow Spectrum (FR) **M. R. Johnson**
2 **BALLINARGH GIRL (IRE)**, 6, b m Footstepsinthesand—Rack And Ruin (IRE) **M. R. Johnson**
3 **LAUDATION**, 4, b g Royal Applause—Calamanco **M. R. Johnson**

MISS DANIELLE MCCORMICK - Continued

4 **LORD WESTHEAD (IRE)**, 5, b g Bach (IRE)—Dawning Day (IRE) **M. R. Johnson**
5 **MILLIE N AIRE**, 4, b f Multiplex—Hillside Girl (IRE) **M. R. Johnson**

Amateur: Miss A. McCormick.

---

421 MR PHIL MCENTEE, Newmarket

Postal: **Racefield Stables, Carriageway, Hamilton Road, Newmarket, Suffolk, CB8 7JQ**
Contacts: **PHONE (01638) 662092 FAX (01638) 662092 MOBILE (07802) 663256**

1 **ISHIAMIRACLE**, 5, ch m Ishiguru (USA)—Sukuma (IRE) **Mrs R. L. McEntee**
2 **JONNIE SKULL (IRE)**, 8, b g Pyrus (USA)—Sovereign Touch (IRE) **Eventmaker Racehorses**
3 **MINIMEE**, 4, b g Dubai Destination (USA)—Malaaq **Eventmaker Racehorses**
4 **MOVES LIKE JAGGER (IRE)**, 4, b g Danehill Dancer (IRE)—Lucky Spin **Eventmaker Racehorses**
5 **PRINCESS BOUNTY**, 4, b f Bahamian Bounty—Regal Magic (IRE) **Mr S. Jakes**
6 **PUTIN (IRE)**, 6, b g Fasliyev (USA)—Consignia (IRE) **Mr S. Jakes**
7 **SILK SKY**, 8, ch m Shahrastani (USA)—Insulate **Mr S. J. March**
8 **SWISS CROSS**, 7, b g Cape Cross (IRE)—Swiss Lake (USA) **Mr S. Jakes**
9 **THE BLUE DOG (IRE)**, 7, b m High Chaparral (IRE)—Jules (IRE) **Mr R. W. Carson**
10 **TORNADO BATTLE**, 4, b g War Chant (USA)—Child Bride (USA) **Mr S. Jakes**
11 **TOYMAKER**, 7, b g Starcraft (NZ)—Eurolink Raindance (IRE) **Eventmaker Racehorses**
12 **TWO NO BIDS (IRE)**, 8, b br g Footstepsinthesand—Milwaukee (FR) **Eventmaker Racehorses**

THREE-YEAR-OLDS

13 **BLACK VALE (IRE)**, b g Moss Vale (IRE)—Limit (IRE) **Mrs R. L. McEntee**
14 **FLYING AUTHOR (IRE)**, b g Authorized (IRE)—Fly Free **Mr S. Jakes**

Other Owners: Mr M. A. Humphris, T. D. Johnson.

---

422 MR MURTY MCGRATH, Maidstone

Postal: **Spicketts House, Kiln Barn Road, East Malling, Kent, ME19 6BJ**
Contacts: **PHONE (01732) 840173 MOBILE (07818) 098073**
E-MAIL mjmcgrath@hotmail.com

1 **FINLODEX**, 7, ch g Pastoral Pursuits—Ela Aphrodite **Mr R. P. Gallagher**
2 **KENT RAGSTONE (USA)**, 5, ch g Stonesider (USA)—Sweet Charity (USA) **Gallagher Equine Ltd**
3 **REZWAAN**, 7, b g Alhaarth (IRE)—Nasij (USA) **Gallagher Equine Ltd**
4 **SALAM ALAYKUM (IRE)**, 6, b g Galileo (IRE)—Alicia (IRE) **Gallagher Equine Ltd**

Assistant Trainer: Heidi McGrath

Jockey (flat): Shane Kelly. **Jockey (NH):** Timmy Murphy.

---

423 MRS JEAN MCGREGOR, Milnathort

Postal: **Wester Tillyrie Steading, Tillyrie, Milnathort, Kinross, KY13 0RW**
Contacts: **PHONE (01577) 861792 MOBILE (07764) 464299**
E-MAIL purebred68@hotmail.co.uk

1 **ASKALOTT (IRE)**, 9, b g Ashkalani (IRE)—Alottalady (IRE) **Miss A. L. McGregor**
2 5, B g Desideratum—Blue Morning
3 **CIGALAS**, 9, ch g Selkirk (USA)—Langoustine (AUS) **Tillyrie Racing Club**
4 **JACKOFHEARTS**, 6, b g Beat Hollow—Boutique **Mr S. Taylor**
5 6, B g Rambling Bear—Lingham Bridesmaid
6 **NELSON DU RONCERAY (FR)**, 13, b g Lute Antique (FR)—Trieste (FR) **Miss A. L. McGregor**
7 **SNOOZE N YOU LOSE**, 9, b g Helissio (FR)—Utmost (IRE) **The Good To Soft Firm**
8 **THEHOODLUM**, 7, b g Fraam—Trilby **Tillyrie Racing Club**
9 **WATERSKI**, 13, b g Petoski—Celtic Waters **Mrs D. Thomson**

Other Owners: Mr Scott Burnett, Mrs Jean McGregor, Miss A. H. McGregor, Mr G Newstead, Mr M O'Conner, Mrs Dorothy Thomson, Mr John Thomson.

Jockey (flat): Andrew Mullen. **Jockey (NH):** Adrian Lane. **Conditional:** Jonathan England, John Kington.
Amateur: Miss A.L. McGregor.

424 MS KAREN MCLINTOCK, Newcastle-Upon-Tyne

Postal: The Byerley Stud, Ingoe, Newcastle-Upon-Tyne NE20 0SZ
Contacts: PHONE (01661) 886356 FAX (01661) 886356 MOBILE (07966) 776710
E-MAIL karen.mclintock@equiname.co.uk WEBSITE www.karenmclintock.co.uk

1 ANOTHER BYGONES (IRE), 5, b g High-Rise (IRE)—Little Chartridge **Mr A. C. Lamont**
2 BYGONES OF BRID (IRE), 11, b g Alderbrook—Glenadore **J. R. Callow**
3 CARLITO BRIGANTE (IRE), 8, b g Haafhd—Desert Magic (IRE) **06 Zoo Ltd**
4 COUSIN GUILLAUME (FR), 5, b g Kapgarde (FR)—Tante Zoe (FR) **Mr A. C. Lamont**
5 DEVENISH ISLAND, 5, b g Multiplex—Wahiba Reason (IRE) **Mrs A. M. O'Sullivan**
6 GURKHA BRAVE (IRE), 6, b g Old Vic—Honeyed (IRE) **Mr A. C. Lamont**
7 4, B g Zerpour (IRE)—Leachestown (IRE) **06 Zoo Ltd**
8 MASON HINDMARSH, 7, ch g Dr Fong (USA)—Sierra Virgen (USA) **B. Chicken**
9 NORTHERN EXECUTIVE (IRE), 6, b g Milan—Letterwoman (IRE) **Mr A. C. Lamont**
10 4, Ch g Sakhee (USA)—Pochard **06 Zoo Ltd**
11 5, B g Old Vic—Raphuca (IRE) **06 Zoo Ltd**
12 ULTIÉP (FR), 6, gr g Ragmar (FR)—Naltiepy (FR) **Mr A. C. Lamont**

TWO-YEAR-OLDS

13 B br c 22/3 Rip Van Winkle (IRE)—Sinister Ruckus (USA) (Trippi (USA)) (70000) **Mr G. R. Stockdale**

Other Owners: Mr D. Eddy, Equiname Ltd.

Assistant Trainer: Donald Eddy

425 MR ED MCMAHON, Lichfield

Postal: Horsley Brook Farm, Tamworth Road, Lichfield, Staffordshire, WS14 9PT
Contacts: PHONE (01543) 481224 FAX (01543) 651100 MOBILE (07787) 951630
E-MAIL comeracing@horsleybrook.fsnet.co.uk WEBSITE www.edmcmahonracing.co.uk

1 ANGELITO, 5, ch g Primo Valentino (IRE)—Supreme Angel **Least Moved Partners**
2 ARLECCHINO (IRE), 4, b g Hernando (FR)—Trullitti (IRE) **The LAM Partnership**
3 ARTISTIC JEWEL (IRE), 5, ch m Excellent Art—Danish Gem **Mrs A. D. Bedding**
4 COLOUR MY WORLD, 4, gr g With Approval (CAN)—Nadeszhda **Mr P. A. Wilkins**
5 DELICIOUS PATRICA, 5, b m Multiplex—Cerulean Rose **Mr J. Loftus**
6 DUSTY STORM (IRE), 4, ch f Kyllachy—Halliwell House **Mrs A. D. Bedding**
7 EMJAYEM, 4, ch g Needwood Blade—Distant Stars (IRE) **Mrs J. McMahon**
8 FLIRTINASKIRT, 4, b f Avonbridge—Talampaya (USA) **Mr P. A. Wilkins**
9 INVINCIBLE LAD (IRE), 10, b g Invincible Spirit (IRE)—Lady Ellen **Mr G. E. French**
10 NOBLE STORM (USA), 8, b h Yankee Gentleman (USA)—Changed Tune (USA) **Mrs A. D. Bedding**
11 PASSIONADA, 5, b br m Avonbridge—Lark In The Park (IRE) **Mia Racing**
12 ROSA LOCKWOOD, 5, b m Needwood Blade—Star of Flanders **Mr J. Loftus**
13 SAKHEE'S ROSE, 4, b f Sakhee's Secret—Isobel Rose (IRE) **Mr J. R. Dwyer**
14 SECRET LOOK, 4, ch g Sakhee's Secret—Look Here's Carol (IRE) **S. L. Edwards**
15 SECRETINTHEPARK, 4, ch g Sakhee's Secret—Lark In The Park (IRE) **Mia Racing**
16 WINNING EXPRESS (IRE), 4, gr f Camacho—Lady Fabiola (USA) **Milton Express Limited**

THREE-YEAR-OLDS

17 AEOLUS, b c Araafa (IRE)—Bright Moll **A. R. F. Buxton**
18 AGE OF DISCOVERY, b c Nayef (USA)—Magic Tree (UAE) **The LAM Partnership**
19 Ch f Dutch Art—All Smiles **Mrs P. J. Toye**
20 ARCHIBALD THORBURN (IRE), br g Duke of Marmalade (IRE)—Winged Harriet (IRE) **Mr R. Allcock**
21 EXPRESS HIMSELF (IRE), b c Dylan Thomas (IRE)—Lightwood Lady (IRE) **Milton Express Limited**
22 B f Firebreak—Fisher Island (IRE)
23 GOLD CLASS, ch g Firebreak—Silken Dalliance **The C H F Partnership**
24 GOLD CLUB, b g Multiplex—Oceana Blue **The C H F Partnership**
25 INCITING INCIDENT (IRE), b g Camacho—Halliwell House **The W.H.O. Society**
26 Ch g Kyllachy—Look Here's Carol (IRE) **S. L. Edwards**
27 THREE PIPS, b c Captain Gerrard (IRE)—Samadilla (IRE) **Whittle, Kent & Lees-Jones**
28 WHERE THE BOYS ARE (IRE), b f Dylan Thomas (IRE)—Promise of Love **Mr P. A. Wilkins**

TWO-YEAR-OLDS

29 LET RIGHT BE DONE, gr c 6/2 Lawman (FR)—Cheerfully (Sadler's Wells (USA)) **The LAM Partnership**
30 B c 1/4 Sakhee's Secret—Look Here's Dee (Dansili) **S. L. Edwards**

MR ED MCMAHON - Continued

31 B f 14/5 Bertolini (USA)—Muara (Wolfhound (USA))
32 B f 4/4 Assertive—Noor El Houdah (IRE) (Fayruz) (13333)
33 B c 22/2 Pastoral Pursuits—Oceana Blue (Reel Buddy (USA)) **Unregistered Partnership**
34 Gr c 12/2 Royal Applause—Secret Night (Dansili) (37000) **J. C. Fretwell**
35 B c 17/1 Firebreak—She Mystifies (Indesatchel (IRE)) (35000) **J. C. Fretwell**
36 B c 20/3 Cockney Rebel (IRE)—Silken Dalliance (Rambo Dancer (CAN)) **Unregistered Partnership**

Other Owners: K. H. Fischer, C. H. Fischer, Dr M. F. Ford, R. Kent, Mrs A. M. Lees-Jones, Mr M. McGuinness, E. S. A. McMahon, Ms L. M. Mulcahy, F. G. Poingdestre, Mr D. Thomas, M. A. Tickle, A. Tickle, Mrs I. M. Tickle, W. T. Whittle.

Assistant Trainer: Bryan Arthur McMahon

---

426 **MR GRAEME MCPHERSON, Stow-On-The-Wold**
Postal: **Martins Hill, Bledington Road, Stow-On-The-Wold, Gloucestershire, GL54 1JH**
Contacts: **PHONE (01451) 830769 MOBILE (07815) 887360**
WEBSITE www.mcphersonracing.co.uk

1 BOBBIE MAGERN, 9, b g Alderbrook—Outfield **Exors of the Late Mr R. Nicholls**
2 CANADIAN DREAMER (IRE), 7, b g Westerner—Ride The Tide (IRE) **The Martins Hill Racing Partnership**
3 CHERRY TIGER, 4, b g Tiger Hill (IRE)—Lolla's Spirit (IRE) **Ms S. A. Howell**
4 CITRUS MARK, 9, b g Mark of Esteem (IRE)—Lemon's Mill (USA) **G. McPherson**
5 CLARION CALL, 6, b g Beat Hollow—Fanfare **The Maugersbury Racegoers**
6 COCACOBANA (IRE), 9, ch g Snurge—Dun Dun (IRE) **Mr R. Dodney**
7 DAISIE CUTTER, 4, b f Tobougg (IRE)—Bowled Out (GER) **G. McPherson**
8 DO BE DASHING, 6, b m Doyen (IRE)—Be Brave (FR) **Mr J. Fildes**
9 EVERVESCENT (IRE), 5, b g Elnadim (USA)—Purepleasureseeker (IRE) **Ever Equine**
10 FLYING LIGHT (IRE), 8, b g Chevalier (IRE)—Light-Flight (IRE)
11 GLACIAL ROCK (IRE), 8, b g Sonus (IRE)—Glacial Princess (IRE) **Mr M. Bell**
12 GREAT VALUE (IRE), 9, b g Revoque (IRE)—Dame de L'oise (USA) **The Martins Hill Racing Partnership**
13 HARRY HUNT, 7, b g Bertolini (USA)—Qasirah (IRE) **Arion Racing**
14 HOLLYWOOD ALL STAR (IRE), 5, b g Kheleyf (USA)—Camassina (IRE) **G. McPherson**
15 KAYF BLANCO, 5, b g Kayf Tara—Land of Glory **Mrs L Day & Mr H Burdett**
16 KILCREA ASLA (IRE), 13, b g Oscar (IRE)—Alottalady (IRE) **Mrs L. Day**
17 MIDNIGHT GEM, 4, b f Midnight Legend—Barton Flower
18 5, B g Needle Gun (IRE)—Miss Millbrook
19 NOMADIC STORM, 8, b g Nomadic Way (USA)—Cateel Bay **Mrs V. Williams**
20 OUR MAIMIE (IRE), 8, b m Luso—Cormac Lady (IRE) **G. McPherson**
21 PANDY WELLS, 5, b m Kayf Tara—Alina Rheinberg (GER) **Mike & Linda Paul**
22 POLO SPRINGS, 7, gr m Baryshnikov (AUS)—Cristal Springs **Denarius Consulting Ltd**
23 PYRSHAN (IRE), 5, b g Pyrus (USA)—Runshangale (IRE)
24 RED ADMIRABLE (IRE), 8, b g Shantou (USA)—Eimears Pet (IRE) **Wildcat Syndicate**
25 SHADY GLEN (IRE), 5, br g Dr Massini (IRE)—Poppins (IRE)
26 SOCIETY SHARES (IRE), 9, ch g Moscow Society (USA)—Presenting Shares (IRE) **Arion Racing**
27 5, B m Erhaab (USA)—Solid Land (FR) **G. McPherson**
28 SPECIAL VINTAGE, 8, br g Grape Tree Road—Special Beat **G. McPherson**
29 5, B g Royal Anthem (USA)—Supreme Baloo (IRE)
30 5, B m Exit To Nowhere (USA)—Sweet Empire (USA) **G. McPherson**
31 TEACHMETOBOUGGIE, 4, ch g Tobougg (IRE)—Teachmetotango **G. McPherson**
32 5, B m Kayf Tara—Teachmetotango
33 THE GOOD GUY (IRE), 11, b g Lord Americo—Lady Farnham (IRE) **The Martins Hill Racing Partnership**
34 TICKATACK (IRE), 9, gr g Tikkanen (USA)—Theflyingcannister (IRE) **Andy Weller & The Drummers**
35 TIMESISHARD (IRE), 7, b g Misternando—Smokey Flavour (IRE) **Mr J. Chamberlain**
36 TITANS APPROACH (IRE), 5, b g High Chaparral (IRE)—Armelles Approach (IRE)
37 TRILLERIN MINELLA (IRE), 6, b g King's Theatre (IRE)—Eva Fay (IRE) **Mrs L. Day**
38 WERENEARLYOUTOFIT (IRE), 6, b g Asian Heights—Ballerina Laura (IRE) **The Ladies Of Martins Hill**
39 ZANIR (FR), 10, b g Munir—Shahmy (USA) **Mrs L. Day**

Other Owners: Mr S. Barnes, Mr H. Burdett, K. R. Elliott, Mr R. J. P. Gilmore, Mr I. J. B. Gray, Mrs S. Mattle, Mrs S. M. McPherson, Mr M. R. Paul, Mrs L. C. Paul, Mr G. J. Styles, Mr A. J. Weller.

Assistant Trainers: Mick Finn, Jodie Mogford

Jockey (NH): Wayne Hutchinson. **Conditional:** Ollie Garner, Killian Moore.

427 MR MARTYN MEADE, Newmarket
Postal: **Sefton Lodge, Bury Road, Newmarket, CB8 7BT**
Contacts: **PHONE (01638) 664435 MOBILE (07879) 891811**
E-MAIL lburgoyne@martynmeaderacing.com WEBSITE www.martynmeaderacing.com

1 DAMBUSTER (IRE), 4, b g Dalakhani (IRE)—Threefold (USA) **Ladyswood Stud**
2 GLANELY (IRE), 4, b g Exceed And Excel (AUS)—Bon Ton Roulet **Ladyswood Stud**
3 SQUIRE OSBALDESTON (IRE), 4, b c Mr Greeley (USA)—Kushnarenkovo **P. Hickman & Mr G. Johns**
4 ZARLIMAN (IRE), 4, ch c Zamindar (USA)—Zarlana (IRE) **Ladyswood Stud**

THREE-YEAR-OLDS
5 ALDERLEY, b f Three Valleys (USA)—Doctor's Note **Ladyswood Stud**
6 ARRANGER (IRE), gr f Bushranger (IRE)—El Morocco (USA) **Ladyswood Stud**
7 GANGSTER SQUAD (FR), b f Astronomer Royal (USA)—Cobblestone Road (USA) **Ladyswood Stud**
8 LEGEND RISING (IRE), ch c Tamayuz—Encouragement **Ladyswood Stud**
9 PROPHETS THUMB (IRE), b c Fastnet Rock (AUS)—Holly Blue **P. Hickman & Mr G. Johns**
10 RINGS OF SATURN (IRE), b g Galileo (IRE)—Hveger (AUS) **P. Hickman & Mr G. Johns**
11 VENEZIA (IRE), gr c Galileo (IRE)—St Roch (IRE) **P. Hickman & Mr G. Johns**

TWO-YEAR-OLDS
12 B f 18/2 Zebedee—Bazelle (Ashkalani (IRE)) (5000)
13 B f 17/3 Azamour (IRE)—Bold Assumption (Observatory (USA)) (12388) **Ladyswood Stud**
14 Ch c 4/4 Bahamian Bounty—Celestial Princess (Observatory (USA)) (19357) **Ladyswood Stud**
15 B c 16/3 Multiplex—Cherry Belle (IRE) (Red Ransom (USA)) (10000)
16 B f 24/2 Footstepsinthesand—Chica Whopa (IRE) (Oasis Dream) (8517) **Ladyswood Stud**
17 B f 8/4 Fast Company (IRE)—Consensus (IRE) (Common Grounds) (23228) **Ladyswood Stud**
18 Ch c 29/4 Paco Boy (IRE)—Cruinn A Bhord (Inchinor) (10000)
19 **DARMA (IRE),** b f 24/2 Acclamation—Dark Dancer (FR) (Danehill (USA)) (22454) **Ladyswood Stud**
20 Ch c 11/5 Halling (USA)—Dawnus (IRE) (Night Shift (USA)) (26000)
21 Ch c 12/4 Kyllachy—Descriptive (IRE) (Desert King (IRE)) **Mr D. A. Farrington**
22 B c 12/3 Pastoral Pursuits—Doctor's Note (Pursuit of Love) (11000)
23 B c 29/3 Iffraaj—Dorothy Dene (Red Ransom (USA)) (18582) **Ladyswood Stud**
24 **FLIGAZ (FR),** ch f 11/4 Panis (USA)—Fligane (FR) (Bering) (6194)
25 Ch f 20/4 Thousand Words—Ide Say (IRE) (Grand Lodge (USA)) (5806)
26 Ch c 30/3 Kyllachy—Lady Broughton (IRE) (Grand Lodge (USA)) (5000)
27 B f 23/1 Strategic Prince—Leopard Creek (Weldnaas (USA)) (7742)
28 Br f 7/2 Yeats (IRE)—Little Empress (IRE) (Holy Roman Emperor (IRE)) (3000)
29 B c 10/4 Makfi—Lure of The Moon (USA) (Lure (USA)) (18582) **Ladyswood Stud**
30 B f 9/3 Bushranger (IRE)—Masela (IRE) (Medicean) (5420) **Ladyswood Stud**
31 **MISS JONH (FR),** ch f 13/4 Deportivo—Flower (Zamindar (USA)) (6968)
32 B br f 27/1 Astronomer Royal (USA)—Miss Possibility (USA) (Chimes Band (USA)) (12388)
33 B f 29/4 Bushranger (IRE)—Miznapp (Pennekamp (USA)) (19000) **Mr D. A. Farrington**
34 MYSTERIOUS STAR (FR), b c 29/3 Iron Mask (USA)—Red Star (USA) (Lure (USA)) (7742)
35 MYSTICAL SPIRIT (FR), ch c 14/4 Spirit One (FR)—Miss Maguilove (FR) (Dyhim Diamond (IRE)) (9291)
36 B f 6/2 Kyllachy—Pulsate (Inchinor) (6194) **Ladyswood Stud**
37 B c 7/2 Indesatchel (IRE)—Rosabee (IRE) (No Excuse Needed) (3000)
38 B c 18/2 Le Cadre Noir (IRE)—Social Upheaval (USA) (Twilight Agenda (USA)) (18582)
39 B f 24/2 Compton Place—Stella Manuela (FR) (Galileo (IRE)) (13000)
40 B c 31/3 Le Cadre Noir (IRE)—Tarrifa (IRE) (Mujtahid (USA)) (4645)
41 B br c 23/3 Vale of York (IRE)—Telesina (ITY) (Marju (IRE)) (6194)
42 B c 24/4 Elusive City (USA)—Testama (FR) (Testa Rossa (AUS)) (36391)

Other Owners: Mr P. J. Hickman, Mr G. C. Johns.

Assistant Trainer: Michael Marshall

428 MR NOEL MEADE, Navan
Postal: **Tu Va Stables, Castletown-Kilpatrick, Navan, Co. Meath, Ireland**
Contacts: **PHONE (00 353) 46 905 4197 FAX (00 353) 46 905 4459 MOBILE (00 353) 87 256 6039**
E-MAIL tuvastables@eircom.net WEBSITE www.noelmeade.com

1 AENGUS (IRE), 4, b g Robin des Champs (FR)—Which Thistle (IRE)
2 ALLY CASCADE (IRE), 6, b g Golan (IRE)—Nikkis Alstar (IRE)
3 ANGE BALAFRE (FR), 5, b g Ange Gabriel (FR)—Balafre Rose (FR)

MR NOEL MEADE - Continued

4 **ANGE BLANC (FR)**, 6, gr g Keltos (FR)—Trasimene
5 **ANOTHER PALM (IRE)**, 9, gr g Great Palm (USA)—Park Rose (IRE)
6 **APACHE STRONGHOLD (IRE)**, 6, b g Milan—First Battle (IRE)
7 4, B f Flemensfirth (USA)—Atomic Winner (IRE)
8 **AVIDIUS CASSIUS (IRE)**, 6, b g Flemensfirth (USA)—Rixdale (FR)
9 **BAROSSA PEARL (IRE)**, 4, b f Milan—What An Answer (IRE)
10 **BENEMEADE (IRE)**, 6, b g Beneficial—Millicent Bridge (IRE)
11 **BLISSFUL MOMENT (USA)**, 7, b br g Dynaformer (USA)—Arabian Spell (IRE)
12 **BONNY KATE (IRE)**, 4, ch f Beneficial—Peppardstown (IRE)
13 **BOSE IKARD (IRE)**, 6, b g Brian Boru—Dolldyedee (IRE)
14 **BUSTY BROWN (IRE)**, 8, b g Mr Combustible—Misty Brown (IRE)
15 **CHAMPOLEON (FR)**, 4, gr g Turtle Bowl (IRE)—Trasimene
16 **CHANCOL (FR)**, 5, b br g Vangelis (USA)—Boreale (FR)
17 **CHRISSIE MC (IRE)**, 5, b m Oscar (IRE)—They Call Me Molly (CAN)
18 **CORSKEAGH ROYALE (IRE)**, 11, ch g Beneficial—Rubys Shadow (IRE)
19 **COULEUR FRANCE (IRE)**, 6, b g Flemensfirth (USA)—Gaye Mercy
20 **CROSS APPEAL (IRE)**, 8, b g Cape Cross (IRE)—Hadeb
21 **CURLEY BILL (IRE)**, 6, b g Heron Island (IRE)—In Excelsis (GER)
22 **DAN BOGAN (IRE)**, 5, b g Windsor Knot (IRE)—Housekeeping
23 **DIDNTITELLYA (IRE)**, 5, b g Presenting—Beauty Star (IRE)
24 **FESTIVE FELON (IRE)**, 7, b g Gold Well—Takara (IRE)
25 **FISHER BRIDGE (IRE)**, 11, ch g Singspiel (IRE)—Kristal Bridge
26 **FLINDERS RIVER (IRE)**, 6, ch g Traditionally—Silver Tassie (FR)
27 **FORMIDABLEOPPONENT (IRE)**, 7, b g Arakan (USA)—Sliding
28 **GAIUS MARIUS (IRE)**, 6, b g Tiger Hill (IRE)—Russian Muse (FR)
29 **GLENMOREANGIE (IRE)**, 5, b g Scorpion (IRE)—Sister Swing
30 **HARVEY LOGAN (IRE)**, 5, b g Saffron Walden (FR)—Baie Barbara (IRE)
31 **HECK THOMAS (IRE)**, 6, b g Oscar (IRE)—Good Heighway (IRE)
32 **HONOURABLE EMPEROR (IRE)**, 5, b g Holy Roman Emperor (IRE)—Belle of Honour (USA)
33 **IKE CLANTON (IRE)**, 5, b g Heron Island (IRE)—Shbrook (IRE)
34 **IL FENOMENO (ITY)**, 8, b g Denon (USA)—Fabulous Charm (ITY)
35 **IPSOS DU BERLAIS (FR)**, 8, gr g Poliglote—Isis Du Berlais (FR)
36 **JACK SLADE (IRE)**, 4, ch g Stowaway—Sharps Express (IRE)
37 **JOHANNISBERGER (IRE)**, 7, b g Arakan (USA)—Housekeeping
38 **KILLEENMORE (IRE)**, 11, b g Flemensfirth (USA)—Clever Move (IRE)
39 **KILLER MILLER (IRE)**, 5, b g Flemensfirth (USA)—Miss Brandywell (IRE)
40 **LITTLEMISSSTUBBORN (IRE)**, 5, b m Heron Island (IRE)—Unabhan (IRE)
41 4, B g Kalanisi (IRE)—Littleton Liberty
42 **LONDON BRIDGE**, 8, br g Beat Hollow—Cantanta
43 4, B f Kalanisi (IRE)—Maggies Oscar (IRE)
44 **MAXIM GORKY (IRE)**, 7, b g Montjeu (IRE)—Altruiste (USA)
45 4, B g Kalanisi (IRE)—Mill Lady (IRE)
46 **MILT YARBERRY**, 5, b g Librettist (USA)—Polar Storm (IRE)
47 4, B g Kalanisi (IRE)—Miss Twinkletoes (IRE)
48 **MONKSLAND (IRE)**, 7, b g Beneficial—Cush Jewel (IRE)
49 **MULLAGHANOE RIVER (IRE)**, 6, b g Beneficial—Wahiba Hall (IRE)
50 4, Br f Arcadio (GER)—Musicienne (IRE)
51 **NAILED ON (IRE)**, 5, b g Milan—Pebble Hill (IRE)
52 **NED BUNTLINE**, 6, b g Refuse To Bend (IRE)—Intrum Morshaan (IRE)
53 **ON YOUR EOIN (IRE)**, 7, b g Brian Boru—Spring Lake (IRE)
54 **ORIGINAL OPTION (IRE)**, 9, br g Anshan—Deepest Thoughts (IRE)
55 **OUTLAWED TUNES (IRE)**, 7, br g Lord Americo—Thousand Springs (IRE)
56 **PANDORAMA (IRE)**, 11, b g Flemensfirth (USA)—Gretchen's Castle (IRE)
57 **PAT GARRETT (IRE)**, 7, b g Fruits of Love (USA)—Junga Connection
58 **PERFECT SMILE (IRE)**, 9, b br g Anshan—Mambo Music (FR)
59 **PLEASE TALK (IRE)**, 8, b g Beneficial—Fresh Partner (IRE)
60 **POWDER HOUND**, 4, b g Lucarno (USA)—Balnaha
61 **PRIMA VISTA**, 9, b g Singspiel (IRE)—Papering (IRE)
62 **PROTARAS (USA)**, 7, b br g Lemon Drop Kid (USA)—Seven Moons (JPN)
63 **REALT DUBH (IRE)**, 10, b g Beneficial—Suez Canal (FR)
64 **RICH COAST**, 6, b g King's Best (USA)—Costa Rica (IRE)
65 **ROAD TO RICHES (IRE)**, 7, b g Gamut (IRE)—Bellora (IRE)
66 **ROCK OF GLENSTAL (IRE)**, 4, b g Mount Nelson—Amandian (IRE)
67 **RORY MAC (IRE)**, 5, b g Flemensfirth (USA)—Wild Fuchsia (IRE)
68 4, B g Double Eclipse (IRE)—Rossbridge Lass (IRE)

MR NOEL MEADE - Continued

69 RUBE BURROW (IRE), 5, b g Presenting—Sarah Massini (IRE)
70 SILVER TASSIE (IRE), 6, b g Shantou (USA)—Silver Castor (IRE)
71 SNOW FALCON (IRE), 4, b g Presenting—Flocon de Neige (IRE)
72 SUCKER PUNCH (IRE), 5, b g Scorpion (IRE)—Lemonfield Lady (IRE)
73 SUE AND ISI (IRE), 5, b m Kalanisi (IRE)—Susy In The Summer (IRE)
74 SUNRAE SHADOW, 5, b g Echo of Light—Please
75 4, Br f Arcadio (GER)—Talk of Rain (FR)
76 4, B f Flemensfirth (USA)—Tart of Tipp (IRE)
77 TEXAS FOREVER (IRE), 5, b g Heron Island (IRE)—Gravinis (FR)
78 TEXAS JACK (IRE), 8, b g Curtain Time (IRE)—Sailors Run (IRE)
79 THE CONTENDER (IRE), 5, b g Scorpion (IRE)—Welsh Rhapsody (IRE)
80 THE HERDS GARDEN, 5, b g Multiplex—Eternal Legacy (IRE)
81 THOMOND (IRE), 6, b g Definite Article—Hushaby (IRE)
82 TOM HORN (IRE), 8, ch g Beneficial—Lady Shackleton (IRE)
83 TULSA JACK (IRE), 5, b g Urban Ocean (FR)—Jessica's Pet (IRE)
84 VERY WOOD (FR), 5, b g Martaline—Ball of Wood (FR)
85 VIRTUOSO ROUGE (FR), 5, b g Laveron—Prompt
86 WAXIES DARGLE, 5, b g Sakhee (USA)—Cup of Love (USA)
87 WESTHAVEN (IRE), 6, b g Alhaarth (IRE)—Dashiba
88 WOUNDED WARRIOR (IRE), 5, b g Shantou (USA)—Sparkling Sword
89 ZIGGER ZAGGER (IRE), 5, b g Mountain High (IRE)—Main Suspect (IRE)
90 ZIP WYATT (IRE), 5, ch g Flemensfirth (USA)—Tricky Present (IRE)

THREE-YEAR-OLDS

91 B g Shantou (USA)—Maidrin Rua (IRE)

TWO-YEAR-OLDS

92 B c 20/2 Jeremy (USA)—Cant Hurry Love (Desert Prince (IRE)) (15485)
93 B c 6/3 Dark Angel (IRE)—Moon Diamond (Unfuwain (USA)) (11614)

Assistant Trainers: Damien McGillick, Nina Carberry

Jockey (NH): Davy Condon, Paul Carberry. **Conditional:** Ger Fox, Donagh Meyler. **Amateur:** Miss Nina Carberry.

---

429 **MR BRIAN MEEHAN, Manton**
Postal: **The Racing Office, Manton House Estate, Marlborough, SN8 1PN**
Contacts: **PHONE (01672) 511264 (01672) 517191 FAX (01672) 516232 MOBILE (07836) 754254**
E-MAIL info@brianmeehan.com WEBSITE www.brianmeehan.com

1 AAIM TO PROSPER (IRE), 10, br g Val Royal (FR)—Bint Al Balad (IRE) **CGA Racing Partnership 2**
2 ARCHBISHOP (USA), 5, b h Arch (USA)—Avaricity (USA) **Mr C. W. Clay**
3 ASBAAB (USA), 4, ch g Jazil (USA)—Alsaabeqa (USA) **Hamdan Al Maktoum**
4 BURANO (IRE), 5, ch h Dalakhani (IRE)—Kalimanta (IRE) **Mr J. R. Harvey**
5 CAPE APPEAL, 4, b f Cape Cross (IRE)—Sheboygan (IRE) **Longview Stud & Bloodstock Ltd**
6 CAPITOL GAIN (IRE), 5, b g Bahamian Bounty—Emmas Princess (IRE) **Mrs B. V. Sangster**
7 CRIMSON KNIGHT, 6, ch g Zafeen (FR)—Kaylianni **W. A. Harrison-Allan**
8 DA DO RUN RUN, 4, b g Sixties Icon—Fascinatin Rhythm **W. A. Harrison-Allan**
9 ESHTIAAL (USA), 4, b g Dynaformer (USA)—Enfiraaj (USA) **Hamdan Al Maktoum**
10 GRANELL (IRE), 4, ch g Excellent Art—Granny Kelly (USA) **Native Colony Partnership**
11 GREAT HALL, 4, b c Halling (USA)—L'affaire Monique **R. C. Tooth**
12 GREGORI (IRE), 4, b c Invincible Spirit (IRE)—Three Wrens (IRE) **S. P. Tucker**
13 HARRY BOSCH, 4, b g Kyllachy—Fen Guest **M. A. C. Buckley**
14 INTIBAAH, 4, b g Elnadim (USA)—Mawaared **Hamdan Al Maktoum**
15 JANIE RUNAWAY (IRE), 4, b f Antonius Pius (USA)—Await (IRE) **Biddestone Racing Club**
16 LEGAL WAVES (IRE), 4, b g Lawman (FR)—Surf The Web (IRE) **Orwell Partnership**
17 LOOKS CAN KILL, 4, b f Dylan Thomas (IRE)—Looker **Invictus**
18 MASTER MING (IRE), 4, b g Excellent Art—China Pink **Mr Michael Wilmshurst&Mr NB Attenborough**
19 MISTER MUSIC, 5, b g Singspiel—Sierra **Longview Stud & Bloodstock Ltd**
20 NUMBER ONE LONDON (IRE), 4, b g Invincible Spirit (IRE)—Vadorga **Mr S. Jones**
21 PATENTLY (IRE), 4, b c Moss Vale (IRE)—Trader Secret (IRE) **Lanesborough**
22 RED ROCKER (IRE), 4, ch c Redback—Feet of Flame (USA) **Lanesborough**
23 SECULAR SOCIETY, 4, b g Royal Applause—Fantastic Santanyi **Orwell Partnership**
24 SINAADI (IRE), 4, b f Kyllachy—Quantum (IRE) **Longview Stud & Bloodstock Ltd**

MR BRIAN MEEHAN - Continued

THREE-YEAR-OLDS

25 **ADAPTABILITY**, ch f Mastercraftsman (IRE)—Sierra **Longview Stud & Bloodstock Ltd**
26 **AGENT MURPHY**, b c Cape Cross (IRE)—Raskutani **W. A. Harrison-Allan**
27 **AHD (USA)**, b f Elusive Quality (USA)—Abby Road (IRE) **Hamdan Al Maktoum**
28 **ALMOST GUILTY (USA)**, ch f Distorted Humor (USA)—Rolling Sea (USA) **Reddam Racing LLC**
29 **ARCHIPELIGO**, b g Archipenko (USA)—Red Slew **R. C. Tooth**
30 **CAPTAIN SWIFT (IRE)**, br g Captain Rio—Grannys Reluctance (IRE) **The Pony Club**
31 **CAYMAN CRY (USA)**, ch f Street Cry (IRE)—On A Cloud (USA) **Reddam Racing LLC**
32 **CLODOALDO (IRE)**, b g Clodovil (IRE)—Salonga (IRE) **Bayardo**
33 **EASTON ARCH (USA)**, b f Arch (USA)—Shoofha (IRE) **Mr A. Rosen**
34 **EMERALD SWELL (IRE)**, gr f Dalakhani (IRE)—Dance of The Sea (IRE) **Ballymacoll Stud Farm Ltd**
35 **FASHION FUND**, b f Oasis Dream—So Silk **Mr A. Rosen**
36 **GREAT FUN**, b c Kyllachy—Have Fun **The Pony Club**
37 **HEADLONG (IRE)**, gr g Aussie Rules (USA)—Trois Graces (USA) **S.Jones,Burrell,Harvey,Palatinate&Taylor**
38 **HEWAYAAT (IRE)**, b f Cape Cross (IRE)—Wink **Hamdan Al Maktoum**
39 **HOOKE'S LAW (IRE)**, b c Lawman (FR)—Woodland Orchid (IRE) **The Pony Club**
40 **J WONDER (USA)**, b f Footstepsinthesand—Canterbury Lace (USA) **Mr A. Rosen**
41 **LAW APPEAL**, b g Lawman (FR)—Demi Voix **Longview Stud & Bloodstock Ltd**
42 **LOVE TANGLE (IRE)**, b g Azamour (IRE)—Dragnet (IRE) **Ballymacoll Stud Farm Ltd**
43 **MADEED**, b c Nayef—Danehill Dreamer (USA) **Hamdan Al Maktoum**
44 **MAJORITIES**, b g Major Cadeaux—Mania (IRE) **Mr T. G. & Mrs M. E. Holdcroft**
45 **MAN AMONGST MEN (IRE)**, b g Holy Roman Emperor (IRE)—Bankeress (IRE) **Qatar Racing Limited**
46 **MANTONIZE (USA)**, ch c Smart Strike (CAN)—L'ile Aux Loups (IRE) **Reddam Racing LLC**
47 **MAWFOOR (IRE)**, b g Iffraaj—Miss Odlum (IRE) **Hamdan Al Maktoum**
48 **MUSTADAAM (IRE)**, br c Dansili—Sundus (USA) **Hamdan Al Maktoum**
49 **NEWTON'S LAW (IRE)**, b c Lawman (FR)—Royal Alchemist **Bayardo**
50 B c Exceed And Excel (AUS)—Only In Dreams **Mascalls Stud**
51 **PIPE DREAM**, ch g Piccolo—Bold Love **M Wilmshurst, N Attenborough Et al**
52 **RACING'S DREAM**, b c Iffraaj—There's Two (IRE) **The Pony Club**
53 **RECANTED (USA)**, b c Empire Maker (USA)—Deaconess Bonnie (USA) **Reddam Racing LLC**
54 **RED LADY (IRE)**, ch f Dutch Art—Felucca (USA) **D. J. Burke**
55 **ROMAN ROYAL**, b f Holy Roman Emperor (IRE)—Favourita **Longview Stud & Bloodstock Ltd**
56 Gr ro c Mastercraftsman (IRE)—Rose Briar (IRE) **The Pony Club**
57 **SAALIB (USA)**, b c War Front (USA)—Dixie Quest (USA) **Hamdan Al Maktoum**
58 **SETAI**, b f Dubawi (IRE)—Zietory **Mr A. Rosen**
59 **SPARK PLUG (IRE)**, b c Dylan Thomas (IRE)—Kournikova (SAF) **Mr J. L. Day**
60 **STORMY PARADISE (IRE)**, br c Excellent Art—Stormy Larissa (IRE) **Decadent Racing**
61 **TAGHREEB**, b c Dubawi (IRE)—Ghaneema (USA) **Hamdan Al Maktoum**
62 **TAJSEER (USA)**, b br g Medaglia d'oro (USA)—Lear's Princess (USA) **Hamdan Al Maktoum**
63 **TASAABOQ**, b g Aqlaam—Seldemosa **Hamdan Al Maktoum**
64 **TAX ENOUGH (USA)**, b br c Awesome Again (CAN)—Unbridled Ambiance (USA) **Reddam Racing LLC**
65 **VILAZ**, ch g Byron—Flamenco Dancer **Mrs P. Good**
66 **WINDFAST (IRE)**, b c Exceed And Excel (AUS)—Fair Sailing (IRE) **Trelawny II**
67 **WINTRY LIGHT**, gr f Archipenko (USA)—Frosty Welcome (USA) **Miss K. Rausing**
68 **ZORA SEAS (IRE)**, b br f Marju (IRE)—Urgele (FR) **Mrs L. O. Sangster**

TWO-YEAR-OLDS

69 **ABLE SPIRIT**, b c 4/3 Invincible Spirit (IRE)—Sierra (Dr Fong (USA)) **Longview Stud & Bloodstock Ltd**
70 B c 17/4 High Chaparral (IRE)—Alexander Divine (Halling (USA)) (35000) **Decadent Racing**
71 **ALKHAYYAM (IRE)**, b c 9/3 Oasis Dream—Tariysha (IRE) (Daylami (USA)) (1100000) **Hamdan Al Maktoum**
72 **ALPINE AFFAIR**, b c 10/4 Invincible Spirit (IRE)—Demi Voix (Halling (USA)) **Longview Stud & Bloodstock Ltd**
73 **ALSHAAHRAMAN (USA)**, b c 9/2 Daaher (CAN)—
                                    Bashoosha (USA) (Distorted Humor (USA)) **Hamdan Al Maktoum**
74 B c 17/1 Azamour (IRE)—Ambria (GER) (Monsun (GER)) (42000) **The Hon E. I. Mack**
75 **ARTIC PROMISE**, gr c 9/3 Verglas (IRE)—Artistry (Night Shift (USA)) **Longview Stud & Bloodstock Ltd**
76 **AWJAB (IRE)**, b g 2/3 Bahamian Bounty—Applause (IRE) (Danehill Dancer (IRE)) (76190) **Hamdan Al Maktoum**
77 **BEACH WALKER**, b f 28/1 Footstepsinthesand—
                                    Danemere (IRE) (Danehill (USA)) **Longview Stud & Bloodstock Ltd**
78 B c 17/4 Kodiac—Bronze Baby (IRE) (Silver Charm (USA)) (37000)
79 **CRITICAL RISK (IRE)**, ch c 9/3 Pivotal—High Reserve (Dr Fong (USA)) (50000) **Mr J. R. Harvey**
80 **ETIBAAR (USA)**, b c 10/5 Kitten's Joy (USA)—
                                    Oh Deanne O (USA) (Dynaformer (USA)) (204498) **Hamdan Al Maktoum**
81 B f 15/3 Big Bad Bob (IRE)—Fair Sailing (IRE) (Docksider (USA)) **Mrs E. Capon**
82 Ch c 2/2 Equiano (FR)—Fame Is The Spur (Motivator) (63491) **Qatar Racing Limited**
83 B c 20/2 Invincible Spirit (IRE)—Leavingonajetplane (IRE) (Danehill (USA)) (45000) **Mrs E. Capon**

MR BRIAN MEEHAN - Continued

84 Ch f 11/3 More Than Ready (USA)—Liberally (IRE) (Statue of Liberty (USA)) **Mr A. Rosen**
85 Ch c 18/4 Equiano (FR)—Lomapamar (Nashwan (USA)) (35000)
86 **MARAAKIB (IRE),** b c 19/4 Dark Angel (IRE)—Mrs Cee (IRE) (Orpen (USA)) (80000) **Hamdan Al Maktoum**
87 B c 28/4 Approve (IRE)—Miss Assertive (Zafonic (USA)) (38095)
88 Br c 21/3 Bushranger (IRE)—Miss Brief (IRE) (Brief Truce (USA)) (50000)
89 Ch f 18/2 Pulpit (USA)—Mousse Au Chocolat (USA) (Hennessy (USA)) **Mr A. Rosen**
90 B c 27/1 Dutch Art—Moyoko (IRE) (Mozart (IRE)) **Mrs N. L. Young**
91 **MUSTADEEM (IRE),** b c 28/3 Arcano (IRE)—Hureya (USA) (Woodman (USA)) **Hamdan Al Maktoum**
92 **MUTARAKEZ (IRE),** ch c 7/5 Fast Company (IRE)—
                                        Nightswimmer (IRE) (Noverre (USA)) (47619) **Hamdan Al Maktoum**
93 **OFFICER SYDNEY (IRE),** b c 6/4 Lawman (FR)—Morena Park (Pivotal) (24777) **Sydney Arms Racing Club III**
94 B c 10/4 Bushranger (IRE)—Open Verse (USA) (Black Minnaloushe (USA)) (35000) **Decadent Racing**
95 **RATHAATH (IRE),** b f 2/2 Oasis Dream—Jamaayel (Shamardal (USA)) **Hamdan Al Maktoum**
96 Ch f 20/4 Eskendereya (USA)—Rebuke (USA) (Carson City (USA)) **Mr A. Rosen**
97 **SULAALAAT,** b f 2/3 New Approach (IRE)—
                                        Danehill Dreamer (USA) (Danehill (USA)) (180000) **Hamdan Al Maktoum**
98 **TADARROJ,** b c 6/4 Exceed And Excel (AUS)—Quintrell (Royal Applause) (78000) **Hamdan Al Maktoum**
99 **TATAWU (IRE),** b c 13/2 Mawatheeq (USA)—Mooteeah (IRE) (Sakhee (USA)) **Hamdan Al Maktoum**
100 Gr c 2/3 Dark Angel (IRE)—Theben (GER) (Monsun (GER)) (20000) **Mr J. S. Dunningham & Mr P. Gore**
101 B c 30/3 Arcano (IRE)—Validate (Alhaarth (IRE)) (55000) **Mr J. S. Dunningham & Mr P. Gore**
102 B f 11/3 Myboycharlie (IRE)—Zacchera (Zamindar (USA)) (11428) **D. J. Irwin Bloodstock**

Other Owners: Mr N. B. Attenborough, Miss M. Blair, Mr J. Bradley, Mrs Carmen Burrell, Mr Edward W. Easton, Mr Jonathan Harvey, Mr Stewart Jones, Mr David Mann, Mr D. McCormick, Mr B. J. Meehan, Mr N. Nunn, Palatinate Thoroughbred Racing Limited, Mr G. E. Sangster, Mr B. V. Sangster, Mr S. E. Sangster, Mr Roger Taylor, Mr Michael Wilmshurst.

Assistant Trainer: R. O'Dowd

---

430 **MISS REBECCA MENZIES, Brandsby**
Postal: Rebecca Menzies Racing, Foulrice Farm, Brandsby, York, North Yorkshire, YO61 4SB
Contacts: PHONE (01347) 889652 MOBILE (07843) 169217
E-MAIL rebecca@rebeccamenzies.com WEBSITE www.rebeccamenzies.com

1 **BALDING BANKER (IRE),** 8, b g Accordion—What A Breeze (IRE) **Club Racing Banker Partnership**
2 **CHAVOY (FR),** 9, br g Saint des Saints (FR)—Dictania (FR) **Mr Masoud Khadem**
3 **DOMOLY (FR),** 11, b g Varese (FR)—Queen d'ouilly (FR) **The Extra Time Partnership**
4 **FORMULATION (IRE),** 7, b g Danehill Dancer (IRE)—
                                        Formal Approval (USA) **Poppies Europe, Clinton, Gale & Menzies**
5 **HALCYON DAYS,** 5, b g Generous (IRE)—Indian Empress **Club Racing Halcyon Partnership**
6 **MACKLYCUDDY (USA),** 8, b g Monashee Mountain (USA)—Exellensea (USA) **Premier Racing Partnerships**
7 **MCNULTY WRAY (IRE),** 6, b g Westerner—Lyphard Abu (IRE) **Poppies Europe Limited**
8 **MISTER WALL STREET (FR),** 9, b br g Take Risks (FR)—Miss Breezy (FR) **Gay & Peter Hartley**
9 **MR UTAH,** 7, b g Presenting—Raphuca (IRE) **Premier Racing Partnerships**
10 **NEW ZAFEEN (IRE),** 4, b g Zafeen (FR)—Modelliste **J. & A. Millar**
11 **OZIER HILL (IRE),** 5, br g Arcadio (GER)—Lady Clara (IRE) **Mrs R. D. Cairns**
12 **PISTOL BASC (FR),** 10, ch g Maille Pistol (FR)—Moldane (FR) **Panther Racing Limited**
13 **POPPIES MILAN (IRE),** 5, b g Milan—Second Best (IRE) **Poppies Europe Limited**
14 **SAMSON COLLONGES (FR),** 8, gr g Fragrant Mix (FR)—Idole Collonges (FR) **Premier Racing Partnerships**
15 **SECRET DESERT,** 8, b g Dubai Destination (USA)—Lady Bankes (IRE) **The Extra Time Partnership**
16 **TEXAS ROSE (IRE),** 7, b m Beneficial—Dusty Melody (IRE) **Mr J. W. Howley**
17 **VUVUZELA,** 8, ch g Sir Harry Lewis (USA)—Clair Valley **Premier Racing Partnerships**

Other Owners: J. Berry, Miss D. M. Clinton, Mrs M. Feely, Ms D. Fields, Mrs S. V. Gale, P. A. H. Hartley, Mrs R. C. Hartley, Mr A. R. Millar, Mrs J. Millar, Mr G. W. Peacock, Major P. H. K. Steveney.

Assistant Trainer: Carly Dixon

431 **MR ANTHONY MIDDLETON, Banbury**
Postal: Culworth Grounds Stables, Culworth, Banbury, Oxfordshire, OX17 2ND
Contacts: PHONE (01844) 292463 FAX (01844) 292463 MOBILE (07894) 909542
E-MAIL tony@granboroughracing.com WEBSITE www.granboroughracing.co.uk

1 AMERICAN LIFE (FR), 7, b br g American Post—Poplife (FR) **Racing Roses Partnership**
2 BALLINALACKEN (IRE), 6, b g Fruits of Love (USA)—Miss Daisy **Miss C. Elks**
3 CAUGHT BY WITNESS (IRE), 9, b g Witness Box (USA)—Donegans Daughter **Mrs D. Dewbery**
4 CUBISM, 8, b g Sulamani (IRE)—Diagonale (IRE) **Ms B. Woodcock**
5 FITANDPROPERJOB, 8, b g Helissio (FR)—Talkasha (IRE) **S.E.D Racing Partnership**
6 FORGET AND FORGIVE (IRE), 6, b g Clouseau (DEN)—Mollunde (IRE) **Byerley Racing Limited**
7 FUTURE SECURITY (IRE), 5, ch g Dalakhani (IRE)—Schust Madame (IRE) **Bloomfields**
8 GRAFITE, 9, gr g Act One—Silver Gyre (IRE) **J Dalton C Shankland P Fitzgerald**
9 ICANBOOGIE, 4, b g Tobougg (IRE)—Dubai Marina **Mr J. Lefevre**
10 JAYA BELLA (IRE), 9, gr m Tikkanen (USA)—Maxis Girl (IRE) **C. H. Shankland**
11 LOUGH COI (IRE), 8, b g Insatiable (IRE)—Roisin Dove **Mrs D. Dewbery**
12 MARLENO (GER), 8, b g Lecroix (GER)—Mondalita (GER) **Pet Necessities Partnership**
13 5, B g Norse Dancer (IRE)—Miss Lewis **Miss C. Elks**
14 REDOUBTABLEFIGHTER (IRE), 8, b g Kayf Tara—La Brigantine (IRE) **D. J. Shorey**
15 SHOCK N FREANEY (IRE), 7, ch g Clouseau (DEN)—Iliner (IRE) **Mrs D. Dewbery**
16 SWANAGE BAY (IRE), 7, b g Dilshaan—Special Mention (IRE) **Dr J. D. Dalton**
17 THE BOOGEYMAN (IRE), 8, br g King's Theatre (IRE)—Market Lass (IRE) **Nic Allen & Paul Frank Barry**
18 VA'VITE (IRE), 7, b m Vinnie Roe (IRE)—Presenting Shares (IRE) **Ms B Woodcock & Mrs D Dewbery**

Other Owners: Mr Nic Allen, Dr Jeff Dalton, Mr Stewart Darvill, Mrs Diane Dewbery, Mr John P. Ferguson, Mrs John Ferguson, Mr Pat Fitzgerald, Mrs Denise Hopkins, Mr S. Mackintosh, Mr F. Mackintosh, Mr J. P. Naylor, Mr J. Peavoy, Mr Christopher Shankland, Ms Barbara Woodcock.

Jockey (NH): James Banks, Paul Moloney. **Conditional:** Mark Marris.

432 **MR PHIL MIDDLETON, Aylesbury**
Postal: The Stables, Dorton Park Farm, Dorton, Aylesbury, Buckinghamshire, HP18 9NR
Contacts: PHONE (01844) 237503 FAX (01844) 237503 MOBILE (07860) 426607

1 ALWAYSTHEOPTIMIST, 11, b g Muhtarram (USA)—Miss Optimist **Mr P. W. Middleton**
2 MARJU KING (IRE), 8, b g Marju (IRE)—Blue Reema (IRE) **Mr P. W. Middleton**
3 REFER, 4, b g Rail Link—Trellis Bay **Mr P. W. Middleton**
4 SAIL AND RETURN, 10, b g Kayf Tara—Maidwell **Mr P. W. Middleton**

Assistant Trainer: Helen Day

433 **MR PAUL MIDGLEY, Westow**
Postal: Sandfield Farm, Westow, York, YO60 7LS
Contacts: Office (01653) 658790 FAX (01653) 658790 MOBILE (07976) 965220
E-MAIL ptmidgley@aol.com WEBSITE www.ptmidgley.com

1 ADAM'S ALE, 5, b g Ishiguru (USA)—Aqua **Mrs M. J. Hills**
2 ANOTHER WISE KID (IRE), 6, b g Whipper (USA)—Romancing **M. Ng**
3 BOSUN BREESE, 9, b g Bahamian Bounty—Nellie Melba **Williams, Lindley, J.Boocock, N.Boocock**
4 CHOC'A'MOCA (IRE), 7, b g Camacho—Dear Catch (IRE) **John Milburn - Andrew Stephenson**
5 EDITH ANNE, 4, b f Sakhee's Secret—Accusation (IRE) **D. Mann**
6 HAAJES, 10, ch g Indian Ridge—Imelda (USA) **Sandfield Racing**
7 IRISH GIRLS SPIRIT (IRE), 5, b m Desert Millennium (USA)—
                                    Shone Island (IRE) **Sheard, Banks, Jackson & Johnson**
8 LINE OF REASON (IRE), 4, br g Kheleyf (USA)—Miss Party Line (USA) **Taylor's Bloodstock Ltd**
9 LINGUINE (FR), 4, ch c Linngari (IRE)—Amerissage (USA) **Mrs A. Cowley**
10 MONSIEUR JOE (IRE), 7, b g Choisir (AUS)—Pascali **Taylor's Bloodstock Ltd**
11 OLDJOESAID, 10, b g Royal Applause—Border Minstral (IRE) **Pee Dee Tee Syndicate & T W Midgley**
12 PHOENIX CLUBS (IRE), 5, b m Red Clubs (IRE)—Hollow Haze (USA) **Williams, Lindley, Turton, Bate**
13 QUAROMA, 9, ch m Pivotal—Quiz Time **The Legend's Syndicate II**
14 SILVANUS, 9, b g Danehill Dancer (IRE)—Mala Mala (IRE) **C. Alton**
15 SNOW BAY, 8, ch g Bahamian Bounty—Goodwood Blizzard **Snow Bay Partnership**

MR PAUL MIDGLEY - Continued

16 **SUNRAIDER (IRE)**, 7, b g Namid—Doctrine **R. Wardlaw**
17 **TARRSILLE (IRE)**, 8, b g Dansili—Tara Gold (IRE) **Sandfield Racing**

THREE-YEAR-OLDS

18 **FUEL INJECTION**, gr g Pastoral Pursuits—Smart Hostess **Mrs M. Verity**
19 **HEBRIDEAN PRINCESS (IRE)**, b f Rock of Gibraltar (IRE)—Jacaranda Ridge **R. Wardlaw**
20 **HIGHLAND PRINCESS (IRE)**, b f Amadeus Wolf—Ten Spot (IRE) **Mr J. A. Hall**
21 **NAGGERS (IRE)**, ch g Excellent Art—Trika **Taylor's Bloodstock Ltd**
22 **ORIENT CLASS**, ch g Orientor—Killer Class **Frank & Annette Brady**
23 **ORIENT SKY**, b g Orientor—Sister Eugenie (IRE) **Frank & Annette Brady**
24 **PRINCESS MYLA (IRE)**, b f Intense Focus (USA)—Romany Princess (IRE) **Mr R Banks & Mr M Lindsay**
25 **SANDFIELD (IRE)**, b g Kodiac—Red Rabbit **T W Midgley & Sandfield Racing**
26 **SICILIAN BAY (IRE)**, b f Jeremy (USA)—Taormina (IRE) **Sandfield Racing**

TWO-YEAR-OLDS

27 Br gr f 17/3 Ferrule (IRE)—Dispol Isle (IRE) (Trans Island) **W. B. Imison**
28 B c 6/4 Strategic Prince—Glencoagh Order (IRE) (Danehill (USA)) (6194)
29 **MISS RUBY ROYALE**, ch f 14/1 Monsieur Bond (IRE)—Amoureuse (Needwood Blade) (1428) **Mrs A. Milburn**
30 Ch c 26/2 Archipenko (USA)—Mme de Stael (Selkirk (USA)) (2167) **P. T. Midgley**
31 B f 26/4 Windsor Knot (IRE)—Policy (Nashwan (USA)) (619)
32 B f 25/4 Tagula (IRE)—Rainbow Nation (Rainbow Quest (USA)) (619)
33 Br c 23/2 Amadeus Wolf—Royal Superlative (King's Best (USA)) (619)
34 B f 1/3 Vale of York (USA)—Spinning Maid (USA) (Forestry (USA)) (3097)
35 **VALENTINE BELLE**, b f 14/2 Monsieur Bond (IRE)—Sheka (Ishiguru (USA)) (2380) **Mrs A. Milburn**

Other Owners: Mr R. Banks, Mr G. Bate, Mr P. Bateson, Mr R. Batty, Mr J. L. Boocock, Mr N. Boocock, F. Brady, Mrs A. Brady, Mr J. Hobson, Mr A. Jackson, E. Jagger, Mr C. Jagger, Mr R. F. Johnson, Mr P. N. Lindley, Mr M. P. Lindsay, Mr T. W. Midgley, J. A. Milburn, Mr J. N. Sheard, T. A. Stephenson, Mr A. Turton, Mr A. D. Ward, A. Williams.

Assistant Trainer: Miss W. Gibson

Jockey (flat): Micky Fenton. **Amateur:** Miss H. Dukes.

---

434 **MR ROD MILLMAN, Cullompton**
Postal: **The Paddocks, Kentisbeare, Cullompton, Devon, EX15 2DX**
Contacts: **PHONE/FAX (01884) 266620 MOBILE (07885) 168447**
E-MAIL rod.millman@ic24.net

1 **BURNT FINGERS (IRE)**, 4, b f Kheleyf (USA)—Play With Fire (FR) **Miss G. J. Abbey**
2 **DANCE**, 5, b m Erhaab (USA)—Shi Shi **Mrs C. Knowles**
3 **GALATIAN**, 7, ch g Traditionally (USA)—Easy To Imagine (USA) **Tarka Racing**
4 **GLADIATRIX**, 5, b m Compton Place—Lady Dominatrix (IRE) **Harry Dutfield & Partners**
5 **ICE TRES**, 5, br m Iceman—Tup Tim **K. L. Dare**
6 **ICEBUSTER**, 6, ch g Iceman—Radiate **The Links Partnership**
7 **ISIS BLUE**, 4, b g Cockney Rebel (IRE)—Bramaputra (IRE) **Cantay Racing**
8 **IVOR'S PRINCESS**, 5, b m Atraf—Rosina May (IRE) **Mr P.G. Gibbins & Mr Ivor Perry**
9 **MADAME KINTYRE**, 6, b m Trade Fair—Chorus **Mrs L. S. Millman**
10 **MASAI MOON**, 10, b g Lujain—Easy To Imagine (USA) **B. R. Millman**
11 **MODEM**, 4, b g Motivator—Alashaan **D. J. Deer**
12 **PRINCESS ANNABELLE**, 5, ch m Sworn In (USA)—Marybelle **B. R. Millman**
13 **SHAVANSKY**, 10, b g Rock of Gibraltar (IRE)—Limelighting (USA) **The Links Partnership**
14 **STARVING MARVIN**, 6, b g Hawk Wing (USA)—Oleana (IRE) **Seasons Holidays**
15 **UNDER MILK WOOD**, 4, b f Montjeu (IRE)—Freni (GER) **Seasons Holidays**
16 **WYNDHAM WAVE**, 5, gr g Dr Fong (USA)—Atlantic Light **Kentisbeare Racing**

THREE-YEAR-OLDS

17 **BIOTIC**, b g Aqlaam—Bramaputra (IRE) **Mrs M. Campbell-Andenaes**
18 **BLUE ANCHOR BAY (IRE)**, b g Ad Valorem (USA)—New Foundation (IRE) **Crowcombe Racing**
19 **CABLE CAR**, br g Pastoral Pursuits—Nina Fontenail (FR) **The Links Partnership**
20 **COTTON CLUB (IRE)**, b g Amadeus Wolf—Slow Jazz (USA) **The Links Partnership**
21 **DOVIL'S DUEL (IRE)**, b g Clodovil (IRE)—Duelling **Always Hopeful Partnership**
22 **DYLAN'S CENTENARY**, b g Kyllachy—Sheka **Seasons Holidays**
23 **EUGENIC**, br g Piccolo—Craic Sa Ceili (IRE) **B. C. Scott**
24 **GRAPHENE**, b g Nayef (USA)—Annapurna (IRE) **The Graphene Partnership**

MR ROD MILLMAN - Continued

25 **KAIZEN FACTOR**, b g Azamour (IRE)—Best Side (IRE) **Mustajed Partnership**
26 **MASTER CARPENTER (IRE)**, ch c Mastercraftsman (IRE)—Fringe **The Links Partnership/Cheveley Park Stud**
27 **MISS TWEEDY**, b f Sleeping Indian—Ile Royale **Mr B. H. Parkhouse**
28 **NAUGHTY SPICE**, b f Three Valleys (USA)—Milldown Story **Mrs J. E. Laws**
29 **SEAHAM**, b g Myboycharlie (IRE)—Be Decisive **Seasons Holidays**
30 **TAWS**, b f Hernando (FR)—Reaf **K. Arrowsmith**
31 **TRIPLE CHIEF (IRE)**, b br g High Chaparral (IRE)—Trebles (IRE) **G. D. Thompson**

TWO-YEAR-OLDS

32 B f 29/2 Sleeping Indian—Azharia (Oasis Dream) (7000)
33 Ch f 23/4 Monsieur Bond (IRE)—Bond Platinum Club (Pivotal) (3500)
34 Gr f 1/3 Hellvelyn—Crofters Ceilidh (Scottish Reel) (7619) **Mrs M. O'Sullivan**
35 B c 29/3 Sir Percy—Great Quest (IRE) (Montjeu (IRE)) **Seasons Holidays**
36 B f 30/3 Jeremy (USA)—Kuwinda (Hunting Lion (IRE)) (2500)
37 **LORELEI**, b f 9/3 Excellent Art—Light Dreams (Fantastic Light (USA)) (19047) **The Links Partnership**
38 **MARCANO (IRE)**, b c 5/2 Arcano (IRE)—Aquatint (Dansili) (55238) **The Links Partnership**
39 B f 26/3 Equiano (FR)—Midnight Sky (Desert Prince (IRE)) (8000)
40 B c 11/4 Hellvelyn—Overcome (Belmez (USA)) (10476) **Mustajed Partnership**
41 B c 18/2 Danehill Dancer (IRE)—Thermopylae (Tenby) (38000) **E. J. S. Gadsden**
42 **ZEBELLA**, b f 15/2 Paco Boy (IRE)—Delitme (IRE) (Val Royal (FR)) (22857) **The Links Partnership**

Other Owners: P. Bartlam, J. Burley, Cheveley Park Stud Limited, A. J. Conway, Mrs A. C. Dominy, Mr D. S. Dormer, Mr H. Dutfield, S. J. Dutfield, Mr R. D. Gamlin, P. G. Gibbins, F. G. Hollis, Mr D. J. Hornby, Mr E. J. Hughes, N. W. Lake, Mr M. Leach, V. B. Lewer, D. A. Little, Mr A. M. Nolan, G. G. Payne, S. M. Perry, W. I. M. Perry, Mr T. Tompkins.

Assistant Trainer: Louise Millman

Jockey (flat): Andrea Atzeni. **Apprentice:** Pat Millman.

---

435 | **MR ROBERT MILLS, Epsom**
Postal: **Loretta Lodge Racing Stables, Tilley Lane, Headley, Surrey, KT18 6EP**
Contacts: **PHONE (01372) 377209 FAX (01372) 386578**
E-MAIL lorettalodge@aol.com

1 **CANADIAN RUN (IRE)**, 4, ch g Hurricane Run (IRE)—Vale View (FR) **Mr B. Kerr**
2 **CHARLTON**, 11, b g Inchinor—Sabina **Mrs B. B. Mills**
3 **CLUB HOUSE (IRE)**, 4, b g Marju (IRE)—Idesia (IRE) **Mrs B B Mills Mr A Foreman**
4 **LITTLE BUXTED (USA)**, 4, b br g Mr Greeley (USA)—Mo Cheoil Thu (IRE) **Buxted Partnership**
5 **SWING EASY**, 4, b c Zamindar (USA)—Shahmina (IRE) **Mrs B B Mills, Mr J Harley, Mr T Jacobs**

THREE-YEAR-OLDS

6 **DANVERS STREET**, b g Avonbridge—Lady of Limerick (IRE) **Mrs B. B. Mills**
7 **MONSIEUR LAVENE (IRE)**, b g Kodiac—Sign of Luck (IRE) **J Harley Mrs B B Mills Mr R A Mills**
8 **RYDAN (IRE)**, ch c Intense Focus (USA)—Lough Mewin (IRE) **Jacobs Construction & Mrs B B Mills**
9 **SWEENEY TODD**, b g Refuse to Bend (IRE)—Ashantiana **SN Racing VII**
10 **TURNBURY**, b g Azamour (IRE)—Scottish Heights (IRE) **Mrs B B Mills, T Jacobs, A Foreman**

TWO-YEAR-OLDS

11 Ch c 25/3 Tagula (IRE)—Kannon (Kyllachy) (38714) **R. A. Mills**
12 Gr f 14/3 Art Connoisseur (IRE)—Ms Sasha Malia (IRE) (Verglas (IRE)) (7742) **Mrs B. B. Mills**
13 B c 28/1 Excellent Art—Shahmina (IRE) (Danehill (USA)) (23228) **Mrs B B Mills, Mr J Harley, Mr T Jacobs**
14 B c 29/1 Strategic Prince—Theebah (Bahamian Bounty) (18582) **Mrs B. B. Mills**

Other Owners: Miss N. F. Davey, Mr A. J. Foreman, J. P. Hanifin, J. E. Harley, T. Jacobs, Jacobs Construction (Holdings) Limited, S. Nunn, Mrs J. Ruthven.

Assistant Trainer: Richard Ryan

436 MR NICK MITCHELL, Dorchester
Postal: **Brick House, Piddletrenthide, Dorchester, Dorset, DT2 7QP**
Contacts: **PHONE (01300) 348049 MOBILE (07770) 892085**
E-MAIL nick.mitch@btinternet.com WEBSITE www.nickmitchellracing.com

1 DANCE FLOOR KING (IRE), 7, b g Generous (IRE)—Strawberry Fool (FR) **N. Elliott**
2 ELECTRIC MAYHEM, 7, b g Alflora (IRE)—She's No Muppet **Mr & Mrs Andrew May**
3 JUST FEE, 7, b m Emperor Fountain—Mabel's Memory (IRE) **A. J. M. Trowbridge**
4 MINISTER OF MAYHEM, 4, ch g Sakhee's Secret—First Fantasy **Mr J. M. Wilson**
5 PHONE HOME (IRE), 7, b br g Heron Island (IRE)—Ancestral Voices (IRE) **Mr & Mrs Andrew May & Nick Elliott**
6 RICKETYROCK, 8, b g Riverwise (USA)—Apatura Cherry **Mrs E. Mitchell**

Other Owners: Mrs Andrew May, Mr Andrew May.

Jockey (NH): Daryl Jacob. **Amateur:** Mr R. G. Henderson.

437 MR PHILIP MITCHELL, Kingston Lisle
Postal: **Blowing Stone Stables, Kingston Lisle, Wantage, Oxfordshire, OX12 9QL**
Contacts: **PHONE (01372) 273729 FAX (01372) 278701 MOBILE (07836) 231462**

1 AL QATARI (USA), 5, b br g Dynaformer (USA)—Where's The Church (USA) **S. P. Tindall**
2 MONT VENTOUX (FR), 4, b br g Elusive City (USA)—Recreation **Mrs P. A. Mitchell**
3 ROBIN HOOD (IRE), 6, b g Galileo (IRE)—Banquise (IRE) **Amelco UK Ltd**
4 SAN SIRO (IRE), 8, b g Milan—Foxtail (IRE) **Mrs P. A. Mitchell**

THREE-YEAR-OLDS
5 CHORAL CLAN (IRE), b c Oratorio (IRE)—Campbellite **Amity Finance Ltd**

TWO-YEAR-OLDS
6 Ch f 22/3 Peintre Celebre (USA)—Virginias Best (King's Best (USA)) (28000)

Jockey (flat): Jack Mitchell.

438 MR RICHARD MITCHELL, Dorchester
Postal: **East Hill Stables, Piddletrenthide, Dorchester, Dorset, DT2 7QY**
Contacts: **PHONE/FAX (01300) 348739 MOBILE (07775) 843136**

1 BENBECULA, 5, b g Motivator—Isle of Flame **Mr & Mrs Andrew May**
2 CATCH THE KATT, 7, b m Wared (USA)—Kittenkat **N. R. Mitchell**
3 ELLYMAC, 6, b m Deltic (USA)—Or Aibrean **Mrs E. Mitchell**
4 MASSINI SUNSET (IRE), 14, b g Dr Massini (IRE)—Burgundy Sunset (IRE) **Mr & Mrs Andrew May**
5 REILLYS DAUGHTER, 6, b m Diktat—Compose **Piddle Valley Racing Club & N R Mitchell**
6 THUNDERING HOME, 7, gr g Storming Home—Citrine Spirit (IRE) **Mrs K. M. Boughey**

Other Owners: Mrs S. H. May, A. J. May.

Assistant Trainer: Mrs E. Mitchell

439 MR JAMES MOFFATT, Grange-Over-Sands
Postal: **Pit Farm Racing Stables, Cartmel, Grange-Over-Sands, Cumbria, LA11 6PJ**
Contacts: **PHONE (01539) 536689 FAX (01539) 536236 MOBILE (07767) 367282**
E-MAIL james@jamesmoffatt.co.uk WEBSITE www.jamesmoffatt.co.uk

1 ABEL J TASMAN (IRE), 6, b g Aussie Rules (USA)—Vin Santo (IRE) **K. Bowron**
2 CAPE ROSA, 4, b f Sir Percy—Cashema (IRE) **Mr M. W. Chapman**
3 CAPTAIN BROWN, 6, b g Lomitas—Nicola Bella (IRE) **K. Bowron**
4 CAPTAIN RHYRIC, 5, ch g Dylan Thomas (IRE)—Nuts In May (USA) **Bowes Lodge Stables**
5 DE LESSEPS (USA), 6, ch g Selkirk (USA)—Suez **Ms A. Hartley**
6 DOLLAR MICK (IRE), 9, b g Presenting—Bula Beag (IRE) **Mr M. W. Chapman**
7 DUMBARTON (IRE), 6, br h Danehill Dancer (IRE)—Scottish Stage (IRE) **K. Bowron**
8 FANTASY KING, 8, b g Acclamation—Fantasy Ridge **Mr V. R. Vyner-Brooks**
9 MAY'S BOY, 6, gr h Proclamation (IRE)—Sweet Portia (IRE) **K. Bowron**

MR JAMES MOFFATT - Continued

10 **MAYBE I WONT**, 9, b g Kyllachy—Surprise Surprise **The Sheroot Partnership**
11 **MOHAWK RIDGE**, 8, b g Storming Home—Ipsa Loquitur **K. Bowron**
12 **MORNING ROYALTY (IRE)**, 7, b g King's Theatre (IRE)—Portryan Native (IRE) **Mrs E. M. Milligan**
13 **PENNINE JOSIE**, 5, b m Josr Algarhoud (IRE)—Pennine Star (IRE) **Mr M. W. Chapman**
14 **QUEL ELITE (FR)**, 10, b g Subotica (FR)—Jeenly (FR) **Mr M. W. Chapman**
15 **REDPENDER (IRE)**, 8, gr g Great Palm (USA)—Josie Murphy (IRE) **K. Bowron**
16 **RUTTERKIN (USA)**, 6, gr g Maria's Mon (USA)—Chilukki Cat (USA) **J. W. Barrett**
17 **SAM LORD**, 10, ch g Observatory (USA)—My Mariam **Bowes Lodge Stables**
18 **SMART RULER (IRE)**, 8, ch g Viking Ruler (AUS)—Celebrated Smile (IRE) **The Vilprano Partnership**
19 **ZUILEKA**, 5, b m Observatory (USA)—Cashema (IRE) **Mr M. W. Chapman**

Other Owners: A. R. Mills, Mr S. Wilson, Mrs J. C. Wilson.

Assistant Trainer: Jennie Moffatt

Jockey (flat): Royston Ffrench, P. J. McDonald. **Jockey (NH):** Brian Harding, Brian Hughes, Wilson Renwick.

---

440 **MR ISMAIL MOHAMMED, Newmarket**
Postal: **Revida Place Stables, Hamilton Road, Newmarket, Suffolk, CB8 7JQ**
Contacts: **PHONE (01638) 669074 MOBILE (07771) 777121**
E-MAIL justina.stone@dubairacingclub.com

1 **ALHAARTH BEAUTY (IRE)**, 4, b f Alhaarth (IRE)—Endis (IRE) **Ismail Mohammed**
2 **ANA SHABABIYA (IRE)**, 4, ch f Teofilo (IRE)—Call Later (USA) **Ahmad Abdulla Al Shaikh**
3 **CAPE SAMBA**, 5, b g Cape Cross (IRE)—Dancing Feather **Ismail Mohammed**
4 **EDUCATE**, 5, b g Echo of Light—Pasithea (IRE) **Sultan Ali**
5 **JANOUB NIBRAS (IRE)**, 4, b g Acclamation—Wildsplash (USA) **Saeed H. Altayer**
6 **LAWMANS THUNDER**, 4, b g Lawman (FR)—Rhapsodize **Sheikh Rashid Dalmook Al Maktoum**
7 **LIGHT BURST (USA)**, 5, b h Hard Spun (USA)—Kew Garden (USA) **Saeed H. Altayer**
8 **MUBTADI**, 6, b g Dr Fong (USA)—Noble Peregrine **Abdulla Al Mansoori**
9 **RED WARRIOR (IRE)**, 4, ch c Iffraaj—Wiolante (GER) **Ismail Mohammed**
10 **RHOMBUS (IRE)**, 4, b g Authorized (IRE)—Mathool (USA) **Sheikh Rashid Dalmook Al Maktoum**
11 **SHAMAAL NIBRAS (USA)**, 5, b h First Samurai (USA)—Sashay Away (USA) **Saeed H. Altayer**

THREE-YEAR-OLDS

12 **CAPE CELEBRATION (IRE)**, b f Cape Cross (IRE)—Miss Champagne (FR) **Sheikh Rashid Dalmook Al Maktoum**
13 **DUBAWI FUN**, b c Dubawi (IRE)—Arabian Treasure (USA) **Sultan Ali**
14 **HATHA HOOH**, b c Exceed And Excel (AUS)—Mystery Ocean **Saeed H. Altayer**
15 **HAWASH**, b c New Approach (IRE)—Al Hasnaa **Sultan Ali**
16 **MOTAMAYEZAH**, ch f Tamayuz—Classical Dancer **Sheikh Juma Dalmook Al Maktoum**
17 **PURE AMBER (IRE)**, b c Shamardal (USA)—Ile Rousse **Abdulla Al Mansoori**
18 **SIGHORA (IRE)**, b f Royal Applause—Singitta **Sheikh Rashid Dalmook Al Maktoum**
19 **STORMARDAL (IRE)**, b c Shamardal (USA)—Dievotchkina (IRE) **Sheikh Juma Dalmook Al Maktoum**
20 B c Iffraaj—Tortue (USA) **Saeed H. Altayer**
21 **TOWER POWER**, b c Nayef (USA)—Voile (IRE) **Abdulla Al Mansoori**
22 **UPDATED (FR)**, ch f New Approach (IRE)—Dance Treat (USA) **Sultan Ali**
23 **WICKHAMBROOK (IRE)**, ch c Dubawi (IRE)—Beautiful Filly **Ali Ridha**

TWO-YEAR-OLDS

24 B c 24/4 Vale of York (IRE)—Bean Island (USA) (Afleet (CAN)) (16000) **Sultan Ali**
25 B c 23/1 Thewayyouare (USA)—Beautiful Dancer (IRE) (Danehill Dancer (IRE)) (16000) **Ismail Mohammed**
26 B c 16/2 Iffraaj—Beautiful Filly (Oasis Dream) (57000) **Ali Ridha**
27 B c 27/4 Big Bad Bob (IRE)—Dievotchkina (IRE) (Bluebird (USA)) (60000) **Sheikh Juma Al Dalmook Maktoum**
28 B c 15/2 Archipenko (USA)—Eminencia (Sadler's Wells (USA)) (20000) **Sheikh Rashid Dalmook Al Maktoum**
29 B f 5/4 Exceed And Excel (AUS)—Impetuous (Inchinor) (42000) **Saeed Manana**
30 B c 22/2 Medicean—Inchberry (Barathea (IRE)) (65000) **Saeed Manana**
31 B c 9/3 Aussie Rules (USA)—Kekova (Montjeu (IRE)) (60000) **Saeed Manana**
32 **KODESTINY (IRE)**, b f 5/4 Kodiac—
                                Singingintherain (IRE) (Kyllachy) (27100) **Sheikh Juma Al Dalmook Maktoum**
33 B f 14/2 Teofilo (IRE)—Petit Calva (FR) (Desert King (IRE)) (40000) **Sultan Ali**
34 B c 22/2 Vale of York (IRE)—Reasonably Devout (CAN) (St Jovite (USA)) (15000) **Sultan Ali**
35 B f 17/3 Vale of York (IRE)—Star Express (Sadler's Wells (USA)) (20000) **Ali Ridha**

441 MRS LAURA MONGAN, Epsom
Postal: **Condover Stables, Langley Vale Road, Epsom, Surrey, KT18 6AP**
Contacts: **PHONE (01372) 271494 FAX (01372) 271494 MOBILE (07788) 122942**
E-MAIL ljmongan@hotmail.co.uk WEBSITE www.lauramongan.co.uk

1 **ALSADAA (USA)**, 11, b g Kingmambo (USA)—Aljawza (USA) **Mrs P. J. Sheen**
2 **ANGINOLA (IRE)**, 5, b m Kodiac—Lady Montekin **The Only Pub In The World**
3 4, B br g Mountain High (IRE)—Ballinacariga Rose (IRE) **Mrs P. J. Sheen**
4 **BELL'ARTE (IRE)**, 4, b f Zamindar (USA)—Art Eyes (USA) **Mr David J Bearman & Charlie's Starrs**
5 **BERT THE ALERT**, 6, b g Proclamation (IRE)—Megalex **Condover Racing**
6 **CINEMATIQUE (IRE)**, 6, br g King's Theatre (IRE)—Chantoue Royale (FR) **Mrs P. J. Sheen**
7 **DIVINE RULE (IRE)**, 6, br g Cacique (IRE)—Island Destiny **Mrs L. J. Mongan**
8 **FIRST AVENUE (IRE)**, 9, b g Montjeu (IRE)—Marciala (IRE) **Mrs L. J. Mongan**
9 **KEPPEL ISLE (IRE)**, 5, b g Heron Island (IRE)—Wadi Khaled (FR) **Mrs P. J. Sheen**
10 **KING'S REQUEST (IRE)**, 4, ch g New Approach (IRE)—Palace Weekend (USA) **Mrs P. J. Sheen**
11 **LADY LUNCHALOT (USA)**, 4, b f More Than Ready (USA)—Betty Johanne (USA) **Charlie's Starrs**
12 **NORFOLK SKY**, 5, ch m Haafhd—Cayman Sound **Condover Racing**
13 **ORSM**, 7, b g Erhaab (USA)—Royal Roulette **Mrs P. J. Sheen**
14 **RIVERMOUTH**, 9, ch g Karinga Bay—Rippling Brook **Mrs P. J. Sheen**
15 **ROSOFF (IRE)**, 12, b g New Frontier (IRE)—Annida (IRE) **Mrs P. J. Sheen**
16 **SEA CADET**, 12, gr g Slip Anchor—Stormy Gal (IRE) **Mrs P. J. Sheen**
17 **SHINE IN TIME (IRE)**, 6, b m Definite Article—Time To Shine **Mrs P. J. Sheen**
18 **SKIDBY MILL (IRE)**, 4, b f Ramonti (FR)—Glasnas Giant **Mr R. F. Coates**
19 **STAY IN MY HEART (IRE)**, 5, ch m Medicean—Christmas Cracker (FR) **Make Way Partnership**
20 **SYNTHE DAVIS (FR)**, 9, b m Saint des Saints (FR)—Trumpet Davis (FR) **Mrs P. J. Sheen**
21 **TUSCAN GOLD**, 7, ch g Medicean—Louella (USA) **Mrs P. J. Sheen**
22 **TWO SUGARS**, 6, b g Val Royal (FR)—Princess Galadriel **Mrs P. Akhurst**

Other Owners: Mr S. W. Bain, Mr A. W. Bain, D. J. Bearman, Mr P. J. Wheatley, T. Zachariades.

Jockey (NH): Tom Cannon. **Conditional:** Nathan Adams.

442 MR ARTHUR MOORE, Naas
Postal: **Dereens, Naas, Co. Kildare, Ireland**
Contacts: **PHONE (00353) 4587 6292 FAX (00353) 4589 9247 MOBILE (00353) 8725 52535**
E-MAIL arthurlmoore@eircom.net

1 **BACK OFF MATE (IRE)**, 6, b g Old Vic—Flyhalf (IRE) **M. Beresford**
2 **DANDRIDGE**, 5, ch g Doyen (IRE)—Arantxa **R. Bartlett**
3 **EL SORO (FR)**, 6, b g Malinas (GER)—La Esplendida (FR) **P. McCarthy**
4 **FEVER PITCH (IRE)**, 8, b g Dushyantor (USA)—Stormey Tune (IRE) **Mr J. P. McManus**
5 **FULL OF MISCHIEF (IRE)**, 6, ch m Classic Cliche (IRE)—Drama Chick **Mrs A. L. T. Moore**
6 **GENTLEMAN DUKE (IRE)**, 6, b g Bachelor Duke (USA)—Housekeeping **Mr J. P. McManus**
7 **GOLDEN HERON (IRE)**, 6, b g Heron Island (IRE)—Dear As Gold (IRE) **S. Haughey**
8 **HARLEY'S HARLEY (IRE)**, 4, b f Cockney Rebel (IRE)—Signella **L. Flood**
9 **HOME FARM (IRE)**, 7, b g Presenting—Tynelucy (IRE) **C. Jones**
10 **HOP IN (IRE)**, 7, b g Flemensfirth (USA)—Prowler (IRE) **C. Hanbury**
11 **LINNEL (IRE)**, 9, b g Moscow Society (USA)—The Last Bank (IRE) **R. Donworth**
12 **MERRYDOWN BLACK**, 6, b g Kayf Tara—Right On Target (IRE) **Mrs P. Sloan**
13 **MITEBEALL FORLUCK**, 6, b g Westerner—Iborga (FR) **C. Hanbury**
14 **ONTOPOFTHEWORLD (IRE)**, 5, ch g Desert King—Zaffre (IRE) **Mrs A. L. T. Moore**
15 **ORGANISEDCONFUSION (IRE)**, 9, b g Laveron—Histologie (FR) **Mr A. Dunlop**
16 **PASS THE HAT (IRE)**, 7, ch g Karinga Bay—Moor Spring **M. Beresford**
17 **POSITIVE VIBES**, 5, ch g Nayef (USA)—Steeple **F. Jones**
18 **SABROCLAIR (FR)**, 5, b g Robin des Champs (FR)—Malicka Madrick (FR) **C. Jones**
19 **SEA BEAT**, 4, ch g Beat Hollow—Maritima **C. Jones**
20 **TALBOT ROAD (IRE)**, 6, b g Old Vic—Over The Glen (IRE) **J. P. Byrne**
21 **TREAT YOURSELF (IRE)**, 7, b g Beat Hollow—Cartesian **L. Breslin**

THREE-YEAR-OLDS

22 **HANNAH'S MAGIC (IRE)**, ch f Lomitas—Cool Storm (IRE) **Mrs A. L. T. Moore**
23 **RAGGEE (IRE)**, b f Ad Valorem (USA)—Recast (IRE) **F. Jones**

MR ARTHUR MOORE - Continued

TWO-YEAR-OLDS

24 B c 12/3 Alfred Nobel (IRE)—Hazarama (IRE) (Kahyasi) (8903) **Mrs A. L. T. Moore**
25 B f 15/2 Footstepsinthesand—Lassie's Gold (USA) (Seeking The Gold (USA)) (15485) **L. Flood**

Assistant Trainer: M. O'Sullivan

Jockey (flat): F. M. Berry, S. Foley. **Jockey (NH):** D. J. Casey, D. Russell. **Conditional:** G. Malone.

443
MR GARY MOORE, Horsham
Postal: **Cisswood Racing Stables, Sandygate Lane, Lower Beeding, Horsham, West Sussex, RH13 6LR**
Contacts: **HOME** (01403) 891997 **YARD** (01403) 891912 **FAX** (01403) 891924
MOBILE (07753) 863123
E-MAIL garyjayne.moore@virgin.net **WEBSITE** www.garymooreracing.com

1 AGINCOURT REEF (IRE), 5, b g Gold Well—Hillside Native (IRE) **Mr A. Head, Mr R. Lockwood & Mr M. Burne**
2 ANJUNA BEACH (USA), 4, b c Artie Schiller (USA)—Hidden Temper (USA) **C. E. Stedman**
3 AUGUSTA BAY, 5, b m Oscar (IRE)—Penneyrose Bay **Sir Christopher Wates**
4 AULD STHOCK (IRE), 6, ch g Definite Article—Native Archive (IRE) **Mark Albon & Chris Stedman**
5 BALLYHEIGUE (IRE), 5, b g High Chaparral (IRE)—Lypharden (IRE) **A. Head**
6 BALTIC BLADE (IRE), 4, b g Baltic King—Anita's Contessa (IRE) **Mr J. R. Craik-White**
7 BE ALL MAN (IRE), 7, b g Dubawi (IRE)—Belle Allemande (CAN) **Mr A. Head, Mr R. Lockwood & Mr M. Burne**
8 BEAUFORT BOY (IRE), 5, b g Heron Island (IRE)—What A Mewsment (IRE) **Mrs A. Gloag**
9 BIRDIE KING, 4, b g Dutch Art—Daughters World **The Golf Partnership**
10 BIRDIE QUEEN, 4, b f Pastoral Pursuits—Silver Miss (FR) **The Golf Partnership**
11 BOW QUEST, 7, b m Rainbow High—Fair Kai (IRE) **E. A. Condon**
12 BRAVE VIC (IRE), 6, b g Old Vic—Baliya (IRE) **R. Henderson**
13 BUILDING ZIET, 4, b g Dubai Destination (USA)—Zietunzeen (IRE) **Mrs M. Shenkin & Dr I. R. Shenkin**
14 BURLINGTON BERTIE (IRE), 6, ch g Old Vic—Clara's Dream (IRE) **D. N. Green**
15 BUSTER BROWN (IRE), 5, ch h Singspiel (IRE)—Gold Dodger (USA) **B. Siddle & B. D. Haynes**
16 CABIMAS, 7, b g King's Best (USA)—Casanga (IRE) **Mr A. D. Bradmore**
17 CHARLIE CHEESECAKE (IRE), 8, br g Kayf Tara—Darabaka (IRE) **Mr G. Gillespie**
18 CHRIS PEA GREEN, 5, b g Proclamation (IRE)—Another Secret **C. Green & Galloping On The South Downs**
19 CIVIL WAR (IRE), 5, b g Scorpion (IRE)—Silvestre (ITY) **Mr A. J. Head**
20 COULOIR EXTREME (IRE), gr g Verglas (IRE)—Chica Roca (USA) **C. E. Stedman**
21 CRUZ ON TED, 7, b g Helissio (FR)—Dublivia **A. Head**
22 CRY FURY, 6, b g Beat Hollow—Cantanta **Mr A. E. Dean**
23 DE BLACKSMITH (IRE), 6, b g Brian Boru—Gift of The Gab (IRE) **Mrs E. A. Kiernan**
24 DEUX ETOILES (IRE), 7, b g Montjeu (IRE)—Onereuse **Heart Of The South Racing**
25 DONNAS PALM (IRE), 10, gr g Great Palm (USA)—Donna's Tarquin (USA) **Mr I. Beach**
26 DUTCH MASTERPIECE, 4, b g Dutch Art—The Terrier **R. Green**
27 DYNAMIC IDOL (USA), 7, b br g Dynaformer (USA)—El Nafis (USA) **Heart Of The South Racing**
28 EXCLUSIVE WATERS (IRE), 4, b g Elusive City (USA)—Pelican Waters (IRE) **The Old Brokers**
29 FANTASY INVADER (IRE), 4, b g Captain Marvelous (IRE)—Fields of Joy (GER) **The Fantasy Fellowship E**
30 FLASHMAN, 5, ch g Doyen (IRE)—Si Si Si **Mr A. D. Bradmore**
31 FLUTE BOWL, 4, b f Black Sam Bellamy (IRE)—Queen's Dancer **C. E. Stedman**
32 FREDDY WITH A Y (IRE), 4, b g Amadeus Wolf—Mataji (IRE) **Mrs M. J. George**
33 FRUITY O'ROONEY, 11, b g Kahyasi—Recipe **Heart Of The South Racing**
34 GAELIC SILVER (FR), 8, b g Lando (GER)—Galatza (FR) **The Winning Hand**
35 GALIOTTO (IRE), 8, b g Galileo (IRE)—Welsh Motto (USA) **Mr A. D. Bradmore**
36 GENEROUS HELPINGS (IRE), 5, ch g Generous (IRE)—
Saffron Pride (IRE) **Galloping On The South Downs Partnership**
37 GEORGEA (IRE), 5, ch m Generous (IRE)—Newbay Lady **The Somner Syndicate**
38 GIGONDAS, 5, ch g Grape Tree Road—Queen's Dancer **C. E. Stedman**
39 GOLANOVA, 5, b g Golan (IRE)—Larkbarrow **Galloping On The South Downs Partnership**
40 GOLD CARROT, 6, b g Beat All (USA)—Emma-Lyne **A. Head**
41 GOOD LUCK CHARM, 5, b g Doyen (IRE)—Lucky Dice **Heart Of The South Racing**
42 GORES ISLAND (IRE), 8, b g Beneficial—Just Leader (IRE) **Collins, Horsfall, Michael & O'Sullivan**
43 GUARDS CHAPEL, 6, b g Motivator—Intaaj (IRE) **Mr A. D. Bradmore**
44 GUN SHY (IRE), 6, b g Norwich—Debbies Scud (IRE) **P. R. Chapman**
45 HALLING'S WISH, 4, br g Halling (USA)—Fair View (GER) **WBC Partnership**
46 HANGA ROA (IRE), 4, b g Hannouma (IRE)—Fine And Mellow (FR) **C. E. Stedman**
47 HIGHFIELDS DANCER, 6, b g Silver Patriarch (IRE)—Linguistic Dancer **Mr L. J. Roberts**
48 JODAWES (USA), 7, b br g Burning Roma (USA)—Venetian Peach (USA) **Stephen Fisher & Pat Wilkins**

MR GARY MOORE - Continued

49 **JUBILEE BRIG**, 4, b g Kheleyf (USA)—Voile (IRE) **Lookout Partnership**
50 **JUPITER STORM**, 5, ch g Galileo (IRE)—Exciting Times (FR) **Heart Of The South Racing**
51 **JUSTIFICATION**, 6, b g Montjeu (IRE)—Colorspin (IRE) **Mrs E. A. Kiernan**
52 **KAMBIS**, 6, b g Tobougg (IRE)—Queen Tomyra (IRE) **Mr & Mrs Leslie Vine**
53 **KINGSFOLD FLARE**, 7, ch m Central Park (IRE)—Kingsfold Blaze **G. L. Moore**
54 **KNIGHT OF PLEASURE**, 5, ch g Exit To Nowhere (USA)—Kim Fontenail (FR) **The Knights Of Pleasure**
55 **KYLLACHY SPIRIT**, 6, b g Kyllachy—Cartuccia (IRE) **Mrs J. R. Jenrick & R. D. Jenrick**
56 5, B g Oscar (IRE)—Lady Meribel
57 **LEO LUNA**, 5, b g Galileo (IRE)—Eva Luna (USA) **Mr P. B. Moorhead**
58 **LIGHT WELL (IRE)**, 6, b g Sadler's Wells (USA)—L'ancresse (IRE) **B. Siddle & B. D. Haynes**
59 **LITTLE LOUIE**, 5, ch g Nomadic Way (USA)—Lillie Lou **R. Fielder**
60 **MAJOR MARTIN (IRE)**, 5, b g Flemensfirth (USA)—Miss Emer (IRE) **Mr A. E. Dean**
61 **MARMALADY (IRE)**, 4, ch f Duke of Marmalade (IRE)—Grecian Glory (IRE) **Heart Of The South Racing**
62 4, B g Kayf Tara—Megalex **Galloping On The South Downs Partnership**
63 **MEGASTAR**, 9, b g Kayf Tara—Megalex **Galloping On The South Downs Partnership**
64 **MOUNT ODELL**, 5, b g Motivator—Oscars Vision (IRE) **Langleys**
65 **MR FICKLE (IRE)**, 5, b g Jeremy (USA)—Mamara Reef **A. J. Perkins**
66 **MY GIGI**, 4, b f Medicean—Choirgirl **Mrs H. J. Moorhead**
67 **NEBULA STORM (IRE)**, 7, b g Galileo (IRE)—Epping **Mr R. H. MacNabb**
68 **NETHERBY**, 8, b g Fair Mix (IRE)—Lissadell (IRE) **R. Green**
69 **OSGOOD**, 7, b g Danehill Dancer (IRE)—Sabreon
70 **PORTRAIT EMOTION (IRE)**, 7, ch g Portrait Gallery (IRE)—Gleann Present (IRE) **Heart Of The South Racing**
71 **PROXIMATE**, 4, b g Nayef (USA)—Contiguous (USA) **Mr P. B. Moorhead**
72 **PUISQUE TU PARS (FR)**, 4, b g Walk In The Park (IRE)—Pierre Azuree (FR) **Dedman Properties Limited**
73 **REBLIS (FR)**, 9, b g Assessor (IRE)—Silbere (FR) **Kingsley, Avery, Farr, Glover, Humphreys**
74 4, B c Midnight Legend—Recipe
75 **REGAL PARK (IRE)**, 7, b g Montjeu (IRE)—Classic Park **Mrs A. Gloag**
76 **REZWAAN**, 7, b g Alhaarth (IRE)—Nasij (USA) **Gallagher Equine Ltd**
77 **ROME**, 4, b g Holy Roman Emperor (IRE)—Magical Cliche (USA) **Heart Of The South Racing**
78 **ROSSETTI**, 6, gr g Dansili—Snowdrops **Sheikh A'Leg Racing**
79 **ROYAL COLLEGE**, 4, b g Pastoral Pursuits—Stroppi Poppi **D. M. Newland**
80 **SANTADELACRUZE**, 5, b g Pastoral Pursuits—Jupiters Princess **Mr D. M. & Mrs M. A. Newland**
81 **SHADARPOUR (IRE)**, 5, b g Dr Fong (USA)—Shamadara (IRE) **G. L. Porter**
82 **SHALIANZI (IRE)**, 4, b g Azamour (IRE)—Shalama (IRE) **Mr A. J. Head**
83 **SHAMAHAN**, 5, b g Shamardal (USA)—Hanella (IRE) **Heart Of The South Racing**
84 **SHOULD I STAY (FR)**, 6, b g Muhtathir—Dusky Royale (FR) **M. L. Bloodstock Ltd**
85 **SILVER BULLITT**, 6, gr g Proclamation (IRE)—Eurolinka (USA) **Dahab Racing**
86 **SIRCOZY (IRE)**, 8, b g Celtic Swing—Furnish **G. L. Moore**
87 **SIRE DE GRUGY (FR)**, 8, ch g My Risk (FR)—Hirlish (FR) **The Preston Family & Friends**
88 **SONG AND DANCE MAN**, 4, b g Danehill Dancer (IRE)—Song **Owner**
89 **SOUTH CAPE**, 11, b g Cape Cross (IRE)—Aunt Ruby (USA) **Heart Of The South Racing & Friends**
90 **STENTORIAN (IRE)**, 6, ch g Street Cry (IRE)—Nomistakeaboutit (CAN) **B. G. Homewood**
91 **SUDDEN WISH (IRE)**, 5, b m Jeremy (USA)—Fun Time **M & R Refurbishments Ltd**
92 5, Gr g Fair Mix (IRE)—Sunley Shines
93 **SWAMPFIRE (IRE)**, 6, b g Anabaa (USA)—Moonfire **Mr I. Beach**
94 **THE GAME IS A FOOT (IRE)**, 7, b g Oscar (IRE)—Cooksgrove Rosie (IRE) **G. L. Moore**
95 **THE GREEN OGRE**, 4, b g Dubai Destination (USA)—Takegawa **Leydens Farm Stud**
96 **TOP DIKTAT**, 6, b g Diktat—Top Romance (IRE) **Miss T. R. Hale**
97 **TOTHEMOONANDBACK (IRE)**, 6, gr g Dr Massini (IRE)—Mrs Jones (FR) **David & Jane George**
98 **UBAK (FR)**, 6, b g Kapgarde (FR)—Gesse Parade (FR) **Mr N. J. Peacock**
99 **VIA SUNDOWN (FR)**, 6, ch g Until Sundown (USA)—Via Fratina (FR) **The Old Brokers**
100 **VIKEKHAL (FR)**, 5, b g Khalkevi (IRE)—Gesse Parade (FR) **The Old Brokers**
101 **VINO GRIEGO (FR)**, 9, b g Kahyasi—Vie de Reine (FR) **C. E. Stedman**
102 **VIOLET DANCER**, 4, b g Bertolini (USA)—Another Secret **D Bessell & Galloping On The South Downs**
103 **WELL REFRESHED**, 10, b g Nikos—Cool Spring (IRE) **P. J. Wilmott**
104 **WHILE YOU WAIT (IRE)**, 5, b g Whipper (USA)—Azra (IRE) **Galloping On The South Downs Partnership**
105 **WHINGING WILLIE (IRE)**, 5, b g Cape Cross (IRE)—Pacific Grove **Mr P. B. Moorhead**
106 **WHITBY JACK**, 7, b g Bering—Sablonne (USA) **C. E. Stedman**
107 **ZOUTI (FR)**, 6, b g Kahyasi—Reine de Sabot (FR) **Mr David Miles & Mr M G Rogers**

THREE-YEAR-OLDS

108 **DAZZA**, ch f Bertolini (USA)—Another Secret **Galloping On The South Downs Partnership**
109 **DIVINE BAY**, b f Dutch Art—Inchcoonan **The Winning Hand**
110 **DRACO'S CODE**, b c Galileo (IRE)—Lady Karr
111 **DUTCH INTERIOR**, ch g Dutch Art—Rotunda **R. Green**

MR GARY MOORE - Continued

112 **DUTCHARTCOLLECTOR,** b g Dutch Art—Censored **R. Green**
113 **DYNAMIC RANGER (USA),** b c U S Ranger (USA)—Dynamous (USA) **Mr M. L. Albon**
114 **JERSEY CREAM (IRE),** ch f Iffraaj—Unicamp **C. E. Stedman**
115 **LADY MARL,** b f Duke of Marmalade (IRE)—Empress Anna (IRE) **Sir Eric Parker**
116 **PUSHKIN MUSEUM (IRE),** gr g Soviet Star (USA)—Chaste **R. Green**
117 **ROMAN RICHES,** b c Holy Roman Emperor (IRE)—Dyna Bowl (USA) **Five Star Racing Group & Partners**
118 **TARA'S TREASURE (IRE),** b c Amadeus Wolf—Bean Island (USA) **G. L. Moore**
119 **THIRD STRIKE,** b c Tertullian (USA)—Shaabra (IRE) **Mr C. E. Stedman & A. R. Blaxland**

TWO-YEAR-OLDS

120 B c 19/4 Galileo (IRE)—
　　　　Beauty Bright (IRE) (Danehill (USA)) (116143) **Galloping On The South Downs Partnership**
121 **BORIS ISLAND,** gr c 26/3 Bushranger (IRE)—
　　　　Someone's Angel (USA) (Runaway Groom (CAN)) (10000) **Mark Albon & Chris Stedman**
122 **DUTCH GOLDEN AGE (IRE),** b c 19/3 Kodiac—Magic Melody (Petong) (30971) **Mr R. A. Green**
123 B f 28/3 Arcano (IRE)—Jazz Up (Cadeaux Genereux) (29000) **Mr Colin Bird**
124 B f 22/3 Kodiac—Millay (Polish Precedent (USA)) (20131) **C. E. Stedman**
125 B c 24/2 Dark Angel (IRE)—Moriches (IRE) (Alhaarth (IRE)) (23228)
126 B c 14/2 Henrythenavigator (USA)—Santolina (Boundary (USA)) (60000) **Newco 1111 Ltd**
127 B c 17/3 Lope de Vega (IRE)—Woodmaven (USA) (Woodman (USA)) (70000) **Newco 1111 Ltd**

Other Owners: Mr M. Albon, Miss Gill Arthur, Mrs E. Avery, Mr David Bessell, Mr A. R. Blaxland, Mr A. Brightwell, Mr R. Brown, Rev L. M. Brown, Mr M. Burne, Mr Don Churston, Mrs M. A. Cole, Mr M. J. Coles, Mr D. J. Coles, Mr J. A. Collins, Mr Gary Fenlon, Mr Bryan Fry, Mr D. W. George, Mrs Jane George, Mr M. Goodrum, Mr R. E. Greatorex, Mr Chris Green, Mr B. D. Haynes, Mr Ashley Head, Mr R. Henderson, Mr Philip Herbert, Mrs L. Jenkins, Mr Kevin Jupp, Mr P. Kingsley, Mr Darren Langley, Mr Richard Lockwood, Mr Steve Michael, Mr D. Miles, Mr G. L. Moore, Mrs M. A. Newland, Mr D. Newland, Sir Eric Parker, Mr Nick Peacock, Mr John Penny, Miss Eloise Penny, Mr N. J. Roach, Mr M. G. Rogers, Mr R. M. Siddle, Mrs S. J. Somner, Mrs Carola Somner, Mr C. E. Stedman, Mr M. C. Waddingham, Mr S. Wishart.

Assistant Trainer: David Wilson

Jockey (flat): George Baker, Ryan Moore, Fergus Sweeney. **Jockey (NH):** Jamie Moore. **Conditional:** Joshua Moore, Lee Oswin. **Apprentice:** Hector Crouch, Jayne Farwell. **Amateur:** Mr George Gorman, Miss Hayley Moore.

444　MR GEORGE MOORE, Middleham

Postal: **Warwick Lodge Stables, Middleham, Leyburn, North Yorkshire, DL8 4PB**
Contacts: **PHONE** (01969) 623823 **FAX** (01969) 623823 **MOBILE** (07711) 321117
E-MAIL georgeandcarolmoore@hotmail.co.uk **WEBSITE** www.george-moore-racing.co.uk

1 **ASEELA (IRE),** 4, b f Teofilo (IRE)—Valse Mystique (IRE) **Mrs S. C. Moore**
2 **BRASINGAMAN ESPEE,** 5, b h Silver Patriarch (IRE)—Serene Pearl (IRE) **Mr R. J. Morgan**
3 **CHARLES DE MILLE,** 6, b g Tiger Hill (IRE)—Apple Town **Mrs Liz Ingham**
4 **COMICAL,** 5, b g Dubai Destination (USA)—Amusing Time (IRE) **The Comedians**
5 **COWSLIP,** 5, b m Tobougg (IRE)—Forsythia **Mrs I. I. Plumb**
6 **DON'T TELL,** 4, ch f Sakhee's Secret—Starry Sky **Evelyn, Duchess of Sutherland**
7 **ERICA STARPRINCESS,** 4, b f Bollin Eric—Presidium Star **Richard J. Phizacklea**
8 **EXCLUSIVE DANCER,** 5, gr m Notnowcato—Exclusive Approval (USA) **D. Parker**
9 **JACK THE GENT (IRE),** 10, b g Anshan—Asidewager (IRE) **J. B. Wallwin**
10 **JUST FABULOUS,** 5, b m Sakhee (USA)—Tipsy Me **S. P. Graham**
11 **LACOCODANZA,** 5, b m Tamure (IRE)—Miss Petronella **A Crute & Partners**
12 **LADY AMAKHALA,** 6, b m Val Royal (FR)—Isla Negra (IRE) **Mrs S. M. Pearson**
13 **LADY BUSANDA,** 4, b f Fair Mix (IRE)—Spirit of Ecstasy **Mrs S. M. Pearson**
14 **LADY POPPY,** 4, b f Kyllachy—Poppets Sweetlove **Ingham Racing Syndicate**
15 **NOT ANOTHER MONDAY (IRE),** 6, b br g Great Palm—Americo Rescue (IRE) **J. B. Wallwin**
16 **PETELLA,** 8, b m Tamure (IRE)—Miss Petronella **Mrs S. C. Moore**
17 **THE SHY MAN (IRE),** 11, b g Grand Plaisir (IRE)—Black Betty **S. P. Graham**
18 **TOMORROW'S LEGEND,** 4, br g Midnight Legend—Colvada **Mrs M. Hatfield & Mrs S. Kramer**
19 **TURF TRIVIA,** 7, gr g Alhaarth (IRE)—Exclusive Approval (USA) **Mrs M. Hatfield & Mrs S. Kramer**
20 **WOLF SHIELD (IRE),** 7, b g King's Theatre (IRE)—Garlucy (IRE) **Mrs J. M. Gray**
21 **WOLF SWORD (IRE),** 5, b g Flemensfirth (USA)—Dame O'neill (IRE) **G. R. Orchard**

THREE-YEAR-OLDS

22 **BENTONS LAD,** br g Bollin Eric—Spirit of Ecstasy **Mr A. G. Benton**
23 **HIGHWAY PURSUIT,** b g Pastoral Pursuits—Extreme Pleasure (IRE) **Mrs G. A. Kendall**

MR GEORGE MOORE - Continued

24 **LADY DANCER (IRE)**, b f Captain Rio—Anessia **Mrs Liz Ingham**
25 **LADY LIZ**, b f Byron—Sister Rose (FR) **Mrs Liz Ingham**
26 **LADY YEATS**, b f Yeats (IRE)—Oblique (IRE) **A Crute & Partners**
27 **MEDICINE HAT**, b g Multiplex—Blushing Heart **Mrs D. N. B. Pearson**
28 **ROKEBY**, b g Byron—Scarlet Royal **Mrs Liz Ingham**

TWO-YEAR-OLDS

29 **EGMONT**, b c 10/5 Notnowcato—Salutare (IRE) (Sadler's Wells (USA)) (40000) **Mr T. S. Ingham**

Other Owners: Mr A. Crute, Mrs C. A. Crute, Mrs J. M. Gray, Mrs Mary Hatfield, Mrs Susan Kramer, Mr G. R. Orchard.

Assistant Trainer: Mrs Susan Moore

Jockey (flat): P. J. McDonald, Andrew Mullen. **Jockey (NH):** Barry Keniry. **Apprentice:** Keiran Schofield.
Amateur: Mr Mathew Garnett.

---

445 **MR J. S. MOORE, Upper Lambourn**
Postal: **Berkeley House Stables, Upper Lambourn, Hungerford, Berkshire, RG17 8QP**
Contacts: **PHONE** (01488) 73887 **FAX** (01488) 73997 **MOBILE** (07860) 811127 / (07900) 402856
E-MAIL jsmoore.racing@btopenworld.com **WEBSITE** www.stanmooreracing.co.uk

1 **PADDY'S SALTANTES (IRE)**, 4, b g Redback—Shall We Tell **Wall To Wall Partnership**
2 **SHEILA'S BUDDY**, 5, ch g Reel Buddy (USA)—Loreto Rose **Mr R. J. Styles**
3 **TEOLAGI (IRE)**, 4, ch g Teofilo (IRE)—Satulagi (USA) **Mrs Fitri Hay**

THREE-YEAR-OLDS

4 **ADIMENDIS (IRE)**, b g Elnadim (USA)—Endis (IRE) **Mr K. Kirkup & J. S. Moore**
5 **ALFIE LUNETE (IRE)**, b f Footstepsinthesand—La Lunete **Mr Ross Peters & J. S. Moore**
6 **BONJOUR STEVE**, b g Bahamian Bounty—Anthea **Iconic Partnership & J. S. Moore**
7 **CAROLINE'S BEACH (IRE)**, ch f Footstepsinthesand—Rohain (IRE) **Mr Kieron Badger & J. S. Moore**
8 **DULY ACCLAIMED (IRE)**, b f Acclamation—Cloonkeary **Mr R. J. Styles, Mr P. Grimes & J. S. Moore**
9 **EMERALD GG (IRE)**, b g Diamond Green (FR)—Florista Gg (URU) **Mrs Fitri Hay**
10 **LADY KNIGHT (IRE)**, b f Champs Elysees—Knight's Place (IRE) **Mr J. Bond-Smith & J. S. Moore**
11 **MARTI'S BOY**, ch g Bertolini (USA)—Rock Art (IRE) **Mr Jim Barnes & J. S. Moore**
12 **MOUNTAIN RIVER (IRE)**, br g Footstepsinthesand—Animalu (IRE) **Mr D. Kerr & J. S. Moore**
13 **MY MY MY DILIZA**, br f Sakhee's Secret—Diliza **Mr R. J. Styles, Mr P. Grimes & J. S. Moore**
14 **POUND PIECE (IRE)**, b g Ad Valorem (USA)—Peps (IRE) **Mr G. B. Watts & J. S. Moore**
15 **SHEILA'S FOOTSTEPS**, b g Footstepsinthesand—Marmaga (IRE) **Mr R. J. Styles & J. S. Moore**
16 **STARLIGHT PRINCESS (IRE)**, b f Mastercraftsman—Definitely Royal (IRE) **J. S. Moore**
17 **SWEET ALIBI (IRE)**, b f Lawman (FR)—Zingari **Mr G. V. March & J. S. Moore**
18 **TABLEFORTEN**, ch g Pastoral Pursuits—Twitch Hill **Eventmasters Racing**
19 **TALKSALOT (IRE)**, b g Thousand Words—Lady Piste (IRE) **Mr J. Bond-Smith & J. S. Moore**
20 **VODKA CHASER (IRE)**, b f Baltic King—Suffer Her (IRE) **Mr N. Attenborough, Mrs L. Mann, J. S. Moore**

TWO-YEAR-OLDS

21 B c 27/4 Duke of Marmalade (IRE)—Abandon (USA) (Rahy (USA)) (1000)
22 B f 17/4 Rip Van Winkle (IRE)—Antinea (Royal Applause) (5032) **Mr Peter Grimes & J. S. Moore**
23 **AREION (IRE)**, gr f 24/4 Zebedee—Grecian Glory (IRE) (Zafonic (USA)) (619) **The Bottom Liners & J. S. Moore**
24 B br c 29/4 More Than Ready (USA)—Balletomaine (IRE) (Sadler's Wells (USA)) (40262) **Mrs Fitri Hay**
25 Br g 9/3 Moss Vale (IRE)—Caro Mio (IRE) (Danehill Dancer (IRE)) (4645)
26 B f 20/4 Indesatchel (IRE)—Darling Buds (Reel Buddy (USA)) (476)
27 B g 30/3 Excellent Art—Diksie Dancer (Diktat) (1904)
28 **ENDLISLIE**, b c 15/2 Amadeus Wolf—
                              Endis (IRE) (Distant Relative) (2167) **Mrs Evelyn Yates Mr T. Yates and J. S. Moore**
29 **EVER PHEASANT (IRE)**, b c 23/2 Alfred Nobel (IRE)—
                              Indian Bounty (Indian Ridge) (14000) **Ever Equine & J. S. Moore**
30 B f 1/3 Alfred Nobel (IRE)—Fantastic Belle (IRE) (Night Shift (USA)) (15485)
31 B f 9/4 Acclamation—Fully Fashioned (IRE) (Brief Truce) (40262) **Mr Abdullateef Al Zeer**
32 **GILDED LACE**, b f 16/3 Virtual—Regal Gallery (IRE) (Royal Academy (USA)) (1200)
33 B g 20/4 Bertolini (USA)—Iamfine (IRE) (Whipper (USA)) (9523)
34 **KIDMEFOREVER**, ch f 2/2 Piccolo—Shore Light (USA) (Gulch (USA)) (1904) **Ever Equine & J. S. Moore**
35 B c 7/5 Alhaarth (IRE)—La Cuvee (Mark of Esteem (IRE)) (10000)
36 B f 1/2 Dylan Thomas (IRE)—Love Thirty (Mister Baileys) (3871) **Mr N. Alrefaie**
37 Ch g 22/3 Makfi—Morinqua (IRE) (Cadeaux Genereux) (6666) **Mr Peter Grimes & J. S. Moore**

MR J. S. MOORE - Continued

38 **MOUNT ISA,** b c 20/1 Bushranger (IRE)—Fee Eria (FR) (Always Fair (USA)) (5714) **The Moore The Merrier**
39 B g 27/3 Excellent Art—Positive Step (IRE) (Footstepsinthesand) (2322)
40 B f 24/3 Major Cadeaux—Reel Cool (Reel Buddy (USA)) (476)
41 B g 1/4 Rock of Gibraltar (IRE)—Reine Violette (FR) (Fly To The Stars) (3871) **Mr G. V. March & J. S. Moore**
42 **SHE'S GOT THE NUTS (IRE),** b f 12/4 Camacho—
Rainbow Above You (IRE) (Mujadil (USA)) (1904) **Poker Boys & J. S. Moore**

Other Owners: Mr N. B. Attenborough, Mr Kieron Badger, Mr Jim Barnes, Mr John Bond-Smith, Mr Gabriel Chrysanthou, Mr Gerry Connor, Mr Ian Gray, Mr P Grimes, Mr Ron Hull, Mr Robin Johnson, Mr Donald M. Kerr, Mr Kevin Kirkup, Mrs Lyndsey Mann, Mr G. V. March, Mr J. S. Moore, Mr Ross Peters, Mr R. J. Rexton, Mrs Denise Sheasby, Mr S. Sheehan, Mr Ray Styles, Mr Gary B. Watts, Mr Stephen Williams, Mr T. Yates, Mrs Evelyn Yates.

Assistant Trainer: Mrs S. Moore

Jockey (flat): Liam Jones. **Apprentice:** Kristy French.

---

446 **MR KEVIN MORGAN, Newmarket**
Postal: Gazeley Park Stables, 13 - 15 Moulton Road, Gazeley, Newmarket, Suffolk, CB8 8RA
Contacts: **PHONE (01638) 551888 FAX (01638) 551888 MOBILE (07768) 996103**
E-MAIL morgan.k@btconnect.com

1 **ANAN,** 8, br g Cape Cross (IRE)—Hawafiz **Roemex Ltd**
2 **CAMERA SHY (IRE),** 10, ch g Pivotal—Shy Danceuse (FR) **Mr M. D. Ogburn**
3 **EZDIYAAD (IRE),** 10, b g Galileo (IRE)—Wijdan (USA) **Roemex Ltd**
4 **FLAMIN JUNE,** 8, ch m Karinga Bay—Nessfield **Mr J. Duckworth**
5 **GO RUBY GO,** 10, b m Karinga Bay—Nessfield **Mr J. Duckworth**
6 **HAAMES (IRE),** 7, b g Kheleyf (USA)—Jumilla (USA) **Roemex Ltd**
7 **ISDAAL,** 7, ch m Dubawi (IRE)—Faydah (USA) **Roemex Ltd**
8 **MAREEF (IRE),** 4, b g Oasis Dream—Katayeb (IRE) **Roemex Ltd**
9 **MY FARMER GIRL,** 8, b m Karinga Bay—See My Girl **Mr J. Duckworth**
10 **RAAMZ (IRE),** 7, ch m Haahld—Tarbiyah **Roemex Ltd**
11 **SHE'S A HONEY,** 4, ch f Firebreak—Manuka Too (IRE) **Mr D. Ablitt**
12 **TAARESH (IRE),** 9, b g Sakhee (USA)—Tanaghum **Roemex Ltd**

Head Lad: S. Rathore

Jockey (flat): Jimmy Quinn. **Jockey (NH):** Leighton Aspell.

---

447 **MR DAVE MORRIS, Newmarket**
Postal: Mokefield, Baxters Green, Wickhambrook, Newmarket, Suffolk, CB8 8UY
Contacts: **PHONE (01284) 850248 FAX (01284) 850248 MOBILE (07711) 010268**

1 **CHEZ VRONY,** 8, b g Lujain (USA)—Polish Abbey **Stag & Huntsman**
2 **JAMAICA GRANDE,** 6, ch g Doyen (IRE)—Mary Sea (FR) **Mr S. C. Wood**

THREE-YEAR-OLDS

3 **WATER FOR LIFE,** ch f Mount Nelson—Echo River (USA) **D. P. Fremel**

Other Owners: Ms C. C. Fagerstrom, Lord Hambleden.

Jockey (flat): Franny Norton.

---

448 **MR M. F. MORRIS, Fethard**
Postal: Everardsgrange, Fethard, Co. Tipperary, Ireland
Contacts: **PHONE (00353) 52 6131474 FAX (00353) 52 6131654**
E-MAIL mouse@eircom.net

1 **AKORAKOR (FR),** 5, ch g Lando (GER)—Great Way (FR) **Gigginstown House Stud**
2 **ALLIED VICTORY (IRE),** 5, b g Old Vic—Echo Creek (IRE) **Gigginstown House Stud**
3 **BAILY DUSK (IRE),** 8, br g Dushyantor (USA)—Gentle Lady (IRE) **A. R. Scott**
4 **BAILY GREEN (IRE),** 8, b g King's Theatre (IRE)—Dream On Boys (IRE) **A. R. Scott**
5 **BALLYSTEEN (IRE),** 8, b g Elnadim (USA)—Winning Jenny (IRE) **Gigginstown House Stud**

MR M. F. MORRIS - Continued

6 **BRUFF (IRE)**, 7, b g Presenting—Aniston (IRE) **J. P. McManus**
7 **CALL RÓG (IRE)**, 6, b g Beneficial—Lady Fancy (IRE) **J. P. McManus**
8 **CARRY EACH OTHER (IRE)**, 8, b g Milan—Jennys Supreme (IRE) **Gigginstown House Stud**
9 **DROMNEA (IRE)**, 7, b br g Presenting—Fifth Imp (IRE) **Mrs A. Daly**
10 **EASTER HUNT (IRE)**, 5, br g Kalanisi (IRE)—Easter Day (IRE) **Gigginstown House Stud**
11 **FIRST LIEUTENANT (IRE)**, 9, ch g Presenting—Fourstargale (IRE) **Gigginstown House Stud**
12 **GORGEOUSREACH (IRE)**, 6, b m Turtle Island (IRE)—Fifth Imp (IRE) **Mrs A. Daly**
13 **HORENDUS HULABALOO (IRE)**, 5, b g Beneficial—Renvyle Society (IRE) **Gigginstown House Stud**
14 **LET'S CELEBRATE (IRE)**, 6, b g Oscar (IRE)—Blooming Quick (IRE) **J. P. McManus**
15 **MIRADANE**, 7, b g Kayf Tara—Coolvawn Lady (IRE) **B. Maloney**
16 **ORYX FALCON (IRE)**, 5, ch g Presenting—Park Athlete (IRE) **B. Maloney**
17 **RATHLIN**, 9, b g Kayf Tara—Princess Timon **Gigginstown House Stud**
18 **RAVISHED (IRE)**, 6, b g Oscar (IRE)—Fair Present (IRE) **Gigginstown House Stud**
19 **ROGUE ANGEL (IRE)**, 6, b g Presenting—Carrigeen Kohleria (IRE) **Gigginstown House Stud**
20 **RULE THE WORLD**, 7, b g Sulamani (IRE)—Elaine Tully (IRE) **Gigginstown House Stud**
21 **RUN WITH THE TIDE (IRE)**, 6, b g Milan—Cullian **J. P. McManus**
22 **SPOT FINE**, 8, b g Kayf Tara—Lily The Lark **M. & J. O'Flynn**
23 **TAKE THE HIT (IRE)**, 6, b g Turtle Island (IRE)—Winged Rocket (IRE) **L. F. Curtin**
24 **THE DOORMAN (IRE)**, 5, b g King's Theatre (IRE)—Amber Light (IRE) **J. P. McManus**
25 **THE MYSTRO (IRE)**, 5, ch g Golan (IRE)—Going For Home (IRE) **S. O'Driscoll**
26 **TINAKELLYLAD (IRE)**, 10, b g Witness Box (USA)—Iora (IRE) **Mrs B. Twomey**

---

449 MR PATRICK MORRIS, Prescot

Postal: **Avenue House, George Hale Avenue, Knowsley Park, Prescot, Merseyside, L34 4AJ**
Contacts: **MOBILE (07545) 425235**
E-MAIL info@patmorrisracing.co.uk WEBSITE www.patmorrisracing.co.uk

1 **BALLESTEROS**, 5, ch g Tomba—Flamenco Dancer **Dr M. B. Q. S. Koukash**
2 **BRAE HILL (IRE)**, 8, b g Fath (USA)—Auriga **Dr M. B. Q. S. Koukash**
3 **CLASSY TRICK (USA)**, 4, b g Hat Trick (JPN)—Classiest Gem (CAN) **Dr M. B. Q. S. Koukash**
4 **ENGLISH SUMMER**, 7, b g Montjeu (IRE)—Hunt The Sun **Dr M. B. Q. S. Koukash**
5 **EWELL PLACE (IRE)**, 5, br g Namid—Miss Gibraltar **Dr M. B. Q. S. Koukash**
6 **GABRIAL THE DUKE (IRE)**, 4, ch g Duke of Marmalade (IRE)—Literacy (USA) **Dr M. B. Q. S. Koukash**
7 **GABRIAL THE HERO (USA)**, 5, b g War Front (USA)—Ball Gown (USA) **Dr M. B. Q. S. Koukash**
8 **GABRIAL THE MASTER (IRE)**, 4, ch g Strategic Prince—Kualke (IRE) **Dr M. B. Q. S. Koukash**
9 **GABRIAL'S BOUNTY (IRE)**, 5, ch g Bahamian Bounty—Social Storm (USA) **Dr M. B. Q. S. Koukash**
10 **GABRIAL'S KAKA (IRE)**, 4, b g Jeremy (USA)—Love In May (IRE) **Dr M. B. Q. S. Koukash**
11 **GATEPOST (IRE)**, 5, br g Footstepsinthesand—Mandama (IRE) **Dr M. B. Q. S. Koukash**
12 **GRAMERCY (IRE)**, 7, b g Whipper—Topiary (IRE) **Dr M. B. Q. S. Koukash**
13 **MANDY THE NAG (USA)**, 4, b br f Proud Citizen (USA)—Storm to Glory (USA) **Dr M. B. Q. S. Koukash**
14 **MEHDI (IRE)**, 5, b g Holy Roman Emperor (IRE)—College Fund Girl (IRE) **Dr M. B. Q. S. Koukash**
15 **MONTASER (IRE)**, 5, b g Rail Link—For Example (IRE) **Dr M. B. Q. S. Koukash**
16 **NASHVILLE (IRE)**, 5, b g Galileo (IRE)—Brown Eyes **Dr M. B. Q. S. Koukash**
17 **OUR JONATHAN**, 7, b g Invincible Spirit (IRE)—Sheik'n Swing **Dr M. B. Q. S. Koukash**
18 **RAINFORD GLORY (IRE)**, 4, ch g Rock of Gibraltar (IRE)—My Dolly Madison (USA) **Dr M. B. Q. S. Koukash**
19 **SUEGIOO (FR)**, 5, ch g Manduro (GER)—Mantesera (IRE) **Dr M. B. Q. S. Koukash**
20 **SUMMERINTHECITY (IRE)**, 7, ch g Indian Ridge—Miss Assertive **Dr M. B. Q. S. Koukash**
21 **TANGO SKY (IRE)**, 5, b g Namid—Sky Galaxy (USA) **Dr M. B. Q. S. Koukash**
22 **VERY GOOD DAY (FR)**, 7, b g Sinndar (IRE)—Picture Princess **Dr M. B. Q. S. Koukash**

THREE-YEAR-OLDS

23 **BRIAN NOBLE**, b c Royal Applause—Little Greenbird **Dr M. B. Q. S. Koukash**
24 **LAYLA'S RED DEVIL (IRE)**, b f Dalakhani (IRE)—Brazilian Samba (IRE) **Dr M. B. Q. S. Koukash**
25 **RANGI CHASE (IRE)**, b c Lawman (FR)—Tirunesh (USA) **Dr M. B. Q. S. Koukash**
26 B f High Chaparral (IRE)—Shakti **Dr M. B. Q. S. Koukash**

450 MR HUGHIE MORRISON, East Ilsley
Postal: Summerdown, East Ilsley, Newbury, Berkshire, RG20 7LB
Contacts: PHONE (01635) 281678 FAX (01635) 281746 MOBILE (07836) 687799
E-MAIL hughie@hughiemorrison.co.uk WEBSITE www.hughiemorrison.co.uk

1 **ABI SCARLET (IRE)**, 5, b m Baltic King—Petarga **H. Morrison**
2 **AIYANA**, 4, ch f Indian Haven—Coventina (IRE) **The End-R-Ways Partnership**
3 **ANOTHER COCKTAIL**, 4, b g Dalakhani (IRE)—Yummy Mummy **M. Kerr-Dineen**
4 **BANOFFEE (IRE)**, 4, b f Hurricane Run (IRE)—Nanabanana (IRE) **Michael Kerr-Dineen & Lord Margardale**
5 **BROTHER BRIAN (IRE)**, 6, b g Millenary—Miner Detail (IRE) **L. A. Garfield**
6 **BURNHAM**, 5, b g Nayef (USA)—Salim Toto **The Hill Stud**
7 **CARRAIG ROCK**, 4, b g Beat Hollow—Riverine **Pangfield Racing III**
8 **CHIL THE KITE**, 5, b g Notnowcato—Copy-Cat **Hazel Lawrence & Graham Doyle**
9 **CONQUESTADIM**, 4, b g Elnadim (USA)—Conquestadora **The Fairy Story Partnership**
10 **COUSIN KHEE**, 7, b g Sakhee (USA)—Cugina **R. C. Tooth**
11 **FANZINE**, 4, ch f Medicean—Dash To The Front **Helena Springfield Ltd**
12 4, Ch f Double Trigger (IRE)—Flirtatious **Mrs M. D. W. Morrison**
13 **LYRIC BALLAD**, 4, b f Byron—Skies Are Blue **Mr T D Rootes & Mr O F Waller**
14 **MAX THE MINISTER**, 4, bl g Pastoral Pursuits—Franciscaine (FR) **Mrs M. D. W. Morrison**
15 **MIDAZ**, 4, br g Zamindar (USA)—Schlague (FR) **Mrs M. T. Bevan & Mr S. de Zoete**
16 **NEARLY CAUGHT (IRE)**, 4, b c New Approach (IRE)—Katch Me Katie **A. N. Solomons**
17 **PASTORAL PLAYER**, 7, b g Pastoral Pursuits—Copy-Cat **The Pursuits Partnership**
18 **PETE THE PASTOR**, 6, b g Pastoral Pursuits—Franciscaine (FR) **Mrs M. D. W. Morrison**
19 **QUIZ MISTRESS**, 6, ch m Doyen (IRE)—Seren Quest **The Fairy Story Partnership**
20 **REALIZE**, 4, b g Zafeen (FR)—Relkida **Deborah Collett & M. J. Watson**
21 **SECRET TALENT**, 4, b g Sakhee's Secret—Aqaba **Wood Street Syndicate IV**
22 **ZIEKHANI**, 4, ch gr c Dalakhani (IRE)—Zietory **The Fairy Story Partnership**

THREE-YEAR-OLDS

23 **ARAB DAWN**, gr c Dalakhani (IRE)—Victoire Celebre (USA) **Eason,Kerr-Dineen,Hughes,Edwards-Jones**
24 **BACKSTAGE GOSSIP**, b f Sakhee's Secret—Theatre Royal **Runs In The Family**
25 **BALTIC BRAVE (IRE)**, b g Baltic King—Negria (IRE) **The Brave Partnership**
26 **BLACK RODDED**, ch f Bahamian Bounty—Palace Affair **The Socrates Partnership**
27 **BON PORT**, b f Major Cadeaux—Miss Poppy **Mr A C Pickford**
28 **BROTHER KHEE**, ch g Sakhee's Secret—Cugina **R. C. Tooth**
29 **CASCADING**, b f Teofilo (IRE)—Angel Falls **Thurloe Thoroughbreds XXXI**
30 **CHUFFT**, b f Sleeping Indian—Relkida **Deborah Collett & M. J. Watson**
31 **COASTAL STORM**, b f Manduro (GER)—Ruff Shod (USA) **Turf Club 2012**
32 **CONCRETE MAC**, b g Mastercraftsman (IRE)—Merry Diva **Adrian Mcalpine & Partners**
33 **DISCREETLY**, b f Sakhee's Secret—Aqaba **Wood Street Syndicate**
34 **FRUIT PASTILLE**, b f Pastoral Pursuits—Classic Millennium **Mrs I. Eavis**
35 **FUN MAC (GER)**, ch c Shirocco (GER)—Favorite (GER) **Mrs Angela McAlpine & Partners**
36 **KELAMITA (IRE)**, ch f Pivotal—Keladora (USA) **M. E. Wates**
37 **KEY TO YOUR HEART**, b f Sakhee (USA)—You Too **Helena Springfield Ltd**
38 **LADY BABOOSHKA**, b f Cape Cross (IRE)—Balalaika **Helena Springfield Ltd**
39 **MARSH DAISY**, ch f Pivotal—Bella Lambada **Sir Thomas Pilkington & Mrs S Rogers**
40 **MISS MOPPET**, b f Nayef (USA)—So Blissful (IRE) **L. A. Garfield**
41 **MOSHE (IRE)**, b c Dansili—Rosinka **Capt J. Macdonald-Buchanan**
42 **NISSAKI KASTA**, ch f Sakhee's Secret—Casterossa **Mr D. P. Barrie**
43 Ch c Black Sam Bellamy (IRE)—Riverine **Pangfield Racing**
44 **SOAK (IRE)**, gr f Verglas (IRE)—Ive Gota Bad Liver (USA) **St Albans Bloodstock LLP**
45 **SOUTHERN CROSS**, ch f Mount Nelson—Bread of Heaven **David Chappell, Rod Lloyd & Partners**
46 **SUPACHAP**, br g High Chaparral (IRE)—Supamova (USA) **Sir Martyn Arbib**
47 **SWEEPING UP**, b f Sea The Stars (IRE)—Farfala (FR) **Ben & Sir Martyn Arbib**
48 **THUNDER PASS (IRE)**, b c High Chaparral (IRE)—Hadarama (IRE) **Thurloe Thoroughbreds XXXIII**
49 **TRIPLE STAR**, b f Royal Applause—Triple Sharp **Lady Hardy**
50 **VENT DE FORCE**, b c Hurricane Run (IRE)—Capriolla **The Fairy Story Partnership**

TWO-YEAR-OLDS

51 **ATALAN**, b c 3/3 Azamour (IRE)—Capriolla (In The Wings) **The Fairy Story Partnership**
52 **COMPTON MILL**, b c 21/2 Compton Place—Classic Millennium (Midyan (USA)) (15000) **Mr M Bevan**
53 **FIELD GAME**, b c 8/2 Pastoral Pursuits—Tarqua (IRE) (King Charlemagne (USA)) **Earl Of Carnarvon**
54 B f 2/2 Kheleyf (USA)—Fleeting Moon (Fleetwood (IRE)) **M. E. Wates**
55 **ICE BOAT (IRE)**, b br c 24/4 Verglas (IRE)—Yawl (Rainbow Quest (USA)) **Mr M. Dixon**
56 Br f 12/2 Rock of Gibraltar (IRE)—Kinetix (Linamix (FR)) (30000) **Helena Springfield Ltd**

MR HUGHIE MORRISON - Continued

57 B c 10/4 Dutch Art—Lawyers Choice (Namid) **R. C. Tooth**
58 **LITTLE PRAIRIE,** ch f 7/4 Exceed And Excel (AUS)—
  Chetwynd (IRE) (Exit To Nowhere) (105000) **Margadale, Scott, Kerr-Dineen & Scott-Barrett**
59 **MAJIC MAC,** b f 14/3 Stimulation (IRE)—
  Supatov (USA) (Johannesburg (USA)) (2857) **Mr Adrian McAlpine & Partners**
60 **MAJOR MAC,** ch c 22/3 Shirocco (GER)—
  Spring Fashion (IRE) (Galileo (IRE)) (31000) **Mr Adrian McAlpine, Mr Paul Brocklehurst & Partners**
61 **MANOLITO,** b c 12/2 High Chaparral (IRE)—
  Break Time (Dansili) (36000) **Malcolm, Hamilton Fairley, Plummer & Wechler**
62 B c 29/3 Stimulation (IRE)—Patteresa Girl (Auction House (USA)) (9000) **Annika Murjahn & Partners**
63 B c 9/2 Authorized (IRE)—
  Pentatonic (Giant's Causeway (USA)) (40000) **Hughes, Kerr-Dineen, Malcolm & Murjahn**
64 **PERCELLA,** b f 2/5 Sir Percy—
  Temple of Thebes (IRE) (Bahri (USA)) (22000) **Gabb, De Zoete, Trenchard, Pakenham**
65 **RESPECTABILITY,** b f 17/3 Echo of Light—Respectfilly (Mark of Esteem (IRE)) **The Fairy Story Partnership**
66 **SARSTED,** ch c 18/3 Paco Boy (IRE)—
  Red Blooded Woman (USA) (Red Ransom (USA)) (14000) **Annika Murjahn & Partners**
67 **SECRET JOURNEY (IRE),** ch c 13/2 Sakhee's Secret—
  Hinokia (IRE) (Forestry (USA)) (36000) **Mr S De Zoete, Mrs A Gabb, Mr T Pickford & Annika Murjahn**
68 Br gr f 30/1 Cape Cross (IRE)—Starfala (Galileo (IRE)) **Ben & Sir Martyn Arbib**
69 B c 30/1 Rip Van Winkle (IRE)—
  Strictly Lambada (Red Ransom (USA)) (50000) **Eason, Hughes, Kerr-Dineen & Malpas**
70 **SWEET SELECTION,** b f 10/2 Stimulation (IRE)—
  Sweet Coincidence (Mujahid (USA)) (29523) **Paul Brocklehurst & Ms Magdalena Gut**
71 B f 14/3 Sakhee's Secret—Yonder (And Beyond (IRE)) **Mrs M. D. W. Morrison**

Other Owners: Mr Ben Arbib, Sir Martyn Arbib, Mr D. P. Barrie, Mr Charles Benson, Mr M. T. Bevan, Mr T. M. Bird, Major D. N. Chappell, Miss D. Collett, Mr Graham Doyle, Mr William Eason, Mr Marcus Edwards-Jones, Mr L. A. Garfield, Mr E. R. Goodwin, Mouse Hamilton-Fairley, Mr Martin Hughes, Mr Michael Kerr-Dineen, Miss Hazel Lawrence, Capt. J. Macdonald-Buchanan, Lord Margadale, Mrs Satu Marks, Mr Adrian McAlpine, Mrs Angela McAlpine, Mr H. Morrison, Mrs M. D. W. Morrison, Mr B. G. W. Parker, Mr O. J. W. Pawle, Mr A. C. Pickford, Mrs Richard Plummer, Mr M. J. Rees, Mr T. D. Rootes, Miss C. S. Scott-Balls, Mr Hugh Scott-Barrett, Mr J. A. B. Stafford, Mr Andrew Stone, Mrs M. F. Stone, Mr G. D. W. Swire, Mr O. F. Waller, Mr M. J. Watson, Mr J. A. Wechsler, Mr Stan West, Mr Simon de Zoete.

Apprentice: Charlie Bennett. **Amateur:** Mr Robert Pooles.

---

451 MR GARRY MOSS, Tickhill
Postal: **The Barn, Moorhouse Farm, Tickhill, Doncaster DN11 9EY**
Contacts: **PHONE (01302) 746456 (07872) 993519 MOBILE (07791) 888129**

1 **GRACE HULL,** 4, gr f Piccolo—Smart Hostess **Mr R. Hull**
2 **LUCKY MARK (IRE),** 5, b g Moss Vale (IRE)—Vracca **Mr R. Hull**
3 **MOORHOUSE LAD,** 11, b g Bertolini (USA)—Record Time **Mr R. Hull**
4 **READY (IRE),** 4, ch g Elnadim (USA)—Fusili **Mr R. Hull**

THREE-YEAR-OLDS

5 **ARROWZONE,** b g Iffraaj—Donna Giovanna **Mr R. Hull**
6 **BOOLOO (IRE),** b g Bushranger (IRE)—Ink Pot (USA) **Mr R. Hull**
7 **FREDRICKA,** ch f Assertive—Vintage Steps **Mr R. Hull**
8 **HULCOLT (IRE),** b c Acclamation—Fusili (IRE) **Mr R. Hull**
9 **SLINKY MCVELVET,** ch f Refuse To Bend (IRE)—Rania (GER) **Mr R. Hull**

---

452 MR WILLIAM MUIR, Lambourn
Postal: **Linkslade, Wantage Road, Lambourn, Hungerford, Berkshire, RG17 8UG**
Contacts: **OFFICE (01488) 73098 HOME (01488) 73748 FAX (01488) 73490**
MOBILE (07831) 457074
E-MAIL william@williammuir.com WEBSITE www.williammuir.com

1 **ALICE'S DANCER (IRE),** 5, br m Clodovil (IRE)—Islandagore (IRE) **Perspicacious Punters Racing Club**
2 **BIG BAZ,** b g Pivotal—Gracefully (IRE) **The Big Baz Partnership**
3 **FLECKERL (IRE),** 4, b g Danehill Dancer (IRE)—Spinola (FR) **F. P. Hope**
4 **GRAYSWOOD,** 4, gr g Dalakhani (IRE)—Argent du Bois (USA) **C. L. A. Edginton**

MR WILLIAM MUIR - Continued

5 **KENNY'S GIRL (IRE)**, 4, b f Manduro (GER)—Tanz (IRE) **D. F. White**
6 **LADY WHO**, 4, b f Sir Percy—Herminoe **Mrs J. M. Muir**
7 **MAGIC SECRET**, 6, b g Trade Fair—Just Devine (IRE) **Carmel Stud**
8 **SECRET MISSILE**, 4, b g Sakhee's Secret—Malelane (GER) **Muir Racing Partnership - Manchester**
9 **SIOUXPERHERO (IRE)**, 5, b g Sleeping Indian—Tintern **Muir Racing Partnership - Bath**
10 **STEPPER POINT**, 5, b g Kyllachy—Sacre Coeur **C. L. A. Edginton**

THREE-YEAR-OLDS

11 **ALYS LOVE**, b f New Approach (IRE)—Porthcawl **Usk Valley Stud**
12 **ARMOURER (IRE)**, b g Azamour (IRE)—Engraving **D. G. Clarke & C. L. A. Edginton**
13 **AVOCADEAU (IRE)**, b g Lawman (FR)—Christmas Cracker (FR) **Mr J. M. O'Mulloy**
14 **BLACK SCHNAPPS (IRE)**, b c Manduro (GER)—Ornellaia (IRE) **O'Mulloy, Collinette, Quaintance, Clark**
15 **BLACKE FOREST**, b f Manduro (GER)—Welsh Cake **M. J. Caddy**
16 **CRY FREEDOM (IRE)**, b f Acclamation—Amistad (GER) **M. J. Caddy**
17 **DIVISION BELLE**, gr f Dalakhani (IRE)—Multiplication **Foursome Thoroughbreds**
18 **GULLAND ROCK**, b g Exceed And Excel (AUS)—Sacre Coeur **C. L. A. Edginton & K. Mercer**
19 **HALEO**, ch g Halling (USA)—Oatey **R. Haim**
20 **IMPROVIZED**, b f Authorized (IRE)—Rhapsodize **Foursome Thoroughbreds**
21 **JAMMY MOMENT**, ch f Duke of Marmalade (IRE)—Special Moment (IRE) **Foursome Thoroughbreds**
22 **LADY HORATIA**, gr f Mount Nelson—Lady Xara (IRE) **Muir Racing Partnership - Ascot**
23 **LOVE SPICE**, b f Cape Cross (IRE)—Zanzibar (IRE) **Usk Valley Stud**
24 **MYSTIC ANGEL (IRE)**, gr f Dark Angel (IRE)—Tintern **Muir Racing Partnership - Sandown**
25 **OPHIR**, b g Nayef (USA)—Ermine (IRE) **Mr J. M. O'Mulloy**
26 **ORACLE BOY**, b c Mount Nelson—Snow Princess (IRE) **The Epicureans**
27 **PINK AND BLACK (IRE)**, b f Yeats (IRE)—Raysiza (IRE) **Mrs D. L. Edginton**
28 **RETROFIT**, b c Exceed And Excel (AUS)—Passe Passe (USA) **Mr J. P. Kok**
29 **ROCHELLE (IRE)**, b f Duke of Marmalade (IRE)—Emilion **Mr & Mrs G. Middlebrook**
30 **ROYAL BRAVE (IRE)**, b c Acclamation—Daqtora **Muir Racing Partnership - Ascot**
31 **SAND STORMER (IRE)**, b g Footstepsinthesand—Claustra (FR) **Mrs J. M. Muir**
32 **SEVERN CROSSING**, br g Authorized (IRE)—Croeso Cariad **Usk Valley Stud**
33 **STRAWBERRY MARTINI**, ch f Mount Nelson—Strawberry Lolly **Newsells Park Stud Limited**

TWO-YEAR-OLDS

34 **BEST ENDEVOUR**, b c 15/2 Medicean—Striving (IRE) (Danehill Dancer (IRE)) (54200) **C. L. A. Edginton**
35 B c 30/4 Sleeping Indian—China Beads (Medicean) (8571)
36 **DUTCH FALCON**, ch c 27/3 Pivotal—
                    Luminance (IRE) (Danehill Dancer (IRE)) (45000) **C Edginton, G Berkeley, R Haim**
37 **EAGER BEAVER**, b f 26/3 Duke of Marmalade (IRE)—Kahlua Kiss (Mister Baileys) **M. J. Caddy**
38 B f 4/4 Misu Bond (IRE)—Enchanting Eve (Risk Me (FR)) **Mr J. M. O'Mulloy**
39 **EQUALLY FAST**, b c 7/2 Equiano (FR)—
                    Fabulously Fast (USA) (Deputy Minister (CAN)) (40263) **Muir Racing Partnership - Haydock**
40 **FINE JUDGMENT**, b f 28/1 Compton Place—
                    Blue Lyric (Refuse To Bend (IRE)) (28000) **Muir Racing Partnership - Goodwood**
41 B c 7/3 Mount Nelson—Franglais (GER) (Lion Cavern (USA)) (45000) **Mr J. P. Kok**
42 B c 22/3 Kyllachy—Glencal (Compton Place) (52000) **The Lavelle Family**
43 Ch c 12/2 Pivotal—Irresistible (Cadeaux Genereux) (60000) **Mr Syed Pervez Hussain**
44 **JET MATE**, b c 21/1 Fast Company (IRE)—Anazah (USA) (Diesis) (35000) **Mr M.P. Graham**
45 Ch c 15/3 Bahamian Bounty—Just Devine (IRE) (Montjeu (IRE)) **Carmel Stud**
46 B f 20/4 Jeremy—Karenaragon (Aragon) (3871)
47 B f 2/2 Medicean—Lyra's Daemon (Singspiel (IRE))
48 B c 22/4 Dark Angel (IRE)—Ornellaia (IRE) (Mujadil (USA)) (7500) **Mr J. O'Mulloy**
49 **RESTORER**, gr c 13/3 Mastercraftsman (IRE)—
                    Moon Empress (FR) (Rainbow Quest (USA)) (35000) **C. L. A. Edginton**
50 B c 27/1 Kyllachy—Riccoche (Oasis Dream) (45000) **Mr Syed Pervez Hussain**
51 B c 6/5 Excellent Art—Space Time (FR) (Bering) (70000) **Mr Syed Pervez Hussain**
52 **SURREY PINK (FR)**, ch f 10/1 Kyllachy—Idle Tears (Selkirk (USA)) (48006) **Mrs D. L. Edginton**

Other Owners: Mr G. W. A. Berkeley, Mr D. G. Clarke, Mr C. L. A. Edginton, Mr Martin P Graham, Mr R. Haim, Mr K. J. Mercer, Mrs S. Mercer, Mrs G. Middlebrook, Mrs L. Middlebrook, Mr Peter Morgan, Mrs Michelle Morgan, Mr W. R. Muir, Mr D. L. Quaintance, Mr P. J. Wheatley.

Jockey (flat): Martin Dwyer.

453 MR CLIVE MULHALL, Scarcroft
Postal: **Scarcroft Hall Farm, Thorner Lane, Scarcroft, Leeds**
Contacts: PHONE **(0113) 2893095** FAX **(0113) 2893095** MOBILE **(07979) 527675**
E-MAIL **clive@scarcrofthallracing.co.uk** WEBSITE **www.scarcrofthallracing.co.uk**

1 **ALIMURE,** 8, b m Tamure (IRE)—Auntie Alice **Carl Chapman & Mrs C M Mulhall**
2 **IFONLYWECUD (IRE),** 5, b g Celtic Swing—Mrs Dalloway (IRE) **Carl Chapman & Mrs C M Mulhall**
3 **LADY LISA JAYNE,** 4, b f Moss Vale (IRE)—Mimic
4 **SHARADIYN,** 11, b g Generous (IRE)—Sharadiya (IRE) **Simon Ballance & Mrs C M Mulhall**
5 **THINK,** 7, ch g Sulamani (IRE)—Natalie Jay **Mrs C M Mulhall & Over The Rainbow**
6 **TUKITINYASOK (IRE),** 7, b g Fath (USA)—Mevlana (IRE) **Carl Chapman & Mrs C M Mulhall**

Other Owners: Mr S. T. Ballance, Mr M. Bisogno, Mr C. Chapman, Mrs C. M. Mulhall, Mr T. D. Wooldridge.

Assistant Trainer: Mrs Martina Mulhall

454 MR NEIL MULHOLLAND, Limpley Stoke
Postal: **Conkwell Grange Stables, Conkwell, Limpley Stoke, Bath, Avon, BA2 7FD**
Contacts: MOBILE **(07739) 258607**
E-MAIL **neil@neilmulhollandracing.com** WEBSITE **www.neilmulhollandracing.com**

1 **ADIYNARA (IRE),** 6, b m Halling (USA)—Adirika (IRE) **J Baigent, D Smith & I Woodward**
2 **AGAPANTHUS (GER),** 9, b g Tiger Hill (IRE)—Astilbe (GER) **Mr S. K. Brown**
3 **ANOTHER BRANDY (IRE),** 6, b g Oscar (IRE)—Reapers Dream (IRE) **D. J. Bridger**
4 **ASHCOTT BOY,** 6, ch g Lahib (USA)—Last Ambition (IRE) **Mr J. Hobbs**
5 **BARTON ANTIX,** 5, b g Fair Mix (IRE)—Barton Dante **Lady H. J. Clarke**
6 **BARTON HEATHER,** 5, b m Midnight Legend—Home From The Hill (IRE) **Lady H. J. Clarke**
7 **BARTON JUBILEE,** 6, ch g Midnight Legend—Home From The Hill (IRE) **Lady H. J. Clarke**
8 **BARTON ROSE,** 5, b m Midnight Legend—Barton Flower **Lady H. J. Clarke**
9 **BENNYS QUEST (IRE),** 11, ch g Beneficial—Wonder Winnie (IRE) **John Hobbs & Dave Harris**
10 **BUCK MAGIC (IRE),** 8, b g Albano (IRE)—Green Sea **B. A. Derrick**
11 **CAROLE'S DESTRIER,** 6, b g Kayf Tara—Barton May **Mrs C. Skipworth**
12 **COMMITMENT,** 5, b g Motivator—Courting **Mrs H. R. Cross**
13 **CORONEA LILLY (IRE),** 10, ch m Busy Flight—Aoife's Joy (IRE) **Wellcroomed Ltd**
14 **EBONY EMPRESS (IRE),** 5, br m Kris Kin (USA)—Auditing Empress (IRE) **Wincanton Race Club**
15 **GENERAL MONTGOMERY (IRE),** 5, b g Desert King (IRE)—
Supreme Course (IRE) **Mrs H R Cross & Mrs S A Keys**
16 **HOBB'S DREAM (IRE),** 10, br m Winged Love (IRE)—La-Greine **John & Jeanette Hobbs & Mr P J Proudley**
17 **HOPATINA (IRE),** 8, b m Flemensfirth (USA)—Bonny Lass **J. R. Baigent**
18 **ISTHEREADIFFERENCE (IRE),** 7, gr g Amilynx (FR)—Jennys Grove (IRE) **Colony Stable Llc**
19 **JIM JOB JONES,** 10, b g Tipsy Creek (USA)—Sulapuff **Dajam Ltd**
20 **KILRUSH (IRE),** 8, gr g Dilshaan—Pride of Passion (IRE) **Six Shades Of Grey**
21 **KING HELISSIO (IRE),** 6, b g Helissio (FR)—Banner Buzz (IRE) **Mrs J. Gerard-Pearse**
22 **KRISTAL HART,** 5, b m Lucky Story (USA)—Moly (FR) **The White Hart Racing Syndicate**
23 **LANGARVE LADY (IRE),** 6, b m Oscar (IRE)—Fashions Monty (IRE) **Mr B. F. Mulholland**
24 **LANGARVE LASS (IRE),** 5, b m Oscar (IRE)—Fashions Monty (IRE) **Mr B. F. Mulholland**
25 **LILY MARS (IRE),** 7, br m Presenting—Tiffany Jazz (IRE) **Mrs H. Dale-Staples**
26 **MAID OF SILK (IRE),** 8, b m Blueprint (IRE)—Silk Style **D. M. Bell**
27 **MATROW'S LADY (IRE),** 7, b m Cloudings (IRE)—I'm Maggy (NZ) **Matrow Properties Limited**
28 **MAYBE ANNIE,** 4, ch f Pasternak—Barton May **Mrs H. R. Cross**
29 **MIDNIGHT SEQUEL,** 5, b m Midnight Legend—Silver Sequel **Dajam Ltd**
30 **MINELLA DEFINITELY (IRE),** 7, br g Definite Article—West Along **Wellcroomed Ltd**
31 **MINELLA PRESENT (IRE),** 5, b g Presenting—Dabaya (IRE) **Lady H. J. Clarke**
32 **MR BURBIDGE,** 6, b g Midnight Legend—Twin Time **Dajam Ltd**
33 **NOVABRIDGE,** 6, ch g Avonbridge—Petrovna **Dajam Ltd**
34 **PASS THE TIME,** 5, b m Passing Glance—Twin Time **Dajam Ltd**
35 **PRIMACY (IRE),** 5, br m Primary (USA)—Seaborne **Prime Of Life 2**
36 **PURE POTEEN (IRE),** 6, ch g Flemensfirth (USA)—Taking My Time (IRE) **Mr N. C. Robinson**
37 **PURSUITOFHAPPINESS (IRE),** 6, b g Classic Cliche (IRE)—Lake Tour (IRE) **B. A. Derrick**
38 **REALTA MO CROI (IRE),** 6, b m Westerner—Solar Quest (IRE) **Neil Mulholland Racing Ltd**
39 **ROSSA PARKS (IRE),** 6, b m Anshan—Alshou (IRE) **Mrs P. L. Bridel**
40 **SIRRAH STAR (IRE),** 6, gr m Great Palm—Simply Deep (IRE) **Wellcroomed Ltd**
41 **SOLID CONCRETE (IRE),** 8, b m Insatiable (IRE)—Official Secret **Neil Mulholland Racing Club**
42 **SPECIAL REPORT (IRE),** 4, b g Mujadil (USA)—Ellistown Lady (IRE) **Neil Mulholland Racing Ltd**
43 **STARSHIP TROUPER,** 6, b g First Trump—Bay of Plenty **David H. Smith**

MR NEIL MULHOLLAND - Continued

44 **STRICTLY THE ONE (IRE)**, 4, b g Robin des Pres (FR)—Rita's Charm (IRE) **Strictly Come Racing**
45 **THE BAY BANDIT**, 7, b g Highest Honor (FR)—Pescara (IRE) **Neil Mulholland Racing Club**
46 **THE YOUNG MASTER**, 5, b g Echo of Light—Fine Frenzy (IRE) **Dajam Ltd**
47 **WAIT NO MORE (IRE)**, 9, ch g Strategic Choice (USA)—Tearaway Lady (IRE) **Mr J. Hobbs**
48 **WALTZING TORNADO (IRE)**, 10, ch g Golden Tornado (IRE)—Lady Dante (IRE) **Mr J. Hobbs**

Other Owners: Mrs J. A. V. Allen, Mr G. J. R. Barry, Mrs M. A. Clark, Mr D. B. Harris, Mrs S. A. Keys, Mr P. H. King, Mr E. A. M. Leatham, Mrs S. E. Leatham, Mrs C. Lewis, B. D. Makepeace, Mr N. P. Mulholland, Mr P. J. Proudley, Mrs D. J. Symes, Mr J. N. Trueman, Mr I. S. Woodward.

Conditional: Andrias Guerin.

---

455 **MR LAWRENCE MULLANEY, Malton**
Postal: Raikes Farm, Great Habton, Malton, North Yorkshire, YO17 6RX
Contacts: PHONE (01653) 668208 MOBILE (07899) 902565

1 **CAPE MARENGO**, 4, gr f Paris House—Cape Charlotte **Wildcard Racing & S Rimmer**
2 **COMETOGRAPHY (IRE)**, 5, b g Teofilo (IRE)—Halle Bop **Wildcard Racing Syndicate X1**
3 **DENISON FLYER**, 7, b g Tobougg (IRE)—Bollin Victoria **L. A. Mullaney**
4 **JACK LUEY**, 7, b g Danbird (AUS)—Icenaslice (IRE) **The Jack Partnership & Mr S Rimmer**
5 **KARA TARA**, 4, b f Kayf Tara—Matilda Too (IRE)
6 **MAGGIE MEY (IRE)**, 6, b m Kodiac—Christmas Kiss **The Ten Commandments**
7 **MR MO JO**, 6, b g Danbird (AUS)—Nampara Bay **L. A. Mullaney**
8 **THROWING ROSES**, 4, b f Clodovil (IRE)—Mizooka **Wildcard Racing Syndicate X1**

TWO-YEAR-OLDS

9 **EDIE WHITE**, b f 21/3 Bahamian Bounty—Croeso Bach (Bertolini (USA)) (9523) **Ian Buckley**

Other Owners: Mr A. J. Bonarius, Mr N. J. Bonarius, M. J. Dyas, Mr A. Fellows, Mrs D. A. Reed, Mr A. P. Reed, Mr S. J. Rimmer, Mr P. Smith.

---

456 **MR MICHAEL MULLINEAUX, Tarporley**
Postal: Southley Farm, Alpraham, Tarporley, Cheshire, CW6 9JD
Contacts: PHONE (01829) 261440 FAX (01829) 261440 MOBILE (07753) 650263
E-MAIL southlearacing@btinternet.com WEBSITE www.southleyfarm.co.uk

1 **BIG FLOE**, 5, b m Alflora (IRE)—Dominie Breeze **Miss L. S. Young**
2 **BRICBRACSMATE**, 6, b g Revoque (IRE)—Blissphilly **P. J. Lawton**
3 4, B g Vita Rosa (JPN)—Common Request (USA)
4 4, Ch f Erhaab (USA)—Dolly Duff **The Weaver Group**
5 **FRANKIE FOUR FEET**, 6, b g Proclamation (IRE)—Miss Holly **D. Ashbrook**
6 **GABRIAL THE BOSS (USA)**, 4, ch g Street Boss (USA)—Bacinella (USA) **H. Clewlow**
7 4, B g Starcraft (NZ)—Jig Time
8 **LORD OF THE DANCE (IRE)**, 8, ch g Indian Haven—Maine Lobster (USA) **H. Clewlow**
9 4, Br f Striking Ambition—Lucky Find (IRE) **M. Mullineaux**
10 **METHAALY (IRE)**, 11, b g Red Ransom (USA)—Santorini (USA) **S. A. Pritchard**
11 **MINTY JONES**, 5, b h Primo Valentino (IRE)—Reveur **P. Clacher**
12 **MOLKO JACK (FR)**, 10, b br g Lavirco (GER)—Line As (FR) **D. Ashbrook**
13 5, B g Revoque (IRE)—Montevelle (IRE)
14 **MUZEY'S PRINCESS**, 8, b m Grape Tree Road—Premier Princess **D. M. Drury**
15 **MY TIME**, 5, b g Mind Games—Tick Tock **Mr M. Kilner**
16 **OLYNARD (IRE)**, 8, b g Exceed And Excel (AUS)—Reddening **Mr G. Cornes**
17 **ORPEN BID (IRE)**, 9, b m Orpen (USA)—Glorious Bid (IRE) **Miss L. S. Young**
18 **PHOENIX EYE**, 13, b g Tragic Role (USA)—Eye Sight **The Hon Mrs S. Pakenham**
19 **POLVERE D'ORO**, 4, b g Revoque (IRE)—Dusty Anne (IRE) **Mr P. R. D'Amato**
20 5, B m Sir Harry Lewis (USA)—Roman Gospel **Mr A. Johnstone**
21 **SMIRFYS BLACKCAT (IRE)**, 5, b m One Cool Cat (USA)—Smirfys Dance Hall (IRE) **Mrs D. Plant**
22 **SMIRFYS COPPER (IRE)**, 7, ch m Choisir (AUS)—Fer de Lance (IRE)
23 **SMIRFYS ERIC (IRE)**, 8, b g Bollin Eric—Smirfys Dance Hall (IRE) **Mrs D. Plant**
24 **STAR OF NAMIBIA (IRE)**, 4, b g Cape Cross (IRE)—Sparkle of Stones (FR) **Mr K. Jones**
25 5, B g Zagreb (USA)—Too Back (IRE) **Mr Denis Gallagher**
26 **TOP LINE BANKER**, 4, b g Top Line Dancer (IRE)—Ice Pack **Miss D. S. Crewe**

MR MICHAEL MULLINEAUX - Continued

27 **TWO TURTLE DOVES (IRE)**, 8, b m Night Shift (USA)—Purple Rain (IRE) **Mr G. Cornes**
28 **VERY FIRST BLADE**, 5, b g Needwood Blade—Dispol Verity **Ogwen Valley Racing**
29 **WYMESWOLD**, 7, b m Alflora (IRE)—Dominie Breeze **The Hon Mrs S. Pakenham**

THREE-YEAR-OLDS

30 **MARKET STORM (FR)**, b g After Market (USA)—Minted (USA) **E. H. Jones (Paints) Ltd**

TWO-YEAR-OLDS

31 B f 30/4 Bushranger (IRE)—Diosper (USA) (Diesis) **Mr & Mrs S Ashbrooke & J P Daly**
32 B c 20/2 Leroidesanimaux (BRZ)—
Kaleidoscopic (USA) (Fortunate Prospect (USA)) (25714) **E. H. Jones (Paints) Ltd**

Other Owners: Mrs M. Ashbrooke, Mr S. Ashbrooke, Mr J. P. Daly, Mr G. Jones, Mr P. Murray, Mr N. Murray-Williams.

Assistant Trainers: Stuart Ross & Susan Mullineaux

Amateur: Miss M. J. L. Mullineaux.

---

457 **MR SEAMUS MULLINS, Amesbury**
Postal: Wilsford Stables, Wilsford-Cum-Lake, Amesbury, Salisbury, Wiltshire, SP4 7BL
Contacts: PHONE/FAX (01980) 626344 MOBILE (07702) 559634
E-MAIL info@jwmullins.co.uk WEBSITE www.seamusmullins.co.uk

1 **ADRENALIN FLIGHT (IRE)**, 8, b g Dr Massini (IRE)—Chapel Queen (IRE) **Mr M. Adams**
2 **ALDER MAIRI (IRE)**, 7, ch m Alderbrook—Amari Queen **F. G. Matthews**
3 **BAHUMBUG**, 4, b g Bahamian Bounty—Stan's Smarty Girl (USA) **Woodford Valley Racing**
4 **BONDS CONQUEST**, 5, ch g Monsieur Bond (IRE)—Another Conquest **F. G. Matthews**
5 **BOSS IN BOOTS (IRE)**, 6, gr g King's Theatre (IRE)—Grey Mo (IRE) **Mr M. Adams**
6 **BRUNETTE'SONLY (IRE)**, 9, ch m Flemensfirth (USA)—Pride of St Gallen (IRE) **Mrs M. M. Rayner**
7 **COMBUSTIBLE LADY (IRE)**, 9, b m Mr Combustible (IRE)—Ladyogan (IRE) **J. W. Mullins**
8 **DERVLA (IRE)**, 6, b m Definite Article—Kennycourt Lady (IRE) **J. W. Mullins**
9 **FERGALL (IRE)**, 7, br g Norwich—Gaybrook Girl (IRE) **Andrew Cocks & Tara Johnson**
10 **FLUGZEUG**, 6, gr g Silver Patriarch (IRE)—Telmar Flyer **New Forest Racing Partnership**
11 **FOREST RHYTHM (IRE)**, 10, b g Great Palm (USA)—Eurythmic **J. W. Mullins**
12 **GENEROUS BOB**, 7, ch g Generous (IRE)—Bob's Finesse **Miss C. A. James**
13 **GIVEAGIRLACHANCE (IRE)**, 5, b m Iffraaj—Farewell To Love (IRE) **The Five Plus One Partnership**
14 **GREATDAY ALLWEEK (IRE)**, 5, ch m Kutub (IRE)—Correct And Right (IRE) **J. W. Mullins**
15 **HEAD SPIN (IRE)**, 6, b g Beneficial—Who Tells Jan **Mr M. Adams**
16 **HILL FORTS HARRY**, 5, ch g Arkadian Hero (USA)—Queen of The Suir (IRE) **Mrs J. C. Scorgie**
17 **KASTANI BEACH (IRE)**, 8, b g Alderbrook—Atomic View (IRE) **Mr G B Balding & Philippa Downing**
18 **KENTFORD LEGEND**, 7, b g Midnight Legend—Quistaquay **D. I. Bare**
19 **KENTFORD MYTH**, 4, b f Midnight Legend—Quistaquay **D. I. Bare**
20 **LANDERBEE (IRE)**, 7, b g Exit To Nowhere (USA)—Ithastobedone (IRE) **Mrs G. Elliott**
21 **MARMALADE MAN**, 8, ch g Karinga Bay—Kentford Duchess **D. I. Bare**
22 **MISS FORTYWINKS**, 5, gr m Act One—Andromache **J. T. Brown**
23 **MISS SASSYPANTS**, 5, ch m Hernando (FR)—Serraval (FR) **J. T. Brown**
24 **RIDDLE ME THIS**, 5, b g Yawmi—Ambience Lady **Caloona Racing**
25 **RUBY GLOW**, 6, b m Septieme Ciel (USA)—Ruby Too **Dr R. Jowett**
26 **RUFF LUCK**, 4, b f Lucarno (USA)—Ruffie (IRE) **Phoenix Bloodstock**
27 **SAPPHIRE ROUGE (IRE)**, 8, ch m Alderbrook—Emerald Express **J. W. Mullins**
28 **SOMCHINE**, 6, b g Volochine (IRE)—Seem of Gold **Mr C. R. Dunning**
29 **SPORTSREPORT (IRE)**, 6, b g Coroner (IRE)—Goforthetape (IRE) **Mr C. J. Baldwin**
30 **STEEL CITY**, 6, gr g Act One—Serraval (FR) **J. T. Brown**
31 **SWING IT**, 5, b g Bahamian Bounty—Haiyfoona **The Calvera Partnership No. 2**
32 **THE INFORMANT**, 8, gr g Central Park (IRE)—Belle Rose (IRE) **Dr & Mrs John Millar**
33 **TIME TO THINK**, 9, b m Alflora (IRE)—Shuil Do (IRE) **Mrs V. F. Hewett**
34 **TOP SMART**, 9, b g Karinga Bay—Clover Dove **The Calvera Partnership No. 2**
35 **UGLY BUG**, 8, b g Runyon (IRE)—Mutual Decision (USA) **Mrs T. P. James**

THREE-YEAR-OLDS

36 **DOUNEEDAHAND**, b f Royal Applause—Our Sheila **Caloona Racing**
37 **JARLATH**, b c Norse Dancer (IRE)—Blue Lullaby (USA) **Phoenix Bloodstock**
38 **SWALE STAR**, b f Three Valleys (USA)—Salim Toto **Caloona Racing**
39 **ULTIMATE ACT**, ro c Act One—Ruffie (IRE) **Phoenix Bloodstock**

MR SEAMUS MULLINS - Continued

Other Owners: P. R. Attwater, Mr H. R. Attwater, G. B. Balding, Mr A. P. Cocks, Mr J. Collins, Mr P. Collins, Miss P. M. Downing, A. A. Goodman, P. Hickey, Mrs E. M. J. James, Mr S. E. James, Mr A. C. James, Miss T. Johnson, D. A. Lucie-Smith, Dr J. W. Millar, Mrs J. D. Millar, Mr R. J. Stammers, D. Sutherland, C. Wilson.

Assistant Trainer: Miss Charlotte Brown

Jockey (NH): Wayne Kavanagh, Andrew Thornton. **Amateur:** Mr K. Jones.

---

458 **MR WILLIAM P. MULLINS, Carlow**
Postal: **Closutton, Bagenalstown, Co. Carlow, Ireland**
Contacts: **PHONE** (00353) 5997 21786 **FAX** (00353) 5997 22709 **MOBILE** (00353) 8725 64940
E-MAIL wpmullins@eircom.net **WEBSITE** www.wpmullins.com

1 ABBEY LANE (IRE), 9, b g Flemensfirth (USA)—Hazel Sylph (IRE) **Martin Lynch**
2 ABBYSSIAL (IRE), 4, ch g Beneficial—Mega d'estruval (FR) **Mrs Violet O'Leary**
3 ADRIANA DES MOTTES (FR), 4, b br f Network (GER)—Daisy des Mottes (FR) **Mrs S. Ricci**
4 AKLAN (IRE), 5, gr h Dalakhani (IRE)—Akdara (IRE) **Coach Partnership**
5 ALELCHI INOIS (FR), 6, b g Night Tango (GER)—Witness Gama (FR) **Mrs M. McMahon**
6 ALONSO (SPA), 5, ch g Green Tune (USA)—Lady Cree (IRE) **Andrea & Graham Wylie**
7 ANDIAMOS (IRE), 7, b g Beneficial—Iron Mariner (IRE) **Roderick Ryan**
8 ANNIE POWER (IRE), 6, ch m Shirocco (GER)—Anno Luce **Mrs S. Ricci**
9 ARCTIC FIRE (GER), 5, b g Soldier Hollow—Adelma (GER) **Wicklow Bloodstock Limited**
10 ARE YA RIGHT CHIEF (IRE), 9, b g Flemensfirth (USA)—River Clyde (IRE) **Mrs M. McMahon**
11 ARVIKA LIGEONNIERE (FR), 9, b g Arvico (FR)—Daraka (FR) **Mrs S. Ricci**
12 ASHJAR (FR), 4, b c Oasis Dream—Asharna (IRE) **Wicklow Bloodstock Limited**
13 AWAY WE GO (IRE), 11, ch g Stowaway—Margurites Pet (IRE) **Michael A. O'Gorman**
14 BACK IN FOCUS (IRE), 9, ch g Bob Back (USA)—Dun Belle (IRE) **Andrea & Graham Wylie**
15 BALLY LONGFORD (IRE), 6, b g Gold Well—Stay On Line (IRE) **Ann & Alan Potts**
16 BALLYCASEY (IRE), 7, gr g Presenting—Pink Mist (IRE) **Mrs S. Ricci**
17 BALNASLOW (IRE), 7, b g Presenting—Noble Choice **Gigginstown House Stud**
18 BELUCKYAGAIN (IRE), 6, b m Old Vic—Whizz **Supreme Horses Racing Club**
19 BISHOPSFURZE (IRE), 9, b g Broadway Flyer (USA)—Supreme Dipper (IRE) **Mrs C. M. Hurley**
20 BLACK HERCULES (IRE), 5, b g Heron Island (IRE)—Annalecky (IRE) **Andrea Wylie**
21 BLACKSTAIRMOUNTAIN (IRE), 9, b g Imperial Ballet (IRE)—Sixhills (FR) **Mrs S. Ricci**
22 BLESS N'JECT (IRE), 9, b g Luso—Lady Renowned (IRE) **Thomas M. Crowe**
23 BLOOD COTIL (FR), 5, b g Enrique—Move Along (FR) **Mrs S. Ricci**
24 BOSMAN RULE (IRE), 6, ch g Gamut—Fairy Blaze (IRE) **Philip J. Reynolds**
25 BOSTON BOB (IRE), 9, b g Bob Back (USA)—Bavaway **Andrea & Graham Wylie**
26 BOXER GEORG (IRE), 12, b g Taipan (IRE)—Country Course (IRE) **Mr W. Murray**
27 BRIAR HILL (IRE), 6, b g Shantou (USA)—Backaway (IRE) **Andrea & Graham Wylie**
28 BUNDLE OF FUN (IRE), 11, ch g Topanoora—Leaden Sky (IRE) **Shanakiel Racing Syndicate**
29 CADSPEED (IRE), 11, b g Vertical Speed (FR)—Cadmina (FR) **Carra Ethos Syndicate**
30 CHAMPAGNE FEVER (IRE), 7, gr g Stowaway—Forever Bubbles (IRE) **Mrs S. Ricci**
31 CHILTERN HILLS (IRE), 7, ch m Beneficial—Mirazur (IRE) **Supreme Horse Racing Club**
32 CITY SLICKER (IRE), 6, b g King's Theatre (IRE)—Donna's Princess (IRE) **J. P. McManus**
33 CLONARD LAD (IRE), 9, ch g Presenting—Furiella **DAFTC Syndicate**
34 CLONDAW COURT (IRE), 7, br g Court Cave (IRE)—Secret Can't Say (IRE) **Mrs S. Ricci**
35 CONNAUGHT MANOR (IRE), 9, ch g Pilsudski (IRE)—Connaught Lace **Kevin W. O'Brien**
36 DANEKING, 5, b g Dylan Thomas (IRE)—Sadie Thompson (IRE) **Mrs S. Ricci**
37 DEVILS BRIDE (IRE), 7, b g Helissio (FR)—Rigorous **Gigginstown House Stud**
38 DIAKALI (FR), 5, gr g Sinndar (IRE)—Diasilixa (FR) **Wicklow Bloodstock Limited**
39 DIGEANTA (IRE), 7, b g Helissio (FR)—
                                Scolboa Gold (IRE) **Dr I. M. P. Moran, Colland Sand & Gravel Syndicate**
40 DJAKADAM (FR), 5, b g Saint des Saints (FR)—Rainbow Crest (FR) **Mrs S. Ricci**
41 DOGORA (FR), 5, gr g Robin des Pres (FR)—Garde de Nuit (FR) **Mrs S. Ricci**
42 DON POLI (IRE), 5, b g Poliglote—Dalamine (FR) **Gigginstown House Stud**
43 DRIVE TIME (USA), 9, b g King Cugat (USA)—Arbusha (USA) **Andrea & Graham Wylie**
44 EQUITY SWAP (IRE), 5, ch g Strategic Prince—Medicean Star (IRE) **Ann & Alan Potts**
45 FAUGHEEN (IRE), 6, b g Germany (USA)—Miss Pickering (IRE) **Mrs S. Ricci**
46 FELIX YONGER (IRE), 8, b g Oscar (IRE)—Marble Sound (IRE) **Andrea & Graham Wylie**
47 FIVEFORTHREE (IRE), 12, gr g Arzanni—What A Queen **Olde Crowbars Syndicate**
48 FLASH OF GENIUS, 8, b g Definite Article—Fortune's Girl **Gigginstown House Stud**
49 FLAT OUT (FR), 9, gr g Sagamix (FR)—Divine Rodney (FR) **M. O'Riordan**
50 GITANE DU BERLAIS (FR), 4, b f Balko (FR)—Boheme du Berlais (FR) **Mr Simon Munir**

MR WILLIAM P. MULLINS - Continued

51 **GLENS MELODY (IRE)**, 6, b m King's Theatre (IRE)—Glens Music (IRE) **Ms Fiona McStay**
52 **GOLDBOY (IRE)**, 6, b g Gold Well—Woodbinesandroses (IRE) **CCR Racing Syndicate**
53 **GORGEOUS SIXTY (FR)**, 6, b m Touch of The Blues (FR)—Sixty Six (IRE) **Mrs S. Ricci**
54 **GRANGECLARE PEARL (IRE)**, 7, b m Old Vic—Grangeclare Rose (IRE) **Ethel Flanagan**
55 **HURRICANE FLY (IRE)**, 10, b g Montjeu (IRE)—Scandisk (IRE) **George Creighton**
56 **IMMEDIATE RESPONSE (IRE)**, 11, b g Strategic Choice (USA)—Rosies All The Way **Kates Monkeys Syndicate**
57 **INISH ISLAND (IRE)**, 8, ch g Trans Island—Ish (IRE) **Susan Flanagan**
58 **IVAN GROZNY (FR)**, 4, b g Turtle Bowl (IRE)—Behnesa (IRE) **Andrea & Graham Wylie**
59 **KALMANN (FR)**, 5, ch g Reste Tranquille (FR)—Sahmat (FR) **Mrs S. Ricci**
60 **KERB APPEAL (IRE)**, 9, b g Needle Gun (IRE)—Great Days (IRE) **Olde Crowbars Syndicate**
61 **KILLULTAGH VIC (IRE)**, 5, b g Old Vic—Killultagh Dawn (IRE) **Mrs Rose Boyd**
62 **LETHERBELUCKY (IRE)**, 7, b m Luso—Silaoce (FR) **Supreme Horse Racing Club**
63 **LOCAL CELEBRITY (IRE)**, 10, b g Bach (IRE)—Shanks Design (IRE) **TCD Horse Racing Society Club**
64 **LUCKY BRIDLE (IRE)**, 5, b h Dylan Thomas (IRE)—Auction Room (USA) **Andrea & Graham Wylie**
65 **MADE IN GERMANY (IRE)**, 6, ch g Germany (USA)—Black Dot Com (IRE) **Gigginstown House Stud**
66 **MAKE YOUR MARK (IRE)**, 7, b g Beneficial—Bell Star (IRE) **Gigginstown House Stud**
67 **MARASONNIEN (FR)**, 8, b g Mansonnien (FR)—Maracay (FR) **Mrs S. Ricci**
68 **MARITO (GER)**, 8, b g Alkalde (GER)—Maratea (USA) **Mrs S. Ricci**
69 **MAX DYNAMITE (FR)**, 4, b c Great Journey (JPN)—Mascara (GER) **Mrs S. Ricci**
70 **MCKINLEY**, 4, b g Kheleyf (USA)—Priera Menta (IRE) **Gigginstown House Stud**
71 **MEASUREOFMYDREAMS (IRE)**, 6, b g Shantou (USA)—Le Bavellen **Gigginstown House Stud**
72 **MIDNIGHT GAME**, 7, b g Montjeu (IRE)—Midnight Angel (GER) **Gigginstown House Stud**
73 **MIDNIGHT OIL**, 6, b g Motivator—One So Marvellous **Gigginstown House Stud**
74 **MIKAEL D'HAGUENET (FR)**, 10, b g Lavirco (GER)—Fleur d'haguenet (FR) **Mrs S. Ricci**
75 **MILSEAN (IRE)**, 5, b g Milan—Boro Supreme (IRE) **Gigginstown House Stud**
76 **MOST PECULIAR (IRE)**, 5, b g Kutub—Oceanide Bleue (FR) **OMG Partnership**
77 **MOURAD (IRE)**, 9, ch g Sinndar (IRE)—Mouramara (IRE) **Teahon Consulting Limited**
78 **MOYLE PARK (IRE)**, 6, ch g Flemensfirth (USA)—Lovely Present (IRE) **Mrs S. Ricci**
79 **MOZOLTOV**, 8, b g Kayf Tara—Fairmead Princess **Martin Lynch**
80 **NOBLE INN (FR)**, 4, b g Sinndar (IRE)—Nataliana **M. J. Mulvaney**
81 **ON HIS OWN (IRE)**, 10, b g Presenting—Shuil Na Mhuire (IRE) **Andrea & Graham Wylie**
82 **OUTLANDER (IRE)**, 6, b g Stowaway—Western Whisper (IRE) **Gigginstown House Stud**
83 **PATANNE (IRE)**, 6, b g Golan (IRE)—Best Wait (IRE) **Shanakiel Racing Syndicate**
84 **PERFECT GENTLEMAN (IRE)**, 9, b g King's Theatre (IRE)—Millennium Lilly (IRE) **Mrs J. M. Mullins**
85 **PINK HAT (IRE)**, 6, b m Presenting—Victorine (USA) **Mrs J. M. Mullins**
86 **PIQUE SOUS (FR)**, 7, gr g Martaline—Six Fois Sept (FR) **Not Just Any Racing Club**
87 **PONT ALEXANDRE (GER)**, 6, b g Dai Jin—Panzella (FR) **Mrs S. Ricci**
88 **POPCORN (FR)**, 11, b g Roakarad—Baie de Chalamont (FR) **Mrs J. M. Mullins**
89 **PRIMROSEANDBLUE (IRE)**, 10, b g Shernazar—Karlybelle (FR) **Mrs J. M. Mullins**
90 **PRINCE DE BEAUCHENE (FR)**, 11, b g French Glory—Chipie d'angron (FR) **Andrea & Graham Wylie**
91 **QUEVEGA (FR)**, 10, b m Robin des Champs (FR)—Vega IV (FR) **Hammer & Trowel Syndicate**
92 **RAISE HELL (IRE)**, 7, b g Presenting—Markiza (IRE) **Gigginstown House Stud**
93 **RAPTOR (FR)**, 9, gr g Caballo Raptor (CAN)—Tiwa (FR) **Aiden Devawey**
94 **RATHVINDEN (IRE)**, 6, b g Heron Island (IRE)—Peggy Cullen (IRE) **R. A. Bartlett**
95 **RENNETI (FR)**, 5, b g Irish Wells (FR)—Caprice Meill (FR) **Mrs S. Ricci**
96 **ROCKYABOYA (IRE)**, 10, ch g Rock Hopper—Motility **P. W. Mullins**
97 **ROLLY BABY (FR)**, 9, b g Funny Baby (FR)—Vancia (FR) **Teahon Consulting**
98 **ROUGH JUSTICE (IRE)**, 6, b g Beneficial—Ringzar (IRE) **Gigginstown House Stud**
99 **ROYAL CAVIAR (IRE)**, 6, b g Vinnie Roe (IRE)—Blackwater Babe (IRE) **Mrs S. Ricci**
100 **ROYAL MOLL (IRE)**, 7, b m King's Theatre (IRE)—Moll Bawn (IRE) **The Hibo Syndicate**
101 **RUBI BALL (FR)**, 9, ch g Network (GER)—Hygie (FR) **Sc Ecurie Madame Patrick Papot**
102 **RUPERT LAMB**, 8, gr g Central Park (IRE)—Charlotte Lamb **Andrea & Graham Wylie**
103 **SARABAD (FR)**, 6, b g Astarabad (USA)—Saraphine (FR) **Mrs S. Ricci**
104 **SECURITY BREACH (IRE)**, 5, b g Red Clubs (IRE)—Lear's Crown (USA) **Gigginstown House Stud**
105 **SEMPRE MEDICI (FR)**, 4, b c Medicean—Sambala (IRE) **Mrs S. Ricci**
106 **SERGENT GUIB'S (FR)**, 8, b br g Califet (FR)—Miss Quessie (FR) **Mrs S. Ricci**
107 **SHAMAR (FR)**, 6, b h Dr Fong (USA)—Shamalana (IRE) **Mrs S. Ricci**
108 **SHAMSIKHAN (IRE)**, 5, ch g Dr Fong (USA)—Shamdala (IRE) **Mrs Audrey Turley**
109 **SHANESHILL (IRE)**, 5, b g King's Theatre (IRE)—Darabaka (IRE) **Andrea & Graham Wylie**
110 **SHESAFOXYLADY (IRE)**, 6, b m Trans Island—Foxed (IRE) **Supreme Horse Racing Club**
111 **SIMENON (IRE)**, 7, b g Marju (IRE)—Epistoliere (IRE) **Wicklow Bloodstock Ltd**
112 **SIN PALO (IRE)**, 10, b g Dushyantor (USA)—Platinum Gold **Downthehatch Syndicate**
113 **SIR DES CHAMPS (FR)**, 8, b br g Robin des Champs (FR)—Liste En Tete (FR) **Gigginstown House Stud**
114 **SIZING BRISBANE (IRE)**, 6, b g Nayef (USA)—Elaine Tully (IRE) **Ann & Alan Potts**
115 **SIZING CHILE (IRE)**, 6, b g Flemensfirth (USA)—Smooching (IRE) **Alan Potts**

MR WILLIAM P. MULLINS - Continued

116 **SIZING SAHARA**, 6, gr g Shirocco (GER)—Aristocratique **Ann & Alan Potts Partnership**
117 **SIZING TENNESSEE (IRE)**, 6, ch g Robin des Champs (FR)—Jolivia (FR) **Ann & Alan Potts**
118 **SMASHING (IRE)**, 4, b f Galileo (IRE)—Adalya (IRE) **Ann & Alan Potts Partnership**
119 **SO YOUNG (FR)**, 8, b g Lavirco (GER)—Honey (FR) **Mrs McMahon**
120 **SUNTIEP (FR)**, 8, b g Ungaro (GER)—Galostiepy (FR) **J. T. Ennis**
121 **SUPREME CAROLINA (IRE)**, 7, b m Traditionally (USA)—Carolina (FR) **Supreme Horse Racing Club**
122 **SURE REEF (IRE)**, 5, ch g Choisir (AUS)—Cutting Reef (IRE) **Andrea & Graham Wylie**
123 **SWEET MY LORD (FR)**, 8, b g Johann Quatz (FR)—Hasta Manana (FR) **Mr A. Devaney**
124 **TARARE (FR)**, 5, b g Astarabad (USA)—Targerine (FR) **Mrs S. Ricci**
125 **TARLA (FR)**, 8, b m Lavirco (GER)—Targerine (FR) **Mrs S. Ricci**
126 **TERMINAL (FR)**, 7, b g Passing Sale (FR)—Durendal (FR) **Favourites Racing Syndicate**
127 **THE BOSSES COUSIN (IRE)**, 9, b g King's Theatre (IRE)—Seductive Dance **Mrs J. M. Mullins**
128 **THE PAPARAZZI KID (IRE)**, 7, b g Milan—Banbury Cross (IRE) **Byerley Thoroughbred Racing**
129 **THELEZE (FR)**, 7, b m Lavirco (GER)—Divette (FR) **Ann & Alan Potts Partnership**
130 **THOUSAND STARS (FR)**, 10, gr g Grey Risk (FR)—Livaniana (FR) **Hammer & Trowel Syndicate**
131 **TOTALLY DOMINANT (USA)**, 5, b g War Chant (USA)—Miss Kilroy (USA) **Mrs S. Ricci**
132 **TOUCH THE EDEN (FR)**, 7, b g Malinas (GER)—Loika (FR) **Mrs S. Ricci**
133 **TURBAN (FR)**, 7, b g Dom Alco (FR)—Indianabelle (FR) **Edward O'Connell**
134 **TURNANDGO (IRE)**, 6, b g Morozov (USA)—Crazy Alice (IRE) **Gigginstown House Stud**
135 **TWINLIGHT (FR)**, 7, b g Muhtathir—Fairlight (GER) **M L Bloodstock Limited**
136 **UN BEAU ROMAN (FR)**, 6, bl g Roman Saddle (FR)—Koukie (FR) **Aiden Devaney**
137 **UN DE SCEAUX (FR)**, 6, b g Denham Red (FR)—Hotesse de Sceaux (FR) **E. O'Connell**
138 **UNCLE JUNIOR (IRE)**, 13, b g Saddlers' Hall (IRE)—Caslain Nua **Mrs M. McMahon**
139 **UNION DUES (FR)**, 6, b br g Malinas (GER)—Royale Dorothy (FR) **Allan McLuckie**
140 **UP THE BEAT**, 9, b br g Beat All (USA)—Everything's Rosy **Mrs A. M. Varmen**
141 **UPAZO (FR)**, 6, b g Enrique—Honey (FR) **Philip J. Reynolds**
142 **UPSIE (FR)**, 6, b m Le Balafre (FR)—Medjie (FR) **J. P. McManus**
143 **URANNA (FR)**, 6, gr m Panoramic—Irresistible Anna (FR) **Supreme Horse Racing Club**
144 **URANO (FR)**, 6, b g Enrique—Neiland (FR) **Mrs M. Mahon**
145 **URTICAIRE (FR)**, 6, b m Mister Sacha (FR)—Opium des Mottes (FR) **Gigginstown House Stud**
146 **VALSEUR LIDO (FR)**, 5, b g Anzillero (GER)—Libido Rock (FR) **Gigginstown House Stud**
147 **VAUTOUR (FR)**, 5, b g Robin des Champs (FR)—Gazelle de Mai (FR) **Mrs S. Ricci**
148 **VEDETTARIAT (FR)**, 5, bl g Lavirco (GER)—Platine (FR) **Mrs S. Ricci**
149 **VESPER BELL (IRE)**, 8, b g Beneficial—Fair Choice (IRE) **Mrs S. Ricci**
150 **VICKY DE L'OASIS (FR)**, 5, b m Ultimately Lucky (IRE)—Japonaise III (FR) **Wicklow Bloodstock Limited**
151 **VIVEGA (FR)**, 5, ch g Robin des Champs (FR)—Vega IV (FR) **Mrs S. Ricci**
152 **WELL READ MAN (IRE)**, 7, b g Presenting—Silent Orders (IRE) **Mrs M. McMahon**
153 **WICKLOW BRAVE**, 5, b g Beat Hollow—Moraine **Wicklow Bloodstock Limited**
154 **WICKLOW GOLD (FR)**, 6, b g Robin des Champs (FR)—Gamine d'ici (FR) **Wicklow Bloodstock Limited**
155 **WOOD BREIZH (FR)**, 4, gr g Stormy River (FR)—Polynevees (FR) **Supreme Horse Racing Club**
156 **ZAIDPOUR (FR)**, 8, b g Red Ransom (USA)—Zainta (IRE) **Mrs S. Ricci**
157 **ZUZKA (IRE)**, 7, b m Flemensfirth (USA)—Downtown Train (USA) **Supreme Horse Racing Club**

Other Owners: A. W. G. Wylie, Mrs A. Wylie.

---

459 MRS ANABEL K. MURPHY, Stratford-upon-Avon
Postal: **Warren Chase, Billesley Road, Wilmcote, Stratford-upon-Avon, Warwickshire, CV37 9XG**
Contacts: **OFFICE** (01789) 205087 **HOME** (01789) 298346 **FAX** (01789) 263260
MOBILE (07774) 117777
E-MAIL anabelking.racing@virgin.net WEBSITE www.anabelkmurphy.co.uk

1 **ASTON CANTLOW**, 6, b g Hurricane Run (IRE)—Princess Caraboo (IRE) **Touchwood Racing**
2 **BEAUMONT COOPER**, 5, b g Invincible Spirit (IRE)—Atlantide (USA) **Touchwood Racing**
3 **CROUCHING HARRY (IRE)**, 5, b g Tiger Hill (IRE)—Catwalk Dreamer (IRE) **Touchwood Racing**
4 **DORMOUSE**, 9, b g Medicean—Black Fighter (USA) **H. A. Murphy**
5 **INDIAN SCOUT**, 6, b g Indesatchel (IRE)—Manderina **Touchwood Racing**
6 **KAKAPUKA**, 7, b g Shinko Forest (IRE)—No Rehearsal (IRE) **Aiden Murphy & All The Kings Horses**
7 **KAUTO THE ROC (FR)**, 10, ch g With The Flow (USA)—Kauto of Realm (FR) **Ridgeway Racing Club**
8 **KING'S ROAD**, 9, ch g King's Best (USA)—Saphire **Mrs A. L. M. Murphy**
9 **LITTLE CHOOSEY**, 4, ch f Cadeaux Genereux—Little Nymph **Ridgeway Racing Club**
10 **RIGOLETTO (IRE)**, 6, b g Ad Valorem (USA)—Jallaissine (IRE) **All The Kings Horses**
11 **VOLITO**, 8, ch g Bertolini (USA)—Vax Rapide **Mrs A. L. M. Murphy**
12 **WALTER DE LA MARE (IRE)**, 7, b g Barathea (IRE)—Banutan (IRE) **Mrs A. L. M. Murphy**

MRS ANABEL K. MURPHY - Continued

THREE-YEAR-OLDS

13 **AUTOPILOT,** b c Kyllachy—Khyber Knight (IRE) **Mrs A. L. M. Murphy**

Assistant Trainer: Aiden Murphy

Amateur: Mr O. J. Murphy.

460

MR COLM MURPHY, Gorey
Postal: **Ballinadrummin, Killena, Gorey, Co. Wexford, Ireland**
Contacts: **PHONE (00353) 53 9482690 FAX (00353) 53 9482690 MOBILE (00353) 862 629538**
E-MAIL murphycolma@hotmail.com WEBSITE www.colmmurphyracing.ie

1 **AFOOTINTHEDOOR (IRE),** 5, b g Milan—Bondi Storm (IRE) **J. P. McManus**
2 **ALADDINS CAVE,** 10, b g Rainbow Quest (USA)—Flight of Fancy **Treasure Hunters Syndicate**
3 **BOUILLABAISSE (IRE),** 8, b m Beat Hollow—Cattermole (USA) **Barry Connell**
4 **CAOLANEOIN (IRE),** 8, b g King's Theatre (IRE)—Queen Plaisir (IRE) **Michael J. Mulligan**
5 **CARA'S OSCAR (IRE),** 8, b g Oscar (IRE)—Distant Gale (IRE) **A. T. Battersby**
6 **CATALAUNIAN FIELDS (IRE),** 5, b g Fair Mix (IRE)—Leading Lady **Gigginstown House Stud**
7 **CORR POINT (IRE),** 7, b g Azamour (IRE)—Naazeq **Declan Hogan**
8 **CRACKING CHAP (IRE),** 5, b g High Chaparral (IRE)—Creaking Step (IRE) **John F. Doyle**
9 **EMPIRE OF DIRT (IRE),** 7, b g Westerner—Rose of Inchiquin (IRE) **Gigginstown House Stud**
10 **EXPRESS DU BERLAIS (FR),** 5, b g Saint des Saints (FR)—Euil Eagle (FR) **Gigginstown House Stud**
11 **FITZGUTENTYTE (IRE),** 9, ch m Beneficial—Joyau (IRE) **Mr E. Allen**
12 **GLAM GERRY (IRE),** 10, b g Dr Massini (IRE)—Daraheen Diamond (IRE) **Barry Connell**
13 **JEWEL STAR (IRE),** 7, b m Flemensfirth (USA)—Thetravellinglady (IRE) **J. P. McManus**
14 **KILLINEY COURT (IRE),** 5, b g King's Theatre (IRE)—Thimble Royale (IRE) **Barry Connell**
15 **MARLBROOK (IRE),** 6, b g Beneficial—Drinadaly (IRE) **J. P. McManus**
16 **MISTER HOTELIER (IRE),** 7, b g Beneficial—Accordian Lady (IRE) **Mark McDonagh**
17 **MY KIND OF TOWN (IRE),** 5, br g Presenting—West Hill Rose (IRE) **J. P. McManus**
18 **PEPELINA (IRE),** 6, b m Vinnie Roe (IRE)—Vallee Doree (FR) **Barry Connell**
19 **PRESENTING BEARA (IRE),** 6, b g Presenting—Ginger Bar (IRE) **Winning Ways Solar Syndicate**
20 **QUITO DE LA ROQUE (FR),** 10, b g Saint des Saints (FR)—Moody Cloud (FR) **Gigginstown House Stud**
21 **RI ULADH (IRE),** 7, b g Needle Gun (IRE)—Jurado Park (IRE) **C. E. Falls**
22 **RYANSBROOK (IRE),** 6, b g Alderbrook—Lost Link (IRE) **Thomas Friel**
23 **RYE MARTINI (IRE),** 7, b g Catcher In The Rye (IRE)—Nocturne In March (IRE) **Gigginstown House Stud**
24 **SUNSHINEANDSHADOW,** 6, b g Kayf Tara—Champagne Lil **Gigginstown House Stud**
25 **THE COOKIE JAR (IRE),** 7, b m Alderbrook—Garrylough (IRE) **M. Fennessy Jnr**

Other Owners: Patrick G. Walsh, S. Delaney.

Assistant Trainer: Patrick Murphy

461

MR MICHAEL MURPHY, Newmarket
Postal: **76 Weston Way, Newmarket, Suffolk, CB8 7SF**
Contacts: **PHONE (01638) 561099 MOBILE (07951) 766035**
E-MAIL mpfequine@hotmail.co.uk

1 **CELTIC LEGACY,** 7, ch m Where Or When (IRE)—An Cailin Rua **Mr M. P. F. Murphy**
2 **IMPRESS ME,** 6, ch m Sulamani (IRE)—An Cailin Rua **Michael P Murphy & Marie Wymer**
3 **LAW HILL,** 5, b g Zamindar (USA)—Absoluta (IRE) **Future Electrical Services Ltd**
4 **LES ANDELYS,** 8, b g Zieten (USA)—Oasis Song (IRE) **Future Electrical Services Ltd**
5 **ROCK OF AGES,** 5, ch g Pivotal—Magic Peak (IRE) **R. W. Smith**
6 **YANBU (USA),** 9, b m Swain (IRE)—Dufoof (USA) **Future Electrical Services Ltd**

Other Owners: Mrs M. Wymer.

MR MIKE MURPHY, Westoning
Postal: **Broadlands, Manor Park Stud, Westoning, Bedfordshire, MK45 5LA**
Contacts: PHONE **(01525) 717305** FAX **(01525) 717305** MOBILE **(07770) 496103**
E-MAIL **mmurphy@globalnet.co.uk** WEBSITE **www.mikemurphyracing.co.uk**

1 **ANGEL WAY (IRE)**, 5, br m Trans Island—Zilayah (USA) **Mr D. J. Ellis**
2 **AVONMORE STAR**, 6, b g Avonbridge—Pooka's Daughter (IRE) **Goff,Hoskins,Hyde,Lobo&Smithx2 & Partner**
3 **BENANDONNER (USA)**, 11, ch g Giant's Causeway—Cape Verdi (IRE) **M. Murphy**
4 **CAPTAIN CAROLINE**, 4, b f Multiplex—Nut (IRE) **Mrs C. J. Barr**
5 **CHAPTER AND VERSE (IRE)**, 8, gr g One Cool Cat (USA)—Beautiful Hill (IRE) **Mr D. J. Ellis**
6 **DANEGLOW (IRE)**, 4, ch f Thousand Words—Valluga (IRE) **Mrs J. Thompson**
7 **DISCUSSIONTOFOLLOW (IRE)**, 4, b g Elusive City (USA)—Tranquil Sky **Mr D. T. Spratt**
8 **DIVIDEND DAN (IRE)**, 4, ch g Danroad (AUS)—Pip'n Judy (IRE) **Mr N. C. F. McLeod-Clarke**
9 **KAKATOSI**, 7, br g Pastoral Pursuits—Ladywell Blaise (IRE) **Mr R. E. Tillett**
10 **LA FORTUNATA**, 7, b m Lucky Story (USA)—Phantasmagoria **Mr J. Patton**
11 **LIMON SQUEEZY**, 5, b m Royal Applause—Limonia (GER) **M. Murphy**
12 4, B g Sakhee's Secret—Limonia (GER)
13 **MUHDIQ (USA)**, 5, b g Hard Spun (USA)—Enfiraaj (USA) **Ms A. D. Tibbett**
14 **RED SOMERSET (USA)**, 11, b g Red Ransom (USA)—Bielska (USA) **M. Murphy**
15 **ROCK ANTHEM (IRE)**, 10, ch g Rock of Gibraltar (IRE)—Regal Portrait (IRE) **R. Bright**
16 **UP TIPP**, 4, ch g Medicean—Jetbeeah (IRE) **Cobby, Williams, O'Connell, Murphy**
17 **VALDAW**, 6, b g Val Royal (FR)—Delight of Dawn **Mr D. T. Spratt**

THREE-YEAR-OLDS
18 **SWEET CHARLIE**, b f Myboycharlie (IRE)—Play Around (IRE) **Charlie's Angels**

Other Owners: Mrs M. Bright, Mr N. Cobby, Mr R. S. Hoskins, Mr B. Rogerson, Mr A. C. Smith.

Assistant Trainer: J.P. Cullinan

MR PAT MURPHY, Hungerford
Postal: **Glebe House Stables, School Lane, East Garston, Nr Hungerford, Berkshire, RG17 7HR**
Contacts: OFFICE **(01488) 648473** FAX **(01488) 649775** MOBILE **(07831) 410409**
E-MAIL **pat@mabberleys.freeserve.co.uk** WEBSITE **www.patmurphyracing.com**

1 **ALPINE MIST**, 4, b f Elusive Quality (USA)—Snowtime (IRE) **Mrs C. C. Regalado-Gonzalez**
2 **CATALINAS DIAMOND (IRE)**, 6, b m One Cool Cat (USA)—Diamondiferous (USA) **Briton International**
3 **CLOUDY BOB (IRE)**, 7, gr g Cloudings (IRE)—Keen Supreme (IRE) **Men Of Stone**
4 **ETERNAL VIEW (IRE)**, 4, b f Pivotal—Alstemeria (IRE) **Mrs C. C. Regalado-Gonzalez**
5 **ISLAND CRUISE (IRE)**, 6, b g Turtle Island (IRE)—Chuckawalla (IRE) **Quintin Friends & Family**
6 **LOVES BLIND (IRE)**, 5, b g Fruits of Love (USA)—Naughty Marietta (IRE) **P. G. Murphy**
7 **VANVITELLI**, 4, b g Shamardal (USA)—Treble Seven (USA) **Mrs C. C. Regalado-Gonzalez**

THREE-YEAR-OLDS
8 B g Assertive—Illustre Inconnue (USA) **P. G. Murphy**
9 **LASTING VIEW (IRE)**, b f Pivotal—Alstemeria (IRE) **Mrs C. C. Regalado-Gonzalez**
10 B c Dylan Thomas (IRE)—Renowned (IRE)
11 **SWEET CHERRY (IRE)**, b f Mastercraftsman (IRE)—Dear Gracie (IRE) **Mrs C. C. Regalado-Gonzalez**

TWO-YEAR-OLDS
12 B c 2/5 Arcano (IRE)—Snowtime (IRE) (Galileo (IRE)) (34843) **Mrs C. C. Regalado-Gonzalez**

Other Owners: B. H. Goldswain, Exors of the Late Mrs J. B. H. Goldswain, Mr R. Guest, Mr P. D. Lloyd, Mrs L. Quintin, Mr R. L. Reynolds.

Assistant Trainer: Mrs Dianne Murphy

Jockey (flat): Steve Drowne, Robert Havlin. **Jockey (NH):** Leighton Aspell, Colin Bolger.

464 MR BARRY MURTAGH, Carlisle
Postal: **Hurst Farm, Ivegill, Carlisle, Cumbria, CA4 ONL**
Contacts: **PHONE (01768) 484649 FAX (01768) 484744 MOBILE (07714) 026741**
E-MAIL **sue@suemurtagh.wanadoo.co.uk**

1 **BARABOY (IRE)**, 4, b g Barathea (IRE)—Irina (IRE) **A. R. White**
2 **BREEZE WITH EASE (IRE)**, 10, b g Fourstars Allstar (USA)—Roses Return (IRE) **Famous Five Racing**
3 **CALDEW LAD (IRE)**, 6, b g Aahsaylad—Princess Le Moss (IRE) **Mr G. Vipond**
4 **CAVITE ETA (IRE)**, 7, br g Spadoun (FR)—Samarinnda (IRE) **Don't Tell Henry**
5 **DALSTONTOSILOTH (IRE)**, 6, b g Gamut (IRE)—The Boss's Dance (USA) **Mr G. Vipond**
6 **FORESTSIDE (IRE)**, 9, br g Zagreb (USA)—Silver Sunset **J. R. Callow**
7 **HORTON**, 6, b g Beat All (USA)—Fen Terrier **Mrs S. Murtagh**
8 **HUNTERS BELT (IRE)**, 10, b g Intikhab (USA)—Three Stars **Mr R. A. Fisher**
9 **JEBULANI**, 4, b g Jelani (IRE)—Susan's Dowry **Mr K. Fitzsimons & Mr G. Fell**
10 **KEALIGOLANE (IRE)**, 10, gr g Beneficial—Leone Des Pres (FR) **J. R. Callow**
11 **KING'S CHORISTER**, 8, ch g King's Best (USA)—Chorist **Woodgate Partnership**
12 **LEROY PARKER (IRE)**, 6, ch g Titus Livius (FR)—Jameela (IRE) **R & K Carter**
13 **LUCKY MELLOR**, 7, b g Lucky Story (USA)—Lady Natilda **Mr Don O'Connor & Mr Derek Wilson**
14 **PETE**, 11, b g Overbury (IRE)—Fen Terrier **Mrs S. Murtagh**
15 **STANLEY BRIDGE**, 7, b g Avonbridge—Antonia's Folly **Mr M. A. Proudfoot**
16 **TARA SPRINGS**, 5, b m Kayf Tara—Moor Spring **Mrs A. Stamper**
17 **TROUBLE IN PARIS (IRE)**, 7, ch g Great Palm (USA)—Ten Dollar Bill (IRE) **Hurst Farm Racing**

Other Owners: Mr R. Allen, Mr James Callow, Mr Robert Carter, Mrs F. K. Carter, Mr G. Fell, Mr K. Fitzsimons, Mrs M. Hutt, Mr A. J. Markley, Mr James Murtagh, Mr F. P. Murtagh, Mr D. O'Connor, Mr Michael A. Proudfoot, Mr Dave Teasdale, Mr Thomas Uprichard, Mr Derek Wilson.

Assistant Trainer: S A Murtagh

465 MR WILLIE MUSSON, Newmarket
Postal: **Saville House, St Mary's Square, Newmarket, Suffolk, CB8 0HZ**
Contacts: **PHONE (01638) 663371 FAX (01638) 667979**
E-MAIL **willie@williemusson.co.uk WEBSITE www.williemusson.co.uk**

1 **BOLD ADVENTURE**, 10, ch g Arkadian Hero (USA)—Impatiente (USA) **The Back To Back Partnership**
2 **BROUGHTONS CHARM (IRE)**, 4, b f Invincible Spirit (IRE)—Parisian Elegance **Broughton Thermal Insulations**
3 **BROUGHTONS RHYTHM**, 5, b g Araafa (IRE)—Broughton Singer (IRE) **Broughton Thermal Insulations**
4 **BROUGHTONS WARRIOR**, 6, b g Where Or When (IRE)—Sleave Silk (IRE) **Broughton Thermal Insulations**
5 **COMMON TOUCH (IRE)**, 6, ch g Compton Place—Flying Finish (FR) **Broughton Thermal Insulations**
6 **LADY COOPER**, 4, b f Ishiguru (USA)—Mistress Cooper **Mrs R. H. Brown**
7 **MAC'S POWER (IRE)**, 8, b g Exceed And Excel (AUS)—Easter Girl **Broughton Thermal Insulations**
8 **MADAME ALLSORTS**, 9, b m Double Trigger (IRE)—Always A Pleasure **Mr R Musson & Mr P Thompson**
9 **MOUNTAIN RANGE (IRE)**, 6, b g High Chaparral (IRE)—Tuscany Lady (IRE) **The Climbers**
10 **NOVELLEN LAD (IRE)**, 9, b g Noverre (USA)—Lady Ellen **Johnson & Broughton**
11 **ROCKET ROB (IRE)**, 8, b g Danetime (IRE)—Queen of Fibres (IRE) **Mr J. R. Searchfield**

THREE-YEAR-OLDS

12 **BROUGHTONS SECRET**, b f Aqlaam—Hidden Meaning **Broughton Thermal Insulations**
13 **DONT HAVE IT THEN**, b g Myboycharlie (IRE)—Mondovi **Mr L. J. Mann**
14 B f Bushranger (IRE)—Larrocha (IRE) **Broughton Thermal Insulations**
15 B f Mount Nelson—Motif **W. J. Musson**
16 **PLOUGH BOY (IRE)**, b c Dandy Man (IRE)—Ribald **K. A. Cosby & Partners**
17 **TASHTU**, b f Tobougg (IRE)—Tashkiyla (FR) **Mrs N. A. Ward**

TWO-YEAR-OLDS

18 Ch f 5/4 Shirocco (GER)—Marrakech (IRE) (Barathea (IRE)) (2000) **Broughton Thermal Insulations**
19 Ch f 8/3 Nayef (USA)—Park Melody (IRE) (Refuse To Bend (IRE)) (32000) **Broughton Thermal Insulations**
20 **SIR ERNIE**, b c 26/4 Azamour (IRE)—Catherine Palace (Grand Lodge (USA)) (15000) **Mr Laurence Mann**

Other Owners: Broughton Thermal Insulation, Mr K. A. Cosby, Mr T. Evans, Mr B. N. Fulton, Mr John Hawksley, Mr I. Johnson, Mr Laurence Mann, Mr W. J. Musson, Mr R. D. Musson, Mr Patrick Thompson.

466 DR JEREMY NAYLOR, Shrewton
Postal: **The Cleeve, Elston Lane, Shrewton, Wiltshire, SP3 4HL**
Contacts: **PHONE (01980) 620804 MOBILE (07771) 740126**
E-MAIL **info@jeremynaylor.com** WEBSITE **www.jeremynaylor.com**

1 ACOSTA, 10, b g Foxhound (USA)—Dancing Heights (IRE) **The Acosta Partnership**
2 PADOVA, 8, b g Shahrastani (USA)—My Song of Songs **Mr A. Brown**
3 PLAIN STRIKING, 5, b m Striking Ambition—Daphne's Doll (IRE) **The Acosta Partnership**
4 POPPY GREGG, 9, b m Tamure (IRE)—Opalette **Mrs S. P. Elphick**
5 TOO TRIGGER HAPPY, 5, b m Double Trigger (IRE)—Hilarious (IRE) **Dr J. R. J. Naylor**
6 TOUS LES DEUX, 11, b g Efisio—Caerosa **Dr J. R. J. Naylor**
7 WASPY, 5, ch m King's Best (USA)—Gib (IRE) **Cleeve Stables Racing Partnership**

THREE-YEAR-OLDS

8 B f Striking Ambition—Sweet Request **Mrs S. P. Elphick**

Jockey (NH): Wayne Kavanagh.

467 MR JOHN NEEDHAM, Ludlow
Postal: **Gorsty Farm, Mary Knoll, Ludlow, Shropshire, SY8 2HD**
Contacts: **PHONE (01584) 872112/874826 FAX (01584) 873256 MOBILE (07811) 451137**

1 BRINGEWOOD BELLE, 11, b m Kayf Tara—Carlingford Belle **J. L. Needham**
2 BRINGEWOOD FOX, 12, gr g Cloudings—Leithall Fox **Miss J. C. L. Needham**
3 COOLDINE RUN (IRE), 10, b g Shernazar—Run A Fairy (IRE) **J. L. Needham**
4 ELTON FOX, 9, br g Bob Back (USA)—Leithall Fox **Miss J. C. L. Needham**
5 MORTIMERS CROSS, 13, b g Cloudings (IRE)—Leithall Doe **J. L. Needham**

Assistant Trainer: P. Hanly

Jockey (NH): Richard Johnson, Paul Moloney. Amateur: Mr R Jarrett.

468 MRS HELEN NELMES, Dorchester
Postal: **Warmwell Stables, 2 Church Cottages, Warmwell, Dorchester, Dorset, DT2 8HQ**
Contacts: **PHONE/FAX (01305) 852254 MOBILE (07977) 510318**
E-MAIL **warmwellstud@tiscali.co.uk** WEBSITE **www.warmwellracing.co.uk**

1 CRANKY CORNER, 10, b g Classic Cliche (IRE)—Pondimari (FR) **Warmwell Racing Club**
2 GOODGOSHMSMOLLY, 5, b m Amrak Ajeeb (IRE)—Larry's Law (IRE) **Warmwell Racing Club**
3 KALMBEFORETHESTORM, 6, ch g Storming Home—Miss Honeypenny (IRE) **Warmwellcome Partnership**
4 MR TOY BOY, 4, b g Phoenix Reach (IRE)—Toy Girl (IRE) **All Sorts Dorset Partnership**
5 MYLITTLEMOUSE (IRE), 6, b m Turtle Island (IRE)—Ballybeg Rose (IRE) **K. A. Nelmes**
6 THE CLYDA ROVER (IRE), 10, ch g Moonax (IRE)—Pampered Molly (IRE) **K. A. Nelmes**
7 THE FINGER POST (IRE), 7, b g Zagreb (USA)—Mystic Madam (IRE) **K. A. Nelmes**
8 UNOWHATIMEANHARRY, 6, b g Sir Harry Lewis (USA)—Red Nose Lady **Miss S. J. Hartley**
9 WEST BAY HOOLIE, 8, b g Nomadic Way (USA)—West Bay Breeze **C. T. & A. Samways**
10 WITCHESINTUNE, 7, b m Beat Hollow—Music Park (IRE) **Miss S. J. Hartley**
11 ZULU PRINCIPLE, 7, b g Tiger Hill (IRE)—Tu Eres Mi Amore **T M W Partnership**

Other Owners: Mrs S. Cobb, Miss V. O. Kardas, Mr M. Miller, Mr C. E. Mundy, Mrs H. R. J. Nelmes, Ms A. M. Neville, Mr D. Price, C. T. Samways, Mrs A. Samways.

Assistant Trainer: K Nelmes

469 MR TONY NEWCOMBE, Barnstaple
Postal: **Lower Delworthy, Yarnscombe, Barnstaple, Devon, EX31 3LT**
Contacts: **PHONE/FAX (01271) 858554 MOBILE (07785) 297210**
E-MAIL **huntshawequineforest@talktalk.net**

1 ALL RIGHT NOW, 7, b g Night Shift (USA)—Cookie Cutter (IRE) **Mr J. Hay**
2 DORBACK, 7, ch g Kyllachy—Pink Supreme **Joli Racing**
3 DUNHOY (IRE), 6, ch g Goodricke—Belle of The Blues (IRE) **D. M. J. Gilbert**

MR TONY NEWCOMBE - Continued

4 **GUNG HO (FR)**, 5, b br h Marju (IRE)—Moonlit Water **Mr A. T. Owen**
5 **HALIFAX (IRE)**, 6, ch g Halling (USA)—Lady Zonda **Mr A. T. Owen**
6 **JOLLY RANCH**, 8, gr m Compton Place—How Do I Know
7 **KAY SERA**, 6, b g Kayf Tara—Inflation **N. P. Hardy**
8 **LUNDY SKY**, 9, b g Zaha (CAN)—Rosina Mae **West Country Partners**
9 **MAMBO SPIRIT (IRE)**, 10, b g Invincible Spirit (IRE)—Mambodorga (USA) **N. P. Hardy**
10 **MY METEOR**, 7, b g Bahamian Bounty—Emerald Peace (IRE) **A. G. Newcombe**
11 **RED ART (IRE)**, 5, b h Excellent Art—All Began (IRE) **D. M. J. Gilbert**
12 **SIGNORA FRASI (IRE)**, 9, b m Indian Ridge—Sheba (IRE) **A. G. Newcombe**
13 **SPELLMAKER**, 5, b g Kheleyf (USA)—Midnight Spell **Joli Racing**
14 4, B c King's Theatre (IRE)—Talinas Rose (IRE) **Reefer Distribution Services Ltd**
15 **TEUTONIC KNIGHT (IRE)**, 7, ch g Daggers Drawn (USA)—Azyaa **R. J. Turton**

Other Owners: C. J. Buckerfield, A. G. Craig, Mr J. W. Heal, Mr M. R. Rhoades.

Assistant Trainer: John Lovejoy

Jockey (flat): Dane O'Neill, Fergus Sweeney, Tom Queally. **Jockey (NH):** Liam Treadwell, Andrew Thornton.

470

DR RICHARD NEWLAND, Claines
Postal: **Newland Associates Ltd, Linacres Farm, Egg Lane, Claines, Worcester, WR3 7SB**
Contacts: **PHONE (07956) 196535**
E-MAIL richard.newland1@btopenworld.com

1 **ACT OF KALANISI (IRE)**, 8, b g Kalanisi (IRE)—
Act of The Pace (IRE) **Mr C. E. Stedman, Dr & Mrs R. D. P. Newland**
2 **AHYAKNOWYERSELF (IRE)**, 8, b g Milan—Summer Break (IRE) **G Carstairs & R Marker**
3 **ANGELOT DU BERLAIS (FR)**, 5, b g Poliglote—Afragha (IRE) **C. E. Stedman**
4 **ANTON DOLIN (IRE)**, 6, ch g Danehill Dancer (IRE)—Ski For Gold **Mrs M L Trow, Barwell & Newland**
5 **ARDKILLY WITNESS (IRE)**, 8, b g Witness Box (USA)—Ardkilly Angel (IRE) **C E Stedman & Dr R D P Newland**
6 **BOBOWEN (IRE)**, 8, b g Bob Back (USA)—Opus One **Mr J. Stewart**
7 **CHANGING THE GUARD**, 8, b g King's Best (USA)—Our Queen of Kings **Mr J. Stewart**
8 **CORNISH BEAU (IRE)**, 7, ch g Pearl of Love (IRE)—Marimar (IRE) **The London Foot & Ankle Centre**
9 **DALMO**, 5, b g Dalakhani (IRE)—Morina (USA) **J. A. Provan**
10 **DISCAY**, 5, b g Distant Music (USA)—Caysue **Foxtrot NH Racing Partnership VIII**
11 **GORTENBUIE (IRE)**, 9, b g Flemensfirth (USA)—Carnival Buck (IRE)
12 **HAWDYERWHEESHT**, 6, b g Librettist (USA)—Rapsgate (IRE) **Mr P. Drinkwater**
13 **MART LANE (IRE)**, 9, b g Stowaway—Western Whisper (IRE) **Mr J. Stewart**
14 **MURTYS DELIGHT (IRE)**, 7, b g Bach (IRE)—Valley Supreme (IRE) **Mr P. C. W. Green**
15 **NIGHT ALLIANCE (IRE)**, 9, ch g Pierre—Next Venture (IRE) **Dr R. D. P. Newland**
16 **ORTHODOX LAD**, 6, ch g Monsieur Bond (IRE)—Ashantiana **Mr P. C. W. Green**
17 **PINEAU DE RE (FR)**, 11, b g Maresca Sorrento (FR)—Elfe du Perche (FR) **J. A. Provan**
18 **REGAL D'ESTRUVAL (FR)**, 9, b g Panoramic—Haie d'estruval (FR) **Mr P. Jenkins**
19 **ROYALE KNIGHT**, 8, b g King's Theatre (IRE)—Gardana (FR) **C. E. Stedman & R. J. Corsan**
20 **SMALIB MONTERG (FR)**, 8, b g Smadoun (FR)—Liberty's (FR) **AP Barwell,Mrs ML Trow & Mrs MJ Sanders**
21 **YOUNG HURRICANE (IRE)**, 8, b g Oscar (IRE)—Georgia On My Mind (FR) **Mr P. Jenkins**

Other Owners: Mr D. Abraham, A. P. Barwell, G. N. Carstairs, Mr M. S. Davies, R. J. T. Marker, Mrs L. J. Newland, Mrs M. J. Sanders, Mrs M. L. Trow.

Assistant Trainer: S. R. Trow

Amateur: Mr T. Weston.

471

MISS ANNA NEWTON-SMITH, Polegate
Postal: **Bull Pen Cottage, Jevington, Polegate, East Sussex, BN26 5QB**
Contacts: **PHONE (01323) 488354 FAX (01323) 488354 MOBILE (07970) 914124**
E-MAIL anna_newtonsmith@o2.co.uk WEBSITE www.annanewtonsmith.co.uk

1 **BUDSSON**, 8, b g Alflora (IRE)—Little Bud **Mrs S. B. S. Grist**
2 **DUDE ALERT (IRE)**, 4, b g Windsor Knot (IRE)—Policy **Mr M. R. Baldry**
3 **GETCARTER**, 8, b g Fasliyev (USA)—Pourquoi Pas (IRE) **Miss H. J. Williams**
4 **GORING ONE (IRE)**, 9, b g Broadway Flyer (USA)—Brigette's Secret **Mr G. E. Goring**
5 **GORING TWO (IRE)**, 9, br g Needle Gun (IRE)—Kam Slave **Mr G. E. Goring**

MISS ANNA NEWTON-SMITH - Continued

6 **HARLEQUINS GLEAMS**, 6, b g Gleaming (IRE)—Harlequin Walk (IRE) **Mrs H. Norman**
7 **HERMOSA VAQUERA (IRE)**, 4, b f High Chaparral (IRE)—Sundown **Mr M. R. Baldry**
8 4, B g Air Quest—Itsinthepost **Mr M. R. Baldry**
9 **LITTLE ROXY (IRE)**, 9, b m Dilshaan—Brunswick **The Ash Tree Inn Racing Club**
10 **SHERREB (IRE)**, 8, b g Zagreb (USA)—Sherberry (IRE) **PPS Racing**

Other Owners: Mr M. K. Baker, Baroness S. Noakes, C. B. Noakes, His Honour Judge A. Patience, His Honour Judge J. R. Peppitt, A. K. Walker.

Assistant Trainer: Sally Harler

Jockey (flat): Hayley Turner. **Jockey (NH):** Mattie Batchelor, Marc Goldstein, Nick Scholfield, Andrew Thornton. **Conditional:** Tom Cannon, Adam Wedge.

---

472   **MR DAVID NICHOLLS**, Thirsk
Postal: **Tall Trees Racing Ltd, Tall Trees, Sessay, Thirsk, North Yorkshire, YO7 3ND**
Contacts: **PHONE** (01845) 501470 **FAX** (01845) 501666 **MOBILE** (07971) 555105
E-MAIL david.nicholls@btconnect.com **WEBSITE** www.davidnichollsracing.com

1 **ADDICTIVE DREAM (IRE)**, 7, ch g Kheleyf (USA)—
                                             Nottambula (IRE) **Brian Morton & Pinnacle Dream Partnership**
2 **BE PERFECT (USA)**, 5, b g Street Cry (IRE)—Binya (GER) **Lady C. J. O'Reilly**
3 **BONNIE CHARLIE**, 8, ch g Intikhab (USA)—Scottish Exile (IRE) **Gaga Syndicate**
4 **DESERT CREEK (IRE)**, 8, ch g Refuse To Bend (IRE)—Flagship **D W Barker & D Nicholls**
5 **DON'T CALL ME (IRE)**, 7, ch g Haafhd—Just Call Me (NZ) **Matt & Lauren Morgan**
6 **FITZ FLYER (IRE)**, 8, b g Acclamation—Starry Night **M. F. Browne**
7 **FREEWHEEL (IRE)**, 4, br c Galileo (IRE)—La Chunga (USA) **B. Morton**
8 **GREENHEAD HIGH**, 6, b g Statue of Liberty (USA)—Artistry **D. Nicholls**
9 **HAMOODY (USA)**, 10, ch g Johannesburg (USA)—Northern Gulch (USA) **Hart Inn I**
10 **IMPERIAL LEGEND (IRE)**, 5, b g Mujadil (USA)—Titian Saga (IRE) **Pinnacle Mujadil Partnership**
11 **INDEGO BLUES**, 5, b g Indesatchel (IRE)—Yanomami (USA) **Pinnacle Indesatchel Partnership**
12 **INDIAN CHIEF (IRE)**, 4, b c Montjeu (IRE)—Buck Aspen (USA) **Castle Construction (NE) LTD**
13 **INXILE (IRE)**, 9, b g Fayruz—Grandel **Mr D. Nicholls & Mrs J. Love**
14 **JOHNNO**, 5, br g Excellent Art—Vert Val (USA) **Gary & Linnet Woodward**
15 **KARAKA JACK**, 7, ch g Pivotal—Mauri Moon **Mr M. Mackay & Mr S. Bruce**
16 **KIMBERELLA**, 4, b g Kyllachy—Gleam of Light (USA) **Mr C. J. Titcomb**
17 **KUANYAO (IRE)**, 8, b g American Post—Nullarbor **Matt & Lauren Morgan**
18 **LAYLA'S HERO (IRE)**, 7, b g One Cool Cat (USA)—Capua (USA) **Hart Inn I**
19 **LEWISHAM**, 4, b g Sleeping Indian—Almunia (IRE) **D. Nicholls**
20 **LLEWELLYN**, 6, b g Shamardal (USA)—Ffestiniog **David Nicholls Racing Club**
21 **MAJESTIC MANANNAN (IRE)**, 5, b g Majestic Missile (IRE)—Miraculous (IRE) **Mark & Maureen Schofield**
22 **MANATEE BAY**, 4, ch g Royal Applause—Dash of Lime **Pinnacle Royal Applause Partnership**
23 **MISTER MANANNAN (IRE)**, 7, b g Desert Style (IRE)—Cover Girl (IRE) **Mrs M. C. Schofield**
24 **MUJAZIF (IRE)**, 4, br c Shamardal (USA)—Red Bandanna (IRE)
25 **PEA SHOOTER**, 5, b g Piccolo—Sparkling Eyes
26 **RASSELAS (IRE)**, 7, b g Danehill Dancer (IRE)—Regal Darcey (IRE) **Mr J Honeyman**
27 **ROCKET RONNIE (IRE)**, 4, b g Antonius Pius (USA)—Ctesiphon (USA) **Mills, Purchase, Fallon**
28 **RODRIGO DE TORRES (IRE)**, 7, ch g Bahamian Bounty—Leonica **Mr B. Morton**
29 **SECRET RECIPE**, 4, ch g Sakhee's Secret—Fudge
30 **STREET ARTIST (IRE)**, 4, ch c Street Cry (IRE)—Portrayal (USA)
31 **TAJNEED (IRE)**, 11, b g Alhaarth (IRE)—Indian Express **Mrs A. A. Nicholls**
32 **TAKE THE LEAD**, 4, ch f Assertive—My Dancer (IRE) **David Nicholls Racing Club**
33 **TAX FREE (IRE)**, 12, b g Tagula (IRE)—Grandel **Mr D. Nicholls & Mrs J. Love**
34 **WEST LEAKE HARE (IRE)**, 5, b g Choisir (AUS)—March Hare **Mr N. Yeoman & Mrs A. Nicholls**
35 **XILERATOR (IRE)**, 7, b g Arakan (USA)—Grandel **Mr J. Law**

THREE-YEAR-OLDS

36 **CAHAL (IRE)**, b g Bushranger (IRE)—Cabopino (IRE) **Mr J. Law**
37 **FALSE WITNESS (IRE)**, b g Amadeus Wolf—Ten Commandments (IRE) **Mr D. Fish**
38 **OLY'ROCCS (IRE)**, b c Tagula (IRE)—Orpendonna (IRE) **Mr C. M. Grech**

TWO-YEAR-OLDS

39 **MAGH MEALL**, b f 1/4 Monsieur Bond (IRE)—Tibesti (Machiavellian (USA)) (15238) **Mark & Maureen Schofield**

MR DAVID NICHOLLS - Continued

Other Owners: Mr D. W. Barker, Mrs Jackie Love, Ms Johan Moncur, Mr Matthew Morgan, Mrs Lauren Morgan, Mr Brian Morton, Mrs Alex Nicholls, Mr D. Nicholls, Mr M. A. Scaife, Mr A. Scaife, Mrs M. Schofield, Mr Mark Schofield.

Assistant Trainer: Ben Beasley

Jockey (flat): Adrian Nicholls, Paul Quinn. **Apprentice:** Anna Hesketh. **Amateur:** Mrs Adele Mulrennan.

473

MR PAUL NICHOLLS, Ditcheat
Postal: Manor Farm Stables, Ditcheat, Shepton Mallet, Somerset, BA4 6RD
Contacts: PHONE (01749) 860656 FAX (01749) 860523 MOBILE (07977) 270706
E-MAIL info@paulnichollsracing.com WEBSITE www.paulnichollsracing.com

1 ABIDJAN (FR), 4, b g Alberto Giacometti (IRE)—Kundera (FR) **Axom L**
2 AERIAL (FR), 8, b g Turgeon (USA)—Fille Formidable (USA) **Tony Hayward & Barry Fulton**
3 AL FEROF (FR), 9, gr g Dom Alco (FR)—Maralta (FR) **Mr J. R. Hales**
4 ALCALA (FR), 4, gr g Turgeon (USA)—Pail Mel (FR) **Andrea & Graham Wylie**
5 ALDOPICGROS (FR), 4, b g Tirwanako (FR)—In'challha (FR) **Million in Mind Partnership**
6 ALIBI DE SIVOLA (FR), 4, b br g Shaanmer (IRE)—Neva de Sivola (FR) **Mr C. M. Giles**
7 ALTO DES MOTTES (FR), 4, b g Dream Well (FR)—Omance (FR) **Giles, Hogarth & Webb**
8 ARPEGE D'ALENE (FR), 4, b g Dom Alco (FR)—Joliette d'alene (FR) **Potensis Limited**
9 ART MAURESQUE (FR), 4, b g Policy Maker (IRE)—Modeva (FR) **Mrs S. De La Hey**
10 AS DE MEE (FR), 4, b br g Kapgarde (FR)—Koeur de Mee (FR) **The Stewart Family & Judi Dench**
11 ATLANTIC ROLLER (IRE), 7, b g Old Vic—Tourist Attraction (IRE) **C. G. Roach**
12 BAR A MINE (FR), 5, b g Martaline—Treekle Toffee (FR) **Walters Plant Hire Ltd**
13 BENVOLIO (IRE), 7, b g Beneficial—Coumeenoole Lady **Dobson, Sutton & Woodhouse**
14 BIG BUCK'S (FR), 11, b br g Cadoudal (FR)—Buck's (FR) **The Stewart Family**
15 BLACK COW (IRE), 6, br g Presenting—Back Market Lass (IRE) **Mr Chris Giles & Mr Richard Webb**
16 BLACK RIVER (IRE), 5, b g Secret Singer—Love River (FR) **Andrea & Graham Wylie**
17 BLACK THUNDER (FR), 7, bl g Malinas (GER)—Blackmika (FR) **Donlon, MacDonald, Fulton & Webb**
18 BRINESTINE (USA), 5, b g Bernstein (USA)—Miss Zafonic (FR) **The Johnson & Stewart Families**
19 BROTHER DU BERLAIS (FR), 5, b br g Saint des Saints (FR)—
King's Daughter (FR) **Mr John Hales & Mr Ian Fogg**
20 BUCK'S BOND (FR), 8, gr g Turgeon (USA)—Buck's Beauty (FR) **Mrs C. E. Penny**
21 BURY PARADE (IRE), 8, br g Overbury (IRE)—
Alexandra Parade (IRE) **HighclereThoroughbredRacing- Bury Parade**
22 CAID DU BERLAIS (FR), 5, b g Westerner—Kenza du Berlais (FR) **Donlon, Doyle, MacDonald & C. Barber**
23 CALIPTO (FR), 4, b g Califet (FR)—Peutiot (FR) **Mr Ian Fogg & Mr Chris Giles**
24 CAPTAIN KELLY (IRE), 7, b g Oscar (IRE)—Tri Folene (FR) **Donlon, Doyle, MacDonald & Webb**
25 CEASAR MILAN (IRE), 6, br g Milan—Standfast (IRE) **The Stewart & Wylie Families**
26 CEDRE BLEU (FR), 7, b g Le Fou (IRE)—Arvoire (IRE) **Mr Paul K. Barber & The Johnson Family**
27 CELESTIAL HALO (IRE), 10, b g Galileo (IRE)—Pay The Bank **The Stewart Family**
28 CHINATOWN BOY (IRE), 6, ch g Presenting—Asian Maze (IRE) **C. G. Roach**
29 COWARDS CLOSE (IRE), 7, br g Presenting—Parsee (IRE) **Mr Barry Fulton & Mr Paul K Barber**
30 CURRENT EVENT (FR), 7, b g Muhtathir—La Curamalal (IRE) **Mrs A. M. Millard**
31 DARK LOVER (GER), 9, b g Zinaad—Dark Lady (GER) **Mr Des Nichols & Mr Peter Hart**
32 DEIREADH RE (IRE), 8, b g Old Vic—Donaghmore Lady (IRE) **Mr Ian J. Fogg & Mrs Wendy Fogg**
33 DILDAR (IRE), 6, b g Red Ransom (USA)—Diamond Tango (FR) **Mrs S. De La Hey**
34 DO WE LIKE HIM (IRE), 4, b g Beneficial—Pattern Queen (IRE) **The Kyle & Stewart Families**
35 DODGING BULLETS (FR), 6, b g Dubawi (IRE)—Nova Cyngi (USA) **Martin Broughton & Friends**
36 DOMTALINE (FR), 7, gr g Martaline—Domna Noune (FR) **Sparkes & Gibson**
37 DORMELLO MO (FR), 4, b g Conillon (GER)—Neogel (USA) **The Kyle & Stewart Families**
38 EARTHMOVES (FR), 4, b g Antarctique (IRE)—Red Rym (FR) **R. M. Penny**
39 EASTER DAY (FR), 6, b g Malinas (GER)—Sainte Lea (FR) **B. Fulton, Broughton Thermal Insulation**
40 EDGARDO SOL (FR), 7, ch g Kapgarde (FR)—Tikiti Dancer (FR) **Axom XXXII**
41 EMPIRE LEVANT (USA), 7, gr g Empire Maker (USA)—
Orellana (USA) **Sir A Ferguson,G Mason,R Wood & P Done**
42 FAGO (FR), 4, b g Balko (FR)—Merciki (FR) **Andrea & Graham Wylie**
43 FAIRYTALE THEATRE (IRE), 7, b m King's Theatre (IRE)—Bay Dove **Mr R. J. H. Geffen**
44 FAR WEST (FR), 5, b g Poliglote—Far Away Girl (FR) **Axom XXXIX**
45 FASCINO RUSTICO, 6, b g Milan—Rustic Charm (IRE) **Mr J. R. Hales**
46 FOGGY'S WALL (IRE), 6, b g Golan (IRE)—Mrs Masters (IRE) **Mr & Mrs Mark Woodhouse**
47 FOR TWO (FR), 5, gr g Act One—Forcat (FR) **Andrea & Graham Wylie**
48 FUNNY STAR (FR), 6, ch g Tot Ou Tard (IRE)—Funny Miss (FR) **Mr & Mrs J. D. Cotton**
49 GRANDIOSO (IRE), 7, b g Westerner—Champagne Warrior (IRE) **Andrea & Graham Wylie**

MR PAUL NICHOLLS - Continued

50 **GREAT TRY (IRE)**, 5, b g Scorpion (IRE)—Cherry Pie (FR) **T. J. Hemmings**
51 **HARRY THE VIKING**, 9, ch g Sir Harry Lewis (USA)—Viking Flame **Sir A Ferguson,G Mason,R Wood & P Done**
52 **HAWKES POINT**, 9, b g Kayf Tara—Mandys Native (IRE) **C. G. Roach**
53 **HINTERLAND (IRE)**, 6, b g Poliglote—Queen Place (FR) **Mr C. M. Giles**
54 **HOWLONGISAFOOT (IRE)**, 5, b g Beneficial—Miss Vic (IRE) **P. J. Vogt**
55 **IRISH SAINT (FR)**, 5, b br g Saint des Saints (FR)—Minirose (FR) **Mrs S. De La Hey**
56 **IRVING**, 6, b g Singspiel (IRE)—Indigo Girl (GER) **Axom XLIX**
57 **JUMP CITY (FR)**, 8, b g Muhtathir—Just Fizzy **Mrs Angela Tincknell & Mr W. Tincknell**
58 **JUST A PAR (IRE)**, 7, b g Island House (IRE)—Thebrownhen (IRE) **C G Roach & Paul K Barber**
59 **KARINGA DANCER (IRE)**, 8, b g Karinga Bay—Miss Flora **H. B. Geddes**
60 **KATGARY (FR)**, 4, b g Ballingarry (IRE)—Kotkira (FR) **Andrea & Graham Wylie**
61 **KAUTO STONE (FR)**, 8, ch g With The Flow (USA)—Kauto Relka (FR) **Mr R. J. H. Geffen**
62 **KELTUS (FR)**, 4, gr g Keltos (FR)—Regina d'orthe (FR) **Donlon & MacDonald**
63 **KEPPOLS HILL (IRE)**, 8, b g Indian Danehill (IRE)—
                                                     Keppols Princess (IRE) **Mr Paul Barber & Mr & Mrs Mark Woodhouse**
64 **LAC FONTANA (FR)**, 5, b g Shirocco (GER)—Fontaine Riant (FR) **Potensis Limited**
65 **LUMPYS GOLD**, 6, b g Tikkanen (USA)—Elegant Accord (IRE) **Elite Racing Club**
66 **MAC'S RETURN (IRE)**, 7, b g Flemensfirth (USA)—Dark Mist (IRE) **Mr J. R. Hales**
67 **MAXI CHOP (FR)**, 6, b g Muhaymin (USA)—Scotch Mockery (FR) **The Stewart Family**
68 **MCLLHATTON (IRE)**, 6, b g Fruits of Love (USA)—Penny Haven (IRE) **Giles, Donlon & Macdonald**
69 **MEREHEAD (FR)**, 8, gr g Al Namix (FR)—Moneda (FR) **Mrs A. B. Yeoman**
70 **MERRION SQUARE (IRE)**, 8, b g Kotashaan (FR)—Parverb (IRE) **The Stewart Family**
71 **MINELLAHALFCENTURY (IRE)**, 6, b g Westerner—Shanakill River (IRE) **Mr Jeffrey Hordle & Mr Peter Hart**
72 **MISTRESS MOLE (IRE)**, 5, br m Definite Article—Emmylou du Berlais (FR) **The Significant Others**
73 **MON PARRAIN (FR)**, 8, b g Trempolino (USA)—Kadaina (FR) **Mr & Mrs J. D. Cotton**
74 **MORE BUCK'S (IRE)**, 4, ch g Presenting—Buck's Blue (FR) **The Stewart Family**
75 **MORITO DU BERLAIS (FR)**, 5, b g Turgeon (USA)—Chica du Berlais (FR) **C. G. Roach**
76 **MR BRIDGER**, 5, ch g Shirocco (GER)—Diamant Noir **The Stewart Family**
77 **MR MOLE (IRE)**, 6, br g Great Pretender (IRE)—Emmylou du Berlais (FR) **J. P. McManus**
78 **NO LOOSE CHANGE (IRE)**, 9, b g Bob Back (USA)—Quit The Noise (IRE) **Donlon, Doyle, MacDonald & Webb**
79 **ON BLUEBERRY HILL**, 5, b g Flemensfirth (USA)—Mrs Malt (IRE) **The Domino Boys Syndicate**
80 **OSCARGO (IRE)**, 10, b g Oscar (IRE)—Broken Rein (IRE) **Hordle, Evans & Nicholls**
81 **OUR BOMBER HARRIS**, 10, b g Saddlers' Hall (IRE)—Gaye Fame **R. P. Fry**
82 **PACHA DU POLDER (FR)**, 7, b g Muhtathir—Ambri Piotta (FR) **The Stewart & Wylie Families**
83 **PAY THE KING (IRE)**, 7, b g King's Theatre (IRE)—Knocktartan (IRE) **Mr R. J. H. Geffen**
84 **PEARL SWAN (FR)**, 9, b g Gentlewave (IRE)—Swanson (USA) **Mr R. J. H. Geffen**
85 **POLISKY (FR)**, 7, b g Poliglote—Dusky Royale (FR) **Mrs S. De La Hey**
86 **PORT MELON (IRE)**, 6, br g Presenting—Omyn Supreme (IRE) **C. G. Roach**
87 **POUNGACH (FR)**, 8, b g Daliapour (IRE)—Shalaine (FR) **Donlon, Doyle, MacDonald & Webb**
88 **PRAETURA (IRE)**, 4, b g Flemensfirth (USA)—Native Side (FR) **Mr Chris Giles & Praetura**
89 **PRESENTING ARMS (IRE)**, 7, b g Presenting—Banningham Blaze **Mr J. M. Dare**
90 **PRESSIES GIRL (IRE)**, 6, b m Presenting—Leader's Hall (IRE) **W. A. Harrison-Allan**
91 **PROSPECT WELLS (FR)**, 9, b g Sadler's Wells (USA)—Brooklyn's Dance (FR) **Andrea & Graham Wylie**
92 **PROVO (IRE)**, 7, br g Presenting—Pairtree **Hilton & Lyn Ramseyer**
93 **PTIT ZIG (FR)**, 5, b g Great Pretender (IRE)—Red Rym (FR) **Barry Fulton, Chris Giles & Richard Webb**
94 **RAINY CITY (IRE)**, 4, b g Kalanisi (IRE)—Erintante (IRE) **Sir A Ferguson,G Mason,R Wood & P Done**
95 **RANJAAN (FR)**, 6, b g Dubai Destination (USA)—Ridafa (IRE) **Highclere Thoroughbred Racing - Ranjaan**
96 **REBEL DU MAQUIS (FR)**, 9, b g Brier Creek (USA)—Jade de Chalamont (FR) **Mrs Kathy Stuart & P F Nicholls**
97 **REBEL REBELLION (IRE)**, 9, b g Lord Americo—
                                                     Tourmaline Girl (IRE) **Mr & Mrs M Woodhouse & Miss R Dobson**
98 **REMILUC (FR)**, 5, b g Mister Sacha (FR)—Markene de Durtal (FR) **Mr Ian Fogg & Mr Chris Giles**
99 **ROB ROBIN (IRE)**, 4, b g Robin des Champs (FR)—Ashwell Lady (IRE) **Mr J. R. Hales**
100 **ROCKY CREEK (IRE)**, 8, b g Dr Massini (IRE)—Kissantell (IRE) **The Johnson & Stewart Families**
101 **ROLLING ACES (IRE)**, 8, b g Whitmore's Conn (USA)—Pay Roll (IRE) **Paul Barber, Ian Fogg & David Martin**
102 **RUBEN COTTER (IRE)**, 8, b g Beneficial—Bonnie Thynes (IRE) **C. G. Roach**
103 **SAINT ROQUE (IRE)**, 8, b g Lavirco (GER)—Moody Cloud (FR) **Mr Chris Giles & Mr Ian Fogg**
104 **SALUBRIOUS (IRE)**, 7, b g Beneficial—Who Tells Jan **The Johnson & Stewart Families**
105 **SAM WINNER (FR)**, 7, b g Okawango (USA)—Noche (IRE) **Mrs A. B. Yeoman**
106 **SAMETEGAL (FR)**, 5, b g Saint des Saints (FR)—Loya Lescribaa (FR) **Mr & Mrs J. D. Cotton**
107 **SAPHIR DU RHEU (FR)**, 5, gr g Al Namix (FR)—Dona du Rheu (FR) **The Stewart Family**
108 **SEA WALL (IRE)**, 6, b g Turgeon (USA)—Si Parfaite (FR) **C. G. Roach**
109 **SERGEANT THUNDER**, 5, ch g Halling (USA)—Dissolve **C. G. Roach**
110 **SHARENI (IRE)**, 5, b g Azamour (IRE)—Sharesha (IRE) **Highclere Thoroughbred Racing - Shareni**
111 **SHOOTERS WOOD (IRE)**, 10, b g Needle Gun (IRE)—Talbot's Hollow (IRE) **W. A. Harrison-Allan**
112 **SILSOL (GER)**, 5, b g Soldier Hollow—Silveria (GER) **Michelle And Dan Macdonald**

MR PAUL NICHOLLS - Continued

113 **SILVINIACO CONTI (FR)**, 8, ch g Dom Alco (FR)—Gazelle Lulu (FR) **Potensis Limited & Mr Chris Giles**
114 **SIN BIN (IRE)**, 8, b g Presenting—Navaro (IRE) **T. J. Hemmings**
115 **SIRE COLLONGES (FR)**, 8, gr g Dom Alco (FR)—Idylle Collonges (FR) **Mrs Angela Tincknell & Mr W. Tincknell**
116 **SOLAR IMPULSE (FR)**, 4, b g Westerner—Moon Glow (FR) **Andrea & Graham Wylie**
117 **SOUND INVESTMENT (IRE)**, 6, b g Dr Massini (IRE)—Drumcay Polly (IRE) **Andrea & Graham Wylie**
118 **SOUTHFIELD THEATRE (IRE)**, 6, b g King's Theatre (IRE)—Chamoss Royale (FR) **Mrs A. B. Yeoman**
119 **SOUTHFIELD VIC (IRE)**, 5, ch g Old Vic—Chamoss Royale (FR) **Mrs A. B. Yeoman**
120 **SUBTLE SOVEREIGN (IRE)**, 7, gr g Subtle Power (IRE)—Katonka **J. Barber**
121 **TAGRITA (IRE)**, 6, b m King's Theatre (IRE)—Double Dream (IRE) **Axom XLVIII**
122 **TARA POINT**, 5, gr m Kayf Tara—Poppet **Mr R. J. H. Geffen**
123 **THE MINACK (IRE)**, 10, b g King's Theatre (IRE)—Ebony Jane **C. G. Roach**
124 **THE OUTLAW (FR)**, 4, b g Presenting—Bonnie Parker (IRE) **Donlon, MacDonald, Giles & Webb**
125 **THERE'S NO PANIC (IRE)**, 9, ch g Presenting—Out Ranking (FR) **The Stewart Family**
126 **TIDAL BAY (IRE)**, 13, b g Flemensfirth (USA)—June's Bride (IRE) **Andrea & Graham Wylie**
127 **ULCK DU LIN (FR)**, 6, b g Sassanian (USA)—Miss Fast (FR) **Mrs S. De La Hey**
128 **UNIONISTE (FR)**, 6, gr g Dom Alco (FR)—Gleep Will (FR) **Mr J. R. Hales**
129 **URBAN DE SIVOLA (FR)**, 6, ch g Le Fou (FR)—Neva de Sivola (FR) **Mr C. M. Giles**
130 **URUBU D'IRLANDE (FR)**, 6, b g Sleeping Car (FR)—Noceane (FR) **Andrea & Graham Wylie**
131 **V NECK (IRE)**, 5, b g Sir Harry Lewis (USA)—Swift Settlement **J. P. McManus**
132 **VAGO COLLONGES (FR)**, 5, b g Voix du Nord (FR)—Kapucine Collonges (FR) **Andrea & Graham Wylie**
133 **VALCO DE TOUZAINE (FR)**, 5, gr g Dom Alco (FR)—Narcisse de Touzaine (FR) **The Gi Gi Syndicate**
134 **VAROM (FR)**, 5, gr g Charming Groom (FR)—Morava (FR) **Mr John & Jordan Lund**
135 **VERY NOBLE (FR)**, 5, b g Martaline—Isati's (USA) **Mr Paul K Barber & Mr Ian J Fogg**
136 **VESPERAL DREAM (FR)**, 5, bl g Network (GER)—Pampanilla (FR) **The Loving Insurance Partnership**
137 **VIBRATO VALTAT (FR)**, 5, gr g Voix du Nord (FR)—La Tosca Valtat (FR) **Axom XLIII**
138 **VICENTE (FR)**, 5, b g Dom Alco (FR)—Ireland (FR) **Mr Ian Fogg & Mr John Hales**
139 **VICENZO MIO (FR)**, 4, b c Corri Piano (FR)—Sweet Valrose (FR) **Mrs S. De La Hey**
140 **VIDE CAVE (FR)**, 5, b g Secret Singer (FR)—Kenna (FR) **Mr Jordan Lund & Mr Brian Taylor**
141 **VIRAK (FR)**, 5, b g Bernebeau (FR)—Nosika d'airy (FR) **Hills of Ledbury Ltd**
142 **VIVALDI COLLONGES (FR)**, 5, b g Dom Alco (FR)—Diane Collonges (FR) **The Gi Gi Syndicate**
143 **WIFFY CHATSBY (IRE)**, 7, br g Presenting—Star Child (GER) **Inch Bloodstock**
144 **WILTON MILAN (IRE)**, 6, b g Milan—Biondo (IRE) **J. T. Warner**
145 **WONDERFUL CHARM (FR)**, 6, b g Poliglote—Victoria Royale (FR) **Mr R. J. H. Geffen**
146 **WOOLCOMBE FOLLY (IRE)**, 11, b br g Presenting—Strong Gara (IRE) **The Hon Mr C. A. Townshend**
147 **ZARKANDAR (IRE)**, 7, b g Azamour (IRE)—Zarkasha (IRE) **Potensis Limited & Mr Chris Giles**

Other Owners: Axom Ltd, P. K. Barber, Mr C. L. Barber, Mrs M. C. Bolton, Mr M. Bower-Dyke, A. R. Bromley, S. W. Broughton, Sir M. F. Broughton, Broughton Thermal Insulations, Mr A. P. Brown, D. J. Coles, Mr M. H. Colquhoun, J. D. Cotton, Mrs B. Cotton, Dame J. O. Dench, Miss R. J. Dobson, Mr I. J. Donaldson, Mr P. E. Done, Mr C. A. Donlon, Mrs K. Donlon, Mr D. Downie, Mr A. Doyle, Mr C. W. Evans, Mrs L. A. Farquhar, Sir A. Ferguson, Mr M. Fletcher, Mr I. J. Fogg, Mrs W. Fogg, B. N. Fulton, Mrs M. J. K. Gibson, G. F. Goode, Miss L. J. Hales, P. L. Hart, A. A. Hayward, The Hon H. M. Herbert, Highclere Thoroughbred Racing Ltd, Mr A. J. Hill, Mr B. M. Hillier, P. H. Hogarth, Mr M. J. Holman, J. G. Hordle, Mr P. J. Inch, Mrs L. Inch, Exors of the Late Mr D. A. Johnson, Mrs D. A. Johnson, Mr S. D. Johnson, Mr C. L. Keey, Mrs C. L. Kyle, Mr J. E. Lund, Mr J. E. Lund, Mrs M. Macdonald, Mr W. D. Macdonald, Mr D. L. Maddocks, Mr P. D. Maddocks, Mr D. J. Martin, G. A. Mason, Mr B. J. McManus, W. D. C. Minton, Mrs M. E. Moody, P. F. Nicholls, Mrs G. Nicholls, Mr D. J. Nichols, Mrs D. C. Nicholson, Miss M. Noden, Mr M. J. O'Shaughnessy, Mr H. Ramseyer, Mrs I. Ramseyer, Mrs L. Scott-MacDonald, Miss Claire Simmonds, Mrs K. M. Sparkes, Mr C. E. M. Staddon, Mr D. D. Stevenson, Mr A. Stewart, Mrs J. A. Stewart, Mrs K. A. Stuart, Ms C. Sutton, Mr B. Taylor, Mrs A. Tincknell, W. C. Tincknell, Mr R. A. Webb, Mr R. J. Wood, M. J. M. Woodhouse, Mrs T. A. Woodhouse, A. W. G. Wylie, Mrs A. Wylie.

Assistant Trainers: Tom Jonason, David Prichard

Jockey (NH): Daryl Jacob, Ryan Mahon, Nick Scholfield, Sam Twiston-Davies. **Conditional:** Alex Chadwick, Harry Derham, Andrias Guerin, Jack Sherwood. **Amateur:** Mr Will Biddick, Mr Andrew Doyle, Mr James King, Miss Megan Nicholls, Mr Billy Page.

---

474 **MR PETER NIVEN, Malton**
Postal: **Clovafield, Barton-Le-Street, Malton, North Yorkshire, YO17 6PN**
Contacts: **PHONE (01653) 628176 FAX (01653) 627295 MOBILE (07860) 260999**
E-MAIL pruniven@btinternet.com

1 **AREGRA (FR)**, 4, gr g Fragrant Mix (IRE)—Elisa de Mai (FR) **Mr G. Wragg**
2 **BARTON BOUNTY**, 7, b g Bahamian Bounty—Tenebrae (IRE) **Francis Green Racing Ltd**
3 **BEAT THE SHOWER**, 8, b g Beat Hollow—Crimson Shower **Mrs K. J. Young**
4 **BLADES LAD**, 5, ch g Haafhd—Blades Girl **Crown Select**

MR PETER NIVEN - Continued

5 **CLEVER COOKIE**, 6, b g Primo Valentino (IRE)—Mystic Memory **Francis Green Racing Ltd**
6 **DESGREY**, 6, gr g Desideratum—Briden **Mr S. W. Knowles**
7 **GOLDEN FUTURE**, 11, b g Muhtarram (USA)—Nazca **The Little Ice Club**
8 **LITTLE POSH (IRE)**, 5, br m Winged Love (IRE)—Lady Oakwell (IRE) **David Bamber**
9 **PINOTAGE**, 6, br g Danbird (AUS)—Keen Melody (USA) **S. J. Bowett**
10 **PITHIVIER (FR)**, 4, b g Poliglote—Kelbelange (FR) **Mr S. W. Knowles**
11 **REVANNA**, 5, b m Revoque (IRE)—Kingennie **Mrs J. A. Niven**
12 **SIR SAFIR**, 4, b g Croco Rouge (IRE)—Angela's Ashes **Francis Green Racing Ltd**
13 **SUGAR TOWN**, 4, b f Elusive City (USA)—Sweetsformysweet (USA) **S. V. Barker**
14 **UNCUT STONE (IRE)**, 6, b g Awesome Again (CAN)—Suitably Discreet (USA) **P. D. Niven**
15 **VALE OF CLARA (IRE)**, 6, b m Iffraaj—Luggala (IRE) **Mr G. Wragg**

THREE-YEAR-OLDS

16 **UNDULATE**, b f Three Valleys (USA)—Singleton **Mr G. Wragg**

Other Owners: M. J. Feneron, D. M. Gibbons, D. Holgate, Mrs J. Iceton, Mr K. J. Little, Ms L. P. Tomkins.

---

475 **MR RAYSON NIXON, Selkirk**
Postal: Oakwood Farm, Ettrickbridge, Selkirk, Selkirkshire, TD7 5HJ
Contacts: **PHONE (01750) 52245 FAX (01750) 52313**

1 **JUST STRIPE**, 7, gr m Supreme Sound—Delightfool **Rayson & Susan Nixon**
2 **WIND ECHO**, 6, br g Supreme Sound—Split The Wind **Rayson & Susan Nixon**

Other Owners: G. R. S. Nixon, Mrs S. Nixon.

Assistant Trainer: Mrs S. Nixon

Jockey (NH): Ryan Mania, Fearghal Davis.

---

476 **MRS LUCY NORMILE, Glenfarg**
Postal: Duncrievie, Glenfarg, Perthshire, PH2 9PD
Contacts: **PHONE (01577) 830330 FAX (01577) 830658 MOBILE (07721) 454818**
E-MAIL lucy@normileracing.co.uk WEBSITE www.normileracing.co.uk

1 **AGRICULTURAL**, 8, b g Daylami (IRE)—Rustic (IRE) **Mrs J. Carnaby**
2 **BADGED**, 5, b g High Chaparral (IRE)—Meshhed (USA) **The Explorers**
3 **BALLYCARBERY**, 8, b g Bollin Eric—Carbery Spirit (IRE) **Mrs F. M. Whitaker**
4 **BERKSHIRE DOWNS**, 4, b f Tiger Hill (IRE)—Cut Corn **Riverside Racing**
5 **CADORE (IRE)**, 6, b g Hurricane Run (IRE)—Mansiya **L B N Racing Club**
6 **CRUACHAN (IRE)**, 5, b g Authorized (IRE)—Calico Moon (USA) **P Carnaby & B Thomson**
7 **DICKIE HENDERHOOP (IRE)**, 9, b g Milan—Merry Breeze **L B N Racing Club**
8 **DIDDLEY DEE**, 10, b g Riverhead (USA)—Ballydiddle **The Fiddlers**
9 **DR PADDY (IRE)**, 7, b g Dr Massini (IRE)—Tina Torus (IRE) **Mrs P. Sinclair**
10 **DUNLEER DIXIE**, 6, b g Erhaab (USA)—Andaleer (IRE) **Riverside Racing**
11 **FLOGAROSE (FR)**, 5, ch m Bonbon Rose (FR)—Rosala (FR) **Tulloch Family Syndicate**
12 **HAIDEES REFLECTION**, 4, b f Byron—Exchanging Glances **Mr A. Doig**
13 **IHTIKAR (USA)**, 4, b g Invasor (ARG)—Ranin **Riverside Racing**
14 **JUST ANNIE**, 6, b m Revoque (IRE)—Carbery Spirit (IRE) **Mrs F. M. Whitaker**
15 **KARINGO**, 7, ch g Karinga Bay—Wild Happening (GER) **Douglas Black,P A Carnaby,P J Carnaby**
16 **LORD REDSGIRTH (IRE)**, 9, ch g Flemensfirth (USA)—Wisebuy (IRE) **L B N Racing Club**
17 **MISS DEEFIANT**, 8, b m Muhtarram (USA)—Hiding Place **Mrs L. B. Normile**
18 **MR MANSSON (IRE)**, 7, b g Millenary—Supreme Dare (IRE) **Mr K. N. R. MacNicol**
19 **REMEMBER ROCKY**, 5, ch g Haafhd—Flower Market **Byrne Racing**
20 **RINNAGREE ROSIE**, 8, gr m Silver Patriarch (IRE)—Gretton **The Silver Tops**
21 **SILVERTON**, 7, gr m Silver Patriarch (IRE)—Gretton **Twentys Plenty**
22 **STROBE**, 10, ch g Fantastic Light (USA)—Sadaka (USA) **Miss P. A. & Mr P. J. Carnaby**
23 **WOLF HEART (IRE)**, 6, b g Dalakhani (IRE)—Lisieux Orchid (IRE) **Twentys Plenty**

TWO-YEAR-OLDS

24 **ROYAL REGENT**, b g 9/3 Urgent Request (IRE)—Royal Citadel (IRE) (City On A Hill (USA)) **Mr S. W. Dick**

MRS LUCY NORMILE - Continued

Other Owners: Mr D. M. Black, P. Byrne, Miss P. A. Carnaby, Mr P. J. Carnaby, Mr P. Carnaby, Miss F. M. Fletcher, Mr A. C. Rodger, B. Thomson, Mr K. F. Tulloch, Mrs S. M. Tulloch, D. A. Whitaker.

Assistant Trainer: Libby Brodie (07947) 592438

Jockey (NH): Lucy Alexander, Dougie Costello. **Conditional:** Alexander Voy. **Amateur:** Mr R. Wilson.

---

477 | MR JOHN NORTON, Barnsley
Postal: **Globe Farm, High Hoyland, Barnsley, South Yorkshire, S75 4BE**
Contacts: **PHONE/FAX (01226) 387633 MOBILE (07970) 212707**
E-MAIL johnrnorton@hotmail.com WEBSITE www.johnrnortonracehorsetrainer.co.uk

1 BLAKEY TOPPING, 4, b g Tiger Hill (IRE)—Ma-Arif (IRE) **J. R. Norton Ltd**
2 CAPTIVE MOMENT, 8, b m Almaty (IRE)—Captive Heart **J. Norton**
3 DEPORTATION, 7, b g Deportivo—Kyle Rhea **J. R. Norton Ltd**
4 DR VICTORIA, 5, ch m Three Valleys (USA)—Spielbound **Mrs H. Tattersall**
5 FIDDLER'S FLIGHT (IRE), 8, b g Convinced—Carole's Dove **J. Norton**
6 FINN MAC, 4, ch g Norse Dancer (IRE)—Strictly Elsie (IRE) **M. R. & T. Simcox**
7 FLYING POWER, 6, b g Dubai Destination (USA)—Rah Wa (USA) **Jaffa Racing Syndicate**
8 GOREY LANE (IRE), 8, b g Oscar (IRE)—Supremely Deep (IRE) **Jaffa Racing Syndicate**
9 SAMTOMJONES (IRE), 6, ch g Presenting—She's All That (IRE) **J. R. Norton Ltd**
10 SNOW ALERT, 8, ch g Where Or When (IRE)—Ela Aphrodite **Fellowship Of The Rose Partnership**

TWO-YEAR-OLDS

11 Ch f 28/2 Monsieur Bond (IRE)—Rapturous (Zafonic (USA)) **R. S. Cockerill (Farms) Ltd**
12 Ch f 4/2 Major Cadeaux—Razzle (IRE) (Green Desert (USA)) (2200) **A. R. Middleton**

Other Owners: Mr R. M. Firth, Mr P. J. Marshall, Mr Tim Simcox, Mr P. Woodcock-Jones.

Amateur: Mr P. Hardy.

---

478 | MR JEREMY NOSEDA, Newmarket
Postal: **Shalfleet, 17 Bury Road, Newmarket, Suffolk, CB8 7BX**
Contacts: **PHONE (01638) 664010 FAX (01638) 664100 MOBILE (07710) 294093**
E-MAIL jeremy@jeremynoseda.com WEBSITE www.jeremynoseda.com

1 COCONELL, 4, b f Rock of Gibraltar (IRE)—Marula (IRE)
2 CONSIGN, 4, b g Dutch Art—Maid To Dance
3 DUTIFUL SON (IRE), 4, b c Invincible Spirit (IRE)—Grecian Dancer
4 EVIDENT (IRE), 4, b g Excellent Art—Vestavia (IRE)
5 FANTASTIC MOON, 4, ch c Dalakhani (IRE)—Rhadegunda
6 GRANDEUR (IRE), 5, gr ro g Verglas (IRE)—Misskinta (IRE)
7 GREEK SPIRIT (IRE), 4, b f Invincible Spirit (IRE)—Greek Symphony (IRE)
8 HAVELOVEWILLTRAVEL (IRE), 4, b f Holy Roman Emperor (IRE)—Strategy
9 JOE PALOOKA (IRE), 4, b c Galileo (IRE)—Glinting Desert (IRE)
10 MAGIQUE (IRE), 4, b f Jeremy (USA)—Misskinta (IRE)
11 MESSILA STAR, 4, ch c Pivotal—Jamboretta (IRE)
12 NOCTURN, 5, b g Oasis Dream—Pizzicato
13 RED BATON, 4, b f Exceed And Excel (AUS)—Ruby Rocket (IRE)
14 THE BEST DOCTOR (IRE), 4, ch c Pivotal—Strawberry Fledge (USA)
15 THE GOLD CHEONGSAM (IRE), 4, b f Red Clubs (IRE)—Fuerta Ventura (IRE)
16 VALBCHEK (IRE), 5, b g Acclamation—Spectacular Show (IRE)
17 WARRIGAL (IRE), 4, ch c Mount Nelson—Waldblume (GER)
18 YEAGER (USA), 4, b br g Medaglia d'oro (USA)—Lucky Flyer (USA)

THREE-YEAR-OLDS

19 ANNA'S FANCY (IRE), gr f Acclamation—Step Too Far (USA)
20 ANNA'S VISION (IRE), b f Invincible Spirit (IRE)—House In Wood (FR)
21 AUTUMNS BLUSH (IRE), b f Kheleyf (USA)—Park Romance (IRE)
22 BASE RATE (USA), b c Exchange Rate (USA)—Colonna Traiana (CHI)

MR JEREMY NOSEDA - Continued

23 **BISHOPS AVENUE (IRE)**, b c Lawman (FR)—Shesasmartlady (IRE)
24 **DANCE OF HEROES**, b c Danehill Dancer (IRE)—Helena Molony (IRE)
25 **DREAMING BEAUTY**, b f Oasis Dream—Independence
26 B gr c Duke of Marmalade (IRE)—Exotic Mix (FR)
27 **EXPECT**, b f Invincible Spirit (IRE)—Expressive
28 **FLAWLESS PINK**, br f More Than Ready (USA)—High Heel Sneakers
29 **GARRAUN (IRE)**, b f Tamayuz—French Fern (IRE)
30 **GONE WITH THE WIND (GER)**, b c Dutch Art—Gallivant
31 B c High Chaparral (IRE)—Hana Dee
32 **IAN'S MEMORY (USA)**, b br c Smart Strike (CAN)—Rite Moment (USA)
33 **JOHN CAESAR (IRE)**, b c Bushranger (IRE)—Polish Belle
34 **KAGAMI**, ch c Teofilo (IRE)—Sky Wonder
35 **MARGARET'S MISSION (IRE)**, b f Shamardal (USA)—Wimple (USA)
36 **MERLETTA**, b f Raven's Pass (USA)—Light Hearted
37 **MOONVOY**, b f Cape Cross (IRE)—Needles And Pins (IRE)
38 **NIGEL'S DESTINY (USA)**, b c Giant's Causeway (USA)—Ticket to Seattle (USA)
39 **NIGHTLIGHT**, b f Pivotal—Floodlit
40 **OUTBACK TRAVELLER (IRE)**, b c Bushranger (IRE)—Blue Holly (IRE)
41 **RED VELOUR**, ch f Pivotal—Regal Velvet
42 **SHAMA'S CROWN (IRE)**, ch f New Approach (IRE)—Classic Park
43 **SLOANE AVENUE (USA)**, ch c Candy Ride (ARG)—Apt (USA)
44 **SMARTIE ARTIE (IRE)**, b c Smart Strike (CAN)—Green Room (USA)
45 **THE SILVER KEBAYA (FR)**, b f Rock of Gibraltar (IRE)—Music House (IRE)
46 **WAKEA (USA)**, b br c Cape Cross (IRE)—Imiloa (USA)
47 **ZESHOV (IRE)**, b c Acclamation—Fathoming (USA)

TWO-YEAR-OLDS

48 **ARABIAN HILLS (IRE)**, b f 30/3 Cape Cross (IRE)—Emirates Hills (Dubawi (IRE)) (45000)
49 Gr c 6/2 Mount Nelson—Bruxcalina (FR) (Linamix (FR)) (60000)
50 Gr ro c 28/4 Street Cry (IRE)—Cable (USA) (Dynaformer (USA)) (233713)
51 B c 26/4 Eskendereya (USA)—Call Mariah (USA) (Dixie Union (USA))
52 Ch f 13/4 Smart Strike (CAN)—Cassis (USA) (Red Ransom (USA))
53 **COURIER**, b f 11/3 Equiano (FR)—Pivotal Drive (IRE) (Pivotal) (45000)
54 Ch f 29/1 Mount Nelson—Darmiana (USA) (Lemon Drop Kid (USA)) (60000)
55 **DUET**, ch f 9/3 Pivotal—Miswaki Belle (USA) (Miswaki (USA))
56 Ch c 19/2 Giant's Causeway (USA)—Element of Truth (USA) (Atticus (USA)) (93485)
57 **EYE CATCHING**, ch f 8/2 Exceed And Excel (AUS)—Rainbow Queen (FR) (Spectrum (IRE)) (50000)
58 **FIRMAMENT**, b c 18/3 Cape Cross (IRE)—Heaven Sent (Pivotal) (65000)
59 B c 12/2 Pivotal—Fondled (Selkirk (USA)) (120000)
60 Br gr f 7/3 Zebedee—Fuerta Ventura (IRE) (Desert Sun) (120000)
61 B c 10/2 Dark Angel (IRE)—Glisten (Oasis Dream) (81300)
62 B c 30/3 New Approach (IRE)—Grecian Air (FR) (King's Best (USA))
63 B c 22/4 Pivotal—Helter Helter (USA) (Seeking The Gold (USA)) (15485)
64 B c 14/4 Lope de Vega (IRE)—Irish Flower (IRE) (Zieten (USA)) (34000)
65 B c 21/3 King's Best (USA)—La Belle Dane (Danetime (IRE))
66 B f 22/4 Equiano (FR)—Luanshya (First Trump) (105000)
67 B c 26/4 Fastnet Rock (AUS)—Myrtle (Batshoof) (60000)
68 B f 6/4 Eskendereya (USA)—Mysterieuse Etoile (USA) (Quiet American (USA))
69 **OVERHEARD (IRE)**, b f 9/4 Lope de Vega (IRE)—Gutter Press (IRE) (Raise A Grand (IRE)) (35000)
70 B f 10/2 Kodiac—Perfect Fun (Marju (IRE)) (13937)
71 **QUEEN'S CHARTER**, b f 1/3 Oasis Dream—Queen's Best (King's Best (USA))
72 B c 11/2 Elnadim (USA)—Relinquished (Royal Applause) (37000)
73 Ch f 18/3 Dutch Art—Semplicita (IRE) (In The Wings) (36190)
74 B br f 1/3 Kodiac—Special Dancer (Shareef Dancer (USA)) (162600)
75 Gr ro f 7/4 War Front (USA)—T K O Lady (USA) (Two Punch (USA)) (210341)
76 **UP TEMPO**, b f 17/3 Pivotal—Light Hearted (Green Desert (USA))
77 **WICKEDLY SMART (USA)**, gr ro f 2/2 Smart Strike (CAN)—Wickedly Wise (USA) (Tactical Cat (USA)) (204498)
78 B f 29/2 Fastnet Rock (AUS)—Winged Harriet (IRE) (Hawk Wing (USA)) (77428)

Assistant Trainer: Dave Bradley

479 MR A. P. O'BRIEN, Ballydoyle

The following list has not been supplied by the trainer and has been compiled from information in the public domain.

1 **ANGEL CHORUS (IRE)**, 5, b m Dylan Thomas (IRE)—Fayre (IRE)
2 **BEACH OF FALESA (IRE)**, 5, b m Dylan Thomas (IRE)—Leonia (IRE)
3 **CARRIGANOG (IRE)**, 5, ch g Shantou (IRE)—Penny Fiction (IRE)
4 **CHICQUITA (IRE)**, 4, b f Montjeu (IRE)—Prudenzia (IRE)
5 **DARWIN (USA)**, 4, b c Big Brown (USA)—Cool Ghoul (USA)
6 **DRACO**, 5, ch g Hernando (FR)—Easibrook Jane
7 **EYE OF THE STORM (IRE)**, 4, ch c Galileo (IRE)—Mohican Princess
8 **FRANCIS OF ASSISI (IRE)**, 4, b g Danehill Dancer (IRE)—Queen Cleopatra (IRE)
9 **KING LEON (IRE)**, 5, b g Mountain High (IRE)—None The Wiser (IRE)
10 **KINGSBARNS (IRE)**, 4, b c Galileo (IRE)—Beltisaal (FR)
11 **LEADING LIGHT (IRE)**, 4, b c Montjeu (IRE)—Dance Parade (USA)
12 **MAASAI (IRE)**, 6, b g Milan (IRE)—Flaming Brandy (IRE)
13 **MACBRIDE (IRE)**, 5, b g Oscar (IRE)—Carioca Dream (USA)
14 **MAGICIAN (IRE)**, 4, b br c Galileo (IRE)—Absolutelyfabulous (IRE)
15 **NOAH WEBSTER (IRE)**, 5, b g Galileo (IRE)—Matikanehanafubuki (IRE)
16 **PLINTH (IRE)**, 4, b g Montjeu (IRE)—Crazy Volume (IRE)
17 **RULER OF THE WORLD (IRE)**, 4, ch c Galileo (IRE)—Love Me True (USA)
18 **SHIELD (IRE)**, 5, b g Dylan Thomas (IRE)—American Queen (FR)
19 **VERRAZANO (USA)**, 4, b c More Than Ready (USA)—Enchanted Rock (USA)

THREE-YEAR-OLDS

20 **A GREATER FORCE (FR)**, gr c Montjeu (IRE)—Dibenoise (FR)
21 **ADELAIDE (IRE)**, b c Galileo (IRE)—Elletelle (IRE)
22 **ADESTE FIDELES (USA)**, b br f Giant's Causeway (USA)—Imagine (IRE)
23 **ADJUSTED (IRE)**, b c Montjeu (IRE)—Belesta
24 **AFFAIRS OF STATE (IRE)**, b c Montjeu (IRE)—Lucina
25 **AGENA (IRE)**, b c Galileo (IRE)—Dietrich
26 **ANNUS MIRABILIS (IRE)**, b c Montjeu (IRE)—Love Me True (USA)
27 **AUSTRALIA**, ch c Galileo (IRE)—Ouija Board
28 **BAZAAR (IRE)**, ch c Galileo (IRE)—One Moment In Time (IRE)
29 **BELISARIUS (IRE)**, b c Montjeu (IRE)—Lasting Chance (USA)
30 **BEYOND BRILLIANCE (IRE)**, b f Holy Roman Emperor (IRE)—Charroux (IRE)
31 **BLUE HUSSAR (IRE)**, b c Montjeu (IRE)—Metaphor (USA)
32 **BRACELET (IRE)**, b f Montjeu (IRE)—Cherry Hinton
33 **BUONARROTI (IRE)**, b c Galileo (IRE)—Beauty Is Truth (IRE)
34 **BYE BYE BIRDIE (IRE)**, b f Oasis Dream—Slink
35 **CARLO BUGATTI (IRE)**, b c Montjeu (IRE)—Marquesa (USA)
36 **CENTURY (IRE)**, b c Montjeu (IRE)—Mixed Blessing
37 **COACH HOUSE (IRE)**, b c Oasis Dream—Lesson In Humility (IRE)
38 **COUGAR MOUNTAIN (IRE)**, b c Fastnet Rock (AUS)—Descant (USA)
39 **DANCE WITH ANOTHER (IRE)**, b f Danehill Dancer (IRE)—Quarter Moon (IRE)
40 **DAZZLING (IRE)**, b f Galileo (IRE)—Secret Garden (IRE)
41 **DESERT TIGER (IRE)**, b c Galileo (IRE)—Khoruna (GER)
42 **DOWN HOUSE**, b c Galileo (IRE)—Guaranda
43 **DYNAMO (IRE)**, b c Galileo (IRE)—Trading Places
44 **FAIR WIND**, b c High Chaparral (IRE)—Night Teeny
45 **FALKIRK (IRE)**, b c Montjeu (IRE)—Jewel In The Sand (IRE)
46 **FAUVE (IRE)**, b c Montjeu (IRE)—Simaat (USA)
47 **FELIX MENDELSSOHN (IRE)**, b c Galileo (IRE)—Ice Queen (IRE)
48 **FIVE STAR GENERAL (IRE)**, b c High Chaparral (IRE)—Rainbow Queen (FR)
49 **FORT DE FRANCE (IRE)**, b c Montjeu (IRE)—Penny's Gold (USA)
50 **FOUNTAIN OF YOUTH (IRE)**, b c Oasis Dream—Attraction
51 **FOUR CARAT (GER)**, b c Montjeu (IRE)—Four Roses (IRE)
52 **FRIENDSHIP (IRE)**, ch c Galileo (IRE)—Squeak
53 **GEOFFREY CHAUCER (USA)**, b c Montjeu (IRE)—Helsinki
54 **GIOVANNI BOLDINI (USA)**, b br c War Front (USA)—Dancing Trieste (USA)
55 **GOVERNMENT HOUSE (USA)**, ch c Giant's Causeway (USA)—Galleon of Gold (USA)
56 **GRANDDUKEOFTUSCANY (IRE)**, b c Galileo (IRE)—Crystal Valkyrie (IRE)
57 **GREAT WHITE EAGLE (USA)**, b c Elusive Quality (USA)—Gender Dance (USA)
58 **GUARD OF HONOUR (IRE)**, b c Galileo (IRE)—Queen of France (USA)

MR A. P. O'BRIEN - Continued

59 **GUERRE (USA)**, b br c War Front (USA)—Golden Toast (USA)
60 **GYPSY KING (IRE)**, b c Galileo (IRE)—Dancing Shoes (IRE)
61 **HORSEGUARDSPARADE**, b c Montjeu (IRE)—Honorlina (FR)
62 **HOUSEHOLD CAVALRY**, b c Oasis Dream—Masskana (IRE)
63 **ILLUSIVE (IRE)**, b c Galileo (IRE)—Looking Back (IRE)
64 **INDIAN MAHARAJA (IRE)**, b c Galileo (IRE)—Again (IRE)
65 **INIESTA (IRE)**, b c Galileo (IRE)—Red Evie (IRE)
66 **JOHANN STRAUSS**, b c High Chaparral (IRE)—Inchmina
67 **JOHN CONSTABLE (IRE)**, b c Montjeu (IRE)—Dance Parade (USA)
68 **JUNIPER TREE (IRE)**, b c Galileo (IRE)—Alexander Goldrun (IRE)
69 **JUST GORGEOUS (IRE)**, b f Galileo (IRE)—Halfway To Heaven (IRE)
70 **KINGFISHER (IRE)**, b c Galileo (IRE)—Mystical Lady (IRE)
71 **MARVELLOUS (IRE)**, b f Galileo (IRE)—You'resothrilling (USA)
72 **MASAI (IRE)**, b c Oasis Dream—I'm In Love (USA)
73 **MEANDERING (IRE)**, ch f Galileo (IRE)—Halland Park Lass (IRE)
74 **MEKONG RIVER (IRE)**, b c Galileo (IRE)—Simply Perfect
75 **MEMORABLE (IRE)**, b f Galileo (IRE)—Doula (USA)
76 **MICHAELMAS (USA)**, b c Elusive Quality (USA)—Christmas Kid (USA)
77 **OKLAHOMA CITY**, b c Oasis Dream—Galaxy Highflyer
78 **ORCHESTRA (IRE)**, b c Galileo (IRE)—Bywayofthestars
79 **PALACE (IRE)**, b f Fastnet Rock (AUS)—Lady Icarus
80 **QUARTZ (IRE)**, b c Fastnet Rock (AUS)—Beltisaal (FR)
81 **RED ROCKS POINT (IRE)**, b c Fastnet Rock (AUS)—My Emma
82 **RUBY TUESDAY (IRE)**, b f Galileo (IRE)—Jude
83 **SHELL HOUSE (IRE)**, b f Galileo (IRE)—Bonnie Byerly (USA)
84 **SIR JOHN HAWKINS (USA)**, b c Henrythenavigator (USA)—Peeping Fawn (USA)
85 **SOLAR ECLIPSE**, b c Montjeu (IRE)—Birmanie (USA)
86 **SPARROW (IRE)**, b f Oasis Dream—All Too Beautiful (IRE)
87 **STUBBS (IRE)**, b c Danehill Dancer (IRE)—Moonstone
88 **TABLE ROCK (IRE)**, b c Fastnet Rock (AUS)—Small Sacrifice (IRE)
89 **TAPESTRY (IRE)**, b f Galileo (IRE)—Rumplestiltskin (IRE)
90 **TERRIFIC (IRE)**, b f Galileo (IRE)—Shadow Song (USA)
91 **THE ISLANDER (IRE)**, b c Fastnet Rock (AUS)—Blue Cloud (IRE)
92 **THOMAS WEDGWOOD (IRE)**, b c Galileo (IRE)—Mythical Echo (USA)
93 **TIGRIS RIVER (IRE)**, b c Montjeu (IRE)—Hula Angel (USA)
94 **TOUR DE FORCE (IRE)**, b c Galileo (IRE)—Ramruma (USA)
95 **WAR COMMAND (USA)**, b c War Front (USA)—Wandering Star (USA)
96 **WILSHIRE BOULEVARD (IRE)**, b c Holy Roman Emperor (IRE)—Tyranny
97 **WONDERFULLY (IRE)**, b f Galileo (IRE)—Massarra

TWO-YEAR-OLDS

98 B c 10/5 Galileo (IRE)—Al Ihsas (IRE) (Danehill (USA))
99 B c 13/5 Galileo (IRE)—Aleagueoftheirown (IRE) (Danehill Dancer (IRE))
100 B c 22/2 Galileo (IRE)—Another Storm (USA) (Gone West (USA)) (321355)
101 B c 15/3 Galileo (IRE)—Ask For The Moon (FR) (Dr Fong (USA))
102 B c 25/3 Galileo (IRE)—Beauty Is Truth (IRE) (Pivotal)
103 B c 9/3 Galileo (IRE)—Belesta (Xaar) (201316)
104 B c 18/4 Duke of Marmalade (IRE)—Beltisaal (FR) (Belmez (USA))
105 B c 28/2 Bernardini (USA)—Christmas Kid (USA) (Lemon Drop Kid (USA))
106 Ch c 24/2 Galileo (IRE)—Circle of Life (USA) (Belong To Me (USA))
107 B c 11/4 High Chaparral (IRE)—Civility Cat (USA) (Tale of The Cat (USA)) (131629)
108 Gr c 19/3 Montjeu (IRE)—Clodora (FR) (Linamix (FR))
109 B c 5/4 Montjeu (IRE)—Crazy Volume (IRE) (Machiavellian (USA))
110 Gr c 10/2 Galileo (IRE)—Dialafara (FR) (Anabaa (USA))
111 B c 14/4 Galileo (IRE)—Dietrich (USA) (Storm Cat (USA))
112 B c 16/2 Montjeu (IRE)—Ecoutila (USA) (Rahy (USA)) (375000)
113 Ch c 8/3 Galileo (IRE)—Field of Hope (IRE) (Selkirk (USA)) (650000)
114 B c 7/3 Montjeu (IRE)—Finsceal Beo (IRE) (Mr Greeley (USA)) (2206736)
115 B c 2/5 Montjeu (IRE)—First Breeze (USA) (Woodman (USA)) (650000)
116 Ch c 11/5 Galileo (IRE)—Golden Ballet (USA) (Moscow Ballet (USA))
117 B c 19/1 Galileo (IRE)—Gwynn (IRE) (Darshaan)
118 Ch c 13/5 Galileo (IRE)—Halfway To Heaven (IRE) (Pivotal)
119 B c 29/4 Galileo (IRE)—Heavenly Bay (USA) (Rahy (USA))
120 B c 21/2 Galileo (IRE)—Hveger (AUS) (Danehill (USA)) (460000)

MR A. P. O'BRIEN - Continued

121 B c 5/2 Montjeu (IRE)—La Sylvia (IRE) (Oasis Dream) (420000)
122 B c 22/1 Fastnet Rock (AUS)—Lady Lupus (IRE) (High Chaparral (IRE))
123 B c 29/4 Galileo (IRE)—Last Love (IRE) (Danehill (USA))
124 B c 6/3 Galileo (IRE)—Latin Love (IRE) (Danehill Dancer (IRE))
125 B c 21/5 Montjeu (IRE)—Llia (Shirley Heights) (50000)
126 Ch c 30/3 Galileo (IRE)—Looking Lovely (IRE) (Storm Cat (USA))
127 Ch c 8/5 Galileo (IRE)—Love Me True (IRE) (Kingmambo (USA))
128 B c 20/4 Galileo (IRE)—Massarra (Danehill (USA))
129 B c 4/4 Galileo (IRE)—Mauralakana (FR) (Muhtathir) (525000)
130 B c 6/4 High Chaparral (IRE)—Middle Persia (Dalakhani (IRE)) (275000)
131 B c 25/4 Galileo (IRE)—Milanova (AUS) (Danehill (USA))
132 B c 3/5 Montjeu (IRE)—Mora Bai (IRE) (Indian Ridge)
133 Ch c 9/5 Galileo (IRE)—Mythical Echo (USA) (Stravinsky (USA))
134 B c 31/3 Montjeu (IRE)—Northern Gulch (USA) (Gulch (USA))
135 B c 14/5 Montjeu (IRE)—Notable (Zafonic (USA))
136 B c 23/2 Galileo (IRE)—One Moment In Time (IRE) (Danehill (USA))
137 B c 3/5 Montjeu (IRE)—Penny's Gold (USA) (Kingmambo (USA))
138 B c 6/2 Galileo (IRE)—Piquetnol (USA) (Private Account (USA))
139 Ch c 3/5 Galileo (IRE)—Play Misty For Me (IRE) (Danehill Dancer (IRE))
140 B c 12/4 Fastnet Rock (AUS)—Race For The Stars (USA) (Fusaichi Pegasus (USA))
141 B c 11/3 Galileo (IRE)—Rafina (USA) (Mr Prospector (USA))
142 B c 18/4 Galileo (IRE)—Rags To Riches (USA) (A P Indy (USA))
143 B c 7/2 Galileo (IRE)—Rumplestiltskin (IRE) (Danehill (USA))
144 B c 20/4 Galileo (IRE)—Saoire (Pivotal) (329074)
145 B c 12/2 Galileo (IRE)—Shastye (IRE) (Danehill (USA)) (3600000)
146 Gr c 26/2 Galileo (IRE)—Simply Perfect (Danehill (USA))
147 B c 26/4 Galileo (IRE)—St Roch (IRE) (Danehill (USA)) (193573)
148 Gr ro c 22/3 Galileo (IRE)—Starlight Dreams (USA) (Black Tie Affair) (817995)
149 B c 9/3 Montjeu (IRE)—Starlight Night (USA) (Distant View (USA))
150 B c 20/4 Montjeu (IRE)—Valdara (Darshaan)
151 B c 7/4 Galileo (IRE)—Withorwithoutyou (IRE) (Danehill (USA))

---

480 **MR DANIEL O'BRIEN, Tonbridge**
Postal: **Knowles Bank, Capel, Tonbridge, Kent, TN11 0PU**
Contacts: **PHONE (01892) 824072**

1 **ACHIEVED,** 11, b g Lahib (USA)—Equity's Darling (IRE) **D. C. O'Brien**
2 **CHARLEY FOX,** 10, ch g Lahib (USA)—Bumpse A Daisy
3 **GOLDEN GAMES (IRE),** 8, b m Montjeu (IRE)—Ski For Gold **D. C. O'Brien**
4 **MINORITY INTEREST,** 5, ch g Galileo (IRE)—Baliya **D. C. O'Brien**
5 **SACRILEGE,** 9, ch g Sakhee (USA)—Idolize **D. C. O'Brien**
6 **SPARTILLA,** 5, b h Teofilo (IRE)—Wunders Dream (IRE) **D. C. O'Brien**

Other Owners: Mr C. Attrell.

Assistant Trainer: Christopher O'Bryan

Jockey (NH): M. Batchelor, Sam Twiston-Davies.

---

481 **MR FERGAL O'BRIEN, Cheltenham**
Postal: **Cilldara Stud, Coln St. Dennis, Cheltenham, Gloucestershire, GL54 3AR**
Contacts: **PHONE (01285) 721150 MOBILE (07771) 702829**
E-MAIL fergaljelly@aol.com

1 **ALLERTON (IRE),** 7, b g Flemensfirth (USA)—Bonny Hall (IRE) **T. M. Evans**
2 **ALVARADO (IRE),** 9, ch g Goldmark (USA)—Mrs Jones (IRE) **Mr & Mrs William Rucker**
3 **ARTHUR MC BRIDE (IRE),** 5, b br g Royal Anthem (USA)—Lucky Diverse (IRE) **John Gaughan & Rob Rexton**
4 **BALLYGROOBY BERTIE (IRE),** 6, b g King's Theatre (IRE)—Vigna Maggio (FR) **Mr H. J. Millar**
5 **BALZACCIO (FR),** 9, b g Marchand de Sable (USA)—Baliyna (USA) **King, Roberts, Flintham & MCL**
6 **BORN TO BENEFIT (IRE),** 8, b m Beneficial—Sister Superior (IRE) **S. D. Hemstock**
7 **BRADLEY,** 10, ch g Karinga Bay—Good Taste **J. C. Collett**

MR FERGAL O'BRIEN - Continued

8 **BRANKSTON (IRE)**, 4, b g Milan—Not So Green (IRE) **T. Barr**
9 **CHASE THE SPUD**, 6, b g Alflora (IRE)—Trial Trip **Mrs C. J. Banks**
10 **DARK ENERGY**, 10, br g Observatory (USA)—Waterfowl Creek (IRE) **The Yes No Wait Sorries**
11 **DOUBLE SILVER**, 7, gr m Silver Patriarch (IRE)—Shadows of Silver **Mr R. C. Mayall**
12 **DOUBLETOILNTROUBLE (IRE)**, 8, b g Hubbly Bubbly (USA)—Boolindrum Lady (IRE) **Peter & Lisa Hall**
13 **DOWN ACE (IRE)**, 7, ch m Generous (IRE)—Full of Birds (FR) **Mr P. Sullivan**
14 **EMILY'S FLYER (IRE)**, 7, b m Oscar (IRE)—Lady Rolfe **Mr C. Cornes**
15 **FAITH KEEPER (IRE)**, 9, ch g Beneficial—Witney Girl **North And South Racing Partnership**
16 **FARMER MATT (IRE)**, 8, b br g Zagreb (USA)—Ashville Native (IRE) **S. D. Hemstock**
17 **FIDDLERS BID**, 7, b g Sulamani (IRE)—Charitini (GER) **The Yes No Wait Sorries**
18 **GALLIC WARRIOR (FR)**, 7, b g Nononito (FR)—Rosa Gallica **Mrs J. Hodgkiss**
19 **GUD DAY (IRE)**, 6, gr g Aussie Rules (USA)—Queen Al Andalous (IRE) **The People's Horse**
20 **GUNNER FIFTEEN (IRE)**, 6, b g Westerner—Grandy Hall (IRE) **Masterson Holdings Limited**
21 **HURRICANE IVAN (IRE)**, 6, b g Golden Tornado (IRE)—Woodram Delight **Mr F. M. O'Brien**
22 **JACKS GREY**, 9, gr g Karinga Bay—Arctic Chick **The Yes No Wait Sorries**
23 **JENNYS SURPRISE (IRE)**, 6, b m Hawk Wing (USA)—Winning Jenny (IRE) **C. S. J. Coley**
24 **KILMACOWEN (IRE)**, 8, b g Flemensfirth (USA)—Baunfaun Run (IRE) **The Kilmacowens**
25 **KING MURO**, 4, b g Halling (USA)—Ushindi (IRE) **The General Asphalte Company Ltd**
26 **LILYWHITE GESTURE (IRE)**, 5, b m Presenting—Loyal Gesture (IRE) **M. Fahy**
27 **LORD LANDEN (IRE)**, 9, br g Beneficial—Agua Caliente (IRE) **The B Lucky Partnership**
28 **MANBALLANDALL (IRE)**, 6, b g Flemensfirth (USA)—Omas Lady (IRE) **Mr G. Kennedy**
29 **ME AND BEN (IRE)**, 7, b m Revoque (IRE)—Rare Gesture (IRE) **M. Fahy**
30 **MR LENNYGREENGRASS (IRE)**, 7, b g Millenary—Grassed **Mrs C. E. M. R. Mackness**
31 **MYSTIFIABLE**, 6, gr g Kayf Tara—Royal Keel **Graham & Alison Jelley**
32 **NURSE RATCHED (IRE)**, 5, b m Presenting—Mascareigne (FR) **The Nurse Ratched**
33 **OWEN NA VIEW (IRE)**, 6, b br g Presenting—Lady Zephyr (IRE) **The Yes No Wait Sorries**
34 **PASTURE BAY (IRE)**, 8, b g Flemensfirth (USA)—Silver Oak (IRE) **The Marvellous Partnership**
35 **PERFECT CANDIDATE (IRE)**, 7, b g Winged Love (IRE)—Dansana (IRE) **ISL Recruitment**
36 **PITTER PATTER**, 4, b f Nayef (USA)—Pixie Ring **N. M. H. Jones**
37 **PRINCESS BELLA (IRE)**, 5, b m Presenting—Miss Cozzene (FR) **Mr A. D. Bradshaw**
38 **RIO MILAN (IRE)**, 8, b g Milan—Lady Medina (IRE) **Mrs J. Cumiskey Mr T. Joyce**
39 **ROCKCHASEBULLETT (IRE)**, 6, b g Catcher In The Rye (IRE)—Last Chance Lady (IRE) **The Yes No Wait Sorries**
40 **SILVER ROQUE (IRE)**, 8, b g Laveron—Bible Gun (FR) **Lord Vestey**
41 **SMART STORY**, 7, b g Iktibas—Clever Nora (IRE) **Mrs R. Outhwaite**
42 **SON OF SUZIE**, 6, gr g Midnight Legend—Suzie Cream Cheese (IRE) **Mrs C. E. M. R. Mackness**
43 **THE GOVANESS**, 5, b m Kayf Tara—Just Kate **C. B. Brookes**
44 **TINELYRA (IRE)**, 8, b g Mr Combustible (IRE)—Ladyogan (IRE) **Mr M. Costello**
45 **UP THE ANTE (IRE)**, 6, b g Royal Anthem (USA)—Mags Benefit (IRE) **Masterson Holdings Limited**

Other Owners: N. B. Attenborough, J. Baldwin, J. R. Bayer, M. A. Blackford, N. J. Chamberlain, Mrs K. T. Cumiskey, Miss O. Curl, J. S. Dale, P A. Deal, G. K. Duncan, Mr J. Gaughan, R. A. Green, Mrs L. Hall, Mr P. Hall, S. Hurst, D. M. Hussey, G. S. Jelley, Mrs A. D. Jelley, T. F. Joyce, G. F. Keeys, Mrs C. M. Keeys, Mrs M. M. Kennedy, Mr J. D. King, Mr C. Levan, C. McFadden, Mr R. J. Rexton, Mr A. J. Roberts, I. Robinson, Mrs G. C. Robinson, W. J. Rucker, Mrs A. Rucker, M. J. Silver, I. F. White.

---

482 MR P. J. O'GORMAN, Newmarket
Postal: **Seven Springs, Newmarket, Suffolk, CB8 7JQ**
Contacts: **PHONE (01638) 667070**

1 **ALBAQAA**, 9, ch g Medicean—Basbousate Nadia **Racing To The Max Limited**
2 **DANESIDE (IRE)**, 7, b g Danehill Dancer (IRE)—Sidecar (IRE) **P. J. O'Gorman**
3 **DONCOSAQUE (IRE)**, 8, b g Xaar—Darabela (IRE) **Racing To The Max Limited**
4 **GOLD EXPRESS**, 11, b g Observatory (USA)—Vanishing Point (USA)
5 **HARRISON GEORGE (IRE)**, 9, b g Danetime (IRE)—Dry Lightning **Racing To The Max Limited**
6 **MONSIEUR CHEVALIER (IRE)**, 7, b g Chevalier (IRE)—Blue Holly (IRE) **Racing To The Max Limited**

THREE-YEAR-OLDS

7 **GENTLEMEN**, ch g Ad Valorem (USA)—Stoney Cove (IRE) **Racing To The Max Limited**
8 **HEBREW MELODIES**, b g Byron—Glorious Colours **Racing To The Max Limited**

483 MR JEDD O'KEEFFE, Leyburn

Postal: Highbeck, Brecongill, Coverham, Leyburn, North Yorkshire, DL8 4TJ
Contacts: **PHONE** (01969) 640330 **FAX** (01969) 640397 **MOBILE** (07710) 476705
E-MAIL jedd@jeddokefferacing.co.uk **WEBSITE** www.jeddokefferacing.co.uk

1 **ANEEDH**, 4, b g Lucky Story (USA)—Seed Al Maha (USA) **Limegrove Racing**
2 **BYRON'S DREAM**, 4, b g Byron—Fresher **Highbeck Racing**
3 **CROWN CHOICE**, 9, b g King's Best (USA)—Belle Allemande (CAN) **Limegrove Racing**
4 **DARK OCEAN (IRE)**, 4, b g Dylan Thomas (IRE)—Neutral **The Fatalists**
5 **OCEAN WAVES (IRE)**, 5, b g Milan—Myown (IRE) **Caron & Paul Chapman**
6 **SATANIC BEAT (IRE)**, 5, br g Dark Angel (IRE)—Slow Jazz (USA) **Caron & Paul Chapman**
7 **SLEEPY EYE (IRE)**, 5, b g Catcher In The Rye (IRE)—Lithica (IRE) **Caron & Paul Chapman**
8 **WATERCLOCK (IRE)**, 5, ch g Notnowcato—Waterfall One **Caron & Paul Chapman**

THREE-YEAR-OLDS

9 **INSTANT ATTRACTION (IRE)**, b g Tagula (IRE)—Coup de Coeur (IRE) **United We Stand**
10 **NEW BIDDER**, b br g Auction House (USA)—Noble Nova **Highbeck Racing**
11 **OFFSHORE BOND**, b g Bahamian Bounty—Miss Rimex (IRE) **Caron & Paul Chapman**
12 **SHARED EQUITY**, b g Elnadim (USA)—Pelican Key (IRE) **Paul & Dale Chapman**
13 **SKETCH MAP (IRE)**, b g Excellent Art—Atlas Silk **Highbeck Racing**
14 **WHERE'S TIGER**, b g Tiger Hill (IRE)—Where's Broughton **Highbeck Racing**

TWO-YEAR-OLDS

15 B f 10/2 Azamour (IRE)—Mischief Making (USA) (Lemon Drop Kid (USA)) (28000) **Caron & Paul Chapman**
16 Ch c 6/4 Bahamian Bounty—Sovereign Abbey (IRE) (Royal Academy (USA)) (70000) **Caron & Paul Chapman**

Assistant Trainer: Miss Leanne Kershaw

Jockey (NH): Brian Harding.

484 MR DAVID O'MEARA, Nawton

Postal: Arthington Barn Stables, Highfield Lane, Nawton, York, North Yorkshire, YO62 7TU
Contacts: **PHONE** (01439) 771400 **FAX** (01439) 771775 **MOBILE** (07747) 825415
E-MAIL helmsleyhorseracing@gmail.com **WEBSITE** www.davidomeara.co.uk

1 **ABLE MASTER (IRE)**, 8, b g Elusive City (USA)—Foresta Verde (USA) **Rasio Cymru Racing 1 & Partners**
2 **AFTER TONIGHT (FR)**, 4, b g Lando (GER)—Affair (FR) **R. Collins**
3 **ALEJANDRO (IRE)**, 5, b g Dark Angel (IRE)—Carallia (IRE) **Mr G. H. Briers**
4 **ANDERIEGO (IRE)**, 6, b g Invincible Spirit (IRE)—Anna Frid (GER) **Ebor Racing Club**
5 **ARCH EBONY (USA)**, 4, b br g Arch (USA)—Dot C C (USA) **Mr & Mrs G. Turnbull**
6 **AUNTIE MILDRED**, 4, b f Elnadim (USA)—Nahrayn (USA) **Direct Racing Partnership**
7 **AWAKE MY SOUL (IRE)**, 5, ch g Teofilo (IRE)—Field of Hope (IRE) **Mr K. Nicholson**
8 **BACK BURNER (IRE)**, 6, br g Big Bad Bob (IRE)—Marl **Middleham Park Racing LXXV**
9 **BALDUCCI**, 7, b g Dansili—Miss Meltemi (IRE) **Direct Racing Partnership**
10 **BARTACK (IRE)**, 4, b g Acclamation—Bentley's Bush (IRE) **Ebor Racing Club III**
11 **BERLUSCA (IRE)**, 5, b g Holy Roman Emperor (IRE)—Shemanikha (FR) **Mr P. Ball**
12 **BEST OF ORDER (IRE)**, 7, ch h Pivotal—Groom Order **R. Walker**
13 **BISPHAM GREEN**, 4, b g Green Desert (USA)—Royal Grace **D. W. Armstrong**
14 **BUNCE (IRE)**, 6, b g Good Reward (USA)—Bold Desire **Wildcard Racing Syndicate X1 & Partners**
15 **CANON LAW (IRE)**, 4, b g Holy Roman Emperor (IRE)—Delisha **Gargate Corporation**
16 **CAPE OF HOPE (IRE)**, 4, b g Cape Cross (IRE)—Bright Hope (IRE) **Middleham Park Racing LIII**
17 **CHANCERY (USA)**, 6, b br g Street Cry (IRE)—Follow That Dream **Hollowdean**
18 **CUSTOM CUT (IRE)**, 5, b g Notnowcato—Polished Gem (IRE) **Mr Gary Douglas & Mr Pat Breslin**
19 **DANSILI DUTCH (IRE)**, 5, gr m Dutch Art—Joyful Leap **Direct Racing Partnership**
20 **DOC HAY (USA)**, 7, b br g Elusive Quality (USA)—Coherent (USA) **Mr S. Laffan**
21 **EASTER SKY (IRE)**, 4, b c Authorized (IRE)—Suedoise
22 **ESTEMAALA (IRE)**, 5, b m Cape Cross (IRE)—Elutrah **Middleham Park Racing XLVI & Partners**
23 **FATTSOTA**, 6, b g Oasis Dream—Gift of The Night (USA) **Middleham Park Racing XXVIII & Partner**
24 **FROG HOLLOW**, 5, gr g Intikhab (USA)—The Manx Touch (IRE) **Dab Hand Racing**
25 **FRONTIER FIGHTER**, 6, b g Invincible Spirit (IRE)—Rawabi **Mr Archibald Nichol & Partners**
26 **GHOST RUNNER (IRE)**, 4, b g Tagula (IRE)—Ball Cat (FR) **Middleham Park Racing L**
27 **GRANDORIO (IRE)**, 4, b g Oratorio (IRE)—Grand Splendour **Hambleton Racing Ltd - Three In One**
28 **HELMSLEY FLYER (IRE)**, 4, b g Baltic King—Dorn Hill **Direct Racing Partnership**
29 **HIT THE JACKPOT (IRE)**, 5, ch g Pivotal—Token Gesture (IRE) **Hambleton Racing Ltd XXV**

MR DAVID O'MEARA - Continued

30 **IFANDBUTWHYNOT (IRE)**, 8, b g Raise A Grand (IRE)—Cockney Ground (IRE) **Claire Hollowood & Henry Dean**
31 **INGLEBY ANGEL (IRE)**, 5, br g Dark Angel (IRE)—Mistress Twister **Mr D. Scott**
32 **LEXINGTON BLUE**, 4, b g Bertolini (USA)—Jasmine Breeze **Middleham Park Racing XLIX & Partners**
33 **LEXINGTON PLACE**, 4, ch g Compton Place—Elidore **Middleham Park Racing XXXI**
34 **LIBRANNO**, 6, b h Librettist (USA)—Annabelle Ja (FR) **McDowell Racing Ltd**
35 **LIGHTNIN HOPKINS (IRE)**, 4, b g Kodiac—Bundle of Joy (IRE) **Wildcard Racing Syndicate**
36 **LOOKBEFOREYOULEAP**, 4, ch f Teofilo (IRE)—One Giant Leap (IRE) **Middleham Park Racing LVII**
37 **MAGNIFIED**, 4, b g Passing Glance—Scrutinize (IRE) **The Maroon Stud**
38 **MAISON DE VILLE (GER)**, 6, b m Sholokhov (IRE)—Morbidezza (GER) **Mr G. Schoeningh**
39 **MARCRET (ITY)**, 7, b g Martino Alonso—Love Secret (USA) **Gargate Corporation**
40 **MONT RAS (IRE)**, 7, ch g Indian Ridge—Khayrat (IRE) **Colne Valley Racing**
41 **MOROCCO**, 5, b g Rock of Gibraltar (IRE)—Shanghai Lily (IRE) **Equality Racing**
42 **MOSS QUITO (IRE)**, 4, b g Moss Vale (IRE)—Gold Majesty **The Fallen Angels**
43 **MUSIC IN THE RAIN (IRE)**, 6, b g Invincible Spirit (IRE)—Greek Symphony (IRE) **Colne Valley Racing**
44 **NURPUR (IRE)**, 4, b f Dark Angel (IRE)—The Good Life (IRE) **Middleham Park Racing XXIX & Partners**
45 **OMNIPRESENT**, 4, b g Rail Link—Protectress **Middleham Park Racing XXXVIII**
46 **OPEN EAGLE (IRE)**, 5, b g Montjeu (IRE)—Princesse de Viane (FR) **Middleham Park Racing LXXIV & Partner**
47 **OUT DO**, 5, ch g Exceed And Excel (AUS)—Ludynosa (USA) **Mr E.M. Sutherland**
48 **PATRONA CIANA (FR)**, 4, b f Falco (USA)—Bavaria Patrona (GER) **Middleham Park Racing LII & Partner**
49 **PENITENT**, 8, b g Kyllachy—Pious **Middleham Park Racing XVII**
50 **PERCI FRENCH**, 4, b g Tiger Hill—Annabelle Ja (FR) **McDowell Racing Ltd**
51 **PHILOSOFY**, 4, ch f Barathea (IRE)—Idealistic (IRE) **Direct Racing Partnership**
52 **POWERFUL PRESENCE (IRE)**, 8, ch g Refuse To Bend (IRE)—
                              Miss a Note (USA) **The Lawton Bamforth Partnership**
53 **REPEATER**, 5, b g Montjeu (IRE)—Time Over **Cheveley Park Stud Limited**
54 **ROBERT THE PAINTER (IRE)**, 6, b g Whipper (USA)—Lidanna **Mr S. Humphreys**
55 **ROSE OF THE MOON (IRE)**, 9, gr g Moonax (USA)—
                              Little Rose (IRE) **Middleham Park Racing XXXIII & Partners**
56 **SAVED BY THE BELL (IRE)**, 4, b g Teofilo (IRE)—Eyrecourt (IRE) **Mr J Blackburn & Mr A Turton**
57 **SIMILARITY (USA)**, 4, b f Street Sense (USA)—Another Aleyna (USA) **Direct Racing Partnership**
58 **SMARTY SOCKS (IRE)**, 10, ch g Elnadim (USA)—Unicamp **Direct Racing Partnership**
59 **SMOOTHTALKINRASCAL (IRE)**, 4, b g Kodiac—Cool Tarifa (IRE) **Cheveley Park Stud Limited**
60 **STAND MY GROUND (IRE)**, 7, b g Cape Cross (IRE)—
                              Perfect Hedge **Middleham Park Racing XLVIII & Partners**
61 **SWEET LIGHTNING**, 9, b g Fantastic Light (USA)—Sweetness Herself **Middleham Park Racing X**
62 **THISTLEANDTWOROSES (USA)**, 4, ch g Lion Heart (USA)—Country Again (USA) **Sir A. Ferguson**
63 **TOTO SKYLLACHY**, 9, b g Kyllachy—Little Tramp **R. Walker**
64 **TROPICAL BEAT**, 6, b g Beat Hollow—Tropical Heights (FR) **Normandie Stud Ltd**
65 **TWO FOR TWO (IRE)**, 6, b h Danehill Dancer (IRE)—D'articleshore (IRE) **High Hopes Partnership & Partner**
66 **VILLA ROYALE**, 5, b m Val Royal (FR)—Villa Carlotta **David Kuss & Tim Pakyurek**
67 **WINTERWELL (USA)**, 4, b f First Defence (USA)—Kinetic Force (USA) **Middleham Park Racing LXIII**
68 **YSPER (FR)**, 4, b f Orpen (USA)—Velda **Middleham Park Racing XL**

THREE-YEAR-OLDS

69 B f Amadeus Wolf—Carranza (IRE)
70 **COIN BROKER (IRE)**, b f Montjeu (IRE)—Cash Run (USA) **Mr Michael Tabor & Mrs John Magnier**
71 **CONVEYOR BELT (IRE)**, br f Pivotal—Gift Range (IRE) **Ballymacoll Stud Farm Ltd**
72 **DIEGO VELAZQUEZ (IRE)**, b g Duke of Marmalade (IRE)—Blessing (USA) **Sir R. Ogden C.B.E., LLD**
73 **ECCLESTON**, b c Acclamation—Miss Meggy **D. W. Armstrong**
74 **EMRYS**, ch g Shirocco (GER)—Movie Star (IRE) **R. Walker**
75 **G FORCE (IRE)**, b c Tamayuz—Flanders (IRE) **Middleham Park Racing XVIII & Partner**
76 **HIGHLAND ACCLAIM (IRE)**, b g Acclamation—Emma's Star (ITY) **Mr E.M. Sutherland**
77 **INNOCENTLY (IRE)**, ch c Kheleyf (USA)—Innocency (USA) **Hollowdean**
78 **LADY IN BLUE (IRE)**, ch f Iffraaj—Compton Girl **The Duchess Syndicate**
79 **LORD OF THE NILE (IRE)**, b c Galileo (IRE)—Magic Carpet (IRE) **Sir R. Ogden C.B.E., LLD**
80 **MADAGASCAR MOLL (IRE)**, b br f Captain Gerrard (IRE)—Fontanally Springs (IRE) **Hambleton Racing XXVIII**
81 **MARINERS MOON (IRE)**, ch g Mount Nelson—Dusty Moon **Stu, Mark, Ed Racing**
82 **MARLISMAMMA (FR)**, ch f Turtle Bowl (IRE)—Karawan **Middleham Park Racing LXVI & Partners**
83 **MAUPITI EXPRESS (FR)**, b g Chineur (FR)—Azucar (FR) **Middleham Park Racing LXVIII & Partners**
84 **MR MCLAREN**, b g Royal Applause—Mamma Morton (IRE) **Middleham Park Racing LXIV & Partner**
85 **PROUD DUCHESS (IRE)**, b f Duke of Marmalade (IRE)—
                              Pride of My Heart **Hambleton Racing Ltd - Two Chances**
86 **RYEOLLIEAN**, ch g Haafhd—Brave Mave **Direct Racing Partnership**
87 **SHERIFF OF NAWTON (IRE)**, b g Lawman (FR)—Pivotal Role
88 **SUNNY HARBOR (IRE)**, b f Indian Haven—Kathy Sun (IRE) **Mr C Maxsted & Miss S Iggulden**

MR DAVID O'MEARA - Continued

89 **THAT IS THE SPIRIT**, b g Invincible Spirit (IRE)—Fraulein **F. Gillespie**
90 **THORNABY NASH**, br g Kheleyf (USA)—Mistress Twister **Mr D. Scott**
91 **UNDER APPROVAL**, b g Captain Gerrard (IRE)—Dockside Strike **R. Collins**
92 B f Duke of Marmalade (IRE)—Vanity (IRE) **Middleham Park Racing LXXVI**
93 **VICTORY DANZ (IRE)**, b c Bushranger (IRE)—Victoria Lodge (IRE) **Hollowdean**
94 **VIVERE (IRE)**, b f Montjeu (IRE)—Valdara **Middleham Park Racing LXII**
95 **WILDCAT LASS**, b br f Street Cry (IRE)—Lexington Girl (USA) **Mr R. G. Fell**

TWO-YEAR-OLDS

96 **BLAZING ROSE (IRE)**, ch f 25/4 Intikhab (USA)—Radhwa (FR) (Shining Steel) (10065) **The Roses Partnership 1**
97 **DANZING GIRL (IRE)**, b f 14/3 Bushranger (IRE)—
                                    Prime Time Girl (Primo Dominie) (8517) **Baker, Hensby, Longden, Baker**
98 **HIGHTIME HERO**, b c 27/2 Pivotal—
                                    Hightime Heroine (IRE) (Danetime (IRE)) (50000) **Cheveley Park Stud Limited**
99 **JEBEDIAH SHINE**, ch f 11/4 Kyllachy—Ardessie (Bahamian Bounty) (7619) **Sterling Racing**
100 B g 2/3 Bahamian Bounty—Noble Desert (FR) (Green Desert (USA)) (25000)
101 B f 5/3 Teofilo—Pirie (USA) (Green Dancer (USA)) (35000) **Hambleton Racing Ltd**
102 **ROSE ACCLAIM (IRE)**, b f 5/3 Acclamation—
                                    Carmona (Rainbow Quest (USA)) (15238) **The Roses Partnership 1**
103 B f 7/3 Moss Vale (IRE)—Sail With The Wind (Saddlers' Hall (IRE)) (619)
104 B g 18/4 Royal Applause—Sindarbella (Sinndar (IRE)) (10000)
105 **THANKSTOMONTY**, b c 10/5 Dylan Thomas (IRE)—Beldarian (IRE) (Last Tycoon) (24000) **Colne Valley Racing**
106 B f 9/4 Kodiac—Thistlestar (USA) (Lion Heart (USA)) (4645)
107 **WHISKY MARMALADE (IRE)**, b f 3/5 Duke of Marmalade (IRE)—Nashatara (USA) (Nashwan (USA)) (27000)

Other Owners: Mr P. I. Baker, Mr R. Baker, P. Bamford, Mr S. H. Bamforth, Mr J. M. Binns, J. N. Blackburn, Mr A. J. Bonarius, Mr N. J. Bonarius, Mr P. Breslin, Mr C. Charlton, Mr L. H. Christie, Lord Daresbury, Mr H. T. H. Dean, A. Dickman, L. L. Dickman, Mr G. J. Douglas, Mr A. W. Ellis, Mr A. Fell, A. Franks, S. Franks, Ms R. Galbraith, Mr M. P. Glass, Mr S. Graham, Helmsley Bloodstock Limited, Mr G. D. Hensby, Dr J. Hollowood, Mrs C. Hollowood, Miss S. L. Iggulden, Mr G. S. Jehu, Mr A. S. Kelvin, Mr E. T. Kilday, Mr D. Kuss, Mr P. Lawton, Mrs S. Magnier, C. A. Maxsted, Mrs L. Millard-Bourne, Mr A. Nichol, Dr W. O'Brien, Mrs S. K. O'Meara, Mr T. Pakyurek, T. S. Palin, D. Pearson, Mr M. Pearson, Mr D. J. Pentney, Mr J. D. Pierce, A. D. Pirie, M. Prince, Mrs A. E. Richardson, Mr A. Ga. Ryan, Mr J. F. Simpson, M. Tabor, Mr M. Taylor, Mr G. Turnbull, Mrs S. E. Turnbull, Mr S. R. H. Turner, Mr A. Turton, Mr I. K. White.

Jockey (flat): Daniel Tudhope. **Apprentice:** Julie Burke, Josh Doyle, Sam James.
Amateur: Miss J. Gillam, Miss R. Heptonstall, Miss S. Murray.

---

485 **MR JOHN O'NEILL, Bicester**
Postal: Hall Farm, Stratton Audley, Nr Bicester, Oxfordshire, OX27 9BT
Contacts: **PHONE (01869) 277202 MOBILE (07785) 394128**
E-MAIL jgoneill4@gmail.com

1 **CABARET GIRL**, 7, ch m Karinga Bay—Little Miss Prim **Ms D. Keane**
2 **IRISH GUARD**, 13, b g Infantry—Sharp Practice **J. G. O'Neill**
3 12, Br m I'm Supposin (IRE)—Laced Up (IRE)
4 **ONURBIKE**, 6, b g Exit To Nowhere (USA)—Lay It Off (IRE) **J. G. O'Neill**

---

486 **MR JONJO O'NEILL, Cheltenham**
Postal: Jackdaws Castle, Temple Guiting, Cheltenham, Gloucestershire, GL54 5XU
Contacts: **PHONE (01386) 584209 FAX (01386) 584219**
E-MAIL reception@jonjooneillracing.com WEBSITE www.jonjooneillracing.com

1 **ABNAKI (IRE)**, 9, b g Milan—Laboc **G. & P. Barker Ltd / Globe**
2 **ALFIE SHERRIN**, 11, b g Kayf Tara—Mandys Native (IRE) **J. P. McManus**
3 **ALLOW DALLOW (IRE)**, 7, b g Gold Well—Russland (GER) **Regulatory Finance Solutions Limited**
4 **ALWAYSENTERTAINING (FR)**, 4, ch g Network (GER)—Castille Eti (FR) **Mrs Peter Bond**
5 **AN TAILLIUR (IRE)**, 5, b g Milan—Tavildara (IRE) **P. Hickey**
6 **ANOTHER HERO (IRE)**, 5, b g Kalanisi (IRE)—Storm Front (IRE) **J. P. McManus**
7 **AT RECEPTION (IRE)**, 7, b g Gamut (IRE)—Receptionist **G & P Barker Ltd / Globe**
8 **BALLYLIFEN (IRE)**, 7, b g Brian Boru—Line Jade (FR) **T. Cole**
9 **BANDIT COUNTRY (IRE)**, 5, b g Flemensfirth (USA)—Calomeria **Mrs John Magnier,Mr D Smith & Mr M Tabor**
10 **BURTON PORT (IRE)**, 10, b g Bob Back (USA)—Despute (IRE) **T. J. Hemmings**

MR JONJO O'NEILL - Continued

11 **CALAF**, 6, b g Dubai Destination (USA)—Tarandot (IRE) **Local Parking Security Limited**
12 **CAPOTE (IRE)**, 6, b g Oscar (IRE)—Kinsellas Rose (IRE) **T. J. Hemmings**
13 **CARLTON JACK**, 7, b g Erhaab (USA)—Harry's Bride **J. P. McManus**
14 **CATCHING ON (IRE)**, 6, b g Milan—Miracle Lady **Mrs G. K. Smith**
15 **CHAMPAGNE AT TARA**, 5, gr g Kayf Tara—Champagne Lil **J. P. McManus**
16 **CHURCH FIELD (IRE)**, 6, b g Heron Island (IRE)—Dante's Thatch (IRE) **J. P. McManus**
17 **CLOUDINGSTAR (IRE)**, 7, gr g Cloudings (IRE)—Different Dee (IRE) **Mrs Peter Bond**
18 **CLOUDY COPPER (IRE)**, 7, gr g Cloudings (IRE)—Copper Supreme (IRE) **Mrs G. K. Smith**
19 **CLUES AND ARROWS (IRE)**, 6, b g Clerkenwell (USA)—
Ballela Girl (IRE) **Mr Peter Piller, Mr John Wade & Eric Brook**
20 **COFFEE (IRE)**, 7, b br g Beneficial—Boro Cruise (IRE) **J. P. McManus**
21 **CROPLEY (IRE)**, 5, gr g Galileo (IRE)—Niyla (IRE) **Mr P. A. Downing**
22 **DAKAR RUN**, 5, gr g Dalakhani (IRE)—Turn of A Century **J. P. McManus**
23 **DEADLY STING (IRE)**, 5, b g Scorpion (IRE)—Gaza Strip (IRE) **Maxilead Limited**
24 **DON PADEJA**, 4, b g Dansili—La Leuze (IRE) **G & P Barker Ltd & Yes No Wait Sorries**
25 **DOWNTOWN MANHATTAN (IRE)**, 7, b br g Presenting—La Speziana (IRE) **Club 40 - 60**
26 **DURSEY SOUND (IRE)**, 6, b g Milan—Glendante (IRE) **J. P. McManus**
27 **EASTLAKE (IRE)**, 8, b g Beneficial—Guigone (FR) **J. P. McManus**
28 **FESTIVE AFFAIR (IRE)**, 6, b g Presenting—Merry Batim (IRE) **J. P. McManus**
29 **FLEMENSON (IRE)**, 5, b g Flemensfirth (USA)—Andrea Cova (IRE) **Mrs G. K. Smith**
30 **FLINSTONE (IRE)**, 5, b g Presenting—Sweet Liss (IRE) **Jackdaws Castle Crew**
31 **FORT WORTH (IRE)**, 8, b g Presenting—Victorine (IRE) **Mrs John Magnier,Mr D Smith & Mr M Tabor**
32 **FOUNDATION MAN (IRE)**, 7, b g Presenting—Function Dream (IRE) **P. Hickey**
33 **GET BACK IN LINE (IRE)**, 6, b g Milan—Daraheen Diamond (IRE) **J. P. McManus**
34 **GET ME OUT OF HERE (IRE)**, 10, b g Accordion—Home At Last (IRE) **J. P. McManus**
35 **GLENS BOY (IRE)**, 10, b g Dushyantor (USA)—Glens Lady (IRE) **Lady Bamford & Alice Bamford**
36 **GOODWOOD MIRAGE (IRE)**, 4, b c Jeremy (USA)—Phantom Waters **Lady Bamford & Alice Bamford**
37 **HAWAII FIVE NIL (IRE)**, 6, b g Gold Well—Polish Rhythm (IRE) **Regulatory Finance Solutions Limited**
38 **HEDLEY LAMARR (IRE)**, 4, b g Gold Well—Donna's Tarquin (IRE) **J. C. & S. R. Hitchins**
39 **HINTON MAGIC**, 5, b m Revoque (IRE)—
Miss Quickly (IRE) **Lisa Butcher, Nicola Moores & Nicholas Sercombe**
40 **HOLYWELL (IRE)**, 7, b g Gold Well—Hillcrest (IRE) **Mrs G. K. Smith**
41 **HURRICANE'S GIRL**, 5, b m Hurricane Run (IRE)—Wise Little Girl **Phil Tufnell Racing Limited**
42 **INTERIOR MINISTER**, 4, b g Nayef (USA)—Sister Maria (USA) **Mr C. Austin**
43 **IT'S A DODDLE (IRE)**, 6, b g Oscar (IRE)—Nic An Ree (IRE) **J. P. McManus**
44 **IVY GATE (IRE)**, 6, b g Westerner—Key Partner **Jeremy & Germaine Hitchins**
45 **J J DANCER (IRE)**, 4, b g Flemensfirth—Shuil Mavourneen (IRE) **Mr P. Hickey**
46 **JOHNS SPIRIT (IRE)**, 7, b g Gold Well—Gilt Ridden (IRE) **Mr C. Johnston**
47 **JOIN THE CLAN (IRE)**, 5, b g Milan—Millicent Bridge (IRE) **J. P. McManus**
48 **JOSIES ORDERS (IRE)**, 6, b g Milan—Silent Orders (IRE) **J. P. McManus**
49 **KAIKIAS (IRE)**, 7, b g Flemensfirth (USA)—Special Case (IRE) **Imperial Racing**
50 **KELVINGROVE (IRE)**, 4, b g Hurricane Run (IRE)—Silversword (FR) **The All In Syndicate**
51 **KNOCKRAHEEN (IRE)**, 6, b g Heron Island (IRE)—Nancy's Stile (IRE) **El Amigas**
52 **LESS TIME (IRE)**, 5, b g Oscar (IRE)—Woodville Princess (IRE) **J. P. McManus**
53 **LOOKOUT MOUNTAIN (IRE)**, 6, b g Flemensfirth (USA)—
Thegoodwans Sister (IRE) **Mrs John Magnier,Mr D Smith & Mr M Tabor**
54 **LOST GLORY (NZ)**, 9, b g Montjeu (IRE)—Joie de Vivre (NZ) **J. P. McManus**
55 **LOST LEGEND (IRE)**, 7, b g Winged Love (IRE)—Well Orchestrated (IRE) **Mrs G. K. Smith**
56 **MAD JACK MYTTON (IRE)**, 4, b g Arcadio (GER)—Gilt Ridden (IRE) **J. C. & S. R. Hitchins**
57 **MADEIRA GIRL (IRE)**, 5, b m Bachelor Duke (USA)—Last Cry (IRE) **Jonjo O'Neill Racing Club**
58 **MAGHERAL EXPRESS (IRE)**, 5, b g Gold Well—Patzanni (IRE) **Mr C. Johnston**
59 **MARKTTAG**, 4, b g Manduro (GER)—Makhsusah (IRE) **The Megsons**
60 **MASQUERADING (IRE)**, 4, b g Singspiel (IRE)—Moonlight Dance (USA) **Masterson Holdings Limited**
61 **MATRIPAJO (IRE)**, 5, b g Westerner—Una Juna (IRE) **P. Hickey**
62 **MERRY KING (IRE)**, 7, ch g Old Vic—Merry Queen (IRE) **F. Gillespie**
63 **MILAN BOUND (IRE)**, 6, b g Milan—Bonnie And Bright (IRE) **J. P. McManus**
64 **MONT ROYALE**, 6, b g Hurricane Run (IRE)—Wild Academy (IRE) **F. Gillespie**
65 **MORE OF THAT (IRE)**, 6, b g Beneficial—Guigone (FR) **J. P. McManus**
66 **MOUNTAIN TUNES (IRE)**, 5, b g Mountain High (IRE)—Art Lover (IRE) **J. P. McManus**
67 **MR SHANTU (IRE)**, 5, b g Shantou (USA)—Close To Shore (IRE) **West Coast Haulage Limited**
68 **MR WATSON (IRE)**, 7, b g Gold Well—Risk And Reward (IRE) **Mrs G. K. Smith**
69 **MUTUAL REGARD (IRE)**, 5, b g Hernando (FR)—Hidden Charm (IRE) **Mr Andrew Tinkler**
70 **OSCAR FORTUNE (IRE)**, 6, b g Oscar (IRE)—Platin Run (IRE) **The Jackdaws Strangers**
71 **OZZY THOMAS (IRE)**, 4, b g Gold Well—Bramble Leader (IRE) **Mr C. Johnston**
72 **PORTOFINO WASP (IRE)**, 5, b g Milan—Kiniohio (FR) **Mrs Peter Bond**

MR JONJO O'NEILL - Continued

73 PRESENCE FELT (IRE), 6, br g Heron Island (IRE)—Faeroe Isle (IRE) Mrs Peter Bond
74 PRESENTINGS RETURN (IRE), 5, b g Presenting—Gales Return (IRE) T. J. Hemmings
75 PROMPTER, 7, b g Motivator—Penny Cross J. P. McManus
76 RAYAK (IRE), 4, b g Invincible Spirit (IRE)—Rayyana (IRE) Mrs Nan Hickey & Bensaranat Club
77 RUM AND BUTTER (IRE), 6, b g Milan—Silent Valley J. P. McManus
78 SHE'S LATE, 4, ch g Pivotal—Courting Mrs D. Carr
79 SHUTTHEFRONTDOOR (IRE), 7, b br g Accordion—Hurricane Girl (IRE) J. P. McManus
80 SMOKING ACES (IRE), 10, b g Old Vic—Callmartel (IRE) J. P. McManus
81 SPOIL ME (IRE), 7, b g Presenting—Akayid Mrs Peter Bond
82 SPOOKYDOOKY (IRE), 6, b g Winged Love (IRE)—Kiora Lady (IRE) Masterson Holdings Limited
83 STORM SURVIVOR (IRE), 8, b g Milan—Lindas Present (IRE) J. P. McManus
84 SUNNYHILLBOY, 11, b g Old Vic—Sizzle J. P. McManus
85 SWEEPS HILL (NZ), 10, b g Montjeu (NZ)—Windfield Dancer (NZ) J. P. McManus
86 TAQUIN DU SEUIL (FR), 7, b br g Voix du Nord (FR)—Sweet Laly (FR) Martin Broughton & Friends 1
87 TENMOKU, 5, b m Westerner—Blast Freeze (IRE) Mrs V. F. Burke
88 THE NEPHEW (IRE), 6, b g Indian River (FR)—Charlottine (IRE) Mr Peter Bond
89 THERE YOU ARE, 5, b g Beat All (USA)—Mandys Native (IRE) J. P. McManus
90 TITCHWOOD (IRE), 6, b g Flemensfirth (USA)—Aker Wood Mrs G. K. Smith
91 TOMINATOR, 7, gr g Generous (IRE)—Jucinda Exors of the Late Mr P. A. Byrne
92 TOUCH BACK (IRE), 8, b g Shantou (USA)—Back Log (IRE) J. P. McManus
93 TWIRLING MAGNET (IRE), 8, b g Imperial Ballet (USA)—Molly Maguire (IRE) Mrs G. K. Smith
94 UBALDO DES MENHIES (FR), 6, b br g Network (GER)—Ker Marie (FR) Mr G. McManus
95 UNSINKABLE (IRE), 4, gr g Verglas (IRE)—Heart's Desire (IRE) Penman Bond Partnership
96 UPSWING (IRE), 6, b g Beneficial—Native Country (IRE) J. P. McManus
97 VAIHAU (IRE), 5, br g Lavirco (GER)—Niponne (FR) J. P. McManus
98 VROMBEL (FR), 5, b g Laveron—Ombrelle (FR) Miss Y. Edwards
99 WELL SHARP (IRE), 6, b g Selkirk (USA)—Saphila (IRE) J. P. McManus
100 WHISKY YANKEE (IRE), 7, br g Presenting—Southcoast Gale (IRE) Walters Plant Hire Ltd
101 4, B g Robin des Champs (FR)—Zaffaran Blends (IRE) Michael & John O'Flynn

Other Owners: Mr Brook Alder, Mr Charlie Austin, Lady Bamford & Alice Bamford, Mrs E. A. M. W. Bellamy, Mrs Peter Bond, Miss Lucinda Bond, Miss Harriet Bond, Mr E. A. Brook, Mrs Jocelyn Broughton, Sir Martin Broughton, Mr Stephen Broughton, Club 40-60, Mr Toby Cole, Mr Paul Downing, Miss N. E. Fetzer, G. & P Barker Ltd/Globe Engineering, Mrs Noel Harwerth, Mrs Nan Hickey, Mr J. C. Hitchins, Mr S. R. Hitchins, Mrs Germaine Hitchins, Mrs R. D. Hodgson, Jackdaws Castle Crew, Mr Stephen Killalea, Local Parking Security, Mrs Felicity Lowden, Mr John Lowden, Mr John Magnier, Maxilead Metals, Mr Peter McCarthy, The Megsons, Ms Mary Miles, Mrs Nicola Moores, Mr M. E. O'Hara, Mrs Jonjo O'Neill, Mr Joe O'Neill, Mr Stephen Perry, Phil Tufnell Racing Club, Mr Peter Piller, Mr Richard Seed, Mr Derrick Smith, Mrs Gay Smith, Mr M. Tabor, The All In Syndicate, Mr John Wade, Mr M. Warren, Mrs S. J. Warren, Ms Zena Ann White.

---

487 MR JOHN O'SHEA, Newnham-on-Severn
Postal: The Stables, Bell House, Lumbars Lane, Newnham, Gloucestershire, GL14 1LH
Contacts: (01452) 760835 FAX (01452) 760233 MOBILE (07917) 124717
WEBSITE www.johnoshearacing.co.uk

1 AFTER THE STORM, 5, b g Dylan Thomas (IRE)—Inchiri The Cross Racing Club
2 BROWN VOLCANO (IRE), 5, b g Waky Nao—Lavish Spirit (USA) Acousta Foam Limited
3 CAPTAIN CARDINGTON (IRE), 5, b g Strategic Prince—Alkaffeyeh (IRE) Mrs R. E. Nelmes
4 CLEMENT (IRE), 4, b g Clodovil (IRE)—Winnifred K. W. Bell
5 DESCARO (USA), 8, gr g Dr Fong (USA)—Miarixa (FR) The Sandcroft Partnership
6 DOUBLE CHOCOLATE, 11, b g Doubletour (USA)—Matching Green Red & Black Racing
7 LITTLEDEAN JIMMY (IRE), 9, b g Indian Danehill (IRE)—Gold Stamp K. W. Bell
8 MONOPOLI, 5, ch m Cadeaux Genereux—Jump Ship The Cross Racing Club
9 MY BOY GEORGE (IRE), 6, br g Artan—Gold Stamp K. W. Bell
10 NATIVE COLONY, 6, b g St Jovite (USA)—Self Esteem The Cross Racing Club
11 NICKY NUTJOB (GER), 8, b g Fasliyev—Natalie Too (USA) Quality Pipe Supports (Q.P.S.) Ltd
12 NINEPOINTSIXTHREE, 4, b g Bertolini—Armada Grove The Cross Racing Club
13 PEAK STORM, 5, b g Sleeping Indian—Jitterbug (IRE) Cross Racing Club & Pete Smith Car Sales
14 PORT AND WARD (IRE), 5, ch m Captain Rio—Gold Stamp The Cross Racing Club
15 RADMORES EXPRESS, 5, b g Primo Valentino (IRE)—Emma Lilley (USA) J. R. Salter
16 RADMORES JEWEL, 4, ch f Primo Valentino (IRE)—Emma Lilley (USA) J. R. Salter
17 RADMORES RETURN, 6, b m Overbury (IRE)—Harvey's Sister J. R. Salter
18 RADMORES SURPRISE, 5, b m Revoque (IRE)—Harvey's Sister J. R. Salter
19 RED SKIPPER (IRE), 9, ch g Captain Rio—Speed To Lead (IRE) K. W. Bell

MR JOHN O'SHEA - Continued

20 **RING EYE (IRE)**, 6, b g Definite Article—Erins Lass (IRE) **The Cross Racing Club**
21 **RIVER CLARE (IRE)**, 6, br g Indian River (FR)—Lakyle Lady (IRE) **TGK Construction Co. Ltd**
22 **STACCATO VALTAT (FR)**, 8, gr g Fragrant Mix (IRE)—Harmonie de Valtat (FR) **Mrs R. E. Nelmes**
23 **STAFFORD CHARLIE**, 8, ch g Silver Patriarch (IRE)—Miss Roberto (IRE) **N. G. H. Ayliffe**
24 **STAFFORD JO**, 5, ch g Silver Patriarch (IRE)—Miss Roberto (IRE) **N. G. H. Ayliffe**
25 **SWENDAB (IRE)**, 6, b g Trans Island—Lavish Spirit (USA) **The Cross Racing Club & Patrick Brady**
26 **THOMAS BELL (IRE)**, 10, b g Moscow Society (USA)—Cottage Girl (IRE) **K. W. Bell**
27 **TO THE SKY (IRE)**, 6, b g Saffron Walden (FR)—Tara Tara (IRE) **J. R. Salter**
28 **TRIBAL DANCE (IRE)**, 8, br g Flemensfirth (USA)—Native Sparkle (IRE) **Quality Pipe Supports (Q.P.S.) Ltd**
29 **WHEN IN ROAM (IRE)**, 5, b m Flemensfirth (USA)—Roaming (IRE) **J. R. Salter**

THREE-YEAR-OLDS

30 **SUPER DANCER (IRE)**, b f Camacho—Super Trouper (FR) **The Cross Racing Club**

Other Owners: P. Brady, Ms J. M. Brooks, C. L. Dubois, Mrs E. A. Huckle, J. G. Huckle, P. Smith, Mrs S. Smith, Miss S. F. Willis.

Jockey (flat): Robert Havlin, Luke Morris, Fergus Sweeney. **Jockey (NH):** Charlie Wallis. **Amateur:** Miss S. Randell.

---

488 **MR JIM OLD, Wroughton**
Postal: **Upper Herdswick Farm, Hackpen, Burderop, Wroughton, Swindon, Wiltshire, SN4 0QH**
Contacts: **PHONE** (01793) 845200 **CAR** (07836) 721459 **OFFICE** (01793) 845200
FAX (01793) 845201 **MOBILE** (07836) 721459
E-MAIL racing@jimold.co.uk **WEBSITE** www.jimoldracing.co.uk

1 **ALDEBURGH**, 5, b g Oasis Dream—Orford Ness **W. E. Sturt**
2 4, B g Erhaab (USA)—Bessie Blues
3 **COUNTING HOUSE (IRE)**, 11, ch g King's Best (USA)—Inforapenny **W. E. Sturt**
4 **OKAFRANCA (IRE)**, 9, b g Okawango (USA)—Villafranca (IRE) **W. E. Sturt**
5 **PINK GIN**, 6, ch g Alflora (IRE)—Miss Mailmit **Mrs J Fowler & Mr C Jenkins**
6 **REVOUGE**, 5, b g Revoque (IRE)—Eva's Edge (IRE) **Mr D. Mee**
7 **ROUND THE HORN (IRE)**, 14, ch g Master Willie—Gaye Fame **Old Fools Partnership**
8 **THEDREAMSTILLALIVE (IRE)**, 14, ch g Houmayoun (FR)—State of Dream (IRE) **J. A. B. Old**
9 **TODAREISTODO**, 8, gr g Fair Mix (IRE)—Its Meant To Be **Mrs J. A. Fowler**
10 **VAL D'ALLIER (FR)**, 5, b g Special Kaldoun (FR)—Exilie (FR) **W. E. Sturt**
11 **VALID POINT (IRE)**, 8, b g Val Royal (FR)—Ricadonna **W. E. Sturt**
12 **WITCH'S HAT (IRE)**, 11, br g Hubbly Bubbly (USA)—Bold Shilling (IRE) **Old Fools Partnership**

Other Owners: Mrs P. V. Antrobus, C. J. Jenkins, B. M. Mathieson, C. C. Walker.

Assistant Trainer: Emma Grierson

Jockey (NH): Jason Maguire, Mark Grant, Timmy Murphy.

---

489 **MR GEOFFREY OLDROYD, Malton**
Postal: **Flint Hall Farm, Moor Lane, Brawby, Malton, North Yorkshire, YO17 6PZ**
Contacts: **PHONE** (01653) 668279 **MOBILE** (07730) 642620

1 **ALFRED HUTCHINSON**, 6, ch g Monsieur Bond (IRE)—Chez Cherie **R. C. Bond**
2 **BOND ARTIST (IRE)**, 5, b m Excellent Art—Pitrizza (IRE) **R. C. Bond**
3 **BOND CLUB**, 4, b g Misu Bond (IRE)—Bond Platinum Club **R. C. Bond**
4 **BOND EMPIRE**, 4, b g Misu Bond (IRE)—At Amal (IRE) **R. C. Bond**
5 **BOND FASTRAC**, 7, b g Monsieur Bond (IRE)—Kanisfluh **R. C. Bond**
6 **BOND'S GIFT**, 4, ch f Monsieur Bond (IRE)—Bond Shakira **South Yorkshire Racing**
7 **CROSSLEY**, 5, ch g Monsieur Bond (IRE)—Dispol Diamond **P. Drewery**
8 **DINKIE**, 4, b f Misu Bond (IRE)—Chez Cherie **Mr R. S. Marshall**
9 **JAMAICAN BOLT (IRE)**, 6, b g Pivotal—Chiming (IRE) **R. C. Bond**
10 **JUST BOND (IRE)**, 12, b g Namid—Give Warning (IRE) **R. C. Bond**
11 **LADIES ARE FOREVER**, 6, b m Monsieur Bond (IRE)—Forever Bond **R. C. Bond**
12 **MON CHIC**, 4, b f Monsieur Bond (IRE)—Chicago Bond (USA) **Mr R. S. Marshall**
13 **MONSIEUR ROYALE**, 4, ch g Monsieur Bond (IRE)—Bond Royale **Casino Royale Racing**
14 **PRINCESS KHELEYF**, 5, b m Kheleyf (USA)—Jugendliebe (IRE) **Mr G. R. Oldroyd**

MR GEOFFREY OLDROYD - Continued

15 **REGGIE BOND,** 4, ch g Monsieur Bond (IRE)—Triple Tricks (IRE) **R. C. Bond**
16 **VEGAS BELLE,** 4, b f Misu Bond (IRE)—Bond Casino **Mr R. S. Marshall**

THREE-YEAR-OLDS

17 **BOND IN RIO,** ch f Captain Gerrard (IRE)—Kanisfluh **R. C. Bond**
18 **ETERNAL BOND,** ch g Monsieur Bond (IRE)—Bond Babe **R. C. Bond**
19 **MAGICAL BOND,** ch f Monsieur Bond (IRE)—Triple Tricks (IRE) **R. C. Bond**
20 **ROCKIN RUBY RED,** b f Monsieur Bond (IRE)—Westcourt Ruby **Mrs M. Lingwood**

TWO-YEAR-OLDS

21 B g 3/3 Misu Bond (IRE)—Bond Babe (Forzando) **R. C. Bond**
22 B c 20/2 Misu Bond (IRE)—Chez Cherie (Wolfhound (USA)) **R. C. Bond**
23 **WHAT USAIN,** b c 2/5 Misu Bond (IRE)—Bond Shakira (Daggers Drawn (USA)) (9523) **R. C. Bond**

Other Owners: Mr C. S. Bond, Mr E. Dupont, Mr W. Standeven.

Amateur: Mr Aaron James.

---

490 **MR HENRY OLIVER, Abberley**
Postal: **Stable End, Worsley Racing Stables, Bank Lane, Abberley, Worcester, Worcestershire, WR6 6BQ**
Contacts: **MOBILE (07701) 068759**

1 **CRESCENT BEACH (IRE),** 7, b g Presenting—Angelas Choice (IRE) **R. G. Whitehead**
2 **FESTIVAL FOLKLORE (IRE),** 6, b m Dr Massini (IRE)—Corsican Pine (IRE) **Mrs S. P. H. Oliver**
3 **KATIE'S MASSINI (IRE),** 6, b m Dr Massini (IRE)—Our Lucky Supreme (IRE) **The Red Filly**
4 **KEEL HAUL (IRE),** 6, br g Classic Cliche (IRE)—Tara Hall **R. G. Whitehead**
5 **MINELLAFORLUNCH (IRE),** 7, b g King's Theatre (IRE)—Loughaderra (IRE) **R. G. Whitehead**
6 **MOSCOW ME (IRE),** 7, b g Moscow Society (USA)—Just Trust Me (IRE) **Ms S. A. Howell**
7 **POWERTAKEOFF (IRE),** 6, b g Court Cave (IRE)—Diminished (IRE) **Mrs H. M. Oliver**
8 **TAKE THE CROWN,** 5, gr g Fair Mix (IRE)—Miss Wizadora **R. G. Whitehead**
9 **TEMPLEBRADEN (IRE),** 7, b g Brian Boru—Baunfaun Run (IRE) **J. Mcgrath**
10 **THEREGOESTHETRUTH (IRE),** 6, b m Flemensfirth (USA)—Beagan Rose (IRE) **Mrs H. M. Oliver**
11 **WHISPERING HARRY,** 5, b g Sir Harry Lewis—Welsh Whisper **R. G. Whitehead**
12 **WITHOUTDEFAVOURITE (IRE),** 6, b g Oscar (IRE)—Camden Confusion (IRE)
13 **YAZDI (IRE),** 5, b g Galileo (IRE)—Lucky Spin **Mrs H. M. Oliver**

Other Owners: Mr J. O'Sullivan.

---

491 **MR JAMIE OSBORNE, Upper Lambourn**
Postal: **The Old Malthouse, Upper Lambourn, Hungerford, Berkshire, RG17 8RG**
Contacts: PHONE **(01488) 73139** FAX **(01488) 73084** MOBILE **(07860) 533422**
E-MAIL **info@jamieosborne.com** WEBSITE **www.jamieosborne.com**

1 **AMADEUS WOLFE TONE (IRE),** 5, b g Amadeus Wolf—Slieve **B. T. McDonald**
2 **CAI SHEN (IRE),** 6, ch g Iffraaj—Collada (IRE)
3 **DALGIG,** 4, b g New Approach—Bright Halo (IRE) **Mr N. A. Jackson**
4 **EASTBURY,** 6, ch gr g Pivotal—Sita (IRE) **Mrs C. Walwyn**
5 **FIELD OF DREAM,** 7, b g Oasis Dream—Field of Hope (IRE) **Mr N. A. Jackson**
6 **GREAT CONQUEST (USA),** 4, b c First Samurai (USA)—Conquestress (USA) **J. A. Osborne**
7 **INKERMAN (IRE),** 4, b g Duke of Marmalade (IRE)—Lady Taufan (IRE)
8 **LIVING THE LIFE (IRE),** 4, b f Footstepsinthesand—Colour And Spice (IRE) **M. A. C. Buckley**
9 **LORAINE,** 4, b f Sir Percy—Emirates First (IRE) **Mrs F Walwyn Mr & Mrs A Pakenham A Taylor**
10 **MR DAVID (USA),** 7, b g Sky Mesa (USA)—Dancewiththebride (USA) **Steve Jakes & S J Piper Partnership**
11 **ORATORIO'S JOY (IRE),** 4, b f Oratorio (IRE)—Seeking The Fun (USA) **Mr D. G. Christian**
12 **PABUSAR,** 6, b g Oasis Dream—Autumn Pearl **Homecroft Wealth Racing & Partner**
13 **POOR DUKE (IRE),** 4, b g Bachelor Duke (USA)—Graze On Too (IRE) **The Duke's Partnership**
14 **RAKAAN (IRE),** 7, ch g Bahamian Bounty—Petite Spectre **Mr L. Marshall**
15 **RED EXPLORER (USA),** 4, b c Henrythenavigator (USA)—Remote (USA) **J. A. Osborne**
16 **SAINT JEROME (IRE),** 4, b g Jeremy (USA)—Eminence Gift **Mrs C. Walwyn**
17 **SYCOPHANTIC (IRE),** 4, b g Cape Cross (IRE)—Amarice **Lady Blyth**
18 **TREADWELL (IRE),** 7, b h Footstepsinthesand—Lady Wells (IRE) **Mrs F Walwyn & A Taylor**

MR JAMIE OSBORNE - Continued

THREE-YEAR-OLDS

19 **AIN'T NO SURPRISE (IRE),** b f Kheleyf (USA)—Harmonist (USA) **Chris Watkins & David N. Reynolds**
20 **BIRD OF LIGHT (IRE),** b f Elnadim (USA)—Lady Docker (IRE) **Chris Watkins & David N. Reynolds**
21 **EXCLUSIVE CONTRACT (IRE),** br f High Chaparral (IRE)—Birthday (IRE) **J. A. Osborne**
22 **FEISTY DRAGON (IRE),** b f Camacho—Ejder (IRE) **Homecroft Wealth Racing**
23 **HARDY BLACK (IRE),** b c Pastoral Pursuits—Wondrous Story (USA) **Patrick Gage & Tony Taylor**
24 **HARDY PINK (IRE),** b f Clodovil (IRE)—Secret Circle **Tony Taylor & Patrick Gage**
25 **HIGH ON LIFE,** b g Invincible Spirit (IRE)—Lovely Thought **M. A. C. Buckley**
26 **INTENSIVE (IRE),** ch f Intense Focus (USA)—Alinea (USA) **J. A. Osborne**
27 **LAWSONG (IRE),** b g Lawman (FR)—Flaming Song (IRE) **Mr D. Margolis & Mr J. P. M. O'Connor**
28 **LLANDANWG,** b f Lawman (FR)—New Light **Dr J. A. E. Hobby**
29 **MONSIEUR CHABAL,** b g Avonbridge—Coup de Torchon (FR) **Homecroft Wealth Racing**
30 **OUTER SPACE,** b c Acclamation—Venoge (IRE)
31 **PRISCA,** b f Holy Roman Emperor (IRE)—Ainia **Chris Watkins & David N. Reynolds**
32 **SUMMERSAULT (IRE),** b g Footstepsinthesand—Sumingasefa **Mrs C. Walwyn, A. Taylor & D. Christian**
33 **THE DANDY YANK (IRE),** b g Dandy Man (IRE)—Bronze Queen (IRE) **Chris Watkins & David N. Reynolds**
34 **THEBEASTUNLEASHED (FR),** gr g Mastercraftsman (IRE)—Prairie Moon **Mr D. Margolis**
35 **TOAST OF NEW YORK (USA),** b c Thewayyouare (USA)—Claire Soleil (USA) **M. A. C. Buckley**

TWO-YEAR-OLDS

36 B c 28/2 Thewayyouare (USA)—Cozzene's Pride (USA) (Cozzene (USA)) (120000) **M. A. C. Buckley & Partners**
37 B c 9/2 Camacho—D'addario (IRE) (Galileo (IRE)) (19047) **Fromthestables.Com**
38 B f 19/1 Jeremy (USA)—Derval (IRE) (One Cool Cat (USA)) (18095) **Mr D. G. Christian**
39 B f 12/4 Monsieur Bond (IRE)—Discover Roma (IRE) (Rock of Gibraltar (IRE)) (17000) **Fromthestables.Com**
40 B c 2/5 Thewayyouare (USA)—Dont Cross Tina (IRE) (Cape Cross (IRE)) (3871) **M. A. C. Buckley**
41 Ch f 30/3 Mastercraftsman (IRE)—Khibraat (Alhaarth (IRE)) (135000) **Mr & Mrs R. G. Kelvin-Hughes**
42 B c 23/3 Arcano (IRE)—Lady of Kildare (Mujadil (USA)) (38714)
43 B c 8/4 Pivotal—Regina (Green Desert (USA)) (72000) **Mr & Mrs R. G. Kelvin-Hughes**
44 B f 16/4 Showcasing—Roodeye (Inchinor) (28000) **M. A. C. Buckley**
45 **SLEIGHT OF HAND (IRE),** b c 18/4 Galileo (IRE)—Queen of France (USA) (Danehill (USA)) **M. A. C. Buckley**
46 B f 24/2 Kodiac—Special Destiny (Tobougg (IRE)) (2095)
47 B f 6/2 Showcasing—Super Midge (Royal Applause) (8500)
48 B c 12/4 Amadeus Wolf—Swynford Lady (IRE) (Invincible Spirit (IRE)) (16260) **Eventmasters Ltd**
49 B c 12/2 Royal Applause—Umniya (IRE) (Bluebird (USA)) (30000) **B. McDonald**
50 B f 18/3 Paco Boy (IRE)—Wafeira (Dansili) (5238)
51 B f 18/3 Lope de Vega (IRE)—Wana Doo (USA) (Grand Slam (USA)) (140000) **Mr & Mrs R. G. Kelvin-Hughes**
52 B c 18/2 Iffraaj—Whazzis (Desert Prince (IRE)) (100000) **Mr & Mrs R. G. Kelvin-Hughes**

Other Owners: Lady Aitken, Mr N. A. Coster, Mr P. J. Gage, B. D. Heath, Mr S. Jakes, D. Margolis, Mr I. G. Martin, Mr J. P. M. O'Connor, A. E. Pakenham, Mrs V. H. Pakenham, Brig A. H. Parker Bowles, S. J. Piper, Mr N. Pogmore, Mr D. N. Reynolds, A. Taylor, C. D. Watkins.

Apprentice: John Lawson.

---

492 MR JOHN M. OXX, Kildare
Postal: **Creeve, Currabeg, Kildare, Co. Kildare, Ireland**
Contacts: **PHONE (00353) 455 21310 FAX (00353) 455 22236**

1 **CASTLE OF ARGH (USA),** 4, b br c Arch (USA)—Xinji (IRE) **Mr F. Fabre**
2 **HARASIYA (IRE),** 4, br f Pivotal—Hazariya (IRE) **H. H. Aga Khan**
3 **NEWELLEN (IRE),** 4, b f Montjeu (IRE)—Maryellen's Spirit (IRE) **Newtown Anner Stud Farm Ltd**
4 **QEWY (IRE),** 4, b c Street Cry (IRE)—Princess Nada **Sheikh Mohammed Obaid Al Maktoum**
5 **SADDLER'S ROCK (IRE),** 6, b h Sadler's Wells (USA)—Grecian Bride (IRE) **Mr M. O'Flynn**
6 **TARANA (IRE),** 4, b f Cape Cross (IRE)—Tarakala (IRE) **H. H. Aga Khan**

THREE-YEAR-OLDS

7 **AFFINISEA (IRE),** b c Sea The Stars (IRE)—Affianced (IRE) **Mr C. Tsui**
8 **ALAFZARA (IRE),** br f Nayef (USA)—Aliyfa (IRE) **H. H. Aga Khan**
9 **ALAYNA (IRE),** b f Cape Cross (IRE)—Alaiyma (IRE) **H. H. Aga Khan**
10 **ALYASAN (IRE),** ch c Sea The Stars (IRE)—Alaya (IRE) **H. H. Aga Khan**
11 **ANTICIPATED (IRE),** b c Whipper (USA)—Foreplay (USA) **Sheikh Mohammed Bin Faleh Al Thani**
12 **AWESOME STAR (IRE),** b c Sea The Stars (IRE)—Always Awesome (USA) **Mr C. E. Fipke**
13 **AZAMA (IRE),** b f Sea The Stars (IRE)—Asmara (USA) **H. H. Aga Khan**

MR JOHN M. OXX - Continued

14 **BABBLING STREAM,** b g Authorized (IRE)—Elasouna (IRE) **Mr J. O'Byrne**
15 **BE MY SEA (IRE),** b c Sea The Stars (IRE)—Bitooh **Mr C. Tsui**
16 B c Cockney Rebel (IRE)—Caeribland (IRE) **Mr M. Valade**
17 **CAILINI ALAINN (IRE),** b f Danehill Dancer (IRE)—Monty's Girl (IRE) **Newtown Anner Stud Farm Ltd**
18 **EBANORAN (IRE),** b c Oasis Dream—Ebadiyla (IRE) **H. H. Aga Khan**
19 **EBASANI (IRE),** ch c Manduro (GER)—Ebatana (GER) **H. H. Aga Khan**
20 B f Invincible Spirit (IRE)—Entre Nous (IRE) **Mr V. I. Araci**
21 **ERINIYA (IRE),** b f Acclamation—Erdiyna (IRE) **H. H. Aga Khan**
22 **FOREST OF SEAS (IRE),** b br f Sea The Stars (IRE)—Epping **Mr C. Tsui**
23 **GENTRY (IRE),** ch c Nayef (USA)—Elegant Way (IRE) **Sheikh Mohammed**
24 **GLOWING REPORT (IRE),** b c Dansili—Campfire Glow (IRE) **Newtown Anner Stud Farm Ltd**
25 **HARRY'S PRINCESS (IRE),** b f Strategic Prince—Harry's Irish Rose (USA) **Mr J. Aherne**
26 **HAZARABA (IRE),** b f Oasis Dream—Hazariya (IRE) **H. H. Aga Khan**
27 **JUPITER AND MARS (IRE),** b c Sea The Stars (IRE)—Hill of Snow **Ms Pinar Araci**
28 **KADAYMA (IRE),** b f Oratorio—Kadayna (IRE) **H. H. Aga Khan**
29 **KAREZAK (IRE),** b g Azamour (IRE)—Karawana (IRE) **H. H. Aga Khan**
30 **KATILAN (IRE),** b c Cape Cross (IRE)—Katiyra (IRE) **H. H. Aga Khan**
31 **KERKENI (IRE),** b g Manduro (GER)—Kerania (IRE) **H. H. Aga Khan**
32 **LONGTON,** b c Myboycharlie (IRE)—Lauren Louise **Sheikh Mohammed Bin Faleh Al Thani**
33 **MARAKOUSH (IRE),** b c Danehill Dancer (IRE)—Mouramara (IRE) **H. H. Aga Khan**
34 **MIA CAPRI (IRE),** gr f Dalakhani (IRE)—Noyelles (IRE) **Sheikh Khalid Al Sabah**
35 **MY TITANIA (IRE),** b f Sea The Stars (IRE)—Fairy of The Night (IRE) **Mr C. Tsui**
36 **NECTAR DE ROSE (FR),** ch f Shamardal (USA)—Bal de La Rose (IRE) **Mr C. Tsui**
37 **NEWTON'S NIGHT (IRE),** b f Galileo (IRE)—Sassenach (IRE) **Mr C. Tsui**
38 **OASIS TOWN,** br f Sleeping Indian—Town And Gown **Sheikh Mohammed Bin Faleh Al Thani**
39 **PONFEIGH (IRE),** gr c Teofilo (IRE)—Water Fountain **T. Barr**
40 **PRIMOGENITURE (IRE),** b g Glory of Dancer—Jacqueline (IND) **K. Dhunjibhoy, B. Desai, V. Shirke**
41 **PRINCE FREDERICK (IRE),** b g Kheleyf (USA)—Royal Crescent (IRE) **Sheikh Mohammed**
42 **RAYNA (IRE),** ch f Selkirk (USA)—Raydiya (IRE) **H. H. Aga Khan**
43 **RIPPLES EFFECT,** b c Sea The Stars (IRE)—Ripples Maid **Mr C. Tsui**
44 **SEA'S ARIA (IRE),** b c Sea The Stars (IRE)—Speed Song **Mr C. Tsui**
45 **SEAS OF WELLS (IRE),** b f Dansili—Kiyra Wells (IRE) **Mr C. Tsui**
46 **SHE'S MINE (IRE),** b f Sea The Stars (IRE)—Scribonia (IRE) **Mr V. I. Araci**
47 **SHERAMA (IRE),** b f Acclamation—Shehira (FR) **H. H. Aga Khan**
48 **SHORANA (IRE),** b f Holy Roman Emperor (IRE)—Sharesha (IRE) **H. H. Aga Khan**
49 **SIR ISSAC (IRE),** b c Sea The Stars (IRE)—Daneleta (IRE) **Mrs S. Rogers**
50 **STARS ALIGHT (IRE),** b f Sea The Stars (IRE)—Alizaya (IRE) **Mr C. Tsui**
51 **STARS SO BRIGHT (IRE),** b f Sea The Stars (IRE)—Night Fairy (IRE) **Mr C. Tsui**
52 **STREETCAR TO STARS (IRE),** b c Sea The Stars (IRE)—Approach **Mr C. Tsui**
53 **TARZIYNA (IRE),** ch f Raven's Pass (USA)—Taraza (IRE) **H. H. Aga Khan**
54 **TITHONUS (IRE),** b g Glory of Dancer—Aurora Aurealis (IND) **K. Dhunjibhoy & B. Desai**
55 **TORNADEA (IRE),** b f Sea The Stars (IRE)—Girouette (IRE) **Mr C. Tsui**
56 **WILD AT SEA (IRE),** ch g Sea The Stars (IRE)—Coyote **Mr C. Tsui**
57 **WRAP STAR (IRE),** b br c Cape Cross (IRE)—Twinkling (NZ) **Mr R. Ancell**
58 **ZINDANA (IRE),** gr f Dalakhani (IRE)—Zarkalia (IRE) **H. H. Aga Khan**

TWO-YEAR-OLDS

59 B c 29/3 Sea The Stars (IRE)—Alizaya (IRE) (Highest Honor (FR)) **Mr C. Tsui**
60 **AMPLIFIER,** b f 15/2 Dubawi (IRE)—
                    The Sound of Music (IRE) (Galileo (IRE)) **Sheikh Mohammed Obaid Al Maktoum**
61 **APPEARED,** b c 22/2 Dubawi (IRE)—Appearance (Galileo (IRE)) **Sheikh Mohammed Obaid Al Maktoum**
62 B f 25/3 Sea The Stars (IRE)—Aquarelle Bleue (Sadler's Wells (USA)) **Mr C. Tsui**
63 **BALLERINA ROSE,** b f 20/2 Duke of Marmalade (IRE)—
                    Roses For The Lady (IRE) (Sadler's Wells (USA)) **Mr N. Jones**
64 Ch f 7/2 Galileo (IRE)—Baraka (IRE) (Danehill (USA)) (140000) **Mrs E. M. Stockwell**
65 B f 30/1 Champs Elysees—Beautiful Lady (IRE) (Peintre Celebre (USA)) **Sheikh Mohammed Bin Faleh Al Thani**
66 **BETT'S GIFT,** b f 28/1 Teofilo (IRE)—Bett's Spirit (IRE) (Invincible Spirit (IRE)) **Miss P. F. O' Kelly**
67 **CAREFREE HIGHWAY,** b c 24/2 Authorized (IRE)—
                    Early Morning Rain (IRE) (Rock of Gibraltar (IRE)) (31000) **Mr J. McStay**
68 **CONTENANCE (IRE),** ch f 11/5 Dansant—Massada (Most Welcome) **Ms B. Keller**
69 **CROSSANDRA (IRE),** b f 9/3 Cape Cross (IRE)—Veneration (Dalakhani (IRE)) **Mr L. Walshe**
70 **DUBAI CROWN (IRE),** b c 22/3 Dubawi (IRE)—
                    Jumaireyah (Fairy King (USA)) **Sheikh Mohammed Obaid Al Maktoum**
71 B f 1/3 Sea The Stars (IRE)—Fairy of The Night (IRE) (Danehill (USA)) **Mr C. Tsui**
72 B c 8/5 Invincible Spirit (IRE)—Farranjordan (Galileo (IRE)) **Newtown Anner Stud Farm Ltd**

MR JOHN M. OXX - Continued

73 Gr c 23/4 Verglas (IRE)—Fine Day (Fantastic Light (USA)) (27874) **Miss E. M. Oxx**
74 FROZEN LAKE (IRE), b c 28/4 Elusive Quality (USA)—
Creative Design (USA) (Stravinsky (USA)) (73557) **Mr T. Pabst & Ms B. Keller**
75 GALILEO ALWAYS (IRE), b f 20/5 Galileo (IRE)—Always Awesome (USA) (Awesome Again (CAN)) **Mr C. Fipke**
76 GELENSCHIK (IRE), b f 2/3 Dalakhani (IRE)—Nunavik (IRE) (Indian Ridge) **Moyglare Stud Farm**
77 B f 11/2 Sea The Stars (IRE)—Germance (USA) (Silver Hawk (USA)) **Mr C. Tsui**
78 Ch f 4/2 Lope de Vega (IRE)—Helen of Sparta (IRE) (Barathea (IRE)) **Newtown Anner Stud Farm Ltd**
79 Ch c 7/3 Dubawi (IRE)—Hidden Silver (Anabaa (USA)) **Mr C. Tsui**
80 B c 17/4 Shirocco (GER)—Jomana (IRE) (Darshaan) **Sheikh Mohammed**
81 B f 26/1 Invincible Spirit (IRE)—Jumooh (Monsun (GER)) **Mr C. Tsui**
82 B f 26/4 Rip Van Winkle (IRE)—Mary Pickford (USA) (Speightstown (USA)) (25000) **Dundalk Racing Club**
83 B f 18/3 Iffraaj—Mas A Fuera (IRE) (Alzao (USA)) (17034) **Mrs C. Oxx**
84 B f 8/2 Pivotal—Nebraas (Green Desert (USA)) **H. E. The President Of Ireland**
85 PIVOTIQUE, b f 12/4 Pivotal—Suba (USA) (Seeking The Gold (USA)) **Sheikh Mohammed Obaid Al Maktoum**
86 POUR DEUX (IRE), b f 26/1 Dansili—
Gagnoa (IRE) (Sadler's Wells (USA)) (260000) **Mrs C. McStay & Lady O'Reilly**
87 ROMEO ROMEO (IRE), b c 15/2 Invincible Spirit (IRE)—
Precious Spring (IRE) (Sadler's Wells (USA)) (110000) **Mr V. I. Araci**
88 ROSALINE (IRE), ch f 6/2 New Approach (IRE)—
Reem Three (Mark of Esteem (IRE)) **Sheikh Mohammed Obaid Al Maktoum**
89 B f 21/1 Rock of Gibraltar (IRE)—So Secret (Barathea (IRE)) **Newtown Anner Stud Farm Ltd**
90 SPINNER (IRE), b c 1/3 Pivotal—Zomaradah (Deploy) **Sheikh Mohammed Obaid Al Maktoum**
91 STARLIGHT DANCE (IRE), b f 19/5 Sea The Stars (IRE)—Cadence (Cadeaux Genereux) **Mrs C. Oxx**
92 Ch c 29/1 Iffraaj—Sweet Folly (IRE) (Singspiel (IRE)) **Sheikh Mohammed**
93 Ch c 12/3 Duke of Marmalade (IRE)—
Taking Liberties (IRE) (Royal Academy (USA)) (19357) **Sheikh Mohammed Bin Faleh Al Thani**
94 Gr c 10/4 Zebedee—Tea Service (USA) (Atticus (USA)) (12388) **Dundalk Racing Club**
95 Ch f 21/1 Rip Van Winkle (IRE)—Truly Mine (IRE) (Rock of Gibraltar (IRE)) **Mrs H. Keaveney**
96 B f 14/3 Equiano (FR)—Vale of Belvoir (IRE) (Mull of Kintyre (USA)) **Sheikh Mohammed Bin Faleh Al Thani**
97 B f 24/2 Iffraaj—Vitoria (IRE) (Exceed And Excel (AUS)) **Sheikh Mohammed**
98 B f 26/4 Sea The Stars (IRE)—What A Picture (FR) (Peintre Celebre (USA)) **Mr C. Tsui**
99 Gr ro c 29/3 Mizzen Mast (USA)—Xinji (IRE) (Xaar) **Mr F. Fabre**
100 B f 16/2 King's Best (USA)—Zeeba (IRE) (Barathea (USA)) **Sheikh Mohammed Obaid Al Maktoum**

Jockey (flat): N. G. McCullagh, B. A. Curtis, D. P. McDonogh.

493
MR HUGO PALMER, Newmarket
Postal: Kremlin Cottage Stables, Snailwell Road, Newmarket, Suffolk, CB8 7DP
Contacts: PHONE (01638) 669880 FAX (01638) 666383 MOBILE (07824) 887886
E-MAIL info@hugopalmer.com WEBSITE www.hugopalmer.com

1 ASCRIPTION (IRE), 5, b g Dansili—Lady Elgar (IRE) **Mr V. I. Araci**
2 AUDACIA (IRE), 4, b f Sixties Icon—Indiannie Moon **Carmichael Simmons Humber**
3 DUBAWI SOUND, 6, b g Dubawi (IRE)—Hannah's Music **Seventh Lap Racing**
4 FREMONT (IRE), 7, b g Marju (IRE)—Snow Peak **Mr H. Palmer**
5 HIGH TIME TOO (IRE), 4, b f High Chaparral (IRE)—Dane Thyme (IRE) **Rathordan Partnership**
6 KHUBALA (IRE), 5, b c g Acclamation—Raghida (IRE) **Mrs P. Araci Bas**
7 KORANTAM (IRE), 4, b c Galileo (IRE)—Miss Beatrix (IRE) **Mr V. I. Araci**
8 SHORT SQUEEZE (IRE), 4, b g Cape Cross (IRE)—Sunsetter (USA) **W Duff Gordon, R Smith, B Mathieson**
9 ZERO MONEY, 8, ch g Bachelor Duke (USA)—Dawn Chorus **Kremlin Cottage III**
10 ZEYRAN (IRE), 5, ch m Galileo (IRE)—Chervil **Mrs Z. Araci Oneren**

THREE-YEAR-OLDS

11 BEWITCHMENT, b f Pivotal—Hypnotize **Windmill Bloodstock Partnership**
12 BREMNER, b c Manduro (GER)—Maggie Lou (IRE) **Gai Waterhouse Racing Partnership**
13 EXTREMITY (IRE), ch c Exceed And Excel (AUS)—Chanterelle (IRE) **Kremlin Cottage II**
14 B f Galileo (IRE)—Jessica's Dream (IRE) **Mr V. I. Araci**
15 KNIFE POINT (GER), b c High Chaparral (IRE)—Knightsbridge (BRZ) **Decadent Racing**
16 LAMORAK (IRE), b c King's Best (USA)—Indian Jewel (GER) **Mr A. Al Mansoori**
17 LOBSTER POT, b f Dylan Thomas (IRE)—Classical Flair **Anglia Bloodstock Syndicate II**
18 MOHOLOHOLO (IRE), b c High Chaparral (IRE)—Pray (IRE) **Mrs P. Araci Bas**
19 B f Rock of Gibraltar (IRE)—Rubileo **Kremlin Cottage I**
20 TACTICAL STRIKE, ch c Pivotal—Alvee (IRE) **Mr V. I. Araci**

MR HUGO PALMER - Continued

21 **THREE HEART'S**, b f Three Valleys (USA)—Heart's Harmony **Mrs D. M. Haynes**
22 **TOORAWEENAH**, br f Notnowcato—Navajo Love Song (IRE) **Mr H. Palmer**

TWO-YEAR-OLDS

23 B f 1/2 Alfred Nobel (IRE)—Applaud (USA) (Rahy (USA)) (28571) **Kremlin Cottage V**
24 Ch c 6/3 Starspangledbanner (AUS)—Blissful Beat (Beat Hollow) (61943) **Flemington Bloodstock Partnership**
25 **BROWN VELVET**, b f 12/2 Kodiac—Silkenveil (IRE) (Indian Ridge) (17142) **Carmichael Humber**
26 B f 20/3 Aussie Rules (USA)—Cliche (IRE) (Diktat) (9291) **Anglia Bloodstock Syndicate V**
27 B f 19/3 Sir Percy—Emirates First (IRE) (In The Wings) (10000) **Kremlin Cottage IV**
28 Ch f 30/3 Raven's Pass (USA)—Fafinta (IRE) (Indian Ridge) **Mr V. I. Araci**
29 B c 9/2 Equiano (IRE)—Fairnilee (Selkirk (USA)) (20000) **Kremlin Cottage VI**
30 B c 10/4 Sir Percy—Fizzy Treat (Efisio) (27874) **Ballymore Downunder Syndicate**
31 **GAME PIE (IRE)**, b c 9/3 Tamayuz—Princess Nala (IRE) (In The Wings) (32520) **De La Warr Racing**
32 B c 10/4 Amadeus Wolf—Hawk Eyed Lady (IRE) (Hawk Wing (USA)) (12388) **Weybridge Mafia**
33 Ch f 29/1 Mastercraftsman (IRE)—La Lunete (Halling (USA)) (17808) **Chris Humber & Amanda Brudenell**
34 **MAZOULA (IRE)**, b f 26/2 Camacho—Molaaf (Shareef Dancer (USA)) (6194) **Anglia Bloodstock Syndicate IV**
35 **NOT NEVER**, ch g 16/4 Notnowcato—Watchoverme (Haafhd) (1428) **Mrs D. M. Haynes**
36 B f 28/1 Bushranger (IRE)—Sheila Blige (Zamindar (USA)) (13000) **Mr A. Al Mansoori**
37 **SILVERY BLUE**, b f 21/4 Paco Boy (IRE)—Blue Echo (Kyllachy) (26000) **Mrs Mary Taylor & Mr James Taylor**
38 B f 19/1 Invincible Spirit (IRE)—Sound of Summer (USA) (Fusaichi Pegasus (USA)) (54200) **Mr V. I. Araci**
39 **SPANISH SQUEEZE (IRE)**, ch c 13/4 Lope de Vega (IRE)—
                                     Appetina (Perugino (USA)) (62000) **W. A. L. Duff Gordon**
40 B c 25/2 Oasis Dream—Splashdown (Falbrav (IRE)) (370000) **Mr V. I. Araci**
41 **STRONG STEPS**, br c 1/5 Aqlaam—Wunders Dream (IRE) (Averti (IRE)) (40000) **Mr V. I. Araci**
42 **TWITCH (IRE)**, b f 23/4 Azamour (IRE)—
                                     Blinking (Marju (IRE)) (30000) **The Duke of Roxburghe & The Duke of Devonshire**
43 B f 14/4 Azamour (IRE)—Wing Stealth (IRE) (Hawk Wing (USA)) (20131) **FOMO Syndicate**
44 **ZIGGURAT**, gr c 24/3 Tagula (IRE)—Visual Element (USA) (Distant View (USA)) (45714) **Mr C. M. Humber**

Other Owners: Lord & Lady Ampthill, Anja Anderson, Daniel Berry, Jonathan Bond, Dan Bovington, Tom Brideoak, Sophia Brudenell, Charlie Budgett, Chris Budgett, Fiona Carmichael, Henry Channon, Colin Chisholm, Lord De La Warr, Mick Donohoe, Nick Donovan, Andrew Dowsett, Eddie Fitzpatrick, Philip Gibbs, Patrick Halloran, Ben Hanbury, Paul Hernon, Craig Hillier, Tim Hyde, Rob Jones, Lord Kimball, MV Magnier, Philippa Mains, Tom Magnier, Lady Manton, Mark Mcstay, David Moodie, Tom Morrison, Donough Murphy, Michael Naylor-Leyland, Andrew Nicholls, Sally Nicholson, Mr & Mrs A E Pakenham, Mrs A E Phillips, Peter Raft, Peter Raftopoulos, Tim Rooney, Paul & Denise Rowe, Sam Sangster, Max Sangster, Stan Saric, Paul Shanahan, Peter Shemilt, Roger Simmons, Jessica Slack, Rob Speers, Jeff Spencer, Frances Stanley, Peter Stanley, David Steen (Jnr), David Steen (Snr), Calie Stone, Mike Styles, Heather Tylor, Lord & Lady Vestey, Mary Vestey, Kerry Wainman.

Apprentice: Noel Garbutt.

---

494 | **MR H. A. PANTALL, Beaupreau**
Postal: Le Bois du Coin, Beaupreau 49600, France
Contacts: **PHONE** (0033) 241 636715 (0033) 685 070620 **FAX** (0033) 241 630530
MOBILE (0033) 607 450647
E-MAIL hapantall@wanadoo.fr

1 **A COEUR OUVERT (FR)**, 8, b g Dano-Mast—Lady Stapara (IRE)
2 **BARONESS DANIELA**, 4, b f Tiger Hill (IRE)—Bedara
3 **BLUEFIRE**, 4, gr f Distorted Humor (USA)—Filarmonia (ARG)
4 **CRYING SHAME (USA)**, 4, b f Street Cry (IRE)—Tout Charmant (USA)
5 **DARK WOMAN**, 4, b br f Manduro (GER)—Sospel
6 **DAWN SALUTE (FR)**, 4, b c Royal Applause—Nice Matin (USA)
7 **DYNAMOON (FR)**, 4, b f Kentucky Dynamite (USA)—Moon Gorge
8 **ENCYIA (FR)**, 4, b f Gold Away (IRE)—Eloisa (GER)
9 **GHOSTFLOWER (IRE)**, 4, b f Dansili—Silkwood
10 **HARBOUR OF HOPE (GER)**, 4, b f Monsun (GER)—Hanami
11 **INGOT OF GOLD**, 4, b f Dubawi (IRE)—Cresta Gold
12 **JOYEUSE MARCHE**, 4, ch f New Approach (IRE)—Last Rhapsody (IRE)
13 **JULIE CLARY (FR)**, 3, b f Dubai Destination (USA)—Queen of Naples
14 **JUST DARCY**, 4, b f Danehill Dancer (IRE)—Jane Austen (IRE)
15 **KENHOPE (FR)**, 4, b f Kendargent (FR)—Bedford Hope (GER)
16 **LADY MCKELL (IRE)**, 4, b f Raven's Pass (USA)—Victoria Star (IRE)
17 **LATINO (SWI)**, 5, b g Meshaheer (USA)—Sun Godess (FR)

MR H. A. PANTALL - Continued

18 **LAW BLADE (FR)**, 9, b g Dashing Blade—Lonia (GER)
19 **LIBRE TEMPS (FR)**, 6, b h Cadeaux Genereux—Nellie Gwyn
20 **LINNGARO (FR)**, 4, ch g Linngari (IRE)—Indochine (BRZ)
21 **LIVING DESERT**, 4, gr g Oasis Dream—Sell Out
22 **LOCAL LOVER (FR)**, 4, b c Choisir (AUS)—La Victoria (IRE)
23 **MATORIO (FR)**, 4, b f Oratorio (IRE)—Matwan (FR)
24 **MISTER BAWI (FR)**, 4, ch c Dubawi (IRE)—Miss Sissy (FR)
25 **PAIZA (IRE)**, 4, b c Zamindar (USA)—Tobermory (IRE)
26 **PASSARINHO (IRE)**, 5, ch h Ad Valorem (USA)—Semiramide (IRE)
27 **PEACE AT LAST (IRE)**, 4, b c Oasis Dream—National Day (IRE)
28 **POLARIX**, 8, gr ro h Linamix (FR)—Freezing (USA)
29 **ROCNA (FR)**, 4, f Nayef (USA)—Rock Chick
30 **ROXANNE (FR)**, 4, b f Falco (USA)—Super Vite (USA)
31 **SILLYLINNY (FR)**, 4, ch f Linngari (IRE)—Syllable
32 **SNAPE MALTINGS (IRE)**, 7, b g Sadler's Wells (USA)—Hanami
33 **SOLYWAY (FR)**, 4, b f Way of Light (USA)—Lasso Calypso (FR)
34 **TANGATCHEK (IRE)**, 5, ch h Mr Greeley (USA)—Tivadare (FR)
35 **THIQA (IRE)**, 4, b f New Approach (IRE)—Sunray Superstar
36 **TREASURE ROCK (FR)**, 4, b f Rock of Gibraltar (IRE)—Tiara
37 **UNFUNNY (USA)**, 4, b f Distorted Humor (USA)—Dubai Escapade (USA)
38 **VALENTINO ANGELI (FR)**, 6, ch g Vespone (IRE)—Speedy Amber (FR)
39 **VALLEY GIRL (FR)**, 4, ch f Motivator—Nanty (IRE)
40 **VANISHING CUPID (SWI)**, 4, b c Galileo (IRE)—Vanishing Prairie (USA)

THREE-YEAR-OLDS

41 **ATHENA (FR)**, b f King's Best (USA)—Saharienne (USA)
42 **ATLANTIC CITY (FR)**, b f Holy Roman Emperor (IRE)—Bog Wild (USA)
43 **AVENTURIER (FR)**, ch c Samum (GER)—Aramina (GER)
44 **BEDOUIN DANCER (IRE)**, gr f Pivotal—Tamarillo
45 **BEST STEPS (IRE)**, gr f Acclamation—Legal Steps (IRE)
46 **BLIND LOVE (FR)**, b f Librettist (USA)—Baracoa (SWI)
47 **BLUE MOOD (IRE)**, b f Invincible Spirit (IRE)—Cabriole
48 **BROKEN TIMES (FR)**, b c Zafeen (FR)—Beriosova (FR)
49 **CAJA (FR)**, ch f Touch Down (GER)—Centinela
50 **CRESSELIA (FR)**, b f Sinndar (IRE)—Honorable Love
51 **CROSSTALK (IRE)**, b f Cape Cross (IRE)—Last Resort
52 **DANCING SANDS (IRE)**, b f Dubawi (IRE)—Past The Post (USA)
53 **DANDIA**, b f Teofilo (IRE)—Danse Arabe (IRE)
54 **DEUXIEME EMPIRE (FR)**, b c Naaqoos—Dentelle (FR)
55 **DUKE OF FRANCE (FR)**, b c Duke of Marmalade (IRE)—Tres Ravi (GER)
56 **EARLY PRIME (FR)**, b f Early March—Valprime (FR)
57 **ELEVENTH HOUR (IRE)**, b f Invincible Spirit (IRE)—Midnight Line (USA)
58 **FAST AND PRETTY (IRE)**, b f Zamindar (USA)—Tres Rapide (IRE)
59 **FLEUR DES MERS**, ch f Mount Nelson—Fidelio's Miracle (USA)
60 **FREEDOM TALES (FR)**, b c Tertullian (USA)—Fridas World
61 **GENTLE BREEZE (IRE)**, b f Dubawi (IRE)—Laureldean Gale (USA)
62 **GOLDY ESPONY (FR)**, f Vespone (IRE)—Goldy Honor (FR)
63 **HAZUMI (GER)**, b c Monsun (GER)—Hanami
64 **HEARTILY (IRE)**, b f Dubawi (IRE)—Heart's Content (IRE)
65 **INSPIRITER**, b f Invincible Spirit (IRE)—Floristry
66 **IRRADIANCE (IRE)**, b f Raven's Pass (USA)—Pure Illusion (IRE)
67 **JOLIE CHANSON (FR)**, ch f Mount Nelson—Slow Down (USA)
68 **KAMELLATA (FR)**, b f Pomellato (GER)—Kamakura (FR)
69 **LADY SPEEDY (IRE)**, gr f Speedmaster (GER)—Carinamix (FR)
70 **LANDYM (FR)**, b c Lando (GER)—Ymlaen (IRE)
71 **LIGHT AND SALT (FR)**, b f Sageburg (IRE)—Take The Light (FR)
72 **MI VIDA (FR)**, b c Meshaheer (USA)—Belle Suisse (FR)
73 **MONATORIO (FR)**, b c Vespone (IRE)—Midyanila (FR)
74 **MORENA**, b f Zafeen (FR)—Star Godess (FR)
75 **MR POMMEROY (FR)**, ch c Linngari (IRE)—Amerissage (USA)
76 **NALOUDIA (IRE)**, ch f Piccolo—Fanciful Dancer
77 **OEIL DE TIGRE (FR)**, b f Footstepsinthesand—Suerte
78 **ORAGE NOIR (FR)**, b c Astronomer Royal (USA)—Atlantic Crossing (GER)
79 **ORION BEST (FR)**, b f King's Best (USA)—Okocha (GER)
80 **PATENT JOY (IRE)**, b f Pivotal—Kitty Matcham (IRE)

MR H. A. PANTALL - Continued

81 **PICATCHU (FR)**, b f King's Best (USA)—Trazando
82 **POLISCHNO (FR)**, b c Country Reel (USA)—Noverings
83 **PRAIRIE SALSA (FR)**, b f Meshaheer (USA)—Prairie Scilla (GER)
84 **PRINCESS BAVAROISE (FR)**, b f Desert Prince (IRE)—Sascilaria
85 **PRISENFLAG (FR)**, gr f Pyrus (USA)—Proud Douna (FR)
86 **PUPA DI SARONNO (ITY)**, b f Orpen (USA)—Olonella
87 **QUOTH**, ch f Raven's Pass (USA)—Hearsay
88 **RACE FOR FAME (IRE)**, b c Meshaheer (USA)—Rocky Mixa (FR)
89 **RAIN ARTIST'S (FR)**, b f Montmartre (USA)—Rain Lily (FR)
90 **RANGALI**, ch c Namid—Tejaara (USA)
91 **RAPHINAE**, b f Dubawi (IRE)—Dodo (IRE)
92 **REAL PROMISE**, ch c Pivotal—Precocious Star (IRE)
93 **RED RUBY (FR)**, b f Hold That Tiger (USA)—Red Kiss (IRE)
94 **REDWHITE AND BLUES (FR)**, b c Bernstein (USA)—Tina Bull (USA)
95 **REMEMBER BABI (FR)**, b f High Chaparral (IRE)—Simay (TUR)
96 **RIDE ON ANGELS (FR)**, ch c Dalakhani (IRE)—Well Groomed (IRE)
97 **SANREMO (FR)**, ch g Manduro (GER)—Gontcharova (IRE)
98 **SARINDA**, ch f Dubawi (IRE)—Viola da Braccio (IRE)
99 **SAYORI (FR)**, gr g Martaline—Shaama Rose (FR)
100 **SEA INTERLUDE**, b c Cape Cross (IRE)—Aldeburgh Music (IRE)
101 **SEE YOU SOON (FR)**, b c Zafeen (FR)—Summer Dance (FR)
102 **SHALLOW LAKE (USA)**, b br f Bernardini (USA)—Scarlet Ibis
103 **SOHO LIGHTNING (IRE)**, b c Royal Applause—Nice Matin (USA)
104 **SON CESIO (FR)**, b c Zafeen (FR)—Slitana (IRE)
105 **SPRING CARNIVAL (USA)**, b f Bernardini (USA)—Shesabullwinkle (USA)
106 **STEEL TRAIN (FR)**, b c Zafeen (FR)—Silent Sunday (IRE)
107 **TALENT SPOTTER**, b f Exceed And Excel (AUS)—Sophie's Girl
108 **TALETELLER (USA)**, b f Bernardini (USA)—Taletobetold (USA)
109 **THIS TIME (FR)**, b f Zafeen (FR)—Scalotta (GER)
110 **TRACE OF SCENT (IRE)**, b f Acclamation—Red Blossom (USA)
111 **TURIN (IRE)**, b f Raven's Pass (USA)—Veronica Cooper (IRE)
112 **VACATIONER**, ch f Dubawi (IRE)—Tropical Breeze (IRE)
113 **VEHEMENCE D'AMOUR (FR)**, ch f Linngari (IRE)—Fire Sale (ARG)
114 **ZAFEEN STYLE (FR)**, b c Zafeen (FR)—Silver Swain (FR)
115 **ZARNIA (FR)**, b f Soldier of Fortune (IRE)—Zarnitza (FR)
116 **ZERKA**, b f Invincible Spirit (IRE)—Hashimiya (USA)

TWO-YEAR-OLDS

117 B c 5/3 Zamindar (USA)—Alpensinfonie (IRE) (Montjeu (IRE))
118 **ALPINKATZE (FR)**, ch f 10/5 Linngari (IRE)—Amerissage (USA) (Rahy (USA)) (3097)
119 **ANA'S BEST (FR)**, b f 27/3 King's Best (USA)—Ana Marie (FR) (Anabaa (USA)) (92915)
120 **ANOTHER DANCE (FR)**, b f 10/2 Zafeen (FR)—American Tune (IRE) (Refuse To Bend (IRE)) (6194)
121 **ARCHANGE (FR)**, b f 30/4 Arcano (FR)—Carinae (USA) (Nureyev (USA)) (13162)
122 B f 20/4 Duke of Marmalade (IRE)—Ballerina Blue (IRE) (High Chaparral (IRE)) (48006)
123 **BARBARA (FR)**, b f 15/4 Samson Happy (JPN)—Ballet Girl (USA) (Theatrical)
124 B c 2/4 Gentlewave (IRE)—Be Yourself (FR) (Marchand de Sable (USA)) (38714)
125 **BIG LETTERS (IRE)**, b f 23/1 Whipper (USA)—Big Monologue (IRE) (Testa Rossa (AUS)) (18583)
126 **BLUE SMOKE (FR)**, b c 21/5 Zafeen (FR)—Blue Roses (IRE) (Oratorio (IRE)) (11614)
127 B c 6/2 Rock of Gibraltar (IRE)—Border Bloom (Selkirk (USA))
128 **CARRY OUT (FR)**, b c 20/3 Air Chief Marshal (IRE)—Respite (Pivotal)
129 B f 19/2 Makfi—Costa Brava (IRE) (Sadler's Wells (USA)) (65814)
130 B c 23/2 Mastercraftsman (IRE)—Decouverte (IRE) (Rainbow Quest (USA)) (11227)
131 **DIAMOND RED (FR)**, b c 2/4 Diamond Green (FR)—Massatixa (FR) (Linamix (FR)) (11614)
132 B c 1/1 Danehill Dancer (IRE)—Dubai Rose (Dubai Destination (USA))
133 **EL SUIZO (FR)**, b c 28/1 Meshaheer (USA)—Belle Suisse (FR) (Hamas (IRE))
134 B f 21/3 Equiano (FR)—Fabulously Red (Red Ransom (USA))
135 **GOKEN (FR)**, b c 18/4 Kendargent (FR)—Gooseley Chope (FR) (Indian Rocket)
136 B f 31/1 Cape Cross (IRE)—Golden Bottle (Giant's Causeway (USA))
137 **GREEN FANCY (FR)**, b f 19/3 Diamond Green (FR)—Fancy Diamond (GER) (Ransom O'war (USA)) (9291)
138 Ch c 15/5 Monsun (GER)—Hanami (Hernando (FR))
139 **KENFREEZE (FR)**, b c 18/4 Kendargent (FR)—Damdam Freeze (FR) (Indian Rocket)
140 **KENOUSKA (FR)**, ch f 3/3 Kendargent (FR)—Dame Anouska (IRE) (Exceed And Excel (AUS))
141 **LOVEMEDO (FR)**, ch f 5/3 Zafeen (FR)—Suvretta Queen (FR) (Polish Precedent (USA))
142 B f 27/3 Acclamation—Lunaskia (FR) (Ashkalani (IRE))
143 B c 15/4 Montjeu (IRE)—Majoune (FR) (Take Risks (FR))

MR H. A. PANTALL - Continued

144 B c 4/3 Oasis Dream—Maroussies Wings (IRE) (In The Wings) (58072)
145 **MIND STORY (FR)**, b f 8/3 Diamond Green (FR)—Mind Master (USA) (Mizzen Mast (USA)) (5420)
146 c 1/1 Pivotal—Miss Emma May (IRE) (Hawk Wing (USA))
147 **MISTER IFF**, b c 5/2 Iffraaj—Miss Sissy (FR) (Sicyos (USA))
148 **MUST BE THE ONE (FR)**, b f 14/2 Meshaheer (USA)—Silver Market (FR) (Marchand de Sable (USA)) (4645)
149 **NACHT (FR)**, b f 12/4 Sabiango (GER)—Nonoalka (GER) (Alkalde (GER)) (10840)
150 B c 9/4 Acclamation—Nice Matin (USA) (Tiznow (USA)) (30971)
151 Gr f 9/3 Aussie Rules (USA)—Nightdance Sun (GER) (Monsun (GER))
152 B f 31/3 American Post—Pink Topaz (USA) (Tiznow (USA)) (21680)
153 **PLAISIR D'AMOUR (FR)**, b f 15/2 Linngari (IRE)—Analfabeta (FR) (Anabaa (USA))
154 **PRADARA (FR)**, b f 26/3 Aussie Rules (USA)—Vaillante (IRE) (Zilzal (USA)) (11614)
155 Br c 28/3 Dansili—Precocious Star (IRE) (Bold Fact (USA))
156 Ch f 4/3 Mount Nelson—Reading Habit (USA) (Half a Year (USA))
157 **ROCKET BOB (FR)**, b c 10/2 Whipper (USA)—Raise In Aspen (FR) (Iron Mask (USA)) (13162)
158 B f 7/3 Motivator—Serpina (IRE) (Grand Lodge (USA)) (19357)
159 B f 5/4 Hannouma (IRE)—Shadai Stone (JPN) (Real Shadai (USA)) (10840)
160 **SHANAKILLA (FR)**, f 16/5 Lord Shanakill (USA)—Carinamix (FR) (Linamix (FR))
161 **SORCIEREBIENAIMEE (FR)**, b f 30/1 Muhtathir—Magie Noire (IRE) (Marju (IRE)) (7742)
162 **SPICY MOMENTS (FR)**, b f 8/3 Elusive City (USA)—Musha Cay (FR) (Hawk Wing (USA)) (23228)
163 B f 24/2 Falco (USA)—Sweetdreams (FR) (Cadeaux Genereux) (7742)
164 **TEJAHAA (FR)**, f 9/3 Haafhd—Tejaara (USA) (Kingmambo (USA))
165 Ch c 14/4 Raven's Pass (USA)—Turtle Point (USA) (Giant's Causeway (USA)) (38714)
166 **VAL D'HIVER (FR)**, bl f 17/1 Zafeen (FR)—Verzasca (IRE) (Sadler's Wells (USA))
167 B c 1/1 Orpen—Ymlaen (FR) (Desert Prince (IRE)) (23228)
168 **ZARIYANO (FR)**, b c 19/3 Linngari (IRE)—Zariyana (IRE) (Desert Prince (IRE)) (15485)

Assistant Trainer: Ludovic Gadbin (0033) 685 070620

Jockey (flat): Fabrice Veron. **Apprentice:** Sebastien Martino, Antoine Werle.

---

495 **MR JOHN PANVERT, Tiverton**
Postal: **Steart Farm Racing Stables, Stoodleigh, Tiverton, Devon, EX16 9QA**
Contacts: **MOBILE (07590) 120314**

1 **CHOISIREZ (IRE)**, 5, b m Choisir (AUS)—Filimeala (IRE) **J. F. Panvert**
2 **EDDY**, 5, b g Exit To Nowhere (USA)—Sharway Lady **J. F. Panvert**
3 **REBEL ISLAND (IRE)**, 5, b m Heron Island (IRE)—Rebel Rebel (FR) **J. F. Panvert**
4 **SISTERBROOKE (IRE)**, 5, ch m Trans Island—Cool Merenda (IRE) **J. F. Panvert**
5 **STUDFARMER**, 4, b g Multiplex—Samadilla (USA) **J. F. Panvert**
6 **WATCHMETAIL (IRE)**, 8, b br g Amilynx (FR)—Ellie Anna (IRE) **J. F. Panvert**

Jockey (flat): Jim Crowley, Luke Morris. **Jockey (NH):** David England, Conor O'Farrell, Charlie Wallis.

---

496 **MRS HILARY PARROTT, Redmarley**
Postal: **Chapel Farm, Chapel Lane, Redmarley, Gloucester, Gloucestershire, GL19 3JF**
Contacts: **PHONE (01452) 840139 FAX (01452) 840139 MOBILE (07972) 125030**
E-MAIL hkparrott@btinternet.com

1 **BERTIES COIN**, 5, b g Sakhee (USA)—Spinning Coin **Mr T. J. & Mrs H. Parrott**
2 **BIT OF A SCRUFF (IRE)**, 7, b g Westerner—Collage **Mr T. J. & Mrs H. Parrott**
3 6, B g Heron Island (IRE)—Clare Hogan (IRE) **Unregistered Partnership**
4 **DAIZY (IRE)**, 5, ch g Presenting—I Remember It Well (IRE) **Mr T. J. & Mrs H. Parrott**
5 **SERIOUS MIXTURE**, 7, b g Fair Mix (IRE)—Bonne Anniversaire **Mr T. J. & Mrs H. Parrott**
6 **SIMPLY CHARLES (IRE)**, 7, ch g Blueprint (IRE)—Stormy Sea (IRE) **Mr T. J. & Mrs H. Parrott**
7 **SPINNING SCOOTER**, 4, b g Sleeping Indian—Spinning Coin **Mr T.J. & Mrs H. Parrott**
8 5, B g Flemensfirth (USA)—Tinopasa (FR) **Unregistered Partnership**
9 **WAYWARD PRINCE**, 10, b g Alflora (IRE)—Bellino Spirit (IRE) **Mr T. J. & Mrs H. Parrott**

497 MR BEN PAULING, Bourton-On-The-Water
Postal: **Bourton Hill Farm, Bourton-On-The-Water, Gloucestershire, GL54 3BJ**
Contacts: PHONE **(01451) 821252** MOBILE **(07825) 232888**

1 **BARTERS HILL**, 4, b g Kalanisi (IRE)—Circle The Wagons (IRE) **Circle Of Friends**
2 **BENEFITOFHINDSIGHT**, 5, ch g Sir Harry Lewis (USA)—Aoninch **Tim Finch & Mike Lanz**
3 **CADEAU GEORGE**, 5, b g Relief Pitcher—Sovereign's Gift **Genesis Racing Partnership**
4 **CASSIE**, 4, b f Refuse To Bend (IRE)—Strictly Cool (USA) **Pump & Plant Services LTD**
5 **COSWAY SPIRIT (IRE)**, 7, ch g Shantou (USA)—Annalisa (IRE) **Alan Marsh & Partners**
6 **HERBALIST**, 4, ch g Haafhd—Puya **Mrs S. Pauling**
7 **KELLYS BROW (IRE)**, 7, b g Golan (IRE)—Eyebright (IRE) **Foxtrot Racing Heythrop Partnership**
8 **LOCK TOWERS (IRE)**, 5, b g Classic Cliche (IRE)—Katieella (IRE) **Mr B. Pauling**
9 **MALIBU SUN**, 7, ch g Needwood Blade—Lambadora **Easy Going Racing**
10 **NEWTON THISTLE**, 7, b g Erhaab (USA)—Newton Venture **J. H. & N. J. Foxon**
11 **RAVEN'S TOWER (USA)**, 4, b g Raven's Pass (USA)—Tizdubai (USA) **Faithful Friends**
12 **RAVENS NEST**, 4, b g Piccolo—Emouna **Mr B. P. Pauling**
13 **RIDE ON TIME (IRE)**, 4, b g Presenting—Polly Anthus **Whatalot**
14 **RONNIE ROCKCAKE**, 4, b g Tiger Hill (USA)—Vitesse (IRE) **Pump & Plant Services Ltd**
15 **SMART FREDDY**, 8, b g Groom Dancer (USA)—Smart Topsy **Mrs R. D. Sumpter**
16 **SPRING STEEL (IRE)**, 5, b g Dushyantor (USA)—Fieldtown (IRE) **Tim Finch & Mike Lanz**
17 **WADSWICK HAROLD**, 4, b g Septieme Ciel (USA)—Miss Flinders **Mr & Mrs T. Barton**

Other Owners: Mr D. Abraham, Mrs L. M. Bugden, Mrs P. M. Colson, Mr J. Deacon, Mr N. C. Deacon, Mr P. M. Drewett, Mr T. P. Finch, Mr R. Foxon, Mrs N. J. Foxon, Mr J. H. Foxon, Mr R. S. Johnson, Mr M. E. Lanz, Mr A. R. W. Marsh, Mrs J. Pauling, Mr R. W. P. Weeks.

Jockey (NH): David Bass, Felix De Giles. **Conditional:** Kielan Woods.

498 MR RAY PEACOCK, Tenbury Wells
Postal: **Elliott House Farm, Vine Lane, Kyre, Tenbury Wells, Worcestershire, WR15 8RL**
Contacts: PHONE **(01885) 410772** MOBILE **(07748) 565574/ 07881440135**

1 **GIFTED HEIR (IRE)**, 10, b g Princely Heir (IRE)—Inzar Lady (IRE) **R. E. Peacock**
2 **INTERCHOICE STAR**, 9, b g Josr Algarhoud (IRE)—Blakeshall Girl **Mr J. P. Evitt**
3 **KOMREYEV STAR**, 12, b g Komaite (USA)—L'ancressaan **R. E. Peacock**
4 **PORTRUSH STORM**, 9, ch m Observatory (USA)—Overcast (IRE) **Mr J. P. Evitt**
5 **RICH HARVEST (USA)**, 9, b br g High Yield (USA)—Mangano **R. E. Peacock**
6 **SAGA LOUT**, 4, b g Assertive—Intellibet One **Mr J. P. Evitt**
7 **SWORDS**, 12, b g Vettori (IRE)—Pomorie (IRE) **R. E. Peacock**

Assistant Trainer: Mrs C Peacock **Jockey (flat):** David Probert. **Apprentice:** Charles Bishop.
Amateur: Miss S. Peacock.

499 MRS LYDIA PEARCE, Newmarket
Postal: **Wroughton House, 37 Old Station Road, Newmarket, Suffolk, CB8 8DT**
Contacts: PHONE **(01638) 664669** MOBILE **(07787) 517864**
E-MAIL **lsp_8@live.co.uk**

1 **ALKHATAAF (USA)**, 7, b g Green Desert (USA)—Elrafa Ah (USA) **R. G. Thurston**
2 **CEELO**, 4, b g Green Desert (USA)—Mindsharp (USA) **S & M Supplies (Aylsham) Ltd**
3 **CORN MAIDEN**, 5, b m Refuse To Bend (IRE)—Namat (IRE) **Ms J. McHugh**
4 **COUNT CEPRANO (IRE)**, 10, b g Desert Prince (IRE)—Camerlata **R. G. Thurston**
5 **DR FINLEY (IRE)**, 7, ch g Dr Fong (USA)—Farrfesheena (USA) **Killarney Glen**
6 **DUKE OF ARICABEAU (IRE)**, 5, ch g Modigliani (USA)—Essential Fear (IRE) **Mr P. J. Stephenson**
7 **GHUFA (IRE)**, 10, b g Sakhee (USA)—Hawriyah (USA) **Mrs L. S. Pearce**
8 **HATTA STREAM (IRE)**, 8, b g Oasis Dream—Rubies From Burma (USA)
9 **MINSTREL LAD**, 6, ch g Where Or When (IRE)—Teal Flower **S & M Supplies (Aylsham) Ltd**
10 **OLNEY LASS**, 7, b m Lucky Story (USA)—Zalebe **Mrs L. J. Marsh**
11 **PICTURE DEALER**, 5, b g Royal Applause—Tychy **Killarney Glen**
12 **SHAMALAD**, 4, b c Shamardal (USA)—Steam Cuisine **Killarney Glen**
13 **SWEET TALKING GUY (IRE)**, 4, b g Oratorio (IRE)—Sweet Namibia (IRE) **Killarney Glen**

MRS LYDIA PEARCE - Continued

Other Owners: S. Andrews, N. M. Hanger, Mr E. Jones, Mrs J. R. Marsh, Mrs L. M. Matthews.

Jockey (flat): Simon Pearce. **Amateur:** Mr Ray Barrett.

---

500 MR OLLIE PEARS, Malton
Postal: **The Office, Old Farmhouse, Beverley Road, Norton, Malton, North Yorkshire, YO17 9PJ**
Contacts: **PHONE (01653) 690746 MOBILE (07760) 197103**
E-MAIL info@olliepearsracing.co.uk WEBSITE www.olliepearsracing.co.uk

1 BOY THE BELL, 7, b g Choisir (AUS)—Bella Beguine **K. C. West**
2 CONFIDENTIAL CREEK, 4, b g Sakhee's Secret—Upstream **Mr John J. Maguire & Mr John H. Sissons**
3 DIZOARD, 4, b f Desideratum—Riviere
4 ITALIAN LADY (USA), 5, b br m Medaglia d'oro (USA)—Way Beyond (USA) **O. J. Pears**
5 LEAN ON PETE (IRE), 5, b g Oasis Dream—Superfonic (FR) **K. C. West**
6 NAUGHTYBYCHOICE, 4, gr g Dubai Destination (USA)—Gracia **Mrs V. A. Pears**
7 NOODLES BLUE BOY, 8, b g Makbul—Dee Dee Girl (IRE) **Mr Keith Taylor & Mr Keith West**
8 POWERFUL PIERRE, 7, ch g Compton Place—Alzianah **T. Elsey**
9 SHAMROCKED (IRE), 5, b g Rock of Gibraltar (IRE)—Hallowed Park (IRE) **John H Sissons & Partners**
10 STAR REQUEST, 4, b f Urgent Request (IRE)—Carahill (AUS) **O. J. Pears**
11 ZAITSEV (IRE), 4, ch g Refuse To Bend (IRE)—Zuniga's Date (USA) **Mrs Z. Wentworth**

THREE-YEAR-OLDS
12 AUGUSTA ADA, b f Byron—Preference **T. J. O'Gram**
13 BREUGHEL (GER), b g Dutch Art—Bezzaaf **C. V. Wentworth**
14 COOL RECEPTION, b f Royal Applause—Winter Ice **Ownaracehorse Ltd**
15 Ch g Strategic Prince—Lurgoe Lady (IRE) **J. J. Maguire**
16 MOVING WAVES (IRE), b f Intense Focus (USA)—Kimola (IRE) **Mrs Z. Wentworth**
17 NO LEAF CLOVER (IRE), b c Kodiac—Rajmahal (UAE) **C. V. Wentworth**

TWO-YEAR-OLDS
18 Ch f 30/4 Sakhee's Secret—China Cherub (Inchinor) (800) **Ownaracehorse Ltd**
19 DIAMOND MELEE, b f 15/4 Monsieur Bond (IRE)—Real Diamond (Bertolini (USA)) **J. H. Sissons**
20 Ch c 23/4 Showcasing—Forrest Star (Fraam) (3000) **Ownaracehorse Ltd**
21 B c 19/3 Sakhee's Secret—Saddlers Bend (IRE) (Refuse To Bend (IRE)) (16000) **D. Scott**

Other Owners: P. Sadler, L. C. Sigsworth, K. Taylor.

Assistant Trainer: Vicky Pears

Jockey (NH): Brian Hughes.

---

501 MR DAVID PEARSON, High Peak
Postal: **Lower Fold Farm, Rowarth, High Peak, Derbyshire, SK22 1ED**
Contacts: **PHONE (01663) 741471 MOBILE (07775) 842009**

1 BALLYCRACKEN (IRE), 10, b g Flemensfirth (USA)—Cons Dual Sale (IRE) **D. Pearson**

Assistant Trainer: Eileen Pearson

---

502 MISS LINDA PERRATT, East Kilbride
Postal: **North Allerton Farm, East Kilbride, Glasgow, Lanarkshire, G75 8RR**
Contacts: **PHONE (01355) 303425 MOBILE (07931) 306147**
E-MAIL linda.perratt@btinternet.com

1 ANITOPIA, 9, gr g Alflora (IRE)—The Whirlie Weevil **Miss L. A. Perratt**
2 BERBICE (IRE), 9, gr g Acclamation—Pearl Bright (FR) **J. K. McGarrity**
3 DISTANT SUN (USA), 10, b g Distant View (USA)—The Great Flora (USA) **Jackton Racing Club**
4 EBONY CLARETS, 5, b m Kyllachy—Pachanga **Linda Perratt Racing Club**
5 FINDOG, 4, b g Pastoral Pursuits—Night Home (ITY) **J. K. McGarrity**
6 GEANIE MAC (IRE), 5, ch m Needwood Blade—Dixie Evans **J. K. McGarrity**
7 JINKY, 6, b g Noverre (USA)—Aries (GER) **Mr J. Murphy**

MISS LINDA PERRATT - Continued

8 **MYSTICAL KING**, 4, b g Notnowcato—Mystical Ayr (IRE) **Jackton Racing Club**
9 **PITT RIVERS**, 5, br g Vital Equine (IRE)—Silca Boo **Mrs H. F. Perratt**
10 **ROCK CANYON (IRE)**, 5, b g Rock of Gibraltar (IRE)—Tuesday Morning **Mrs H. F. Perratt**
11 **ROYAL STRAIGHT**, 9, ch g Halling (USA)—High Straits **J. K. McGarrity**
12 **SAXONETTE**, 6, b m Piccolo—Solmorin **Mr J. Murphy**
13 **SCHMOOZE (IRE)**, 5, b m One Cool Cat (USA)—If Dubai (USA) **Jackton Racing Club**
14 **SILVER RIME (FR)**, 9, gr g Verglas (IRE)—Severina **J. K. McGarrity**
15 **TADALAVIL**, 9, gr g Clodovil (IRE)—Blandish (USA) **J. K. McGarrity**

THREE-YEAR-OLDS

16 **DARK CRYSTAL**, b f Multiplex—Glitz (IRE) **Mrs H. F. Perratt**

TWO-YEAR-OLDS

17 Gr f 25/3 Zebedee—Mystical Ayr (IRE) (Namid) (13333) **Mrs H. F. Perratt**

Other Owners: Mr B. Atkins, M. Sawers.

Jockey (flat): Tom Eaves, Paul Hanagan, Graham Lee, Phillip Makin. **Jockey (NH):** Brian Hughes, Wilson Renwick.
Conditional: Callum Whillans. **Apprentice:** Ross Smith.

---

503 **MRS AMANDA PERRETT, Pulborough**
Postal: **Coombelands Racing Stables, Pulborough, West Sussex, RH20 1BP**
Contacts: **OFFICE (01798) 873011 HOME (01798) 874894 FAX (01798) 875163**
MOBILE (07803) 088713
E-MAIL aperrett@coombelands-stables.com WEBSITE www.amandaperrett.com

1 **ARCH VILLAIN (IRE)**, 5, b g Arch (USA)—Barzah (IRE) **Mr & Mrs F Cotton,Mr & Mrs P Conway**
2 **BLACK MINSTREL (IRE)**, 5, b g Dylan Thomas (IRE)—Overlook **Mrs A. J. Perrett**
3 **BLUE SURF**, 5, ch g Excellent Art—Wavy Up (IRE) **John Connolly And Partners**
4 **BRAMSHAW (USA)**, 7, gr ro g Langfuhr (CAN)—Milagra (USA) **Mrs A. J. Perrett**
5 **BRAMSHILL LASS**, 5, ch m Notnowcato—Disco Ball **Mrs K. J. L. Hancock**
6 **CZECH IT OUT (IRE)**, 4, b g Oratorio (IRE)—Naval Affair (IRE) **G. D. P. Materna**
7 **EXTRASOLAR**, 4, b g Exceed And Excel (AUS)—Amicable Terms **Odile Griffith & John Connolly**
8 **HARWOODS STAR (IRE)**, 4, b g Danehill Dancer (IRE)—Showbiz (IRE) **Harwoods Racing Club Limited**
9 **LION BEACON**, 4, ch g Beat Hollow—Second of May **Mrs A. J. Chandris**
10 **MOONDAY SUN (USA)**, 5, gr h Mizzen Mast (USA)—Storm Dove (USA) **Moonday Sun Partnership**
11 **OVATORY**, 4, b g Acclamation—Millsini **John Connolly & Odile Griffith**
12 **PENCHESCO (IRE)**, 5, b g Orpen (USA)—Francesca (IRE) **Mrs K. J. L. Hancock**
13 **PIVOTAL SILENCE**, 4, ch f Vita Rosa (JPN)—Tara Moon **M. H. and Mrs G. Tourle**
14 **PRESTO VOLANTE (IRE)**, 6, b g Oratorio (IRE)—
Very Racy (USA) **Mrs S Conway Mr & Mrs M Swayne Mr A Brooke Mrs R Doel**
15 **SABORIDO (USA)**, 8, gr g Dixie Union (USA)—Alexine (ARG) **Mrs A. J. Perrett**
16 **SAUCY MINX (IRE)**, 4, b f Dylan Thomas (IRE)—Market Day **Mr & Mrs F Cotton,Mr & Mrs P Conway**

THREE-YEAR-OLDS

17 **A LEGACY OF LOVE (IRE)**, b f Sea The Stars (IRE)—Nashmiah (IRE) **Mrs B. A. Karn-Smith**
18 **ALZANTI (USA)**, b f Arch (USA)—Proud Fact (USA) **K. Abdullah**
19 **APPROACHING (IRE)**, ch c New Approach (IRE)—Dust Dancer **Bluehills Racing Limited**
20 **ARTFUL ROGUE (IRE)**, b g Excellent Art—Szabo (IRE) **Mr & Mrs F Cotton,Mr & Mrs P Conway**
21 **ARTISTIC FLAME**, b g Archipenko (USA)—Umlilo **Coombelands Racing Syndicate**
22 **ASTRONEREUS (IRE)**, ch c Sea The Stars (IRE)—Marie Rheinberg (GER) **John Connolly & Odile Griffith**
23 **BEST KEPT**, ch c Sakhee's Secret—Ashlinn (IRE) **Coombelands Racing Syndicate 3**
24 **BLACK SHADOW**, b c New Approach (IRE)—Shadow Dancing **A. D. Spence**
25 **CELEBRATORY**, ch f Peintre Celebre (USA)—Inchberry **Woodcote Stud Ltd**
26 **DREAMING BRAVE**, b g Sleeping Indian—Beechnut (IRE) **Coombelands Racing Syndicate 2**
27 **EXCEDO PRAECEDO**, b g Exceed And Excel (AUS)—Merle **John Connolly & Odile Griffith**
28 **FAINTLY**, b c Kitten's Joy (USA)—Tinge **K. Abdullah**
29 **FIELD FORCE**, b c Champs Elysees—Fairy Steps **K. Abdullah**
30 **FIGHTING BACK**, b c Galileo (IRE)—Maroochydore (IRE) **A. D. Spence**
31 **HARWOODS VOLANTE (IRE)**, ch g Kheleyf (USA)—Semiquaver (IRE) **Harwoods Racing Club Limited**
32 B c New Approach (IRE)—Intaaj (IRE)
33 **JELLY FISH**, ch g Observatory (USA)—Grand Coral **K. Abdullah**
34 **KALIFI (USA)**, b br f First Defence (USA)—Out of Reach **K. Abdullah**

MRS AMANDA PERRETT - Continued

35 **LADY BRIGID (IRE)**, b f Holy Roman Emperor (IRE)—Brigids Cross (IRE) **M. H. and Mrs G. Tourle**
36 **PACK LEADER (IRE)**, b g Hurricane Run (IRE)—Bright Enough **G. D. P. Materna**
37 B c Reel Buddy (USA)—Papality **Mrs A. J. Chandris**
38 Ch f Champs Elysees—Second of May **Mrs A. J. Chandris**
39 **SUNNY AGAIN**, ch f Shirocco (GER)—Spotlight **Bluehills Racing Limited**
40 **TEMPLATE (IRE)**, ch g Iffraaj—Sagaing **Mrs R. M. Ward**
41 **TORRID**, ch c Three Valleys (USA)—Western Appeal (USA) **K. Abdullah**

TWO-YEAR-OLDS

42 **BOUNCING CZECH**, b c 28/2 Dandy Man (IRE)—
    Correlandie (USA) (El Corredor (USA)) (100658) **G. D. P. Materna**
43 **CHAPPARACHIK**, b c 18/3 High Chaparral (IRE)—
    Musique Magique (IRE) (Mozart (IRE)) (110000) **John Connolly & Odile Griffith**
44 B c 29/2 Oasis Dream—Double Crossed (Caerleon (USA)) **K. Abdullah**
45 **FLIGHTY FILIA (IRE)**, gr f 7/3 Raven's Pass (USA)—Coventina (IRE) (Daylami (IRE)) (40000) **Cotton, Conway**
46 **FRONT FIVE (IRE)**, b c 7/5 Teofilo (IRE)—Samdaniya (Machiavellian (USA)) (50000) **G. D. P. Materna**
47 **GENTLE PERSUASION**, b f 3/4 Rock of Gibraltar (IRE)—Play Bouzouki (Halling (USA)) (38000) **A. D. Spence**
48 B c 26/3 Nayef (USA)—Dorabella (Dansili) **K. Abdullah**
49 **ISAMOL**, b c 3/2 Intikhab (USA)—Uvinza (Bertolini (USA)) (170000) **John Connolly & Odile Griffith**
50 **LIGHTNING CHARLIE**, b c 8/3 Myboycharlie (IRE)—Lighted Way (Kris) (30000) **Lightning Charlie Partnership**
51 Ch c 23/4 Apotheosis (USA)—Nephetriti Way (Docksider (USA)) **Mrs A. J. Chandris**
52 B c 4/3 Showcasing—Night Symphonie (Cloudings (IRE)) (65000) **A. D. Spence**
53 **OPEN THE RED**, b c 17/2 Lawman (FR)—Acquainted (Shamardal (USA)) (87000) **G. D. P. Materna**
54 B f 25/2 Harmonic Way—Papality (Giant's Causeway (USA)) **Mrs A. J. Chandris**
55 B c 16/3 Rock Hard Ten (USA)—Proud Fact (USA) (Known Fact (USA)) **K. Abdullah**
56 **PROVATO (IRE)**, ch c 20/3 Approve (IRE)—
    Sagemacca (IRE) (Danehill Dancer (IRE)) (42000) **The Provato Partnership**
57 Ch f 12/2 Harmonic Way—Rainbow Way (High Chaparral (IRE)) **Mrs A. J. Chandris**
58 **REST EASY**, b f 3/5 Rip Van Winkle (IRE)—Early Evening (Daylami (IRE)) (4000)
59 B c 1/2 Zamindar (USA)—Rule of Nature (Oasis Dream) **K. Abdullah**
60 Ch f 7/4 Reel Buddy (USA)—Second of May (Lion Cavern (USA))

Other Owners: Mr S. W. Barnett, A. W. Brooke, J. P. Connolly, Mrs S. M. Conway, F. G. Cotton, Mrs S. H. Cotton, Mrs R. J. Doel, Mrs J. M. V. Freeman, Ms O. L. Griffith, Guy Harwood, Mr M. B. Swayne, Mrs A. J. Swayne, Mr M. H. Tourle, Mrs G. O. Tourle.

Assistant Trainer: Mark Perrett

---

504 | MR PAT PHELAN, Epsom
Postal: **Ermyn Lodge, Shepherds Walk, Epsom, Surrey, KT18 6DF**
Contacts: **PHONE (01372) 229014 FAX (01372) 229001 MOBILE (07917) 762781**
E-MAIL **pat.phelan@ermynlodge.com** WEBSITE **www.ermynlodge.com**

1 **ASSEMBLY**, 4, ch g Kyllachy—Constitute (USA) **Epsom Racegoers No.2**
2 **BINT ALZAIN (IRE)**, 5, b m Marju (IRE)—Barconey (IRE) **T. Zachariades**
3 **CELTIC CHARLIE (FR)**, 9, ch g Until Sundown (USA)—India Regalona (USA) **Celtic Contractors Limited**
4 **COUNTESS LOVELACE**, 4, b f Byron—Muwasim (USA) **Mr W. Bocking**
5 **COUP DE GRACE (IRE)**, 5, b g Elusive City (USA)—No Way (IRE) **Mr J. F. Lang**
6 **DELLBUOY**, 5, b g Acclamation—Ruthie **Timesquare Ltd**
7 **DOUBLE U DOT EDE'S**, 5, b g Rock of Gibraltar (IRE)—Reveuse de Jour (IRE) **Ede's (UK) Ltd**
8 **EPSOM SALTS**, 9, b g Josr Algarhoud (USA)—Captive Heart **Epsom Racegoers**
9 **ERMYNTRUDE**, 7, b br m Rock of Gibraltar (IRE)—Ruthie **Mr W. Bocking**
10 **FLEETWOOD NIX**, 4, b f Acclamation—Antediluvian **I. W. Harfitt**
11 **GALLOPING GREEN (IRE)**, 6, b g Ad Valorem (USA)—Gladstone Street (IRE) **G. D. Newton**
12 **PROUTS PUB (IRE)**, 5, b g Catcher In The Rye (IRE)—A Woman In Love **Mr E. Gleeson**
13 **REGGIE PERRIN**, 6, ch g Storming Home—Tecktal (FR) **Ermyn Lodge Stud Limited**
14 **THE WONGA COUP (IRE)**, 7, b g Northern Afleet (USA)—Quichesterbahn (USA) **Celtic Contractors Limited**
15 **YOUNG DOTTIE**, 8, b m Desert Sun—Auntie Dot Com **Chelgate Public Relations Ltd**

THREE-YEAR-OLDS

16 **CHARLEYS ANGEL**, b f Myboycharlie (IRE)—Muwasim (USA) **Epsom Racegoers No.3**
17 **EDE'S THE BUSINESS**, ch f Halling (USA)—My Amalie (IRE) **Ede's (UK) Ltd**
18 **FLYING KYTE**, b br g Pastoral Pursuits—Red Kyte **Timesquare Ltd**
19 **GUESSHOWMUCHILOVEU (IRE)**, b c Cape Cross (IRE)—Overruled (IRE) **Miss H. Loder**

MR PAT PHELAN - Continued

Other Owners: Ermyn Lodge Stud, Mr R. G. Mappley, Mr Tony Smith, Timesquare Ltd, Mr P. Wheatley.

Jockey (NH): Colin Bolger. **Amateur:** Mr. Freddie Mitchell.

---

505 **MR RICHARD PHILLIPS, Moreton-in-Marsh**
Postal: Adlestrop Stables, Adlestrop, Moreton-in-Marsh, Gloucestershire, GL56 0YN
Contacts: PHONE (01608) 658710 FAX (01608) 658713 MOBILE (07774) 832715
E-MAIL info@richardphillipsracing.com WEBSITE www.richardphillipsracing.com

1 **ARCTIC CHIEF**, 4, b g Sleeping Indian—Neiges Eternelles (FR) **Too Many Chiefs**
2 **ATA BOY (IRE)**, 8, br g Key of Luck (USA)—Atalina (FR) **The Adlestrop Club**
3 **CALL ME EMMA (IRE)**, 6, b m Beneficial—Clody Girl (IRE) **Upthorpe Racing**
4 **CATKIN COPSE**, 6, b m Alflora (IRE)—Run Tiger (IRE) **Mrs S. C. Welch**
5 4, B f Kayf Tara—Ceoperk (IRE) **R. T. Phillips**
6 **CRYSTAL SWING**, 7, b g Trade Fair—Due West **Enjoy The Journey**
7 **FAIR BREEZE**, 7, b m Trade Fair—Soft Touch (IRE) **The Summer Club**
8 **FIRE TOWER**, 6, ch m Firebreak—Lamper's Light **The Firebirds**
9 **IFITS A FIDDLE**, 5, b m Kalanisi (IRE)—Fiddling Again **Mrs E. C. Roberts**
10 **JUST BENNY (IRE)**, 9, b g Beneficial—Artic Squaw (IRE) **Upthorpe Racing**
11 4, Gr br g Rail Link—Karsiyaka (IRE) **Nut Club Partnership**
12 **LISHEEN HILL (IRE)**, 8, b g Witness Box (USA)—Lady Lamb (IRE) **The Aspirationals**
13 **LUCKY THIRTEEN**, 6, b g Passing Glance—Lingua Franca **Mr D. Stockdale**
14 6, B m Flemensfirth (USA)—Mandys Native (IRE) **Dozen Dreamers Partnership**
15 **MASTER VINTAGE**, 6, b g Kayf Tara—What A Vintage (IRE) **The Someday's Here Racing Partnership**
16 **MISS LILLY LEWIS**, 6, b m Sir Harry Lewis (USA)—Theme Arena **The Pink Ladies**
17 **MISTER NEWBY (IRE)**, 8, b g Oscar (IRE)—Sallie's Girl (IRE) **C. Pocock**
18 **MOTOU (FR)**, 9, b g Astarabad (USA)—Picoletta (FR) **The Summer Club**
19 **MOVEMENTNEVERLIES**, 4, ch f Medicean—Frabjous **Mr Nicholas Roberts & Mrs E Roberts**
20 **MR TINGLE**, 10, br g Beat All (USA)—Dianthus (IRE) **Mr & Mrs W. Brogan-Higgins & Gryffindor**
21 **NO COMPROMISE**, 5, b m Avonbridge—Highly Liquid **The Summer Club**
22 **OCEAN POWER (IRE)**, 4, b g Papal Bull—Petticoat Power (IRE) **Mr W. McLuskey**
23 **ORGAN MORGAN**, 4, b g Dylan Thomas (IRE)—Abide (FR) **C Humber & SM Smith**
24 **PRINCE DU SEUIL (FR)**, 11, b g Lucky Dream (FR)—Hermione III (FR) **Mrs E. A. Prowting**
25 **RAFAAF (IRE)**, 6, b g Royal Applause—Sciunfona (USA) **J. A. Gent**
26 **RICH BUDDY**, 8, b g Kayf Tara—Silver Gyre (IRE) **Mrs E. A. Prowting**
27 **SHEELBEWHATSHEELBE (IRE)**, 4, b f Oscar (IRE)—Cheerymount (IRE) **B. J. Duckett**
28 **THORNTON ALICE**, 9, b m Kayf Tara—Lindrick Lady (IRE) **The Listeners**
29 **VINAIGRETTE**, 5, b m Kayf Tara—What A Vintage (IRE) **The Someday's Here Racing Partnership**
30 **VIVA RAFA (IRE)**, 4, b g Scorpion (IRE)—Back To Stay (IRE) **Ms F. Baxter**
31 **WHICHEVER**, 8, ch m Where Or When (IRE)—Pips Way (IRE) **Upthorpe Racing**

Other Owners: Mr C. A. J. Allan, Ms K. M. Anderson, J. E. Barnes, Mr J. R. Brown, Mr E. G. Brown, Mr J. E. S. Colling, Lady S. Davis, Mrs S. J. Harvey, Mr C. M. Humber, Mrs H. M. Nixseaman, M. T. Phillips, Mr N. W. Roberts, S. M. Smith, Dr E. D. Theodore.

Conditional: Daniel Hiskett.

---

506 **MISS IMOGEN PICKARD, Leominster**
Postal: The Granary, Sodgeley Stables, Kingsland, Leominster, Herefordshire, HR6 9PY
Contacts: MOBILE (07884) 437720
E-MAIL bundlepickardracing@yahoo.co.uk

1 **COIN OF THE REALM (IRE)**, 9, b g Galileo (IRE)—Common Knowledge **G. Byard**
2 **JAUNTY DOVE**, 12, b m Atraf—Flossy Dove **Mrs M. J. Wilson**
3 **MISTER FIZZ**, 6, b g Sulamani (IRE)—Court Champagne **Mrs M. J. Wilson**
4 **NINNY NOODLE**, 4, b f Proclamation (IRE)—Court Champagne
5 **PRIVATE JONES**, 5, br g Trade Fair—Dafne **A Bit Of Fun**

Other Owners: Miss S. Bather, Mr N. R. Hodge, Mr G. Provost, A. P. Rogers.

Amateur: Mr Jonny Flook.

507 MR DAVID PIPE, Wellington

Postal: **Pond House, Nicholashayne, Wellington, Somerset, TA21 9QY**
Contacts: **PHONE (01884) 840715 FAX (01884) 841343**
E-MAIL **david@davidpipe.com** WEBSITE **www.davidpipe.com**

1 **AINSI FIDELES (FR)**, 4, ch g Dream Well (FR)—Loya Lescribaa (FR) **Mr Simon Munir & Mr Isaac Souede**
2 **ALDERLUCK (IRE)**, 11, ch g Alderbrook—Cecelia's Charm (IRE) **Mrs C. J. Rayner**
3 **ALL FORCE MAJEURE (FR)**, 4, gr g Dom Alco (FR)—
                                        Naiade du Moulin (FR) **Professor Caroline Tisdall & Bryan Drew**
4 **AMIGO (FR)**, 7, b g Ballingarry (IRE)—Allez Y (FR) **A. L. Cohen & Willsford Racing**
5 **ARAB LEAGUE (IRE)**, 9, b g Dubai Destination (USA)—Johnny And Clyde (USA) **S. M. Mercer**
6 **ARIBO D'ALBAIN (FR)**, 4, ch g Dom Alco (FR)—Kandy de Vonnas (FR) **Mr R. J. H. Geffen**
7 **AZZA (FR)**, 4, b br f Great Pretender (IRE)—Indecise (FR) **Prof C. Tisdall**
8 **BALGARRY (FR)**, 7, ch g Ballingarry (IRE)—Marie de Motreff (FR) **Brocade Racing**
9 **BALLYNAGOUR (IRE)**, 8, b g Shantou (USA)—Simply Deep (IRE) **A. Stennett**
10 **BALTIMORE ROCK (IRE)**, 5, b g Tiger Hill (IRE)—La Vita E Bella (IRE) **R. S. Brookhouse**
11 **BARTON STACEY (IRE)**, 9, b g Snurge—Life's Treasure (IRE) **Pipe Monkees**
12 5, B g Presenting—Be My Belle (IRE) **M. C. Denmark**
13 **BEL HUGO (FR)**, 10, b br g Astarabad (USA)—La Pitchoun (FR) **Mr J. T. Chalmers**
14 4, B f Kalanisi (IRE)—Belle Magello (FR) **Mr R. J. H. Geffen**
15 **BLADOUN (FR)**, 6, gr g Smadoun (FR)—Blabliramic (FR) **H. M. W. Clifford**
16 **BOIS DES AIGLES (FR)**, 5, gr g Stormy River (FR)—Silver Fun (FR) **Prof C. Tisdall**
17 **BORDER BREAKER (IRE)**, 5, br g Indian Danehill (IRE)—Flying Answer (IRE) **Jimmy Hack Racing Partners 1**
18 **BROADWAY BUFFALO (IRE)**, 6, ch g Broadway Flyer (USA)—Benbradagh Vard (IRE) **The Broadway Partnership**
19 **BUDDY BOLERO (IRE)**, 8, b g Accordion—Quinnsboro Ice (IRE) **M. C. Denmark**
20 **BYGONES SOVEREIGN (IRE)**, 8, b g Old Vic—Miss Hollygrove (IRE) **Arnie & Alan Kaplan**
21 **CABORA (FR)**, 6, ch m Prince Kirk (FR)—Cabiria (FR) **Exors of the Late Mr D. A. Johnson**
22 4, B g Kayf Tara—Caitlin Rose (IRE) **Mr R. J. H. Geffen**
23 **CENTASIA**, 7, b m Presenting—Cent Prime **R. S. Brookhouse**
24 **CHIC THEATRE (IRE)**, 4, gr g King's Theatre—La Reine Chic (FR) **Mr B. J. C. Drew**
25 4, Ch f Beneficial—Christdalo (IRE) **M. C. Pipe**
26 **CLOSE HOUSE**, 7, b g Generous (IRE)—Not Now Nellie **R. S. Brookhouse**
27 **CONSIGLIERE (FR)**, 11, ch g Trempolino (USA)—Gianna Nannini (ITY) **Mr E. A. P. Scouller**
28 **COUNT DANILO (IRE)**, 5, b g Zagreb (USA)—Miss Bobby Bennett **B. A. Kilpatrick**
29 **DAN BREEN (IRE)**, 9, b g Mull of Kintyre (USA)—Kunuz **Mr Stuart & Simon Mercer**
30 **DAVY DOUBT (IRE)**, 5, b g Kalanisi (IRE)—Trompe L'oeil (IRE) **R. S. Brookhouse**
31 **DECOY (FR)**, 8, b g Della Francesca (USA)—Vagualame (FR) **Stefanos Stefanou**
32 **DELL' ARCA (IRE)**, 5, b g Sholokhov (IRE)—Daisy Belle (GER) **Prof C. Tisdall**
33 6, Ch h Tobougg (IRE)—Denica (IRE) **Skeltools Ltd**
34 **DIAMOND LIFE**, 8, b g Silver Patriarch—Myrrh **M. C. Denmark**
35 5, B g King's Theatre (IRE)—Disallowed (IRE) **M. C. Denmark**
36 **DOCTOR HARPER (IRE)**, 6, b g Presenting—Supreme Dreamer (IRE) **The Johnson Family**
37 **DUKES ART**, 8, b g Bachelor Duke (USA)—Creme Caramel (USA) **Mr J. Diver**
38 **DYNASTE (FR)**, 8, gr g Martaline—Bellissima de Mai (FR) **A. J. White**
39 **EDMUND KEAN (IRE)**, 7, b g Old Vic—Baliya (IRE) **Walters Plant Hire & James & Jean Potter**
40 **FAMOUSANDFEARLESS (IRE)**, 6, b g Presenting—Clandestine **The Bravo Partnership**
41 **FRANKLIN ROOSEVELT (IRE)**, 8, b g Beneficial—Glen's Gale (IRE) **M. C. Denmark**
42 **GARRYLEIGH (IRE)**, 7, b g Statue of Liberty (USA)—Hunter's Valley **Brocade Racing**
43 **GEVREY CHAMBERTIN (FR)**, 6, gr g Dom Alco (FR)—Fee Magic (FR) **Roger Stanley & Yvonne Reynolds III**
44 **GOTHAM CITY (IRE)**, 5, b g September Storm (GER)—Open Miss **Mr C. N. C. Denmark**
45 **GOULANES (IRE)**, 8, b g Mr Combustible (IRE)—Rebolgiane (IRE) **R. S. Brookhouse**
46 **GRANDS CRUS (FR)**, 9, gr g Dom Alco (FR)—Fee Magic (FR) **Roger Stanley & Yvonne Reynolds III**
47 **GREAT CHOICE (IRE)**, 5, b g Westerner—Granuale (IRE) **Mrs J. Gerard-Pearse**
48 **GUESS AGAIN (IRE)**, 9, b g Milan—Guess Twice **M. C. Denmark**
49 **HEATH HUNTER (IRE)**, 7, b g Shantou (USA)—Deep Supreme (IRE) **The Heath Hunter Partnership**
50 **HELLFIRE CLUB**, 11, b g Overbury (IRE)—Tapua Taranata (IRE) **M. C. Denmark**
51 **HIS EXCELLENCY (IRE)**, 6, ch g King's Best (USA)—Road Harbour (USA) **Mrs J. Tracey**
52 **HOME RUN (GER)**, 6, ch g Motivator—Hold Off (IRE) **W. F. Frewen**
53 **JIGSAW PUZZLE (IRE)**, 8, b g Presenting—Star Child (GER) **M. C. Denmark**
54 **JUNIOR**, 11, ch g Singspiel (IRE)—For More (FR) **Middleham Park Racing LI**
55 **KATKEAU (FR)**, 7, b g Kotky Bleu (FR)—Levine (FR) **Prof C Tisdall, Mr A J Gent, Mr R Wilkin**
56 **KEEP THE CASH (IRE)**, 6, b g Oscar (IRE)—Waterloo Ball (IRE) **Kelly, Pipe & Fawkhandles**
57 **KILRYE (IRE)**, 7, b g Catcher In The Rye (USA)—Kiladante (IRE) **A. J. White & Mrs A. Underhill**
58 **KINGS PALACE (IRE)**, 6, b g King's Theatre—Sarahs Quay (IRE) **Drew, George & The Johnson Family**
59 **KNIGHT OF NOIR (IRE)**, 5, b g Winged Love (IRE)—At Dawn (IRE) **H. M. W. Clifford**
60 **LEADER OF THE GANG**, 8, b g Karinga Bay—Material Girl **M. C. Denmark**

MR DAVID PIPE - Continued

61 **LEGACY GOLD (IRE)**, 6, b m Gold Well—Durgams Delight (IRE) **R. S. Brookhouse**
62 **LOLA GALLI**, 6, br m Old Vic—Tahoe (IRE) **M. B. Jones**
63 **MAKADAMIA**, 5, b m Kahyasi—Makounji (FR) **R. B. Waley-Cohen**
64 **MARTIAL LAW (IRE)**, 8, ch g Galileo (IRE)—Tree Tops **Mr Stuart & Simon Mercer**
65 **MASSANNIE (IRE)**, 6, b m Dr Massini (IRE)—Bathwick Annie **H. M. W. Clifford**
66 **MASTER OVERSEER (IRE)**, 11, b g Old Vic—Crogeen Lass **Brocade Racing**
67 **MILOR DE LA BORIE (FR)**, 5, gr g Turgeon (USA)—Trop Tard (FR) **Prof Caroline Tisdall With R Wilkin**
68 **MOLLY OSCAR (IRE)**, 8, b m Oscar (IRE)—Bishop's Folly **Mrs S. Clifford**
69 **MONCARNO**, 4, b g Lucarno (USA)—Sparkling Jewel **David & Elaine Long**
70 5, B g Kayf Tara—Monsignorita (IRE) **M. C. Denmark**
71 **MOST ELIGIBLE**, 7, b g Pursuit of Love—Danzig's Heiress **Skeltools Ltd**
72 **MR TRILBY (IRE)**, 7, b g Millenary—Bamji (IRE) **M. C. Pipe**
73 **MY BROTHER SYLVEST**, 8, b g Bach (IRE)—Senna da Silva **Teddington Racing Club**
74 **MYSTICAL FLAME (IRE)**, 5, b m Flemensfirth (USA)—Lizzie Bathwick (IRE) **Mrs S. Clifford**
75 **NO SECRETS (IRE)**, 10, b g King's Theatre (IRE)—Happy Native (IRE) **M. C. Denmark**
76 **NOTUS DE LA TOUR (FR)**, 8, b g Kutub (IRE)—Ridiyla (IRE) **D Bradshaw,J Dale,P Deal,J Smee,W Walsh**
77 **OBISTAR (FR)**, 4, b g Astarabad (USA)—Vallee du Luy (FR) **Brocade Racing**
78 **OFF THE WALL (IRE)**, 7, ch g Presenting—Ginger Bar (IRE) **M. C. Denmark**
79 **ON KHEE**, 7, b m Sakhee (USA)—Star Precision **Palatinate Thoroughbred Racing Limited**
80 **OUR CHIEF (IRE)**, 5, b g Old Vic—Torsha (IRE) **The Johnson Family**
81 **OUR FATHER (IRE)**, 8, gr g Shantou (USA)—Rosepan (IRE) **The Ives & Johnson Families**
82 **PARTY GIRLS (FR)**, 6, b m Astarabad (USA)—Canadiane (FR) **M. C. Pipe**
83 **PLEASANT COMPANY (IRE)**, 6, b g Presenting—Katie Flame (IRE) **M. C. Denmark**
84 **POOLE MASTER**, 9, ch g Fleetwood (IRE)—Juste Belle (FR) **G. D. Thompson**
85 **PRASINA RUSSATA (IRE)**, 7, b g Accordion—Henrietta (IRE) **B. A. Kilpatrick**
86 **PRIDEOFTHECASTLE (IRE)**, 7, b g Waky Nao—Park's Pet (IRE) **Mr B. J. C. Drew**
87 **PROBLEMA TIC (FR)**, 8, b g Kapgarde (FR)—Atreide (FR) **Mrs J. Tracey**
88 **PUNJABI**, 11, b g Komaite (USA)—Competa **R. C. Tooth**
89 **QALINAS (FR)**, 7, gr g Malinas (GER)—Tabletiere (FR) **Middleham Park Racing XX & M C Pipe**
90 **RED SEVENTY**, 5, b g Sakhee (USA)—Dimakya (USA) **T. Neill**
91 **RED SHERLOCK**, 5, ch g Shirocco (GER)—Lady Cricket (FR) **The Johnson Family**
92 **RONALDO DES MOTTES (FR)**, 9, b g Rifapour (IRE)—Gemma (FR) **K & D Ives**
93 5, Ch g Presenting—Roxbury **M. C. Denmark**
94 **ROYAL PEAK (IRE)**, 7, b g Bach (IRE)—Dante's Ville (IRE) **Robert Aplin & M C Pipe**
95 5, B g Halling (USA)—Ryde On **M. C. Denmark**
96 **SAINT JOHN HENRY (FR)**, 4, b g Saint des Saints (FR)—Noceane (FR) **Mr B. J. C. Drew**
97 **SALUT FLO (FR)**, 9, b g Saint des Saints (FR)—Royale Marie (FR) **A. Stennett**
98 **SEVEN NATION ARMY (IRE)**, 5, gr g Rock of Gibraltar (IRE)—Crepe Ginger (IRE) **R. S. Brookhouse**
99 **SHAKALAKA (IRE)**, 8, b g Montjeu (IRE)—Sweet Times **Mr A. Wichser**
100 **SHAKING HANDS (IRE)**, 10, b g Bach (IRE)—Picton Lass **Brocade Racing**
101 **SHALLOW BAY**, 7, b g Shamardal (USA)—Yawl **Mr P. J. McGee**
102 **SHOEGAZER (IRE)**, 9, b g Bach (IRE)—American Native (IRE) **H. M. W. Clifford**
103 **SHOTAVODKA (IRE)**, 8, ch g Alderbrook—Another Vodka (IRE) **Mrs J. Gerard-Pearse**
104 **SIVRON (IRE)**, 6, b g Laveron—Maille Sissi (FR) **Prof C. Tisdall**
105 **SMILES FOR MILES (IRE)**, 6, b g Oscar (IRE)—Native Kin (IRE) **Prof C. Tisdall**
106 5, Br g Definite Article—Snipe Hunt (IRE) **M. C. Denmark**
107 **STANDING OVATION (IRE)**, 7, b g Presenting—Glittering Star (IRE) **The Bravo Partnership**
108 **STAR OF SALFORD**, 5, b m Hernando (FR)—City of Angels **R. S. Brookhouse**
109 **STREET ENTERTAINER (IRE)**, 7, br g Danehill Dancer (USA)—Opera Ridge (FR) **Barnett, Manasseh & Partners**
110 **SWING BILL (FR)**, 13, gr g Grey Risk (FR)—Melodie Royale (FR) **Halewood International Ltd**
111 **SWING BOWLER**, 7, b m Galileo (IRE)—Lady Cricket (FR) **Mr K. Alexander**
112 5, B g Definite Article—Talk of Rain (FR) **M. C. Denmark**
113 **TANERKO EMERY (FR)**, 8, b g Lavirco (GER)—Frequence (FR) **Walters Plant Hire Ltd Egan Waste Ltd**
114 **THE DARLING BOY**, 9, b g Medicean—Silver Top Hat (USA) **The Hon Mrs D. Hulse**
115 **THE LIQUIDATOR**, 6, b g Overbury (IRE)—Alikat (IRE) **R. S. Brookhouse**
116 **THE PACKAGE**, 11, br g Kayf Tara—Ardent Bride **The Johnson Family**
117 **THE WEALERDEALER (IRE)**, 7, b g Vinnie Roe (IRE)—Lantern Liz (IRE) **Govier & Brown**
118 **THOMAS JUNIOR (FR)**, 5, b g Dylan Thomas (IRE)—Smiling **Walters Plant Hire Ltd**
119 **TOGIAK (IRE)**, 7, b g Azamour (IRE)—Hawksbill Special (IRE) **Omega**
120 **TOO GENEROUS**, 6, b m Generous (IRE)—Little Feat **A. E. Frost**
121 **TOP GAMBLE (IRE)**, 6, ch g Presenting—Zeferina (IRE) **Walters Plant Hire & James & Jean Potter**
122 5, Ch g Presenting—Top Her Up (IRE) **M. C. Denmark**
123 **TOP WOOD (FR)**, 7, ch g Kotky Bleu (FR)—Heure Bleu (FR) **Lady H. J. Clarke**
124 **TULLYESKER HILL (IRE)**, 5, b g Shantou (USA)—Couture Daisy (IRE) **Mr B. J. C. Drew**

MR DAVID PIPE - Continued

125 **UN TEMPS POUR TOUT (IRE),** 5, b g Robin des Champs (FR)—
Rougedespoir (FR) **Professor Caroline Tisdall & Bryan Drew**
126 **VAZARO DELAFAYETTE (FR),** 5, bl g Robin des Champs (FR)—Etoile du Merze (FR) **Mr B. J. C. Drew**
127 **VIEUX LION ROUGE (FR),** 5, ch g Sabiango (GER)—Indecise (FR) **Prof Caroline Tisdall & Mr John Gent**
128 **VIF ARGENT (FR),** 5, b g Dom Alco (FR)—Formosa (FR) **Stefanos Stefanou**
129 **VILJA (IRE),** 5, ch m Bach (IRE)—Dapples (IRE) **B. A. Kilpatrick**
130 **VOLT FACE (FR),** 5, ch g Kapgarde (FR)—Jourenuit (FR) **R. S. Brookhouse**
131 **WATERUNDER (IRE),** 7, br g Vinnie Roe (IRE)—Be My Katie (IRE) **Mrs S. Clifford**
132 **WEATHER BABE,** 6, b m Storming Home—Bathwick Babe (IRE) **H. M. W. Clifford**
133 **WESTERN DIVA (IRE),** 5, b m Westerner—Duck 'n' Dive (IRE) **R. S. Brookhouse**
134 **WESTERN WARHORSE (IRE),** 6, b g Westerner—An Banog (IRE) **R. S. Brookhouse**
135 **WETAK (FR),** 7, b g Antarctique (IRE)—Rhapsodie (FR) **T. Neill**

Other Owners: Mr R. J. Aplin, Mr J. Barnett, Mr D. M. Bradshaw, Mrs R. C. V. Brook, Mr G. R. Broom, Mrs A. E. M. Broom, G. S. Brown, Mr S. W. Buckley, Exors of the Late Mr P. A. Byrne, A. L. Cohen, Mr S. F. Coton, Mr M. J. Cueto, J. S. Dale, P. A. Deal, Egan Waste Services Ltd, J. T. Ennis, Mrs L. A. Farquhar, J. A. Gent, Mr P. George, Mr P. Govier, Mr P. F. Govier, R. B. Gray, J. J. Hathorn, Mrs F. K. Hathorn, Mr K. R. Ives, Mrs D. A. Johnson, Mr S. D. Johnson, Mr R. Jones, Alan Kaplan, N. R. Kelly, D. J. Long, Mrs E. Long, Mr D. C. Manasseh, Mr S. S. Mercer, S. E. Munir, T. S. Palin, Mr D. J. Peel, Mr M. Peterlechner, J. E. Potter, Mrs M. J. Potter, Mr A. T. Powell, M. Prince, D. J. Reid, Mrs Y. J. Reynolds, Mr P. S. Russell, Mr J. Smee, Mr I. Souede, R. K. Stanley, Mrs A. Underhill, W. T. Walsh, Mr R. C. Wilkin, Willsford Racing Ltd.

Assistant Trainer: Mr M. C. Pipe C.B.E.

Jockey (NH): Mikey Ennis, Hadden Frost, Timmy Murphy, Conor O'Farrell, Tom Scudamore.
Conditional: Tom Bellamy, Kieron Edgar, Anthony Fox. **Amateur:** Mr Ed Barrett, Mr Michael Heard, Mr David Noonan.

---

508 **MR TIM PITT, Market Drayton**
Postal: **Helshaw Grange, Warrant Road, Stoke Heath, Market Drayton, Shropshire, TF9 2JP**
Contacts: **PHONE (01630) 639883 FAX (01630) 639883 MOBILE (07917) 541341**
E-MAIL timjoelpitt@aol.com WEBSITE www.timpittracing.com

1 **AN CAT DUBH (IRE),** 5, b g One Cool Cat (USA)—Bella Estella (GER) **Mr P. E. Wildes**
2 **DARK RANGER,** 8, b g Where Or When (IRE)—Dark Raider (IRE) **Recycled Products Limited**
3 **FIRST WARNING,** 4, b g Rail Link—Tricked **Mr P. E. Wildes**
4 **HEJAZ (IRE),** 4, ch g Manduro (GER)—Halawanda (IRE) **Miss E. Watkinson**
5 **INTREPID (IRE),** 4, b g Invincible Spirit (IRE)—Imiloa (USA) **Mr J. Roberts**
6 **PEARL SPICE (IRE),** 4, ch g Dalakhani (IRE)—Cinnamon Rose (USA) **Decadent Racing**
7 **PILGRIMS REST (IRE),** 5, ch g Rock of Gibraltar (IRE)—Holly Blue **Wildehall Bloodstock Limited**
8 **SERGIO'S SON (IRE),** 4, b g Zamindar (USA)—Mail Express (IRE) **Saintly Racing**
9 **SIR MAXIMILIAN (IRE),** 5, b g Royal Applause—Nebraska Lady (IRE) **Mr P. E. Wildes**

THREE-YEAR-OLDS

10 **BELLE CAROLINE (IRE),** b f Street Sense (USA)—Ebaraya (IRE) **Mrs C. J. Wildes**
11 **CAPTAIN MYLES (IRE),** ch g Captain Rio—Untimely **Mr P. E. Wildes**
12 **CHORLTON MANOR (IRE),** b g Kheleyf (USA)—Pearl of The Sea (IRE) **Mr P. E. Wildes**
13 **DARK TSARINA (IRE),** b f Soviet Star (USA)—Dark Raider (IRE) **Recycled Products Limited**
14 **EMERALD BREEZE (IRE),** b f Tagula (IRE)—Rebel Aclaim (USA) **Decadent Racing II**
15 **ENNISCORTHY MYLES (USA),** b g Forestry (USA)—Sans Reward (USA) **Mr P. E. Wildes**
16 B f Tobougg (IRE)—Maidenhair (IRE) **Saintly Racing**
17 **MINNIE MAGIC (IRE),** b f Manduro (GER)—Amarice **Mrs C. J. Wildes**
18 **ONE CHANCE (IRE),** b f Invincible Spirit (IRE)—Towards (USA) **Recycled Products Limited**
19 **SECOND OF DECEMBER (IRE),** ch g Duke of Marmalade (IRE)—
Coquette Rouge (IRE) **Wildehall Bloodstock Limited**
20 **VINEGAR HILL BOY (IRE),** b g Oratorio (IRE)—Lovealoch (IRE) **Mr P. E. Wildes**
21 **WILDES (IRE),** b g Manduro (GER)—Balloura (USA) **Mr P. E. Wildes**

TWO-YEAR-OLDS

22 B br c 23/4 Kodiac—Bobby Jane (Diktat) (15485) **Wildehall Bloodstock Limited**
23 **CALCULATOR (FR),** b c 1/3 Siyouni (FR)—Addition (FR) (Numerous (USA)) (27874) **Mr P. E. Wildes**
24 B c 19/3 Zamindar (USA)—Glorious Dreams (USA) (Honour And Glory (USA)) **Mr J. O'Donnell**
25 Ch f 23/1 Dutch Art—Mookhlesa (Marju (IRE)) (26666) **Wildehall Bloodstock Limited**
26 B f 26/3 Sakhee's Secret—Numerus Clausus (FR) (Numerous (USA)) (13549) **Mr P. E. Wildes**

MR TIM PITT - Continued

27 Ch c 28/1 Compton Place—Really Ransom (Red Ransom (USA)) (39047) **Wildehall Bloodstock Limited**
28 B c 14/4 Bushranger (IRE)—Triple Zero (IRE) (Raise A Grand (IRE)) (12775) **Mr P. E. Wildes**

Other Owners: J. Burke, Mr C. B. Hills, Mr D. A. Mccormick, T. Pitt, Mr S. E. Sangster.

Jockey (flat): Stevie Donohoe. **Jockey (NH):** Dougie Costello.

509
MR CHARLES POGSON, Newark
Postal: **Allamoor Farm, Mansfield Road, Farnsfield, Nottinghamshire, NG22 8HZ**
Contacts: **PHONE (01623) 882275 MOBILE (07977) 016155**

1 **ALL FOR LILY,** 5, b m Alflora (IRE)—Who Let The Foxout **C. T. Pogson**
2 **AUDACIOUS,** 6, b g Motivator—Flash of Gold **C. T. Pogson**
3 **COUNTERSIGN,** 5, b g Authorized (IRE)—Circle of Love **C. T. Pogson**
4 **CUSHEEN BRIDGE (IRE),** 6, b h Oscar (IRE)—One Hell Ofa Woman **Wordingham Plant Hire**
5 **HOPEAND,** 9, b m King's Theatre (IRE)—Land of Glory **C. T. Pogson**
6 **KAYFTON PETE,** 8, b g Kayf Tara—Jonchee (FR) **Wordingham Plant Hire & Partner**
7 **MILAN OF HOPE (IRE),** 7, b g Milan—Miss Bertaine (IRE) **C. T. Pogson**
8 **MONDO CANE (IRE),** 7, b g Beneficial—La Vita E Bella (FR) **C. T. Pogson**
9 **NOBLE WITNESS (IRE),** 11, b g Witness Box (USA)—Jennas Pride (IRE) **Wordingham Plant Hire & Partner**
10 **WORDY'S BOY,** 9, b g Kayf Tara—Wordy's Wonder **Wordingham Plant Hire**

Other Owners: P. L. Wordingham, Mrs P. A. Wordingham.

Assistant Trainer: Adam Pogson

Jockey (NH): Adam Pogson.

510
MR NICHOLAS POMFRET, Tilton-on-the-Hill
Postal: **Red Lodge Farm, Marefield Lane, Tilton-on-the-Hill, Leicester, Leicestershire, LE7 9LJ**
Contacts: **PHONE (01162) 597537 MOBILE (07885) 598810**

1 **FIRST LAD,** 7, ch g First Trump—Intrepid Gal **J. N. Cheatle**

511
MR JONATHAN PORTMAN, Upper Lambourn
Postal: **Whitcoombe House Stables, Upper Lambourn, Hungerford, Berkshire, RG17 8RA**
Contacts: **PHONE (01488) 73894 FAX (01488) 72952 MOBILE (07798) 824513**
E-MAIL jonathan@jonathanportmanracing.com WEBSITE www.jonathanportmanracing.com

1 **ANNECDOTE,** 4, b f Lucky Story (USA)—May Fox **Tom Edwards & Partners**
2 **BALMORAL CASTLE,** 5, b g Royal Applause—Mimiteh (USA) **J. G. B. Portman**
3 **BRAVE HELIOS,** 4, b g High Chaparral (IRE)—Renowned (IRE) **Mrs J. A. Watts**
4 **CUNNING ACT,** 6, ch g Act One—Saffron Fox **M. J. Vandenberghe**
5 **HALLINGHAM,** 4, b g Halling (USA)—In Luck **The Ladies Of The Manor Syndicate**
6 **JEBRIL (FR),** 4, b g Astronomer Royal (USA)—Happy Clapper **Mr L. Raissi**
7 **JOE PACKET,** 7, ch g Joe Bear (IRE)—Costa Packet (IRE) **P. Moulton**
8 **KYLEAKIN LASS,** 5, b m Kyllachy—Local Fancy **C.R. Lambourne, M. Forbes, D. Losse**
9 **LEAD THE WAY,** 4, b f Indian Haven—Way To The Stars **Tom Edwards & Partners**
10 **MONSIEUR RIEUSSEC,** 4, bl g Halling (USA)—Muscovado (USA) **Mr J. T. Habershon-Butcher**
11 **MR PYRAMUS,** 6, b g Act One—Eiszeit (GER) **Mr J. T. Habershon-Butcher**
12 **NOW WHAT,** 7, ch m Where Or When (IRE)—Vallauris **Mrs S. J. Portman**
13 **PASAKA BOY,** 4, ch g Haafhd—Shesha Bear **RWH Partnership**
14 **PLAY STREET,** 5, ch m Tobougg (IRE)—Zoena **A. R. Boswood**
15 **TREGERETH (IRE),** 4, b f Footstepsinthesand—Ringmoor Down **Prof C. D. Green**
16 **UNCLE PETTIT (IRE),** 6, b br g Heron Island (IRE)—Special Ballot (IRE) **A. R. Boswood**
17 **ZEN FACTOR,** 9, b g Josr Algarhoud (USA)—Zabelina (USA) **Mr J. T. Habershon-Butcher**
18 **ZINNOBAR,** 4, gr f Ishiguru (USA)—Demolition Jo **Prof C. D. Green**

THREE-YEAR-OLDS

19 B f Azamour (IRE)—Akarita (IRE) **Soho Partnership**
20 **ARCHIEBEAU,** gr g Archipenko (USA)—Si Belle (IRE)

MR JONATHAN PORTMAN - Continued

21 **ASTRAL ROSE,** b f Pastoral Pursuits—Rosapenna (IRE) **C.R. Lambourne, M. Forbes, D. Losse**
22 **BENOORDENHOUT (IRE),** br g Footstepsinthesand—Tara Too (IRE) **Prof C. D. Green**
23 **CLASSIC MISSION,** ch g Bahamian Bounty—Triple Cee (IRE) **David & Gwyn Joseph**
24 **CONNAUGHT WATER (IRE),** b c Aussie Rules (USA)—Chingford (IRE) **Prof C. D. Green**
25 **CUECA (FR),** b f Country Reel (USA)—Costa Packet (IRE) **Stuart McPhee & Partners**
26 **FENELLA FOGHORN,** b f Elnadim (USA)—Bundle Up (USA) **Mr D. Redvers**
27 **FERNGROVE (USA),** gr g Rockport Harbor (USA)—Lucky Pipit **Mr J. T. Habershon-Butcher**
28 **FLY A KITE,** b g Assertive—High Bird (IRE) **Lady Whent**
29 **JACK BEAR,** b c Joe Bear (IRE)—Colins Lady (FR) **Joe Bear Racing**
30 **MOLLASSES,** b f Authorized (IRE)—Muscovado (USA) **Mrs J. Wigan**
31 **NELSON OF THE NILE,** b g Mount Nelson—Appleby **Looks A Bright Prospect Racing**
32 **PETALE NOIR,** b f Mount Nelson—Apple Blossom (IRE) **Dr A. J. F. Gillespie**
33 **PINK MIRAGE (IRE),** gr f Verglas (IRE)—Deira (USA) **Whitcoombe Park Racing**
34 **POLAR EXPRESS,** ch g Sakhee's Secret—Polar Dawn **Berkeley Racing**
35 **RUSSIAN REMARQUE,** b c Archipenko (USA)—Accede **The Traditionalists**
36 **SUMMERLING (IRE),** b f Excellent Art—Sun Seasons (IRE) **A. H. Robinson**

TWO-YEAR-OLDS

37 Br f 6/3 Intense Focus (USA)—Acquiesced (IRE) (Refuse To Bend (IRE)) (8571) **Berkeley Racing**
38 B f 26/4 Hellvelyn—Anneliina (Cadeaux Genereux) (13333)
39 B g 2/5 Tobougg (IRE)—Balsamita (FR) (Midyan (USA)) (5238)
40 **BOLLYWOOD DREAM,** b f 15/2 Sleeping Indian—Act Three (Beat Hollow) **Mrs G Hamilton-Fairley**
41 **CELESTIAL MAGIC,** b g 31/3 Black Sam Bellamy (IRE)—Mighty Merlin (Royal Applause) **Mrs J. A. Watts**
42 Ch f 3/3 Zebedee—Chingford (IRE) (Redback) **Prof C. D. Green**
43 B f 20/3 Pastoral Pursuits—Halfwaytoparadise (Observatory (USA)) (800) **Mascalls Stud**
44 Ch f 10/3 Medicean—Honky Tonk Sally (Dansili) (10476) **Mrs J Maitland-Jones**
45 **HOUND MUSIC,** ch f 12/4 Ashkalani (IRE)—Saffron Fox (Safawan) **Mrs E. J. Edwards Heathcote**
46 **ICKYMASHO,** b f 8/3 Multiplex—
   Icky Woo (Mark of Esteem (IRE)) (13000) **C.R. Lambourne, M. Forbes, D. Losse**
47 B f 2/4 Monsieur Bond—Kanisfluh (Pivotal) **David & Gwyn Joseph & Partners**
48 **MADAME LAFITE,** b f 15/4 Dutch Art—
   Poppo's Song (CAN) (Polish Navy (USA)) (46000) **Mr J. T. Habershon-Butcher**
49 **MAYBELATER,** b f 14/4 Mount Nelson—Muscovado (USA) (Mr Greeley (USA)) **Mrs J. Wigan**
50 Gr f 16/4 Hellvelyn—Pelican Key (IRE) (Mujadil (USA)) **Mrs J. Watts**
51 B f 3/4 Bushranger (IRE)—Ringmoor Down (Pivotal) **Prof C. D. Green**
52 B f 22/1 Hellvelyn—Rioliina (IRE) (Captain Rio) (14285) **Mrs J. A. Watts**
53 B f 21/3 Monsieur Bond (IRE)—Rose of Coma (IRE) (Kheleyf (USA))
54 **RUSSIAN RADIANCE,** ch f 12/3 Paco Boy (IRE)—Russian Ruby (FR) (Vettori (IRE)) (17142) **The Traditionalists**
55 **SECRET BAY (IRE),** ch f 18/4 Arcano (IRE)—Caribbean Escape (Pivotal) (20952) **un-registered partnership**
56 Ch c 29/4 Sakhee's Secret—Smart Hostess (Most Welcome) (9523)
57 B c 22/4 Excellent Art—Tara Too (IRE) (Danetime (IRE)) **Prof C. D. Green**
58 B f 4/3 Zamindar (USA)—Tereshkina (IRE) (Sadler's Wells (USA)) (7000) **Mrs M. D. Stewart**
59 Ch f 21/4 Lope de Vega (IRE)—Twiggy's Sister (IRE) (Flying Spur (AUS)) (15000) **David & Gwyn Joseph**
60 Ch f 11/3 Joe Bear (IRE)—Veni Babi Vici (Horse Chestnut (SAF)) (761) **Mike Webly & Stuart McPhee**

Other Owners: Mr Jim Atkinson, Mr G. Bishop, Mr Jeremy Brownlee, Mr D. Cadger, Mr G. Clark, Mr Steve Dawes, Mr S. Dawes, Mr R. Dollar, Mr Tom F. Edwards, Mr Tony Edwards, Mr M. I. Forbes, Mrs S. Hearn, Mr J. Hobson, Mr J. Homan, Mr C. R. Lambourne, Mr D. R. Losse, Mr L. J. Losse, Mr D. Powell, Mr M. A. Ransom, Mr S. M. Ransom, Mrs H. Stalder, Mrs S. A. Symonds, Mrs C. S. Whitaker, Mr G. C. Wickens.

Assistant Trainer: Sophie Portman

Apprentice: Ned Curtis, Matthew Lawson. **Amateur:** Mr J. Harding.

---

512 **MR JAMIE POULTON, Lewes**
Postal: **White Cottage, Telscombe, Lewes, East Sussex, BN7 3HZ**
Contacts: **YARD** (01273) 300515 **HOME** (01273) 300127 **FAX** (01273) 300915
MOBILE (07980) 596952
E-MAIL jamie@poulton8.orangehome.co.uk

1 **BANGKOK PETE (IRE),** 9, b g Alflora (IRE)—Kinnegads Pride (IRE) **The Never Dropped Partnership**
2 **DOUBLE DEALITES,** 4, b f Double Trigger (IRE)—Linden Grace (USA) **Miss V. Markowiak**
3 **FARBREAGA (IRE),** 8, b g Shernazar—Gleann Alainn **Miss V. Markowiak**
4 **FEATHER DANCER,** 4, b f Norse Dancer (IRE)—Featherlight **Oceana Racing**

MR JAMIE POULTON - Continued

    5 **GORHAMS GIFT**, 6, b g Double Trigger (IRE)—Linden Grace (USA) **The Never Dropped Partnership**
    6 **SULTRY LADY**, 4, b f Pastoral Pursuits—Naemi (GER) **J. R. Poulton**

THREE-YEAR-OLDS
    7 B c Sakhee (USA)—Featherlight **Unregistered Partnership**

Other Owners: Mr A. Baker, Mr I. C. Cusselle, Mr K. Farmer, J. Harrison.

Assistant Trainer: Mrs C D Poulton

Jockey (NH): Mattie Batchelor.

---

513   **MR BRENDAN POWELL, Upper Lambourn**
Postal: Newlands Stables, Upper Lambourn, Hungerford, Berkshire, RG17 8QX
Contacts: **PHONE (01488) 73650 FAX (01488) 73650 MOBILE (07785) 390737**
E-MAIL brendan.powell@btconnect.com WEBSITE www.brendanpowellracing.com

  1 **ALWAYS MANAGING**, 5, b m Oscar (IRE)—Sunshine Rays **H. Redknapp**
  2 **AMAZING SCENES (IRE)**, 5, b br g Desert King (IRE)—Lady Leila (IRE) **Let's Get Ready To Rumble Partnership**
  3 **ANTON CHIGURH**, 5, b g Oasis Dream—Barathiki **A. J. Barker**
  4 **AWARD WINNER**, 11, b g Alflora (IRE)—Blackwater Bay (IRE) **J. P. McManus**
  5 **BENEFITS WELL (IRE)**, 7, b g Beneficial—Farran Lady (IRE) **B. G. Powell**
  6 **BOB TUCKER (IRE)**, 7, b g Brian Boru—Acumen (IRE) **Mr N. Davies**
  7 **BRACKLOON HIGH (IRE)**, 9, b g Bob Back (USA)—Homebird (IRE) **Mr T Conway,Mrs Conway&Mr T G Warren**
  8 **BRIANS WELL (IRE)**, 7, b g Brian Boru—Cons Dual Sale (IRE) **The Arkle Bar Partnership**
  9 **CANADIAN DIAMOND (IRE)**, 7, ch g Halling (USA)—Six Nations (USA) **Nicholls Family**
10 **CERTAVI (IRE)**, 5, b g Antonius Pius (USA)—The Quiet Woman (IRE) **Mr N. Davies**
11 **DARK AMBER**, 4, b f Sakhee (USA)—Donna Vita **Mrs M Fairbairn & Mr P Dean**
12 **DARK AND DANGEROUS (IRE)**, 6, b g Cacique (IRE)—Gilah (IRE) **North South Alliance**
13 **DARK EMERALD (IRE)**, 4, gr c Dark Angel (IRE)—Xema **Mr K. R. E. Rhatigan**
14 **DESERT RECLUSE (IRE)**, 7, ch g Redback—Desert Design **The Hill Top Partnership**
15 **DUNKELLY CASTLE (IRE)**, 10, ch g Old Vic—Nanna's Joy (IRE) **Vetlab Supplies Ltd**
16 **FAIRYINTHEWIND (IRE)**, ch m Indian Haven—Blue Daze **Mr R. J. Delnevo**
17 **GLEN COUNTESS (IRE)**, 7, b m Pilsudski (IRE)—Countessdee (IRE) **The Naughty Partnership**
18 **GRAFFITI ART**, 5, b m Kayf Tara—Art Affair (GER) **Mr R. L. Fanshawe**
19 **GUANCIALE**, 7, b g Exit To Nowhere (USA)—Thenford Lass (IRE) **The Beefeaters**
20 **HOT WHISKEY (IRE)**, 6, ch g Flemensfirth (USA)—Fair Gina (USA) **H. Redknapp**
21 **INSTINCTUAL**, 4, ch g Observatory (USA)—Be Glad **Mr N. Davies**
22 **ITALIAN SYMPHONY (IRE)**, 4, b f Galileo (IRE)—Tea Break **J. S. Warner**
23 **JULIE PRINCE (IRE)**, 8, b g Desert Prince (IRE)—Daniella Ridge (IRE) **B. G. Powell**
24 **KEYCHAIN (IRE)**, 4, b g Key of Luck (USA)—Sarifa (IRE) **T. H. Chadney**
25 **KING SPIRIT (IRE)**, 6, b g Fruits of Love (USA)—Tariana (IRE) **Mr J. J. King**
26 **KNOCKGRAFFON LAD (USA)**, 7, b g Forestry (USA)—Miss Dahlia (USA) **Mr N. Davies**
27 **LADY FROM GENEVA**, 7, ch m Generous (IRE)—Schizo-Phonic **Geneva Finance PLC**
28 **LINKABLE**, 5, b h Rail Link—Fashionable **Mr J. Henwood-Ross**
29 **MERCHANT OF MILAN**, 6, b g Milan—Repunzel **Mr & Mrs A. J. Mutch**
30 **MILANS WELL (IRE)**, 8, b g Milan—Panoora Queen (IRE) **A. Head**
31 **MORESTEAD (IRE)**, 9, ch g Traditionally (USA)—Itsy Bitsy Betsy (USA) **L. Gilbert**
32 **NEWFORGE HOUSE (IRE)**, 6, b g High-Rise (IRE)—Treasure Island **The Beefeaters**
33 **ONE PURSUIT (IRE)**, 6, br g Pastoral Pursuits—Karinski (USA) **Mr N. J. E. Maher**
34 **ONLY WITNESS (IRE)**, 9, b g Witness Box (USA)—Shiny Button **R. K. Stanley**
35 **OPHELIA'S KISS**, 7, b m Karinga Bay—Baileys Baby **J. S. Warner**
36 **PHANTOM PRINCE (IRE)**, 5, b g Jeremy (USA)—Phantom Waters **C. F. Harrington**
37 **REACH THE BEACH**, 5, ch m Phoenix Reach (IRE)—Comtesse Noire (CAN) **Winterbeck Manor Stud Ltd**
38 **RIVER PAGEANT (AUS)**, 4, ch c Choisir (AUS)—Royal Pageant (AUS)
39 **ROCK DIAMOND (IRE)**, 4, b f Rock of Gibraltar (IRE)—Yaky Romani (IRE) **The Hill Top Partnership**
40 **SHIPTON**, 5, b g Nayef (USA)—Silk Road **Mr N. Davies**
41 **SIR FREDLOT (IRE)**, 5, b g Choisir (AUS)—Wurfklinge (GER) **Rupert Williams & P Winkworth**
42 **SONORAN SANDS (IRE)**, 6, b g Footstepsinthesand—Atishoo (IRE) **C. F. Harrington**
43 **STOCKHILL DIVA**, 4, ch f Haafhd—April Stock **Mrs M. Fairbairn & E. Gadsden**
44 **STRICTLY CISSBURY**, 5, b g Sakhee (USA)—Distant Music **B. G. Powell**
45 **SUGARFORMYHONEY (IRE)**, 5, ch m Dutch Art—Sweetsformysweet (USA) **W. A. Harrison-Allan**
46 **SUN AND STARS**, 6, ch g Haafhd—Leading Role **J. H. Widdows**
47 **TERRA FIRMA**, 4, b g Lucarno (USA)—Solid Land (FR) **P. L. Winkworth**

MR BRENDAN POWELL - Continued

48 **TODOISTODARE**, 4, b f Tobougg (IRE)—Misrepresented (IRE) **T. G. Warren**
49 **UNCLE DERMOT (IRE)**, 6, b g Arakan (USA)—Cappadoce (IRE) **Mr K. R. E. Rhatigan**
50 **VIOLETS BOY (IRE)**, 7, br g King's Theatre (IRE)—Sunshine Rays **H. Redknapp**

THREE-YEAR-OLDS

51 **ARABIAN SUNSET (IRE)**, b f Dubawi (IRE)—Summer Sunset (IRE) **Newlands Bloodstock Ltd**
52 **CLEAR FOCUS (IRE)**, ch f Intense Focus (USA)—Sofistication (IRE) **Mr K. R. E. Rhatigan**
53 **GANNICUS**, b g Phoenix Reach (IRE)—Rasmani **Winterbeck Manor Stud Ltd**
54 **LITERALLY ON FIRE (IRE)**, ch g Rock of Gibraltar (IRE)—Toolentidhaar (USA) **I. S. Smith**
55 **MY ESCAPADE (IRE)**, ch f Tamayuz—Highly Respected (IRE) **Newlands Bloodstock Ltd**
56 **PRIM AND PROPER**, b f Sleeping Indian—Quite Fantastic (IRE) **Mr & Mrs A. J. Mutch**
57 **SECRET KODE (IRE)**, b f Kodiac—Finty **Newlands Bloodstock Ltd**
58 **THUNDERING CLOUD (IRE)**, b f Clodovil (IRE)—Porky Pie (IRE) **Newlands Bloodstock Ltd**

Other Owners: P. Burgoyne, T. Conway, Mrs M. Conway, P. Dean, Mrs A. Ellis, Mrs M. Fairbairn, G. M. Flood, E. J. S. Gadsden, Miss W. J. Leighton, D. Leon, Mr D. J. Martin, Mr P Morris, Mrs S. Mutch, Mr A. J. Mutch, Mr R. Nicholls, Mrs E. Nicholls, Mr J. R. Peppiatt, Mrs E. Smith, A. J. Viall, Mr R. E. Williams.

Jockey (flat): Kirsty Milczarek, Seb Sanders. **Jockey (NH):** A P McCoy, Andrew Tinkler. **Conditional:** Brendan Powell. **Apprentice:** Matthew Lawson. **Amateur:** Miss Jenny Powell.

---

514 | **MR TED POWELL, Reigate**
Postal: Nutwood Farm, Gatton Park Road, Reigate, Surrey, RH2 0SX
Contacts: **PHONE (01737) 765612**

1 **AJJAADD (USA)**, 8, b g Elusive Quality (USA)—Millstream (USA) **Katy & Lol Pratt**
2 **SNOW KING (USA)**, 4, ch g Elusive Quality (USA)—Cloudspin (USA) **Mr D. G. Acomb**

Other Owners: Mrs K. J. Pratt, L. C. Pratt.

---

515 | **SIR MARK PRESCOTT BT, Newmarket**
Postal: Heath House, Newmarket, Suffolk, CB8 8DU
Contacts: **PHONE (01638) 662117 FAX (01638) 666572**

1 **ALCAEUS**, 4, b c Hernando (FR)—Alvarita **Ne'er Do Wells IV**
2 **ALWILDA**, 4, gr f Hernando (FR)—Albanova **Miss K. Rausing**
3 **ATHENIAN (IRE)**, 5, b m Acclamation—Ziria (IRE) **AXOM (XXXI)**
4 **BIG THUNDER**, 4, gr g Dalakhani (IRE)—Charlotte O Fraise (IRE) **John Brown & Megan Dennis**
5 **CURIOUS MIND**, 4, b f Dansili—Intrigued **Denford Stud**
6 **MAN FROM SEVILLE**, 4, ch g Duke of Marmalade (IRE)—Basanti (USA) **Mr & Mrs William Rucker**
7 **PALLASATOR**, 5, b g Motivator—Ela Athena **Baxter, Gregson, Jenkins & Warman**
8 **SOLAR VIEW (IRE)**, 5, ch g Galileo (IRE)—Ellen (IRE) **Neil Greig - Osborne House**

THREE-YEAR-OLDS

9 **ABOODY**, b g Dutch Art—Rabshih (IRE) **Fawzi Abdulla Nass**
10 **ALBA VERDE**, grf Verglas (IRE)—Algarade **Miss K. Rausing**
11 **ANJIN (IRE)**, b c Danehill Dancer (IRE)—Twyla Tharp (IRE) **Syndicate 2012**
12 **CHARLOTTE'S DAY**, b f Dalakhani (IRE)—Charlotte O Fraise (IRE) **Lord Derby**
13 **CHINESE JADE**, gr g Cape Cross (IRE)—Chinese White (IRE) **Lady O'Reilly**
14 **FLORA MEDICI**, b f Sir Percy—Florentia **Neil Greig**
15 **FOREMOST**, b g Hernando (FR)—Flor Y Nata (USA) **W. E. Sturt - Osborne House**
16 **HARBOURED (USA)**, b f Rockport Harbor (USA)—Gulch Girl (USA) **Axom XLI**
17 **HIGH SECRET (IRE)**, b g High Chaparral (IRE)—Secret Question (USA) **Charles C. Walker - Osborne House**
18 **JOLIE BLONDE**, ch f Sir Percy—Affaire d'amour **Miss K. Rausing**
19 **LADY BINGO (IRE)**, b f Galileo (IRE)—Sharp Lisa (USA) **Qatar Racing Ltd**
20 **LEGAL SHARK (IRE)**, b c Lawman (FR)—Sea Searcher (USA) **Tim Bunting - Osborne House II**
21 **LIBRA ROMANA (IRE)**, b f Holy Roman Emperor (IRE)—Sliding Scale **Mr & Mrs J Kelsey-Fry**
22 **MOSCATO**, gr g Hernando (FR)—Alba Stella **The Green Door Partnership**
23 **MOUNTAIN KINGDOM (IRE)**, b g Montjeu (IRE)—Althea Rose (IRE) **Tim Bunting - Osborne House**

SIR MARK PRESCOTT BT - Continued

24 **NAMELY (IRE)**, b f Rock of Gibraltar (IRE)—Viz (IRE) **Mrs Sonia Rogers**
25 **PALACE DRAGON (IRE)**, b g Lawman (FR)—Mayonga (IRE) **Palace House Turf Club**
26 **REAL JAZZ (IRE)**, b f Marju (IRE)—Sedna (IRE) **T. J. Rooney**
27 **RED PASSIFLORA**, b f Danehill Dancer (IRE)—Red Peony **Cheveley Park Stud**
28 **ROHESIA**, b f High Chaparral (IRE)—Common Knowledge **Qatar Racing Ltd**
29 **SARPECH (IRE)**, b c Sea The Stars (IRE)—Sadima (IRE) **Qatar Racing Ltd**
30 **SEA PRIDE (IRE)**, b f Sea The Stars (IRE)—Claxon **Bluehills Racing Ltd**
31 **SECRET KEEPER**, ch f New Approach (IRE)—Confidante (USA) **Cheveley Park Stud**
32 **SHAFT OF LIGHT**, b c Exceed And Excel (AUS)—Injaaz **B. Haggas**
33 **SOIREE D'ETE**, b f Selkirk (USA)—Souvenance **Miss K. Rausing**
34 **THE STEWARD (USA)**, b c Street Cry (IRE)—Candlelight (USA) **Donald R. Dizney**
35 **THREETIMESALADY**, b f Royal Applause—Triple Joy **Bluehills Racing Ltd**
36 **UPSHOT**, b f Pivotal—Soar **Cheveley Park Stud**
37 **WILLIAM OF ORANGE**, b g Duke of Marmalade (IRE)—Critical Acclaim **Nicholas Jones**
38 **WINDSHIELD**, b f Montjeu (IRE)—Westerly Air (USA) **Cheveley Park Stud**
39 **WUNDERKIND (USA)**, b f Langfuhr (CAN)—Traum (USA) **Donald R. Dizney**

TWO-YEAR-OLDS

40 **AMOUR DE NUIT (IRE)**, b c 11/4 Azamour (IRE)—
                     Umthoulah (IRE) (Unfuwain (USA)) (16000) **L. A. Larratt - Osborne House**
41 B f 25/2 Zamindar (USA)—Brooklyn's Storm (USA) (Storm Cat (USA)) **Qatar Racing Ltd**
42 **CELESTIAL PATH (IRE)**, b br c 8/3 Footstepsinthesand—
                     Miss Kittyhawk (IRE) (Hawk Wing (USA)) (85171) **Gordon C. Woodall**
43 **COURSING**, b br f 21/4 Kyllachy—Granuaile O'malley (IRE) (Mark of Esteem (IRE)) (64000) **Denford Stud**
44 **EL DRAQUE (USA)**, b c 26/4 Henrythenavigator (USA)—
                     Miss Fanny (USA) (Theatrical) **Mt. Brilliant Farm & Ranch**
45 **ELECT (IRE)**, b f 19/3 Intikhab (USA)—Kawaha (IRE) (Danehill Dancer (IRE)) (28000) **Denford Stud**
46 **GALLO GALANTE**, ch c 17/3 Galileo (IRE)—Spacious (Nayef (USA)) (350000) **J. L. C. Pearce**
47 **KACHOU**, b f 5/4 Excellent Art—
                     Milwaukee (FR) (Desert King (IRE)) (24000) **Lady Fairhaven & The Hon C & H Broughton**
48 **LIGHT BREAKS (IRE)**, b c 15/2 Dylan Thomas (IRE)—Anywaysmile (IRE) (Indian Ridge) **Moyglare Stud**
49 B c 26/4 Sea The Stars (IRE)—Maid of Killeen (IRE) (Darshaan) **Lady Bamford**
50 **MISS CAP D'AIL**, b f 16/2 Invincible Spirit (IRE)—Miss Cap Ferrat (Darshaan) **J. L. C. Pearce**
51 **MISS MINUTY**, gr f 23/2 Verglas (IRE)—Miss Provence (Hernando (FR)) **J. L. C. Pearce**
52 **MISS TURPAN**, ch f 3/4 Hernando (FR)—Miss Katmandu (IRE) (Rainbow Quest (USA)) **J. L. C. Pearce**
53 **NAVAL ACTION**, b c 16/2 Lawman (FR)—
                     Dance of The Sea (IRE) (Sinndar (IRE)) (80000) **J. E. Fishpool - Osborne House**
54 **NIGHT GENERATION (GER)**, ch c 8/3 Sholokhov (IRE)—
                     Night Woman (GER) (Monsun (GER)) (50000) **John Brown & Megan Dennis**
55 **OVERLORD**, b c 19/3 Lawman (FR)—Hip (Pivotal) (34000) **Cheveley Park Stud**
56 **POETIC LICENSE (IRE)**, b c 3/4 Dylan Thomas (IRE)—
                     Bright Bank (IRE) (Sadler's Wells (USA)) (80000) **Mr & Mrs William Rucker**
57 **RAINBOW PRIDE (IRE)**, gr c 21/4 Clodovil (IRE)—
                     Rahila (IRE) (Kalanisi (IRE)) (25000) **W. E. Sturt - Osborne House IV**
58 **SEYCHELLOISE**, b f 5/5 Pivotal—Starlit Sands (Oasis Dream) **Miss K. Rausing**
59 **SINGOALLA**, b f 5/3 Arch (USA)—Songerie (Hernando (FR)) **Miss K. Rausing**
60 B f 1/5 Dylan Thomas (IRE)—Sliding Scale (Sadler's Wells (USA)) **Mr & Mrs J. Kelsey-Fry**
61 **SONRISA**, b f 23/2 Hernando (FR)—Sourire (Domedriver (IRE)) **Miss K. Rausing**
62 B f 17/3 Galileo (IRE)—Specifically (USA) (Sky Classic (CAN)) (375000) **Qatar Racing Partnership**
63 **VEJOVIS**, b c 9/2 Fastnet Rock (AUS)—
                     Violet (IRE) (Mukaddamah (USA)) (57000) **William Charnley & Richard Pegum**
64 **WEDLOCK**, ch f 7/3 Pivotal—Wedding Party (Groom Dancer (USA)) **Cheveley Park Stud**

Other Owners: Mr E. A. Baxter, Mr B. D. Burnet, Mr Terry Corden, Mr Darren Ellis, Mr Phil Fry, Mr Greg Goodman, Mr P. G. Goulandris, The Hon. Mrs G. Greenwood, Mrs Caroline Gregson, Mr Chris Jenkins, Mr L. A. Larratt, Mr Mike Rudd, Mr & Mrs Dennis Russell, Prince Faisal Salman, Mr Barry Taylor, Mrs J. Taylor, Mr Mark Tracey, The Hon. Lady Troubridge, Mrs S. L. Warman, Mr E. J. Williams.

Assistant Trainer: William Butler, **Pupil Assistant:** James Ferguson

Jockey (flat): L. Morris, C. Catlin. **Apprentice:** R. Jessop, J. Gilligan.

516 | MR ANDREW PRICE, Leominster
Postal: **Eaton Hall Farm, Leominster, Herefordshire, HR6 0NA**
Contacts: PHONE **(01568) 611137** FAX **(01568) 611137** MOBILE **(07729) 838660**
E-MAIL **helen@aepriceracing.plus.com**

1 BOBBY DOVE, 7, b g Fraam—Flakey Dove **A. E. Price**
2 6, B g Beat All (USA)—Flakey Dove **A. E. Price**
3 FLORA LEA, 7, b m Alflora (IRE)—Castanet **Mrs C. Davis**
4 MISS TILLY DOVE, 6, b m Overbury (IRE)—Scratch The Dove **A. E. Price**
5 SPENCER LEA, 6, b g Overbury (IRE)—Castanet **Mrs C. Davis**

Assistant Trainer: Mrs H L Price

517 | MR JOHN PRICE, Ebbw Vale
Postal: **41 Beaufort Terrace, Ebbw Vale, Gwent, NP23 5NW**
Contacts: PHONE **(01495) 306113** MOBILE **(07870) 475156**

1 TINCTORIA, 4, b f Oratorio (IRE)—Blue Indigo (FR) **J. K. Price**

Assistant Trainer: A J Price

518 | MR RICHARD PRICE, Hereford
Postal: **Criftage Farm, Ullingswick, Hereford, Herefordshire, HR1 3JG**
Contacts: PHONE **(01432) 820263** FAX **(01432) 820785** MOBILE **(07929) 200598**

1 ARGAUM (IRE), 7, ch g Medicean—Poppy Carew (IRE) **My Left Foot Racing Syndicate**
2 CHEERS BIG EARS (IRE), 8, gr g Kheleyf (USA)—Grey Galava **B. Veasey**
3 CHEVETON, 10, ch g Most Welcome—Attribute **Mrs K. E. Oseman**
4 GREYEMKAY, 6, gr g Fair Mix (IRE)—Magic Orb **Richard Price & Maria Slade**
5 HURAKAN (IRE), 8, gr g Daylami (IRE)—Gothic Dream **Mr & Mrs D. C. Holder**
6 IGUACU, 10, b g Desert Prince (IRE)—Gay Gallanta (USA) **Mr & Mrs D. C. Holder**
7 ROWLESTONE LASS, 4, b f Hernando (FR)—Charmante Femme **Ocean's Five**
8 TAURUS TWINS, 8, b g Deportivo—Intellibet One **G. E. Amey & G. D. Bailey**
9 TRANSFER, 9, br g Trans Island—Sankaty Light (USA) **G. Ivall & R. J. Price**

Other Owners: Mr G. E. Amey, Mr G. D. Bailey, Mr Douglas Boddy, Mr A. J. Chance, Mr P. J. Hoare, Mr Derek C. Holder, Mrs Cheryl Holder, Mr G. Ivall, Mr R. J. Price, Mrs Maria Slade.

Assistant Trainer: Jane Price

Amateur: Mr M. Price.

519 | MR PETER PRITCHARD, Shipston-on-Stour
Postal: **The Gate House, Whatcote, Shipston-on-Stour, Warwickshire, CV36 5EF**
Contacts: PHONE **(01295) 680689**

1 COWBRIDGE (IRE), 8, b g Pilsudski (IRE)—Clyde Goddess (IRE) **Trustmark**
2 EARCOMESTHEDREAM (IRE), 11, b g Marignan (USA)—
Play It By Ear (IRE) **Woodland Generators & Mr D R Pritchard**
3 JUBILEE JOY (IRE), 8, b m Windsor Castle—Icy Allstar (IRE) **Mr R. W. Stowe**
4 OVERTON LAD, 13, gr g Overbury (IRE)—Safe Arrival (USA) **D. R. Pritchard**
5 SAFARI SUNBEAM, 6, br g Primo Valentino (IRE)—Bathwick Finesse (IRE) **D. R. Pritchard**
6 SHADESOFNAVY, 8, ch g Fleetwood (IRE)—Safe Arrival (USA) **Whittington Racing Club**
7 TIKKETORIDE, 6, gr g Tikkanen (USA)—Safe Arrival (USA) **D. R. Pritchard**
8 TISFREETDREAM (IRE), 8, b g Oscar (IRE)—Gayley Gale (IRE) **Woodland Generators & Mr D R Pritchard**

Other Owners: Mr W. R. Evans, Mr R. A. Evans, Mrs V. L. Pryor, Mr C. S. White, Woodlands (Worcestershire) Ltd.

Assistant Trainer: Mrs. E. Gardner

Jockey (NH): Jack Doyle, Jamie Moore.

520 **MR PETER PURDY, Bridgwater**
Postal: **Fyne Court Farm, Broomfield, Bridgwater, Somerset, TA5 2EQ**
Contacts: **PHONE (01823) 451632 FAX (01823) 451632 MOBILE (07860) 392786**
E-MAIL **purdy844@btinternet.com**

1 BOWMANS WELL (IRE), 9, b m Cadeaux Genereux—Guignol (IRE) **P. D. Purdy**
2 COURT FINALE, 13, ch g One Voice (USA)—Tudor Sunset **P. D. Purdy**
3 MAY COURT, 7, b g Groomsbridge May I—Tudor Sunset **P. D. Purdy**
4 5, Ch m Mutazayid (IRE)—Tudor Blonde **P. D. Purdy**

Jockey (NH): Wayne Kavanagh.

521 **MR NOEL QUINLAN, Newmarket**
Postal: **Harraton Stables, Chapel Street, Exning, Newmarket, Suffolk, CB8 7HA**
Contacts: **PHONE (01638) 578674 FAX (01638) 577831 MOBILE (07815) 072946**
E-MAIL **noelquinlanracing@hotmail.co.uk**

1 BETTER VALUE (IRE), 4, b g Ad Valorem (USA)—Varmint Lady (IRE) **Miss M. A. Quinlan**
2 FIRE IN BABYLON (IRE), 6, b g Montjeu (IRE)—Three Owls (IRE) **Mrs F. A. Shaw**
3 IMPERTINENT, 4, b f Halling (USA)—Incarnation (IRE) **Mr G. Wilding**
4 LOUCAL, 4, b c Lucky Story (USA)—Penny Ha'penny **Mr B. Dick**
5 SLIPPER SATIN (IRE), 4, b f Excellent Art—In The Ribbons **Miss M. A. Quinlan**
6 SUPER COOKIE, 4, b f Dylan Thomas (IRE)—Dance Lesson **Miss M. A. Quinlan**

THREE-YEAR-OLDS

7 BELLE STAR, b f Royal Applause—Dixie Belle **Burns Farm Racing**
8 FIZZOLO, b f Piccolo—Fizzy Treat **Mrs N McGreavy, W Flynn, S Fordham**
9 GOLDEN SPEAR, ch c Kyllachy—Penmayne **Newtown Anner Stud Farm Ltd**
10 PAY THE GREEK, b c Sleeping Indian—To Grace (IRE) **R Morris J Russell T Obrien O Doyle**
11 PINDORA (GER), ch f Sholokhov (IRE)—Poule d'essai (GER) **Mr Tommy Cummings**
12 SPEEDFIEND, b c Bahamian Bounty—Vive Les Rouges **Newtown Anner Stud Farm Ltd**
13 THE DOYLE MACHINE (IRE), b g Camacho—Berenica (IRE) **R Morris J Russell T Obrien O Doyle**

TWO-YEAR-OLDS

14 B f 10/4 Bahamian Bounty—Broughtons Revival (Pivotal) (6500) **Peter Hollingsworth**
15 B br f 23/4 Equiano (FR)—Jenny Lake (USA) (Danzig) (75000) **Newtown Anner Stud Farm Ltd**
16 Ch c 20/2 Iffraaj—Kelowna (IRE) (Pivotal) (50000) **Newtown Anner Stud Farm Ltd**
17 B c 26/4 Iffraaj—La Jwaab (Alhaarth) (52000) **Newtown Anner Stud Farm Ltd**
18 B c 28/1 Shirocco (GER)—Moxby (Efisio) **Mr G. Wilding**
19 B f 12/4 Tagula (IRE)—Notley Park (Wolfhound (USA)) (3483) **Mrs C Cashman**
20 Ch f 28/3 Footstepsinthesand—Perfect Peach (Lycius (USA)) (6968) **Rachel Robinson**
21 B f 23/4 Azamour (IRE)—Portrait of A Lady (IRE) (Peintre Celebre) (50000) **Newtown Anner Stud Farm Ltd**
22 B f 15/2 Intikhab (USA)—Tell Mum (Marju (IRE)) (12388) **Mr R. Morris**
23 B f 21/2 Kyllachy—Three Ducks (Diktat) (5000) **Ian Horman**

Other Owners: Mr Wayne Asquith, Mr R. Morris, Miss M. A. Quinlan, Mrs Gay Scott.

522 **MR DENIS QUINN, Newmarket**
Postal: **Marlborough House Stables, Old Station Road, Newmarket, Suffolk, CB8 8DW**
Contacts: **MOBILE (07435) 340008**

1 DESERT AL (IRE), 11, b g Desert Style (IRE)—Glass Lady
2 JJS PRIDE (IRE), 5, b g One Cool Cat (USA)—Yaselda **Mr M. McGovern**
3 WINGS OF FIRE (IRE), 4, b g Verglas (IRE)—Allspice **Mr M. McGovern**

THREE-YEAR-OLDS

4 Ch g Firebreak—Alula
5 DIAMOND BACK (IRE), b c Diamond Green (FR)—Raqiqah **Mr M. McGovern**

523 MR JOHN QUINN, Malton

Postal: **Bellwood Cottage Stables, Settrington, Malton, North Yorkshire, YO17 8NR**
Contacts: **PHONE (01944) 768370 MOBILE (07899) 873304**
E-MAIL johnquinnracing@btconnect.com

1 **AN CAPALL MOR (IRE)**, 8, b g Flemensfirth (USA)—Corravilla (IRE) **Boretech Ltd**
2 **ARTHURS SECRET**, 4, ch g Sakhee's Secret—Angry Bark (USA) **David Scott & Chris Simmonds**
3 **AURORE D'ESTRUVAL (FR)**, 4, ch f Nickname (FR)—Option d'estruval (FR) **Mr C. S. Hinchy**
4 **CALCULATED RISK**, 5, ch g Motivator—Glen Rosie (IRE) **J. T. Warner**
5 **CHEBSEY BEAU**, 4, b c Multiplex—Chebsey Belle (IRE) **Kent & Greaves**
6 **CHIEFTAIN'S CHOICE (IRE)**, 5, b g King's Theatre (IRE)—Fairy Native (IRE) **Distillery Stud**
7 **COCKNEY SPARROW**, 5, b m Cockney Rebel (IRE)—Compose **Mr & Mrs Paul Gaffney**
8 **DAN EMMETT (USA)**, 4, ch g Flower Alley (USA)—Singing Dixie (USA) **Mrs S. Quinn**
9 **DISTIME (IRE)**, 8, b g Flemensfirth (USA)—Technohead (IRE) **Middleham Park Racing, Mr & Mrs P Gaffney**
10 **EVANESCENT (IRE)**, 5, b g Elusive City (USA)—Itsanothergirl **Mrs S. Quinn**
11 **EXNING HALT**, 5, b g Rail Link—Phi Phi (IRE) **Highfield Racing 4**
12 **FANTASY GLADIATOR**, 8, b g Ishiguru (USA)—Fancier Bit **The Fantasy Fellowship**
13 4, B c Primo Valentino (IRE)—Flaming Rose (IRE) **Mrs M. L. Luck**
14 **FORCED FAMILY FUN**, 4, b g Refuse To Bend (IRE)—Juniper Girl (IRE) **The Top Silk Syndicate**
15 **HAWK MOUNTAIN (UAE)**, 9, b g Halling (USA)—Friendly (IRE) **N. E. F. Luck**
16 **HIDDEN JUSTICE (IRE)**, 5, b g Lawman (FR)—Uncharted Haven **Highfield Racing 2**
17 **INNSBRUCK**, 4, b g Tiger Hill (IRE)—Lille Hammer **Riverdee Stable, Acorn P'Ship, M Lindsay**
18 **IVAN VASILEVICH (IRE)**, 6, b g Ivan Denisovich (IRE)—Delisha **Mr C. S. Hinchy**
19 **JOE EILE (IRE)**, 6, b g Iffraaj—Encouragement **HD Partnership**
20 **KASHMIR PEAK (IRE)**, 5, b g Tiger Hill (IRE)—Elhareer (IRE) **Win Only SP Only Partnership**
21 **LEVITATE**, 6, ch g Pivotal—Soar **Mr Charles Wentworth**
22 **MANY LEVELS**, 4, br g Nayef (USA)—Polygueza (FR) **The Acorn Partnership**
23 **MOIDORE**, 5, b g Galileo (IRE)—Flash of Gold **Estio Racing**
24 4, B g Kayf Tara—Mrs Malt (IRE) **Robert Robinson**
25 **O MA LAD (IRE)**, 6, ch g Redback—Raydaniya (IRE) **Mr Bob McMillan**
26 **PEARL CASTLE (IRE)**, 4, b g Montjeu (IRE)—Ghurra (USA) **Mr & Mrs Paul Gaffney**
27 **POETIC VERSE**, 4, gr f Byron—Nina Fontenail (FR) **J. N. Blackburn**
28 **RACING PULSE (IRE)**, 5, b g Garuda (IRE)—Jacks Sister (IRE) **Mr C. S. Hinchy**
29 **RECESSION PROOF (FR)**, 8, ch g Rock of Gibraltar (IRE)—Elevate **Mr P Taylor & Mr J Stone**
30 **RUTHERGLEN**, 4, b g Tiger Hill (IRE)—Hanella (IRE) **The Beer Swigging Strangers**
31 **SCOTS GAELIC (IRE)**, 7, ch g Tomba—Harmonic (IRE) **Mr C. S. Hinchy**
32 **TAHIRA (GER)**, 4, ch f Doyen (IRE)—Tennessee Queen (GER) **Mr C. S. Hinchy**
33 **TARTAN TIGER (IRE)**, 8, ch g Flemensfirth (USA)—River Clyde (IRE) **Distillery Stud**
34 **THINGS CHANGE (IRE)**, 6, b g Old Vic—Northwood May **Mrs E. Wright**
35 **VILLORESI (IRE)**, 5, b g Clodovil (IRE)—Villafranca (IRE) **Mr S. Burns**
36 **VIOLENT VELOCITY (IRE)**, 11, b g Namid—Lear's Crown (USA) **Mrs S. Quinn**
37 **ZAPLAMATION (IRE)**, 9, b g Acclamation—Zapatista **Mr Andrew Turton & Mr David Barker**
38 **ZERMATT (IRE)**, 5, ch g Strategic Prince—Await (IRE) **Mr R. L. Houlton**

THREE-YEAR-OLDS

39 **BOLD CAPTAIN (IRE)**, ch g Captain Rio—Indianaca (IRE) **Highfield Racing**
40 **CAPTAIN GEE**, b c Captain Gerrard (IRE)—Gagajulu **R. Kent**
41 **DARLING BOYZ**, ch g Auction House (USA)—Summertime Parkes **J. N. Blackburn**
42 **EL BEAU (IRE)**, ch g Camacho—River Beau (IRE) **Highfield Racing (Camacho)**
43 **ELUSIVE GEORGE (IRE)**, b c Elusive City (USA)—Sur Ma Vie (USA) **Mrs S Quinn**
44 **GIANT SAMURAI (USA)**, ch c First Samurai (USA)—Willow Point (USA) **Mr & Mrs Paul Gaffney**
45 **L'ARTISTE (IRE)**, gr f Mastercraftsman (IRE)—Sepia **Mr & Mrs Paul Gaffney**
46 **MAKIN THE RULES (IRE)**, b g Lawman (FR)—Shinto Duchess (IRE) **Mr Chris Makin**
47 **MAY WHI (IRE)**, b f Whipper (USA)—May **Shropshire Wolves 6**
48 **MORNIN MR NORRIS**, b g Byron—Fractured Foxy **Mrs E. Wright**
49 **MR GALLIVANTER (IRE)**, ch g Heliostatic (IRE)—Purepleasuresealer (IRE) **Mr R. Harmon**
50 **NOBLE ASSET**, ch g Compton Place—Chance For Romance **Mr Paul Chapman**
51 **SNUGFIT SAM**, b g Acclamation—Swanky Lady **Mr A. G. Greenwood**
52 **STRICTLY GLITZ (IRE)**, b f Kodiac—Dancing Steps **N. S. Cooper**
53 **TY COBB (IRE)**, b g Dandy Man (IRE)—Mrs Moonlight **C. V. Wentworth**

TWO-YEAR-OLDS

54 **ARTISTIC FLARE**, ch f 18/2 Dutch Art—Pantile (Pivotal) (71428) **Mr & Mrs Paul Gaffney**
55 **DONT TELL CHRIS**, b c 16/4 Lawman (FR)—Enigma (GER) (Sharp Victor (USA)) (42585) **Mr C. W. Makin**
56 Ch c 16/2 Zebedee—Florida City (IRE) (Pennekamp (USA)) (40000) **Highfield Racing 5**

MR JOHN QUINN - Continued

57 **HARRY'S DANCER (IRE)**, b f 2/2 Kodiac—Dance On (Caerleon (USA)) (12775) **Mr T. G. S. Wood**
58 **MAKIN A STATEMENT (IRE)**, b c 13/2 Bahamian Bounty—Star Now (Librettist (USA)) (69685) **Mr Chris Makin**
59 **MAKIN TROUBLE (IRE)**, b c 27/2 Lawman (FR)—
　　　　　　　　　　　　　　Crafty Notion (IRE) (Viking Ruler (AUS)) (46457) **Mr Chris Makin**
60 B c 9/4 Dark Angel (IRE)—Monsusu (IRE) (Montjeu (IRE)) (45714) **Mr & Mrs Paul Gaffney**
61 B c 20/4 Sir Percy—Salydora (FR) (Peintre Celebre (USA)) (40000) **Mr C. S. Hinchy**
62 **SILVER TYCOON (IRE)**, br gr c 20/2 Arcano (IRE)—Sailanches (USA) (Gone West (USA)) (45000) **Mr S. Burns**
63 Ch c 5/3 Sir Percy—Suertuda (Domedriver (IRE)) (20131) **Mr C. S. Hinchy**
64 Ch c 17/4 Fast Company (IRE)—Titian Saga (IRE) (Titus Livius (FR)) (40000) **Mr R. Harmon**
65 **YOUONLYLIVEONCE (IRE)**, b c 9/4 Lawman (FR)—
　　　　　　　　　　　　　　Caerlonore (IRE) (Traditionally (USA)) (23000) **J. N. Blackburn**

Other Owners: Mr Steve Avery, Mr J. Babb, Mr D. W. Barker, Mr A. M. Blewitt, Mr Sean Clancy, Mr Peter Coll, Mr Paul Gaffney, Mrs Joanne Gaffney, Mr G. A. Greaves, Mr Mark Grier, Mr P. Halkett, Mr Jason Hathorn, Mrs Fiona Hathorn, Mr Richard Jones, Mr R. Kent, Mr Maurice P. Lindsay, Mr I. A. Marmion, Mr Justin Murphy, Mr T. S. Palin, Mr M. Prince, Mrs S. Quinn, Mr S. A. T. Quinn, Mr Robert Robinson, Mrs Margaret Robinson, Mr Richard Simpson, Mr John Stone, Mr P. M. Taylor, Mr Mike Thomas, Mr Robert Turner, Mr Andrew Turton.

524　**MR MICK QUINN, Newmarket**
Postal: **Southgate Barn, Hamilton Road, Newmarket, Suffolk, CB8 0WY**
Contacts: **PHONE (01638) 660017 FAX (01638) 660017 MOBILE (07973) 260054**
E-MAIL mick@quinn2562.fsnet.co.uk

1 **EAST TEXAS RED (IRE)**, 4, ch c Danehill Dancer (IRE)—Evangeline **M. Quinn**
2 **ROYAL DEFENCE (IRE)**, 8, b g Refuse To Bend (IRE)—Alessia (GER) **M. Quinn**
3 **WATERLOO DOCK**, 9, b g Hunting Lion (IRE)—Scenic Air **M. Quinn**
4 **WHISKEY JUNCTION**, 10, b g Bold Edge—Victoria Mill **S. Astaire**

THREE-YEAR-OLDS

5 **ANFIELD**, b f Captain Gerrard (IRE)—Billie Holiday **A. Viner**

Assistant Trainer: Miss Karen Davies

Jockey (flat): Franny Norton.

525　**MR W. T. REED, Haydon Bridge**
Postal: **Moss Kennels, Haydon Bridge, Hexham, Northumberland, NE47 6NL**
Contacts: **PHONE (01434) 344016 MOBILE (07703) 270408 / (07889) 111885**
E-MAIL timreed8@aol.com

1 **HIE MOSSY (IRE)**, 7, ch g Moscow Society (USA)—Sarah's Smile **Mr W. T. Reed**
2 **JOHANNA FOSIE (IRE)**, 5, ch m Peintre Celebre (USA)—Yding (IRE) **Mr W. T. Reed**
3 **PRINCESS OF ROCK**, 5, ch m Rock of Gibraltar (IRE)—Principessa **Mr W. T. Reed**
4 **SILENT SNOW (IRE)**, 9, ch g Moscow Society (USA)—Miss Ogan (IRE) **Mr W. T. Reed**
5 **VIKING REBEL (IRE)**, 12, b g Taipan (IRE)—Clodagh's Dream **Mr W. T. Reed**

Assistant Trainer: Mrs E. J. Reed

Jockey (NH): Peter Buchanan. **Amateur:** Mr Harry Reed.

526　**MR WILLIAM REED, Umberleigh**
Postal: **Stowford Farm, East Stowford, Chittlehampton, Umberleigh, Devon, EX37 9RU**
Contacts: **PHONE (01769) 540292 MOBILE (07967) 130991**

1 **ALMOST HERE (IRE)**, 11, b g Lear Spear (USA)—Second Violin (IRE)
2 **J R HAWK (IRE)**, 6, b br g Hawk Wing (USA)—Miss Shivvy (IRE) **W. J. Reed**
3 **LITTLE WADHAM**, 9, b m Bandmaster (USA)—Sport of Fools (IRE) **W. J. Reed**
4 **WADHAM HILL**, 12, b m Bandmaster (USA)—Sport of Fools (IRE) **W. J. Reed**
5 **WHAT A JOKE (IRE)**, 7, b g Vinnie Roe (IRE)—Shaping **W. J. Reed**

527 MR DAVID REES, Haverfordwest
Postal: **The Grove Yard, Clarbeston Road, Haverfordwest, Pembrokeshire, SA63 4SP**
Contacts: **PHONE (01437) 731308 FAX (01437) 731551 MOBILE (07775) 662463**
E-MAIL davidreesfencing@lineone.net

1 CASCO BAY (IRE), 10, b g Fath (USA)—Montana Miss (IRE) **Mr R. P. Patrick**
2 CAWDOR HOUSE BERT, 7, b g Kayf Tara—Lady Shanan (IRE) **A. J. & Dai Rees**
3 CHANGING LANES, 11, b g Overbury (IRE)—Snowdon Lily **Mr E. W. Morris**
4 COMEHOMEQUIETLY (IRE), 10, b g King's Theatre (IRE)—Windswept Lady (IRE) **IWEC International Ltd**
5 DREAM BOLT (IRE), 6, ch g Urban Ocean (FR)—Riviera Dream **D. A. Rees**
6 FISHING BRIDGE (IRE), 9, ch g Definite Article—Rith Ar Aghaidh (IRE) **D. A. Rees**
7 MACARTHUR, 10, b g Montjeu (IRE)—Out West (USA) **Mr D. Rees & Mr B. Evans**
8 MOLON LABE (IRE), 7, ch g Footstepsinthesand—Pillars of Society (IRE) **Mr D Rees & Mr P Evans**
9 NISHAY (IRE), 7, b br g Classic Cliche (IRE)—Winged Victory (IRE) **D. A. Rees**
10 ROMEO IS BLEEDING (IRE), 8, b g Carroll House—Ean Eile (IRE) **D. A. Rees**
11 SANDEEL BAY (IRE), 8, ch g Gulland—Dollar Bay (IRE) **D. A. Rees**
12 SUPERMAN DE LA RUE (FR), 8, b g Akhdari (USA)—Impala de La Rue (FR) **Crew Racing**

Other Owners: Mr M. Cole, Mr P. Evans, Mr W. J. Evans, Mr D. Rees, Mr A. J. Rees, Mr Mark Williams.

528 MRS HELEN REES, Dorchester
Postal: **Distant Hills, Chalmington, Dorchester, Dorset, DT2 0HB**
Contacts: **PHONE (01300) 320683 MOBILE (07115) 558289**
E-MAIL helen-rees@live.co.uk

1 CNOC MOY (IRE), 10, b g Mull of Kintyre (USA)—Ewar Sunrise **Mrs H. E. Rees**
2 RESIDENCE AND SPA (IRE), 6, b g Dubai Destination (USA)—Toffee Nosed **Mrs H. E. Rees**

Assistant Trainer: Mr Rupert Rees

529 MR SEAN REGAN, Middleham
Postal: **Low Beck, Coverham, Middleham, Leyburn, North Yorkshire, DL8 4TJ**
Contacts: **MOBILE (07866) 437476**
E-MAIL sean@seanreganracing.com WEBSITE www.seanreganracing.com

1 6, Ch m Distant Music (USA)—Emma May **Mrs L. Grasby**
2 LUNACORN (IRE), 8, ch m Flemensfirth (USA)—Coppervega (IRE) **Mrs C. D. Taylor**
3 MILL RUN, 8, b m Tamure (IRE)—Seul Moi (IRE) **Mr M. S. U. Hustler**
4 MOISSANITE, 5, b m Danbird (AUS)—Nikita Sunrise (IRE) **Mrs L. Grasby**
5 PTOLOMEOS, 11, b g Kayf Tara—Lucy Tufty **Mrs C. D. Taylor**
6 7, B m Midnight Legend—Seul Moi (IRE) **Mr M. S. U. Hustler**
7 SHEILA'S CASTLE, 10, b m Karinga Bay—Candarela **S. Regan**

530 MR ANDREW REID, Mill Hill, London
Postal: **Highwood Lodge, Highwood Hill, Mill Hill, London, NW7 4HB**
Contacts: **PHONE (07836) 214617 (07747) 751603 FAX (02089) 061255**
E-MAIL clathell2000@yahoo.co.uk

1 ASCENDANT, 8, ch g Medicean—Ascendancy **A. S. Reid**
2 ATHLETIC, 5, b g Doyen (IRE)—Gentle Irony **A. S. Reid**
3 MALTEASE AH, 5, br m Librettist (USA)—Manic **A. S. Reid**
4 MR PLOD, 9, ch g Silver Patriarch (IRE)—Emily-Mou (IRE) **A. S. Reid**
5 UNDERWHELM, 4, ch f Bahamian Bounty—Depressed **A. S. Reid**

TWO-YEAR-OLDS

6 Ch g 13/3 Bahamian Bounty—Depressed (Most Welcome) **A. S. Reid**
7 B f 9/3 Teofilio (IRE)—Manic (Polar Falcon (USA)) **A. S. Reid**

Jockey (flat): Jim Crowley.

531 **MR KEITH REVELEY, Saltburn**
Postal: **Groundhill Farm, Lingdale, Saltburn-by-the-Sea, Cleveland, TS12 3HD**
Contacts: **OFFICE (01287) 650456 FAX (01287) 653095 MOBILE (07971) 784539**
E-MAIL **reveleyracing@yahoo.co.uk**

1 **ASH RED (IRE)**, 5, b g Ashkalani (IRE)—La Femme En Rouge **Reveley Farms**
2 **BALMUSETTE**, 5, b m Halling (USA)—Tcherina (IRE) **Mr & Mrs W. J. Williams**
3 **BRAVE SPARTACUS (IRE)**, 8, b g Spartacus (IRE)—Peaches Polly **R. Collins**
4 **BROCTUNE PAPA GIO**, 7, b g Tobougg (IRE)—Fairlie **Broctune Partners I**
5 **CATEGORICAL**, 11, b g Diktat—Zibet **Rug, Grub & Pub Partnership**
6 **CORKAGE (IRE)**, 11, b g Second Empire—Maslam (IRE) **The Scarth Racing Partnership**
7 **CORSAIR PRINCE**, 4, b g Black Sam Bellamy (IRE)—Nobratinetta (FR) **Supreme Aliance**
8 **CROWNING JEWEL**, 8, b g Sulamani (USA)—Pennys Pride (IRE) **Sir Ian Good**
9 **DANCE OF TIME**, 7, b g Presenting—Northern Native (IRE) **Mrs S. A. Smith**
10 **DANCING ART (IRE)**, 8, b g Definite Article—Seductive Dance **R. Collins**
11 **DELTA FORTY**, 6, b m Aflora (IRE)—Northern Native (IRE) **Mrs S. A. Smith**
12 **DONNA'S PRIDE**, 5, b m Beat All (USA)—Pennys Pride (IRE) **Sun King Partnership & Partner**
13 4, Ch f Black Sam Bellamy (IRE)—Fairlie **Reveley Farms**
14 **HARVEY'S HOPE**, 8, b g Sinndar (IRE)—Ancara **The Home & Away Partnership**
15 **I GOT POWER**, 5, ch g Grape Tree Road—I Got Rhythm **Thomson & Fyffe Racing**
16 **IVAN BORU (IRE)**, 6, b g Brian Boru—Miranda's Lace (IRE) **Thwaites Furness & Zetland**
17 **JESSICA VALENTINE (IRE)**, 7, b m King's Theatre (IRE)—Jessica One (IRE) **Mr I. Valentine**
18 **KINGS GREY (IRE)**, 10, gr g King's Theatre (IRE)—Grey Mo (IRE) **J. Wade**
19 6, B g Overbury (IRE)—Marello **Mr & Mrs W. J. Williams**
20 **MR BEATLE**, 5, br g Beat All (USA)—Northern Native (IRE) **Mrs I. C. Sellars & Major & Mrs P. Arkwright**
21 **MR PUCK (IRE)**, 7, gr g Tikkanen (USA)—Vicky's Music (IRE) **Mrs I. C. Sellars & Major & Mrs P. Arkwright**
22 **MR SUPREME (IRE)**, 9, b g Beneficial—Ardfallon (IRE) **Mrs S. P. Granger**
23 **NIGHT IN MILAN (IRE)**, 8, b g Milan—Chione (IRE) **R. Collins**
24 4, Ch f Double Trigger (IRE)—Pennys Pride (IRE) **Reveley Farms**
25 **REDKALANI (IRE)**, 6, b g Ashkalani (IRE)—La Femme En Rouge **Cristiana's Crew & Reveley Farms**
26 **ROBBIE**, 10, b g Robellino (USA)—Corn Lily **Mrs S. McDonald**
27 **SAMBELUCKY (IRE)**, 9, b g Barathea (IRE)—Kalimar (IRE) **Maurice Foxton, JBP & DAG Partnership**
28 **SAMEDI SOIR**, 4, b f Black Sam Bellamy (IRE)—Bonne Anniversaire **Shade Oak Stud**
29 **SEREN GRIS**, 8, gr m Fair Mix (IRE)—Bayrouge (IRE) **Reveley Farms**
30 **SHADRACK (IRE)**, 10, gr g Tamayaz (CAN)—Alba Dancer **Mrs S. P. Granger**
31 **SPECIAL CATCH (IRE)**, 7, b g Catcher In The Rye (IRE)—Top Quality **Mr Mike Browne & Mr William McKeown**
32 **SPICULAS (IRE)**, 5, ch g Beneficial—Alicia's Charm (IRE) **R. Collins**
33 **STAR LILY (IRE)**, 5, b m King's Theatre (IRE)—Mrs Battleaxe (IRE) **Mr I. Valentine**
34 **STEELTEESCOMPONENT**, 5, gr g Tillerman—Out of The Shadows **Tees Components Ltd**
35 **TEESCOMPONENTS MAX**, 5, b g Grape Tree Road—Our Tees Component (IRE) **Tees Components Ltd**
36 **THURNHAM**, 8, b g Tobougg (IRE)—Nobratinetta (FR) **J. M. & Mrs M. R. Edwardson**
37 **VICTOR HEWGO**, 9, b g Old Vic—Pennys Pride (IRE) **Sir Ian Good**
38 **WALTZ DARLING (IRE)**, 6, b g Iffraaj—Aljafliyah **Mrs M B Thwaites & Mr M E Foxton**
39 **WHICHWAYTOBOUGIE**, 5, b g Tobougg (IRE)—Whichway Girl **The Supreme Partnership**

THREE-YEAR-OLDS

40 **BOOK AT BEDTIME**, b f Midnight Legend—Northern Native (IRE) **Mrs S. A. Smith**
41 B g Black Sam Bellamy (IRE)—I Got Rhythm **Thomson & Fyffe Racing**
42 **SAMSASWINGER**, b g Black Sam Bellamy (IRE)—Nobratinetta (FR) **The Lingdale Optimists**

TWO-YEAR-OLDS

43 Ch g 10/3 Monsieur Bond (IRE)—Fairlie (Halling (USA)) **Reveley Farms**
44 **HOOKERGATE GRAMMAR,** b g 29/4 Yeats (IRE)—Oulianovsk (IRE) (Peintre Celebre (USA)) (42000) **Mr M. Joyce**
45 Ch f 30/4 Sulamani (USA)—Let It Be (Entrepreneur) **Mr A. Frame**

Other Owners: Mr C. Alessi, Mr C. Anderson, Mr Philip Arkwright, Mrs Philip Arkwright, Mr Doug Bauckham, Mr D. E. Baxter, Mr D. Bowen, Mr M. Bradley, Mr Mike Browne, Mr Andy Clewer, Mr J. W. Coates, Mr A. E. Corbett, Mr M. Cressey, Mr Bernard Drinkall, Mr J. M. Edwardson, Mrs M. R. Edwardson, Mr M. E. Foxton, Mr Ian Fraser, Mrs J. W. Furness, Mr J. Fyffe, Mr Brian W. Goodall, Mr George Gray, Mr David A. Green, Mrs D. Greenhalgh, Mr Roger Hart, Mr P. Henry, Mr Gary Hopkins, Mr Anthony Iceton, Mrs Christine Lally, Mr P. Longstaff, Mr D. Lovell, Mr Ron MacDonald, Mr Robert McAlpine, Mr W. McKeown, Mr T. M. McKain, Mrs Lynn Morrison, Mrs D. A. Oliver, Mr D. Playforth, Mr Graeme Renton, Exors of the Late Mr John Renton, Mr Douglas Renton, Reveley Farms, Mr D. M. D. Robinson, Mr J. Scarth, Mrs Ian Sellars, Mr Richard V. Smith, Mr Richard Stephens, Mr Jim Struth, Mr G. Thomson, Mr J. Thoroughgood, Mrs M. B. Thwaites, Mr Michael Walsh, Mr W. J. Williams, Mrs M. Williams, Mrs C. M. Yates, Mr D. Young, Lord Zetland.

Assistant Trainer: Fiona Reveley **Jockey (NH):** James Reveley. **Conditional:** Elliot Brookbanks, Colm McCormack.

532 MR DAVID RICHARDS, Abergavenny
Postal: **White House, Llantilio Crossenny, Abergavenny, Gwent, NP7 8SU**
Contacts: **PHONE (01600) 780235**

1 **ANOTHER KATE (IRE)**, 10, gr m Norwich—Cracking Kate (IRE) **D. M. Richards**
2 **KATES BROTHER (IRE)**, 6, gr g Vertical Speed (FR)—Cracking Kate (IRE) **D. M. Richards**

Jockey (NH): Sam Thomas.

533 MRS LYDIA RICHARDS, Chichester
Postal: **Lynch Farm, Hares Lane, Funtington, Chichester, West Sussex, PO18 9LW**
Contacts: **YARD (01243) 574379 HOME (01243) 574882 MOBILE (07803) 199061**
E-MAIL lydia.richards@sky.com

1 **AALY**, 7, b g Milan—Leyaaly **Mrs Lydia Richards**
2 **BAYTOWN BERTIE**, 5, b g Orientor—Baytown Flyer **Mrs Lydia Richards**
3 **BEEP**, 4, b f Beat Hollow—Dialing Tone (USA) **The Beep Partnership**
4 **DEMOISELLE BOND**, 6, ch m Monsieur Bond (IRE)—Baytown Flyer **The Demoiselle Bond Partnership**
5 **INNER STEEL (IRE)**, 9, b g Zagreb (USA)—Mrs McClintock (IRE) **The Inner Steel Partnership**
6 **LEYLA'S GIFT**, 5, b m Milan—Leyaaly **Mrs Lydia Richards**
7 **MIGHTY THOR**, 4, b g Norse Dancer (IRE)—Leyaaly **M. P. Merwood**
8 **MYETTA**, 6, gr m Silver Patriarch (IRE)—Henrietta Holmes (IRE) **Mrs E. F. J. Seal**
9 **NOVEL DANCER**, 6, b g Dansili—Fictitious **Mrs Lydia Richards**
10 **VENETIAN LAD**, 5, ro g Midnight Legend—Henrietta Holmes (IRE) **The Venetian Lad Partnership**
11 **ZIGZAGA (IRE)**, 8, b g Zagreb (USA)—Mrs McClintock (IRE) **The Zigzaga Partnership**

Other Owners: Mr Hamish Kinmond, Mr Graeme Musker, Mrs Lydia Richards, Mrs Judy Seal, Mr M. Thompsett, Mr E. T. Wright.

534 MR NICKY RICHARDS, Greystoke
Postal: **Rectory Farm, Greystoke, Penrith, Cumbria, CA11 0UJ**
Contacts: **OFFICE (01768) 483392 HOME (01768) 483160 FAX (01768) 483933**
MOBILE (07771) 906609
E-MAIL n.g.richards@virgin.net WEBSITE www.nickyrichardsracing.com

1 **ACCORDINGTOTHEBOSS (IRE)**, 9, b g Accordion—Wooden Pass (IRE) **Miss J. R. Richards**
2 4, Br g Arcadio (GER)—Anck Su Namun (IRE) **Langdale Bloodstock**
3 **AND THE MAN**, 8, ch g Generous (IRE)—Retro's Lady (IRE) **Little Green Syndicate**
4 **ANOTHER BILL (IRE)**, 4, ch g Beneficial—Glacier Lilly (IRE) **Langdale Bloodstock**
5 4, Ch g Trans Island—Ashanti Dancer (IRE) **D. Wesley-Yates**
6 **AZURE GLAMOUR (IRE)**, 5, br g Golan (IRE)—Mirazur (IRE) **Mr Geoff Tunstall**
7 **BENMADIGAN (IRE)**, 12, ch g Presenting—Dont Tell Nell (IRE) **Charlie & Nick Fortescue**
8 **BERNARDELLI (IRE)**, 6, b g Golan (IRE)—Beautiful Blue (IRE) **Henriques & Lloyd-Bakers**
9 **BISHOPS GATE (IRE)**, 8, br g Bishop of Cashel—
Lischelle Star (IRE) **Mrs T. H. Barclay/Mrs F. D. McInnes Skinner**
10 **BRIJOMI QUEEN (IRE)**, 7, b m King's Theatre (IRE)—Tempest Belle (IRE) **M S Borders Racing Club & Partners**
11 **CARINENA (IRE)**, 5, b m Shantou (USA)—Dinny Kenn (IRE) **Mrs C. A. Torkington**
12 5, Br g Winged Love (IRE)—Cerise de Totes (FR) **David & Nicky Robinson**
13 **CHIDSWELL (IRE)**, 5, b g Gold Well—Manacured (IRE) **Langdale Bloodstock**
14 **COTTENWOOD (IRE)**, 6, br g Tillerman—Chavi (JPN) **Miss J. R. Richards**
15 5, B g Gold Well—Different Level (IRE) **D. Wesley-Yates**
16 **DUKE OF NAVAN (IRE)**, 6, b br g Presenting—Greenfieldflyer (IRE) **David & Nicky Robinson**
17 **EARLY APPLAUSE**, 6, b g Royal Applause—Early Evening **C. W. Jenkins**
18 **EDUARD (IRE)**, 6, b g Morozov (USA)—Dinny Kenn (IRE) **Kingdom Taverns Ltd**
19 **GLINGERBURN (IRE)**, 6, b g King's Theatre (IRE)—Wychnor Dawn **James Westoll**
20 **GOLD FUTURES (IRE)**, 5, b g Gold Well—Don't Discount Her (IRE) **Mrs C. A. Torkington**
21 **HOUSTON DYNIMO (IRE)**, 9, b g Rock of Gibraltar (IRE)—Quiet Mouse (USA) **Miss J. R. Richards**
22 4, B g Gold Well—Itsonlyraheen (IRE)
23 **JOFFREY (IRE)**, 5, b g Brian Boru—Ballyknock Present (IRE) **Miss J. R. Richards**
24 4, B f Robin des Champs (FR)—Lizzy Langtry (IRE)
25 **MALIN BAY (IRE)**, 9, b g Milan—Mirror of Flowers **David & Nicky Robinson**
26 **MERRYDOWN (IRE)**, 11, b g Oscar (IRE)—Euro Coin Lady (IRE) **Mrs Pat Sloan**
27 **MISTER MARKER (IRE)**, 10, ch g Beneficial—Bavards Girl (IRE) **J. A. Dudgeon**

MR NICKY RICHARDS - Continued

28 **NEDDY BOGLE (IRE)**, 4, br g Trans Island—Tranquil Sunset (IRE) **David & Nicky Robinson**
29 4, B g Milan—Newcastlebeauty (IRE)
30 **NOBLE ALAN (GER)**, 11, gr g King's Theatre (IRE)—Nirvavita (FR) **C. Bennett**
31 **ONE FOR HARRY (IRE)**, 6, b g Generous (IRE)—Strawberry Fool (FR) **The Fife Boys + 1**
32 **ONE FOR HOCKY (IRE)**, 6, b g Brian Boru—Wire Lady (IRE) **Kingdom Taverns Ltd**
33 **PARC DES PRINCES (USA)**, 8, b br g Ten Most Wanted (USA)—Miss Orah **Bob Bennett & Bill Graham**
34 **PEACHEY MOMENT (USA)**, 9, b br g Stormin Fever (USA)—Given Moment (USA)
35 4, B g Westerner—Ryehill Lady (IRE)
36 **SCARLET FIRE (IRE)**, 7, b g Helissio (FR)—Ross Dana (IRE) **Miss J. R. Richards**
37 **SIMPLY NED (IRE)**, 7, ch g Fruits of Love (USA)—Bishops Lass (IRE) **David & Nicky Robinson**
38 **SIR VINSKI (IRE)**, 5, ch g Vinnie Roe (IRE)—Mill Emerald **Langdale Bloodstock**
39 **ST GREGORY (IRE)**, 6, ch m Presenting—Ardrom **The Grafton Lounge Partnership**
40 **STREAMS OF WHISKEY (IRE)**, 7, br g Spadoun (FR)—Cherry Tops (IRE) **Mr & Mrs R. G. Kelvin Hughes**
41 **TALKIN THOMAS (IRE)**, 8, b g Talkin Man (CAN)—Keerou Lady (IRE) **Henriques & Lloyd-Bakers**
42 **TEDDY TEE (IRE)**, 5, b g Mountain High (IRE)—Knocksouna Lady (IRE) **David & Nicky Robinson**
43 **THAT'LL DO NICELY (IRE)**, 11, b g Bahhare (USA)—Return Again (IRE) **Miss J. R. Richards**
44 **TOP BILLING**, 5, br g Monsun (GER)—La Gandilie (FR) **Jimmy Dudgeon & Partners**
45 **TUTCHEC (FR)**, 7, gr g Turgeon (USA)—Pocahontas (FR) **Club 4 Racing**
46 **UN NOBLE (FR)**, 4, gr g Near Honor (GER)—Noble Gary (FR) **Mrs C. A. Torkington**
47 **WARRIORS TALE**, 5, b g Midnight Legend—Samandara (FR) **Langdale Bloodstock**
48 **WICKED SPICE (IRE)**, 5, b g Old Vic—Afdala (IRE) **Mrs Pat Sloan**
49 **WINTER ALCHEMY (IRE)**, 9, b g Fruits of Love (USA)—Native Land **The Alchemy Partnership**

Other Owners: Mr Noel Anderson, Mr M. Brown, Mr D. Burdon, Mr A. Clark, Mr J. Dobson, Mr Gerard Dowling, Mrs R. L. Elliot, Mr I. Forrester, Mrs Judy Fortescue, Mr M. Henriques, Miss Rhonda Hill, Mr C. G. M. Lloyd-Baker, Mr H. M. A. Lloyd-Baker, Mr H. Mattocks, Mr Edward Melville, Mr Darren Moore, Mr Walter Morris, Mr B. Ridley, Mr J. Whitehead, Mr K. Wilson.

Assistant Trainer: Miss Joey Richards **Jockey (NH):** Brian Harding. **Amateur:** Mr J. Nuttall, Miss J. R. Richards.

535

MR MARK RIMELL, Witney
Postal: **Fairspear Racing Stables, Fairspear Road, Leafield, Witney, Oxfordshire, OX29 9NT**
Contacts: **PHONE (01993) 878551 MOBILE (07778) 648303/(07973) 627054**
E-MAIL rimell@rimellracing.com WEBSITE www.rimellracing.com

1 **BHAKTI (IRE)**, 7, b g Rakti—Royal Bossi (IRE) **M. G. Rimell**
2 **DEFINITE LADY (IRE)**, 8, b m Definite Article—Phillis Hill **M. G. Rimell**
3 **JAZZ MAN (IRE)**, 7, ch g Beneficial—Slaney Jazz **M. G. Rimell**
4 **JUST BLUE**, 8, gr g Silver Patriarch (IRE)—Miss Millie **W. W. Stroud**
5 **PONCHO**, 5, b m Cape Cross (IRE)—Pixie Ring **M. G. Rimell**
6 **ROYAL ROO**, 5, b m Overbury (IRE)—Royal Roxy **Mrs A. Rimell**
7 4, B f Black Sam Bellamy (IRE)—Royal Roxy (IRE)
8 **SO SUDDEN**, 5, b m Needwood Blade—Sudden Spirit (FR) **M. G. Rimell**
9 **SPIRAEA**, 4, ch f Bahamian Bounty—Salvia **M. G. Rimell**
10 **TOP CHIEF**, 6, b g Doyen (IRE)—For More (FR) **M. G. Rimell**
11 **TWOWAYS (IRE)**, 8, br g Bob's Return (IRE)—Braw Lass **M. G. Rimell**

TWO-YEAR-OLDS

12 B f 25/3 Kayf Tara—Royal Roxy (IRE) (Exit To Nowhere (USA))

Assistant Trainer: Anne Rimell

536

MR MARK RIMMER, Newmarket
Postal: **2 Pinetree Bungalows, Philipps Close, Newmarket, Suffolk, CB8 0PB**
Contacts: **PHONE (01638) 577498 MOBILE (07913) 111205**

1 **EMERALD WILDERNESS (IRE)**, 10, b g Green Desert (USA)—Simla Bibi **Mr F. J. Perry**

THREE-YEAR-OLDS

2 **ECLIPTIC SUNRISE**, b f Compton Place—Winter Moon **M. E. Rimmer**
3 **IVAN MAZEPPA**, ch g Byron—Stealthy Times **Mr F. J. Perry**

Amateur: Mr J. Pearce.

537 MISS BETH ROBERTS, Bridgend
Postal: **14 Pwllcarn Terrace, Pontycymmer, Bridgend, Mid-Glamorgan, CF32 8AS**
Contacts: **PHONE (01656) 870076**

1 CHESNUT ANNIE (IRE), 13, ch m Weld—Leaden Sky (IRE) **Miss H. E. Roberts**
2 COPPER CARROLL (IRE), 10, b m Carroll House—Edermine Sunset (IRE) **Miss H. E. Roberts**
3 KIMS QUEST (IRE), 6, b m Needle Gun (IRE)—Flyingagain (IRE) **Miss H. E. Roberts**
4 MAGNUM TOO (IRE), 5, b g Westerner—Glenair Lucy (IRE) **Miss H. E. Roberts**
5 TWO SHADES OF BLUE, 7, b m Advise (FR)—Smilingatstrangers **Miss H. E. Roberts**

538 MR DAVE ROBERTS, Shrewsbury
Postal: **Leasowes Farm, Kenley, Shrewsbury, Shropshire, SY5 6NY**
Contacts: **PHONE (01746) 785255**

1 CAT SIX (USA), 10, b m Tale of The Cat (USA)—Hurricane Warning (USA) **Dave Roberts Racing**
2 CHICAGO ALLEY, 13, br m Bob Back (USA)—Winnetka Gal (IRE) **Dave Roberts Racing**
3 COCKNEY CLASS (USA), 7, gr ro g Speightstown (USA)—Snappy Little Cat (USA) **D. B. Roberts**
4 5, b g Revoque (IRE)—Cool Spring (IRE) **D. B. Roberts**
5 DEFINITE FUTURE (IRE), 5, b g Definite Article—Miss Marilyn (IRE) **Mr P. Rowley**
6 GREEN AND WHITE (ITY), 4, b g Denon (USA)—Sequita (GER) **Mr F. Sheridan**
7 GREEN SPECIAL (ITY), 4, ch g Denon (USA)—Groove (ITY) **Mr F. Sheridan**
8 HIGHLAND RIVER, 8, b g Indian Creek—Bee One (IRE) **Dave Roberts Racing**
9 MOANING BUTCHER, 4, b g Lucarno (USA)—Musical Chimes **J. Jones Racing Ltd**
10 MY FRIEND RIQUET (FR), 7, b g Laveron—Brave Chartreuse (FR) **D. B. Roberts**
11 4, Ch g Halling (USA)—Opera de Luna **Dr M. Voikhansky**
12 SCOGLIO, 6, b g Monsieur Bond (IRE)—Ex Mill Lady **D. B. Roberts**
13 SPIRIT RIVER (FR), 9, b g Poliglote—Love River (FR) **D. B. Roberts**
14 TANTALIZED, 5, b m Authorized (IRE)—Tarabela (CHI) **Dave Roberts Racing**
15 THATCHERS GOLD (IRE), 6, b g Gold Well—Chesterfield Lady (IRE) **Miss J. M. Green**
16 THE MOBB (IRE), 6, b g Westerner—Marlogan (IRE) **Dave Roberts Racing**

TWO-YEAR-OLDS

17 B c 3/3 What A Caper (IRE)—Squirtle (IRE) (In The Wings) **J. Jones Racing Ltd**

Other Owners: Mrs D. M. Roberts.

539 MR MIKE ROBERTS, Hailsham
Postal: **Summertree Farm, Bodle Street Green, Hailsham, East Sussex, BN27 4QT**
Contacts: **PHONE (01435) 830231 FAX (01435) 830887**
E-MAIL **mike@summertree-racing.com**

1 SNIPPETYDOODAH, 6, b m King's Theatre (IRE)—Kimpour (FR) **M. J. Roberts**
2 UNDERWOOD (FR), 6, b g Assessor (IRE)—Attualita (FR) **M. J. Roberts**
3 UTALY (FR), 6, b g Shaanmer (IRE)—Nataly (FR) **M. J. Roberts**

540 MRS RENEE ROBESON, Newport Pagnell
Postal: **Fences Farm, Tyringham, Newport Pagnell, Buckinghamshire, MK16 9EN**
Contacts: **PHONE/FAX (01908) 611255 MOBILE (07831) 579898**
E-MAIL **robesons@btconnect.com**

1 AESCHYLUS, 7, b gr g Act One—Circe **A D G Oldrey, G C Hartigan & S F Oldrey**
2 AULIS, 5, gr g Act One—Circe **A D G Oldrey, G C Hartigan & S F Oldrey**
3 BENEFIT CUT (IRE), 8, b g Beneficial—I'm Maggy (NZ) **Howard Cooke & Terence Jenner**
4 CAROLINA WREN, 5, b m Sir Harry Lewis (USA)—Wren Warbler **Mrs R. L. M. Robeson**
5 COFFERS, 4, ch g Bahamian Bounty—Fabuleux Millie (IRE) **Mrs R. L. M. Robeson**
6 COLEBROOKE, 6, b g Shamardal (USA)—Shimna **TMT Grand**
7 DAWN COMMANDER (GER), 7, gr g Mamool (IRE)—Dark Lady (GER) **Nick Brown Racing**
8 EREYNA, 5, gr m Erhaab (USA)—Tereyna **Mrs R. L. M. Robeson**
9 4, B f Tobougg (IRE)—Forest Pride (IRE) **The Oakley Partnership**
10 GENNY WREN, 8, ch m Generous (IRE)—Wren Warbler **Mrs R. L. M. Robeson**

MRS RENEE ROBESON - Continued

11 **MAYPOLE LASS**, 4, ch f Halling (USA)—Maigold Lass **Mr B. H. Turner**
12 **NORSE WREN**, 6, ch g Norse Dancer (IRE)—Wren Warbler **Mrs R. L. M. Robeson**
13 **OGEE**, 11, ch g Generous (IRE)—Aethra (USA) **Sir E. de Rothschild**
14 **REYNO**, 6, b g Sleeping Indian—Tereyna **Mrs R. L. M. Robeson**
15 **SAN TELM (IRE)**, 9, b g Oscar (IRE)—Magical Mist (IRE) **The Tyringham Partnership**
16 **SILVER WREN**, 7, gr m Silver Patriarch (IRE)—Wren Warbler **Mrs R. L. M. Robeson**
17 **SMART EXIT (IRE)**, 7, b g Exit To Nowhere (USA)—Navaro (IRE) **The Ravenstone Partnership**

Other Owners: Mr N. J. Brown, Mr H. J. Cooke, G. C. Hartigan, Mr T. A. Jenner, A. D. G. Oldrey, S. F. Oldrey, D. Yates.

Assistant Trainer: Stuart Edmunds

---

541 **MISS SARAH ROBINSON, Bridgwater**
Postal: **Newnham Farm, Shurton, Stogursey, Bridgwater, Somerset, TA5 1QG**
Contacts: **PHONE (01278) 732357 FAX (01278) 732357 MOBILE (07866) 435197 / (07971) 475947**
E-MAIL info@sarahrobinsonracing.co.uk WEBSITE www.sarahrobinsonracing.co.uk

1 **FIRST SPIRIT**, 8, ch m First Trump—Flaming Spirt **Mr B. Robinson**
2 **NEWNHAM FLYER (IRE)**, 12, gr m Exit To Nowhere (USA)—Paper Flight **Mr B. Robinson**
3 **THEROADTOGOREY (IRE)**, 8, b g Revoque (IRE)—Shannon Mor (IRE) **Mr B. Robinson**

Assistant Trainer: Mr B. Robinson

Jockey (NH): Ian Popham. **Conditional:** Kevin Jones. **Amateur:** Miss S. Robinson.

---

542 **MISS PAULINE ROBSON, Capheaton**
Postal: **Kidlaw Farm, Capheaton, Newcastle Upon Tyne, NE19 2AW**
Contacts: **PHONE (01830) 530241 MOBILE (07721) 887489 or (07814) 708725 (David)**
E-MAIL pauline.robson@virgin.net

1 **DON'T TELL ANYONE (IRE)**, 7, b g Rashar (USA)—Crossgales Flutter (IRE) **Foley Brothers**
2 **FULL JACK (FR)**, 7, b g Kahyasi—Full Contact (FR) **Mr & Mrs Raymond Anderson Green**
3 **GET THE PAPERS**, 7, b g Kayf Tara—Smart Topsy **Non Stop Racing**
4 **HUMBIE (IRE)**, 10, b g Karinga Bay—South Queen Lady (IRE) **Mr & Mrs Raymond Anderson Green**
5 **RIVAL D'ESTRUVAL (FR)**, 9, b g Khalkevi (IRE)—
　　　　　　　　　　　　　　　　　Made In Law (FR) **Mr & Mrs Raymond Anderson Green**
6 **SCIMON TEMPLAR (FR)**, 6, b br g Saint des Saints (FR)—
　　　　　　　　　　　　　　　　　Kermesse d'estruval (FR) **Mr & Mrs Raymond Anderson Green**
7 **SHANEN (IRE)**, 8, b g Tikkanen (USA)—Ursha (FR) **Mr & Mrs Raymond Anderson Green**
8 **UPSILON BLEU (FR)**, 6, b g Panoramic—Glycine Bleue (FR) **Mr & Mrs Raymond Anderson Green**
9 **VISION DE LA VIE (FR)**, 4, ch g Sin Kiang (FR)—Vidahermosa (FR) **I Couldn't Switch Club**

Other Owners: S. P. Graham, R. A. Green, Mrs A. Green, Mr D. J. A. Green, Mr M. J. Jenkins, Mr D. Parker, Miss P. Robson.

Assistant Trainer: David Parker

Jockey (NH): Timmy Murphy, Richie McGrath.

---

543 **MR FRANCOIS ROHAUT, Pau**
Postal: **Chermin du Champ de Tir, Domaine de Sers, 64000 Pau, France**
Contacts: **PHONE (0033) 59 32 44 58 FAX (0033) 59 62 46 52 MOBILE (0033) 6727 75619**
E-MAIL ecurie.rohaut@wanadoo.fr

Trainer did not supply details of his older horses

TWO-YEAR-OLDS
1 **AUDERVILLE (FR)**, b f 1/2 Le Havre (IRE)—Artana (FR) (Sendawar (IRE)) **G. Augustin Normand**
2 B c 30/1 Turtle Bowl (IRE)—Baldamelle (FR) (Dansili) (15485) **F. Rohaut**
3 **BAROOD (FR)**, b c 13/5 Soldier of Fortune (IRE)—
　　　　　　　　　Beau Fete (ARG) (Beau Sultan (USA)) **Shiekh Abdullah Bin Khalifa Al Thani**
4 Ch f 8/2 Siyouni (FR)—Fonage (Zafonic (USA)) (20905)
5 **HADAYAANA**, ch f 14/2 Shamardal (USA)—Bahja (USA) (Seeking The Gold (USA)) **Hamdan Al Maktoum**

MR FRANCOIS ROHAUT - Continued

6 Gr f 18/4 Verglas (IRE)—Hideaway (FR) (Cape Cross (IRE)) **Skymarc Farm**
7 **L'ECRIVAIN DORE (FR),** b c 5/2 Literato (FR)—Golden Lily (FR) (Dolphin Street (FR)) (25551) **Pandora Racing**
8 B c 6/5 Elusive City (USA)—Lady Golconda (FR) (Kendor (FR)) **B. Van Dalfsen**
9 **LANDIGOU (FR),** b c 30/4 Le Havre (IRE)—Landskia (FR) (Lando (GER)) **G. Augustin Normand**
10 **LARMINA (FR),** b f 31/3 Thewayyouare (USA)—Lilac Charm (IRE) (Marju (IRE)) (9291)
11 **LONGUEIL (FR),** b c 23/3 Le Havre (IRE)—Love Queen (IRE) (Val Royal (FR)) **G. Augustin Normand**
12 **MAHIR (FR),** b c 18/2 Makfi—Shifting Sands (FR) (Hernando) **Shiekh Abdullah Bin Khalifa Al Thani**
13 Ch c 26/3 King's Best (USA)—Monava (FR) (El Prado (IRE)) **N. Elwes**
14 B c 7/3 Teofilo (IRE)—Mulled Wine (FR) (Night Shift (USA)) (65814) **Khalifa Dasmal**
15 B c 11/2 Sholokhov (IRE)—Peaceful Love (GER) (Dashing Blade) (46457) **Pandora Racing**
16 B c 12/3 Arcano (IRE)—Subilita (GER) (Dr Fong (USA)) (38714) **Hamdan Al Maktoum**
17 **SUSANNA VASSA (FR),** ch f 9/2 Equiano (FR)—Anasy (USA) (Gone West (USA)) **Pandora Racing**
18 **TAGADIRT,** b c 18/2 Aqlaam—Latent Lover (IRE) (In The Wings) **Pandora Racing**
19 **THAKERAH (IRE),** ch f 30/4 New Approach (IRE)—Tadris (USA) (Red Ransom (USA)) **Hamdan Al Maktoum**
20 B f 19/4 Teofilo (IRE)—Winning Family (IRE) (Fasliyev (USA)) **Haras D'Etreham**

544

MR W. M. ROPER, Curragh
Postal: **French Furze, Maddenstown, The Curragh, Co. Kildare, Ireland**
Contacts: **PHONE (00353) 45 441821 MOBILE (00353) 86 823 4279**
E-MAIL markroper1@eircom.net

1 **CLARIOR EX OBSCURO (IRE),** 8, br g Morozov (USA)—Achates (IRE) **Mr W. M. Roper**
2 **COURTLY CONDUCT (IRE),** 9, b g Court Cave (IRE)—Regency Charm (IRE) **Mr P. E. I. Newell**
3 **LARSEN BEE (IRE),** 8, ch m Frenchmans Bay (FR)—Surabaya (FR) **Mr W. M. Roper**
4 **SIX BOOKS (IRE),** 6, b g Kutub (IRE)—Love's Always Game (IRE) **Mr P. E. I. Newell**
5 **VAALWATER (IRE),** 9, b g Danehill Dancer (USA)—Amaranthus (USA) **Mr W. M. Roper**

Assistant Trainer: Barry Heffernan

545

MR BRIAN ROTHWELL, Malton
Postal: **Old Post Office, Oswaldkirk, York, North Yorkshire, YO62 5XT**
Contacts: **PHONE (01439) 788859 MOBILE (07969) 968241**
E-MAIL brian.rothwell1@googlemail.com

1 **BONNIE BURNETT (IRE),** 7, b br m Hawk Wing (USA)—Chameleon **Mrs G. Sparks**
2 **DOUBLE HAPPINESS,** 4, ch f Sakhee (USA)—Fu Wa (USA) **B. S. Rothwell**
3 **LADY NORLELA,** 8, b m Reset (AUS)—Lady Netbetsports (IRE) **B. S. Rothwell**
4 **MAJESTIC ANGEL (IRE),** 5, b m Majestic Missile (IRE)—Free Angel (USA) **B. S. Rothwell**
5 **QUEEN OF EPIRUS,** 6, ch m Kirkwall—Andromache **B. S. Rothwell**
6 5, b g Olden Times—Reasoning **B. S. Rothwell**
7 **TINSELTOWN,** 8, b g Sadler's Wells (USA)—Peony **Mr A. F. Arnott**

THREE-YEAR-OLDS

8 **BERTHA BURNETT (IRE),** gr f Verglas (IRE)—Starsazi **Mrs G. Sparks**
9 **PETERGATE,** b g Alhaarth (IRE)—Shamayel **Mrs G. Sparks**
10 **TAKEMYBREATHAWAY,** b f Court Masterpiece—Corblets **Mrs M. Lingwood**
11 **TAWAN,** b g Tiger Hill (USA)—Lady Netbetsports (IRE) **P. Moorhouse**
12 **TELL ME WHEN,** b f Monsieur Bond (IRE)—Giffoine **Sparks, Valentine & Lingwood**

Other Owners: Mr A. J. Sparks, B. Valentine.

546

MR J. C. ROUGET, Pau
Postal: **Chemin de la Foret Bastard, Domaine de l'Aragnon, 64000 Pau, France**
Contacts: **PHONE (0033) 5593 32790 FAX (0033) 5593 32930 MOBILE (0033) 6102 70335**
E-MAIL societerouget@orange.fr

1 **AGY (IRE),** 4, b c Dylan Thomas (IRE)—Diamond Star (IRE) **G. Augustin-Normand**
2 **CAMARETZ (USA),** 4, ch g Mr Greeley (USA)—Drums of Freedom (USA) **Ecurie Tagada SAS**
3 **CHANCELIER (FR),** 4, b g Peer Gynt (JPN)—Particuliere **G. Augustin-Normand & Mme B. Hermelin**
4 **COURCY (FR),** 4, b g Mizzen Mast (USA)—Insan Mala (IRE) **G. Augustin-Normand**

MR J. C. ROUGET - Continued

5 **CRICKEL WOOD (FR)**, 4, b c Muhtathir—Tanguista (FR) **A. Caro**
6 **ESPERO (FR)**, 5, gr h Verglas (IRE)—Queen's Conquer **G. Augustin-Normand & J-C Rouget**
7 **ETALONDES (FR)**, 4, b c Royal Applause—Fancy Dance **G. Augustin-Normand**
8 **FIVE AVENUE (IRE)**, 4, ch c Tamayuz—Luminata (IRE) **Mme M.T. Dubuc-Grassa & Mme F. Teboul**
9 **FREE WALK (FR)**, 4, b c Librettist (USA)—River Ballade (USA) **J. F. Gribomont**
10 **GAILY GAME**, 6, b g Montjeu (IRE)—Gaily Tiara (USA) **Ecurie I.M. Fares**
11 **HECTOMARE (IRE)**, 5, b g Hurricane Run (IRE)—Overruled (IRE) **G. Augustin-Normand**
12 **HIGH STAR (FR)**, 7, ch g High Yield (USA)—Étoile d'or (FR) **S. Brogi & J-C Rouget**
13 **KEIRA (FR)**, 5, b m Turtle Bowl (IRE)—Nazlia (FR) **B. Benaych**
14 **KERMIYAN (FR)**, 7, b g Green Desert (USA)—Kerasha (FR) **S. A. Aga Khan**
15 **LASTUCE (FR)**, 4, b f Orpen (USA)—Labamba (FR) **Lauray & Beziat**
16 **MISTER GIBRALTAR (IRE)**, 8, ch g Rock of Gibraltar (IRE)—Carisheba (USA) **J-C Rouget**
17 **SILAS MARNER (FR)**, 7, b h Muhtathir—Street Kendra (FR) **A. Jathiere**
18 **SNAP CALL**, 4, ch g Tamayuz—Sister Agnes (IRE) **D-Y Treves**
19 **STAR PRINCE (FR)**, 4, b c Green Tune (USA)—Princess Love (FR) **A. Caro**
20 **SUNNY (FR)**, 5, b g Muhtathir—Vol Sauvage (FR) **B. Margrez Horses & J-C Rouget**
21 **VAUNOISE (IRE)**, 4, b f Teofilo (IRE)—Tipperary Honor (FR) **G. Augustin-Normand**
22 **WIGHT IS WIGHT (IRE)**, 4, b g Peintre Celebre (USA)—Alenteja (IRE) **D-Y Treves**
23 **YARUBO (FR)**, 6, ch g Muhtathir—Miss Mission (IRE) **A. Caro**

THREE-YEAR-OLDS

24 **AMFREVILLE**, b f Le Havre (IRE)—Alyousufeya (IRE) **G. Augustin-Normand**
25 **ANAHITA (FR)**, b f Turtle Bowl (IRE)—Nazlia (FR) **Ecurie J.-L. Tepper**
26 **ANNALULU (IRE)**, b f Hurricane Run (IRE)—Louve de Saron (FR) **C. Marzocco**
27 **AR POULGWENN (IRE)**, b g Nayef (USA)—Ballerina Blue (IRE) **J. Seche & J.P. Vallee Lambert**
28 **ARANIYA**, b f Elusive City (USA)—Artistica (IRE) **H. H. Aga Khan**
29 **AREOS (USA)**, b br c Henrythenavigator (USA)—Momix **B. Margrez Horses & J.-C. Rouget**
30 **ARTHUR'S QUEEN (FR)**, b f Soldier of Fortune (IRE)—Tintagel **J.-C. Rouget**
31 **ASHKOUN**, b c Sinndar (IRE)—Ashalina (FR) **H. H. Aga Khan**
32 **AVENIR CERTAIN (FR)**, b f Le Havre (IRE)—Puggy (IRE) **A. Caro & G. Augustin-Normand**
33 **BAINO HOPE (FR)**, b f Jeremy (USA)—Baino Ridge (FR) **Ecurie I.M. Fares**
34 **BALFOUR (FR)**, b c Myboycharlie (IRE)—Phone the Diva (USA) **D.-Y. Treves**
35 **BEAUTY PARLOR (USA)**, b f Elusive Quality (USA)—Moon Queen (FR) **J. Allen**
36 **BRIONES (FR)**, gr f Green Tune (USA)—Golden Glare (FR) **M. Schwartz**
37 **BRYNICA (FR)**, b f Desert Style (IRE)—Brusca (USA) **H. H. Aga Khan**
38 **CARAMANTA (FR)**, b f Zamindar (USA)—Clodovina (FR) **H. H. Aga Khan**
39 **CERTAIN IN PARIS (FR)**, b g Lawman (FR)—Last Cast (FR) **Ecurie J.-L. Tepper**
40 **CERTITUDE (IRE)**, b f Oasis Dream—Coquerelle (IRE) **Ecurie Des Monceaux**
41 **CRISOLLES (FR)**, b f Le Havre (IRE)—Sandsnow (IRE) **G. Augustin-Normand**
42 **DANAM (FR)**, b c Doctor Dino (FR)—Desarmante (FR) **Mme. M.-T. Dubuc-Grassa**
43 **DAVANTAGE**, ch f Galileo (IRE)—Delicieuse Lady **Ecurie Des Monceaux**
44 **DIYOUDAR**, b c Elusive City (USA)—Diasilixa (FR) **H. H. Aga Khan**
45 **DNIEPER (USA)**, b c Giant's Causeway (USA)—Volga (USA) **J. Allen**
46 **DONTSTOPLOVINGME (FR)**, ch f Creachadoir (IRE)—Save Me The Waltz (FR) **J.-F. Gribomont**
47 **DYE FORE (FR)**, b c Giant's Causeway (USA)—Homebound (USA) **J. Allen**
48 **ELUSIVE KAY (FR)**, b c Elusive City (USA)—Lunashkaya **A. Jathiere**
49 **ENNAYA**, b f Nayef (USA)—Elva (IRE) **S. A. Aga Khan**
50 **FIRST AIRBORNE**, b c Medaglia d'oro (USA)—My Annette (USA) **J. Allen**
51 **FLAMBOYANT (FR)**, b c Peer Gynt (JPN)—Relicia Bere (FR) **Mme B. Hermelin & J-C Rouget**
52 **FOURDRINIER (USA)**, b c Dynaformer (USA)—Grande Melody (IRE) **J. Allen**
53 **FRIARDEL (FR)**, ch g Le Havre (IRE)—Fancy Dance **G. Augustin-Normand**
54 **GLADSTONE (FR)**, b c Mizzen Mast (USA)—Bahia Gold (USA) **D-Y Treves**
55 **GONNA RUN (FR)**, b c Hurricane Cat (USA)—Realdad (ARG) **D-Y Treves**
56 **GRACE OF LOVE (IRE)**, b f Lawman (FR)—Rampoldina **P. Augier & J-C Rouget**
57 **HONEYMOON COCKTAIL (FR)**, gr c Martaline—Caipirinia (FR) **D-Y Treves**
58 **ITERATION (FR)**, b f Astronomer Royal (USA)—Lunaba (FR) **Ecurie La Vallee Martigny & M. Zerolo**
59 **JALLY (IRE)**, ch g Tamayuz—Miss Beatrix (IRE) **Hamdan Al Maktoum**
60 **JUST MARRIED (IRE)**, b f Tamayuz—Wedding Gown **E. Puerari**
61 **KATIOUSHKA**, b f Mastercraftsman (IRE)—Minor Point **A. Jathiere**
62 **KEENA**, b f Acclamation—Kerasha (FR) **S. A. Aga Khan**
63 **KENDEMAI (FR)**, b c Carlotamix (FR)—Kendorya (FR) **B. Belinguier & J-C Rouget**
64 **KENZADARGENT (FR)**, b f Kendargent (FR)—Quiza Bere (FR) **M. Schwartz**
65 **KIFAAH**, b c Dubawi (IRE)—Mokaraba **Hamdan Al Maktoum**
66 **KIRAM (FR)**, b c Elusive City (USA)—King Luna (FR) **H. H. Aga Khan**
67 **KOZIDEH (FR)**, ch f Gold Away (IRE)—Kozaka (FR) **S. A. Aga Khan**

MR J. C. ROUGET - Continued

68 **L'ARDENT (FR)**, b c Soldier of Fortune (IRE)—Princesse de Viane (FR) **B. Magrez Horses**
69 **LA HOGUETTE (FR)**, b f Le Havre (IRE)—Isanous (FR) **Mr G. Augustin-Normand**
70 **LA TEMPERANTE (IRE)**, gr f Naaqoos—Magical Hawk (USA) **B. Magrez Horses**
71 **LESSTALK IN PARIS (IRE)**, b f Cape Cross (IRE)—Top Toss (IRE) **Ecurie J-L Tepper**
72 **LORESHO (FR)**, b c Halling (USA)—Luna Gulch (FR) **H. H. Aga Khan**
73 **LOVABLE (CAN)**, b f Survivalist (USA)—Zawaahy (USA) **M. C. Byrne**
74 **LOVE STRIKE (IRE)**, b c Zamindar (USA)—Sculpted (FR) **J-C Rouget**
75 **LUANNAN (IRE)**, b c Zamindar (USA)—Laxlova (FR) **H. H. Aga Khan**
76 **MAJRAA (IRE)**, b f Invincible Spirit (IRE)—Santa Louisia **Hamdan Al Maktoum**
77 **MARSOUD (USA)**, b br c Dixie Union (USA)—Paris Rose (USA) **Hamdan Al Maktoum**
78 **MUBASHERA (USA)**, b f Medaglia d'oro (USA)—Nuqoosh **Zerolo, Puerari & Shanahan**
79 **MUSAADAQA (IRE)**, b f Tamayuz—Million Waves (IRE) **Hamdan Al Maktoum**
80 **MUSTAHDAF (USA)**, b c Dynaformer (USA)—Tabrir (IRE) **Hamdan Al Maktoum**
81 **NABBAASH**, b c Aqlaam—Poppo's Song (CAN) **Hamdan Al Maktoum**
82 **ORANGEFIELD (FR)**, b c Soave (GER)—Moon Serenade **Mme. B. Hermelin & J-C Rouget**
83 **ORBEC (FR)**, b c Le Havre (IRE)—Langrune (IRE) **G. Augustin-Normand**
84 **PASSION BLANCHE**, b f Dutch Art—Siren Sound **B. Magrez Horses & J-C Roget**
85 **PETITE PARISIENNE**, b f Montmartre (FR)—Ejina (FR) **Ecurie Tagadettes**
86 **PRAVDA**, b f Nayef (USA)—Bay Tree (IRE) **F. Salman**
87 **PRINCE GIBRALTAR (FR)**, ch c Rock of Gibraltar (IRE)—
　　　　　　　　　　Princess Sofia (UAE) **Gribomont, Pokrovsky & Ecurie La Vallee Martigny**
88 **RANEK (IRE)**, ch c Medicean—Spirit of South (AUS) **D-Y Treves**
89 **RUN IN PARIS (IRE)**, b f Hurricane Run (IRE)—Epistole (IRE) **Ecurie J-L Tepper**
90 **SAANE (FR)**, b g Le Havre (IRE)—Salamon **G Augustin-Normand**
91 **SAINT GREGOIRE (FR)**, b c Le Havre (IRE)—Scapegrace (IRE) **G Augustin-Normand**
92 **SAINT POIS (FR)**, b g Le Havre (IRE)—Our Dream Queen **G Augustin-Normand**
93 **SAINTE CROIX (FR)**, b f Le Havre (IRE)—Sainte Adresse **G Augustin-Normand**
94 **SALAI (FR)**, b c Myboycharlie (IRE)—Mabadi (USA) **Schwartz & Ecurie La Vallee Martigny**
95 **SANABOWL (FR)**, b g Turtle Bowl (IRE)—Sanagora (IRE) **D-Y Treves**
96 **SOURIYAN**, b c Alhaarth (IRE)—Serasana **S. A. Aga Khan**
97 **SPEED ROAD (FR)**, b c King's Best (USA)—Life On The Road (IRE) **L. Dassault**
98 **STEP AND GO (IRE)**, b c Footstepsinthesand—Fresh Laurels (IRE) **Pokrovsky, NcNulty & Elissalt**
99 **SUMMER MOON**, b f Elusive City (USA)—Kalatuna (FR) **Zerolo, Haras De Saint Pair & Puerari**
100 **TAKE THE CROWN (FR)**, ch c Creachadoir (IRE)—Taking Haven (FR) **J-C Weill**
101 **TALEMA (FR)**, ch f Sunday Break (JPN)—Algoa (FR) **J-C Weill**
102 **TAPAAN ZEE (IRE)**, br f Holy Roman Emperor (IRE)—Belle Rebelle (IRE) **D-Y Treves**
103 **TRADER OF FORTUNE (FR)**, b c Soldier of Fortune (IRE)—
　　　　　　　　　　Back The Winner (IRE) **Ecurie J-L Tepper & F. McNulty**
104 **TRIPTYKA (IRE)**, br gr f Mastercraftsman (IRE)—
　　　　　　　　　　Acatama (USA) **Fellous, Zribi, Fellous, Saada, Giaoui & Blaisse**
105 **VERDURA (USA)**, ch f Smart Strike (CAN)—Wonder Woman (USA) **J. Allen**
106 **VISORIYNA (FR)**, b f Dansili—Visorama (IRE) **H. H. Aga Khan**
107 **VITA (FR)**, gr f Elusive City (USA)—Vezina (FR) **D-Y Treves**
108 **VOLKOVKHA**, b f Holy Roman Emperor (IRE)—Armanda (GER) **A. Jathiere**
109 **WAKINA LUTA (IRE)**, b f King's Best (USA)—Top Crystal (IRE) **Zerolo & Gravereaux**
110 **WAR EFFORT (USA)**, b f War Front (USA)—Louve Royale (IRE) **J. Allen**
111 **WAR OFFICE (USA)**, b f War Front (USA)—Storybook (UAE) **J. Allen**
112 **WIRELESS (FR)**, ch c Kentucky Dynamite (USA)—Sachet (USA) **Ecurie I M Fares**
113 **ZABROV (IRE)**, b c Mastercraftsman (IRE)—Fine And Mellow (FR) **A. Jathiere**
114 **ZLATAN IN PARIS (FR)**, b c Slickly (FR)—Tossup (USA) **Ecurie J-L Tepper & F. McNulty**
115 **ZVAROV (IRE)**, b c Elusive City (USA)—Marie Rossa **A. Jathiere**

TWO-YEAR-OLDS

116 **A SPACE IN TIME**, b f 5/4 Lord Shanakill (USA)—Market Index (IRE) (Danehill Dancer (IRE)) (27100) **D-Y Treves**
117 **ADARA (FR)**, ch f 13/4 Charge d'affaires—
　　　　　　　　　　Malinday (FR) (Lord of Men) (54200) **O. Carli & M. G. Augustin-Normand**
118 **AIMLESS LADY**, b f 14/1 Peer Gynt (JPN)—Poet's Studio (USA) (Bertrando (USA)) (11614) **J.-C. Rouget (s)**
119 **AKWABA**, b c 6/2 Kentucky Dynamite (USA)—
　　　　　　　　　　Funny Line (FR) (Emperor Jones (USA)) (20131) **P. Augier & O. Carli**
120 **ALIOCHKA (IRE)**, b f 23/2 Intikhab (USA)—Luna Royale (FR) (Royal Applause) (123886) **Cuadra Montalban**
121 **ALL THE NEWS (USA)**, b c 3/4 Bernardini (USA)—Black Speck (USA) (Arch (USA)) **J. Allen**
122 **ANNOUVILLE (FR)**, b f 7/4 Air Chief Marshal (IRE)—Langrune (IRE) (Fasliyev (USA)) **G. Augustin-Normand**
123 **ANTOGNONI (FR)**, b c 4/5 Nayef (USA)—
　　　　　　　　　　Tanguista (FR) (War Chant (USA)) (19357) **Mme L. Urano & J.-C. Rouget (s)**
124 **ARDAHAN (FR)**, gr c 28/1 Azamour (IRE)—Artistica (IRE) (Spectrum (IRE)) **H. H. Aga Khan**

MR J. C. ROUGET - Continued

125 **AUCUN DOUTE (IRE)**, b f 11/3 Elusive City (USA)—
Corrozal (GER) (Cape Cross (IRE)) (24777) **B. Magrez Horses**
126 **BELOIT (USA)**, b c 1/1 Dynaformer (USA)—Louve des Reves (IRE) (Sadler's Wells (USA)) **J. Allen**
127 **BLUEGRASS (FR)**, ch c 19/2 Kentucky Dynamite (USA)—Little Jaw (Footstepsinthesand) **Ecurie I M Fares**
128 **BROADWAY BOOGIE (IRE)**, b c 18/4 Distorted Humor (USA)—Grande Melody (IRE) (Grand Lodge (USA)) **J. Allen**
129 **BUKHARI (FR)**, gr c 4/4 Dalakhani (IRE)—Brofalya (FR) (Fasliyev (USA)) **H. H. Aga Khan**
130 **CARLO BAY**, b c 16/3 Diktat—Lady Cree (IRE) (Medicean) (51877) **Mme L. Urano**
131 **CERTES**, b c 25/4 Astronomer Royal (USA)—Mabadi (USA) (Sahm (USA)) (34843) **E. Pokrovsky & F. Le Clec'h**
132 B c 10/4 Paco Boy (IRE)—Cherryxma (FR) (Linamix (FR)) **H. H. Aga Khan**
133 B c 21/1 Medicean—Clarinda (FR) (Montjeu (IRE)) **H. H. Aga Khan**
134 **CLISHET**, b c 12/5 Sinndar (IRE)—Sachet (USA) (Royal Academy (USA)) **Ecurie I. M. Fares**
135 **CLOSER TO HOME (IRE)**, b c 5/4 Soldier of Fortune (IRE)—
Maid For Music (IRE) (Dubai Destination (USA)) (17034) **J.-C. Rouget (S)**
136 **COUPESARTE**, gr f 26/3 Kendargent (FR)—Coconino (IRE) (Okawango (USA)) (42586) **G. Augustin-Normand**
137 **DACHENKA**, b f 18/4 Dansili—Blaze of Colour (Rainbow Quest (USA)) (162601) **Caudra Montalban**
138 **DAKOTA QUEEN (USA)**, b f 1/1 War Front (USA)—Moon Queen (IRE) (Sadler's Wells (USA)) **J. Allen**
139 **DANCE ON THE HILL (IRE)**, br f 6/4 Danehill Dancer (IRE)—
Hitra (USA) (Langfuhr (CAN)) (69686) **Ecurie J.-L. Tepper**
140 **DELIVRANCE**, b f 1/1 Makfi—
Mrs Ting (USA) (Lyphard (USA)) (38714) **Ecurie La Vallee Martigny / Lachaud / De Villeneuve**
141 **DR KING**, b c 4/5 Dr Fong (USA)—Sommerflora (GER) (Pivotal) (10840) **D. Y. Treves**
142 **DUKE OF DUNDEE (FR)**, b g 1/1 Duke of Marmalade (IRE)—
Santa Louisia (Highest Honor (FR)) (21680) **Ecurie J. - L. Tepper**
143 **EASY FEELING**, b f 5/5 Elusive Quality (USA)—Wonder Woman (USA) (Storm Cat (USA)) **J. Allen**
144 B f 14/3 Azamour (IRE)—Elbasana (IRE) (Indian Ridge) **S. A. Aga Khan**
145 **ELKA (IRE)**, b f 28/4 Elusive City (USA)—Lunashkaya (Muhtathir) **A. Jathiere**
146 **ELUSIVE PARTICLE**, b c 16/3 Elusive City (USA)—
From This Day On (USA) (El Prado (IRE)) (30971) **Sheikh J. Bin Hamad Al Thani**
147 **EPONYME (IRE)**, b f 25/2 Zamindar (USA)—
Ballyvarra (IRE) (Sadler's Wells (USA)) (32520) **Ecurie La Vallee Martigny & E. Pokrovsky**
148 **ERVEDYA (FR)**, b f 13/4 Siyouni (FR)—Elva (IRE) (King's Best (USA)) **S. A. Aga Khan**
149 **FAWAASEL (IRE)**, b c 1/4 Haatef (USA)—Insaaf (Averti (IRE)) **Hamdan Al Maktoum**
150 B c 22/2 Galileo (IRE)—Festoso (IRE) (Diesis) **P. Shanahan**
151 **FIRST COMPANY**, b c 30/4 Elusive City (USA)—
Amnesia (USA) (Septieme Ciel (USA)) (19357) **C. Ben Lassin & Ecurie J.L. Tepper**
152 **FLAG OFFICER**, b c 1/1 War Front (USA)—My Annette (USA) (Red Ransom (USA)) **J. Allen**
153 **GOLD DUST (FR)**, b f 15/1 Le Havre (IRE)—
Golding Star (FR) (Gold Away (IRE)) (30971) **G. Augustin-Normand & Mme. E. Vidal**
154 **GOLDEN EARRING**, b c 23/3 Orpen (USA)—Summer Exhibition (Royal Academy (USA)) (38714) **F. McNulty**
155 **GWALCHAVED**, b c 26/2 Silver Frost (IRE)—
Good Hope (GER) (Seattle Dancer (USA)) (23228) **Mme. B. Hermelin & J.-C. Rouget**
156 B c 20/3 Elusive City (USA)—Heliocentric (FR) (Galileo (IRE)) **M. Schwartz**
157 **HENRI'S DELIGHT**, b f 29/1 Henrythenavigator (USA)—
Belle Turquoise (FR) (Tel Quel (IRE)) (8764) **Ecurie I. M. Fares**
158 **HOMESTEADING (USA)**, b f 26/3 Unbridled's Song (USA)—Homebound (USA) (Dixie Union (USA)) **J. Allen**
159 **ILIOUSHKA (IRE)**, b f 29/3 Iffraaj—Pearlescence (USA) (Pleasantly Perfect (USA)) **A. Jathiere**
160 **INTO THE MYSTIC (IRE)**, ch f 3/5 Galileo (IRE)—Tamazirte (IRE) (Danehill Dancer (IRE)) (247773) **Fox Hill Farm**
161 **JAY GATSBY**, b c 1/1 Giant's Causeway (USA)—Starry Dreamer (USA) (Rubiano (USA)) **J. Allen**
162 **KARBADINO (IRE)**, b c 11/4 Azamour (IRE)—Tulipe Rose (FR) (Shamardal (USA)) (37166) **Mme L. Urano**
163 **KARENINE**, b f 19/3 High Chaparral (IRE)—
Louvain (IRE) (Sinndar (IRE)) (309717) **Cuadra Montalban & E. Puerari**
164 **KERMAN (FR)**, b c 17/4 Invincible Spirit (IRE)—Kerasha (FR) (Daylami (IRE)) **S. A. Aga Khan**
165 **KHAYRAWANI (FR)**, b c 23/3 Oratorio (IRE)—Khazina (FR) (Alhaarth (IRE)) **S. A. Aga Khan**
166 B c 1/1 Siyouni (FR)—King Luna (FR) (King's Best (USA)) **H. H. Aga Khan**
167 **LA CORNICHE**, b f 2/5 Naaqoos—
Mademoisellechichi (FR) (Chichicastenango (FR)) (30971) **Augier, Rouget, Tepper**
168 **LA RENAISSANCE**, b f 13/4 Astronomer Royal (USA)—
America Nova (FR) (Verglas (IRE)) (139372) **Ecurie La Boetie**
169 **KERMAN (FR)**, b c 7/3 Cape Cross (IRE)—Lady Elgar (IRE) (Sadler's Wells (USA)) (50329) **Ecurie I.M. Fares**
170 **LARVOTTO**, b c 4/3 Astronomer Royal (USA)—Senderlea (IRE) (Giant's Causeway (USA)) (17034) **Mme L. Urano**
171 **LE DEPUTE (FR)**, b c 27/1 Literato (FR)—
Hamida (Johannesburg (USA)) **La Vallee Martigny/ C-A. du Buisson de Courson/P. Vigier/ J. L. Dupont**
172 **LE SENATEUR (FR)**, b c 9/4 Desert Style (IRE)—
Birdy Namnam (USA) (Langfuhr (CAN)) **La Vallee Martigny/ C-A. du Buisson de Courson/P. Vigier/ J. L. Dupont**
173 **LE VAGABOND (FR)**, bl c 1/1 Footstepsinthesand—Miryale (FR) (Anabaa (USA)) (61943) **B. Magrez Horses**

MR J. C. ROUGET - Continued

174 **LIGHT IN PARIS (IRE)**, b f 16/4 Aussie Rules (USA)—
    Grande Rousse (FR) (Act One) (32520) **Ecurie J.-L. Tepper & G. Ben Lassin**
175 **LONGRAY (FR)**, ch c 1/5 Le Havre (IRE)—Isanous (FR) (Zamindar (USA)) **G. Augustin-Normand**
176 B f 28/3 Le Havre (IRE)—Love In Paradise (Dalakhani (IRE)) (46457) **G. Augustin Normand**
177 **MAFAAHIM**, ch c 7/2 Arcano (IRE)—Mawaakeb (USA) (Diesis) **Hamdan Al Maktoum**
178 **MALTA BADIA (IRE)**, b f 11/3 Fastnet Rock (AUS)—M'oubliez Pas (USA) (El Corredor (USA)) **N. Radwan**
179 **MALVASIA**, b f 8/4 Hannouma (IRE)—
    Charmer Sweet (USA) (Afternoon Deelites (USA)) (9291) **S. Brogi & J.-C. Rouget**
180 **MANCORA (FR)**, b f 21/1 Iffraaj—Mantadive (FR) (Okawango (USA)) (58072) **P. Segalot**
181 **MAPATONICK (FR)**, b c 13/4 Peer Gynt (JPN)—
    Symphonie Bere (FR) (Della Francesca (USA)) (23228) **Seche, Vallee Lambert & Rouget**
182 **MARILLANA (FR)**, b f 24/3 Elusive City (USA)—Marque Royale (Royal Academy (USA)) **H. H. Aga Khan**
183 **MARTINENGO (ITY)**, b c 23/3 Red Rocks (IRE)—
    Queen Cheap (Daylami (IRE)) (10840) **M. B. Weill & M. D.-Y. Treves**
184 **MEAN STREET**, b c 11/4 Hannouma (IRE)—Spark Sept (FR) (Septieme Ciel (USA)) (46457) **M. D.-Y. Treves**
185 Ch f 30/3 Malibu Moon (USA)—Miss Salsa (USA) (Unbridled (USA)) 15485) **Ecurie I.M. Fares**
186 **MOONLIGHT IN PARIS (FR)**, b f 6/4 Literato (FR)—Isalou (FR) (Unfuwain (USA)) **Ecurie J-L Tepper**
187 **MOVIETONE (USA)**, b c 1/1 Blame (USA)—Wandering Star (USA) (Red Ransom (USA)) **M. J. Allen**
188 **MY YEAR IS A DAY,** b f 24/4 King's Best (USA)—Aliyeska (FR) (Fasliyev (USA)) (58072) **D.-Y. Treves**
189 **NEVERTALK IN PARIS (IRE)**, b c 29/4 Azamour (IRE)—
    Top Toss (IRE) (Linamix (FR)) (120015) **Ecurie J.-L. Tepper**
190 **NIGHT RUN (FR)**, gr c 17/4 Martaline—Spring Morning (FR) (Ashkalani (IRE)) (58072) **D.-Y Treves**
191 **PABLO,** b c 26/2 Astronomer Royal (USA)—Hoosick Falls (USA) (Precise End (USA)) (19357) **Mme L. Urano**
192 **PENEBSCOT (IRE)**, b c 2/4 Lawman (FR)—Curgell (FR) (Peintre Celebre (USA)) (54200) **D.-Y. Treves**
193 **PEPPY MILLER (FR)**, ch f 27/3 Iffraaj—Shining Vale (USA) (Twilight Agenda (USA)) (42586) **D.-Y. Treves**
194 **PLUMETOT (FR)**, ch c 20/3 Le Havre (IRE)—Polysheba (FR) (Poliglote) **G. Augustin-Normand**
195 **POLITICAL ACT,** b f 2/3 Political Force (USA)—Rare Blend (USA) (Bates Motel (USA)) **J. Allen**
196 **PONTORSON (FR)**, ch c 17/3 Le Havre (IRE)—Pennedepie (Tiger Hill (IRE)) **G. Augustin-Normand**
197 **PRINCE DES LOGES,** b c 18/2 Le Havre (IRE)—
    Haridiyna (IRE) (Verglas (IRE)) (46457) **Pokrovsky, Le Clec'h & Pattou**
198 **RAFAADAH**, br f 5/2 Oasis Dream (GB)—Joanna (IRE) (High Chaparral (IRE)) **Hamdan Al Maktoum**
199 **RAT PACK (IRE)**, gr c 29/3 Verglas (IRE)—
    How High The Sky (IRE) (Danehill Dancer (IRE)) (34843) **D.-Y. Treves & G. Augustin-Normand**
200 **RIFJAH (IRE)**, b f 2/3 Dubawi (IRE)—Mohafazaat (IRE) (Sadler's Wells (USA)) **Hamdan Al Maktoum**
201 **ROMAN DE SAINT CYR (FR)**, b c 12/3 Sageburg (IRE)—La Romagne (FR) (Art Francais (USA)) (34843) **A. Caro**
202 **ROMEO LIMA**, b c 1/1 Medaglia d'oro (USA)—Storybook (UAE) (Halling (USA)) **J. Allen**
203 B f 22/3 Invincible Spirit (IRE)—
    Romie's Kastett (GER) (Halling (USA)) (600000) **H.E. Sheikh J. B. H. B. K. Al Thani**
204 **SAON**, ch c 23/2 Le Havre (IRE)—Absolute Lady (IRE) (Galileo (IRE)) **G. Augustin-Normand**
205 B f 31/3 Sea The Stars (IRE)—Sefroua (USA) (Kingmambo (USA) (131629) **N. Radwan**
206 **SENORA DE LA PLATA (FR)**, b f 18/5 Evasive—Quellaffaire (FR) (Charge d'affaires) **M. Chartier**
207 **SLON HE**, b c 8/2 Danehill Dancer (IRE)—
    Key Figure (Beat Hollow) (100658) **Zerolo, McNulty, Puerari & Gravereaux**
208 **STAND UP IN PARIS**, b f 11/2 Rip Van Winkle (IRE)—
    Mixfeeling (IRE) (Red Ransom (USA)) (15485) **Ecurie J.-L. Tepper**
209 **STAY THE NIGHT (USA)**, b f 15/5 Arch (USA)—Louve Royale (FR) (Peintre Celebre (USA)) **J. Allen**
210 **SUJOUD**, br c 17/3 Iffraaj—Nidhaal (IRE) (Observatory (USA)) **Hamdan Al Maktoum**
211 **SUPER SISTER (ITY)**, b f 8/5 Orpen (USA)—Torrian (IRE) (Intikhab (USA)) (11227) **D.-Y. Treves**
212 B c 31/1 Zamindar (USA)—Talon Bleu (FR) (Anabaa Blue) (30971) **A. Caro**
213 **TANIYAR (IRE)**, b c 17/2 Shamardal (USA)—Tanoura (IRE) (Dalakhani (IRE)) **S. A. Aga Khan**
214 **TEAM COLORS,** b c 1/1 Street Cry (IRE)—Teammate (A P Indy (USA)) **J. Allen**
215 Ch f 21/2 New Approach (IRE)—
    Tierra Luna (IRE) (Giant's Causeway (USA)) (232288) **Sheikh. J. Bin Hamad Al Thani**
216 **TOTSIYAH (IRE)**, b f 29/4 Dalakhani (IRE)—
    Marie Laurencin (Peintre Celebre (USA)) (7742) **M. Zerolo & Mme A. Gravereaux**
217 **UNION SACREE,** b f 27/4 Naaqoos—
    Queen's Conquer (King's Best (USA)) (28648) **Mme. B. Hermelin & J.-C. Rouget**
218 **URAKANA (IRE)**, b f 3/2 Teofilo (IRE)—
    Faviva (USA) (Storm Cat (USA)) (28648) **Pokrovsky, Le Clec'h & Elissalt**
219 B f 1/1 Sea The Stars (IRE)—Valima (FR) (Linamix (FR)) **H. H. Aga Khan**
220 B f 27/3 Makfi—Ventura (IRE) (Spectrum (USA)) (278745) **Puerari & Seydoux De Clausonne**
221 **VILLEDIEU (FR),** b c 23/2 Le Havre (IRE)—Vidiyna (FR) (Danehill Dancer (IRE)) **G. Augustin-Normand**
222 **VISANDI,** b c 1/1 Azamour (IRE)—Vadaza (FR) (Zafonic (USA)) **H. H. Aga Khan**
223 f 1/1 Nayef (USA)—Visionnaire (FR) (Linamix (FR)) **H. H. Aga Khan**
224 **VIYANA (IRE)**, b f 12/5 Azamour (IRE)—Virana (IRE) (King's Best (USA)) **S. A. Aga Khan**

MR J. C. ROUGET - Continued

225 WAR DISPATCH, b c 1/1 War Front (USA)—Photograph (USA) (Unbridled's Song (USA)) **J. Allen**
226 WATHAAB (IRE), b c 25/2 Shamardal (USA)—Sulaalah (IRE) (Darshaan) **Hamdan Al Maktoum**
227 WEEKELA, b f 19/2 Hurricane Run (IRE)—Moonrise (GER) (Grand Lodge (USA)) (69686) **D.-Y. Treves**
228 WELCOME IN PARIS, b f 27/2 Azamour (IRE)—
                  Caipirinia (FR) (Hawk Wing (USA)) (54200) **Ecurie J.-L. Tepper & Mme G. Forien**
229 WINTERS GOLD (FR), gr c 14/4 Silver Frost (IRE)—Jetarsu (IRE) (King's Theatre (IRE)) (12388) **J.-C. Rouget**
230 B f 7/3 Galileo (IRE)—Zaneton (FR) (Mtoto) (503290) **Sheikh J. Bin Hamad Al Thani**
231 ZARIDIYA (IRE), b f 23/2 Duke of Marmalade (IRE)—Zarkalia (IRE) (Red Ransom (USA)) **S. A. Aga Khan**
232 Ch c 4/2 Rock of Gibraltar (IRE)—Zariziyna (IRE) (Dalakhani (IRE)) **S. A. Aga Khan**
233 ZVETKA (IRE), b f 28/2 Lawman (FR)—
                  Shepton Mallet (FR) (Ocean of Wisdom (USA)) (77429) **Cuadra Montalban**

Assistant Trainers: Jean Bernard Roth, Jean Rene Dubosq, Simone Brogi.

Jockey (flat): Christophe Soumillon, Jean-Bernard Eyquem, Thomas Henderson, Ioritz Mendizabal.
Apprentice: Jefferson Smith, Sofiane Saadi.

547

MR RICHARD ROWE, Pulborough
Postal: **Ashleigh House Stables, Sullington Lane, Storrington, Pulborough, West Sussex, RH20 4AE**
Contacts: **PHONE** (01903) 742871 **MOBILE** (07831) 345636
E-MAIL r.rowe.racing@virgin.net **WEBSITE** www.richardrowe-racing.co.uk

1 ALTERANTHELA (IRE), 10, br g Alderbrook—Anthela (GER) **T. L. Clowes**
2 FATHER ARTHUR, 6, gr g Silver Patriarch (IRE)—Amber Starlight **Winterfields Farm Ltd**
3 GRACE AND FORTUNE, 7, b m Grape Tree Road—Nouveau Cheval **Fortune Racing**
4 I NO UNDERSTAND (IRE), 8, b g Overbury (IRE)—Falika (FR) **Richard Rowe Racing Partnership**
5 4, b c Multiplex—Lacounsel (FR) **Capt Adrian Pratt & Friends**
6 MARBLE WALK (IRE), 9, b g Oscar (IRE)—Clowater Lassie (IRE) **Winterfields Farm Ltd**
7 PASTORAL DANCER, 5, b g Pastoral Pursuits—Dancing Flame **B. H. Page**
8 PASTORAL JET, 6, b br h Pastoral Pursuits—Genteel (IRE) **R. Rowe**
9 STRANGE BIRD (IRE), 9, b m Revoque (IRE)—Ethel's Bay (IRE) **Richard Rowe Racing Partnership**
10 TANG ROYAL (FR), 7, ch g Epalo (GER)—Bea de Forme (FR) **R. Rowe**
11 TATANIANO (FR), 10, b g Sassanian (USA)—Rosa Carola (FR) **The Stewart Family**
12 TATENEN (FR), 10, b g Lost World (USA)—Tamazula (FR) **The Stewart Family**
13 WHATAGOA (IRE), 7, b m Bishop of Cashel—Gotta Goa (IRE) **Richard Rowe Racing Partnership**
14 WILD LEGEND (IRE), 5, ch m Flying Legend (USA)—Burren View (IRE) **T. Thompson**

Other Owners: M. W. Barber, Mr D. M. Bradshaw, Mrs H. C. G. Butcher, Mrs J. Case, Mrs J. E. Debenham, M. D. P. Fortune, Mrs F. M. Gordon, Capt. A. Pratt, Mr A. Stewart, Mrs J. A. Stewart, T. W. Wellard.

548

MISS MANDY ROWLAND, Lower Blidworth
Postal: **Kirkfields, Calverton Road, Lower Blidworth, Nottingham, Nottinghamshire, NG21 0NW**
Contacts: **PHONE** (01623) 794831 **MOBILE** (07768) 224666
E-MAIL kirkfieldsriding@hotmail.co.uk

1 ACE OF SPIES (IRE), 9, br g Machiavellian (USA)—Nadia **Miss M. E. Rowland**
2 ANNIES IDEA, 5, ch m Yoshka—Danum Diva (IRE) **Miss M. E. Rowland**
3 GILDED AGE, 8, b g Cape Cross (IRE)—Sweet Folly (IRE) **Solihull Racing Club**
4 HAZARD WARNING (IRE), 4, b c Haafef (USA)—Hazardous **Miss M. E. Rowland**
5 HITTIN'THE SKIDS (IRE), 6, ch m Fruits of Love (USA)—Hush Deal **Mr R. Morris**
6 JOHNSON'S CAT (IRE), 5, b g One Cool Cat (USA)—Takanewa (IRE) **Johnson Racing**
7 MR CHOCOLATE DROP (IRE), 10, b g Danetime (IRE)—Forest Blade (USA) **Miss M. E. Rowland**
8 6, B m Pierre—Ronni Pancake **Mr J. P. Keogh**
9 ROXY MADAM, 5, br m Generous (USA)—Masouri Sana (IRE) **Miss M. E. Rowland**
10 SILAS MARINER (IRE), 7, b g Indian Danehill (IRE)—Fancy Boots (IRE) **Miss M. E. Rowland**
11 SONG OF PRIDE (GER), 10, ch g Platini (GER)—Song of Peace (GER) **Miss M. E. Rowland**

Other Owners: Mr John Lynch, Mrs Gill Summers, Mr C. Wing, Mr S. J. Wood.

Assistant Trainer: Sarah Mitchel

Jockey (flat): Adam Kirby, Jimmy Quinn. **Jockey (NH):** Adam Pogson. **Apprentice:** Nathan Alison.

549 MR A. DE ROYER-DUPRE, Chantilly

Postal: **3 Chemin des Aigles, 60500 Chantilly, France**
Contacts: **PHONE (0033) 34458 0303 FAX (0033) 34457 3538 MOBILE (0033) 6702 32901**
E-MAIL de-royer-dupre@wanadoo.fr

1 **ARCH DUCHESS (FR)**, 4, b f Arch (USA)—Jacira (FR) **Mme Magalen Bryant**
2 **BELLA QATARA (IRE)**, 4, b f Dansili—Alexandrova (IRE) **H. H. Sheikh Mohammed bin Khalifa**
3 **CHERANA (FR)**, 4, b f Sinndar (IRE)—Cherryxma (FR) **H. H. Aga Khan**
4 **DAANA QATAR**, 4, b f Galileo (IRE)—Evita **H. H. Sheikh Mohammed bin Khalifa**
5 **DANSILITO**, 4, b c Dansili—Caesarine (FR) **Mme Chantal Sanglier**
6 **DIBAJJ (FR)**, 4, ch f Iffraaj—Goleta (USA) **Abdullah Al Maddah**
7 **EBIYZA (FR)**, 4, ch f Rock of Gibraltar (IRE)—Ebalista (IRE) **S. A. Aga Khan**
8 **HAPPY VALENTINE (SAF)**, 4, ch f Silvano (GER)—Happy Ever After (SAF) **Team Valor**
9 **HIDDEN COVE (IRE)**, 4, b f Nayef (USA)—Pas d'heure (IRE) **Mise de Moratalla**
10 **IPSWICH (IRE)**, 4, ch f Danehill Dancer (IRE)—Imperial Beauty (USA) **Ecurie Wildenstein**
11 **KADESHA (FR)**, 4, b f Azamour (IRE)—Kadiana (FR) **S. A. Aga Khan**
12 **KING OF ENGLAND**, 4, ch c Galileo (IRE)—Royal Highness (GER) **Waratah Thoroughbreds Pty Ltd**
13 **LAGO MINTO**, 5, ch g Galileo (IRE)—Maroussie (FR) **Mise de Moratalla**
14 **MANDOUR (USA)**, 5, ch h Smart Strike (CAN)—Mandesha (FR) **Princess Z. P. Aga Khan**
15 **MANNDAWI (FR)**, 4, gr c Dalakhani (IRE)—Mintly Fresh (USA) **J. M. Haseler**
16 **NARNIYN (IRE)**, 4, b f Dubawi (IRE)—Narmina (IRE) **S. A. Aga Khan**
17 **SANO DI PIETRO**, 6, gr g Dalakhani (IRE)—Special Delivery (IRE) **A. Krauliger**
18 **SHAZANA**, 13, gr m Key of Luck (USA)—Shawanni **S. A. Aga Khan**
19 **SINDAJAN (FR)**, 9, b h Medicean—Sinndiya (IRE) **S. A. Aga Khan**
20 **SIYENICA (FR)**, 4, b f Azamour (IRE)—Sichilla (IRE) **H. H. Aga Khan**
21 **VADAPOUR (FR)**, 4, b c Cape Cross (IRE)—Vadapolina (FR) **H. H. Aga Khan**
22 **VALIRANN (FR)**, 4, b c Nayef (USA)—Valima (FR) **H. H. Aga Khan**

THREE-YEAR-OLDS

23 **AGAMON LAKE (FR)**, ch c Montjeu (IRE)—Agathe (USA) **Ecurie Wildenstein**
24 **AJANTA (IRE)**, b f Monsun (GER)—Alloway **Haras de la Perelle**
25 **AL JASSASIYAH (IRE)**, b f Galileo (IRE)—Alluring Park (IRE) **Sheikh Joaan bin Hamad Al Thani**
26 Gr c Dalakhani (IRE)—Alava (IRE) **Viktor Timoshenko**
27 **AMIRLI (IRE)**, ch c Medicean—Amenapinga (FR) **H. H. Aga Khan**
28 **ASHKANND (FR)**, b c Sinndar (IRE)—Ashalanda (FR) **H. H. Aga Khan**
29 **BEHESHT (FR)**, b c Sea The Stars (IRE)—Behkara (IRE) **S. A. Aga Khan**
30 **BLARNEY STONE (IRE)**, ch f Peintre Celebre (USA)—Bastet (IRE) **Ecurie Wildenstein**
31 **BOCCA LUPO (FR)**, b c Falco (USA)—Bocanegra (FR) **P-Y Lefevre**
32 **CAREFUL CHARLIE (IRE)**, ch f Tapit (USA)—Careless Charlie (USA) **Charles E. Fipke**
33 **CLADOCERA (GER)**, b f Oasis Dream—Caesarine (FR) **Haras de la Perelle**
34 **CORESSOS (FR)**, b c Dalakhani (IRE)—Nearthyka (IRE) **San Paolo Agri-Stud SRL**
35 **DALISHAN (FR)**, b c Sinndar (IRE)—Daltaiyma (IRE) **S. A. Aga Khan**
36 **DARAYBI (FR)**, b c Street Cry (IRE)—Daryaba (IRE) **S. A. Aga Khan**
37 **DARDIZA (IRE)**, b f Street Cry (IRE)—Darkara (IRE) **Princess Z. P. Aga Khan**
38 **DARENJANA (FR)**, b f Sea The Stars (IRE)—Darinska (IRE) **Princess Z. P. Aga Khan**
39 **DAURAN (IRE)**, b c Manduro (GER)—Dawera (IRE) **S. A. Aga Khan**
40 **DEBUTANTE (FR)**, b f Gold Away (IRE)—Danedrop (IRE) **Ecurie des Monceaux**
41 **DEFROST MY HEART (IRE)**, b f Fastnet Rock (AUS)—Perfect Hedge **Haras de Vieux Pont**
42 **DJIBI (FR)**, gr c Dalakhani (IRE)—Darjina (FR) **Princess Z. P. Aga Khan**
43 **DOLNIYA (FR)**, b f Azamour (IRE)—Daltama (IRE) **S. A. Aga Khan**
44 **DONCELLA (IRE)**, b f High Chaparral (IRE)—Onereuse **Waratah Thoroughbreds Pty Ltd**
45 **DOUBLE POWER (FR)**, b c Sageburg (IRE)—Double Dollar **Sheikh Joaan bin Hamad Al Thani**
46 **DOUMARAN (FR)**, b c Authorized (IRE)—Diamond Tango (FR) **H. H. Aga Khan**
47 **DOURADA (FR)**, b f Invincible Spirit (IRE)—Dardania **S. A. Aga Khan**
48 **EBARAN (IRE)**, b c Desert Style (IRE)—Ebareva (IRE) **S. A. Aga Khan**
49 **EDKHAN (IRE)**, gr c Sea The Stars (IRE)—Alpine Rose (FR) **Sheikh Joaan bin Hamad Al Thani**
50 **FAZAL (FR)**, b c Montjeu (IRE)—Fraloga (IRE) **H. H. Aga Khan**
51 **GERTSOGINYA (IRE)**, ch f Kentucky Dynamite (USA)—Golubushka (USA) **Viktor Timoshenko**
52 **GRACIOUSLY**, b f Shamardal (USA)—Gracefully (FR) **Mise de Moratalla**
53 **HARGAM (FR)**, gr c Sinndar (IRE)—Horasana (FR) **H. H. Aga Khan**
54 **INVOCADA (IRE)**, b f Dalakhani (IRE)—Classira (IRE) **Julio Gerin Almeida Camargo**
55 **JARADA (USA)**, b f Sea The Stars (IRE)—Love To Dance (USA) **Sheikh Joaan bin Hamad Al Thani**
56 **LESSAADY (IRE)**, b c Montjeu (IRE)—Alleviate (IRE) **Sheikh Joaan bin Hamad Al Thani**
57 **MANALI (FR)**, ch c Sea The Stars (IRE)—Mintly Fresh (USA) **H. H. Aga Khan**
58 **MANDALAYA (USA)**, b f Elusive Quality (USA)—Mandesha (FR) **Princess Z. P. Aga Khan**

MR A. DE ROYER-DUPRE - Continued

59 **MARALIKA (FR),** b f Dubawi (IRE)—Marasima (IRE) **S. A. Aga Khan**
60 **MINTAKA (FR),** gr f Zamindar (USA)—Minatlya (FR) **H. H. Aga Khan**
61 **MONSIEUR OK,** b c Nayef (USA)—Bold Classic (USA) **H. H. Sheikh Mohammed bin Khalifa**
62 **NAZMIA (IRE),** b f Holy Roman Emperor (IRE)—Narmina (IRE) **S. A. Aga Khan**
63 **NISMA (IRE),** b f Montjeu (IRE)—Maggie Jordan (USA) **H. H. Sheikh Mohammed bin Khalifa**
64 **OAK HARBOUR,** b c Sinndar (IRE)—Onega Lake (IRE) **Ecurie Wildenstein**
65 **PARATONNERRE,** b f Montjeu (IRE)—Platonic (USA) **Ecurie des Monceaux**
66 **PARNAIOCA,** b f Muhtathir—Wadjeka (USA) **Julio Gerin Almeida Camargo**
67 **PEPIN LE BREF,** ch c Galileo (IRE)—Porlezza (FR) **Ecurie Wildenstein**
68 **PILAGEYA (IRE),** b f New Approach (IRE)—Pine Chip (USA) **Viktor Timoshenko**
69 **PRAIRIE DALE (FR),** b br c Dalakhani (IRE)—Prairie Runner (IRE) **Ecurie Wildenstein**
70 **PROMETHEUS (IRE),** b c Montjeu (IRE)—Ahdaab (USA) **H.H. Sheikh Mohammed bin Khalifa Al-Thani**
71 **QINGDAO (IRE),** b f Dansili—Quezon Sun (GER) **Haras de la Parelle**
72 **RAYA STYLE (IRE),** b c Nayef (USA)—Menesteem (IRE) **S. Munir**
73 **REDBROOK (IRE),** b c Raven's Pass (USA)—Nawal (FR) **Sheikh Joaan bin Hamad Al Thani**
74 **SANAIJA,** ch f Pivotal—Sanjida (IRE) **Haras de la Parelle**
75 **SANDY'S CHOICE (FR),** b f Footstepsinthesand—Zafonia (FR) **Mme Magalen Bryant**
76 **SANEMA (FR),** b f Elusive City (USA)—Sanaya (IRE) **S. A. Aga Khan**
77 **SARZANA (FR),** b f Azamour (IRE)—Sarlisa (FR) **S. A. Aga Khan**
78 **SEMPRE SPERANZA (IRE),** b f Muhtathir—Million Dollargirl (USA)
79 **SHAMKALA (FR),** b f Pivotal—Shamakiya (USA) **S. A. Aga Khan**
80 **SHAMKIYR (FR),** b c Sea The Stars (IRE)—Shemaya (IRE) **S. A. Aga Khan**
81 **SHE LOVES YOU,** b f Lawman (FR)—On Fair Stage (IRE) **Fair Salinia Ltd**
82 **SHEMYA (FR),** gr f Dansili—Shemima **S. A. Aga Khan**
83 **SHIVANA (FR),** b f Sinndar (IRE)—Shivera (FR) **S. A. Aga Khan**
84 **SINAKAR (IRE),** b c Manduro (GER)—Siniyya (IRE) **S. A. Aga Khan**
85 **STRIKING CREATION (IRE),** b f Smart Strike (CAN)—Anabaa's Creation (IRE) **W. J. Preston**
86 **TASHIRIYAN (FR),** b c Dubawi (IRE)—Tashiriya (IRE) **S. A. Aga Khan**
87 **TELOPEA,** b f Pivotal—Fermion (IRE) **Waratah Thoroughbreds Pty Ltd**
88 **TOMOE (FR),** f Shirocco (GER)—Sanada (FR) **G. T. Ryan**
89 **VADIRIMA (FR),** ch f Selkirk (USA)—Vadiya (FR) **H. H. Aga Khan**
90 **VALDIYANA (FR),** b f Sinndar (IRE)—Vadasouna (FR) **S. A. Aga Khan**
91 **VAYASA (FR),** gr f Zamindar (USA)—Visionnaire (FR) **H. H. Aga Khan**
92 **VAZIRA (FR),** b f Sea The Stars (IRE)—Vadaza (FR) **H. H. Aga Khan**
93 **VEDA (FR),** b f Dansili—Vadapolina (FR) **H. H. Aga Khan**
94 **VERRIYA (FR),** b f Zamindar (USA)—Vermentina (IRE) **S. A. Aga Khan**
95 **WALDFEST (FR),** ch f Hurricane Run (IRE)—Gifted Icon (IRE) **Haras de la Perelle**
96 **ZARKASH (FR),** b c Sea The Stars (IRE)—Zarkava (FR) **S. A. Aga Khan**
97 **ZARSHANA (IRE),** b f Sea The Stars (IRE)—Zarkasha (FR) **S. A. Aga Khan**
98 **ZAVALLYA (FR),** b f Elusive City (USA)—Zewara (IRE) **S. A. Aga Khan**
99 **ZOTILLA (IRE),** b f Zamindar (USA)—Louvain (IRE) **Finn Blichfeldt**
100 **ZOURNABAD (IRE),** b c Invincible Spirit (IRE)—Zafaraniya (FR) **S. A. Aga Khan**

TWO-YEAR-OLDS

101 **AFSHEEN (FR),** b f 13/2 Invincible Spirit (IRE)—Asharna (IRE) (Darshaan) **S. A. Aga Khan**
102 **AKATEA (IRE),** ch f 30/4 Shamardal (USA)—Altamira (Peintre Celebre (USA)) **Ecurie Wildenstein**
103 **ALMIYR (FR),** gr c 2/2 Dubawi (IRE)—Alnamara (FR) (Linamix (FR)) **H. H. Aga Khan**
104 **ASHLAN (FR),** b c 8/4 Dansili—Ashalanda (FR) (Linamix (FR)) **H. H. Aga Khan**
105 B c 6/2 New Approach (IRE)—Balankiya (IRE) (Darshaan) **S. A. Aga Khan**
106 **BEHNASA (FR),** b f 27/4 Dansili—Behkara (IRE) (Kris) **S. A. Aga Khan**
107 **BLUE KIMONO (IRE),** b f 13/4 Invincible Spirit (IRE)—Bastet (IRE) (Giant's Causeway (USA)) **Ecurie Wildenstein**
108 Gr f 27/1 Dalakhani (IRE)—Candara (FR) (Barathea (IRE)) **H. H. Aga Khan**
109 **DARADIYNA (FR),** b f 22/3 Sea The Stars (IRE)—Dardania (Dalakhani (IRE)) **S. A. Aga Khan**
110 **DARIYAN (FR),** b c 4/3 Shamardal (USA)—Daryakana (FR) (Selkirk (USA)) **S. A. Aga Khan**
111 B f 27/1 Invincible Spirit (IRE)—Darsha (FR) (Sakhee (USA)) **S. A. Aga Khan**
112 **DHORSELL (IRE),** gr f 11/2 Mastercraftsman (IRE)—Dacca (Deploy) **Zaro SRL**
113 Br c 9/5 Pivotal—Fraloga (IRE) (Grand Lodge (USA)) **H. H. Aga Khan**
114 B c 24/2 High Chaparral (IRE)—Karawana (IRE) (King's Best (USA)) **S. A. Aga Khan**
115 B c 18/2 Shamardal (USA)—Kastoria (IRE) (Selkirk (USA)) **S.A. Aga Khan**
116 B f 16/2 Raven's Pass (USA)—Katiykha (IRE) (Darshaan) **S.A. Aga Khan**
117 Ch c 15/1 Dalakhani (IRE)—Khelwa (FR) (Traditionally (USA)) **S.A. Aga Khan**
118 B c 1/1 Cape Cross (IRE)—Ludiana (FR) (Dalakhani (IRE)) **H. H. Aga Khan**
119 **MANDHEERA (USA),** b f 30/3 Bernardini—Mandesha (FR) (Desert Style (IRE)) **Princess Z. P. Aga Khan**
120 **MARUNOUCHI (IRE),** ch f 10/3 Peintre Celebre (USA)—Morning Line (FR) (Anabaa (USA)) **Ecurie Wildenstein**
121 **MINYA (FR),** b f 28/2 Sinndar (IRE)—Minatlya (FR) (Linamix (FR)) **H. H. Aga Khan**

MR A. DE ROYER-DUPRE - Continued

122 MONISHA (FR), b f 27/3 Sinndar (IRE)—Minty Fresh (USA) (Rubiano (USA)) **H. H. Aga Khan**
123 PARADE MUSIC (USA), b f 31/1 Giant's Causeway (USA)—
Parade Militaire (IRE) (Peintre Celebre (USA)) **Ecurie Wildenstein**
124 PERLE RARE (USA), ch f 8/2 Distorted Humor (USA)—
Peinture Rare (IRE) (Sadler's Wells (USA)) **Ecurie Wildenstein**
125 ROYANA (FR), b f 28/2 Sea The Stars (IRE)—Rosanara (FR) (Sinndar (IRE)) **H. H. Aga Khan**
126 B c 1/1 Selkirk (USA)—Sadiyna (FR) (Sinndar (IRE)) **H. H. Aga Khan**
127 f 1/1 Azamour (IRE)—Sagalina (IRE) (Linamix (FR)) **H. H. Aga Khan**
128 SAGAMI (USA), b br f 1/2/2 Street Cry (IRE)—Special Delivery (IRE) (Danehill (USA)) **Ecurie Wildenstein**
129 SAMADRISA (IRE), b f 12/2 Oasis Dream—Sanarira (IRE) (Darshaan) **S. A. Aga Khan**
130 SANAM (USA), gr ro c 24/2 More Than Ready (USA)—Saliyna (FR) (Linamix (FR)) **H. H. Aga Khan**
131 SAYANA (FR), b f 1/1 Galileo (IRE)—Sichilla (IRE) (Danehill (USA)) **H. H. Aga Khan**
132 SHAHNILA (FR), b f 20/2 Elusive City (USA)—Shamakiya (IRE) (Intikhab (USA)) **S. A. Aga Khan**
133 SHAYWAN (IRE), b c 8/5 Sinndar (IRE)—Shawara (IRE) (Barathea (IRE)) **S. A. Aga Khan**
134 B f 6/3 Tale of The Cat (USA)—Shediyama (FR) (Red Ransom (USA)) **S. A. Aga Khan**
135 SHENDINI (IRE), b c 1/4 Medicean—Shehira (IRE) (Sendawar (IRE)) **S. A. Aga Khan**
136 SHERINGA (FR), gr f 15/4 Oasis Dream—Shemima (Dalakhani (IRE)) **S. A. Aga Khan**
137 VADARIYA (IRE), b f 6/5 Sea The Stars (IRE)—Vadapolina (FR) (Trempolino (USA)) **H. H. Aga Khan**
138 VAITAHU (FR), b c 3/4 Soldier of Fortune (IRE)—Verveine (USA) (Lear Fan (USA)) **Ecurie Wildenstein**
139 B f 1/1 Sea The Stars (IRE)—Valasyra (FR) (Sinndar (IRE)) **H. H. Aga Khan**
140 VAZIRABAD (FR), b c 8/3 Manduro (GER)—Visorama (IRE) (Linamix (FR)) **H. H. Aga Khan**
141 ZALZALI (FR), c 1/1 Dalakhani (IRE)—Zalaiyka (FR) (Royal Academy (USA)) **S. A. Aga Khan**
142 ZARKAR (FR), b c 20/2 Galileo (IRE)—Zarkava (IRE) (Zamindar (USA)) **S. A. Aga Khan**
143 ZAZIYR (FR), b c 2/2 Cape Cross (IRE)—Zayanida (IRE) (King's Best (USA)) **S. A. Aga Khan**
144 ZOURKHANE (IRE), b c 2/5 Shamardal (USA)—Zarkasha (IRE) (Kahyasi) **S. A. Aga Khan**
145 ZUBAYR (IRE), b c 13/4 Authorized (IRE)—Zaziyra (IRE) (Dalakhani (IRE)) **S. A. Aga Khan**

Assistant Trainer: Laurent Metais

Jockey (flat): Antoine Hamelin, Gerald Mosse, Christophe Soumillon. **Apprentice:** Mickael Berto.

550
MS LUCINDA RUSSELL, Kinross
Postal: **Arlary House Stables, Milnathort, Kinross, Tayside, KY13 9SJ**
Contacts: **PHONE** (01577) 865512 **FAX** (01577) 861171 **MOBILE** (07970) 645261
E-MAIL lucinda@arlary.fsnet.co.uk **WEBSITE** www.lucindarussell.com

1 ALBATROS TRESOR (FR), 4, b g Network (GER)—Itiga (FR) **Ms D. Thomson**
2 ALIZEE DE JANEIRO (FR), 4, b f Network (GER)—Katana (GER) **Ms D. Thomson**
3 AMORE MIO (GER), 9, b g Trempolino (USA)—Amore (GER) **CMC - W & P Marzouk & Team Kirkton**
4 BADGER FOOT (IRE), 9, br g Beneficial—Droim Alton Gale (IRE) **P. J. S. Russell**
5 BALLYBEN (IRE), 6, ch g Beneficial—I'm Maggy (NZ) **Drew & Ailsa Russell**
6 BALLYBILL (IRE), 4, ch g Presenting—Corrieann (IRE) **Drew & Ailsa Russell**
7 BALLYCOOL (IRE), 7, b g Helissio (FR)—Carnoustie (USA) **Mr & Mrs T. P. Winnell**
8 BE MY DEPUTY (IRE), 9, b g Oscar (IRE)—Have A Myth (IRE) **Mr W. T. Scott**
9 BEIDH TINE ANSEO (IRE), 8, b g Rock of Gibraltar (IRE)—Siamsa (USA) **Mr I. D. Miller**
10 BEN AKRAM (IRE), 6, b g Beneficial—Ring Four (IRE) **Mrs M. Gleeson**
11 BESCOT SPRINGS (IRE), 9, b g Saddlers' Hall (IRE)—Silver Glen (IRE) **Mrs J. Tracey**
12 BIGGAR (IRE), 6, b g Court Cave (IRE)—Native Success (IRE) **Mr A. McAllister**
13 BLENHEIM BROOK (IRE), 9, br g Alderbrook—Blenheim Blinder (IRE) **The County Set Three**
14 BLUESIDE BOY (IRE), 6, b g Blueprint (IRE)—Asidewager (IRE) **Mr G. F. Adam**
15 CARINYA (IRE), 6, br m Iffraaj—Ma N'ieme Biche (USA) **Mr R. M. Boyd**
16 CASTLELAWN (IRE), 7, b g Runyon (IRE)—Pure Magic (IRE) **J. R. Adam**
17 CATCHTHEMOONLIGHT, 6, b m Generous (IRE)—Moon Catcher **Dig In Racing**
18 CHAMPAGNE AGENT (IRE), 8, b g Smadoun (FR)—Madame Jean (FR) **Star Racing**
19 CLIFF LANE (IRE), 5, b g Scorpion (IRE)—Susan's Dream (IRE) **Lynne & Angus Maclennan**
20 CLONDAW FLICKA (IRE), 6, ch g Stowaway—Bealaha Essie (IRE) **Dan & Michelle Macdonald, Mackie, Levein**
21 CLONDAW KNIGHT (IRE), 6, b g Heron Island (IRE)—Sarah Supreme (IRE) **Mr A. N. Seymour**
22 CRACKERJACK LAD (IRE), 11, b g Exit To Nowhere (USA)—Crowther Homes **Mr I. D. Miller**
23 DELIGHTFULLY (FR), 10, br m Sagacity (FR)—Green House (FR) **Mr R. M. Boyd**
24 DOTTIES DILEMA (IRE), 6, b g Pierre—Tellarue (IRE) **Stewart Dempster Mitchell**
25 ELFEGO BACA (IRE), 5, br g Kalanisi (IRE)—Lady Padivor (IRE) **Mrs J. Tracey**
26 ETXALAR (FR), 11, b g Kingsalsa (USA)—Tender To Love (FR) **Dig In Racing**
27 FARRAGON (IRE), 4, b g Marienbard (IRE)—Oath of Allegiance (IRE) **Mrs S Russell & A M Russell**
28 FIGHT AWAY BOYS (IRE), 6, ch g Vertical Speed (FR)—Say Ya Love Me (IRE) **R. H. T. Barber**

MS LUCINDA RUSSELL - Continued

29 **FINAL ASSAULT (IRE)**, 5, b br g Beneficial—Last Campaign (IRE) **Mrs S Russell & A M Russell**
30 **FOG PATCHES (IRE)**, 8, br g Oscar (IRE)—Flash Parade **Sunny Days**
31 **GARTH (IRE)**, 6, b g Sayadaw (FR)—Zaffaran Express (IRE) **Mr A. M. Russell**
32 **GREEN FLAG (IRE)**, 7, b g Milan—Erin Go Brea (IRE) **J. R. Adam**
33 **HALLMARK STAR**, 5, b g Nayef (USA)—Spring **The County Set (Two)**
34 4, B f Kalanisi (IRE)—Hamari Gold (IRE)
35 **HAPPY RIVER (IRE)**, 7, b g Pierre—Breezy River (IRE) **BSN Racing**
36 **HELIOPSIS (IRE)**, 9, b g Beneficial—Bright Note **Douglas & George Godsman**
37 **IMJOEKING (IRE)**, 7, b g Amilynx (FR)—Go Franky (IRE) **Mr K. Alexander**
38 **INNOCENT GIRL (IRE)**, 5, b m King's Theatre (IRE)—Belle Innocence (FR) **John J. Murray & Niall Farrell**
39 **ISLAND HEIGHTS (IRE)**, 5, b g Heron Island (IRE)—La Reina (IRE) **Straightline Construction Ltd**
40 **IT'S HIGH TIME (IRE)**, 6, b g Kalanisi (IRE)—Windsor Dancer (IRE) **Straightline Construction Ltd**
41 **ITSTIMEFORAPINT (IRE)**, 6, b g Portrait Gallery (IRE)—Executive Pearl (IRE) **IMEJ Racing**
42 **JUST CHILLY**, 5, b m Kayf Tara—Your Punishment (IRE) **Mrs V. J. McKie**
43 **JUST FOR PLEASURE (IRE)**, 4, b f Kayf Tara—Heltornic (IRE) **Let's Live Racing**
44 **KAI BROON (IRE)**, 7, b g Marju (IRE)—Restiv Star (FR) **John R. Adam & Sons Ltd**
45 **KILBREE CHIEF (IRE)**, 6, b g Dr Massini (IRE)—Lame Excuse (IRE) **J. R. Adam**
46 **KINGS FOLLY (IRE)**, 6, b g Dushyantor (USA)—Beltane Queen (IRE) **Mrs M. C. Coltman**
47 **KINGSWELL THEATRE**, 5, b g King's Theatre (IRE)—Cresswell Native (IRE) **Mr J. J. Murray**
48 **KRIS CROSS (IRE)**, 5, b g Kris Kin (USA)—Perfidia (IRE) **Ms D. Thomson**
49 **LADY OF VERONA (IRE)**, 7, b m Old Vic—Innovate (IRE) **Peter K. Dale Ltd**
50 **LIE FORRIT (IRE)**, 10, b g Subtle Power (IRE)—Ben Roseler (IRE) **Mr JW McNeill Mr C McNeill Ms L Gillies**
51 **LONE FOOT LADDIE (IRE)**, 5, b g Red Clubs—Alexander Phantom (IRE) **Dr J. Wilson**
52 **LORD OF DRUMS (IRE)**, 8, b g Beat of Drums—Treat A Lady (IRE) **The Ormello Way**
53 **MARAWEH (IRE)**, 4, b g Muhtathir—Itqaan (USA) **Tay Valley Chasers Racing Club**
54 4, Ch g Ad Valorem (USA)—Mindanao **Anna Noble & Andy Bell**
55 4, B f Robin des Champs (FR)—Miss Poutine (FR) **Mr A. N. Seymour**
56 **MOMKINZAIN (USA)**, 7, b g Rahy (USA)—Fait Accompli (USA) **John R. Adam & Sons Ltd**
57 **MORNING TIME (IRE)**, 8, b g Hawk Wing (USA)—Desert Trail (IRE) **Mr W. G. H. Forrester**
58 **MUMGOS DEBUT (IRE)**, 6, b g Royal Anthem (USA)—Black Queen (IRE) **Mrs Suzy Brown & Mr Peter R Brown**
59 **MYSTEREE (IRE)**, 6, b g Gold Well—Hillside Native (IRE) **Mrs L. Maclennan**
60 **NO DEAL (IRE)**, 8, b g Revoque (IRE)—Noble Choice **Fraser McClung & Belinda Wares**
61 **NUTS N BOLTS**, 8, b g Marju (IRE)—Anniversary **The County Set**
62 **ON BROADWAY (IRE)**, 8, b g Broadway Flyer (USA)—Snap Out of It (IRE) **Mr G. Truscott**
63 **ONE FOR ARTHUR (IRE)**, 5, b g Milan—Nonnetia (FR) **Miss B. Wares**
64 **OUTLAW TOM (IRE)**, 10, b g Luso—Timely Approach (IRE) **Milnathort Racing Club**
65 **PRESENT FLIGHT (IRE)**, 5, ch g Presenting—Grangeclare Flight (IRE) **Kilco (International) Ltd**
66 **PRESENT LODGER (IRE)**, 6, b g Presenting—Hannigan's Lodger (IRE) **Mr A. N. Seymour**
67 **PRESENTING REBEL (IRE)**, 8, ch g Presenting—Random Bless (IRE) **Mr W. T. Scott**
68 **PROSECCO (IRE)**, 12, b g Perpendicular—Bay Gale (IRE) **Tay Valley Chasers Racing Club**
69 **PULPITARIAN (USA)**, 6, b g Pulpit (USA)—Bedanken (USA) **Two Black Labs**
70 **QUITO DU TRESOR (FR)**, 10, b g Jeune Homme (USA)—Itiga (FR) **Mrs A. E. Giles**
71 **REAPING THE REWARD (IRE)**, 10, b g Sylvan Express—Zamaine (IRE) **Mr & Mrs Raymond Anderson Green**
72 **REVOCATION**, 6, b g Revoque (IRE)—Fenella **Mr Michael & Lady Jane Kaplan**
73 **RHYMERS HA'**, 7, br g Kasakov—Salu **Mr G. F. Adam**
74 **RHYMERS STONE**, 6, b g Desideratum—Salu **Mr G. F. Adam**
75 **RUDEMEISTER (IRE)**, 8, b g Rudimentary (USA)—Boardroom Belle (IRE) **Mr A. McAllister**
76 **RYTON RUNNER (IRE)**, 6, b g Sadler's Wells (USA)—Love For Ever (IRE) **County Set Four**
77 **SAPHIR RIVER (FR)**, 8, gr g Slickly (FR)—Miss Bio (FR) **Mr A. N. Seymour**
78 **SETTLEDOUTOFCOURT (IRE)**, 8, b g Court Cave (IRE)—Ardagh Princess **Mr A. McAllister**
79 **SHINE A DIAMOND (IRE)**, 6, gr g St Jovite—Mossy Grey (IRE) **Kilco (International) Ltd**
80 **SHOOTING TIMES**, 9, b g Commanche Run—Rainbow Times (IRE) **Mrs J. M. R. Lancaster**
81 **SIMARTHUR**, 7, gr g Erhaab (USA)—Dusty Too **R. A. Bartlett**
82 **SKI GUIDE**, 4, b g Three Valleys (USA)—Dansara **Mr C. G. W. Bruce**
83 **SONNY THYNE**, 5, b g Overbury (IRE)—This Thyne **G. S. Brown**
84 **STARPLEX**, 4, b g Multiplex—Turtle Bay **G & J Park**
85 **SUPERIOR COMMAND (IRE)**, 5, b g Lahib (USA)—Decent Dime (IRE) **P. J. S. Russell**
86 **TANTAMOUNT**, 5, b g Observatory (USA)—Cantanta **Mutual Friends**
87 **TAP NIGHT (USA)**, 7, ch g Pleasant Tap (USA)—Day Mate (USA) **J. P. McManus**
88 **THE FRIARY (IRE)**, 7, b g Kris Kin (USA)—Native Design (IRE) **Mrs S Russell & A M Russell**
89 **THE SQUINTY BRIDGE**, 6, b g Heron Island (IRE)—The Storm Bell (IRE) **Mrs J. Perratt**
90 **THE STARBOARD BOW**, 7, b g Observatory (USA)—Overboard (IRE) **John R. Adam & Sons Ltd**
91 **THE TOFT**, 5, b m Kayf Tara—Gretton **P. J. S. Russell**
92 **THE VILLAGE (IRE)**, 5, b g Lahib (USA)—Melisande **Milnathort Racing Club**
93 **THORPE (IRE)**, 4, b g Danehill Dancer (IRE)—Minkova (IRE) **Mr Graham Truscott & Dr John Wilson**

MS LUCINDA RUSSELL - Continued

94 THROTHETHATCH (IRE), 5, b g Beneficial—Castletownroche (IRE) **Mrs A. E. Giles**
95 UISGE BEATHA (IRE), 6, b g Alderbrook—Me Grannys Endoors (IRE) **Last Alders**
96 ULTRA DU CHATELET (FR), 6, b g Network (GER)—Grandeur Royale (FR) **Brahms & Liszt**
97 URBAN KODE (IRE), 6, b g Kodiac—Urbanize (USA) **Suzy Brown, John Baird, Tony Evans**
98 VALLANI (IRE), 9, ch m Vettori (IRE)—Hecuba **Mr R. M. Boyd**
99 VENGEUR DE GUYE (FR), 5, b g Dom Alco (FR)—Mascotte de Guye (FR) **Brahms & Liszt**
100 VENITZIA (IRE), 8, b br g Presenting—Bloom Berry **Hadrian's Warriors**
101 VOYAGE A NEW YORK (FR), 5, b g Kapgarde (FR)—Pennsylvanie (FR) **Straightline Construction Ltd**
102 WAYNE MANOR (IRE), 5, br g Cape Cross (IRE)—Inchmahome **Mrs B. Smith**
103 WILD GEESE (IRE), 7, br g Cape Cross (IRE)—Intrepidity **Tay Valley Chasers Racing Club**
104 YOU'RESOMEDREAMER (IRE), 6, b br g Cloudings (IRE)—
Criaire Nouveau (IRE) **Mrs S. Bruce & Mrs L. Mackay**

Other Owners: Mr G. G. Adamson, Mr W. Agnew, R. D. Anderson, Mr J. B. Baird, M. Ball, M. Ball, M. Bamlet, G. F. Bear, Mr A. Bell, Mrs A. J. Boswell, Mrs S. Brown, Mr P. R. Brown, Mrs S. E. Bruce, E. Bruce, H. A. Brydon, A. Cadger, Mr K. Carruthers, Mr J. E. Chernouski, Chiltern Medicare Ltd, Mr C. Dempster, Mr E. W. Dempster, Mr D. J. Eggie, Mr Gary Etheridge, Mrs B. V. Evans, Mr A. Evans, N. Farrell, L. R. Frampton, Mrs L. M. Gillies, G. Godsman, D. Godsman, Mrs I. M. Grant, R. A. Green, Mrs A. Green, Mr M. J. Guthrie, E. D. Haggart, Mrs M. Hamilton, Mr A. W. Henderson, Mrs M Kennedy, Mr J. S. Lessells, Mr C. W. Levein, Ms F. E. MacInnes, Mr W. D. Macdonald, Mr J. C. McNeill, Mr J. M. Mcintyre, Mr M. G. Mellor, Mr J. D. Miller, Mr J. Mitchell, Mr J. M. Murphy, Mr W. E. Nicholson, Mrs A. M. Noble, Mr G. Park, Miss J. Park, Mrs A.M. Rhind, Mr G. G. Ritchie, Ms L. V. Russell, Mrs S. C. Russell, Mrs A. Russell, A. J. R. Russell, Mr A. Savage, Mr A. B. Shepherd, Mr B. T. E. Shrubsall, A. W. Sinclair, Mr D. R. Skinner, A. D. Stewart, Mrs S. A. Taylor, Mr A. C. Todd, Mrs C. A. Todd, Mr T. P Winnell, Mrs M. Winnell, Mrs M. Winnell.

Assistant Trainers: Peter Scudamore, Jaimie Duff, Nick Orpwood

Jockey (NH): Peter Buchanan. **Conditional:** Grant Cockburn, Derek Fox, Craig Nichol, Graham Watters.
Amateur: Mr Steven Fox, Mr Jamie Lyttle, Miss Rachael Macdonald, Mr Nick Orpwood.

---

551 **MR JOHN RYALL, Yeovil**
Postal: Higher Farm, Rimpton, Yeovil, Somerset, BA22 8AD
Contacts: **PHONE/FAX** (01935) 850222 **MOBILE** (07592) 738848
E-MAIL bjmryall@btconnect.com

1 CYPRESS GROVE (IRE), 11, b g Windsor Castle—Grecian Queen **B. J. M. Ryall**
2 HI BRONCO, 7, b g Emperor Fountain—Win A Hand **B. J. M. Ryall**
3 SPRING WOLF, 6, br g Loup Sauvage (USA)—Spring Grass **B. J. M. Ryall**
4 5, B g Emperor Fountain—Win A Hand **B. J. M. Ryall**

Assistant Trainer: Mrs R C Ryall

---

552 **MR JOHN RYAN, Newmarket**
Postal: John Ryan Racing, Cadland Stables, Moulton Road, Newmarket, Suffolk, CB8 8DU
Contacts: **PHONE** (01638) 664172 **MOBILE** (07739) 801235
E-MAIL john.ryan@jryanracing.com **WEBSITE** www.jryanracing.com

1 MICK DUNDEE (IRE), 4, b g Aussie Rules (USA)—Lucky Oakwood (USA) **Power Bloodstock Ltd**
2 OCEAN APPLAUSE, 4, b g Royal Applause—Aldora **Mr W. McLuskey**
3 OCEAN TEMPEST, 5, gr g Act One—Ipsa Loquitur **Mr W McLuskey & Mr C Little**
4 TENOR (IRE), 4, b g Oratorio (IRE)—Cedar Sea (IRE) **Kilco International**
5 THECORNISHCOCKNEY, 5, bl g Cockney Rebel (IRE)—Glittering Image (IRE) **Mr C Letcher & Mr J Ryan**
6 THECORNISHCOWBOY, 5, b g Haafhd—Oriental Dance **Mr C Letcher & Mr J Ryan**

THREE-YEAR-OLDS

7 APPLEJACK LAD, ch g Three Valleys (USA)—Fittonia (FR) **Mr G. R. McGladery**
8 Ch f Rock of Gibraltar (IRE)—Balliasta (IRE)
9 EVACUSAFE LADY, ch f Avonbridge—Snow Shoes **Evacusafe UK Ltd & Mr G Hicks**
10 FINALITY, b g Henrythenavigator (USA)—Dear Daughter
11 B f Oratorio (IRE)—Glittering Image (IRE)
12 PLUCKY DIP, b g Nayef (USA)—Plucky **Mr Byron, Mr Lavallin & Mr Donnison**

MR JOHN RYAN - Continued

TWO-YEAR-OLDS

13 BIG MCINTOSH (IRE), b c 4/2 Bushranger (IRE)—
Three Decades (IRE) (Invincible Spirit (IRE)) (85000) **Kilco International**
14 Ch c 16/5 Duke of Marmalade (IRE)—Chance For Romance (Entrepreneur) (2800)
15 B f 22/2 Stimulation (IRE)—Crystal Gale (IRE) (Verglas (IRE)) (800)
16 B f 28/1 Exceed And Excel (AUS)—Muja Farewell (Mujtahid (USA)) (45000) **M. Byron**
17 B c 2/5 Humbel (USA)—Tamara Moon (Acclamation) (4000) **Mr W. McLuskey**
18 THECORNISHBARRON (IRE), b c 27/4 Bushranger (IRE)—
Tripudium (IRE) (Night Shift (USA)) (8000) **Mr C. Letcher**

Other Owners: Mr M. Byron, Mr P. J. Donnison, Evacusafe UK Limited, Mr Gary Hicks, Mr S. Lavallin, Mr Christopher Letcher, Mr C. W. Little, Mr W. McLuskey, Mr J. Ryan.

Apprentice: Caroline Kelly, Jordon McMurray.

---

553 **MR KEVIN RYAN, Hambleton**
Postal: Hambleton Lodge, Hambleton, Thirsk, North Yorkshire, YO7 2HA
Contacts: PHONE Office (01845) 597010 / (01845)597622 FAX (01845) 597622
MOBILE (07768) 016930
E-MAIL kevin.hambleton@virgin.net WEBSITE www.kevinryanracing.com

1 **A STAR IN MY EYE (IRE),** 4, b f Authorized (IRE)—Vyatka **Sultan Ali**
2 **ARDMAY (IRE),** 5, b g Strategic Prince—Right After Moyne (IRE) **A. C. Henson**
3 **AU RENOIR,** 4, ch f Peintre Celebre (USA)—Goodbye **Guy Reed Racing**
4 **BAPAK BANGSAWAN,** 4, b g Pastoral Pursuits—Nsx **H.R.H. Sultan Ahmad Shah**
5 **BAPAK CHINTA (USA),** 5, gr ro g Speightstown (USA)—Suena Cay (USA) **Mr T. A. Rahman**
6 **BAPAK MUDA (USA),** 4, ch c Distorted Humor (USA)—Shiva (JPN) **Mr T. A. Rahman**
7 **BAPAK PESTA (IRE),** 4, b g Haatef (USA)—Penny Fan **Mr T. A. Rahman**
8 **BAPAK SAYANG (USA),** 4, b g Medaglia d'oro (USA)—Emily Ring (USA) **Mr T. A. Rahman**
9 **BLAINE,** 4, ch g Avonbridge—Lauren Louise **Matt & Lauren Morgan**
10 **BOGART,** 5, ch g Bahamian Bounty—Lauren Louise **Mrs A. Bailey**
11 **BOUSATET (FR),** 4, b f Muhtathir—Miss Mission (IRE) **Highbank Stud**
12 **BURNING BLAZE,** 4, b g Danroad (AUS)—Demeter (USA) **Qatar Racing Limited**
13 **CAPAILL LIATH (IRE),** 6, gr g Iffraaj—Bethesda **Mr T. A. Rahman**
14 **CAPTAIN RAMIUS (IRE),** 8, b g Kheleyf (USA)—Princess Mood (GER) **Mrs Clodagh McStay**
15 **CARDS,** 4, b f Tobougg (IRE)—Card Games **Guy Reed Racing**
16 **CHOOSEDAY (IRE),** 5, b g Choisir (AUS)—Break of Day (USA) **Mrs S. J. Barker**
17 **CLAYTON,** 5, b g Peintre Celebre (USA)—Blossom **Guy Reed Racing**
18 **DELORES ROCKET,** 4, b f Firebreak—Artistic (IRE) **J. Nixon**
19 **EQUITY RISK (USA),** 4, b g Henrythenavigator (USA)—Moon's Tune (USA) **Clipper Logistics**
20 **FORGET ME NOT LANE (IRE),** 5, b g Holy Roman Emperor (IRE)—Mrs Arkada (FR) **Mr J Hanson**
21 **GLORY AWAITS (IRE),** 4, ch c Choisir (AUS)—Sandbox Two (IRE) **Ahmad Abdulla Al Shaikh & Co**
22 **HAMZA (IRE),** 5, b g Amadeus Wolf—Lady Shanghai (IRE) **Mr Mubarak Al Naemi**
23 **HOPES N DREAMS (IRE),** 6, b m Elusive City (USA)—Hope of Pekan (IRE) **J. C. G. Chua**
24 **LIGHTNING CLOUD (IRE),** 6, gr g Sleeping Indian—Spree (IRE) **Hambleton Racing Ltd XVIII**
25 **PINTURA,** 7, ch g Efisio—Picolette **Mr Michael Beaumont**
26 **RED PALADIN (IRE),** 4, b g Red Clubs (IRE)—Alexander Goldmine **Hambleton Racing Ltd XXII**
27 **SARDANAPALUS,** 5, b g Byron—Crinkle (IRE) **Mr J. Nixon**
28 **STAR UP IN THE SKY (USA),** 4, gr ro f Speightstown (USA)—Prenuptial Plans (USA) **Matt & Lauren Morgan**
29 **SWEHAN (IRE),** 4, b g Diamond Green (FR)—Golden (FR) **Mr Mubarak Al Naemi**
30 **TRAIL BLAZE (IRE),** 5, b g Tagula (IRE)—Kingpin Delight **Mr & Mrs Julian & Rosie Richer**
31 **WARFARE,** 5, b g Soviet Star (USA)—Fluffy **Guy Reed Racing**
32 **YORK GLORY (USA),** 4, gr ro h Five Star Day (USA)—Minicolony (USA) **Salman Rashed & Mohamed Khalifa**

THREE-YEAR-OLDS

33 **ANA ETTIHADY (ITY),** b g Red Rocks (IRE)—American Beauty (GER) **Mr Ahmad Abdulla Al Shaikh**
34 **ASTAIRE (IRE),** b c Intense Focus (USA)—Runway Dancer **Mrs A. Bailey**
35 **BELAYER (IRE),** b g Whipper (USA)—Stella Del Mattino (USA) **Mr T. A. Rahman**
36 **BRAVE IMP,** b g Sleeping Indian—Impetious **Hambleton Racing Ltd XXVI**
37 **COMINO (IRE),** b g Tagula (IRE)—Malta (USA) **Mr D. W. Barker**
38 **DERBYSHIRE (IRE),** b g Green Tune (USA)—Statia (FR) **Matt & Lauren Morgan**
39 **DESERT COLOURS,** b g Exceed And Excel (AUS)—Awwal Malika (USA) **Mrs J. H. Ryan**
40 **DISTANT PAST,** b g Pastoral Pursuits—Faraway Lass **Mr M. Wynne**
41 **FINITO,** b c Peintre Celebre (USA)—Polo **Guy Reed Racing**

MR KEVIN RYAN - Continued

42 **GALVANIZE**, b g Bahamian Bounty—Xtrasensory **Matt & Lauren Morgan**
43 **HOT STREAK (IRE)**, ch c Iffraaj—Ashirah (USA) **Qatar Racing Limited**
44 **INJAZ**, ch g Compton Place—Belle's Edge **Salman Rashed & Mohamed Khalifa**
45 **KEEP TO THE BEAT**, b f Beat Hollow—Cadeau Speciale **Hambleton Racing Ltd XXIX**
46 **LESHA (IRE)**, b g Amadeus Wolf—Dane Blue (IRE) **Mr Mubarak Al Naemi**
47 **LEXINGTON ABBEY**, b g Sleeping Indian—Silvereine (FR) **Middleham Park Racing XIX**
48 **LIGHT WEIGHT (IRE)**, b f Danehill Dancer (IRE)—Foofaraw (USA) **Qatar Racing Limited**
49 **LOCKY TAYLOR (IRE)**, b g Bushranger (IRE)—Hawk Eyed Lady (IRE) **Kenneth MacPherson**
50 **MADAME MIRASOL (IRE)**, b f Sleeping Indian—Confidentiality (IRE) **Mrs M. Forsyth**
51 **MON PETIT SECRET**, b f Sakhee's Secret—Crabapple **Mrs S. Kelly**
52 **MOONLIGHT VENTURE**, ch g Tobougg (IRE)—Evening **Guy Reed Racing**
53 **NELSON'S PRIDE**, b f Mount Nelson—Bandanna **Hambleton Racing Ltd XXVII**
54 **ONLINE ALEXANDER (IRE)**, b f Acclamation—Dance Club (IRE) **Mr Noel O'Callaghan**
55 **OUTBACK WARRIOR (IRE)**, b c Bushranger (IRE)—Choice House (USA) **Saeed Manana**
56 **PATIENCE'S ROCK (IRE)**, b c Rock of Gibraltar (IRE)—Shakeeba (IRE) **Mr Michael Beaumont**
57 **PROCLAMATIONOFWAR (IRE)**, b g Proclamation (IRE)—Rockburst **Mr Michael Beaumont**
58 **RADEBE (USA)**, b c Distorted Humor (USA)—Sweet Hope (USA) **Highbank Stud**
59 **SEARCHLIGHT**, b g Kyllachy—Baralinka (IRE) **Elite Racing Club**
60 **SHAMOUTI (IRE)**, ch f Duke of Marmalade (IRE)—Pitrizza (IRE) **Racegoers Club Owners Group**
61 **SLEEPER KING (IRE)**, b c Holy Roman Emperor (IRE)—Catherine Palace **Mrs J. Bownes**
62 **SOUL INSTINCT**, b g Myboycharlie (IRE)—However (IRE) **Mr D. Cork**
63 **STRAITS OF MALACCA**, ch g Compton Place—Cultural Role **J. C. G. Chua**
64 **THE BOSS OF ME**, ch g Bahamian Bounty—Orange Pip **B. T. McDonald**
65 **THE GREY GATSBY (IRE)**, gr c Mastercraftsman (IRE)—Marie Vison (IRE) **Mr F. Gillespie**
66 **TOUCH THE CLOUDS**, b g Sleeping Indian—Aptina (USA) **Matt & Lauren Morgan 1**
67 **UPLIFTED (IRE)**, b g Jeremy (USA)—Misty Peak (IRE) **Mr Michael & Jacqueline Beaumont**

TWO-YEAR-OLDS

68 B f 30/1 Speightstown (USA)—African Skies (Johannesburg (USA)) **Hillen & Cockerill**
69 Gr c 18/4 Zebedee—Baby Bunting (Wolfhound (USA)) (30000) **Mr Mubarak Al Naemi**
70 B c 2/4 Tagula (IRE)—Bold Bunny (Piccolo) (14285)
71 B c 20/1 Kodiac—Callanish (Inchinor) (90000) **Qatar Racing Limited**
72 **CAN YOU REVERSE**, b c 28/2 Piccolo—Give Her A Whirl (Pursuit of Love) **Guy Reed Racing**
73 B g 4/5 Exceed And Excel (AUS)—Capistrano Day (USA) (Diesis) (45000) **Matt & Lauren Morgan**
74 B f 28/2 Approve (IRE)—Causeway Charm (Giant's Causeway (USA)) (25714) **Hambleton Racing Ltd**
75 B f 3/4 Acclamation—Church Melody (Oasis Dream) (46457) **Mr Mubarak Al Naemi**
76 B f 16/4 Exceed And Excel (AUS)—Crystal Mountain (Monashee Mountain (USA))
77 **CYRIL**, b c 20/3 Rail Link—Nurse Gladys (Dr Fong (USA)) **Guy Reed Racing**
78 B c 15/3 Acclamation—Dorelia (IRE) (Efisio) (140000) **Qatar Racing Limited**
79 **ELEUTHERA**, ch c 14/3 Bahamian Bounty—Cha Cha Cha (Efisio) **Guy Reed Racing**
80 B c 3/2 Bernstein (USA)—Escape To Victory (Salse (USA)) (5714) **Mrs R. G. Hillen**
81 B f 2/5 Dandy Man (IRE)—Gala Style (IRE) (Elnadim (USA)) **Mr Mubarak Al Naemi**
82 B f 18/3 Rock of Gibraltar (IRE)—Gamra (IRE) (Green Desert (USA)) **Highbank Stud**
83 **GEOLOGY**, b c 2/5 Rock of Gibraltar (IRE)—Baralinka (IRE) (Barathea (IRE)) **Elite Racing Club**
84 Br gr c 2/3 Zebedee—Giusina Mia (USA) (Diesis) (34000) **Kenneth MacPherson**
85 Ch c 28/1 Danehill Dancer (IRE)—Inca Trail (USA) (Royal Academy (USA)) **Mr Mubarak Al Naemi**
86 **INDIAN CHAMP**, b g 20/4 Sleeping Indian—Bebe de Cham (Tragic Role (USA)) (8571) **Mr M. Beaumont**
87 **INDIAN KEYS**, ch c 26/2 Sleeping Indian—Newkeylets (Diktat) (9047) **Mr M. Beaumont**
88 Ch c 2/3 Tagula (IRE)—Just Tallulah (Tomba) (9523) **Mr M. Beaumont**
89 **KATY IRAE (IRE)**, b f 5/4 Amadeus Wolf—Lady From Limerick (IRE) (Rainbows For Life (CAN)) (9523) **J. Berry**
90 **LET'S TWIST**, ch c 12/2 Piccolo—Takes Two To Tango (Groom Dancer (USA)) **Guy Reed Racing**
91 B c 13/4 Makfi—Liberty Chery (Statue of Liberty (USA)) (61942) **Qatar Racing Limited**
92 B c 15/4 Alfred Nobel (IRE)—Lintera (GER) (Night Shift (USA)) (11428) **Tariq Al Nisf**
93 B c 7/4 Dutch Art—Little Greenbird (Ardkinglass) (30476) **Kenneth MacPherson**
94 B c 17/4 Fast Company (IRE)—Nofa's Magic (IRE) (Rainbow Quest (USA)) **Mr Jaber Abdullah**
95 Ch c 16/4 Fast Company (IRE)—Nullarbor (Green Desert (USA)) (33333) **Hambleton Racing Ltd**
96 **QUESTO**, ch g 1/2 Monsieur Bond (IRE)—Ex Gracia (Efisio) **Guy Reed Racing**
97 Ch c 24/2 Bahamian Bounty—Rainbow End (Botanic (USA)) (35238) **Matt & Lauren Morgan**
98 B c 15/1 Kyllachy—Raskutani (Dansili) (15238) **Geoff & Sandra Turnbull**
99 B c 22/2 Dandy Man (IRE)—Red Beach (Turtle Island (IRE)) (26666) **Qatar Racing Limited**
100 B c 3/3 Acclamation—Red Shareef (Marju (IRE)) (47619) **Qatar Racing Limited**
101 **SHAMAZING**, ch f 7/4 Makfi—Rababah (USA) (Woodman (USA)) (50000) **Mrs R. G. Hillen**
102 B c 11/4 Zebedee—Sheba Five (USA) (Five Star Day (USA)) (33333) **Mr T. A. Rahman**
103 B gr c 15/1 Exceed And Excel (AUS)—Si Belle (IRE) (Dalakhani (IRE)) (16000) **Matt & Lauren Morgan**
104 Gr c 29/3 Zebedee—Spinning Gold (Spinning World (USA)) **Mr Mubarak Al Naemi**

MR KEVIN RYAN - Continued

105 Gr c 12/4 Jeremy (USA)—Spree (IRE) (Dansili) **Hambleton Racing Ltd**
106 Br c 24/3 Big Bad Bob (IRE)—Toberanthawn (IRE) (Danehill Dancer (IRE)) (33333) **Matt & Lauren Morgan**
107 WELD AL EMARAT, b c 14/2 Dubawi (IRE)—Spirit of Dubai (IRE) (Cape Cross (IRE)) **Ahmad Abdulla Al Shaikh**
108 B f 21/2 Paco Boy (IRE)—Xtrasensory (Royal Applause) (42857) **Mrs A. Bailey**
109 Ch ro c 30/1 Mastercraftsman (IRE)—Yacht Woman (USA) (Mizzen Mast (USA)) **Mr Mubarak Al Naemi**

Other Owners: Shaikh Mohammed Alkhalifa, Mrs Jacqueline Beaumont, Mr Michael Beaumont, Sir Alex Ferguson, Hambleton Racing Ltd, Mr J. Hanson, Mrs R. G. Hillen, Mr Matthew Morgan, Mrs Lauren Morgan, Mr Salman Rashed, Mrs J. Ryan, Mr S. R. H. Turner, Mrs I. M. Wainwright, Mr M. Wainwright.

Assistant Trainer: Joe O'Gorman

Jockey (flat): Amy Ryan. **Apprentice:** Shane Gray, Kevin Stott.

---

554 **MR AYTACH SADIK, Kidderminster**
Postal: **Wolverley Court Coach House, Wolverley, Kidderminster, Worcestershire, DY10 3RP**
Contacts: **PHONE (01562) 852362 MOBILE (07803) 040344**

1 APACHE DAWN, 10, ch g Pursuit of Love—Taza **A. M. Sadik**
2 BLIZZARD BLUES (USA), 8, ch g Mr Greeley (USA)—Blush Damask (USA) **A. M. Sadik**
3 FINCH FLYER (IRE), 7, ch g Indian Ridge—Imelda (USA) **A. M. Sadik**
4 ZAFARABAN (IRE), 7, gr g Dalakhani (IRE)—Zafaraniya (IRE) **A. M. Sadik**

---

555 **MRS DEBORAH SANDERSON, Retford**
Postal: **Poplar Cottage, Wheatley Road, Sturton-le-Steeple, Retford, Nottinghamshire, DN22 9HU**
Contacts: **PHONE (01777) 818751 (01427) 884692 FAX (01777) 818751 MOBILE (07968) 821074**
E-MAIL debbie.sanderson@btconnect.com WEBSITE www.wisetonstables.co.uk

1 MOORGATE LASS, 6, b m Danbird (AUS)—Bolham Lady **Mr J. M. Lacey**
2 NINE BEFORE TEN (IRE), 6, ch m Captain Rio—Sagaing **W. McKay**
3 PRIGSNOV DANCER (IRE), 9, ch g Namid—Brave Dance (IRE) **Mr J. M. Lacey**
4 ROGER THORPE, 5, b g Firebreak—Nunthorpe **Mr J. M. Lacey**

THREE-YEAR-OLDS
5 POCO PICCOLO, b g Piccolo—Angel Maid **Lacey, Sanderson & Amos**

Other Owners: Mr S. Amos, Mrs D. J. Sanderson.

Jockey (flat): Edward Creighton, Silvestre De Sousa. **Amateur:** Miss Dora Lenge.

---

556 **MR MALCOLM SAUNDERS, Wells**
Postal: **Blue Mountain Farm, Wells Hill Bottom, Haydon, Wells, Somerset, BA5 3EZ**
Contacts: **OFFICE/FAX (01749) 841011 MOBILE (07771) 601035**
E-MAIL malcolm@malcolmsaunders.co.uk WEBSITE www.malcolmsaunders.co.uk

1 BALTIC GIN (IRE), 4, b f Baltic King—Deeday Bay (IRE) **Mr P. K. Hancock**
2 GINZAN, 6, b m Desert Style (IRE)—Zyzania **Mr P. S. G. Nicholas**
3 LADY BAYSIDE, 6, ch m Ishiguru (USA)—Seldemosa **Biddestone Racing Club 1**
4 SARANGOO, 6, b m Piccolo—Craic Sa Ceili (IRE) **Lockstone Business Services Ltd**
5 SILVERRICA (IRE), 4, gr f Ad Valorem (USA)—Allegorica (IRE) **Mrs V. L. Nicholas**
6 SUNNY FUTURE, 8, b g Masterful (USA)—Be Magic **M. S. Saunders**
7 WOODEN KING (IRE), 9, b g Danetime (IRE)—Olympic Rock (IRE) **Mr P. K. Hancock**

THREE-YEAR-OLDS
8 B g Amadeus Wolf—Allegorica (IRE) **M. S. Saunders**
9 BABYFACT, b f Piccolo—Pennyspider (IRE) **Mrs V. L. Nicholas**
10 CAMELEY DAWN, b f Alhaarth (IRE)—Apply Dapply **Mr & Mrs J Harris**
11 DANZ STAR (IRE), ch g Ad Valorem (USA)—Await (IRE) **Mr P. S. G. Nicholas**
12 PERMSIRI (IRE), b f Ad Valorem (USA)—Swiss Roll (IRE) **M. S. Saunders**
13 Ch f Lucky Story (USA)—Willisa **M. S. Saunders**

MR MALCOLM SAUNDERS - Continued

TWO-YEAR-OLDS

14 B f 23/2 Pastoral Pursuits—Ballyalla (Mind Games) (22857) **M. S. Saunders**
15 Ch f 20/3 Sakhee's Secret—Craic Sa Ceili (IRE) (Danehill Dancer (IRE)) (1142) **M. S. Saunders**
16 Ch c 27/4 Sakhee's Secret—Crimson Fern (IRE) (Titus Livius (FR)) **M. S. Saunders**
17 B c 10/3 Aussie Rules (USA)—Polynesian Queen (IRE) (Statue of Liberty (USA)) (5806) **M. S. Saunders**
18 B f 11/3 Vale of York (IRE)—Star Port (Observatory (USA)) (9291) **M. S. Saunders**

Other Owners: T. Al-Mazeedi, T. P. Bostwick, Mr J. E. Harris, Mrs P. A. Harris.

---

557 MRS DIANNE SAYER, Penrith
Postal: **Town End Farm, Hackthorpe, Penrith, Cumbria, CA10 2HX**
Contacts: **PHONE (01931) 712245 MOBILE (07980) 295316**

1 **ALLOW ME,** 9, b g Daylami (IRE)—Time Honoured **The Polnud Partnership**
2 **BAILEYS CONCERTO (IRE),** 8, b g Bach (IRE)—None The Wiser (IRE) **United Five Racing & Mr Andrew Sayer**
3 **BORUMA (IRE),** 4, b g Brian Boru—Itiallendintears (IRE) **Tony Price & Mrs Linda White**
4 **BRIGHT ABBEY,** 6, ch g Halling (USA)—Bright Hope (IRE) **A. R. White**
5 **CALL OF DUTY (IRE),** 9, br g Storming Home—Blushing Barada (USA) **T. W. Rebanks**
6 **COOL BARANCA (GER),** 8, b m Beat Hollow—Cool Storm (IRE) **Mr D. J. Coppola**
7 **DISCOVERIE,** 6, b g Runyon (IRE)—Sri (IRE) **Mr D. J. Coppola**
8 **ENDEAVOR,** 9, ch g Selkirk (USA)—Midnight Mambo (USA) **Mrs M. Coppola**
9 **FANNYTHEWUNDAHORSE (IRE),** 7, b m Alderbrook—Woodford Beauty (IRE) **Suzanne & Nigel Williams**
10 **GOLD CHAIN (IRE),** 4, b f Authorized (IRE)—Mountain Chain (USA) **J. A. Sayer**
11 **GREAT DEMEANOR (USA),** 4, b g Bernstein (USA)—Hangin Withmy Buds (USA) **Mr D. J. Coppola**
12 **JACK ALBERT (IRE),** 7, gr g Cloudings (IRE)—Lisdoylelady (IRE) **E F Sporting**
13 **LANGLEY HOUSE (IRE),** 7, b m Milan—No Moore Bills **S J D Racing**
14 **MARKADAM,** 8, b g Mark of Esteem (IRE)—Elucidate **Mr R. A. Harrison**
15 5, B g Classic Cliche (IRE)—Mighty Mandy (IRE)
16 **MORE EQUITY,** 12, b m Classic Cliche (IRE)—Sillymore **Mrs M. Coppola**
17 **MY FRIEND GEORGE,** 8, ch g Alflora (IRE)—Snowgirl (IRE) **J. A. Sayer**
18 **NEWDANE DANCER (IRE),** 7, b m Golan (IRE)—Flagofconvienience (IRE) **E. G. Tunstall**
19 **OH RIGHT (IRE),** 10, b g Zagreb (USA)—Conna Bride Lady (IRE) **J. A. Sayer**
20 **SENDIYM (FR),** 7, b g Rainbow Quest (USA)—Seraya (FR) **United Five Racing & Mr Andrew Sayer**
21 **SERGEANT PINK (IRE),** 8, b g Fasliyev (USA)—Ring Pink (USA) **J. A. Sayer**
22 **SHOAL BAY DREAMER,** 8, b m Central Park (IRE)—Ninfa (IRE) **The Transatlantics**
23 **SOLIS (GER),** 11, ch g In The Wings—Seringa (GER) **Mr D. J. Coppola**

THREE-YEAR-OLDS

24 **TASHBEEH (IRE),** b g Iffraaj—Kayak **J. A. Sayer**

Other Owners: Mr K. J. Burrow, Mr A. J. Burrow, Mr I. T. Conroy, Mr R. Hamilton, Mrs J. D. Howard, Mr D. Hunter, R. Kent, Mr P. Moorby, Mr K. E. Moorby, Mr S. Nicholson, Mr D. A. Price, Mrs H. D. Sayer, Mrs C. Tunstall, Mr A. Wardrop, Mrs L. White, Mrs S. E. Williams, N. Williams.

Assistant Trainer: Miss Joanna Sayer

Conditional: Emma Sayer. **Apprentice:** Emma Sayer. **Amateur:** Miss Liz Butterworth.

---

558 DR JON SCARGILL, Newmarket
Postal: **Red House Stables, Hamilton Road, Newmarket, Suffolk, CB8 0TE**
Contacts: PHONE (01638) 663254 MOBILE (07785) 350705
E-MAIL scargill@redhousestables.freeserve.co.uk WEBSITE www.jonscargill.co.uk

1 **ASIA MINOR (IRE),** 5, ch m Pivotal—Anka Britannia (USA) **Strawberry Fields Stud**
2 **FANOOS,** 5, b m Dutch Art—Miss Otis **Theme Tune Partnership**
3 **MAN IN THE ARENA,** 4, b g Bertolini (USA)—Torver **Mrs S. M. Scargill**
4 **THE GINGER BERRY,** 4, ch g First Trump—Dolly Coughdrop (IRE) **Strawberry Fields Stud & S. J. Howard**
5 **YOU'RE A RICH GIRL,** 4, b f Proclamation (IRE)—Ribh **J P T Partnership**

THREE-YEAR-OLDS

6 B c Bertolini (USA)—Torver **J P T Partnership**

DR JON SCARGILL - Continued

TWO-YEAR-OLDS

7 B c 27/3 Sakhee (USA)—Chine (Inchinor) **Strawberry Fields Stud**
8 B c 12/5 Footstepsinthesand—Contemplate (Compton Place) **Silent Partners**
9 Ch c 16/2 Sir Percy—Great White Hope (IRE) (Noverre (USA)) **Silent Partners**
10 Ch f 28/4 Showcasing—La Gazzetta (IRE) (Rossini (USA)) **Silent Partners**
11 B f 9/4 Kheleyf (USA)—Snow Shoes (Sri Pekan (USA)) **Silent Partners**

Other Owners: G. Bridgford, P. Darlington, J. Dutton, W. Eacott, P. Edwards, A. Holness, S. Howard, L. Meadows, D. Meilton, Mr G. F. L. Robinson, K. Ruttle, Mr P. J. Scargill, P. Scargill, S. E. Scargill, P. Stanton, B. Watson, R. Watson, Mr Basil White, Mrs A. L. J. White.

---

559 **MR DERRICK SCOTT, Minehead**
Postal: East Lynch, Minehead, Somerset, TA24 8SS
Contacts: **PHONE (01643) 702430 FAX (01643) 702430**

1 LUPITA (IRE), 10, ch m Intikhab (USA)—Sarah (IRE) **Mrs R. Scott**
2 ROYBUOY, 7, b g Royal Applause—Wavy Up (IRE) **Mrs R. Scott**

---

560 **MR JEREMY SCOTT, Dulverton**
Postal: Higher Holworthy Farm, Brompton Regis, Dulverton, Somerset, TA22 9NY
Contacts: **PHONE (01398) 371414 MOBILE (07709) 279483**
E-MAIL holworthyfarm@yahoo.com

1 ADDICTION, 9, b m Alflora (IRE)—Premier Princess **Gale Force Four**
2 ALBEROBELLO (IRE), 6, b g Old Vic—Tourist Attraction (IRE) **Bradley Partnership**
3 ALFIE'S BIRD, 6, b g Alflora (IRE)—Thornbird **Mr D. J. Bluett**
4 BALLINAHOW STAR (IRE), 8, b m Definite Article—Ballinahowliss (IRE) **Pillhead House Partners**
5 BEST BOY BARNEY (IRE), 8, b g Rashar (USA)—Graigue Lass (IRE) **G. T. Lever**
6 BOOGIE IN THE BARN (IRE), 6, b g Milan—Presenting Mist (IRE) **Bradley Partnership**
7 BRAVE DEED (IRE), 8, b g Kadeed (IRE)—Merlins Return (IRE) **Gale Force Seven**
8 DASHAWAY (IRE), 5, ch g Shantou (USA)—Backaway (IRE) **The Town & Country Partnership 2**
9 DAVERON (IRE), 6, b g Winged Love (IRE)—Double Doc (IRE) **Mr N. A. Holder**
10 DECIMUS (IRE), 7, b g Bienamado (USA)—Catch Me Dreaming (IRE) **The Ten 2 One Gang**
11 DREAM DEAL (IRE), 6, b g Presenting—Rowlands Dream (IRE) **Mrs Messer-Bennetts,Clarke Hall & Gilbert**
12 DUKE'S AFFAIR (IRE), 6, b g Fair Mix (IRE)—Dunsfold Duchess (IRE) **Mrs H. L. Stoneman**
13 EXMOOR CHALLENGE, 5, b g Thank Heavens—Bullys Maid
14 FEATHERED FRIEND, 8, b g Teofilio (IRE)—Thornbird **Mr D. J. Bluett**
15 FIVE STAR WILSHAM (IRE), 10, b g Bob's Return (IRE)—Riverpauper (IRE) **Mr & Mrs Richard Organ**
16 GLENWOOD PRINCE (IRE), 8, b g King's Theatre (IRE)—Moll Bawn (IRE) **Gale Force Seven**
17 GOLDEN GAEL, 8, ch m Generous (IRE)—Gaelic Gold (IRE) **The Wild Bunch**
18 GUNNA BE A DEVIL (IRE), 10, b g Alflora (IRE)—Gunna Be Precious **Mr R. J. Lock**
19 KILMURVY (IRE), 6, b g Shantou (USA)—Spagna (IRE) **I. R. Murray**
20 KNAVE OF CLUBS (IRE), 5, b g Red Clubs (IRE)—Royal Bounty (IRE) **Mr J. P. Carrington**
21 MASTER MAX, 7, b g Reset (AUS)—Folly Finnesse **Mrs P. J. Pengelly**
22 MELODIC RENDEZVOUS, 8, ch g Where Or When (IRE)—Vic Melody (FR) **Cash For Honours**
23 MIDNIGHT MINT, 4, b f Midnight Legend—Calamintha **Mrs K. Holmes**
24 MINER DISTRACTION, 6, b m Desert King (IRE)—Miner Yours **Mrs D. C. Webb**
25 MOORLANDS GEORGE, 6, b g Grape Tree Road—Sandford Springs (USA) **Mrs L. M. Williams**
26 MOORLANDS JACK, 9, b g Cloudings (IRE)—Sandford Springs (USA) **Mrs L. M. Williams**
27 MYSTIC APPEAL (IRE), 8, b r g Alderbrook—Piseog (IRE) **Gale Force Two**
28 NIGHT OF PASSION (IRE), 6, b m Winged Love (IRE)—Miss Dundee (FR) **Mrs P. J. Pengelly**
29 NOTARFBAD (IRE), 8, b g Alderbrook—Angels Flame (IRE) **Govier & Brown**
30 ON THE BRIDGE (IRE), 9, b g Milan—Bay Dove **Mr C. J. James**
31 OSCAR THE MYTH (IRE), 8, b g Oscar (IRE)—Have A Myth (IRE) **Langleys**
32 PEACEFUL GARDENS, 5, b m Franklins Gardens—So Peaceful **Twelve Twelve Twelve**
33 PORTERS WAR (IRE), 12, ch g Flemensfirth (USA)—Grainne Geal **Sarah Waugh & Paul Porter**
34 QUADDICK LAKE (IRE), 11, br g Blueprint—Wondermac (IRE) **The Exmoor Pack**
35 SHOOFLY MILLY (IRE), 5, b m Milan—Jacksister (IRE) **Gale Force One**
36 SPECIAL ACCOUNT (IRE), 9, b g Luso—Thegirlfromslane (IRE) **Mrs J. M. Perry**
37 THE SNAPPY POET, 5, ch g Byron—Runaway Star **Jeremy Scott Racing Club**

MR JEREMY SCOTT - Continued

Other Owners: Mr M. P. Ansell, Mr J. F. C. Atkins, Mr J. Bagwell-Purefoy, G. S. Brown, Mrs C. Clarke-Hall, Mr C. Cole, Mrs M. A. Cole, D. J. Coles, Mr R. J. L. Flood, Mr A. P. Gale, Mrs A. G. Gale, Mrs K. Gilbert, Mrs G. D. Giles, Mr P. Govier, Mr P. F. Govier, Mr C. F. Hayes, Mr W. M. Izaby-White, Mr D. E. Langley, Mr S. J. Loosemore, Miss N. Martin, Mrs S. D. Messer-Bennetts, Mr R. H. Organ, Mr J. Organ, P Porter, Mrs S. M. Ragg, Mr J. R. M. Scott, Mrs R. Scott, Mrs C. C. Scott, Mr J. Simpson, Mr M. J. Swallow, Miss S. M. Waugh, Mr A. Westwood.

Assistant Trainer: Camilla Scott

Jockey (NH): Nick Scholfield. **Conditional:** Matt Griffiths, Chris Meehan. **Amateur:** Miss V. Wade.

---

561 MR BERNARD SCRIVEN, Taunton
Postal: **Cogload Farm, Durston, Taunton, Somerset, TA3 5AW**
Contacts: **PHONE (01823) 490208**

1 PUERTO AZUL (IRE), 10, ch g Beneficial—Droichidin **B. Scriven**

Assistant Trainer: Miss Kay Scriven

---

562 MR MICHAEL SCUDAMORE, Bromsash
Postal: **Ecclesswall Court, Bromsash, Nr. Ross-on-Wye, Herefordshire, HR9 7PP**
Contacts: **PHONE (01989) 750844 FAX (01989) 750281 MOBILE (07901) 853520**
E-MAIL michael.scu@btconnect.com WEBSITE www.scudamoreracing.co.uk

1 BENENDEN (IRE), 6, b g Moscow Society (USA)—Ashanti Dancer (IRE) **Mr M. R. Blandford**
2 BOUNDS AND LEAPS, 9, b m Laveron—Geisha **Mason Scudamore Racing**
3 CHRISTOPHER CHUA (IRE), 5, gr g Clodovil (IRE)—Pearls of Wisdom **C. G. J. Chua**
4 EASTERN DRAGON (IRE), 4, b g Elnadim (USA)—Shulammite Woman (IRE) **JCG Chua & CK Ong**
5 LINE D'AOIS (IRE), 6, b g Craigsteel—Old Line (IRE) **S. M. Smith**
6 MONBEG DUDE (IRE), 9, b g Witness Box (USA)—Ten Dollar Bill (IRE) **Oydunow**
7 MR GOOFY (IRE), 13, b g Rock Hopper—Jamie's Lady **Mrs L. J. Sluman**
8 NEXT SENSATION (IRE), 7, b g Brian Boru—Road Trip (IRE) **Mr M. R. Blandford**
9 NO THROUGH ROAD, 7, b g Grape Tree Road—Pendil's Delight **A. P. Barwell**
10 PRINCESSE FLEUR, 5, b m Grape Tree Road—Princesse Grec (FR) **The Honfleur Syndicate**
11 RED CURRENT, 10, b m Soviet Star (USA)—Fleet Amour (USA) **Simpson-Daniel & Scudamore Racing**
12 RETROSON (IRE), 6, b g Lahib (USA)—Retro's Girl (IRE) **Mr. M. Scudamore**
13 RIPTIDE, 8, b g Val Royal (FR)—Glittering Image (IRE) **Middletons**
14 SHADES OF SILVER, 4, b g Dansili—Silver Pivotal (IRE) **M. Scudamore**
15 UNCLE TOM COBLEY (IRE), 10, b g King's Theatre—Platinum Leader (IRE) **M. Scudamore**
16 UNE DES BIEFFES (FR), 6, b m Le Fou—Belle D'ecajeul (FR) **Michael Fitzpatrick & Mark Blandford**
17 VON GALEN (IRE), 13, b g Germany (USA)—Castle Carrig (IRE) **Mrs B. V. Evans**
18 WOTSTHECATCH (IRE), 6, b g Fruits of Love (USA)—Miss Perky (IRE) **Mr M. R. Blandford**

Other Owners: S. A. Baker, Mr M. J. Fitzpatrick, K. L. Hunter, Mr A. Mason, Mr G. D. Middleton, A. D. Middleton, Mr F. Ong, Dr S. M. Readings, Mrs M. L. Scudamore, Mr J. D. Simpson-Daniel.

---

563 MR IAN SEMPLE, Haddington
Postal: **Stoneypath Tower, Haddington, East Lothian, EH41 4QB**
Contacts: **PHONE (01620) 830233 MOBILE (07950) 175207**
E-MAIL ian.semple48@yahoo.com

1 BELLGROVE (IRE), 6, b g Gold Well—Less Hassle (IRE) **M. Sawers**
2 CALTON ENTRY (IRE), 5, b g Bahri (USA)—Gaybrook (IRE) **M. Sawers**
3 CHLOE'S DREAM (IRE), 4, gr f Clodovil (IRE)—Extravagance (IRE) **P. Tsim**
4 COMMANDABLE (AUS), 10, b g Commands (AUS)—Achievable (AUS) **Stoneypath Racing Club**
5 JOSHUA THE FIRST, 5, br g Kheleyf (USA)—Newkeylets **Mr J. Gaffney**
6 L'AMI LOUIS (IRE), 6, b g Elusive City (USA)—Princess Electra (IRE) **Mr Kenny Robson & Billy Robinson**
7 SHE'S SOME GIRL (IRE), 4, ch f Camacho—Tea Service (IRE) **Mr J. Gaffney**

THREE-YEAR-OLDS

8 BIFOCAL, b g Footstepsinthesand—Clear Vision **D. W. Shaw**
9 CLABARE, b g Proclamation (IRE)—Choral Singer **Mr Ian Anderson**

MR IAN SEMPLE - Continued

10 **DRINKS FOR LOSERS (IRE),** b g Mastercraftsman (IRE)—Heart's Desire (IRE) **Mrs J. Penman**
11 B f Art Connoisseur (IRE)—Jinxy Jill **Matt Sawers**

TWO-YEAR-OLDS

12 B c 29/4 Dutch Art—Dance Card (Cape Cross (IRE)) (28571) **Mrs J. Penman**
13 B g 9/4 Myboycharlie (IRE)—Dead Womans Pass (IRE) (High Chaparral (IRE)) **Exchange Court Properties Ltd**

Other Owners: Miss Laura Davidson, Mr W. Gibb, D. Irvine, A. Irvine, Miss Rona Mowbray, Mr G. Ritchie, Mr M Sawers, Mr D W Shaw, Mr Peter Tsim.

Assistant Trainer: David Shaw **Pupil Assistant:** Annie Mowbray

Jockey (flat): Tom Eaves. **Jockey (NH):** Dougie Costello, Ryan Mania. **Apprentice:** Jason Hart.

---

564 **MR DEREK SHAW, Sproxton**
Postal: **The Sidings, Saltby Road, Sproxton, Melton Mowbray, Leicestershire, LE14 4RA**
Contacts: **PHONE (01476) 860578 FAX (01476) 860578 MOBILE (07721) 039645**
E-MAIL **mail@derekshawracing.com** WEBSITE **www.derekshawracing.com**

1 **ARASHI,** 8, b g Fantastic Light (USA)—Arriving **Mr P. Derbyshire**
2 **BABY STRANGE,** 10, gr g Superior Premium—The Manx Touch (IRE) **Market Avenue Racing Club Ltd**
3 **BLACKSTONE VEGAS,** 8, ch g Nayef (USA)—Waqood (USA) **Shakespeare Racing**
4 **BOROUGH BOY (IRE),** 4, b g Jeremy (USA)—Ostrusa (AUT) **Mr B. Johnson**
5 **CHATEAU LOLA,** 5, b m Byron—Glensara **D McLiesh & Ownaracehorse**
6 **CLIMAXFORTACKLE (IRE),** 6, b m Refuse To Bend (IRE)—Miss Asia Quest **Shakespeare Racing**
7 **INVIGILATOR,** 6, b g Motivator—Midpoint (USA) **The Warren Partnership**
8 **LAST CHANCE RANCH,** 4, b g Manduro (GER)—Rakata (USA) **Mr D. Shaw**
9 **LOYALTY,** 7, b g Medicean—Ecoutila (USA) **Mr B. Johnson**
10 **MATAAJIR (USA),** 6, b g Redoute's Choice (AUS)—Hamasah (USA) **Mr B. Johnson**
11 **MAX THE MACHINE,** 4, b g Intikhab (USA)—Digamist Girl (IRE) **Mr B. Johnson**
12 **MIDNITE MOTIVATION,** 5, b m Motivator—Tamise (USA) **The Whiteman Partnership**
13 **OUR PRINCESS ELLIE (USA),** 6, ch m Borrego (USA)—Dear Abigail (USA) **Mrs L. J. Shaw**
14 **PRINCE OF PASSION (CAN),** 6, ch g Roman Ruler (USA)—Rare Passion (CAN) **Mr C. B. Hamilton**
15 **REELWILL (FR),** 9, gr m Dom Alco (FR)—Jeep Will (FR) **Mr D. J. W. Edmunds**
16 **REFLECT (IRE),** 6, b g Hurricane Run (IRE)—Raphimix (FR) **Mr P. Derbyshire**
17 **SAKTOON (USA),** 6, b m El Prado (IRE)—Galore (USA) **Mrs L. J. Shaw**
18 **SAM SPADE (IRE),** 4, gr g Clodovil (IRE)—Red Empress **The Warren Partnership**
19 **SHAWKANTANGO,** 7, b g Piccolo—Kitty Kitty Cancan **Shawthing Racing Partnership**
20 **SIX SILVER LANE,** 6, gr g Aussie Rules (USA)—Aurelia **Mr D. Shaw**
21 **STUN GUN,** 4, b g Medicean—Tapas En Bal (FR) **Mr J. R. Saville**
22 **TEENAGE DREAM (IRE),** 6, b g Antonius Pius (USA)—Lucayan Star (IRE) **Market Avenue Racing Club Ltd**
23 **THORNCLIFFER,** 10, ch g Generous (IRE)—Recipe **Moorland Racing & Mr P R Whilock**
24 **TOP BOY,** 4, b g Exceed And Excel (AUS)—Injaaz **Mr B. Johnson**
25 **TWIST AND TWIRL,** 4, b f Cockney Rebel (IRE)—Silent Miracle (IRE) **Mr D. Shaw**
26 **WELLIESINTHEWATER (IRE),** 4, b g Footstepsinthesand—Shadow Ash (IRE) **The Whiteman Partnership**

THREE-YEAR-OLDS

27 **ARGENT TOUCH,** gr g Elnadim (USA)—The Manx Touch (IRE) **Mr B. Johnson**
28 **CAESARS GIFT (IRE),** b g Holy Roman Emperor (IRE)—Jazz Up **Mr B. Johnson**
29 **DAY STAR LAD,** b g Footstepsinthesand—Eurolink Mayfly **Mr B. Johnson**
30 **DIAMONDSINTHESKY (IRE),** b f Dandy Man (IRE)—Colourpoint (USA) **Mr D. Shaw**
31 **DONT TELL NAN,** b f Major Cadeaux—Charlie Girl **Mr B. Johnson**
32 **DYNAMO WALT (IRE),** b g Acclamation—Cambara **Mr B. Johnson**
33 **EXTREME SUPREME,** b c Piccolo—Kitty Kitty Cancan **Mrs L. J. Shaw**
34 **KINGSWAY LAD (IRE),** b g New Approach (IRE)—Obsessive (USA) **Mr B. Johnson**
35 **MARO,** b g Royal Applause—Meditation **P. E. Barrett**
36 **ROYAL BUSHIDA,** b g Royal Applause—Moonmaiden **Mr B. Johnson**
37 Ch g Pivotal—Visualize **Mr B. Johnson**

TWO-YEAR-OLDS

38 B f 29/5 Tagula (IRE)—Cambara (Dancing Brave (USA)) (11000) **Mr B. Johnson**
39 Ro f 23/3 Dark Angel (IRE)—Cappella (IRE) (College Chapel) (21680) **Mr B. Johnson**
40 Br f 16/4 Alfred Nobel (IRE)—Colourpoint (USA) (Forest Wildcat (USA)) (7742) **Mr B. Johnson**
41 B f 2/3 Tamayuz—Final Opinion (IRE) (King's Theatre (IRE)) (25000) **Mr B. Johnson**

MR DEREK SHAW - Continued

42 B c 15/2 Exceed And Excel (AUS)—Inaminute (IRE) (Spectrum (IRE)) (49523) **Mr B. Johnson**
43 B c 22/3 Piccolo—Kitty Kitty Cancan (Warrshan (USA)) **Mrs L. J. Shaw**
44 B br f 6/3 Equiano (FR)—Meditation (Inchinor) **P. E. Barrett**
45 B c 18/2 Bluegrass Cat (USA)—Meniatarra (USA) (Zilzal (USA)) (14285) **Mr B. Johnson**
46 B c 26/4 Exceed And Excel (AUS)—Oatcake (Selkirk (USA)) (19000) **Mr B. Johnson**
47 B c 20/3 Equiano (FR)—Pretty Girl (IRE) (Polish Precedent (USA)) (36190) **Mr B. Johnson**
48 Gr c 26/4 Strategic Prince—Rofan (USA) (Cozzene (USA)) (12388) **Mr B. Johnson**
49 B br f 9/2 Medicean—Specific Dream (Danehill Dancer (IRE)) (45000) **Mr B. Johnson**
50 Ch f 26/3 Exceed And Excel (AUS)—Stravella (IRE) (Stravinsky (USA)) (11000) **Mr B. Johnson**
51 B c 7/3 Invincible Spirit (IRE)—Super Sleuth (IRE) (Selkirk (USA)) (55000) **Mr B. Johnson**
52 B f 8/4 Paco Boy (IRE)—Swanky Lady (Cape Cross (IRE)) **P. E. Barrett**
53 B c 9/4 Excellent Art—Teddy Bears Picnic (Oasis Dream) (17808) **Mr B. Johnson**

Other Owners: Mrs H. Franklin, Mr N. Higginson, Mr T. Lively, S. A. Mace, Mrs A. M. Mace, D. N. McLiesh, Ownaracehorse Ltd, Mr S. Warren, Mr P. R. Whilock, S. A. Whiteman.

Yard Sponsor: Grosvenor Contracts Leasing Ltd

Jockey (flat): Martin Dwyer. **Apprentice:** Adam McLean.

---

565 **MRS PATRICIA SHAW, Looe**
Postal: **Kilminorth Park, Looe, Cornwall, PL13 2NE**

1 FIREWELD, 7, b m Weld—Bella Astra **Mr D. C. Odgers**
2 JOAACI (IRE), 14, b g Presenting—Miss Sarajevo (IRE) **Mr D. C. Odgers**
3 MOBAASHER (USA), 11, ch g Rahy (USA)—Balistroika (USA) **Mr D. C. Odgers**

---

566 **MR MARK SHEARS, Newton Abbot**
Postal: **Lower Nattadon Farm, Chagford, Newton Abbot, Devon, TQ13 8ER**
Contacts: PHONE (01647) 432356 FAX (01647) 432356 MOBILE (07881) 745314
E-MAIL markshearsracing@gmail.com

1 MEADSTOWN (IRE), 6, gr g Talkin Man (CAN)—Little Rose (IRE) **J. B. Shears**
2 RUBY'S FROM MILAN (IRE), 6, b m Milan—Rubita (IRE) **J. B. Shears**
3 WAR TREATY (IRE), 6, b g Wareed (IRE)—Via Viaduct (IRE) **J. B. Shears**

Assistant Trainer: Mr J. B. Shears

Jockey (NH): James Davies. **Conditional:** Ollie Garner, Kevin Jones, Mark Quinlan.

---

567 **MR MATT SHEPPARD, Ledbury**
Postal: **Home Farm Cottage, Eastnor, Ledbury, Herefordshire, HR8 1RD**
Contacts: FAX (01531) 634846 MOBILE (07770) 625061
E-MAIL matthew.sheppard@cmail.co.uk WEBSITE www.mattsheppardracing.co.uk

1 ANOTHER FLUTTER (IRE), 10, b g Lahib (USA)—Golden Fizz **Mr A. J. Scrivin**
2 COOL BOB (IRE), 11, b g Bob Back (USA)—Rosie Jaques **Mrs N. Sheppard**
3 FAUSTINA PIUS (IRE), 6, b m Antonius Pius (USA)—Out In The Sun (USA) **Lost In The Summer Wine**
4 IKORODU ROAD, 11, b g Double Trigger (IRE)—Cerisier (IRE) **W. J. Odell**
5 LOUGHALDER (IRE), 8, ch g Alderbrook—Lough Lein Leader (IRE) **Mr Simon Gegg & Mr Tony Scrivin**
6 MODELIGO (IRE), 5, b g Indian Danehill (IRE)—Glens Lady (IRE) **S. J. D. Gegg**
7 ROCK ON ROCKY, 6, b g Overbury (IRE)—Tachometer (IRE) **Mrs J. M. Johnson**

Other Owners: R. A. Kujawa, Mr P. R. W. Smith.

Amateur: Mr S. Sheppard.

568   **MR OLIVER SHERWOOD, Upper Lambourn**
Postal: **Rhonehurst House, Upper Lambourn, Hungerford, Berkshire, RG17 8RG**
Contacts: **PHONE (01488) 71411 FAX (01488) 72786 MOBILE (07979) 591867**
E-MAIL oliver.sherwood@virgin.net WEBSITE www.oliversherwood.com

1 **ARKOSE (IRE)**, 10, b g Luso—Endless Patience (IRE) **D. P. Barrie & Partners 'A'**
2 **BEFOREALL (IRE)**, 6, b g Spadoun (FR)—Maggie Howard (IRE) **Beforeall Partnership**
3 **BELLUCIA**, 5, b m Kayf Tara—L'ultima (FR) **T. D. J. Syder**
4 **BERTIE'S DESIRE**, 6, b g King's Theatre (IRE)—Temptation (FR) **T. D. J. Syder**
5 **CAMDEN (IRE)**, 8, b g Old Vic—Electric View (IRE) **T. D. J. Syder**
6 **CARRIGEEN ASPEN**, 7, gr m Indian River (FR)—Carrigeen Acer (IRE) **Will Watt & Jeremy Dougall**
7 **CARRY ON SYDNEY**, 4, ch g Notnowcato—River Fantasy (USA) **The Sydney Arms Partnership**
8 **COCO SHAMBHALA**, 6, b m Indian Danehill (IRE)—Kohinor **Mr R. J. Chugg**
9 **DANVINNIE**, 5, b g Midnight Legend—Top Gale (IRE) **Unregistered Partnership**
10 **DEPUTY DAN (IRE)**, 6, b g Westerner—Louisas Dream (IRE) **T. D. J. Syder**
11 **DRUM VALLEY**, 6, b g Beat Hollow—Euippe **A Taylor & A Signy**
12 **EASTERN CALM**, 5, b m Kayf Tara—New Dawn **Mr M. A. Burton**
13 **EVENING STANLEY (IRE)**, 4, b g Stowaway—Suzy Q (IRE) **M. St Quinton & T. Syder**
14 **EXITAS (IRE)**, 8, b g Exit To Nowhere (USA)—Suntas (IRE) **Fawley House Stud**
15 **FAIR BRAMBLE**, 8, b m Fair Mix (IRE)—Briery Ann **Weatherbys Racing Club & P. Deal**
16 **FIGHT COMMANDER (IRE)**, 5, b g Oscar (IRE)—Creidim (IRE) **Mr J. C. D. Rathbone**
17 **FINANCIAL CLIMATE (IRE)**, 7, b g Exit To Nowhere (USA)—Claudia's Pearl **Mrs S. C. Fillery**
18 **FLORAFERN**, 9, b m Alflora (IRE)—Mossy Fern **G. R. Waters**
19 **GREEN HACKLE (IRE)**, 9, b g Stowaway—Honey Mustard (IRE) **Mrs C. G. Watson**
20 **JEANO DE TOULOUSE (FR)**, 7, b g Lavirco (GER)—Indecidable (FR) **D P Barrie & D Redhead**
21 **KASBADALI (FR)**, 9, b g Kahyasi—Nikalie (FR) **T. D. J. Syder**
22 **LEMONY BAY**, 5, b g Overbury (IRE)—Lemon's Mill (USA) **G. R. Waters**
23 **LIARS POKER (IRE)**, 7, b g Beneficial—Strong Willed **Ian Barratt, Stephen Short & Adam Signy**
24 **LUCI DI MEZZANOTTE**, 6, ch m Sulamani (IRE)—Dissolve **P. K. Gardner T/A Springcombe Park Stud**
25 **MAJORIA KING (FR)**, 8, b g Kahyasi—Majorica Queen (FR) **Mrs S. Griffiths**
26 **MANY CLOUDS (IRE)**, 7, br g Cloudings (IRE)—Bobbing Back (IRE) **T. J. Hemmings**
27 **MISCHIEVOUS MILLY (IRE)**, 6, b m Old Vic—Jennifers Diary (IRE) **A. Stewart & A. Taylor**
28 **MORNING REGGIE**, 5, gr g Turgeon (USA)—Nile Cristale (FR) **T. D. J. Syder**
29 **MOULIN DE LA CROIX**, 10, b m Muhtarram (USA)—Brambly Hedge **Luksonwood Partnership**
30 **MR CARDLE (IRE)**, 5, b g Golan (IRE)—Leave Me Be (IRE) **Mr M. A. Burton**
31 **NIMBUS GALE (IRE)**, 5, b g Cloudings (IRE)—Barton Gale (IRE) **T. J. Hemmings**
32 **PECTORA (IRE)**, 5, b m Kalanisi (IRE)—Nerissa (IRE) **Swanbridge Bloodstock Limited**
33 **PUFFIN BILLY (IRE)**, 6, b g Heron Island (IRE)—Downtown Train (IRE) **T. D. J. Syder**
34 **ROBINSSON (IRE)**, 4, b g Robin des Champs (FR)—Silver Proverb **A. Taylor**
35 **ROUGE ET BLANC (FR)**, 9, ch g Mansonnien (FR)—Fidelety (FR) **O Sherwood & T Syder**
36 **ROYALRAISE (IRE)**, 5, b g Royal Anthem (USA)—
         Raise The Issue (IRE) **Ian Barratt, Stephen Short & Adam Signy**
37 **SANTA'S SECRET (IRE)**, 6, b g Basanta (IRE)—Rivers Town Rosie (IRE) **Barratt, Gumienny, Johnsons & Signys**
38 **SECURE INVESTMENT**, 6, b g Alflora (IRE)—Ivy Edith **Furrows Ltd**
39 **SPIRIT OSCAR (IRE)**, 6, b m Oscar (IRE)—Grange Classic (IRE) **Million in Mind Partnership**
40 **STAR DATE (IRE)**, 5, b g Galileo (IRE)—Play Misty For Me (IRE) **Mr B. T. E. Shrubsall**
41 **STIFF UPPER LIP (IRE)**, 4, b c Sakhee's Secret—Just In Love (FR) **Richard Hitchcock Alan King**

Other Owners: Mr I. J. Barratt, D. P. Barrie, A. R. Bromley, P. A. Deal, Mrs S. V. Donald, J. M. Dougall, G. F. Goode, Mr M. S. Gumienny, R. G. Hitchcock, A. E. King, Mrs A. T. Lambert, Mrs J. K. Lukas, Mrs S. D. McGrath, Mr R. H. Mcgrath, W. D. C. Minton, Mrs D. C. Nicholson, Mr T. J. Ramsden, Mr D. P. Redhead, Mr M. E. Sangster, The Hon Mrs L. J. Sherwood, O. M. C. Sherwood, Mr A. Signy, M. G. St Quinton, Mr A. R. Stewart, Lady Thompson, W. S. Watt, Mr J. R. Weatherby, Mr R. N. Weatherby.

Assistant Trainer: Tom Fillery **Head Lad:** Stefan Namesansky

Jockey (NH): Sam Jones, Leighton Aspell, Dominic Elsworth. **Amateur:** Mr J. Sherwood.

569   **MR RAYMOND SHIELS, Jedburgh**
Postal: **Thickside Farm, Jedburgh, Roxburghshire, TD8 6QY**
Contacts: **PHONE (01835) 864060 MOBILE (07790) 295645**

1 6, B m Overbury (IRE)—Cool Island (IRE) **R. Shiels**
2 **TIKKANDEMICKEY (IRE)**, 8, gr g Tikkanen (USA)—Miss Vikki (IRE) **R. Shiels**
3 **ZOREN (FR)**, 10, b g Robin des Champs (FR)—Zianini (FR) **R. Shiels**

570 **MR SIMON SHIRLEY-BEAVAN, Hawick**
Postal: **Gatehousecote, Bonchester Bridge, Hawick, Roxburghshire, TD9 8JD**
Contacts: **PHONE (01450) 860210**

1 **HEART DANCER (FR)**, 8, b g Dark Moondancer—Petite Emilie (FR) **Mrs P. M. Shirley-Beavan**
2 **RAPIDOLYTE DE LADALKA (FR)**, 9, b g Network (GER)—Emeraude du Moulin (FR) **Mrs P. M. Shirley-Beavan**
3 **TAMBOUR MAJOR (FR)**, 7, b g Myrakalu (FR)—Joaillere (FR) **Mrs P. M. Shirley-Beavan**
4 **TRACKANAIS (FR)**, 7, b g Milford Track (IRE)—Havanaise (FR) **Mrs P. M. Shirley-Beavan**

571 **MISS LYNN SIDDALL, Tadcaster**
Postal: **Stonebridge Farm, Colton, Tadcaster, North Yorkshire, LS24 8EP**
Contacts: **PHONE (01904) 744291 FAX (01904) 744291 MOBILE (07778) 216692/4**

1 **ANNIE'S DAUGHTER**, 7, b m Danbird (AUS)—Moondance **Podso Racing**
2 **BACH STREET GIRL (IRE)**, 10, ch m Bach (IRE)—Millmount (IRE) **G. Kennington**
3 **BLUE COVE**, 9, ch g Karinga Bay—Meadow Blue **G. Kennington**
4 **BROTHER RODNEY**, 10, ch g Karinga Bay—Meadow Blue **G. Kennington**
5 **CADGERS HOLE**, 7, b g Helissio (FR)—Not So Prim **Mrs D. Ibbotson**
6 **DIRECT APPROACH (IRE)**, 10, b g Tel Quel (FR)—Miss Telimar (IRE) **G. Kennington**
7 **FIRST OF NEVER (IRE)**, 8, b g Systematic—Never Promise (FR) **Lynn Siddall Racing II**
8 **I KNOW THE CODE (IRE)**, 9, b g Viking Ruler (AUS)—Gentle Papoose **Lynn Siddall Racing II**
9 **LISDONAGH HOUSE (IRE)**, 12, b g Little Bighorn—Lifinsa Barina (IRE) **J. P. G. Cooke**
10 **RUBYMINX**, 8, b m Grape Tree Road—Windfola **Miss J. M. Slater**
11 **WESTWIRE TOBY (IRE)**, 12, ch g Anshan—Ware It Well (IRE) **Stonebridge Racing II**

Other Owners: Mr C. Abbott, Mrs P. J. Clark, Mrs E. W. Cooper, Mr B. Donkin, Mr I. Grice, Mrs P. M. Hornby, Mr R. Jenkins, Mrs K. M. Kennington, Mr G. Kennington, Miss S. Lythe, Mr H. Pilling, Miss L. C. Siddall, Miss S. E. Vinden.

Assistant Trainer: Stephen Hackney

Jockey (NH): Tom Siddall.

572 **MR DAVID SIMCOCK, Newmarket**
Postal: **The Office, Trillium Place, Birdcage Walk, Newmarket, Suffolk, CB8 ONE**
Contacts: **PHONE (01638) 662968 FAX (01638) 663888 MOBILE (07808) 954109**
E-MAIL david@davidsimcock.co.uk WEBSITE www.davidsimcock.co.uk

1 **APOSTLE (IRE)**, 5, gr g Dark Angel (IRE)—Rosy Dudley (IRE)
2 **AQUILLA (IRE)**, 5, b m Teofilo (IRE)—Dance Troupe
3 **BIRDMAN (IRE)**, 4, b g Danehill Dancer (IRE)—Gilded Vanity (IRE)
4 **BRETON ROCK (IRE)**, 4, b g Bahamian Bounty—Anna's Rock (IRE)
5 **CAFE SOCIETY (FR)**, 4, b g Motivator—Mishina (FR)
6 **CASPAR NETSCHER**, 5, b h Dutch Art—Bella Cantata
7 **CASTILO DEL DIABLO (IRE)**, 5, br g Teofilo (IRE)—Hundred Year Flood (USA)
8 **GABRIAL'S KING (IRE)**, 5, b g Hurricane Run (IRE)—Danella (IRE)
9 **GLASS OFFICE**, 4, gr c Verglas (IRE)—Oval Office
10 **MABAIT**, 8, b g Kyllachy—Czarna Roza
11 **MAJEED (IRE)**, 4, b g Mount Nelson—Clever Millie (USA)
12 **MOMENT IN TIME (IRE)**, 5, b m Tiger Hill (IRE)—Horatia (IRE)
13 **NAVE (USA)**, 7, b g Pulpit (USA)—Lakabi (USA)
14 **NOBLE CITIZEN (USA)**, 9, b g Proud Citizen (USA)—Serene Nobility (USA)
15 **PEREIRA**, 4, b f Tiger Hill (IRE)—Manoeuvre (IRE)
16 **POSTSCRIPT (IRE)**, 6, ch g Pivotal—Persian Secret (FR)
17 **RAY WARD (IRE)**, 4, b g Galileo (IRE)—Kentucky Warbler (IRE)
18 **RELATED**, 4, b g Kheleyf (USA)—Balladonia
19 **SILK TRAIN**, 4, b f Rail Link—Monsoon Wedding
20 **STASIO (USA)**, 4, b g Street Boss (USA)—Believe (USA)
21 **VAINGLORY (USA)**, 10, ch g Swain (IRE)—Infinite Spirit (USA)
22 **WHISPERING WARRIOR (IRE)**, 5, b g Oasis Dream—Varenka (IRE)

THREE-YEAR-OLDS

23 **AFFAIRE DE COEUR**, b f Dalakhani (IRE)—Divergence (USA)
24 **AL SHOOGH**, b f Nayef (USA)—Bakhoor (IRE)

MR DAVID SIMCOCK - Continued

25 **ALPS,** b f Danehill Dancer (IRE)—Mountain Chain (USA)
26 **ARTISTIC CHARM,** b f Dutch Art—Greenfly
27 **BARYE,** b c Archipenko (USA)—Oblige
28 **BRETON COMMANDER,** b g Zamindar (USA)—Lady Donatella
29 **CAN'T CHANGE IT (IRE),** gr g Verglas (IRE)—All Tied Up (IRE)
30 **CAPTAIN MORLEY,** b c Hernando (FR)—Oval Office
31 **COLONEL ALI,** b g Halling (USA)—Preceder
32 **CURBYOURENTHUSIASM (IRE),** gr c Mastercraftsman (IRE)—Mohican Princess
33 **DOCTOR SARDONICUS,** ch c Medicean—Never A Doubt
34 B f High Chaparral (IRE)—English Ballet
35 **ERRONEOUS (IRE),** br g Footstepsinthesand—Atir Love (USA)
36 **FRACTAL,** b c High Chaparral (IRE)—Clincher Club
37 **GREAT WAVE (IRE),** gr f Duke of Marmalade (IRE)—Rosamixa (FR)
38 **JOIE DE REVE (IRE),** b f Footstepsinthesand—La Caprice (USA)
39 **LORD EMPIRE (IRE),** b c Invincible Spirit (IRE)—Miss Ghena (USA)
40 B c Thewayyouare (USA)—Luck Be A Lady (IRE)
41 **MADAME CHIANG,** b f Archipenko (USA)—Robe Chinoise
42 **MANIPULATION (IRE),** b g Elnadim (USA)—Intriguing (IRE)
43 Ch g Street Cry (IRE)—Modesty Blaise (USA)
44 **MOMENTUS (IRE),** b f Montjeu (IRE)—Race For The Stars (USA)
45 **MORE ADORA (IRE),** br f Dylan Thomas (IRE)—Niner's Home (USA)
46 **SARIYAH,** b f Shirocco (GER)—Sakhya (IRE)
47 **SOME SITE (IRE),** b f Nayef (USA)—Horatia (IRE)
48 **SWAN LAKES (IRE),** gr f Dalakhani (IRE)—Rock Salt
49 B f Giant's Causeway (USA)—Swan Nebula (USA)
50 **THE CORSICAN (IRE),** b c Galileo (IRE)—Walklikeanegyptian (IRE)
51 **TIGERS IN RED (USA),** ch c Speightstown (USA)—Gaudete (USA)
52 **UCHENNA (IRE),** b f Fastnet Rock (AUS)—Uriah (GER)
53 **WHISPERING STAR (USA),** b f War Front (USA)—Eclisse (FR)

TWO-YEAR-OLDS

54 **ALLIANCE FRANCAISE,** ch f 14/4 Archipenko (USA)—Affaire d'amour (Hernando (FR))
55 B f 1/1 Mastercraftsman (IRE)—Anna of Dubai (GER) (Dubai Destination (USA)) (27874)
56 B f 25/1 Pivotal—Arabian Mirage (Oasis Dream) (160000)
57 Ch f 24/4 King's Best (USA)—Arabian Treasure (USA) (Danzig (USA))
58 **BELLONAISE,** b f 20/2 Authorized (IRE)—Bellona (IRE) (Bering) (32520)
59 Gr ro c 2/2 Mastercraftsman (IRE)—Capriole (Noverre (USA)) (77428)
60 B f 26/3 Makfi—Cartimandua (Medicean) (42000)
61 B f 19/3 Azamour (IRE)—Centime (Royal Applause)
62 B c 12/4 Invincible Spirit (IRE)—Combust (USA) (Aptitude (USA)) (70000)
63 **CONSORTIUM (IRE),** b c 17/1 Teofilo (IRE)—Wish List (IRE) (Mujadil (USA)) (40000)
64 B c 16/3 Street Sense (USA)—Delighted (IRE) (Danehill (USA))
65 B f 29/2 Arabian Gleam—Desert Liaison (Dansili)
66 B c 12/4 Intikhab (USA)—Don't Tell Mum (IRE) (Dansili) (160000)
67 B c 12/2 Sea The Stars (IRE)—Drifting (IRE) (Sadler's Wells (USA))
68 Ch c 22/3 Shamardal (USA)—Elle Galante (GER) (Galileo (IRE))
69 B c 10/2 Aqlaam (USA)—Fifty (IRE) (Fasliyev (USA)) (22000)
70 Ch c 19/3 Fast Company (IRE)—Five of Wands (Caerleon (USA)) (50000)
71 Ch c 18/3 Tamayuz—Frivolity (Pivotal)
72 **GRAHAMLUCAS (CAN),** b c 29/4 North Light (IRE)—Perfect Sting (USA) (Red Ransom (USA)) (8179)
73 B c 27/4 Cape Cross (IRE)—High Barn (Shirley Heights) (7000)
74 B f 29/3 Cape Cross (IRE)—Honours Stride (IRE) (Red Ransom (USA))
75 B c 6/5 Cape Cross (IRE)—Illuminise (IRE) (Grand Lodge (USA)) (15000)
76 B c 12/3 Halling (USA)—La Chicana (IRE) (Invincible Spirit (IRE)) (32000)
77 B f 8/2 Makfi—La Conquistadora (Pivotal) (50000)
78 **LADY HARE (IRE),** b f 25/4 Approve (IRE)—Peaceful Kingdom (USA) (King of Kings (IRE)) (34000)
79 B f 7/4 Mastercraftsman (IRE)—Market Day (Tobougg (IRE)) (64761)
80 **MAYBE TOMORROW,** b f 30/3 Zamindar (USA)—Appointed One (USA) (Danzig (USA))
81 Br f 21/3 Royal Applause—Meredith (Medicean)
82 Ch f 20/3 Shamardal (USA)—Miss Marvellous (USA) (Diesis) (30000)
83 B c 5/5 Elusive City (USA)—My Heart's Deelite (USA) (Afternoon Deelites (USA))
84 **OUD METHA,** ch f 9/4 Manduro (GER)—Royal Secrets (IRE) (Highest Honor (FR))
85 B f 25/2 Teofilo (IRE)—Penang (IRE) (Xaar) (22000)
86 B c 21/3 Danehill Dancer (IRE)—Phrase (Royal Anthem (USA)) (85000)
87 **PRECAST,** ch f 23/3 Halling (USA)—Preceder (Polish Precedent (USA))

MR DAVID SIMCOCK - Continued

88 **RESOLVE**, ch f 28/2 Dutch Art—Crooked Wood (USA) (Woodman (USA)) (18000)
89 B br f 3/3 U S Ranger (USA)—Saudia (USA) (Gone West (USA)) (85000)
90 B c 4/4 Mastercraftsman (IRE)—Shamara (IRE) (Spectrum (IRE)) (44000)
91 B f 5/5 Kodiac—Slow Jazz (USA) (Chief's Crown (USA))
92 **SONNYTHENAVIGATOR (USA)**, b br c 27/3 Henrythenavigator (USA)—
Lady Simpson (Yankee Victor (USA)) (46457)
93 B f 21/1 Authorized (IRE)—Sovereign's Honour (USA) (Kingmambo (USA))
94 B f 28/1 Equiano (FR)—Tanasie (Cadeaux Genereux)
95 B c 8/4 Galileo (IRE)—Thought Is Free (Cadeaux Genereux)
96 B c 14/2 Fastnet Rock (AUS)—Timeless Dream (Oasis Dream) (65000)
97 B c 15/2 Dark Angel (IRE)—Zoudie (Ezzoud (IRE)) (34000)

Owners: Abdulla Al Mansoori, Jaber Abdullah, Al Asayl Bloodstock Ltd, Mrs J. M. Annable, Mr Simon Bamber, Mr James Barnett, Black Gold Partnership, Oliver Brendon, Mr R. G. W. Brown, Marcella Burns, CJJR Partnership, Mr Malcolm Caine, Chippenham Lodge Stud, Mr John Cook, Sheikh Rashid Dalmook Al Maktoum, Sheikh Juma Dalmook Al Maktoum, Khalifa Dasmal, Jane Forman-Hardy, Nicholas Forman-Hardy, Ziad Galadari, Mr M. P. Gibbens, Happy Valley Racing & Breeding Ltd, Mrs Fitri Hay, Anthony Hogarth, Simon Hope, Ahmed Jaber, Alison Jackson, Barbara Keller, Dr M. B. Q. S. Koukash, Mrs John Magnier, Millingbrook Racing, Nabil Mourad, New Dreamers, Eliza Park, Mr Daniel Pittack, Qatar Racing Ltd, Ms Kirsten Rausing, Dr Ali Ridha, Ali Saeed, St Albans Bloodstock, Mr Andrew Stone, Mrs M. F. Stone, Saeed Suhail, Mr M. Tabor, Charles Wentworth, Zorka Wentworth, Andrew Whitlock, Windborne Partnership, C. G. P. Wyatt, Major M. Wyatt, Mr W. P. Wyatt.

Assistant Trainer: Tom Clover

Jockey (flat): Martin Lane, Jamie Spencer. **Apprentice:** George Buckell, Paige Ranger, Lewis Walsh.
Amateur: Mr Daryl McLaughlin.

573 MR DAN SKELTON, Alcester
Postal: **Lodge Hill, Shelfield Green, Alcester, Warwickshire, B49 6JR**
Contacts: **PHONE (01789) 336339**
E-MAIL **office@danskeltonracing.com** WEBSITE **www.danskeltonracing.com**

1 **AT THE TOP (FR)**, 4, b f Network (GER)—Quaiou (FR)
2 **AWESOME FREDDIE**, 9, b g Karinga Bay—Awesome Aunt (IRE) **Mrs Gwen Meacham & Mr & Mrs D. Thornhill**
3 **BAILE ANRAI (FR)**, 10, b g Norwich—Rose Ana (IRE) **Massive**
4 **BALLINCURRIG (IRE)**, 8, b g Craigsteel—Flora Rambler **H. B. Hodge**
5 **BEATRIX KIDDO (IRE)**, 5, b m Scorpion (IRE)—Garden City (IRE) **Donlon, Doyle & MacDonald**
6 **BEAUTIFUL GEM (FR)**, 4, ch f Muhtathir—Hunorisk (FR) **Mr & Mrs J. D. Cotton**
7 **BELLENOS (FR)**, 4, b g Apsis—Palmeria (FR) **Mr & Mrs J. D. Cotton**
8 **BJORNLUCKY (IRE)**, 4, b g Key of Luck (USA)—Super Trouper (USA) **Donlon, Doyle & MacDonald**
9 **BLUE HERON (IRE)**, 6, b g Heron Island (IRE)—American Chick (IRE) **Horwood Harriers Partnership**
10 **CATWALK BABE (IRE)**, 4, br f Presenting—Supreme Dreamer (IRE) **Mr T. Spraggett**
11 **CHARLIE'S OSCAR (IRE)**, 4, b g Oscar (IRE)—Blue Gallery (IRE) **Universal Recycling Company**
12 **COLLEEN BAWN (FR)**, 4, b f Cockney Rebel (IRE)—Compose **P. Cunningham**
13 4, B g Beneficial—Fennor Rose (IRE) **A Chandler,L Westwood,D Balchin,K Jones**
14 **FOREST WALKER (IRE)**, 7, b g Morozov (USA)—Queen Polly (IRE) **Mr K. W. Price**
15 **GAYE MEMORIES**, 6, b m Overbury (IRE)—Gaye Memory **Mrs J. S. Allen**
16 **GO ODEE GO (IRE)**, 6, b g Alkaadhem—Go Franky (IRE) **N. W. Lake**
17 **GOING WRONG**, 11, b g Bob Back (USA)—Lucy Glitters **Universal Recycling Company**
18 **HERONS HEIR (IRE)**, 6, b g Heron Island (IRE)—Kyle Lamp (IRE) **HighclereThoroughbredRacing-Herons Heir**
19 **JOHN REEL (FR)**, 5, b g Country Reel (USA)—John Quatz (FR) **Walters Plant Hire Ltd**
20 **LAWSONS THORNS (IRE)**, 5, b g Presenting—Ardnurcher (IRE) **Mr N. Skelton**
21 **LIKE MINDED**, 10, b g Kayf Tara—Sun Dante (IRE) **D. J. Coles**
22 **MANY STARS (IRE)**, 6, b g Oscar (IRE)—Tempest Belle (IRE) **James Hughes,John Hughes,Charles Hughes**
23 **MIDNIGHT TUESDAY (FR)**, 9, b g Kapgarde (FR)—Deat Heat (FR) **A. C. Eaves**
24 **MISTER GREZ (FR)**, 8, gr g Turgeon (USA)—Yoruba (FR) **Gilmans Point Racing Syndicate**
25 **MY FLORA**, 10, b m Alflora (IRE)—Bishop's Folly **Mr W D Edwards & Mr J Whitfield**
26 **RASCAL (IRE)**, 5, b g Milan—Montagues Lady (IRE) **The Really Wild Bunch**
27 **ROSE PAGEANT**, 5, ch m Loup Sauvage (USA)—Realms of Roses **Mrs S. C. Welch**
28 **SANTO DE LUNE (FR)**, 4, gr g Saint des Saints (FR)—Tikidoun (FR) **Donlon & MacDonald**
29 **SIKSIKA (IRE)**, 6, b m Golan—Native Delight (IRE) **Mrs D. Bowley**
30 **SQUIRE TRELAWNEY**, 8, b g Domedriver (IRE)—Crockadore (USA) **P. J. Haycock**
31 **STEPHANIE FRANCES (IRE)**, 6, b m King's Theatre (IRE)—Brownlow Castle (IRE) **Miss M. J. Hall**
32 **STEPHEN HERO**, 4, br g Celtic Swing—Albaiyda (IRE) **Three Celts**
33 **STORM OF SWORDS (IRE)**, 6, ch g Beneficial—Crossbar Lady (IRE) **The McKilocon Syndicate**

MR DAN SKELTON - Continued

34 **TASHKALDOU (FR)**, 5, b g Kaldou Star—Tashka (FR) **Rebel Racing**
35 **TOBY LERONE (IRE)**, 7, b g Old Vic—Dawn's Double (IRE) **G.Regan, A.Pettey, J.Dunning & S.Morgan**
36 **TOUBAB (FR)**, 8, gr g Martaline—Tabachines (FR) **Hills of Ledbury Ltd**
37 **TWICE RETURNED (IRE)**, 8, b g Old Vic—Almost Regal (IRE) **N. W. Lake**
38 **UNEX MODIGLIANI (IRE)**, 5, ch g Hurricane Run (IRE)—Chronicle **W. J. Gredley**
39 **WALK ON AL (IRE)**, 6, b g Alflora (IRE)—Wave Back (IRE) **Donlon, MacDonald & McGowan**
40 **WILLOW'S SAVIOUR**, 7, ch g Septieme Ciel (USA)—Willow Gale **Triple F Partnership**
41 **WORKBENCH (FR)**, 6, b g Network (GER)—Danhelis (FR) **N. W. Lake**

Other Owners: Mr D. Balchin, Mr H. F. Bowley, Mr A. Chandler, P. F. Charter, J. D. Cotton, Mrs B. Cotton, Mrs M. A. Cuff, P. M. Cunningham, Mr C. A. Donlon, Mr A. Doyle, W. D. Edwards, Mr D. J. Flynn, Mr J. B. Gilruth, The Hon H. M. Herbert, Highclere Thoroughbred Racing Ltd, Mr J. C. Hughes, Mr J. R. Hughes, Mr K. D. Jones, Mr T. Kilroe, Ms L. Kraut, Mr A. N. McGowan, Mrs G. Meacham, Mr S. Morgan, Mr D. Noble, Mr T. O'Connor, G. J. P Regan, Mrs L. Scott-MacDonald, Mr D. N. Skelton, Mr K. Sumner, Mr D. Thornhill, Mrs C. Thornhill, Mr L. J. Westwood, Mr E. J. Whitfield.

Assistant Trainer: Josh Guerriero

Jockey (NH): Harry Skelton.

574

MRS EVELYN SLACK, Appleby
Postal: **Stoneriggs, Hilton, Appleby, Cumbria, CA16 6LS**
Contacts: **PHONE (01768) 351354 MOBILE (07503) 161240**

1 **AUBERGE (IRE)**, 10, ch m Blueprint (IRE)—Castlegrace (IRE) **Mrs D. E. Slack**
2 **GRAND VINTAGE (IRE)**, 8, gr g Basanta (IRE)—Rivers Town Rosie (IRE) **A. Slack**
3 **OMID**, 6, b g Dubawi (IRE)—Mille Couleurs (FR) **Mrs D. E. Slack**

Assistant Trainer: K. A. A. Slack (01768) 351922 Or (07931) 137413

575

MRS PAM SLY, Peterborough
Postal: **Singlecote, Thorney, Peterborough, Cambridgeshire, PE6 0PB**
Contacts: **PHONE (01733) 270212 MOBILE (07850) 511267**

1 **ABIJOE**, 5, b m Fair Mix (IRE)—Casewick Mist **The Kickers Racing Syndicate**
2 **ACERTAIN CIRCUS**, 4, ch g Definite Article—Circus Rose **Mrs P. M. Sly**
3 **ARKAIM**, 6, b g Oasis Dream—Habariya (IRE) **G.A.Libson D.L.Bayliss G.Taylor P.M.Sly**
4 **BARNACK**, 8, b g Karinga Bay—Ima Delight **Mrs P. M. Sly**
5 **BONNET'S VINO**, 6, b m Grape Tree Road—Bonnet's Pieces **Mrs P. M. Sly**
6 **BOUGGIETOPIECES**, 4, b g Tobougg (IRE)—Bonnet's Pieces **Mrs P. M. Sly**
7 **BOUNTIFUL BESS**, 4, ch f Bahamian Bounty—Saida Lenasera (FR) **Mrs P. M. Sly**
8 **CHICKLEMIX**, 8, gr m Fair Mix (IRE)—Chichell's Hurst **M. H. Sly, Dr T. Davies & Mrs P. Sly**
9 **HELPSTON**, 10, b g Sir Harry Lewis (USA)—Chichell's Hurst **Mrs P. M. Sly**
10 **ICONIC ROSE**, 7, ch m Sir Harry Lewis (USA)—Standing Bloom **The Stablemates**
11 **KAYAAN**, 7, br g Marju (IRE)—Raheefa (USA) **D. L. Bayliss**
12 **SPECIALTY (IRE)**, 4, b f Oasis Dream—Speciosa (IRE) **M. H. Sly, Dr T. Davies & Mrs P. Sly**
13 **SYNCOPATE**, 5, b g Oratorio (IRE)—Millistar **Pam's People**
14 **UNMOOTHAJ**, 4, b g Green Desert—Sundus (USA) **G.A.Libson D.L.Bayliss G.Taylor P.M.Sly**
15 **VERMUYDEN**, 5, b g Oasis Dream—Speciosa (IRE) **M. H. Sly, Dr T. Davies & Mrs P. Sly**
16 **WILHANA (IRE)**, 4, b f Singspiel (IRE)—Jathaabeh **D. L. Bayliss**

THREE-YEAR-OLDS

17 **ASTEROIDEA**, b f Sea The Stars (IRE)—Speciosa (IRE) **M. H. Sly, Dr T. Davies & Mrs P. Sly**
18 **GHINIA (IRE)**, b f Mastercraftsman (IRE)—Jorghinia (IRE) **D. L. Bayliss**

TWO-YEAR-OLDS

19 B f 19/4 Sir Percy—Black Salix (USA) (More Than Ready (USA)) **Mrs P. M. Sly**

Other Owners: Mr David L. Bayliss, Mr R. S. Blundell, Mr J. Cleeve, Dr T. J. W. Davies, Mr Danny Duncombe, Mrs S. E. Godfrey, Mr G. A. Libson, Mr Michael H. Sly, Mrs P. M. Sly, Mr A. J. Talton, Mr G. Taylor.

Conditional: Kielan Woods. **Amateur:** Miss Gina Andrews.

576 MR DAVID SMAGA, Lamorlaye

Postal: **17 Voie de la Grange des Pres, 60260 Lamorlaye, France**
Contacts: **PHONE (0033) 3442 15005 FAX (0033) 3442 15556 MOBILE (0033) 6078 37287**
E-MAIL david-smaga@wanadoo.fr

1 BOOKEND, 10, b g Dansili—Roupala (USA) **Mr D. Smaga**
2 COMMUTE, 4, b f Rail Link—Zorleni **Mme M-J Goetschy**
3 DON BOSCO (FR), 7, ch h Barathea (IRE)—Perfidie (IRE) **Mr O. El Sharif**
4 FAIR MOON (FR), 4, b f Gold Away (IRE)—La Fee de Breizh (FR) **Mr A. Louis-Dreyfus**
5 FOFA MELECA (URU), 6, b m Quinze Quilates (BRZ)—Tessy Slew (BRZ) **Mr B. Steinbruch**
6 FRED LALLOUPET, 7, b h Elusive City (USA)—Firm Friend (IRE) **Mr M. Lagasse**
7 FRENCH GARDEN (FR), 8, b h Kendor (FR)—Girl of France **Mr D. Smaga**
8 GAGA A (URU), 5, gr ro m T H Approval (USA)—Yin (BRZ) **Mr B. Steinbruch**
9 GAS TOTAL (BRZ), 5, b m Sulamani (IRE)—Club Med (BRZ) **Mr B. Steinbruch**
10 GOING SOMEWHERE (BRZ), 5, ch h Sulamani (IRE)—Angel Star (BRZ) **Mr B. Steinbruch**
11 HIDDEN RAINBOW (IRE), 11, ch g Spectrum (IRE)—Grecian Urn **Mr D. Smaga**
12 LUCKY LOOK (FR), 4, b f Teofilo (IRE)—Victoria College (FR) **Mr A. M. Haddad**
13 OMY, 4, b c Zamindar (USA)—Galipette (USA) **Mr O. El Sharif**
14 PARATY DREAM (FR), 4, b f Elusive Quality (USA)—Sur Ma Vie (USA) **Mr R. Nahas**
15 ROYAL MANIFICO (IRE), 4, b c Hannouma (IRE)—Poltava (FR) **Mr D. Smaga**
16 SAINT ELIER (FR), 5, b h Stormy River (FR)—Basse Besogne (IRE) **Mr G. Augustin-Normand**
17 SAPHIRSIDE (FR), 5, b g Elusive City (USA)—Silirisa (FR) **Mr G. Augustin-Normand**

THREE-YEAR-OLDS

18 ALLEGREZZA, b f Sir Percy—Allegro Viva (USA) **K. Abdulla**
19 ALMERIA, b f Shamardal (USA)—Suedoise **Mr A. M. Haddad**
20 ARABIAN LADY (FR), ch f Gentlewave (USA)—Sometime (FR) **Mr R. Nahas**
21 FEE DE LUNE (FR), gr f Kentucky Dynamite (USA)—La Fee de Breizh (FR) **Mr A. Louis-Dreyfus**
22 FRIDA LA BLONDE (FR), b f Elusive City (USA)—Firm Friend (IRE) **Mr M. Lagasse**
23 GENERATA (USA), gr ro f Mizzen Mast (USA)—Gateway (USA) **K. Abdulla**
24 INCIDENT, b f Dansili—Emergency **K. Abdulla**
25 LARC (FR), b c Cape Cross (IRE)—Luminosity **Haras D'Etreham**
26 MAGICIENMAKE MYDAY, b c Whipper (USA)—Whisper To Dream (USA) **Mr R. Nahas**
27 MASTERMAMBO (IRE), b f Mastercraftsman (IRE)—Poltava (FR) **Mr M. Parrish**
28 MIMADO (FR), ch c Falco (USA)—Spring Fun (FR) **Mr R. Nahas**
29 NOLLEVAL (FR), b c Gold Away (IRE)—Amazing Story (FR) **Mr G. Augustin-Normand**
30 OBVIOUS REASONS (IRE), b f Slickly (FR)—Vezara (IRE) **Mr R. Nahas**
31 PRIMUS INCITATUS (IRE), ch c Mastercraftsman (IRE)—Chaibia (IRE) **Mr A. M. Haddad**
32 PRIVET HEDGE (USA), b f First Defence (USA)—Privity (USA) **K. Abdulla**
33 RAFFINEE (FR), b f Air Eminem (IRE)—Gioconda Umbra (ITY) **Mme M. Fougy**
34 SAILING CLUB (USA), b br c Mizzen Mast (USA)—Storm Dove (USA) **K. Abdulla**
35 SERIOUS TO RUN (FR), ch f Hurricane Run (IRE)—Arrow of Desire **Mr R. Nahas**
36 SKIPPY, b f Gold Away (IRE)—Zghorta (USA) **Mr A. Louis-Dreyfus**
37 STARFLOWER, b f Champs Elysees—Posteritas (USA) **K. Abdulla**
38 VICTORIOUS CHAMP (FR), b c New Approach (IRE)—Sasanuma (USA) **Mr R. Nahas**

TWO-YEAR-OLDS

39 Gr ro c 21/2 Mizzen Mast (USA)—Arboreta (USA) (Empire Maker (USA)) **K. Abdulla**
40 B f 1/1 King's Best (USA)—Arrow of Desire (Danehill Dancer (IRE)) **Mr R. Nahas**
41 B br f 12/2 Mizzen Mast (USA)—Deep Feeling (USA) (Empire Maker (USA)) **K. Abdulla**
42 Ch c 16/1 Beat Hollow—Disclose (Dansili) **K. Abdulla**
43 DJIGUITE (FR), b c 19/2 Makfi—Envoutement (FR) (Vettori (IRE)) **Mr A. Louis-Dreyfus**
44 B br f 26/1 Mizzen Mast (USA)—Gainful (USA) (Gone West (USA)) **K. Abdulla**
45 B f 27/4 Whipper (USA)—Larme (IRE) (Soviet Star (USA)) **Mr R. Nahas**
46 MARCHAND CELEBRE (FR), b f 10/3 High Chaparral (IRE)—
    Anestasia (IRE) (Anabaa (USA)) (100658) **Mr O. Thomas**
47 MEZZO MEZZO (FR), ch f 26/3 Mount Nelson—Ibizane (USA) (Elusive Quality (USA)) (23228) **Mme M. Fougy**
48 MISS DERNA (FR), b f 25/1 Air Chief Marshal (USA)—Lamask (USA) (Bahri (USA)) (54200) **Mr A. Louis-Dreyfus**
49 OJALA (FR), ch f 20/5 Dunkerque (FR)—Gioconda Umbra (ITY) (Sicyos (USA)) **Mr A. M. Haddad**
50 B f 12/2 Champs Elysees—Plum Fairy (Sadler's Wells (USA)) **K. Abdulla**
51 B c 23/3 Dansili—Pretty Face (Rainbow Quest (USA)) **K. Abdulla**
52 B f 6/4 Aqlaam—Pyrana (USA) (42586) **Mr B. Steinbruch**
53 B c 3/6 Elusive City (USA)—Sasanuma (USA) (Kingmambo (USA)) **Mr R. Nahas**
54 B c 1/3 Whipper (USA)—Sometime (FR) (Anabaa (USA)) **Mr R. Nahas**
55 B f 30/3 Whipper (USA)—Spring Fun (FR) (Kingmambo (USA)) **Mr R. Nahas**

MR DAVID SMAGA - Continued

56 B c 25/1 Elusive City (USA)—Stefer (USA) (Johannesburg (USA)) **Mr R. Nahas**
57 **STRELKITA (FR)**, b f 4/3 Dr Fong (USA)—Olonella (Selkirk (USA)) (42586) **Mr A. Louis-Dreyfus**
58 B c 14/2 High Chaparral (IRE)—Vezara (IRE) (Grand Lodge (USA)) **Mr R. Nahas**
59 B f 18/2 Elusive City (USA)—Victoria College (FR) (Rock of Gibraltar (IRE)) **Mr A. M. Haddad**
60 B c 4/1 Medicean—Wadjeka (USA) (Oasis Dream) (24777) **Mr G. Augustin-Normand**
61 f 1/1 Makfi—Whisper To Dream (USA) (Gone West (USA)) **Mr R. Nahas**

577 **MR BRYAN SMART, Hambleton**
Postal: **Hambleton House, Sutton Bank, Thirsk, North Yorkshire, YO7 2HA**
Contacts: **PHONE** (01845) 597481 **FAX** (01845) 597480 **MOBILE** (07748) 634797
E-MAIL office@bryansmart.plus.com **WEBSITE** www.bryansmart-racing.com

1 **ARMADA BAY (IRE)**, 4, b g Tamayuz—Yara (IRE) **B. Smart**
2 **CHESSFIELD PARK**, 4, ch g Byron—Annie Harvey **Mrs V. Smart**
3 **DA'QUONDE (IRE)**, 6, br m Pivotal—Bobcat Greeley (USA) **The Barber Girls**
4 **DIFFERENT**, 4, ch f Bahamian Bounty—Hill Welcome **Mrs F. Denniff**
5 **DUBAI HILLS**, 8, b g Dubai Destination (USA)—Hill Welcome **Mrs F. Denniff**
6 **ENDERBY (GER)**, 8, gr g Invincible Spirit (IRE)—Arctic Ice (IRE) **Mrs P. M. Brown**
7 **FEEL THE HEAT**, 7, ch g Firebreak—Spindara (IRE) **B. Smart**
8 **FLASH CITY (ITY)**, 6, b g Elusive City (USA)—Stefer **Ceffyl Racing**
9 **FREE ZONE**, 5, b g Kyllachy—Aldora **Fromthestables.Com Racing**
10 **HENRY MORGAN**, 7, ch h Bahamian Bounty—Hill Welcome **Mrs F. Denniff**
11 **ICHIMOKU**, 4, b g Indesatchel (IRE)—Mythicism **Crossfields Racing**
12 **KALANI'S DIAMOND**, 4, ch f Kalani Bay (IRE)—Cryptonite Diamond (USA) **The Armstrong Family**
13 **LUCY MINAJ**, 4, b f Dylan Thomas (IRE)—Keyaki (IRE) **M. Barber**
14 **MANDY LAYLA (IRE)**, 4, ch f Excellent Art—Chervil **Mrs V. Smart & Miss C. Derighetti**
15 **MONTE CASSINO (IRE)**, 9, ch g Choisir (AUS)—Saucy Maid (IRE) **Woodcock Electrical Limited**
16 **MOVIESTA (USA)**, 4, b g Hard Spun (USA)—Miss Brickyard (USA) **Redknapp, Salthouse & Fiddes**
17 **ORWELLIAN**, 5, b g Bahamian Bounty—Trinny **B. Smart**
18 **SMALLJOHN**, 8, ch g Needwood Blade—My Bonus **B. Smart**
19 **SPACE ARTIST (IRE)**, 4, b g Captain Marvelous (IRE)—Dame Laura (IRE) **The Smart Dame Laura Partnership**
20 **TANGERINE TREES**, 9, b g Mind Games—Easy To Imagine (USA) **Tangerine Trees Partnership**

THREE-YEAR-OLDS

21 **ANNIE'S ROSE**, b f Captain Gerrard (IRE)—Annie Harvey **Mrs V. Smart**
22 **APPLICATION**, ch g Major Cadeaux—Choisette **Crossfields Racing**
23 **CHUCKAMENTAL**, b g Captain Marvelous (IRE)—Stoneacre Sarah **The Smart Stoneacre Sarah Partnership**
24 **ICE MAYDEN**, b f Major Cadeaux—Reel Cool **Mr J. Ball**
25 **JACQUOTTE DELAHAYE**, ch f Kyllachy—Mary Read **Just For Girls Partnership**
26 **KINKOHYO**, b f Indesatchel (IRE)—Mythicism **Crossfields Racing**
27 **LEXINGTON ROSE**, b f Captain Gerrard (IRE)—Silca Destination **Middleham Park Racing VIII & Partners**
28 **MAJOR ROWAN**, b g Captain Gerrard (IRE)—Julie's Gift **David H. Cox**
29 **MEADWAY**, b g Captain Gerrard (IRE)—Tibesti **Mr Michael Moses & Mr Terry Moses**
30 **MODIFY**, ch f New Approach (IRE)—Hill Welcome **Mrs F. Denniff**
31 **NZHOO**, ch g Major Cadeaux—Nizhoni (USA) **Crossfields Racing**
32 **OMAHA GOLD (IRE)**, b f Kodiac—Naraina (IRE) **Mr P. J. Shaw**
33 **PLAYTOTHEWHISTLE**, b g Sakhee's Secret—Prima Ballerina **Mr S. Tolley**
34 **RED PIKE (IRE)**, ch g Kheleyf (USA)—Fancy Feathers (IRE) **Sir A. Ferguson, P. Deal & G. Lowe**
35 **REET THICKNSTRONG**, b f Captain Gerrard (IRE)—Dazzling Quintet **Spot On Racing**
36 **RIO RANGER (IRE)**, b f Bushranger (IRE)—Desert d'argent (IRE) **Woodcock Electrical Limited**
37 **SECRET OASIS**, b f Captain Gerrard (IRE)—Annellis (UAE) **The Smart Annellis Partnership**
38 **TINCHY RYDER**, b g Dylan Thomas (IRE)—Keyaki (IRE) **M. Barber**

TWO-YEAR-OLDS

39 B c 15/4 Kyllachy—Choisette (Choisir (AUS)) (9523) **Crossfields Racing**
40 **EMBLAZE**, b f 19/2 Showcasing—Chushka (Pivotal) (5714) **Crossfields Racing**
41 **ESPECIAL**, b c 24/3 Misu Bond (IRE)—Lady In The Bath (Forzando) (3809) **David H. Cox**
42 **GREYBOOTER (IRE)**, gr c 28/4 Dark Angel (IRE)—
              Babacora (IRE) (Indian Ridge) (70000) **Mr R. Fiddes & Mr S. Chapell**
43 B f 13/4 Dark Angel (IRE)—Halliwell House (Selkirk (USA)) (20000) **Ritchie Fiddes**
44 **HAPPY AS HARRY**, ch c 31/3 Monsieur Bond (IRE)—
              The Washerwoman (Classic Cliche (IRE)) **Pastures New Partnership**
45 **HELVIS**, br gr c 20/2 Hellvelyn—Easy Mover (IRE) (Bluebird (USA)) (6190) **Woodcock Electrical Limited**

MR BRYAN SMART - Continued

46 B c 26/4 Compton Place—Inagh River (Fasliyev (USA)) (9523) **The Smart Inagh River Partnership**
47 KI KI, ch f 6/5 Kheleyf (USA)—Peryllys (Warning) **Mrs P.A. Clarke**
48 LITTLE SISTA, ch f 15/1 Equiano (FR)—Clifton Dancer (Fraam) (27619) **Ritchie Fiddes**
49 MYTHMAKER, b c 20/4 Major Cadeaux—Mythicism (Oasis Dream) (7619) **Crossfields Racing**
50 B c 2/2 Captain Gerrard (IRE)—Park's Girl (Averti (IRE)) (14285) **Middleham Park Racing**
51 B f 2/2 Iffraaj—Poppets Sweetlove (Foxhound (USA)) (62000) **R. C. Bond**
52 B f 14/3 Hellvelyn—Positivity (Monsieur Bond (IRE)) (4761) **The Smart Positivity Partnership**
53 B c 24/3 Acclamation—Praesepe (Pivotal) (16260) **Ceffyl Racing**
54 Br f 23/2 Lord Shanakill (USA)—Rakiza (IRE) (Elnadim (USA)) (21000) **Mr R. S. Fiddes**
55 B c 6/3 Captain Gerrard (IRE)—Saorocain (IRE) (Kheleyf (USA)) (15238) **The Smart Saorocain Partnership**
56 SHOOTINGSTA (IRE), b c 20/4 Fast Company (IRE)—
                                                            Kiva (Indian Ridge) (44761) **Redknapp, Salthouse & Fiddes**
57 YTHAN WATERS, b c 24/3 Hellvelyn—Primrose Queen (Lear Fan (USA)) (20952) **BEFG Partnership**
58 B c 30/4 Zebedee—Zuzu (IRE) (Acclamation) (7742) **Ceffyl Racing**

Other Owners: Mr Neil Armstrong, Mr Ronny Armstrong, Mr M. Barber, Mr S. A. Barningham, Mrs Patricia Barrell, Mr M. G. Bullock, Mrs Tina Bullock, Mr N. A. Coster, Mr P.A. Deal, Mrs F. Denniff, Miss Chanelle Derighetti, Mr Dave Elders, Sir Alex Ferguson, Mr Ritchie Fiddes, Mr Bill Fraser, Mr John M. Glendinning, Mrs A. C. Hudson, Mr G. Lowe, Mr I. G. Martin, Mrs B. A. Matthews, Mr T. J. Moses, Mr M. Moses, Mr Richard Page, Mr T. S. Palin, Mr M. Prince, Mr Harry Redknapp, Mr W. J. Salthouse, Mr B. Smart, Mrs V. R. Smart, Mrs Judy Youdan.

Assistant Trainers: Mrs V. R. Smart, Mr K. Edmunds

Jockey (flat): Graham Lee, Paul Mulrennan.

---

578 **MR CHARLES SMITH, Bawtry**
Postal: **Martin Grange Lodge, Martin Common, Bawtry, Doncaster, South Yorkshire, DN10 6DD**
Contacts: **PHONE/FAX (01526) 833245 MOBILE (07778) 149188**

1 GENERAL TUFTO, 9, b g Fantastic Light (USA)—Miss Pinkerton **Mr J. R. Theaker**
2 GOAL (IRE), 6, b g Mujadil (USA)—Classic Lin (FR) **W. McKay**
3 SAIRAAM (IRE), 8, b m Marju (IRE)—Sayedati Eljamilah (USA) **J. Martin-Hoyes**
4 6, Br m Kayf Tara—Santa Ana **Mr N. J. Baines**

THREE-YEAR-OLDS

5 DONNY ROVER (IRE), b g Excellent Art—My Lass **W. McKay**
6 Ch c Monsieur Bond (IRE)—Free Flow **Mr N. J. Baines**
7 ROBBIAN, b c Bertolini (USA)—Crathes **R. J. Lewin**

---

579 **MR JULIAN SMITH, Tirley**
Postal: **Tirley Court, Tirley, Gloucester**
Contacts: **PHONE (01452) 780461 FAX (01452) 780461 MOBILE (07748) 901175**
E-MAIL nicola.smith9156@o2.co.uk

1 CRYSTAL CLICHE, 9, b m Classic Cliche (IRE)—Tirley Pop Eye **Exors of the Late Mr D. E. S. Smith**
2 EMERALD ROSE, 7, b m Sir Harry Lewis (USA)—Swiss Rose **Grand Jury Partnership**
3 FORTUNA ROSE, 8, b m Sir Harry Lewis (USA)—Swiss Rose **Grand Jury Partnership**
4 HARRIET'S ARK, 7, ch m Sir Harry Lewis (USA)—Brush The Ark **Exors of the Late Mr D. E. S. Smith**
5 HERO'S CALL, 9, b m Arkadian Hero (USA)—Sense of Value **Exors of the Late Mr D. E. S. Smith**
6 IONA DAYS (IRE), 9, br g Epistolaire (IRE)—Miss Best (FR) **Mrs J.A. Benson & Miss S.N. Benson**
7 NO PRINCIPLES, 11, b g Overbury (IRE)—Selective Rose **Exors of the Late Mr D. E. S. Smith**
8 PENNIES AND POUNDS, 7, b m Sir Harry Lewis (USA)—Sense of Value **Exors of the Late Mr D. E. S. Smith**
9 PETIT FLEUR, 12, b m Nomadic Way (USA)—Sense of Value **Exors of the Late Mr D. E. S. Smith**
10 SAILOR'S SOVEREIGN, 13, b g Sovereign Water (FR)—Tirley Pop Eye **Exors of the Late Mr D. E. S. Smith**
11 THE HERB, 11, b g Sovereign Water (FR)—Sail On Sunday **D. H. Morgan**
12 THE LAST SELECTION, 8, b g Sir Harry Lewis (USA)—Deep Selection (IRE) **Exors of the Late Mr D. E. S. Smith**
13 TIRLEY BAY, 10, b m Karinga Bay—Tirley Pop Eye **Mr M J Smith**

Other Owners: Mrs J. A. Benson, Miss S. N. Benson, A. W. Brookes, R. Brookes, Mr M J Smith.

Assistant Trainer: Mrs Nicky Smith

Jockey (NH): Mark Grant, Timmy Murphy, Sam Twiston-Davies. **Amateur:** Mr J. M. Ridley.

580 MR MARTIN SMITH, Newmarket
Postal: **Cedar Lodge Stables, Hamilton Road, Newmarket, Suffolk, CB8 0NQ**
Contacts: **MOBILE (07712) 493589**

1 AMBERJAM (IRE), 4, b g Duke of Marmalade (IRE)—Makarova (IRE) **Amblyn Racing**
2 BALTI'S SISTER (IRE), 5, b m Tiger Hill (IRE)—Itsibitsi (IRE) **Mrs M. E. Smith**
3 BORIS THE BOLD, 5, b g Librettist (USA)—Santiburi Girl **Wee 3 Women**
4 DOUGLAS PASHA (IRE), 4, b g Compton Place—Lake Nayasa **The Trojan Horse Partnership**
5 HILLBILLY BOY (IRE), 4, b g Haafhd—Erreur (IRE) **Mr P. D. Moore**
6 INVISIBLE TOUCH, 4, gr f Act One—Zarma (FR) **Four Winds Racing Partnership**
7 MILLIES QUEST, 5, b m Generous (IRE)—Alexander Star (IRE) **M. C. Whatley**
8 OSSIE'S DANCER, 5, ch g Osorio (GER)—Nina Ballerina **Mrs V. Garner**
9 SPECIAL MIX, 6, b g Proclamation (IRE)—Flaming Spirt **Little Princess Racing**

THREE-YEAR-OLDS
10 B f Kheleyf (USA)—Fanny's Fancy **Little Princess Racing**

TWO-YEAR-OLDS
11 B f 9/4 Arakan (USA)—Angel Rays (Unfuwain (USA)) (7000) **The Trojan Horse Partnership**
12 BOUNTY'S SPIRIT, b f 21/2 Bahamian Bounty—
          Scarlet Buttons (IRE) (Marju (IRE)) (8571) **The Trojan Horse Partnership**
13 INDOMITABLE SPIRIT, b c 5/3 Zebedee—Gayala (IRE) (Iron Mask (USA)) (5714)
14 B br f 12/2 Pastoral Pursuits—Spirito Libro (USA) (Lear Fan (USA)) (6000) **Little Princess Racing**

Other Owners: Miss L. Cowdrey, Miss Lynn Douglas, Ms L. K. Heaton-Jacques, S. J. Mear, Mrs E. A. Mear, Miss A. L. Mortlock, Mrs J. Smith, Mr M. P. B. Smith, Mr G. Walker.

581 MR MICHAEL SMITH, Newcastle Upon Tyne
Postal: **Toft Hall Farm, Kirkheaton, Newcastle Upon Tyne, Tyne and Wear, NE19 2DH**
Contacts: **PHONE (01830) 530044 MOBILE (07976) 903233**
E-MAIL **michaelsmithracing@hotmail.co.uk**

1 5, B m Pierre—Bannow Island (IRE)
2 BLAST MARTHA (IRE), 5, b m Definite Article—Calendula **Unnamed Partnership**
3 BOP ALONG (IRE), 7, b g Double Eclipse (IRE)—Bob Girl (IRE) **East-West Partnership**
4 5, B g Pierre—Brushaside Spa (IRE)
5 DANTE'S FROLIC, 6, b m Overbury (IRE)—Dusky Dante (IRE) **East-West Partnership**
6 DREAM FLYER (IRE), 7, ch g Moscow Society (USA)—Bright Choice (IRE) **J. W. Stephenson**
7 IMPERIAL VIC (IRE), 9, b br g Old Vic—Satco Rose (IRE) **J. W. Stephenson & W. J. Muir**
8 INDIGO ROCK (IRE), 8, b g Pierre—Thethirstyscholars (IRE) **Sprayclad UK & Cockton Hill Punters Club**
9 KILGEFIN STAR (IRE), 6, b g Saddlers' Hall (IRE)—High Church Annie (IRE) **J. W. Stephenson**
10 MAKBULLET, 7, gr g Makbul—Gold Belt (IRE) **Mrs S. Smith & DD Armstrong LTD**
11 MASTERLEADERMAN (IRE), 6, b g Beneficial—Atagirl (IRE) **East-West Partnership**
12 MONT ROYALE, 6, b g Hurricane Run (IRE)—Wild Academy (IRE) **Mrs S. Smith & W. J. Muir**
13 MOST HONOURABLE, 4, b g Halling (USA)—Her Ladyship **Mrs S. Smith & W. J. Muir**
14 NATIVE SPA (IRE), 6, b g Norwich—Thethirstyscholars (IRE) **J. W. Stephenson**
15 ORSIPPUS (USA), 8, b br g Sunday Break (JPN)—Mirror Dancing (USA) **Mrs S. Smith**
16 5, B g Subtle Power (IRE)—Satco Rose (IRE) **J. W. Stephenson & W. J. Muir**
17 5, Br m Beneficial—Thethirstyscholars (IRE)

THREE-YEAR-OLDS
18 BLACK INK, b g Black Sam Bellamy (IRE)—Incony **J. W. Stephenson**

Other Owners: Mr Lee Aldsworth, Mr L. Ellison, Mr William Muir, Mrs Sandra Smith, Mr J. Stephenson.

Assistant Trainer: Sandra Smith

Jockey (NH): Danny Cook, Ryan Mania. **Conditional:** Adam Nicol. **Amateur:** Mr Brendan Wood.

582 MR R. MIKE SMITH, Galston
Postal: **West Loudoun Farm, Galston, Ayrshire, KA4 8PB**
Contacts: **PHONE (01563) 822062 MOBILE (07711) 692122**
E-MAIL mike@mikesmithracing.co.uk WEBSITE www.mikesmithracing.co.uk

1 EILEAN MOR, 6, ch g Ishiguru (USA)—Cheviot Heights **R. M. Smith**
2 GOOD BOY JACKSON, 6, b g Firebreak—Fisher Court (IRE) **Mrs A. D. Matheson**
3 HOPEFULL, 4, br bl f Overbury (IRE)—Maryscross (IRE) **R. M. Smith**
4 KATIES CHOICE (IRE), 6, gr g Croco Rouge (IRE)—Rosetown Girl (IRE) **Smith & Kelly**
5 KNIGHT WOODSMAN, 10, ch g Sir Harry Lewis (USA)—Jowoody **Smith & Lawson**
6 OSCAR DALLAS (IRE), 7, b g Oscar (IRE)—Ring Mam (IRE) **Mrs A. D. Matheson**
7 SCOTCH WARRIOR, 10, ch g Karinga Bay—Tarda **R. M. Smith**
8 WEST BRIT (IRE), 6, b g High Chaparral—Aldburgh **R. M. Smith**

Other Owners: Mr T. Kelly, Mr R. Lawson.

583 MR RALPH SMITH, Chipstead
Postal: **Stud Managers Cottage, Cheval Court Stud, High Road, Chipstead, Surrey, CR5 3SD**
Contacts: **PHONE (01737) 201693 FAX (01737) 201693 MOBILE (07795) 327003**
E-MAIL rjsmith.racing@hotmail.com WEBSITE www.rjsmithracing.com

1 KINGSWOOD HEIGHTS, 5, b g Night Shift (USA)—Call Me Roxane (GER) **Mr Fred Wilson**
2 MAYGO'S JOY, 4, b g Josr Algarhoud (IRE)—Nikki Bea (IRE) **Surrey Elite**
3 THE CASH GENERATOR (IRE), 6, b g Peintre Celebre (USA)—
Majestic Launch **The Cash Generator Racing Corporation**
4 TWO IN THE PINK (IRE), 4, b f Clodovil (IRE)—Secret Circle **Homecroft Wealth & Mr Kevin Old**
5 WHO'S THAT CHICK (IRE), 5, ch m Footstepsinthesand—
Poule de Luxe (IRE) **Piper, Harris, Churchill, Hirschfeld**

THREE-YEAR-OLDS
6 B c Araafa (IRE)—Angel Kate (IRE)
7 BEAVER CREEK, ch c Three Valleys (USA)—Delta **Mr Tony Hirschfeld**

Other Owners: Mr Nigel Bailey, Mrs Sheila Bailey, Mr Steve Churchill, Mr Rob E. L. Frost, Mrs Charlotte Harris, Mr Tony Hirschfeld, Mr Steven Lang, Mr Kevin Old, Mr S. J. Piper, Mr Nick Pogmore, Mr Anthony Stocker, Mr S. Wilkinson.

Assistant Trainer: Jayne Smith

Amateur: Miss Ella Smith.

584 MRS SUE SMITH, Bingley
Postal: **Craiglands Farm, High Eldwick, Bingley, West Yorkshire, BD16 3BE**
Contacts: **PHONE (01274) 564930 FAX (01274) 560626**
E-MAIL craiglandsracing@yahoo.com

1 ALBA KING (IRE), 8, b g Beauchamp King—Alba Dancer **Mrs S. J. Smith**
2 ALF THE AUDACIOUS, 8, gr g Alflora (IRE)—Rua Ros (IRE) **Mr R. Preston**
3 ALTA ROCK (IRE), 9, b g Luso—Princess Lulu (IRE) **Mrs S. J. Smith**
4 BACCALAUREATE (FR), 8, b g High Chaparral (IRE)—Rose d'or (IRE) **The Cartmel Syndicate**
5 BALTIC PATHFINDER (IRE), 10, b g Alflora (IRE)—Boro Bow (IRE) **John Regan & John Conroy**
6 BE A DREAMER, 6, ch g Dreams End—Miss Fahrenheit (IRE) **Mrs S. J. Smith**
7 BELMORE BARON, 12, ch g Double Trigger (IRE)—Belmore Cloud
8 BENNYS WELL (IRE), 8, b g Beneficial—Alure (IRE) **Mrs A. Ellis**
9 BLAKE DEAN, 6, b g Halling (USA)—Antediluvian **Widdop Wanderers**
10 BLAKEMOUNT (IRE), 6, br g Presenting—Smashing Leader (IRE) **Mrs J. Conroy**
11 BOLD SLASHER (IRE), 6, b g Millenary—Witney Girl **A. D. Hollinrake**
12 BOLLIN SAM, 8, b g Bollin Eric—Cranborne (IRE) **Mrs S. J. Smith**
13 BROTHER SCOTT, 7, b g Kirkwall—Crimson Shower **Mrs S. J. Smith**
14 BUZZARD FLIGHT, 5, b g Kayf Tara—Im Busy **Mrs S. J. Smith**
15 CAMDEN GEORGE (IRE), 13, b g Pasternak—Triple Town Lass (IRE) **R. H. Scholey & M. B. Scholey**
16 CLAN WILLIAM (IRE), 6, b g Antonius Pius (USA)—Celebrated Smile (IRE) **Mr A. M. Phillips**
17 CLOUDY DAWN, 9, gr g Cloudings (IRE)—Persistent Gunner **Mrs S. J. Smith**
18 CLOUDY TOO (IRE), 8, b g Cloudings (IRE)—Curra Citizen (IRE) **Formulated Polymer Products Ltd**

MRS SUE SMITH - Continued

19 **COMEBACK COLIN**, 6, b g Beat Hollow—Queen G (USA) **Beningtonbury Stud/Laundry Cottage Stud**
20 **DARTFORD WARBLER (IRE)**, 7, b br g Overbury (IRE)—Stony View (IRE) **Mrs S. J. Smith**
21 **DE BOITRON (FR)**, 10, b g Sassanian (USA)—Pondiki (FR) **Mrs J. Morgan & Mrs Lindsey J. Shaw**
22 **EMRAL SILK**, 6, b g Revoque (IRE)—Silk Stockings (FR) **Mrs A. Ellis**
23 **FILL THE POWER (IRE)**, 8, b g Subtle Power (IRE)—Our Alma (IRE) **McGoldrick Racing Syndicates**
24 **FLEMERINA (IRE)**, 5, b m Flemensfirth (USA)—Ballerina Laura (IRE) **Mrs S. J. Smith**
25 **FORWARD FLIGHT (IRE)**, 8, b g Dilshaan—Too Advanced (USA) **J. P. McManus**
26 **FRED ARCHER (IRE)**, 6, b g Iffraaj—Fairy Contessa (IRE) **Mrs S. J. Smith**
27 **GANSEY (IRE)**, 12, br g Anshan—Ebony Jane **T. J. Hemmings**
28 **GRATE FELLA (IRE)**, 6, b g King's Best (USA)—Moonlight Paradise (USA) **Mrs M. Ashby**
29 **GREEN WIZARD (IRE)**, 8, b g Wizard King—Ajo Green (IRE) **Mrs S. J. Smith**
30 **GROOMED (IRE)**, 6, b g Acclamation—Enamoured **Mrs S. J. Smith**
31 **HELENA OF TROY**, 8, b m Largesse—Just Julia **Mrs S. J. Smith**
32 **HERDSMAN (IRE)**, 9, b g Flemensfirth (USA)—My Sunny South **T. J. Hemmings**
33 **HERISING (IRE)**, 6, b g Heron Island (IRE)—Lady Rising (IRE) **Mrs S. J. Smith**
34 **HIGH HOYLANDER**, 8, b g Aljabr (USA)—Ma-Arif (IRE) **McGoldrick Racing Syndicates**
35 **HIT THE TOP (IRE)**, 7, b g Gold Well—Smooth Leader (IRE) **Mrs S. J. Smith**
36 5, Ch g Grape Tree Road—Its Meant To Be **Mrs S. J. Smith**
37 **KARINGA DANDY (IRE)**, 8, b g Karinga Bay—Well Then Now Then (IRE) **Mrs M B Scholey & Mrs S J Smith**
38 **KARISMA KING**, 5, b g Supreme Sound—Hollybush (IRE) **Broadway Racing Club 15**
39 **KENT STREET (IRE)**, 9, ch g Flemensfirth (USA)—Fernhill (IRE) **K. Nicholson**
40 **LACKAMON**, 9, b g Fleetwood (IRE)—Pearlossa **Mrs S. J. Smith**
41 **LAVELLA WELLS**, 6, b m Alflora (IRE)—Jazzy Refrain (IRE) **Mrs S. J. Smith**
42 **LITTLE LONDON (IRE)**, 7, b g Croco Rouge (IRE)—Katty Barry (IRE) **Mrs S. J. Smith**
43 **MARINE BAND**, 8, b g Bandmaster (USA)—Darakah **Mrs S. J. Smith**
44 **MAXED OUT KING (IRE)**, 6, ch g Desert King (IRE)—Lady Max (IRE) **Mrs S. J. Smith**
45 **MISTER JONES**, 6, b g Val Royal (FR)—Madame Jones (IRE) **McGoldrick Racing Syndicates**
46 **MR MOONSHINE (IRE)**, 10, b g Double Eclipse (IRE)—Kinross **DG Pryde,J Beaumont,DP van der Hoeven 1**
47 **MR PEPPERPOT**, 5, b g Sir Harry Lewis (USA)—Parslin **The Trevor-McDonald Partnership**
48 **MWALESHI**, 9, b g Oscar (IRE)—Roxy River **Mrs S. J. Smith**
49 **NEXT HIGHT (IRE)**, 7, b g High Chaparral (IRE)—Night Petticoat (GER) **Mrs S. J. Smith**
50 **NO PLANNING**, 7, b g Kayf Tara—Poor Celt **Mrs J. Conroy**
51 5, B g Grape Tree Road—Nortonthorpe-Rose **Mrs S. J. Smith**
52 **OORAYVIC (IRE)**, 7, ch g Snurge—Miss Murtle (IRE) **Mrs S. J. Smith**
53 **OPTICAL HIGH**, 5, b g Rainbow High—Forsweets **Mrs S. J. Smith**
54 **PALM GREY (IRE)**, 6, gr g Great Palm (USA)—Lucy Cooper (IRE) **Mrs S. J. Smith**
55 **PAPA CARUSO**, 10, b g Kayf Tara—Madonna da Rossi **Mrs S. J. Smith**
56 **PERSIAN HERALD**, 6, gr g Proclamation (IRE)—Persian Fortune **The Cartmel Syndicate**
57 5, B g Phoenix Reach (IRE)—Piddies Pride (IRE) **Mrs S. J. Smith**
58 **PINEROLO**, 8, b g Milan—Hollybush (IRE) **McGoldrick Racing Syndicates (2)**
59 **RATTLIN**, 6 b m Bollin Eric—Broadband **Partnership**
60 **REGGIE PARROT**, 7, ch g Soviet Star (USA)—Jazzy Refrain (IRE) **Mrs S. J. Smith**
61 **SILVER SOPHFIRE**, 8, gr m Silver Patriarch (IRE)—Princess Timon **Mrs S. J. Smith**
62 **SILVER VOGUE**, 6, gr g Revoque (IRE)—Pusslin **Mrs S. J. Smith**
63 **SMOOTH STEPPER**, 5, b g Alflora (IRE)—Jazzy Refrain (IRE) **Mrs S. J. Smith**
64 **SPARKLING TARA**, 9, b g Kayf Tara—Sparkling Yasmin **Mrs S. J. Smith**
65 **SPARKLING WINE (IRE)**, 6, b g Kayf Tara—Sparkling Yasmin **Mrs S. J. Smith**
66 **SPECIAL WELLS**, 5, ch g Alflora (IRE)—Oso Special **Mrs S. J. Smith**
67 **STAGECOACH HARRY**, 8, b g Sir Harry Lewis (USA)—Linwood **Mrs S. J. Smith**
68 **STAGECOACH JASPER**, 8, b g Sir Harry Lewis (USA)—Flintwood **Mrs J. Conroy**
69 **STAGECOACH PEARL**, 10, gr g Classic Cliche (IRE)—Linwood **John Conroy Jaqueline Conroy**
70 **STRAIDNAHANNA (IRE)**, 5, gr g Medaaly—Sue's Song **M. B. Scholey & R. H. Scholey**
71 **SWINDY**, 6, b g Hurricane Run (IRE)—Red Passion **Mrs S. J. Smith**
72 **SWING HARD (IRE)**, 6, br g Zagreb (USA)—Hurricane Jane (IRE) **DP van der Hoeven, DG Pryde & J Beaumon**
73 **TAHITI PEARL (IRE)**, 10, b g Winged Love (IRE)—Clara's Dream (IRE) **M. B. Scholey & R. H. Scholey**
74 **THE KNOXS (IRE)**, 11, b g Close Conflict (USA)—
                                            Nicola Marie (IRE) **AprilStrangSteelJimBeaumont&DouglasPryde**
75 **TIPSY INDIAN**, 11, ch g Commanche Run—Dubelle **Mrs S. J. Smith**
76 **TROOPER ROYAL**, 4, b g Zafeen (FR)—Faithful Beauty (IRE) **Mrs C. Steel**
77 **TWICE LUCKY**, 10, b g Mtoto—Foehn Gale (IRE) **Mrs S. J. Smith**
78 **VINTAGE STAR (IRE)**, 8, b g Presenting—Rare Vintage (IRE) **T. J. Hemmings**
79 **WAKANDA (IRE)**, 5, b g Westerner—Chanson Indienne (FR) **M. B. Scholey & R. H. Scholey**
80 **WAKHAN (IRE)**, 6, b g Dalakhani (IRE)—Wrapitraise (USA) **Jim Beaumont & Douglas Pryde**
81 **WHATDOIDOWITHTHAT**, 11, ch g Minster Son—Wynyard Lady **M. F. Spence**
82 **WHISKEY RIDGE (IRE)**, 8, b g High-Rise (IRE)—Little Chartridge **Widdop Wanderers**

MRS SUE SMITH - Continued

83 WILLY C, 8, b g Zamindar (USA)—Rosa Canina **M. F. Spence**
84 YOU KNOW YOURSELF (IRE), 11, b g Dr Massini (IRE)—Gift of The Gab (IRE) **Mrs S. J. Smith**

Other Owners: J. J. Beaumont, Mr R. S. Bebb, R. F. Broad, Mrs M. Bryce, J. Conroy, Mrs E. M. Grundy, W. S. D. Lamb, R. J. Longley, C. C. S. MacMillan, P. J. Martin, S. McDonald, Mrs J. Morgan, D. Musgrave, Mr M. Norcliffe, D. G. Pryde, Mrs J. B. Pye, J. Regan, R. H. Scholey, Mrs M. B. Scholey, Mrs L. J. Shaw, Mrs A. E. Strang Steel, S. P. Trevor, Mr D. P. van der Hoeven.

Assistant Trainer: Ryan Clavin

Jockey (NH): Ryan Mania. **Conditional:** Callum Bewley, Shane Byrne, Jonathan England, Zachery-James Gaughan.

---

585 **MISS SUZY SMITH, Lewes**
Postal: **County Stables, The Old Racecourse, Lewes, East Sussex, BN7 1UR**
Contacts: **PHONE (01273) 477173 FAX (01273) 477173 MOBILE (07970) 550828**
E-MAIL suzy@suzysmithracing.co.uk WEBSITE www.suzysmithracing.co.uk

1 AIMIGAYLE, 11, b m Midnight Legend—Cherrygayle (IRE) **David Cliff, Phillipa Clunes & P Mercer**
2 BEAU LAKE (IRE), 10, b br g Heron Island (IRE)—
        Brennan For Audits (IRE) **Sergio Gordon-Watson & Graham Willetts**
3 BRAVE DECISION, 7, gr g With Approval (CAN)—Brave Vanessa (USA) **Mr R. I. Knight**
4 5, B m Oscar (IRE)—Golden Bay
5 INVICTA LAKE (IRE), 7, b g Dr Massini (IRE)—Classic Material **Bernard & Jan Wolford**
6 JENNIFER ECCLES, 4, b f Midnight Legend—Cherrygayle (IRE) **P. J. Mercer**
7 LAUGHTON PARK, 9, ch g Karinga Bay—Brass Castle (IRE) **Exors of the Late Mr A. G. C. Russell**
8 MALIBU ROCK, 6, b g Tiger Hill (IRE)—High Straits **Mr D. R. Jinks**
9 MARIET, 5, ch m Dr Fong (USA)—Medway (IRE) **Miss S. Smith**
10 MATERIAL STAR, 5, b g Kayf Tara—Material World **Material World Racing Club**
11 NATURAL SPRING, 9, b m Generous (IRE)—Highbrook (USA) **The Natural Spring Partnership**
12 O MALLEY'S OSCAR (IRE), 9, b g Oscar (IRE)—Notre Dame (IRE) **Mr R. I. Knight**
13 OURMANMASSINI (IRE), 6, b g Dr Massini (IRE)—Aunty Dawn (IRE) **The Seagull Partnership**
14 SAMURAI LEGEND, 6, b g Midnight Legend—Cherrygayle (IRE)
15 SHANTY TOWN (IRE), 5, b g Zagreb (USA)—Rapsan (IRE) **Mrs E. C. Stewart**
16 SHE'S NOBLE, 7, b m Karinga Bay—Alta **Mr N. L. Crawford-Smith**
17 TED SPREAD, 7, b g Beat Hollow—Highbrook (USA) **False Nose 'n Glasses Partnership**

THREE-YEAR-OLDS

18 STORM PATROL, b f Shirocco (GER)—Material World **Storm Force Ten**

Other Owners: Mrs D. J. Arstall, Mr S. A. Ashley, Mr G. Barrett, D. Cliff, Mrs P. K. Clunes, S. Gordon-Watson, Mr D. J. Harrison, Mr M. Hess, J. A. A. S. Logan, Mr A. J. McDonald, Mr G. Pettit, R. F. Smith, Mr G. J. Willetts, B. Wolford, Mrs J. Wolford, Mrs H. M. T. Woods.

Assistant Trainer: Mr S E Gordon-Watson

Jockey (flat): Luke Morris. **Jockey (NH):** Paddy Brennan. **Conditional:** Gavin Sheehan.

---

586 **MR GILES SMYLY, Broadway**
Postal: **Garden Cottage, Wormington Grange, Broadway, Worcestershire, WR12 7NJ**
Contacts: **PHONE (01386) 584085 FAX (01386) 584085 MOBILE (07747) 035169**
E-MAIL gilessmiler@aol.com WEBSITE www.smylyracing.co.uk

1 BADGER WOOD, 5, b g Overbury (IRE)—Parlour Game **A. C. Ward-Thomas**
2 DANNERS (IRE), 8, b br g Old Vic—The Great O'malley (IRE) **Mark Hingley & David Doolittle**
3 JUNE FRENCH (FR), 6, b m Jimble (FR)—Sunbelt Broker **Brigadier Racing**
4 LETEMGO (IRE), 6, b g Brian Boru—Leteminletemout (IRE) **A. C. Ward-Thomas**
5 MINERFORTYNINER (IRE), 5, br g Catcher In The Rye (IRE)—Hungry Eyes (IRE) **D. Maxwell**
6 SPIRIT MINDED, 6, b m Silver Patriarch—Dickies Girl **B. P. Wilson**
7 STELLA'S FELLA, 6, b g Septieme Ciel (USA)—Gaspaisie (FR) **Mr A. Agnew**
8 TAIGAN (FR), 7, b g Panoramic—Lazary (FR) **M. Burford**
9 VENEZ HORACE (FR), 5, b g Polish Summer—Fripperie (FR) **M. Burford**

MR GILES SMYLY - Continued

Other Owners: D. J. Bussell, D. W. Doolittle, M. Hingley, Mr R. J. Moore, Mrs L. G. Thomas.

Assistant Trainer: Kim Smyly

Jockey (NH): David England, Liam Treadwell. **Conditional:** Ed Cookson.

---

587 **MR JAMIE SNOWDEN, Lambourn**
Postal: **Folly House, Upper Lambourn Road, Lambourn, Hungerford, Berkshire, RG17 8QG**
Contacts: **PHONE (01488) 72800 (office) Twitter: @jamiesnowden MOBILE (07779) 497563**
E-MAIL info@jamiesnowdenracing.co.uk WEBSITE www.jamiesnowdenracing.co.uk

1 **ALANJOU (FR)**, 4, b g Maresca Sorrento (FR)—Partie Time (FR) **The Cherry Pickers**
2 **BATU FERRINGHI (FR)**, 8, b g Numerous (USA)—Dara (IRE) **The Sandylini Racing Partnership I**
3 **BLACKDOWN HILLS**, 4, b f Presenting—Lady Prunella (IRE) **Mrs P. De. W. Johnson**
4 **BORGUY (FR)**, 4, b g Irish Wells (FR)—Bally Borg (FR) **Mrs S. F. Snowden**
5 **BREAKING BRIKS**, 7, b br g Oscar (IRE)—Lantern Lark (IRE) **Colin Peake & John H W Finch Partnership**
6 **BUXOM (IRE)**, 7, b m Milan—Bermuda Bay (IRE) **Ward, Smith & Harper Families**
7 **CAMINERO (IRE)**, 7, b g Cloudings (IRE)—Sounds Confident (IRE) **Mrs L. E. Snowden**
8 **CENTORIA (IRE)**, 6, ch m Generous (IRE)—Cent Prime **The Wife Loves It Partnership**
9 **COMEDINEWITHME**, 6, b m Milan—Skipcarl (IRE) **The Lynch Wood Syndicate**
10 **DENBOY (IRE)**, 4, b g King's Theatre (IRE)—Miss Denman (IRE) **Sir Martin Broughton & Friends**
11 **ETHELRED**, 6, b g Alflora (IRE)—Navale (FR) **Mr David Hearson**
12 **FUTURE GILDED (FR)**, 5, b g Lost World (IRE)—Doree du Pin (FR) **Owners For Owners: Future Gilded**
13 **HOUNDSCOURT (IRE)**, 7, b g Court Cave (IRE)—Broken Rein (IRE) **Owners For Owners: Houndscourt**
14 **JEAN FLEMING (IRE)**, 7, b m Flemensfirth (USA)—Dromhale Lady (IRE) **Mrs K. Gunn**
15 **JOANNE ONE (IRE)**, 6, ch m Vinnie Roe (IRE)—Bobs Star (IRE) **Sir Chippendale Keswick**
16 **LEMONS GROUND**, 5, ch g Generous (IRE)—Misty Move (IRE) **L G Partnership**
17 **LOUGH DERG WAY (IRE)**, 8, b g Dushyantor (USA)—Lotschberg Express **The Folly Partnership**
18 **LUCYS GIRL (IRE)**, 7, b m Portrait Gallery (IRE)—Bubbleover (IRE) **J. H. W. Finch**
19 **MAJOR MILBORNE**, 6, ch g Exit To Nowhere (USA)—Motown Melody (IRE) **Nowhere To Run Friends**
20 **MARODIMA (IRE)**, 11, b g Robin des Pres (FR)—Balbeyssac (FR) **Mareildar Racing Part 2**
21 **MISS MILBORNE**, 8, b m Tamure (IRE)—Motown Melody (IRE) **Adrian Brown and Friends**
22 **MONBEG THEATRE (IRE)**, 5, b g King's Theatre (IRE)—Amberina (IRE) **Tim Dykes & Lynda Lovell**
23 **NIKI ROYAL (FR)**, 9, b m Nikos—Balgarde (FR) **Jamie Snowden Racing Club**
24 **PRESENT VIEW**, 6, b g Presenting—Carry Me (IRE) **Sir Chippendale Keswick**
25 **REVES D'AMOUR (IRE)**, 5, ch m Midnight Legend—Poppy Maroon **The TTF Partnership**
26 **ROYAL MACNAB (IRE)**, 6, b g Beneficial—Tina McBride (IRE) **Jeremy Sykes & Jamie Snowden**
27 **SANDY'S DOUBLE**, 8, ch g Double Trigger (IRE)—Skipcarl (IRE) **Ms L. V. Agran**
28 **SCUDERIA (IRE)**, 7, b g Kris Kin (USA)—Class Society (IRE) **Whites 'n Oops**
29 **STAGE TWENTY (IRE)**, 4, b f King's Theatre (IRE)—Last Century (IRE) **Mr Tim Dykes**
30 **TEA CADDY**, 8, b m Kadastrof (FR)—Little Tern (IRE) **R. T. S. Matthews**
31 **TOM SANG (FR)**, 7, b g Dom Alco (FR)—Idee (FR) **Pat & Tony Bath**
32 **ULTRA KLASS (FR)**, 6, b g Ungaro (GER)—Leathou (FR) **Ultra Klass Racing**
33 **WYFIELD ROSE**, 5, b m Kayf Tara—Miniature Rose **Mrs Nicholas Jones & Friends**
34 **ZAVA RIVER (FR)**, 7, b g Zagreb (USA)—Great Accord (IRE) **Chalke Valley Racing Partnership**

THREE-YEAR-OLDS

35 **MANGOWAVE (FR)**, b f Gentlewave (IRE)—Sous Kai Mango (FR) **Mr Ian Snowden**

Other Owners: Mr Reg Allen, Mr Ray Antell, Mr Tony Bath, Mrs Pat Bath, Mr Oliver Battersby, Mr L. H. Brewin, Mr A. P. Brown, Mr Tim Dykes, Mr John H. W. Finch, Mr R. J. Galpin, Mr H. M. Glyn-Davies, Mr Chris Guy, Mr Matt Harper, Mr C. Hellyer, Mr Jon Hughes, Mrs Nicholas Jones, Mr O. C. S. Lazenby, Mrs L. R. Lovell, Mr A. Morley, Mr M. Pike, Mr D. C. Ross, Mr David Sanger, Mr M. Smith, Mrs Ian Snowden, Mr J. E. Snowden, Mrs L. Snowden, Mr Jeremy Sykes, Mr William Wallace, Mr A. J. Ward, Mrs Janet Ward, Miss Anna Yorke.

Assistant Trainer: Kate Robinson

Jockey (NH): Tom O'Brien, Brendan Powell, Sam Twiston-Davies. **Conditional:** Gavin Sheehan.

588 MR MIKE SOWERSBY, York
Postal: **Southwold Farm, Goodmanham Wold, Market Weighton, York, East Yorkshire, YO43 3NA**
Contacts: **PHONE (01430) 810534 MOBILE (07855) 551056**

1 AGENT LOUISE, 6, b m Alflora (IRE)—Oso Special M. E. Sowersby
2 AUTO MAC, 6, b g Auction House (USA)—Charlottevalentina (USA) **Mounted Gamess Assoc Syndicate**
3 CARMELA MARIA, 9, b m Medicean—Carmela Owen Mrs Janet Cooper & Mr M. E. Sowersby
4 DAVE THE DAUPHIN, 5, b g Alflora (IRE)—Ma Jolie F. M. Holmes
5 FROSTY DAWN, 6, b m Desideratum—Frosty Petal Mrs J. M. Plummer
6 HAMMER, 9, b g Beat Hollow—Tranquil Moon J. Payne
7 INKA EXPRESS, 4, b f Rail Link—Coolberry (USA) The Southwold Set
8 MOON MELODY (GER), 11, b g Montjeu (IRE)—Midnight Fever (IRE) Mrs J. H. Cooper
9 ONEOFAPEAR (IRE), 8, b g Pyrus (USA)—Whitegate Way Mr B. W. Gibson
10 SPITHEAD, 4, b g Tiger Hill (IRE)—Cyclone Connie B. Valentine
11 SYCHO FRED (IRE), 13, b g Buster King—Rebecca Steel (IRE) Mrs E. A. Verity
12 TREGARO (FR), 8, b g Phantom Breeze—Touques (FR) A. Lyons
13 TRENTSIDE WILLIAM, 7, b g Bollin William—Aunt Gladys (IRE) J. Payne

Other Owners: Mr P. W. Clifton, Mr J. E. Scott, Mrs C. J. Zetter-Wells.

Assistant Trainer: Mary Sowersby

Jockey (flat): Tom Eaves. **Jockey (NH):** Keith Mercer. **Conditional:** Edmond Linehan.

589 MR JOHN SPEARING, Kinnersley
Postal: **Kinnersley Racing Limited, Kinnersley Racing Stables, Kinnersley, Severn Stoke, Worcestershire, WR8 9JR**
Contacts: **PHONE (01905) 371054 FAX (01905) 371054 MOBILE (07801) 552922**
E-MAIL jlspearing@aol.com

1 ADDIKT (IRE), 9, b h Diktat—Frond Good Breed Limited
2 ASHPAN SAM, 5, b g Firebreak—Sweet Patoopie Advantage Chemicals Holdings Ltd
3 BARTON GIFT, 7, b g Alflora (IRE)—Marina Bird Mercy Rimell & Kate Ive
4 BLACK EIDER, 4, b f Piccolo—The Dark Eider Kinnersley Partnership II
5 CASHEL'S MISSILE (IRE), 4, b g Majestic Missile (IRE)—Cashel Mead Masonaires
6 CLEAR LOCH, 4, gr g Proclamation (IRE)—Loch Shiel (IRE) Mr H. James
7 CLEAR SPRING (IRE), 6, b h Chineur (FR)—Holly Springs Mr H. James
8 CROESO MAWR, 8, ch m Bertolini (USA)—Croeso-I-Cymru Mrs S. A. Evans
9 FARMERS DREAM (IRE), 7, b m Antonius Pius (USA)—Beucaire (IRE) D. J. Oseman
10 FROSTED OFF, 4, gr g Verglas (IRE)—Dispol Veleta Advantage Chemicals Holdings Ltd
11 FULL SHILLING (IRE), 6, b m Intikhab (USA)—Full Cream (USA) Not The Full Shilling Syndicate
12 GRACIE'S GAMES, 8, b m Mind Games—Little Kenny Mr D. Prosser & Mr K. Warrington
13 HAWK MOTH (IRE), 6, b g Hawk Wing (USA)—Sasimoto (USA) Kinnersley Partnership
14 HEAVENSTOWN (IRE), 8, ch g Bienamado (USA)—Little Bliss (IRE) Mr M. Page
15 IDOLISE (IRE), 5, b g Elusive Quality (USA)—Victoria Star (IRE) Kinnersley Partnership II
16 LUCKY LEOPARDSFOOT, 4, b c Echo of Light—Je Suis Belle
17 OVER THE AIR, 6, br m Overbury (IRE)—Moonlight Air Mrs P. Badger
18 PEARLS LEGEND, 7, b g Midnight Legend—Pearl's Choice (IRE) The Corsairs
19 ROCK ON CANDY, 5, b m Excellent Art—Rock Candy (IRE) T. M. Hayes
20 SANTERA (IRE), 10, br m Gold Away (FR)—Sainte Gig (FR) Mr J. Tucker
21 TABLE BLUFF (IRE), 5, ch g Indian Haven—Double Deal Advantage Chemicals Holdings Ltd
22 TARANTELLE, 5, br m Kayf Tara—Suave Shot H. M. Porter
23 WHITECREST, 6, ch m Ishiguru (USA)—Risky Valentine G. M. Eales

THREE-YEAR-OLDS
24 HOWZ THE FAMILY (IRE), b c Myboycharlie (IRE)—Lady Raj (USA) G. Barot
25 INSIGHT (IRE), b f Bushranger (IRE)—Ribbon Glade (UAE) G. Barot
26 LITTLE BRIAR ROSE, ch f Sleeping Indian—Penrice Castle Kinnersley Partnership II

TWO-YEAR-OLDS
27 B f 14/4 Excellent Art—Clinging Vine (USA) (Fusaichi Pegasus (USA)) (4258) G. M. Gales
28 Ch g 12/3 Strategic Prince—Miss Dilletante (Primo Dominie) (3483)
29 B f 7/3 Kodiac—Namu (Mujahid (USA)) (24000) Advantage Chemicals Ltd
30 B f 1/3 Strategic Prince—Pixie's Blue (IRE) (Hawk Wing (USA)) (3483)

MR JOHN SPEARING - Continued

Other Owners: Mr S. J. Court, Mr Eddie Devereaux, Mr J. Eccleson, Mr W. J. Goddard, Miss C. Ive, Mr Andrew O'Brien, Major H. R. M. Porter, Mr D. J. Prosser, Mrs Mercy Rimell, Mr J. Spearing, Mr Keith Warrington.

Assistant Trainer: Miss C Ive

---

590 MR MICHAEL SQUANCE, Newmarket
Postal: 36 Golden Miller Close, Newmarket, Suffolk, CB8 7RT
Contacts: **PHONE** (01638) 661824 **MOBILE** (07532) 372557
WEBSITE www.michaelsquanceracing.co.uk

1 **CALLISTO LIGHT**, 7, ch m Medicean—Luminda (IRE) **G. D. J. Linder**
2 **DIPLOMATIC (IRE)**, 9, b g Cape Cross (IRE)—Embassy **Miss K. L. Squance**
3 **HARROGATE FAIR**, 4, b g Trade Fair—Starbeck (IRE) **K. D. Crabb**
4 **MISTER FROSTY (IRE)**, 8, gr g Verglas (IRE)—La Chinampina (FR) **Mr M. Bartram**
5 **ONCEAPONATIME (IRE)**, 9, b g Invincible Spirit (IRE)—Lake Nyasa (IRE) **Miss K. L. Squance**
6 **SAFWAAN**, 7, b g Selkirk (USA)—Kawn **Roberto Felicia Favarulo, Miss K Squance**

Other Owners: Mr R. Favarulo.

---

591 MR TOMMY STACK, Cashel
Postal: Thomastown Castle Stud, Golden, Cashel, Co. Tipperary, Ireland
Contacts: **PHONE** (00353) 62 54129
E-MAIL tommystack@eircom.net

1 **ALIVE ALIVE OH**, 4, b f Duke of Marmalade (IRE)—Higher Love (IRE)
2 **ALMANACK**, 4, b c Haatef (USA)—Openness
3 **BARBEQUE (IRE)**, 4, b f Elusive City (USA)—Babberina (IRE)
4 **BEACON LODGE (IRE)**, 9, b g Clodovil (IRE)—Royal House (FR)
5 **CAPE OF APPROVAL (IRE)**, 5, b g Cape Cross (IRE)—Wyola (USA)
6 **CROI AN OR (IRE)**, 5, b g Windsor Knot (IRE)—Exponent (USA)
7 **GREAT MINDS (IRE)**, 4, ch g Bahamian Bounty—Raja (IRE)
8 **OVERLAND EXPRESS (IRE)**, 4, b f Dylan Thomas (IRE)—No Way (IRE)
9 **SCREAM BLUE MURDER (IRE)**, 4, b f Oratorio—Holly Blue
10 **SNAKES AND LADDERS (IRE)**, 4, br c Rock of Gibraltar (IRE)—Jalisco (IRE)
11 **STRADATER (IRE)**, 5, b g Catcher In The Rye (IRE)—Starring Role (IRE)
12 **TOOREEN LEGEND (IRE)**, 4, ch g Rakti—Annmary Girl
13 **WANNABE BETTER (IRE)**, 4, b f Duke of Marmalade (IRE)—Wannabe

THREE-YEAR-OLDS
14 **AGERA CASS (IRE)**, gr f Mastercraftsman (IRE)—Fand (USA)
15 **ASHTAROTH**, b f Royal Applause—Asheyana (IRE)
16 B f Sea The Stars (IRE)—Blas Ceoil (USA)
17 **BOQA (IRE)**, b c Danehill Dancer (IRE)—Mowaadah (IRE)
18 **CELESTIAL FABLE (IRE)**, br f Intense Focus (USA)—Angels Story (IRE)
19 **DASH (IRE)**, ch f Danehill Dancer (IRE)—Challow Hills (USA)
20 **FINE CUT (IRE)**, gr c Dark Angel (IRE)—Non Dimenticar Me (IRE)
21 **GRADATIM (IRE)**, b g High Chaparral (IRE)—Fear And Greed (IRE)
22 **HAPPY GATHERING (IRE)**, b f Shamardal (USA)—Home You Stroll (IRE)
23 **IRISH ARROW (IRE)**, b c Montjeu (IRE)—Miss Khaya (IRE)
24 B f Fastnet Rock (AUS)—Mer de Corail (IRE)
25 **ONENIGHTIDREAMED (IRE)**, ch c Footstepsinthesand—Pivotalia (USA)
26 **ROBIN'S CHOICE (IRE)**, b f Bushranger (IRE)—Creekhaven (IRE)
27 **SIRIKOI**, gr f Myboycharlie (IRE)—Misty Eyed (IRE)
28 **WALTZING MATILDA (IRE)**, b f Danehill Dancer (IRE)—Simadartha (USA)

TWO-YEAR-OLDS
29 B f 9/2 Oratorio (IRE)—Arionella (Bluebird (USA)) (20905)
30 B c 26/3 Rock of Gibraltar (IRE)—Asheyana (IRE) (Soviet Star (USA)) (108400)
31 Ch c 20/4 Approve (IRE)—Birthday Present (Cadeaux Genereux) (29422)
32 B c 26/2 Kyllachy—Broadway Dancer (Fantastic Light (USA)) (31428)
33 B f 24/4 Zebedee—Exponent (USA) (Exbourne (USA)) (54200)
34 B f 28/2 Fastnet Rock (AUS)—Fand (USA) (Kingmambo (USA))

MR TOMMY STACK - Continued

35 Ch f 28/3 Raven's Pass (USA)—Fraulein (Acatenango (GER)) (48000)
36 B c 21/3 Duke of Marmalade (IRE)—Golden Mask (USA) (Seeking The Gold (USA))
37 B f 24/4 Montjeu (IRE)—Inkling (USA) (Seeking The Gold (USA))
38 Ch c 5/5 Galileo (IRE)—Kindling (Dr Fong (USA)) (201316)
39 B f 30/3 Myboycharlie (IRE)—Lauren Louise (Tagula (IRE)) (60000)
40 Ch c 12/2 Galileo (IRE)—Maine Lobster (USA) (Woodman (USA)) (216801)
41 B br c 26/2 Thewayyouare (USA)—Mini Dane (IRE) (Danehill (USA))
42 B f 26/3 Arcano (IRE)—Oh Nellie (USA) (Tilt The Stars (CAN)) (40262)
43 Ch f 28/2 Duke of Marmalade (IRE)—Peace Signal (USA) (Time For A Change (USA)) (50000)
44 B c 28/4 Dubawi (IRE)—Pennegale (IRE) (Pennekamp (USA)) (348432)
45 B c 14/5 Holy Roman Emperor (IRE)—Pure Greed (IRE) (Galileo (IRE)) (3483)
46 B c 7/3 Hurricane Run (IRE)—Rahya Cass (IRE) (Rahy (USA))
47 B f 6/3 Kyllachy—Starry Sky (Oasis Dream) (26666)
48 B f 23/1 Starspangledbanner (AUS)—Summer Bliss (Green Desert (USA)) (23228)
49 B c 28/4 Zebedee—Unfortunate (Komaite (USA)) (50000)

Owners: Mr Michael Begley, Mr John Byrne, Mr Arunas Cicenas, Mr John Connaughton, Mr Terry Corden, Mr T. Hyde Jnr, JSC Kasandros Grupe, Mr D. Keoghan, Lady Laidlaw, Mrs J. Magnier, Mr Casey McLiney, J. P McManus, Eimear Mulhearne, Newtownanner Stud, Mr M. J. O'Flynn, Mr Peter Piller, Mary Slack, Mr David Slater, Mr Michael Tabor, The New Pension Fund Syndicate, Ms Kinvara Vaughan.

Jockey (flat): Wayne Lordan. **Jockey (NH):** W. J. Lee.

---

592 | **MR EUGENE STANFORD, Newmarket**
Postal: **Lemberg Stables, Hamilton Road, Newmarket, Suffolk, CB8 7JQ**
Contacts: **PHONE (01638) 660142**

1 CHANDLER BING, 5, b g Librettist (USA)—Gina Tribbiani **C. Woof**
2 GODWIT, 6, b m Noverre (USA)—Hen Harrier **Lemberg Stables**
3 LADY OF YUE, 4, b f Manduro (GER)—Desert Royalty (IRE) **Mrs J. M. Quy**
4 THE HAPPY HAMMER (IRE), 8, b g Acclamation—Emma's Star (ITY) **C. Woof**
5 TWO MINDS (FR), 7, ch g Choisir (AUS)—Dynamic Dream (USA) **Lemberg Stables**
6 UNTIL MIDNIGHT (IRE), 4, b g Moss Vale (IRE)—Emma's Star (ITY) **C. Woof**

---

593 | **MR DANIEL STEELE, Henfield**
Postal: **Blacklands House, Wheatsheaf Road, Wineham, nr Henfield, West Sussex, BN5 9BE**
Contacts: **MOBILE (07500) 556398**
E-MAIL danielsteele14@hotmail.co.uk

1 ACCORDING TO THEM (IRE), 10, ch g Quws—Any Old Music (IRE) **Mr D. R. Steele**
2 HOLD THE BUCKS (USA), 8, b g Hold That Tiger (USA)—Buck's Lady (USA) **Mr D. R. Steele**
3 HUDIBRAS (IRE), 10, b g Bluebird—Mannequin (IRE) **Mr D. R. Steele**
4 KASBAN, 10, b g Kingmambo (USA)—Ebaraya (IRE) **Mr D. R. Steele**
5 NICEBOY (IRE), 10, br g Environment Friend—Take The Catch **Mr D. R. Steele**

---

594 | **MRS JACKIE STEPHEN, Inverurie**
Postal: **Conglass Farmhouse, Inverurie, Aberdeenshire, AB51 5DN**

1 AMILLIONTIMES (IRE), 6, b g Olden Times—Miss Million (IRE) **Mr P. G. Stephen**
2 MO ROUGE (IRE), 6, b g Croco Rouge (IRE)—Just A Mo (IRE) **Mrs J. S. Stephen**
3 RELAND (FR), 9, ch g Shaanmar (IRE)—Falkland III (FR) **Mr P. G. Stephen**

595 MR ROBERT STEPHENS, Caldicot
Postal: **The Knoll, St. Brides Netherwent, Caldicot, Gwent, NP26 3AT**
Contacts: **MOBILE (07717) 477177**

1 4, B g Trade Fair—Amica
2 **CHAPELLE DU ROI (USA)**, 5, ch g Danehill Dancer (IRE)—Capilla Bonita (USA) **Ms M. Ryan**
3 5, Ch g Halling (USA)—Friend For Life **D. J. Deer**
4 **GIORGIO'S DRAGON (IRE)**, 5, b g Le Vie Dei Colori—Broadways Millie (IRE) **Mr R. D. Stephens**
5 **GLAMOROUS SISTER (IRE)**, 4, b f Jeremy (USA)—Glamorous Air (IRE) **Robert & Nina Bailey**
6 **LEADER OF THE LAND (IRE)**, 7, ch g Halling (USA)—Cheerleader **Mark Duthie & Partners**
7 **MODUS**, 4, ch g Motivator—Alessandra **D. J. Deer**
8 **NORTHERN MEETING (IRE)**, 4, b f Dylan Thomas (IRE)—Scottish Stage (IRE) **Ms M. Ryan**
9 **PICODEAN**, 6, b g Tikkanen (USA)—Gipsy Girl **Mr D. O. Stephens**
10 **SANCTIONED**, 5, b g Authorized (IRE)—Kazeem **D. J. Deer**

THREE-YEAR-OLDS

11 **RIVER DREAMER (IRE)**, ch f Intense Focus (USA)—Guard Hill (USA) **Mr R. D. Stephens**

Other Owners: R. M. Bailey, Mrs J. H. Bailey, M. Duthie.

596 MR OLLY STEVENS, Chiddingfold
Postal: **Robins Farm Stables, Fisher Lane, Chiddingfold, Godalming, Surrey, GU8 4TB**
Contacts: **PHONE (01428) 682059 FAX (01428) 682466 MOBILE (07585) 123178**
E-MAIL ostevens@robinsfarmracing.com WEBSITE www.robinsfarmracing.com

1 **BOOKMAKER**, 4, b g Byron—Cankara (IRE) **Giles, McCarthy, Stephens & Newton**
2 **PEARL BELL (IRE)**, 4, b f Camacho—Magnificent Bell (IRE) **Pearl Bloodstock Limited**

THREE-YEAR-OLDS

3 B f Azamour (IRE)—Aladiyna (IRE) **Pearl Bloodstock Limited**
4 B g Kyllachy—Ellens Princess (IRE) **Pearl Bloodstock Limited**
5 **EXTORTIONIST (IRE)**, b c Dandy Man (IRE)—Dream Date (IRE) **Sheikh S. A. K. H. Al Thani**
6 B f Kyllachy—Forest Prize **Mr Oliver Stevens & Chris Fahy**
7 **GAMESOME (FR)**, b c Rock of Gibraltar (IRE)—Hot Coal (USA) **Qatar Racing & Essafinaat**
8 **GOLD RUN**, b c Hurricane Run (IRE)—Trick (IRE) **Mrs J K Powell & Pearl Bloodstock Ltd**
9 **GREEN DOOR (IRE)**, b c Camacho—Inourhearts (IRE) **Mr D Redvers & Mr Michael H Watt**
10 **ILLEGAL ACTION (USA)**, b c Smart Strike (CAN)—Polar Circle (USA) **Clipper Group Holdings Ltd**
11 B f Thousand Words—Islandagore (IRE) **Pearl Bloodstock Limited**
12 B g Medicean—Light Impact (IRE) **Pearl Bloodstock Limited**
13 **LIGHTNING THUNDER**, b f Dutch Art—Sweet Coincidence **Mr Mohd Al Kubasi & Pearl Bloodstock Ltd**
14 B c Teofilo (IRE)—Luminata (IRE) **Qatar Racing Limited**
15 **MICROWAVE (IRE)**, b f Fastnet Rock (AUS)—Chrisalice (GR) **Qatar Racing Limited**
16 **PEARL PRINCESS (FR)**, b f Astronomer Royal (USA)—Tambura (FR) **Pearl Bloodstock Limited**
17 **PRAIRIE ROSE (GER)**, b f Exceed And Excel (AUS)—Prairie Lilli (GER)
18 **ROCK N ROUGE (IRE)**, ch f Rock of Gibraltar (IRE)—Samorra (IRE) **Qatar Racing Limited**
19 **ROLY TRICKS**, b f Pastoral Pursuits—Freya Tricks **Mr I. Wilson**
20 **SPLASHOFCHOCOLATE (IRE)**, b f Intikhab (USA)—Saramacca (IRE) **K Altaji, R Sayegh & Pearl Bloodstock Ltd**
21 **STREETHOWLINGMAMA (USA)**, b br f Street Cry (IRE)—Mama Nadine (USA) **Easton Park Stud**
22 **SWEET LILY PEA (USA)**, ch f Hard Spun (USA)—Tree Pipit (USA) **Lamont Racing**
23 **SWEETNESS LADY**, ch f Sleeping Indian—Eforetta (GER) **Mr M. Al Suwaidi**

TWO-YEAR-OLDS

24 B f 16/4 Montjeu (IRE)—Arbella (Primo Dominie) (300000) **QRL/Sheikh Suhaim Al Thani/M Al Kubaisi**
25 B br f 13/4 Iffraaj—Banyu Dewi (GER) (Poliglote) (170344) **Sheikh Suhaim Al Thani/QRL/M Al Kubaisi**
26 **DESIRE TO WIN (IRE)**, b f 31/3 Lawman (FR)—
          Perfidie (IRE) (Monsun (GER)) (69686) **M Al Kubaisi/Sheikh Suhaim Al Thani/QRL**
27 B f 24/3 Makfi—Elegant Pride (Beat Hollow) (25000) **Isidore Carivalis & Pearl Bloodstock Ltd**
28 B f 1/4 Royal Applause—Fatal Attraction (Oasis Dream) (28571)
29 Ch f 2/4 Linngari (GER)—Fire Sale (ARG) (Not For Sale (ARG)) (17034)
30 **GOTASINGGOTADANCE**, b f 3/2 Royal Applause—Water Gipsy (Piccolo) **Mrs S. R. Wadman**
31 B f 5/3 Duke of Marmalade (IRE)—
          Guantanamera (IRE) (Sadler's Wells (USA)) (185829) **QRL/Sheikh Suhaim Al Thani/M Al Kubaisi**
32 B br f 12/3 Invincible Spirit (IRE)—Malyana (Mtoto) (61942) **M Al Kubaisi/Sheikh Suhaim Al Thani/QRL**

MR OLLY STEVENS - Continued

33 B f 1/3 Fastnet Rock (AUS)—Mark of An Angel (IRE) (Mark of Esteem (IRE)) (52000)
34 B f 3/4 Acclamation—
Miss Tango Hotel (Green Desert (USA)) (42585) **QRL/Sheikh Suhaim Al Thani/M Al Kubaisi**
35 **NEXT GENERATION (IRE),** b f 14/4 Royal Applause—
Gazebo (Cadeaux Genereux) (50328) **QRL/Sheikh Suhaim Al Thani/M Al Kubaisi**
36 **PEACE AND WAR (USA),** b f 21/4 War Front (USA)—
More Oats Please (USA) (Smart Strike (CAN)) (175284) **Sheikh Suhaim Al Thani/QRL/M Al Kubaisi**
37 **QATAR SUCCESS,** b f 29/2 Kyllachy—
Cherokee Stream (IRE) (Indian Ridge) (47619) **Chris Fahy, Jon Collins & R Williams**
38 B c 21/3 Kyllachy—Rustam (Dansili) (23000) **Pearl Bloodstock Limited**
39 B c 26/4 Dark Angel (IRE)—Saffron Crocus (Shareef Dancer (USA)) (27100)
40 **SENSE OF VICTORY (IRE),** b f 9/3 Montjeu (IRE)—
Shaanara (IRE) (Darshaan) (116143) **M Al Kubaisi/Sheikh Suhaim Al Thani/QRL**
41 B br c 25/4 Zebedee—Sharplaw Destiny (IRE) (Petardia) (48000)
42 B f 31/1 Equiano (FR)—Tembladora (IRE) (Docksider (USA)) (22857) **Pearl Bloodstock Limited**
43 B c 10/2 Royal Applause—Thara'a (IRE) (Desert Prince (IRE)) (15000) **Pearl Bloodstock Limited**
44 **THE BIG LAD,** ch c 7/2 Kheleyf (USA)—Cultured Pride (IRE) (King's Best (USA)) **Lookout Partnership**
45 **THE PACO KID,** b c 5/3 Paco Boy (IRE)—
Linea (King's Best (USA)) (30476) **Dobson, Milln, Fahy, Collins & Williams**
46 **TOP OF THE ART (IRE),** gr f 22/2 Dark Angel (IRE)—
Thawrah (IRE) (Green Desert (USA)) (123809) **M Al Kubaisi/Sheikh Suhaim Al Thani/QRL**
47 B c 2/4 Duke of Marmalade (IRE)—Wrong Key (IRE) (Key of Luck (USA)) (65814) **Qatar Racing Limited**

Other Owners: Mr M. A. M. K. Al-Kubaisi, Sheikh M. B. K. Al Maktoum, Mr K. A. A. Altaji, Mr I. Carivalis, D. G. Churston, Mr J. A. Collins, Mr C. J. Fahy, R. E. Greatorex, B. E. Holland, Mrs E. McClymont, Mr D. McClymont, Mr B. P. Newton, Sir Eric Parker, Mrs J. K. Powell, Mr D. Redvers, Mr R. Sayegh, Mr C. A. Stephens, Mr O. Stevens, Mr C. P. Watson, Mr Peter Watson, M. H. Watt, Mr R. E. Williams.

Assistant Trainer: Hetta Stevens

---

597 **MR JOHN STIMPSON, Newcastle-under-Lyme**
Postal: **Trainers Lodge, Butterton Racing Stables, Off Park Road, Butterton, Newcastle-under-Lyme, Staffordshire, ST5 4DZ**
Contacts: **PHONE (01782) 636020 FAX (01782) 633533 MOBILE (07768) 213531**
E-MAIL info@jtsintltd.co.uk

1 **APACHE GLORY (USA),** 6, b br m Cherokee Run (USA)—Jumeirah Glory (USA) **J. Stimpson**
2 **CANDY HOUSE GIRL (USA),** 4, b f Hard Spun (USA)—Princess Mitterand (USA) **J. T. S. (International) Ltd**
3 **DILETTA TOMMASA (IRE),** 4, ch f Dylan Thomas (IRE)—Chronicle **J. Stimpson**
4 **FLUMPS,** 5, ch m Auction House (USA)—Demolition Jo **Marshmallows International S. L.**
5 **HAWAIIAN FREEZE,** 5, b m Avonbridge—Autumn Affair **J. T. S. (International) Ltd**
6 **JAWBREAKERONASTICK,** 5, b g Striking Ambition—Danalia (IRE) **J. T. S. (International) Ltd**
7 **JUMBO PRADO (USA),** 5, gr ro g El Prado (IRE)—Sant Elena **J. Stimpson**
8 **POKER HOSPITAL,** 5, b m Rock of Gibraltar (IRE)—Empress Anna (IRE) **J. Stimpson**
9 **ZED CANDY GIRL,** 4, ch f Sakhee's Secret—Musical Twist (USA) **J. T. S. (International) Ltd**

THREE-YEAR-OLDS

10 **TORNADO POP,** b f Firebreak—Shady Glint (IRE) **J. T. S. (International) Ltd**

---

598 **MISS ANN STOKELL, Southwell**
Postal: **2 Chippendale Road, Lincoln, Lincolnshire, LN6 3PP**
Contacts: **MOBILE (07814) 579982**
E-MAIL ann.stokell@gmail.com

1 **AL KHAN (IRE),** 5, b g Elnadim (USA)—Popolo (IRE) **Pallet And Recycling Sales Ltd**
2 **AMBER MOON,** 9, ch m Singspiel (IRE)—Merewood (USA) **Ms C. Stokell**
3 **AMENABLE (IRE),** 7, b g Bertolini (USA)—Graceful Air (IRE) **Pallet And Recycling Sales Ltd**
4 **ATHENIAN GARDEN (USA),** 7, b m Royal Academy (USA)—Webee (USA) **Pallet And Recycling Sales Ltd**
5 **BERTIE BOB,** 8, b g Bertolini (USA)—Quartermark (IRE) **Mr S. H. Glover**
6 **BRAVO KING (IRE),** 6, b g Sakhee (USA)—Ashbilya (USA) **Pallet And Recycling Sales Ltd**
7 **BROWN PETE (IRE),** 6, b br g Aussie Rules (USA)—Banba (IRE) **Pallet And Recycling Sales Ltd**
8 **CAME BACK (IRE),** 11, ch g Bertolini (USA)—Distant Decree (USA) **Ms C. Stokell**

MISS ANN STOKELL - Continued

9 **CATALYZE**, 6, b g Tumblebrutus (USA)—Clarita Dear (CHI) **Pallet And Recycling Sales Ltd**
10 **DANCING FREDDY (IRE)**, 7, b g Chineur (FR)—Majesty's Dancer (IRE) **Pallet And Recycling Sales Ltd**
11 **DANIEL THOMAS (IRE)**, 12, b g Dansili—Last Look **Pallet And Recycling Sales Ltd**
12 **DECENT FELLA (IRE)**, 8, b g Marju (IRE)—Mac Melody (IRE) **Pallet And Recycling Sales Ltd**
13 **ELUSIVE**, 8, b m Reel Buddy (USA)—Love Is All (IRE) **Ms C. Stokell**
14 **FAIRY WING (IRE)**, 7, b g Hawk Wing (USA)—Mintaka (IRE) **Pallet And Recycling Sales Ltd**
15 **FROGNAL (IRE)**, 8, b g Kheleyf (USA)—Shannon Dore (IRE) **Pallet And Recycling Sales Ltd**
16 **GYPSY JAZZ (IRE)**, 7, b m Antonius Pius (USA)—Dawn's Folly (IRE) **Ms C. Stokell**
17 **HOLD THE STAR**, 8, b m Red Ransom (USA)—Sydney Star **Ms C. Stokell**
18 **ISLAND EXPRESS (IRE)**, 7, b g Chineur (FR)—Cayman Expresso (IRE) **Ms C. Stokell**
19 **KNEESY EARSY NOSEY**, 8, ch m Compton Place—Evie Hone (IRE) **Ms C. Stokell**
20 **MAJURO (IRE)**, 10, b g Danetime (IRE)—First Fling (IRE) **Pallet And Recycling Sales Ltd**
21 **MCCONNELL (USA)**, 9, ch g Petionville (USA)—Warsaw Girl (USA) **Pallet And Recycling Sales Ltd**
22 **MRS MEDLEY**, 8, b m Rambling Bear—Animal Cracker **Ms C. Stokell**
23 **ON THE CUSP (IRE)**, 7, b g Footstepsinthesand—Roman Love (IRE) **Pallet And Recycling Sales Ltd**
24 **PAWAN (IRE)**, 14, ch g Cadeaux Genereux—Born To Glamour **Ms C. Stokell**
25 **PROFILE STAR (IRE)**, 5, b g Kodiac—Fingal Nights (IRE) **Pallet And Recycling Sales Ltd**
26 **PULL THE PIN (IRE)**, 5, b g Kheleyf (USA)—Inscribed (IRE) **Pallet And Recycling Sales Ltd**
27 **ROYAL INTRUDER**, 9, b g Royal Applause—Surprise Visitor (IRE) **Pallet And Recycling Sales Ltd**
28 **SATWA LAIRD**, 8, b g Johannesburg (USA)—Policy Setter (USA) **Ms C. Stokell**
29 **SIX DIAMONDS**, 7, b m Exceed And Excel (AUS)—Daltak **Pallet And Recycling Sales Ltd**
30 **STEEL CITY BOY (IRE)**, 11, b g Bold Fact (USA)—Balgren (IRE) **Ms C. Stokell**
31 **THE WHICH DOCTOR**, 9, b g Medicean—Oomph **Pallet And Recycling Sales Ltd**
32 **UNBREAK MY HEART (IRE)**, 9, ch g Bahamian Bounty—Golden Heart **Pallet And Recycling Sales Ltd**
33 **WAABEL**, 7, b br g Green Desert (USA)—Najah (IRE) **Pallet And Recycling Sales Ltd**
34 **WE HAVE A DREAM**, 9, b br g Oasis Dream—Final Shot **Pallet And Recycling Sales Ltd**

Assistant Trainer: Caron Stokell

599
MR WILLIAM STONE, West Wickham
Postal: The Meadow, Streetly End, West Wickham, Cambridge, Cambridgeshire, CB21 4RP
Contacts: PHONE (01223) 894617 MOBILE (07788) 971094
E-MAIL williamstone1@hotmail.co.uk

1 **CLOCK OPERA (IRE)**, 4, b f Excellent Art—Moving Diamonds **Caroline Scott & Shane Fairweather**
2 **IMJIN RIVER (IRE)**, 7, b g Namid—Lady Nasrana (FR) **Miss C. M. Scott**
3 **LACONICOS (IRE)**, 12, ch g Foxhound (USA)—Thermopylae **Miss C. M. Scott**
4 **OUTRAGEOUS REQUEST**, 8, ch g Rainbow Quest (USA)—La Sorrela (IRE) **Miss C. M. Scott**
5 **THREE CHOIRS (IRE)**, 4, br f Rock of Gibraltar (IRE)—Three Owls (IRE) **The Plenipo Partnership**
6 **WARDEN BOND**, 6, ch g Monsieur Bond (IRE)—Warden Rose **Mr J A Ross & Miss C Scott**

THREE-YEAR-OLDS

7 **TOUCH THE CLOUDS**, b g Sleeping Indian—Aptina (USA) **Miss C. M. Scott**

Other Owners: Mr Shane Fairweather, Plenips Partnership, Mr J. A. Ross, Miss Caroline Scott.

600
MR BRIAN STOREY, Kirklinton
Postal: Low Dubwath, Kirklinton, Carlisle, Cumbria, CA6 6EF
Contacts: PHONE (01228) 675376 FAX (01228) 675977 MOBILE (07950) 925576/ (07912) 898740
E-MAIL jackie@brianstoreyracing.co.uk WEBSITE www.brianstoreyracing.co.uk

1 **BIRNIES BOY**, 10, b g Thowra (FR)—Drumkilly Lilly (IRE) **Mr G. Wilkinson**
2 **COURT RISE (IRE)**, 5, br g Court Cave (IRE)—Raise A Flag (IRE) **Mr G. Wilkinson**
3 **DIAMOND NATIVE (IRE)**, 6, b g Alderbrook—Native Sylph (IRE) **B. Storey**
4 6, B gr m Overbury (IRE)—Ladylliat (FR) **Mr G. Wilkinson**
5 **QUO VISTA (IRE)**, 9, b g Anshan—Miss Cooline (IRE) **F. S. Storey**

Assistant Trainer: Mrs Jackie Storey

Jockey (flat): P. J. McDonald. **Jockey (NH):** Brian Hughes, Richie McGrath. **Amateur:** Miss Jackie Coward.

601 MR WILF STOREY, Consett
Postal: **Grange Farm & Stud, Muggleswick, Consett, Co. Durham, DH8 9DW**
Contacts: **PHONE (01207) 255259 FAX (01207) 255259 MOBILE (07860) 510441**
E-MAIL wlstorey@metronet.co.uk WEBSITE www.wilfstorey.com

1 **CARD HIGH (IRE)**, 4, b g Red Clubs (IRE)—Think (FR) **Gremlin Racing**
2 **DAN'S HEIR**, 12, b g Dansili—Million Heiress **P. Tomlinson**
3 **JAN SMUTS (IRE)**, 6, b g Johannesburg (USA)—Choice House (USA) **H. S. Hutchinson & W. Storey**
4 **MONTHLY MEDAL**, 11, b g Danehill Dancer (IRE)—Sovereign Abbey (IRE) **W. Storey**
5 **NELSON'S BAY**, 5, b g Needwood Blade—In Good Faith (USA) **W. Storey**
6 **TRISKAIDEKAPHOBIA**, 11, b g Bertolini (USA)—Seren Teg **W. Storey**

THREE-YEAR-OLDS
7 **NONAGON**, b g Pastoral Pursuits—Nine Red **W. Storey**

Other Owners: Mark Burton, Mr D. D. Gillies, Alan Henderson, Stephen Howie, Mr H. S. Hutchinson, David McPharlane, Paul McVey, Stewart Meikle, Andrew Morrison, Andrew Rugg, Peter Serginson, Mr W. Storey, Joseph Swanson.

Assistant Trainer: Miss S. Storey

Jockey (flat): Graham Lee. **Amateur:** Miss S. M. Doolan.

602 SIR MICHAEL STOUTE, Newmarket
Postal: **Freemason Lodge, Bury Road, Newmarket, Suffolk, CB8 7BY**
Contacts: **PHONE (01638) 663801 FAX (01638) 667276**

1 **ABSEIL (USA)**, 4, b c First Defence (USA)—Intercontinental
2 **ARAB SPRING (IRE)**, 4, b c Monsun (GER)—Spring Symphony (IRE)
3 **ASTONISHING (IRE)**, 4, b f Galileo (IRE)—Amazing Krisken (USA)
4 **BAIHAS**, 4, b g Nayef (USA)—Allegretto (IRE)
5 **BOLD SNIPER**, 4, b g New Approach (IRE)—Daring Aim
6 **DANK**, 5, b m Dansili—Masskana (IRE)
7 **ECONOMY**, 4, gr g Dalakhani (IRE)—Quiff
8 **ELIK (IRE)**, 4, b f Dalakhani (IRE)—Elopa (GER)
9 **ENOBLED**, 4, b c Dansili—Peeress
10 **ESTIMATE (IRE)**, 5, b m Monsun (GER)—Ebaziya (IRE)
11 **GOSPEL CHOIR**, 5, ch g Galileo (IRE)—Chorist
12 **HILLSTAR**, 4, b c Danehill Dancer (IRE)—Crystal Star
13 **INTEGRAL**, 4, b f Dalakhani (IRE)—Echelon
14 **MANGO DIVA**, 4, b f Holy Roman Emperor (IRE)—Mango Mischief (IRE)
15 **PAVLOSK (USA)**, 4, b f Arch (USA)—Tsar's Pride
16 **RUSSIAN REALM**, 4, b c Dansili—Russian Rhythm (USA)
17 **RYE HOUSE (IRE)**, 5, b g Dansili—Threefold (USA)
18 **STOMACHION (IRE)**, 4, b g Duke of Marmalade (IRE)—Insight (FR)
19 **TELESCOPE (IRE)**, 4, b c Galileo (IRE)—Velouette
20 **VITAL EVIDENCE (USA)**, 4, b g Empire Maker (USA)—Promising Lead
21 **WAILA**, 4, ch f Notnowcato—Crystal Cavern (USA)

THREE-YEAR-OLDS
22 **ADORE**, b f Oasis Dream—Fantasize
23 **ALEX VINO (IRE)**, b c High Chaparral (IRE)—Rare Ransom
24 **ALMUHEET**, b c Dansili—Arwaah (IRE)
25 **ALONG AGAIN (IRE)**, b f Elusive City (USA)—American Adventure (USA)
26 **ALTAAYIL (IRE)**, br c Sea The Stars (IRE)—Alleluia
27 **ARBAAB**, br c Dynaformer (USA)—Kaseema (USA)
28 **ASYAD (IRE)**, b f New Approach (IRE)—Elle Danzig (GER)
29 **BRAGGING (USA)**, b br f Exchange Rate (USA)—Boasting (USA)
30 **CANNOCK CHASE (USA)**, b c Lemon Drop Kid (USA)—Lynnwood Chase (USA)
31 **DALMATIA (IRE)**, gr f Cape Cross (IRE)—Dalataya (IRE)
32 **DIANORA**, b f New Approach (IRE)—Nannina
33 **EXECUTRIX**, b f Oasis Dream—Exclusive
34 **EXTENT**, ch f Exceed And Excel (AUS)—Selkirk Sky
35 **EYE CONTACT**, br c Dansili—Modern Look
36 **FESTIVAL THEATRE (IRE)**, ch c Danehill Dancer (IRE)—Scottish Stage (IRE)

SIR MICHAEL STOUTE - Continued

37 **FREEMASON**, b c Cape Cross (IRE)—Candy Mountain
38 **GHAAWY**, b c Teofilo (IRE)—Asawer (IRE)
39 **GOOD VALUE**, ch g Champs Elysees—Change Course
40 **GOTHIC**, b c Danehill Dancer (IRE)—Riberac
41 **HEHO**, b f Dansili—Nitya (FR)
42 **IDEA (USA)**, gr c Mizzen Mast (USA)—Discuss (USA)
43 **INHERITANCE**, b f Oasis Dream—Peeress
44 **JONE DES CHAMPS (IRE)**, b g Montjeu (IRE)—Desert Bloom (IRE)
45 **KINGS FETE**, b c King's Best (USA)—Village Fete
46 **LONG VIEW (IRE)**, b f Galileo (IRE)—Highland Gift (IRE)
47 **MAIRISE**, b c Authorized (IRE)—Maigold Lass
48 **MARDIE GRAS**, ch f Galileo (IRE)—Midnight Angel (GER)
49 **MATRAVERS**, b c Oasis Dream—Maakrah
50 **MONTONE (IRE)**, ch g Danehill Dancer (IRE)—Leocorno (IRE)
51 **MUNAASER**, b c New Approach (IRE)—Safwa (IRE)
52 **NOBLE DESCENT**, ch f Pivotal—Noble Lady
53 **PAS DE CHEVAL (IRE)**, ch g Pivotal—Olympienne (IRE)
54 **PIVOTAL BRIDE**, ch f Dubawi (IRE)—Brazilian Bride (IRE)
55 **PROVENANCE**, b f Galileo (IRE)—Echelon
56 **PSYCHOMETRY (FR)**, b f Danehill Dancer (IRE)—Seven Magicians (USA)
57 **QAFFAAL (USA)**, b g Street Cry (IRE)—Wasseema (USA)
58 **QUEEN'S PRIZE**, b f Dansili—Daring Aim
59 **RADIATOR**, b f Dubawi (IRE)—Heat Haze
60 **RAMSHACKLE**, b f Dansili—Purissima (USA)
61 **ROCKET SHIP**, b g Sinndar (IRE)—Bimini
62 **ROYAL SEAL**, b f Dansili—Queen's Best
63 **SAHARA DESERT (IRE)**, b g Montjeu (IRE)—Festoso (IRE)
64 **SAINT'S VICTORY**, b f Oasis Dream—Hi Calypso (IRE)
65 **SAVANT (IRE)**, gr c Oasis Dream—Shreyas (IRE)
66 **SEA THE BLOOM**, b f Sea The Stars (IRE)—Red Bloom
67 **SHAMA (IRE)**, b f Danehill Dancer (IRE)—Shamadara (IRE)
68 **SHAMA'S SONG (IRE)**, b f Teofilo (IRE)—Green Dollar (IRE)
69 **SIR ROSCO**, b g Sir Percy—Rosacara
70 **SNOW SKY**, b c Nayef (USA)—Winter Silence
71 **SONG OF NAMIBIA (IRE)**, br c Cape Cross (IRE)—Spring Symphony (IRE)
72 **STAMPEDE (IRE)**, b c High Chaparral (IRE)—Summerhill Parkes
73 **SURCINGLE (USA)**, b f Empire Maker (USA)—Promising Lead
74 **TALL SHIP (IRE)**, b c Sea The Stars (IRE)—Magical Romance (IRE)
75 **TAMASHA**, ch f Sea The Stars (IRE)—Tamarind (IRE)
76 **TERCEL (IRE)**, b c Monsun (GER)—Kitty Hawk
77 **TIME SIGNAL**, b f Champs Elysees—Sandglass
78 **TOP TUG (IRE)**, ch c Halling (USA)—Top Romance (IRE)
79 **UPPER STREET (IRE)**, b f Dansili—Islington (IRE)

TWO-YEAR-OLDS

80 B c 9/3 Dansili—African Rose (Observatory (USA))
81 **AKWAAN**, br c 17/2 Oasis Dream—Tanfidh (Marju (IRE))
82 **ALLA BREVE**, b f 23/4 Dansili—Allegretto (IRE) (Galileo (IRE))
83 B f 25/1 Oasis Dream—Alumni (Selkirk (USA))
84 **AMBASSADRICE**, b f 16/2 Oasis Dream—Agathe Rare (IRE) (Sadler's Wells (USA))
85 **ANDRETTI**, b c 15/4 Oasis Dream—Anna Amalia (IRE) (In The Wings)
86 **ANGEL VISION (IRE)**, b f 7/2 Oasis Dream—Islington (IRE) (Sadler's Wells (USA))
87 **AREIOPAGOS (IRE)**, br c 25/5 Lawman (FR)—Athene (IRE) (Rousillon (USA))
88 B c 13/2 Iffraaj—Assertive Lass (AUS) (Zeditave (AUS))
89 B f 6/5 Galileo (IRE)—Blue Rhapsody (Cape Cross (IRE)) (210000)
90 Ch c 3/3 New Approach (IRE)—Calakanga (Dalakhani (IRE))
91 **CAPE ROSIE**, b f 27/3 Cape Cross (IRE)—Rosika (Sakhee (USA))
92 Ch c 15/2 Intikhab (USA)—Cayman Sunrise (IRE) (Peintre Celebre (USA)) (42585)
93 **CHAPEL CHOIR**, b f 29/3 Dalakhani (IRE)—Chorist (Pivotal)
94 **CHRISTMAS HAMPER (IRE)**, b c 12/2 Dubawi (IRE)—Gift Range (IRE) (Spectrum (IRE))
95 B f 20/1 Dansili—Codename (Sadler's Wells (USA))
96 **CRYSTAL ZVEZDA**, ch f 2/3 Dubawi (IRE)—Crystal Star (Mark of Esteem (IRE))
97 **DANEGA**, b f 3/2 Galileo (IRE)—Danelissima (IRE) (Danehill (USA))
98 **DANNYDAY**, b c 9/4 Dansili—Dayrose (Daylami (IRE))

SIR MICHAEL STOUTE - Continued

99 **DISEGNO (IRE)**, b c 17/2 Fastnet Rock (AUS)—Seven Magicians (USA) (Silver Hawk (USA))
100 **EBEN DUBAI (IRE)**, b c 1/3 New Approach (IRE)—Eldalil (Singspiel (IRE))
101 **ENTITY**, ch f 24/3 Shamardal (USA)—Echelon (Danehill (USA))
102 B c 26/2 Sir Percy—Fairy Flight (USA) (Fusaichi Pegasus (USA)) (50000)
103 B c 13/3 Dubawi (IRE)—Galatee (FR) (Galileo (IRE))
104 **GOCEL**, ch c 7/4 Exceed And Excel (AUS)—Maigold Lass (Mark of Esteem (IRE))
105 **GRAND INQUISITOR**, b c 9/2 Dansili—Dusty Answer (Zafonic (USA)) (250000)
106 **HORSESHOE BAY (IRE)**, b c 25/1 Arch (USA)—Sweepstake (IRE) (Acclamation) (250000)
107 B c 4/2 Galileo (IRE)—Ice Queen (Danehill Dancer (IRE))
108 **INDELIBLE INK (IRE)**, b c 31/1 Invincible Spirit (IRE)—Serres (IRE) (Daylami (IRE)) (100000)
109 **INSHAA**, b c 3/3 Dansili—Hidden Brief (Barathea (IRE)) (210000)
110 B c 31/1 Dansili—Insinuate (USA) (Mr Prospector (USA))
111 **INTIMATION**, b f 25/4 Dubawi (IRE)—Infallible (Pivotal)
112 Ch f 25/3 Dubawi (IRE)—Kaseema (USA) (Storm Cat (USA))
113 Br f 5/2 Dansili—La Divina (IRE) (Sadler's Wells (USA))
114 B c 17/2 Clodovil (IRE)—March Star (IRE) (Mac's Imp (USA)) (70000)
115 B f 28/4 Oasis Dream—Midsummer (Kingmambo (USA))
116 B br c 2/3 Street Cry (IRE)—Miss Lucifer (IRE) (Noverre (USA))
117 **MONASADA**, b f 16/4 Nayef (USA)—Asawer (IRE) (Darshaan)
118 **MUKHAYYAM**, b c 25/2 Dark Angel (IRE)—Caster Sugar (USA) (Cozzene (USA)) (120000)
119 Gr c 10/2 Lope de Vega (IRE)—Mundus Novus (USA) (Unbridled's Song (USA)) (150000)
120 **MUNTADAB (IRE)**, b c 1/3 Invincible Spirit (IRE)—Chibola (ARG) (Roy (USA)) (72000)
121 **MUSHARRIF**, b c 22/3 Arcano (IRE)—Cefira (Distant View (USA)) (300000)
122 **MUSIC AND DANCE**, b f 2/5 Galileo (IRE)—Jamboretta (IRE) (Danehill (USA))
123 **MUSICAL BEAT (IRE)**, b f 22/1 Acclamation—Musical Bar (Barathea (IRE)) (193573)
124 **MUSTAAQEEM (USA)**, b c 14/2 Dynaformer (USA)—Wasseema (Danzig (USA))
125 **MUSTARD**, b c 8/2 Motivator—Flash of Gold (Darshaan)
126 **MUTAMAKKIN (USA)**, b br c 30/4 War Front (USA)—La Laja (USA) (El Prado (IRE)) (511247)
127 **ONDA DISTRICT (IRE)**, b c 9/3 Oasis Dream—Leocorno (IRE) (Pivotal)
128 **PHANTASMAGORIC (IRE)**, b f 4/4 Dansili—Sacred Song (USA) (Diesis)
129 **PLANE SONG (IRE)**, ch c 25/1 Nayef (USA)—Kitty Hawk (Danehill Dancer (IRE))
130 **PLENARY POWER**, b c 4/4 Danehill Dancer (IRE)—Plethora (Sadler's Wells (USA))
131 B c 14/5 New Approach (IRE)—Portodora (USA) (Kingmambo (USA))
132 **PROFUSION**, b c 14/3 Dansili—Red Bloom (Selkirk (USA)) (105000)
133 **QUICK DEFENCE (USA)**, b c 27/2 First Defence (USA)—Quickfire (Dubai Millennium)
134 **RADDEH**, gr f 26/4 Shamardal (USA)—Hathrah (IRE) (Linamix (FR))
135 **RADHAADH (IRE)**, b f 25/2 Nayef (USA)—Safwa (IRE) (Green Desert (USA))
136 **REFERENDUM (IRE)**, b c 21/2 Cape Cross (IRE)—Mary Stuart (IRE) (Nashwan (USA))
137 **RIB RESERVE (IRE)**, b c 5/2 Azamour (IRE)—Fringe Success (IRE) (Selkirk (USA))
138 **RUSSIAN HEROINE**, b f 2/4 Invincible Spirit (IRE)—Russian Rhythm (USA) (Kingmambo (USA))
139 **SANDY CAY (USA)**, gr f 19/4 Mizzen Mast (USA)—Camanoe (USA) (Gone West (USA))
140 **SEA SCENT (USA)**, ch f 4/2 Mizzen Mast (USA)—July Jasmine (USA) (Empire Maker (USA))
141 B c 29/3 Arcano (IRE)—Seraphina (IRE) (Pips Pride) (89042)
142 B c 28/2 Rip Van Winkle (IRE)—Star Ruby (IRE) (Rock of Gibraltar (IRE))
143 B f 24/3 Henrythenavigator (USA)—Sweet Temper (USA) (Stormy Atlantic (USA)) (147115)
144 **TAMARIN**, ch f 24/4 Paco Boy (IRE)—Les Hurlants (IRE) (Barathea (IRE))
145 **TEALIGHT**, b f 18/4 Teofilo (IRE)—Floodlit (Fantastic Light (USA))
146 **TINGLEO**, ch f 15/3 Galileo (IRE)—Tingling (USA) (Storm Cat (USA))
147 B f 10/3 Invincible Spirit (IRE)—Towanda (USA) (Dynaformer (USA)) (90000)
148 **VALLEMI (IRE)**, b f 15/3 Invincible Spirit (IRE)—Vologda (IRE) (Red Ransom (USA))
149 **VIVI'S CHARIS (IRE)**, ch f 14/2 Rock of Gibraltar (IRE)—Amathusia (Selkirk (USA))
150 B c 14/2 Lawman (FR)—Whole Grain (Polish Precedent (USA)) (240000)
151 B c 2/4 Aqlaam—Winner's Call (Indian Ridge) (20000)

Owners: HM The Queen, Mr Khalid Abdullah, Sheikh Joaan Al Thani, Antoniades Family, Ballymacoll Stud, Ballymore Thoroughbred Ltd, Bermuda Thoroughbred Racing Ltd, Mr Nurlan Bizakov, Cheveley Park Stud, Mr Athos Christodoulou, Sir Alex Ferguson, Mr Hamdan Al Maktoum, Mrs Elizabeth Haynes, Highclere Throughbred Racing, Mrs John Magnier, Miss Anne Marshall, Newsells Park Stud, Mr Philip Newton, Mr Robert Ng, Niarchos Family, Sir Evelyn de Rothschild, Lady Rothschild, Mr Derrick Smith, Mr Saeed Suhail, Mr Michael Tabor, Mrs Anita Wigan, Mr James Wigan.

MISS KRISTIN STUBBS, Malton
Postal: **Beverley House, Beverley Road, Norton, Malton, North Yorkshire, YO17 9PJ**
Contacts: **PHONE (01653) 698731 FAX (01653) 698724 MOBILE (07932) 977279 / (07801) 167707**
E-MAIL **l.stubbs@btconnect.com**

1 BOGSNOG (IRE), 4, b g Moss Vale (IRE)—Lovers Kiss **Facts & Figures**
2 BRONZE BEAU, 7, ch g Compton Place—Bella Cantata **D. G. Arundale**
3 GOLD BEAU (FR), 4, b g Gold Away (IRE)—Theorie (FR) **D. G. Arundale**
4 MAGNOLIA RIDGE (IRE), 4, b c Galileo (IRE)—Treasure The Lady (IRE) **Mr D. R. Grieve**
5 MEGAMUNCH (IRE), 4, b g Camacho—Liscoa (IRE) **P & L Partners**
6 MIDNIGHT DREAM (FR), 4, b br g Country Reel (USA)—Tatante **O. J. Williams**
7 REPETITION, 4, b g Royal Applause—Uno **The B.P.J. Partnership**
8 SILVERWARE (USA), 6, b br g Eurosilver (USA)—Playing Footsie (USA) **Paul & Linda Dixon**
9 TARQUIN (IRE), 5, b g Excellent Art—Umlani (IRE) **D. G. Arundale**

THREE-YEAR-OLDS
10 DANFAZI (IRE), ch g Dandy Man (IRE)—Distant Shore (IRE) **Facts & Figures**
11 IDAMANTE, b g Amadeus Wolf—Gower Valentine **O. J. Williams**
12 RIO YUMA (ITY), b f Gold Sphinx (USA)—Selsey **Mr D. R. Grieve**
13 TOO ELUSIVE, b g Major Cadeaux—Elusive Kitty (USA) **Paul & Linda Dixon**

TWO-YEAR-OLDS
14 BAHANGO (IRE), b c 14/4 Bahamian Bounty—
Last Tango (IRE) (Lion Cavern (USA)) (17034) **Chester Racing Club Ltd**
15 COMPETANT, b c 15/2 Compton Place—Pantita (Polish Precedent (USA)) (45000) **Chester Racing Club Ltd**
16 DANCRUISE (IRE), b c 19/4 Dandy Man (IRE)—Crua Mna (Bahamian Bounty) (9523) **Chester Racing Club Ltd**
17 MON GRIS (IRE), gr c 16/3 Falco (USA)—Turpitude (Caerleon (USA)) (23228) **P & L Partners**
18 MULTIPLIER, b c 27/3 Multiplex—Best Bidder (Mr Greeley (USA)) (4761) **Chester Racing Club Ltd**
19 PAFIYA (IRE), b c 23/4 Paco Boy (IRE)—Tafiya (Bahri (USA)) (30000) **Chester Racing Club Ltd**
20 SOIE D'LEAU, b g 4/3 Monsieur Bond (IRE)—Silky Silence (High Chaparral (IRE)) **F.A.T.J Partnership**

Other Owners: P. Dixon, Mrs L. J. Dixon, J. P. Hames, Mr F. Harrison, Mr A. T. Larkin, Mr N. P. Lyons, Mr B. Midgley, G. Pickering, Mrs V. J. Pittman, Mr T S Pople, P. A. Saxton, P. G. Shorrock, Mr R. W. Stubbs, Mr J. Wright.

Jockey (flat): Tom Eaves. **Apprentice:** Georgina Baxter, Jacob Butterfield.

MR ROB SUMMERS, Solihull
Postal: **Summerhill Cottage, Danzey Green, Tanworth-in-Arden, Solihull**
Contacts: **PHONE (01564) 742667 MOBILE (07775) 898327**

1 MASSACHUSETTS, 7, ch g Singspiel (IRE)—Royal Passion **Miss G. L. Henderson**
2 PHOTOGENIQUE (FR), 11, b m Cyborg (FR)—Colombia (FR) **Solihull Racing Club**
3 QUINOLA DES OBEAUX (FR), 10, b g Useful (FR)—Zaouia (FR) **O. P. J. Meli**
4 RED ROSSO, 9, ch g Executive Perk—Secret Whisper **Solihull Racing Club**
5 RED WHISPER, 10, ch g Midnight Legend—Secret Whisper **Solihull Racing Club**
6 ROSE RED, 7, ch m Weld—Secret Whisper **Solihull Racing Club**

Other Owners: Mrs G. M. Summers, Mr S. J. Wood. **Assistant Trainer:** Mrs G. M. Summers

MR JOHN A. SUPPLE, Abbeyfeale
Postal: **Feale View Stud, Coolaneelig, Abbeyfeale P.O., Co. Limerick, Ireland**
Contacts: **PHONE (00353) 68 45890 FAX (00353) 68 45890 MOBILE (00353) 86 7390841**
E-MAIL **Lorna.Preston@ymail.com**

1 BLACKWELL SYNERGY (FR), 8, b g Antarctique (IRE)—Pyu (GER) **Mr J. J. Byrne**
2 4, B g Catcher In The Rye (IRE)—Dangerous Business (IRE) **Mr W. J. Byrne**
3 4, B g Milan—Kashmir Lady (FR) **Mr J. J. Byrne**
4 KNOCKANAR (IRE), 8, b g Kalanisi (IRE)—Fairy Dawn (IRE) **Mr J. J. Byrne**
5 ROADTOABBEYFEALE (IRE), 9, b g Milan—Lady Bramble (IRE) **Mr J. J. Byrne**
6 THELIFEOF (IRE), 8, b g Brian Boru—Dream Adventure (IRE) **Miss Julianna Byrne**

Other Owners: Mr Nolan Byrne, Miss Lorna Preston.

Assistant Trainer: Lorna Preston **Jockey (NH):** E. J. O'Connell.

606 MR C. F. SWAN, Cloughjordan
Postal: **Modreeny Stables, Cloughjordan, Co. Tipperary, Ireland**
Contacts: **PHONE (00353) 5054 2128 FAX (00353) 505 42128 MOBILE (00353) 8625 73194**
E-MAIL cswan@iol.ie WEBSITE www.charlieswanracing.com

1 AGENT JAMES (IRE), 7, b g Oscar (IRE)—Savanagh (IRE) **J. Reddington**
2 ALCHIMIX (FR), 4, b g Al Namix (FR)—Julie Noire (FR)
3 BALLAGH (IRE), 5, b g Shantou (USA)—Go Along (IRE) **Mrs T. P. Hyde**
4 BOB THE GOON (IRE), 6, b g Golan (IRE)—Caslain Og (IRE) **Noel O'Flaherty**
5 BOUND TO FLY (IRE), 6, b g Flemensfirth (USA)—Wayward Winnie (IRE) **J. P. McManus**
6 COURAGE (IRE), 5, b g Invincible Spirit (IRE)—Mamonta **Philip McGee Partnership**
7 DRUMLEE (IRE), 6, b g Helissio (FR)—Wigwambrave (IRE) **J. P. McManus**
8 ERIC THE GREY (IRE), 4, gr g Verglas (IRE)—Queens Wharf (IRE) **Michael D Mee**
9 EVER SO MUCH (IRE), 5, b g Westerner—Beautiful World (IRE) **J. P. McManus**
10 FLAMMETTA, 4, b f Milan—Carry Me (IRE) **The Lucky Bags Syndicate**
11 FOLK VILLAGE, 4, b g Gold Well—Fleur de Tal **Mrs T. E. Hyde**
12 FULTON (IRE), 5, b g Flemensfirth (USA)—Tonaphuca Girl (IRE) **R. A. Bartlett**
13 GETOUTWHENYOUCAN, 5, br g Beneficial—Ballycleary (IRE) **J. P. McManus**
14 GRANDMA DOTTY (IRE), 5, b m Hurricane Run (IRE)—High Reef (FR) **Mrs M.R. Sheahan**
15 HARETH (IRE), 4, b g Jeremy (USA)—Princess Leona (IRE) **Philip McGee Partnership**
16 4, B g Kayf Tara—Liss A Chroi (IRE) **Mrs T. E. Hyde**
17 LO SIENTO (IRE), 6, b g Oscar (IRE)—Notsophar (IRE) **Philip Reynolds**
18 MAKE A TRACK (IRE), 8, ch g Hernando (FR)—Tracker **Gigginstown House Stud**
19 4, Gr g Scorpion (IRE)—Mondeo Rose (IRE) **Mrs T. E. Hyde**
20 MR RAJ (IRE), 6, b g Oscar (IRE)—Chapel Wood Lady (IRE) **John Reddington**
21 RASTELLI (IRE), 5, b g Milan—Slush Fund (IRE) **Mrs T. E. Hyde**
22 SHAUNAS DREAM (IRE), 6, b m Milan—Cloone Leader (IRE) **Kathleen Gillane**
23 4, B g Gold Well—Tatiana (IRE) **J. Carthy**
24 THE DUTCHMAN (IRE), 4, b g King's Theatre (IRE)—Shivertimember (IRE) **John Roche**
25 THE GAME CHANGER (IRE), 5, b g Arcadio (GER)—Gilt Ridden (IRE) **Gigginstown House Stud**
26 THREE MUSKETEERS (IRE), 4, b g Flemensfirth (USA)—Friendly Craic (IRE) **Mrs T. P. Hyde**
27 THREE WISE MEN (IRE), 4, b g Presenting—Bilboa (FR) **Mrs P. Shanahan**
28 YOUR DEAL (IRE), 4, b g Flemensfirth (USA)—Quadrennial (IRE) **Mrs P. Shanahan**

THREE-YEAR-OLDS

29 I'VEGOTAFEELING, b c Rock of Gibraltar (IRE)—Italian Connection **Mrs P. Shanahan**
30 LADY CLITICO (IRE), b f Bushranger (IRE)—Villa Nova (IRE) **Philip Reynolds**

Jockey (flat): Fran Berry, William Lee. **Jockey (NH):** David Casey. **Apprentice:** Conor Banaghan.

607 MR ALAN SWINBANK, Richmond
Postal: **Western House Stables, East Road, Melsonby, Richmond, North Yorkshire, DL10 5NF**
Contacts: **PHONE (01325) 339964 FAX (01325) 377113 MOBILE (07860) 368365 / (07711) 488341**
E-MAIL info@alanswinbank.com WEBSITE www.alanswinbank.com

1 ARAMIST (IRE), 4, gr g Aussie Rules (USA)—Mistic Sun **Mrs Pam Ellis**
2 ARYIZAD (IRE), 4, b m Hurricane Run (IRE)—Daziyra (IRE) **Mrs J. Porter**
3 BIG WATER (IRE), 6, ch g Saffron Walden (FR)—Magic Feeling (IRE) **T. B. Tarn**
4 BOBS LORD TARA, 4, b g Kayf Tara—Bob Back's Lady (IRE) **Mr J. R. Wills**
5 CHEVALGRIS, 4, gr g Verglas—Danzelline **Ms A. J. Findlay**
6 DARK RULER (IRE), 5, b g Dark Angel (IRE)—Gino Lady (IRE) **Mr K. Walters**
7 DUBAI SONNET, 5, b g Dubai Destination—Twilight Sonnet **Solway Stayers**
8 EBONY EXPRESS, 5, bl g Superior Premium—Coffee Ice **Mrs T. Blackett**
9 ENTIHAA, 6, b g Tiger Hill (GER)—Magic Tree (UAE) **Elsa Crankshaw & G. Allan**
10 EUTROPIUS (IRE), 5, b g Ad Valorem—Peps (IRE) **Ontoawinner 2**
11 FAIR TRADE, 7, ch g Trade Fair—Ballet **Raymond Tooth**
12 FLY HOME HARRY, 5, b g Sir Harry Lewis (USA)—Fly Home **Panther Racing Limited**
13 FLY SOLO, 5, b g Soviet Star (USA)—Vino **Exors of the Late Mr G. Reed**
14 FRIDAYNIGHT GIRL (IRE), 5, b m Red Ransom (USA)—Miss Amanpuri **Mr & Mrs M. Miller**
15 GEORGIAN FIREBIRD, 4, b f Firebreak—Skovshoved **Mrs E. A. Wilson**
16 GIOVANNI JACK, 4, ch g Three Valleys (USA)—Marching West (USA) **Mr C. G. Harrison**
17 GOGEO (IRE), 7, b g Val Royal (FR)—Steal 'em **Mrs J. Porter**
18 HAIL BOLD CHIEF (USA), 7, b g Dynaformer (USA)—Yanaseeni (USA) **Mr D. Connolly**
19 HALKIRK (IRE), 5, b g Nayef (USA)—Sil Sila (IRE) **Miss S. R. Haynes**

MR ALAN SWINBANK - Continued

20 **I'M SUPER TOO (IRE)**, 7, b g Fasliyev (USA)—Congress (IRE) **D. C. Young**
21 4, B f Millkom—Island Path (IRE) **Mr J Nelson**
22 **LADY KASHAAN (IRE)**, 5, b m Manduro (GER)—Lady's Secret (IRE) **Mr G. Brogan**
23 **LEGAL WAVES (IRE)**, 4, b g Lawman (FR)—Surf The Web (IRE) **Mr B Sangster**
24 **LOTHAIR (IRE)**, 5, b g Holy Roman Emperor (IRE)—Crafty Example (USA) **Mrs J. Porter**
25 **MITCHELL'S WAY**, 7, ch g Needwood Blade—Ghana (GER) **Ontoawinner 2**
26 **MOLLY CAT**, 4, ch f Dylan Thomas (IRE)—Pentatonic **Elm Row Racing Syndicate**
27 **NABURN**, 6, b g Cape Cross (IRE)—Allespagne (USA) **Elsa Crankshaw & G. Allan**
28 **NORTHSIDE PRINCE (IRE)**, 8, b g Desert Prince (IRE)—Spartan Girl (IRE) **Mrs J. M. Penney**
29 **ONE IN A ROW (IRE)**, 7, ch g Saffron Walden (FR)—Rostarr (IRE) **Elm Row Racing Syndicate**
30 **PAINTED TAIL (IRE)**, 7, b m Mark of Esteem (IRE)—Bronwen (IRE) **Ms A. L. I. Winbergh**
31 **PERSIAN PERIL**, 10, br g Erhaab (USA)—Brush Away **Mrs J. Porter**
32 **PHOENIX RETURNS (IRE)**, 6, br g Phoenix Reach (IRE)—Oscar's Lady (IRE) **Mrs J. Porter**
33 **REGAL SWAIN (IRE)**, 6, b g Ivan Denisovich (IRE)—Targhyb (IRE) **Mr A. J. Sparks**
34 **SAMOSET**, 4, b g Sir Percy—Great Quest (IRE) **Mr Arnold Headdock & Mrs Kath Headdock**
35 **SHOWTIME STAR**, 4, b g Byron—Piddies Pride (IRE) **Countrywide Classics Ltd**
36 **TINY DANCER (IRE)**, 6, b g Darsi (FR)—Taipans Girl (IRE) **Ms A. J. Findlay**

THREE-YEAR-OLDS

37 **CRAKEHALL LAD (IRE)**, ch c Manduro (GER)—My Uptown Girl **Mr G. Brogan**
38 **DEEP RESOLVE (IRE)**, b g Intense Focus (USA)—I'll Be Waiting **Panther Racing Limited**
39 B f Duke of Marmalade (IRE)—Dreams Come True (FR) **Mr D. C. Young**
40 B c Papal Bull—Enchanted Wood (IRE) **Mr I Twedall**
41 **IN FOCUS (IRE)**, ch c Intense Focus (USA)—Reine de Neige **Mr G. H. Bell**
42 **LIBRAN (IRE)**, b g Lawman (FR)—True Crystal (IRE) **Mrs J. Porter**
43 Br f Strategic Prince—Love Thirty **Mr D. C. Young**
44 Gr g Verglas (IRE)—Malaisienne (FR) **Mr D. C. Young**
45 B c Tiger Hill (IRE)—Mamoura (IRE) **Miss S. Haynes**
46 **MINIONETTE (IRE)**, b f Manduro (GER)—La Vita E Bella (IRE) **Elsa Crankshaw & G. Allan**
47 **NATIVE FALLS (IRE)**, ch g Elnadim (USA)—Sagrada (GER) **Ms A. J. Findlay**
48 Ch g Bahamian Bounty—Phoebe Woodstock (IRE) **Mr G McCann**
49 **PRIVATE DANCER**, b g Halling (USA)—Anamilina (IRE) **Ms A. J. Findlay**
50 **RALPHY LAD (IRE)**, b g Iffraaj—Hawattef (IRE) **The Trio Syndicate**
51 **SILVER CRAFTSMAN (IRE)**, gr g Mastercraftsman (IRE)—Shining Hour (USA) **Mrs I. Gibson**
52 B f Byron—Skiddaw Wolf **J. R. Wills**
53 **SMART ALEC (IRE)**, br g Dandy Man (IRE)—Art Critic (USA) **Ms A. J. Findlay**
54 **STANARLEY PIC**, b g Piccolo—Harlestone Lady **The Twopin Partnership**
55 Ch f Mr Greeley (USA)—Tink So (USA) **Mr I Twedall**

TWO-YEAR-OLDS

56 B c 10/3 Lope de Vega (IRE)—Ballet Dancer (IRE) (Refuse To Bend (IRE)) (23228) **Mr G McCann**
57 B c 2/2 Beat Hollow—Dombeya (Danehill (USA)) (19357) **Mr G McCann**
58 Br g 22/3 Pastoral Pursuits—Goldeva (Makbul) (20905) **Mr B Valentine**
59 B g 6/4 Le Havre (IRE)—Mambo Mistress (USA) (Kingmambo (USA)) (11614) **Mr G McCann**
60 B c 25/3 Bushranger (IRE)—Prealpina (IRE) (Indian Ridge) (10000) **Mr B Valentine**
61 B c 29/5 Equiano (FR)—Sharplaw Venture (Polar Falcon (USA)) (18000) **Mr B Valentine**

Other Owners: G. Allan, G. Allen, Ann Bell, P. Blackett, Mr Andy Bonarius, Miss E. Crankshaw, Mr Mac Creedon, R. Ellis, Fantails Restaurant, Mrs T. Harrison, Mr Arnold Headdock, Mrs Kath Headdock, Mr K. Hogg, Mrs D. Jeromson, J. Jeromson, Mr G. McCann, Mr M. Miller, Mrs C. Miller, Mr N. J. O'Brien, Dr Roy Palmer, W. Perrett, J. Perrett, Mrs B. V. Sangster, Ben Sangster, Miss M. Swinbank, Mrs T. Tarn, Mr I. S. Tweddall.

Assistant Trainers: Mr W.W. Haigh & Miss Sally Haynes

Jockey (flat): Ben Curtis, Robert Winston. **Jockey (NH):** Paddy Brennan. **Conditional:** Jake Greenall.
Amateur: Mr O. R. J. Sangster.

---

608 **MR TOM SYMONDS, Hentland**
Postal: **Dason Court Cottage, Hentland, Ross-on-Wye, Herefordshire, HR9 6LW**
Contacts: **PHONE (01989) 730869 MOBILE (07823) 324649**
E-MAIL dasoncourt@gmail.com WEBSITE www.thomassymonds.co.uk

1 **ABRUZZI**, 6, b g Milan—Shannon Native (IRE) **G & M Roberts Churchward Frost Green W-Williams**
2 **ALBERTO'S DREAM**, 5, b g Fantastic Spain (USA)—Molly's Folly **Wallys Dream Syndicate**

MR TOM SYMONDS - Continued

3 **AMBER FLUSH**, 5, b m Sir Harry Lewis (USA)—Sari Rose (FR) **The Mumbo Jumbos**
4 **ARDEN DENIS (IRE)**, 5, ch g Generous (IRE)—Christian Lady (IRE) **T. C. and A. Winter & Partners**
5 **ASHDOWN LAD**, 5, ch g Sir Percy—Antibes (IRE) **Foster, Coe, Stagg, Rowlinson**
6 **AVOCA PROMISE (IRE)**, 9, b g Oscar (IRE)—High Ace (IRE) **Bailey-Carvill Equine**
7 **BALLYCASSEL (IRE)**, 9, ch g Presenting—Sara's Gold (IRE) **Celia & Michael Baker**
8 **BAR BOY (IRE)**, 5, gr g Acambaro (GER)—Carminda Thyne (IRE) **Sir Peter & Lady Gibbings**
9 **BRIERY BLOSSOM**, 5, b m Norse Dancer (IRE)—
Hong Kong Classic **Mrs H Plumbly J Trafford K Deane S Holme**
10 **BRIERY BUBBLES**, 6, b m Grape Tree Road—Hong Kong Classic
11 **CARHUE PRINCESS (IRE)**, 8, b m Desert Prince (IRE)—Carhue Journey (IRE) **The Ever Hopeful Partnership**
12 **DARNBOROUGH (IRE)**, 8, b g Darnay—Princesse Sharpo (USA) **Mr & Mrs John Wall**
13 **DIXIE BULL (IRE)**, 9, br g Milan—Calora (USA) **Bailey-Carvill Equine**
14 **DUC DE REGNIERE (FR)**, 12, b g Rajpoute (FR)—Gladys de Richerie (FR) **Mr T. R. Symonds**
15 **DUNMALLET BELLE**, 5, b m Kayf Tara—Magic Mistress **Brian J Griffiths & John Nicholson**
16 **EATON LOUIE**, 5, b m Rocamadour—La Feuillarde (FR) **Mr K. J. Price**
17 **EATON ROCK (IRE)**, 5, b g Rocamadour—Duchess of Kinsale (IRE) **Mr K. J. Price**
18 **FOXCUB (IRE)**, 6, b g Bahri (USA)—Foxglove Leaf (IRE) **Celia & Michael Baker**
19 **GRILYNE (FR)**, 5, b g Kapgarde (FR)—Marie de Valois (FR) **Bradley Partnership**
20 **GWENDOLINER (IRE)**, 5, b m Flemensfirth (USA)—Clandestine **Brian,Gwen,Terri & Kelly Griffiths**
21 **HIDDEN LINK**, 4, b g Rail Link—Gloved Hand **Mr T. R. Symonds**
22 4, B f Midnight Legend—Holy Smoke
23 **HOME FOR TEA**, 5, b g Westerner—Wolnai **Mr Ian Low & Mr Peter Crawford**
24 **KAKI DE LA PREE (FR)**, 7, b g Kapgarde (FR)—Kica (FR) **Sir Peter & Lady Gibbings**
25 **KATARRHINI**, 5, b m Kayf Tara—Dedrunknmunky (IRE)
26 **KINGS APOLLO**, 5, b g King's Theatre (IRE)—
Temple Dancer **G & M Roberts Churchward Frost Green W-Williams**
27 **MARICO (FR)**, 6, b br g Lavirco (GER)—Mary Bay (FR) **Mr T. R. Symonds**
28 **MIDNIGHT BELLE**, 7, b m Midnight Legend—Cherry Alley (IRE) **Mrs P. E. Holtorp**
29 **MIDNIGHT REQUEST**, 5, b g Midnight Legend—Friendly Request **W E Donohue J M Donohue**
30 **OSCAR'S PET (IRE)**, 6, b m Oscar (IRE)—Kilcoleman Lady (IRE) **J. Palmer-Brown**
31 **SCHOLASTICA**, 7, b m Old Vic—La Perrotine (FR) **Dominic Burke & Jonathan Palmer-Brown**
32 **STRAITS OF MESSINA (IRE)**, 5, b g Mountain High (IRE)—Scylla **Lost In Space**
33 **SUMMER SOUNDS (IRE)**, 5, b br g Definite Article—Marble Sound (IRE) **Sir Peter & Lady Gibbings**
34 **TED DOLLY (IRE)**, 10, b br g Bob's Return (IRE)—Little Pearl (IRE) **Galway Bay Partnership**
35 **THEATREBAR**, 6, b g King's Theatre (IRE)—Ardenbar **Exors of the Late Mr T. J. Wyatt**
36 **TROJAN SUN**, 8, b br g Kayf Tara—Sun Dante (IRE) **I. A. Low**
37 **TWEEDLEDRUM**, 7, b m Beat Hollow—Tweed Mill **Wainwright,Hill,Atkin,Cheshire&Rowlinson**

Other Owners: Mr A. Abbott, Mr P. J. Andrews, R. F. Bailey, Mrs C. A. M. Baker, Mr M. J. Baker, Mrs P. J. Buckler, D. J. Burke, R. K. Carvill, Mr P. G. Crawford, Mrs K. M. Deane, W. E. Donohue, Mrs J. M. Donohue, Mr B. Foster, Sir Peter Gibbings, The Hon Lady Gibbings, Mr L. Gore, F. M. Green, B. J. Griffiths, Mrs G. E. A. Griffiths, Mrs S. E. Holme, Miss N. Martin, J. G. G. Mason, J. M. Nicholson, Mrs H. Plumbly, Mr R. T. R. Price, G. A. Roberts, Mrs J. Rowlinson, Mr J. Simpson, Mrs J. E. Symonds, Mrs E. J. Trafford, Mr M. J. Wainwright, Mr J. H. Wall, Mrs S. M. Wall, Mr T. W. Winter, Mr A. L. Winter, Mr C. W. Winter.

Jockey (NH): Felix De Giles. **Conditional:** Ben Poste. **Amateur:** Mr James Nixon.

609

MR JAMES TATE, Newmarket
Postal: **Jamesfield Place, Hamilton Road, Newmarket, Suffolk, CB8 7JQ**
Contacts: PHONE **(01638) 669861** FAX **(01638) 676634** MOBILE **(07703) 601283**
E-MAIL **james@jamestateracing.com** WEBSITE **www.jamestateracing.com**

1 **BIN SINGSPIEL**, 4, br g Singspiel (IRE)—Mexican Hawk (USA) **Saif Ali**
2 **GENIUS BOY**, 4, ch c New Approach (IRE)—One So Marvellous **Sheikh Juma Dalmook Al Maktoum**
3 **IPTISAM**, 5, ch g Rahy (USA)—Grain of Truth **Saeed Manana**
4 **MIRSAALE**, 4, ch c Sir Percy—String Quartet (IRE) **Saif Ali**
5 **REGAL HAWK**, 4, br f Singspiel (IRE)—Elegant Hawk **Saeed Manana**
6 **RUWAIYAN (USA)**, 5, b br h Cape Cross (IRE)—Maskunah (IRE) **Saeed Manana**

THREE-YEAR-OLDS

7 **APPROACH THE WEST (IRE)**, b f New Approach (IRE)—Damsel **Saeed Manana**
8 Ch f Art Connoisseur (IRE)—Aquatint **Saeed Manana**
9 **ARAMADYH**, gr f Authorized (IRE)—Swift Dispersal **Saif Ali**
10 **BEREKA**, b f Firebreak—Alexander Ballet **Saif Ali**

MR JAMES TATE - Continued

11 **BINT MALYANA (IRE)**, b f Bahamian Bounty—Malyana **Saif Ali**
12 **BLHADAWA (IRE)**, b f Iffraaj—Trois Heures Apres **Sheikh Juma Dalmook Al Maktoum**
13 **BLOCKADE (IRE)**, br f Kheleyf (USA)—Barracade (IRE) **Saeed Manana**
14 B f Royal Applause—Choosey Girl (IRE) **Saeed Manana**
15 B f Street Cry (IRE)—Cloud Castle **Saeed Manana**
16 **DREESE (IRE)**, b c Dandy Man (IRE)—Lucky Flirt (USA) **Saeed Manana**
17 **DUBAWI COAST**, b f Dubawi (IRE)—Portmeirion **Saif Ali**
18 **DUBAWI LIGHT**, b c Dubawi (IRE)—Shesadelight **Saeed Manana**
19 **DUTCH RIFLE**, b f Dutch Art—Vodka Shot (USA) **Saeed Manana**
20 B f Dutch Art—Ellway Queen (USA) **Saif Ali**
21 **EXCEL'S BEAUTY**, b f Exceed And Excel (AUS)—Continua (USA) **Sheikh Juma Dalmook Al Maktoum**
22 **FREE CODE (IRE)**, b g Kodiac—Gerobies Girl (USA) **Sheikh Rashid Dalmook Al Maktoum**
23 **HADYA (IRE)**, b f Teofilo (IRE)—Lafleur (IRE) **Sheikh Rashid Dalmook Al Maktoum**
24 **HALLOUELLA**, ch f Halling (USA)—Louella (USA) **Saif Ali**
25 **ICE FALCON (IRE)**, gr f Verglas (IRE)—Katimont (IRE) **Saeed Manana**
26 **INVINCIBLE STRIKE (IRE)**, gr c Invincible Spirit (IRE)—Lazaretta (IRE) **Sheikh Juma Dalmook Al Maktoum**
27 **L'AVENUE (IRE)**, b f Champs Elysees—Mrs Seek **Saeed Manana**
28 **LAMAR (IRE)**, b f Cape Cross (IRE)—Deveron (IRE) **Saif Ali**
29 Ch f Shamardal (USA)—Miss Hepburn (USA) **Saeed Manana**
30 **MOONLIT SKY**, b c Myboycharlie (IRE)—Calico Moon (USA) **Saeed Manana**
31 **MUSTAMIR (IRE)**, b c Medicean—Perfect Plum (IRE) **Sheikh Rashid Dalmook Al Maktoum**
32 **NEW TARABELA**, ch c New Approach (IRE)—Tarabela (CHI) **Saif Ali**
33 **OCEAN STORM (IRE)**, b c Royal Applause—Cedar Sea (IRE) **Saeed Manana**
34 **REGAL FALCON**, b f Royal Applause—Clinet (IRE) **Saeed Manana**
35 **RUWASI**, b c Authorized (IRE)—Circle of Love **Saeed Manana**
36 **SBRAASE**, ch c Sir Percy—Hermanita **Saeed Manana**
37 **SECRET SUSPECT**, b f Invincible Spirit (IRE)—Madura (GER) **Saeed Manana**
38 **SKY RANGER (IRE)**, b f Bushranger (IRE)—Cassava (IRE) **Saeed Manana**
39 **SORRY SAEED**, b f Raven's Pass (USA)—Clear Impression (IRE) **Saif Ali**
40 **TOBOUGG HAPPY**, b f Tobougg (IRE)—Happy Lady (FR) **Saif Ali**
41 **TOP DOLLAR**, ch f Elusive Quality (USA)—Elrehaan **Saeed Manana**
42 **UMNEYATI**, b f Iffraaj—Honky Tonk Sally **Sheikh Rashid Dalmook Al Maktoum**
43 **ZAMRA (IRE)**, b f Azamour (IRE)—Deauville Vision (IRE) **Saif Ali**

TWO-YEAR-OLDS

44 B f 28/2 Vale of York (IRE)—Alexander Ridge (IRE) (Indian Ridge) (25000) **Saif Ali**
45 B c 31/1 Archipenko (USA)—Alta Moda (Sadler's Wells (USA)) (70000) **Sheikh Juma Dalmook Al Maktoum**
46 **AMBIGUOUS**, b f 3/5 Kheleyf (USA)—
             Easy To Imagine (USA) (Cozzene (USA)) (64761) **Sheikh Rashid Dalmook Al Maktoum**
47 Ch f 9/3 Iffraaj—Bratislava (Dr Fong (USA)) (68137) **Saeed Manana**
48 B f 1/2 Azamour (IRE)—Causeway Queen (IRE) (Giant's Causeway (USA)) (40262) **Saif Ali**
49 **CEASELESS (IRE)**, b f 14/4 Iffraaj—
             Sheer Bliss (IRE) (Sadler's Wells (USA)) (65814) **Sheikh Rashid Dalmook Al Maktoum**
50 B br f 16/2 Arch (USA)—Classic West (USA) (Gone West (USA)) (116856) **Sheikh Juma Dalmook Al Maktoum**
51 **CLODOVIL DOLL (IRE)**, gr f 17/3 Clodovil (IRE)—
             Titus Wood (IRE) (Titus Livius (FR)) (35000) **Sheikh Juma Dalmook Al Maktoum**
52 **DARKENING NIGHT**, b c 28/4 Cape Cross (IRE)—
             Garanciere (FR) (Anabaa (USA)) (70000) **Sheikh Juma Dalmook Al Maktoum**
53 B c 7/5 Dubawi (IRE)—Darrfonah (IRE) (Singspiel (IRE)) **Saeed Manana**
54 B f 14/1 Bahamian Bounty—Dream In Waiting (Oasis Dream) (26000) **Saif Ali**
55 Ch f 15/4 Raven's Pass (USA)—Edetana (IRE) (Diesis) (12000) **Saeed Manana**
56 **FREE ENTRY (IRE)**, b f 31/3 Approve (IRE)—
             Dear Catch (IRE) (Bluebird (USA)) (55000) **Sheikh Rashid Dalmook Al Maktoum**
57 Br f 17/3 Sea The Stars (IRE)—Independant (Medicean) (58071) **Saeed Manana**
58 B f 18/2 Bahamian Bounty—Intermission (IRE) (Royal Applause) (7619) **Saeed Manana**
59 B f 27/3 King's Best (USA)—Jane Austen (IRE) (Galileo (IRE)) (10000) **Saeed Manana**
60 B f 17/4 Dansili—Jira (Medicean) **Saeed Manana**
61 **KODIAC LADY (IRE)**, b f 5/3 Kodiac—
             Weeping Willow (IRE) (Kheleyf (USA)) (26666) **Sheikh Rashid Dalmook Al Maktoum**
62 Ch c 23/2 Aqlaam—Kunda (IRE) (Intikhab (USA)) (26000) **Saeed Manana**
63 B f 10/4 Cape Cross (IRE)—Lil's Jessy (IRE) (Kris) (26000) **Saeed Manana**
64 Ch c 18/3 Kheleyf (USA)—Miss McGuire (Averti (IRE)) (42857) **Saeed Manana**
65 B c 24/2 Iffraaj—Najam (Singspiel (IRE)) **Saeed Manana**
66 Ch f 3/3 Iffraaj—Neshla (Singspiel (IRE)) (40000) **Saeed Manana**
67 B f 23/3 Sir Percy—Place de Moscou (IRE) (Rock of Gibraltar (IRE)) (30000) **Saeed Manana**

MR JAMES TATE - Continued

68 B c 25/2 Kheleyf (USA)—Posy Fossil (USA) (Malibu Moon (USA)) (52000) **Saeed Manana**
69 B f 7/5 Medaglia d'oro (USA)—Rajeem (Diktat) **Saeed Manana**
70 Gr c 18/2 Iffraaj—Ronaldsay (Kirkwall) (48000) **Saeed Manana**
71 B f 29/4 New Approach (IRE)—Saabiq (USA) (Grand Slam (USA)) **Saif Ali**
72 B f 14/4 Kodiac—Scottish Heights (IRE) (Selkirk (USA)) (30476) **Saeed Manana**
73 **SECRET LIAISON (IRE)**, b f 3/2 Dandy Man (IRE)—
                 Kiss And Don'tell (USA) (Rahy (USA)) (45714) **Sheikh Rashid Dalmook Al Maktoum**
74 B f 31/3 Iffraaj—Shining Hour (USA) (Red Ransom (USA)) (70000) **Saif Ali**
75 B c 3/3 Invincible Spirit (IRE)—
                 Silver Bracelet (Machiavellian (USA)) (40000) **Sheikh Juma Dalmook Al Maktoum**
76 B f 7/4 Makfi—Sinndiya (IRE) (Pharly (FR)) (20000) **Saif Ali**
77 B f 2/4 Sir Percy—Siren Sound (Singspiel (IRE)) (50000) **Saif Ali**
78 Ch f 13/1 Iffraaj—Slieve Mish (IRE) (Cape Cross (IRE)) (92914) **Saeed Manana**
79 B f 1/4 Lope de Vega (IRE)—Statua (USA) (Statoblest) (33333) **Saeed Manana**
80 B f 21/2 Aqlaam—Tara Moon (Pivotal) (40000) **Saeed Manana**
81 B c 22/3 Paco Boy (IRE)—Tincture (Dr Fong (USA)) (26000) **Saeed Manana**
82 B f 15/2 Teofilo (IRE)—Wadaat (Diktat) (205000) **Saeed Manana**
83 B c 28/2 Shamardal (USA)—Zacheta (Polish Precedent (USA)) (65000) **Saif Ali**
84 Ch f 13/2 Teofilo (IRE)—Zam Zoom (IRE) (Dalakhani (IRE)) **Saeed Manana**
85 B c 27/3 Halling (USA)—Zamhrear (Singspiel (IRE)) (19000) **Saeed Manana**
86 B f 27/3 Equiano (FR)—Zia (GER) (Grand Lodge (USA)) (36190) **Saif Ali**

Assistant Trainer: Mrs Lucinda Tate

MR TOM TATE, Tadcaster
Postal: **Castle Farm, Hazelwood, Tadcaster, North Yorkshire, LS24 9NJ**
Contacts: **PHONE (01937) 836036 FAX (01937) 530011 MOBILE (07970) 122818**
E-MAIL tomtate@castlefarmstables.fsnet.co.uk WEBSITE www.tomtate.co.uk

1 **EAGLE ROCK (IRE)**, 6, b g High Chaparral (IRE)—Silk Fan (IRE) **The Ivy Syndicate**
2 **ELAND ALLY**, 6, b g Striking Ambition—Dream Rose (USA) **T T Racing**
3 **GOOD SPEECH (IRE)**, 4, ch f Haatef (USA)—Privileged Speech (USA) **T T Racing**
4 **KUDU COUNTRY (IRE)**, 8, gr g Captain Rio—Nirvavita (FR) **The Flat Cap Syndicate**
5 **PRINCE OF JOHANNE (IRE)**, 8, gr g Johannesburg (USA)—Paiute Princess (FR) **Mr D. Storey**
6 **SKY CROSSING**, 5, b g Cape Cross (IRE)—Sky Wonder **T T Racing**

THREE-YEAR-OLDS

7 **AHOY THERE (IRE)**, ch g Captain Rio—Festivite (IRE) **Ms M. F. Cassidy & Mr T. P. Tate**
8 **EMPRESS ALI (IRE)**, b f Holy Roman Emperor (IRE)—Almansa (IRE) **T T Racing**
9 Ch f Shamardal (USA)—Excellent **T T Racing**
10 **MIGHTY MISSILE (IRE)**, ch g Majestic Missile (IRE)—Magdalene (FR) **T T Racing**
11 **PETITE CADEAUX (IRE)**, ch f Bahamian Bounty—Travel On (USA) **T T Racing**
12 **WALK LIKE A GIANT**, b g Sir Percy—Temple of Thebes (IRE) **The Ivy Syndicate**

TWO-YEAR-OLDS

13 Ch g 11/4 Winker Watson—Cibenze (Owington) (3333) **T T Racing**
14 **DON'T TELL BERTIE**, b f 17/2 Bertolini (USA)—Rockburst (Xaar) (19047) **Don't Tell Bertie Partnership**
15 Ch g 7/3 Shirocco (GER)—Leonica (Lion Cavern (USA)) (32000) **T T Racing**

Other Owners: Mr D. M. W. Hodgkiss, Mrs S. Hodgkiss, Mr T. P. Tate, Mrs Hazel Tate.

Assistant Trainer: Hazel Tate

Jockey (flat): Micky Fenton, Graham Lee. **Jockey (NH):** Dougie Costello.

MRS SUSAN TAYLOR, Morpeth
Postal: **The Gate, Longframlington, Morpeth, Northumberland, NE65 8EL**

1 **CHESTER LEGEND**, 7, ch g Pasternak—Sally Smith **Mrs S. Taylor**
2 **RAKERIN LAD (IRE)**, 11, b g New Frontier (IRE)—Lotta (IRE) **Mrs S. Taylor**

612 **MR COLIN TEAGUE, Wingate**
Postal: **Bridgefield Farm, Trimdon Lane, Station Town, Wingate, Co. Durham, TS28 5NE**
Contacts: PHONE (01429) 837087 MOBILE (07967) 330929
E-MAIL colin.teague@btopenworld.com

1 **CASTLE EDEN (IRE)**, 4, ch g Where Or When (IRE)—Brilliant Trees (IRE) **P. Maddison**
2 **DURHAM EXPRESS (IRE)**, 7, b g Acclamation—Edwina (IRE) **Mr J. C. Johnson**
3 4, B g Overbury (IRE)—Ghana (GER) **P. Maddison**
4 6, Ch m Millkom—Habla Me (IRE)
5 **MONTE PATTINO (USA)**, 10, ch g Rahy (USA)—Jood (USA) **A. Rice**
6 **NOBODYS HERO (IRE)**, 5, b g Indian Danehill (IRE)—Smooth Voyage (IRE) **P. Maddison**
7 **ON THE HIGH TOPS (IRE)**, 6, b g Kheleyf (USA)—Diplomats Daughter **Mr J. R. Bowman**
8 **RUBICON BAY (IRE)**, 7, b m One Cool Cat (USA)—Mrs Moonlight **Collins Chauffeur Driven Executive Cars**
9 6, Ch g Where Or When (IRE)—Sovereign Seal
10 **STAR BETA**, 5, b g Danbird (AUS)—Lady Rock **Mr J. R. Bowman**
11 6, B m Garrison Savannah (NZ)—Transylvania

THREE-YEAR-OLDS

12 B f Sixties Icon—Solemn Vow **P. Maddison**

TWO-YEAR-OLDS

13 Ch c 7/3 Phoenix Reach (IRE)—Pink Supreme (Night Shift (USA)) (3809) **A. Rice**
14 B c 2/5 Arabian Gleam—Renee (Wolfhound (USA))

613 **MR ROGER TEAL, Epsom**
Postal: **Thirty Acre Barn Stables, Shepherds Walk, Epsom, Surrey, KT18 6BX**
Contacts: PHONE (01372) 279535 FAX (01372) 271981 MOBILE (07710) 325521
E-MAIL rteal@thirtyacre.co.uk WEBSITE www.thirtyacrestables.co.uk

1 **CHARLOTTE ROSINA**, 5, b m Choisir (AUS)—Intriguing Glimpse **Homecroft Wealth Racing**
2 **CHRISSYCROSS (IRE)**, 5, b m Cape Cross (IRE)—Penang (IRE) **A. J. Morton**
3 **CLASSIC ART**, 4, ch g Excellent Art—Sensibility **John Morton & Andrew Sharpe**
4 **FREDDY Q (IRE)**, 5, ch g Iffraaj—Barnabas (ITY) **H. Hunt**
5 **JACK OF DIAMONDS (IRE)**, 5, b g Red Clubs (IRE)—Sakkara Star (IRE) **Inside Track Racing Club**
6 **JOHNNY SPLASH (IRE)**, 5, b g Dark Angel (IRE)—Ja Ganhou **Epping Racing**
7 **LANGLEY VALE**, 5, b g Piccolo—Running Glimpse (IRE) **Dr G. F. Forward & Mr F. C. Taylor**
8 **PUCON**, 5, b m Kyllachy—The Fugitive **Mr J. A. Redmond**
9 **SUPER DUPLEX**, 7, b g Footstepsinthesand—Penelope Tree (IRE) **K. S. Thomas**
10 **THE TICHBORNE (IRE)**, 6, b g Shinko Forest (IRE)—Brunswick **Mr Chris Simpson & Mick Waghorn**
11 **TIGERS TALE (IRE)**, 5, b g Tiger Hill (IRE)—Vayenga (FR) **Mr B. Kitcherside & Big Cat Partnership**
12 **TILSTARR (IRE)**, 4, b f Shamardal—Vampire Queen (IRE) **Homecroft Wealth Racing**

THREE-YEAR-OLDS

13 **BERKELEY VALE**, b c Three Valleys (USA)—Intriguing Glimpse **Mrs Muriel Forward & Dr G C Forward**
14 **LORD LEXINGTON**, ch g Dutch Art—Spiralling **Mr John Morton**
15 **MISS LILLIE**, b f Exceed And Excel (AUS)—Never Lose **Mr M. Vickers**
16 **MR CARTOGRAPHER (USA)**, b br c Henrythenavigator (USA)—Humble Clerk (USA) **A. J. Morton**
17 **ORLANDO STAR (CAN)**, b g Henrythenavigator (USA)—Clayton's Lass (USA) **Mr F. C. Taylor**
18 **SON OF FEYAN (IRE)**, ch g Nayef (USA)—Miss Penton **The Rat Racers**
19 **STORM RUN (IRE)**, ch f Hurricane Run (IRE)—Jabroot (IRE) **The Thirty Acre Racing Partnership**
20 **SYLVAN SPIRIT (IRE)**, gr f Camacho—Spree (IRE) **Mrs R. Morton**
21 **VILLARRICA LADY**, b f Sakhee (USA)—The Fugitive **Mr J. A. Redmond**

TWO-YEAR-OLDS

22 B c 16/3 Cockney Rebel (IRE)—Intriguing Glimpse (Piccolo) (4000) **J. A. Morton**

Other Owners: Mrs Emma Curley, Mr Stephen Fisher, Mr Barry Kitcherside, Mr R. Kolien, Mr John Morton, Mr S. J. Piper, Mr Nick Pogmore, Mrs R. Pott, Mr C. Roase, Mr Andrew Sharpe, Mr Chris Simpson, Mr Mick Waghorn, Mr S. Wylde, Mr Martin Wynn.

614 **MR DAVID THOMPSON, Darlington**
Postal: South View Racing, Ashley Cottage, South View, Bolam, Darlington, Co. Durham, DL2 2UP
Contacts: PHONE (01388) 835806 (01388) 832658 FAX (01325) 835806 MOBILE (07795) 161657
E-MAIL dwthompson61@hotmail.co.uk WEBSITE www.dwthompson.co.uk

1 BALLYTHOMAS, 7, b g Kayf Tara—Gregale **Mr Alan Moore & Mr Tony Livingston**
2 BOLD AND FREE, 4, b g Bertolini (USA)—Lady Broughton (IRE) **A. J. Duffield**
3 BOWDLER'S MAGIC, 7, b g Hernando (FR)—Slew The Moon (ARG) **A. J. Duffield**
4 CAP BENAT (IRE), 10, br g Lahib (USA)—Final Peace (IRE) **D. W. Thompson**
5 GIOIA DI VITA, 4, b c Sakhee (USA)—Dhuyoof (IRE) **Seneca Investments & Developments Ltd**
6 LOGICAL APPROACH (IRE), 7, b g Tikkanen (USA)—Anntella (IRE) **A. J. Duffield**
7 MITCHELL, 4, ch g Haafhd—Maid To Matter **A. J. Duffield**
8 ROYAL AND ANCIENT (IRE), 7, b g Danehill Dancer (IRE)—Champaka (IRE) **A. J. Duffield**
9 SILVER SPEECH, 6, gr m Proclamation (IRE)—Sophies Symphony **A. J. Duffield**
10 STAND CLEAR, 9, b m Sir Harry Lewis (USA)—Clair Valley **Mr T. J. A. Thompson**
11 THE THIRSTY BRICKY (IRE), 12, b g Saddlers' Hall (IRE)—Splendid Choice (IRE) **Mr T. J. A. Thompson**
12 WEYBRIDGE LIGHT, 9, b g Fantastic Light (USA)—Nuryana **J. A. Moore**

Other Owners: Mr A. J. Livingston.

Assistant Trainer: A Dickman

Jockey (flat): Andrew Elliott, Tony Hamilton.

615 **MR VICTOR THOMPSON, Alnwick**
Postal: Link House Farm, Newton By The Sea, Embleton, Alnwick, Northumberland, NE66 3ED
Contacts: PHONE (01665) 576272

1 ALPHAZOV (IRE), 8, b g Morozov (USA)—Alphablend (IRE) **Mr Mark Thompson**
2 ANZINGER (IRE), 8, b g Milan—Tarmons Duchess (IRE) **V. Thompson**
3 BACKTOTHEBANK, 6, b g Zafeen (FR)—Natalie **V. Thompson**
4 CAMDEN VINE, 6, b m Grape Tree Road—Camden Bella **V. Thompson**
5 CHANCEOFA LIFETIME (IRE), 7, ch g Beneficial—Bounty Queen (IRE) **V. Thompson**
6 CHOSEN KEYS (IRE), 8, b m Well Chosen—Lost Keys (IRE) **V. Thompson**
7 DUHALLOWCOUNTRY (IRE), 8, b g Beneficial—Milltown Lass (IRE) **Mr Mark Thompson**
8 GIN COBBLER, 8, b g Beneficial—Cassia **V. Thompson**
9 HAVE ONE FOR ME (IRE), 7, b g Sonus (IRE)—Dunmanogue (IRE) **V. Thompson**
10 HEATHER GLEN (IRE), 8, b m Luso—Kadara (IRE) **Mr Mark Thompson**
11 INDIAN PRINT (IRE), 10, ch g Blueprint (IRE)—Commanche Glen (IRE) **V. Thompson**
12 KING OF THE DARK (IRE), 7, b g Zagreb (USA)—Dark Bird (IRE) **V. Thompson**
13 KNACKY LAD (IRE), 8, b g Bach—Sin Ceist Eile (IRE) **Mr Mark Thompson**
14 MISSING YOU (IRE), 8, b g Witness Box (USA)—Mega Drama (IRE) **V. Thompson**
15 MONOGRAM, 10, ch g Karinga Bay—Dusky Dante (IRE) **V. Thompson**
16 MR SHAHADY (IRE), 9, b g Xaar—Shunaire (USA) **V. Thompson**
17 MR STINT (IRE), 7, b g Jammaal—Shamrock's Pet **V. Thompson**
18 RED MYST (IRE), 9, ch g Beneficial—That's Not Fair (IRE) **V. Thompson**
19 SENOR ALCO (FR), 8, gr g Dom Alco (FR)—Alconea (FR) **V. Thompson**
20 SHARIVARRY (FR), 8, ch g Ballingarry (IRE)—Sharsala (IRE) **V. Thompson**
21 SIR TAMBURLANE (IRE), 9, b g Tamayaz (CAN)—Lady Lupin **Mr Mark Thompson**
22 TOM'S PRIDE (IRE), 11, br g Witness Box (USA)—Proverb's Way **V. Thompson**
23 TOMMYS LAD (IRE), 8, br g Luso—Monalee Dream (IRE) **V. Thompson**
24 TOMMYSTEEL (IRE), 9, br g Craigsteel—Sarahs Music (IRE) **V. Thompson**
25 TWO STROKE (IRE), 8, b br g Turtle Island (IRE)—Bannockburn (IRE) **V. Thompson**

Assistant Trainer: M Thompson

616 **MR SANDY THOMSON, Greenlaw**
Postal: Lambden, Greenlaw, Duns, Berwickshire, TD10 6UN
Contacts: PHONE (01361) 810211 MOBILE (07876) 142787
E-MAIL sandy@lambdenfarm.co.uk WEBSITE www.lambdenracing.co.uk

1 ANY GIVEN MOMENT (IRE), 8, b g Alhaarth (IRE)—Shastri (USA) **Mr & Mrs A. M. Thomson**
2 BLUE KASCADE (IRE), 7, ch g Kaieteur (USA)—Lydia Blue (IRE) **Mrs Q. R. Thomson**
3 CHANDOS (IRE), 6, b g Heron Island (IRE)—Park Belle (IRE) **J. R. Adam**

MR SANDY THOMSON - Continued

4 **DANEBROOK LAD (IRE)**, 8, b g Indian Danehill (IRE)—Lady Brookvale (IRE) **Mr J. Szkudro**
5 **JUST AWAKE**, 7, b g Prince Daniel (USA)—Katinka **Mr & Mrs A. M. Thomson**
6 **KILQUIGGAN (IRE)**, 6, gr g Vinnie Roe (IRE)—Irene's Call (IRE) **Mrs Q. R. Thomson**
7 **NETMINDER (IRE)**, 8, b g Insatiable (IRE)—
Princess Douglas **Quona Thomson, David Spratt, Kevin McMunigal**
8 **OSCAR LATEEN (IRE)**, 6, b g Oscar (IRE)—Storm Call **Mr J. R. Adam**
9 **OSCAR TOO (IRE)**, 5, b g Oscar (IRE)—Biddy Earley (IRE) **Mr J. R. Adam**
10 5, B m Kayf Tara—Portland Row (IRE) **W. A. Walker**
11 **PRAIRIE LAD**, 6, b g Alflora (IRE)—An Bothar Dubh **Mr J. R. Adam**
12 5, B m And Beyond (IRE)—Quonarose **Mrs Q. M. Thomson**
13 **SEEYOUATMIDNIGHT**, 6, b g Midnight Legend—Morsky Baloo **Mrs Q. R. Thomson**
14 **SELDOM INN**, 6, ch g Double Trigger (IRE)—Portland Row (IRE) **W. A. Walker**
15 **THE SHRIMP (IRE)**, 7, gr g Indian Danehill (IRE)—Rheban Lass (IRE) **Mrs Q. R. Thomson**

Other Owners: Mr Kevin McMunigal, Mr D. Spratt, Mrs A. M. Thomson, Mr A. M. Thomson.

Assistant Trainer: Mrs A. M. Thomson

---

617 **MR KARL THORNTON, Dublin**
Postal: **Balcunnin, Skerries, Co. Dublin, Ireland**
Contacts: **PHONE (00353) 1 8490964 MOBILE (00353) 86 3371887**

1 5, Ch g Beneficial—African Waters (IRE) **Sean Thornton**
2 **BEARLY LEGAL (IRE)**, 8, b g Court Cave (IRE)—Fair Size (IRE) **Sean Thornton**
3 **CITY LINE (IRE)**, 7, b g Antonius Pius (USA)—Indian Myth (USA) **Sean Thornton**
4 **LORTZING (IRE)**, 7, b g Spartacus (IRE)—Lowtown **Sean Thornton**
5 **STREET RUNNER**, 8, b g Rainbow Quest (USA)—Dansara **Sean Thornton**

Assistant Trainer: Sean Thornton

Jockey (flat): Ian Brennan. **Jockey (NH):** Eddie O'Connell. **Conditional:** Conor David Maxwell.
Apprentice: Charlie Elliott. **Amateur:** Mr J. C. Barry.

---

618 **MR NIGEL TINKLER, Malton**
Postal: **Woodland Stables, Langton, Malton, North Yorkshire, YO17 9QR**
Contacts: **PHONE (01653) 658245**

1 **COMBAT JET**, 4, ch g Sleeping Indian—Strawberry Leaf **Sunrise**
2 **MISPLACED FORTUNE**, 9, b m Compton Place—Tide of Fortune **W. F. Burton**
3 **MY CLAIRE**, 4, b f Piccolo—Aymara **Mr J. O'Doherty**
4 **REASON TO SMILE**, 4, b c Teofilo (IRE)—Easy To Love (USA) **Maze Rattan Limited & Lady Cecil**
5 **TEETOTAL (IRE)**, 4, ch g Footstepsinthesand—Tea Service (USA) **Raybould & Scott**
6 **THOMAS BLOSSOM (IRE)**, 4, b g Dylan Thomas (IRE)—Woman Secret (IRE) **Mr H. K. Ma**

THREE-YEAR-OLDS

7 **BASHIBA (IRE)**, ch c Iffraaj—Nightswimmer (IRE) **Mr Y. T. Szeto**
8 **ELUALLA (IRE)**, b f Elusive City (USA)—Cote Quest (USA) **Sunrise**
9 B g Dylan Thomas (IRE)—Foreign Language (USA) **Mr Y. T. Szeto**
10 B c Bushranger (IRE)—Fuerta Ventura (IRE) **Mr H. K. Ma**
11 **GENIUSINRHYME**, b g Amadeus Wolf—Ardessie **Mr Y. T. Szeto**
12 **GREEN ZONE (IRE)**, b g Bushranger—Incense **Sunrise**
13 **HENKE (IRE)**, b g Elnadim (USA)—Miss Frangipane (IRE)
14 **NU FORE FIRE (IRE)**, b g Footstepsinthesand—Maimana (IRE) **Mr E. Carswell**
15 **ORIENTAL DREAM (IRE)**, b c Shamardal (USA)—Oriental Melody (IRE) **Leeds Plywood & Doors Ltd**
16 **RED TIGER LILY**, ch f Piccolo—Juncea **Exors of the Late Mr K. P. Beecroft**
17 **SAN REMO ROSE (IRE)**, b f Tagula (IRE)—Satin Rose **W. F. Burton**
18 B g Archipenko (USA)—Stormy View (USA) **Mr H. K. Ma**
19 **TINSILL**, ch g Firebreak—Concentration (IRE)
20 B c Tagula (IRE)—Westlife (IRE) **Mr Y. T. Szeto**

Other Owners: Lady J. Cecil, Maze Rattan Limited, J. Raybould, D. Scott, N. Tinkler, Mr W. Tsang.

619 **MR COLIN TIZZARD, Sherborne**
Postal: **Venn Farm, Milborne Port, Sherborne, Dorset, DT9 5RA**
Contacts: **PHONE (01963) 250598 FAX (01963) 250598 MOBILE (07976) 778656**
E-MAIL info@colintizzard.co.uk WEBSITE www.colintizzard.co.uk

1 **BEARS RAILS**, 4, b g Flemensfirth (USA)—Clandestine **P. M. Warren**
2 **BILLY NO NAME (IRE)**, 6, b g Westerner—Just Little **Mrs J. R. Bishop**
3 **BOLD CUFFS**, 5, b g Dutch Art—Chambray **Mr J. P. Romans**
4 **BUCKHORN TIMOTHY**, 5, b g Tamure (IRE)—Waimea Bay **The Buckhorn Racing Team**
5 **BUCKHORN TOM**, 6, b g Tamure (IRE)—Waimea Bay **The Buckhorn Racing Team**
6 4, B g Flemensfirth (USA)—Crystal Ballerina (IRE) **T. H. Chadney**
7 **CUE CARD**, 8, b g King's Theatre (IRE)—Wicked Crack (IRE) **Mrs J. R. Bishop**
8 **DARK DESIRE**, 5, br g Generous (IRE)—Diletia **Chasing Gold Limited**
9 **DEAR DARLING**, 4, b f Midnight Legend—Easibrook Jane **Barrow Hill**
10 4, B g Morozov (USA)—Enistar (IRE) **Moonrakers**
11 **FALCON ISLAND**, 9, b g Turtle Island (IRE)—Dolly Sparks (IRE) **The Butterwick Syndicate**
12 **FINAL FLOW**, 5, ch g With The Flow (USA)—The Final One
13 **FLAMING CHARMER (IRE)**, 6, ch g Flemensfirth (USA)—Kates Charm (IRE) **Tom Chadney & Peter Green**
14 **FOURTH ACT (IRE)**, 5, b g King's Theatre (IRE)—Erintante (IRE) **Mrs J. R. Bishop**
15 **FOXES BRIDGE**, 4, b g Tamure (IRE)—Risky May **Glanvilles Stud Partners**
16 **GENTLEMAN JON**, 6, b g Beat All (USA)—Sudden Spirit (FR) **Mr J. P. Romans**
17 **GOLDEN CHIEFTAIN**, 9, b g Tikkanen (USA)—Golden Flower (GER) **Brocade Racing**
18 **GRAND VISION (IRE)**, 8, gr g Old Vic—West Hill Rose (IRE) **J. T. Warner**
19 **HANDY ANDY (IRE)**, 8, b g Beneficial—Maslam (IRE) **Brocade Racing**
20 **HEALTH IS WEALTH**, 9, br g Anshan—Cherry Black (IRE) **Gale Force Five**
21 **HENWOOD (IRE)**, 6, ch g Old Vic—Katty Barry (IRE) **C. L. Tizzard**
22 **HEY BIG SPENDER (IRE)**, 11, b g Rudimentary (USA)—Jims Monkey **Brocade Racing**
23 **INSIDE DEALER (IRE)**, 10, b g Presenting—Sea Gale (IRE) **J. M. Dare, T. Hamlin, J. W. Snook**
24 5, B g Alflora (IRE)—Island Hopper
25 **IVOR'S KING (IRE)**, 7, b g King's Theatre (IRE)—Christelle (IRE) **W. I. M. Perry**
26 **IVOR'S QUEEN (IRE)**, 5, b m King's Theatre (IRE)—Sonnerschien (IRE) **Ivor Perry & Ashton Selway**
27 **JUMPS ROAD**, 7, b g Clerkenwell (USA)—Diletia **Chasing Gold Limited**
28 **KINGFISHER CREEK**, 4, b g Kayf Tara—Symbiosis **Brocade Racing**
29 **KINGS LAD (IRE)**, 7, b g King's Theatre (IRE)—Festival Leader (IRE) **G. F. Gingell**
30 **LORD OF THE DUNES**, 6, b g Desert King (IRE)—Dame Fonteyn **Barrow Hill**
31 **LUCULLAN**, 4, b g Lucarno (USA)—Towaahi (IRE) **Five Horses Ltd**
32 **MASTERS HILL (IRE)**, 8, gr g Tikkanen (USA)—Leitrim Bridge (IRE) **K S B, Mr M Doughty & Mrs Sarah Tizzard**
33 **MIBLEU (IRE)**, 14, b g Agent Bleu (FR)—Eauseille (FR) **Chasing Gold Limited**
34 **MIDNIGHT THUNDER**, 5, ch g Beneficial—
Peppardstown (IRE) **Brocade Racing J P Romans Terry Warner**
35 **MILARROW (IRE)**, 7, b g Milan—Fleeting Arrow (IRE) **P. M. Warren**
36 **MORELLO ROYALE (IRE)**, 4, b f King's Theatre (IRE)—Mystic Cherry (IRE) **Ann & Tony Gale**
37 **MULTITUDE OF SINS**, 7, b g Lucky Owners (NZ)—Lady Turk (FR) **Tizzard Racing One**
38 **MURRAYANA (IRE)**, 4, b g King's Theatre (IRE)—Royalrova (FR) **Mrs S. I. Tainton**
39 **OHIO GOLD (IRE)**, 8, b g Flemensfirth (USA)—Kiniohio (FR) **P. M. Warren**
40 **OISEAU DE NUIT (FR)**, 12, b g Evening World (FR)—Idylle du Marais (FR) **J. T. Warner**
41 **OLD TRICKS (IRE)**, 7, br g Flemensfirth (USA)—Cabin Glory **J K Farms**
42 **QUITE BY CHANCE**, 9, b g Midnight Legend—Hop Fair **T Hamlin,J M Dare,J W Snook,J T Warner**
43 **ROBINSFIRTH (IRE)**, 5, b g Flemensfirth (USA)—Phardester (IRE) **Christine Knowles & Wendy Carter**
44 **ROCKET SCIENTIST**, 5, b g Proclamation (IRE)—Motown Melody (IRE) **Barrow Hill**
45 **ROYAL VACATION (IRE)**, 4, b g King's Theatre (IRE)—Summer Break (IRE) **Mrs J. R. Bishop**
46 **SANDY BEACH**, 4, b g Notnowcato—Picacho (IRE) **Brocade Racing**
47 4, Ch f Apple Tree (FR)—Seemarye **Glanvilles Stud Partners**
48 **SEW ON TARGET (IRE)**, 9, b g Needle Gun (IRE)—Ballykea (IRE) **A. G. Selway**
49 4, B g Tikkanen (USA)—Shilling Hill (IRE)
50 **SONNY THE ONE**, 4, ch g Tobougg (IRE)—Annie Fleetwood
51 **SPENDING TIME**, 5, b g King's Theatre (IRE)—Karello Bay **Brocade Racing**
52 **SUMMERTIME LADY**, 6, b m Desert King (IRE)—Shelayly (IRE) **Mrs S. I. Tainton**
53 **THE CIDER MAKER**, 4, b g Kayf Tara—Dame Fonteyn **Barrow Hill**
54 **THEATRE GUIDE (IRE)**, 7, b g King's Theatre (IRE)—Erintante (IRE) **Mrs J. R. Bishop**
55 **THEATRICAL STAR**, 8, b g King's Theatre (IRE)—Lucy Glitters **Brocade Racing**
56 **THIRD ACT (IRE)**, 5, b g King's Theatre (IRE)—Starry Lady (IRE) **Mrs J. R. Bishop**
57 **THIRD INTENTION (IRE)**, 7, b g Azamour (IRE)—Third Dimension (FR) **Mr & Mrs R. Tizzard**
58 **TIKKAPICK (IRE)**, 4, b g Tikkanen (USA)—Takeanotherpick (IRE) **Mrs S. I. Tainton**
59 **TIME BOOK (IRE)**, 8, b g Galileo (IRE)—Pocket Book (IRE) **D. V. Stevens**
60 **ULTRAGOLD (FR)**, 6, b br g Kapgarde (FR)—Hot d'or (FR) **Brocade Racing J P Romans Terry Warner**

MR COLIN TIZZARD - Continued

61 **VIRGINIA ASH (IRE)**, 6, ch g Definite Article—Peace Time Girl (IRE) **Mr J. P. Romans**
62 **WHEN BEN WHEN (IRE)**, 5, b g Beneficial—Almnadia (IRE) **Mrs S. I. Tainton**
63 **XAARCET (IRE)**, 7, b g Xaar—Anoukit **The Missiles**

Other Owners: Mrs S. J. Biggins, Mr K. W. Biggins, Mr G. R. Broom, Mrs A. E. M. Broom, Mrs W. Carter, Mr C. Cole, Mr C. E. G. Collier, Mr J. M. Dare, Mr M. Doughty, Mr A. P. Gale, Mrs A. G. Gale, Mr P. C. W. Green, Dr G. W. Guy, T. Hamlin, Mr K. F. Honeybun, Mrs J. Honeybun, M. M. Hooker, Mrs C. Knowles, Mr D. A. Mayes, Mr W. D. Procter, J. W. Snook, Mr D. J. Stevens, R. G. Tizzard, Mrs S. L. Tizzard, Mr E. R. Vickery.

Assistant Trainer: Mrs K. Gingell

Jockey (NH): Brendan Powell, Joe Tizzard. **Amateur:** Mr M. Legg.

---

620 | **MR MARTIN TODHUNTER, Penrith**
Postal: **The Park, Orton, Penrith, Cumbria, CA10 3SD**
Contacts: **PHONE (01539) 624314 FAX (01539) 624811 MOBILE (07976) 440082**
WEBSITE www.martintodhunter.co.uk

1 **ACORDINGTOSCRIPT (IRE)**, 8, ch g Accordion—Jane Jones (IRE) **The Surf & Turf Partnership**
2 **ALLANARD (IRE)**, 10, b g Oscar—Allatrim (IRE) **Mr E. R. Madden**
3 **BADEA**, 5, b g Cockney Rebel (IRE)—Gibraltar Bay (IRE) **Park Farms Racing Syndicate 1**
4 **CARTHAGINIAN (IRE)**, 5, b g Azamour (IRE)—Khayrat (IRE) **P. G. Airey**
5 **CLARAGH NATIVE (IRE)**, 9, ch g Beneficial—Susy In The Summer (IRE) **Mrs S. J. Matthews**
6 **CLOUD MONKEY (IRE)**, 4, b br c Marju (IRE)—Sweet Clover **Mr & Mrs Ian Hall**
7 **CLOUDY DEAL (IRE)**, 7, b g Cloudings (IRE)—Native Gift (IRE) **D. M. Proos**
8 **COTTIERS DEN (IRE)**, 7, b g Snurge—Silvretta (IRE) **Leeds Plywood & Doors Ltd**
9 **DE CHISSLER (IRE)**, 7, b g Zagreb (USA)—Lady Lola (IRE) **Mr A. Bell**
10 **EL CABALLO**, 5, b g Sir Harry Lewis (USA)—Woodwind Down **Park Farms Racing Syndicate 2**
11 **INDEPUB**, 5, b g Indesatchel (IRE)—Champenoise **The Dun Deal**
12 **MARTIN CHUZZLEWIT (IRE)**, 5, ch g Galileo (IRE)—Alta Anna (FR) **Island Intermodal Services Limited**
13 **MISS MACNAMARA (IRE)**, 5, b m Dylan Thomas (IRE)—Kincob (USA) **Javas Charvers**
14 **MONBEG (IRE)**, 7, b g Revoque (IRE)—Dikler Gale (IRE) **Island Intermodal Services Limited**
15 **MORNING WITH IVAN (IRE)**, 4, b f Ivan Denisovich (IRE)—Grinneas (IRE) **Island Intermodal Services Limited**
16 **OSCAR TANNER (IRE)**, 6, br g Oscar (IRE)—Rose Tanner (IRE) **Murphy's Law & Vyner-Brooks**
17 **PAIRC NA LEASA (IRE)**, 8, b g Beat All (USA)—Seymour Roses
18 **PRESENTING JUNIOR (IRE)**, 7, b g Presenting—Dr Alice (IRE) **Mr W. & Mrs J. Garnett**
19 **ROCKABILLY RIOT (IRE)**, 4, br g Footstepsinthesand—Zawariq (IRE) **J. D. Gordon**
20 **ROYAL SAM (IRE)**, 9, ch g Bach (IRE)—Dereenavurrig (IRE) **Mrs K. Hall**
21 **SEE WHAT HAPPENS (IRE)**, 8, b g Tikkanen (USA)—Fontanalia (FR) **J. D. Gordon**
22 4, B f Lucarno (USA)—Woodwind Down **P. G. Airey**

THREE-YEAR-OLDS

23 **QUESTION OF FAITH**, b f Yeats (IRE)—Anastasia Storm **P. G. Airey**

Other Owners: P. W. Clement, Mr P. M. Croan, W. Downs, Mr J. W. Fryer-Spedding, Mr W. W. Garnett, Mrs J. M. Garnett, Mr D. Gillespie, Mr J. D. Graves, Mr N. Haughan, Mr C. G. Snoddy, Mr J. I. A. Spedding, D. M. Todhunter, Mr V. R. Vyner-Brooks.

Jockey (NH): Wilson Renwick, Lucy Alexander, Henry Brooke, Denis O'Regan.

---

621 | **MR JAMES TOLLER, Newmarket**
Postal: **Eve Lodge Stables, Hamilton Road, Newmarket, Suffolk, CB8 0NY**
Contacts: **PHONE (01638) 668918 FAX (01638) 669384 MOBILE (07887) 942234**
E-MAIL james.toller@btconnect.com / jamestoller@btconnect.com

1 **GIVE US A REASON**, 4, b f Motivator—Ela's Giant **Mr G. E. M. Wates**
2 **LOVING SPIRIT**, 6, b g Azamour (IRE)—Lolla's Spirit (IRE) **Loving Spirit Partnership**
3 **RED PILGRIM (IRE)**, 4, b g Authorized (IRE)—Plenty of Action (USA) **Mr James C Cummings**
4 **SMOKETHATTHUNDERS (IRE)**, 4, gr g Elusive City (USA)—Zinstar (IRE) **M. E. Wates**
5 **SOHAR**, 6, b m Iceman—Desert Joy **G. B. Partnership**

MR JAMES TOLLER - Continued

THREE-YEAR-OLDS
6 **GANGES (IRE),** b c Shamardal (USA)—Quantum (IRE) **P. C. J. Dalby & R. D. Schuster**
7 **MAJESTIC SONG,** b f Royal Applause—Sakhee's Song (IRE) **P. C. J. Dalby & R. D. Schuster**
8 **REEDCUTTER,** b c Passing Glance—Violet's Walk **M. E. Wates**
9 **SATURATION POINT,** b f Beat Hollow—Query (USA) **P. Pearce & S. A. Herbert**

TWO-YEAR-OLDS
10 B f 13/4 Zamindar (USA)—Bolsena (USA) (Red Ransom (USA)) (4800)
11 **DEMONSTRATION (IRE),** b c 26/2 Cape Cross (IRE)—Quiet Protest (USA) (Kingmambo (USA)) (48000)
12 B f 15/4 Azamour (IRE)—Lolla's Spirit (IRE) (Montjeu (IRE))
13 **WISEWIT,** b c 22/4 Royal Applause—Loveleaves (Polar Falcon (USA)) (42000)

Other Owners: A. N. C. Bengough, Mr N. J. Charrington, Mr P. C. J. Dalby, J. F. Dean, D. W. Dennis, Mr M. G. H. Heald, Mr Andrew Heald, Mr S. A. Herbert, Mrs Anna Pearce, Mr Philip Pearce, Mr Richard Schuster, Andrew Stone, Mr R. A. C. Toller, Mr J. A. R. Toller, Lady Sophia Topley.

Jockey (flat): Robert Havlin.

---

622 **MR MARK TOMPKINS, Newmarket**
Postal: **Exeter Ride, The Watercourse, Newmarket, Suffolk, CB8 8LW**
Contacts: **PHONE (01638) 661434 FAX (01638) 668107 MOBILE (07799) 663339**
E-MAIL mht@marktompkins.co.uk WEBSITE www.marktompkins.co.uk

1 **AKULA (IRE),** 7, ch g Soviet Star (USA)—Danielli (IRE) **Jay Three Racing**
2 **COMRADE BOND,** 6, ch g Monsieur Bond (IRE)—Eurolink Cafe **Raceworld**
3 **LIKE CLOCKWORK,** 5, b g Rail Link—Tenpence **Mrs J. I. Simpson**
4 **LIKELIKELIKELIKEIT,** 4, b f Avonbridge—Rutland Water (IRE) **Michael Harvey & Partners**
5 **MY GUARDIAN ANGEL,** 5, b g Araafa (IRE)—Angels Guard You **Sarabex**
6 **TOPAMICHI,** 4, b g Beat Hollow—Topatori (IRE) **Roalco Ltd**
7 **TOPTEMPO,** 5, ch m Halling (USA)—Topatoo **Roalco Ltd**
8 **ZENARINDA,** 7, b m Zamindar (USA)—Tenpence **Dullingham Park**

THREE-YEAR-OLDS
9 **ASTROCAT,** b f Zamindar (USA)—Mega (IRE) **Mystic Meg Limited**
10 **ASTRODIAMOND,** b f Black Sam Bellamy (IRE)—Astromancer (USA) **Mystic Meg Limited**
11 **ASTROVIRTUE,** b c Virtual—Astrolove (IRE) **Mystic Meg Limited**
12 **ASTROWOLF,** b g Halling (USA)—Optimistic **Mystic Meg Limited**
13 **BLUE BOUNTY,** ch g Bahamian Bounty—Laheen (IRE) **Raceworld**
14 **CRYSTAL PEARL,** b f Beat Hollow—Missouri **J. Brenchley**
15 **LITTLE TINKA,** b f Three Valleys (USA)—Tenpence **Dullingham Park**
16 **NANCY,** b f Rail Link—Feabhas (IRE) **J. Brenchley**
17 **SWILKEN,** ch c Halling (USA)—Azure Mist **Mr D. P. Noblett**
18 **TOPALING,** ch f Halling (USA)—Topatori (IRE) **M. P. Bowring**

TWO-YEAR-OLDS
19 **ASTROMAJOR,** b c 23/2 Royal Applause—Astromancer (USA) (Silver Hawk (USA)) **Mystic Meg Ltd**
20 **ASTROVALOUR,** ch c 2/3 Shirocco (GER)—Mega (IRE) (Petardia) (13000) **Mystic Meg Ltd**
21 B f 29/2 Champs Elysees—Azure Mist (Bahamian Bounty) **Mr David Noblett**
22 Ch c 15/3 Motivator—Dolls House (Dancing Spree (USA)) **Dullingham Park**
23 B f 14/3 Champs Elysees—Dulcie (Hernando (FR)) **Dullingham Park**
24 B c 9/2 Refuse To Bend (IRE)—Four Miracles (Vettori (IRE)) **Mr Richard Farleigh**
25 **LEXI GRADY ALICE,** b f 10/4 Royal Applause—Missoula (IRE) (Kalanisi (IRE)) **Steve Ashley**
26 Ch c 8/4 Pastoral Pursuits—Nice Time (IRE) (Tagula (IRE)) **Sarabex**
27 B c 14/2 Virtual—Qilin (IRE) (Second Set (IRE)) **Dullingham Park**
28 Ch f 9/3 Dutch Art—Sosumi (Be My Chief (USA)) **The Sakal Family**
29 B f 24/4 Champs Elysees—Tenpence (Bob Back (USA)) **Dullingham Park**
30 B f 10/2 Rail Link—Topatoo (Bahamian Bounty) **Mr M. P. Bowring**
31 B f 14/4 Authorized (IRE)—Trew Class (Inchinor) **Russell Trew Ltd**
32 Ch f 14/4 Halling (USA)—Twelfth Night (IRE) (Namid) **Pollards Stables**

MR MARK TOMPKINS - Continued

Other Owners: Mr Bryan Agar, Mr Stuart Andrews, Mr M. P Bowring, Judi Dench, Mr N. M. Hanger, Mr Michael D. Harvey, Mr Eric Jones, Mr R. D. E. Marriott, Mr Gary Pettit, Mrs P. M. Rickett, Mr W. H. Simpson, Mr R. J. Thornalley, Mr M. H. Tompkins, Mrs M. H. Tompkins, Mr David Tompkins.

Assistant Trainer: Steven Avery

Jockey (NH): Colin Bolger. **Amateur:** Miss Nikki McCaffrey.

---

623 MR KEVIN TORK, Leigh
Postal: Westcoats Farm, Clayhill Road, Leigh, Reigate, Surrey, RH2 8PB
Contacts: **PHONE (01306) 611616 MOBILE (07988) 206544**

1 LIEUTENANT NELSON, 4, ch g Mount Nelson—Franglais (GER) **K. Tork**
2 6, B gr g Exit To Nowhere (USA)—Rosie (IRE) **K. Tork**
3 TYDRAW PARC, 6, b m Central Park (IRE)—In A Whirl (USA) **K. Tork**
4 UPTON MEAD (IRE), 7, b g Jimble (FR)—Inchinnan **Tork Racing**
5 ZHUKOV (IRE), 12, b g Saddlers' Hall (IRE)—Tamasriya (IRE) **K. Tork**

Other Owners: Mr P. Grimes, Mr K. Tork.

Assistant Trainer: Mr Max Tork

Amateur: Mr F. Penford.

---

624 MR MARCUS TREGONING, Whitsbury
Postal: Whitsbury Manor Racing Stables, Whitsbury, Fordingbridge, Hampshire, SP6 3QQ
Contacts: PHONE (01725) 518889 FAX (01725) 518042 MOBILE (07767) 888100
E-MAIL info@marcustregoningracing.co.uk WEBSITE www.marcustregoningracing.co.uk

1 ATALANTA BAY (IRE), 4, b f Strategic Prince—Wood Sprite **Miss S. M. Sharp**
2 BOOM AND BUST (IRE), 7, b g Footstepsinthesand—Forest Call **Mr J. Singh**
3 BRONZE ANGEL (IRE), 5, b g Dark Angel (IRE)—Rihana **Lady Tennant**
4 BROON TROOT (IRE), 4, b g Jeremy (USA)—Special Park (USA) **M. P. Tregoning**
5 CATARIA GIRL (USA), 5, b m Discreet Cat (USA)—Elaflaak (USA) **Mr & Mrs A. E. Pakenham**
6 CAVALEIRO (IRE), 5, ch g Sir Percy—Khibraat **Mr G. C. B. Brook**
7 FLASHHEART (IRE), 4, b g Nayef (USA)—Emerald Peace (IRE) **Mr G. C. B. Brook**
8 MISS BLAKENEY, 5, b m Sir Percy—Misplace (IRE) **Mr & Mrs A. E. Pakenham**
9 OPERA BOX, 6, b m Singspiel (IRE)—Annex **Efemera Stud**
10 PERDU, 4, b c Sir Percy—Misplace (IRE) **Mr & Mrs A. E. Pakenham**
11 SWEEPING ROCK (IRE), 4, b g Rock of Gibraltar (IRE)—Sweeping Story (USA) **Mr J. Singh**
12 VALAIS GIRL, 4, b f Holy Roman Emperor (IRE)—Ellen (IRE) **Mr G. C. B. Brook**

THREE-YEAR-OLDS
13 AYERS ROCK (IRE), b g Bushranger (IRE)—Red Fuschia **Lady Tennant**
14 BETWEEN WICKETS, b c Compton Place—Intermission (IRE) **R. C. C. Villers**
15 BIRETTA, ch f Kirkwall—Burqa **R. J. McCreery**
16 BOWSERS BOLD, b g Firebreak—Cristal Clear (IRE) **Mrs J. R. A. Aldridge**
17 CASTLE COMBE (IRE), b c Dylan Thomas (IRE)—Mundus Novus (USA) **Gaskell, Wallis & Partners**
18 B g Authorized (IRE)—Elizabethan Age (FR)
19 EMPEROR FERDINAND (IRE), b g Holy Roman Emperor (IRE)—Moon Flower (IRE) **Lady Tennant**
20 FYRECRACKER (IRE), ch g Kheleyf (USA)—Spirit of Hope (IRE) **Mrs Lynn Turner & Mr Guy Brook**
21 HAYDN'S LASS, b f Sir Percy—String Quartet (IRE) **Mr & Mrs A. E. Pakenham**
22 HESBAAN (IRE), b c Acclamation—Celestial Dream (IRE) **Hamdan Al Maktoum**
23 MAJOR BOBBY, b c Exceed And Excel (AUS)—Dominica **Exors of the Late Mrs R. B. Kennard**
24 MONEYPENNIE, b f Captain Gerrard (IRE)—Snoozy **Miss S. M. Sharp**
25 NAWL (IRE), b g Bushranger (IRE)—Crystalline Stream (FR) **M. P. Tregoning**
26 NEW COLOURS, gr g Verglas (IRE)—Briery (IRE) **Mr J. A. Tabet**
27 Ch c Hernando (FR)—Protectorate **Lady N. F. Cobham**
28 SECRET PURSUIT (IRE), b f Lawman (FR)—Secret Melody (FR) **Mr G. C. B. Brook**
29 SERENA GRAE, gr f Arakan (USA)—Success Story **Mrs H. B. Raw**
30 SIR PERCY BLAKENEY, b g Sir Percy—Sulitelma (USA) **Home Marketing Limited**
31 SNOW TROUBLE (USA), gr c Tapit (USA)—Smara (USA) **Mr G. C. B. Brook**

MR MARCUS TREGONING - Continued

32 **STILLA AFTON,** b br f Nayef (USA)—Sourire **Miss K. Rausing**
33 **SWEET P,** b f Sir Percy—Desert Run (IRE) **M. P. Tregoning**

TWO-YEAR-OLDS

34 **AFRAAS (IRE),** b f 7/2 Elnadim (USA)—Aadaat (USA) (Dixie Union (USA)) **Hamdan Al Maktoum**
35 B c 12/3 Mawatheeq (USA)—Amhooj (Green Desert (USA)) (18095) **Park Walk Racing**
36 Ch f 25/2 Sakhee's Secret—Belle des Airs (IRE) (Dr Fong (USA)) (2380) **Mrs H. I. Slade**
37 B c 16/2 Sir Percy—Bermondsey Girl (Bertolini (USA)) (52000) **R. C. C. Villers**
38 **DIAMOND BLAISE,** b f 10/4 Iffraaj—See You Later (Emarati (USA)) (95000) **Mrs H. I. Slade**
39 Ch f 25/3 Sir Percy—La Peinture (GER) (Peintre Celebre (USA))
40 **MAGICAL THOMAS,** ch c 27/3 Dylan Thomas (IRE)—
Magical Cliche (USA) (Affirmed (USA)) (7500) **G. P. and Miss S. J. Hayes**
41 **MAISRAH (IRE),** b c 30/4 Invincible Spirit (IRE)—
Virginia Rose (IRE) (Galileo (IRE)) (110000) **Hamdan Al Maktoum**
42 **MULAASEQ,** b c 8/3 Showcasing—Lonely Heart (Midyan (USA)) (57142) **Hamdan Al Maktoum**
43 **ROYAL ROSLEA,** b f 19/2 Royal Applause—
Roslea Lady (IRE) (Alhaarth (IRE)) (13000) **G. P. and Miss S. J. Hayes**
44 **SAHAAYEF (IRE),** b f 30/1 Mawatheeq (USA)—Nasheed (USA) (Riverman (USA)) **Hamdan Al Maktoum**
45 **SHAAKIS (IRE),** br gr c 15/4 Dark Angel (IRE)—
Curious Lashes (IRE) (Footstepsinthesand) (80000) **Hamdan Al Maktoum**
46 **TAZYEEN,** ch f 26/1 Tamayuz—Shohrah (IRE) (Giant's Causeway (USA)) **Hamdan Al Maktoum**

Other Owners: R. F. U. Gaskell, Mr G. P. Hayes, Miss S. J. Hayes, A. E. Pakenham, Mrs V. H. Pakenham, Mr N. A. Penston, Mr R. J. Penston, Mrs L. Turner, J. R. Wallis.

Assistant Trainer: Angie Kennedy

Jockey (flat): Martin Dwyer, Hayley Turner.

 MR EDWIN TUER, Northallerton
625 Postal: Granary Barn, Birkby, Northallerton, North Yorkshire, DL7 0EF
Contacts: **PHONE (01609) 881798 FAX (01609) 881798 MOBILE (07808) 330306**

1 **AILSA CRAIG (IRE),** 8, b m Chevalier (IRE)—Sharplaw Destiny (IRE) **Ontoawinner**
2 **BLUE MAISEY,** 6, b m Monsieur Bond (IRE)—Blue Nile (IRE) **Ontoawinner**
3 **BULAS BELLE,** 4, b f Rob Roy (USA)—Bula Rose (IRE) **E. Tuer**
4 **DORA'S GIFT,** 5, b m Cadeaux Genereux—Conquestadora **E. Tuer**
5 **EASY TERMS,** 7, b m Trade Fair—Effie **E. Tuer**
6 **FAZZA,** 7, ch g Sulamani (IRE)—Markievicz (IRE) **E. Tuer**
7 **GOLD SHOW,** 5, gr m Sir Percy—Pearl Bright (FR) **Ontoawinner**
8 **MYSTICAL MOMENT,** 4, ch f Dutch Art—Tinnarinka **E. Tuer**
9 **PATAVIUM (IRE),** 11, b g Titus Livius (FR)—Arcevia (IRE) **Mr J. A. Nixon**
10 **SALLY FRIDAY (IRE),** 6, b m Footstepsinthesand—Salee (IRE) **E. Tuer**
11 **SPRING BACK,** 6, b m Silver Patriarch (IRE)—Dancebaak (IRE)
12 **THE BLUE BANANA (IRE),** 5, b g Red Clubs (IRE)—Rinneen (IRE) **Mr E Tuer & Mr & Mrs C Tompkins**

Other Owners: Mr N. J. O'Brien, Mr Charles Tompkins, Mrs Angela Tompkins, Mr E. Tuer.

Assistant Trainer: Fergus King (07813) 153982

 MR JOSEPH TUITE, Great Shefford
626 Postal: Shefford Valley Stables, Great Shefford, Lambourn, Berkshire, RG17 7EF
Contacts: **MOBILE (07769) 977351**
E-MAIL joe.tuite@tuiteracing.com **WEBSITE** www.tuiteracing.co.uk

1 **CAMACHE QUEEN (IRE),** 6, b m Camacho—Alinda (IRE) **Mr A. Liddiard**
2 **DOZY JOE,** 6, b g Sleeping Indian—Surrey Down (USA) **P. E. Barrett**
3 **INTERAKT,** 7, b m Rakti—Amelie Pouliche (FR) **www.isehove.com**
4 **IWILSAYZISONLYONCE,** 4, ch g Kyllachy—Resistance Heroine **Shefford Valley Racing**
5 **LADY SYLVIA,** 5, ch m Haafhd—Abide (FR) **Mr D. J. Keast**
6 **PRESBURG (IRE),** 5, b g Balmont (USA)—Eschasse (USA) **www.isehove.com**
7 **THANE OF CAWDOR (IRE),** 5, b g Danehill Dancer (IRE)—Holy Nola (USA) **Alan & Christine Bright**

MR JOSEPH TUITE - Continued

THREE-YEAR-OLDS

8 **CINCUENTA PASOS (IRE)**, ch c Footstepsinthesand—Sweet Nicole **Mr Mark Wellbelove & Mr Peter Gleeson**
9 **COISTE BODHAR (IRE)**, b g Camacho—Nortolixa (FR) **Shefford Valley Racing**
10 **FLASHY QUEEN (IRE)**, ch f Bahamian Bounty—Somersault **Mr B. Woodward**
11 **LADY KATHIAN (IRE)**, gr f Verglas (IRE)—Nurama **I & K Prince**
12 **MISTRESS AND MAID**, ch f Dutch Art—Passing Fancy **Mrs D. Lochhead**

Other Owners: Mr Alan Bright, Mrs Christine Bright, Mrs Penny Burton, Mr Lawrence Eke, Mr P. Gleeson, Mr R. J. Lampard, Mr Andrew Liddiard, Mr I. Prince, Mrs K. Prince, Mr Joseph Tuite, Mr Mark Wellbelove.

---

627 **MR ANDREW TURNELL, Swindon**
Postal: Elmcross House, Broad Hinton, Swindon, Wiltshire, SN4 9PF
Contacts: **PHONE** (01793) 731481 **FAX** (01793) 739001 **MOBILE** (07973) 933450
E-MAIL info@andyturnellracing.com **WEBSITE** www.andyturnellracing.com

1 **DAN'S WEE MAN**, 5, b g Kayf Tara—Hazel Bank Lass (IRE) **Mr M. J. Tedham**
2 **FAHA (IRE)**, 8, b m Catcher In The Rye (IRE)—Tarayib **Mr V Askew & CCC Partnership**
3 **RIVER DANCING (IRE)**, 7, b g Muhtarram (USA)—Peacefull River (IRE) **John & Heather Snook**
4 **ROUGH FIGHTER (USA)**, 5, b g Mizzen Mast (USA)—Louis d'or (USA) **Maori Partnership**
5 **SABLAZO (FR)**, 8, b g Ragmar (FR)—Daytona II (FR) **Miss S. Douglas-Pennant**
6 **SPANISH TREASURE (GER)**, 8, b g Black Sam Bellamy (IRE)—Santa Zinaada (GER) **Mr M. J. Tedham**
7 **SUBORDINATE (GER)**, 5, b g Echo of Light—Suborneuse (USA) **The Jumping Stars**
8 **THE DRUIDS NEPHEW (IRE)**, 7, b g King's Theatre (IRE)—Gifted **The Stonehenge Druids**
9 **ULLSWATER (IRE)**, 6, b g Singspiel (IRE)—Uluwatu (IRE) **The Jumping Stars**
10 **WHILEAWAY (USA)**, 5, b g Mizzen Mast (USA)—Routine (USA) **Maori Partnership**

Other Owners: V. Askew, Mrs L. S. Atwell, Mr S. M. Brown, Mr D. C. Codling, Mrs A. C. Crofts, Mr L. P. Dunne, Mrs A. M. Dunne, Mrs R. M. Hill, Mr L. G. Kimber, Mr S. T. Merry, Mrs D. J. Merry, Mrs C. A. Moysey, J. W. Snook, Mrs H. A. Snook, Mrs M. R. Taylor, Mr G. J. Villis.

Jockey (NH): James Banks, Nick Scholfield, Gerard Tumelty.

---

628 **MR BILL TURNER, Sherborne**
Postal: Sigwells Farm, Sigwells, Corton Denham, Sherborne, Dorset, DT9 4LN
Contacts: **PHONE** (01963) 220523 **FAX** (01963) 220046 **MOBILE** (07932) 100173
E-MAIL billturnerracing@gmail.com

1 **COCONUT KISSES**, 4, ch f Bahamian Bounty—Royal Mistress **Mr P. Venner**
2 **DEMOLITION BLUE (IRE)**, 5, b m Diamond Green (FR)—Amoras (IRE) **Miss Karen Theobald**
3 **DEW REWARD (IRE)**, 6, b g Aussie Rules (USA)—Shariyfa (FR) **Mrs D. Tucker**
4 **EDLOMOND (IRE)**, 8, gr g Great Palm (USA)—Samardana (IRE) **Mrs P. A. Turner**
5 **FLORAL SPINNER**, 7, b m Alflora (IRE)—Dawn Spinner **The Floral Farmers**
6 **FRECKLE FACE**, 7, br g Septieme Ciel (USA)—Wavet **Mrs C. M. Goldsmith**
7 **GILLY'S FILLY**, 4, b f With The Flow (USA)—True Dove **Mrs G Scott & Mr P & Mrs G Turner**
8 **HILLBILLY BOY (IRE)**, 4, b g Haafhd—Erreur (IRE) **Mr P. D. Moore**
9 **LAGAN KATIE**, 8, b m Kayf Tara—Bichette **Mrs S. E. Clarke**
10 **MISTERAY**, 4, ch g Singspiel (IRE)—Hannda (IRE) **Ansells Of Watford**

THREE-YEAR-OLDS

11 **ASPIRANT**, b g Rail Link—Affluent **Mrs P. A. Turner**
12 **EL DUQUE**, b g Byron—Royal Tavira Girl (IRE) **Ansells Of Watford**
13 **HIJA**, b f Avonbridge—Pantita **Titan Assets**
14 **PARADISE CHILD**, ch f Compton Place—Halfwaytoparadise **Mascalls Stud**
15 **PRINCESS TILLY**, ch f Proclamation (IRE)—Dusty Dazzler (IRE) **Trowbridge Office Cleaning Services Ltd**
16 **SHE'S A LUCKY LADY**, ch f Avonbridge—Lady Killer (IRE) **Mrs M. S. Teversham**
17 **TASHTU**, b f Tobougg (IRE)—Tashkiyla (FR) **Mrs C. W. Ward**

TWO-YEAR-OLDS

18 B f 17/3 Moss Vale (IRE)—Belle Watling (IRE) (Street Cry (IRE)) (1316) **Mrs S. E. Clarke**
19 B gr c 2/3 Hellvelyn—Bengers Lass (USA) (Orientate (USA)) (11428) **Mr E. A. Brook**
20 B f 13/4 Showcasing—Bling Bling (IRE) (Indian Ridge) **Mrs M. S. Teversham**
21 B f 25/4 Kodiac—Coral Dawn (IRE) (Trempolino (USA)) (16000) **The Huxley Partnership**

MR BILL TURNER - Continued

22 **DANCING SPRINGS (IRE)**, b f 18/4 Bushranger (IRE)—
                                     Deep Springs (USA) (Storm Cat (USA)) (1702) **Mr David Bell**
23 B c 3/3 Jeremy (USA)—House Rebel (IRE) (Spartacus (IRE)) (6580) **Mr E. A. Brook**
24 Gr c 19/3 Proclamation (IRE)—Lady Filly (Atraf) **Mrs M. S. Teversham**
25 Gr f 19/3 Hellvelyn—Lady Smith (Greensmith) **Mrs. M. S. Teversham**
26 B c 27/2 Showcasing—Lucky Dip (Tirol) **Tracy Turner**
27 **MAGIC ROUND (IRE)**, gr c 21/1 Zebedee—Street Kitty (IRE) (Tiger Hill (IRE)) (12000) **Gongolfin Syndicate**
28 Ch f 2/2 Aqlaam—Millsini (Rossini (USA)) **Tracy Turner**
29 Br c 25/3 Hellvelyn—Miss Brookie (The West (USA)) **Mrs M. S. Teversham**
30 B c 18/3 Strategic Prince—Moon Crest (IRE) (Singspiel (IRE)) **Tracy Turner**
31 B c 3/4 Moss Vale (IRE)—Rubilini (Bertolini (USA)) **Tracy Turner**
32 Br f 27/3 Striking Ambition—Straight As A Die (Pyramus (USA)) **Unity Farm Holiday Centre Ltd**
33 B c 25/4 Hellvelyn—Wavet (Pursuit of Love) **Mr B. Goldsmith**

Other Owners: Mr B. C. Ansell, Mrs B. C. Ansell, Mr R. L. Ansell, Mrs Natasha Ansell, Mrs Susan Hearn, Mr Barry Hearn, Mr Stuart George Lake, Mrs M. O'Sullivan, Mrs Gill Scott, Mr P. R. Turner, Mrs G. S. Turner.

Conditional: Ryan While. **Apprentice:** Ryan While.

---

629 MR JAMES TURNER, Helperby
Postal: Mayfield Farm, Norton-le-Clay, Helperby, York
Contacts: PHONE (01423) 322239 FAX (01423) 322239

1 **BONDI BEACH BOY**, 5, b g Misu Bond (IRE)—Nice One **Mr G. R. Turner & Mr H. Turner**
2 **NEEDY MCCREDIE**, 8, ch m Needwood Blade—Vocation (IRE) **J. R. Turner**
3 **SQUEALY KEELY**, 6, b m Kahyasi—Granny Shona (IRE) **J. R. Turner**

Other Owners: Mr G. R. Turner, Mr H. Turner.

Assistant Trainer: Oliver J. Turner

---

630 MRS KAREN TUTTY, Northallerton
Postal: Trenholme House Farm, Osmotherley, Northallerton, North Yorkshire, DL6 3QA
Contacts: PHONE (01609) 883624 FAX 01609 883624 MOBILE (07967) 837406
E-MAIL karentutty@btinternet.com WEBSITE www.karentuttyracing.co.uk

1 **BITUSA (USA)**, 4, b g Roman Ruler (USA)—Richen (USA) **Thoroughbred Homes Ltd**
2 **CROWN AND GLORY (IRE)**, 7, b g Turtle Island (IRE)—Monteleena (IRE) **Mr & Mrs W. H. Woods**
3 **LOYAL N TRUSTED**, 6, b g Motivator—Baby Don't Cry (USA) **Ivor Fox & Thoroughbred Homes Ltd**
4 **MERCERS ROW**, 7, b g Bahamian Bounty—Invincible **K. Fitzsimons**
5 **MONTJEN (IRE)**, 4, b f Montjeu (IRE)—Nuriva (USA) **Keep The Faith Partnership**
6 **SADDLERS MOT**, 10, b m Saddlers' Hall (IRE)—Be My Mot (IRE) **Grange Park Racing**
7 **SUNNY SIDE UP (IRE)**, 5, b m Refuse To Bend (IRE)—Feeling Wonderful (IRE) **Mrs S Atkinson & Mr S Leggott**
8 **TALENT SCOUT (IRE)**, 8, b g Exceed And Excel (AUS)—Taalluf (USA) **Thoroughbred Homes Ltd**

THREE-YEAR-OLDS

9 **EMILY DAVISON (IRE)**, gr f Moss Vale (IRE)—Carabine (USA) **Thoroughbred Homes Ltd**
10 **JACBEQUICK**, b g Calcutta—Toking N' Joken (IRE) **Cherry Garth Racing**
11 **PERCY'S GAL**, ch f Sir Percy—Galette **Arrand & Tutty**

TWO-YEAR-OLDS

12 Ch f 27/3 Arcano (IRE)—Dhuyoof (IRE) (Sinndar (IRE)) (3500) **Thoroughbred Homes Ltd**
13 B f 6/3 Sir Percy—Fly In Style (Hernando (FR)) (4761) **Thoroughbred Homes Ltd**
14 **FREIDA**, b f 16/2 Mullionmileanhour (IRE)—La Corujera (Case Law) (2666) **Keep The Faith Partnership**
15 B f 19/2 Royal Applause—Grasshoppergreen (IRE) (Barathea (IRE)) (1500) **Thoroughbred Homes Ltd**

Other Owners: Mr & Mrs C. G. Arrand, Miss S Atkinson & Mr S Leggott, Cherry Garth Racing, A. D. Crombie, Grange Park Racing, Keep The Faith Partnership, Mr E. Surr, J. M. Swinglehurst, Mrs G. M. Swinglehurst, Mr W. H. Woods, Mrs G. H. Woods.

Apprentice: Gemma Tutty. **Amateur:** Miss Phillipa Tutty.

631 MR NIGEL TWISTON-DAVIES, Cheltenham
Postal: T/a Grange Hill Farm Limited, Grange Hill Farm, Naunton, Cheltenham, Gloucestershire, GL54 3AY
Contacts: PHONE (01451) 850278 FAX (01451) 850101 MOBILE (07836) 664440
E-MAIL nigel@nigeltwistondavies.co.uk WEBSITE www.nigeltwistondavies.co.uk

1 ACCORDING TO TREV (IRE), 8, ch g Accordion—Autumn Sky (IRE) Mr F. J. Mills & Mr W. Mills
2 AFRICAN GOLD (IRE), 6, b g King's Theatre (IRE)—Mrs Dempsey (IRE) Walters Plant, J & J Potter & Egan
3 ALGERNON PAZHAM (IRE), 5, b g Milan—Kitty Star (IRE) Graham & Alison Jelley
4 ARTIC NIGHT (FR), 8, gr g Take Risks (FR)—Just Win (FR) The I.O.U. Partnership
5 ASTRACAD (FR), 8, br g Cadoudal (FR)—Astre Eria (FR) H. R. Mould
6 BALLY BRAES (IRE), 6, b g Old Vic—Gaelic Stream (IRE) Chris Haughey
7 BALLYBOLLEY (IRE), 5, b g Kayf Tara—Gales Hill (IRE) N. A. Twiston-Davies
8 BENBENS (IRE), 9, ch g Beneficial—Millicent Bridge (IRE) Mrs S. E. Such
9 BIG CASINO, 8, b g Court Cave (IRE)—Migsy Malone R. N. Jukes
10 BILLIE MAGERN, 10, b g Alderbrook—Outfield Exors of the Late Mr R. Nicholls
11 BROUSSE EN FEUX (FR), 11, ch m April Night (FR)—Antoniola (FR) N. A. Twiston-Davies
12 BUDDY LOVE, 7, gr m Silver Patriarch (IRE)—O My Love Mr S. Cottrill
13 CHURCH BRAY, 6, b g Kayf Tara—Castle Lynch (IRE) The Yes No Wait Sorries
14 COGRY, 5, b g King's Theatre (IRE)—Wyldello Graham & Alison Jelley
15 COLIN'S BROTHER, 4, b g Overbury (IRE)—Dd's Glenalla (IRE) Caroline Beresford-Wylie
16 COOTEHILL (IRE), 10, b g Alflora (IRE)—Dancing Dove Mrs F. E. Griffin
17 COUNT GUIDO DEIRO (IRE), 7, b g Accordion—Ivy Lane (IRE) R. Bevis
18 DOUBLE ROSS (IRE), 8, ch g Double Eclipse (IRE)—Kinross Options O Syndicate
19 FLEET FOX, 7, b g Alflora (IRE)—Minora (IRE) Tim Hardie & Gregg Robb
20 FOND MEMORY (IRE), 6, b g Dr Massini (IRE)—Glacier Lilly (IRE) The Stirling Partnership
21 FRONTIER SPIRIT (IRE), 10, b g New Frontier (IRE)—Psalmist Jump For Fun Racing
22 FRONTIER VIC, 7, b g Old Vic—Right On Target (IRE) Jump For Fun Racing
23 GALEB WARRIOR, 4, b g Duke of Marmalade (IRE)—Katrina (IRE) Tony Bloom
24 GETTING READY (IRE), 7, b g Westerner—Last Campaign (IRE) The I.O.U. Partnership
25 GINJO, 4, b f Sakhee (USA)—Gulshan Mrs J. K. Powell
26 GOAT CASTLE (IRE), 10, b g Goldmark (USA)—Rolands Girl (IRE) N. A. Twiston-Davies
27 GOLDEN JUBILEE (USA), 5, b br g Zavata (USA)—Love Play (USA) Mrs J. K. Powell
28 GOLDIE HORN, 6, ch m Where Or When (IRE)—Gulshan Mrs J. K. Powell
29 HAVE YOU SEEN ME (IRE), 11, b g Beneficial—Silent Supreme (IRE) The Maple Hurst Partnership
30 HE'S THE DADDY, 7, b g Generous (IRE)—Brambly Hedge Mr A. Gillman
31 HERECOMESTHEHOLLOW (IRE), 8, ch g Flemensfirth (USA)—
Drumcay Polly (IRE) The Hollow Bottom Partnership
32 HOLLOW BLUE SKY (FR), 7, gr g Turgeon (USA)—Run For Laborie (FR) The Hollow Partnership
33 HUNTERS LODGE (IRE), 8, ch g Subtle Power (IRE)—Native Orchid (IRE) Exors of the Late Mr R. Nicholls
34 I AM COLIN, 5, b g Zafeen (FR)—Dd's Glenalla (IRE) Mrs C. S. C. Beresford-Wylie
35 IMPERIAL LEADER (IRE), 6, b g Flemensfirth (USA)—
Glamorous Leader (IRE) Imperial Racing Partnership No.2
36 JAUNTY JOURNEY, 13, b g Karinga Bay—Jaunty June Mr C. Roberts
37 KAYLIF ARAMIS, 7, b g Kayf Tara—Ara The Grangers
38 KILVERGAN BOY (IRE), 10, br g Zagreb (USA)—Brigante (IRE) The Yes No Wait Sorries
39 KING'S TEMPEST, 5, b h Act One—Queen of Spades (IRE) Rita Vaughan
40 LADY FINGERS, 6, b m Kirkwall—Wellfield N. A. Twiston-Davies
41 LISTEN BOY (IRE), 8, ch g Presenting—Buckalong (IRE) Bryan & Philippa Burrough
42 LITTLE JON, 6, b g Pasternak—Jowoody N. A. Twiston-Davies
43 LITTLE POP, 6, b g Pasternak—Flagship Daisy May (IRE) Mrs S. E. Such
44 LODGICIAN (IRE), 12, b g Grand Lodge (USA)—Dundel (IRE) The Yes No Wait Sorries
45 MAHOGANY BLAZE (FR), 12, b g Kahyasi—Mahogany River Mrs L. M. Berryman
46 MAJOR MALARKEY (IRE), 11, b g Supreme Leader—Valley (IRE) Baker Dodd & Cooke
47 MASTER RAJEEM (USA), 5, b br g Street Cry (IRE)—Rajeem Million in Mind Partnership
48 MINI MUCK, 8, b m Kayf Tara—Madam Muck N. A. Twiston-Davies
49 MISSION TO MARS (IRE), 5, b g Presenting—Nivalf Staplegrove Racing & David Langdon
50 MUCKLE ROE (IRE), 5, b g Westerner—Island Crest Mrs V. J. Lane
51 MY BOY PADDY (IRE), 10, ch g Accordion—Securon Rose (IRE) Miss K. J. Holland
52 NIGHT SAFE, 13, b g Safety Catch (USA)—Rock All Night (IRE) Ian Dimmer
53 NOWWEARESEVEN, 7, b m Court Cave (IRE)—Migsy Malone Richard Jukes
54 OSCAR MAGIC, 7, b br g Oscar (IRE)—Just An Illusion (IRE) Mrs L. M. Berryman
55 PAPRADON, 10, b g Tobougg (IRE)—Salvezza (IRE) Alf Cresser
56 PETTIFOUR (IRE), 12, b g Supreme Leader—Queen of Natives (IRE) Mr J. B. Pettifer
57 PIGEON ISLAND (IRE), 11, gr g Daylami (IRE)—Morina (USA) H. R. Mould
58 POWER PACK JACK (IRE), 11, b g Rudimentary (USA)—Monas Jem (IRE) N. A. Twiston-Davies

MR NIGEL TWISTON-DAVIES - Continued

59 **PURE SCIENCE (IRE)**, 6, ch g Galileo (IRE)—Rebelline (IRE) **H. R. Mould**
60 **RED RIVERMAN**, 6, b g Haafhd—Mocca (IRE) **N. A. Twiston-Davies**
61 **RED ROCCO (IRE)**, 7, ch g Croco Rouge (IRE)—Youbetido (IRE) **Glen's Fools 2**
62 **RHUM (FR)**, 9, ch g Dark Moondancer—Ireland (IRE) **N. A. Twiston-Davies**
63 **RIDDLEOFTHESANDS (IRE)**, 10, b br g Oscar (IRE)—Flaxen Pride (IRE) **N. A. Twiston-Davies**
64 **ROSSONERI (IRE)**, 7, b g Milan—Native Crystal (IRE) **P. J. Dixon**
65 **ROYAL RIVIERA**, 8, b g Nayef (USA)—Miss Cap Ferrat **N. A. Twiston-Davies**
66 **SAME DIFFERENCE (IRE)**, 8, b g Mr Combustible (IRE)—Sarahs Reprive (IRE) **Mrs R. I. Vaughan**
67 **SAUDI PEARL (IRE)**, 6, br g Rakti—Cheeky Weeky **The New Club Partnership**
68 **SPEED MASTER (IRE)**, 8, b g King's Theatre (IRE)—Handy Lass **Walters Plant Hire Spiers & Hartwell**
69 **SPLASH OF GINGE**, 6, b g Oscar (IRE)—Land of Honour **Mr J. Neild**
70 **STORMHOEK (IRE)**, 9, ch g Alderbrook—Auntie Honnie (IRE) **The New Club Partnership**
71 **SUSQUEHANNA RIVER (IRE)**, 7, b g Indian River (FR)—Calistoga (IRE) **The Wasting Assets**
72 **SYBARITE (FR)**, 8, b br g Dark Moondancer—Haida III (FR) **H. R. Mould**
73 **TARA MUCK**, 7, b m Kayf Tara—Madam Muck **N. A. Twiston-Davies**
74 **TARA ROSE**, 9, br m Kayf Tara—True Rose (IRE) **Jimmy & Susie Wenman**
75 **THE COCKNEY MACKEM (IRE)**, 8, b g Milan—Divine Prospect (IRE) **Mills & Mason Partnership**
76 **THE MUSICAL GUY (IRE)**, 8, b g Lahib (USA)—Orchestral Sport (IRE) **The Musical Guy's Girls**
77 **THE NEW ONE (IRE)**, 6, b g King's Theatre (IRE)—Thuringe (FR) **Mrs S. E. Such**
78 **TOUR DES CHAMPS (FR)**, 7, b br g Robin des Champs (FR)—Massada (FR) **H. R. Mould**
79 **TRAFALGAR (FR)**, 7, b g Laveron—Dzaoudzie (FR) **Mr & Mrs Gordon Pink**
80 **TULLYRAINE (IRE)**, 10, b g Winged Love (IRE)—Struell Princess **Geoffrey & Donna Keeys**
81 **VIKING BLOND (FR)**, 9, ch g Varese (FR)—Sweet Jaune (FR) **Mrs C. M. Mould**
82 **WHAT A GOOD NIGHT (IRE)**, 6, br g Westerner—Southern Skies (IRE) **Mr & Mrs Gordon Pink**
83 **WHAT A WARRIOR (IRE)**, 7, b g Westerner—Be Right (IRE) **Mr & Mrs Gordon Pink**
84 **WHAT AN OSCAR (IRE)**, 9, b g Oscar (IRE)—Katie Buckers (IRE) **Mr & Mrs Gordon Pink**
85 **WINGED CRUSADER (IRE)**, 6, b g Winged Love (IRE)—Reine Berengere (FR) **Imperial Racing Partnership No.6**
86 **WOOD YER (IRE)**, 8, ch g Anshan—Glenasheen (IRE) **Miss K. J. Holland**
87 **ZAYFIRE ARAMIS**, 5, ch g Zafeen (FR)—Kaylifa Aramis **Aramis Racing**

Other Owners: Mr Dave Arthur, Mr John B. Baker, Mr B. R. H. Burrough, Mrs Philippa Burrough, Mr John Cantrill, Mr Chris Coley, Mr Peter G. Cooke, Mr G. T. G. Dodd, Mr Ian Dunbar, Mr Peter Earl, Egan Waste Services Ltd, Mrs Judy England, Mr Graham Jelley, Mrs Alison Jelley, Mr Geoffrey Keeys, Mrs Donna Keeys, Mr H. J. Kelly, Mr David Langdon, Mrs S. A. MacEchern, Mr David Mason, Mr Martin Maxted, Mrs Susan Maxted, Mr F. J. Mills, Mr W. R. Mills, Mr Nigel Payne, Mrs Scilla Phillips, Mrs Isobel Phipps Coltman, Mr G. K. G. Pink, Mrs K. M. Pink, Mr J. E. Potter, Mrs J. E. Potter, Mr Ian A. Robinson, Mrs C. M. Scott, Spiers & Hartwell Ltd, Mr N. A. Twiston-Davies, Walters Plant Hire Ltd, Mr Jimmy Wenman, Mrs Susie Wenman, Mr S. Wignall.

Assistant Trainer: Carl Llewellyn

Jockey (NH): Sam Twiston-Davies, David England. **Conditional:** Ryan Hatch. **Apprentice:** William Twiston-Davies.

---

632 MR JAMES UNETT, Oswestry
Postal: **Garden Cottage, Tedsmore, West Felton, Oswestry, Shropshire, SY11 4HD**
Contacts: PHONE **(01691) 610001** FAX **(01691) 610001** MOBILE **(07887) 534753**
E-MAIL **jamesunett1327@yahoo.co.uk** WEBSITE **www.jamesunettracing.com**

1 **CHES JICARO (IRE)**, 6, ch g Majestic Missile (IRE)—Kelso Magic (USA) **J. W. Unett**
2 **CLARATY**, 4, b f Firebreak—Claradotnet **G. D. Kendrick**
3 **CLARY (IRE)**, 4, b f Clodovil (IRE)—Kibarague **Exors of the Late Mr P. Fetherston-Godley**
4 5, B g Fair Mix (IRE)—Firebird Annie (IRE)
5 **LABYRINTHINE (IRE)**, 4, ch f Pivotal—Madame Cerito (USA) **Miss C. Doyle**
6 **MCCOOL BANNANAS**, 6, b g Firebreak—Dances With Angels (IRE) **Mark Sheehy & Malcolm Hall**
7 **MONUMENTAL MAN**, 5, b g Vital Equine (IRE)—Spark Up **Exors of the Late Mr P. Fetherston-Godley**

THREE-YEAR-OLDS

8 B c Cockney Rebel (IRE)—Dances With Angels (IRE) **Mr M. A. Sheehy**
9 **DUTCH LADY ROSEANE**, b f Dutch Art—Lady Rose Anne (IRE) **Exors of the Late Mr P. Fetherston-Godley**
10 **MINNYVINNY**, b f Multiplex—Bounty Reef **Black & Whites**
11 B c Rob Roy (USA)—Spark Up

Other Owners: Mr M. B. Hall, Ms V. Saxon, Mr M. A. Smith.

Assistant Trainer: Miss C. H. Jones

633 MR JOHN UPSON, Towcester
Postal: **Glebe Stables, Blakesley Heath, Maidford, Towcester, Northamptonshire, NN12 8HN**
Contacts: **PHONE (01327) 860043 FAX (01327) 860238**

1 **DRAMATIC VICTORY (IRE)**, 7, b g Old Vic—Pinky The Nose (IRE) **The Peter Partnership**
2 **DUNE ISLAND**, 6, b m Compton Admiral—Desert Island Disc **Mrs J. M. Owen**
3 **HALIANA**, 5, ch m Sakhee (USA)—Boojum **Mr N. A. Price**
4 **ISAAC'S WARRIOR (IRE)**, 8, b g Pushkin (IRE)—Point The Finger (IRE) **Lord Nicholas Wilson**
5 **KEVIN FANCY (IRE)**, 8, b m Zagreb (USA)—Top Flight Travel (IRE) **The Nap Hand Partnership**
6 **OAK WOOD (IRE)**, 6, ch g Bienamado (USA)—Oakum (IRE) **Lord Nicholas Wilson**
7 **QUEL BRUERE (FR)**, 10, gr g Sassanian (USA)—Housseliere (FR) **Miss Tracey Leeson**
8 **ROSE OF MARRON (IRE)**, 7, b g Dilshaan—Sunset Park (IRE) **The Marron Partnership**
9 **SAMIZDAT (FR)**, 11, b g Soviet Star (USA)—Secret Account (FR) **Honorvell Partnership**
10 **THEFRIENDLYGREMLIN**, 6, b g Vinnie Roe (IRE)—Queens Fantasy **The Nap Hand Partnership**

Other Owners: M. H. Beesley, D. Deveney, G. G. Fowler, Mr R. W. George, Mrs K. Hopewell, Mrs J. M. Letts, Miss K. J. Letts, M. E. White.

634 MR MARK USHER, Lambourn
Postal: **Saxon House Stables, Upper Lambourn, Hungerford, Berkshire, RG17 8QH**
Contacts: **PHONE (01488) 72598 FAX (01488) 73630 MOBILE (07831) 873531**
E-MAIL markusherracing@btconnect.com WEBSITE www.markusherracing.co.uk

1 **BAY FORTUNA**, 5, b g Old Vic—East Rose **The Ridgeway Partnership**
2 **BLACK TRUFFLE (FR)**, 4, b c Kyllachy—Some Diva **Ushers Court**
3 **BULLSEYE BABE**, 4, ch f Notnowcato—Mary Sea (FR) **Mr Clark Fortune**
4 **DIRECT TRADE**, 4, ch f Trade Fair—Bold Love **Saxon House Racing**
5 **HAATEFINA**, 4, b f Haatef (USA)—Felona **Ushers Court**
6 **HONOURABLE KNIGHT (IRE)**, 6, b g Celtic Swing—Deemeh (IRE) **Mrs T. J. Channing-Williams**
7 **HOPE POINT**, 6, b m Overbury (IRE)—East Rose **The Ridgeway Partnership**
8 **KATMAI RIVER (IRE)**, 7, b g Choisir (AUS)—Katavi (USA)
9 **LADY PERCY (IRE)**, 5, b m Sir Percy—Genuinely (IRE) **Ushers Court**
10 **LITTLECOTE LADY**, 5, b m Byron—Barefooted Flyer (USA) **Littlecote House Racing**
11 **NOOR AL HAYA (IRE)**, 4, b f Tamayuz—Hariya (IRE) **Imran Butt & High Five Racing**
12 6, B m Cadeaux Genereux—Persea (IRE)
13 **REGINALD CLAUDE**, 6, b g Monsieur Bond (IRE)—Miller's Melody **High Five Racing**
14 **RIDGEWAY HAWK**, 6, ch g Monsieur Bond (IRE)—Barefooted Flyer (USA) **Goodracing Partnership**
15 **SPICE FAIR**, 7, ch g Trade Fair—Focosa (ITY) **Saxon House Racing**

THREE-YEAR-OLDS
16 **BIRIKYNO**, b g Piccolo—Alvarinho Lady **Saxon House Racing**
17 B f Dr Massini (IRE)—Focosa (ITY) **Mrs D J Hughes**
18 **HARLEQUIN JINKS**, b f Lucky Story (USA)—Crofters Ceilidh **The High Jinks**
19 **IGNIGHT**, ch c Compton Place—Time Clash **Mrs D. J. Hughes**
20 **KRACKERJILL (IRE)**, b f Kheleyf (USA)—Knockenduff **High Five Racing**
21 **MINNIE MIRACLE**, ch f Compton Place—Splicing **Ushers Court**
22 **MIRACLE OF MEDINAH**, ch c Milk It Mick—Smart Ass (IRE) **The High Jinks Partnership**
23 **SAXONY**, b f Bertolini (USA)—Just Down The Road (IRE) **Saxon House Racing**
24 **SEE NO SHIPS**, b f Compton Place—Queen of Havana (USA)

TWO-YEAR-OLDS
25 **ARLECCHINO'S LEAP**, b c 29/2 Kheleyf (USA)—Donna Giovanna (Mozart (IRE)) (20000) **Mr Kevin Senior**
26 Ch f 29/2 Monsieur Bond (IRE)—Dazzling Daisy (Shareef Dancer (USA)) (4285) **High Five Racing**
27 Ch c 24/3 Bahamian Bounty—Eternity Ring (Alzao (USA)) (12000) **High Five Racing**
28 B c 3/3 Rip Van Winkle (IRE)—Foolish Ambition (GER) (Danehill Dancer (IRE)) (15485) **Mr Imran Butt**

Other Owners: Mr R. H. Brookes, Mr Imran Butt, Mrs Jean Johnson, Mr C. A. Kneller, Mr M. Swinswood, Mr M. D. I. Usher, Mr Carl West-Meads.

Jockey (flat): Liam Keniry, Racheal Kneller, David Probert. **Jockey (NH):** David Crosse. **Apprentice:** Charlotte Jenner.

635 MR ROGER VARIAN, Newmarket

Postal: **Kremlin House Stables, Fordham Road, Newmarket, Suffolk, CB8 7AQ**
Contacts: **PHONE (01638) 661702 FAX (01638) 667018**
E-MAIL office@varianstable.com WEBSITE www.varianstable.com

1 **AGERZAM**, 4, b g Holy Roman Emperor (IRE)—Epiphany **Saleh Al Homaizi & Imad Al Sagar**
2 **ALJAMAAHEER (IRE)**, 5, ch h Dubawi (IRE)—Kelly Nicole (IRE) **Hamdan Al Maktoum**
3 **AMBIVALENT (IRE)**, 5, b m Authorized (IRE)—Darrery **A. Saeed**
4 **CAMERON HIGHLAND (IRE)**, 5, b h Galileo (IRE)—Landmark (USA) **H.R.H. Sultan Ahmad Shah**
5 **EKTIHAAM (IRE)**, 5, b g Invincible Spirit (IRE)—Liscune (IRE) **Hamdan Al Maktoum**
6 **ELKAAYED (USA)**, 4, ch c Distorted Humor (USA)—Habibti (USA) **Hamdan Al Maktoum**
7 **ELSINIAAR**, 4, bl g New Approach (IRE)—Comic (IRE) **Hamdan Al Maktoum**
8 **ETON FOREVER (IRE)**, 7, b g Oratorio (IRE)—True Joy (IRE) **H.R.H. Sultan Ahmad Shah**
9 **EXCEPTIONELLE**, 4, br f Exceed And Excel (AUS)—Turning Leaf (IRE) **Thurloe Thoroughbreds XXX**
10 **FAMILLIARITY**, 4, ch f Nayef (USA)—Millistar **Helena Springfield Ltd**
11 **FARRAAJ (IRE)**, 5, b g Dubai Destination (USA)—Pastorale **Sheikh Ahmed Al Maktoum**
12 **FRASERS HILL**, 5, ch g Selkirk (USA)—Shemriyna (IRE) **H.R.H. Sultan Ahmad Shah**
13 **HASHEEM**, 4, ch g New Approach (IRE)—Masaafat **Hamdan Al Maktoum**
14 **HORSTED KEYNES (FR)**, 4, ch g Giant's Causeway (USA)—Viking's Cove (USA) **Mrs F. H. Hay**
15 **JALADEE**, 4, b g Cape Cross (IRE)—Atamana (IRE) **Sheikh Ahmed Al Maktoum**
16 **JUSTINEO**, 5, b h Oasis Dream—Loulwa (IRE) **Saleh Al Homaizi & Imad Al Sagar**
17 **MIGUEL GRAU (IRE)**, 4, b g City Zip (USA)—Zuri Ridge (USA) **Mr J. Barton & Mr C. Pizarro**
18 **MORAWIJ**, 4, ch c Exceed And Excel (AUS)—Sister Moonshine (FR) **Sheikh Ahmed Al Maktoum**
19 **MUTASHADED (USA)**, 4, b c Raven's Pass (USA)—Sortita (GER) **Hamdan Al Maktoum**
20 **ONE PEKAN (IRE)**, 4, b g Hard Spun (USA)—Stormy Blessing (USA) **H.R.H. Sultan Ahmad Shah**
21 **PANETTONE (IRE)**, 5, b m Montjeu (IRE)—Tea Break **Mr Duncan Jones & Dr Sosie Kassab**
22 **PERFECT HEART**, 5, gr g Dalakhani (IRE)—Maid To Perfection **Normandie Stud Ltd**
23 **POOLE HARBOUR (IRE)**, 5, b g Elusive City (USA)—Free Lance (IRE) **Hamdan Al Maktoum**
24 **PRINCESS LOULOU (IRE)**, 4, ch f Pivotal—Aiming **Saleh Al Homaizi & Imad Al Sagar**
25 **PUTRA ETON (IRE)**, 4, b c Danehill Dancer (IRE)—Anna Pallida (USA) **H.R.H. Sultan Ahmad Shah**
26 **ROCKY GROUND (IRE)**, 4, b c Acclamation—Keriyka (IRE) **Clipper Logistics & Cheveley Park Stud**
27 **SEVERIANO (USA)**, 4, b g Danehill Dancer (IRE)—Time Control **Merry Fox Stud Limited**
28 **SOUND HEARTS (USA)**, 5, b br m Sir Percy—Crystal Seas **Mr Y. Masuda**
29 **SPORTING GOLD (IRE)**, 5, b g Shirocco (GER)—Pink Stone (FR) **A. D. Spence**
30 **STEPS (IRE)**, 6, br g Verglas (IRE)—Killinallan **Michael Hill**
31 **TAFAWUK (USA)**, 5, b g Nayef (USA)—Yaqeen **Michael Hill**
32 **WANDSWORTH (IRE)**, 4, br g Authorized (IRE)—Henties Bay (IRE) **H.R.H. Sultan Ahmad Shah**
33 **WANNABE YOUR MAN**, 4, b c Halling (USA)—Wannabe Posh (IRE) **Normandie Stud Ltd**

THREE-YEAR-OLDS

34 **ALJAAZIAH**, b br f Medaglia d'oro (USA)—Eswarah **Hamdan Al Maktoum**
35 **ALMASHOOQA (USA)**, b br f Dubai (IRE)—Almoutezah (USA) **Hamdan Al Maktoum**
36 **AMASEENA (IRE)**, gr f Shamardal (USA)—Indian Belle (IRE) **Clipper Group Holdings Ltd**
37 **AMBIANCE (IRE)**, b c Camacho—Thawrah (IRE) **Prince A. A. Faisal**
38 **ANIPA**, ch f Sea The Stars (IRE)—Anna Amalia (IRE) **N. Bizakov**
39 **AYRAD (IRE)**, ch c Dalakhani (IRE)—Sweet Firebird (IRE) **Saleh Al Homaizi & Imad Al Sagar**
40 **BAAREZ (USA)**, ch c Hard Spun (USA)—Sortita (GER) **Hamdan Al Maktoum**
41 **BATTERSEA**, b c Galileo (IRE)—Gino's Spirits **H.R.H. Sultan Ahmad Shah**
42 **CERTIFICATE**, ch c Pivotal—Graduation **Cheveley Park Stud Limited**
43 **CLASSICAL ART (IRE)**, ch c Excellent Art—Ask Carol **Mrs S. M. Roy**
44 **DANCING SHIROCCO (IRE)**, b f Shirocco (GER)—Danzelline **Sheikh J. Al Dalmook Maktoum**
45 **DEADLINE DAY (IRE)**, b c Montjeu (IRE)—Madame Cerito (USA) **A. D. Spence**
46 **DORRAAR (IRE)**, b f Shamardal (USA)—Dorrati (USA) **Sheikh Ahmed Al Maktoum**
47 **DOUBLE UP**, b c Exceed And Excel (AUS)—My Love Thomas (IRE) **Mr A D Spence & Mr M B Spence**
48 **DYNAMIC VISION (IRE)**, b c Shamardal (USA)—Mazaaya (USA) **S. Ali**
49 **EJADAH (IRE)**, b f Clodovil (IRE)—Bintalreef (USA) **Hamdan Al Maktoum**
50 **EL NAJMM (IRE)**, ch c Sea The Stars (IRE)—My Dubai (IRE) **Sheikh Ahmed Al Maktoum**
51 **ELSHAADIN**, gr f Dalakhani (IRE)—Distinctive Look (IRE) **Hamdan Al Maktoum**
52 **EMARATIYA ANA (IRE)**, b f Excellent Art—Tina Heights **A. Al Shaikh**
53 **EMIRATI SPIRIT**, b c New Approach (IRE)—Dance Lively (USA) **A. Al Shaikh**
54 **FERAYHA (IRE)**, b f Cape Cross (IRE)—Albahja **Sheikh Ahmed Al Maktoum**
55 **GO SAKHEE**, br g Sakhee's Secret—Bling Bling (IRE) **K Allen G Moss R & S Marchant & G Jarvis**
56 **HADAATHA (IRE)**, gr f Sea The Stars (IRE)—Hathrah (IRE) **Hamdan Al Maktoum**
57 **HIGHLY EXCITED (USA)**, ch g Exchange Rate (USA)—Miss Delta Dawn (USA) **Mrs F. H. Hay**
58 **HUMOUR (IRE)**, b c Invincible Spirit (IRE)—Hucking Hot **Highclere Thoroughbred Racing - Heritage**

MR ROGER VARIAN - Continued

59 **IDDER (IRE)**, br c Authorized (IRE)—Epiphany **Saleh Al Homaizi & Imad Al Sagar**
60 **IGIDER (IRE)**, b c Teofilo (IRE)—Changeable **Saleh Al Homaizi & Imad Al Sagar**
61 **JAAHIEZ (USA)**, b c More Than Ready (USA)—Nasmatt **Sheikh Ahmed Al Maktoum**
62 **KAFEEL (USA)**, b g First Samurai (USA)—Ishraak (USA) **Hamdan Al Maktoum**
63 **KEEPER'S RING (USA)**, b f Street Cry (IRE)—Liffey Dancer (IRE) **Merry Fox Stud Limited**
64 **KHATIBA (IRE)**, b f Kheleyf (USA)—Tempete **Sheikh Ahmed Al Maktoum**
65 **KING'S PROCESSION (IRE)**, ch c Teofilo (IRE)—Sateen **S. Suhail**
66 **KINGSTON HILL**, gr ro c Mastercraftsman (IRE)—Audacieuse **Mr P. D. Smith**
67 **KNAVERY (USA)**, b br c Candy Ride (ARG)—Tight Spin (USA) **Qatar Racing Limited**
68 **LABJAAR**, ch g Dutch Art—Interlace **Sheikh Ahmed Al Maktoum**
69 **LADY SPARKLER (IRE)**, b f Tamayuz—Capote West (USA) **Sotirios Hassiakos & Maurice Manasseh**
70 **LAFTAH (IRE)**, b f Invincible Spirit (IRE)—Liscune (IRE) **Hamdan Al Maktoum**
71 **MADAME MERE (IRE)**, b f Dalakhani (IRE)—Napoleon's Sister (IRE) **Normandie Stud Ltd**
72 **MADE WITH LOVE**, b c Exceed And Excel (AUS)—Maid To Perfection **Normandie Stud Ltd**
73 **MAHAABA (IRE)**, b f Oasis Dream—Masaafat **Hamdan Al Maktoum**
74 **MASTER OF ALKMAAR**, ch c Dutch Art—Lalina (GER) **Mr Michael Hill & Mrs Hanako Varian**
75 **MUHAWALAH (IRE)**, ch f Nayef (USA)—Al Ishq (FR) **Hamdan Al Maktoum**
76 **MUNATAS**, b c Sea The Stars (IRE)—Dashing (USA) **Saleh Al Homaizi & Imad Al Sagar**
77 **MUSHIR**, b c Oasis Dream—Shimah (USA) **Hamdan Al Maktoum**
78 **MUSTAJJID**, b c Byron—Skara Brae **Hamdan Al Maktoum**
79 **MUTARAADIF (USA)**, b c Dynaformer (USA)—Dawla **Hamdan Al Maktoum**
80 **OXBOW LAKE (IRE)**, b br f Dynaformer (USA)—Shelly River (USA) **S. Ali**
81 **PERYZAT (IRE)**, b f Mastercraftsman (IRE)—Plethora **N. Bizakov**
82 **POPPING CANDY**, br f Oasis Dream—Blessing **Lordship Stud**
83 **PRETZEL (IRE)**, ch c New Approach (IRE)—Foodbroker Fancy (IRE) **Normandie Stud Ltd**
84 **PRINCESS NOOR (IRE)**, b f Holy Roman Emperor (IRE)—Gentle Night **Saleh Al Homaizi & Imad Al Sagar**
85 **QUASQAZAH**, ch g Bahamian Bounty—Rock Lily **Hamdan Al Maktoum**
86 **QUEEN'S DREAM (IRE)**, b f Oasis Dream—Queen of Pentacles (IRE) **Normandie Stud Ltd**
87 **RAINBEAM**, b f Rock of Gibraltar (IRE)—Rainbow Queen **Cheveley Park Stud Limited**
88 **RAPID ADVANCE**, b c Medicean—Snow Gretel (IRE) **S. Suhail**
89 **REESHA**, b f Teofilo (IRE)—Sana Abel (IRE) **Hamdan Al Maktoum**
90 **REKDHAT (IRE)**, b br f Shamardal (USA)—Taarkod (IRE) **Sheikh Ahmed Al Maktoum**
91 **SHERIFF'S STAR (IRE)**, gr g Lawman (FR)—Silver Bandana (USA) **S. Suhail**
92 **STAR JET (IRE)**, b gr f Teofilo (IRE)—Silver Shoon (IRE) **Ladas**
93 **STEVE ROGERS (IRE)**, b c Montjeu (IRE)—Three Owls (IRE) **N. Bizakov**
94 **SYNERGISE**, ch c Danehill Dancer (IRE)—Splashdown **Mr K. J. P. Gundlach**
95 **TA AMMOL**, b f Halling (USA)—Anaamil (IRE) **Sheikh Ahmed Al Maktoum**
96 **TAKREYM (IRE)**, b g Clodovil (IRE)—Somoushe (IRE) **Sheikh Ahmed Al Maktoum**
97 **TALMADA (USA)**, b f Cape Cross (IRE)—Aryaamm (IRE) **Sheikh Ahmed Al Maktoum**
98 **TAWEYLA (IRE)**, b f Teofilo (IRE)—Qasirah (IRE) **Sheikh Ahmed Al Maktoum**
99 **TEARS OF THE SUN**, b f Mastercraftsman (IRE)—Perfect Star **Qatar Racing Limited**
100 **THREE CLIFFS**, b c Exceed And Excel (AUS)—Gower Song **H.R.H. Sultan Ahmad Shah**
101 **THURAYAAT**, b f Tamayuz—Ghaidaa (IRE) **Hamdan Al Maktoum**
102 **TOOFI (FR)**, b c Henrythenavigator (USA)—Silver Bark **Saleh Al Homaizi & Imad Al Sagar**
103 **TWEEDSWOOD (IRE)**, ch c New Approach (IRE)—Rafting (IRE) **Mrs F. H. Hay**
104 **TWILIGHT SKY**, b f Authorized (IRE)—La Sky (IRE) **Lordship Stud**
105 **YAGHEER (IRE)**, b c Lawman (FR)—Dawn Raid (IRE) **Sheikh Ahmed Al Maktoum**

TWO-YEAR-OLDS

106 B f 27/4 Iffraaj—Albahja (Sinndar (IRE)) **Sheikh Ahmed Al Maktoum**
107 **ALMOHTASEB**, b c 20/2 Oasis Dream—Cuis Ghaire (IRE) (Galileo (IRE)) **Hamdan Al Maktoum**
108 **ALMUTAMARRED (USA)**, ch c 21/1 Street Cry (USA)—Sortita (GER) (Monsun (GER)) **Hamdan Al Maktoum**
109 **AMERICAN ARTIST (IRE)**, ch c 25/4 Danehill Dancer (IRE)—
American Adventure (USA) (Miswaki (USA)) (86000) **Thurloe Thoroughbreds XXXV**
110 **ATLETICO (IRE)**, b c 26/2 Kodiac—Queenofthefairies (Pivotal) (80000) **A. D. Spence**
111 B c 10/3 Oasis Dream—Balalaika (Sadler's Wells (USA)) **Unregistered Partnership**
112 B c 22/2 Mastercraftsman (IRE)—Chanter (Lomitas) (120000) **Mrs F. H. Hay**
113 Gr f 31/1 Verglas (IRE)—Cover Look (SAF) (Fort Wood (USA)) (17034) **K. A. Dasmal**
114 **DASAATEER (IRE)**, b c 6/3 Mount Nelson—Trishuli (Indian Ridge) (82000) **Hamdan Al Maktoum**
115 B c 1/4 Dansili—Dashing (Sadler's Wells (USA)) **Saleh Al Homaizi & Imad Al Sagar**
116 **EFFECTUAL**, b f 22/2 Exceed And Excel (AUS)—Our Faye (College Chapel) (72000) **Cheveley Park Stud Limite**
117 Gr ro c 13/2 Henrythenavigator (USA)—
Eightyfivebroadst (USA) (Unbridled's Song (USA)) (116143) **Saleh Al Homaizi & Imad Al Sagar**
118 B c 23/3 Acclamation—Emerald Peace (IRE) (Green Desert (USA)) (75000) **Sheikh Ahmed Al Maktoum**
119 B c 29/4 Vale of York (IRE)—Endless Peace (IRE) (Russian Revival (USA)) (28000)

MR ROGER VARIAN - Continued

120 **ESTIKHRAAJ**, b c 24/3 Dansili—Shimah (USA) (Storm Cat (USA)) **Hamdan Al Maktoum**
121 **ETTIHADI (IRE)**, b f 19/4 Duke of Marmalade (IRE)—
                     Naval Affair (IRE) (Last Tycoon) (23228) **Ahmad Abdulla Al Shaikh & Co**
122 **FAVORINA (GER)**, b f 21/3 Desert Prince (IRE)—Fantasia (GER) (Monsun (GER)) (10065) **Mr Y. Masuda**
123 **FIVE OF DIAMONDS (FR)**, b f 19/2 Peintre Celebre (USA)—
                     Give Me Five (GER) (Monsun (GER)) (115000) **A. D. Spence**
124 Br c 13/4 Lawman (FR)—Fonda (USA) (Quiet American (USA)) (280000) **Saleh Al Homaizi & Imad Al Sagar**
125 **FRENCH DRESSING**, b f 19/3 Sea The Stars (IRE)—Foodbroker Fancy (IRE) (Halling (USA)) **Normandie Stud Ltd**
126 B f 7/2 Exceed And Excel (AUS)—Gimasha (Cadeaux Genereux) **Z. A. Galadari**
127 **GUILTY TWELVE (USA)**, b f 23/3 Giant's Causeway (USA)—
                     Arkadina (IRE) (Danehill (USA)) **Merry Fox Stud Limited**
128 B f 29/3 Arcano (IRE)—Heart's Desire (IRE) (Royal Applause) (23228) **Saleh Al Homaizi & Imad Al Sagar**
129 **INTILAAQ (USA)**, b c 12/4 Dynaformer (USA)—Torrestrella (IRE) (Orpen (USA)) **Hamdan Al Maktoum**
130 **KHAWAATER**, ch f 25/1 Haatef (USA)—Balaagha (USA) (Mr Greeley (USA)) **Hamdan Al Maktoum**
131 **KNIGHT OF SWORDS**, b c 24/2 Cape Cross (IRE)—Queen of Pentacles (IRE) (Selkirk (USA)) **Normandie Stud Ltd**
132 **KNIGHT OF WANDS**, b c 13/3 Azamour (IRE)—
                     Maid To Treasure (IRE) (Rainbow Quest (USA)) **Normandie Stud Ltd**
133 B c 9/4 Kyllachy—Labisa (IRE) (High Chaparral (IRE)) (80000) **Sheikh Ahmed Al Maktoum**
134 **LADY IN WHITE (IRE)**, gr f 10/2 Zebedee—
                     Alexander Phantom (IRE) (Soviet Star (USA)) (32000) **Cheveley Park Stud Limited**
135 **LAYALEE (IRE)**, b f 19/3 Lawman (FR)—Red Feather (IRE) (Marju (IRE)) (340000) **Hamdan Al Maktoum**
136 B f 9/2 Iffraaj—Loulwa (IRE) (Montjeu (IRE)) **Saleh Al Homaizi & Imad Al Sagar**
137 **MALJAA**, ch c 7/2 Paco Boy (IRE)—Kerry's Dream (Tobougg (IRE)) (76190) **Hamdan Al Maktoum**
138 **MANHATTAN PRINCESS**, ch f 1/4 Pivotal—
                     Fibou (USA) (Seeking The Gold (USA)) (70000) **Mr Simon Munir & Mr Isaac Souede**
139 **MARKABAH (IRE)**, b f 14/4 Dubawi (IRE)—Ghaidaa (IRE) (Cape Cross (IRE)) **Hamdan Al Maktoum**
140 **MASTER OF SPEED (IRE)**, ch c 14/2 Mastercraftsman (IRE)—
                     Mango Groove (Unfuwain (USA)) (26325) **Jon Collins, Chris Fahy & Hanako Varian**
141 B c 15/3 Sakhee's Secret—Moody Margaret (Bahamian Bounty) (476) **Ms Y. Ferguson**
142 **MUDAMMERA (IRE)**, b f 1/3 Dubawi (IRE)—Fatanah (IRE) (Green Desert (USA)) **Hamdan Al Maktoum**
143 Ch c 1/3 Exceed And Excel (AUS)—Muffled (USA) (Mizaaya) (100000) **Sheikh Ahmed Al Maktoum**
144 **MUJASSAM**, ch c 23/2 Kyllachy—Naizak (Medicean) (180000) **Hamdan Al Maktoum**
145 **MUQTASER (USA)**, b c 4/3 Distorted Humor (USA)—
                     Life Well Lived (Tiznow (USA)) (306748) **Hamdan Al Maktoum**
146 **MURAHANA (IRE)**, b f 16/3 Invincible Spirit (IRE)—
                     By Request (Giant's Causeway (USA)) (300000) **Hamdan Al Maktoum**
147 **MUTANAAWAL**, ch c 13/3 Intikhab (USA)—Pikaboo (Pivotal) (85714) **Hamdan Al Maktoum**
148 Ch c 11/2 Galileo (IRE)—Pearling (USA) (Storm Cat (USA)) **Saleh Al Homaizi & Imad Al Sagar**
149 B c 28/3 Dark Angel (IRE)—Penicuik (Hernando (FR)) (70000) **HighclereThoroughbredRacing(Coronation)**
150 B c 8/2 Getaway (GER)—Persian Heroine (IRE) (Intikhab (USA)) (75000) **Mr Y. Masuda**
151 B c 2/4 Invincible Spirit (IRE)—Pharmacist (IRE) (Machiavellian (USA)) (77428) **Mrs F. H. Hay**
152 Ch f 8/5 Dutch Art—Pink Stone (FR) (Bigstone (IRE)) (85000) **Sheikh Ahmed Al Maktoum**
153 B f 27/3 Arcano (IRE)—Popolo (IRE) (Fasliyev (USA)) **Z. A. Galadari**
154 **PRIVILEGED (IRE)**, b f 9/2 Exceed And Excel (AUS)—
                     Almaviva (IRE) (Grand Lodge (USA)) (75000) **Cheveley Park Stud Limited**
155 **PROPEL (IRE)**, ch f 12/3 Dubawi (IRE)—Hit The Sky (IRE) (Cozzene (USA)) (1161440) **Mr J. M. Camilleri**
156 B f 16/2 Elusive Quality (USA)—Raymi Coya (CAN) (Van Nistelrooy (USA)) **Qatar Racing Limited**
157 B gr f 21/1 Acclamation—Red Boots (IRE) (Verglas (IRE)) (95000) **Highclere T'Bred Racing(Prince Of Wales)**
158 **RIFLE RANGE (IRE)**, b c 26/3 Shamardal (USA)—Ratukidul (FR) (Danehill (USA)) (178087) **Mr J. M. Camilleri**
159 B c 8/2 Camacho—Salinia (IRE) (Rainbow Quest (USA)) (75000) **Sheikh Ahmed Al Maktoum**
160 **SEARCHING (IRE)**, b c 31/3 Mastercraftsman (IRE)—Miracolia (IRE) (Montjeu (IRE)) (90000) **A. D. Spence**
161 **SHAHRALASAL (IRE)**, b f 20/2 Oasis Dream—Khulood (USA) (Storm Cat (USA)) **Hamdan Al Maktoum**
162 B c 3/3 Rip Van Winkle (IRE)—Shanghai Lily (IRE) (King's Best (USA)) (230000) **Mr P. D. Smith**
163 **SINGAPORE DREAM (IRE)**, b c 16/5 Teofilo (IRE)—
                     Rainbow Queen (Dynaformer (USA)) (80000) **Mr Simon Munir & Mr Isaac Souede**
164 B f 2/3 Zebedee—Sonny Sunshine (Royal Applause) (61904) **Saleh Al Homaizi & Imad Al Sagar**
165 B c 5/5 High Chaparral (IRE)—Sri Kandi (Pivotal) **Mrs F. H. Hay**
166 **SYLVETTE**, ch f 30/3 Selkirk (USA)—Souvenace (Hernando (FR)) **Miss K. Rausing**
167 B f 4/3 Shamardal (USA)—Taarkod (IRE) (Singspiel (IRE)) **Sheikh Ahmed Al Maktoum**
168 B f 18/1 Iffraaj—Tarfshi (Mtoto) **Sheikh Ahmed Al Maktoum**
169 **TAWAASHEEH (IRE)**, b c 22/3 New Approach (IRE)—Sana Abel (IRE) (Alhaarth (IRE)) **Hamdan Al Maktoum**
170 B f 20/2 Kheleyf (USA)—Tempete (Dubai Millennium) **Sheikh Ahmed Al Maktoum**
171 **TIGRILLA (IRE)**, gr f 29/3 Clodovil (IRE)—
                     Lisieux Orchid (IRE) (Sadler's Wells (USA)) (90000) **Cheveley Park Stud Limited**
172 **TUTTI FRUTTI**, b f 5/3 Teofilo (IRE)—Soft Centre (Zafonic (USA)) **Normandie Stud Ltd**

MR ROGER VARIAN - Continued

173 B c 10/3 Rip Van Winkle (IRE)—Vas Y Carla (USA) (Gone West (USA)) (150000) **Mrs S. Magnier**
174 B f 16/2 Stimulation (IRE)—Wolumla (IRE) (Royal Applause) (9291) **Mrs H. Varian**

Other Owners: Mr A. A. Al Shaikh, I. J. Al-Sagar, Mr K. Allen, J. Barton, Mr J. A. Collins, Mrs H. S. Ellingsen, Mr C. J. Fahy, T. F. Harris, Mrs E. A. Harris, S. Hassiakos, The Hon H. M. Herbert, Highclere Thoroughbred Racing Ltd, Saleh Al Homaizi, Mrs G. A. S. Jarvis, Mr D. Jones, Dr S. C. Kassab, M. Manasseh, Mr R. P. Marchant, Mr S. Marchant, Mr G. Moss, Mr C. Mullin, Mrs M. T. Mullin, S. E. Munir, O. J. W. Pawle, Mr C. Pizarro, Mr I. Souede, Mr M. B. Spence, Mr J. A. B. Stafford, M. Weinfeld.

Assistant Trainer: David Eustace

Jockey (flat): Andrea Atzeni. **Apprentice:** Ross Atkinson.

---

636 **MR ED VAUGHAN, Newmarket**
Postal: **Machell Place Cottage, Old Station Road, Newmarket, Suffolk, CB8 8DW**
Contacts: **PHONE (01638) 667411 FAX (01638) 667452 MOBILE (07799) 144901**
E-MAIL ed@efvaughan.com WEBSITE www.efvaughan.com

1 **DANCE AND DANCE (IRE)**, 8, b g Royal Applause—Caldy Dancer (IRE)
2 **FLAMBOROUGH BREEZE**, 5, ro m Ad Valorem (USA)—Lothian Lass (IRE)
3 **IT'S COMPLICATED**, 3, b f Cape Cross (IRE)—Only Alone (USA)
4 **LEGENDARY**, 5, b g Exceed And Excel (AUS)—Red Carnation (IRE)
5 **OLIVERS MOUNT**, 4, ch g Mount Nelson—Phoebe Woodstock (IRE)
6 **REDVERS (IRE)**, 6, br g Ishiguru (USA)—Cradle Brief (IRE)
7 **ROBIN HOODS BAY**, 6, b g Motivator—Bijou A Moi
8 **WHITBY JET (IRE)**, 6, b g Mujadil (USA)—Anazah (USA)

THREE-YEAR-OLDS

9 **ADVENTURE SEEKER (IRE)**, gr c Dalakhani (IRE)—Adventure (USA)
10 **CARNT CASH SORRY**, b g Authorized (IRE)—Eternity Ring
11 **CHINDENI**, b f Teofilo (IRE)—Choysia
12 **CLAIM THE ROSES (USA)**, b br c Speightstown (USA)—Reboot (USA)
13 **COSTA FILEY**, b g Pastoral Pursuits—Cosmic Destiny (IRE)
14 **COURAGEOUS ROCK (USA)**, b br c Rock Hard Ten (USA)—To The Brim (CAN)
15 **CYPRESS POINT (FR)**, gr f Oratorio (IRE)—Miss Sazanica (FR)
16 **INTERCONNECTION**, ch g Mount Nelson—Lacework
17 **REAFFIRMED (IRE)**, ch g Pivotal—Quiet Protest (USA)
18 **ROYAL ENCOUNTER**, b c Royal Applause—Alhufoof (USA)
19 **SI SENOR (IRE)**, b g Dansili—Kotsi (USA)

TWO-YEAR-OLDS

20 B f 7/2 Exceed And Excel (AUS)—Caldy Dancer (IRE) (Soviet Star (USA))
21 **CAYTON BAY**, br f 25/3 Equiano (FR)—Hearsay (Dubai Destination (USA)) (6000)
22 B f 13/3 Paco Boy (IRE)—Isla Azul (IRE) (Machiavellian (USA)) (15000)
23 B c 30/3 Fast Company (IRE)—Lost Shilling (IRE) (Noverre (USA)) (82000)
24 Ch f 7/3 Duke of Marmalade (IRE)—Midpoint (USA) (Point Given (USA)) (12000)
25 Ch f 3/2 Iffraaj—Miss University (USA) (Beau Genius (CAN)) (65000)
26 B f 19/4 Lemon Drop Kid (USA)—Missing Miss (USA) (Unaccounted For (USA)) (67192)
27 Br f 15/2 Makfi—Playwithmyheart (Diktat)
28 **PRIMROSE VALLEY**, b f 20/4 Pastoral Pursuits—Cosmic Destiny (IRE) (Soviet Star (USA))
29 **PUSS MOTH**, b f 21/2 Paco Boy (IRE)—Seeking Dubai (Dubawi (IRE)) (7619)
30 Ch f 24/3 Duke of Marmalade (IRE)—Time Ahead (Spectrum (IRE)) (21000)

---

637 **MR TIM VAUGHAN, Cowbridge**
Postal: **Tim Vaughan Racing Ltd., Pant Wilkin Stables, Aberthin, Cowbridge, South Glamorgan, CF71 7GX**
Contacts: **PHONE (01446) 771626 FAX (01446) 774371 MOBILE (07841) 800081**
E-MAIL tim@timvaughanracing.com WEBSITE www.timvaughanracing.com

1 **ACKERTAC (IRE)**, 9, ch g Anshan—Clonsingle Native (IRE) **The Mount Fawcus Partnership**
2 **ALBORZ (IRE)**, 5, b g Dubai Destination (USA)—Mount Elbrus **Diamond Racing Ltd**
3 **ALPHABETICAL ORDER**, 6, b g Alflora (IRE)—Lady Turk (FR) **Great Northern Partnership**

MR TIM VAUGHAN - Continued

4 **ASHFORD WOOD (IRE)**, 6, b g Stowaway—Shambala (IRE) **David & Susan Luke**
5 **AWBEG MASSINI (IRE)**, 8, b g Dr Massini (IRE)—Awbeg Flower (IRE) **Mr R. I. Clay**
6 **BALLYMOAT**, 7, b g Grape Tree Road—Frosty Mistress **Mr J. Goodrick**
7 **BALLYROCK (IRE)**, 8, b g Milan—Ardent Love (IRE) **Pearn's Pharmacies Ltd**
8 **BE BOP BORU (IRE)**, 7, b g Brian Boru—Henrietta Howard (IRE) **The Oak Syndicate**
9 **BE KIND**, 8, b m Generous (IRE)—Aquavita **Mr W. Jones**
10 **BENABILITY (IRE)**, 4, b g Beneficial—Whataliability (IRE) **Mrs L. Bowtell**
11 **BENNACHIE (IRE)**, 5, b g Milan—Stormy Lady (IRE) **Oceans Racing**
12 **BENS MOOR (IRE)**, 9, b g Beneficial—Moor Lady **Mrs M. A. O'Sullivan**
13 **BILLYBO**, 11, b g Kayf Tara—Pollys Perk (IRE) **Oceans Racing**
14 **BO'S RETURN**, 4, b g Tobougg (IRE)—Lamp's Return **Bovian Racing**
15 **BOB WILL (IRE)**, 9, b g Bob's Return (IRE)—Mini Moo Min **Mr W. Jones**
16 **BUCKING THE TREND**, 6, b g Kayf Tara—Macklette (IRE) **The Marinades**
17 **CAPE SAFARI (IRE)**, 5, b m Cape Cross (IRE)—Finnmark **Pinehurst Stud**
18 **CEEVEE**, 4, ch g Vita Rosa (JPN)—Calonnog (IRE) **Mr & Mrs D. D. Clee**
19 4, B g Tobougg (IRE)—Champagne Lil **Mrs M. A. O'Sullivan**
20 **DESTROYER DEPLOYED**, 8, b g Deploy—Supreme Cove **The Craftsmen**
21 **DONNACHAS CHANT (USA)**, 9, b g War Chant (USA)—
                            Super Supreme (IND) **Folly Road Racing Partners (1996)**
22 **DOVILS DATE**, 5, gr g Clodovil (IRE)—Lucky Date (IRE) **Exors of the Late Mr R. H. D. Smith**
23 **DUNEEN POINT (IRE)**, 10, b g Saddlers' Hall (IRE)—Miss Ogan (IRE) **Mr R. I. Clay**
24 **ELSAFEER (IRE)**, 9, b g Sakhee (USA)—Nabadhaat (USA) **Delamere Cottage Racing Partners (1996)**
25 **ESSTEEPEE**, 5, b g Double Trigger (IRE)—Lamper's Light **Shoot The Pot Racing**
26 **EXPERIMENTALIST**, 6, b g Monsieur Bond (IRE)—Floppie (FR) **Two Gents & An Orange Bloke Racing**
27 **EXPLAINED (IRE)**, 7, b g Exit To Nowhere (USA)—All Told (IRE) **D N V Churton & Mrs C Wilson**
28 **FALCARRAGH (IRE)**, 7, ch g Alderbrook—Maghereeragh Lady (IRE) **Mr M. A. Stratford**
29 **FAYETTE COUNTY (IRE)**, 7, b g Golden Lariat (USA)—Midsyn Lady (IRE) **J. P. McManus**
30 **FIELDS OF GLORY (FR)**, 4, b g King's Best (USA)—Lavandou **Exors of the Late Mr R. H. D. Smith**
31 **FIGARO**, 6, ch g Medicean—Chorist **Pearn's Pharmacies Ltd**
32 **FIRST FANDANGO**, 7, b g Hernando (FR)—First Fantasy **WRB Racing 40 & Premier Chance Racing**
33 **FOUR SHUCK MEN (IRE)**, 6, b g Spartacus (IRE)—Shed **Craig and Maureen Buckingham**
34 **GALLOX BRIDGE**, 9, b g Kayf Tara—Explorer **Mr D. W. Fox**
35 4, B g Presenting—Gemini Lucy (IRE) **Mr J. P. M. Bowtell**
36 **GEMINIUS (IRE)**, 6, b g Choisir (AUS)—Macca Luna (IRE) **W R B Racing 54**
37 **GOLAN WAY**, 10, b g Golan (IRE)—Silk Daisy **W R B Racing 58**
38 **GRACIE B (IRE)**, 5, b m Golan (IRE)—Me Grannys Endoors (IRE) **Diamond Racing Ltd**
39 **GREAT OAK (IRE)**, 8, b m Dushyantor (USA)—Reginella (IRE) **Mrs M. A. O'Sullivan**
40 **HAWKHILL (IRE)**, 8, b g Hawk Wing (USA)—Crimphill (IRE) **Exors of the Late Mr R. H. D. Smith**
41 **HELLESBELLES (IRE)**, 6, b m Helissio (FR)—Madame Luso (IRE) **Great Northern Partnership**
42 **HIDDEN IDENTITY (IRE)**, 8, b m Beneficial—Swanbrook Leader (IRE) **Mr J. P. M. Bowtell**
43 **HUNTING TOWER**, 10, b g Sadler's Wells (USA)—Fictitious **Mighty Macs Syndicate**
44 **IFAN (IRE)**, 6, b g Ivan Denisovich (IRE)—Montana Miss (IRE) **WRB Racing 61 & Derek & Jean Clee**
45 **JIMBILL (IRE)**, 8, br g Flying Legend (USA)—Ah Gowan (IRE) **Mr M. E. Moore & Mr B. Ead**
46 **JUNO THE MUFFINMAN (IRE)**, 5, b g Holy Roman Emperor (IRE)—Mackenzie's Friend **Itsfuninit**
47 **KALIMANTAN (IRE)**, 4, b c Azamour (IRE)—Kalamba (IRE) **D. J. Wallis**
48 **KING ROLFE (IRE)**, 6, b g King's Theatre (IRE)—Lady Rolfe (IRE) **Four Corners Syndicate**
49 **KNIGHT'S REWARD**, 4, b g Sir Percy—Wardeh **The Mount Fawcus Partnership**
50 **LECALE LAD (IRE)**, 7, b g Revoque (IRE)—Thyngreesa **R. M. Kirkland**
51 **LIBERTY COURT (IRE)**, 7, b g Court Cave—Miss Vikki (IRE) **Passant & Butt**
52 4, B g Turtle Island (IRE)—Life Support (IRE) **Oceans Racing**
53 **LORD LIR (IRE)**, 8, b g Oscar Schindler (IRE)—Milford Woman (IRE) **Two Gents & An Orange Bloke Racing**
54 **MASSINI'S MAGUIRE (IRE)**, 13, b g Dr Massini (IRE)—Molly Maguire (IRE) **A. E. Peterson**
55 **MASTER HIDE (IRE)**, 4, b g Stowaway—Carrigeen Acer (IRE) **R. M. Kirkland**
56 **MILBOROUGH (IRE)**, 8, b g Milan—Fox Burrow (IRE) **Pinehurst Stud**
57 **MISIRLOU (IRE)**, 4, b br g Limnos (JPN)—Other Salsa (FR) **The Misirlou Gang**
58 **MIST THE BOAT**, 6, b g Generous (IRE)—Baily Mist (IRE) **Craftsmen2**
59 **MONART DIAMOND**, 5, gr g Presenting—Line White (FR) **Mr G Handley & Mr G Pesticcio**
60 **MR CRACKER (IRE)**, 9, ch g Anshan—Sesame Cracker **Oceans Racing**
61 **MY OH MOUNT BROWN (IRE)**, 7, b g Millenary—My O Mio (IRE) **Craig and Maureen Buckingham**
62 **NASH POINT (IRE)**, 5, ch g Kris Kin (USA)—Ten Dollar Bill (IRE) **Mr G Handley & Mr G Pesticcio**
63 **NATHANS PRIDE (IRE)**, 6, ch g Definite Article—Tricias Pride (IRE) **Mr J. P. M. Bowtell**
64 **NINE IRON (IRE)**, 4, gr g Verglas (IRE)—Sevi's Choice (USA) **T. E. Vaughan**
65 **OFFICER HOOLIHAN**, 4, b g Kayf Tara—Major Hoolihan **R. M. Kirkland**
66 **OPERATIC HEIGHTS (IRE)**, 5, b g Golan (IRE)—Opera Lover (IRE) **Craig and Maureen Buckingham**
67 **OSCARS DEN (IRE)**, 6, b g Oscar (IRE)—Lyre Hill (IRE) **Mrs Z. Wentworth**

MR TIM VAUGHAN - Continued

68 **OUR ISLAND (IRE)**, 9, b g Turtle Island (IRE)—Linda's Leader (IRE) **Oceans Racing**
69 **PARTING WAY (IRE)**, 6, b g Golan (IRE)—Best Mother (IRE) **Mr B Ead & Mr M E Moore**
70 **POWER OF GOD (IRE)**, 6, b g Heron Island (IRE)—Aruba Dam (IRE) **Mr J. H. Frost**
71 **PRESENTING RED (IRE)**, 4, b g Presenting—Bolly (IRE) **R. M. Kirkland**
72 **PURE ANTICIPATION (IRE)**, 9, gr m Old Vic—Lady of Gortmerron (IRE) **Cloud Nine**
73 **QUALVIRO (FR)**, 10, b g Lavirco (GER)—French County (FR) **Double Trouble Partnership**
74 **REV IT UP (IRE)**, 8, b g Revoque (IRE)—Von Carty (IRE) **The Bill & Ben Partnership**
75 **ROBBERS ROOST (IRE)**, 6, b g Flemensfirth (USA)—Chapel Queen (IRE) **The Oxymorons**
76 **ROCK DOCTOR (IRE)**, 4, b g Flemensfirth (USA)—Often Quoted (IRE) **Oceans Racing**
77 **SAFFERANO (IRE)**, 8, b g Saffron Walden (FR)—Parviana (IRE) **Exors of the Late Mr R. H. D. Smith**
78 **SAINT ARE (FR)**, 8, b br g Network (GER)—Fortanea (FR) **Mr D. W. Fox**
79 **SASH OF HONOUR (IRE)**, 5, ch h Galileo (IRE)—Adoration (USA) **Exors of the Late Mr R. H. D. Smith**
80 **SAVED BY JOHN (IRE)**, 9, b g Revoque (IRE)—Lady Appeal (IRE) **S. Clarke & and the Late Mr M. S. Clarke**
81 **SHARPASAKNIFE (IRE)**, 4, b g Flemensfirth (USA)—Omas Lady (IRE) **The Mount Fawcus Partnership**
82 **SHOUT IT ALOUD**, 5, b g Proclamation (IRE)—Party Charmer **The Mount Fawcus Partnership**
83 **SILENTPLAN**, 6, b g Blueprint (IRE)—Sprig Muslin **Craig and Maureen Buckingham**
84 **SKI SUNDAY**, 9, b g King's Best (USA)—Lille Hammer **Four Leaf Clover Partnership**
85 **SOLARAS EXHIBITION (IRE)**, 6, b g Great Exhibition (USA)—Solara (GER) **Mr C. Davies**
86 **SPANISH OPTIMIST (IRE)**, 8, b g Indian Danehill (IRE)—La Traviata **Hugh Doubtfire & Tony Evans**
87 **STONETHROWER (IRE)**, 9, b g Dushyantor (USA)—
                                    Ciaras Charm (IRE) **S. Clarke & and the Late Mr M. S. Clarke**
88 **SWIFT ESCAPE**, 7, b g Exit To Nowhere (USA)—Vivre Aimer Rire (FR) **Diamond Racing Ltd**
89 **TIME AND AGAIN (FR)**, 4, b g Sassanian (USA)—Petillante Royale (FR) **Oceans Racing**
90 **TIME ON YOUR HANDS (IRE)**, 4, b g Beneficial—Zalda **Pearn's Pharmacies Ltd**
91 **TIPSY GYPSY (IRE)**, 7, b g Milan—Montanara (IRE) **Mr J. P. M. Bowtell**
92 **TOMSK (FR)**, 4, ch g Priolo (USA)—Kauto Relstar (FR) **Oceans Racing**
93 **TWOPOUNDSOFBUTTER (IRE)**, 8, b g Beneficial—Jezel (IRE) **T. E. Vaughan**
94 **VINTAGE VIXON (IRE)**, 7, b m Moscow Society (USA)—Bar Un'que (IRE) **Exors of the Late Mr R. H. D. Smith**
95 **WINDMILLS EDGE (IRE)**, 4, b g Presenting—Mawly Day (IRE) **R. M. Kirkland**
96 **WINGS OF SMOKE (IRE)**, 9, gr g King's Theatre (IRE)—Grey Mo (IRE) **Pearn's Pharmacies Ltd**
97 **WISTARI ROCKS (IRE)**, 5, b g Heron Island (IRE)—Hi Honey (IRE) **Four Leaf Clover Partnership**
98 **YES DADDY (IRE)**, 5, b g Golan (IRE)—Hollygrove Samba (IRE) **Mr P. M. Cooper**

THREE-YEAR-OLDS

99 **BELIZE**, b g Rail Link—Costa Rica (IRE) **Mr D. R. Passant**
100 **MARIGNY**, b g Enrique—Gastina (FR) **T. E. Vaughan**
101 **NIXYBA**, b f Cockney Rebel (IRE)—Hisaronu (IRE) **Diamond Racing Ltd**

Other Owners: Mr P. G. Amos, A. W. A. Bates, Mr A. Bott, Mr C. Buckingham, Mrs M. Buckingham, Mr G. W. T. Butt, Mr R. J. Churches, Mr D. N. V. Churton, Mr S. A. Clarke, Exors of the Late Mr M. S. Clarke, D. D. Clee, Mrs J. P. Clee, Mr P. G. Connolly, Mr R. Denness, H. G. Doubtfire, Mr B. Ead, Mr P. C. Etty, T. L. Evans, Mrs M. W. Fawcus, Mr D. S. Fawcus, K. H. Foster, Mr M. Gear, Mr A. L. Gregg, Miss M. Gut, Mr G. Handley, Mr R. Jackson, Mr B. Jagger, Mr I. C. Jenkins, D. M. Jenkins, T. E. Kerfoot, G. T. Lever, Mrs S. Luke, Mr D. A. Luke, Dr C. H. Mason, Mr E. McEntee, Mr F. M. McGuinness, Mr R. Middleton, Mr S. Middleton, Mr M. E. Moore, Mr J. M. Mordecai, Mr G. P. O'Shea, Mr J. C. Peak, Mr G. Pesticcio, Mr J. T. Phillips, Mr A. J. Pigott, Mr M. Pou, Mr R. G. Price, Mr N. S. C. Proctor, Mr P. Pyatt, Mr P. Ragan, Mr T. J. Roberts, Mr N. J. Robinson, A. Robinson, Mr J. Sanders, D. A. Shinton, Mr A. Smallman, Wetherby Racing Bureau Ltd, Mr N. D. Whitham, Mrs C. S. Wilson.

Assistant Trainer: Jonathan Phillips

Jockey (flat): Fergus Sweeney. **Jockey (NH):** Richard Johnson, Aidan Coleman, Dougie Costello.
Conditional: Alan Johns, Jason Kiely, Michael Byrne. **Apprentice:** Chloe Ingram.
Amateur: Mr Evan David, Mr Bradley Gibbs.

---

638 **MR CHRISTIAN VON DER RECKE, Weilerswist**
Postal: **Rennstall Recke**, Hovener Hof, D-53919, Weilerswist, Germany
Contacts: **PHONE** (0049) 2254 84 53 14 **FAX** (0049) 2254 845315 **MOBILE** (0049) 171 542 50 50
E-MAIL recke@t-online.de WEBSITE www.rennstall-recke.de

1 **AEGEAUS**, 5, b g Monsun (GER)—Ouija Board **M-B-A Racing**
2 **AL MAMZAR (IRE)**, 5, b g Teofilo (IRE)—Avila **Frau R & A Hacker**
3 **ANTANO (GER)**, 5, b g Manduro (GER)—A Beautiful Mind (GER) **Frau M. Kammermeier**
4 **BAITSILEIR (IRE)**, 6, b g Bachelor Duke (USA)—Alamanta (IRE) **M. Himmelsbach & C. F. von der Recke**
5 **BE MY LION (GER)**, 5, b g Areion (GER)—Boucheron (GER) **Galopp Club Deutschland**

MR CHRISTIAN VON DER RECKE - Continued

6 **BIRTHDAY GUEST (GER)**, 5, ch h Areion (GER)—Birthday Spectrum (GER) **Stall Waldhaus**
7 **BURGOYNE (USA)**, 4, b g Officer (USA)—Married for Money (USA) **C. F. von der Recke**
8 **BURMA BEACH (GER)**, 4, b f Rock of Gibraltar (IRE)—Bougainvillea (GER) **Stall Steigenberger**
9 **CAFE AU LAIT (GER)**, 4, b c Nicaron (GER)—Cariera (GER) **Stall Nizza**
10 **CASHMERE CAT (IRE)**, 5, b rm One Cool Cat (USA)—Pink Cashmere (IRE) **Stall Karlshorst**
11 **CIOCCO SAM (GER)**, 6, b g Samum (GER)—Cioccolata (GER) **Stall Blankenese**
12 **DARING RUDOLPH (GER)**, 7, b g Soviet Star (USA)—Delightful Sofie (GER) **Frau R & A Hacker**
13 **DOUBLE TROUBLE (GER)**, 4, b f Liquido (GER)—Double Dagger Lady (USA) **Frau A. Lammertz**
14 **DREAMSPEED (IRE)**, 7, b g Barathea (IRE)—Kapria (FR) **BMK Racing**
15 **EARLSALSA (GER)**, 10, b g Kingsalsa (USA)—Earthly Paradise (GER) **Stall Blankenese**
16 **FEUERFUCHS (GER)**, 4, b c Lord of England (GER)—Flair Sensation (GER) **Stall Blau-Weiss**
17 **FILUN**, 9, b g Montjeu (IRE)—Sispre (FR) **C. F. von der Recke**
18 **HEADSTIGHT (IRE)**, 5, b m Holy Roman Emperor (IRE)—Regal Star (USA) **C. F. von der Recke**
19 **INPUT (GER)**, 8, ch g Areion (GER)—Icandra (GER) **Frau M. Hoffmann**
20 **KONIG HALL**, 6, b g Halling (USA)—Konigin Shuffle (GER) **Stall Fly Baby Fly**
21 **MAGIC DASH**, 4, ch g Call Me Big—Magic Love **M-B-A Racing**
22 **NEPHELE (GER)**, 4, ch f Salutino (GER)—Nostana (GER) **G. Neu**
23 **OASIS KNIGHT (GER)**, 8, b g Oasis Dream—Generous Lady **Stall Chevalex**
24 **OSCAN (USA)**, 5, b g Street Cry (IRE)—Moyesii (USA) **M-B-A Racing**
25 **PANESIDORA (GER)**, 4, b f Soviet Star (USA)—Paradise Search (IRE) **Stall Karlshorst**
26 **PARIGINO (FR)**, 6, b g Panis (USA)—Loretta Gianni (FR) **M-B-A Racing**
27 **PRE TAX PROFIT (IRE)**, 6, b g Ad Valorem (USA)—Civic Duty (IRE) **Stall Saarbrucken**
28 **RAVAISCH**, 4, b g Kalatos—Rajputana **H F v.Hodenberg**
29 **SKY FLYER (HOL)**, 6, ch g Urgent Request (USA)—Day Diesis (USA) **A. Mulder**
30 **TINLEY LODGE**, 5, b g Montjeu (IRE)—Shining Bright **Frau U & H Alck**
31 **TOUCH OF TEXAS (FR)**, 4, b c Touch Down (GER)—Texas Melody (GER) **R. Wolfermann**
32 **WELCOME IN LIFE (GER)**, 7, b m Tertullian (USA)—Wind In Her Hair (GER) **Gestut Romerhof**
33 **WINNING BABY (GER)**, 5, b m Lord of England (GER)—Winning Time (IRE) **Gestut Romerhof**

THREE-YEAR-OLDS

34 **ADLERAUGE (GER)**, b g Adlerflug (GER)—Abazzia (GER) **Stall Burg Muggenhausen**
35 **BAVARIAN BEAUTY (GER)**, b f Desert Prince (IRE)—Best Moving (GER) **M. E. Veeck**
36 **CHE SERA (GER)**, b f Nicaron (GER)—Chato's Girl (GER) **Stall Nizza**
37 **ERIC (GER)**, ch c Tertullian (USA)—Ericarrow (IRE) **Frau G. Gaul**
38 **IBECKE**, b f Exceed And Excel (AUS)—Granted (FR) **Dr K. Wurtenberger**
39 **IGNAZ**, ch g Peppercorn—Isi Going **P. Vogt**
40 **LADY KATE (GER)**, b f Liquido (GER)—Lady Di (GER) **Home Farm Racing**
41 B f Shirocco (GER)—Lisa La Fleur (GER) **Stall Karlshorst**
42 **OSTARAKOV (GER)**, b f Sholokhov (GER)—Orsina (IRE) **Stall Weiss-Blau**
43 **PERFECT CARE (SWI)**, b c Captain Rio—Perfectly Chilled (IRE) **Stall Klosters-Serneus**
44 **PHOENIX SHADOW (GER)**, b g Mamool (IRE)—Pawella (GER) **Stall Walcheren**
45 Ch f Literato (FR)—Queen's Diamond (GER) **Quadriga Ltd**

TWO-YEAR-OLDS

46 **ATTILA (GER)**, b c 1/1 Nicaron (GER)—Alte Rose (GER) (Monsun (GER)) **Stall Nizza**
47 **CALL ME NUMBER ONE (GER)**, b c 26/2 Touch Down (GER)—Carrie Anne (Piccolo) **H H Brand**
48 **EASTSITE ONE (GER)**, b c 16/4 Mamool (IRE)—Ericarrow (IRE) (Bollin Eric) (35617) **Frau G. Gaul**
49 **FUJI (GER)**, b f 25/4 Liquido (GER)—Fanfare (GER) (Surumu (GER)) (929) **Gestut Lindenhof**
50 **JAMES COOK (GER)**, b c 1/1 Nicaron (GER)—Jalta (GER) (Platini (GER)) **Stall Nizza**
51 **JUNGLEBOOGIE (GER)**, b c 20/3 Nicaron (GER)—Jive (GER) (Montjeu (IRE)) **Stall Nizza**
52 **LASCALINA (GER)**, b f 1/1 Kallisto (GER)—Lajana (GER) (Goofalik (USA)) **H. Lohmann**
53 **PETITE PARADISE (FR)**, ch f 17/3 Lord of England (GER)—
Paradise Rain (Compton Place) (23228) **Frau R & A Hacker**
54 **ROXI (GER)**, b f 1/1 Tertullian (GER)—Rosaly (GER) (Kallisto (GER)) **H. Lohmann**
55 **SHADOW SADNESS (GER)**, b c 14/2 Soldier Hollow—Shadow Queen (Lando (GER)) **Stall Weiss-Blau**

---

639 | **MR JOHN WADE, Sedgefield**
Postal: **Howe Hills, Mordon, Sedgefield, Cleveland, TS21 2HG**
Contacts: PHONE **(01740) 630310** FAX **(01740) 630310** MOBILE **(07831) 686968**

1 **AIAAM AL NAMOOS**, 5, b g Teofilo (IRE)—Deveron (USA) **J. Wade**
2 **ALLEZ COOL (IRE)**, 5, ch g Flemensfirth (USA)—La Fisarmonica (IRE) **J. Wade**
3 **ALWAYS RIGHT (IRE)**, 12, ch g Right Win (IRE)—Kemal Brave (IRE) **J. Wade**

MR JOHN WADE - Continued

4 **APACHE BLUE (IRE)**, 10, b g Presenting—La Eile (IRE) **J. Wade**
5 **BELLRINGER**, 4, b g Black Sam Bellamy (IRE)—Reamzafonic **J. Wade**
6 **BENNY BE GOOD**, 11, b g Benny The Dip (USA)—Hembane (FR) **J. Wade**
7 **CALL ME MULLIGAN (IRE)**, 10, ch g Bach (IRE)—They Call Me Molly (CAN) **J. Wade**
8 **CASUAL CAVALIER (IRE)**, 6, br g Presenting—Asklynn (IRE) **J. Wade**
9 **CHICAGO OUTFIT (IRE)**, 9, b g Old Vic—Lambourne Lace (IRE) **J. Wade**
10 **COURT RED (IRE)**, 8, b g Court Cave (IRE)—An Bonnan Bui (IRE) **J. Wade**
11 **DEAN'S WALK (IRE)**, 5, b g Craigsteel—Killashee (IRE) **J. Wade**
12 **DIAMOND FRONTIER (IRE)**, 11, gr g Sadler's Wells (USA)—Diamond Line (FR) **J. Wade**
13 **DINGO BAY**, 8, b g Karinga Bay—Do It On Dani **Miss M. D. Myco**
14 **DISSIDANCER (IRE)**, 6, b g Bishop of Cashel—Dancing At Lunasa (IRE) **J. Wade**
15 **EYRE SQUARE (IRE)**, 11, b g Publisher (USA)—Eyre Eile (IRE) **J. Wade**
16 **FORTY CROWN (IRE)**, 8, b g Court Cave (IRE)—Forty Quid (IRE) **Miss M. D. Myco**
17 **GENERAL HARDI**, 13, b g In Command (IRE)—Hardiprincess **J. Wade**
18 **GLENCREE (IRE)**, 10, b g Presenting—Hidden Ability (IRE) **J. Wade**
19 **GREEN PASTURES (IRE)**, 6, b g Diamond Green (FR)—Continuous (IRE) **J. Wade**
20 **GREY SHADOW (IRE)**, 8, gr g Tikkanen (USA)—Prospect Lady (IRE) **Miss M. D. Myco**
21 **HARRIS HAWK**, 9, b g Karinga Bay—Harristown Lady **J. Wade**
22 **IRISH BY NAME (IRE)**, 8, ch g Definite Article—Rosies All The Way **J. Wade**
23 **JAGO RIVER (IRE)**, 8, b g Milan—Light And Airy **J. Wade**
24 **JOKERS AND ROGUES (IRE)**, 6, b g Beneficial—Ashfield Girl (IRE) **J. Wade**
25 **JUKEBOX MELODY (IRE)**, 8, b g Brian Boru—Carmels Cottage (IRE) **J. Wade**
26 **MANNERED**, 9, b g Alflora (IRE)—Manettia (IRE) **J. Wade**
27 **MOON INDIGO**, 8, b g Sadler's Wells (USA)—Solo de Lune (IRE) **J. Wade**
28 **NEW ACADEMY**, 6, ch g Zamindar (USA)—New Abbey **J. Wade**
29 **NEW SHUIL (IRE)**, 10, b g New Frontier (IRE)—Shuil Ura (IRE) **J. Wade**
30 **NEWSPAGE (IRE)**, 8, b g Blueprint (IRE)—Newlineview (IRE) **J. Wade**
31 **OTTO QUERCUS (FR)**, 9, b g Saint Cyrien (FR)—La Haie Blanche (FR) **J. Wade**
32 **PEGASUS PRINCE (USA)**, 10, b g Fusaichi Pegasus (USA)—Avian Eden (USA) **J. Wade**
33 **PUDSEY HOUSE**, 7, b g Double Trigger—Dara's Pride (IRE) **J. Wade**
34 **RISKIER**, 9, gr g Kier Park (IRE)—Risky Girl **J. Wade**
35 **RIVER MUSIC (IRE)**, 9, b g Flemensfirth (USA)—Shean Bracken (IRE) **J. Wade**
36 **ROSEVILLE COTTAGE (IRE)**, 7, b g Kris Kin (USA)—Johnny's Idea (IRE) **J. Wade**
37 **RUNSWICK DAYS (IRE)**, 7, b g Presenting—Miss Lauren Dee (IRE) **J. Wade**
38 **RUNSWICK RELAX**, 8, ch g Generous (IRE)—Zany Lady **J. Wade**
39 **SAGLIERE**, 9, gr g Sagamix (FR)—D'egliere (FR) **J. Wade**
40 **SILVER CROSSING**, 5, b g Avonbridge—Silver Purse **J. Wade**
41 **SPANISH FLEET**, 6, b g Cadeaux Genereux—Santisima Trinidad (IRE) **J. Wade**
42 **TAKAATUF (IRE)**, 8, b g Dubai Destination (USA)—Karlaka (IRE) **J. Wade**
43 **TOPLANDER (IRE)**, 10, ch g Topanoora—Okeemo Hall (IRE) **J. Wade**
44 **VIKING CHIEF (IRE)**, 7, b g Westerner—Diamond Sal **J. Wade**
45 **WALSER (IRE)**, 7, b g Milan—Brass Neck (IRE) **J. Wade**
46 **WHATS UP WOODY (IRE)**, 9, b g Beneficial—Lady Noellei (IRE) **J. Wade**

THREE-YEAR-OLDS

47 **SADDLE UP SAM**, b g Black Sam Bellamy (IRE)—Reamzafonic **J. Wade**

Assistant Trainer: Miss Maria Myco (07798) 775932

Jockey (NH): Brian Hughes, Wilson Renwick, James Reveley. **Conditional:** John Dawson.

---

640 **MRS LUCY WADHAM, Newmarket**
Postal: **The Trainer's House, Moulton Paddocks, Newmarket, Suffolk, CB8 7PJ**
Contacts: **PHONE (01638) 662411 FAX (01638) 668821 MOBILE (07980) 545776**
E-MAIL lucy.wadham@virgin.net WEBSITE www.lucywadhamracing.co.uk

1 **ALIZEE JAVILEX (FR)**, 4, b f Le Fou (IRE)—Etoile du Lion (FR) **J. J. W. Wadham**
2 **AMIDON (FR)**, 4, b g Dom Alco (FR)—Immage (FR) **P. H. Betts**
3 **ARTIFICE SIVOLA (FR)**, 4, gr g Dom Alco (FR)—Kerrana (FR) **R. B. Holt**
4 **BABY SHINE (IRE)**, 8, b m King's Theatre (IRE)—
Brambleshine (IRE) **P.A.Philipps,T.S.Redman & Mrs L. Redman**
5 **CANUSPOTIT**, 7, b g Nomadic Way (USA)—Play Alone (IRE) **D. A. Wales & S. J. Wood**
6 **CRESTA ONE**, 4, gr f Act One—Collect **Miss C. Blockley**
7 **DALIANCE (IRE)**, 5, ch g Dalakhani (IRE)—Everlasting Love **Black Eyed Mara**

MRS LUCY WADHAM - Continued

8 **DAWN TWISTER (GER)**, 7, br g Monsun (GER)—Dawn Side (CAN) **Mr R. Davies**
9 **ELEAZAR (GER)**, 13, b br g Alkalde (GER)—Eicidora (GER) **J. J. W. Wadham**
10 **HORTENSE MANCINI**, 5, ch m King's Best (USA)—Have Fun **The Woughton Partnership**
11 **KALAHARI (IRE)**, 5, b g Halling (USA)—Semaphore **J. Gill, H. Spiller, G. Waterhouse**
12 **LE REVE (IRE)**, 6, br g Milan—Open Cry (IRE) **P. H. Betts**
13 **MIDNIGHT MACARENA**, 9, ch m Midnight Legend—Royal Tango **The Bees**
14 **MINSTRELS GALLERY (IRE)**, 5, ch g Refuse To Bend (IRE)—Lilakiya (IRE) **G. Pascoe & S. Brewer**
15 **MISTRAL REINE**, 5, b m King's Theatre (IRE)—Classic Gale (USA) **Sara Dennis and Dominic and Sarah Reilly**
16 **NOBLE SILK**, 5, gr g Sir Percy—Tussah **The FOPS**
17 **NULLARBOR SKY (IRE)**, 4, gr f Aussie Rules (USA)—Grenouillere (USA) **Mr T. R. Wood**
18 **OPUS (IRE)**, 5, br g Danehill Dancer (IRE)—Mixed Blessing **J. J. W. Wadham**
19 **PERNICA**, 4, b f Sir Percy—Nicola Bella (IRE) **Mr & Mrs A. E. Pakenham**
20 **RASHEED**, 6, b g Oasis Dream—Alexandrine (IRE) **Peter Howell & Richard S Keeley**
21 **RENDEZVOUS PEAK**, 5, b g High-Rise (IRE)—Jurado Park (IRE) **Tom Ford & Tony Regan**
22 **RISING TEAL**, 5, b m Phoenix Reach (IRE)—Tealby **The Dyball Partnership**
23 **ROAD TO FREEDOM**, 5, b g Revoque (IRE)—Go Classic **Mr R. S. Keeley**
24 **RUBY RAMBLER**, 4, b f Notnowcato—Arruhan (IRE) **Sara Dennis,J J W Wadham & J C S Wilson**
25 **SONGSMITH**, 6, b g Librettist (USA)—Venus Rising **Team Supreme**
26 **SPYDER**, 6, b g Resplendent Glory (IRE)—Collect **Miss KJ Austin & Miss Christina Blockley**
27 **TEALISSIO**, 8, b g Helissio (FR)—Tealby **The Dyball Partnership**
28 **WATERED SILK**, 6, gr g Encosta de Lago (AUS)—Tussah **Mr & Mrs A. E. Pakenham**
29 **WHISPERING SPEED (IRE)**, 4, ch g Vertical Speed (FR)—Midnight Lover **The A. T. Partnership**
30 **WIESENTRAUM (GER)**, 8, ch g Next Desert (IRE)—Wiesenblute (GER) **G. Pascoe & S. Brewer**
31 **ZIGGY'S SECRET**, 4, b f Sakhee's Secret—Ziggy Zaggy **Mr & Mrs A. E. Pakenham**

THREE-YEAR-OLDS

32 **LADY TIANA**, b f Sir Percy—Cartoon **The FOPS**
33 B f Shirocco (GER)—Lumiere d'espoir (IRE) **Vogue Development Company (Kent) Ltd**
34 **MARY LE BOW**, b f Sir Percy—Bermondsey Girl **The FOPS**
35 **SUNSHINE CORNER (IRE)**, b f King's Theatre (IRE)—Coolgreaney (IRE) **P. A. Philipps & Mrs G. J. Redman**

TWO-YEAR-OLDS

36 **ASHDOWN LASS**, b f 21/1 Sir Percy—Antibes (IRE) (Grand Lodge (USA)) **The FOPS**
37 Br f 12/3 Sakhee (USA)—Atwirl (Pivotal) (3000) **The Calculated Speculators**
38 B f 9/3 Kyllachy—Elhareer (IRE) (Selkirk (USA)) (10000) **The Calculated Speculators**
39 **LADY VIOLA**, b f 6/4 Sir Percy—String Quartet (IRE) (Sadler's Wells (USA)) **Mr & Mrs A. E. Pakenham**

Other Owners: Mr A. Black, Mr S. J. Brewer, Mr D. J. S. Dyball, Mrs C. A. Dyball, Mr Tom Ford, Mr Simon Hall, Mr S. J. High, Mr Peter Howell, Richard S. Keeley, Mrs B. Lockhart-Smith, Mr R. Maddison, Mr Jeff O'Leary, Mrs S. F. O'Leary, Mrs Victoria Pakenham, Mr A. E. Pakenham, Mr G. J. Pascoe, Mr P. A. Philipps, Mr T. S. Redman, Mrs L. E. Redman, Mr A. W. Regan, Mrs Lucy Wadham, Mr J. J. W. Wadham, Mr Edward Wakelin, Mr Simon Wood.

Jockey (NH): Leighton Aspell. **Conditional:** Matt Crawley, Luke Ingram. **Amateur:** Mr Sam Davis.

 641 **MISS TRACY WAGGOTT, Spennymoor**
Postal: **Awakening Stables, Merrington Lane, Spennymoor, Co. Durham, DL16 7HB**
Contacts: **PHONE (01388) 819012 MOBILE (07979) 434498**

1 **BORDER BANDIT (USA)**, 6, b g Selkirk (USA)—Coretta (IRE) **Elsa Crankshaw Gordon Allan**
2 **BRIGHT APPLAUSE**, 6, b g Royal Applause—Sadaka (USA) **Littlethorpe Park Racing**
3 **CAPTAIN ROYALE (IRE)**, 9, ch g Captain Rio—Paix Royale **H. Conlon**
4 **COPT HILL**, 6, b g Avonbridge—Lalique (IRE) **H. Conlon**
5 **DEAN IARRACHT (IRE)**, 8, b g Danetime (IRE)—Sirdhana **Mr M. J. Howarth**
6 **KING PIN**, 9, b g Pivotal—Danehurst **H. Conlon**
7 **KORNGOLD**, 6, b g Dansili—Eve **N. Waggott**
8 **MISSION IMPOSSIBLE**, 9, gr g Kyllachy—Eastern Lyric **H. Conlon**
9 **NO QUARTER (IRE)**, 7, b g Refuse To Bend (IRE)—Moonlight Wish (IRE) **Miss T. Waggott**
10 **PIVOTAL PROSPECT**, 6, b m Nayef (USA)—Buon Amici **Miss T. Waggott**
11 **RUNNING REEF (IRE)**, 5, b g Hurricane Run (IRE)—Half-Hitch (USA) **Elsa Crankshaw Gordon Allan**
12 **SHADOWTIME**, 9, b g Singspiel (IRE)—Massomah (USA) **H. Conlon**
13 **SHEARIAN**, 4, b g Royal Applause—Regal Asset **Mr D. Tate**
14 **SOLAR SPIRIT (IRE)**, 9, b g Invincible Spirit (IRE)—Misaayef (USA) **Elsa Crankshaw Gordon Allan**
15 **THRUST CONTROL (IRE)**, 7, ch g Fath (USA)—Anazah (USA) **Mr D. Tate**
16 **TUIBAMA (IRE)**, 5, ch g Bertolini (USA)—Supportive (USA) **H. Conlon**

MISS TRACY WAGGOTT - Continued

17 **VALANTINO OYSTER (IRE)**, 7, b g Pearl of Love (IRE)—Mishor **Mr S. Sawley**
18 **WHISPERED TIMES (USA)**, 7, b br g More Than Ready (USA)—Lightning Show (USA) **Miss T. Waggott**
19 **WINDFORPOWER (IRE)**, 4, b g Red Clubs (IRE)—Dubai Princess (IRE) **Mr D. Tate**

THREE-YEAR-OLDS

20 **KING'S PROSPECT**, b g Authorized (IRE)—Sovereign's Honour (USA) **H. Conlon**

Other Owners: G. Allan, Miss E. Crankshaw, J. M. Hughes, Mr A. Stainton.

---

642 **MR JOHN WAINWRIGHT, Malton**
Postal: **Granary House, Beverley Road, Norton, Malton, North Yorkshire, YO17 9PJ**
Contacts: **PHONE (01653) 692993 MOBILE (07798) 778070**
E-MAIL jswainwright@googlemail.com

1 **BENIDORM**, 6, b g Bahamian Bounty—Famcred **Miss J. M. Slater**
2 **BLUE NOODLES**, 8, b g Reset (AUS)—Gleam of Light (IRE) **P. W. Cooper**
3 **EXIT TO FREEDOM**, 8, ch g Exit To Nowhere (USA)—Bobanvi **I. J. Barran**
4 **FROSTY BERRY**, 5, gr m Proclamation (IRE)—Star Entry **Ms J. A. French**
5 **KNOCKAMANY BENDS (IRE)**, 4, b g Majestic Missile (IRE)—Sweet Compliance **D. R. & E. E. Brown**
6 **MEDECIS MOUNTAIN**, 5, b g Medecis—Moon Cat (IRE) **J. S. Wainwright**
7 **OBBOORR**, 5, b g Cape Cross (IRE)—Felawnah (USA) **J. S. Wainwright**
8 **ROSSINGTON**, 5, b g Gentleman's Deal (IRE)—Ettrbee (IRE) **Brian Robb. David Hoyes. Mark Phillips.**
9 **ZAINDA (IRE)**, 4, b f Dr Fong (USA)—Zafayra (IRE) **Ms J. A. French**

THREE-YEAR-OLDS

10 **ACQUAINT (IRE)**, gr f Verglas (IRE)—Azia (IRE) **FRT Racing Club**

Other Owners: Mr Wayne Bavill, Mr D. Bavill, Mr A. P. Bluck, Mr D. R. Brown, Mrs E. E. Brown, Mr David Hoyes, Mr J. Lamerton, Mr Mark Phillips, Mr Brian Robb, Mr P. R. Walker.

Assistant Trainer: Mrs Fiona Wainwright

Jockey (flat): Tom Eaves, Paddy Aspell, Tony Hamilton. **Amateur:** Mr Alexander French, Mr Kaine Wood.

---

643 **MR MARK WALFORD, Sheriff Hutton**
Postal: **Cornborough Manor, Sheriff Hutton, York, YO60 6QN**
Contacts: **PHONE (01347) 878382 FAX (01347) 878547 MOBILE (07734) 265689**
E-MAIL g_walford@hotmail.com WEBSITE www.timwalford.co.uk

1 **BIG SOUND**, 7, b g Supreme Sound—Tarbolton Moss **Hanson & Hamilton**
2 **BLUE TOP**, 5, b g Millkom—Pompey Blue **Mr Brown, Evans, Lister, Cowley**
3 **CEDAR GLORY**, 5, b m Josr Algarhoud (IRE)—Cedar Jeneva **Sarah Hills & Mr Midgley**
4 **DANCING LANCER**, 5, b g Alhaarth (IRE)—Mafatin (IRE) **A. C. Birkle**
5 **EVERLASTING LIGHT**, 4, b f Authorized (IRE)—Blue Rocket (IRE) **Mrs G. B. Walford**
6 **FENTARA**, 9, b m Kayf Tara—Miss Fencote **Chasing Gold Limited**
7 **FLEXIBLE FLYER**, 5, b g Exceed And Excel (AUS)—Windermere Island **Mrs G. B. Walford**
8 **FLY BY KNIGHT**, 5, b g Desert King—Lox Lane (IRE) **Townroe & Mitchell**
9 **FRANK'S FOLLY (IRE)**, 5, b g Tiger Hill (IRE)—Pocket Book (IRE) **Mrs F Horsfield**
10 **GRANWOOD**, 8, ch m Midnight Legend—Half Each **Mrs C. A. Watson**
11 **HIGHLANDER TED**, 6, b g Midnight Legend—Half Each **Quench Racing Partnership 3**
12 **KING OF STRINGS (IRE)**, 5, b g Desert King (IRE)—Lemon Cello (IRE) **F. M. & Mrs E. Holmes**
13 **KODICIL (IRE)**, 6, b g Kodiac—Miss Caoimhe (IRE) **Mr D. & Mr S. Woodall**
14 **LILLY'S LEGEND**, 4, ch f Midnight Legend—Daltica (FR) **Grindal & Skinner**
15 **MEDIEVAL BISHOP (IRE)**, 5, b g Bachelor Duke (USA)—
　　On The Backfoot (IRE) **K Hamilton,D Dickson,N Skinner**
16 **MISSY WELLS**, 4, b f Misu Bond (IRE)—Aqua **Mrs M. J. Hills**
17 **MR SNOOZY**, 5, b g Pursuit of Love—Hard To Follow **T. W. Heseltine**
18 **MULTILICIOUS**, 4, b f Multiplex—Ryan's Quest (IRE) **Mrs G. B. Walford**
19 **NORTHERN OSCAR (IRE)**, 6, b g Oscar (IRE)—Cailin's Princess (IRE) **Allott Bowler Roberts Stanser Gittus**
20 **OLIVER'S GOLD**, 6, b g Danehill Dancer (IRE)—Gemini Gold (IRE) **Quench Racing Partnership**
21 **RUBY BAY (IRE)**, 9, ch g Beneficial—Ruby Supreme (IRE) **Chasing Gold Limited**
22 **SHIMLA DAWN (IRE)**, 6, b g Indian Danehill (IRE)—Tina Thyne (IRE) **Mrs M. Cooper**
23 **UNO VALOROSO (FR)**, 6, b g Voix du Nord (FR)—Danse d'avril (FR) **Mr C. R. Herman**

MR MARK WALFORD - Continued

THREE-YEAR-OLDS

24 **BARLEYCORN LADY (IRE)**, b f Nayef (USA)—Partly Sunny **G. Mett Racing & Chadney**
25 **CRAGGAKNOCK**, b g Authorized (IRE)—Goodie Twosues **Mrs Mary & David Longstaff**
26 **LORIMER'S LOT (IRE)**, ch f Camacho—Alwiuda (USA) **Lorimer Walford**
27 **SIRPERTAN**, b g Sir Percy—Tanwir **Mr D. & Mr S. Woodall**

TWO-YEAR-OLDS

28 B c 11/4 Mount Nelson—Amiata (Pennekamp (USA)) (9291) **Cornborough Racing Club**
29 B f 9/4 Misu Bond (IRE)—Salalah (Lion Cavern (USA)) (1142) **Cornborough Racing Club**
30 B f 29/1 Bushranger (IRE)—Vanilla Loan (IRE) (Invincible Spirit (IRE)) (9291) **Cornborough Racing Club**

Other Owners: Mr J. Allott, Mr M. A. Blades, Mr J. Bowler, Mr M. Brown, Lady Cobham, Mr Eric Cowley, Mr David Dickson, Mr Brian Downard, Mr. Chris Evans, Miss Jill Gittus, Mrs Jayne Hamilton, Mr Karl Hamilton, Mr Keith Hanson, Mr Brian Harris, Ms Sarah Hills, Mr M. Holmes, Mrs Elaine Holmes, Mrs F. Horsfield, Miss Rosemary Lister, Mrs M. Longstaff, Mr D. Longstaff, Mr P. P. Lorimer, S. N. Lorimer, Mr K. Midgley, Mr J. C. Mitchell, Mr Mal Preedy, Mr M. G. Roberts, Mr N. D. Skinner, Mr Robert Smeaton, Mr M. T. Stanser, Mrs C. Townroe, Mr J. Walford, Mrs Carol Watson, Mr Derek Woodall, Mr Stephen Woodall.

Assistant Trainer: Tim Walford

Jockey (flat): Duran Fentiman, Graham Gibbons. **Apprentice:** Jason Hart.

---

644 **MR ROBERT WALFORD, Blandford**
Postal: **Heart of Oak Stables, Okeford Fitzpane, Blandford, Dorset, DT11 0LW**
Contacts: **MOBILE (07815) 116209**
E-MAIL robertwalford1@gmail.com

1 **ASTRE DE LA COUR (FR)**, 4, b br g Khalkevi (IRE)—Gracieuse Delacour (FR) **The Front Runners Partnership**
2 **BRODY BLEU (FR)**, 7, b g Kotky Bleu (FR)—Brodie Blue (FR) **Mr R. J. Brown**
3 **CAPEL LE FERNE (IRE)**, 6, ch g Anabaa Blue—Lox Lane (IRE) **Lady N. F. Cobham**
4 **CAROLE'S LORD**, 5, b g Hernando (FR)—Carole's Crusader **P. Murphy**
5 **CAROLE'S SPIRIT**, 6, b m Hernando (FR)—Carole's Crusader **P. Murphy**
6 **CASTARNIE**, 6, b g Afflora (IRE)—Just Jenny (IRE) **Sue & Clive Cole & Ann & Tony Gale**
7 **ITS RUBY**, 8, bm Midnight Legend—Lorgnette **A. J. M. Trowbridge**
8 **JUST CLOUDY**, 10, b g Cloudings (IRE)—Tycoon Tina **R. H. Alner**
9 **PILGREEN (FR)**, 9, ch g Green Tune (USA)—Galinetta (FR) **Mrs S. De Wilde**
10 **ROSA IMPERIALIS**, 5, ch m Imperial Dancer—Motcombe (IRE) **Lady N. F. Cobham**
11 **SUN WILD LIFE (FR)**, 4, b g Antarctique (IRE)—Nidelia (FR) **The Keightley Lambert Partnership**
12 **SWINCOMBE STAR**, 5, b g With The Flow (USA)—Lady Felix **Yeo Racing Partnership**
13 **TRIBULATION (IRE)**, 6, br g Diktat—Royal York **Mrs C. A. Lewis-Jones**
14 **UMBERTO D'OLIVATE (FR)**, 6, b g Alberto Giacometti (IRE)—Komunion (FR) **Mrs S. De Wilde**
15 **VOLTCHESKO (FR)**, 5, b g Della Francesca (USA)—Mass Media (FR) **Chris Pugsley & Nigel Skinner**

Other Owners: Mr C. Cole, Mrs S. S. Cole, Mr A. P. Gale, Mrs A. G. Gale, Mr P. Goodwin, Mrs C. Keightley, Mr T P Lambert, K. B. W. Parkhouse, C. C. Pugsley, Mr S. Reed, N. Skinner, Mrs K. D. Yeo.

Jockey (NH): Dougie Costello, Daryl Jacob, Felix De Gilles.

---

645 **MR ED WALKER, Newmarket**
Postal: **Warren Place, Newmarket, Suffolk, CB8 8QQ**
Contacts: **PHONE (01638) 660464 FAX (01638) 663282 MOBILE (07787) 534145**
E-MAIL ed@edwalkerracing.com WEBSITE www.edwalkerracing.com

1 **ANYA**, 5, b m Monsieur Bond (IRE)—Dyanita **Mrs L. M. Alexander**
2 **DARING DRAGON**, 4, gr g Intikhab (USA)—The Manx Touch (IRE) **Mrs A. A. Yap**
3 **DUKE OF DESTINY (IRE)**, 5, br g Bachelor Duke (USA)—Marghelan (FR) **Dubai Thoroughbred Racing**
4 **GLORIOUS PROTECTOR (IRE)**, 4, b g Azamour (IRE)—Hasaiyda (IRE) **Mrs A. A. Yap**
5 **GLORIOUS STAR (USA)**, 4, ch g Soviet Star (USA)—Caerlonore (IRE) **Mrs A. A. Yap**
6 **INDIAN JACK (IRE)**, 6, ch g Indian Haven—Almaviva (IRE) **Forza Azzurri**
7 **INDIAN TRIFONE (IRE)**, 4, ch c Indian Haven—Almaviva (IRE) **Forza Azzurri**
8 **LIVIA'S DREAM (IRE)**, 5, b m Teofilo (IRE)—Brindisi **Mrs O. Hoare**
9 **MEMORIZE (IRE)**, 4, b g Dark Angel (IRE)—Cape Cod (IRE) **L. A. Bellman**
10 **NICHOLASCOPERNICUS (IRE)**, 5, ch g Medicean—Ascendancy **Greenwood, Halsall and Pegum**

MR ED WALKER - Continued

11 **TUMBLEDOWN (USA)**, 4, b f Bernardini (USA)—Freeroll (USA) **Sheikh Juma Dalmook Al Maktoum**
12 **WILLIE WAG TAIL (USA)**, 5, b g Theatrical—Night Risk (USA) **Qatar Racing Limited**

THREE-YEAR-OLDS

13 **AYA'S GIFT**, ch c Compton Place—Ringarooma **K. A. Dasmal**
14 **BEASTFROMTHEEAST**, b g Oratorio (IRE)—Bronze Star **Benatom Racing 2**
15 **BUSHCRAFT (IRE)**, b c Bushranger (IRE)—Lady Lucia (IRE) **L. A. Bellman**
16 **CENSORIUS**, b c Notnowcato—Meredith **Al Ansari, Greenwood, Pegum**
17 **CHUCK HATCH**, b c Sakhee (USA)—Forest Fire (SWE) **Mrs M. Campbell-Andenaes**
18 **CHUNGHUA (USA)**, ch c Elusive Quality (USA)—Mananiyya (IRE) **Mr R. Ng**
19 **CLEAR SPELL (IRE)**, b g Tamayuz—Beat The Rain **De La Warr Racing**
20 **FULL MOON FEVER (IRE)**, b f Azamour (IRE)—Hasaiyda (IRE) **Bellman, Donald, Walker & Walker**
21 **GLORIOUS EMPIRE (IRE)**, br g Holy Roman Emperor (IRE)—
                                                    Humble And Proud (IRE) **Ms Judy Yap & Ms Salina Yang**
22 **GLORIOUS SUN**, b c Medicean—Sweet Cando (IRE) **Ms Judy Yap & Ms Salina Yang**
23 **GRACEFILLY**, b f Invincible Spirit (IRE)—Marula (IRE) **L. A. Bellman**
24 **HOPEFILLY (IRE)**, b f Compton Place—Kondakova (IRE) **L. A. Bellman**
25 **ITSNOWCATO**, b c Notnowcato—Blaenavon **Sheikh Juma Dalmook Al Maktoum**
26 **KINEMA (IRE)**, b g Galileo (IRE)—Bon Nuit (IRE) **Mr M. Keller**
27 **LIGHTNING MOON (IRE)**, b c Shamardal (USA)—Catch The Moon (IRE) **Mr M. Betamar**
28 **MUTATIS MUTANDIS (IRE)**, gr f Mastercraftsman (IRE)—Amathia (IRE) **Chasemore Farm**
29 **OUTLAWED**, b c Kyllachy—Regent's Park **L. A. Bellman**
30 **PERSONA GRATA**, b f Sir Percy—Kaldounya **Miss K. Rausing**
31 **PRESIDENTE**, b c Myboycharlie (IRE)—Madam President **S. Manana**
32 **REROUTE (IRE)**, b f Acclamation—Divert (IRE) **Sheikh R. D. Al Maktoum**
33 **SCOTTISH STRAND**, b c Selkirk (USA)—Starlit Sands **S. Ali**
34 **SMART BOUNTY**, b f Bahamian Bounty—Loveleaves **Mr B. T. C. Liu**
35 **SMART SALUTE**, b c Royal Applause—Naizak **Mr B. T. C. Liu**
36 **TWENTY ROSES (IRE)**, b f Mastercraftsman (IRE)—Stunning Rose (IRE) **Highland Yard LLC**
37 **URBAN SANCTUARY**, ch c Mount Nelson—White Dress (IRE) **John Nicholls (Trading) & John Moorhouse**
38 B f Compton Place—Vellena **Clipper Group Holdings Ltd**
39 **VINCERE**, b c Tiger Hill (IRE)—Valoria **Mr S. A. Stuckey**
40 **XANTHOS**, ch g Medicean—My Girl Jode **Mr M. J. Cottis**

TWO-YEAR-OLDS

41 B c 18/4 Arcano (IRE)—Acicula (IRE) (Night Shift (USA)) (40000) **E. C. D. Walker**
42 **ARTFILLY (IRE)**, b f 10/3 Art Connoisseur (IRE)—Tallassee (Indian Ridge) (25714) **L. A. Bellman**
43 B c 17/4 Authorized (IRE)—Awwal Malika (USA) (Kingmambo (USA)) (11000) **N. Mourad**
44 B c 16/3 Intikhab (USA)—Bufera (IRE) (King's Best (USA)) (27874) **Laurence Bellman & Matthew Cottis**
45 **BUSHEPHALUS (IRE)**, br c 17/2 Dark Angel (IRE)—
                                White Daffodil (IRE) (Footstepsinthesand) (45714) **Mr E. Bush**
46 B c 22/2 Acclamation—Divine Power (Kyllachy) (65000) **Sheikh Juma Dalmook Al Maktoum**
47 B c 22/1 Fast Company (IRE)—Es Que (Inchinor) (75000) **Mr M. Keller**
48 **FILLOTHEWISP**, b f 3/4 Teofilo (IRE)—Euroceleb (IRE) (Peintre Celebre (USA)) (240030) **Mrs O. Hoare**
49 **LA MARCHESA (IRE)**, b f 19/3 Duke of Marmalade (IRE)—Brindisi (Dr Fong (USA)) **Mrs O. Hoare**
50 B f 26/3 Lawman (FR)—Leopard Hunt (USA) (Diesis) (15485) **Round Hill Stud**
51 B c 4/2 Bushranger (IRE)—Munaawashat (IRE) (Marju (IRE)) (37000) **E. C. D. Walker**
52 Ch f 24/2 Pastoral Pursuits—Nihal (IRE) (Singspiel (IRE)) (5714) **Dubai Thoroughbred Racing**
53 B c 6/3 Dutch Art—Popocatepetl (FR) (Nashwan (USA)) (105000) **Mr C. F. Ma**
54 Br c 8/2 Royal Applause—Provence (Averti (IRE)) (27000) **Mrs A. A. Yap**
55 Br c 27/2 Bushranger (IRE)—Rafelite (Fraam) (10000) **Alpine Racing**
56 B c 2/3 Aqlaam—Regal Asset (USA) (Regal Classic (CAN)) (55000) **Mrs A. A. Yap**
57 B c 19/4 Dark Angel (IRE)—Rose's Destination (IRE) (Dubai Destination (USA)) (60000) **Mr C. U. F. Ma**
58 B c 4/2 Lord Shanakill (USA)—Roskeen (IRE) (Grand Lodge (USA)) (58000) **Mr C. U. F. Ma**
59 Ch g 28/3 Zebedee—Rule Britannia (Night Shift (USA)) (30000) **Mr C. U. F. Ma**
60 B f 30/1 Cape Cross (IRE)—Russian Symbol (Danehill Dancer (IRE)) **Mr M. Keller**
61 B c 8/4 Dark Angel (IRE)—Sassari (IRE) (Darshaan) (115000) **K. M. Yeung**
62 **SHOWBIRD**, b f 8/5 Showcasing—Dancing Feather (Suave Dancer (USA)) (23000) **K. A. Dasmal**
63 B f 17/3 Kyllachy—Stormy Weather (Nashwan (USA)) **Buckmaster Racing**
64 B f 28/3 Azamour (IRE)—Suzy Bliss (Spinning World (USA)) (31000) **Chasemore Farm**
65 B c 26/3 Kodiac—Undulation (Alhaarth (IRE)) (42000) **Sheikh R. D. Al Maktoum**
66 B f 16/3 Kyllachy—Upskittled (Diktat) (55000) **Sheikh R. D. Al Maktoum**
67 B c 28/3 Invincible Spirit (IRE)—Urgele (FR) (Zafonic (USA)) (110000) **Mr John Coleman & Mr Clarence Cheng**
68 B f 2/2 Sir Percy—Valoria (Hernando (FR)) **Mr S. A. Stuckey**

MR ED WALKER - Continued

69 Ch f 29/3 Compton Place—Where's Broughton (Cadeaux Genereux) (13000) **L. A. Bellman**
70 B f 9/4 Shamardal (USA)—Wiener Wald (USA) (Woodman (USA)) **Car Colston Hall Stud Syndicate**

Other Owners: Mr S. Al Ansari, Mr Laurence A. Bellman, Mr Philip Corbisiero, Mr Matthew Cottis, Mr Alastair Donald, Mr P. Gleeson, Mr B. Greenwood, Mr Alan Halsall, Mr T. F. Harris, John Nicholls (Trading) Ltd, Mr John Moorhouse, Mr R. A. Pegum, Mr Onofrio Tona, Mr E. C. D. Walker, Mrs T. Walker, Ms Salina Yang, Mrs A. A. Yap.

---

646 | **MR CHRIS WALL, Newmarket**
Postal: **Induna Stables, Fordham Road, Newmarket, Suffolk, CB8 7AQ**
Contacts: **OFFICE (01638) 661999 HOME (01638) 668896 FAX (01638) 667279
MOBILE (07764) 940255**
E-MAIL christianwall@btconnect.com WEBSITE www.chriswallracing.co.uk

1 **BALLYSHONAGH**, 4, b f Tiger Hill (IRE)—Shamara (IRE) **Lady Juliet Tadgell**
2 **BASSARA (IRE)**, 5, b m Oasis Dream—Sauvage (FR) **Ms Aida Fustoq**
3 **EMERALD SEA**, 4, b f Green Desert (USA)—Wind Surf (USA) **Lady Juliet Tadgell**
4 **FEVER FEW**, 5, b m Pastoral Pursuits—Prairie Oyster **Mrs C. A. Wall & Mr R. Wayman**
5 **GRAVITATIONAL (IRE)**, 4, b g Invincible Spirit (IRE)—Flower of Kent (USA) **D. M. J. Gilbert**
6 **MEET ME HALFWAY**, 4, b f Exceed And Excel (AUS)—Pivotal Drive (IRE) **Mr D. M. Thurlby**
7 **MIDNIGHT RIDER (IRE)**, 6, b g Red Ransom (USA)—Foreplay (USA) **The Leap Year Partnership**
8 **OH SO SASSY**, 4, b f Pastoral Pursuits—Almasi (IRE) **The Eight of Diamonds**
9 **OH SO SPICY**, 7, ch m Pastoral Pursuits—Almasi (IRE) **The Eight of Diamonds**
10 **PEARL BLUE (IRE)**, 6, b m Exceed And Excel (AUS)—Sanfrancullinan (IRE) **Archangels 2**
11 **POSH BOY (IRE)**, 4, b g Duke of Marmalade (IRE)—Sauvage (FR) **Mr D. M. Thurlby**
12 **PREMIO LOCO (USA)**, 10, ch g Prized (USA)—Crazee Mental **B. R. Westley**
13 **QANAN**, 5, b g Green Desert (USA)—Strings **Alan & Jill Smith**
14 **RAVENSBURG**, 4, ch f Raven's Pass (USA)—Generous Lady **Ms Aida Fustoq**
15 **ROCKSILLA**, 4, b f Rock of Gibraltar (IRE)—Hope Island (IRE) **Moyns Park Stud Ltd**
16 **ROYAL ROCK**, 10, b g Rock (USA)—Vanishing Point (USA) **Ms Aida Fustoq**
17 **SILVALA DANCE**, 4, b f Kyllachy—Bride of The Sea **Mrs D. Lochhead**
18 **SILVER LACE (IRE)**, 5, br gr m Clodovil—Rockahoolababy (IRE) **The Equema Partnership**
19 **TRUCANINI**, 4, b f Mount Nelson—Jalissa **Dolly's Dream Syndicate**
20 **ZE KING**, 5, b g Manduro (GER)—Top Flight Queen **Ms Aida Fustoq**

THREE-YEAR-OLDS

21 **BURMESE BREEZE**, b g Shirocco (GER)—Crimson Topaz **Mr D. M. Thurlby**
22 **DIRE STRAITS (IRE)**, b c Teofilo (IRE)—Kalagold (IRE) **Mr D. S. Lee**
23 **DISTANT SHADOW**, gr f Rock of Gibraltar (IRE)—Daheeya **Follow The Flag Partnership**
24 **ELEUSIS**, b f Elnadim (USA)—Demeter (USA) **Lady Juliet Tadgell**
25 **FLIGHT FIGHT**, b c Raven's Pass (USA)—Sunspear (IRE) **Ms Aida Fustoq**
26 **JOHARA (IRE)**, b f Iffraaj—Hurricane Irene (IRE) **Mrs Claude Lilley**
27 **KATAWI**, b f Dubawi (IRE)—Purring (USA) **Moyns Park Stud Ltd**
28 **LUCKY JIM**, b g Lucky Story (USA)—Lateralle (IRE) **Follow The Flag Partnership**
29 **MAY QUEEN**, ch f Shamardal (USA)—Mango Lady **Ms Aida Fustoq**
30 **MR WIN (IRE)**, b c Intikhab (USA)—Midnight Oasis **Mr D. M. Thurlby**
31 **NORFOLK SOUND**, b f Pastoral Pursuits—Cayman Sound **Far and Wide Partners**
32 **NOT ANOTHER BILL**, ch g Notnowcato—Composing (IRE) **P. J. W. Botham**
33 **QUEEN OF THE NILE**, b f Sakhee (USA)—Vanishing Point (USA) **Ms Aida Fustoq**
34 **SEMARAL (IRE)**, b f High Chaparral (IRE)—Semaphore **Moyns Park Stud Ltd**
35 **SOUVILLE**, b f Dalakhani (IRE)—Royale Danehill (IRE) **Hughes & Scott**
36 **SYRIAN PEARL**, gr f Clodovil—Syrian Queen **The Clodhoppers**
37 **THE NEW PHARAOH (IRE)**, b c Montjeu (IRE)—Out West (USA) **Ms Aida Fustoq**
38 **VENUS MARINA**, b f Tiger Hill (USA)—Danvers **Highgrounds Partnership**
39 **WINDY CITI**, ch f Zamindar (USA)—Windy Britain **Scuderia Giocri SNC**

TWO-YEAR-OLDS

40 **BELVOIR DIVA**, br f 22/2 Exceed And Excel (AUS)—Merry Diva (Bahamian Bounty) (26000) **Mr Barry Green**
41 B f 5/4 Clodovil (IRE)—Celtic Lynn (IRE) (Celtic Swing) (30971) **Qatar Racing Limited**
42 **CLOUD SEVEN**, br c 11/2 New Approach (IRE)—Regrette Rien (USA) (Unbridled's Song (USA)) **Ms Aida Fustok**
43 **COOLCALMCOLLECTED (IRE)**, b f 6/4 Acclamation—Jalissa (Mister Baileys) (67000) **Mr Des Thurlby**
44 B f 24/2 Mastercraftsman (IRE)—Eve (Rainbow Quest (USA)) (35000) **Mr D. S. Lee**
45 B f 19/5 Lawman (FR)—Gentle Thoughts (Darshaan) (34000) **Mr D. S. Lee**
46 **KRISTJANO (GER)**, b c 6/4 Nayef (USA)—Kalahari Dancer (Dalakhani (IRE)) (8000) **B. R. Westley**

MR CHRIS WALL - Continued

47 **LAURA B**, b f 20/3 Acclamation—New Design (IRE) (Bluebird (USA)) (3000) **Lady Juliet Tadgell**
48 **OASIS SPEAR**, b c 28/2 Oasis Dream—Sunspear (IRE) (Montjeu (IRE)) **Ms Aida Fustok**
49 **STAMP OF APPROVAL (IRE)**, b f 3/4 Approve (IRE)—
Wassendale (Erhaab (USA)) (18000) **Induna Racing Partners (Two)**
50 **SUFFOLK SKY**, b f 7/3 Pastoral Pursuits—
Charlevoix (IRE) (King Charlemagne (USA)) (2857) **Mr J. Sims & Mr M Sinclair**

Other Owners: Mr T. J. Bater, Mr N Belcher, Mr H. Bethell, Mrs S & Mr M Burrows, Mrs J Carlisle, Mrs V. Carpenter, Mrs V Carpenter, Mr D. Cherry, Mrs R Cooper, Mr & Mrs J G Davies, Mrs J. E. Dobie, Mr Stuart Feast, Mrs S Feast, Mrs S Fleet, Mr R. Fraiser, Mr P Hanmer, Mr C Harker, Mr P Hitchcock, Mr C. J. A. Hughes, Mrs Jill Kerr-Smiley, Mrs M Middleton, Mr Roger Nash, Mr R. B. Norden, Mr J Norden, Mr B Payne, Mr D. Popely, Mr R. A. Popely, Mr R Rice, Mr D Rice, Mrs T. Rigby, Prudence Lady Salt, Mr Kieran D. Scott, Mrs A Shuckburgh, Mr A Stearn, Mr A Stearn, Lady Stuttaford, R. Sutton & R Machin, Lady Juliet Tadgell, Mrs C. J. Walker, Mrs C. A. Wall, Mrs E Wass, Miss H Wass, Mr R. J. Wayman, Mr M Wayman, Mrs P Williams.

Assistant Trainer: Richard Freeman

Jockey (flat): George Baker, Ted Durcan. **Apprentice:** Sam Clarke, Jess Sharp.

---

647 **MRS SARAH WALL, Dallington**
Postal: **Little Pines, Bakers Lane, Heathfield, East Sussex, TN21 9JS**
Contacts: **PHONE/FAX (01435) 831048 MOBILE (07783) 370856**
E-MAIL sarah55french@btinternet.com

1 **BACH TO FRONT (IRE)**, 9, b m Bach (IRE)—Celtic Leader (IRE) **J. P. C. Wall**
2 **BALLINHASSIG (IRE)**, 9, ch g Beneficial—Dear Polly (IRE) **Mrs S. Wall**
3 **TIGRIDIA (IRE)**, 7, br m Brian Boru—Indian Legend (IRE) **Mrs S. Wall**

Assistant Trainer: Jeremy Wall

---

648 **MR TREVOR WALL, Craven Arms**
Postal: **Hope Farm Stables, Twitchen, Clunbury, Craven Arms, Shropshire, SY7 0HN**
Contacts: **PHONE (01694) 724144 FAX (01694) 724144 MOBILE (07972) 732080**

1 **CELTS ESPERE**, 11, ch g Samraan (USA)—Celtic Dream **Ricochet Management Limited**
2 **FAIRY ALISHA**, 6, ch m Doyen (IRE)—Regal Fairy (IRE) **Moorland Racing**
3 **FEMME D'ESPERE**, 8, b m Celts Espere—Drummer's Dream (IRE) **Ricochet Management Limited**
4 **MAXI MAC (IRE)**, 4, ch g Thousand Words—Crimada (IRE) **D. Pugh**

Other Owners: S. A. Mace, Mrs A. M. Mace.

Assistant Trainer: Mrs J. A. Wall **Conditional:** Josh Wall.

---

649 **MRS JANE WALTON, Otterburn**
Postal: **Dunns Houses, Otterburn, Newcastle Upon Tyne, Tyne and Wear, NE19 1LB**
Contacts: **PHONE (01830) 520677 FAX (01830) 520677 MOBILE (07808) 592701**
E-MAIL dunnshouses@hotmail.com WEBSITE www.janewaltonhorseracing.co.uk

1 **ALWAYSRECOMMENDED (IRE)**, 5, ch g Gamut (IRE)—
Awbeg Beauty (IRE) **Highly Recommended Partnership 2**
2 **CHARMING KNIGHT (IRE)**, 13, b g Mohaajir (USA)—Arctic Laura **Mrs J. M. Walton**
3 **HAVE YOU HAD YOURS (IRE)**, 8, br g Whitmore's Conn (USA)—
Mandys Moynavely (IRE) **Highly Recommended Partnership**
4 **HEEZ A STEEL (IRE)**, 13, b g Naheez (USA)—Ari's Fashion **Mrs J. M. Walton**
5 **MASTER MURPHY (IRE)**, 9, b g Flemensfirth (USA)—Awbeg Beauty (IRE) **Mrs J. M. Walton**
6 **THEDFACTOR (IRE)**, 5, b g Kalanisi (IRE)—Insan Magic (IRE) **Fresh Start Partnership**
7 **WESTEND THEATRE (IRE)**, 5, b g Darsi (FR)—Ballyvelig Lady (IRE) **Mrs J. M. Walton**
8 **WILDEST DREAMS (IRE)**, 5, b g Flemensfirth (USA)—Suspicious Minds **Joyce Rutherford Jane Walton**

Other Owners: Mrs L. Duncan, Mr J. McCreanor, Mr D. Parkins, Recommended Freight Ltd, Mrs M. R. Ridley, Miss J. Rutherford.

Assistant Trainer: Mrs Patricia Robson **Jockey (NH):** Alistair Findlay.

650 MR JASON WALTON, Morpeth
Postal: **Flotterton Hall, Thropton, Morpeth, Northumberland, NE65 7LF**
Contacts: **PHONE (01669) 640253 FAX (01669) 640288 MOBILE (07808) 592701**

1 **BOSSY BECCY**, 5, b m And Beyond (IRE)—Merry Tina **Exors of the late Mr & Mrs F. T. Walton**
2 **CENTRAL FLAME**, 6, ch g Central Park (IRE)—More Flair **Exors of the late Mr & Mrs F. T. Walton**
3 **HIGHLAND CATHEDRAL**, 10, ch g Minster Son—Celtic Waters **Exors of the late Mr & Mrs F. T. Walton**
4 **JOB FOR ERIC**, 7, b g Bollin Eric—Gone Astray **Exors of the late Mr & Mrs F. T. Walton**
5 **MERRY MIX**, 6, br m Fair Mix (IRE)—Merry Tina **Exors of the late Mr & Mrs F. T. Walton**
6 **RUPERT BEAR**, 8, b g Rambling Bear—Glittering Stone **Exors of the late Mr & Mrs F. T. Walton**
7 **SACRED MOUNTAIN**, 13, b g Primitive Rising (USA)—Gone Astray **Exors of the late Mr & Mrs F. T. Walton**
8 **SADDLE PACK (IRE)**, 11, b g Saddlers' Hall (IRE)—Zuhal **Exors of the late Mr & Mrs F. T. Walton**

Other Owners: J. B. Walton, F. A. Walton.

651 MRS SHEENA WALTON, Hexham
Postal: **Linacres, Wark, Hexham, Northumberland, NE48 3DP**
Contacts: **PHONE (01434) 230656 MOBILE (07752) 755184**
E-MAIL rchrdwltn@aol.com

1 4, B g Kayf Tara—Bonchester Bridge **Rede Tyne Racing**
2 **DYSTONIA'S REVENGE (IRE)**, 9, b g Woods of Windsor (USA)—Lady Isaac (IRE) **Mr J. L. Blacklock**
3 4, B g Gamut (IRE)—Elleena Rose (IRE) **Linacres Racing Partnership**
4 **HOBSONS BAY (IRE)**, 9, b g Flemensfirth (USA)—Ou La La (IRE) **R. H. Walton**
5 **NATIVE OPTIMIST (IRE)**, 7, b g Broadway Flyer (USA)—Native Orchid (IRE) **Rede Tyne Racing**
6 6, Ch m And Beyond (IRE)—Reeker Pike **R. H. Walton**
7 **THE BOOZY BISHOP (IRE)**, 9, b g Bishop of Cashel—Ann's River (IRE) **R. H. Walton**

Other Owners: Mrs M. Rogerson.

Assistant Trainer: Mr R. H. Walton

Amateur: Miss C. Walton.

652 MR JASON WARD, Middleham
Postal: **The Dante Yard, Manor House Stables, Middleham, Leyburn, North Yorkshire, DL8 4QL**
Contacts: **PHONE (01969) 622730 MOBILE (07967) 357595**
E-MAIL info@jasonwardracing.co.uk WEBSITE www.jasonwardracing.co.uk

1 **HEROSTATUS**, 7, ch g Dalakhani (IRE)—Desired **R. Naylor**
2 **HOPE FOR GLORY**, 5, b g Proclamation (IRE)—Aissa **Pear Tree Partnership**
3 **IMPERIAL BOND**, 5, b g Misu Bond (IRE)—Liability (IRE) **Mr S. J. Matheson**
4 **LONGSHADOW**, 4, ch g Monsun (GER)—La Felicita **B. Harker & Jill Ward**
5 **MOSS HILL**, 5, b g Moss Vale (IRE)—Borders Belle (IRE) **Mrs J. Ward**
6 **MY NEW ANGEL (IRE)**, 5, gr m Dark Angel (IRE)—Mynu Girl (IRE) **Mr C. J. Dingwall**
7 **SWEETNESSANDLIGHT**, 5, b m Aussie Rules (USA)—Taschlynn (IRE) **Mrs J. Ward**
8 **TROUBLED WATERS**, 5, b m Kayf Tara—Air of Affection **Miss S. R. Robertson**
9 **YPRES**, 5, b g Byron—Esligier (IRE) **Brian Harker, J. Teal, M. Walmsley, S. Roebuck**

THREE-YEAR-OLDS

10 **BAHAMA DANCER**, ch f Bahamian Bounty—Arlene Phillips **21st Century Racing**
11 **HELLO SWEETNESS**, b f Aqlaam—Atnab (USA) **P. Adams & J Morphet**
12 **SOLID JUSTICE (IRE)**, b g Rock of Gibraltar (IRE)—Burnin' Memories (USA) **N. Carr, R. Naylor, T. Whitehead**

TWO-YEAR-OLDS

13 B c 21/2 Mullionmileanhour (IRE)—Fangfoss Girls (Monsieur Bond (IRE)) (3333) **Mr S. J. Matheson**
14 Gr c 26/3 Proclamation (IRE)—Los Organos (IRE) (Turtle Island (IRE)) **Mr S. J. Matheson**

Other Owners: Mr B. Harker, Mr J. A. Morphet, Barry Roebuck & Family, Mr C. Teal, Deidre Throup, Mrs Jill Ward.

Assistant Trainer: Tim Ward

Jockey (flat): Tom Eaves, P J McDonald. **Jockey (NH):** Brian Hughes. **Amateur:** Mr Ross Turner.

653 **MR FREDERICK WATSON, Sedgefield**
Postal: **Beacon Hill, Sedgefield, Stockton-On-Tees, Cleveland, TS21 3HN**
Contacts: PHONE **(01740) 620582** MOBILE **(07773) 321472**
E-MAIL **fredwatson@talktalk.net**

1 **BILLY REDPATH**, 6, b g Distant Music (USA)—Shardda **Mr B. Emery**
2 **CONJUROR'S BLUFF**, 6, b g Tiger Hill (IRE)—Portmeirion **F. Watson**
3 **DESTINATION AIM**, 7, b g Dubai Destination (USA)—Tessa Reef (IRE) **F. Watson**
4 **FREDDIE BOLT**, 8, b g Diktat—Birjand **F. Watson**
5 **JOYFUL STAR**, 4, b g Teofilo (IRE)—Extreme Beauty (USA) **F. Watson**
6 **SPOKESPERSON (USA)**, 6, b g Henny Hughes (USA)—Verbal (USA) **F. Watson**

654 **MRS SHARON WATT, Richmond**
Postal: **Rosey Hill Farm, Scorton Road, Brompton on Swale, Richmond, North Yorkshire, DL10 7EQ**
Contacts: PHONE **(01748) 812064** FAX **(01748) 812064** MOBILE **(07970) 826046**
E-MAIL **wattfences@aol.com**

1 **JEWELLED DAGGER (IRE)**, 10, b g Daggers Drawn (USA)—Cappadoce (IRE) **Rosey Hill Partnership**
2 **MADAM LILIBET (IRE)**, 5, b m Authorized (IRE)—Foxilla (IRE) **D. H. Montgomerie**
3 **STRANDFIELD BAY (IRE)**, 8, b m Wizard King—Stylish Chic (IRE) **Major E. J. Watt**
4 **VODKA MOON**, 5, gr g Beat All (USA)—Auntie Kathleen **Mrs S A Watt & Mrs G Handley**

THREE-YEAR-OLDS

5 **CHAMPAGNE RULES**, gr g Aussie Rules (USA)—Garabelle (IRE) **Rosey Hill Partnership**
6 **THE BUNNY CATCHER**, b f Jeremy (USA)—Passionforfashion (IRE) **Rosey Hill Partnership**

TWO-YEAR-OLDS

7 B f 5/5 Royal Applause—Choysia (Pivotal)
8 Ch c 24/3 Monsieur Bond (IRE)—Hula Ballew (Weldnaas (USA))

Other Owners: Mrs N. M. Handley, F. C. Previtali, Mrs S. A. Watt.

Jockey (NH): Keith Mercer. **Conditional:** Joseph Palmowski.

655 **MR SIMON WAUGH, Morpeth**
Postal: **A G Waugh & Sons Limited, Molesden House, Molesden, Morpeth, Northumberland, NE61 3QF**
Contacts: MOBILE **(07860) 561445**
E-MAIL **swaugh@dircon.co.uk**

1 **BIG GEORGE**, 7, b g Alflora (IRE)—Petrea **Mrs S. A. York**
2 **BORIC**, 6, b g Grape Tree Road—Petrea **Mrs S. A. York**
3 **CLASSIC ORANGE**, 4, ch f Assertive—Classical Song (IRE) **S. G. Waugh**
4 **GRANDE MONSIEUR (IRE)**, 11, b g Houmayoun (FR)—Lady Suntan **A. R. G. Waugh**
5 **NEWYEARSRESOLUTION (IRE)**, 10, b g Mr Combustible (IRE)—That's Magic (IRE) **S. G. Waugh**
6 **PADDY THE PLUMBER (IRE)**, 8, b g Dr Massini—Heather Ville (IRE) **S. G. Waugh**
7 **REAR VIEW (IRE)**, 7, b g Alhaarth (IRE)—Sadinga (IRE) **S. G. Waugh**
8 **TOTAL ASSETS**, 6, b m Alflora (IRE)—Maid Equal **Northumberland Racing Club**

Other Owners: Mrs V. A. Y. Knox.

656 **MISS AMY WEAVER, Newmarket**
Postal: **Green Lodge, The Severals, Newmarket, Suffolk, CB8 7BS**
Contacts: MOBILE **(07947) 442083**
E-MAIL **amy@amyweaverracing.com** WEBSITE **www.amyweaverracing.com**

1 **ABSENT AMY (IRE)**, 5, b m Redback—Twitcher's Delight **N. P. Hardy**
2 **ANGELA'S DREAM (IRE)**, 4, b f Chineur (FR)—Church Mice (IRE) **North Star Racing**
3 **CONSERVE (IRE)**, 4, b f Duke of Marmalade (IRE)—Minor Point **Bringloe, Clarke & North Star Racing**
4 **COUNTRYMAN**, 4, b g Pastoral Pursuits—Baileys Silver (USA) **North Star Racing**
5 **EMKANAAT**, 6, b g Green Desert (USA)—Miss Anabaa **Bringloe, Powell & Executive Bloodlines**

MISS AMY WEAVER - Continued

6 **IT'S MY TIME,** 5, b m Green Desert (USA)—Soviet Terms **Mrs D. M. Swinburn**
7 **TARIQ TOO,** 7, ch g Kyllachy—Tatora **Bringloe Clarke Spain Hensby Partridge**
8 **WRECKING BALL (IRE),** 4, b g Royal Applause—Shatarah **Partridge, Parkin & Friends**

THREE-YEAR-OLDS

9 **APPLESTORY,** b f Lucky Story (USA)—Applesnap (IRE) **Mr M. J. Bringloe**
10 **D'ARCY INDIANA,** b g Royal Applause—Prowse (USA) **A Roberts & S Hassiakos**
11 **ONE PENNY PIECE,** b f Archipenko (USA)—Silken Promise (USA) **North Star Racing**
12 **PARTY RULER (IRE),** b g Holy Roman Emperor—Calypso Dancer (FR) **North Star Racing**
13 **RISK 'N' REWARD (IRE),** ch g Dandy Man (IRE)—Sharp Diversion (USA) **Miss A. K. Weaver**
14 **SILVER TREASURE (FR),** gr c Clodovil (IRE)—Ardesia Si (FR) **Bringloe, Goddard, Hitchcock & Friends**

Other Owners: M. L. Ayers, Mr R. A. Clarke, Mrs C. Goddard, S. Hassiakos, Mr C. Hensby, Mr M. G. Hitchcock, Mr M. J. McCotter, Mr K. Parkin, Mr R. E. Partridge, Mr S. Powell, Mr A. Roberts, Mr P. J. Spain, Mr C. P. White.

Apprentice: David Kenny.

---

657 | **MR ROBERT WEBB-BOWEN, Wincanton**
Postal: **Sycamore Farm, Stoke Trister, Wincanton, Somerset, BA9 9PE**
Contacts: **PHONE (01963) 31647 FAX (01963) 31647 MOBILE (07919) 884895**
E-MAIL **robert@webb-bowen.co.uk** WEBSITE **www.camrosestud.org.uk**

1 **VINMIX DE BESSY (FR),** 13, gr g River Bay (USA)—Hesse (FR) **Mrs D. J. Webb-Bowen**

Assistant Trainer: Mrs Dinah Webb-Bowen

---

658 | **MR PAUL WEBBER, Banbury**
Postal: **Cropredy Lawn, Mollington, Banbury, Oxfordshire, OX17 1DR**
Contacts: **PHONE (01295) 750226 FAX (01295) 758482 MOBILE (07836) 232465**
E-MAIL **paul@paulwebberracing.com** WEBSITE **www.paulwebberracing.com**

1 **ALASI,** 10, b m Alflora (IRE)—Anamasi **Swanbridge Bloodstock Limited**
2 **ALFIBOY,** 4, b g Alflora (IRE)—Cloudy Pearl **D. C. R. Allen**
3 **AMORUCCIO (FR),** 4, b g Le Fou (IRE)—Mandchou (FR) **Mr S. A. Al Helaissi**
4 **AUSTRALIA DAY (IRE),** 11, gr g Key of Luck (USA)—Atalina (FR) **Skippy & The Partners**
5 **BAYLEY'S DREAM,** 5, b g Presenting—Swaythe (USA) **The Sweep Stakes Partnership**
6 **BUFFLERS HOLT (IRE),** 5, b m Flemensfirth (USA)—Water Stratford (IRE) **C. W. Booth**
7 **CANTLOW (IRE),** 9, b g Kayf Tara—Winnowing (IRE) **J. P. McManus**
8 **COULDHAVEHADITALL (IRE),** 6, b g Milan—Night Leader (IRE) **D. C. R. Allen**
9 **DANVILLA,** 7, b m Dansili—Newtown Villa **Mr S. Liebermann**
10 **DASHING OVER,** 6, b g Overbury (IRE)—Dashing Executive (IRE) **Fawley House Stud**
11 **DEFINITELY GLAD (IRE),** 7, b m Definite Article—Gladys May (IRE) **Mr S. Liebermann**
12 **DEIA SUNRISE (IRE),** 5, gr g Clodovil (IRE)—Hedera (USA) **M Hughes & M Kerr-Dineen**
13 **DEVON DRUM,** 6, b g Beat Hollow—West Devon (USA) **Mr D. Carrington**
14 **DOG OR DIVORCE,** 5, b m Midnight Legend—Time For A Glass **Mr & Mrs A D Mitchell**
15 **DUNLOUGH BAY (IRE),** 8, ch g Flemensfirth (USA)—Loch Lomond (IRE) **The Horwoods Partnership**
16 **ENDOFDISCUSSION (IRE),** 7, b g Flemensfirth (USA)—Fake Tan (IRE) **D. C. R. Allen**
17 **FINGERS CROSSED (IRE),** 4, b g Bach (IRE)—Awesome Miracle (IRE) **D. C. R. Allen**
18 **FIRM ORDER (IRE),** 9, b g Winged Love (IRE)—Fairylodge Scarlet (IRE) **The Syndicators**
19 **GRAVITATE,** 5, ch g Pivotal—Spacecraft (USA) **Mrs P. V. E. Morrell**
20 **HALUCHA (IRE),** 9, b g Luso—Rose Basket (IRE) **R. W. Barnett**
21 **HONOUR A PROMISE,** 6, b m Norse Dancer (IRE)—Motcombe (IRE) **Honour A Promise**
22 **ICY COLT (ARG),** 8, br g Colonial Affair (USA)—Icy Desert (USA) **P. R. Webber**
23 **KOOLALA (IRE),** 6, b m Kayf Tara—Squaw Talk (USA) **Lady Wellesley**
24 **LADY KATHLEEN,** 7, b m Hernando (FR)—Lady of Fortune (IRE) **Mr S. Liebermann**
25 **LEMON DROP RED (USA),** 6, b g Lemon Drop Kid (USA)—Skipper's Mate (USA) **John Nicholls (Trading) Ltd**
26 **LEMON'S GENT,** 7, br g Generous (IRE)—Lemon's Mill (USA) **G. R. Waters**
27 **MAETRUFEL ANNIE,** 5, b m Flemensfirth (USA)—Materiality **Jolly Wolf Racing**
28 **MARLEY ROCA (IRE),** 10, b br g Tamayaz (CAN)—Gaye Gordon **R. V. Shaw**
29 **MASTER WICKHAM (IRE),** 5, b g Darsi (FR)—Beechberry (IRE) **Economic Security 1**
30 **NOTNOWIVORHEADACHE,** 5, b m Notnowcato—Inchcoonan **The Attwood-Coggon-Edwards-Neville**
31 **OBSTACLE,** 4, ch g Observatory (USA)—Stage Left **P. R. Webber**

MR PAUL WEBBER - Continued

32 **PERFECT TIMING (FR)**, 4, b f Sassanian (USA)—Royale Sulawesie (FR) **D. C. R. Allen**
33 **PINAMAR**, 4, ch f Shirocco (GER)—Highland Ceilidh (IRE) **C. Humphris**
34 **RESOURCEFUL MISS**, 5, b m Dubai Destination (USA)—Resourceful (IRE) **The Resourceful Partnership**
35 **RHAPANDO**, 5, b g Hernando (FR)—Rhapsody Rose **D. C. R. Allen**
36 **ROYALRACKET (IRE)**, 6, b g Royal Anthem (USA)—Allaracket (IRE) **D. C. R. Allen**
37 **RUBBER SOLE (IRE)**, 5, gr g Milan—Silver Sonus (IRE) **Mrs A. W. Timpson**
38 **RUN ON STERLING**, 5, b g Dr Fong (USA)—Dansara **Mr A. J. Rowland**
39 **SEPTEMBER BLAZE**, 7, b m Exit To Nowhere (USA)—Mid Day Chaser (IRE) **The Blaze Partnership**
40 **SHUIL GEALACH (IRE)**, 6, b m Flemensfirth (USA)—Rith Ar Aghaidh (IRE) **R. C. Moody**
41 **SIX ONE AWAY (IRE)**, 5, gr g Tikkanen (USA)—Surfing France (FR) **Mrs A. W. Timpson**
42 **SIXTY SOMETHING (FR)**, 8, gr g Dom Alco (FR)—Jaunas (FR) **Mrs A. W. Timpson**
43 **SOLE SURVIVOR (FR)**, 7, gr g Smadoun (FR)—Sellaginella **Mrs A. W. Timpson**
44 **STAR PRESENTER (IRE)**, 6, b g Presenting—Star Councel (IRE) **Archie's Partnership**
45 **SUGAR TRAIN**, 4, b c Rail Link—Plum Fairy **P. R. Webber**
46 **TAFIKA**, 10, b g Kayf Tara—Shiwa **The Tafika Partnership**
47 **THISGUNSFORHIRE (IRE)**, 6, b g Flemensfirth (USA)—Midnight Lover **Mrs L. M. Shanahan**
48 **THOM THUMB (IRE)**, 8, ch g Flemensfirth (USA)—Ardlea Dawn (IRE) **Mr S. A. Helaissi**
49 **TIME FOR RUPERT (IRE)**, 10, ch g Flemensfirth (USA)—Bell Walks Run (IRE) **Littlecote Racing Partnership**
50 **TINDARO (FR)**, 7, gr g Kingsalsa (USA)—Star's Mixa (FR) **The Tindaro Partnership**
51 **TOO MUCH TOO SOON (IRE)**, 5, b g Craigsteel—Zara Rose (IRE) **Dunton Racing Partnership**
52 **TURKEY CREEK (IRE)**, 5, b g Scorpion (IRE)—Emesions Lady (IRE) **R. C. Moody**
53 **VERVE ARGENT (FR)**, 5, gr g Fragrant Mix (IRE)—Devise II (FR) **Mr I. R. Watters**
54 **VERY LIVE (FR)**, 5, b h Secret Singer (FR)—Iona Will (FR) **R. V. Shaw**

THREE-YEAR-OLDS

55 **EMILY YEATS**, b f Yeats (IRE)—Lasso **Lady Richard Wellesley**
56 **RED COSSACK (CAN)**, ch g Rebellion—Locata (USA) **Solario Racing (Banbury)**

TWO-YEAR-OLDS

57 **MICHAELA**, ch f 4/4 Sholokhov (IRE)—La Capilla (Machiavellian (USA)) **John Nicholls (Trading) Ltd**

Other Owners: Mr Troy Attwood, Mr Nigel Birch, Mr P. Bowden, Mr H. F. Bowley, Mr A. Brooks, Mr D. G. Carrington, Mr W. H. Carson, Mr Peter Charter, Mr Jim Clay, Mr S. J. Coggon, Mr Javier Dela Rosa Maura, Mrs Sarah Drysdale, Mr M. G. Edwards, Mr Robert Frosell, Mrs Margaret Gardiner, Mr Peter Hewett, Mr D. W. Higgins, Mr David Howard, Mr Martin Hughes, Mr Michael Kerr-Dineen, Mr P. S. Lewis, Sir I. Magee, Mr M. V. Magnier, Mrs S. McGrath, Mr R. McGrath, Professor David Metcalf, Mr A. Mitchell, Mrs D. Mitchell, Mr J. Neville, Mr Martin Pepper, Mr Tony Roche, Mr Philip Rocher, Mr Nicholas Sercombe, Mr Giles Sim, Mr Jonty Southan, Mrs John Webber, Mr Paul Webber.

Jockey (NH): Denis O'Regan. **Conditional:** Luke Watson.

---

659 **MR D. K. WELD, Curragh**
Postal: Rosewell House, Curragh, Co. Kildare, Ireland
Contacts: **PHONE** (00353) 4544 1273 / 441 476 **FAX** (00353) 4544 1119
E-MAIL dkweld@eircom.net

1 **BIG BREAK**, 4, br f Dansili—Fame At Last (USA) **K. Abdullah**
2 **CALIBRATE**, 4, b f Rail Link—Valentine Girl **K. Abdullah**
3 **DIPLOMAT (USA)**, 5, b g Kitten's Joy (USA)—Waki Affair (USA) **Dr R. Lambe**
4 **FORGOTTEN RULES (IRE)**, 4, b g Nayef (USA)—Utterly Heaven (IRE) **Moyglare Stud Farms Ltd**
5 **GALILEO'S CHOICE (IRE)**, 8, b g Galileo (IRE)—Sevi's Choice (USA) **Dr M. W. J. Smurfit**
6 **GAMBLE**, 4, ch f Galileo (IRE)—Pretty Face **Calumet Farm**
7 **HISABAAAT (IRE)**, 6, b g Dubawi (IRE)—Phariseek (IRE) **Mr Dominick Glennane**
8 **MANHATTAN SWING (IRE)**, 4, b g Invincible Spirit (IRE)—Bluebell Park (IRE) **Mr J. Higgins**
9 **NOTABLE GRADUATE (IRE)**, 6, b g Galileo (IRE)—Market Slide (USA) **Chanelle Pharmaceuticals Ltd**
10 **PALE MIMOSA (IRE)**, 5, b m Singspiel (IRE)—Katch Me Katie **Dr R. Lambe**
11 **PAY DAY KITTEN (USA)**, 4, b br f Kitten's Joy (USA)—Annual Dues (USA) **Mr Kenneth & Mr Sarah Ramsey**
12 **SHOW COURT (IRE)**, 5, b g Vinnie Roe (IRE)—Sparkling Gem (IRE) **Mr K. Weld**
13 **SILVER CONCORDE**, 6, b g Dansili—Sacred Pearl (IRE) **Dr R. Lambe**
14 **TALWEEN**, 5, b m Nayef (USA)—Zaqrah (USA) **Mr M. Weld**
15 **WAAHEB (USA)**, 7, b br g Elusive Quality (USA)—Nafisah (IRE) **J. P. McManus**
16 **WANDERING STAR (IRE)**, 5, gr m Verglas (IRE)—Legend Has It (IRE) **Mr G. Devlin**
17 **WINDSOR PARK (IRE)**, 5, b g Galileo (IRE)—Blissful (USA) **Dr R. Lambe**

MR D. K. WELD - Continued

THREE-YEAR-OLDS

18 **AFTERNOON SUNLIGHT (IRE)**, ch f Sea The Stars (IRE)—Lady Luck (IRE) **Moyglare Stud Farm Ltd**
19 **AKILIYNA (IRE)**, b f Holy Roman Emperor (IRE)—Akdara (IRE) **H. H. Aga Khan**
20 **ALKASSER (IRE)**, b c Shamardal (USA)—Alexander Queen (IRE) **Hamdan Al Maktoum**
21 **ANTIQUE PLATINUM (IRE)**, b f Holy Roman Emperor (IRE)—Summer Trysting (USA) **Moyglare Stud Farm Ltd**
22 **BACKDROP (USA)**, b f First Defence (USA)—Hasardeuse (USA) **K. Abdullah**
23 **BALANSIYA (IRE)**, b f Shamardal (USA)—Baliyana (IRE) **H. H. Aga Khan**
24 **BOBBY'S HEART (IRE)**, b g Dandy Man (IRE)—Almatlaie (USA) **Dr R. Lambe**
25 **BROOCH (USA)**, b f Empire Maker (USA)—Daring Diva **K. Abdullah**
26 **BUSH PILOT (IRE)**, br g Bushranger (IRE)—Dame Noir (IRE) **Dr R. Lambe**
27 **CARLA BIANCA (IRE)**, gr f Dansili—Majestic Silver (IRE) **Moyglare Stud Farms Ltd**
28 **COUMLARA (IRE)**, b f High Chaparral (IRE)—Perfect Touch (USA) **Mrs C. L. Weld**
29 **EBEYINA (IRE)**, b f Oasis Dream—Ebalista (IRE) **H. H. Aga Khan**
30 **EDELMIRA (IRE)**, ch f Peintre Celebre (USA)—Elbasana (IRE) **H. H. Aga Khan**
31 **EMERITA (IRE)**, gr f Mizzen Mast (USA)—Ebaza (IRE) **H. H. Aga Khan**
32 **ENZANI (IRE)**, b c Cape Cross (IRE)—Eytarna (IRE) **H. H. Aga Khan**
33 **FLYING JIB**, ro f Oasis Dream—Jibboom (USA) **K. Abdullah**
34 **FREE EAGLE (IRE)**, b c High Chaparral (IRE)—Polished Gem (IRE) **Moyglare Stud Farms Ltd**
35 **GAMBRINUS (USA)**, b c Dynaformer (USA)—Cyclorama (USA) **Calumet Farm**
36 **GO FOR GOAL (IRE)**, gr g Verglas (IRE)—Triple Try (IRE) **Mr G. Devlin**
37 **GOOD TRADITION (IRE)**, b c Pivotal—Token Gesture (IRE) **Moyglare Stud Farms Ltd**
38 **HELLENISTIC (USA)**, ch f English Channel (USA)—Garimpeiro (USA) **Calumet Farm**
39 **I'M YOURS**, b f Invincible Spirit (IRE)—Rebelline (IRE) **Moyglare Stud Farms Ltd**
40 **INTISAAB**, b g Elnadim (USA)—Katoom (IRE) **Hamdan Al Maktoum**
41 **KALEEFA (IRE)**, b f Sinndar (IRE)—Kalarouna (IRE) **H. H. Aga Khan**
42 **KEYBOARD MELODY (IRE)**, gr g Verglas (IRE)—Wrong Key (IRE) **Dr R. Lambe**
43 **LANYARD (USA)**, gr f Mizzen Mast (USA)—Geographic (USA) **K. Abdullah**
44 **LEAFCUTTER (IRE)**, b g Shamardal (USA)—Bee Eater (IRE) **Sheikh Mohammed**
45 **LELIANI (IRE)**, ch c Mr Greeley (USA)—Lidakiya (IRE) **H. H. Aga Khan**
46 **MADAKHEEL (USA)**, b f Mr Greeley (USA)—Manaal (USA) **Hamdan Al Maktoum**
47 **MUSTAJEEB**, ch c Nayef (USA)—Rifqah (USA) **Hamdan Al Maktoum**
48 **NEXT BEND (IRE)**, b g Azamour (IRE)—Polite Reply (IRE) **Moyglare Stud Farms Ltd**
49 **NIDHAAM**, ch f Nayef (USA)—Malakaat (USA) **Hamdan Al Maktoum**
50 **NIEVE (USA)**, b f English Channel (USA)—November Snow (USA) **Calumet Farm**
51 **NONCHALANT**, gr c Oasis Dream—Comeback Queen **K. Abdullah**
52 **PIRITA (IRE)**, br f Invincible Spirit (IRE)—Spinamix **Moyglare Stud Farm Ltd**
53 **RENOWN**, ch g Champs Elysees—Fame At Last (USA) **K. Abdullah**
54 **ROUSAYAN (IRE)**, b c Invincible Spirit (IRE)—Rose Quartz **H. H. The Aga Khan**
55 **SAILORS SWAN (USA)**, b c Henrythenavigator (USA)—Society Hostess (USA) **Moyglare Stud Farm Ltd**
56 **SARAFIYLA (IRE)**, b f Azamour (IRE)—Sarima (IRE) **H. H. Aga Khan**
57 **SCHOLARLY**, b f Authorized (IRE)—Historian (IRE) **Sheikh Mohammed**
58 **SEREZA (IRE)**, b f Pivotal—Seraya (FR) **H. H. Aga Khan**
59 **SIERRA SUN (IRE)**, b f Hernando (FR)—Sierra Slew **Lady O' Reilly**
60 **SILVER GAUNTLET (IRE)**, gr g Verglas (IRE)—Katch Me Katie **Dr R. Lambe**
61 **SILWANA (IRE)**, b f Peintre Celebre (USA)—Simawa (IRE) **H. H. Aga Khan**
62 **SINKAL (USA)**, b c Smart Strike (CAN)—Sindirana (IRE) **H. H. Aga Khan**
63 **SPARKLE FACTOR (IRE)**, b f Arch—Thoughtless Moment (IRE) **Moyglare Stud Farm Ltd**
64 **STARLET (IRE)**, b f Sea The Stars (IRE)—Treasure The Lady (IRE) **Mrs C. L. Weld**
65 **STAY DE NIGHT (IRE)**, b c Shamardal (USA)—Where We Left Off **Moyglare Stud Farms Ltd**
66 **TAHAANY (IRE)**, b f Raven's Pass (USA)—Photophore (IRE) **Hamdan Al Maktoum**
67 **TARFASHA (IRE)**, ch f Teofilo (IRE)—Grecian Bride (IRE) **Hamdan Al Maktoum**
68 **TESTED**, b f Selkirk (USA)—Prove **K. Abdullah**
69 **TIMIYAN (USA)**, b c Ghostzapper (USA)—Timarwa (IRE) **H. H. Aga Khan**
70 **VINTAGE NOUVEAU (IRE)**, b f Montjeu (IRE)—Utterly Heaven (IRE) **Moyglare Stud Farm Ltd**
71 **VOTE OFTEN**, b f Beat Hollow—Minority **K. Abdullah**
72 **WATEED (IRE)**, b g Iffraaj—Miss Adelaide (IRE) **Hamdan Al Maktoum**
73 **WELD ARAB (USA)**, b c Shamardal (USA)—Itqaan (USA) **Hamdan Al Maktoum**
74 **WHITEY O' GWAUN (IRE)**, gr g Dalakhani (IRE)—Angel of The Gwaun (IRE) **Sheikh Mohammed**
75 **ZAFAYAN (IRE)**, b c Acclamation—Zafayra (IRE) **H. H. Aga Khan**
76 **ZARAWI (IRE)**, b g Marju (IRE)—Zarwala (IRE) **H. H. Aga Khan**

TWO-YEAR-OLDS

77 **ALFARAABY (IRE)**, ch c 20/2 Tamayuz—Aphorism (Halling (USA)) **Hamdan Al Maktoum**
78 **ALMELA (IRE)**, b f 29/2 Sea The Stars (IRE)—Aliya (IRE) (Darshaan) **H. H. Aga Khan**
79 **ALVEENA (IRE)**, ch f 11/5 Medicean—Aliyfa (IRE) (Spinning World (USA)) **H. H. Aga Khan**

MR D. K. WELD - Continued

80 B c 11/2 Vale of York (IRE)—Always Friendly (High Line) **Sheikh Mohammed**
81 **ASHRAF (IRE),** b c 19/1 Cape Cross (IRE)—Askeria (IRE) (Sadler's Wells (USA)) **H. H. Aga Khan**
82 **BLEU CIEL ET ROUGE (IRE),** br f 8/2 Manduro (GER)—
Burren Rose (USA) (Storm Cat (USA)) **Moyglare Stud Farm Ltd**
83 Gr f 30/3 Dalakhani (IRE)—Chiang Mai (IRE) (Sadler's Wells (USA)) **Lady O' Reilly**
84 Gr ro c 9/2 Langfuhr (CAN)—Dalmiya (IRE) (Kalanisi (IRE)) **Calumet Farm**
85 **EDELPOUR (IRE),** gr c 24/3 Mastercraftsman (IRE)—Ebadiyla (IRE) (Sadler's Wells (USA)) **H. H. Aga Khan**
86 Ch f 3/3 Fast Company (IRE)—Elegant Ridge (IRE) (Indian Ridge) (92914) **Mrs Anne Coughlan**
87 **FASEEHA (IRE),** ch f 25/3 Teofilo (IRE)—Turkana Girl (Hernando (FR)) (123886) **Hamdan Al Maktoum**
88 Ch c 2/4 English Channel (USA)—Fiji (Rainbow Quest (USA)) **Calumet Farm**
89 B f 15/3 Arch (USA)—Firey Red (IRE) (Pivotal) **Moyglare Stud Farm Ltd**
90 Ch f 29/1 Paco Boy (IRE)—Genuine Charm (IRE) (Sadler's Wells (USA)) **Moyglare Stud Farm Ltd**
91 B br f 21/2 Smart Strike (CAN)—Hasanka (IRE) (Kalanisi (IRE)) **H. H. Aga Khan**
92 **HAWRAA,** br f 31/1 Dansili—Bethrah (IRE) (Marju (IRE)) **Hamdan Al Maktoum**
93 B f 24/1 Oasis Dream—Honest Quality (USA) (Elusive Quality (USA)) **K. Abdullah**
94 B c 18/3 Dansili—Imroz (IRE) (Nureyev (USA)) **K. Abdullah**
95 B f 5/3 Street Cry (IRE)—Irresistible Jewel (IRE) (Danehill (USA)) **Moyglare Stud Farm Ltd**
96 B c 22/4 Invincible Spirit (IRE)—Ishitaki (ARG) (Interprete (ARG)) **Sheikh Mohammed**
97 **JACK BLUE (IRE),** b c 2/2 Duke of Marmalade (IRE)—
Key Secure (IRE) (Sadler's Wells (USA)) **Moyglare Stud Farm Ltd**
98 B c 9/3 First Defence (USA)—Kithira (Danehill (USA)) **K. Abdullah**
99 B c 8/4 Iffraaj—Magna Graecia (IRE) (Warning) **Sheikh Mohammed**
100 B f 7/4 Dubawi (IRE)—Majestic Silver (IRE) (Linamix (FR)) **Moyglare Stud Farm Ltd**
101 **MALINKA (IRE),** b f 4/2 Pivotal—Mad About You (IRE) (Indian Ridge) **Moyglare Stud Farm Ltd**
102 **MARIFAH (IRE),** b f 25/4 Dubawi (IRE)—Itqaan (USA) (Danzig (USA)) **Hamdan Al Maktoum**
103 B f 1/6 Montjeu (IRE)—Market Slide (USA) (Gulch (USA)) **Moyglare Stud Farm Ltd**
104 **MESADAH (IRE),** b f 3/2 Raven's Pass (USA)—Albisola (IRE) (Montjeu (IRE)) (402632) **Hamdan Al Maktoum**
105 B br f 5/4 More Than Ready (USA)—Milago (USA) (Danzig (USA)) **Calumet Farm**
106 B f 24/3 Showcasing—Mirthful (USA) (Miswaki (USA)) **K. Abdullah**
107 B c 12/4 Lope de Vega (IRE)—Misty Daylight (USA) (Seeking Daylight (USA)) **Calumet Farm**
108 **MOALLEF (IRE),** b f 7/4 Iffraaj—Laywaan (USA) (Fantastic Light (USA)) **Hamdan Al Maktoum**
109 B f 28/2 Dalakhani (IRE)—Sahool (Unfuwain (USA)) **Hamdan Al Maktoum**
110 **MULKEYYA (IRE),** b f 21/3 Mawatheeq (USA)—Rifqah (USA) (Elusive Quality (USA)) **Hamdan Al Maktoum**
111 **MUTADHAMEN,** ch c 29/1 Arcano (IRE)—Janina (Namid) **Hamdan Al Maktoum**
112 **MUTAWAASEL,** ch c 23/3 Teofilo (IRE)—Muwakleh (Machiavellian (USA)) **Hamdan Al Maktoum**
113 **MUTAZEN (USA),** b c 19/4 Candy Ride (ARG)—
Wynyard (CAN) (Mr Greeley (USA)) (292141) **Hamdan Al Maktoum**
114 B f 4/3 Fastnet Rock (AUS)—Nightime (IRE) (Galileo (IRE)) **Mrs C. C. Regalado Gonzalez**
115 B f 25/2 English Channel (USA)—Notable Career (USA) (Avenue of Flags (USA)) **Calumet Farm**
116 B c 28/4 Invincible Spirit (IRE)—Out of Thanks (IRE) (Sadler's Wells (USA)) **Moyglare Stud Farm Ltd**
117 B c 15/4 Sir Percy—Pearl Bright (FR) (Kaldoun (FR)) (75000) **Calumet Farm**
118 B c 3/5 Dark Angel (IRE)—Polished Gem (IRE) (Danehill (USA)) **Moyglare Stud Farm Ltd**
119 **POSTULATION (USA),** b c 11/3 Harlan's Holiday (USA)—Supposition (Dansili) **K. Abdullah**
120 B f 21/2 Sea The Stars (IRE)—Proportional (Beat Hollow) **K. Abdullah**
121 B c 15/2 New Approach (IRE)—Prove (Danehill (USA)) **K. Abdullah**
122 **RADANPOUR (IRE),** b c 18/4 Sea The Stars (IRE)—Rose Quartz (Lammtarra (USA)) **H. H. Aga Khan**
123 **RAVENS HEART (IRE),** b c 3/2 Dansili—Hymn of Love (IRE) (Barathea (IRE)) **Moyglare Stud Farm Ltd**
124 Ch gr f 30/1 Galileo (IRE)—Rosa Grace (Lomitas) (100658) **Mrs J. Magnier**
125 B c 22/2 Oasis Dream—Sandglass (Zafonic (USA)) **K. Abdullah**
126 **SASUKA (IRE),** br f 23/2 Pivotal—Desert Ease (IRE) (Green Desert) **Moyglare Stud Farm Ltd**
127 B c 3/2 Footstepsinthesand—Seraya (FR) (Danehill (USA)) **H. H. Aga Khan**
128 **SHINGHARI (IRE),** b c 22/2 Cape Cross (IRE)—Sindiyma (IRE) (Kalanisi (IRE)) **H. H. Aga Khan**
129 B f 4/2 Oasis Dream—Short Dance (USA) (Hennessy (USA)) **K. Abdullah**
130 **SIDRA (IRE),** b f 4/5 Elusive Quality (USA)—Sindirana (IRE) (Kalanisi (IRE)) **H. H. Aga Khan**
131 Ch f 20/4 Teofilo (IRE)—Spacecraft (USA) (Distant View (USA)) **K. Abdullah**
132 B f 2/5 Areion (GER)—Step With Style (USA) (Gulch (USA)) **Moyglare Stud Farm Ltd**
133 **STORMFLY (IRE),** gr f 22/5 Dark Angel (IRE)—Intaglia (GER) (Lomitas) (29422) **Dieu Bros Syndicate**
134 **SUMMAYA (IRE),** b f 21/2 Azamour (IRE)—Simawa (IRE) (Anabaa (USA)) **H. H. Aga Khan**
135 B c 25/2 Fastnet Rock (AUS)—Super Gift (IRE) (Darshaan) (85171) **Calumet Farm**
136 B c 29/2 Kyllachy—Swingle (Dubawi (IRE)) (77428) **Calumet Farm**
137 **TADAANY (IRE),** b c 21/3 Acclamation—Park Haven (IRE) (Marju (IRE)) **Hamdan Al Maktoum**
138 **TAHREEM (IRE),** br f 25/2 Manduro (GER)—Tarakala (IRE) (Dr Fong (USA)) **H. H. Aga Khan**
139 B f 1/4 Cape Cross (IRE)—Thoughtless Moment (IRE) (Pivotal) **Moyglare Stud Farm Ltd**
140 B c 6/3 Montjeu (IRE)—Timabiyra (IRE) (Linamix (FR)) **H. H. Aga Khan**
141 Ch c 14/4 Galileo (IRE)—Utterly Heaven (IRE) (Danehill (USA)) **Moyglare Stud Farms Ltd**

MR D. K. WELD - Continued

142 B br c 22/4 Smart Strike (CAN)—Wild Intention (USA) (A P Indy) (USA) **Calumet Farm**
143 B c 2/3 Azamour (IRE)—Zafayra (IRE) (Nayef (USA)) **H. H. Aga Khan**
144 ZANNDA (IRE), b f 14/2 Azamour (IRE)—Zanoubiya (IRE) (Dalakhani (IRE)) **H. H. Aga Khan**
145 B c 6/2 Arch (USA)—Zaralanta (IRE) (Danehill Dancer (IRE)) **H. H. Aga Khan**
146 ZAWRAQ (IRE), b c 25/4 Shamardal (USA)—Sundus (USA) (Sadler's Wells (USA)) **Hamdan Al Maktoum**

Jockey (flat): P. J. Smullen. **Apprentice:** S. M. Gorey, L. F. Roche.

660

MISS SHEENA WEST, Lewes
Postal: **5 Balmer Farm Cottages, Brighton Road, Lewes, East Sussex, BN7 3JN**
Contacts: **PHONE (01273) 621303 FAX (01273) 622189 MOBILE (07748) 181804**
E-MAIL sheenawest11@aol.com WEBSITE www.sheenawest.com

1 ALFRAAMSEY, 6, b g Fraam—Evanesce **Tapestry Partnership**
2 BRILLIANT BARCA, 6, b g Imperial Dancer—Fading Away **Mrs S. D. Flight**
3 CANNON FODDER, 7, b m Nomadic Way (USA)—Grace Dieu **The Cheapskates**
4 FEB THIRTYFIRST, 5, ch g Shirocco (GER)—My Mariam **M. Moriarty**
5 HI NOTE, 6, b m Acclamation—Top Tune **G. West**
6 IMPERIAL STARGAZER, 5, gr g Imperial Dancer—Sky Light Dreams **Tapestry Partnership**
7 JUSTANOTHER MUDDLE, 5, gr g Kayf Tara—Spatham Rose **Saloop**
8 4, B c Tobougg (IRE)—Kalmina (USA)
9 LEG IRON (IRE), 9, b g Snurge—Southern Skies (IRE) **M. Moriarty**
10 MR MUDDLE, 7, gr g Imperial Dancer—Spatham Rose **Saloop**
11 SPANISH FORK (IRE), 5, br g Trans Island—Wings Awarded **G. West**
12 UNIDEXTER (IRE), 4, br g Footstepsinthesand—Run To Jane (IRE) **The Cheapskates**
13 WARRANT OFFICER, 4, gr g Misu Bond (IRE)—Kilmovee **M. Moriarty**
14 YA HAFED, 6, ch g Haafhd—Rule Britannia **Mr A. J. Head**

Other Owners: Mr R. C. G. Dodds, Mr L. T. Morris, Mrs C. S. Muddle, R. A. Muddle, Mrs E. Turner, D. M. Woodward.

Jockey (NH): M. Goldstein.

661

MR SIMON WEST, Middleham
Postal: **Castle Stables, Middleham, Leyburn, North Yorkshire, DL8 4QQ**
Contacts: **MOBILE (07855) 924529**
E-MAIL simonwest21@hotmail.co.uk WEBSITE www.mkmracing.co.uk

1 CAPTAIN CLAYTON (IRE), 7, b g Subtle Power (IRE)—Dont Hurry (IRE) **Wild West Racing**
2 5, Br m Waveney (UAE)—Corravilla (IRE) **Mr S. G. West**
3 KUKURUDU (IRE), 7, b g Tikkanen (USA)—Tullyfoyle (IRE) **Mr P. Hothersall**
4 LAYLA'S BOY, 7, ch g Sakhee (USA)—Gay Romance **Miss M. K. Milligan**
5 SAINT BRIEUC (FR), 5, br g Saint des Saints (FR)—Merci Allamee (FR) **Mr C. R. Hirst**
6 TURJUMAN (USA), 9, ch g Swain (IRE)—Hachiyah (IRE) **Mr S. G. West**
7 WHERE'S THE CATCH, 5, ch m Kapgarde (FR)—Indienne Efi (FR) **Mr P. Hothersall**

THREE-YEAR-OLDS
8 NAM MA PROW, ch g Bahamian Bounty—Charlotte Vale **Mr C. R. Hirst**

Other Owners: Mr K. Flint, Mr P. Fowlie.

Apprentice: Paul Pickard.

662

MISS JESSICA WESTWOOD, Minehead
Postal: **Monkham House, Exford, Minehead, Somerset, TA24 7NA**
Contacts: **MOBILE (07536) 021449**
E-MAIL JessWestwoodracing@gmail.com

1 FORRARDON XMOOR, 5, gr g Fair Mix (IRE)—The Nuns Song **Mrs J. Baskerville**
2 MONKERTY TUNKERTY, 11, b g Silver Patriarch (IRE)—Orphan Annie **Miss J. J. Westwood**
3 SIROP DE MENTHE (FR), 4, ch g Discover d'auteuil (FR)—Jolie Menthe (FR) **Mrs J. Baskerville**

Other Owners: Mr A. Westwood.

663   MR JOHN WEYMES, Middleham
Postal: **Ashgill, Coverham, Leyburn, North Yorkshire, DL8 4TJ**
Contacts: **PHONE (01969) 640420 FAX (01969) 640505 MOBILE (07753) 792516**
E-MAIL kirsty@johnweymesracing.co.uk WEBSITE www.johnweymesracing.co.uk

1 ALMATY EXPRESS, 12, b g Almaty (IRE)—Express Girl **Highmoor Racing 4 & Tag Racing**
2 ARCH WALKER (IRE), 7, ch g Choisir (AUS)—Clunie **High Moor & Thoroughbred Partners**
3 BIGINDIE (IRE), 4, ch g Indian Haven—Graceful Air (IRE) **High Moor & Thoroughbred Partners**
4 CELESTIAL DAWN, 5, b m Echo of Light—Celestial Welcome **Grange Park Racing & T'Bred Partners**
5 DARK OPAL (IRE), 4, b f Camacho—Dark Albatross (USA) **Scothern, Leadbetter & Partners**
6 ELIZABETH COFFEE (IRE), 6, b m Byron—Queens Wharf (IRE) **Thoroughbred Partners & Tag Racing**
7 FALCON'S GINGER, 4, ch f Grape Tree Road—Sheriff's Falcon (IRE) **Falcon's Line Ltd**
8 FALCON'S LEGEND, 4, ch f Midnight Legend—Bling Noir (FR) **Falcon's Line Ltd**
9 FALCON'S PRESENT, 6, br m Presenting—Mini Mandy **Falcon's Line Ltd**
10 JUST FIVE (IRE), 8, b g Olmodavor (USA)—Wildsplash (USA) **Ed Kingsley & Thoroughbred Partners**
11 SILVER FAWN (IRE), 4, gr g Clodovil (IRE)—Tinareena **Thoroughbred Partners**
12 SILVER SONGSTRESS, 4, b f Singspiel (IRE)—Composing (IRE) **Thoroughbred Partners**
13 TIGHT KNIT (USA), 4, b g Hard Spun (USA)—Tamdiid (USA) **Mr E. P. Kingsley**
14 UNDERWRITTEN, 5, b g Authorized (IRE)—Grain of Gold **Thoroughbred Partners**

THREE-YEAR-OLDS
15 PRINCESS ROSE, b f Royal Applause—Mystical Spirit (IRE) **T. A. Scothern**

TWO-YEAR-OLDS
16 B f 26/1 Equiano (FR)—Forest Prize (Charnwood Forest (IRE)) (12857) **Mr T A Scothern & Mrs R L Heaton**
17 B f 1/1 Firebreak—Linden's Lady (Compton Place) **Highmoor Racing**
18 B f 15/3 Acclamation—Sister Clement (IRE) (Oasis Dream) (13937) **T. A. Scothern**

Other Owners: Mr P.D. Bickley, Miss K. Buckle, Mr Alan D. Crombie, Mr Richard Gayton, Mrs R. L. Heaton, Mr Edward Kingsley, Mr M. J. Leadbetter, Mr T. A. Scothern, Mr E. Surr, Mr J. Weymes.

Assistant Trainer: Kirsty Buckle

Jockey (flat): Darryll Holland, Philip Makin. **Jockey (NH):** Dougie Costello, Keith Mercer.

664   MR ERIC WHEELER, Pangbourne
Postal: **15 St Michaels Close, Lambourn, Hungerford, Berkshire, RG17 8FA**
Contacts: **PHONE (07795) 844185 FAX (01189) 841924 MOBILE (07795) 844185**

1 BEGGERS LUCK, 4, b f Lucky Story (USA)—Dropitlikeit's Hot (IRE) **Mr G. W. Witheford**
2 CLIFFORDS REPRIEVE, 6, b g Kheleyf (USA)—Bijan (IRE) **Mr G. W. Witheford**
3 DON'T BE SCILLY, 6, ch m Reel Buddy (USA)—Batchworth Breeze **Mr G. W. Witheford**
4 EL LIBERTADOR (USA), 8, b br g Giant's Causeway (USA)—Istikbal (USA) **Mr J. L. Day**
5 EVEN BOLDER, 11, ch g Bold Edge—Level Pegging (IRE) **E. A. Wheeler**
6 FLEUR DE FORTUNE, 7, ch m Best of The Bests (IRE)—Fortuitious (IRE) **Mr G. K. Hall**
7 KISS MY HEART, 5, br m Byron—Kisses **Wedgewood Estates**

Assistant Trainer: Miss C Nosworthy

Apprentice: Joey Haynes.

665   MR ALISTAIR WHILLANS, Hawick
Postal: **Esker House, Newmill-On-Slitrig, Hawick, Roxburghshire, TD9 9UQ**
Contacts: **PHONE (01450) 376642 FAX (01450) 376082 MOBILE (07771) 550555**
E-MAIL acwracing@hotmail.com

1 AHHDEHKEN, 9, b g Cloudings (IRE)—Swazi Princess (IRE) **Jethart Justice**
2 ALEXANDRAKOLLONTAI (IRE), 4, b f Amadeus Wolf—Story **Chris Spark & William Orr**
3 APACHEE PRINCE (IRE), 5, b g Indian Danehill (IRE)—Wheredidthemoneygo (IRE) **J. D. Wright**
4 CLAUDE CARTER, 4, b g Elmaamul (USA)—Cruz Santa **Mrs L. M. Whillans**
5 DANCING GIZMO, 9, b g Where Or When (IRE)—Tactile **A. C. Whillans**
6 EUSTON SQUARE, 8, b g Oasis Dream—Krisia **Mrs L. M. Whillans**
7 FILBERT FOX (IRE), 8, b g Snurge—Shean Storm (IRE) **Ms S. J. Burns**
8 FUNKY MUNKY, 9, b g Talaash (IRE)—Chilibang Bang **The Twelve Munkys**

MR ALISTAIR WHILLANS - Continued

9 **GALILEE CHAPEL (IRE)**, 5, b g Baltic King—Triple Zero (IRE) **The Blues Gang**
10 **GLEANN NA NDOCHAIS (IRE)**, 8, b g Zagreb (USA)—Nissereen (USA) **Mr W J E Scott & Mrs M A Scott**
11 **HEART O ANNANDALE (IRE)**, 7, b g Winged Love (IRE)—She's All Heart **K. Milligan Partnership**
12 **HENPECKED**, 4, b f Footstepsinthesand—Poule de Luxe (IRE) **Eildon Hill Racing**
13 **JON (IRE)**, 6, ch g Refuse To Bend (IRE)—Calgarth (IRE) **Mr F. Lowe**
14 **LADY BLUESKY**, 11, gr m Cloudings (IRE)—M N L Lady **Mrs S. Harrow Mrs L. M. Whillans**
15 **LOVE MARMALADE (IRE)**, 4, ch c Duke of Marmalade (IRE)—Green Castle (IRE) **Akela Construction Ltd**
16 5, B m Milan—Martha Reilly (IRE) **Mrs L. M. Whillans**
17 **MEADOWCROFT BOY**, 5, bd g Kayf Tara—Blackbriery Thyne (IRE) **Mr W J E Scott & Mrs M A Scott**
18 **OPT OUT**, 4, ch g Pivotal—Easy Option (IRE) **Akela Construction Ltd**
19 **PIXIE CUT (IRE)**, 4, b f Chineur (FR)—Fantastic Cee (IRE) **J Wilson, C Spark, W Orr**
20 **SAMSTOWN**, 7, b g Kingsalsa (USA)—Red Peony **Mrs E. B. Ferguson**
21 **SCRAPPER SMITH (IRE)**, 8, b g Choisir (AUS)—Lady Ounavarra (IRE) **A. C. Whillans**
22 **SOCIAL RHYTHM**, 10, b m Beat All (USA)—Highly Sociable **Mrs L. M. Whillans**
23 **STORM BRIG**, 9, b g Heron Island (IRE)—The Storm Bell (IRE) **Mr W J E Scott & Mrs M A Scott**
24 **TEIDE MISTRESS (USA)**, 4, b br f Medaglia d'oro (USA)—Chandelle No. Five (USA) **Mrs H. Greggan**
25 **THATLLDOFORUS**, 6, b m Double Trigger (IRE)—Bantel Bargain **A. Gilchrist**
26 **TURTLE CASK (IRE)**, 5, b g Turtle Island (IRE)—Sayce (IRE) **Distillery Racing Club**
27 **VICKY VALENTINE**, 4, b f Rock of Gibraltar (IRE)—Silcasue **Mr F. Lowe**
28 **VITTACHI**, 7, b g Bertolini (USA)—Miss Lorilaw (FR) **Sutherland View**
29 **W SIX TIMES**, 8, b m Double Trigger (IRE)—Be My Mot (IRE) **Mrs L. M. Whillans**
30 **WEE JOCK ELLIOT**, 4, b g Overbury (IRE)—Caitlin Ash **John & Liz Elliot**
31 **WHADAURMEDDLEWIMEI**, 4, b g Central Park (IRE)—Thorterdykes Lass (IRE) **John & Liz Elliot**
32 **WHAT A STEEL (IRE)**, 10, b g Craigsteel—Sonya's Pearl (IRE) **J. D. Wright**

Other Owners: W. M. Ballantyne, C. Bird, Mr N. Dalgarno, J. J. Elliot, Mrs E. J. Elliot, Mr R. J. Goodfellow, E. Graham, T. D. Griffiths, Mr J. S. B. Harrold, Mrs S. Harrow, Mr B. Melrose, K. J. Milligan, Mr W. Orr, R. Robinson, W. J. E. Scott, Mrs M. A. Scott, Mr C. Spark, Mr S. A. Taylor, Mr J. R. L. Wilson, Mrs S. L. Wright.

---

666 **MR DONALD WHILLANS, Hawick**
Postal: Dodlands Steading, Hawick, Roxburghshire, TD9 8LG
Contacts: BUSINESS (01450) 373128 HOME (01450) 379810 FAX (01450) 376082
MOBILE (07771) 550556
E-MAIL donaldwhillans@aol.com WEBSITE www.donaldwhillansracing.com

1 **BOLLIN FIONA**, 10, ch m Silver Patriarch (IRE)—Bollin Nellie **C. N. Whillans**
2 **BOLLIN JULIE**, 7, b m Bollin Eric—Bollin Nellie **C. N. Whillans**
3 **CHARLIE BUCKET**, 11, ch g Sugarfoot—Stoproveritate **D. W. Whillans**
4 **ELLISTRIN BELLE**, 6, b m Helissio (FR)—Hannah Park (IRE) **The Potassium Partnership**
5 **HARTFORTH**, 6, ch g Haathd—St Edith (IRE) **The Brave Lads Partnership**
6 **HAWAII KLASS**, 9, ch g Classic Cliche (IRE)—Youandi **Star Racing**
7 **MINI THE MINX (IRE)**, 8, br m Accordion—Gypsy Run **D. W. Whillans**
8 **NEARLY MAY**, 6, b m Winged Love (IRE)—Lindajane (IRE) **D. W. Whillans**
9 **NODDA HIGH KID**, 8, ch g Sir Harry Lewis (USA)—Lindajane (IRE) **D. W. Whillans**
10 **SAM PATCH**, 11, ch g Weldnaas (USA)—Youandi **Star Racing**
11 **SHADOW BOXER**, 9, gr g Makbul—Shadows of Silver **The Peeskie Partnership**
12 **SNAPPING TURTLE (IRE)**, 9, b g Turtle Island (IRE)—Rachael's Dawn **D. W. Whillans**
13 8, B m Meadowbrook—Wee Willow **D. W. Whillans**
14 6, B g River Falls—Wee Willow **D. W. Whillans**

Other Owners: Mr R. Bannerman, H. G. Beeby, D. W. Whillans, H. M. Whillans.

Jockey (flat): Garry Whillans. **Conditional:** Ryan Nichol, Callum Whillans.

---

667 **MR RICHARD WHITAKER, Scarcroft**
Postal: Hellwood Racing Stables, Hellwood Lane, Scarcroft, Leeds, West Yorkshire, LS14 3BP
Contacts: PHONE (01132) 892265 FAX (01132) 893680 MOBILE (07831) 870454
E-MAIL rmwhitaker@btconnect.com WEBSITE www.richardwhitaker.org

1 **AVON BREEZE**, 5, b m Avonbridge—African Breeze **Grange Park Racing II & Partner**
2 **BAVARIAN NORDIC (USA)**, 9, b g Barathea (IRE)—Dubai Diamond **Six Iron Partnership**
3 **ICY BLUE**, 6, b g Iceman—Bridal Path **Country Lane Partnership**
4 **LICHEN ANGEL**, 4, gr f Dark Angel (IRE)—Moss Likely (IRE) **Mr Robert Macgregor & Mr David Walker**

MR RICHARD WHITAKER - Continued

5 **LOVE ISLAND**, 5, b m Acclamation—Sally Traffic **J Barry Pemberton & R M Whitaker**
6 **MEY BLOSSOM**, 9, ch m Captain Rio—Petra Nova **Waz Developments Ltd**
7 **MISS ELLA JADE**, 5, b m Danbird (AUS)—Keen Melody (USA) **R. M. Whitaker**
8 **PIPERS NOTE**, 4, ch g Piccolo—Madam Valentine **Six Iron Partnership & Partner**
9 **RIO SANDS**, 9, b g Captain Rio—Sally Traffic **The Barflys**
10 **RIO'S ROSANNA (IRE)**, 7, b m Captain Rio—Ling Lane **Mr James Marshall & Mr Chris Marshall**
11 **TUMBLEWIND**, 4, ch f Captain Rio—African Breeze **Nice Day Out Partnership**
12 **WOODACRE**, 7, b g Pyrus (USA)—Fairy Ring (IRE) **Mrs R. M. Whitaker**
13 **WOTALAD**, 4, b g Bertolini (USA)—Cosmic Song **Mrs J. M. Willows**

THREE-YEAR-OLDS

14 **CHATSWORTH EXPRESS**, b g Redoubtable (USA)—Teo Torriate (IRE) **The Hainworth Syndicate**
15 **EDWARD ELGAR**, ch g Avonbridge—Scooby Dooby Do **Paul Davies & R. M. Whitaker**
16 **SPINNER LANE**, ch f Three Valleys (USA)—Petra Nova **Mr A. Melville**

TWO-YEAR-OLDS

17 B g 4/5 Kheleyf (USA)—African Breeze (Atraf)
18 B f 21/4 Royal Applause—Cosmic Song (Cosmonaut) (10000)
19 B f 31/3 Captain Rio—Hypocrisy (Bertolini (USA))
20 B g 3/3 Monsieur Bond (IRE)—Scooby Dooby Do (Atraf) **Paul Davies H/gate & R M Whitaker**
21 Ro f 27/2 Monsieur Bond (IRE)—Velvet Band (Verglas (IRE)) **Nice Day Out Partnership**

Other Owners: K. M. Brown, A. D. Crombie, P. Davies, Robert Macgregor, J. R. Marshall, Mr C. R. Marshall, Mr A. Norrington, J. B. Pemberton, G. Sanderson, Mr D. A. Walker, Mr R. Wright, Mrs E. L. Wright.

Assistant Trainer: Simon R Whitaker

Apprentice: Casey Wilcox.

---

668 **MR ARTHUR WHITEHEAD, Craven Arms**
Postal: **Lawn Farm, Beambridge, Aston on Clun, Craven Arms, Shropshire, SY7 0HA**
Contacts: **PHONE (01588) 660424**

1 **DELLA SUN (FR)**, 8, b g Della Francesca (USA)—Algarve Sunrise (IRE) **A. J. Whitehead**
2 **JAWAHAL DU MATHAN (FR)**, 6, b g Smadoun (FR)—Stone's Glow (USA) **A. J. Whitehead**
3 **JEANRY (FR)**, 11, b g Marathon (USA)—Envergure **A. J. Whitehead**
4 **ZALGARRY (FR)**, 7, b g Ballingarry (IRE)—Spleen (FR) **A. J. Whitehead**

Conditional: Josh Wall.

---

669 **MR ARTHUR WHITING, Dursley**
Postal: **38 Barrs Lane, North Nibley, Dursley, Gloucestershire, GL11 6DT**
Contacts: **PHONE (01453) 546375 MOBILE (07786) 152539**

1 **BARRS LANE**, 6, b m Sir Harry Lewis (USA)—Cashel Dancer **A. J. Whiting**
2 **CHARLIE RUFFLES (IRE)**, 6, b g Milan—Rosie Ruffles (IRE) **A. J. Whiting**
3 **DRIVING WELL (IRE)**, 6, b g Oscar (IRE)—Polly Anthus **A. J. Whiting**
4 **ITSUPTOYOU (IRE)**, 10, b g Dr Massini (IRE)—I Blame Theparents **A. J. Whiting**
5 **THE WEE LASS**, 7, b m Act One—Fragrant Rose **A. J. Whiting**
6 **THE WEE MIDGET**, 9, b g Mtoto—Fragrant Rose **A. J. Whiting**

---

670 **MR CHARLES WHITTAKER, Radstock**
Postal: **West Forest Farm, Gare Hill, Frome, Somerset, BA11 5EZ**
Contacts: **PHONE (01373) 836500**

1 **CUT THE LUGSREILLY**, 10, ch g Flemensfirth (USA)—Minora (IRE) **C. R. Whittaker**
2 **NOW LISTEN TO ME**, 11, br g Slip Anchor—Calendula **C. R. Whittaker**
3 **PERTINENT (FR)**, 11, b g Sleeping Car (FR)—Jamais de La Vie (FR) **C. R. Whittaker**
4 **RUAPEHU (IRE)**, 8, b g Presenting—Silver Prayer (IRE) **C. R. Whittaker**
5 **STARBURST DIAMOND (IRE)**, 12, gr g Old Vic—Camlin Rose (IRE) **C. R. Whittaker**

671 MR HARRY WHITTINGTON, Sparsholt
Postal: **Hill Barn, Sparsholt, Wantage, Oxfordshire, OX12 9XB**
Contacts: **MOBILE (07734) 388357**
E-MAIL **harry@harrywhittington.co.uk** WEBSITE **www.harrywhittington.co.uk**

1 CUBAN PIECE (IRE), 6, b g Azamour (IRE)—Naazeq **C. H. O. Whittington**
2 DUBAI KISS, 5, b g Dubai Destination (USA)—Smooch **Leading The Way Partnership**
3 FOUROVAKIND, 9, b g Sir Harry Lewis (USA)—Four M's **Andrew F Sawyer, G W Hazell & C Bosley**
4 GRAASP THE NETTLE, 4, br g Araafa (IRE)—Beacon Silver **The King's Men**
5 4, Br f Grape Tree Road—Look of Eagles
6 POLSTAR (FR), 5, b g Poliglote—Star Dancing **Dixon,Ellis,Lynds,Travers,Watkins**
7 4, B g Westerner—Quel Bleu (IRE)
8 TOMIBOLA (IRE), 6, b g Definite Article—Cebola (FR) **Laurence Bellman & Harry Whittington**

Other Owners: L. A. Bellman, C. M. Bosley, R. B. Denny, P. J. Dixon, Mr D. Ellis, Mr R. W. Green, M. G. Hazell, Mr G. W. Hazell, E. J. Saunders, Mr A. F. Sawyer.

672 MR MICHAEL WIGHAM, Newmarket
Postal: **Hamilton Stables, Hamilton Road, Newmarket, Suffolk, CB8 7JQ**
Contacts: **PHONE (01638) 668806 FAX (01638) 668806 MOBILE (07831) 456426**
E-MAIL **michaelwigham@hotmail.co.uk**

1 BARBADOS BOB (USA), 4, b g Speightstown (USA)—Lemon Lady (USA) **D. Hassan**
2 CHAIN OF EVENTS, 7, ch g Nayef (USA)—Ermine (IRE) **Mr P. J. Edwards**
3 CHARTER (IRE), 4, b g Elusive City (USA)—Lucky Norwegian (IRE) **Healwayswantstopullthetrigger**
4 CREDIT SWAP, 9, b g Diktat—Locharia **Palatinate Thoroughbred Racing Limited**
5 FAIRWAY TO HEAVEN (IRE), 5, b h Jeremy (USA)—Luggala (IRE) **Palatinate Thoroughbred Racing Limited**
6 FOXY FOREVER (IRE), 4, b g Kodiac—Northern Tara (IRE) **D. Hassan, J. Cullinan**
7 GIN AND TONIC, 4, ch g Phoenix Reach (IRE)—Arctic Queen **The Gin & Tonic Partnership**
8 SHOTGUN START, 4, b g Kyllachy—Fly In Style **Palatinate Thoroughbred Racing Limited**
9 SUPERBOOT (IRE), 4, b g Holy Roman Emperor (IRE)—
                                         Balting Lass (IRE) **Palatinate Thoroughbred Racing Limited**
10 TEE IT UP TOMMO (IRE), 5, gr g Clodovil (IRE)—Lamh Eile (IRE) **Palatinate Thoroughbred Racing Limited**
11 TROJAN ROCKET (IRE), 6, b g Elusive City (USA)—Tagula Bay (IRE) **G Linder, D Hassan, R Warner**
12 ZAMMY, 5, ch g Zamindar (USA)—Barbs Pink Diamond (USA) **J Williams & D Hassan**

THREE-YEAR-OLDS

13 ADAM FOREVER, b g Myboycharlie (IRE)—Dust **D. Hassan**
14 HAPPY JACK (IRE), b c Elusive City (USA)—Miss Pelling (IRE) **G Linder, D Hassan, B Green**

Other Owners: Mr C. T. Appleton, J. Cullinan, Mr B. Green, W. R. Hinge, G. D. J. Linder, R. Warner, M. Wigham, Mr J. B. Williams.

Assistant Trainer: Sharon Kenyon

673 MR MARTIN WILESMITH, Dymock
Postal: **Bellamys Farm, Dymock, Gloucestershire, GL18 2DX**
Contacts: **PHONE (01531) 890410 (01684) 561238 FAX (01684) 893428 MOBILE (07970) 411638**
E-MAIL **martin@mswilesmith.co.uk**

1 AT YOUR PERIL, 12, b g Alflora (IRE)—Teenero **M. S. Wilesmith**
2 LORD BELLAMY (IRE), 12, b g Lord Americo—Paean Express (IRE) **M. S. Wilesmith**
3 RED OATS, 8, ch m Alflora (IRE)—Silk Oats **M. S. Wilesmith**
4 SHE'SOLOVELY, 10, b m Alflora (IRE)—Cashmere Lady **M. S. Wilesmith**
5 SILK ROSE, 10, gr m Terimon—Silk Oats **M. S. Wilesmith**
6 THE HUMBEL BUTLER (IRE), 13, b g Humbel (USA)—Butler's Lady **M. S. Wilesmith**

Assistant Trainer: Ms E. C. Wilesmith (07976 926906)

Amateur: Mr M. C. Wilesmith.

674 **MR EVAN WILLIAMS, Llancarfan**
Postal: **Aberogwrn Farm, Llancarfan, Nr Barry, Vale of Glamorgan**
Contacts: PHONE **(01446) 754069 (01446) 754045** FAX **(01446) 754069** MOBILE **(07950) 381227**
E-MAIL **evanwilliamsracing@hotmail.co.uk**

1 AJMAN (IRE), 9, b g Orpen (USA)—Grand Madam **Mr R. P. O'Neil**
2 ARMCHAIR THEATRE (IRE), 4, b g King's Theatre (IRE)—Oh Susannah (FR) **Ms S. A. Howell**
3 4, B g Stowaway—B Greenhill
4 BALLYGLASHEEN (IRE), 4, ch g Galileo (IRE)—Luas Line (IRE) **Mr R. J. Gambarini**
5 BALLYMACAHILLCROSS (IRE), 6, br g Presenting—Topanberry (IRE) **Mr & Mrs William Rucker**
6 BARRAKILLA (IRE), 7, b g Milan—Kigali (IRE) **Mr & Mrs William Rucker**
7 5, B g Fair Mix (IRE)—Beetle Bug
8 BONOBO (IRE), 7, b g Quws—Better Folly (IRE)
9 BULLET STREET (IRE), 6, ch g Arakan (USA)—Play A Tune (IRE) **Mrs Janet Davies & Mrs C Williams**
10 BUYWISE (IRE), 7, b g Tikkanen (USA)—Greenogue Princess (IRE) **T. H. Jones**
11 CANICALLYOUBACK, 6, b g Auction House (USA)—Island Colony (USA) **R. E. R. Williams**
12 CAPILLA (IRE), 6, gr g Beneficial—Cap The Rose (IRE) **Mrs J. Davies**
13 CAPPA BLEU (IRE), 12, b g Pistolet Bleu (IRE)—Cappagale (IRE) **Mr & Mrs William Rucker**
14 CAPTAIN PAULIE (IRE), 11, b g Lahib (USA)—Garvivonne **R. E. R. Williams**
15 4, B g Stowaway—Carrigeen Kerria (IRE)
16 CLYNE, 4, b g Hernando (FR)—Lauderdale (GER) **Mr D. M. Williams**
17 COPPER BIRCH (IRE), 6, ch g Beneficial—Givehertime (IRE) **Mrs J. Davies**
18 COURT MINSTREL (IRE), 7, b g Court Cave—Theatral **Mrs J. Davies**
19 DANCING ECCO (IRE), 5, b g Elnadim (USA)—Ecco Mi (IRE) **Mr James W. Barrett**
20 DARK SPIRIT (IRE), 6, b m Whipper (USA)—Dark Raider (IRE) **Richard Abbott & Mario Stavrou**
21 DE FAOITHESDREAM (IRE), 8, br g Balakheri (USA)—Cutteen Lass (IRE) **Mr R Abbott & Mr M Stavrou**
22 DEFINITE DREAM (IRE), 5, b g Definite Article—Brooks Chariot (IRE) **Mr R. J. H. Geffen**
23 DEVIL'S DYKE (USA), 6, b br g Redoute's Choice (AUS)—Kotuku **Mr R Abbott & Mr M Stavrou**
24 EXTREME IMPACT, 8, b g Rock of Gibraltar (IRE)—
                                    Soviet Moon (IRE) **Gareth Morse, Iwan Thomas, Charles Footman**
25 FIREBIRD FLYER (IRE), 7, b g Winged Love (IRE)—Kiora Lady (IRE) **R. E. R. Williams**
26 FORGIVIENNE, 7, b m Alflora (IRE)—Always Forgiving **Gwili Syndicate**
27 GAMBO (IRE), 8, b g Oscar (IRE)—River Thyne (IRE) **Mr R. J. Gambarini**
28 GET IT ON (IRE), 9, b g King's Theatre (IRE)—Keshia **Mr J. L. Jones**
29 5, B g Kalanisi (IRE)—Glen Ten (IRE)
30 GOING CONCERN (IRE), 7, b g Overbury (IRE)—Scorpio Girl **Mr P. M. Langford**
31 GRAN TORINO (IRE), 9, b g Milan—Miss Greinton (GER) **W. J. Evans**
32 HO LEE MOSES (IRE), 4, b g Kalanisi (IRE)—Tipsy Miss (IRE) **Ms S. A. Howell**
33 HOLD COURT (IRE), 7, br g Court Cave—Tipsy Miss (IRE) **Edwards & Howell**
34 HUGHESIE (IRE), 5, b g Indian Danehill (IRE)—Collatrim Choice (IRE) **Mr A. Turton & Mr P. Langford**
35 ISLANDMAGEE (IRE), 7, b g Heron Island (IRE)—Sakanda (IRE) **Mr W. J. Eddy-Williams**
36 4, Br g Indian River (FR)—Jurado Park (IRE)
37 KAYALAR (IRE), 6, b g Noverre (USA)—Katiykha (IRE) **Mrs J. Davies**
38 KING MASSINI (IRE), 8, b g Dr Massini (IRE)—King's Linnet (IRE) **Border Pointers**
39 LANCETTO (FR), 9, b g Dubai Destination (USA)—Lanciana (IRE) **Mr R. J. Gambarini**
40 LAVA LAMP (GER), 7, b g Shamardal (USA)—La Felicita **Mrs J. Davies**
41 LIENOSUS (IRE), 8, b g Old Vic—Red Supporter **Mr & Mrs William Rucker**
42 LIKE A DIAMOND (IRE), 4, b g Antonius Pius (USA)—Silk Law (IRE) **R. E. R. Williams**
43 MAC BERTIE, 5, b g Beat All (USA)—Macnance (IRE) **Keith & Sue Lowry**
44 4, Ch g Lucarno (USA)—Makeabreak (IRE)
45 MAKETHE MOSTOFNOW (IRE), 9, b g Milan—Pass The Leader (IRE) **Mrs J. Davies**
46 4, B g Presenting—Mardi Roberta (IRE)
47 4, Br g Kalanisi (IRE)—Maxis Girl (IRE)
48 4, B g King's Theatre (IRE)—Merrill Gaye (IRE)
49 MILO MAN (IRE), 6, b g Milan—Rilmount (IRE) **Mr & Mrs William Rucker**
50 MINELLA FRIEND (IRE), 5, b g King's Theatre (IRE)—Don't Waste It (IRE) **Mr & Mrs William Rucker**
51 4, B g Touch of Land (FR)—Miss McCormick (IRE)
52 MR MOSS (IRE), 9, b g Moscow Society (USA)—Yesterdays Gorby (IRE) **Mr & Mrs William Rucker**
53 MY DADS HORSE, 8, ch g Exit To Nowhere (USA)—Fruity Farm **Mr & Mrs William Rucker**
54 NODIVIDENDSAGAIN, 6, b g Kayf Tara—Catherine's Run (IRE) **POS Partnership**
55 4, B g Beneficial—Nordic Abu (IRE)
56 ON TOUR (IRE), 6, b g Croco Rouge (IRE)—Galant Tour (IRE) **T. H. Jones**
57 ONE IN A MILAN (IRE), 9, b g Milan—Kitty Star (IRE) **Mr P. M. Langford**
58 OSCAR HALFPENNY (IRE), 4, b g Oscar (IRE)—Temporary Setback (IRE) **Geoff & Anne Price**
59 OSCAR SUNSET (IRE), 7, b g Oscar (IRE)—Derravarra Sunset (IRE) **Geoff & Anne Price**
60 PADGE (IRE), 5, b g Flemensfirth (USA)—Mona Vic (IRE) **Mr & Mrs William Rucker**

MR EVAN WILLIAMS - Continued

61 4, B g Act One—Pequenita
62 **POBBLES BAY (IRE)**, 4, b g Oscar (IRE)—Rose de Beaufai (FR) **Mr D. M. Williams**
63 **PRIMA PORTA**, 8, b m American Post—Porta Marzia (CHI) **D.P. Barrie & H.A.F. Parshall**
64 **PRIMO MILANO**, 5, b g Milan—She's Our Native (IRE) **I. C. Brice**
65 **QUARTON (IRE)**, 7, b g Peintre Celebre (USA)—Marjie (IRE) **Mr C. T. Cromwell**
66 4, Br g Westerner—Reticent Bride (IRE)
67 **SHAYS RIVER (IRE)**, 9, b g Heron Island (IRE)—Miss Flic **R. E. R. Williams**
68 **SPARKSFROMMYHEELS (IRE)**, 4, b g Oscar (IRE)—Shesourpresent (IRE) **Ms S. A. Howell**
69 **STILL BELIEVING (IRE)**, 6, ch m Blueprint (IRE)—Im A Believer (IRE) **R. E. R. Williams**
70 **STORMYISLAND AHEAD**, 9, b g Turtle Island (IRE)—Queen's Banquet **Mr D. M. Williams**
71 **SUBLIME TALENT (IRE)**, 8, b g Sadler's Wells (USA)—Summer Trysting (USA) **Mrs C. A. Williams**
72 **TEDNEY EXPRESS (IRE)**, 7, b g Presenting—Persian Argument (IRE)
73 **THINK ITS ALL OVER (USA)**, 7, b g Tiznow (USA)—A P Petal (USA) **R. E. R. Williams**
74 **TIGER O'TOOLE (IRE)**, 9, gr g King's Theatre (IRE)—Memsahib Ofesteem **Ms S. A. Howell**
75 **TIMESAWASTIN (IRE)**, 8, b g Curtain Time (IRE)—Innocent Approach (IRE) **Mrs C. A. Waters**
76 **TIN POT MAN (IRE)**, 8, br g Tillerman—White-Wash **Oaks**
77 **TORNADO IN MILAN (IRE)**, 8, b g Milan—Julika (GER) **Mr & Mrs William Rucker**
78 **TRADITIONAL BOB (IRE)**, 9, b g Saddlers' Hall (IRE)—Portia's Delight (IRE) **Mr W. J. Eddy-Williams**
79 **TRAIN OF THOUGHT (IRE)**, 6, b g Sadler's Wells (USA)—Cool Clarity (IRE) **I. Struel**
80 4, B g Indian River (FR)—Treasure Island
81 **TROOPER CLARENCE**, 10, b g Trempolino (USA)—Ten To Six **Mrs S. De Wilde**
82 **UPSANDDOWNS (IRE)**, 6, b g Definite Article—Courtain (USA) **ARC**
83 **VINNIE RED (IRE)**, 5, ch g Vinnie Roe (IRE)—Conzara (IRE) **Mr & Mrs William Rucker**
84 **WESTER ROSS (IRE)**, 10, b g Fruits of Love (USA)—Diabaig **T. H. Jones**
85 **WILLIAM'S WISHES (IRE)**, 9, b g Oscar (IRE)—Strong Wishes (IRE) **Mrs D. E. Cheshire**
86 **WYCHWOODS BROOK**, 8, b g Midnight Legend—Miss Millbrook **Kevin & Anne Glastonbury**
87 **ZAMA ZAMA**, 7, b g Sakhee (USA)—Insinuation (IRE) **R. E. R. Williams**
88 **ZARZAL (IRE)**, 6, b g Dr Fong (USA)—Zarwala (IRE) **Mrs J. Davies**

Other Owners: R. J. Abbott, D. P. Barrie, M. V. Dawson, J. R. Edwards, Mr D. C. Footman, K. J. Glastonbury, Mrs A. J. Glastonbury, Mr P. Griffiths, Mrs S. B. Lowry, K. R. Lowry, W. J. G. Morse, Mr H. A. F. Parshall, Mr G. Price, Mrs A. C. Price, W. J. Rucker, Mrs A. Rucker, Mr P. Sevenoaks, Mr D. G. Sevenoaks, M. Stavrou, D. I. Thomas, Mr C. Trigg, Mr A. Turton, Mr S. Williams.

Assistant Trainers: James Tudor, Cath Williams

Jockey (NH): Paul Moloney, Christian Williams.

---

675 **MR IAN WILLIAMS, Alvechurch**
Postal: Dominion Racing Stables, Seafield Lane, Alvechurch, Birmingham, B48 7HL
Contacts: PHONE (01564) 822392 FAX (01564) 829475 MOBILE (07976) 645384
E-MAIL info@ianwilliamsracing.com WEBSITE www.ianwilliamsracing.com

1 **A TAIL OF INTRIGUE (IRE)**, 6, b g Tillerman—
Princess Commanche (IRE) **Mr Oscar Singh & Miss Priya Purewal**
2 **AAZIF (IRE)**, 5, ch g Nayef (USA)—Ayun (USA) **Askew Dick Hernon Reynard**
3 **AGLAOPHONOS**, 4, ch g Dutch Art—Lasting Image **Jobarry Partnership**
4 **AMBELLA (IRE)**, 4, gr f Dark Angel (IRE)—Showmesomething (IRE) **Mr P. L. Mousley**
5 **AMPLEFORTH**, 6, ch g Pivotal—Anna Amalia (IRE) **Macable Partnership**
6 **ARABIAN HEIGHTS**, 6, gr g Araafa (IRE)—Makhsusah (IRE) **Macable Partnership**
7 **BALLYALTON (IRE)**, 7, b g Pierre—Almilto (IRE) **Mr J. Westwood**
8 **BOBCATBILLY (IRE)**, 8, b g Overbury (IRE)—Cush Jewel (IRE) **P. J. Vogt**
9 **BODEGA**, 6, b g Grape Tree Road—Gurleigh (IRE) **Mr P. R. Williams**
10 **BRUNSTON**, 8, gr g High Chaparral (USA)—Molly Mello (GER) **Mr P. F. Barry**
11 **C J MACKINTOSH**, 8, b m Beat All (USA)—Fringe Benefit (IRE) **Macable Partnership**
12 **CHAPTER FIVE**, 7, b m Grape Tree Road—Northern Shadows **Mr & Mrs Hutton & Mrs Laing**
13 **CHELLALLA**, 5, b m Elnadim (USA)—Cheloca **Global Commodity Imports Ltd**
14 **COMMISSAR**, 5, b g Soviet Star (USA)—Sari **S. Hassiakos**
15 **CONRY (IRE)**, 8, ch g Captain Rio—Altizaf **I. P. Williams**
16 **COTILLION**, 8, b g Sadler's Wells (USA)—Riberac **P. J. Vogt**
17 **CRAIGLANDS (IRE)**, 12, b g Dushyantor (USA)—Fernhill (IRE) **J. Tredwell**
18 **DONAPOLLO**, 6, b g Kayf Tara—Star of Wonder (FR) **Mr J. P. D. Stead**
19 **DRUMLANG (IRE)**, 8, b g Soviet Star (USA)—Sherekiya (IRE) **M Roberts J O'Shea S Hunt R Stearman**
20 **DUSTLAND FAIRYTALE (IRE)**, 6, b m Noverre (USA)—Subtle Affair (IRE) **I. P. Williams**
21 **EARLS QUARTER (IRE)**, 8, b g Shantou (USA)—Par Street (IRE) **P. Kelly**

MR IAN WILLIAMS - Continued

22 **ESCORT'MEN (FR)**, 8, ch g Robin des Champs (FR)—Escortee (FR) **Macable Partnership**
23 **ETANIA**, 6, b m King's Theatre (IRE)—Linnet (GER) **Mr & Mrs H. Parmar**
24 **FERRYVIEW PLACE**, 5, b g Compton Place—Songsheet **Mr J. O'Shea**
25 **FREDO (IRE)**, 10, ch g Lomitas—Felina (GER) **Mrs J. S. Allen**
26 **FREEDOM FIGHTER (IRE)**, 4, b c Danehill Dancer (IRE)—Rose of Petra (IRE) **Global Commodity Imports Ltd**
27 **GHOST OF A SMILE (IRE)**, 6, b g Oscar (IRE)—Dix Huit Brumaire (FR) **Mr S. Cox**
28 **GIFTED LEADER (USA)**, 9, b g Diesis—Zaghruta (USA) **The Ferandlin Peaches**
29 **GRAND GIGOLO (FR)**, 5, b g Enrique—Belle D'ecajeul (FR) **Mr P. A. Downing**
30 **HENRYBROWNEYES (IRE)**, 5, ch g Goldmark (USA)—The Vine Browne (IRE) **Mr P. R. Williams**
31 **HIGHWAY JOE**, 7, b m Central Park (IRE)—Fringe Benefit (IRE) **Mr P. M. Mannion**
32 **IL PRESIDENTE (GER)**, 7, ch g Royal Dragon (USA)—Independent Miss (GER) **P. J. Vogt**
33 **INCENDO**, 8, ch g King's Best (USA)—Kindle **Mr C. G. Adam**
34 **IOANNOU**, 5, b h Excellent Art—Sandtime (IRE) **A & P Skips Limited**
35 **KAYF HILL**, 6, b g Kayf Tara—Fulwell Hill **J. Tredwell**
36 **KONZERT (ITY)**, 4, b g Hurricane Cat (USA)—Known Alibi (USA) **Global Commodity Imports Ltd**
37 **LEATH ACRA MOR (IRE)**, 8, b g King's Theatre (IRE)—
Happy Native (IRE) **John O'Shea Stephen Hunt Craig Gardner**
38 **LILY LITTLE LEGS (IRE)**, 5, gr m Westerner—Silvers Promise (IRE) **J. P. Hanifin**
39 **MANDY'S BOY (IRE)**, 4, b g Kyllachy—African Queen (IRE) **Mr P. M. Mannion**
40 **MISS LUCKY PENNY**, 8, ch m Karinga Bay—Singing Cottage **S. G. Adams**
41 **MR VENDMAN (IRE)**, 4, b g Whipper (USA)—So Precious (IRE) **Vendman Systems Limited**
42 **NUBAR BOY**, 7, ch g Compton Place—Out Like Magic **Mr P. Slater**
43 **PORTWAY FLYER (IRE)**, 6, br g King's Theatre (IRE)—Next Best Thing (IRE) **P. Kelly**
44 **REMIX (IRE)**, 5, b m Oratorio (IRE)—Miss Lopez (IRE) **Global Commodity Imports Ltd**
45 **ROCKNROLLRAMBO (IRE)**, 7, b g Winged Love (IRE)—Lady Padivor (IRE) **Miss J. M. Foran**
46 **SOLIX (FR)**, 8, b br g Al Namix (FR)—Solimade (FR) **P. J. Vogt**
47 **SONOFAGUN (FR)**, 8, b g Turgeon (USA)—Detonante (FR) **The Piranha Partnership**
48 **STEVIE THUNDER**, 9, ch g Storming Home—Social Storm (USA) **S. L. Gray**
49 **SWINGING HAWK (GER)**, 8, ch g Hawk Wing (USA)—Saldenschwinge (GER) **Jamie Roberts & Jack Turton**
50 **TELLOVOI (IRE)**, 6, b h Indian Haven—Kloonlara (IRE) **Miss M. Gut**
51 **THE PERFECT CRIME (IRE)**, 5, b g Oscar (IRE)—Gimme Peace (IRE) **Mr S. Cox**
52 **TOUGHNESS DANON**, 8, b g Tiger Hill (IRE)—Templerin (GER) **Mr P. F. Barry**
53 **TWOJAYSLAD**, 5, b g Kayf Tara—Fulwell Hill **J. Tredwell**
54 **TYRANA (GER)**, 11, ch m Acatenango (GER)—Tascalina (GER) **The Piranha Partnership**
55 **WATT BRODERICK (IRE)**, 5, ch g Hawk Wing (USA)—Kingsridge (IRE) **P. Kelly**
56 **WESTERN APPROACHES**, 7, b m Westerner—Bayariyka (IRE) **I. P. Williams**
57 **WISHFORMORE (IRE)**, 7, b m Chevalier (IRE)—Terra Nova **Mr P. M. Mannion**
58 **ZAFRANAGAR (IRE)**, 9, b g Cape Cross (IRE)—Zafaraniya (IRE) **Mr P. A. Downing**

THREE-YEAR-OLDS

59 Ch g Medicean—Amzara (IRE)
60 **ANNOUNCEMENT**, ch f Proclamation (IRE)—Anapola (GER) **O C Racing**
61 **IZBUSHKA (IRE)**, b g Bushranger (IRE)—Zaynaba (IRE) **The Slurry Tavern Partnership**
62 B c Multiplex—Plead (FR)

TWO-YEAR-OLDS

63 B c 20/2 Rail Link—Cyclone Connie (Dr Devious (IRE)) (31000) **I. P. Williams**
64 Ch c 23/5 Footstepsinthesand—Ellen (IRE) (Machiavellian (USA)) (8000) **Buxted Partnership**
65 Ch f 10/3 Dandy Man (IRE)—Petticoat Hill (UAE) (Timber Country (USA)) (16190) **Mr P. Slater**
66 **ROMAN DE BRUT (IRE)**, ch c 3/3 Rock of Gibraltar (IRE)—
Nesmeh (More Than Ready (USA)) (33333) **Mr P. Slater**
67 B c 17/3 High Chaparral (IRE)—Senta's Dream (Danehill (USA)) (35000) **I. P. Williams**
68 B c 12/3 Duke of Marmalade (IRE)—Thewaytosanjose (IRE) (Fasliyev (USA)) (35000)

Other Owners: Mr B. A. Adams, Mr A. Chandler, Mr A. D. Dick, Mr C. Gardner, P. V. Harris, Ms R. J. Harris, T. Hart, Mr S. Hunt, M. J. Hutton, Mrs F. M. Laing, Mr S. Mackintosh, Mr F. W. Mackintosh, C. D. Massey, Mrs J. Massey, Mr A. Miles, Mr R. P. O'Donnell, Mr J. Parker, Mr H. Parmar, Mrs K. Parmar, Miss P. Purewal, Mr J. A. Reynard, Mr M. G. Roberts, Mr J. Roberts, Mrs J. Ruthven, Mr A. Singh, Mr R. Stearman, R. J. Turton, Mr L. J. Westwood.

Assistant Trainer: Richard Ryan

Jockey (NH): Dougie Costello, Harry Skelton. **Conditional:** Robbie McCarth.

676 MR NICK WILLIAMS, South Molton

Postal: Culverhill Farm, George Nympton, South Molton, Devon, EX36 4JE
Contacts: HOME (01769) 574174 FAX (01769) 573661 MOBILE (07855) 450379

1 ABRACADABRA SIVOLA (FR), 4, b g Le Fou (IRE)—Pierrebrune (FR) **The Arthur White Partnership**
2 AFTER EIGHT SIVOLA (FR), 4, b g Shaanmer (IRE)—Eva de Chalamont (FR) **Larkhills Racing Partnership III**
3 ALCO SIVOLA (FR), 4, gr g Dom Alco (FR)—Oeuvre Vive (FR) **Mr P R Noott & Mrs S A Noott**
4 ALFIE SPINNER (FR), 9, b g Afflora (IRE)—Little Red Spider **Alan Beard & Brian Beard**
5 AMORE ALATO, 5, b g Winged Love (IRE)—Sardagna (FR) **Mrs S. J. Faulks**
6 ATTENTE DE SIVOLA (FR), 4, gr ro f Dom Alco (FR)—Gamine d'ici (FR) **Potensis Limited**
7 AUBUSSON (FR), 5, b g Ballingarry (IRE)—Katioucha (FR) **Mrs J. R. Williams**
8 BEAU DE TABEL (FR), 6, b g Assessor (IRE)—Garde Aux Armes (FR) **Larkhills Racing Partnership II**
9 BENEFIQUE ROYALE, 6, ch m Beneficial—Royale De Vassy (FR) **Len, Davies, Downes, Hewlett, White, Booth**
10 COMTE D'ANJOU, 5, b g Desert King (IRE)—Delayed (FR) **Mrs S. J. Faulks**
11 CORNAS (NZ), 12, b g Prized (USA)—Duvessa (NZ) **The Gascoigne Brookes Partnership III**
12 DIAMOND HARRY, 11, b g Sir Harry Lewis (USA)—Swift Conveyance (IRE) **Paul Duffy Diamond Partnership**
13 DOLORES DELIGHTFUL (FR), 4, b f Saint des Saints (FR)—Us Et Coutumes (FR) **Miss E. Morgan**
14 FOX NORTON (FR), 4, b g Lando (GER)—Natt Musik (FR) **B. Dunn**
15 GREYWELL BOY, 7, gr g Fair Mix (IRE)—Rakajack **Chasing Gold Limited**
16 HINT OF MINT, 5, b g Passing Glance—Juno Mint **Sandie & David Newton**
17 HORATIO HORNBLOWER (IRE), 6, b br g Presenting—Countess Camilla **Huw & Richard Davies**
18 LE ROCHER (FR), 6, b g Saint des Saints (FR)—Belle du Roi (FR) **A. J. White & Mrs A. Underhill**
19 MALJIMAR (FR), 14, b g Un Desperado (FR)—Marble Miller (IRE) **Mrs J. R. Williams**
20 REVE DE SIVOLA (FR), 9, b g Assessor (IRE)—Eva de Chalamont (FR) **Paul Duffy Diamond Partnership**
21 RIO DE SIVOLA (FR), 5, bl g Caballo Raptor (CAN)—Pierrebrune (FR) **Forty Winks Syndicate**
22 ROYALE'S CHARTER, 8, ch g Karinga Bay—Royale De Vassy (FR) **Jakeman, Davies, Downes, & Friends**
23 SARIKA (FR), 8, b g Grand Tresor—Arika (FR) **Mrs J. R. Williams**
24 SHALIMAR FROMENTRO (FR), 8, gr g Martaline—Miss des Ormeaux (FR) **Mrs J. R. Williams**
25 TEA FOR TWO, 4, b g Kayf Tara—One For Me **Mrs J. R. Williams**
26 THE ITALIAN YOB (IRE), 6, b g Milan—The Rebel Lady (IRE) **The Macaroni Beach Society**
27 ULIS DE VASSY (FR), 6, b g Voix du Nord (FR)—
                    Helathou (FR) **Len & White, Hewlett, Robinson, Banyard & Booth**
28 UN BON P'TIT GARS (FR), 6, b g Robin des Champs (FR)—Nee A Saint Voir (FR) **K Alexander/ R Watts**
29 VEAUCE DE SIVOLA (FR), 5, b g Assessor (IRE)—Eva de Chalamont (FR) **D. P. Duffy**

THREE-YEAR-OLDS

30 AMOUR D'OR, b f Winged Love (IRE)—Diletia **French Gold**
31 BASILIC D'ALENE (FR), gr g Fragrant Mix (IRE)—Haïfa du Noyer (FR) **Mr J White & Mrs A Underhill**
32 BRISE COEUR (FR), b g Daramsar (FR)—Rose Bombon (FR) **French Gold**
33 BRISE VENDEENNE (FR), gr f Dom Alco (FR)—Naiade Mag (FR) **B. Dunn**
34 SAINT LINO (FR), b g Saint des Saints (FR)—Dona Rez (FR) **French Gold**

Other Owners: Mr K. Alexander, Mr Kerry Barker, Mr Alan Beard, Mr B. Beard, Dr Martin Booth, Mr N. Brookes, Mr Kevin Conlan, Dr Chris Cowell, Mr Huw Davies, Mr R. L. Davies, Mr Paul Duffy, Mr Tony Gale, Mr C. Garner, Mr D. A. Gascoigne, Mr A. Holt, Mr Len Jakeman, Mr Joe Lawrence, Mrs Sarah Ling, Miss Eliisa Morgan, Mr David Morgan, Mr David Newton, Mrs Sandie Newton, Mr Ian Paye, Mr Martin Pepper, Mr G. C. Pratt, Mr J. Robinson, Miss Alice Simmons, Mrs A. Underhill, Mr Ron Watts, Mr A. J. White.

Assistant Trainer: Mrs Jane Williams

Amateur: Miss Lizzie Kelly.

---

677 MR NOEL WILLIAMS, Blewbury

Postal: White Shoot, Woodway Road, Blewbury, Didcot, Oxfordshire, OX11 9EY
Contacts: PHONE (01235) 850806

1 BRIERY QUEEN, 5, b m King's Theatre (IRE)—Briery Gale **Helen Plumbly & Kathryn Leadbeater**
2 CHANCE TAKEN, 6, b m Overbury (IRE)—New Dawn **Unregistered Partnership**
3 FREDDIE ED, 13, b g Makbul—Miss Mirror **R. Bevis**
4 FRIENDLY SOCIETY (IRE), 9, ch g Moscow Society (USA)—Friendly Breeze **Whiteshoot Racing**
5 HOT WHISKEY N ICE (IRE), 5, b g Milan—Fair Gina **Whitehorsemen**
6 KINCORA FORT (IRE), 5, b g Brian Boru—Glenview Rose (IRE) **Miss C. Ludlow**
7 KING KAYF, 5, b g Kayf Tara—Firecracker Lady (IRE) **J.C.Harrison Lee & T.Howard Partnership**
8 KRACKATOA KING, 6, b g Kayf Tara—Firecracker Lady (IRE) **J.C.Harrison Lee & T.Howard Partnership**
9 LEGAL EAGLE (IRE), 9, b g Invincible Spirit (IRE)—Lupulina (CAN) **Mr N. Williams**

MR NOEL WILLIAMS - Continued

10 **PATTARA**, 5, b m Kayf Tara—Fortunes Course (IRE) **J. E. Garrett**
11 **PRIMO BLUE**, 4, b g Primo Valentino (IRE)—Flintwood **Mr R. Skillen**

Other Owners: Ms J. Harrison-Lee, Miss T. Howard, Mrs K. B. Leadbeater, Mrs H. Plumbly, Mrs L. L. Skillen.

---

678 **MR STUART WILLIAMS, Newmarket**
Postal: **Diomed Stables, Hamilton Road, Newmarket, Suffolk, CB8 0PD**
Contacts: **STABLES/OFFICE (01638) 663984 HOME (01638) 560143 MOBILE (07730) 314102**
E-MAIL **stuart@stuartwilliamsracing.co.uk**
WEBSITE **www.stuartwilliamsracing.co.uk Twitter:@Williamsstuart**

1 **BAHAMA BAY**, 4, b f Bahamian Bounty—Green Bonnet (IRE) **Mrs J. E. Wallsgrove**
2 **BOOTS AND SPURS**, 5, b g Oasis Dream—Arctic Char **Mr S. E. Chappell**
3 **CHAPTER SEVEN**, 5, ch g Excellent Art—My First Romance **Pearl Bloodstock Limited**
4 **CHERRY PRINCESS**, 4, ch gr f Act One—Francia **Mr B. Piper**
5 **CINCINNATI KIT**, 5, br m Cape Cross (IRE)—Princess Georgina **J. W. Parry**
6 **COMPTON**, 5, ch g Compton Place—Look So **The Morley Family**
7 **CREW CUT (IRE)**, 6, gr g Acclamation—Carabine (USA) **P. W. Stevens**
8 **DOCTOR PARKES**, 8, b g Diktat—Lucky Parkes **Mrs S Mason & Partners**
9 **ETON RIFLES (IRE)**, 9, b g Pivotal—Maritsa (IRE) **The Eton Riflemen**
10 **EX ORIENTE (IRE)**, 5, b g Azamour (IRE)—Little Whisper (IRE) **Mrs J. Morley & GJSS**
11 **HOLLEY SHIFTWELL**, 4, ch f Bahamian Bounty—Persario **J. W. Parry**
12 **LADY GUINEVERE**, 4, b f Pivotal—Birdie **J. W. Parry**
13 **LUNAR DEITY**, 5, b g Medicean—Luminda (IRE) **The Morley Family**
14 **MEZZOTINT (IRE)**, 5, b g Diamond Green (FR)—Aquatint **Mr S. E. Chappell**
15 **MILL I AM (USA)**, 4, b f Henny Hughes (USA)—Courageous (USA) **Eclipse Horse Racing**
16 **MY KINGDOM (IRE)**, 8, b g King's Best (USA)—Nebraas **My Kingdom For A Horse**
17 **RESONARE**, 5, b g Echo of Light—Pretty Kool **G. D. Thompson**
18 **TWO DAYS IN PARIS (FR)**, 5, b m Authorized (IRE)—Isalou (FR) **J. W. Parry**
19 **TYCHAIOS**, 4, b g Green Desert (USA)—Tychy **Mr P. Ellinas**
20 **WELEASE BWIAN (IRE)**, 5, b g Kheleyf (USA)—Urbanize (USA) **W. E. Enticknap**
21 **WELSH SUNRISE**, 4, b f Vita Rosa (JPN)—Chapel Corner (IRE) **Seize The Day Racing Partnership**

THREE-YEAR-OLDS

22 **DAISY BOY (IRE)**, b c Cape Cross (IRE)—Muluk (IRE) **Mr G. M. C. Johnson**
23 **DRINKUPTRIG (IRE)**, b c Bushranger (IRE)—Maybe in May (USA) **Mr G. M. C. Johnson**
24 **FREDERIC CHOPIN**, ch g Tamayuz—Eliza Gilbert **Mrs M. Shone**
25 **GLOBAL EXPLORER (USA)**, b g Henrythenavigator (USA)—Trulips (USA) **T W Morley & Mrs J Morley**
26 **GRACESOME (IRE)**, b f Shirocco (GER)—Simonda **S. P. Tindall**
27 **MR SOPRANO**, ch g Halling (USA)—Rima Baciata **Mr P. Kendall**
28 **NATIONAL CENTRE (USA)**, b g War Chant (USA)—Cotton Club Ballet (USA) **T. W. Morley**
29 **NOVA CHAMP (IRE)**, ch c Intikhab (USA)—Baby Bunting **Qatar Racing Limited**
30 **ORIENTAL TIGER**, b g Tiger Hill (IRE)—Cal Norma's Lady (IRE) **J. G. Thom**
31 **PACTOLUS (IRE)**, b g Footstepsinthesand—Gold Marie (IRE) **T W Morley & Mrs J Morley**
32 **POUNCING TIGER**, b f Tiger Hill (IRE)—Ipsa Loquitur **Mr A. Simpson**
33 **ROCK CHARM**, b g Araafa (IRE)—Evening Charm (IRE) **P. J. Ransley**
34 **ROYAL BIRTH**, b c Exceed And Excel (AUS)—Princess Georgina **Qatar Racing Limited**
35 **SPINNING COBBLERS**, b c Royal Applause—Tychy **Brian Roper & David Cobill**
36 **STAPLEFORD LAD**, b c Shirocco (GER)—World Spirit **Stapleford Racing Ltd**
37 **SYBILICIOUS**, b f Royal Applause—Tora Bora **J. W. Parry**
38 **TETE ORANGE**, ch f Pastoral Pursuits—Imperialistic (IRE) **J. W. Parry**
39 **TSARGLAS**, gr g Verglas (IRE)—Russian Empress (IRE) **Essex Racing Club**
40 **WIKI TIKI**, br f Dixie Union (USA)—Witten (USA) **J. W. Parry**

TWO-YEAR-OLDS

41 **AUTHORIZED SPIRIT**, b f 7/4 Authorized (IRE)—World Spirit (Agnes World (USA)) (7000) **Stapleford Racing Ltd**
42 B f 9/4 Pastoral Pursuits—Carollan (IRE) (Marju (IRE)) (24777) **Happy Valley Racing & Breeding Limited**
43 B c 2/4 Observatory (USA)—Chapel Corner (IRE) (Alhaarth (IRE)) (6190) **Seize The Day Racing Partnership**
44 Ch f 6/4 Summer Bird (USA)—Lady Amira (USA) (Langfuhr (CAN)) (60000) **J. W. Parry**
45 Ch c 30/3 Exceed And Excel (AUS)—
                    Monnavanna (IRE) (Machiavellian (USA)) (130000) **Happy Valley Racing & Breeding Limited**
46 B f 20/3 Kheleyf (USA)—Overwing (IRE) (Fasliyev (USA)) **Mr Keith Robinson**
47 B f 19/4 Sir Percy—Pivotting (Pivotal) (80000) **Mr J. W. Parry**

MR STUART WILLIAMS - Continued

48 B c 28/4 Exceed And Excel (AUS)—Princess Georgina (Royal Applause) (45000) **Mr D. A. Shekells**
49 RED HOUSE REBEL (IRE), b c 26/1 Cockney Rebel (IRE)—Avril Rose (IRE) (Xaar) (14000) **Mr B. Ralph**
50 Ch f 3/4 Intense Focus (USA)—Spinning Well (IRE) (Pivotal) (70000) **Happy Valley Racing & Breeding Limited**
51 B c 18/2 Excellent Art—Starfish (IRE) (Galileo (USA)) (92914) **Qatar Racing Limited**
52 Ch f 28/3 Sakhee's Secret—Warden Rose (Compton Place) (22000) **The Secretly Hopeful Partnership**

Other Owners: Mr Damian Bourke, Mr L. Ellinas, Miss Brigid Hennessy, Mr P. Kendall, Mrs F. Kendall, Mrs S. Mason, Mrs F. M. Midwood, Mr M. Montague, Mr J. Montague, Mr T. W. Morley, Mrs J. Morley, Mr R. R. Morris, Mr Barry Root, Mrs Joan Root, Dr Paula Sells, Mr Stuart C. Williams.

Assistant Trainer: Kirstine Wright

---

679 **MISS VENETIA WILLIAMS, Hereford**
Postal: **Aramstone, Kings Caple, Hereford, Herefordshire, HR1 4TU**
Contacts: **PHONE (01432) 840646 MOBILE (07770) 627108**
E-MAIL venetia.williams@virgin.net WEBSITE www.venetiawilliams.com

1 AACHEN, 10, b g Rainbow Quest (USA)—Anna of Saxony **Mr A. G. Bloom**
2 ABUNDANTLY, 5, b m Sakhee (USA)—Composing (IRE) **Mrs Fay Kempe & Deborah North**
3 AMINAH, 4, b f Dubawi (IRE)—Why Dubai (USA) **John & Zara Johnstone**
4 ART PROFESSOR (IRE), 10, b g In The Wings—Itab (USA) **J. P. Hancock**
5 ARTHUR'S OAK, 6, b g Kayf Tara—Myumi **Mrs J. K. Burt**
6 ASTIGOS (FR), 7, b br g Trempolino (USA)—Astonishing (BRZ) **Mr A. L. Brooks**
7 BALLYOLIVER, 10, b g Kayf Tara—Macklette (IRE) **Mr R. M. Britten-Long**
8 BARADARI (IRE), 4, b g Manduro (GER)—Behra (IRE) **Mr A. L. Brooks**
9 BECAUSESHESAIDSO (IRE), 6, b g Winged Love (IRE)—Huit de Coeur (FR) **Lady M. A. Bolton**
10 BENNYS MIST (IRE), 8, b g Beneficial—Dark Mist (IRE) **Mezzone Family**
11 BOBBLE BORU (IRE), 6, b m Brian Boru—Balreask Lady (IRE) **Mrs B. B. Grainger**
12 BRICK RED, 7, ch g Dubawi (IRE)—Duchcov **Julian Taylor & Andrew Brooks**
13 BROWNS BROOK (IRE), 8, b g Bob Back (USA)—All Over Now (IRE) **Mrs V. A. Bingham**
14 CALL CARLO, 7, ch g Karinga Bay—Lady Widd (IRE) **A. J. Pye-Jeary**
15 CARRICKBOY (IRE), 10, b g Silver Patriarch (IRE)—Alaskan Princess (IRE) **T. J. Hemmings**
16 CICERON (IRE), 8, b g Pivotal—Aiglonne (USA) **Verrier, Bowditch, Secretan**
17 CITIZENSHIP, 8, b g Beat Hollow—Three More (USA) **The Fizz Fund**
18 DARE ME (IRE), 10, b g Bob Back (USA)—Gaye Chatelaine (IRE) **Shire Birds**
19 DRUMSHAMBO (USA), 8, b g Dynaformer (USA)—Gossamer (USA) **The Grouse Partnership**
20 DUAISEOIR (IRE), 8, b g Bachelor Duke (USA)—Masnada (IRE) **Mezzone Family**
21 DUBAWI ISLAND (FR), 5, b g Dubawi (IRE)—Housa Dancer (FR) **Andrew Brooks & Julian Taylor**
22 DUNGENESS, 6, b g Beat All (USA)—Maydoo (IRE) **The Bellamy Partnership**
23 EASTERN WITNESS (IRE), 7, b g Witness Box (USA)—Eastertide (IRE) **Robert & Prudence Cooper**
24 ELENIKA (FR), 6, gr g Martaline—Nika Glitters (FR) **Janet Bromet & Andrew Brooks**
25 EMPEROR'S CHOICE (IRE), 7, b g Flemensfirth (USA)—House-of-Hearts (IRE) **The Bellamy Partnership**
26 ERSAAL, 4, b g Dubawi (IRE)—Makaaseb (USA) **Mr T. Fawcett**
27 FARASI KUBWA, 6, b g Millenary—Lily Grey (FR) **Mrs C Davies & Mrs W Dice**
28 FINE LILY, 5, gr m Fair Mix (USA)—Lily Grey (FR) **Allen & Monica Powley**
29 GORGEOUS LLIEGE (FR), 8, b g Lavirco (GER)—Charme d'estruval (FR) **Mr A. L. Brooks**
30 GOTOYOURPLAY (IRE), 10, ch g Definite Article—Johnston's Flyer (IRE) **Miss S. Douglas-Pennant**
31 GREEN BELT ELITE (FR), 10, b g Astarabad (USA)—Vallee Bleue (FR) **Green Belt Foresters**
32 HADA MEN (USA), 9, b g Dynaformer (USA)—Catchy (USA) **Gay & Peter Hartley**
33 HOUBLON DES OBEAUX (FR), 7, b g Panoramic—Harkosa (FR) **Mrs J. Blackwell**
34 HOWARD'S LEGACY (IRE), 8, b g Generous (IRE)—Ismene (FR) **A. G. Parker**
35 HUFF AND PUFF, 7, b g Azamour (IRE)—Coyote (USA) **Gay & Peter Hartley**
36 HURRICANE JOHN (IRE), 4, b g Hurricane Run (USA)—Top Lady (IRE) **John Nicholls (Trading) Ltd**
37 JOHN LOUIS, 6, ch g Bertolini (USA)—Native Ring (FR) **Mr A. L. Brooks**
38 KAPGA DE CERISY (FR), 6, ch g Kapgarde (FR)—Non Liquet **Mr A. L. Brooks**
39 KATENKO (FR), 8, b g Laveron—Katiana (FR) **Mr A. L. Brooks**
40 KING OF GLORY, 6, b g Kayf Tara—Glory Be **Mrs B. M. Willcocks**
41 KINGCORA (FR), 6, b g King's Theatre—Coralisse Royale (FR) **Mrs J. Blackwell**
42 KINGS RIVER (FR), 5, b br g Lost World (IRE)—Si Parfaite (FR) **Mrs J. Blackwell**
43 LAST SHOT (FR), 7, b g Le Fou (IRE)—Lucky Shot (FR) **Mr Basil Richards & Lady Bolton**
44 LEVIATHAN, 7, b g Dubawi (IRE)—Gipsy Moth **H. E. Ansell**
45 LOCHNAGAR (GER), 5, b g Sholokhov (IRE)—Lindenblute **Richard Britten-Long & Sarah Williams**
46 LUCKY SUNNY (IRE), 11, b g Pasternak—Flying Fur (IRE) **Suzanne & Nigel Williams**
47 MARCILHAC (FR), 5, b g Smadoun (FR)—One Way (FR) **Mr A. L. Brooks**

MISS VENETIA WILLIAMS - Continued

48 **MARKET OPTION (IRE)**, 8, b g Lord Americo—Ticklepenny (IRE) **The Gambling Cousins**
49 **MENTALIST (FR)**, 6, b g Westerner—Lady Carole (FR) **Brooks, Burke & Cunningham**
50 **MIRACLE CURE (IRE)**, 5, b g Whipper (USA)—Bring Back Matron (IRE) **R. J. Cadoret**
51 **MISS TIQUE (FR)**, 6, b m Network (GER)—Berthevine (FR) **Mrs A. W. Timpson**
52 **MISTARIUA**, 7, b g Kris Kin (USA)—Mrs Battleaxe (IRE) **A. J. Pye-Jeary**
53 **MONETARY FUND (USA)**, 8, b g Montjeu (IRE)—Maddie G (USA) **Mr A. L. Brooks**
54 **MOUJIK BORGET (FR)**, 6, ch g Layman (USA)—Fancy Tune (FR) **Sunday Lunch Partnership**
55 **MRS JORDAN (IRE)**, 6, b m King's Theatre (IRE)—Regents Dancer (IRE) **The Hon J. R. Drummond**
56 **MUDITA MOMENT (IRE)**, 9, b g Heron Island (IRE)—
                                       Woodville Leader (IRE) **John Moorhouse & John Nicholls (Trading)**
57 **NICEONEFRANKIE**, 8, b g Ishiguru (USA)—Chesnut Ripple **Old Carthusian Racing Society**
58 **OLD WAY (IRE)**, 8, b g Gold Away (IRE)—Brooklyn's Dance (FR) **B. C. Dice**
59 **OPERA OG (IRE)**, 8, b g Oscar (IRE)—Maspaloma (IRE) **Craig, Dick, Duckworth & Matthewman**
60 **OTAGO TRAIL (IRE)**, 6, b g Heron Island (IRE)—Cool Chic (IRE) **Mrs M. L. Shone**
61 **PANAMA PETRUS (IRE)**, 6, b g Alflora (IRE)—Pride 'n' Joy (IRE) **Andrew Brooks & Julian Taylor**
62 **PEPITE ROSE (FR)**, 7, b br m Bonbon Rose (FR)—Sambre (FR) **Falcon's Line Ltd**
63 **QUARTZ DE THAIX (FR)**, 10, b g Ragmar (FR)—Une Amie (FR) **ROA Arkle Partnership**
64 **RADICAL IMPACT (IRE)**, 6, ch g Beneficial—Shean Alainn (IRE) **Mr C. A. J. Drury**
65 **RELAX (FR)**, 9, b g Fragrant Mix (IRE)—Magik (FR) **The Bellamy Partnership**
66 **RENARD (FR)**, 9, b br g Discover d'auteuil (FR)—Kirmelia (FR) **ROA Arkle Partnership**
67 **RENARD D'IRLANDE (FR)**, 9, gr g April Night (FR)—Isati's (FR) **Hills of Ledbury Ltd**
68 **RICHMOND (FR)**, 9, b g Assessor (IRE)—Hirondel de Serley (FR) **Hills of Ledbury Ltd**
69 **RIGADIN DE BEAUCHENE (FR)**, 9, b br g Visionary (FR)—Chipie d'angron (FR) **Mr A. O. Wiles**
70 **ROCKY BENDER (IRE)**, 9, b g Saddlers' Hall (IRE)—Silver Spirit (IRE) **S Douglas-Pennant, J Young & P Nathan**
71 **ROSA FLEET (IRE)**, 6, b m Alflora (IRE)—Crimond (IRE) **Mezzone Family**
72 **ROYAL PALLADIUM (FR)**, 6, gr g King's Theatre (IRE)—Dent Sucree (FR) **Mrs A. W. Timpson**
73 **RYDALIS (FR)**, 9, b m Kapgarde (FR)—Fleurissa (FR) **Mrs V. A. Bingham**
74 **SAND ARTIST (IRE)**, 6, b g Sandmason—Belon Breeze (IRE) **John Nicholls (Trading) Ltd**
75 **SANTO THOMAS (FR)**, 8, gr g Chichicastenango (FR)—European Style (FR) **Mrs B. B. Grainger**
76 **SAROQUE (IRE)**, 7, b g Revoque (IRE)—Sarakin (FR) **Mr A. L. Brooks**
77 **SHANGANI (USA)**, 8, b g Giant's Causeway (USA)—Tanzania (IRE) **The Bellamy Partnership**
78 **SMART MONEY (FR)**, 7, br g Spadoun (FR)—Victoria Day **Mrs Louise Jones & Mrs Peter Andrews**
79 **SOMEMOTHERSDOHAVEM**, 5, ch g Avonbridge—Show Off **The Neighbours Partnership**
80 **STONE LIGHT (FR)**, 6, ch m Ballingarry (IRE)—Yellow Light (FR) **Mr A. L. Brooks**
81 **SUMMERY JUSTICE (IRE)**, 10, b g Witness Box (USA)—Kinsellas Rose (IRE) **Mrs P. Brown**
82 **SUSTAINABILITY (IRE)**, 9, ch g Old Vic—Over The Glen (IRE) **The Silver Cod Partnership**
83 4, B g Kayf Tara—Swaythe (USA) **R J H Geffen & P Bennett-Jones**
84 **TAKE THE MICK**, 7, b g Ishiguru (USA)—Michaelmas Daizy **Sir Geoffrey & Lady Vos**
85 **TARRACO (FR)**, 7, b g Sassanian (USA)—Marie Esther (FR) **Mrs V. A. Bingham**
86 **THE CLOCK LEARY (IRE)**, 6, b g Helissio (FR)—Kiwi Babe **Brooks, Vanderson, Pummell & Martin**
87 **TIDAL DANCE (IRE)**, 7, b g Craigsteel—Musical Waves (IRE) **Pinks Gym & Leisure Wear Ltd**
88 **TORGAMAH LAD (IRE)**, 6, b g High-Rise (IRE)—Brook Forte **Mr T. B. James**
89 **TOUBEERA**, 8, b m Tobougg (IRE)—Efizia **Mr R. M. Britten-Long**
90 **TROZULON (FR)**, 7, b g Roli Abi (FR)—Manza (FR) **J. P. Hancock**
91 **UHLAN BUTE (FR)**, 6, ch g Brier Creek (USA)—Jonquiere (FR) **R Elliott & N Coe**
92 **UNION JACK D'YCY (FR)**, 6, b g Bonnet Rouge (FR)—Jacady (FR) **Mr I. R. P. Josephs**
93 **UPEPITO (FR)**, 6, b g Khalkevi (IRE)—Friandise Ii (FR) **Mr A. L. Brooks**
94 **URANIUM (FR)**, 6, ch g Dear Doctor (FR)—Kalgary (FR) **P & T Brooks & A Brooks**
95 **VIVACCIO (FR)**, 5, b g Antarctique (IRE)—Cybelle (FR) **Boultbee Brooks Ltd**
96 **WALDORF SALAD (FR)**, 6, b g Millenary—Ismene (FR) **A. G. Parker**
97 **WING MIRA (IRE)**, 6, b g Winged Love (IRE)—Miraflores (IRE) **You Can Be Sure**
98 **YELLOW BALL (FR)**, 6, ch m Ballingarry (IRE)—Louve Antique (FR) **John & Zara Johnstone**
99 **ZAMDY MAN**, 5, b g Authorized (IRE)—Lauderdale (GER) **Mr M. N. Khan**

Other Owners: Sir John Becher, Mrs C. Belloc Lowndes, Dr Martin Booth, Mrs C. Boultbee-Brooks, Mr James Bowditch, Mr P. L. Brooks, Mrs E. T. L. Brooks, Mr D. J. Burke, Mrs Pat Churchward, Mr T. H. G. Cooper, Dr Chris Cowell, Mr Phil Cunningham, Mr J. S. Dale, Mr P Davies, Mr Michael J. Davies, Mrs C. Davies, Mr P. A. Deal, Mrs W. Dice, Mr Andrew Dick, Mr Andrew Duckworth, Mr R. J. Elliott, Mrs Sadie Evans, Mrs Lisa Fellows, Miss H. Frankham, Mrs J. E. Gorton, Mr Christopher James, Mr S. A. Martin, Mr Graham Mezzone, Mr John O'Reilly, Mr M. A. R. Pummell, Mr T. D. Rose, Mr Maurice Ryan, Mr M. Secretan, Mr James Richard Terry, Mr Lee Vanderson.

Jockey (NH): Aidan Coleman, Liam Treadwell. **Conditional:** Harry Challoner, Callum Whillans. **Amateur:** Mr Jamie Hamilton, Mr Joe Knox, Mr Darragh Lordan, Miss Lucy Turner.

680 MRS LISA WILLIAMSON, Chester

Postal: **Saighton Hall, Saighton, Chester, Cheshire, CH3 6EE**
Contacts: **PHONE (01244) 314254 FAX (01244) 314254 (please ring before sending)**
MOBILE **(07970) 437679**
E-MAIL **info@lisawilliamson.co.uk** WEBSITE **www.lisawilliamson.co.uk**

1 **ANOTHER JOURNEY**, 5, b g Rail Link—Singasongosixpence **Heath House Racing**
2 **BERTIE BLU BOY**, 6, b g Central Park (IRE)—Shaymee's Girl **B & B Hygiene Limited**
3 **CHESTER DEELYTE (IRE)**, 6, b m Desert Style (IRE)—Bakewell Tart (IRE) **Hindford Oak Racing**
4 6, B g Pursuit of Love—Classic Quartet **Mrs L. V. Williamson**
5 **GARDE VILLE (FR)**, 4, ch g Kapgarde (FR)—Ville Eagle (FR) **Mrs Y. Fleet**
6 **HINDFORD OAK GOLD**, 6, ch g Grape Tree Road—Sharp Susy
7 **JOHN CRABBIES (FR)**, 7, b g Super Celebre (FR)—Clelia La Belle (FR) **Halewood International Ltd**
8 **LA BRAVA**, 4, ch f Kheleyf (USA)—La Belga (ARG) **Danron Syndicate**
9 **LA DANZA**, 4, b f Country Reel (USA)—Freedom Song **Danron Syndicate**
10 6, B g Grape Tree Road—Lambrini Queen
11 **MUSICAL BRIDGE**, 8, b g Night Shift (USA)—Carrie Pooter **Mr A. J. Conway**
12 **ODD BALL (IRE)**, 7, b g Redback—Luceball (IRE) **Mr A. T Sykes**
13 **PINBALL (IRE)**, 8, b m Namid—Luceball (IRE)
14 **RAT CATCHER (IRE)**, 4, b g One Cool Cat (USA)—Molly Marie (IRE) **Mr R. Jones**
15 **ROUGHLYN**, 5, ch g Haafhd—Dime Bag **Mrs L. V. Williamson**
16 **RYAN STYLE (IRE)**, 8, b g Desert Style (IRE)—Westlife (IRE) **Mrs S. M. O'Reilly Hyland**
17 **SANTINHO (IRE)**, 11, b g Double Eclipse (IRE)—Gina's Love **Mr K. W. Peach**
18 **SENORA LOBO (IRE)**, 4, b f Amadeus Wolf—Valencia (FR) **Mr G. H. Briers**
19 **SERAPHIMA**, 4, b f Fusaichi Pegasus (USA)—Millestan (IRE) **Danron Syndicate**
20 **TIME FOR CRABBIES (IRE)**, 4, b g Moss Vale (IRE)—Westlife (IRE) **Halewood International Ltd**
21 **TIME FOR LAMBRINI (IRE)**, 4, b f Amadeus Wolf—Princess Madaen (IRE) **Halewood International Ltd**
22 **YOUR GIFTED (IRE)**, 7, b m Trans Island—Dame Laura (IRE) **Mr A. T Sykes**

THREE-YEAR-OLDS

23 **COUNTESS LUPUS (IRE)**, b f Amadeus Wolf—Papaha (FR) **Miss H. J. Roberts**
24 **IMPERIAL IKE**, b g Imperial Dancer—Betws Y Coed (IRE) **Tregarth Racing**

TWO-YEAR-OLDS

25 B f 23/2 Misu Bond (IRE)—Gunalt Joy (Blue Dakota (IRE)) (761) **Mr J. Levenson**
26 B f 23/3 Monsieur Bond (IRE)—Lavernock Lady (Don't Forget Me) (2380) **Mr J. Levenson**
27 Ch c 18/3 Three Valleys (USA)—Miss Dixie (Bertolini (USA))

Other Owners: Mrs E. L. Berry, Mr H. Hall, Exors of the Late M. S. Heath, Miss C. L. Howard, Mr S. Jennings, Mr J. H. Martin, Mr M. L. Rush, Mr T. H. Tan, Mr R. L. Williams, Mr K. S. Wong.

Assistant Trainer: Mark Williamson

Jockey (flat): Mr Alexander French. **Jockey (NH):** Brian Hughes. **Conditional:** Harry Challoner.
Amateur: Mr C. Ellingham.

681 MR ANDREW WILSON, Greystoke

Postal: **Silver Howe, Orton, Penrith, Cumbria, CA10 3RQ**
Contacts: **PHONE (01539) 624071 MOBILE (07813) 846768**

1 **REXMEHEAD (IRE)**, 13, b g Fort Morgan (USA)—Moon Rose (IRE) **Mrs H. J. Wilson**
2 **SO BAZAAR (IRE)**, 7, b g Xaar—Nature Girl (USA) **Mrs H. J. Wilson**

682 MR CHRISTOPHER WILSON, Darlington

Postal: **Manor Farm, Manfield, Darlington, Co. Durham, DL2 2RW**
Contacts: **PHONE (01325) 374595 FAX (01325) 374595 MOBILE (07815) 952306/(07721) 379277**
E-MAIL **wilsonracing@aol.com**

1 **ESME RIDES A GAINE**, 12, gr m Doubletour (USA)—Silver Penny **Mrs J. Wilson**
2 **INGENTI**, 6, ch m Blue Dakota (IRE)—Kungfu Kerry **D. A. J. Bartlett**
3 **LATEST FASHION (IRE)**, 8, ch m Ashkalani (IRE)—Musical Bramble (IRE) **Mrs J. Wilson**

MR CHRISTOPHER WILSON - Continued

4 **NICEONEMYSON**, 5, b g Misu Bond (IRE)—Kungfu Kerry **D. A. J. Bartlett**
5 **NO TIME TO CRY**, 5, b m Josr Algarhoud (IRE)—Autumn Bloom (IRE) **Miss H. J. Wilson**
6 **SHARP SHOES**, 7, br g Needwood Blade—Mary Jane **Mrs J. Wilson**
7 **URSUS**, 9, ch g Rambling Bear—Adar Jane **Mrs J. Wilson**

Assistant Trainer: Julie Wilson

Jockey (flat): Paddy Aspell, Silvestre De Sousa. **Jockey (NH):** Keith Mercer, Ewan Whillans. **Apprentice:** Julie Burke.

---

683 **MR JIM WILSON, Cheltenham**
Postal: **Glenfall Stables, Ham, Charlton Kings, Cheltenham, Gloucestershire, GL52 6NH**
Contacts: **PHONE (01242) 244713 FAX (01242) 226319 MOBILE (07932) 157243**
E-MAIL ajwglenfall@aol.com

1 **CAPTAIN SULLY (IRE)**, 9, b g Pairumani Star (IRE)—Ginger Lily (IRE) **The Cotswold Partnership**
2 **RUBY VALENTINE (FR)**, 11, b m Kayf Tara—A Ma Valentine (FR) **The Winbledon Partnership**
3 **SEYMOUR LEGEND**, 8, b g Midnight Legend—Rosehall **Mrs M. J. Wilson**
4 5, B m Kayf Tara—Vivante (IRE) **Mrs M. J. Wilson**

Other Owners: H. H. J. Fentum, J. W. Griffin, B. J. Hughes, D. B. O'Beirne, Mrs C. L. Troke.

---

684 **MISS MAIRI WILSON, Bawtry**
Postal: **Martin Common Farm, Bawtry, Doncaster, South Yorkshire, DN10 6DB**

1 **COFFEE KING (IRE)**, 5, b g King's Best (USA)—Passarelle (USA) **Mrs M. F. and Miss M. C. Wilson**
2 **ITS A STORY**, 7, ch m Lucky Story (USA)—Inchmore **Mrs M. F. and Miss M. C. Wilson**
3 **RHYME ROYAL**, 5, b m Byron—Burton Ash **Mrs M. F. and Miss M. C. Wilson**

Other Owners: Mrs M. F. Wilson, Miss M. C. Wilson.

---

685 **MR NOEL WILSON, Middleham**
Postal: **Caphall Lodge, Coverham, Middleham, Leyburn, North Yorkshire, DL8 4TL**
Contacts: **PHONE (01969) 622780 FAX (01969) 622780 MOBILE (07718) 613206**
E-MAIL nlwilson69@live.com

1 4, Gr g Iffraaj—Alphilda **Mrs J. Bartley**
2 **BACKFORCE**, 6, b g Jelani (IRE)—Scoffera **Mrs J. Wandless**
3 **ECHO OF LIGHTNING**, 4, b g Echo of Light—Classic Lass **Victoria Greetham & Emily Beasley**
4 **GREAT ROAR (USA)**, 6, b g Thunder Gulch (USA)—Boasting (USA) **N. Wilson**
5 **KOOLGREYCAT (IRE)**, 5, gr m One Cool Cat (USA)—Brooks Masquerade **Mr & Mrs D Walker, Mr N Wilson**
6 **PAVERS STAR**, 5, ch g Pastoral Pursuits—Pride of Kinloch **Mrs C. K. Paver**
7 **SHATIN SECRET**, 4, b g Sakhee's Secret—Al Corniche (IRE) **N. Wilson**

THREE-YEAR-OLDS

8 **BOUNTIFUL FOREST**, ch f Bahamian Bounty—Through The Forest (USA) **N. Wilson**
9 **FUJIN**, b g Oasis Dream—Phantom Wind (USA) **Mrs D. Robinson**
10 **PAVERS BOUNTY**, ch g Bahamian Bounty—Pride of Kinloch **Mrs M. J. Paver**

TWO-YEAR-OLDS

11 B f 22/4 Champs Elysees—Anthea (Tobougg (IRE)) (5500)
12 **GHOSTLY ART (IRE)**, b c 13/3 Arcano (IRE)—
                                   Cheyenne's Spirit (IRE) (Sadler's Wells (USA)) (19357) **Mr G. Paver**
13 B f 13/3 Kodiac—Hollow Haze (Woodman (USA)) (10840)
14 B c 6/3 Captain Rio—Karenka (IRE) (Arakan (USA)) (3871)
15 **LAZY DAYS IN LOULE (IRE)**, b f 3/3 Approve (IRE)—Lazy Lady (Selkirk (USA)) (6194) **Mr G. Paver**

MR NOEL WILSON - Continued

16 **MR CHRISTOPHER (IRE)**, b c 4/4 Bahamian Bounty—
Embassy Pearl (IRE) (Invincible Spirit (IRE)) (23228) **Mrs M. C. Antrobus**
17 B f 5/2 Sakhee's Secret—Regal Run (USA) (Deputy Minister (CAN)) (5000)

Other Owners: Mrs Emily Beasley, Miss Victoria Greetham, Mr Gary Kennedy, Mr Ian B. Pallister, Mr F. Tobin, Mr David Walker (Stafford), Mrs Julie Walker, Mr N. Wilson.

Assistant Trainer: Miss Alex Porritt

Jockey (flat): Duran Fentiman, Daniel Tudhope. **Jockey (NH):** Wilson Renwick. **Apprentice:** Neil Farley, Joey Haynes.

686

MR KEN WINGROVE, Bridgnorth
Postal: **6 Netherton Farm Barns, Netherton Lane, Highley, Bridgnorth, Shropshire, WV16 6NJ**
Contacts: **HOME (01746) 861534 MOBILE (07974) 411267**
E-MAIL kenwingrove@btinternet.com

1 **ANTOELLA (IRE)**, 7, gr m Antonius Pius (USA)—Bella Estella (GER)
2 **ARTY FARMER**, 10, b g Karinga Bay—One of Those Days
3 **BRUNDON**, 5, ch m Refuse To Bend (IRE)—Anna of Brunswick
4 **COPPICE LAD**, 5, b g Thethingaboutitis (USA)—Coppice Lane
5 **FERNANDO (IRE)**, 10, b g Fruits of Love (USA)—Dancing Venus
6 **FEROCIOUS FRAN (IRE)**, 6, b m Footstepsinthesand—Tipsy Lady
7 **GRAND FELLA (IRE)**, 9, ch g Raise A Grand (IRE)—Mummys Best
8 **KWANTO**, 4, b f Piccolo—Craic Sa Ceili (IRE)
9 **LEAHNESS (IRE)**, 7, br m Arakan (USA)—En Retard (IRE)
10 **MARSHALL ART**, 5, b g Lawman (FR)—Portrait of A Lady (IRE)
11 **REINVIGORATE (IRE)**, 4, b f Invincible Spirit (IRE)—Miss Serendipity (IRE)
12 **STREELE (USA)**, 4, gr f Thunder Gulch (USA)—Crown Capers (USA)
13 **WEET IN NERJA**, 8, b g Captain Rio—Persian Fortune
14 **WINROB**, 8, b g Exceed And Excel (AUS)—High Standard
15 **WOR JOSIE (IRE)**, 6, br m Zagreb (USA)—Garw Valley

Assistant Trainer: Isobel Willer

687

MR PETER WINKS, Barnsley
Postal: **Homefield, Rotherham Road, Little Houghton, Barnsley, South Yorkshire, S72 0HA**
Contacts: **MOBILE (07846) 899993**

1 **DASHING GEORGE (IRE)**, 12, ch g Beneficial—Here It Is **Mr P. Winks**
2 **HARTSIDE (GER)**, 5, b g Montjeu (IRE)—Helvellyn (USA) **Mr P. Winks**
3 **RULER OF ALL (IRE)**, 8, b g Sadler's Wells (USA)—Shabby Chic (USA) **Mr P. Winks**
4 **SOLSTICE DAWN**, 6, b m Lyphento (USA)—Ryders Hill **Mr P. Winks**

688

MR ADRIAN WINTLE, Westbury-On-Severn
Postal: **Yew Tree Stables, Rodley, Westbury-on-Severn, Gloucestershire, GL14 1QZ**
Contacts: **MOBILE (07767) 351144**

1 4, B g Beneficial—Beautiful Night (FR) **A. A. Wintle**
2 4, B g Presenting—Escrea (IRE) **A. A. Wintle**
3 **HALLINGS COMET**, 5, ch g Halling (USA)—Landinium (ITY) **Lord J. Blyth**
4 **LE TIGRE DE BRONZE**, 4, b g Tiger Hill (IRE)—Papillon de Bronze (IRE) **Lord J. Blyth**
5 **MILLY MALONE (IRE)**, 8, b m Milan—Sharp Single (IRE) **Mr S. R. Whistance**
6 **NOBLE PERK**, 9, ch g Executive Perk—Far From Perfect (IRE) **A. J. Williams**
7 **SHALONE**, 10, ch g Tobougg (IRE)—Let Alone **Mrs Jeni Fisher & Mr A A Wintle**
8 **SILVER COASTER (IRE)**, 10, b m Presenting—Silver Castor (IRE) **A. A. Wintle**
9 **VIC VENTURI (IRE)**, 14, ch g Old Vic—Carmen Lady **Mr S. W. Dunn**

Other Owners: Mrs J. A. Fisher.

689   MR STEVE WOODMAN, Chichester

Postal: Parkers Barn Stables, 8 Pook Lane, East Lavant, Chichester, West Sussex, PO18 0AU
Contacts: OFFICE (01243) 527136 FAX (01243) 527136 MOBILE (07889) 188519
E-MAIL stevewoodman83@msn.com

1 **CHEVISE (IRE)**, 6, b m Holy Roman Emperor (IRE)—Lipica (IRE) **The Chevise Partnership**
2 4, B f Robin des Pres (FR)—Evangelica (USA)
3 **GOING TWICE**, 9, b g Josr Algarhoud (IRE)—Its Your Bid **Mrs S. B. Woodman**
4 **HIGHLY LIKELY (IRE)**, 5, b g Elnadim (USA)—Height of Fantasy (IRE) **Mrs S. B. Woodman**
5 **LORD ALDERVALE (IRE)**, 7, br g Alderbrook—Monavale (IRE) **Mr D. N. Boxall**

THREE-YEAR-OLDS

6 B f Tikkanen (USA)—Like A Bolt (IRE)
7 B f Winged Love (IRE)—Luck's A Lady (IRE)

Other Owners: Mrs P. M. Tyler.

690   MR GARRY WOODWARD, Retford

Postal: 21 Camden Grove, Maltby, Rotherham, South Yorkshire, S66 8GE
Contacts: HOME (01709) 813431 MOBILE (07709) 382052
E-MAIL gwoodwardracing@aol.com WEBSITE www.garrywoodward.co.uk

1 **ERRIGAL LAD**, 9, ch g Bertolini (USA)—La Belle Vie **Mrs E. Cash**
2 **INSIDE KNOWLEDGE (USA)**, 8, gr ro g Mizzen Mast (USA)—Kithira **Mrs E. Cash**
3 **KINGAROO (IRE)**, 8, b g King Charlemagne (USA)—Lady Naomi (USA) **J. Pownall**
4 **PRINCEOFTHEDESERT**, 8, b g Nayef (USA)—Twilight Sonnet **G. Woodward**
5 **SECRET LODGE**, 6, ch m Needwood Blade—Obsessive Secret (IRE) **Mrs E. Cash**
6 **SELF EMPLOYED**, 7, b g Sakhee (USA)—Twilight Sonnet **G. Woodward**

691   MR RICHARD WOOLLACOTT, South Molton

Postal: Nethercott Manor, Rose Ash, South Molton, Devon, EX36 4RE
Contacts: PHONE (01769) 550483
WEBSITE www.richardwoollacottracing.co.uk

1 **ANGLES HILL (IRE)**, 7, b g Heron Island (IRE)—No Tails Told (IRE) **R. G. Westacott**
2 **BLAZING BOUNCER**, 9, b g Relief Pitcher—Blazing Miracle **Ms R. C. Heard**
3 **CASH INJECTION**, 5, b g Halling (USA)—Cape Siren **Eight Ball Partnership**
4 **CIVIL DISOBEDIENCE**, 10, b g Roi de Rome (USA)—Biddles **R Mitford-Slade & Lucy Johnson**
5 **CRIDDA BOY**, 8, ch g Mark of Esteem (IRE)—Second Affair (IRE) **D. G. Staddon**
6 **DELPHI MOUNTAIN (IRE)**, 9, b g Oscar (IRE)—Summer Break (IRE) **Mr D Stevens & Mrs S Stevens**
7 **DREAM LUCKY**, 9, b g Bandmaster (USA)—Sheilas Dream **S. G. Searle**
8 **FOLLY FARM (IRE)**, 6, gr g Definite Article—West Hill Rose (IRE) **D. G. Staddon**
9 **GENSON**, 5, b g Generous (IRE)—Gaynor **R. Woollacott**
10 **KUDU SHINE**, 8, b g Karinga Bay—Flora Bright **Mr D Stevens & Mr G Jewell**
11 **LIBERTY ONE (IRE)**, 8, b g Milan—Same Old Story (IRE) **D. G. Staddon**
12 **MILLANISI BOY**, 5, b g Kalanisi (IRE)—Millennium Rose (IRE) **Mrs S. E. Stevens**
13 **MISS TINKS**, 8, ch m Exit To Nowhere (USA)—Miss O'grady (IRE) **Taunton Racecourse Owners Club**
14 **PISTOLET NOIR (FR)**, 8, b g Maille Pistol (FR)—Black Et Or (FR) **Angus Mcalpine & Richard Gower**
15 **POSSIBLY FLORA**, 9, b m Rakaposhi King—Calling Flora **R Mitford-Slade & Lucy Johnson**
16 **ROBIN WILL (FR)**, 9, bl g Dark Moondancer—Gleep Will (FR) **J. F. G. Symes**
17 **SILVERGROVE**, 6, b g Old Vic—Classic Gale (USA) **Nicholas Piper & Claire E. Phillipson**
18 **SIR KEZBAAH (IRE)**, 10, b g Oscar (IRE)—Madam Chloe **The Spoofers**
19 **VALOROSO**, 9, b g Laveron—Millennium Rose (IRE) **Mrs A. E. R. Goodwin**
20 **VINTAGE TEA**, 7, b g Beat All (USA)—Come To Tea (IRE) **The Moonlighters**

Other Owners: M. J. Bevan, G. S. Brown, Mrs V. A. Butcher, Mr R. C. Butcher, Mr G. J. Evans, Mrs L. Fielding-Johnson, Mr P. Govier, Mr P. F. Govier, Mr R. I. A. Gower, Mr M. Higgs, Mr G. D. C. Jewell, Mr S. Kidston, Mr A. P. Maddox, Mr A. N. A. McAlpine, R. C. Mitford-Slade, Miss C. E. Phillipson, Mr N. Piper, Mr S. C. C. Stacey, Mr D. J. Stevens.

692 **MR RAYMOND YORK, Cobham**
Postal: **Newmarsh Farm, Horsley Road, Cobham, Surrey, KT11 3JX**
Contacts: **PHONE (01932) 863594 MOBILE (07808) 344131**
E-MAIL **ray.york@virgin.net**

1 **CHOMOLUNGMA,** 7, b m Amber Life—Manrella **Mrs K. H. York**
2 **CRAIGS DREAM (IRE),** 8, b g Craigsteel—Sinead's Dream (IRE) **R. H. York**
3 **CUNNING PLAN (IRE),** 7, ch g Bachelor Duke—Madamaa (IRE) **Mrs K. H. York**
4 **DANCING JACK (FR),** 10, b br g True Brave (USA)—Line Saj (FR) **Mrs K. H. York**
5 **ENCANTADORA,** 7, ch m Generous (IRE)—Sninfia (IRE) **R. H. York**
6 **HARRY'S CHOICE,** 6, b g Sir Harry Lewis (USA)—Chosen (IRE) **R. H. York**
7 **LADY IDA,** 9, b m Dolpour—La Princesse **Mrs K. H. York**
8 6, B m Definite Article—Nut Eile (IRE) **R. H. York**
9 **QUEEN'S PAWN (IRE),** 7, br g Strategic Choice (USA)—Curragh Queen (IRE) **F. D. Camis**
10 **SORSE,** 8, b g Central Park (IRE)—Tachelle (IRE) **R. H. York**
11 **SPIRITOFCHARTWELL,** 6, ch g Clerkenwell (USA)—Rollin Rock **Stoney's Bloodstock**
12 5, B g Bollin Eric—Woodford Consult **R. H. York**

THREE-YEAR-OLDS

13 Gr g Jeremy (USA)—Million All Day (IRE)

Other Owners: Mr M. A. Adams, R. Gurney.

Amateur: Mr P. York.

693 **MRS LAURA YOUNG, Bridgwater**
Postal: **Rooks Castle Stables, Broomfield, Bridgwater, Somerset, TA5 2EW**
Contacts: **PHONE (01278) 661555 FAX (01278) 661555 MOBILE (07766) 514414**
E-MAIL **ljyracing@hotmail.com**

1 **ADMIRAL BLAKE,** 7, b g Witness Box (USA)—Brenda Bella (FR) **Mrs L. J. Young**
2 **BANDOL (IRE),** 6, b g Zagreb (USA)—Formal Affair **Total Plumbing Supporters Club**
3 **BUCKBORU (IRE),** 6, b m Brian Boru—Buckland Filleigh (IRE) **Mrs L. J. Young**
4 **CAMPTOWN LADY,** 5, b m Doyen (IRE)—Ballyquintet (IRE) **Mrs L. J. Young**
5 **CASTANUM (IRE),** 5, ch g Kris Kin (USA)—Persian Argument (IRE) **The Isle Of Frogs Partnership**
6 **CASTLETOWN (IRE),** 6, b g Oscar (IRE)—Closing Thyne (IRE) **The Isle Of Frogs Partnership**
7 **FINTAN,** 11, ch g Generous (IRE)—Seeker **Total Plumbing Supporters Club**
8 **JIGSAW FINANCIAL (IRE),** 8, b g Brian Boru—Ardcolm Cailin (IRE) **Mrs L. J. Young**
9 **KAP WEST (FR),** 9, b g Kapgarde (FR)—Themis Eria (FR) **Mrs S. A. White**
10 **OSRIC (IRE),** 11, b g Mister Mat (FR)—Miss Ondee (FR) **Total Plumbing Supporters Club**
11 **WOLFTRAP (IRE),** 5, b g Mountain High (IRE)—Dear Money (IRE) **Mrs S. A. White**

Other Owners: C. E. Handford, Mr I. D. Moses, Mr G. C. Vining, Mr C. V. Vining.

Assistant Trainer: James Young

694 **MR WILLIAM YOUNG, Carluke**
Postal: **Watchknowe Lodge, Crossford, Carluke, Lanarkshire, ML8 5QT**
Contacts: **PHONE (01555) 860856 (01555) 860226 FAX (01555) 860137 MOBILE (07900) 408210**
E-MAIL **watchknowe@talktalk.net**

1 **ELLANDSHE (IRE),** 14, b br g Topanoora—Fox Glen **W. G. Young**
2 **JOHN'S RUBY,** 4, b f Sixties Icon—Sakaka **W. G. Young**
3 **LEWLAUR SUPREME (IRE),** 11, b g Supreme Leader—Dark Dame (IRE) **W. G. Young**
4 **TIM'S APPROACH (IRE),** 9, b g Luso—Creative Approach (IRE) **W. G. Young**

Assistant Trainer: William G Young Snr

INDEX TO HORSES

The Figure before the name of the horse refers to the number of the team in which it appears and **The Figure after** the name of the horse supplies a ready reference to each animal. Horses are indexed strictly alphabetically, e.g. THE OLDLADYSAYS NO appears in the T's, MR BOSSY BOOTS in the MR's, ST DOMINICK in the ST's etc.

267 BEECHILL DANCER (IRE) G 6
39 BEECHNUT (IRE) F 35
291 BEEDEE (GB) 4
357a BEEKY 25
533 BEEP (GB) 3
674 BEETLE BUG (GB) G 7
418 BEEVES (IRE) 11
568 BEFOREALL (IRE) 2
155 BEGGERS BELIEF (GB) 4
664 BEGGARS LUCK (GB) 1
247 BEGLAWELLA G 2
398 BEGUIN D'ESTIVAUX (FR) 45
549 BEHESHT (FR) 29
178 BEHIND THE BUSH (IRE) 16
549 BEHNASA (IRE) 106
550 BEIDH TINÉ ANSEO (IRE) 9
318 BEIJING STAR (GB) 78
63 BEL AMI RICH (GB) 4
507 BEL HUGO (FR) 13
279 BELAHODOOD (GB) 28
190 BELANNA (GB) 7
553 BELAYER (IRE) 35
130 BELDALE MEMORY (IRE) 26
479 BELESTA (GB) C 102
17 BELFILO (IRE) 52
16 BELGIAN BILL (GB) 5
344 BELINSKY (IRE) 4
479 BELISARIUS (IRE) 28
637 BELIZE (GB) 99
441 BELL'ARTE (IRE) 4
62 BELL'S CROSS (IRE) 2
65 BELLA ALAMOTO (GB) 20
291 BELLA BERTOLINI (GB) C 169
366 BELLA BIJOU (GB) 1
549 BELLA QATARA (IRE) 2
148 BELLACOOLA (GER) F 52
75 BELLE ALLEMANDE (CAN) F 20
296 BELLE BAYARDO (IRE) 2
508 BELLE CAROLINE (USA) 10
260 BELLE D'OR (USA) 24
171 BELLE DE FONTENAY (FR) 3
40 BELLE DE LAWERS (GB) 13
371 BELLE DE LONDRES (IRE) 6
624 BELLE DES AIRS (IRE) F 36
217 BELLE INTRIGUE (IRE) 2
507 BELLE MAGELLO (FR) F 14
130 BELLE OF THE BLUES (IRE) F 64
245 BELLE PARK (IRE) 2
17 BELLE REINE (GB) C 129
521 BELLE STAR (GB) 7
628 BELLE WATLING (IRE) F 18
573 BELLENOS (IRE) 7
376 BELLETRISTE (FR) 14
563 BELLGROVE (IRE) 1
356 BELLINGO (GB) 2
5 BELLO (AUS) 6
572 BELLONAISE (GB) 58
144 BELLOROPHON (IRE) 4
639 BELLRINGER (GB) 5
568 BELLUCIA (GB) 3
584 BELMORE BARON (GB) 7
540 BELOIT (USA) 126
89 BELOW THE DECK (IRE) 1
32 BELROG (GB) 21
479 BELTISAAL (FR) C 103
169 BELTOR (GB) 20
397 BELTS AND BRACES (IRE) 15
458 BELUCKYAGAIN (IRE) 18

646 BELVOIR DIVA (GB) 40
550 BEN AKRAM (IRE) 10
196 BEN CEE PEE M (IRE) 10
637 BENABILITY (IRE) 10
462 BENANDONNER (USA) 3
365 BENBANE HEAD (USA) 5
438 BENBECULA (GB) 1
631 BENBENS (IRE) 8
284 BENDANT (GB) 2
75 BENEDICTE (IRE) C 21
409 BENEFFICIENT (IRE) 1
676 BENEFIQUE ROYALE (GB) 9
540 BENEFIT CUT (IRE) 3
497 BENEFITOFHINDSIGHT (GB) 2
513 BENEFITS WELL (IRE) 5
428 BENEMEADE (IRE) 10
562 BENENDEN (IRE) 1
31 BENEVOLENT (IRE) 2
628 BENGERS LASS (USA) C 19
642 BENIDORM (GB) 1
534 BENMADIGAN (IRE) 7
637 BENNACHIE (IRE) 11
102 BENNELONG (GB) 5
639 BENNY BE GOOD (GB) 6
295 BENNY BLANCO (IRE) 55
258 BENNY THE SWINGER (IRE) 2
679 BENNYS MIST (IRE) 10
454 BENNYS QUEST (IRE) 9
584 BENNYS WELL (IRE) 8
511 BENOORDENHOUT (IRE) 22
637 BENS MOOR (IRE) 12
213 BENTELIMAR (IRE) 7
444 BENTONS LAD (GB) 22
105 BENTWORTH BOY (GB) 18
473 BENVOLIO (IRE) 13
418 BENZANON (IRE) 12
502 BERBICE (IRE) 2
27 BERCHED (FR) 60
54 BEREA BORU (IRE) 4
609 BEREKA (GB) 10
106 BERGAN (GER) 50
267 BERKELEY AVENUE (IRE) 4
321 BERKELEY BARRON (IRE) 8
108 BERKELEY STREET (USA) 3
613 BERKELEY VALE (GB) 13
120 BERKSHIRE (IRE) 13
17 BERKSHIRE BEAUTY (GB) 130
476 BERKSHIRE DOWNS (GB) 4
17 BERKSHIRE HONEY (GB) 131
484 BERLUSCA (IRE) 11
393 BERMACHA (GB) 2
137 BERMONDSEY (GB) 77
624 BERMONDSEY GIRL (GB) C 37
534 BERNARDELLI (IRE) 5
39 BERRAHRI (IRE) 17
441 BERT THE ALERT (GB) 5
545 BERTHA BURNETT (IRE) 8
367 BERTIE BABY (GB) 14
680 BERTIE BLU BOY (GB) 2
598 BERTIE BOB (GB) 9
321 BERTIE BORU (IRE) 5
1 BERTIE MILAN (IRE) 5
161 BERTIE MOON (GB) 3
568 BERTIE'S DESIRE (GB) 4
306 BERTIELICIOUS (GB) 1
496 BERTIES COIN (GB) 1
25 BERTIEWHITTLE (GB) 2
376 BERWIN (IRE) 1

550 BESCOT SPRINGS (IRE) 11
488 BESSIE BLUES (GB) G 2
97 BEST BETTE (GB) 1
560 BEST BOY BARNEY (IRE) 5
452 BEST ENDEAVOUR (GB) 34
503 BEST KEPT (GB) 23
484 BEST OF ORDER (IRE) 12
6 BEST SIDE (IRE) F 58
494 BEST STEPS (IRE) 45
196 BEST TRIP (IRE) 11
211 BETHAN (GB) 5
260 BETIMES (GB) 25
492 BETT'S GIFT (GB) 66
44 BETTER CHANCE (IRE) 69
521 BETTER VALUE (IRE) 1
84 BETTY BERE (FR) 28
297 BETTY BOO (IRE) 1
148 BETTY THE THIEF (IRE) 25
225 BETTY'S PRIDE (GB) 2
247 BETWEEN ME AND YOU (IRE) 3
624 BETWEEN WICKETS (GB) 14
398 BEUVRON (FR) 11
244 BEWARE CHALK PIT (IRE) 4
493 BEWITCHMENT (GB) 11
6 BEYEH (IRE) 6
358 BEYLERBEY (USA) 3
479 BEYOND BRILLIANCE (IRE) 29
17 BEYOND CONCEIT (IRE) 5
50 BEYOND INTENSITY (IRE) 18
306 BEYONDTEMPTATION (GB) 2
6 BEZANT (FR) F 59
535 BHAKTI (IRE) 1
136 BIANCA SFORZA (GB) F 1
142 BIASCA (GB) C 13
398 BIEN PLACEE (FR) 46
563 BIFOCAL (GB) 8
44 BIG AUDIO (IRE) 10
452 BIG BAZ 2
180 BIG BONED (USA) 19
659 BIG BREAK (GB) 1
473 BIG BUCK'S (FR) 14
631 BIG CASINO (GB) 5
318 BIG CHILL (GB) 79
309 BIG DUKE (IRE) 3
321 BIG EASY (GER) 10
246 BIG FELLA THANKS (GB) 7
456 BIG FLOE (GB) 1
655 BIG GEORGE (GB) 1
310 BIG HANDS HARRY (GB) 13
152 BIG JOHN CANNON (IRE) 2
25 BIG JOHNNY D (IRE) 3
201 BIG KENNY (GB) 34
494 BIG LETTERS (IRE) 125
552 BIG MCINTOSH (GB) 13
339 BIG MIKE (IRE) 3
39 BIG MOZA (GB) 2
385 BIG NEWS (GB) 2
303 BIG NIGHT OUT (GB) 2
33 BIG ORANGE (GB) 17
28 BIG RED (GB) 16
246 BIG SOCIETY (IRE) 8
643 BIG SOUND (GB) 1
25 BIG SWIFTY (IRE) C 51
66 BIG TALK (IRE) 4
515 BIG THUNDER (GB) 4
607 BIG WATER (IRE) 3
342 BIG WAVE (IRE) 1
134 BIG WHISKEY (IRE) 1

58 **BOB THE BUTCHER** (GB) 3
606 **BOB THE GOON** (IRE) 4
513 **BOB TUCKER** (IRE) 6
637 **BOB WILL** (IRE) 15
335 **BOB'S CALL** (IRE) 5
4 **BOB'S DREAM** (IRE) 3
375 **BOB'S TICKET** (IRE) 5
93 **BOB'S WORLD** (GB) 6
321 **BOBBIE DEE** (GB) G 13
426 **BOBBIE MAGERN** (GB) 1
287 **BOBBINA** (IRE) 1
280 **BOBBISOX** (IRE) 1
679 **BOBBLE BORU** (IRE) 11
143 **BOBBY BENTON** (IRE) 12
516 **BOBBY DOVE** (GB) 1
508 **BOBBY JANE** (GB) C 22
355 **BOBBY TWO SHOES** (GB) 3
659 **BOBBY'S HEART** (IRE) 24
675 **BOBCATBILLY** (IRE) 8
470 **BOBOWEN** (IRE) 6
40 **BOBS HER UNCLE** (GB) 1
22 **BOBS LADY TAMURE** (GB) 3
607 **BOBS LORD TARA** (GB) 1
310 **BOBS WORTH** (IRE) 15
250 **BOBTAIL** (GB) 2
135 **BOCAMIX** (FR) 4
295 **BOCCA BACIATA** (IRE) 73
549 **BOCCA LUPO** (FR) 31
675 **BODEGA** (GB) 9
809 **BODY AND SOUL** (IRE) 8
397 **BODY BEAUTIFUL** (IRE) 18
27 **BOETIE'S DREAM** (IRE) 22
409 **BOG WARRIOR** (IRE) 1
398 **BOGADOR** (FR) 47
553 **BOGART** (GB) 10
205 **BOGEY HOLE** (IRE) 3
336 **BOGNOR** (USA) 16
111 **BOGSIDE** (IRE) 2
603 **BOGSNOG** (IRE) 1
184 **BOHEMIAN RHAPSODY** (IRE) 1
507 **BOIS DES AIGLES** (FR) 16
810 **BOITE** (IRE) 2
105 **BOLACHOIR** (IRE) 2
465 **BOLD ADVENTURE** (GB) 1
614 **BOLD AND FREE** (GB) 2
32 **BOLD APPEAL** (GB) 78
357a **BOLD ARIAL** 8
427 **BOLD ASSUMPTION** (GB) F 13
553 **BOLD BUNNY** (GB) C 70
523 **BOLD CAPTAIN** (GB) 39
236 **BOLD CHIEF** (GB) 6
335 **BOLD CONQUEST** (IRE) 9
41 **BOLD CROSS** (IRE) 1
619 **BOLD CUFFS** (GB) 3
41 **BOLD DUKE** (GB) 2
382 **BOLD LASS** (IRE) 16
84 **BOLD MARC** (IRE) 3
155 **BOLD MAX** (GB) 32
335 **BOLD OPTIMIST** (IRE) 10
317 **BOLD PERK** (IRE) 2
84 **BOLD PREDICTION** (IRE) 4
134 **BOLD RING** (GB) 2
138 **BOLD RUNNER** (IRE) 19
584 **BOLD SLASHER** (IRE) 11
602 **BOLD SNIPER** (GB) 5
291 **BOLD SPIRIT** (GB) 43
365 **BOLD TARA** (GB) 6
203 **BOLDWOOD** (GB) 1

44 **BOLINGBROKE** (IRE) 11
328 **BOLLIN ACROSS** (GB) 5
666 **BOLLIN FIONA** (GB) 1
190 **BOLLIN GRETA** (GB) 9
38 **BOLLIN JUDITH** (GB) 2
666 **BOLLIN JULIE** (GB) 2
131 **BOLLIN RITA** (GB) C 25
584 **BOLLIN SAM** (GB) 12
511 **BOLLYWOOD DREAM** (GB) 40
621 **BOLSENA** (USA) F 10
209 **BOMBARDIER** (GB) 3
5 **BOMBARDMENT** (USA) 65
189 **BON CHANCE** (GB) 57
398 **BON CHEVAL** (FR) 48
450 **BON PORT** (GB) 27
291 **BON VOYAGE** (GB) 44
137 **BONANZA CREEK** (IRE) 6
398 **BONBON AU MIEL** (FR) 49
651 **BONCHESTER BRIDGE** (GB) G 1
489 **BOND ARTIST** (IRE) 2
489 **BOND BABE** (GB) G 21
232 **BOND BLADE** (GB) 2
489 **BOND CLUB** (GB) 3
489 **BOND EMPIRE** (GB) 4
489 **BOND FASTRAC** (GB) 5
489 **BOND IN RIO** (GB) 17
434 **BOND PLATINUM CLUB** (GB) F 33
489 **BOND'S GIFT** (GB) 6
289 **BONDI BABE** (IRE) G 2
629 **BONDI BEACH BOY** (GB) 1
244 **BONDI MIST** (GB) 5
457 **BONDS CONQUEST** (GB) 4
9 **BONGO BEAT** (GB) 27
397 **BONJOUR BOB** (IRE) 19
445 **BONJOUR STEVE** (GB) 5
398 **BONNE MAMAN** (FR) 50
575 **BONNET'S VINO** (GB) 5
545 **BONNIE BURNETT** (IRE) 1
472 **BONNIE CHARLIE** (GB) 3
169 **BONNIE ECHO** (GB) 3
6 **BONNIE FAIRY** (GB) 49
198 **BONNIE MAJOR** (GB) 1
428 **BONNY KATE** (IRE) 12
674 **BONOBO** (IRE) 8
293 **BONZO BING** (GB) 1
144 **BOOGANGOO** (IRE) 40
560 **BOOGIE IN THE BARN** (IRE) 6
531 **BOOK AT BEDTIME** (GB) 40
54 **BOOK'EM DANNO** (IRE) 5
576 **BOOKEND** (GB) 1
596 **BOOKMAKER** (GB) 1
68 **BOOKTHEBAND** (IRE) 3
36 **BOOLAVARD KING** (IRE) 4
451 **BOOLOO** (IRE) 1
624 **BOOM AND BUST** (IRE) 2
63 **BOOM TO BUST** (IRE) 6
319 **BOOMERANG BOB** (IRE) 4
16 **BOOMSHACKERLACKER** (IRE) 6
187 **BOOMTOWN** (GB) 1
110 **BOONGA ROOGETA** (GB) 1
274 **BOOSHA** (GB) 2
678 **BOOTS AND SPURS** (GB) 2
581 **BOP ALONG** (IRE) 3
591 **BOQA** (IRE) 17
181 **BORDER BALLET** (IRE) F 20
641 **BORDER BANDIT** (USA) 1
494 **BORDER BLOOM** (GB) C 127
507 **BORDER BREAKER** (IRE) 17

59 **BORDER GUARD** (GB) 27
112 **BORDER LEGEND** (GB) 1
4 **BORDER MIST** (IRE) G 4
29 **BORDER STATION** (IRE) 1
28 **BORDERLESCOTT** (GB) 1
214 **BORDONI** (USA) 3
587 **BORGUY** (FR) 4
655 **BORIC** (GB) 2
189 **BORIS GRIGORIEV** (IRE) 10
443 **BORIS ISLAND** (GB) 121
345 **BORIS THE BLADE** (GB) 1
580 **BORIS THE BOLD** (GB) 3
17 **BORN IN BOMBAY** (GB) 54
44 **BORN SOMETHING** (IRE) C 104
481 **BORN TO BENEFIT** (IRE) 6
298 **BORN TO FLY** (IRE) 10
33 **BORN TO REIGN** (GB) 18
102 **BORN TO SURPRISE** (GB) 6
94 **BOROUGH BELLE** (GB) 19
564 **BOROUGH BOY** (IRE) 4
557 **BORUMA** (IRE) 3
428 **BOSE IKARD** (IRE) 13
458 **BOSMAN RULE** (IRE) 24
457 **BOSS IN BOOTS** (IRE) 5
109 **BOSSA NOVA BABY** (IRE) 3
281 **BOSSTIME** (IRE) 3
650 **BOSSY BECCY** (GB) 1
155 **BOSSY JANE** (GB) 5
23 **BOSTIN** (IRE) 1
100 **BOSTON BLUE** (GB) 5
458 **BOSTON BOB** (IRE) 25
433 **BOSUN BREESE** (GB) 3
297 **BOTANIST** (GB) 3
145 **BOTSWANA** (GB) 3
137 **BOUCLIER** (IRE) 7
312 **BOUGGATTI** (GB) 3
575 **BOUGGIETOPIECES** (GB) 6
383 **BOUGGLER** (GB) 3
460 **BOUILLABAISSE** (IRE) 3
503 **BOUNCING CZECH** (GB) 42
358 **BOUND COPY** (USA) 6
606 **BOUND TO FLY** (IRE) 5
562 **BOUNDS AND LEAPS** (GB) 2
575 **BOUNTIFUL BESS** (GB) 7
685 **BOUNTIFUL FOREST** (GB) 8
408 **BOUNTIFUL SIN** (GB) 16
580 **BOUNTY'S SPIRIT** (GB) 1
16 **BOUNTYBEAMADAM** (GB) 7
33 **BOURBON PRINCE** (GB) 19
15 **BOURDELLO** (GB) 3
301 **BOURGELAT** (IRE) 2
418 **BOURNE** (GB) 16
553 **BOUSATET** (FR) 11
99 **BOUSFIELD** (GB) 15
352 **BOW BELLE** (GB) 6
189 **BOW BRIDGE** (GB) C 68
358 **BOW CREEK** (IRE) 66
330 **BOW FIDDLE** (IRE) 2
443 **BOW QUEST** (GB) 11
285 **BOW SCHOOL** (IRE) 2
130 **BOWBERRY** (GB) 27
614 **BOWDLER'S MAGIC** (GB) 3
369 **BOWIE** (IRE) 2
32 **BOWIE BOY** (IRE) 22
520 **BOWMANS WELL** (IRE) 1
624 **BOWSERS BOLD** (GB) 16
9 **BOWSTAR** (GB) 3
33 **BOWSTRING** (IRE) C 20

184 **BUGSY** (GB) 3
38 **BUGSY'S GIRL** (IRE) 3
443 **BUILDING ZIET** (GB) 13
546 **BUKHARI** (FR) 129
625 **BULAS BELLE** (GB) 3
371 **BULL AND BUSH** (IRE) 9
359 **BULL MARKET** (IRE) 3
674 **BULLET STREET** (IRE) 9
295 **BULLOCK HARBOUR** (IRE) 3
634 **BULLSEYE BABE** (GB) 3
50 **BUN NA SPEIRE** (IRE) 60
86 **BUN OIR** (USA) 1
484 **BUNCE** (GB) 14
112 **BUNDITTEN** (IRE) F 59
458 **BUNDLE OF FUN** (IRE) 28
106 **BUNGLE INTHEJUNGLE** (GB) 5
291 **BUNKER** (IRE) 48
50 **BUNREACHT** (USA) 2
68 **BUNTINGFORD** (IRE) 4
479 **BUONARROTI** (IRE) 32
429 **BURANO** (IRE) 4
358 **BUREAU** (IRE) 69
279 **BUREDYMA** (GB) 31
638 **BURGOYNE** (USA) 7
443 **BURLINGTON BERTIE** (IRE) 14
638 **BURMA BEACH** (GER) 8
646 **BURMESE BREEZE** (GB) 21
295 **BURN AND TURN** (IRE) 4
397 **BURN THE BOATS** (IRE) 2
104 **BURNER** (IRE) 42
40 **BURNESTON** (GB) 22
450 **BURNHAM** (GB) 6
166 **BURNHOPE** (GB) 2
553 **BURNING BLAZE** (GB) 12
199 **BURNING THREAD** (IRE) 5
375 **BURNS NIGHT** (GB) 8
20 **BURNSWOOD** (IRE) 2
52 **BURNT CREAM** (GB) 2
434 **BURNT FINGERS** (IRE) 1
187 **BURNTHILL** (IRE) 2
190 **BURREN VIEW LADY** (IRE) 10
486 **BURTON PORT** (IRE) 10
180 **BURWAAZ** (GB) 3
473 **BURY PARADE** (IRE) 21
358 **BUSATTO** (USA) 8
68 **BUSH BEAUTY** (IRE) 17
68 **BUSH BRANCH** (IRE) 18
659 **BUSH PILOT** (IRE) 26
193 **BUSH WARRIOR** (IRE) 5
645 **BUSHCRAFT** (IRE) 15
214 **BUSHEL** (USA) 5
645 **BUSHEPHALUS** (IRE) 45
27 **BUSHIDO** (FR) 23
25 **BUSHTIGER** (IRE) 52
211 **BUSHY GLADE** (IRE) 20
116 **BUSINESS BAY** (USA) 1
85 **BUSINESSMONEY JUDI** (GB) 1
201 **BUSSA** (GB) 4
443 **BUSTER BROWN** (IRE) 15
5 **BUSTOPHER** (USA) 8
428 **BUSTY BROWN** (IRE) 14
35 **BUSY BIMBO** (GB) 3
214 **BUTHELEZI** (USA) 6
295 **BUTTERFLY DANCER** (IRE) 58
17 **BUTTERFLY MCQUEEN** (USA) 7
104 **BUTTON DOWN** (IRE) 17
587 **BUXOM** (IRE) 6
343 **BUXTON** (GB) 1

336 **BUY OUT BOY** (GB) 17
674 **BUYWISE** (IRE) 10
84 **BUZZ LAW** (IRE) 5
584 **BUZZARD FLIGHT** (GB) 14
33 **BY JUPITER** (GB) 5
13 **BY THE BOARDWALK** (IRE) 10
479 **BYE BYE BIRDIE** (IRE) 33
356 **BYGONES FOR COINS** (IRE) 3
424 **BYGONES OF BRID** (IRE) 2
507 **BYGONES SOVEREIGN** (IRE) 20
65 **BYRD IN HAND** (IRE) 1
138 **BYRON AGAIN** (GB) 3
53 **BYRON GALA** (GB) 37
483 **BYRON'S DREAM** (GB) 2
160 **BYRON'S GOLD** (GB) 8
403 **BYRONESS** (GB) 2
675 **C J MACKINTOSH** (GB) 11
259 **C'EST MA SOUER** (IRE) 1
206 **CA LE FERRA** (FR) 6
135 **CABAL** (GB) 5
485 **CABARET GIRL** (GB) 4
172 **CABARETUNE** (FR) 2
443 **CABIMAS** (GB) 16
32 **CABIN FEVER** (GB) 23
478 **CABLE** (USA) C 50
318 **CABLE BAY** (IRE) 21
434 **CABLE CAR** (GB) 19
507 **CABORA** (FR) 21
201 **CABUCHON** (GB) 5
50 **CACHE CREEK** (IRE) C 61
112 **CACTUS VALLEY** (IRE) 2
497 **CADEAU GEORGE** (GB) 3
166 **CADEAUX PEARL** (GB) 3
68 **CADEAUX POWER** (GB) 19
571 **CADGERS HOLE** (GB) 5
181 **CADMIUM** (GB) 8
328 **CADMIUM LOCH** (GB) 6
476 **CADORE** (IRE) 5
394 **CADOUDOFF** (FR) 5
458 **CADSPEED** (FR) 29
492 **CAERIBLAND** (IRE) C 16
167 **CAERLAVEROCK** (IRE) 8
100 **CAERWYN** (GB) 7
564 **CAESARS GIFT** (IRE) 28
638 **CAFE AU LAIT** (GER) 9
572 **CAFE SOCIETY** (FR) 5
120 **CAFETIERE** (GB) 14
27 **CAGOULE** (GB) 24
472 **CAHAL** (IRE) 81
335 **CAHERONAUN** (IRE) 12
491 **CAI SHEN** (IRE) 2
473 **CAID DU BERLAIS** (FR) 22
295 **CAILIN ANNAMH** (IRE) 5
492 **CAILINI ALAINN** (IRE) 17
50 **CAILIUIL** (IRE) 62
213 **CAIM HILL** (IRE) 5
507 **CAITLIN ROSE** (IRE) G 22
267 **CAITYS JOY** (GB) 8
494 **CAJA** (IRE) 49
358 **CAKESTOWN LADY** (IRE) C 151
486 **CALAF** (GB) 11
602 **CALAKANGA** (IRE) C 90
32 **CALAMITY JANE** (GB) 24
9 **CALANDO** (USA) C 114
418 **CALCON** (IRE) 18
523 **CALCULATED RISK** (GB) 4
508 **CALCULATOR** (FR) 23
203 **CALDERCRUIX** (USA) 3

464 **CALDEW LAD** (IRE) 3
256 **CALDEY** (GB) 1
636 **CALDY DANCER** (IRE) F 20
254 **CALEDONIA** (GB) 4
336 **CALEDONIA LADY** (GB) 3
336 **CALEDONIA LAIRD** (GB) 18
418 **CALENDULA** (GB) G 19
659 **CALIBRATE** (GB) 2
260 **CALIFORNIA** (IRE) 109
318 **CALIMA BREEZE** (GB) 80
473 **CALIPTO** (FR) 23
103 **CALL A TRUCE** (IRE) 5
679 **CALL CARLO** (GB) 14
339 **CALL HIM SOMETHING** (IRE) 4
375 **CALL IT ON** (GB) 9
478 **CALL MARIAH** (USA) C 51
505 **CALL ME EMMA** (IRE) 3
145 **CALL ME KATE** (GB) 7
639 **CALL ME MULLIGAN** (GB) 2
638 **CALL ME NUMBER ONE** (GER) 47
246 **CALL ME VIC** (IRE) 9
557 **CALL OF DUTY** (GB) 5
448 **CALL ROG** (IRE) 7
310 **CALL THE COPS** (IRE) 17
290 **CALL THE DETECTIVE** (IRE) 5
553 **CALLANISH** (GB) C 71
295 **CALLHERWHATULIKE** (IRE) F 6
281 **CALLISTAN** (IRE) 33
590 **CALLISTO LIGHT** (IRE) 2
276 **CALM ATTITUDE** (IRE) 2
349 **CALRISSIAN** (IRE) 14
563 **CALTON ENTRY** (IRE) 2
321 **CALUSA STAR** (GB) 16
626 **CAMACHE QUEEN** (IRE) 1
53 **CAMACHOICE** (IRE) 1
32 **CAMAGUEYANA** (GB) 80
281 **CAMAKASI** (IRE) 34
300 **CAMANCHE GREY** (IRE) 16
546 **CAMARETZ** (USA) 2
169 **CAMATINI** (IRE) 22
564 **CAMBARA** (GB) F 38
260 **CAMBORNE** (GB) 2
318 **CAMBRIDGE** (GB) 22
99 **CAMBRIDGE BEE** (GB) 2
568 **CAMDEN** (IRE) 5
584 **CAMDEN GEORGE** (IRE) 15
615 **CAMDEN VINE** (GB) 4
598 **CAME BACK** (IRE) 8
556 **CAMELEY DAWN** (GB) 10
121 **CAMELOPARDALIS** (GB) 1
291 **CAMEO TIARA** (IRE) 49
446 **CAMERA SHY** (IRE) 2
635 **CAMERON HIGHLAND** (IRE) 4
217 **CAMEROONEY** (GB) 3
241 **CAMINEL** (GB) 23
587 **CAMINERO** (IRE) 7
260 **CAMLANN** (IRE) 29
51 **CAMONDO** (IRE) 10
279 **CAMP RIVERSIDE** (USA) F 88
129 **CAMPANNELLO** (GB) F 2
148 **CAMPBELLITE** (GB) F 53
64 **CAMPBONNAIS** (FR) 2
271 **CAMPIGLIA** (FR) F 12
693 **CAMPTOWN LADY** (GB) 4
189 **CAN YOU CONGA** (GB) 11
553 **CAN YOU REVERSE** (GB) 72
572 **CAN'T CHANGE IT** (IRE) 29
106 **CANADIAN CAPERS** (GB) C 103

366 **CASH IN HAND** (IRE) 4
691 **CASH INJECTION** (GB) 3
389 **CASH IS KING** (GB) 2
201 **CASHEL DANCER** (GB) F 54
589 **CASHEL'S MISSILE** (IRE) 5
638 **CASHMERE CAT** (IRE) 10
358 **CASILA** (IRE) 153
213 **CASINO MARKETS** (IRE) 9
572 **CASPAR NETSCHER** (GB) 6
35 **CASPER LEE** (IRE) 21
100 **CASPIAN PRINCE** (IRE) 9
291 **CASSAVA** (IRE) C 175
409 **CASSELLS ROCK** (IRE) 5
497 **CASSIE** (GB) 4
478 **CASSIS** (USA) F 52
346 **CAST IRON CASEY** (IRE) 1
118 **CASTAGNA GIRL** (GB) 9
27 **CASTAGNOU** (IRE) 25
693 **CASTANUM** (IRE) 5
644 **CASTARNIE** (GB) 6
572 **CASTILO DEL DIABLO** (IRE) 7
365 **CASTING IN PARIS** (IRE) 39
624 **CASTLE CHEETAH** (IRE) 7
145 **CASTLE COMBE** (IRE) 17
612 **CASTLE CONFLICT** (IRE) 9
281 **CASTLE EDEN** (IRE) 1
492 **CASTLE GUEST** (IRE) 4
406 **CASTLE OF ARGH** (USA) 1
550 **CASTLE WINGS** (IRE) 3
23 **CASTLELAWN** (IRE) 16
693 **CASTLEMORRIS KING** (GB) 2
16 **CASTLETOWN** (IRE) 6
639 **CASTORIENTA** (GB) 37
17 **CASUAL CAVALIER** (IRE) 8
39 **CASUAL GLANCE** (GB) C 133
17 **CASUAL MOVER** (IRE) 3
5 **CASUAL SMILE** (GB) 56
538 **CAT O'MOUNTAIN** (USA) 10
112 **CAT SIX** (USA) 1
118 **CATADUPA** (GB) 19
460 **CATAKANTA** (GB) 17
463 **CATALAUNIAN FIELDS** (IRE) 6
598 **CATALINAS DIAMOND** (IRE) 2
624 **CATALYZE** (GB) 9
438 **CATARIA GIRL** (USA) 5
412 **CATCH THE KATT** (GB) 2
249 **CATCHAROSE** (IRE) 1
486 **CATCHER STAR** (IRE) 5
235 **CATCHING ON** (IRE) 14
550 **CATCHING ZEDS** (GB) 1
531 **CATCHTHEMOONLIGHT** (GB) 17
305 **CATEGORICAL** (GB) 5
159 **CATFLAP** (GB) 1
393 **CATHEDRAL** (GB) 2
505 **CATIVO CAVALLINO** (GB) 3
573 **CATKIN COPSE** (GB) 4
260 **CATWALK BABE** (GB) 10
431 **CAUCUS** (GB) 3
1 **CAUGHT BY WITNESS** (IRE) 3
303 **CAUGHT IN THE ACT** (IRE) 8
383 **CAUGHT INTHE LIGHT** (GB) 3
318 **CAULFIELDS VENTURE** (IRE) 8
553 **CAUSE CELEBRE** (IRE) F 25
280 **CAUSEWAY CHARM** (USA) F 74
609 **CAUSEWAY KING** (USA) 3
624 **CAUSEWAY QUEEN** (IRE) F 48
375 **CAVALEIRO** (GB) 6
    CAVALIERI (IRE) 10

25 **CAVALLO BELLA** (GB) 31
419 **CAVALRY GUARD** (USA) 1
44 **CAVALRYMAN** (GB) 12
85 **CAVITE ALPHA** (IRE) 2
464 **CAVITE ETA** (IRE) 4
527 **CAWDOR HOUSE BERT** (GB) 2
291 **CAY DANCER** (GB) 52
429 **CAYMAN CRY** (USA) 31
214 **CAYMAN ISLANDS** (GB) 7
602 **CAYMAN SUNRISE** (GB) C 92
44 **CAYMANS** (AUS) 13
358 **CAYSUE** (GB) G 70
636 **CAYTON BAY** (GB) 21
355 **CAYUGA** (GB) 4
473 **CEASAR MILAN** (GB) 25
609 **CEASELESS** (IRE) 49
281 **CEBUANO** (GB) 5
643 **CEDAR GLORY** (GB) 3
473 **CEDRE BLEU** (FR) 26
499 **CEELO** (GB) 2
637 **CEEVEE** (GB) 18
33 **CEFIRA** (USA) F 22
1 **CEILIDH** (IRE) 9
50 **CEISTEACH** (IRE) 19
503 **CELEBRATORY** (GB) 25
280 **CELEBRIAN** (GB) 4
295 **CELESTE** (GB) F 74
376 **CELESTIAL BAY** (GB) 3
663 **CELESTIAL DAWN** (GB) 4
591 **CELESTIAL FABLE** (IRE) 18
209 **CELESTIAL FIRE** (GB) 56
473 **CELESTIAL HALO** (IRE) 27
238 **CELESTIAL ISLAND** (GB) 3
209 **CELESTIAL KNIGHT** (GB) 26
511 **CELESTIAL MAGIC** (GB) 41
515 **CELESTIAL PATH** (IRE) 42
427 **CELESTIAL PRINCESS** (GB) C 14
354 **CELESTIAL RAY** (GB) 1
211 **CELESTINE ABBEY** (GB) 25
172 **CELTIC CELEB** (IRE) 3
504 **CELTIC CHARLIE** (IRE) 3
284 **CELTIC FELLA** (IRE) 4
461 **CELTIC LEGACY** (GB) 1
646 **CELTIC LYNN** (IRE) F 41
369 **CELTIC SIXPENCE** (GB) 1
648 **CELTS ESPERE** (IRE) 1
645 **CENSORIUS** (GB) 16
507 **CENTASIA** (GB) 23
572 **CENTIME** (GB) F 61
587 **CENTORIA** (IRE) 2
650 **CENTRAL FLAME** (GB) 2
395 **CENTRAL SCHOOL** (IRE) 1
25 **CENTRE HAAFHD** (GB) 32
53 **CENTURIUS** (GB) 2
479 **CENTURY** (IRE) 35
505 **CEOPERK** (GB) F 5
534 **CERISE DE TOTES** (FR) G 12
513 **CERTAVI** (GB) 2
281 **CERTERACH** (IRE) 6
546 **CERTES** 131
635 **CERTIFICATE** (GB) 42
214 **CERTIFICATION** (IRE) 8
5 **CERTIFY** (USA) 11
546 **CERTITUDE** (IRE) 40
259 **CEST NOTRE GRIS** (IRE) 2
278 **CHABLIS** (FR) 2
31 **CHAC DU CADRAN** (FR) 3
187 **CHADFORD** (GB) 3

394 **CHAIN OF BEACONS** (GB) 6
94 **CHAIN OF DAISIES** (GB) 41
672 **CHAIN OF EVENTS** (GB) 2
267 **CHALK IT DOWN** (IRE) 10
51 **CHAMEUR** (FR) 11
550 **CHAMPAGNE AGENT** (IRE) 18
486 **CHAMPAGNE AT TARA** (GB) 15
458 **CHAMPAGNE FEVER** (IRE) 30
637 **CHAMPAGNE LIL** (GB) G 19
391 **CHAMPAGNE LOU LOU** (GB) F 1
407 **CHAMPAGNE N CAVIAR** (IRE) 6
139 **CHAMPAGNE RIAN** (IRE) 12
654 **CHAMPAGNE RULES** (GB) 5
291 **CHAMPAGNE SYDNEY** (IRE) 53
321 **CHAMPAGNE WEST** (IRE) 19
365 **CHAMPION COURT** (IRE) 8
260 **CHAMPION PLACE** (GB) C 110
291 **CHAMPIONSHIP** (IRE) 54
428 **CHAMPOLEON** (FR) 15
53 **CHAMPS D'OR** (GB) 40
321 **CHANCE DU ROY** (IRE) 20
46 **CHANCE ENCOUNTER** (IRE) 1
552 **CHANCE FOR ROMANCE** (GB) C 14
677 **CHANCE TAKEN** (GB) 2
546 **CHANCELIER** (FR) 3
615 **CHANCEOFA LIFETIME** (IRE) 5
484 **CHANCERY** (USA) 17
367 **CHANCEUSE** (GB) 16
428 **CHANCOL** (FR) 16
592 **CHANDLER BING** (GB) 1
616 **CHANDOS** (IRE) 3
393 **CHANDRAYAAN** (GB) 4
527 **CHANGING LANES** (GB) 3
470 **CHANGING THE GUARD** (GB) 7
152 **CHANKILLO** (GB) 4
331 **CHANSON DE MARINS** (FR) 14
177 **CHANT** (IRE) 1
380 **CHANT DE SABLE** (IRE) 15
332 **CHANTARA ROSE** (GB) 3
635 **CHANTER** (GB) C 112
104 **CHANTREA** (IRE) 18
602 **CHAPEL CHOIR** (GB) 93
678 **CHAPEL CORNER** (IRE) C 43
294 **CHAPEL HOUSE** (GB) 1
595 **CHAPELLE DU ROI** (USA) 2
277 **CHAPELLERIE** (IRE) 6
316 **CHAPOLIMOSS** (FR) 2
503 **CHAPPARACHIK** (GB) 43
462 **CHAPTER AND VERSE** (IRE) 5
675 **CHAPTER FIVE** (GB) 12
678 **CHAPTER SEVEN** (GB) 3
397 **CHAPTER SEVEN** (GB) 3
13 **CHARINGWORTH** (IRE) 11
53 **CHARITY LINE** (IRE) 3
277 **CHARLEMAGNE DIVA** (GB) 7
376 **CHARLES CAMOIN** (IRE) 4
444 **CHARLES DE MILLE** (GB) 3
94 **CHARLES MOLSON** (GB) 20
272 **CHARLES PARNELL** (GB) 2
480 **CHARLEY FOX** (GB) 2
504 **CHARLEYS ANGEL** (GB) 16
666 **CHARLIE BUCKET** (GB) 3
443 **CHARLIE CHEESECAKE** (IRE) 17
279 **CHARLIE GIRL** (GB) C 89
669 **CHARLIE RUFFLES** (IRE) 2
573 **CHARLIE'S OSCAR** (IRE) 1
357a **CHARLIE WELLS** (IRE) 9
39 **CHARLIES MATE** (GB) 18

220 **CLAPPERBOARD** (GB) 8
269 **CLARA PEGGOTTY** (GB) 3
620 **CLARAGH NATIVE** (IRE) 5
632 **CLARATY** (GB) 2
496 **CLARE HOGAN** (IRE) G 3
196 **CLARENCE BEEKS** (IRE) 15
383 **CLARET CLOAK** (IRE) 9
180 **CLARIETTA** (GB) F 57
546 **CLARINDA** (FR) C 133
426 **CLARION CALL** (GB) 5
544 **CLARIOR EX OBSCURO** (IRE) 1
380 **CLARMINA** (GB) 61
632 **CLARY** (IRE) 3
613 **CLASSIC ART** (GB) 3
138 **CLASSIC CASE** (IRE) 4
5 **CLASSIC DEVOTION** (USA) 68
398 **CLASSIC DIVA** (GER) 12
187 **CLASSIC FANTASY** (GB) G 5
183 **CLASSIC HART** (GB) 10
511 **CLASSIC MISSION** (GB) 23
418 **CLASSIC MOVE** (IRE) 21
655 **CLASSIC ORANGE** (GB) 3
119 **CLASSIC PEARL** (GB) 1
199 **CLASSIC PUNCH** (IRE) 3
296 **CLASSIC PURSUIT** (GB) 28
680 **CLASSIC QUARTET** (GB) G 4
351 **CLASSIC RALLY** (GB) 5
262 **CLASSIC STATEMENT** (IRE) 12
609 **CLASSIC WEST** (USA) F 50
635 **CLASSICAL ART** (IRE) 43
99 **CLASSICAL DIVA** (GB) 16
348 **CLASSY CHASSIS** (IRE) 2
449 **CLASSY TRICK** (USA) 3
665 **CLAUDE CARTER** (GB) 4
140 **CLAUDE GREENWOOD** (GB) 3
172a **CLAUDE MONET** (BRZ) 2
553 **CLAYTON** (GB) 17
5 **CLEAN LIVING** (GB) 69
513 **CLEAR FOCUS** (IRE) 52
333 **CLEAR HILLS** (IRE) 4
589 **CLEAR LOCH** (GB) 6
240 **CLEAR MIX** (GB) 4
172a **CLEAR PRAISE** (USA) 2
645 **CLEAR SPELL** (IRE) 19
589 **CLEAR SPRING** (IRE) 7
68 **CLEARED TO GO** (GB) 24
56 **CLEARING** (GB) 2
327 **CLEETONS TURN** (GB) 5
263 **CLEEVE CLOUD** (IRE) 1
487 **CLEMENT** (IRE) 4
104 **CLEPSYDRA** (GB) C 43
350 **CLERK'S CHOICE** (IRE) 2
375 **CLEVE COTTAGE** (GB) 12
474 **CLEVER COOKIE** (GB) 5
148 **CLEVER MILLIE** (USA) F 55
417 **CLEVER MISS** (GB) 20
493 **CLICHE** (IRE) F 26
550 **CLIFF LANE** (IRE) 19
664 **CLIFFORDS REPRIEVE** (GB) 2
334 **CLIFTON MIST** (GB) F 2
564 **CLIMAXFORTACKLE** (IRE) 6
408 **CLINCHER CLUB** (GB) F 23
589 **CLINGING VINE** (USA) F 27
546 **CLISHET** 134
189 **CLOCK ON TOM** (GB) 13
599 **CLOCK OPERA** (IRE) 1
171 **CLOCKMAKER** (IRE) 4
429 **CLODOALDO** (IRE) 32

479 **CLODORA** (FR) C 107
609 **CLODOVIL DOLL** (IRE) 51
44 **CLON BRULEE** (IRE) 14
207 **CLONALIG HOUSE** (IRE) 7
458 **CLONARD LAD** (IRE) 33
7 **CLONDALEE** (IRE) G 1
310 **CLONDAW BANKER** (IRE) 24
458 **CLONDAW COURT** (IRE) 34
418 **CLONDAW DRAFT** (IRE) 22
290 **CLONDAW FARMER** (IRE) 6
550 **CLONDAW FLICKA** (IRE) 20
418 **CLONDAW HERO** (IRE) 23
418 **CLONDAW KAEMPFER** (IRE) 24
550 **CLONDAW KNIGHT** (IRE) 21
253 **CLONEA POWER** (IRE) 1
25 **CLONEDEN** (IRE) C 53
354 **CLONUSKER** (IRE) 2
507 **CLOSE HOUSE** (GB) 26
310 **CLOSE TOUCH** (GB) 25
546 **CLOSER TO HOME** (IRE) 135
352 **CLOSEST FRIEND** (GB) 9
383 **CLOSING CEREMONY** (IRE) 10
139 **CLOUD BROOK** (IRE) 15
609 **CLOUD CASTLE** (GB) F 15
321 **CLOUD CREEPER** (IRE) 22
279 **CLOUD LINE** (GB) 32
620 **CLOUD MONKEY** (IRE) 6
646 **CLOUD SEVEN** (GB) 42
486 **CLOUDANTE** (IRE) 25
486 **CLOUDINGSTAR** (IRE) 17
313 **CLOUDS OF GLORY** (GB) 8
260 **CLOUDSCAPE** (IRE) 30
463 **CLOUDY BOB** (IRE) 3
486 **CLOUDY COPPER** (IRE) 18
584 **CLOUDY DAWN** (IRE) 9
620 **CLOUDY DEAL** (IRE) 7
418 **CLOUDY JOKER** (IRE) 26
364 **CLOUDY LADY** (GB) 4
191 **CLOUDY SMITH** (IRE) 1
328 **CLOUDY SPIRIT** (GB) 7
362 **CLOUDY START** (GB) 3
584 **CLOUDY TOO** (IRE) 18
358 **CLOVERDALE** (GB) 9
122 **CLOVERHILL LAD** (IRE) 2
112 **CLOWANCE** (GB) C 60
112 **CLOWANCE ESTATE** (IRE) 4
51 **CLOWN** (IRE) 22
435 **CLUB HOUSE** (IRE) 3
50 **CLUB WEXFORD** (IRE) 20
55 **CLUBLAND** (IRE) 2
486 **CLUES AND ARROWS** (IRE) 19
75 **CLUMBER STREET** (GB) 9
383 **CLYFFE DANCER** (GB) 11
674 **CLYNE** (GB) 16
528 **CNOC MOY** (IRE) 1
311 **CNOC SEODA** (IRE) 7
479 **COACH HOUSE** (IRE) 36
183 **COACH MONTANA** (IRE) 1
298 **COALBURN** (GB) 2
450 **COASTAL STORM** (GB) 31
330 **COAX** (GB) 1
426 **COCACOBANA** (IRE) 6
103 **COCHINILLO** (IRE) 6
58 **COCK OF THE ROCK** (IRE) 5
397 **COCKALEEKIE** (USA) C 48
538 **COCKNEY CLASS** (USA) 3
523 **COCKNEY SPARROW** (GB) 7
310 **COCKTAILS AT DAWN** (GB) 26

568 **COCO SHAMBHALA** (GB) 8
207 **COCOA'S PRINCESS** (GB) 56
478 **COCONELL** (GB) 1
628 **COCONUT KISSES** (GB) 1
44 **CODE OF HONOUR** (GB) 15
602 **CODENAME** (GB) F 95
403 **CODY WYOMING** (GB) 3
398 **COELHO** (FR) 13
486 **COFFEE** (IRE) 20
684 **COFFEE KING** (IRE) 1
540 **COFFERS** (GB) 5
631 **COGRY** (GB) 14
395 **COILLTE CAILIN** (IRE) 2
484 **COIN BROKER** (IRE) 70
506 **COIN OF THE REALM** (IRE) 1
11 **COINCIDENTLY** (GB) 2
626 **COISTE BODHAR** (IRE) 9
291 **COLD COLD WOMAN** (GB) C 179
335 **COLDABRI** (IRE) G 16
380 **COLDSTONE** (FR) 62
267 **COLE HARDEN** (IRE) 12
540 **COLEBROOKE** (GB) 6
631 **COLIN'S BROTHER** (GB) 15
110 **COLINCA'S LAD** (IRE) 2
17 **COLLABORATION** (GB) 59
573 **COLLEEN BAWN** (FR) 12
183 **COLLEGE DOLL** (GB) 2
209 **COLLIDER** (GB) 57
243 **COLLINGBOURNEDUCIS** (IRE) 2
140 **COLLODI** (GER) 4
169 **COLLOSIUM** (IRE) 34
26 **COLLS CORNER** (IRE) 1
572 **COLONEL ALI** (GB) 31
214 **COLONEL IAIN** (GB) 10
25 **COLONEL MAK** (GB) 4
260 **COLORADO DAWN** (GB) C 111
425 **COLOUR MY WORLD** (GB) 4
190 **COLOUR OF THE WIND** (GB) 65
321 **COLOUR SQUADRON** (IRE) 23
59 **COLOURBEARER** (IRE) 2
104 **COLOURFUL** (GB) 19
564 **COLOURPOINT** (USA) F 40
318 **COLUMBIAN ROULETTE** (GB) 27
136 **COMADOIR** (IRE) 3
17 **COMANCHERO** (IRE) 60
618 **COMBAT JET** (GB) 1
308 **COMBINATION** (FR) 16
572 **COMBUST** (USA) C 62
395 **COMBUSTIBLE** (IRE) 3
369 **COMBUSTIBLE KATE** (IRE) 4
457 **COMBUSTIBLE LADY** (IRE) 7
291 **COME APRIL** (GB) C 180
182 **COME ON ANNIE** (GB) 3
142 **COME ON BLUE CHIP** (IRE) 1
280 **COME ON HARRIET** (GB) 5
316 **COME ON LAURIE** (IRE) 3
280 **COME ON LILA** (GB) 26
297 **COME ON LULU** (GB) 22
196 **COME ON SUNSHINE** (GB) 96
584 **COMEBACK COLIN** (GB) 19
587 **COMEDINEWITHME** (GB) 9
402 **COMEDY HOUSE** (GB) 2
137 **COMEDY KING** (IRE) 38
527 **COMEHOMEQUIETLY** (IRE) 4
258 **COMEONGINGER** (IRE) 5
218 **COMERAGH KING** (GB) 2
455 **COMETOGRAPHY** (IRE) 2
102 **COMFORT AND JOY** (IRE) 7

383 **COURT IN MOTION** (IRE) 15
365 **COURT IN SESSION** (IRE) 9
674 **COURT MINSTREL** (IRE) 18
639 **COURT RED** (IRE) 10
600 **COURT RISE** (IRE) 2
383 **COURT VICTORY** (IRE) 16
310 **COURTESY CALL** (IRE) 28
544 **COURTLY CONDUCT** (IRE) 2
375 **COURTOWN OSCAR** (IRE) 14
335 **COUSIN BILL** (IRE) 7
424 **COUSIN GUILLAUME** (FR) 4
450 **COUSIN KHEE** (GB) 8
109 **COUVERTURE** (USA) C 37
249 **COVE** (IRE) 7
379 **COVENANT** (GB) 14
635 **COVER LOOK** (SAF) F 113
473 **COWARDS CLOSE** (IRE) 29
519 **COWBRIDGE** (IRE) 1
444 **COWSLIP** (GB) 5
32 **COY** (IRE) C 85
365 **COYABA** (GB) 10
491 **COZZENE'S PRIDE** (USA) C 36
190 **CRACKENTORP** (GB) 15
32 **CRACKER** (GB) 86
15 **CRACKERJACK** (GB) 5
550 **CRACKERJACK LAD** (IRE) 22
460 **CRACKING CHAP** (IRE) 8
180 **CRADLE OF LIFE** (IRE) 22
358 **CRAFTED** (IRE) 73
193 **CRAFTSMANSHIP** (FR) 6
378 **CRAFTY EXIT** (GB) 24
280 **CRAFTY ROBERTO** (GB) 6
358 **CRAFTY SPELL** (GB) 74
355 **CRAFTYBIRD** (GB) 10
643 **CRAGGAKNOCK** (GB) 25
50 **CRAIC AGUS SPRAOI** (IRE) 24
556 **CRAIC SA CEILI** (IRE) F 15
173 **CRAIGANEE** (IRE) 5
675 **CRAIGLANDS** (IRE) 17
692 **CRAIGS DREAM** (IRE) 2
607 **CRAKEHALL LAD** (IRE) 37
468 **CRANKY CORNER** (GB) 1
38 **CRANNAGHMORE BOY** (IRE) 4
159 **CRAVAT** (GB) 3
106 **CRAZEE DIAMOND** (GB) 54
66 **CRAZY** (GER) 5
295 **CRAZY ABOUT YOU** (IRE) F 75
172 **CRAZY CAT** (FR) 17
189 **CRAZY CHESTER** (IRE) 15
53 **CRAZY CHIC** (IRE) 42
269 **CRAZY JANE** (IRE) 4
479 **CRAZY VOLUME** (IRE) C 108
50 **CREAKY VOICE** (IRE) 63
42 **CREAM OF SOCIETY** (IRE) G 2
349 **CREAM TEASE** (GB) F 16
394 **CREDIT FOR LIFE** (IRE) 7
672 **CREDIT SWAP** (GB) 9
365 **CREEPY** (IRE) 11
490 **CRESCENT BEACH** (IRE) 1
494 **CRESSELIA** (FR) 50
332 **CRESSWELL WILLOW** (IRE) F 6
640 **CRESTA ONE** (GB) 6
11 **CRESTA RISE** (GB) 13
678 **CREW CUT** (IRE) 7
546 **CRICKEL WOOD** (FR) 5
291 **CRICKLEWOOD GREEN** (USA) 60
691 **CRIDDA BOY** (GB) 5
556 **CRIMSON FERN** (IRE) C 16

429 **CRIMSON KNIGHT** (GB) 7
318 **CRINOLETTE** (IRE) F 85
207 **CRISIS AVERTED** (IRE) 57
546 **CRISOLLES** (FR) 41
397 **CRISTAL FASHION** (IRE) 22
260 **CRITERIA** (IRE) 31
429 **CRITICAL RISK** (IRE) 79
379 **CRIUS** (IRE) 1
8 **CROCO BAY** (IRE) 1
242 **CROCO MISTER** (IRE) 3
247 **CROCON SI** (IRE) 6
589 **CROESO MAWR** (GB) 2
434 **CROFTERS CEILIDH** (GB) F 34
165 **CROFTON ARCH** (GB) 2
165 **CROFTON LANE** (GB) 1
36 **CROGHILL TUPPENCE** (IRE) 8
591 **CROI AN OR** (IRE) 6
217 **CROOKED ARROW** (IRE) 4
103 **CROOKSTOWN** (IRE) 7
486 **CROPLEY** (IRE) 21
159 **CROQUEMBOUCHE** (IRE) 4
428 **CROSS APPEAL** (IRE) 20
137 **CROSS COUNTRY** (IRE) 40
180 **CROSS CURRENT** (GB) C 58
93 **CROSS KENNON** (IRE) 9
394 **CROSS OF HONOUR** (IRE) 8
32 **CROSS YOUR FINGERS** (IRE) 3
492 **CROSSANDRA** (IRE) 69
376 **CROSSHARE** (GB) 15
489 **CROSSLEY** (GB) 7
358 **CROSSOVER** (GB) F 155
494 **CROSSTALK** (GB) 51
459 **CROUCHING HARRY** (IRE) 3
45 **CROWCOMBE PARK** (GB) 2
139 **CROWD CONTROL** (IRE) 16
358 **CROWDMANIA** (GB) 75
148 **CROWLEY'S LAW** (GB) 29
630 **CROWN AND GLORY** (IRE) 2
483 **CROWN CHOICE** (GB) 3
68 **CROWN PLEASURE** (IRE) 25
531 **CROWNING JEWEL** (GB) 8
351 **CROXTON KERRIAL** (GB) 7
130 **CROZON** (GB) F 66
476 **CRUACHAN** (IRE) 6
82 **CRUCHAIN** (IRE) 1
379 **CRUCIBLE** (GB) 7
106 **CRUCK REALTA** (GB) 9
358 **CRUEL SEA** (USA) C 156
50 **CRUIDIN** (IRE) 64
180 **CRUINN A BHORD** (GB) F 23
427 **CRUINN A BHORD** (GB) C 18
178 **CRUINNEAS** (IRE) 1
45 **CRUISE IN STYLE** (IRE) 3
296 **CRUISE LINE** (GB) C 40
54 **CRUISING BYE** (GB) 8
351 **CRUSHED ICE** (GB) 8
443 **CRUZ ON TED** (GB) 21
452 **CRY FREEDOM** (IRE) 16
443 **CRY FURY** (GB) 7
5 **CRY JOY** (USA) 71
494 **CRYING SHAME** (USA) 4
619 **CRYSTAL BALLERINA** (IRE) G 6
358 **CRYSTAL BULL** (USA) F 157
579 **CRYSTAL CLICHE** (GB) 1
318 **CRYSTAL CROSSING** (IRE) F 86
552 **CRYSTAL GALE** (IRE) F 15
32 **CRYSTAL LAKE** (IRE) 28
291 **CRYSTAL MALT** (IRE) 183

279 **CRYSTAL MOMENTS** (GB) F 90
553 **CRYSTAL MOUNTAIN** (USA) F 76
382 **CRYSTAL MUSIC** (USA) F 17
291 **CRYSTAL NYMPH** (IRE) 61
622 **CRYSTAL PEARL** (GB) 14
17 **CRYSTAL REEF** (GB) C 136
279 **CRYSTAL SWAN** (IRE) C 91
505 **CRYSTAL SWING** (GB) 5
318 **CRYSTAL VALKYRIE** (IRE) F 87
602 **CRYSTAL ZVEZDA** (GB) 96
344 **CRYSTALIZED** (IRE) 31
402 **CTAPPERS** (GB) 3
671 **CUBAN PIECE** (IRE) 1
32 **CUBANITA** (GB) 4
431 **CUBISM** (GB) 4
619 **CUE CARD** (GB) 7
511 **CUECA** (FR) 25
42 **CUMBRIAN FARMER** (GB) 3
50 **CUNEIFORM** (IRE) 65
511 **CUNNING ACT** (GB) 4
692 **CUNNING PLAN** (IRE) 3
310 **CUP FINAL** (IRE) 29
572 **CURBYOURENTHUSIASM** (IRE) 32
515 **CURIOUS MIND** (GB) 5
173 **CURLEW** (GB) 6
428 **CURLEY BILL** (IRE) 21
247 **CURRACLOE ROSE** (IRE) F 7
88 **CURRAGH DANCER** (FR) 2
473 **CURRENT EVENT** (FR) 30
291 **CURSORY** (GB) C 184
258 **CURTAIN RAZER** (IRE) 6
104 **CURVED** (GB) 20
509 **CUSHEEN BRIDGE** (IRE) 4
279 **CUSTER** (GB) 33
484 **CUSTOM CUT** (IRE) 18
393 **CUSTOM HOUSE** (IRE) 5
382 **CUT SHORT** (USA) F 34
670 **CUT THE LUGSREILLY** (IRE) 1
155 **CUT'N'SHUT** (GB) 1
159 **CUTE** (GB) F 5
126 **CUTE COURT** (IRE) 3
9 **CUTHBERT** (IRE) 7
675 **CYCLONE CONNIE** (GB) C 63
271 **CYFLYMDER** (IRE) 1
54 **CYGNET** (GB) 3
551 **CYPRESS GROVE** (IRE) 1
636 **CYPRESS POINT** (FR) 15
406 **CYPRUSORMILAN** (GB) 4
205 **CYPRUSORMILAN** (GB) 5
145 **CYRIEN STAR** (GB) 11
553 **CYRIL** (GB) 77
4 **CYRUS DARIUS** (GB) 7
503 **CZECH IT OUT** (IRE) 6
491 **D'ADDARIO** (IRE) C 37
656 **D'ARCY INDIANA** (GB) 10
196 **D'ARGENT CLOUD** (IRE) 16
260 **D'AVIGNON** (USA) 32
429 **DA DO RUN RUN** (GB) 8
577 **DA'QUONDE** (IRE) 3
549 **DAANA QATAR** (GB) 4
44 **DAAREE** (IRE) 17
1 **DAASIJ** (IRE) 11
281 **DABADIYAN** (IRE) 7
281 **DABASAN** (IRE) 35
394 **DABINETT MOON** (GB) 9
546 **DACHENKA** (GB) 137
60 **DAHTESTE** (GB) 4
124 **DAIS RETURN** (IRE) 2

478 **DARMIANA** (USA) F 54
142 **DARNATHEAN** (GB) 2
608 **DARNBOROUGH** (IRE) 12
281 **DARRAM** (GB) 64
609 **DARRFONAH** (IRE) C 53
396 **DARROUN** (IRE) 2
549 **DARSHA** (FR) F 111
122 **DARSI DANCER** (IRE) 3
584 **DARTFORD WARBLER** (IRE) 21
17 **DARTING** (GB) 6
479 **DARWIN** (USA) 5
635 **DASAATEER** (IRE) 114
591 **DASH** (IRE) 19
209 **DASH TO THE FRONT** (GB) F 58
560 **DASHAWAY** (IRE) 8
635 **DASHING** (GB) C 115
687 **DASHING GEORGE** (IRE) 1
236 **DASHING OSCAR** (IRE) 9
658 **DASHING OVER** (GB) 10
197 **DASHING PRINCE** (IRE) 16
241 **DASHING STORM** (GB) 5
68 **DATE MATE** (USA) C 60
380 **DAUGHTER DAWN** (IRE) 63
172 **DAUPHINE** (SAF) F 34
172 **DAUPHINE DOREE** (GB) 18
549 **DAURAN** (IRE) 39
546 **DAVANTAGE** 43
588 **DAVE THE DAUPHIN** (GB) 4
560 **DAVERON** (IRE) 9
72 **DAVID'S SECRET** (GB) 2
178 **DAVIS ROCK** (GB) G 2
507 **DAVY DOUBT** (GB) 30
310 **DAWALAN** (FR) 30
333 **DAWERANN** (IRE) 5
161 **DAWN CATCHER** (GB) 4
540 **DAWN COMMANDER** (GER) 7
279 **DAWN MISSILE** (GB) 94
172a **DAWN ROCK** 4
494 **DAWN SALUTE** (FR) 6
382 **DAWN SKY** (GB) 2
640 **DAWN TWISTER** (GER) 8
148 **DAWN'S EARLY LIGHT** (IRE) 57
143 **DAWNFROMTHEPAST** (IRE) 13
427 **DAWNUS** (IRE) C 20
278 **DAWSON CITY** (GB) 3
291 **DAY OF CONQUEST** (GB) 63
189 **DAY OF THE EAGLE** (IRE) 16
564 **DAY STAR LAD** (GB) 29
335 **DAYDREAM ISLAND** (IRE) 18
279 **DAYDREAMER** (GB) 35
131 **DAYLAN** (IRE) 3
1 **DAYLIGHT** (GB) 11
383 **DAYMAR BAY** (IRE) 17
383 **DAYS GONE BY** (GB) 18
152 **DAZINSKI** (GB) 6
443 **DAZZA** (GB) 108
479 **DAZZLING** (IRE) 39
634 **DAZZLING DAISY** (IRE) F 26
1 **DAZZLING VALENTINE** (GB) 3
126 **DBANKS** (IRE) 4
58 **DBOBE** (GB) 7
443 **DE BLACKSMITH** (IRE) 23
584 **DE BOITRON** (FR) 22
620 **DE CHISSLER** (GB) 9
674 **DE FAOITHESDREAM** (IRE) 21
321 **DE LA BECH** (GB) 26
439 **DE LESSEPS** (USA) 5
268 **DE REPENTE** (IRE) 11

130 **DEA CAELESTIS** (FR) F 67
563 **DEAD WOMANS PASS** (IRE) G 13
635 **DEADLINE DAY** (IRE) 45
5 **DEADLY APPROACH** (GB) 72
486 **DEADLY STING** (IRE) 23
174 **DEAL DONE** (IRE) 2
12 **DEALING RIVER** (GB) 4
641 **DEAN IARRACHT** (IRE) 3
639 **DEAN'S WALK** (IRE) 11
30 **DEAR BEN** (GB) 6
619 **DEAR DARLING** (GB) 9
121 **DEAR MAURICE** (GB) 2
290 **DEAR MONEY** (IRE) G 11
408 **DEAREST DAISY** (GB) C 24
312 **DEAUVILLE DANCER** (IRE) 10
148 **DEAUVILLE PRINCE** (FR) 13
389 **DEAVIN** (GB) 10
17 **DEBDEBDEB** (GB) 12
130 **DEBIT** (GB) 30
189 **DEBT FREE DAME** (GB) 69
143 **DEBT SETTLER** (IRE) 14
225 **DEBT TO SOCIETY** (IRE) 1
549 **DEBUTANTE** (FR) 40
598 **DECENT FELLA** (IRE) 12
93 **DECENT LORD** (IRE) 10
160 **DECIDING MOMENT** (IRE) 2
560 **DECIMUS** (IRE) 10
201 **DECISION BY ONE** (GB) 7
291 **DECISIVE** (IRE) 189
104 **DECLAN** (GB) 44
494 **DECOUVERTE** (IRE) C 130
507 **DECOY** (FR) 31
409 **DEDIGOUT** (FR) 6
16 **DEE AITCH DOVE** (GB) 11
106 **DEEDS NOT WORDS** (IRE) 55
357a **DEEP BLEU** F 29
576 **DEEP FEELING** (USA) F 41
36 **DEEP INSPIRATION** (IRE) 9
418 **DEEP MARGIN** (GB) 30
607 **DEEP RESOLVE** (IRE) 38
103 **DEEP TROUBLE** (IRE) 9
190 **DEEPSAND** (IRE) 19
69 **DEFENCE COUNCIL** (IRE) 5
257 **DEFICIT** (IRE) 5
50 **DEFINED BENEFIT** (IRE) 67
125 **DEFINITE APPEAL** (IRE) 3
674 **DEFINITE DREAM** (IRE) 22
538 **DEFINITE FUTURE** (IRE) 5
535 **DEFINITE LADY** (IRE) 2
66 **DEFINITE MEMORIES** (IRE) 7
310 **DEFINITE RUBY** (IRE) 31
246 **DEFINITELY BETTER** (IRE) 12
658 **DEFINITELY GLAD** (IRE) 11
257 **DEFINITLY RED** (IRE) 6
549 **DEFROST MY HEART** (IRE) 41
418 **DEGOOCH** (IRE) 31
25 **DEHBANU** (IRE) C 54
658 **DEIA SUNRISE** (IRE) 12
473 **DEIREADH RE** (IRE) 32
418 **DEISE DYNAMO** (IRE) 32
376 **DELAGOA BAY** (IRE) 5
37 **DELATITE** (GB) 14
372 **DELGANY DEMON** (GB) 6
142 **DELGANY DEVIL** (GB) 3
27 **DELHI** (GB) 27
425 **DELICIOUS PATRICA** (GB) 5
572 **DELIGHTED** (IRE) C 64
201 **DELIGHTFUL SLEEP** (GB) 8

550 **DELIGHTFULLY** (FR) 23
414 **DELINEATE** (IRE) 1
546 **DELIVRANCE** 140
507 **DELL' ARCA** (IRE) 32
668 **DELLA SUN** (FR) 1
504 **DELLBUOY** (GB) 6
553 **DELORES ROCKET** (GB) 18
691 **DELPHI MOUNTAIN** (IRE) 6
531 **DELTA FORTY** (GB) 11
291 **DELUXE** (GB) 190
179 **DEMETRIUS** (IRE) 2
2 **DEMISEMIQUAVER** (GB) C 118
383 **DEMOGRAPHIC** (USA) 19
27 **DEMOISELLE** (IRE) 28
533 **DEMOISELLE BOND** (GB) 4
628 **DEMOLITION BLUE** (IRE) 2
621 **DEMONSTRATION** (IRE) 11
12 **DENALI HIGHWAY** (IRE) 5
587 **DENBOY** (IRE) 10
507 **DENICA** (IRE) C 33
455 **DENISON FLYER** (GB) 3
190 **DENNIS** (GB) 20
290 **DENOMINATOR** (GB) 12
120 **DENOTE** (GB) 3
308 **DENTELLE** (FR) 35
291 **DENWAY PARK** (GB) 191
326 **DENY** (GB) 1
50 **DEONTAS** (IRE) 68
477 **DEPORTATION** (GB) 3
530 **DEPRESSED** (GB) G 6
568 **DEPUTY DAN** (IRE) 10
17 **DER MEISTER** (IRE) 62
553 **DERBYSHIRE** (IRE) 38
184 **DERFENNA ART** (IRE) 4
12 **DERMATOLOGISTE** (GB) 6
262 **DERMO'S DILEMMA** (GB) 13
155 **DERRYOGUE** (IRE) 8
491 **DERVAL** (IRE) F 38
457 **DERVLA** (IRE) 8
487 **DESCARO** (USA) 5
427 **DESCRIPTIVE** (IRE) C 21
130 **DESERT ACE** (IRE) 31
522 **DESERT AL** (IRE) 1
553 **DESERT COLOURS** (GB) 39
17 **DESERT COMMAND** (IRE) 13
472 **DESERT CREEK** (IRE) 4
418 **DESERT CRY** (IRE) 33
48 **DESERT FLUTE** (GB) 22
65 **DESERT ISLAND DUSK** (GB) 15
371 **DESERT JOE** (IRE) 13
44 **DESERT LAW** (IRE) 18
572 **DESERT LIAISON** (GB) F 65
397 **DESERT NIGHTS** (GB) C 51
92 **DESERT NOVA** (IRE) 3
332 **DESERT QUEEN** (GB) 8
513 **DESERT RECLUSE** (IRE) 14
371 **DESERT ROBE** (GB) 14
213 **DESERT ROE** (IRE) 10
169 **DESERT ROYALTY** (IRE) G 36
171 **DESERT STRIKE** (GB) 5
479 **DESERT TIGER** (IRE) 40
5 **DESERT WINGS** (IRE) 13
213 **DESERTMORE STREAM** (IRE) 11
474 **DESGREY** (GB) 6
62 **DESIDERATA** (IRE) 3
596 **DESIRE TO WIN** (GB) 26
380 **DESMIOS** (FR) 64
418 **DESOTO COUNTY** (GB) 34

503 **EXCEDO PRAECEDO** (GB) 27
408 **EXCEED AND EXCEED** (GB) 18
162 **EXCEED POLICY** (GB) 17
53 **EXCEEDER** (GB) 47
171 **EXCEEDEXPECTATIONS** (IRE) 7
33 **EXCEEDING POWER** (GB) 24
260 **EXCEEDINGLY** (GB) 115
609 **EXCEL'S BEAUTY** (GB) 21
610 **EXCELLENT** (GB) F 9
408 **EXCELLENT AIM** (GB) 3
106 **EXCELLENT DAY** (IRE) F 111
408 **EXCELLENT GUEST** (GB) 4
223 **EXCELLENT NEWS** (IRE) 1
396 **EXCELLENT PUCK** (GB) 3
44 **EXCELLENT RESULT** (IRE) 20
318 **EXCELLENT ROYALE** (IRE) 34
44 **EXCELLENT VIEW** (IRE) 74
128 **EXCELLO** (GB) C 34
635 **EXCEPTIONELLE** (GB) 9
148 **EXCLUSIVE APPROVAL** (USA) C 63
491 **EXCLUSIVE CONTRACT** (IRE) 21
444 **EXCLUSIVE DANCER** (GB) 8
443 **EXCLUSIVE WATERS** (IRE) 28
300 **EXECUTIVE'S HALL** (IRE) 6
602 **EXECUTRIX** (GB) 33
252 **EXHIBITOR** (USA) C 30
642 **EXIT TO FREEDOM** (GB) 3
568 **EXITAS** (IRE) 14
241 **EXKALIBER** (GB) 7
560 **EXMOOR CHALLENGE** (GB) 13
147 **EXMOOR MIST** (GB) 3
523 **EXNING HALT** (GB) 11
94 **EXOPLANET BLUE** (GB) 42
17 **EXORCET** (FR) F 138
98 **EXOTIC GUEST** (GB) 10
478 **EXOTIC MIX** (FR) C 26
100 **EXPANDING UNIVERSE** (IRE) 13
478 **EXPECT** (GB) 27
68 **EXPECTATION** (IRE) F 61
637 **EXPERIMENTALIST** (GB) 26
291 **EXPERT** (IRE) 68
44 **EXPERT FIGHTER** (USA) 21
637 **EXPLAINED** (IRE) 27
591 **EXPONENT** (USA) F 33
6 **EXPOSE** (GB) 10
460 **EXPRESS DU BERLAIS** (FR) 10
425 **EXPRESS HIMSELF** (IRE) 21
602 **EXTENT** (GB) 34
596 **EXTORTIONIST** (IRE) 5
32 **EXTRA NOBLE** (GB) 33
503 **EXTRASOLAR** (GB) 7
207 **EXTRATERRESTRIAL** (GB) 14
674 **EXTREME IMPACT** (GB) 24
377 **EXTREME PLEASURE** (IRE) F 21
564 **EXTREME SUPREME** (GB) 33
173 **EXTREMELY SO** (GB) 8
493 **EXTREMITY** (IRE) 13
336 **EXZACHARY** (GB) 7
478 **EYE CATCHING** (GB) 57
602 **EYE CONTACT** (GB) 35
479 **EYE OF THE STORM** (IRE) 7
170 **EYE OF THE TIGER** (GER) 1
328 **EYELINE** (GB) 11
639 **EYRE SQUARE** (IRE) 15
446 **EZDIYAAD** (IRE) 3
192 **EZETIGER** (GB) 2
22 **FA'SIDE CASTLE** (IRE) 7
40 **FAB LOLLY** (IRE) 2

318 **FABINE** (GB) F 94
144 **FABLED CITY** (USA) 9
310 **FABRIKA** (GB) 35
494 **FABULOUSLY RED** (GB) F 134
318 **FACT** (GB) F 95
375 **FACTOR FIFTY** (IRE) 22
396 **FADE TO GREY** (IRE) 4
319 **FADHAYYIL** (IRE) 32
106 **FADING AWAY** (GB) C 112
493 **FAFINTA** (IRE) F 28
473 **FAGO** (FR) 42
627 **FAHA** (IRE) 2
503 **FAINTLY** (USA) 28
96 **FAIR ADELAIDE** (IRE) 12
568 **FAIR BRAMBLE** (GB) 15
505 **FAIR BREEZE** (GB) 7
73 **FAIR BUNNY** (GB) 2
49 **FAIR COMMENT** (GB) 5
406 **FAIR DILEMMA** (IRE) 6
236 **FAIR DREAMER** (GB) 11
207 **FAIR FLUTTER** (IRE) 61
84 **FAIR LOCH** (GB) 8
418 **FAIR MONEY** (GB) 46
576 **FAIR MOON** (FR) 4
429 **FAIR SAILING** (IRE) F 81
104 **FAIR SHARE** (GB) 23
607 **FAIR TRADE** (GB) 11
172a **FAIR VALUE** (IRE) 6
169 **FAIR VENTURE** (IRE) 38
479 **FAIR WIND** (GB) 43
253 **FAIRLEE GREY** (GB) 1
531 **FAIRLIE** (GB) F 13
135 **FAIRLIE** (GB) F 25
531 **FAIRLIE** (GB) G 43
493 **FAIRNILEE** (GB) C 29
308 **FAIRWATER** (USA) 17
672 **FAIRWAY TO HEAVEN** (IRE) 5
93 **FAIRWEATHER FRIEND** (GB) 12
648 **FAIRY ALISHA** (GB) 2
130 **FAIRY CONTESSA** (IRE) C 68
602 **FAIRY FLIGHT** (USA) C 102
65 **FAIRY MIST** (IRE) 4
492 **FAIRY OF THE NIGHT** (IRE) F 71
249 **FAIRY RATH** (IRE) 10
99 **FAIRY STEPS** (GB) G 25
598 **FAIRY WING** (IRE) 14
513 **FAIRYINTHEWIND** (IRE) 16
473 **FAIRYTALE THEATRE** (IRE) 43
242 **FAIRYTALEOFNEWYORK** (IRE) G 5
481 **FAITH KEEPER** (IRE) 15
349 **FAITHER** (GB) 3
296 **FAITHFUL RULER** (USA) 7
143 **FAJRY** (USA) 75
59 **FALASTEEN** (IRE) 9
637 **FALCARRAGH** (IRE) 28
619 **FALCON ISLAND** (GB) 11
663 **FALCON'S GINGER** (GB) 7
663 **FALCON'S LEGEND** (GB) 8
663 **FALCON'S PRESENT** (GB) 9
6 **FALCON'S REIGN** (FR) 11
279 **FALDAL** (GB) C 103
479 **FALKIRK** (IRE) 44
260 **FALLEN FOR A STAR** (GB) 116
260 **FALLEN IN LINE** (IRE) 41
120 **FALMOUTH HARBOUR** (GB) 38
333 **FALSE ECONOMY** (IRE) 10
472 **FALSE WITNESS** (IRE) 37
90 **FAMA MAC** (GB) 2

189 **FAME AGAIN** (GB) 17
429 **FAME IS THE SPUR** (GB) C 82
635 **FAMILLIARITY** (GB) 10
258 **FAMILY MOTTO** (GB) 7
50 **FAMILY PRIDE** (IRE) 73
36 **FAMOUS BALLERINA** (IRE) 10
44 **FAMOUS POET** (GB) 22
49 **FAMOUS TALES** 6
507 **FAMOUSANDFEARLESS** (IRE) 40
591 **FAND** (USA) F 34
652 **FANGFOSS GIRLS** (GB) C 13
44 **FANN** (USA C 108
118 **FANNY AGAIN** (GB) 18
580 **FANNY'S FANCY** (GB) F 10
557 **FANNYTHEWUNDAHORSE** (IRE) 9
558 **FANOOS** (GB) 2
136 **FANTASTIC ACCOUNT** (GB) G 5
445 **FANTASTIC BELLE** (IRE) F 30
478 **FANTASTIC MOON** (GB) 5
523 **FANTASY GLADIATOR** (GB) 12
443 **FANTASY INVADER** (IRE) 29
296 **FANTASY JUSTIFIER** (IRE) 30
439 **FANTASY KING** (GB) 8
25 **FANTASY PRINCESS** (USA) C 34
450 **FANZINE** (GB) 11
260 **FANZINE** (USA) F 117
28 **FAOLAN** (IRE) 3
473 **FAR WEST** (FR) 44
380 **FARADAN** (FR) 22
99 **FARANG BER SONG** (GB) 18
679 **FARASI KUBWA** (GB) 27
512 **FARBREAGA** (IRE) 3
207 **FARLOW** (IRE) 15
286 **FARM PIXIE** (IRE) 2
481 **FARMER MATT** (IRE) 16
399 **FARMER'S FRIEND** (GB) 3
369 **FARMER'S PET** (GB) F 8
589 **FARMERS DREAM** (IRE) 9
109 **FARQUHAR** (IRE) 17
635 **FARRAAJ** (IRE) 11
550 **FARRAGON** (IRE) 27
492 **FARRANJORDAN** (GB) C 72
279 **FARSAKH** (USA) 104
473 **FASCINO RUSTICO** (GB) 45
659 **FASEEHA** (IRE) 87
311 **FASHION FAUX PAS** (IRE) 10
429 **FASHION FUND** (GB) 35
177 **FASHION GUIDE** (IRE) F 21
33 **FASHION LINE** (IRE) 1
32 **FASHION ROCKS** (IRE) F 92
178 **FASHION TRADE** (GB) F 17
50 **FAST AND NOW** (GB) 74
494 **FAST AND PRETTY** (GB) 58
44 **FAST DELIVERY** (GB) 76
142 **FAST FINIAN** (IRE) 4
172 **FAST FLIGHT** (FR) 5
279 **FAST OR FREE** (GB) 7
120 **FAST ROMANCE** (USA) 39
190 **FAST SHOT** (GB) 21
25 **FAST TRACK** (GB) 35
181 **FASTBACK** (IRE) F 26
148 **FAT GARY** (GB) 16
596 **FATAL ATTRACTION** (GB) F 28
547 **FATHER ARTHUR** (GB) 2
190 **FATHER BERTIE** (GB) 102
214 **FATHER EDWARD** (IRE) 17
335 **FATHER JACK** (IRE) 23
297 **FATHER SHINE** (IRE) 5

50 **FISCAL FOCUS** (IRE) 27
293 **FISCAL NOMAD** (IRE) 2
428 **FISHER BRIDGE** (GB) 25
425 **FISHER ISLAND** (IRE) F 22
527 **FISHING BRIDGE** (IRE) 6
139 **FISHOUTOFWATER** (IRE) 19
246 **FIT THE BRIEF** (GB) 16
431 **FITANDPROPERJOB** (GB) 5
472 **FITZ FLYER** (IRE) 6
410 **FITZ VOLONTE** (GB) 1
53 **FITZGERALD** (IRE) 48
460 **FITZGUTENTYTE** (IRE) 11
73 **FITZOLINI** (GB) 3
106 **FITZWILLY** (GB) 12
546 **FIVE AVENUE** (IRE) 8
106 **FIVE BELLS** (IRE) C 113
196 **FIVE IN A ROW** (IRE) 27
635 **FIVE OF DIAMONDS** (FR) 123
572 **FIVE OF WANDS** (GB) C 70
125 **FIVE RIVERS** (IRE) 4
479 **FIVE STAR GENERAL** (GB) 1
560 **FIVE STAR WILSHAM** (IRE) 15
458 **FIVEFORTHREE** (IRE) 47
383 **FIX IT RIGHT** (IRE) 23
521 **FIZZOLO** (GB) 8
493 **FIZZY TREAT** (GB) C 30
314 **FLAG OF GLORY** (GB) 3
546 **FLAG OFFICER** 152
44 **FLAG WAR** (GER) 78
516 **FLAKEY DOVE** G 2
380 **FLAMBEUSE** (GB) 24
636 **FLAMBOROUGH BREEZE** (GB) 2
546 **FLAMBOYANT** (FR) 51
358 **FLAMELET** (USA) C 165
41 **FLAMENCO FLYER** (GB) 3
317 **FLAMENCO LAD** (GB) 6
446 **FLAMIN JUNE** (GB) 4
619 **FLAMING CHARMER** (IRE) 13
302 **FLAMING GORGE** (IRE) 3
523 **FLAMING ROSE** (IRE) C 13
331 **FLAMING STAR** (GB) 9
183 **FLAMINGO BEAT** (GB) 4
279 **FLAMME FANTASTIQUE** (GER) 105
606 **FLAMMETTA** (GB) 10
577 **FLASH CITY** (ITY) 8
101 **FLASH CRASH** (GB) 2
458 **FLASH OF GENIUS** (GB) 48
52 **FLASH TOMMIE** (IRE) 6
624 **FLASHHEART** (IRE) 7
443 **FLASHMAN** (GB) 30
94 **FLASHY DIVA** (GB) 43
126 **FLASHY LAD** (IRE) 6
626 **FLASHY QUEEN** (IRE) 10
311 **FLASHY STAR** (GB) 11
33 **FLASHY WINGS** (GB) C 67
197 **FLASHYFRANK** (GB) 7
458 **FLAT OUT** (FR) 49
105 **FLAVIUS VICTOR** (IRE) 7
134 **FLAWLESS DIAMOND** (IRE) F 12
167 **FLAWLESS FILLY** (IRE) 6
478 **FLAWLESS PINK** (GB) 28
59 **FLAXEN LAKE** (GB) 11
452 **FLECKERL** (IRE) 3
345 **FLEDERMAUS** (IRE) 2
196 **FLEET DAWN** (GB) 28
631 **FLEET FOX** (GB) 19
354 **FLEETING INDIAN** (IRE) 3
450 **FLEETING MOON** (GB) F 54

504 **FLEETWOOD NIX** (GB) 10
201 **FLEETWOODSANDS** (IRE) 12
13 **FLEMENSMIX** (GB) 16
486 **FLEMENSON** (IRE) 29
365 **FLEMENTIME** (IRE) 15
584 **FLEMERINA** (IRE) 25
339 **FLEMI TWO TOES** (IRE) 7
83 **FLEMISH DANCER** (GB) 3
197 **FLEMISH SCHOOL** (GB) 4
236 **FLETCHERS FLYER** (IRE) 12
664 **FLEUR DE FORTUNE** (GB) 6
32 **FLEUR DE LA VIE** (IRE) 5
398 **FLEUR DEFENDUE** (FR) 60
494 **FLEUR DES MERS** (GB) 59
132 **FLEURTILLE** (GB) 1
643 **FLEXIBLE FLYER** (GB) 7
127 **FLICHITY** (IRE) 2
267 **FLICK THROUGH** (IRE) 16
131 **FLICKA WILLIAMS** (IRE) 5
296 **FLICKSTA** (USA) 31
427 **FLIGAZ** (FR) 24
646 **FLIGHT FIGHT** (GB) 25
44 **FLIGHT OFFICER** (GB) 79
335 **FLIGHT PLAN** (IRE) 24
50 **FLIGHT RISK** (IRE) 28
207 **FLIGHTY CLARETS** (IRE) 16
503 **FLIGHTY FILIA** (IRE) 45
428 **FLINDERS RIVER** (IRE) 26
167 **FLING ME** (IRE) 7
486 **FLINSTONE** (IRE) 30
60 **FLINTHAM** (GB) 6
33 **FLIP FLOP** (FR) F 68
279 **FLIPPANT** (IRE) 43
377 **FLIPPING** (GB) 2
450 **FLIRTATIOUS** (GB) F 12
425 **FLIRTINASKIRT** (GB) 8
206 **FLIXX** (GB) 40
384 **FLOBURY** (GB) 3
398 **FLOGAPA** (FR) 61
476 **FLOGAROSE** (FR) 11
398 **FLOGASORTE** (FR) 14
395 **FLOODS OF TEARS** (GB) F 22
16 **FLOPPIE** (FR) C 56
516 **FLORA LEA** (GB) 3
515 **FLORA MEDICI** (GB) 14
152 **FLORABURY** (GB) 11
568 **FLORAFERN** (GB) 18
196 **FLORAL PATCHES** (GB) 29
628 **FLORAL SPINNER** (GB) 5
82 **FLORIDA BEAT** (GB) 2
523 **FLORIDA CITY** (IRE) C 56
17 **FLORIDA HEART** (GB) G 140
162 **FLORIDA QUAYS** (IRE) 5
99 **FLORRIE** (IRE) 26
104 **FLOW** (USA) 3
266 **FLOW CHART** (IRE) 4
131 **FLOWER POWER** (GB) 26
391 **FLOWERBUD** (GB) 5
57 **FLOWING AIR** (IRE) 1
457 **FLUGZEUG** (GB) 10
597 **FLUMPS** (GB) 4
418 **FLUSHTOWN VALE** (IRE) G 48
443 **FLUTE BOWL** (GB) 31
16 **FLUTTERBEE** 57
32 **FLUTTERING ROSE** (GB) C 93
511 **FLY A KITE** (GB) 28
643 **FLY BY KNIGHT** (GB) 8
307 **FLY HOME** (GB) C 7

607 **FLY HOME HARRY** (GB) 12
630 **FLY IN STYLE** (GB) F 13
607 **FLY SOLO** (GB) 13
207 **FLYCATCHER** (IRE) 62
55 **FLYING APPLAUSE** (GB) 5
421 **FLYING AUTHOR** (IRE) 14
240 **FLYING AWARD** (IRE) 5
241 **FLYING BEAR** (IRE) 24
276 **FLYING BY** (GB) 15
328 **FLYING CAPE** (IRE) 35
54 **FLYING EAGLE** (IRE) 15
279 **FLYING FANTASY** (GB) 106
209 **FLYING FINISH** (FR) G 31
336 **FLYING GIANT** (IRE) 8
190 **FLYING HIGHEST** (GB) C 103
659 **FLYING JIB** (GB) 33
504 **FLYING KYTE** (GB) 18
426 **FLYING LIGHT** (IRE) 10
260 **FLYING OFFICER** (USA) 5
48 **FLYING PHOENIX** (GB) 5
477 **FLYING POWER** (GB) 7
144 **FLYLOWFLYLONG** (IRE) C 42
207 **FLYMAN** (GB) 17
372 **FOCAIL MAITH** (GB) 8
50 **FOCAS MOR** (IRE) 29
634 **FOCOSA** (ITY) F 17
50 **FOCUS ON LIGHT** (IRE) 75
50 **FOCUS ON VENICE** (IRE) 30
178 **FOCUSSED** (IRE) 14
576 **FOFA MELECA** (URU) 5
397 **FOG OF WAR** (GB) 23
550 **FOG PATCHES** (IRE) 30
473 **FOGGY'S WALL** (IRE) 46
186 **FOIE GRAS** (GB) 3
205 **FOILED** (GB) 8
122 **FOL HOLLOW** (IRE) 5
32 **FOLCARA** (IRE) C 94
383 **FOLIE DANCER** (GB) G 70
5 **FOLK MELODY** (IRE) 80
606 **FOLK VILLAGE** (IRE) 11
106 **FOLLOW THE FAITH** (GB) 114
227 **FOLLOW THE MASTER** (GB) 2
23 **FOLLOW THE TRACKS** (IRE) 4
691 **FOLLY FARM** (IRE) 8
397 **FOLLY LODGE** (GB) C 54
543 **FONAGE** (GB) F 4
631 **FOND MEMORY** (IRE) 20
635 **FONDA** (USA) C 124
128 **FONDLED** (GB) G 25
478 **FONDLED** (GB) C 59
343 **FONTERUTOLI** (IRE) 3
634 **FOOLISH AMBITION** (GER) C 28
158 **FOOLSANDORSES** (IRE) 2
330 **FOOT THE BILL** (GB) 5
251 **FOOTSIEONEHUNDRED** 4
382 **FOOTSTEPSINTHERAIN** (IRE) 4
184 **FOR AYMAN** (GB) 15
56 **FOR EVVA SILCA** (GB) C 19
393 **FOR LIFE** (IRE) 7
395 **FOR SHIA AND LULA** (IRE) 6
473 **FOR TWO** (FR) 47
382 **FOR WHAT** (USA) 5
229 **FORCE OF HABIT** (GB) 4
157 **FORCE TO SPEND** (GB) 4
523 **FORCED FAMILY FUN** (GB) 14
172a **FORCEFUL APPEAL** (USA) 8
618 **FOREIGN LANGUAGE** (USA) G 9
24 **FOREIGN RHYTHM** (IRE) 3

109 **FUNKY COLD MEDINA** (GB) 5
665 **FUNKY MUNKY** (GB) 8
106 **FUNNY GIRL** (GB) F 115
473 **FUNNY STAR** (FR) 48
44 **FURAS** (IRE) 80
68 **FURIOUSLY FAST** (IRE) 63
383 **FURTHER MORE** (IRE) 25
279 **FURY** (GB) 8
247 **FURZE FLYER** (IRE) 9
82 **FUSE WIRE** (GB) 3
587 **FUTURE GILDED** (FR) 12
44 **FUTURE REFERENCE** (IRE) 24
431 **FUTURE SECURITY** (IRE) 7
308 **FUTURISTIC** (FR) 40
6 **FUWALA** (GB) F 53
624 **FYRECRACKER** (IRE) 20
484 **G FORCE** (GB) 75
54 **G'DAI SYDNEY** (GB) 16
241 **GABBIANO** (GB) 8
398 **GABO** (FR) 15
456 **GABRIAL THE BOSS** (USA) 6
449 **GABRIAL THE DUKE** (IRE) 6
418 **GABRIAL THE GREAT** (IRE) 51
449 **GABRIAL THE HERO** (USA) 7
449 **GABRIAL THE MASTER** (IRE) 8
449 **GABRIAL'S BOUNTY** (IRE) 9
166 **GABRIAL'S GIFT** (GB) 9
449 **GABRIAL'S KAKA** (IRE) 10
572 **GABRIAL'S KING** (IRE) 8
343 **GABRIAL'S WAWA** (GB) 4
118 **GABRIEL'S LAD** (IRE) 2
371 **GABRIELLA ROSE** (GB) 25
193 **GAELIC O'REAGAN** (GB) 9
443 **GAELIC SILVER** (GB) 34
215 **GAELIC WIZARD** (GB) 6
576 **GAGA** (URU) 8
546 **GAILY GAME** (GB) 10
576 **GAINFUL** (USA) F 44
113 **GAINSBOROUGH'S ART** (IRE) 4
126 **GAIR LEAT** (IRE) 7
310 **GAITWAY** (GB) 43
428 **GAIUS MARIUS** (IRE) 28
553 **GALA STYLE** (IRE) F 81
104 **GALACTIC HALO** (GB) 24
252 **GALACTIC HEROINE** (GB) 14
602 **GALATEE** (FR) C 103
434 **GALATIAN** (GB) 3
417 **GALAXY** (IRE) 21
209 **GALE FORCE** (GB) 33
631 **GALEB WARRIOR** (GB) 23
17 **GALEOTTI** (GB) 141
51 **GALEOTTO** (FR) 24
665 **GALILEE CHAPEL** (IRE) 9
492 **GALILEO ALWAYS** (IRE) 75
659 **GALILEO'S CHOICE** (IRE) 5
134 **GALILEO'S STAR** (IRE) F 13
172a **GALINTHIAS** 22
443 **GALIOTTO** (IRE) 35
291 **GALISTIC** (IRE) F 204
33 **GALIZZI** (USA) 27
409 **GALLANT OSCAR** (IRE) 11
348 **GALLEONS WAY** (GB) 4
13 **GALLERY EXHIBITION** (IRE) 17
281 **GALLEY** (GB) C 67
107 **GALLEY SLAVE** (IRE) 5
17 **GALLIC DESTINY** (IRE) 70
481 **GALLIC WARRIOR** (IRE) 18
308 **GALLICE** (IRE) 41

308 **GALLIUM** (FR) 42
291 **GALLIVANT** (GB) C 205
515 **GALLO GALANTE** (GB) 46
504 **GALLOPING MINISTER** (IRE) 11
637 **GALLOX BRIDGE** (GB) 34
137 **GALUPPI** (GB) 47
553 **GALVANIZE** (GB) 42
12 **GALWAY JACK** (IRE) 7
412 **GALWAY VIEW** (IRE) 2
659 **GAMBLE** (GB) 6
295 **GAMBLING GIRL** (IRE) 11
674 **GAMBO** (IRE) 27
319 **GAMBOL** (GB) 8
659 **GAMBRINUS** (USA) 35
341 **GAME DORABELLA** (GB) 1
100 **GAME MASCOT** (GB) 14
493 **GAME PIE** (IRE) 31
596 **GAMESOME** (FR) 7
148 **GAMESTERS LAD** (GB) 66
553 **GAMRA** (GB) F 82
7 **GANDALFE** (FR) 3
621 **GANGES** (IRE) 8
427 **GANGSTER SQUAD** (FR) 7
513 **GANNICUS** (GB) 53
584 **GANSEY** (IRE) 28
357a **GANYMEDE** 13
298 **GAOTH NA MARA** (IRE) G 6
54 **GAP OF DUNLOE** (IRE) 17
308 **GARANTIE** (FR) 43
311 **GARDE FOU** (FR) 12
321 **GARDE LA VICTOIRE** (FR) 34
680 **GARDE VILLE** (FR) 5
409 **GARDELITO** (FR) 12
22 **GARLETON** (GB) 8
66 **GARNOCK** (IRE) 13
164 **GARRAHALISH** (IRE) 11
478 **GARRAUN** (IRE) 29
507 **GARRYLEIGH** (IRE) 42
207 **GARSWOOD** (GB) 18
550 **GARTH** (IRE) 31
86 **GARTH MOUNTAIN** (GB) 2
236 **GARTON STAR** (IRE) 3
321 **GAS LINE BOY** (IRE) 35
576 **GAS TOTAL** (BRZ) 9
385 **GASSIN GOLF** (GB) 7
139 **GATE PLEASE** (IRE) 22
449 **GATEPOST** (IRE) 11
207 **GATEPOST** (IRE) 19
260 **GATEWOOD** (GB) 7
33 **GAUCHITA** (GB) 28
321 **GAUVAIN** (GER) 36
378 **GAVLAR** (GB) 25
260 **GAY MARRIAGE** (IRE) 44
573 **GAYE MEMORIES** (GB) 15
502 **GEANIE MAC** (IRE) 6
343 **GEBAYL** (GB) 15
195 **GEE HI** (IRE) 6
53 **GEE KEL** (IRE) C 100
91 **GEE SHARP** (GB) 10
314 **GEEAITCH** (GB) 4
318 **GEESALA** (IRE) C 97
492 **GELENSCHIK** (IRE) 76
637 **GEMINI LUCY** (IRE) G 35
382 **GEMINIANI** (GB) C 37
637 **GEMINUS** (IRE) 36
277 **GENAX** (IRE) 27
364 **GENERAL GIRLING** (GB) 7
639 **GENERAL HARDI** (GB) 17

454 **GENERAL MONTGOMERY** (IRE) 15
84 **GENERAL TIBERIUS** (GB) 10
578 **GENERAL TUFTO** (GB) 1
160 **GENERALYSE** (GB) 3
576 **GENERATA** (USA) 23
457 **GENEROUS BOB** (GB) 5
262 **GENEROUS CHIEF** (IRE) 16
69 **GENEROUS DREAM** (GB) 5
443 **GENEROUS HELPINGS** (IRE) 36
38 **GENEROUS JACK** (IRE) 7
88 **GENEROUS JUNE** (IRE) 4
408 **GENEROUS LADY** (GB) C 25
249 **GENEROUS RANSOM** (IRE) 11
119 **GENEROUS SPENDER** (GB) 2
6 **GENES QUEST** (GB) 14
5 **GENIUS BEAST** (USA) 22
609 **GENIUS BOY** (GB) 2
618 **GENIUSINRHYME** (GB) 11
540 **GENNY WREN** (GB) 10
691 **GENSON** (GB) 9
371 **GENSTONE TRAIL** (GB) 26
494 **GENTLE BREEZE** (IRE) 61
503 **GENTLE PERSUASION** (GB) 47
646 **GENTLE THOUGHTS** (GB) F 45
242 **GENTLEMAN ANSHAN** (IRE) 6
442 **GENTLEMAN DUKE** (IRE) 6
619 **GENTLEMAN JON** (GB) 16
56 **GENTLEMAX** (FR) 4
482 **GENTLEMEN** (GB) 7
492 **GENTRY** (IRE) 23
361 **GENUINE ART** (GB) 2
659 **GENUINE CHARM** (IRE) F 90
169 **GENUINELY** (IRE) C 39
479 **GEOFFREY CHAUCER** (USA) 52
553 **GEOLOGY** (GB) 83
17 **GEORDAN MURPHY** (GB) 71
192 **GEORDIE MAN** (GB) 3
249 **GEORGE ARTHUR** (GB) 12
16 **GEORGE BAKER** (IRE) 15
33 **GEORGE CINQ** (GB) 2
177 **GEORGE DRYDEN** (IRE) 22
171 **GEORGE FENTON** (GB) 8
290 **GEORGE FERNBECK** (GB) 16
9 **GEORGE GURU** (GB) 12
23 **GEORGE NYMPTON** (IRE) 6
443 **GEORGEA** (GB) 37
84 **GEORGIAN BAY** (IRE) 11
607 **GEORGIAN FIREBIRD** (GB) 15
365 **GEORGIAN KING** (GB) 16
50 **GEORGIE HYDE** (GB) 77
321 **GEORGIE LAD** (IRE) 37
94 **GERALD** (GB) 44
492 **GERMANCE** (USA) F 77
394 **GERMANY CALLING** (IRE) 16
549 **GERTSOGINYA** (IRE) 51
486 **GET BACK IN LINE** (IRE) 33
188 **GET BACK TO ME** (IRE) 2
54 **GET HOME NOW** (GB) 18
674 **GET IT ON** (IRE) 28
486 **GET ME OUT OF HERE** (IRE) 34
225 **GET READY TO GO** (IRE) 4
542 **GET THE PAPERS** (GB) 3
190 **GETABUZZ** (GB) 22
471 **GETCARTER** (GB) 3
606 **GETOUTWHENYOUCAN** (IRE) 13
631 **GETTING READY** (IRE) 24
507 **GEVREY CHAMBERTIN** (FR) 43
384 **GHAABESH** (IRE) 4

494 **GOLDEN BOTTLE** (USA) F 136
54 **GOLDEN CALF** (IRE) 20
93 **GOLDEN CALL** (IRE) 13
619 **GOLDEN CHIEFTAIN** (IRE) 17
172a **GOLDEN DESERT** (IRE) 9
546 **GOLDEN EARRING** 154
27 **GOLDEN FASTNET** (FR) 67
409 **GOLDEN FIRTH** (IRE) 16
474 **GOLDEN FUTURE** (GB) 7
560 **GOLDEN GAEL** (GB) 17
480 **GOLDEN GAMES** (IRE) 3
330 **GOLDEN GROOM** (GB) 6
442 **GOLDEN HERON** (IRE) 7
310 **GOLDEN HOOF** (IRE) 46
260 **GOLDEN HORN** (GB) 122
50 **GOLDEN INK** (IRE) 79
130 **GOLDEN JOURNEY** (IRE) 35
631 **GOLDEN JUBILEE** (USA) 27
591 **GOLDEN MASK** (USA) C 36
139 **GOLDEN MILAN** (IRE) 23
397 **GOLDEN ROSE** (FR) C 56
395 **GOLDEN SANDSTORM** (IRE) 7
408 **GOLDEN SHADOW** (IRE) C 26
259 **GOLDEN SHOE** (IRE) 6
179 **GOLDEN SPARKLE** (IRE) 5
521 **GOLDEN SPEAR** (GB) 9
53 **GOLDEN STEPS** (FR) 49
44 **GOLDEN TOWN** (IRE) 82
357a **GOLDEN WEDDING (IRE) 31**
32 **GOLDENROD** (GB) 36
607 **GOLDEVA** (GB) G 58
631 **GOLDIE HORN** (GB) 28
172 **GOLDIE JOLIE** (FR) 7
252 **GOLDMADCHEN** (GER) 4
398 **GOLDMANTIS** (FR) 62
27 **GOLDMETAL JACKET** (IRE) 68
128 **GOLDREAM** (GB) 5
50 **GOLDSMITH** (IRE) 80
30 **GOLDSTORM** (GB) 8
494 **GOLDY ESPONY** (FR) 62
53 **GOLEADOR** (USA) 50
308 **GOLF JUAN** (USA) 5
241 **GOLLY MISS MOLLY** (GB) 25
369 **GONALSTON CLOUD** (IRE) 9
44 **GONBARDA** (GER) C 110
209 **GONE DUTCH** (GB) 7
196 **GONE FOREVER** (GB) 32
371 **GONE TOO FAR** (GB) 29
478 **GONE WITH THE WIND** (GER) 30
410 **GONEINAGLANCE** (GB) 2
546 **GONNA RUN** (FR) 55
381 **GOOCHYPOOCHYPRADER** (GB) 1
245 **GOOD AUTHORITY** (IRE) 4
582 **GOOD BOY JACKSON** (GB) 2
230 **GOOD EGG** (IRE) 1
33 **GOOD HOPE** (GB) 29
33 **GOOD LADY** (IRE) C 71
443 **GOOD LUCK CHARM** (GB) 41
106 **GOOD MORNING LADY** (GB) 60
267 **GOOD OF LUCK** (GB) 17
246 **GOOD ORDER** (GB) 20
610 **GOOD SPEECH** (IRE) 3
659 **GOOD TRADITION** (FR) 37
602 **GOOD VALUE** (GB) 39
468 **GOODGOSHMSMÓLLY** (GB) 2
144 **GOODLUKIN LUCY** (GB) 12
280 **GOODTIME BOY** (IRE) 9
385 **GOODTOKNOW** (GB) 8

486 **GOODWOOD MIRAGE** (IRE) 36
378 **GOODWOOD MOONLIGHT** (GB) 39
378 **GOODWOOD STORM** (GB) 27
145 **GOOHAR** (IRE) 13
443 **GORES ISLAND** (IRE) 42
477 **GOREY LANE** (IRE) 8
679 **GORGEHOUS LLIEGE** (FR) 29
458 **GORGEOUS SIXTY** (FR) 53
448 **GORGEOUSREACH** (IRE) 12
512 **GORHAMS GIFT** (GB) 5
471 **GORING ONE** (IRE) 4
471 **GORING TWO** (IRE) 5
246 **GORSKY ISLAND** (GB) 21
470 **GORTENBUIE** (IRE) 11
398 **GORVELLO** (FR) 17
602 **GOSPEL CHOIR** (GB) 11
100 **GOT ATTITUDE** (IRE) 16
32 **GOT TO DANCE** (GB) 37
596 **GOTASINGGOTADANCE** (GB) 30
40 **GOTCHA** (GB) 16
507 **GOTHAM CITY** (IRE) 44
602 **GOTHIC** (GB) 40
679 **GOTOYOURPLAY** (IRE) 30
507 **GOULANES** (IRE) 45
479 **GOVERNMENT HOUSE** (USA) 54
296 **GOWER PRINCESS** (GB) 33
197 **GOWER SONG** (GB) F 27
318 **GOWN** (IRE) 36
671 **GRAASP THE NETTLE** (GB) 4
17 **GRACE AND FAVOUR** (GB) 72
547 **GRACE AND FORTUNE** (GB) 3
451 **GRACE HULL** (GB) 1
546 **GRACE OF LOVE** (FR) 56
645 **GRACEFILLY** (GB) 23
24 **GRACEFUL ACT** (GB) 4
393 **GRACEFUL WILLOW** (IRE) 3
678 **GRACESOME** (IRE) 26
637 **GRACIE B** (IRE) 38
589 **GRACIE'S GAMES** (GB) 12
231 **GRACIOUS GEORGE** (IRE) 3
17 **GRACIOUS LADY** (GB) 73
549 **GRACIOUSLY** (GB) 52
591 **GRADATIM** (IRE) 21
32 **GRADUATION** (GB) G 97
513 **GRAFFITI ART** (GB) 18
431 **GRAFITE** (GB) 8
572 **GRAHAMLUCAS** (CAN) 72
196 **GRAIN ONLY** (GB) F 112
176 **GRAINEUAILE** (IRE) F 7
449 **GRAMERCY** (IRE) 12
221 **GRAMS AND OUNCES** (GB) 1
98 **GRAN MAESTRO** (USA) 12
674 **GRAN TORINO** (IRE) 31
285 **GRANARUID** (IRE) 5
129 **GRAND ARTICLE** (IRE) 3
686 **GRAND FELLA** (IRE) 7
675 **GRAND GIGOLO** (FR) 29
602 **GRAND INQUISITOR** (GB) 105
196 **GRAND JIPECK** (IRE) 33
252 **GRAND LIAISON** (GB) 5
13 **GRAND MARCH** (GB) 11
33 **GRAND MEISTER** (GB) 30
17 **GRAND PIANO** (IRE) 15
137 **GRAND SPIRIT** (IRE) 83
270 **GRAND TOUR** (GB) 15
174 **GRAND VINTAGE** (IRE) 2
619 **GRAND VISION** (IRE) 18
123 **GRANDAD MAC** (GB) 2

394 **GRANDADS HORSE** (GB) 18
479 **GRANDDUKEOFTUSCANY** (IRE) 55
655 **GRANDE MONSIEUR** (IRE) 4
260 **GRANDEST** (GB) 49
478 **GRANDEUR** (IRE) 6
196 **GRANDILOQUENT** (GB) 34
473 **GRANDIOSO** (IRE) 49
398 **GRANDISSIME** (FR) 18
606 **GRANDMA DOTTY** (IRE) 14
13 **GRANDMA SMITH** (GB) 19
484 **GRANDORIO** (IRE) 27
310 **GRANDOUET** (FR) 47
507 **GRANDS CRUS** (FR) 46
429 **GRANELL** (IRE) 10
335 **GRANGECLARE LARK** (IRE) F 27
458 **GRANGECLARE PEARL** (IRE) 54
93 **GRANNIES PRIDE** (IRE) C 14
247 **GRANNYS GARDEN** (IRE) 10
93 **GRANVILLE ISLAND** (IRE) 15
643 **GRANWOOD** (GB) 10
54 **GRAPE TREE FLAME** (GB) 21
434 **GRAPHENE** (GB) 24
279 **GRAPHIC** (IRE) 9
106 **GRAPHIC GUEST** (GB) 14
104 **GRASPED** (GB) 4
630 **GRASSHOPPERGREEN** (IRE) F 15
584 **GRATE FELLA** (IRE) 29
106 **GRATZIE** (GB) 61
658 **GRAVITATE** (GB) 19
646 **GRAVITATIONAL** (IRE) 5
164 **GRAYLYN AMBER** (GB) 12
164 **GRAYLYN RUBY** (FR) 13
452 **GRAYSWOOD** (GB) 4
75 **GRAZED KNEES** (IRE) 24
50 **GREANTA** (IRE) 33
507 **GREAT CHOICE** (IRE) 47
491 **GREAT CONQUEST** (USA) 6
295 **GREAT CULLEN** (IRE) 3
557 **GREAT DEMEANOR** (USA) 11
352 **GREAT EXPECTATIONS** (GB) 14
44 **GREAT FIGHTER** (GB) 26
429 **GREAT FUN** (GB) 36
32 **GREAT GLEN** (GB) 98
429 **GREAT HALL** (GB) 11
100 **GREAT LINK** (GB) 17
591 **GREAT MINDS** (IRE) 7
637 **GREAT OAK** (IRE) 39
434 **GREAT QUEST** (GB) C 35
685 **GREAT ROAR** (USA) 4
172 **GREAT SILENCE** (FR) 20
473 **GREAT TRY** (GB) 50
426 **GREAT VALUE** (IRE) 12
572 **GREAT WAVE** (IRE) 37
479 **GREAT WHITE EAGLE** (USA) 56
558 **GREAT WHITE HOPE** (IRE) C 9
457 **GREATDAY ALLWEEK** (IRE) 14
409 **GREATNESS** (IRE) 17
120 **GRECIAN** (IRE) 21
478 **GRECIAN AIR** (FR) C 62
318 **GREEB** (GB) 37
397 **GREEK CANYON** (IRE) 4
134 **GREEK ISLANDS** (GB) 5
478 **GREEK SPIRIT** (IRE) 7
49 **GREELEY BRIGHT** (USA) C 18
358 **GREELEYS LOVE** (USA) 16
538 **GREEN AND WHITE** (ITY) 6
172 **GREEN BANANAS** (FR) 8
394 **GREEN BANK** (IRE) 19

44 **HANDSOME MAN** (IRE) 28
236 **HANDSOME RANSOM** (GB) 14
11 **HANDSOME STRANGER** (IRE) 5
358 **HANDWOVEN** (GB) 87
619 **HANDY ANDY** (IRE) 19
443 **HANGA ROA** (IRE) 46
150 **HANK SCHRADER** (GB) 6
387 **HANNAH JUST HANNAH** (GB) 7
343 **HANNAH LOUISE** (IRE) 9
442 **HANNAH'S MAGIC** (IRE) 2
267 **HANNAH'S PRINCESS** (IRE) 19
186 **HANNAHS TURN** (GB) 4
394 **HANNIBAL THE GREAT** (IRE) 21
17 **HANNINGTON** (GB) 75
180 **HANNO** (USA) 28
333 **HANS CRESCENT** (FR) 14
260 **HANSEATIC** (GB) 9
59 **HANSOMIS** (IRE) F 30
390 **HANSUPFORDETROIT** (IRE) 7
144 **HAPIPI** (GB) G 66
577 **HAPPY AS HARRY** (GB) 44
403 **HAPPY FAMILIES** (GB) 5
591 **HAPPY GATHERING** (IRE) 22
672 **HAPPY JACK** (IRE) 14
550 **HAPPY RIVER** (IRE) 35
549 **HAPPY VALENTINE** (SAF) 8
183 **HAPPYDOINGNOTHING** (GB) 13
492 **HARASIYA** (IRE) 2
106 **HARBINGER LASS** (GB) 16
494 **HARBOUR OF HOPE** (GER) 10
291 **HARBOUR PATROL** (IRE) 209
515 **HARBOURED** (USA) 16
196 **HARD CORE DEBT** (GB) 35
32 **HARD TO HANDEL** (GB) 100
491 **HARDY BLACK** (IRE) 23
491 **HARDY PINK** (IRE) 24
118 **HARDY PLUME** (GB) 3
606 **HARETH** (IRE) 15
549 **HARGAM** (FR) 53
634 **HARLEQUIN JINKS** (GB) 18
471 **HARLEQUINS GLEAMS** (GB) 6
309 **HARLESTONE WOOD** (GB) 7
442 **HARLEY'S HARLEY** (IRE) 8
125 **HARLEYS MAX** (GB) 5
54 **HAROUET** (FR) 25
272 **HARPERS RUBY** (GB) 2
579 **HARRIET'S ARK** (GB) 4
1 **HARRIETFIELD** (GB) G 15
374 **HARRIS** (IRE) 8
129 **HARRIS GARDEN** (IRE) 4
639 **HARRIS HAWK** (GB) 21
279 **HARRIS TWEED** (GB) 10
482 **HARRISON GEORGE** (IRE) 5
394 **HARRISTOWN** (GB) 22
590 **HARROGATE FAIR** (GB) 3
429 **HARRY BOSCH** (GB) 13
426 **HARRY HUNT** (GB) 13
16 **HARRY HURRICANE** 58
206 **HARRY THE LEMMON** (IRE) 10
473 **HARRY THE VIKING** (GB) 51
13 **HARRY TOPPER** (GB) 21
692 **HARRY'S CHOICE** (GB) 6
523 **HARRY'S DANCER** (IRE) 57
278 **HARRY'S FAREWELL** (GB) 5
492 **HARRY'S PRINCESS** (IRE) 25
389 **HARRY'S SUMMER** (USA) 11
666 **HARTFORTH** (GB) 5
40 **HARTLEBURY** (GB) 4

358 **HARTNELL** (GB) 88
687 **HARTSIDE** (GER) 2
148 **HARVEST JOY** (IRE) C 67
396 **HARVEST MIST** (IRE) 6
27 **HARVESTIDE** (IRE) 69
428 **HARVEY LOGAN** (IRE) 30
531 **HARVEY'S HOPE** (GB) 14
503 **HARWOODS STAR** (IRE) 8
503 **HARWOODS VOLANTE** (IRE) 31
659 **HASANKA** (IRE) F 91
333 **HASH BROWN** (GB) 15
635 **HASHEEM** (GB) 13
27 **HASNA** (FR) 6
53 **HASOPOP** (IRE) 15
48 **HASSADIN** (GB) 7
130 **HASSLE** (IRE) 6
225 **HASTY LADY** (GB) G 5
440 **HATHA HOOH** (GB) 14
68 **HATSAWAY** (IRE) 33
499 **HATTA STREAM** (IRE) 8
64 **HATTERS RIVER** (IRE) 4
106 **HATTIE JACQUES** (GB) 17
383 **HATTON BANK** (GB) 30
17 **HAVANA BEAT** (IRE) 16
137 **HAVANA COOLER** (IRE) 11
181 **HAVANA GIRL** (IRE) 12
291 **HAVE FAITH** (IRE) C 210
615 **HAVE ONE FOR ME** (IRE) 9
649 **HAVE YOU HAD YOURS** (IRE) 3
631 **HAVE YOU SEEN ME** (IRE) 29
478 **HAVELOVEWILLTRAVEL** (IRE) 8
161 **HAVING A BALL** (GB) 9
365 **HAVINGOTASCOOBYDO** (IRE) 18
17 **HAVISHAM** (GB) 143
486 **HAWAII FIVE NIL** (IRE) 37
666 **HAWAII KLASS** (GB) 6
597 **HAWAIIAN FREEZE** (GB) 5
440 **HAWASH** (GB) 7
130 **HAWATTEF** (IRE) C 70
470 **HAWDYERWHEESHT** (GB) 12
493 **HAWK EYED LADY** (IRE) C 32
78 **HAWK GOLD** (IRE) 2
190 **HAWK HIGH** (IRE) 25
589 **HAWK MOTH** (IRE) 13
523 **HAWK MOUNTAIN** (UAE) 15
214 **HAWKER** (GB) 19
473 **HAWKES POINT** (GB) 52
254 **HAWKEYETHENOO** (IRE) 7
637 **HAWKHILL** (IRE) 40
32 **HAWKIN** (IRE) 101
659 **HAWRAA** (GB) 92
358 **HAWSA** (USA) C 168
180 **HAYDAR** (IRE) 65
624 **HAYDN'S LASS** (GB) 21
190 **HAYEK** (GB) 26
144 **HAYHAR Z** (GB) 44
394 **HAYJACK** (GB) 23
178 **HAYWARD'S HEATH** (GB) F 3
492 **HAZARABA** (IRE) 26
442 **HAZARAMA** (GB) C 24
548 **HAZARD WARNING** (IRE) 4
283 **HAZEL BROOK** (GB) 2
329 **HAZEL'S SONG** (GB) 6
190 **HAZELRIGG** (IRE) 27
268 **HAZIUM** (IRE) F 20
281 **HAZLEDOC** (IRE) 39
494 **HAZUMI** (GER) 63
260 **HAZY DANCER** (GB) C 124

394 **HAZY TOM** (IRE) 24
277 **HAZZA THE JAZZA** (GB) 10
298 **HAZZAAT** (IRE) 7
48 **HE'S A STRIKER** (IRE) 8
209 **HE'S MY BOY** (IRE) 34
130 **HE'S NO ANGEL** (IRE) 7
631 **HE'S THE DADDY** (GB) 30
279 **HEAD COACH** (GB) 108
288 **HEAD OF STEAM** (USA) 10
290 **HEAD OF THE CLASS** (IRE) 17
267 **HEAD RUSH** (GB) 20
98 **HEAD SPACE** (IRE) 15
457 **HEAD SPIN** (IRE) 15
397 **HEADBOROUGH LASS** (IRE) C 57
88 **HEADING TO FIRST** (GB) 5
429 **HEADLONG** (IRE) 37
188 **HEADLY'S BRIDGE** (IRE) 3
638 **HEADSTIGHT** (IRE) 18
53 **HEALING MUSIC** (FR) C 101
619 **HEALTH IS WEALTH** (IRE) 20
570 **HEART DANCER** (FR) 1
50 **HEART FOCUS** (IRE) 34
665 **HEART O ANNANDALE** (IRE) 11
27 **HEART OF HEARTS** (GB) C 70
635 **HEART'S DESIRE** (IRE) F 128
279 **HEARTBREAK HERO** (GB) 109
494 **HEARTILY** (IRE) 64
238 **HEARTSONG** (IRE) 5
106 **HEARTSTRINGS** (GB) 64
291 **HEAT OF THE NIGHT** (GB) C 211
507 **HEATH HUNTER** (IRE) 49
615 **HEATHER GLEN** (IRE) 10
409 **HEATHFIELD** (IRE) 18
381 **HEATHYARDS FLYER** (GB) 2
318 **HEATSTROKE** (IRE) 101
207 **HEAVEN'S GUEST** (IRE) 21
172 **HEAVEN'S HELP** (USA) C 35
169 **HEAVEN'S VAULT** (IRE) C 40
479 **HEAVENLY BAY** (USA) C 118
84 **HEAVENLY RIVER** (FR) 33
411 **HEAVENS EDGE** (GB) 4
589 **HEAVENSTOWN** (IRE) 14
358 **HEAVY METAL** (IRE) 18
482 **HEBREW MELODIES** (GB) 8
433 **HEBRIDEAN PRINCESS** (IRE) 19
428 **HECK THOMAS** (IRE) 31
546 **HECTOMARE** (IRE) 11
403 **HECTOR'S CHANCE** (FR) 11
385 **HECTOR'S CHOICE** (FR) 11
205 **HECTOR'S HOUSE** (GB) 9
486 **HEDLEY LAMARR** (IRE) 38
279 **HEERAAT** (IRE) 11
649 **HEEZ A STEEL** (IRE) 4
244 **HEEZARARITY** (GB) 8
602 **HEHO** (GB) 41
177 **HEIDI'S DELIGHT** (IRE) 2
376 **HEINRICH** (USA) 20
508 **HEJAZ** (IRE) 4
342 **HELAMIS** (GB) 2
492 **HELEN OF SPARTA** (IRE) F 78
201 **HELEN SHARP** (GB) C 57
584 **HELENA OF TROY** (GB) 32
546 **HELIOCENTRIC** (FR) C 156
550 **HELIOPSIS** (IRE) 36
382 **HELIOSPHERE** (USA) 38
182 **HELIUM** (FR) 6
162 **HELL'S SPIRIT** (IRE) 6
297 **HELLBENDER** (IRE) 7

608 **HOME FOR TEA** (GB) 23
357 **HOME GIRL** (IRE) 1
507 **HOME RUN** (GER) 52
112 **HOME YOU STROLL** (IRE) F 66
201 **HOMEBOY** (IRE) 15
27 **HOMEPAGE** (GB) C 72
188 **HOMER RUN** (IRE) 4
180 **HOMERIC** (IRE) 6
295 **HOMERIC HYMN** (FR) 59
546 **HOMESTEADING** (USA) 158
106 **HOMESTRETCH** (GB) 65
257 **HONEST JOHN** (GB) 9
659 **HONEST QUALITY** (USA) F 93
395 **HONEST STRIKE** (USA) 8
287 **HONEY BACH** (IRE) 3
239 **HONEY BADGER** (GB) 4
193 **HONEY MEADOW** (GB) 10
290 **HONEY MUSTARD** (IRE) G 19
201 **HONEY OF A KITTEN** (USA) 16
546 **HONEYMOON COCKTAIL** (FR) 57
211 **HONEYMOON EXPRESS** (IRE) 9
190 **HONEYSUCKLE LIL** (IRE) 104
27 **HONEYSUCKLE ROSE** (FR) 37
319 **HONITON LACE** (GB) 16
511 **HONKY TONK SALLY** (GB) F 44
32 **HONOR BOUND** (GB) 39
17 **HONORINE** (FR) F 147
658 **HONOUR A PROMISE** (GB) 21
214 **HONOUR SYSTEM** (GB) 20
274 **HONOUR THE KING** (IRE) 2
428 **HONOURABLE EMPEROR** (FR) 32
167 **HONOURABLE GENT** (GB) 8
634 **HONOURABLE KNIGHT** (IRE) 6
6 **HONOURED** (IRE) 17
572 **HONOURS STRIDE** (IRE) F 74
112 **HOODED** (USA) 29
44 **HOODNA** (IRE) 29
189 **HOOF IT** (GB) 19
189 **HOOF'S SO LUCKY** (GB) 59
189 **HOOFALONG** (GB) 20
189 **HOOFITRITA** (GB) 21
429 **HOOKE'S LAW** (IRE) 39
531 **HOOKERGATE GRAMMAR** (GB) 44
192 **HOONOSE** (GB) 5
104 **HOOP OF COLOUR** (USA) 25
58 **HOOPY** (GB) 13
442 **HOP IN** (IRE) 10
454 **HOPATINA** (IRE) 17
315 **HOPE CHEST** (GB) F 13
652 **HOPE FOR GLORY** (GB) 2
634 **HOPE POINT** (GB) 7
509 **HOPEAND** (GB) 5
645 **HOPEFILLY** (GB) 24
582 **HOPEFULL** (GB) 3
553 **HOPES N DREAMS** (IRE) 23
71 **HOPSTRINGS** (GB) 1
332 **HORACE HAZEL** (GB) 14
676 **HORATIO HORNBLOWER** (IRE) 17
448 **HORENDUS HULABALOO** (IRE) 13
321 **HORIZONTAL SPEED** (IRE) 39
209 **HORS DE COMBAT** (GB) 35
479 **HORSEGUARDSPARADE** (GB) 60
602 **HORSESHOE BAY** (IRE) 106
635 **HORSTED KEYNES** (FR) 14
267 **HORSTED VALLEY** (GB) 22
640 **HORTENSE MANCINI** (GB) 10
464 **HORTON** (GB) 7
159 **HOSTILE FIRE** (IRE) 18

128 **HOT AMBER** (USA) 26
148 **HOT COFFEE** (IRE) 36
33 **HOT MUSTARD** (GB) 3
173 **HOT PEPPER** (GB) 10
84 **HOT RIGHT NOW** (IRE) 12
189 **HOT SPICE** (GB) 22
336 **HOT STOCK** (FR) 25
553 **HOT STREAK** (IRE) 43
6 **HOT SUGAR** (USA) 18
513 **HOT WHISKEY** (IRE) 20
677 **HOT WHISKEY N ICE** (IRE) 5
679 **HOTGROVE BOY** (GB) 8
679 **HOUBLON DES OBEAUX** (FR) 33
511 **HOUND MUSIC** (GB) 45
587 **HOUNDSCOURT** (IRE) 13
291 **HOUSE CAPTAIN** (GB) 79
27 **HOUSE OF DREAMS** (JPN) 38
628 **HOUSE REBEL** (GB) C 23
61 **HOUSEHOLD CAVALRY** (GB) 61
155 **HOUSEPARTY** (GB) 13
40 **HOUSEWIVES CHOICE** (GB) 18
534 **HOUSTON DYNIMO** (IRE) 21
199 **HOW FORTUNATE** (GB) 4
69 **HOW RUDE** (GB) 18
95 **HOW'S MY FRIEND** (GB) 2
418 **HOWABOUTNEVER** (IRE) 60
418 **HOWABOUTNOW** (IRE) 61
679 **HOWARD'S LEGACY** (IRE) 34
22 **HOWIZEE** (GB) 3
233 **HOWLETT** (IRE) 1
9 **HOWLIN MOON** (GB) 13
473 **HOWLONGISAFOOT** (IRE) 54
371 **HOWWRONGCANYOUBE** (GB) 35
589 **HOWZ THE FAMILY** (IRE) 24
106 **HOY HOY** (IRE) 66
155 **HUBOOD** (GB) 14
39 **HUCKING HARMONY** (IRE) F 23
39 **HUCKING HARMONY** (IRE) F 37
593 **HUDIBRAS** (IRE) 3
50 **HUDSON'S BAY** (IRE) 4
206 **HUEHUECOYOTLE** (GB) 13
380 **HUELIN** (GB) 25
679 **HUFF AND PUFF** (GB) 35
674 **HUGHESIE** (IRE) 34
654 **HULA BALLEW** (GB) C 8
451 **HULCOLT** (IRE) 8
382 **HUMAN** (USA) 40
359 **HUMBEL BEN** (IRE) 6
542 **HUMBLE** (IRE) 4
16 **HUMIDOR** (IRE) 17
635 **HUMOUR** (IRE) 58
1 **HUMPHREY BEE** (IRE) 16
318 **HUNDI** (GB) 103
50 **HUNDRED YEAR FLOOD** (USA) C 82
371 **HUNG PARLIAMENT** (FR) 36
20 **HUNKY DOREY** (GB) 3
310 **HUNT BALL** (IRE) 51
44 **HUNTER'S LIGHT** (IRE) 30
464 **HUNTERS BELT** (IRE) 8
310 **HUNTERS HOOF** (IRE) 52
631 **HUNTERS LODGE** (IRE) 33
358 **HUNTING GROUND** (USA) 20
335 **HUNTING PARTY** (IRE) 29
637 **HUNTING TOWER** (GB) 43
112 **HUNTSMANS CLOSE** (GB) 5
518 **HURAKAN** (IRE) 5
335 **HURLER AND FARMER** (IRE) 30
458 **HURRICANE FLY** (IRE) 55

318 **HURRICANE HARRIET** (GB) F 104
378 **HURRICANE HARRY** (GB) 28
358 **HURRICANE HIGGINS** (IRE) 21
144 **HURRICANE HOLLOW** (GB) 14
481 **HURRICANE IVAN** (IRE) 21
679 **HURRICANE JOHN** (IRE) 36
295 **HURRICANE RIDGE** (IRE) 15
371 **HURRICANE VIC** (GB) 37
486 **HURRICANE'S GIRL** (GB) 41
399 **HURRY HOME POPPA** (IRE) 6
32 **HURRY UP GEORGE** (GB) 8
69 **HUSSAR BALLAD** (USA) 8
75 **HUSTLE BUSTLE** (IRE) 10
91 **HUTCHINSON** (USA) F 11
6 **HUZZAH** (IRE) 19
479 **HVEGER** (AUS) C 119
277 **HYDRANT** (GB) 11
109 **HYDROGEN** (GB) 22
291 **HYMENAIOS** (IRE) 80
296 **HYPNOTISM** (GB) 9
667 **HYPOCRISY** (GB) F 19
318 **HYPOTENEUSE** (IRE) C 105
631 **I AM COLIN** (GB) 34
349 **I AM NOT HERE** (IRE) 20
348 **I AM WHO I AM** (GB) 9
292 **I CONFESS** (GB) 11
259 **I FOUGHT THE LAW** (IRE) 8
531 **I GOT POWER** (GB) 15
531 **I GOT RHYTHM** (GB) G 41
254 **I GOT SUNSHINE** (GB) 10
291 **I KNOW** (GB) 213
571 **I KNOW THE CODE** (IRE) 8
418 **I NEED GOLD** (IRE) 62
547 **I NO UNDERSTAND** (IRE) 4
418 **I TOLD YOU SO** (IRE) 63
22 **I'LL BE FRANK** (GB) 10
35 **I'LL BE GOOD** (GB) 6
339 **I'M A JOKER** (GB) 9
418 **I'M A ROCKER** (IRE) 64
44 **I'M BACK** (IRE) 31
16 **I'M FRAAM GOVAN** (GB) 18
16 **I'M HARRY** (IRE) 19
354 **I'M LUCY** (IRE) 13
95 **I'M NOT TELLING** (IRE) 3
178 **I'M SHEIKRA** (IRE) 4
106 **I'M SO GLAD** (GB) 19
357 **I'M SO SPECIAL** (IRE) 2
607 **I'M SUPER TOO** (IRE) 20
659 **I'M YOURS** (GB) 39
606 **I'VEGOTAFEELING** (GB) 29
445 **IAMFINE** (IRE) G 33
478 **IAN'S MEMORY** (USA) 32
638 **IBECKE** (GB) 38
431 **ICANBOOGIE** (GB) 9
187 **ICANMOTOR** (GB) 9
380 **ICARIUM** (FR) 26
394 **ICE 'N' EASY** (GB) 25
393 **ICE APPLE** (GB) 9
450 **ICE BOAT** (GB) 55
126 **ICE COOL BREEZE** (IRE) 9
609 **ICE FALCON** (IRE) 25
189 **ICE GIRL** (GB) C 71
577 **ICE MAYDEN** (GB) 24
377 **ICE NELLY** (GB) 4
148 **ICE PIE** (GB) 17
602 **ICE QUEEN** (IRE) C 107
200 **ICE SLICE** (IRE) 12
434 **ICE TRES** (GB) 5

9 **KINDIA** (IRE) 14
389 **KINDLELIGHT STORM** (USA) 4
591 **KINDLING** (GB) C 38
383 **KINDLY NOTE** (GB) 37
137 **KINDU** (GB) 15
645 **KINEMA** (IRE) 26
450 **KINETIX** (GB) F 56
137 **KING BOLETE** (IRE) 87
383 **KING BORU** (IRE) 38
1 **KING BREX** (DEN) 19
118 **KING CALYPSO** (GB) 19
258 **KING EDMUND** (GB) 12
454 **KING HELISSIO** (IRE) 21
677 **KING KAYF** (GB) 7
479 **KING LEON** (GB) 9
546 **KING LUNA** (IRE) C 166
674 **KING MASSINI** (IRE) 38
481 **KING MURO** (GB) 25
264 **KING OF ARAN** (IRE) 4
3 **KING OF EDEN** (IRE) 6
549 **KING OF ENGLAND** (GB) 12
679 **KING OF GLORY** (GB) 40
54 **KING OF JAZZ** (IRE) 30
166 **KING OF KUDOS** (IRE) 13
358 **KING OF MACEDON** (GB) 93
3 **KING OF PARADISE** (IRE) 7
643 **KING OF STRINGS** (IRE) 12
190 **KING OF THE CELTS** (IRE) 30
615 **KING OF THE DARK** (IRE) 12
351 **KING OF THE NIGHT** (GER) 18
409 **KING OF THE REFS** (IRE) 19
351 **KING OF THE WOLDS** (IRE) 19
100 **KING OLAV** (UAE) 21
316 **KING OZZY** (IRE) 10
641 **KING PIN** (GB) 6
637 **KING ROLFE** (IRE) 48
513 **KING SPIRIT** (IRE) 25
98 **KING TORUS** (IRE) 17
356 **KING VAHE** (IRE) 8
384 **KING ZEAL** (IRE) 5
464 **KING'S CHORISTER** (GB) 11
138 **KING'S CIEL** (GB) 11
236 **KING'S ENCORE** (IRE) 19
418 **KING'S GRACE** (GB) 72
44 **KING'S LAND** (GB) 86
118 **KING'S ODYSSEY** (IRE) 5
13 **KING'S OPUS** (IRE) 24
635 **KING'S PROCESSION** (IRE) 65
641 **KING'S PROSPECT** (GB) 10
441 **KING'S REQUEST** (IRE) 10
459 **KING'S ROAD** (GB) 8
32 **KING'S SIREN** (GB) C 104
162 **KING'S SONG** (IRE) 8
631 **KING'S TEMPEST** (GB) 39
246 **KING'S WARRIOR** (IRE) 28
690 **KINGAROO** (IRE) 3
679 **KINGCORA** (FR) 41
259 **KINGDOMFORTHEBRIDE** (IRE) 11
479 **KINGFISHER** (GB) 69
619 **KINGFISHER CREEK** (GB) 28
275 **KINGLAMI** (GB) 2
260 **KINGMAN** (GB) 53
608 **KINGS APOLLO** (GB) 26
418 **KINGS BANDIT** (IRE) 73
371 **KINGS BAYONET** (GB) 43
241 **KINGS CHAPEL** (USA) 26
602 **KINGS FETE** (GB) 45
173 **KINGS FLAGSHIP** (GB) 14

550 **KINGS FOLLY** (IRE) 46
531 **KINGS GREY** (IRE) 18
619 **KINGS LAD** (IRE) 29
310 **KINGS LODGE** (GB) 58
507 **KINGS PALACE** (GB) 58
679 **KINGS RIVER** (FR) 42
281 **KINGS RYKER** (IRE) 42
479 **KINGSBARNS** (IRE) 10
354 **KINGSCOMBE** (USA) 6
35 **KINGSCROFT** (IRE) 9
443 **KINGSFOLD FLARE** (GB) 53
159 **KINGSGATE CHOICE** (IRE) 8
128 **KINGSGATE NATIVE** (IRE) 10
172 **KINGSMAN** (FR) 21
145 **KINGSMERE** (GB) 18
197 **KINGSTON EUCALYPT** (GB) 6
635 **KINGSTON HILL** (GB) 66
197 **KINGSTON SASSAFRAS** (GB) 30
564 **KINGSWAY LAD** (IRE) 34
550 **KINGSWELL THEATRE** (GB) 47
583 **KINGSWOOD HEIGHTS** (GB) 1
144 **KINGZINNI** (IRE) 16
577 **KINKOHYO** (GB) 26
291 **KINLOSS** (GB) 86
137 **KINSHASA** (GB) 45
120 **KIPUKA** (GB) 43
546 **KIRAM** (FR) 66
85 **KIRBYS GLEN** (IRE) 4
120 **KIRKINOLA** (GB) C 44
40 **KIRKMAN** (IRE) 19
131 **KIRKSTALL ABBEY** (IRE) 28
137 **KIRTHILL** (IRE) 16
144 **KIRTLING BELLE** (GB) 47
106 **KISANJI** (GB) 74
664 **KISS MY HEART** (GB) 7
318 **KISS OF SPRING** (IRE) 41
56 **KISSED BY FIRE** (GB) 7
382 **KISSES** (GB) F 42
418 **KITCHAPOLY** (FR) 74
164 **KITEGEN** (IRE) 16
659 **KITHIRA** (GB) C 98
564 **KITTY KITTY CANCAN** (GB) C 43
375 **KIWAYU** (GB) 33
169 **KIWI BAY** (GB) 9
318 **KIYOSHI** (GB) 42
377 **KLEITOMACHOS** (IRE) 6
137 **KLEO** (GB) 46
98 **KLYNCH** (GB) 18
615 **KNACKY LAD** (IRE) 13
560 **KNAVE OF CLUBS** (IRE) 20
635 **KNAVERY** (USA) 67
69 **KNAVESMIRE** (IRE) C 25
598 **KNEESY EARSY NOSEY** (GB) 19
89 **KNICKERBOKERGLORY** (GB) 3
493 **KNIFE POINT** (GER) 15
58 **KNIGHT BLAZE** (GB) 15
367 **KNIGHT CHARM** (GB) 3
399 **KNIGHT IN PURPLE** (GB) 1
507 **KNIGHT OF NOIR** (IRE) 59
443 **KNIGHT OF PLEASURE** (GB) 1
635 **KNIGHT OF SWORDS** (GB) 131
635 **KNIGHT OF WANDS** (GB) 132
364 **KNIGHT OFTHE REALM** (GB) 10
209 **KNIGHT OWL** (GB) 11
89 **KNIGHT VALLIANT** (GB) 4
582 **KNIGHT WOODSMAN** (GB) 5
637 **KNIGHT'S REWARD** (GB) 49
196 **KNIGHTLY ESCAPADE** (GB) 41

295 **KNIGHTSONE** (IRE) 19
385 **KNOCK A HAND** (IRE) 14
106 **KNOCK HOUSE** (IRE) 23
642 **KNOCKAMANY BENDS** (IRE) 5
605 **KNOCKANAR** (IRE) 4
13 **KNOCKANRAWLEY** (IRE) 25
111 **KNOCKARA BEAU** (IRE) 3
376 **KNOCKATOTAUN** (GB) F 41
179 **KNOCKCAIRN** (IRE) 6
418 **KNOCKGRAFFON KING** (IRE) 75
513 **KNOCKGRAFFON LAD** (USA) 26
486 **KNOCKRAHEEN** (IRE) 51
17 **KNOCKROON** (GB) 81
147 **KNOW MORE OATS** (IRE) 5
387 **KNOW NO FEAR** (GB) 10
201 **KNOW YOUR NAME** (GB) 41
209 **KOALA BEAR** (GB) 12
398 **KOBROUK** (FR) 68
201 **KODAFINE** (IRE) 42
440 **KODESTINY** (IRE) 32
609 **KODIAC LADY** (IRE) 61
643 **KODICIL** (IRE) 13
404 **KOHARU** (GB) 2
17 **KOKOVOKO** (IRE) 82
169 **KOLONEL KIRKUP** (IRE) 10
295 **KOMITOE** (IRE) 61
169 **KOMMANDER KIRKUP** (GB) 23
4 **KOMPETE** (GB) G 10
498 **KOMREYEV STAR** (GB) 3
638 **KONIG HALL** (GB) 20
378 **KONIYA** (IRE) F 41
675 **KONZERT** (ITY) 36
196 **KOOL ACCLAIM** (GB) C 113
658 **KOOLALA** (IRE) 23
685 **KOOLGREYCAT** (IRE) 5
137 **KOORA** (GB) 88
159 **KOPENHAGEN** (IRE) 20
36 **KOPI LUWAK** (GB) 12
493 **KORANTAM** (IRE) 7
57 **KORBOUS** (IRE) 3
641 **KORNGOLD** (GB) 7
358 **KOSIKA** (USA) 24
33 **KOTDIJI** (GB) C 34
371 **KOTKIRI** (FR) 44
10 **KOUP DE KANON** (FR) 76
161 **KOVOLINI** (GB) 11
546 **KOZIDEH** (FR) 67
390 **KOZMINA BAY** (GB) 11
677 **KRACKATOA KING** (GB) 8
634 **KRACKERJILL** (IRE) 20
189 **KRAKA GYM** (IRE) 60
277 **KRASOTKA** (IRE) G 35
550 **KRIS CROSS** (IRE) 48
385 **KRIS SPIN** (IRE) 15
454 **KRISTAL HART** (GB) 22
646 **KRISTJANO** (GER) 46
241 **KRITZIA** (GB) F 27
84 **KRUPSKAYA** (FR) 14
418 **KRUZHLININ** (GB) 77
295 **KRYNICA** (USA) F 62
118 **KUALA QUEEN** (IRE) 11
120 **KUANTAN ONE** (IRE) 7
472 **KUANYAO** (IRE) 17
387 **KUBEBA** (IRE) 22
321 **KUBLAI** (FR) 46
371 **KUDA HURAA** (IRE) 45
610 **KUDU COUNTRY** (IRE) 4
691 **KUDU SHINE** (GB) 10

104 **LAKE ALFRED** (USA) 27
180 **LAKE CHAMPLAIN** (IRE) 67
291 **LAKE LADOGA** (GB) C 228
164 **LAKE LEGEND** (GB) 18
295 **LAKE SUPERIOR** (IRE) 63
326 **LAKEFIELD REBEL** (IRE) 5
148 **LALECTRA** (GB) C 70
279 **LAMANKA LASS** (USA) F 116
609 **LAMAR** (IRE) 28
296 **LAMASSU** (IRE) F 44
321 **LAMB OR COD** (IRE) 48
250 **LAMB'S CROSS** (GB) 10
291 **LAMBADORA** (GB) F 229
314 **LAMBERT PEN** (USA) 5
265 **LAMBLORD** (IRE) 4
54 **LAMBORO LAD** (IRE) 31
680 **LAMBRINI QUEEN** (GB) G 10
29 **LAMBRO RIVER** (IRE) 2
493 **LAMORAK** (FR) 16
48 **LAMPS** (GB) 2
318 **LAMYAA** (GB) 110
358 **LANARK** (IRE) 95
291 **LANARK BELLE** (GB) C 230
344 **LANCELOT DU LAC** (ITY) 15
674 **LANCETTO** (FR) 39
389 **LANCIANA** (IRE) G 5
54 **LAND OF VIC** (GB) 32
44 **LANDAMAN** (IRE) 34
1 **LANDECKER** (IRE) 20
112 **LANDELA** (GB) F 69
339 **LANDENSTOWN PEARL** (IRE) 11
250 **LANDENSTOWN STAR** (IRE) 11
457 **LANDERBEE** (IRE) 22
141 **LANDESHERR** (GER) 2
543 **LANDIGOU** (FR) 9
131 **LANDMARQUE** (GB) 8
176 **LANDULPH LASS** (GB) 8
209 **LANDWADE LAD** (GB) 64
494 **LANDYM** (FR) 70
454 **LANGARVE LADY** (IRE) 23
454 **LANGARVE LASS** (IRE) 24
339 **LANGHAM LILY** (USA) 12
557 **LANGLEY HOUSE** (IRE) 13
613 **LANGLEY VALE** (GB) 7
210 **LANSDOWNE PRINCESS** (IRE) 7
659 **LANYARD** (USA) 43
201 **LAPIS BLUE** (IRE) 19
6 **LAPWORTH** (IRE) 26
108 **LARA LIPTON** (IRE) 13
100 **LARAGHCON BOY** (GB) 23
576 **LARC** (FR) 25
395 **LARGHETTO** (USA) 10
364 **LARKS RISING** (GB) 12
364 **LARKS WING** (IRE) 13
576 **LARME** (FR) F 45
543 **LARMINA** (FR) 10
465 **LARROCHA** (IRE) F 14
148 **LARSEN BAY** (IRE) 38
544 **LARSEN BEE** (IRE) 5
339 **LARTETA** (FR) 13
546 **LARVOTTO** 170
260 **LAS FLORES** (IRE) C 130
207 **LAS VERGLAS STAR** (IRE) 30
638 **LASCALINA** (GER) 52
143 **LASCAUX** (GB) 10
371 **LASER BLAZER** (GB) 49
241 **LASER BLAZER** (GB) 11
260 **LASHKAAL** (GB) 131

442 **LASSIE'S GOLD** (USA) F 25
564 **LAST CHANCE RANCH** (GB) 8
32 **LAST ECHO** (IRE) 43
213 **LAST INSTALMENT** (IRE) 16
479 **LAST LOVE** (IRE) C 122
376 **LAST MINUTE LISA** (IRE) 7
50 **LAST RESORT** (GB) C 91
679 **LAST SHOT** (FR) 43
221 **LASTCHANCEFORLISA** (IRE) 3
99 **LASTCHANCELUCAS** (GB) 6
463 **LASTING VIEW** (IRE) 9
171 **LASTKINGOFSCOTLAND** (IRE) 11
409 **LASTOFTHELEADERS** (IRE) 20
546 **LASTUCE** (FR) 15
318 **LATE NIGHT MARK** (IRE) 43
263 **LATE REG** (GB) 3
358 **LATE SHIPMENT** (GB) 96
407 **LATELO** (GB) 12
207 **LATENIGHTREQUEST** (GB) 71
203 **LATERAL THINKING** (IRE) 8
682 **LATEST FASHION** (IRE) 3
260 **LATICE** (FR) C 132
53 **LATIN CHARM** (IRE) 56
479 **LATIN LOVE** (IRE) C 123
290 **LATIN MISTRESS** (GB) G 22
254 **LATIN REBEL** (IRE) 15
494 **LATINO** (SWI) 17
207 **LAUDATE DOMINUM** (IRE) 31
420 **LAUDATION** (GB) 4
310 **LAUDATORY** (GB) 61
112 **LAUGHARNE** (GB) 31
16 **LAUGHING JACK** (GB) 23
21 **LAUGHING MUSKETEER** (IRE) 5
358 **LAUGHSOME** (GB) C 170
585 **LAUGHTON PARK** (GB) 7
126 **LAUNCESTON** (GB) F 11
646 **LAURA B** (GB) 47
403 **LAURA SECORD** (CAN) 7
264 **LAUREL CREEK** (IRE) 5
16 **LAURELITA** (IRE) 44
395 **LAUREN ERIA** (GB) C 23
591 **LAUREN LOUISE** (GB) F 39
137 **LAURENCE** (GB) 91
310 **LAURIUM** (GB) 62
674 **LAVA LAMP** (GER) 40
584 **LAVELLA WELLS** (GB) 42
349 **LAVENDAR FIELDS** (IRE) 23
680 **LAVERNOCK LADY** (GB) F 26
429 **LAW APPEAL** (GB) 41
494 **LAW BLADE** (FR) 18
461 **LAW HILL** (GB) 3
279 **LAW KEEPER** (IRE) 48
440 **LAWMANS THUNDER** (GB) 6
491 **LAWSONG** (FR) 27
573 **LAWSONS THORNS** (IRE) 20
137 **LAWYER** (IRE) 47
450 **LAWYERS CHOICE** (GB) C 57
50 **LAWYERS TALK** (IRE) 92
635 **LAYALEE** (IRE) 135
358 **LAYL** (USA) 25
661 **LAYLA'S BOY** (GB) 4
472 **LAYLA'S HERO** (IRE) 18
207 **LAYLA'S OASIS** (GB) 32
449 **LAYLA'S RED DEVIL** (IRE) 24
207 **LAYLA'S RED DEVIL** (IRE) 72
367 **LAYLINE** (IRE) 4
73 **LAZARUS BELL** (GB) 7
685 **LAZY DAYS IN LOULE** (IRE) 15

100 **LE BACARDY** (FR) 24
398 **LE BARON NOIR** (FR) 71
383 **LE BEC** (FR) 39
5 **LE BERNARDIN** (USA) 28
169 **LE CHAT D'OR** (GB) 11
398 **LE COSTAUD** (FR) 72
189 **LE DELUGE** (FR) 29
546 **LE DEPUTE** (FR) 171
386 **LE GRAND CHENE** (FR) 11
166 **LE LAITIER** (FR) 30
130 **LE MAITRE CHAT** (USA) 40
303 **LE PERGOLESE** (FR) 6
640 **LE REVE** (FR) 12
676 **LE ROCHER** (FR) 18
546 **LE SENATEUR** (FR) 172
688 **LE TIGRE DE BRONZE** (GB) 4
94 **LE TORRENT** (GB) 48
259 **LE TROISIEME GRIS** (IRE) 21
546 **LE VAGABOND** (FR) 173
424 **LEACHESTOWN** (IRE) G 7
376 **LEAD A MERRY DANCE** (GB) 24
511 **LEAD THE WAY** (GB) 9
507 **LEADER OF THE GANG** (GB) 60
595 **LEADER OF THE LAND** (IRE) 6
479 **LEADING LIGHT** (IRE) 11
206 **LEADING SCORE** (IRE) 14
659 **LEAFCUTTER** (IRE) 44
50 **LEAFY APPROACH** (IRE) 93
50 **LEAFY SUBURB** (IRE) 38
686 **LEAHNESS** (IRE) 9
221 **LEAHNOR** (IRE) 4
384 **LEAN BURN** (GB) 6
500 **LEAN ON PETE** (IRE) 5
75 **LEAST SAID** (USA) C 28
675 **LEATH ACRA MOR** (IRE) 37
210 **LEAVE IT BE** (IRE) 8
189 **LEAVE IT TO ARNO** (GB) 73
429 **LEAVINGONAJETPLANE** (IRE) C 83
190 **LEBANNA** (GB) 32
637 **LECALE LAD** (IRE) 50
154 **LEEROAR** (IRE) 6
69 **LEES ANTHEM** (GB) 9
660 **LEG IRON** (IRE) 9
507 **LEGACY GOLD** (IRE) 61
677 **LEGAL EAGLE** (IRE) 9
102 **LEGAL LEGACY** (GB) 9
41 **LEGAL PURSUIT** (GB) 4
515 **LEGAL SHARK** (IRE) 20
607 **LEGAL WAVES** (IRE) 23
429 **LEGAL WAVES** (IRE) 16
427 **LEGEND RISING** (IRE) 8
636 **LEGENDARY** (GB) 4
31 **LEGENDARY HOP** (GB) 7
173 **LEGION D'HONNEUR** (UAE) 16
394 **LEITH HILL LEGASI** (GB) 32
50 **LEITIR MOR** (IRE) 5
279 **LEITRIM PASS** (USA) 13
659 **LELIANI** (IRE) 45
658 **LEMON DROP RED** (USA) 25
52 **LEMON GROVE** (GB) 8
308 **LEMON PEARL** (GB) 6
658 **LEMON'S GENT** (GB) 26
587 **LEMONS GROUND** (GB) 16
568 **LEMONY BAY** (GB) 22
354 **LENA PLAYER** (SWE) 14
131 **LENDAL BRIDGE** (GB) 29
107 **LENDERKING** (IRE) 9
285 **LENEY COTTAGE** (IRE) 6

631 **LITTLE POP** (GB) 43	336 **LONDON BRIDGE** (USA) 12	484 **LORD OF THE NILE** (IRE) 79
474 **LITTLE POSH** (IRE) 8	160 **LONDON SILVER** (GB) 4	291 **LORD OFTHE SHADOWS** (IRE) 12
450 **LITTLE PRAIRIE** (GB) 58	200 **LONDON SKOLAR** (GB) 4	328 **LORD PAGET** (GB) 16
16 **LITTLE PUDDING** (GB) 24	550 **LONE FOOT LADDIE** (IRE) 51	321 **LORD PROTECTOR** (IRE) 50
52 **LITTLE RED NELL** (IRE) 9	201 **LONE WARRIOR** (IRE) 44	476 **LORD REDSGIRTH** (IRE) 16
335 **LITTLE ROCKY** (GB) 36	150 **LONELY ONE** (GB) G 7	111 **LORD USHER** (IRE) 4
471 **LITTLE ROXY** (IRE) 9	25 **LONG AWAITED** (GB) 10	230 **LORD VALENTINE** (GB) 3
358 **LITTLE SHAMBLES** (GB) 97	260 **LONG CROSS** (GB) 56	420 **LORD WESTHEAD** (IRE) 5
577 **LITTLE SISTA** (GB) 48	5 **LONG JOHN** (AUS) 31	206 **LORD WISHES** (IRE) 15
622 **LITTLE TINKA** (GB) 15	176 **LONG JOHN** (GB) 9	356 **LORDENSHAWS** (IRE) 7
526 **LITTLE WADHAM** (GB) 3	394 **LONG LUNCH** (GB) 34	246 **LORDOFTHEHOUSE** (IRE) 29
634 **LITTLECOTE LADY** (GB) 10	310 **LONG RUN** (FR) 65	269 **LORDSHIP** (IRE) 9
487 **LITTLEDEAN JIMMY** (IRE) 7	602 **LONG VIEW** (IRE) 46	434 **LORELEI** (GB) 37
121 **LITTLEMISSBLAKENEY** (GB) 18	394 **LONG WAVE** (IRE) 35	546 **LORESHO** (FR) 72
428 **LITTLEMISSSTUBBORN** (IRE) 40	279 **LONGING TO DANCE** (GB) C 119	643 **LORIMER'S LOT** (IRE) 26
358 **LITTLPEACEPADDOCKS** (IRE) C 98	546 **LONGRAY** (FR) 175	617 **LORTZING** (IRE) 4
155 **LITTLETON LAD** (IRE) 20	652 **LONGSHADOW** (GB) 32	254 **LOS NADIS** (GER) 17
428 **LITTLETON LIBERTY** (GB) G 41	492 **LONGTON** (GB) 32	652 **LOS ORGANOS** (GB) C 14
144 **LIVE DANGEROUSLY** (GB) 17	543 **LONGUEIL** (FR) 11	486 **LOST GLORY** (NZ) 54
418 **LIVELY BARON** (IRE) 81	148 **LOOBY LOO** (GB) F 71	369 **LOST IN NEWYORK** (IRE) 12
196 **LIVIA DRUSILLA** (IRE) 101	240 **LOOK FOR LOVE** (GB) 7	131 **LOST IN PARIS** (IRE) 9
645 **LIVIA'S DREAM** (IRE) 8	425 **LOOK HERE'S CAROL** (IRE) G 26	44 **LOST IN THE MOMENT** (IRE) 36
494 **LIVING DESERT** (GB) 21	425 **LOOK HERE'S DEE** (GB) C 30	486 **LOST LEGEND** (IRE) 55
159 **LIVING IT LARGE** (FR) 9	50 **LOOK LIVELY** (IRE) 96	636 **LOST SHILLING** (IRE) C 23
389 **LIVING LEADER** (GB) 6	671 **LOOK OF EAGLES** (GB) F 5	607 **LOTHAIR** (IRE) 24
409 **LIVING NEXT DOOR** (IRE) 21	98 **LOOK ON BY** (GB) 20	371 **LOTUS POND** (IRE) 53
491 **LIVING THE LIFE** (IRE) 8	27 **LOOK OVER** (GB) 40	521 **LOUCAL** (GB) 4
17 **LIZZIE TUDOR** (GB) 23	484 **LOOKBEFOREYOULEAP** (GB) 36	358 **LOUD** (GB) 29
534 **LIZZY LANGTRY** (IRE) F 24	336 **LOOKER** (GB) C 36	431 **LOUGH COI** (IRE) 11
28 **LIZZY'S DREAM** (GB) 8	479 **LOOKING LOVELY** (IRE) C 125	587 **LOUGH DERG WAY** (IRE) 17
269 **LL COOL HORSE** (GB) 8	257 **LOOKING ON** (GB) 13	295 **LOUGH LASS** (IRE) 21
196 **LLANARMON LAD** (IRE) 44	486 **LOOKOUT MOUNTAIN** (IRE) 53	567 **LOUGHALDER** (IRE) 5
491 **LLANDANWG** (GB) 28	429 **LOOKS CAN KILL** (GB) 17	21 **LOUGHMORE VIC** (IRE) 3
472 **LLEWELLYN** (GB) 20	372 **LOOKS LIKE MAGIC** (GB) 12	130 **LOUIE DE PALMA** (GB) 74
479 **LLIA** (GB) C 124	284 **LOOKS LIKE POWER** (IRE) 5	46 **LOUIS PHILLIPE** (IRE) 2
190 **LLYN** (GB) 106	160 **LOOKS LIKE SLIM** (GB) 5	72 **LOUIS VEE** (IRE) 5
305 **LLYRICAL** (GB) 10	291 **LOOKSLIKEANANGEL** (GB) 95	308 **LOUIS' LOVER** (FR) F 45
606 **LO SIENTO** (IRE) 17	139 **LOOKSLIKERAINTED** (IRE) 28	190 **LOUKOUMI** (GB) 34
493 **LOBSTER POT** (GB) 17	394 **LOOSE CHIPS** (GB) 36	329 **LOULOU VUITTON** (GB) 3
458 **LOCAL CELEBRITY** (IRE) 63	252 **LOPITO DE VEGA** (IRE) 31	635 **LOULWA** (IRE) F 136
257 **LOCAL HERO** (GER) 12	39 **LOQUACITY** (IRE) F 26	177 **LOUVOLITE** (FR) F 24
494 **LOCAL LOVER** (FR) 22	491 **LORAINE** (GB) 9	546 **LOVABLE** (CAN) 73
44 **LOCAL SPIRIT** (USA) C 117	207 **LORD AERYN** (IRE) 34	371 **LOVCEN** (GER) 54
106 **LOCH BA** (IRE) 24	689 **LORD ALDERVALE** (IRE) 5	260 **LOVE BALLAD** (IRE) 135
50 **LOCH GARMAN** (IRE) 7	135 **LORD AVONBROOK** (GB) 8	5 **LOVE CHARM** (GB) C 119
180 **LOCH MA NAIRE** (IRE) 34	673 **LORD BELLAMY** (IRE) 2	358 **LOVE D'ORO** (USA) 99
32 **LOCH VERDI** (GB) C 106	84 **LORD BEN STACK** (IRE) 65	5 **LOVE DIVINE** (GB) C 120
378 **LOCHALSH** (IRE) 29	106 **LORD BRANTWOOD** (GB) 76	318 **LOVE EXCEL** (GB) 5
679 **LOCHNAGAR** (GER) 45	356 **LORD BRENDY** (GB) 6	546 **LOVE IN PARADISE** (GB) F 176
196 **LOCHNELL** (IRE) 45	277 **LORD BUFFHEAD** (GB) 14	281 **LOVE IN THE MIST** (USA) C 69
4 **LOCHORE** (IRE) 11	207 **LORD CLYDE** (GB) 73	667 **LOVE ISLAND** (GB) 5
497 **LOCK TOWERS** (IRE) 8	69 **LORD CONYERS** (IRE) C 27	665 **LOVE MARMALADE** (IRE) 15
53 **LOCKEDOUTATHEAVEN** (IRE) 58	572 **LORD EMPIRE** (IRE) 39	279 **LOVE ME ONLY** (IRE) C 120
44 **LOCKWOOD** (GB) 35	297 **LORD FOX** (IRE) 8	101 **LOVE ME TENDER** (GB) C 11
553 **LOCKY TAYLOR** (IRE) 49	3 **LORD FRANKLIN** (GB) 9	479 **LOVE ME TRUE** (USA) C 126
631 **LODGICIAN** (IRE) 44	274 **LORD GALE** (IRE) 3	68 **LOVE OF DUBAI** (USA) F 37
395 **LOGANS LAD** (IRE) 11	145 **LORD GRANTHAM** (IRE) 20	180 **LOVE ROI** (ITY) F 68
614 **LOGICAL APPROACH** (IRE) 6	280 **LORD KENNEDY** (IRE) 12	452 **LOVE SPICE** (GB) 23
84 **LOKI'S STRIKE** (GB) 7	481 **LORD LANDEN** (IRE) 27	546 **LOVE STRIKE** (FR) 74
507 **LOLA GALLI** (GB) 62	321 **LORD LESCRIBAA** (FR) 49	429 **LOVE TANGLE** (IRE) 42
382 **LOLA MONTEZ** (IRE) 21	613 **LORD LEXINGTON** (GB) 14	260 **LOVE THE RAIN** (GB) F 136
134 **LOLITA'S GOLD** (USA) C 15	637 **LORD LIR** (IRE) 53	607 **LOVE THIRTY** (GB) F 43
621 **LOLLA'S SPIRIT** (IRE) F 12	66 **LORD NAVITS** (IRE) 15	445 **LOVE THIRTY** (GB) F 36
417 **LOMA MOR** (IRE) 9	550 **LORD OF DRUMS** (IRE) 52	259 **LOVEINASANDDUNE** (GB) 13
429 **LOMAPAMAR** (GB) C 85	407 **LORD OF HOUSE** (GER) 13	318 **LOVELOCKS** (IRE) 45
19 **LOMBARDY BOY** (IRE) 2	371 **LORD OF SCOTLAND** (IRE) 52	494 **LOVEMEDO** (FR) 141
144 **LOMOND LASSIE** (IRE) 49	456 **LORD OF THE DANCE** (IRE) 8	144 **LOVER MAN** (IRE) 18
428 **LONDON BRIDGE** (GB) 42	619 **LORD OF THE DUNES** (GB) 30	463 **LOVES BLIND** (IRE) 6

576 **MAGICIENMAKE MYDAY** (GB) 26
53 **MAGIKA** (GB) 17
478 **MAGIQUE** (IRE) 10
214 **MAGISTRAL** (GB) 23
308 **MAGISTRATE** (FR) 46
128 **MAGLIETTA FINA** (IRE) 11
310 **MAGNA CARTOR** (GB) 71
659 **MAGNA GRAECIA** (IRE) C 99
484 **MAGNIFIED** (GB) 37
394 **MAGNIFIQUE ETOILE** (GB) 37
50 **MAGNO CLAMORE** (IRE) 101
397 **MAGNOLIA BEACH** (IRE) 21
603 **MAGNOLIA RIDGE** (IRE) 4
537 **MAGNUM TOO** (IRE) 4
291 **MAGNUS MAXIMUS** (GB) 96
53 **MAGNUS ROMEO** (GB) 61
295 **MAGPIE** (USA) C 80
635 **MAHAABA** (GB) 73
353 **MAHAB EL SHAMAAL** (GB) 2
159 **MAHADEE** (IRE) 10
214 **MAHICAN** (IRE) 24
543 **MAHIR** (FR) 12
631 **MAHOGANY BLAZE** (FR) 45
201 **MAHON FALLS** (GB) 45
260 **MAHSOOB** (GB) 58
180 **MAHSOOBA** (USA) 71
197 **MAID A MILLION** (GB) 7
358 **MAID IN RIO** (IRE) 101
190 **MAID IN ROME** (IRE) 107
515 **MAID OF KILLEEN** (IRE) C 49
60 **MAID OF OAKSEY** (GB) 8
454 **MAID OF SILK** (IRE) 26
207 **MAIDEN APPROACH** (GB) 74
161 **MAIDEN AUNT** (GB) G 12
508 **MAIDENHAIR** (IRE) F 16
33 **MAIDIN MAITH** (GB) C 75
428 **MAIDRIN RUA** (IRE) G 91
646 **MAIL DE BIEVRE** (FR) 30
291 **MAIL THE DESERT** (IRE) C 236
330 **MAILLOT JAUNE** (IRE) 9
591 **MAINE LOBSTER** (USA) C 40
50 **MAINICIN** (IRE) 102
281 **MAIRA** (IRE) 70
602 **MAIRISE** (GB) 47
247 **MAISIE MC** (IRE) 13
175 **MAISON BRILLET** (IRE) 1
484 **MAISON DE VILLE** (GER) 38
624 **MAISRAH** (IRE) 41
204 **MAIZY MISSILE** (IRE) 1
246 **MAJALA** (IRE) 31
572 **MAJEED** (GB) 11
545 **MAJESTIC ANGEL** (IRE) 4
189 **MAJESTIC DREAM** (IRE) 31
472 **MAJESTIC MANANNAN** (IRE) 21
207 **MAJESTIC MOON** (IRE) 35
207 **MAJESTIC MYLES** (IRE) 36
209 **MAJESTIC NIGHT** (IRE) C 65
279 **MAJESTIC ROI** (USA) F 121
659 **MAJESTIC SILVER** (IRE) F 100
621 **MAJESTIC SONG** (IRE) 7
109 **MAJESTIC SUN** (IRE) 25
387 **MAJESTIC ZAFEEN** (IRE) 11
5 **MAJEYDA** (USA) 86
450 **MAJIC MAC** (GB) 59
624 **MAJOR BOBBY** (GB) 23
200 **MAJOR CRISPIES** (GB) 13
351 **MAJOR IVAN** (IRE) 22
112 **MAJOR JACK** (GB) 34

450 **MAJOR MAC** (GB) 60
631 **MAJOR MALARKEY** (IRE) 46
443 **MAJOR MARTIN** (IRE) 60
587 **MAJOR MILBORNE** (GB) 19
344 **MAJOR MINOR** (IRE) G 36
297 **MAJOR MUSCARI** (IRE) 9
418 **MAJOR PARKES** (GB) 83
238 **MAJOR PUSEY** (GB) 14
577 **MAJOR ROWAN** (GB) 28
568 **MAJORICA KING** (IRE) 25
429 **MAJORITIES** (GB) 44
494 **MAJOUNE** (FR) C 143
546 **MAJRAA** (IRE) 76
598 **MAJURO** (IRE) 20
27 **MAJVER** (IRE) 77
353 **MAJY D'AUTEUIL** (FR) 3
507 **MAKADAMIA** (GB) 63
137 **MAKAFEH** (GB) 17
310 **MAKARI** (GB) 72
581 **MAKBULLET** (GB) 10
198 **MAKE A FUSS** (GB) 2
606 **MAKE A TRACK** (IRE) 18
257 **MAKE ME A FORTUNE** (IRE) 14
458 **MAKE YOUR MARK** (IRE) 66
674 **MAKEABREAK** (IRE) G 44
225 **MAKELLYS BLACKPOOL** (GB) 8
674 **MAKETHE MOSTOFNOW** (IRE) 45
1 **MAKHZOON** (USA) 22
523 **MAKIN A STATEMENT** (IRE) 58
523 **MAKIN THE RULES** (IRE) 46
523 **MAKIN TROUBLE** (IRE) 59
350 **MAKING WAVES** (IRE) C 22
319 **MAKRUMA** (GB) 19
260 **MAKTABA** (IRE) 138
106 **MALABAR** (GB) 123
291 **MALACHIM MIST** (IRE) 97
260 **MALAF** (USA) 139
308 **MALAISIE** (USA) F 47
607 **MALAISIENNE** (FR) G 44
172a **MALAYSIAN BOLEH** 12
100 **MALANOS** (IRE) 25
58 **MALCOLM THE MOON** (GB) 17
371 **MALDIVIAN REEF** (IRE) 55
585 **MALIBU ROCK** (GB) 8
497 **MALIBU SUN** (GB) 9
344 **MALICHO** (GB) 17
130 **MALILLA** (IRE) 10
534 **MALIN BAY** (IRE) 25
659 **MALINKA** (IRE) 101
635 **MALJAA** (GB) 137
676 **MALJIMAR** (IRE) 19
162 **MALLER TREE** (IRE) 9
137 **MALLORY HEIGHTS** (IRE) 18
396 **MALLUSK** (IRE) 8
209 **MALORY TOWERS** (GB) 40
207 **MALRAAJ** (GB) 75
310 **MALT MASTER** (IRE) 73
546 **MALTA BADIA** (IRE) 178
530 **MALTEASE AH** (GB) 3
546 **MALVASIA** 179
596 **MALYANA** (GB) F 32
403 **MAM RATAGAN** (GB) 8
271 **MAMBO FEVER** (GB) 8
358 **MAMBO HALO** (USA) F 174
32 **MAMBO JAMBO** (USA) F 108
607 **MAMBO MISTRESS** (USA) G 59
358 **MAMBO RHYTHM** (GB) 102
469 **MAMBO SPIRIT** (IRE) 10

5 **MAMONTA** (GB) F 121
291 **MAMOUNIA** (IRE) C 237
607 **MAMOURA** (IRE) C 45
429 **MAN AMONGST MEN** (IRE) 45
515 **MAN FROM SEVILLE** (GB) 6
558 **MAN IN THE ARENA** (IRE) 3
17 **MAN OF HARLECH** (GB) 84
332 **MAN OF LEISURE** (IRE) 19
180 **MAN OF PLENTY** (GB) 8
54 **MAN OF STEEL** (IRE) 34
549 **MANALI** (FR) 57
472 **MANATEE BAY** (GB) 22
481 **MANBALLANDALL** (IRE) 28
207 **MANCHESTAR** (GB) 37
546 **MANCORA** (FR) 180
281 **MANDA HILL** (GER) C 71
217 **MANDALAY KING** (IRE) 5
549 **MANDALAYA** (USA) 58
291 **MANDARIN GIRL** (GB) 238
206 **MANDARIN SUNSET** (IRE) 17
50 **MANDATARIO** (GB) 39
44 **MANDELLICHT** (IRE) C 119
291 **MANDERLEY** (GB) 98
549 **MANDHEERA** (USA) 119
549 **MANDOUR** (USA) 14
577 **MANDY LAYLA** (IRE) 14
449 **MANDY THE NAG** (USA) 13
675 **MANDY'S BOY** (IRE) 39
505 **MANDYS NATIVE** (IRE) F 14
279 **MANGE ALL** (GB) 50
398 **MANGENIE** (FR) 73
63 **MANGER HANAGMENT** (IRE) 8
602 **MANGO DIVA** (GB) 14
587 **MANGOWAVE** (FR) 35
635 **MANHATTAN PRINCESS** (GB) 138
659 **MANHATTAN SWING** (IRE) 8
148 **MANIA** (IRE) C 72
530 **MANIC** (GB) F 7
338 **MANILA MAN** (GB) 1
144 **MANILA SELECTION** (USA) F 69
572 **MANIPULATION** (IRE) 42
53 **MANNARO** (IRE) 62
549 **MANNDAWI** (FR) 15
639 **MANNERED** (GB) 26
395 **MANNERIST** (GB) 24
279 **MANOEUVRE** (IRE) C 122
450 **MANOLITO** (GB) 61
68 **MANOMINE** (GB) 6
394 **MANOR BROOK** (IRE) 38
291 **MANOR WAY** (IRE) 99
147 **MANQUE PAS D'AIR** (FR) F 26
358 **MANSHAA** (IRE) 175
418 **MANSONIEN L'AS** (FR) 84
397 **MANSURI** (GB) 28
429 **MANTONIZE** (USA) 46
33 **MANTOU** (IRE) 35
568 **MANY CLOUDS** (IRE) 26
523 **MANY LEVELS** (GB) 22
187 **MANY MOONS** (FR) 12
573 **MANY STARS** (IRE) 22
371 **MANYRIVERSTOCROSS** (IRE) 56
345 **MANYSHADESOFBLACK** (IRE) 6
93 **MAOI CHINN TIRE** (IRE) 18
546 **MAPATONICK** (IRE) 181
172 **MAPLE GROVE** (FR) 22
190 **MAPPIN TIME** (IRE) 35
5 **MAPUTO** (GB) 32
44 **MAR MAR** (IRE) 37

190 **MAVREE** (IRE) 73
352 **MAWAAKEF** (IRE) 19
328 **MAWAARED** (GB) F 38
418 **MAWAQEET** (USA) 87
319 **MAWASEEL** (GB) 20
429 **MAWFOOR** (IRE) 47
279 **MAWJOOD** (GB) 123
13 **MAX BYGRAVES** (GB) 28
458 **MAX DYNAMITE** (FR) 69
19 **MAX LAURIE** (FR) 3
7 **MAX MILAN** (IRE) 4
564 **MAX THE MACHINE** (GB) 11
450 **MAX THE MINISTER** (GB) 14
72 **MAXDELAS** (FR) 6
584 **MAXED OUT KING** (GB) 45
473 **MAXI CHOP** (FR) 67
648 **MAXI MAC** (IRE) 4
358 **MAXIE T** (GB) 105
383 **MAXILIAN** (IRE) 40
428 **MAXIM GORKY** (IRE) 44
674 **MAXIS GIRL** (IRE) G 47
377 **MAY BE SOME TIME** (GB) 8
520 **MAY COURT** (GB) 3
101 **MAY HAY** (GB) 5
646 **MAY QUEEN** (GB) 29
197 **MAY WEST** (GB) F 32
523 **MAY WHI** (IRE) 47
439 **MAY'S BOY** (GB) 9
342 **MAYA DE VENTURA** (GB) 5
100 **MAYAN FLIGHT** (IRE) 26
454 **MAYBE ANNIE** (GB) 28
439 **MAYBE I WONT** (GB) 10
572 **MAYBE TOMORROW** (GB) 80
190 **MAYBEAGREY** (GB) 37
511 **MAYBELATER** (GB) 49
90 **MAYBEME** (GB) 8
310 **MAYFAIR MUSIC** (IRE) 75
69 **MAYFIELD BOY** (GB) 19
69 **MAYFIELD GIRL** (IRE) 12
583 **MAYGO'S JOY** (GB) 2
158 **MAYLAN** (IRE) F 3
158 **MAYLAN** (IRE) C 5
376 **MAYMYO** (IRE) 26
260 **MAYNOOTH** (GB) 142
540 **MAYPOLE LASS** (GB) 11
131 **MAYSVILLE** (IRE) 31
205 **MAYTHETENTH** (IRE) 12
319 **MAZAAHER** (GB) 11
68 **MAZAAYA** (USA) F 65
314 **MAZIJ** (GB) 6
175 **MAZIONA** (GB) F 4
493 **MAZOULA** (IRE) 34
107 **MAZOVIAN** (USA) 10
103 **MAZURATI** (IRE) 12
358 **MBHALI** (IRE) 106
142 **MCBIRNEY** (USA) 7
598 **MCCARTHY MOR** (IRE) 76
598 **MCCONNELL** (USA) 21
632 **MCCOOL BANNANAS** (GB) 6
112 **MCCREERY** (GB) 71
161 **MCDELTA** (GB) 13
50 **MCGUIGAN** (IRE) 103
458 **MCKINLEY** (GB) 70
473 **MCLLHATTON** (GB) 68
73 **MCMONAGLE** (USA) 9
351 **MCMURROUGH** (IRE) 23
430 **MCNULTY WRAY** (IRE) 7
371 **MCVICAR** (GB) 58

481 **ME AND BEN** (IRE) 29
665 **MEADOWCROFT BOY** (GB) 17
566 **MEADSTOWN** (IRE) 1
577 **MEADWAY** (GB) 29
546 **MEAN STREET** 184
479 **MEANDERING** (IRE) 72
73 **MEANDMYSHADOW** (GB) 10
53 **MEANING OF LIFE** (IRE) 65
201 **MEAON** (IRE) F 59
458 **MEASUREOFMYDREAMS** (IRE) 71
169 **MECCA'S ANGEL** (IRE) 24
250 **MEDAL OF VALOUR** (JPN) 12
68 **MEDALLERO** (USA) 38
297 **MEDAM** (GB) 10
16 **MEDBURN CUTLER** (GB) 26
142 **MEDDLE** (GB) F 14
211 **MEDDLING** (GB) 11
642 **MEDECIS MOUNTAIN** (GB) 6
380 **MEDEO** (FR) 31
371 **MEDERMIT** (FR) 59
84 **MEDIA HYPE** (GB) 16
241 **MEDICEAN MAN** (GB) 13
68 **MEDICEAN QUEEN** (IRE) 39
190 **MEDICI TIME** (GB) 38
444 **MEDICINE HAT** (GB) 27
643 **MEDIEVAL BISHOP** (IRE) 15
310 **MEDIEVAL CHAPEL** (FR) 76
371 **MEDINAS** (FR) 60
564 **MEDITATION** (GB) F 44
352 **MEDITERRANEAN SEA** (IRE) 20
295 **MEDUSE BLEU** (GB) C 81
352 **MEEBO** (GB) 39
281 **MEEK APPEAL** (USA) F 72
362 **MEESON** (GB) 10
646 **MEET ME HALFWAY** (GB) 6
56 **MEETHA ACHAR** (GB) 10
64 **MEETINGS MAN** (IRE) 6
321 **MEETMEATTHEMOON** (IRE) 51
209 **MEETYOUTHERE** (IRE) F 68
65 **MEGALALA** (IRE) 6
11 **MEGALEKA** (IRE) 6
443 **MEGALEX** (GB) G 62
310 **MEGALYPOS** (FR) 77
603 **MEGAMUNCH** (IRE) 5
443 **MEGASTAR** (GB) 63
225 **MEGLIO ANCORA** (GB) 10
449 **MEHDI** (IRE) 11
321 **MEIRIG'S DREAM** (IRE) 52
371 **MEISTER ECKHART** (IRE) 61
479 **MEKONG RIVER** (IRE) 73
69 **MELANDRE** (GB) C 28
260 **MELBOURNE SHUFFLE** (USA) 143
560 **MELODIC RENDEZVOUS** (GB) 22
382 **MELODRAMATIC** (IRE) C 43
358 **MELPOMENE** (GB) F 177
32 **MELROSE ABBEY** (IRE) 47
371 **MEMBEROF** (FR) 62
214 **MEMORABILIA** (GB) 25
479 **MEMORABLE** (GB) 74
181 **MEMORIES GALORE** (IRE) 29
645 **MEMORIZE** (IRE) 9
196 **MEMORY CLOTH** (GB) 50
17 **MEMSAHIB** (GB) C 153
159 **MEN DON'T CRY** (IRE) 11
380 **MENANDORE** (FR) 32
16 **MENDACIOUS HARPY** (IRE) 46
207 **MENDELITA** (GB) 77
236 **MENDIP EXPRESS** (IRE) 21

380 **MENEAS** (FR) 7
148 **MENELIK** (IRE) 19
564 **MENIATARRA** (USA) C 45
291 **MENNETOU** (IRE) F 243
321 **MENORAH** (IRE) 53
679 **MENTALIST** (FR) 49
591 **MER DE CORAIL** (IRE) F 24
372 **MERCERS COURT** (IRE) 13
630 **MERCERS ROW** (GB) 4
254 **MERCHANT OF DUBAI** (GB) 18
288 **MERCHANT OF MEDICI** (GB) 14
513 **MERCHANT OF MILAN** (GB) 29
84 **MERCREDI** (FR) F 66
32 **MERCURY MAGIC** (GB) 48
211 **MERCY ME** (GB) 28
572 **MEREDITH** (GB) F 81
473 **MEREHEAD** (FR) 69
298 **MERIDIUS** (IRE) 8
120 **MERITOCRACY** (IRE) 23
478 **MERLETTA** (GB) 36
365 **MERLIN'S WISH** (GB) 23
674 **MERRILL GAYE** (IRE) G 48
473 **MERRION SQUARE** (IRE) 70
486 **MERRY KING** (IRE) 62
17 **MERRY ME** (FR) 85
650 **MERRY MIX** (GB) 5
534 **MERRYDOWN** (IRE) 26
442 **MERRYDOWN BLACK** (GB) 12
659 **MESADAH** (IRE) 104
98 **MESHARDAL** (GER) 22
11 **MESPONE** (FR) 7
478 **MESSILA STAR** (GB) 11
42 **MESSINA STRAIGHTS** (GB) 8
331 **METAL MICKY** (GB) 3
137 **METAVOS** (GB) 94
104 **METEOROID** (USA) 28
456 **METHAALY** (IRE) 10
83 **METROPOLITAN CHIEF** (IRE) 4
394 **MEXICAN MICK** (GB) 39
667 **MEY BLOSSOM** (GB) 6
27 **MEZAMOUR** (FR) 78
243 **MEZARAT** (ITY) 6
281 **MEZOGIORNO** (IRE) 43
576 **MEZZO MEZZO** (FR) 47
678 **MEZZOTINT** (IRE) 14
207 **MFIFTYTHREEDOTCOM** (IRE) 78
360 **MI MAN SAM** (IRE) 2
144 **MI RUBINA** (IRE) F 70
494 **MI VIDA** (FR) 72
492 **MIA CAPRI** (IRE) 34
109 **MIA SAN TRIPLE** (GB) 27
186 **MIA'S BOY** (GB) 5
134 **MIA'S VIC** (FR) 6
6 **MIAKO** (USA) 31
84 **MIAMI GATOR** (IRE) 17
207 **MIAPLACIDUS** (IRE) 79
619 **MIBLEU** (FR) 33
412 **MIC AUBIN** (FR) 3
147 **MIC'S DELIGHT** (IRE) 7
387 **MICA MIKA** (IRE) 39
387 **MICHAEL'S NOOK** (GB) 12
658 **MICHAELA** (GB) 57
126 **MICHAELA'S CHOICE** (IRE) 12
479 **MICHAELMAS** (USA) 75
284 **MICHIGAN ASSASSIN** (IRE) 6
324 **MICK DUGGAN** (GB) 5
552 **MICK DUNDEE** (IRE) 1
99 **MICK SLATES** (IRE) 7

44 **MOUNTAIN LION** (IRE) 88
204 **MOUNTAIN OF ANGELS** (GB) 2
46 **MOUNTAIN OF MOURNE** (IRE) 3
465 **MOUNTAIN RANGE** (IRE) 9
112 **MOUNTAIN RESCUE** (IRE) 75
445 **MOUNTAIN RIVER** (IRE) 12
486 **MOUNTAIN TUNES** (IRE) 66
385 **MOUNTAINOUS** (IRE) 17
458 **MOURAD** (IRE) 77
53 **MOURIYANA** (IRE) C 68
417 **MOUSIE** (GB) 12
429 **MOUSSE AU CHOCOLAT** (USA) F 89
505 **MOVEMENTNEVERLIES** (GB) 19
421 **MOVES LIKE JAGGER** (IRE) 4
65 **MOVIE MAGIC** (GB) 18
402 **MOVIE MOGUL** (GB) G 11
577 **MOVIESTA** (USA) 16
546 **MOVIETONE** (USA) 187
500 **MOVING WAVES** (IRE) 16
254 **MOWHOOB** (GB) 20
521 **MOXBY** (GB) C 18
150 **MOXEY** (GB) 8
397 **MOY JOY** (IRE) C 64
339 **MOYALIFF** (IRE) 16
458 **MOYLE PARK** (IRE) 78
196 **MOYODE WOOD** (GB) 55
429 **MOYOKO** (IRE) C 90
409 **MOYVIC** (IRE) 23
458 **MOZOLTOV** (IRE) 79
385 **MR BACHSTER** (IRE) 18
531 **MR BEATLE** (GB) 20
32 **MR BOSSY BOOTS** (IRE) 53
473 **MR BRIDGER** (GB) 76
454 **MR BURBIDGE** (GB) 32
568 **MR CARDLE** (IRE) 30
613 **MR CARTOGRAPHER** (USA) 16
418 **MR CHIPPY** (IRE) 89
548 **MR CHOCOLATE DROP** (IRE) 7
685 **MR CHRISTOPHER** (IRE) 16
177 **MR COOL CASH** (GB) 25
637 **MR CRACKER** (GB) 60
296 **MR DANDY MAN** (IRE) 34
491 **MR DAVID** (USA) 10
443 **MR FICKLE** (IRE) 65
295 **MR FIFTYONE** (IRE) 26
154 **MR FITZROY** (IRE) 8
523 **MR GALLIVANTER** (IRE) 49
278 **MR GARDNER** (IRE) 7
562 **MR GOOFY** (IRE) 7
103 **MR GREY** (IRE) 16
245 **MR HICHENS** (GB) 6
418 **MR HOPEFUL** (IRE) 90
187 **MR JAY DEE** (IRE) 13
481 **MR LENNYGREENGRASS** (IRE) 30
476 **MR MANSSON** (IRE) 18
84 **MR MATTHEWS** (IRE) 37
484 **MR MCLAREN** (GB) 84
455 **MR MO JO** (GB) 7
473 **MR MOLE** (GB) 77
584 **MR MOONSHINE** (IRE) 47
674 **MR MOSS** (IRE) 52
660 **MR MUDDLE** (GB) 10
584 **MR PEPPERPOT** (GB) 48
209 **MR PICKWICK** (GB) 71
530 **MR PLOD** (GB) 4
494 **MR POMMEROY** (FR) 75
531 **MR PUCK** (IRE) 21
511 **MR PYRAMUS** (GB) 11

17 **MR QUICKSILVER** (GB) 154
606 **MR RAJ** (IRE) 20
6 **MR RED CLUBS** (GB) 33
418 **MR SATCO** (IRE) 91
615 **MR SHAHADY** (IRE) 16
486 **MR SHANTU** (IRE) 67
260 **MR SMITH** (GB) 62
643 **MR SNOOZY** (GB) 17
678 **MR SOPRANO** (IRE) 14
366 **MR SQUIRREL** (IRE) 6
615 **MR STINT** (IRE) 17
531 **MR SUPREME** (IRE) 22
218 **MR SYNTAX** (IRE) 4
307 **MR TED** (GB) 3
505 **MR TINGLE** (GB) 20
468 **MR TOY BOY** (GB) 4
507 **MR TRILBY** (IRE) 72
430 **MR UTAH** (GB) 9
675 **MR VENDMAN** (IRE) 41
486 **MR WATSON** (IRE) 68
39 **MR WICKFIELD** (GB) 28
646 **MR WIN** (IRE) 30
42 **MRS AVERY** (IRE) C 14
99 **MRS BIGGS** (GB) 29
375 **MRS EFF** (GB) 40
11 **MRS EVE** (GB) 22
330 **MRS GORSKY** (GB) 10
306 **MRS GRASS** (GB) 3
679 **MRS JORDAN** (IRE) 55
523 **MRS MALT** (IRE) G 24
291 **MRS MARSH** (GB) F 249
598 **MRS MEDLEY** (GB) 22
13 **MRS PEACHEY** (IRE) 32
16 **MRS WARREN** (IRE) 28
364 **MRS WINCHESTER** (IRE) 17
295 **MRS WOMAN** (IRE) F 27
17 **MS GRANDE CORNICHE** (IRE) 155
308 **MS MONIQUE** (FR) 23
435 **MS SASHA MALIA** (IRE) F 12
318 **MS SOPHIE ELEANOR** (USA) F 115
358 **MU'AJIZA** (GB) 32
425 **MUARA** (GB) F 31
180 **MUBARAZA** (IRE) 9
546 **MUBASHERA** (USA) 78
196 **MUBROOK** (USA) 56
440 **MUBTADI** (GB) 8
279 **MUBTAGHAA** (IRE) 124
5 **MUCH FASTER** (IRE) F 122
260 **MUCH PROMISE** (GB) 63
631 **MUCKLE ROE** (IRE) 50
342 **MUCKY MOLLY** (GB) 6
635 **MUDAMMERA** (IRE) 142
68 **MUDHISH** (IRE) 8
679 **MUDITA MOMENT** (IRE) 56
659 **MUFARAQAAT** (IRE) 109
319 **MUFFARREH** (USA) 40
25 **MUFFIN MCLEAY** (IRE) 13
635 **MUFFLED** (USA) C 143
279 **MUFFRI'HA** (IRE) 125
319 **MUGHARRED** 41
318 **MUHAAFIZ** (IRE) 116
318 **MUHAARAR** (GB) 117
169 **MUHARRER** (GB) 14
635 **MUHAWALAH** (IRE) 75
462 **MUHDIQ** (USA) 13
279 **MUHTADIM** (IRE) 126
214 **MUHTARIS** (IRE) 27
17 **MUIR LODGE** (GB) 89

552 **MUJA FAREWELL** (GB) F 16
635 **MUJASSAM** (GB) 144
472 **MUJAZIF** (IRE) 24
279 **MUKHADRAM** (GB) 14
602 **MUKHAYYAM** (GB) 118
358 **MUKHMAL** (IRE) 186
624 **MULAASEQ** (GB) 42
233 **MULAAZEM** (GB) 2
13 **MULDOON'S PICNIC** (GB) 33
659 **MULKEYYA** (IRE) 110
108 **MULL OF KILLOUGH** (IRE) 6
428 **MULLAGHANOE RIVER** (IRE) 49
409 **MULLEADY** (GB) 24
543 **MULLED WINE** (FR) C 14
418 **MULLIGAN'S MAN** (IRE) 92
39 **MULLIONHEIR** (GB) 39
291 **MULTICOLOUR WAVE** (IRE) F 250
643 **MULTILICIOUS** (GB) 18
603 **MULTIPLIER** (GB) 8
402 **MULTITASK** (GB) 6
619 **MULTITUDE OF SINS** (GB) 37
54 **MUMBLES BAY** (IRE) 35
54 **MUMBLES HEAD** (IRE) 36
291 **MUMFORD** (GB) 251
550 **MUMGOS DEBUT** (IRE) 58
291 **MUMTAZA** (GB) 104
602 **MUNAASER** (GB) 51
645 **MUNAAWASHAT** (IRE) C 51
271 **MUNAAWIB** (GB) 2
635 **MUNATAS** (GB) 76
602 **MUNDUS NOVUS** (USA) C 119
75 **MUNFALLET** (IRE) 12
367 **MUNGO PARK** (GB) 5
391 **MUNICH** (IRE) 7
291 **MUNJALLY** (GB) 105
260 **MUNJAZ** (GB) 64
394 **MUNSAAB** (IRE) 41
102 **MUNSARIM** (IRE) 12
602 **MUNTADAB** (IRE) 120
635 **MUQTASER** (USA) 145
635 **MURAHANA** (IRE) 146
126 **MURCAR** (GB) 13
190 **MURIELLE** (GB) C 74
407 **MURRAY MOUNT** (IRE) 15
619 **MURRAYANA** (IRE) 38
318 **MURTASSIM** (IRE) 118
470 **MURTYS DELIGHT** (IRE) 14
546 **MUSAADAQA** (GB) 79
44 **MUSADDAS** (GB) 38
180 **MUSALAHA** (IRE) 39
197 **MUSCHANA** (GB) F 19
602 **MUSHARRIF** (GB) 121
635 **MUSHIR** (GB) 77
602 **MUSIC AND DANCE** (GB) 122
484 **MUSIC IN THE RAIN** (IRE) 43
136 **MUSIC MAN** (IRE) 6
94 **MUSIC MASTER** (GB) 10
5 **MUSIC THEORY** (IRE) 90
602 **MUSICAL BEAT** (GB) 123
680 **MUSICAL BRIDGE** (GB) 11
291 **MUSICAL COMEDY** (GB) 106
196 **MUSICAL MOLLY** (IRE) 104
312 **MUSICAL MOON** (GB) 7
187 **MUSICAL WEDGE** (GB) 14
428 **MUSICIENNE** (IRE) F 50
375 **MUSIKHANI** (GB) 41
120 **MUSKOKA DAWN** (USA) C 45
112 **MUSSOORIE** (FR) C 76

607 **NATIVE FALLS** (IRE) 47
160 **NATIVE GALLERY** (IRE) 6
106 **NATIVE HEART** (GB) 81
43 **NATIVE NOVEL** (IRE) G 4
651 **NATIVE OPTIMIST** (IRE) 5
247 **NATIVE PALM** (IRE) 14
581 **NATIVE SPA** (IRE) 14
44 **NATURAL CHOICE** (GB) 92
585 **NATURAL SPRING** (GB) 11
144 **NATURES LAW** (IRE) 22
434 **NAUGHTY SPICE** (GB) 28
500 **NAUGHTYBYCHOICE** (GB) 6
351 **NAUTICAL TWILIGHT** (GB) 24
349 **NAVAJO CHIEF** (GB) 6
515 **NAVAL ACTION** (GB) 53
572 **NAVE** (USA) 13
318 **NAWAASY** (USA) 119
624 **NAWL** (IRE) 25
549 **NAZMIA** (IRE) 62
290 **NEAREST THE PIN** (IRE) 26
450 **NEARLY CAUGHT** (IRE) 16
666 **NEARLY MAY** (GB) 8
335 **NEARLY NAMA'D** (IRE) 42
128 **NEAT SHILLING** (IRE) C 29
492 **NEBRAAS** (GB) F 84
443 **NEBULA STORM** (IRE) 67
492 **NECTAR DE ROSE** (FR) 36
428 **NED BUNTLINE** (GB) 52
371 **NED STARK** (IRE) 74
534 **NEDDY BOGLE** (GB) 28
106 **NEDWA** (GB) C 129
106 **NEEDLESS SHOUTING** (IRE) 82
201 **NEEDS THE RUN** (GB) 46
132 **NEEDWOOD PARK** (GB) 2
629 **NEEDY MCCREDIE** (GB) 3
207 **NEIGHBOTHER** (GB) 82
203 **NEIGHBOURHOOD** (USA) 10
39 **NEISSA** (USA) C 41
386 **NELLIE FORBUSH** (GB) 13
6 **NELLIES QUEST** (GB) 34
423 **NELSON DU RONCERAY** (FR) 6
511 **NELSON OF THE NILE** (GB) 31
241 **NELSON QUAY** (IRE) 14
601 **NELSON'S BAY** (GB) 5
310 **NELSON'S BRIDGE** (GB) 87
137 **NELSON'S HILL** (GB) 21
121 **NELSON'S MUSE** (GB) 3
553 **NELSON'S PRIDE** (GB) 53
108 **NELSON'S VICTORY** (GB) 7
187 **NELTARA** (GB) 16
16 **NENGE MBOKO** (GB) 29
50 **NEOPHILIA** (IRE) 8
192 **NEPALESE PEARL** (GB) 9
638 **NEPHELE** (GB) 22
503 **NEPHETRITI WAY** (IRE) C 51
105 **NEPHETRITI WAY** (IRE) F 42
196 **NEPTUNE EQUESTER** (GB) 58
609 **NESHLA** (GB) F 66
310 **NESTERENKO** (GER) 88
324 **NESTON GRACE** (GB) 6
13 **NET WORK ROUGE** (FR) 34
162 **NETHER STREAM** (IRE) 11
443 **NETHERBY** (GB) 68
616 **NETMINDER** (IRE) 7
189 **NETWORK PERFECTION** (GB) 62
189 **NETWORK STORY** (GB) 34
144 **NEUF DES COEURS** (GB) 50
405 **NEUILLY** (GB) 6

148 **NEUTRINA** (IRE) F 73
318 **NEVER A DOUBT** (GB) F 120
241 **NEVER A QUARREL** (IRE) 15
254 **NEVER FOREVER** (GB) 22
80 **NEVER SAYS NEVER** (GB) 3
260 **NEVER TO BE** (USA) 66
5 **NEVERLETME GO** (IRE) C 123
117 **NEVEROWNUP** (IRE) 2
546 **NEVERTALK IN PARIS** (IRE) 189
295 **NEVERUSHACON** (IRE) 64
321 **NEVILLE** (GB) 58
253 **NEVILLE WOODS** (GB) 3
367 **NEW ABBEY DANCER** (IRE) 26
639 **NEW ACADEMY** (GB) 28
50 **NEW ALLIANCE** (IRE) 105
483 **NEW BIDDER** (GB) 10
173 **NEW CHRISTMAS** (USA) 21
624 **NEW COLOURS** (GB) 26
59 **NEW DECADE** (GB) 17
50 **NEW DIRECTION** (IRE) 106
17 **NEW FFOREST** (GB) 27
310 **NEW HORIZONS** (IRE) 89
50 **NEW REGALIA** (IRE) 9
357a **NEW RICH** 2
350 **NEW ROW** (GB) 16
639 **NEW SHUIL** (IRE) 29
68 **NEW STREAM** (IRE) 40
207 **NEW STREET** (IRE) 83
609 **NEW TARABELA** (GB) 32
214 **NEW YEAR'S EVE** (GB) 28
52 **NEW YOUMZAIN** (FR) 11
430 **NEW ZAFEEN** (IRE) 10
295 **NEWBERRY HILL** (GB) 28
330 **NEWBURY STREET** (GB) 11
534 **NEWCASTLEBEAUTY** (IRE) G 29
557 **NEWDANE DANCER** (IRE) 18
492 **NEWELLEN** (IRE) 3
148 **NEWERA** (GB) 74
513 **NEWFORGE HOUSE** (IRE) 32
131 **NEWGATE QUEEN** (GB) 32
33 **NEWMARKET WARRIOR** (IRE) 38
541 **NEWNHAM FLYER** (IRE) 2
639 **NEWSPAGE** (IRE) 30
358 **NEWSREADER** (USA) 34
25 **NEWSTEAD ABBEY** (GB) 14
497 **NEWTON THISTLE** (GB) 10
429 **NEWTON'S LAW** (IRE) 49
492 **NEWTON'S NIGHT** (IRE) 37
231 **NEWTOWN CROSS** (IRE) 4
655 **NEWYEARSRESOLUTION** (IRE) 5
144 **NEXIUS** (IRE) 23
659 **NEXT BEND** (IRE) 48
25 **NEXT DOOR** (IRE) 15
375 **NEXT EDITION** (IRE) 43
127 **NEXT EXIT** (IRE) 4
596 **NEXT GENERATION** (IRE) 35
584 **NEXT HIGHT** (IRE) 50
311 **NEXT OASIS** (IRE) 19
562 **NEXT SENSATION** (IRE) 8
102 **NEXT STOP** (GB) 16
366 **NEXT TO NOWHERE** (IRE) 7
116 **NEZAMI** (IRE) 3
279 **NEZAR** (IRE) 53
87 **NIBANI** (IRE) 7
120 **NIBBLING** (IRE) 24
251 **NICE 'N' SLEAZY** (IRE) 1
39 **NICE FELLOW** (FR) 30
44 **NICE LIFE** (IRE) 93

494 **NICE MATIN** (USA) C 150
622 **NICE TIME** (IRE) C 26
593 **NICEBOY** (IRE) 5
386 **NICENE CREED** (GB) 14
32 **NICEOFYOUTOTELLME** (GB) 11
679 **NICEONEFRANKIE** (GB) 57
682 **NICEONEMYSON** (GB) 4
645 **NICHOLASCOPERNICUS** (IRE) 10
336 **NICK THE ODDS** (IRE) 28
164 **NICKS POWER** (IRE) 22
487 **NICKY NUTJOB** (GER) 11
104 **NICOISE** (IRE) G 30
350 **NICOLA BELLA** (IRE) C 25
104 **NICTATE** (IRE) 31
659 **NIDHAAM** (GB) 49
659 **NIEVE** (USA) 50
52 **NIFTY KIER** (GB) 12
104 **NIGEL** (GB) 52
478 **NIGEL'S DESTINY** (USA) 38
404 **NIGELLA** (GB) G 19
470 **NIGHT ALLIANCE** (IRE) 15
212 **NIGHT CLUB** (GB) C 3
260 **NIGHT FEVER** (GB) 67
515 **NIGHT GENERATION** (GER) 54
33 **NIGHT HAVEN** (GB) C 78
531 **NIGHT IN MILAN** (IRE) 29
49 **NIGHT KISS** (FR) F 19
291 **NIGHT OF JOY** (IRE) F 255
27 **NIGHT OF LIGHT** (IRE) 81
560 **NIGHT OF PASSION** (IRE) 28
291 **NIGHT OF THUNDER** (IRE) 110
44 **NIGHT PARTY** (IRE) 94
107 **NIGHT REVELLER** (IRE) 12
546 **NIGHT RUN** (FR) 190
631 **NIGHT SAFE** (IRE) 52
260 **NIGHT SONG** (GB) 68
503 **NIGHT SYMPHONIE** (GB) C 52
184 **NIGHT SYMPHONIE** (IRE) F 16
296 **NIGHT TRADE** (IRE) 18
50 **NIGHT VISIT** (GB) F 107
350 **NIGHT'S WATCH** (GB) 6
494 **NIGHTDANCE SUN** (GER) F 151
659 **NIGHTIME** (IRE) F 114
478 **NIGHTLIGHT** (GB) 39
145 **NIGHTLINE** (GB) 23
645 **NIHAL** (IRE) F 52
587 **NIKI ROYAL** (IRE) 23
380 **NIKODAMOS** (GR) 8
291 **NIKOLENKA** (IRE) F 256
13 **NILE CRISTALE** (FR) F 35
200 **NIMBLE KIMBLE** (GB) 14
568 **NIMBUS GALE** (IRE) 31
555 **NINE BEFORE TEN** (IRE) 2
637 **NINE IRON** (IRE) 64
5 **NINE REALMS** (GB) 36
32 **NINE RED** (GB) F 110
487 **NINEPOINTSIXTHREE** (GB) 12
39 **NINETY MINUTES** (IRE) 31
22 **NINETYNINE** (IRE) 14
247 **NINEVAH** (IRE) F 15
372 **NINFEA** (IRE) 16
291 **NINJAGO** (IRE) 18
506 **NINNY NOODLE** (GB) 4
3 **NIQNAAQPAADIWAAQ** (GB) 21
32 **NIRVA** (IRE) 54
527 **NISHAY** (GB) 9
549 **NISMA** (GB) 63
450 **NISSAKI KASTA** (GB) 42

137 **PICK POCKETT** (GB) 55
145 **PICKAMUS** (FR) 28
380 **PICKAWAY** (GB) 77
5 **PICKLE** (GB) C 125
375 **PICKS MILAN** (IRE) 49
336 **PICKS PINTA** (GB) 29
376 **PICNIC IN THE GLEN** (GB) 31
595 **PICODEAN** (GB) 9
106 **PICOLETTE** (GB) C 132
114 **PICOT DE SAY** (GB) 2
499 **PICTURE DEALER** (GB) 11
235 **PIDDIE'S POWER** (GB) 5
584 **PIDDIES PRIDE** (IRE) G 58
44 **PIED A TERRE** (AUS) 42
394 **PIED DU ROI** (FR) 51
308 **PIEDRA** (IRE) 24
101 **PIEMAN'S GIRL** (GB) 12
259 **PIERRE D'OR** (IRE) 14
326 **PIERRERS BOUNTY** (IRE) 9
27 **PIETRA SANTA** (FR) F 82
106 **PIFFLING** (GB) F 133
631 **PIGEON ISLAND** (GB) 57
358 **PIGEON PIE** (GB) 117
549 **PILAGEYA** (IRE) 68
358 **PILATES** (IRE) 39
644 **PILGREEN** (FR) 9
508 **PILGRIMS REST** (IRE) 7
279 **PILLAR BOX** (IRE) 130
241 **PINACOTHEQUE** (IRE) C 16
658 **PINAMAR** (GB) 33
680 **PINBALL** (GB) 13
229 **PINDAR** (GER) 5
521 **PINDORA** (GER) 11
470 **PINEAU DE RE** (FR) 17
584 **PINEROLO** (GB) 59
452 **PINK AND BLACK** (IRE) 27
380 **PINK ANEMONE** (GB) 9
300 **PINK CADILLAC** (IRE) 5
172 **PINK CHALICE** (GB) 25
335 **PINK COAT** (GB) 49
357a **PINK DIAMOND** 18
488 **PINK GIN** (GB) 5
458 **PINK HAT** (IRE) 85
352 **PINK LIPS** (GB) 28
511 **PINK MIRAGE** (IRE) 33
135 **PINK MISCHIEF** (GB) 12
376 **PINK RIBBON** (IRE) 45
635 **PINK STONE** (FR) F 152
612 **PINK SUPREME** (GB) C 13
494 **PINK TOPAZ** (USA) F 152
474 **PINOTAGE** (GB) 9
40 **PINTRADA** (GB) 6
553 **PINTURA** (GB) 25
5 **PINZOLO** (GB) 94
44 **PIONEER BRIDE** (USA) C 123
429 **PIPE DREAM** (GB) 51
131 **PIPER HILL** (IRE) 13
667 **PIPERS NOTE** (GB) 8
291 **PIPING DREAM** (GB) 272
310 **PIPPA GREENE** (GB) 99
458 **PIQUE SOUS** (FR) 86
479 **PIQUETNOL** (USA) C 137
378 **PIRA PALACE** (IRE) 14
303 **PIRANS CAR** (GB) 11
371 **PIRATES CAY** (GB) 81
409 **PIRES** (GB) 27
397 **PIRI WANGO** (IRE) 6
484 **PIRIE** (USA) F 101

659 **PIRITA** (IRE) 52
50 **PIROLO** (IRE) 109
363 **PISCEAN** (USA) 3
281 **PISTE NOIRE** (USA) F 75
321 **PISTOL** (IRE) 65
430 **PISTOL BASC** (FR) 12
691 **PISTOLET NOIR** (FR) 14
398 **PISTOLETTO** (SPA) 82
281 **PIT STOP** (IRE) 44
380 **PITAMORE** (USA) 78
474 **PITHIVIER** (FR) 10
358 **PITON** (GB) 118
502 **PITT RIVERS** (GB) 9
481 **PITTER PATTER** (GB) 36
109 **PIVERINA** (IRE) C 43
184 **PIVKA** (GB) C 17
602 **PIVOTAL BRIDE** (GB) 54
641 **PIVOTAL PROSPECT** (GB) 10
503 **PIVOTAL SILENCE** (GB) 13
120 **PIVOTALIA** (IRE) C 46
492 **PIVOTIQUE** (GB) 85
189 **PIVOTMAN** (GB) 40
678 **PIVOTTING** (GB) F 47
190 **PIXEY PUNK** (GB) 115
665 **PIXIE CUT** (IRE) 19
589 **PIXIE'S BLUE** (FR) F 30
367 **PIXILATED** (GB) 6
169 **PIZZICATO** (GB) C 43
270 **PLACE D'ARMES** (IRE) G 5
609 **PLACE DE MOSCOU** (IRE) F 67
57 **PLACERE** (IRE) 4
382 **PLACIDIA** (IRE) 22
466 **PLAIN STRIKING** (GB) 3
53 **PLAISIR** (IRE) 106
494 **PLAISIR D'AMOUR** (IRE) 153
279 **PLAISIR DES YEUX** (FR) C 131
50 **PLAMAS** (IRE) 42
418 **PLAN AGAIN** (IRE) 102
602 **PLANE SONG** (IRE) 129
321 **PLANET OF SOUND** (GB) 66
85 **PLANET ROCK** (GB) 13
380 **PLANETAIRE** (GB) 51
38 **PLANETOID** (IRE) 15
375 **PLATINUM** (IRE) 50
109 **PLATINUM PEARL** (GB) 28
6 **PLATINUM PREFERRED** (CAN) C 62
196 **PLATINUM PROOF** (USA) 65
377 **PLAUSEABELLA** (GB) 19
479 **PLAY MISTY FOR ME** (FR) C 138
511 **PLAY STREET** (GB) 14
215 **PLAY THE BLUES** (IRE) 11
295 **PLAY THE MARKET** (IRE) 37
32 **PLAYBOY MANSION** (IRE) F 116
16 **PLAYFUL** (GB) C 61
310 **PLAYHARA** (IRE) 100
164 **PLAYING WITH FIRE** (IRE) 24
577 **PLAYTOTHEWHISTLE** (GB) 33
636 **PLAYWITHMYHEART** (GB) F 27
44 **PLAZA** (USA) C 124
675 **PLEAD** (FR) C 62
507 **PLEASANT COMPANY** (IRE) 83
137 **PLEASANT VALLEY** (IRE) 56
50 **PLEASCACH** (IRE) 110
91 **PLEASE LET ME GO** (GB) 12
428 **PLEASE TALK** (IRE) 59
137 **PLEASURE BENT** (GB) 24
602 **PLENARY POWER** (GB) 130
138 **PLETTENBURG BAY** (IRE) 14

479 **PLINTH** (IRE) 16
465 **PLOUGH BOY** (IRE) 16
9 **PLOVER** (GB) 20
552 **PLUCKY DIP** (GB) 12
576 **PLUM FAIRY** (GB) F 50
66 **PLUM PUDDING** (FR) 19
407 **PLUM STONE** (GB) 16
546 **PLUMETOT** (FR) 194
35 **PLUNDER** (GB) 14
254 **PLUS JAMAIS** (FR) 23
382 **PLUTOCRACY** (IRE) 9
357a **PLYMOUTH SOUND** 36
674 **POBBLES BAY** (IRE) 62
424 **POCHARD** (GB) G 10
154 **POCKET WARRIOR** (IRE) 17
555 **POCO PICCOLO** (GB) 5
364 **POD** (GB) 19
17 **POEM** (GB) 32
130 **POET** (GB) 16
389 **POETIC CHOICE** (GB) 13
515 **POETIC LICENSE** (IRE) 56
335 **POETIC LORD** (GB) 50
187 **POETIC POWER** (IRE) 21
105 **POETIC PRINCE** (GB) 23
300 **POETIC STAR** (GB) 13
523 **POETIC VERSE** (GB) 27
96 **POINT GUARD** (IRE) 8
18 **POINT NORTH** (IRE) 4
164 **POINT OF ATTACK** (IRE) 25
196 **POINTING NORTH** (USA) F 115
181 **POITIN** (GB) 3
403 **POKER GOLD** (GB) 14
597 **POKER HOSPITAL** (GB) 8
236 **POLAMCO** (IRE) 24
511 **POLAR EXPRESS** (GB) 34
109 **POLAR EYES** (GB) 29
277 **POLAR FOREST** (GB) 18
138 **POLAR KITE** (IRE) 15
130 **POLAR VORTEX** 82
418 **POLARBROOK** (IRE) 103
494 **POLARIX** (GB) 28
33 **POLDHU** (GB) C 82
433 **POLICY** (GB) F 31
494 **POLISCHNO** (FR) 82
120 **POLISH BALLET** (GB) 26
659 **POLISHED GEM** (IRE) C 118
295 **POLISHED ROCK** (IRE) 38
473 **POLISKY** (FR) 85
189 **POLITBUREAU** (GB) 41
356 **POLITELYSED** (GB) 9
167 **POLITENESS** (FR) 12
546 **POLITICAL ACT** 195
260 **POLITICO** (GB) 150
156 **POLLY LIGHTFOOT** (GB) 4
310 **POLLY PEACHUM** (IRE) 101
295 **POLLY PERKINS** (FR) F 82
237 **POLLY WIGGLE** (GB) 3
426 **POLO SPRINGS** (GB) 22
207 **POLSKI MAX** (GB) 42
671 **POLSTAR** (FR) 6
456 **POLVERE D'ORO** (IRE) 19
382 **POLYBIUS** (GB) 23
100 **POLYDAMOS** (GB) 33
556 **POLYNESIAN QUEEN** (IRE) C 17
357a **POMME DE GUERRE** (IRE) 37
260 **POMOLOGY** (USA) 12
535 **PONCHO** (GB) 5
492 **PONFEIGH** (IRE) 39

434 **PRINCESS ANNABELLE** (GB) 12
358 **PRINCESS ATOOSA** (USA) F 198
260 **PRINCESS AURORA** (GB) F 151
494 **PRINCESS BAVAROISE** (FR) 84
481 **PRINCESS BELLA** (IRE) 37
131 **PRINCESS BLUE** (GB) 43
421 **PRINCESS BOUNTY** (GB) 5
162 **PRINCESS CAETANI** (IRE) 12
65 **PRINCESS CAMMIE** (IRE) 8
238 **PRINCESS FLORENTIA** (GB) 10
678 **PRINCESS GEORGINA** (GB) C 48
118 **PRINCESS HANANE** (IRE) 14
136 **PRINCESS ICICLE** (GB) 9
489 **PRINCESS KHELEYF** (GB) 14
635 **PRINCESS LOULOU** (IRE) 24
433 **PRINCESS MYLA** (IRE) 24
635 **PRINCESS NOOR** (GB) 84
525 **PRINCESS OF ROCK** (GB) 3
40 **PRINCESS PEACHES** (GB) 28
281 **PRINCESS PEARLITA** (IRE) 46
207 **PRINCESS PHEENY** (IRE) 88
106 **PRINCESS QUEST** (GB) 29
663 **PRINCESS ROSE** (GB) 15
408 **PRINCESS SPEEDFIT** (FR) F 32
134 **PRINCESS SPIRIT** (GB) 7
54 **PRINCESS TARA** (IRE) 38
628 **PRINCESS TILLY** (GB) 15
164 **PRINCESS TIMON** (GB) F 27
393 **PRINCESS WILLOW** (GB) 11
562 **PRINCESSE FLEUR** (GB) 10
34 **PRINCESSE KATIE** (IRE) 2
32 **PRINCIPLE EQUATION** (IRE) 58
167 **PRINT SHIRAZ** (IRE) 14
50 **PRINTHA** (IRE) 43
190 **PRINTMAKER** (IRE) 45
17 **PRIORS BROOK** (GB) 99
491 **PRISCA** (GB) 31
494 **PRISENFLAG** (FR) 85
380 **PRIVATE** (GB) 37
607 **PRIVATE DANCER** (GB) 49
506 **PRIVATE JONES** (GB) 5
576 **PRIVET HEDGE** (USA) 32
635 **PRIVILEGED** (IRE) 154
131 **PROBABLY SORRY** (GB) 14
507 **PROBLEMA TIC** (FR) 87
130 **PROCKS GIRL** (GB) 46
553 **PROCLAMATIONOFWAR** (GB) 57
308 **PROCUREMENT** (GB) 25
291 **PRODUCER** (GB) 22
598 **PROFILE STAR** (GB) 25
310 **PROFIT COMMISSION** (IRE) 104
103 **PROFIT MONITOR** (IRE) 20
130 **PROFITABLE** 84
602 **PROFUSION** (GB) 132
128 **PROHIBIT** (GB) 15
352 **PROM DRESS** (GB) 30
394 **PROMANCO** (GB) 53
549 **PROMETHEUS** (IRE) 70
44 **PROMISE YOU** (GB) 95
258 **PROMISED WINGS** (GER) 19
486 **PROMPTER** (GB) 75
291 **PROPAGANDA** (IRE) F 277
635 **PROPEL** (GB) 155
102 **PROPER CHARLIE** (GB) 13
278 **PROPER JOB** (GB) 2
99 **PROPHESY** (IRE) 9
383 **PROPHETS HONOR** (FR) F 50
427 **PROPHETS THUMB** (IRE) 9

659 **PROPORTIONAL** (GB) F 120
291 **PROPOSED** (GB) 278
473 **PROSECCO** (GB) 68
473 **PROSPECT WELLS** (FR) 91
330 **PROSTATE AWARENESS** (IRE) 17
428 **PROTARAS** (USA) 62
291 **PROTECTED** (GB) 119
624 **PROTECTORATE** (GB) C 27
112 **PROTECTRESS** (GB) F 79
295 **PROTESTANT** (IRE) 39
388 **PROUD CHIEFTAIN** (GB) 1
484 **PROUD DUCHESS** (IRE) 85
503 **PROUD FACT** (GB) C 55
286 **PROUD JACK** (GB) 4
64 **PROUD TIMES** (GB) 8
397 **PROUDEYES** (GER) C 65
504 **PROUTS PUB** (IRE) 12
249 **PROUTS PUB** (IRE) 8
503 **PROVATO** (IRE) 56
659 **PROVE** (GB) C 121
602 **PROVENANCE** (GB) 55
645 **PROVENCE** (GB) C 54
260 **PROVIDENT SPIRIT** (GB) 73
473 **PROVO** (IRE) 92
443 **PROXIMATE** (GB) 71
204 **PRU** (GB) 3
50 **PRUDENT APPROACH** (IRE) 44
260 **PSILOVEYOU** (GB) 74
602 **PSYCHOMETRY** (FR) 56
473 **PTIT ZIG** (FR) 93
25 **PTOLEMY** (GB) 19
529 **PTOLOMEOS** (GB) 5
75 **PUCKER UP** (GB) 6
613 **PUCON** (GB) 8
104 **PUDDING** 53
639 **PUDSEY HOUSE** (GB) 33
561 **PUERTO AZUL** (IRE) 1
568 **PUFFIN BILLY** (IRE) 33
443 **PUISQUE TU PARS** (FR) 72
598 **PULL THE PIN** (IRE) 26
99 **PULL THE PLUG** (IRE) 21
311 **PULLMEN** (GB) 21
550 **PULPITARIAN** (USA) 69
427 **PULSATE** (GB) F 36
178 **PUNCH BAG** (IRE) 15
358 **PUNCTILIOUS** (GB) C 199
507 **PUNJABI** (GB) 88
169 **PUNK ROCKER** (IRE) 44
494 **PUPA DI SARONNO** (ITY) 86
291 **PUPIL** (GB) 120
358 **PUPPET THEATRE** (IRE) 41
381 **PUR DE SIVOLA** (FR) 4
17 **PURCELL** (IRE) 34
167 **PURCELL'S BRIDGE** (IRE) 15
440 **PURE AMBER** (IRE) 17
637 **PURE ANTICIPATION** (IRE) 72
54 **PURE FAITH** (IRE) 39
591 **PURE GREED** (GB) C 45
291 **PURE INCENTIVE** (USA) C 279
32 **PURE LINE** (GB) 117
454 **PURE POTEEN** (IRE) 36
631 **PURE SCIENCE** (IRE) 59
84 **PURE SPECULATION** (GB) C 69
9 **PURFORD GREEN** (GB) 21
104 **PURISSIMA** (USA) F 80
214 **PURPLE BAY** (GB) 30
5 **PURPLE GLOW** (IRE) C 126
345 **PURPLE HARRY** (GB) 8

279 **PURPLE SPECTRUM** (GB) 60
454 **PURSUITOFHAPPINESS** (IRE) 37
238 **PUSEY STREET VALE** (GB) 11
348 **PUSH ME** (IRE) 8
364 **PUSH TO EXIT** (GB) 20
443 **PUSHKIN MUSEUM** (IRE) 116
636 **PUSS MOTH** (GB) 29
421 **PUTIN** (IRE) 6
309 **PUTMEINTHESWINDLE** (GB) 11
635 **PUTRA ETON** (IRE) 25
61 **PUZZLE TIME** (GB) 5
167 **PYJAMA GAME** (IRE) 16
365 **PYLEIGH LASS** (GB) 27
576 **PYRANA** (USA) F 52
426 **PYRSHAN** (GB) 23
291 **QAARIB** (IRE) 280
602 **QAFFAAL** (USA) 57
507 **QALINAS** (GB) 89
646 **QANAN** (GB) 13
177 **QATAR PRINCESS** (IRE) 18
596 **QATAR SUCCESS** (GB) 37
318 **QAWAASEM** (IRE) 54
492 **QEWY** (IRE) 4
383 **QIANSHAN LEADER** (IRE) 51
106 **QIBTEE** (FR) 30
622 **QILIN** (FR) C 27
549 **QINGDAO** (IRE) 71
131 **QOUBILAI** (FR) 15
560 **QUADDICK LAKE** (IRE) 34
75 **QUADRI** (GB) F 33
193 **QUADRIGA** (IRE) 3
321 **QUADRILLER** (GB) 69
291 **QUAE SUPRA** (GB) 281
279 **QUAKE** (GB) 132
380 **QUALIDA** (FR) 38
277 **QUALITY ART** (USA) 30
637 **QUALVIRO** (FR) 73
148 **QUANTUM DOT** (IRE) 42
433 **QUAROMA** (GB) 13
406 **QUARRYVALE** (IRE) 12
674 **QUARTON** (FR) 65
479 **QUARTZ** (FR) 79
679 **QUARTZ DE THAIX** (FR) 63
635 **QUASQAZAH** (GB) 85
187 **QUAYSIDE COURT** (IRE) 22
5 **QUE PUNTUAL** (ARG) C 127
201 **QUEEN AGGIE** (IRE) 24
318 **QUEEN CATRINE** (GB) 55
324 **QUEEN CEE** (GB) 12
196 **QUEEN COBRA** (IRE) C 116
44 **QUEEN CONSORT** (USA) C 125
207 **QUEEN OF ARTS** (GB) 89
545 **QUEEN OF EPIRUS** (GB) 5
279 **QUEEN OF ICE** (GB) 19
53 **QUEEN OF MEAN** (GB) F 107
106 **QUEEN OF NARNIA** (GB) F 136
6 **QUEEN OF SKIES** (GB) 37
106 **QUEEN OF STARS** (USA) F 137
646 **QUEEN OF THE NILE** (GB) 33
12 **QUEEN OLIVIA** (GB) 13
279 **QUEEN PADME** (IRE) F 133
53 **QUEEN SARRA** (GB) 77
145 **QUEEN SPUD** (GB) 30
478 **QUEEN'S CHARTER** (GB) 71
638 **QUEEN'S DIAMOND** (GER) F 45
635 **QUEEN'S DREAM** (IRE) 86
279 **QUEEN'S LOGIC** (IRE) F 134
692 **QUEEN'S PAWN** (IRE) 9

394 **READY TOKEN** (IRE) 54
636 **REAFFIRMED** (IRE) 17
515 **REAL JAZZ** (IRE) 26
418 **REAL MILAN** (IRE) 108
494 **REAL PROMISE** (GB) 92
213 **REAL STEEL** (IRE) 19
308 **REALISATOR** (FR) 49
106 **REALITY CHECK** (IRE) C 138
297 **REALITY SHOW** (GB) 13
450 **REALIZE** (GB) 20
508 **REALLY RANSOM** (GB) C 27
172 **REALLY TONIC** (FR) 37
428 **REALT DUBH** (IRE) 63
454 **REALTA MO CROI** (IRE) 38
550 **REAPING THE REWARD** (IRE) 71
189 **REAR ADMIRAL** (IRE) 42
655 **REAR VIEW** (IRE) 7
31 **REARRANGE** (GB) 10
180 **REASON TO DANCE** (GB) F 77
618 **REASON TO SMILE** (GB) 4
440 **REASONABLY DEVOUT** (CAN) C 34
545 **REASONING** (GB) G 6
118 **REBECCA ROMERO** (GB) 7
82 **REBECCAS CHOICE** (IRE) 9
252 **REBEL CODE** (USA) 20
473 **REBEL DU MAQUIS** (FR) 96
233 **REBEL HIGH** (IRE) 4
495 **REBEL ISLAND** (IRE) 3
473 **REBEL REBELLION** (IRE) 97
106 **REBEL YELL** (GB) 139
5 **REBELLINE** (IRE) C 128
408 **REBELLIOUS GUEST** (GB) 10
443 **REBLIS** (FR) 73
429 **REBUKE** (USA) F 96
429 **RECANTED** (IRE) 53
523 **RECESSION PROOF** (FR) 29
443 **RECIPE** C 74
189 **RECKLESS HUNTER** (GB) 76
225 **RECKLESS ROMEO** (IRE) 15
169 **RECTIFY** (IRE) F 45
260 **RECTITUDE** (GB) 75
170 **RECWAY LASS** (GB) 4
426 **RED ADMIRABLE** (IRE) 24
68 **RED AGGRESSOR** (IRE) 10
354 **RED ANCHOR** (IRE) 7
469 **RED ART** (IRE) 12
180 **RED AVENGER** (USA) 11
3 **RED BARON** (IRE) 11
478 **RED BATON** (GB) 3
553 **RED BEACH** (IRE) C 99
417 **RED BIBA** (IRE) 25
635 **RED BOOTS** (IRE) F 157
180 **RED CADEAUX** (GB) 12
98 **RED CAPE** (FR) 26
408 **RED CATKIN** (GB) 11
177 **RED CHARMER** (IRE) 3
190 **RED COBRA** (IRE) 46
417 **RED CONNECT** (GB) 36
658 **RED COSSACK** (CAN) 56
562 **RED CURRENT** (GB) 11
139 **RED DEVIL LADS** (IRE) 39
49 **RED DRAGON** (IRE) 10
491 **RED EXPLORER** (USA) 15
417 **RED FLUTE** (GB) 37
35 **RED FOREVER** (GB) 26
16 **RED FOUR** (GB) 31
180 **RED GALILEO** (GB) 44
389 **RED HARRY** (IRE) 16

216 **RED HOTT ROBBIE** (GB) 5
271 **RED HOUSE** (GB) 9
678 **RED HOUSE REBEL** (IRE) 49
196 **RED INCA** (GB) 70
318 **RED INVADER** (IRE) 9
135 **RED JOKER** (IRE) 13
429 **RED LADY** (IRE) 54
281 **RED LASER** (IRE) 16
154 **RED LILAC** (IRE) 11
418 **RED MERLIN** (IRE) 109
615 **RED MYST** (GB) 18
22 **RED MYSTIQUE** (IRE) 20
188 **RED NOT BLUE** (IRE) 7
193 **RED OASIS** (GB) 13
673 **RED OATS** (GB) 3
38 **RED ORATOR** (GB) 17
553 **RED PALADIN** (IRE) 26
515 **RED PASSIFLORA** (GB) 27
577 **RED PIKE** (IRE) 34
621 **RED PILGRIM** (IRE) 3
417 **RED PRIMO** (IRE) 26
631 **RED RIVERMAN** (GB) 60
35 **RED ROAR** (IRE) 16
631 **RED ROCCO** (IRE) 61
383 **RED ROCK** (FR) 52
429 **RED ROCKER** (IRE) 22
479 **RED ROCKS POINT** (IRE) 80
33 **RED ROSES STORY** (FR) F 83
604 **RED ROSSO** (GB) 4
494 **RED RUBY** (FR) 93
180 **RED RUNAWAY** (GB) 13
507 **RED SEVENTY** (GB) 90
73 **RED SHADOW** (GB) 14
553 **RED SHAREEF** (GB) C 100
507 **RED SHERLOCK** (GB) 91
74 **RED SHUTTLE** (GB) 2
487 **RED SKIPPER** (IRE) 19
462 **RED SOMERSET** (USA) 14
297 **RED STAR LADY** (IRE) 14
25 **RED STARGAZER** (IRE) 44
401 **RED TANBER** (IRE) 2
417 **RED TIDE** (IRE) 27
618 **RED TIGER LILY** (IRE) 34
130 **RED TO AMBER** (IRE) 17
131 **RED TRANCE** (IRE) F 44
180 **RED TYCOON** (IRE) 78
417 **RED UNICO** (IRE) 38
478 **RED VELOUR** (GB) 41
440 **RED WARRIOR** (IRE) 9
604 **RED WHISPER** (GB) 5
417 **RED WIFEY** (IRE) 28
393 **RED WILLOW** (GB) 12
73 **REDALANI** (IRE) 15
549 **REDBROOK** (IRE) 73
45 **REDGRAVE DANCER** (GB) 7
380 **REDING** (FR) 41
354 **REDINGA** (GB) 8
130 **REDINHA** (GB) 48
531 **REDKALANI** (IRE) 25
279 **REDKIRK** (GB) 62
16 **REDLORRYELLOWLORRY** (IRE) 48
431 **REDOUBTABLEFIGHTER** (IRE) 14
439 **REDPENDER** (IRE) 15
335 **REDUNDANT MAN** (GB) 53
636 **REDVERS** (IRE) 6
494 **REDWHITE AND BLUES** (FR) 94
9 **REDY TO RUMBLE** (GB) 28
56 **REE'S RASCAL** (IRE) 13

621 **REEDCUTTER** (GB) 8
3 **REEFLEX** (GB) 18
651 **REEKER PIKE** (GB) F 6
445 **REEL COOL** (GB) F 40
180 **REELING N' ROCKING** (IRE) C 79
260 **REELTOP** (GB) 153
564 **REELWILL** (FR) 15
635 **REESHA** (GB) 89
169 **REET PETITE** (IRE) 46
577 **REET THICKNSTRONG** (GB) 35
432 **REFER** (GB) 3
602 **REFERENDUM** (IRE) 136
291 **REFLATION** (GB) 282
564 **REFLECT** (IRE) 16
276 **REFLECTED IMAGE** (IRE) F 39
30 **REFLECTION** (GB) 20
382 **REFLECTIVE** (GB) F 45
16 **REFRESHESTHEPARTS** (USA) 32
268 **REFUSE COLETTE** (IRE) 8
148 **REFUSE TO GIVE UP** (IRE) C 80
290 **REFUSED A NAME** (GB) 36
645 **REGAL ASSET** (USA) C 56
470 **REGAL D'ESTRUVAL** (FR) 18
318 **REGAL DAN** (IRE) 10
54 **REGAL DIAMOND** (IRE) 40
332 **REGAL ENCORE** (IRE) 24
609 **REGAL FALCON** (GB) 34
209 **REGAL FLAME** (GB) 75
364 **REGAL FLOW** (GB) 21
609 **REGAL HAWK** (GB) 5
105 **REGAL MISS** (GB) 27
66 **REGAL ONE** (IRE) 21
59 **REGAL PARADE** (GB) 19
443 **REGAL PARK** (GB) 75
147 **REGAL PRESENCE** (IRE) 10
685 **REGAL RUN** (GB) F 17
68 **REGAL SULTANA** (GB) 44
607 **REGAL SWAIN** (IRE) 33
358 **REGAL WAYS** (IRE) 201
32 **REGARDEZ** (GB) 61
489 **REGGIE BOND** (GB) 15
584 **REGGIE PARROT** (GB) 61
504 **REGGIE PERRIN** (GB) 13
207 **REGIMENT** (GB) 91
491 **REGINA** (GB) C 43
634 **REGINALD CLAUDE** (GB) 13
281 **REGULATION** (IRE) 17
180 **REHANAAT** (USA) 45
438 **REILLYS DAUGHTER** (GB) 5
192 **REIMPOSE** (GB) 20
445 **REINE VIOLETTE** (FR) G 41
686 **REINVIGORATE** (IRE) 11
4 **REIVERS MOON** (GB) G 18
635 **REKDHAT** (IRE) 90
594 **RELAND** (FR) 3
572 **RELATED** (GB) 14
142 **RELATION ALEXANDER** (IRE) 12
679 **RELAX** (FR) 65
259 **RELAY** (GB) 15
38 **RELENTLESS** (IRE) 18
139 **RELENTLESS DREAMER** (IRE) 40
397 **RELENTLESS PURSUIT** (IRE) 32
257 **RELIC ROCK** (IRE) 16
190 **RELIGHT MY FIRE** (GB) 47
478 **RELINQUISHED** (GB) C 72
291 **REMBRANDT** (GB) 283
382 **REMBRANDT VAN RIJN** (IRE) 25
135 **REMEDIO** (IRE) 14

148 **ROAD TO REALITY** (IRE) C 81
428 **ROAD TO RICHES** (IRE) 65
605 **ROADTOABBEYFEALE** (IRE) 5
321 **ROALCO DE FARGES** (FR) 75
44 **ROAYH** (USA) 45
321 **ROB CONTI** (FR) 76
473 **ROB ROBIN** (IRE) 99
213 **ROBBER BARON** (IRE) 20
637 **ROBBERS ROOST** (IRE) 75
578 **ROBBIAN** (GB) 5
531 **ROBBIE** (GB) 26
484 **ROBERT THE PAINTER** (IRE) 54
60 **ROBERT'S STAR** (IRE) 9
310 **ROBERTO GOLDBACK** (IRE) 110
371 **ROBERTO PEGASUS** (GB) 86
209 **ROBERTSON** (IRE) 18
213 **ROBIN DU FAN** (FR) 21
437 **ROBIN HOOD** (IRE) 3
636 **ROBIN HOODS BAY** (GB) 7
277 **ROBIN THE RICH** (IRE) 21
691 **ROBIN WILL** (IRE) 16
591 **ROBIN'S CHOICE** (IRE) 26
167 **ROBIN'S COMMAND** (IRE) 18
310 **ROBINS REEF** (IRE) 111
619 **ROBINSFIRTH** (IRE) 43
568 **ROBINSSON** (IRE) 34
38 **ROBOBAR** (IRE) 20
25 **ROBOT BOY** (IRE) 20
166 **ROBYN** (GB) 20
213 **ROBYN'S ROSE** (IRE) 22
349 **ROBYNELLE** (GB) 26
246 **ROC D'APSIS** (FR) 44
203 **ROC DE GUYE** (FR) 14
206 **ROC DE PRINCE** (GB) 20
112 **ROCHAMBEAU** (IRE) 41
308 **ROCHEFORT** (FR) 27
452 **ROCHELLE** (IRE) 29
109 **ROCK 'N' ROLL STAR** (GB) 30
282 **ROCK A DOODLE DOO** (IRE) 4
462 **ROCK ANTHEM** (IRE) 15
502 **ROCK CANYON** (IRE) 10
678 **ROCK CHARM** (GB) 33
279 **ROCK CHOIR** (IRE) 19
513 **ROCK DIAMOND** (IRE) 39
637 **ROCK DOCTOR** (IRE) 76
197 **ROCK EXHIBITION** (GB) C 38
389 **ROCK HARMONIE** (FR) G 14
260 **ROCK KRISTAL** (GB) 155
596 **ROCK N ROUGE** (IRE) 18
461 **ROCK OF AGES** (GB) 5
318 **ROCK OF DREAMS** (IRE) 58
428 **ROCK OF GLENSTAL** (GB) 66
33 **ROCK OF LEON** (GB) 43
218 **ROCK ON BOLLINSKI** (GB) 5
589 **ROCK ON CANDY** (GB) 19
567 **ROCK ON ROCKY** (GB) 7
236 **ROCK ON RUBY** (IRE) 29
295 **ROCK ON THE MOOR** (IRE) 41
262 **ROCK RELIEF** (IRE) 30
399 **ROCK SONG** (GB) 15
295 **ROCK THE WORLD** (IRE) 42
335 **ROCK'S FIELD** (IRE) 55
620 **ROCKABILLY RIOT** (IRE) 19
37 **ROCKAHOOLABABY** (IRE) F 16
206 **ROCKAWANGO** (FR) 21
481 **ROCKCHASEBULLETT** (IRE) 39
121 **ROCKED THE BOAT** (GB) 14
494 **ROCKET BOB** (FR) 157

465 **ROCKET ROB** (IRE) 11
472 **ROCKET RONNIE** (IRE) 27
619 **ROCKET SCIENTIST** (GB) 44
602 **ROCKET SHIP** (GB) 61
118 **ROCKFELLA** (GB) 8
268 **ROCKIE ROAD** (IRE) 15
259 **ROCKIN N REELIN** (USA) 17
489 **ROCKIN RUBY RED** (GB) 20
167 **ROCKING BLUES** (IRE) 19
318 **ROCKING THE BOAT** (IRE) 130
145 **ROCKITEER** (IRE) 32
148 **ROCKNROLLRAMBO** (IRE) 45
646 **ROCKSEE** (IRE) 44
15 **ROCKSILLA** (GB) 15
169 **ROCKTHERUNWAY** (IRE) 19
257 **ROCKWEILLER** (GB) 19
679 **ROCKY BENDER** (IRE) 70
473 **ROCKY CREEK** (IRE) 100
7 **ROCKY ELSOM** (USA) 5
635 **ROCKY GROUND** (GB) 26
417 **ROCKY HILL RIDGE** (GB) 29
93 **ROCKY ISLAND** (IRE) 21
48 **ROCKY REBEL** (GB) 14
38 **ROCKY RYAN** (IRE) 21
418 **ROCKY STONE** (IRE) 112
458 **ROCKYABOYA** (IRE) 96
268 **ROCLETTE** (USA) F 21
494 **ROCN** (FR) 29
405 **ROCQUAINE** (IRE) 9
472 **RODRIGO DE TORRES** (GB) 28
246 **RODY** (FR) 45
213 **ROE YOUR OWN BOAT** (IRE) 23
564 **ROFAN** (USA) C 48
155 **ROGER BEANTOWN** (IRE) 26
555 **ROGER THORPE** (GB) 4
448 **ROGUE ANGEL** (IRE) 19
19 **ROGUE DANCER** (FR) 4
349 **ROGUE WAVE** (IRE) 27
397 **ROHERYN** (FR) 33
515 **ROHESIA** (GB) 28
372 **ROJA DOVE** (IRE) 18
326 **ROJO VIVO** (GB) 10
444 **ROKEBY** (GB) 28
33 **ROLE PLAYER** (GB) 6
286 **ROLECARR** (IRE) 5
321 **ROLL THE DICE** (IRE) 77
9 **ROLLIN 'N TUMBLIN** (GB) 22
473 **ROLLING ACES** (IRE) 101
215 **ROLLING DICE** (GB) 14
386 **ROLLING DOUGH** (GB) 23
54 **ROLLING MAUL** (IRE) 41
310 **ROLLING STAR** (FR) 112
103 **ROLLO'S REFLECTION** (IRE) 21
458 **ROLLY BABY** (FR) 97
596 **ROLY TRICKS** (GB) 19
675 **ROMAN DE BRUT** (IRE) 66
546 **ROMAN DE SAINT CYR** (FR) 201
162 **ROMAN FLIGHT** (IRE) 14
456 **ROMAN GOSPEL** (GB) F 20
443 **ROMAN RICHES** (GB) 117
429 **ROMAN ROYAL** (GB) 55
370 **ROMANCE DANCE** (GB) 1
84 **ROMANTIC BLISS** (FR) 39
207 **ROMANTIC SETTINGS** (GB) 44
313 **ROMANTICIZE** (GB) 10
279 **ROMANY PRINCESS** (IRE) C 136
46 **ROMANY QUEST** (GB) 4
42 **ROMANY RYME** (GB) 12

443 **ROME** (GB) 77
527 **ROMEO IS BLEEDING** (IRE) 10
546 **ROMEO LIMA** 202
180 **ROMEO MONTAGUE** (GB) 14
492 **ROMEO ROMEO** (IRE) 87
546 **ROMIE'S KASTETT** (GER) F 203
140 **ROMNEY MARSH** (GB) 9
131 **ROMPING HOME** (IRE) F 45
260 **ROMSDAL** (GB) 77
254 **RONALD GEE** (IRE) 25
371 **RONALDINHO** (GB) 87
507 **RONALDO DES MOTTES** (FR) 92
609 **RONALDSAY** (GB) C 70
105 **RONDEAU** (GB) 13
548 **RONNI PANCAKE** (GB) F 8
214 **RONNIE LAWSON** (IRE) 33
497 **RONNIE ROCKCAKE** (GB) 14
54 **RONS DREAM** (GB) 42
84 **RONYA** (IRE) 40
491 **ROODEYE** (GB) F 44
358 **ROOKERY** (IRE) 123
190 **ROOMIE** (GB) 79
357a **ROOM KEY** 38
273 **ROPARTA AVENUE** (GB) 8
16 **RORING SAMSON** (IRE) 49
135 **RORY BOY** (USA) 16
428 **RORY MAC** (IRE) 67
167 **ROS CASTLE** (IRE) 20
106 **ROS THE BOSS** (IRE) C 141
679 **ROSA FLEET** (IRE) 71
659 **ROSA GRACE** (GB) F 124
644 **ROSA IMPERIALIS** (GB) 10
425 **ROSA LOCKWOOD** (GB) 12
308 **ROSA MUNDI** (GB) C 50
427 **ROSABEE** (IRE) C 37
288 **ROSAIRLIE** (GB) 31
492 **ROSALINE** (IRE) 88
136 **ROSARINA** (GB) 17
17 **ROSE ABOVE** (GB) 161
484 **ROSE ACCLAIM** (GB) 102
225 **ROSE BOUNTY** (GB) G 16
429 **ROSE BRIAR** (GB) C 56
106 **ROSE CHEVAL** (USA) F 142
260 **ROSE CUT** (IRE) C 156
169 **ROSE DE FRANCE** (IRE) C 47
382 **ROSE DIAMOND** (GB) F 46
100 **ROSE GARNET** (GB) 36
53 **ROSE KAZAN** (IRE) 81
511 **ROSE OF COMA** (IRE) F 53
633 **ROSE OF MARRON** (IRE) 8
484 **ROSE OF THE MOON** (GB) 55
154 **ROSE OF THE WORLD** (IRE) 12
367 **ROSE OF ZOLLERN** (IRE) C 27
573 **ROSE PAGEANT** (GB) 27
604 **ROSE RED** (GB) 6
645 **ROSE'S DESTINATION** (IRE) C 57
137 **ROSEBURG** (IRE) 59
318 **ROSEHILL ARTIST** (IRE) 59
280 **ROSENEATH** (IRE) 17
17 **ROSERROW** (GB) 38
358 **ROSES FROM RIDEY** (IRE) F 202
77 **ROSES LEGEND** (GB) 2
32 **ROSEUM** (GB) F 121
639 **ROSEVILLE COTTAGE** (IRE) 36
623 **ROSIE** (GB) G 2
310 **ROSIE PROBERT** (GB) 113
343 **ROSIE PROSPECTS** (GB) 11
276 **ROSIE REBEL** (GB) 9

33 **RUTLAND BOY** (GB) 7
439 **RUTTERKIN** (USA) 16
609 **RUWAIYAN** (USA) 6
609 **RUWASI** (GB) 35
309 **RUZEIZ** (USA) 12
680 **RYAN STYLE** (IRE) 16
460 **RYANSBROOK** (IRE) 22
679 **RYDALIS** (FR) 73
435 **RYDAN** (IRE) 8
310 **RYDE BY KNIGHT** (GB) 116
507 **RYDE ON** (GB) G 95
317 **RYDON PYNES** (GB) 9
602 **RYE HOUSE** (IRE) 17
460 **RYE MARTINI** (IRE) 23
161 **RYEDALE LASS** (GB) 16
534 **RYEHILL LADY** (IRE) G 35
291 **RYELLA** (USA) C 288
484 **RYEOLLIEAN** (GB) 86
277 **RYLEE MOOCH** (GB) 22
550 **RYTON RUNNER** (IRE) 76
206 **SA SUFFIT** (FR) 22
209 **SAAB ALMANAL** (GB) 42
609 **SAABIQ** (USA) F 71
207 **SAAKHEN** (IRE) 95
429 **SAALIB** (USA) 57
546 **SAANE** (FR) 90
260 **SAARREM** (USA) 78
279 **SAAYERR** (GB) 64
73 **SAB LE BEAU** (FR) 17
290 **SABBATICAL** (IRE) G 37
349 **SABHA** (IRE) 33
627 **SABLAZO** (FR) 5
315 **SABLONNE** (USA) C 15
503 **SABORIDO** (USA) 15
39 **SABRE ROCK** (GB) 12
442 **SABROCLAIR** (FR) 18
158 **SACHIKO** (GB) C 6
244 **SACRAMENTO KING** (IRE) 10
206 **SACRE TOI** (FR) 23
260 **SACRED ACT** (GB) 79
650 **SACRED MOUNTAIN** (GB) 7
418 **SACRED SQUARE** (GER) 113
480 **SACRILEGE** (GB) 5
394 **SACROBLEU** (FR) 56
166 **SACROSANCTUS** (GB) 21
650 **SADDLE PACK** (IRE) 8
639 **SADDLE UP SAM** (GB) 47
492 **SADDLER'S ROCK** (IRE) 5
500 **SADDLERS BEND** (IRE) C 21
321 **SADDLERS ENCORE** (GB) 80
630 **SADDLERS MOT** (GB) 6
92 **SADDLERS' SECRET** (IRE) 5
5 **SADEEK'S SONG** (USA) 44
350 **SADIE THOMPSON** (IRE) C 28
5 **SADIMA** (IRE) F 129
549 **SADIYNA** (FR) C 126
48 **SADLER'S STAR** (GER) 16
519 **SAFARI SUNBEAM** (GB) 5
316 **SAFE INVESTMENT** (USA) 14
5 **SAFETY CHECK** (IRE) 96
637 **SAFFERANO** (IRE) 77
11 **SAFFIRE SONG** (GB) 15
596 **SAFFRON CROCUS** (GB) C 39
66 **SAFFRON PRINCE** (GB) 23
372 **SAFFRON WELLS** (IRE) 19
145 **SAFRAN DE COTTE** (FR) 33
590 **SAFWAAN** (GB) 6
180 **SAGA CELEBRE** (FR) F 80

498 **SAGA LOUT** (GB) 6
180 **SAGACIOUS** (IRE) C 81
549 **SAGALINA** (IRE) F 127
549 **SAGAMI** (USA) 128
213 **SAGE MONKEY** (IRE) 24
639 **SAGLIERE** (GB) 39
104 **SAGUA LA GRANDE** (IRE) 14
318 **SAGUNA** (FR) 132
319 **SAHAAFY** (USA) 44
624 **SAHAAYEF** (IRE) 44
602 **SAHARA DESERT** (IRE) 63
395 **SAHARIA** (IRE) 21
318 **SAHRA AL KHADRA** (GB) 60
137 **SAIGON CITY** (GB) 25
432 **SAIL AND RETURN** (GB) 4
484 **SAIL WITH THE WIND** (GB) F 103
576 **SAILING CLUB** (USA) 34
215 **SAILING DAYS** (GB) F 15
579 **SAILOR'S SOVEREIGN** (GB) 10
659 **SAILORS SWAN** (USA) 55
637 **SAINT ARE** (FR) 78
5 **SAINT BAUDOLINO** (IRE) 45
265 **SAINT BREIZ** (FR) 7
661 **SAINT BRIEUC** (FR) 5
576 **SAINT ELIER** (FR) 16
546 **SAINT GREGOIRE** (FR) 91
38 **SAINT HELENA** (IRE) 22
491 **SAINT JEROME** (IRE) 16
507 **SAINT JOHN HENRY** (FR) 96
676 **SAINT LINO** (FR) 34
260 **SAINT LUCY** (GB) 80
80 **SAINT PERAY** (FR) 4
546 **SAINT POIS** (FR) 92
473 **SAINT ROQUE** (FR) 103
399 **SAINT THOMAS** (IRE) 16
602 **SAINT'S VICTORY** (GB) 64
51 **SAINTE ADELE** (FR) 26
546 **SAINTE CROIX** (FR) 93
308 **SAINTES** (FR) 51
189 **SAINTS AND SINNERS** (IRE) 43
578 **SAIRAAM** (IRE) 3
352 **SAKASH** (GB) 33
277 **SAKHALIN STAR** (IRE) 30
117 **SAKHEE'S ALROUND** (GB) 4
425 **SAKHEE'S ROSE** (GB) 13
53 **SAKHEE'S SOUL** (IRE) F 109
138 **SAKHEE'SSQUIRREL** (GB) 21
564 **SAKTOON** (USA) 17
205 **SAKURAMACHI** (GB) 17
546 **SALAI** (FR) 94
643 **SALALAH** (GB) F 29
422 **SALAM ALAYKUM** (IRE) 4
342 **SALBATORE** (GB) 7
37 **SALEAL** (GB) 10
197 **SALFORD PRINCE** (IRE) 9
9 **SALIENT** (GB) 23
352 **SALINGERS STAR** (IRE) F 35
635 **SALINIA** (IRE) C 159
134 **SALLY BRUCE** (GB) 8
625 **SALLY FRIDAY** (IRE) 10
371 **SALMANAZAR** (GB) 88
382 **SALMON SUSHI** (GB) 26
308 **SALOME** (FR) 52
116 **SALSKA** (GB) G 5
116 **SALSKA** (GB) F 4
318 **SALT ISLAND** (GB) 133
418 **SALTO CHISCO** (IRE) 114
33 **SALTWATER CREEK** (IRE) 44

134 **SALTY AIR** (IRE) C 17
473 **SALUBRIOUS** (IRE) 104
507 **SALUT FLO** (FR) 97
280 **SALUT HONORE** (FR) 19
240 **SALUT L'AS** (FR) 11
358 **SALUTATION** (IRE) 42
85 **SALVATOR'S LEGACY** (IRE) 6
144 **SALVATORE FURY** (IRE) 26
523 **SALYDORA** (FR) C 61
439 **SAM LORD** (GB) 17
666 **SAM PATCH** (GB) 10
564 **SAM SPADE** (IRE) 18
473 **SAM WINNER** (FR) 105
549 **SAMADRISA** (IRE) 129
125 **SAMANDY** (GB) 10
84 **SAMAR QAND** (GB) C 72
44 **SAMAWI** (FR) 48
531 **SAMBELUCKY** (IRE) 27
322 **SAMBULANDO** (FR) 1
631 **SAME DIFFERENCE** (IRE) 66
531 **SAMEDI SOIR** (GB) 28
180 **SAMEEK** (IRE) 82
473 **SAMETEGAL** (FR) 106
75 **SAMHAIN** (GB) 14
303 **SAMINGARRY** (FR) 12
27 **SAMIRE** (FR) 84
633 **SAMIZDAT** (FR) 9
49 **SAMMYMAN** (GB) 11
35 **SAMOAN** (IRE) 17
607 **SAMOSET** (GB) 34
531 **SAMSASWINGER** (GB) 42
430 **SAMSON COLLONGES** (FR) 14
665 **SAMSTOWN** (GB) 20
288 **SAMTHEMAN** (GB) 22
477 **SAMTOMJONES** (IRE) 9
68 **SAMTU** (IRE) 46
585 **SAMURAI LEGEND** (GB) 14
98 **SAN CASSIANO** (IRE) 27
124 **SAN MARINO** (FR) 4
618 **SAN REMO ROSE** (IRE) 17
27 **SAN SICARIO** (USA) 48
437 **SAN SIRO** (IRE) 4
540 **SAN TELM** (FR) 15
546 **SANABOWL** (FR) 95
549 **SANAIJA** (GB) 74
549 **SANAM** (USA) 130
595 **SANCTIONED** (GB) 10
679 **SAND ARTIST** (IRE) 74
291 **SAND DANCER** (IRE) 124
452 **SAND STORMER** (IRE) 31
269 **SANDANSKI** (IRE) 10
130 **SANDAURA** (IRE) 18
27 **SANDBAR** (GB) C 85
148 **SANDBOX TWO** (GB) C 82
527 **SANDEEL BAY** (IRE) 11
433 **SANDFIELD** (IRE) 25
133 **SANDFRANKSKIPSGO** (GB) 5
659 **SANDGLASS** (GB) C 125
207 **SANDIVA** (IRE) 96
144 **SANDRA'S DIAMOND** (IRE) 53
252 **SANDS CHORUS** (GB) 36
407 **SANDS COVE** (IRE) 18
252 **SANDSMAN'S GIRL** (IRE) 21
619 **SANDY BEACH** (GB) 46
602 **SANDY CAY** (USA) 139
200 **SANDY COVE** (GB) 15
281 **SANDY SMILE** (IRE) 48
549 **SANDY'S CHOICE** (FR) 75

260 **SOLAR MAGIC** (GB) 86
197 **SOLAR SKY** (GB) 11
641 **SOLAR SPIRIT** (IRE) 14
515 **SOLAR VIEW** (GB) 8
637 **SOLARAS EXHIBITION** (IRE) 85
55 **SOLARMAITE** (GB) 9
291 **SOLDIER SAM** (GB) 299
59 **SOLE DANSER** (IRE) 20
658 **SOLE SURVIVOR** (FR) 43
59 **SOLEMN** (GB) 21
612 **SOLEMN VOW** (GB) F 12
193 **SOLENT LAD** (USA) 16
454 **SOLID CONCRETE** (IRE) 41
652 **SOLID JUSTICE** (IRE) 12
426 **SOLID LAND** (FR) F 27
5 **SOLIDARITY** (GB) 100
86 **SOLIS** (GB) 5
557 **SOLIS** (GER) 23
181 **SOLITAIRY GIRL** (GB) 4
675 **SOLIX** (FR) 46
336 **SOLL** (GB) 15
201 **SOLO HUNTER** (GB) 50
291 **SOLOLA** (GER) C 300
350 **SOLSTALLA** (GB) 32
687 **SOLSTICE DAWN** (GB) 4
332 **SOLSTICE SON** (GB) 30
332 **SOLSTICE STAR** (GB) 31
299 **SOLWAY BAY** (GB) 2
299 **SOLWAY DANDY** (GB) 3
299 **SOLWAY DONAL** (IRE) F 4
299 **SOLWAY DORNAL** (GB) 5
299 **SOLWAY LEGEND** (GB) 6
299 **SOLWAY ROSE** (GB) C 7
299 **SOLWAY SAM** (GB) 8
299 **SOLWAY SILVER** (GB) 9
299 **SOLWAY STAR** (GB) 10
494 **SOLYWAY** (FR) 33
457 **SOMCHINE** (GB) 28
285 **SOME LAD** (IRE) 7
173 **SOME SECRET** (GB) 28
94 **SOME SHOW** (GB) 61
572 **SOME SITE** (IRE) 47
335 **SOME TIKKET** (IRE) 61
679 **SOMEMOTHERSDOHAVEM** (GB) 79
254 **SOMEONE'S DARLING** (GB) 28
226 **SOMERBY** (IRE) 3
148 **SOMERSAULT** (GB) C 85
106 **SOMERSBY** (IRE) 35
80 **SOMERSET LIAS** (IRE) 5
192 **SOMERTON STAR** (GB) 12
318 **SOMETHING BLUE** (GB) 11
90 **SOMETHINGBOUTMARY** (GB) 10
25 **SOMETHINGROYAL** (IRE) 61
335 **SOMETHINGWONDERFUL** (IRE) 62
576 **SOMETIME** (FR) C 54
358 **SOMETIME** (IRE) C 207
358 **SOMEWHAT** (USA) 127
201 **SOMMERSTURM** (GER) 30
494 **SON CESIO** (FR) 104
206 **SON DU SILENCE** (IRE) 27
613 **SON OF FEYAN** (IRE) 18
131 **SON OF FLICKA** (GB) 19
481 **SON OF SUZIE** (GB) 42
58 **SON OF SWALLOW** (IRE) 24
62 **SON OF YORK** (IRE) 4
260 **SONA** (GB) 87
443 **SONG AND DANCE MAN** (GB) 88
197 **SONG LIGHT** (GB) 12

318 **SONG OF MY HEART** (IRE) F 136
602 **SONG OF NAMIBIA** (IRE) 71
404 **SONG OF NORWAY** (GB) 17
266 **SONG OF PARKES** (GB) 10
291 **SONG OF PASSION** (GB) C 301
548 **SONG OF PRIDE** (GER) 11
359 **SONG OF ROWLAND** (IRE) 17
329 **SONG OF THE DESERT** (GB) F 7
246 **SONG SAA** (GB) 51
44 **SONGCRAFT** (IRE) 53
640 **SONGSMITH** (GB) 25
410 **SONIC WELD** (GB) 3
56 **SONNETATION** (IRE) 14
17 **SONNOLENTO** (IRE) 167
635 **SONNY SUNSHINE** (GB) F 164
619 **SONNY THE ONE** (GB) 50
550 **SONNY THYNE** (GB) 83
572 **SONNYTHENAVIGATOR** (USA) 92
675 **SONOFAGUN** (FR) 47
513 **SONORAN SANDS** (GB) 42
515 **SONRISA** (GB) 61
128 **SONTIME** (GB) F 38
69 **SOOQAAN** (GB) 22
107 **SOPHIE'S BEAU** (USA) 18
494 **SORCIEREBIENAIMEE** (FR) 161
106 **SORELLA BELLA** (IRE) 36
293 **SORRENTINA** (IRE) F 9
270 **SORROW** (FR) 7
609 **SORRY SAEED** (GB) 39
692 **SORSE** (GB) 10
380 **SOSIA** (GER) 43
318 **SOSPIRA** (GB) F 137
622 **SOSUMI** (GB) F 28
53 **SOTISE** (IRE) 87
161 **SOUBRETTE** (GB) 17
257 **SOUDAIN** (FR) 21
397 **SOUFFLE** (GB) C 67
44 **SOUL** (AUS) 54
228 **SOUL ANGEL** (GB) 7
190 **SOUL ARTIST** (IRE) 82
190 **SOUL BROTHER** (IRE) 83
553 **SOUL INSTINCT** (GB) 62
319 **SOUL INTENT** (IRE) 12
261 **SOUL MAGIC** (IRE) 7
367 **SOUL OF MOTION** (GB) 22
144 **SOUND ADVICE** (GB) 30
99 **SOUND AMIGO** (IRE) 11
85 **SOUND APPEAL** (GB) F 7
635 **SOUND HEARTS** (USA) 28
473 **SOUND INVESTMENT** (IRE) 117
276 **SOUND OF LIFE** (IRE) 21
493 **SOUND OF SUMMER** (USA) F 38
5 **SOUND REFLECTION** (USA) 101
238 **SOUNDBYTE** (GB) 8
378 **SOUNDTRACK** (IRE) 31
546 **SOURIYAN** 96
443 **SOUTH CAPE** (GB) 89
403 **SOUTH KENTER** (USA) 9
13 **SOUTH STACK** (GB) 40
450 **SOUTHERN CROSS** (GB) 45
364 **SOUTHFIELD BELLE** (IRE) 23
473 **SOUTHFIELD THEATRE** (IRE) 118
473 **SOUTHFIELD VIC** (IRE) 119
139 **SOUTHSEA ISLAND** (IRE) 42
183 **SOUTHWARKNEWSFLASH** (GB) G 14
240 **SOUTHWAY QUEEN** (GB) 12
308 **SOUVERAINE** (FR) 53
646 **SOUVILLE** (GB) 35

483 **SOVEREIGN ABBEY** (IRE) C 16
33 **SOVEREIGN DEBT** (IRE) 9
612 **SOVEREIGN SEAL** (GB) G 9
572 **SOVEREIGN'S HONOUR** (USA) F 93
17 **SOVIET ROCK** (IRE) 43
39 **SOWETO STAR** (IRE) 14
200 **SPA'S DANCER** (IRE) 7
577 **SPACE ARTIST** (IRE) 19
452 **SPACE TIME** (FR) C 51
181 **SPACE WALKER** (IRE) 16
189 **SPACE WAR** (GB) 46
366 **SPACECRAFT** (IRE) 11
659 **SPACECRAFT** (USA) F 131
409 **SPACIOUS SKY** (USA) 33
66 **SPAGETTI WESTERN** (IRE) 24
394 **SPANISH ARCH** (IRE) 61
405 **SPANISH BOUNTY** (GB) 11
639 **SPANISH FLEET** (GB) 41
660 **SPANISH FORK** (IRE) 11
637 **SPANISH OPTIMIST** (IRE) 86
328 **SPANISH PLUME** (GB) 27
493 **SPANISH SQUEEZE** (IRE) 39
366 **SPANISH TRAIL** (GB) 12
627 **SPANISH TREASURE** (IRE) 6
429 **SPARK PLUG** (IRE) 59
632 **SPARK UP** (GB) C 11
659 **SPARKLE FACTOR** (IRE) 63
190 **SPARKLE GIRL** (GB) 120
8 **SPARKLING HAND** (GB) 2
357a **SPARKLING ICE** (IRE) 20
118 **SPARKLING MONTJEU** (FR) F 19
584 **SPARKLING TARA** (GB) 65
584 **SPARKLING WINE** (IRE) 66
674 **SPARKSFROMMYHEELS** (IRE) 68
479 **SPARROW** (IRE) 85
158 **SPARTACULOUS** (GB) 4
310 **SPARTAN ANGEL** (GB) 124
399 **SPARTAN BELLE** (GB) 18
480 **SPARTILLA** (GB) 6
13 **SPARVILLE** (IRE) 41
75 **SPATE RISE** (GB) C 35
3 **SPAVENTO** (IRE) 14
121 **SPEAK SOFTLY TO ME** (USA) F 22
38 **SPEAR THISTLE** (GB) 25
560 **SPECIAL ACCOUNT** (IRE) 36
310 **SPECIAL AGENT** (GB) 125
531 **SPECIAL CATCH** (IRE) 31
478 **SPECIAL DANCER** (GB) F 74
491 **SPECIAL DESTINY** (GB) F 46
308 **SPECIAL DUTY** (GB) F 54
358 **SPECIAL FIGHTER** (IRE) 128
53 **SPECIAL MISS** (GB) 88
580 **SPECIAL MIX** (GB) 9
454 **SPECIAL REPORT** (IRE) 42
426 **SPECIAL VINTAGE** (GB) 28
584 **SPECIAL WELLS** (GB) 67
249 **SPECIALAGENT ALFIE** (GB) 20
575 **SPECIALTY** (IRE) 12
564 **SPECIFIC DREAM** (GB) F 49
515 **SPECIFICALLY** (USA) F 62
5 **SPECKLED** (USA) 47
12 **SPECKLED DOOR** (GB) 16
17 **SPECTATOR** (GB) 111
197 **SPECULATIVE BID** (IRE) 21
53 **SPEECHDAY** (IRE) 89
17 **SPEED COP** (GB) F 168
128 **SPEED HAWK** (USA) 32
120 **SPEED MACHINE** (IRE) 52

40 **STARBOTTON** (GB) 9
670 **STARBURST DIAMOND** (IRE) 5
450 **STARFALA** (GB) F 68
678 **STARFISH** (IRE) C 51
136 **STARFLEET** (GB) F 18
576 **STARFLOWER** (GB) 37
291 **STARISA** (IRE) C 303
659 **STARLET** (IRE) 64
296 **STARLIGHT ANGEL** (IRE) 23
492 **STARLIGHT DANCE** (IRE) 149
479 **STARLIGHT DREAMS** (USA) C 147
479 **STARLIGHT NIGHT** (USA) C 148
445 **STARLIGHT PRINCESS** (IRE) 16
32 **STARLIGHT SERENADE** (GB) 68
383 **STARLIGHT SONATA** (GB) 55
357a **STARLIGHT SYMPHONY (IRE)** 5
357a **STARLIT CANTATA** 22
156 **STARLIT EVE** (GB) 7
371 **STARPARTY** (USA) G 129
550 **STARPLEX** (GB) 84
591 **STARRY SKY** (GB) F 47
112 **STARS ABOVE ME** (GB) 49
492 **STARS ALIGHT** (GB) 50
291 **STARS ALIGNED** (IRE) 133
137 **STARS AND STRIPES** (GB) 107
249 **STARS ROYALE** (IRE) 21
492 **STARS SO BRIGHT** (IRE) 51
454 **STARSHIP TROUPER** (GB) 43
209 **STARSTONE** (GB) C 80
148 **START THE MUSIC** (GB) C 86
318 **STARTARETTE** (USA) F 139
209 **STARTARETTE** (USA) F 47
33 **STARTORI** (GB) F 88
434 **STARVING MARVIN** (GB) 14
65 **STARWATCH** (GB) 11
572 **STASIO** (USA) 20
321 **STATE DEPARTMENT** (GB) 83
291 **STATE OF THE UNION** (IRE) 304
296 **STATE SECRET** (GB) C 45
230 **STATION CLOSED** (IRE) 4
609 **STATUA** (IRE) F 79
44 **STATUTORY** (IRE) 55
659 **STAY DE NIGHT** (GB) 65
441 **STAY IN MY HEART** (IRE) 19
546 **STAY THE NIGHT** (USA) 209
397 **STAYLILY** (GB) C 68
332 **STEADY GIRLFRIEND** (GB) 32
291 **STEAL THE SCENE** (IRE) 305
68 **STEALTH MISSILE** (IRE) 48
85 **STEEL A TUNE** (GB) 9
457 **STEEL CITY** (GB) 30
598 **STEEL CITY BOY** (IRE) 30
402 **STEEL FREE** (GB) F 12
335 **STEEL GREY LADY** (IRE) F 64
32 **STEEL PRINCESS** (IRE) C 124
205 **STEEL RAIN** (GB) 13
69 **STEEL STOCKHOLDER** (GB) 14
162 **STEEL SUMMIT** (IRE) 15
494 **STEEL TRAIN** (FR) 106
81 **STEELCUT** (GB) 3
109 **STEELE RANGER** (GB) 31
5 **STEELER** (IRE) 48
40 **STEELRIVER** (IRE) 10
531 **STEELTEESCOMPONENT** (GB) 34
353 **STEEPLEOFCOPPER** (IRE) 4
576 **STEFER** (USA) C 56
50 **STEIP AMACH** (GB) 119
260 **STELLA BELLISSIMA** (IRE) 89

25 **STELLA ETOILE** (IRE) 62
427 **STELLA MANUELA** (FR) F 39
27 **STELLA RIVER** (FR) 50
586 **STELLA'S FELLA** (GB) 7
397 **STELLAR BRILLIANT** (USA) C 69
6 **STELLAR EXPRESS** (IRE) 43
246 **STELLAR NOTION** (IRE) 52
49 **STELLARTA** (GB) 17
27 **STELWOOD** (FR) 89
279 **STENCIVE** (GB) 20
443 **STENTORIAN** (IRE) 90
546 **STEP AND GO** (GB) 98
291 **STEP TO THE SHEARS** (GB) 306
659 **STEP WITH STYLE** (USA) F 132
573 **STEPHANIE FRANCES** (IRE) 31
573 **STEPHEN HERO** (IRE) 32
27 **STEPHILL** (FR) 51
94 **STEPPE BY STEPPE** (GB) 35
118 **STEPPE DAUGHTER** (IRE) 16
452 **STEPPER POINT** (GB) 10
84 **STEPPING AHEAD** (FR) 21
148 **STEPPING OUT** (IRE) 46
635 **STEPS** (IRE) 30
295 **STEPS TO FREEDOM** (IRE) 45
130 **STEREO LOVE** (FR) 51
126 **STERLING GENT** (IRE) 15
27 **STEROPE** (FR) C 90
358 **STETCHWORTH** (IRE) 129
635 **STEVE ROGERS** (IRE) 93
11 **STEVENTON STAR** (GB) 17
81 **STEVIE GEE** (IRE) 4
675 **STEVIE THUNDER** (GB) 48
353 **STICKERS** (GB) 5
288 **STICKLEBACK** (GB) 24
568 **STIFF UPPER LIP** (IRE) 41
674 **STILL BELIEVING** (GB) 69
276 **STILL SMALL VOICE** (GB) F 22
624 **STILLA AFTON** (GB) 32
318 **STINKY SOCKS** (GB) 140
17 **STIRRING BALLAD** (GB) 44
167 **STITCHED IN TIME** (IRE) 23
513 **STOCKHILL DIVA** (GB) 43
94 **STOIC BOY** (GB) 62
602 **STOMACHION** (IRE) 18
112 **STOMP** (GB) 50
679 **STONE LIGHT** (FR) 80
39 **STONE OF FOLCA** (GB) 15
33 **STONE ROSES** (IRE) 89
266 **STONEACRE BRIGITTE** (IRE) 11
266 **STONEACRE HULL** (IRE) 12
266 **STONEACRE LAD** (IRE) 13
266 **STONEACRE OSKAR** (GB) 14
266 **STONEACRE THIRSK** (IRE) 15
266 **STONEACRE TILLY** (IRE) 16
418 **STONEBROOK** (IRE) 125
72 **STONECRABSTOMORROW** (IRE) 8
53 **STONECUTTER** (IRE) 91
144 **STONEFIELD FLYER** (GB) 31
106 **STONEHAM** (GB) 91
637 **STONETHROWER** (IRE) 87
335 **STONEY** 65
144 **STONEY QUINE** (IRE) 57
371 **STONEY'S TREASURE** (GB) 99
203 **STONEYLEY MINSTREL** (GB) 17
301 **STOP N STARE** (IRE) 5
375 **STOPPED OUT** (GB) 54
277 **STOREY HILL** (USA) 24
318 **STORM** (IRE) 12

240 **STORM ALERT** (GB) 13
665 **STORM BRIG** (GB) 23
17 **STORM FORCE TEN** (GB) 112
192 **STORM HAWK** (GB) 13
67 **STORM LIGHTNING** (GB) 13
9 **STORM OF CHOICE** (GB) 30
398 **STORM OF SAINTLY** (FR) 27
573 **STORM OF SWORDS** (IRE) 33
585 **STORM PATROL** (GB) 18
271 **STORM PRINCESS** (GB) 15
291 **STORM RIDER** (IRE) 134
181 **STORM ROCK** 36
613 **STORM RUN** (IRE) 19
408 **STORM RUNNER** (IRE) 12
486 **STORM SURVIVOR** (IRE) 83
237 **STORM TO PASS** (GB) 5
291 **STORM TROOPER** (IRE) 135
440 **STORMARDAL** (IRE) 19
120 **STORMBOUND** (IRE) 11
659 **STORMFLY** (IRE) 133
631 **STORMHOEK** (IRE) 70
254 **STORMIN EXIT** (IRE) 30
418 **STORMING GALE** (IRE) 126
164 **STORMING HARRY** (GB) 44
209 **STORMING SIOUX** (GB) C 81
246 **STORMING STRUMPET** (GB) 53
32 **STORMY BLESSING** (USA) F 125
375 **STORMY MORNING** (GB) 55
429 **STORMY PARADISE** (IRE) 60
618 **STORMY VIEW** (USA) G 18
196 **STORMY WEATHER** (FR) 75
645 **STORMY WEATHER** (GB) F 63
674 **STORMYISLAND AHEAD** (GB) 70
378 **STORY WRITER** (GB) 17
190 **STORYLINE** (IRE) 84
367 **STOSUR** (IRE) 23
358 **STOUT CORTEZ** (GB) 130
48 **STOW** (GB) 17
290 **STOWAWAY SHARK** (IRE) 38
591 **STRADATER** (IRE) 11
584 **STRAIDNAHANNA** (IRE) 71
628 **STRAIGHT AS A DIE** (GB) F 32
35 **STRAIGHT GIN** (GB) 27
291 **STRAIT RUN** (IRE) 136
553 **STRAITS OF MALACCA** (GB) 63
608 **STRAITS OF MESSINA** (IRE) 32
157 **STRAND LINE** (IRE) 5
654 **STRANDFIELD BAY** (IRE) 3
547 **STRANGE BIRD** (IRE) 9
251 **STRANGELITTLEGIRL** (GB) 3
354 **STRATEGIC ACTION** (IRE) 11
130 **STRATEGIC FORCE** (IRE) 52
120 **STRATEGIC STRIKE** (IRE) 12
5 **STRATEGICAL** (USA) 104
135 **STRATHAIRD** (IRE) 21
564 **STRAVELLA** (IRE) F 50
328 **STRAVERSJOY** (GB) 28
391 **STRAVITA** (GB) 9
276 **STRAWBERRIESNCREAM** (IRE) 23
364 **STRAWBERRY HILL** (IRE) 24
452 **STRAWBERRY MARTINI** (GB) 33
189 **STRAWBERRY MOON** (IRE) C 80
399 **STREAM OF LIGHT** (GB) 19
534 **STREAMS OF WHISKEY** (IRE) 40
686 **STREELE** (USA) 12
472 **STREET ARTIST** (IRE) 30
190 **STREET BOSS** (IRE) 85
507 **STREET ENTERTAINER** (IRE) 109

260 **SWAIN'S GOLD** (USA) C 159
457 **SWALE STAR** (GB) 38
225 **SWALEDALE LAD** (IRE) 19
383 **SWALLOWSHIDE** (GB) 56
443 **SWAMPFIRE** (IRE) 93
572 **SWAN LAKES** (IRE) 48
572 **SWAN NEBULA** (USA) F 49
17 **SWAN SONG** (GB) 45
75 **SWAN WINGS** (GB) C 37
431 **SWANAGE BAY** (IRE) 16
564 **SWANKY LADY** (GB) F 52
291 **SWANWICK SHORE** (IRE) 137
418 **SWATOW TYPHOON** (IRE) 130
679 **SWAYTHE** (USA) G 83
435 **SWEENEY TODD** (GB) 9
624 **SWEEPING ROCK** (IRE) 11
450 **SWEEPING UP** (GB) 47
486 **SWEEPS HILL** (NZ) 85
445 **SWEET ALIBI** (IRE) 17
252 **SWEET ANGELICA** (GB) 24
258 **SWEET BOY VIC** (IRE) 23
462 **SWEET CHARLIE** (GB) 18
463 **SWEET CHERRY** (IRE) 11
310 **SWEET DEAL** (IRE) 132
426 **SWEET EMPIRE** (IRE) F 30
492 **SWEET FOLLY** (IRE) C 92
128 **SWEET HOME ALABAMA** (IRE) C 39
484 **SWEET LIGHTNING** (GB) 61
596 **SWEET LILY PEA** (GB) 22
17 **SWEET MANDOLIN** (GB) C 170
378 **SWEET MARTONI** (GB) 18
136 **SWEET MARWELL** (IRE) 10
458 **SWEET MY LORD** (FR) 123
291 **SWEET NAMIBIA** (IRE) F 308
106 **SWEET NICOLE** (GB) C 148
624 **SWEET P** (GB) 33
88 **SWEET PICCOLO** (GB) 8
192 **SWEET POSSESSION** (USA) 14
466 **SWEET REQUEST** (GB) F 8
450 **SWEET SELECTION** (GB) 70
201 **SWEET SORROW** (IRE) F 65
352 **SWEET SUGAR** (FR) 35
331 **SWEET SUMMER** (GB) 13
499 **SWEET TALKING GUY** (IRE) 13
602 **SWEET TEMPER** (USA) F 143
67 **SWEET VINTAGE** (IRE) 14
494 **SWEETDREAMS** (FR) F 163
378 **SWEETHEART ABBEY** (GB) 32
596 **SWEETNESS LADY** (GB) 23
652 **SWEETNESSANDLIGHT** (GB) 7
553 **SWEHAN** (IRE) 29
487 **SWENDAB** (IRE) 25
418 **SWIFT ARROW** (IRE) 131
312 **SWIFT BLADE** (GB) 9
260 **SWIFT CAMPAIGN** (IRE) 90
637 **SWIFT ESCAPE** (GB) 88
99 **SWIFTLY DONE** (IRE) 12
622 **SWILKEN** (GB) 17
66 **SWINCOMBE ROCK** (GB) 25
644 **SWINCOMBE STAR** (GB) 12
332 **SWINCOMBE STONE** (GB) 33
584 **SWINDY** (GB) 72
367 **SWING ALONE** (IRE) 9
507 **SWING BILL** (GB) 110
507 **SWING BOWLER** (GB) 111
435 **SWING EASY** (GB) 5
584 **SWING HARD** (IRE) 73
457 **SWING IT** (GB) 31

172 **SWING STATE** (FR) 40
269 **SWING STATE** (GB) 11
301 **SWING THE LEAD** (IRE) F 6
262 **SWINGBRIDGE** (IRE) 31
675 **SWINGING HAWK** (IRE) 49
659 **SWINGLE** (GB) C 136
421 **SWISS CROSS** (GB) 8
260 **SWISS KISS** (GB) 91
197 **SWISS LAIT** (GB) 22
235 **SWITCHED OFF** (GB) 8
281 **SWITCHER** (IRE) 25
358 **SWIVEL** (GB) 131
139 **SWYNMOR** (IRE) 43
33 **SWORD OF THE LORD** (GB) 10
209 **SWORDBEARER** (GB) 48
498 **SWORDS** (GB) 7
491 **SWYNFORD LADY** (IRE) C 48
631 **SYBARITE** (FR) 72
678 **SYBILICIOUS** (GB) 37
588 **SYCHO FRED** (IRE) 11
491 **SYCOPHANTIC** (IRE) 17
318 **SYDNEY HEIGHTS** (IRE) 141
102 **SYDNEY JAMES** (IRE) 18
418 **SYDNEY PAGET** (IRE) 132
291 **SYDNEY RUFFDIAMOND** (GB) 309
364 **SYLVAN LEGEND** (GB) 25
613 **SYLVAN SPIRIT** (IRE) 20
635 **SYLVETTE** (IRE) 166
106 **SYMBOLINE** (GB) 38
291 **SYMBOLIST** (IRE) 310
50 **SYMMETRICAL** (USA) 12
398 **SYMPATHIQUE** (FR) 86
82 **SYMPHONY OF ANGELS** (GB) 4
82 **SYMPHONY OF HEAVEN** (GB) 15
100 **SYMPHONY OF KINGS** (GB) 61
82 **SYMPHONY OF PEARLS** (GB) 13
104 **SYNAESTHESIA** (FR) 36
575 **SYNCOPATE** (GB) 13
380 **SYNDROMOS** (FR) 87
635 **SYNERGISE** (GB) 94
382 **SYNODIC** (USA) 48
319 **SYNONYM** (ITY) 25
441 **SYNTHE DAVIS** (FR) 20
646 **SYRIAN PEARL** (GB) 36
189 **SYROS** (IRE) 64
397 **SYSTEM OVERLOAD** (IRE) 35
398 **SYSTEMIQUE** (FR) 30
478 **T K O LADY** (USA) F 75
635 **TA AMMOL** (GB) 95
133 **TAAJUB** (IRE) 6
189 **TAANIF** (GB) 65
446 **TAARESH** (IRE) 12
635 **TAARKOD** (IRE) F 167
589 **TABLE BLUFF** (IRE) 21
479 **TABLE ROCK** (IRE) 87
445 **TABLEFORTEN** (GB) 18
291 **TABREEK** (USA) 138
53 **TAC DE BOISTRON** (FR) 28
178 **TACA D'OLI** (FR) G 10
493 **TACTICAL STRIKE** (GB) 20
104 **TACTICUS** (USA) 37
659 **TADAANY** (IRE) 137
502 **TADALAVIL** (GB) 15
429 **TADARROJ** (GB) 98
358 **TADARROK** (GB) 211
279 **TADPOLE** (GB) 147
279 **TADQEEQ** (IRE) 148
319 **TAFAHOM** (IRE) 48

635 **TAFAWUK** (USA) 31
371 **TAFFY DARE** (IRE) 102
54 **TAFFY THOMAS** (GB) 49
658 **TAFIKA** (GB) 46
543 **TAGADIRT** (GB) 18
29 **TAGGIA** (FR) 5
429 **TAGHREEB** (GB) 61
260 **TAGHROODA** (GB) 92
473 **TAGRITA** (IRE) 121
344 **TAGULA NIGHT** (IRE) 25
659 **TAHAANY** (IRE) 66
295 **THADDI HALL** (IRE) G 46
106 **TAHADEE** (IRE) 92
209 **TAHCHEE** (GB) 49
523 **TAHIRA** (GER) 32
584 **TAHITI PEARL** (IRE) 74
659 **TAHREEM** (IRE) 138
586 **TAIGAN** (FR) 8
180 **TAJATHUB** (GB) 87
472 **TAJNEED** (IRE) 31
429 **TAJSEER** (USA) 62
639 **TAKAATUF** (IRE) 42
318 **TAKAFOL** (IRE) 142
136 **TAKARNA** (IRE) F 20
310 **TAKE A BOW** (GB) 133
132 **TAKE A BREAK** (GB) 4
105 **TAKE A NOTE** (GB) 15
386 **TAKE OF SHOC'S** (IRE) 28
418 **TAKE THE CASH** (GB) 133
546 **TAKE THE CROWN** (FR) 100
490 **TAKE THE CROWN** (GB) 8
112 **TAKE THE HINT** (GB) C 85
448 **TAKE THE HIT** (IRE) 23
472 **TAKE THE LEAD** (GB) 32
679 **TAKE THE MICK** (GB) 84
280 **TAKE TWO** (GB) 23
315 **TAKEGAWA** (GB) C 16
545 **TAKEMYBREATHAWAY** (GB) 10
386 **TAKEROC** (FR) 29
492 **TAKING LIBERTIES** (IRE) C 93
161 **TAKITWO** (GB) 19
635 **TAKREYM** (IRE) 96
442 **TALBOT ROAD** (IRE) 20
27 **TALE OF LIFE** (JPN) 91
546 **TALEMA** (FR) 101
32 **TALENT** (GB) 81
630 **TALENT SCOUT** (IRE) 8
494 **TALENT SPOTTER** (GB) 107
358 **TALENTED KID** (GB) 52
207 **TALES OF GRIMM** (USA) 48
494 **TALETELLER** (USA) 108
469 **TALINAS ROSE** (IRE) C 15
507 **TALK OF RAIN** (GB) F G 112
428 **TALK OF RAIN** (FR) F 75
122 **TALKIN SENCE** (IRE) 13
534 **TALKIN THOMAS** (IRE) 41
321 **TALKONTHESTREET** (IRE) 84
445 **TALKSALOT** (IRE) 19
602 **TALL SHIP** (IRE) 74
387 **TALLULAH MAI** (GB) 19
635 **TALMADA** (USA) 97
546 **TALON BLEU** (GB) C 212
106 **TALQAA** (GB) 39
659 **TALWEEN** (GB) 14
83 **TAMALETTA** (IRE) 9
62 **TAMAM NAMOOSE** (IRE) 5
552 **TAMARA MOON** (IRE) C 17
386 **TAMARILLO GROVE** (IRE) 30

552 TENOR (IRE) 4
622 TENPENCE (GB) F 29
206 TEO VIVO (IRE) 19
267 TEOCHEW (IRE) 35
178 TEODOLITE (IRE) 11
445 TEOLAGI (IRE) 3
68 TEOSROYAL (IRE) 71
328 TEPMOKEA (IRE) 30
602 TERCEL (IRE) 76
358 TERENTIA (GB) F 212
511 TERESHKINA (IRE) F 58
260 TERHAAB (USA) 94
279 TERHAAL (IRE) 151
458 TERMINAL (FR) 126
93 TERNTHEOTHERCHEEK (GB) 25
513 TERRA FIRMA (GB) 47
308 TERRE BRULEE (FR) 32
479 TERRIFIC (IRE) 89
27 TERRUBI (IRE) 15
295 TERTIA (IRE) F 47
176 TESS DE WODELAND (GB) 12
254 TESTA ROSSA (IRE) 31
427 TESTAMA (FR) C 42
659 TESTED (GB) 68
358 TESTING (FR) 134
678 TETE ORANGE (GB) 38
310 TETLAMI (IRE) 136
196 TETRAVELLA (IRE) F 78
469 TEUTONIC KNIGHT (IRE) 16
170 TEVEZ (GB) 6
428 TEXAS FOREVER (IRE) 77
428 TEXAS JACK (IRE) 78
264 TEXAS ROCK (IRE) 11
430 TEXAS ROSE (IRE) 16
44 THA'IR (IRE) 59
208 THACKERAY (GB) 7
209 THAI NOON (IRE) 82
543 THAKERAH (IRE) 19
279 THAMES PAGEANT (GB) 152
180 THANAAYA (IRE) 88
626 THANE OF CAWDOR (IRE) 7
310 THANKS FOR COMING (GB) 137
52 THANKS HARRY (GB) 16
484 THANKSTOMONTY (GB) 105
40 THANKYOU VERY MUCH (GB) 11
596 THARA'A (IRE) C 43
187 THARAYA (GB) 23
329 THARWA (FR) F 8
297 THAT BE GRAND (GB) 24
484 THAT IS THE SPIRIT (GB) 89
534 THAT'LL DO NICELY (GB) 43
127 THAT'S THE DEAL (IRE) 7
148 THATABOY (IRE) 47
33 THATCHEREEN (IRE) 49
131 THATCHERITE (IRE) 21
538 THATCHERS GOLD (IRE) 15
120 THATCHIT (IRE) 29
358 THATCHMASTER (USA) 54
262 THATILDEE (IRE) 33
665 THATLLDOFORUS (GB) 25
269 THATS BEN (IRE) 12
46 THATS YER MAN (IRE) 6
367 THATS YOUR OPINION (GB) C 28
122 THATSMYLOT (IRE) 15
164 THE ABSENT MARE (GB) 33
417 THE ART OF RACING (IRE) 16
418 THE BACKUP PLAN (IRE) 135
398 THE BARBER (FR) 87

454 THE BAY BANDIT (GB) 45
139 THE BEAR TRAP (IRE) 46
478 THE BEST DOCTOR (IRE) 14
596 THE BIG LAD (GB) 44
625 THE BLUE BANANA (IRE) 12
421 THE BLUE DOG (IRE) 9
431 THE BOOGEYMAN (IRE) 17
651 THE BOOZY BISHOP (IRE) 7
553 THE BOSS OF ME (GB) 64
458 THE BOSSES COUSIN (IRE) 127
89 THE BRAVETRAVELLER (IRE) 5
225 THE BROCKSTER (GB) 22
6 THE BULL HAYES (IRE) 45
654 THE BUNNY CATCHER (GB) 6
583 THE CASH GENERATOR (IRE) 3
226 THE CAT'S AWAY (IRE) 4
385 THE CHAZER (IRE) 24
619 THE CIDER MAKER (GB) 53
679 THE CLOCK LEARY (IRE) 86
468 THE CLYDA ROVER (IRE) 6
631 THE COCKNEY MACKEM (IRE) 75
49 THE COMPOSER (GB) 13
94 THE CONFESSOR (GB) 15
293 THE CONKER CLUB (IRE) 10
428 THE CONTENDER (IRE) 79
460 THE COOKIE JAR (IRE) 25
572 THE CORSICAN (IRE) 50
333 THE CRAFTY BUTCHER (IRE) 22
355 THE DANCING LORD (GB) 8
491 THE DANDY YANK (IRE) 33
507 THE DARLING BOY (GB) 114
164 THE DE THAIX (FR) 34
321 THE DISENGAGER (IRE) 85
303 THE DODGY DEALER (GB) 16
448 THE DOORMAN (IRE) 24
521 THE DOYLE MACHINE (IRE) 13
627 THE DRUIDS NEPHEW (IRE) 8
211 THE DUCKING STOOL (IRE) 16
606 THE DUTCHMAN (IRE) 24
291 THE FAIRIES DID IT (USA) F 312
468 THE FINGER POST (IRE) 7
1 THE FLAMING MATRON (IRE) 34
418 THE FLYING COLUMN (IRE) 136
406 THE FLYING DOC (IRE) 14
323 THE FRENCH GREY (FR) 13
550 THE FRIARY (GB) 88
260 THE FUGUE (IRE) 15
606 THE GAME CHANGER (IRE) 25
443 THE GAME IS A FOOT (IRE) 94
332 THE GEEGEEZ GEEGEE (GB) 35
70 THE GENERAL LEE (IRE) 5
66 THE GIANT BOLSTER (GB) 27
558 THE GINGER BERRY (GB) 4
478 THE GOLD CHEONGSAM (IRE) 15
426 THE GOOD GUY (GB) 33
481 THE GOVANESS (GB) 43
417 THE GREAT GABRIAL (GB) 17
443 THE GREEN OGRE (GB) 95
553 THE GREY GATSBY (IRE) 65
257 THE GREY TAYLOR (IRE) 22
207 THE GRUMPY GNOME (IRE) 101
592 THE HAPPY HAMMER (IRE) 4
80 THE HAPPY WARRIOR (GB) 6
579 THE HERB (GB) 11
428 THE HERDS GARDEN (GB) 80
318 THE HERMITAGE (FR) F 144
136 THE HOLYMAN (IRE) 11
190 THE HOODED CLAW (IRE) 88

673 THE HUMBEL BUTLER (IRE) 6
457 THE INFORMANT (GB) 32
154 THE IRON MAIDEN (GB) 13
479 THE ISLANDER (IRE) 90
676 THE ITALIAN YOB (IRE) 26
333 THE JOB IS RIGHT (GB) 23
235 THE KICKING LORD (GB) 9
148 THE KID (GB) 48
584 THE KNOXS (IRE) 75
365 THE KVILLEKEN (GB) 31
33 THE LARK (GB) 11
357 THE LAST BRIDGE (GB) 1
383 THE LAST NIGHT (FR) 57
418 THE LAST SAMURI (IRE) 137
579 THE LAST SELECTION (GB) 12
507 THE LIQUIDATOR (GB) 115
6 THE LOCK MASTER (IRE) 46
351 THE MAGIC BISHOP (GB) 34
258 THE MASTER REMOVER (IRE) 25
473 THE MINACK (IRE) 123
538 THE MOBB (IRE) 16
201 THE MONGOOSE (GB) 32
371 THE MUMPER (IRE) 104
40 THE MUNSHI (GB) 29
631 THE MUSICAL GUY (IRE) 76
448 THE MYSTRO (IRE) 25
250 THE NAME IS FRANK (GB) 18
307 THE NAMES HARRY (GB) 6
486 THE NEPHEW (IRE) 88
631 THE NEW ONE (IRE) 77
646 THE NEW PHARAOH (IRE) 37
376 THE NOBLE ORD (IRE) 10
84 THE OLDLADYSAYS NO (IRE) C 74
1 THE ORANGE ROGUE (IRE) 35
150 THE OSTEOPATH (IRE) 4
53 THE OSTLER (IRE) 93
417 THE OTHER LADY (GB) 39
473 THE OUTLAW (IRE) 124
507 THE PACKAGE (GB) 116
596 THE PACO KID (GB) 45
1 THE PADDY PREMIUM (IRE) 36
351 THE PANAMA KID (IRE) 35
458 THE PAPARRAZI KID (IRE) 128
288 THE PEAKY BLINDER (GB) 26
675 THE PERFECT CRIME (IRE) 51
371 THE PIRATE'S QUEEN (IRE) 105
409 THE PLAN MAN (IRE) 36
106 THE POCKET DOT (GB) 94
144 THE POETS NEPHEW (IRE) 59
383 THE POTTING SHED (IRE) 58
323 THE QUARTERJACK (GB) 11
13 THE RAINBOW HUNTER (GB) 44
288 THE RAMBLIN KID (GB) 27
317 THE RATTLER OBRIEN (IRE) 12
290 THE REBEL PANTHER (IRE) 39
372 THE RED LAIRD (GB) 21
100 THE RIGHT TIME (GB) 46
54 THE ROAD AHEAD (GB) 50
139 THE ROMFORD PELE (IRE) 47
13 THE SCARLETT WOMAN (GB) 45
106 THE SCREAMER (IRE) F 149
258 THE SELECTOR (GB) 26
616 THE SHRIMP (IRE) 15
444 THE SHY MAN (IRE) 17
478 THE SILVER KEBAYA (FR) 45
321 THE SKYFARMER (GB) 86
560 THE SNAPPY POET (GB) 37
182 THE SNEEZER (IRE) 12

330 **TIME OF MY LIFE** (IRE) 14
637 **TIME ON YOUR HANDS** (IRE) 90
602 **TIME SIGNAL** (GB) 77
100 **TIME SQUARE** (FR) 49
457 **TIME TO THINK** (GB) 33
191 **TIMEFORAGIN** (GB) 7
572 **TIMELESS DREAM** (GB) C 96
180 **TIMES UP** (GB) 15
674 **TIMESAWASTIN** (IRE) 75
426 **TIMESISHARD** (IRE) 35
383 **TIMESREMEMBERED** (IRE) 60
659 **TIMIYAN** (USA) 69
5 **TIMONEER** (USA) 51
315 **TIMOTHY T** (GB) 3
145 **TIMPO** (FR) 37
674 **TIN POT MAN** (IRE) 76
448 **TINAKELLYLAD** (IRE) 26
577 **TINCHY RYDER** (GB) 38
517 **TINCTORIA** (GB) 1
609 **TINCTURE** (GB) C 81
658 **TINDARO** (FR) 50
481 **TINELYRA** (IRE) 44
32 **TINGA** (IRE) 71
318 **TINGE** (USA) F 146
382 **TINGHIR** (FR) 10
100 **TINGLE TANGLE** (USA) 50
602 **TINGLEO** (GB) 146
7 **TINGO IN THE TALE** (IRE) 10
607 **TINK SO** (USA) F 55
80 **TINKER TIME** (IRE) 7
638 **TINLEY LODGE** (GB) 30
376 **TINNARINKA** (GB) F 49
496 **TINOPASA** (FR) G 8
545 **TINSELTOWN** (GB) 7
305 **TINSHU** (IRE) 8
618 **TINSILL** (GB) 19
607 **TINY DANCER** (IRE) 36
138 **TINY HAVEN** (GB) 16
120 **TIOGA PASS** (GB) 30
313 **TIP THE SPIRIT** (GB) F 12
406 **TIPP ON AIR** (IRE) 15
201 **TIPPERARY BOUTIQUE** (IRE) C 66
102 **TIPPOTINA** (GB) 15
637 **TIPSY GYPSY** (IRE) 91
584 **TIPSY INDIAN** (GB) 76
190 **TIPTOEAWAY** (IRE) 56
378 **TIPTREE LACE** (GB) 33
321 **TIQRIS** (GB) 89
359 **TIQUER** (FR) 15
352 **TIRADIA** (FR) 37
246 **TIRE LARIGOT** (FR) 54
50 **TIRGHRA** (IRE) 48
579 **TIRLEY BAY** (GB) 13
320 **TIROL LIVIT** (IRE) 5
519 **TISFREETDREAM** (IRE) 8
310 **TISTORY** (FR) 139
9 **TITAN TRIUMPH** (GB) 25
426 **TITANS APPROACH** (IRE) 36
486 **TITCHWOOD** (IRE) 90
492 **TITHONUS** (IRE) 54
318 **TITIAN QUEEN** (GB) C 147
523 **TITIAN SAGA** (IRE) C 64
17 **TITIVATION** (GB) C 171
254 **TITUS BOLT** (IRE) 33
84 **TIZ MY TIME** (USA) F 75
358 **TIZLOVE REGARDLESS** (USA) 136
190 **TO BEGIN** (GB) 89
247 **TO CHOOSE** (IRE) 19

487 **TO THE SKY** (IRE) 27
125 **TOARMANDOWITHLOVE** (IRE) 12
491 **TOAST OF NEW YORK** (USA) 35
260 **TOAST OF THE TOWN** (IRE) 16
50 **TOBACCO ROAD** (IRE) 27
50 **TOBANN** (IRE) 13
553 **TOBERANTHAWN** (IRE) C 106
177 **TOBOGGAN STAR** (GB) 19
177 **TOBOGGAN'S GIFT** (GB) 33
609 **TOBOUGG HAPPY** (GB) 40
6 **TOBOUGGAN** (GB) 63
573 **TOBY LERONE** (IRE) 35
383 **TOCCA FERRO** (FR) 61
397 **TOCCATA BLUE** (IRE) 8
18 **TOCORORO** (IRE) 89
488 **TODAREISTODO** (GB) 9
513 **TODOISTODARE** (GB) 48
361 **TOE TO TOE** (IRE) 7
319 **TOFFEE VODKA** (IRE) F 51
241 **TOGA TIGER** (IRE) 21
507 **TOGIAK** (IRE) 119
325 **TOKAY** (GB) G 5
279 **TOKEN OF LOVE** (GB) 70
403 **TOKYO BROWN** (USA) 11
303 **TOKYO JAVILEX** (FR) 17
22 **TOLEDO GOLD** (IRE) 22
147 **TOLKEINS TANGO** (IRE) 21
211 **TOLLY MCGUINESS** (GB) 23
137 **TOLMIAS** (GB) 63
380 **TOLOX** (FR) 88
202 **TOM BACH** (IRE) 1
291 **TOM HARK** (IRE) 317
428 **TOM HORN** (IRE) 82
164 **TOM O'TARA** (GB) 37
587 **TOM SANG** (FR) 31
91 **TOM SAWYER** (GB) 9
297 **TOM WADE** (IRE) 19
615 **TOM'S PRIDE** (IRE) 22
671 **TOMIBOLA** (IRE) 8
486 **TOMINATOR** (GB) 91
144 **TOMINTOUL SINGER** (IRE) C 76
144 **TOMMY DOCC** (IRE) 77
214 **TOMMY O'DWYER** (IRE) 42
108 **TOMMY'S SECRET** (GB) 11
615 **TOMMYS LAD** (IRE) 23
615 **TOMMYSTEEL** (IRE) 24
371 **TOMOCHICHI** (IRE) 109
549 **TOMOE** (FR) 88
412 **TOMORROW NIGHT** (GB) 4
444 **TOMORROW'S LEGEND** (GB) 18
36 **TOMPATPEG** (IRE) 16
637 **TOMSK** (FR) 92
418 **TONVADOSA** (GB) 142
54 **TONY DINOZZO** (FR) 52
6 **TONY HOLLIS** (GB) 48
321 **TONY STAR** (FR) 90
456 **TOO BACK** (IRE) G 25
105 **TOO BEND** (GB) 25
254 **TOO COOL TO FOOL** (IRE) 34
603 **TOO ELUSIVE** (GB) 13
371 **TOO FAR GONE** (IRE) 130
507 **TOO GENEROUS** (GB) 120
65 **TOO GRAND** (GB) F 23
658 **TOO MUCH TOO SOON** (IRE) 51
260 **TOO THE STARS** (IRE) 96
466 **TOO TRIGGER HAPPY** (GB) 5
635 **TOOFI** (FR) 102
249 **TOOHIGHFORME** (IRE) 22

375 **TOOLA BOOLA** (GB) 57
279 **TOOLENTIDHAAR** (USA) C 153
493 **TOORAWEENAH** (GB) 22
591 **TOOREEN LEGEND** (IRE) 12
291 **TOORMORE** (IRE) 143
321 **TOOWOOMBA** (IRE) 91
294 **TOP BENEFIT** (IRE) 3
534 **TOP BILLING** (GB) 44
564 **TOP BOY** (GB) 24
535 **TOP CHIEF** (GB) 10
296 **TOP COP** (GB) 24
267 **TOP DANCER** (FR) 36
443 **TOP DIKTAT** (GB) 96
609 **TOP DOLLAR** (GB) 41
507 **TOP GAMBLE** (IRE) 121
507 **TOP HER UP** (IRE) G 122
456 **TOP LINE BANKER** (GB) 26
398 **TOP NOTCH** (FR) 88
196 **TOP NOTCH TONTO** (IRE) 81
596 **TOP OF THE ART** (IRE) 46
349 **TOP OF THE GLAS** (IRE) 31
27 **TOP OF THE MOON** (IRE) 55
310 **TOP OF THE RANGE** (IRE) 140
133 **TOP OFFER** (GB) 7
344 **TOP SHOW** (GB) 26
457 **TOP SMART** (GB) 34
145 **TOP TOTTI** (GB) 38
172 **TOP TRIP** (GB) 13
602 **TOP TUG** (GB) 78
507 **TOP WOOD** (FR) 123
622 **TOPALING** (GB) 18
622 **TOPAMICHI** (GB) 6
622 **TOPATOO** (GB) F 30
380 **TOPAZE BLANCHE** (IRE) 12
394 **TOPAZE COLLONGES** (FR) 68
172 **TOPKA** (FR) 41
639 **TOPLANDER** (IRE) 43
315 **TOPOFTHEDROPS** (IRE) 10
7 **TOPOLSKI** (IRE) 11
622 **TOPTEMPO** (GB) 7
52 **TOPTHORN** (GB) 15
358 **TORCHLIGHTER** (IRE) 137
264 **TORDASIA** (IRE) F 15
273 **TORERO** (GB) 3
679 **TORGAMAH LAD** (IRE) 88
308 **TORIDE** (FR) 56
339 **TORNADE D'ESTRUVAL** (FR) 18
492 **TORNADEA** (IRE) 55
421 **TORNADO BATTLE** (GB) 10
418 **TORNADO BOB** (IRE) 143
358 **TORNADO CHALLENGE** (GB) 138
235 **TORNADO FORCE** (IRE) 10
674 **TORNADO IN MILAN** (IRE) 77
597 **TORNADO POP** (GB) 10
291 **TORONADO** (IRE) 28
316 **TORRAN SOUND** (GB) 17
48 **TORRENTIAL RAINE** (IRE) 18
276 **TORREON** (FR) 26
355 **TORRES DEL PAINE** (GB) 9
503 **TORRID** (GB) 41
358 **TORRIDON** (GB) 139
351 **TORRINGTON DEAL** (GB) 36
277 **TORTOISE** (GB) 31
440 **TORTUE** (IRE) C 20
558 **TORVER** (GB) C 6
239 **TOSCA** (GER) 2
655 **TOTAL ASSETS** (GB) 8
320 **TOTAL OBSESSION** (GB) 6

WHAT'S UP DOC (IRE) 18
WHATAGOA (IRE) 13
WHATAMI (GB) F 67
WHATCAMEOVERME (USA) C 121
WHATDOIDOWITHTHAT (GB) 82
WHATS HAPPENING (IRE) 61
WHATS ON THE MENU (IRE) 18
WHATS UP WOODY (IRE) 46
WHATSTHECRACK JACK (IRE) 16
WHATWHAZZ (GB) 92
WHATWILLWEDONEXT (IRE) 15
WHAZZIS (GB) C 52
WHEELAVHER (GB) 24
WHEELAVIM (GB) 25
WHEELAVIT (IRE) 26
WHEELS OF FORTUNE (GB) 74
WHEN BEN WHEN (IRE) 62
WHEN IN ROAM (IRE) 29
WHEN WILL IT END (IRE) 323
WHENINDOUBTDOIT (IRE) 14
WHERE THE BOYS ARE (IRE) 28
WHERE'S BROUGHTON (GB) F 69
WHERE'S REILEY (USA) 26
WHERE'S SUSIE (GB) 12
WHERE'S THE CATCH (GB) 7
WHERE'S TIGER (GB) 14
WHEYAYE (GB) 4
WHICHEVER (GB) 31
WHICHWAYTOBOUGIE (GB) 39
WHILE YOU WAIT (IRE) 104
WHILEAWAY (USA) 10
WHINGING WILLIE (IRE) 105
WHIPCRACKAWAY (IRE) 18
WHIPLASH WILLIE (GB) 49
WHIPPER SNAPPER (IRE) 19
WHIPPETTE (FR) 89
WHIPPHOUND (GB) 17
WHISKEY CHASER (IRE) 158
WHISKEY JUNCTION (GB) 4
WHISKEY N STOUT (IRE) 16
WHISKEY RIDGE (IRE) 83
WHISKY BRAVO (GB) 3
WHISKY MARMALADE (IRE) 107
WHISKY YANKEE (IRE) 100
WHISPER (FR) 153
WHISPER ROCK (IRE) 30
WHISPER TO DREAM (USA) F 61
WHISPERED TIMES (USA) 18
WHISPERING BLUES (IRE) F 84
WHISPERING BOB (IRE) 73
WHISPERING BOY (IRE) 32
WHISPERING GALLERY (GB) 43
WHISPERING HARRY (IRE) 11
WHISPERING JACK (GB) 11
WHISPERING SPEED (IRE) 29
WHISPERING STAR (USA) 53
WHISPERING WARRIOR (IRE) 22
WHISTFILLY (GB) F 64
WHITBY HIGH LIGHT (GB) 36
WHITBY JACK (GB) 106
WHITBY JET (IRE) 8
WHITE FLAG (GB) 94
WHITE LAKE (GB) 108
WHITE NILE (IRE) 16
WHITE ROSE RUNNER (GB) 23
WHITE RUSSIAN (GB) 38
WHITE STAR LINE (IRE) 72
WHITE TURF (GER) F 18

WHITECREST (GB) 23
WHITEY O' GWAUN (IRE) 74
WHO AM I (GB) 8
WHO DARES WINS (IRE) 324
WHO OWNS ME (IRE) 26
WHO SPLASHED ME (GB) 43
WHO'S CROSS (IRE) 154
WHO'S JEFF (IRE) 101
WHO'S SHIRL (GB) 9
WHO'S THAT CHICK (IRE) 5
WHO'STHEDADDY (GB) 20
WHOLE GRAIN (GB) C 150
WHOS MINDIN WHO (IRE) F 76
WHOZTHECAT (IRE) 14
WHY AREEB (IRE) 11
WHY NOT NOW (GB) 53
WHY WORRY (FR) C 53
WICKED SPICE (IRE) 48
WICKED WILMA (IRE) 20
WICKEDLY SMART (USA) 77
WICKHAMBROOK (IRE) 23
WICKLEWOOD (GB) 19
WICKLOW BRAVE (GB) 153
WICKLOW GOLD (IRE) 154
WICKLOW LAD (GB) 37
WIENER WALD (USA) F 70
WIESENTRAUM (GER) 30
WIFFY CHATSBY (IRE) 143
WIGHT IS WIGHT (IRE) 22
WIGMORE HALL (IRE) 12
WIKI TIKI (GB) 40
WILAYA (USA) C 155
WILBERFOSS (IRE) 24
WILCOS MO CHARA (IRE) 159
WILD AFFAIR (IRE) 67
WILD AT SEA (IRE) 56
WILD CARD (GB) 160
WILD DESERT (FR) 56
WILD FOREST (USA) F 156
WILD GEESE (IRE) 103
WILD GUEST (GB) 18
WILD HILL BOY (GB) 4
WILD INTENTION (USA) C 142
WILD LEGEND (IRE) 14
WILD TOBACCO (GB) 325
WILDCAT LASS (USA) 95
WILDE BLUE YONDER (IRE) 121
WILDE INSPIRATION (IRE) 13
WILDE OAK (IRE) 39
WILDE PASTURES (IRE) 38
WILDES (IRE) 21
WILDEST DREAMS (IRE) 8
WILDOMAR (GB) 57
WILFRED PICKLES (IRE) 13
WILFUL MINX (FR) 25
WILHANA (IRE) 16
WILL (GB) 17
WILLBEME (GB) 12
WILLIAM HENRY (GB) 155
WILLIAM HOGARTH (GB) 4
WILLIAM OF ORANGE (GB) 37
WILLIAM'S WISHES (IRE) 85
WILLIE HALL (GB) 1
WILLIE WAG TAIL (USA) 12
WILLING FOE (USA) 63
WILLISA (GB) F 13
WILLOUGHBY (IRE) 166
WILLOUGHBY HEDGE (GB) 122

WILLOW BECK (GB) 17
WILLOW VIEW (USA) 67
WILLOW'S SAVIOUR (GB) 40
WILLOWING (USA) 13
WILLPOWER (IRE) 156
WILLY BRENNAN (IRE) 116
WILLY C (GB) 84
WILSHIRE BOULEVARD (IRE) 95
WILTON MILAN (IRE) 144
WILY FOX (GB) 9
WIMBOLDSLEY (GB) 34
WIN A HAND (GB) G 4
WIN CASH (IRE) F 135
WIN FOR US (IRE) 7
WIND ECHO (GB) 2
WIND FIRE (USA) 16
WIND PLACE AND SHO (GB) 20
WIND SURF (USA) C 109
WINDFAST (IRE) 66
WINDFORPOWER (IRE) 19
WINDHOEK (GB) 64
WINDLASS (IRE) 106
WINDMILLS EDGE (IRE) 95
WINDPFEIL (IRE) 12
WINDS AND WAVES (IRE) 42
WINDS OF TIME (IRE) F 157
WINDSHEAR (GB) 151
WINDSHIELD (GB) 38
WINDSOR PARK (IRE) 17
WINDSOR SECRET (GB) 36
WINDY CITI (GB) 39
WINESONG (IRE) C 20
WING MIRA (IRE) 97
WING STEALTH (IRE) F 43
WINGED CRUSADER (IRE) 85
WINGED FARASI (GB) 6
WINGED HARRIET (IRE) F 78
WINGS OF FIRE (IRE) 3
WINGS OF SMOKE (IRE) 96
WINGTIPS (FR) 40
WINK (GB) F 74
WINNER'S CALL (GB) C 151
WINNEYS BOY (GB) 16
WINNIFRED (GB) C 91
WINNING BABY (GER) 33
WINNING EXPRESS (IRE) 16
WINNING FAMILY (IRE) F 20
WINNING SPARK (USA) 13
WINROB (GB) 14
WINSTON CHURCHILL (IRE) 31
WINSTONE (IRE) 6
WINTER ALCHEMY (IRE) 49
WINTER PICNIC (IRE) 16
WINTER SILENCE (GB) C 60
WINTER SPICE (IRE) 60
WINTER SUNRISE (GB) C 167
WINTERED WELL (IRE) 28
WINTERLUDE (IRE) 55
WINTERS GOLD (GB) 229
WINTERVAL (GB) 110
WINTERWELL (USA) 67
WINTOUR LEAP (GB) 54
WINTRY LIGHT (GB) 67
WIRE (USA) 56
WIRELESS (FR) 112
WISE HAWK (GB) 14
WISEWIT (GB) 13
WISHES AND STARS (IRE) 4

LATE ENTRIES

MR AIDAN F. FOGARTY, Golden
Postal: **Ballymacady, Golden, Co Tipperary, Ireland**
Contacts: **PHONE (00353) 87 9183907**
E-MAIL fogartyaidan@yahoo.ie

 1 5, B m Portrait Gallery (IRE)—Aiguille (IRE) **J. P. Fogarty**
 2 **BACKOFTHEROCK**, 5, b g Scorpion (IRE)—Oscars Vision (IRE)
 3 **BALLINARD BILLY (IRE)**, 9, b g Anshan—Haunted For Sure (IRE) **Donal Cullen**
 4 4, Gr f Portrait Gallery (IRE)—Distinctly Flo Jo (IRE) **J. P. Fogarty**
 5 5, B g Shantou (USA)—Go For Grogan (IRE) **J. P. Fogarty**
 6 **LIKE THE DA (IRE)**, 11, b g Close Conflict (USA)—Commanche Flyer (IRE) **J. P. Fogarty**
 7 **LUCKY PIGEON (IRE)**, 7, b m Portrait Gallery (IRE)—Trip To Knock **J. P. Fogarty**
 8 **NATIVE CONFLICT (IRE)**, 6, b g Close Conflict (USA)—Native Bev (IRE) **Matt O'Dowd**
 9 **SAMANNTOM (IRE)**, 6, ch g Portrait Gallery (IRE)—Native Ocean (IRE) **J. P. Fogarty**
10 5, B m Portrait Gallery (IRE)—Shernazette (IRE) **J. P. Fogarty**
11 **SHESAPORTRAIT (IRE)**, 6, gr m Portrait Gallery (IRE)—Shesnotthelast (IRE) **J. P. Fogarty**

THREE-YEAR-OLDS

12 **CABARETE (IRE)**, b g Yeats (IRE)—Suma Flamenca (IRE) **Edward Pakenham**

TWO-YEAR-OLDS

13 B f 9/5 Fastnet Rock (AUS)—Ziffany (Taufan (USA)) **J. P. Fogarty**

MR CONOR O'DWYER, Kildare
Postal: **Rossmore House, Friarstown, Kildare, Co. Kildare, Ireland**
Contacts: **PHONE (00 353) 45 533458   FAX (00 353) 45 533458 MOBILE (00 353) 87 2555692**
E-MAIL codwyerracing@gmail.com WEBSITE www.conorodwyer.ie

 1 **BELLELINE (IRE)**, 6, b m Norwich—Hot Line (IRE) **The Moonlux Partnership**
 2 4, B g Shirocco (GER)—Biagiotti (GER) **Audrey O'Dwyer**
 3 **BLOW THE DOORS OFF**, 5, b g Medicean—Mini Driver **J. P. McManus**
 4 **CABALLO DE MARCUS (USA)**, 7, b g Black Sam Bellamy (IRE)—Zizi Top **Philip J. Reynolds**
 5 **COLLEGE BOY (IRE)**, 7, b g Oscar (IRE)—Fleur (GER) **J. P. McManus**
 6 **COMPETITIVE EDGE (IRE)**, 7, b g Presenting—Sanghasta (IRE) **J. P. McManus**
 7 **COURT FRONTIER (IRE)**, 6, b g Court Cave (IRE)—Dame En Rouge (IRE) **Barry Connell**
 8 **EBAZAN (USA)**, 5, ch g Lemon Drop Kid (USA)—Ebaza (IRE) **Jafhica Syndicate**
 9 5, B g High-Rise (IRE)—Eliza Everett (IRE) **Audrey O' Dwyer**
10 **FLAME AND FLOWER (IRE)**, 5, b g Scorpion (IRE)—Gilt Benefit (IRE) **Gigginstown House Stud**
11 **FOLSOM BLUE (IRE)**, 7, b g Old Vic—Spirit Leader (IRE) **Gigginstown House Stud**
12 **HEROES BLEED (IRE)**, 5, ch g Old Vic—Lerichi (IRE) **Gigginstown House Stud**
13 **LOGATRINA (IRE)**, 7, b m Shantou (USA)—Good Laugh (IRE) **Anne McDermott**
14 **MAC TIGUE (IRE)**, 6, b g Celtic Swing—Mary Anastatia (USA) **McLoughlin Family Syndicate**
15 **NICHOLASVILLE (IRE)**, 5, b g Flemensfirth (USA)—Cansalrun (IRE) **Gabriel Duignan**
16 **PROSPERITY SQUARE (IRE)**, 9, ch g Anshan—Raheen River (IRE) **Owen Curtin**
17 4, B g Craigsteel—Raheen River (IRE) **Owen Curtin**
18 **STONEHALL VIC (IRE)**, 6, b g Old Vic—Penny Apples (IRE) **J. P. McManus**
19 4, B g Milan—Supreme Eile (IRE) **Owen Curtin**
20 **VOLT SUN (FR)**, 5, b g Network (GER)—Flaming Sun (FR) **Gigginstown House Stud**

Assistant Trainer: Audrey O'Dwyer

Jockey (NH): Ben Dalton.

STOP PRESS Additional horses

MR J. S. BOLGER, Carlow

TWO-YEAR-OLDS

B f 23/2 Sea The Stars (IRE)—Glinting Desert (IRE) (Desert Prince (IRE)) **Mrs Patricia Burns**
B f 13/3 Galileo (IRE)—Tyranny (Machiavellian (USA)) (600000) **Mrs Joan Brosnan**

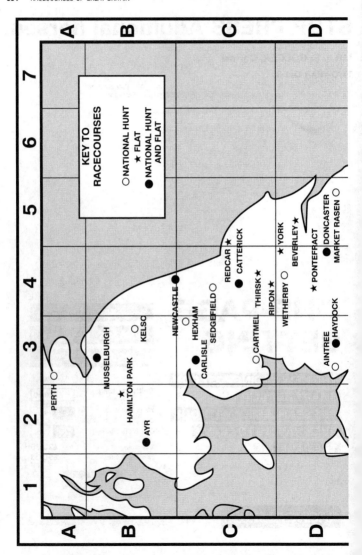

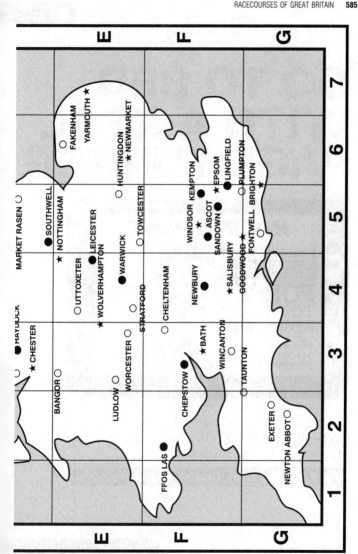

GO TO BED WITH A REAL PAGE TURNER

The Racing Post iPad edition.
Available from 8pm the night
before it's in the shops.

Free 30-day trial. On the app store now.

RACECOURSES OF GREAT BRITAIN

AINTREE (L.H)
Grand National Course: Triangular, 2m 2f (16) 494y run-in with elbow. Perfectly flat. A severe test for both horse and rider, putting a premium on jumping ability, fitness and courage.
Mildmay Course: Rectangular, 1m 4f (8) 260y run-in. A very fast, flat course with sharp bends.
Address: Aintree Racecourse, Ormskirk Road, Aintree, Liverpool, L9 5AS Tel: 0151 523 2600
Fax: 01515 222920 E-mail: aintree@rht.net Website: www.aintree.co.uk
Regional Director: John Baker
Clerk of the Course: Andrew Tulloch 07831 315104
Going Reports: 01515 232600.
Stabling: Boxes allocated in strict rotation. Facilities are available on the course for up to 100 stable staff.
01515 222937.
By Road: North of the City, near the junction of the M57 and M58 with the A59 (Preston).
By Rail: Aintree Station is adjacent to the Stands, from Liverpool Central.
By Air: Liverpool (John Lennon) Airport is 10 miles. Helicopter landing facility by prior arrangement.

ASCOT (R.H)
Flat: Right-handed triangular track just under 1m 6f in length. The Round course descends from the 1m 4f start into Swinley Bottom, the lowest part of the track. It then turns right-handed and joins the Old Mile Course, which starts on a separate chute. The course then rises to the right-handed home turn over a new underpass to join the straight mile course. The run-in is about 3f, rising slightly to the winning post. The whole course is of a galloping nature with easy turns.
N.H. Triangular, 1m 6f (10) 240y run-in mostly uphill. A galloping course with an uphill finish, Ascot provides a real test of stamina. The fences are stiff and sound jumping is essential, especially for novices.
Address: Ascot Racecourse, Ascot, Berkshire SL5 7JX Tel: 08707 271234 Fax: 08704 601250
Website: www.ascot.co.uk
Clerk of the Course: Chris Stickels 01344 878502 / 07970 621440
Chief Executive: Charles Barnett
Going Reports: Day: 01344 878502
Stabling: 175 boxes. Free, with shavings, straw or paper provided. Tel: 01344 878454 Fax: 08704 214755
By Road: West of the town on the A329. Easy access from the M3 (Junction 3) and the M4 (Junction 6). Car parking adjoining the course and Ascot Heath.
By Rail: Regular service from Waterloo to Ascot (500y from the racecourse).
By Air: Helicopter landing facility at the course. London (Heathrow) Airport 15 miles, White Waltham Airfield 12 miles (01427) 718800.

AYR (L.H)
Flat: A left-handed, galloping, flat oval track of 1m 4f with a 4f run-in. The straight 6f is essentially flat.
N.H. Oval, 1m 4f (9) 210y run-in. Relatively flat and one of the fastest tracks in Great Britain.
It is a well-drained course and the ground rarely becomes testing. Suits the long-striding galloper.
Address: Ayr Racecourse, Whitletts Road, Ayr KA8 0JE Tel: 01292 264179 Fax: 01292 610140
Website: www.ayr-racecourse.co.uk
Clerk of the Course: Emma Marley 07881 908702
Managing Director: David Marley
Going Reports: Contact Clerk of the Course as above.
Stabling: 175 boxes. Free stabling and accommodation for lads and lasses. Tel: 01292 264179 ext 141.
By Road: East of the town on the A758. Free parking for buses and cars.
By Rail: Ayr Station (trains on the half hour from Glasgow Central). Journey time 55 minutes. Buses and taxis also to the course.
By Air: Prestwick International Airport (10 minutes), Glasgow Airport (1 hour).

BANGOR-ON-DEE (L.H)

N.H. Circular, 1m 4f (9) 325y run-in. Apart from some 'ridge and furrow', this is a flat course notable for three sharp bends, especially the paddock turn. Suits handy, speedy sorts.
Address: Bangor-On-Dee Racecourse, Overton Road, Bangor-On-Dee, Wrexham. LL13 0DA
Tel: 01978 782081, Fax: 01978 780985 Website: www.bangorondeeraces.co.uk
Racecourse Manager & Clerk of the Course: Andrew Morris
Chief Executive: Richard Thomas
General Manager: Jeannie Chantler
Going Reports: Contact Clerk of the Course as above.
Stabling: 85 stables, allotted on arrival. Shavings (straw on request). Applications to the Manager.
Tel: 01978 782081.
By Road: 5 miles southeast of Wrexham, off the B5069.
By Rail: Wrexham Station (bus or taxi to the course).
By Air: Helicopters may land by prior arrangement with Clerk of the Course at entirely their own risk.

BATH (L.H)

Flat: Galloping, left-handed, level oval of 1m 4f 25y, with long, stiff run-in of about 4f which bends to the left. An extended chute provides for races over 5f 11y and 5f 161y.
Address: The Racecourse, Lansdown, Bath BA1 9BU. Tel: 01225 424609 Fax: 01225 444415.
Website: www.bath-racecourse.co.uk
General Manager & Clerk of the Course : Katie Stephens
Going Reports: Contact Clerk of the Course as above.
Stabling: 120 boxes. Free stabling and accommodation for lads and lasses. Tel: 01225 424609
By Road: 2 miles northwest of the City (M4 Junction 18) at Lansdown. Unlimited free car and coach parking space immediately behind the stands. Special bus services operate from Bath to the racecourse.
By Rail: Bath Station (from Paddington).
By Air: Bristol or Colerne Airports. Helicopter landing facilities available by prior arrangement.

BEVERLEY (R.H)

Flat: A right-handed oval of 1m 3f, generally galloping, with an uphill run-in of two and a half furlongs. The 5f course is very stiff.
Address: Beverley Race Co. Ltd., York Road, Beverley, Yorkshire HU17 9QZ
Tel: 01482 867488 / 882645.Website: www.beverley-racecourse.co.uk
General Manager & Clerk of the Course: Sally Iggulden 07850 458605
Going Reports: Tel: 01482 867488 / 882645 or Head Groundsman (John Morley) 07885 678186
Stabling: 111 boxes. Free stabling. Accommodation available for lads and lasses
Tel: 01482 867488 / 882645.
By Road: 7 miles from the M62 (Junction 38) off the A1035. Free car parking opposite the course.
Owners and trainers use a separate enclosure.
By Rail: Beverley Station (Hull-Scarborough line). Occasional bus service to the course (1 mile).

BRIGHTON (L.H)

Flat: Left-handed, 1m 4f horseshoe with easy turns and a run-in of three and a half furlongs. Undulating and sharp, the track suits handy types.
Address: Brighton Racecourse, Brighton, East Sussex BN2 2XZ Tel: 01273 603580 Fax: 01273 673267
Website: www.brighton-racecourse.co.uk
Clerk of the Course: Edward Arkell 07977 587713
General Manager: Stuart Dorn
Going Reports: Available on www.brighton-racecourse.co.uk or contact main office/Clerk of the Course as above
Stabling: 102 boxes. Stabling & accommodation: Tel: 01273 603580, available on request.
By Road: East of the city on the A27 (Lewes Road). There is a car park adjoining the course.
By Rail: Brighton Station (from Victoria on the hour, London Bridge or Portsmouth). Special bus service to the course from the station (approx 2 miles).
By Air: Helicopters may land by prior arrangement.

CARLISLE (R.H)

Flat: Right-handed, 1m 4f pear-shaped track. Galloping and undulating with easy turns and a stiff uphill run-in of three and a half furlongs. The 6f course begins on an extended chute.

N.H. Pear-shaped, 1m 5f (9) 300y run-in uphill. Undulating and a stiff test of stamina, ideally suited to the long-striding thorough stayer. Three-mile chases start on a chute, and the first fence is only jumped once.

Address: Carlisle Racecourse, Durdar Road, Carlisle CA2 4TS Tel: 01228 554700 Fax: 01228 554747

Website: www.carlisle-races.co.uk

Regional Director: John Baker

Clerk of the Course: Andrew Tulloch 07831 315104

General Manager: Geraldine McKay

Going Reports: 01228 554700 recorded or contact Clerk of the Course above

Stabling: 98 boxes. Stabling and accommodation available on request. Please phone Head Groundsman on 07889 987542, or Fax Stable Office on 01228 554747 by 1pm day before racing.

By Road: 2 miles south of the city (Durdar Road). Easy access from the M6 (Junction 42). The car park is free (adjacent to the course).

By Rail: Carlisle Station (2 miles from the course).

By Air: Helicopter landing facility by prior arrangement.

CARTMEL (L.H)

N.H.: Oval, 1m 1f (6) 800y run-in. Almost perfectly flat but very sharp, with the longest run-in in the country, approximately half a mile. The fences are stiff but fair.

Address: Cartmel Racecourse, Cartmel, nr Grange-Over-Sands, Cumbria LA11 6QF Tel: 01539 536340. Out of season: 01539 533335 Fax: 01539 536004 Website: www.cartmel-racecourse.co.uk

Managing Director: Jonathan Garratt

Clerk of the Course: Anthea Morshead 07837 559861

Going Reports: 01539 536340 or contact Clerk of the Course as above.

Stabling: 75 boxes. Boxes and accommodation for lads and lasses is limited. Prior booking is required by 12 noon the day before racing 01539 534609.

By Road: 1 mile west of the town, 2 miles off the B5277 (Grange-Haverthwaite road). M6 (Junction 36).

By Rail: Cark-in-Cartmel Station (2 miles) (Carnforth-Barrow line). Raceday bus service.

By Air: Light aircraft facilities available at Cark Airport (4 miles from the course). Helicopter landing facility at the course, by prior arrangement only.

CATTERICK (L.H)

Flat: A sharp, left-handed, undulating oval of 1m 180y with a downhill run-in of 3f.

N.H. Oval, 1m 1f (9) 240y run-in. Undulating, sharp track that favours the handy, front-running sort, rather than the long-striding galloper.

Address: The Racecourse, Catterick Bridge, Richmond, North Yorkshire DL10 7PE Tel: 01748 811478 Fax: 01748 811082 Website: www.catterickbridge.co.uk

General Manager & Clerk of the Course: Fiona Needham 07831 688625

Going Reports: Contact Clerk of the Course as above

Stabling: 116 Boxes. Allotted on arrival.

By Road: The course is adjacent to the A1, 1 mile northwest of the town on the A6136. There is a free car park.

By Rail: Darlington Station (special buses to course - 14 mile journey).

By Air: Helicopters can land by prior arrangement. Fixed wing planes contact RAF Leeming Tel: 01677 423041

CHELTENHAM (L.H)

Old Course: Oval, 1m 4f (9) 350y run-in. A testing, undulating track with stiff fences. The ability to stay is essential.

New Course: Oval, 1m 5f (10) 220y run-in. Undulating, stiff fences, testing course, uphill for the final half-mile.

Address: Cheltenham Racecourse, Prestbury Park, Cheltenham, Gloucestershire GL50 4SH

Tel: 01242 513014 Fax: 01242 224227

Website: www.cheltenham.co.uk

Regional Director: Ian Renton

Director of Racing & Clerk of the Course: Simon Claisse 07785 293966

Going Reports: Available from six days before racing 01242 513014 (option 2, then 6)

Stabling: 299 boxes. Ample stabling and accommodation for lads.

Apply to the Stable Manager 01242 537602 or 521950.

By Road: 1.5 miles north of the town on the A435. M5 (Junction 10 or 11).
By Rail: Cheltenham Spa Station. Buses and taxis to course.
By Air: Helicopter landing site to the northeast of the stands.

CHEPSTOW (L.H)

Flat: A left-handed, undulating oval of about 2m, with easy turns, and a straight run-in of 5f. There is a straight track of 1m 14y.
N.H. Oval, 2m (11) 240y run-in. Many changing gradients, five fences in the home straight. Favours the long-striding front-runner, but stamina is important.
Address: Chepstow Racecourse, Chepstow, Monmouthshire NP16 6BE Tel: 01291 622260
Fax: 01291 627061 Website: www.chepstow-racecourse.co.uk
Clerk of the Course: Keith Ottesen 07813 043453
Executive Director: Phil Bell
Going Reports: Contact Clerk of the Course as above.
Stabling: 106 boxes, allotted on arrival. Limited accommodation for lads and lasses. Apply: 01291 622260.
By Road: 1 mile North-West of the town on the A466. (1 mile from Junction 22 of the M4 (Severn Bridge) or M48 Junction 2. There is a free public car park opposite the entrance.
By Rail: Chepstow Station (from Paddington, change at Gloucester or Newport). The course is a mile from the station.
By Air: Helicopter landing facility in the centre of the course.

CHESTER (L.H)

Flat: A level, sharp, left-handed, circular course of 1m 73y, with a short run-in of 230y.
Chester is a specialists' track which generally suits the sharp-actioned horse.
Address: The Racecourse, Chester CH1 2LY Tel: 01244 304600 Fax: 01244 304648 Website:
www.chester-races.co.uk
Racecourse Manager & Clerk of the Course: Andrew Morris
Chief Executive: Richard Thomas
Going Reports: Contact Main Office 01244 304600
Stabling: 138 boxes and accommodation. Tel: 01244 324880 or 01244 304610
By Road: The course is near the centre of the city on the A548 (Queensferry Road). The Owners' and Trainers' car park is adjacent to the Leverhulme Stand. There is a public car park in the centre of the course.
By Rail: Chester Station (¾ mile from the course). Services from Euston, Paddington and Northgate.
By Air: Hawarden Airport (2 miles). Helicopters are allowed to land on the racecourse by prior arrangement only.

DONCASTER (L.H)

Flat: A left-handed, flat, galloping course of 1m 7f 110y, with a long run-in which extends to a straight mile.
N.H. Conical, 2m (11) 247y run-in. A very fair, flat track ideally suited to the long-striding galloper.
Address: Doncaster Racecourse, Leger Way, Doncaster DN2 6BB Tel: 01302 304200, Fax: 01302 323271
Email: info@doncaster-racecourse.co.uk Website: www.doncaster-racecourse.co.uk
Clerk of the Course: Roderick Duncan 07772 958685
Managing Director: Mark Spincer
Going Reports: Contact Clerk of the Course as above or Estate Manager 07831 260373.
Stabling: 147 boxes. Free stabling and accommodation. Tel: 01302 304200
By Road: East of the town, off the A638 (M18 Junctions 3 & 4). Club members' car park reserved. Large public car park free and adjacent to the course.
By Rail: Doncaster Central Station (from King's Cross). Special bus service from the station (1 mile).
By Air: Helicopter landing facility by prior arrangement only. Doncaster Robin Hood Airport is 15 minutes from the racecourse.

EPSOM (L.H)

Flat: Left-handed and undulating with easy turns, and a run-in of just under 4f. The straight 5f course is also undulating and downhill all the way, making it the fastest 5f in the world.
Address: The Racecourse, Epsom Downs, Surrey, KT18 5LQ. Tel: 01372 726311, Fax: 01372 748253
Website: www.epsomderby.co.uk
Regional Director: Rupert Trevelyan
Clerk of the Course: Andrew Cooper. Tel: 01372 726311, Mobile: 07774 230850
General Manager: Simon Durrant

Going Reports: Contact Clerk of the Course as above.
Stabling: 108 boxes. Free stabling and accommodation. Tel: 01372 460454
By Road: Two miles south of the town on the B290 (M25 Junctions 8 & 9). For full car park particulars apply to: The Club Secretary, Epsom Grandstand, Epsom Downs, Epsom Downs, Surrey KT18 5LQ. Tel: 01372 726311.
By Rail: Epsom, Epsom Downs or Tattenham Corner Stations (trains from London Bridge, Waterloo, Victoria). Regular bus services run to the course from Epsom and Morden Underground Station.
By Air: London (Heathrow) and London (Gatwick) are both within 30 miles of the course.
Heliport (Derby Meeting only) apply to Hascombe Aviation. Tel: 01279 680291.

EXETER (R.H)

N.H.: Oval, 2m (11) 300y run-in uphill. Undulating with a home straight of half a mile. A good test of stamina, suiting the handy, well-balanced sort.
Address: Exeter Racecourse, Kennford, Exeter, Devon EX6 7XS Tel: 01392 832599 Fax: 01392 833454
Email: Exeter@thejockeyclub.co.uk Website: www.exeter-racecourse.co.uk
Regional Director: Ian Renton
Clerk of the Course: Barry Johnson 07976 791578
General Manager: Tim Darby
Going Reports: Contact Clerk of the Course as above.
Stabling: 90 loose boxes at the course. Sleeping accommodation and canteen for both lads and lasses by prior arrangement. Apply to Racecourse Office. Tel: 01392 832599 by 12 noon on day before racing.
By Road: The course is at Haldon, 5 miles southwest of Exeter on the A38 (Plymouth) road, 2 miles east of Chudleigh.
By Rail: Exeter (St Davids) Station. Free bus service to course.
By Air: Helicopters can land by prior arrangement.

FAKENHAM (L.H)

N.H. Square, 1m (6) 200y run-in. On the turn almost throughout and undulating, suiting the handy front-runner. The going rarely becomes heavy.
Address: The Racecourse, Fakenham, Norfolk NR21 7NY Tel: 01328 862388 Fax: 01328 855908 email: info@fakenhamracecourse.co.uk Website: www.fakenhamracecourse.co.uk
Clerk of the Course & Chief Executive: David Hunter Tel: 01328 862388 Mobile: 07767 802206.
Going Reports: Contact Clerk of the Course as above.
Stabling: 70 boxes available. Tel: 01328 862388 Fax: 01328 855908.
By Road: A mile south of the town on the B1146 (East Dereham) road.
By Rail: Norwich Station (26 miles) (Liverpool Street line), King's Lynn (22 miles) (Liverpool Street/Kings Cross).
By Air: Helicopter landing facility in the centre of the course by prior arrangement only.

FFOS LAS (L.H)

Flat & N.H. : The track is a 60m wide, basically flat, 1m4f oval with sweeping bends. Races over 5f and 6f start on a chute.
Address: Ffos Las Racecourse, Trimsaran, Carmarthenshire, SA17 4DE Tel: 01554 811092
Fax: 01554 811037 Website: www.ffoslasracecourse.com
Clerk of the Course & General Manager: Tim Long 07966 893531
Going Reports: Contact Clerk of the Course as above.
Stabling: 120 box stable yard.
By Road: From the east take J48 from the M4 and join the A4138 to Llanelli, then follow the brown tourist signs to the racecourse. From the west take the A48 to Carmarthen then the A484 to Kidwelly before following the brown signs.
By Air: The course has the facilities to land helicopters on race days.

FONTWELL PARK (Fig. 8)

N.H. 2m (7) 230y run-in with left-hand bend close home. The figure-of-eight chase course suits handy types and is something of a specialists' track. The left-handed hurdle course is oval, one mile round with nine hurdles per two and a quarter miles.
Address: Fontwell Park Racecourse, nr Arundel, West Sussex BN18 0SX Tel: 01243 543335
Fax: 01243 543904 Website: www.fontwellpark.co.uk
Clerk of the Course: Edward Arkell 07977 587713
General Manager: T.B.A.
Executive Director: Phil Bell

Going Reports: 01243 543335 during office hours.
Stabling: 90 boxes. Limited accommodation. If arriving the day before the meeting, contact: Tel: 01243 543335.
By Road: South of village at the junction of the A29 (Bognor) and A27 (Brighton-Chichester) roads.
By Rail: Barnham Station (2 miles). Brighton-Portsmouth line (access via London Victoria).
By Air: Helicopter landing facility by prior arrangement with the Clerk of the Course.

GOODWOOD (R.H)

Flat: A sharp, undulating, essentially right-handed track with a long run-in. There is also a straight 6f course.
Address: Goodwood Racecourse Ltd., Goodwood, Chichester, West Sussex PO18 0PX
Tel: 01243 755022, Fax: 01243 755025 Website: www.goodwood.co.uk
Managing Director: Adam Waterworth
Clerk of the Course: Seamus Buckley 07774 100223
Going Reports: 01243 755022 (recorded message) or Clerk of the Course.
Stabling: Free stabling and accommodation for runners (130 well equipped boxes at Goodwood House). Please book in advance. Subsidised canteen and recreational facilities. Tel: 01243 755022 / 755036.
By Road: 6 miles north of Chichester between the A286 & A285. There is a car park adjacent to the course. Ample free car and coach parking.
By Rail: Chichester Station (from Victoria or London Bridge). Regular bus service to the course (6 miles).
By Air: Helicopter landing facility by prior arrangement 01243 755030. Goodwood Airport 2 miles (taxi to the course).

HAMILTON PARK (R.H)

Flat: Sharp, undulating, right-handed course of 1m 5f with a five and a half-furlong, uphill run-in. There is a straight track of 6f.
Address: Hamilton Park Racecourse, Bothwell Road, Hamilton, Lanarkshire ML3 0DW Tel: 01698 283806
Fax: 01698 286621 Website: www.hamilton-park.co.uk
Racing Manager & Clerk of the Course: Hazel Peplinski 01698 283806 (raceday). Mobile: 07774 116733.
Fax: 01698 286621
Chief Executive: Vivien Kyles 01698 283806
Going Reports: Track Manager: 07736 101130 or Clerk of the Course.
Stabling: Free stabling (102 boxes) and accommodation on request. Tel: 01698 284892 or Office.
By Road: Off the A72 on the B7071 (Hamilton-Bothwell road). (M74 Junction 5). Free parking for cars and buses.
By Rail: Hamilton West Station (1 mile).
By Air: Glasgow Airport (20 miles).

HAYDOCK PARK (L.H)

Flat: A galloping, almost flat, oval track, 1m 5f round, with a run-in of four and a half furlongs and a straight six-furlong course.
N.H. Oval, 1m 5f (10) 440y run-in. Flat, galloping chase course. The hurdle track, which is sharp, is inside the chase course and has some tight bends.
Address: Haydock Park Racecourse, Newton-le-Willows, Merseyside WA12 0HQ Tel: 01942 402609
Fax: 01942 270879 Website: www.haydock-park.co.uk
Regional Director: John Baker
General Manager: Garry Fortune
Clerk of the Course: Kirkland Tellwright 01942 725963 or 07748 181595
Going Reports: Contact Clerk of the Course as above or Head Groundsman 07831 849298
Stabling: 124 boxes. Applications to be made to the Racecourse for stabling and accommodation.
Tel: 01942 725963 or 01942 402615 (racedays).
By Road: The course is on the A49 near Junction 23 of the M6.
By Rail: Newton-le-Willows Station (Manchester-Liverpool line) is 2.5 miles from the course. Earlstown 3 miles from the course. Warrington Bank Quay and Wigan are on the London to Carlisle/Glasgow line.
By Air: Landing facilities in the centre of the course for helicopters and planes not exceeding 10,000lbs laden weight. Apply to the Sales Office.

HEXHAM (L.H)
N.H. Oval, 1m 4f (10) 220y run-in. An undulating course that becomes very testing when the ground is soft, it has easy fences and a stiff uphill climb to the finishing straight, which is on a separate spur.
Address: Hexham Racecourse, The Riding, Hexham, Northumberland NE46 2JP Tel: 01434 606881
Fax: 01434 605814, Racedays: 01434 603738. Email: admin@hexham-racecourse.co.uk
Website: www.hexham-racecourse.co.uk
Chief Executive: Charles Enderby
Clerk of the Course: James Armstrong 01434 606881 or 07801 166820
Going Reports: Contact Clerk of the Course as above
Stabling: 93 Boxes allocated in rotation. Please book stabling and accommodation the day before by Fax: 01434 605814.
By Road: 1.5 miles southwest of the town off the B6305.
By Rail: Hexham Station (Newcastle-Carlisle line). Free bus to the course.
By Air: Helicopter landing facility in centre of course (by special arrangement only).

HUNTINGDON (R.H)
N.H. Oval, 1m 4f (9) 200y run-in. Perfectly flat, galloping track with a tricky open ditch in front of the stands. The two fences in the home straight can cause problems for novice chasers. Suits front runners.
Address: The Racecourse, Brampton, Huntingdon, Cambridgeshire PE28 4NL Tel: 01480 453373
Fax: 01480 455275 Website: www.huntingdon-racecourse.co.uk
Regional Director: Amy Starkey
Clerk of the Course: Sulekha Varma
Managing Director: Nadia Gollings
Going Reports: Tel: 01480 453373 or 07990 774295
Stabling: 100 boxes available. Allotted on arrival. Telephone Racecourse Office.
By Road: The course is situated at Brampton, 2 miles west of Huntingdon on the A14. Easy access from the A1 (½ mile from the course).
By Rail: Huntingdon Station. Buses and taxis to course.
By Air: Helicopter landing facility by prior arrangement.

KELSO (L.H)
N.H. Oval, 1m 3f (8), uphill run-in reduced to just over a furlong for the 2012-13 season. Rather undulating with two downhill fences opposite the stands, it suits the nippy, front-running sort, though the uphill finish helps the true stayer. The hurdle course is smaller and very sharp with a tight turn away from the stands.
Address: Kelso Racecourse, Kelso, Roxburghshire TD5 7SX Tel: 01668 280800
Website: www.kelso-races.co.uk
Clerk of the Course: Hazel Peplinski 07774 116733
Managing Director: Richard Landale
Going Reports: Racecourse: 01573 224822 Groundsman Tel: 07774 172527
Stabling: 94 boxes allotted in rotation. Reservations for stabling and accommodation for lads and lasses at the racecourse, please phone Head Groundsman Tel: 01573 224767 or Racecourse stables: 01573 224822 from 3pm the day before racing.
By Road: 1 mile north of the town, off the B6461.
By Rail: Berwick-upon-Tweed Station. 23-mile bus journey to Kelso.
By Air: Helicopters can land at course by arrangement, fixed wing aircraft Winfield, regular aircraft Edinburgh.

KEMPTON PARK (R.H)
Flat: A floodlit Polytrack circuit. A 1m 2f outer track accommodates races over 6f, 7f, 1m, 1m 3f, 1m 4f and 2m. The 1m inner track caters for races over 5f and 1m 2f.
N.H. Triangular, 1m 5f (10) 175y run-in. Practically flat; sharp course where the long run between the last obstacle on the far side and the first in the home straight switches the emphasis from jumping to speed. The hurdles track is on the outside of the chase track. The course crosses the Polytrack at two points on each circuit.
Address: Kempton Park Racecourse, Sunbury-on-Thames, Middlesex TW16 5AQ Tel: 01932 782292
Fax: 01932 782044 Raceday Fax: 01932 779525 Website: www.kempton.co.uk Email: kempton@rht.net
Regional Director: Rupert Trevelyan
Clerk of the Course & Director of Racing: Brian Clifford 07880 784484
General Manager: Phil White
Going Reports: 01932 782292 if unavailable contact Clerk of the Course as above
Stabling: 117 boxes. Allocated on arrival. Prior booking required for overnight stay. Tel: 01932 782292

By Road: On the A308 near Junction 1 of the M3.
By Rail: Kempton Park Station (from Waterloo).
By Air: London (Heathrow) Airport 6 miles.

LEICESTER (R.H)

Flat: Stiff, galloping, right-handed oval of 1m 5f, with a 5f run-in. There is a straight course of seven furlongs.
N.H. Rectangular, 1m 6f (10) 250y run-in uphill. An undulating course with an elbow 150y from the finish, it can demand a high degree of stamina, for the going can become extremely heavy and the last three furlongs are uphill.
Address: Leicester Racecourse, Oadby, Leicester LE2 4AL. Tel: 01162 716515 Fax: 01162 711746
Website:www.leicester-racecourse.co.uk
Clerk of the Course: Jimmy Stevenson 01162 712115 or 07774 497281
General Manager: T.B.A.
Going Reports: Recorded message 01162 710875 or contact Clerk of the Course as above.
Stabling: 108 boxes. Allocated on arrival. Canteen opens at 7.30a.m. Tel: 01162 712115.
By Road: The course is 2.5 miles southeast of the City on the A6 (M1, Junction 21). The car park is free.
By Rail: Leicester Station (from St Pancras) is 2.5 miles.
By Air: Helicopter landing facility in the centre of the course.

LINGFIELD PARK (L.H)

Flat, Turf: A sharp, undulating left-handed circuit, with a 7f 140y straight course.
Flat, Polytrack: The left-handed Polytrack is 1m 2f round, with an extended chute to provide a 1m 5f start. It is a sharp, level track with a short run-in.
N.H. Conical, 1m 5f (10) 200y run-in. Severely undulating with a tight downhill turn into the straight, the chase course suits front runners and those of doubtful resolution.
Address: Lingfield Park Racecourse, Lingfield, Surrey RH7 6PQ Tel: 01342 834800 Fax: 01342 832833
Website: www.lingfield-racecourse.co.uk
Clerk of the Course: Neil Mackenzie Ross 01342 831720 Mobile: 07917 326977
Executive Manager: Andrew Perkins
Going Reports: Contact Clerk of the Course as above.
Stabling: 106 boxes. For details of accommodation Tel: 01342 831718. Advance notice for overnight accommodation required before 12 noon on the day before racing.
By Road: Southeast of the town off the A22 M25 (Junction 6). Ample free parking.
By Rail: Lingfield Station (regular services from London Bridge and Victoria). ½ mile walk to the course.
By Air: London (Gatwick) Airport 10 miles. Helicopter landing facility south of wind-sock.

LUDLOW (R.H)

N.H. Oval, 1m 4f (9) 185y run-in. The chase course is flat and has quite sharp bends into and out of the home straight, although long-striding horses never seem to have any difficulties. The hurdle course is on the outside of the chase track and is not so sharp.
Address: Ludlow Race Club Ltd, The Racecourse, Bromfield, Ludlow, Shropshire SY8 2BT
Tel: 01584 856221 (Racedays) or see below. Website:www.ludlowracecourse.co.uk
Clerk of the Course: Simon Sherwood
General Manager: Bob Davies. Tel: 01584 856221, Mobile 07970 861533, Fax: 01584 856217 Email:
bobdavies@ludlowracecourse.co.uk
Going Reports: Contact Clerk of the Course as above or Groundsman Tel: 01584 856289 or 07970 668353
Stabling: Free and allocated on arrival. 100 stables, mainly cardboard with a limited number of shavings and straw. Tel: 01584 856221.
By Road: The course is situated at Bromfield, 2 miles north of Ludlow on the A49.
By Rail: Ludlow Station (Hereford-Shrewsbury line) 2 miles.
By Air: Helicopter landing facility in the centre of the course by arrangement with the Clerk of the Course and entirely at own risk.

MARKET RASEN (R.H)

N.H. Oval, 1m 2f (8) 250y run-in. A sharp, undulating course with a long run to the straight, it favours the handy, front-running type.
Address: Market Rasen Racecourse, Legsby Road, Market Rasen, Lincolnshire LN8 3EA
Tel: 01673 843434 Fax: 01673 844532 Website: www.marketrasenraces.co.uk
Regional Director: Amy Starkey

Clerk of the Course: Jane Hedley
Managing Director: Pip Kirkby
Going Reports: Contact Clerk of the Course as above.
Stabling: 86 boxes at the course, allocated on arrival. Accommodation for lads and lasses is by reservation only. Tel: 01673 842307 (racedays only)
By Road: The town is just off the A46, and the racecourse is one mile east of the town on the A631. Free car parks.
By Rail: Market Rasen Station 1 mile (King's Cross - Cleethorpes line).
By Air: Helicopter landing facility by prior arrangement only.

MUSSELBURGH (R.H)

Flat: A sharp, level, right-handed oval of 1m 2f, with a run-in of 4f. There is an additional 5f straight course.
N.H. Rectangular, 1m 3f (8) 150y run-in (variable). A virtually flat track with sharp turns, suiting the handy, front-running sort. Drains well.
Address: Musselburgh Racecourse, Linkfield Road, Musselburgh, East Lothian EH21 7RG
Tel: 01316 652859 (Racecourse) Fax: 01316 532083 Website:www.musselburgh-racecourse.co.uk
Clerk of the Course: Harriet Graham 07843 380401
General Manager: Bill Farnsworth 07710 536134
Going Reports: Contact main office as above or Clerk of the Course.
Stabling: 101 boxes. Free stabling. Accommodation provided. Tel: 07773 048638, Stables (racedays): 01316 652796.
By Road: The course is situated at Musselburgh, 5 miles east of Edinburgh on the A1. Car park, adjoining course, free for buses and cars.
By Rail: Waverley Station (Edinburgh). Local Rail service to Musselburgh.
By Air: Edinburgh (Turnhouse) Airport 30 minutes

NEWBURY (L.H)

Flat: Left-handed, oval track of about 1m 7f, with a slightly undulating straight mile. The round course is level and galloping with a four and a half furlong run-in. Races over the round mile start on the adjoining chute.
N.H. Oval, 1m 6f (11) 255y run-in. Slightly undulating, wide and galloping in nature. The fences are stiff and sound jumping is essential. One of the fairest tracks in the country.
Address: The Racecourse, Newbury, Berkshire RG14 7NZ Tel: 01635 40015 Fax: 01635 528354
Website: www.newbury-racecourse.co.uk
Chief Executive: Julian Thick
Raceday Clerk: Richard Osgood 07977 426947
Going Reports: Clerk of the Course as above.
Stabling: 164 boxes. Free stabling and accommodation for lads and lasses. Tel: 01635 40015.
By Road: East of the town off the A34 (M4, Junction 12 or 13). Car park, adjoining enclosures, free.
By Rail: Newbury Racecourse Station adjoins the course.
By Air: Light Aircraft landing strip East/West. 830 metres by 30 metres wide. Helicopter landing facilities.

NEWCASTLE (L.H)

Flat: Galloping, easy, left-handed oval of 1m 6f, with an uphill 4f run-in. There is a straight course of 1m 3y.
N.H. Oval, 1m 6f (11) 220y run-in. A gradually rising home straight of four furlongs makes this galloping track a true test of stamina, especially as the ground can become very heavy.
Address: High Gosforth Park, Newcastle-Upon-Tyne NE3 5HP Tel: 01912 362020 Fax: 01912 367761
Website: www.newcastle-racecourse.co.uk
Clerk of the Course: James Armstrong 07801 166820
Executive Director: David Williamson
Stabling: 135 boxes. Stabling Free. It is essential to book accommodation in advance. Apply via the Racecourse Office.
Going Reports: Contact Clerk of the Course as above or Head Groundsman 07860 274289.
By Road: 4 miles north of the city on the A6125 (near the A1). Car and coach park free.
By Rail: Newcastle Central Station (from King's Cross). A free bus service operates from South Gosforth and Regent Centre Metro Station.
By Air: Helicopter landing facility by prior arrangement. The Airport is 4 miles from the course.

NEWMARKET (R.H)

Rowley Mile Course: There is a straight ten-furlong course, which is wide and galloping. Races over 1m 4f or more are right-handed. The Rowley Mile course has a long run-in and a stiff finish.

July Course: Races up to a mile are run on the Bunbury course, which is straight. Races over 1m 2f or more are right-handed, with a 7f run-in. Like the Rowley Mile course, the July Course track is stiff.

Address: Newmarket Racecourse, Newmarket, Suffolk CB8 0TG Tel: 01638 663482 (Main Office), 01638 663762 (Rowley), 01638 675416 (July) Fax: Rowley 01638 675340. Fax: July 01638 675410
Website: www.newmarketracecourses.co.uk

Clerk of the Course: Michael Prosser, Westfield House, The Links, Newmarket. Tel: 01638 675504 or 07802 844578

Regional Director: Amy Starkey

Going Reports: Contact main office or Clerk of the Course as above

Stabling: 100 boxes. Free accommodation available at the Links Stables. Tel: 01638 662200 or 07747 766614

By Road: Southwest of the town on the A1304 London Road (M11 Junction 9). Free car parking at the rear of the enclosure. Annual Badge Holders' car park free all days. Free courtesy bus service from Newmarket Station, Bus Station and High Street, commencing 90 minutes prior to the first race, and return trips up to 60 minutes after the last race.

By Rail: Infrequent rail service to Newmarket Station from Cambridge (Liverpool Street) or direct bus service from Cambridge (13-mile journey).

By Air: Landing facilities for light aircraft and helicopters on racedays at both racecourses. See Flight Guide. Cambridge Airport 11 miles.

NEWTON ABBOT (L.H)

N.H. Oval, 1m 2f (7) 300y run-in. Flat with two tight bends and a water jump situated three fences from home. The nippy, agile sort is favoured. The run-in can be very short on the hurdle course.

Address: Newton Abbot Races Ltd., Kingsteignton Road, Newton Abbot, Devon TQ12 3AF
Tel: 01626 353235 Fax: 01626 336972 Website: www.newtonabbotracing.com

Clerk of the Course: Jason Loosemore 07766 228109

Managing Director: Pat Masterson. Tel: 01626 353235 Fax: 01626 336972 Mobile: 07917 830144.

Going reports: Clerk of the Course as above.

Stabling: 80 boxes, allocated on arrival. Tel: 07766 202938

By Road: North of the town on the A380. Torquay 6 miles, Exeter 17 miles.

By Rail: Newton Abbot Station (from Paddington) ¾ mile. Buses and taxis operate to and from the course.

By Air: Helicopter landing pad in the centre of the course.

NOTTINGHAM (L.H)

Flat: Left-handed, galloping, oval of about 1m 4f, and a run-in of four and a half furlongs. Flat with easy turns.

Address: Nottingham Racecourse, Colwick Park, Nottingham NG2 4BE Tel: 0870 8507634
Fax: 01159 584515 Website: www.nottinghamracecourse.co.uk

Regional Director: Amy Starkey

Clerk of the Course: Jane Hedley

Managing Director: Pip Kirkby

Going Reports: Contact main office as above or Clerk of the Course.

Stabling: 122 boxes allotted on arrival. Hostel for lads and lasses. Tel: 08708 507634

By Road: 2 miles east of the city on the B686.

By Rail: Nottingham (Midland) Station. Regular bus service to course (2 miles).

By Air: Helicopter landing facility in the centre of the course.

PERTH (R.H)

N.H. Rectangular, 1m 2f (8) 283y run-in. A flat, easy track with sweeping turns. Not a course for the long-striding galloper. An efficient watering system ensures that the ground rarely gets hard.

Address: Perth Racecourse, Scone Palace Park, Perth PH2 6BB Tel: 01738 551597 Fax: 01738 553021
Website: www.perth-races.co.uk

Clerk of the Course: Harriet Graham 07843 380401

General Manager: Sam Morshead Tel: 01738 551597 Mobile: 07768 868848

Going Reports: Groundsman: 07899 034012 or contact Clerk of the Course as above.

Stabling: 96 boxes and accommodation for lads and lasses Tel: 01738 551597. Stables Tel: 01738 621604 (racedays only).

By Road: 4 miles north of the town off the A93.

By Rail: Perth Station (from Dundee) 4 miles. There are buses to the course.
By Air: Scone Airport (3.75 miles). Edinburgh Airport 45 minutes.

PLUMPTON (L.H)

N.H. Oval, 1m 1f (7) 200y run-in uphill. A tight, undulating circuit with an uphill finish, Plumpton favours the handy, fast jumper. The ground often gets heavy, as the course is based on clay soil.
Address: Plumpton Racecourse, Plumpton, East Sussex, BN7 3AL Tel: 01273 890383 Fax: 01273 891557
Website: www.plumptonracecourse.co.uk
Clerk of the Course: Mark Cornford 07759 151617
Chief Executive: Michael Moloney
Going Reports: Tel: 01273 890383 / 07759 151617.
Stabling: 76 boxes. Advance notice required for overnight arrival. Tel: 07759 151617
By Road: 2 miles north of the village off the B2116.
By Rail: Plumpton Station (from Victoria) adjoins course.
By Air: Helicopter landing facility by prior arrangement with the Clerk of the Course.

PONTEFRACT (L.H)

Flat: Left-handed oval, undulating course of 2m 133y, with a short run-in of 2f. It is a particularly stiff track with the last 3f uphill.
Address: Pontefract Park Race Co. Ltd., The Park, Pontefract, West Yorkshire Tel: 01977 781307
(Racedays) Fax: 01977 781850 Website: www.pontefract-races.co.uk
Managing Director & Clerk of the Course: Norman Gundill 01977 781307
Assistant Manager & Clerk of the Course: Richard Hamill
Going Reports: Contact Office as above, or Clerk of the Course
Stabling: 113 boxes. Stabling and accommodation must be reserved. They will be allocated on a first come-first served basis. Tel: 01977 702323
By Road: 1 mile north of the town on the A639. Junction 32 of M62. Free car park adjacent to the course.
By Rail: Pontefract Station (Tanshelf, every hour to Wakefield), 1½ miles from the course. Regular bus service from Leeds.
By Air: Helicopters by arrangement only. (Nearest Airfields: Robin Hood (Doncaster), Sherburn-in-Elmet, Yeadon (Leeds Bradford).

REDCAR (L.H)

Flat: Left-handed, level, galloping, oval course of 1m 6f with a straight run-in of 5f. There is also a straight mile.
Address: Redcar Racecourse, Redcar, Cleveland TS10 2BY Tel: 01642 484068 Fax: 01642 488272
Website: www.redcarracing.com
Clerk of the Course: Jonjo Sanderson Tel: 01642 484068 Mobile: 07766 022893
General Manager: Amy Fair
Going Reports: Contact main office as above or Clerk of the Course.
Stabling: 144 Boxes available. Tel: Stables 01642 484068 or racedays only 01642 484254.
By Road: In town off the A1085. Free parking adjoining the course for buses and cars.
By Rail: Redcar Station (¼ mile from the course).
By Air: Landing facilities at Turners Arms Farm (600yds runway) Yearby, Cleveland. Two miles south of the racecourse - transport available. Durham Tees Valley airport (18 miles west of Redcar).

RIPON (R.H)

Flat: A sharp, undulating, right-handed oval of 1m 5f, with a 5f run-in. There is also a 6f straight course.
Address: Ripon Racecourse, Boroughbridge Road, Ripon, North Yorkshire HG4 1UG Tel: 01765 530530
Fax: 01765 698900 E-mail: info@ripon-races.co.uk Website: www.ripon-races.co.uk
Clerk of the Course & Managing Director: James Hutchinson
Going Reports: Tel: 01765 603696 or Head Groundsman 07976 960177
Stabling: Trainers requiring stabling (103 boxes available) are requested to contact the Stable Manager prior to 12 noon the day before racing. Tel: 01765 604135
By Road: The course is situated 2 miles southeast of the city, on the B6265. There is ample free parking for cars and coaches. For reservations apply to the Secretary.
By Rail: Harrogate Station (11 miles), or Thirsk (15 miles). Bus services to Ripon.
By Air: Helicopters only on the course. Otherwise Leeds/Bradford airport.

SALISBURY (R.H)

Flat: Right-handed and level, with a run-in of 4f. There is a straight mile track. The last half-mile is uphill, providing a stiff test of stamina.
Address: Salisbury Racecourse, Netherhampton, Salisbury, Wiltshire SP2 8PN Tel: 01722 326461
Fax: 01722 412710 Website: www.salisburyracecourse.co.uk
Clerk of the Course & General Manager: Jeremy Martin 07880 744999
Going Reports: Contact Clerk of the Course as above
Stabling: Free stabling (114 boxes) and accommodation for lads and lasses, apply to the Stabling Manager 01722 327327.
By Road: 3 miles southwest of the city on the A3094 at Netherhampton. Free car park adjoins the course.
By Rail: Salisbury Station is 3.5 miles (from London Waterloo). Bus service to the course.
By Air: Helicopter landing facility near the 1m 2f start.

SANDOWN PARK (R.H)

Flat: An easy right-handed oval course of 1m 5f with a stiff straight uphill run-in of 4f. Separate straight 5f track is also uphill. Galloping.
N.H. Oval, 1m 5f (11) 220y run-in uphill. Features seven fences on the back straight; the last three (the Railway Fences) are very close together and can often decide the outcome of races. The stiff climb to the finish puts the emphasis very much on stamina, but accurate-jumping, free-running sorts are also favoured. Hurdle races are run on the Flat course.
Address: Sandown Park Racecourse, Esher, Surrey KT10 9AJ Tel: 01372 464348 Fax: 01372 470427
www.sandown.co.uk
Regional Director: Rupert Trevelyan
Clerk of the Course: Andrew Cooper, Sandown Park, Esher, Surrey. Tel: 01372 461213
Mobile: 07774 230850.
Going Reports: 01372 461212.
Stabling: 110 boxes. Free stabling and accommodation for lads and lasses. Tel: 01372 463511.
By Road: Four miles southwest of Kingston-on-Thames, on the A307 (M25 Junction 10).
By Rail: Esher Station (from Waterloo) adjoins the course.
By Air: London (Heathrow) Airport 12 miles.

SEDGEFIELD (L.H)

N.H. Oval, 1m 2f (8) 200y run-in: Hurdles 200y run-in. Undulating with fairly tight turns, it doesn't suit big, long-striding horses.
Address: Sedgefield Racecourse, Sedgefield, Stockton-on-Tees, Cleveland TS21 2HW Tel: 01740 621925
Office Fax: 01740 620663 Website: www.sedgefield-racecourse.co.uk
Clerk of the Course: Sophie Barton
General Manager: Jill Williamson
Going Reports: Tel: 01740 621925 or contact Clerk of the Course as above
Stabling: 116 boxes filled in rotation. No forage. Accommodation for horse attendants: Tel: 01740 621925
By Road: ¾ mile southwest of the town, near the junction of the A689 (Bishop Auckland) and the A177 (Durham) roads. The car park is free.
By Rail: Darlington Station (9 miles). Durham Station (12 miles).
By Air: Helicopter landing facility in car park area by prior arrangement only.

SOUTHWELL (L.H)

Flat, Turf: Tight left-handed track.
Flat, Fibresand: Left-handed oval, Fibresand course of 1m 2f with a 3f run-in. There is a straight 5f. Sharp and level, Southwell suits front-runners.
N.H. Oval, 1m 1f (7) 220y run-in. A tight, flat track with a short run-in, suits front-runners.
Address: Southwell Racecourse, Rolleston, Newark, Nottinghamshire NG25 0TS Tel: 01636 814481
Fax: 01636 812271 Website: www.southwell-racecourse.co.uk
Clerk of the Course: Roderick Duncan 07772 958685
General Manager: Amanda Boby
Going Reports: Contact Clerk of the Course as above.
Stabling: 113 boxes at the course. Applications for staff and horse accommodation to be booked by noon the day before racing on 01636 814481.
By Road: The course is situated at Rolleston, 3 miles south of Southwell, 5 miles from Newark.
By Rail: Rolleston Station (Nottingham-Newark line) adjoins the course.
By Air: Helicopters can land by prior arrangement.

STRATFORD-ON-AVON (L.H)

N.H. Triangular, 1m 2f (8) 200y run-in. Virtually flat with two tight bends, and quite a short home straight. A sharp and turning course, Stratford-on-Avon suits the well-balanced, handy sort.
Address: Stratford Racecourse, Luddington Road, Stratford-upon-Avon, Warwickshire CV37 9SE
Tel: 01789 267949 Fax: 01789 415850 Website: www.stratfordracecourse.net
Clerk of the Course & Managing Director: Stephen Lambert. Mobile 07836 384932.
Assistant to Managing Director: Ilona Barnett
Going reports: Contact main office as above or Head Groundsman Tel: 07770 623366.
Stabling: 89 boxes allotted on arrival. Advance notice must be given for overnight stays.
Tel: 01789 267949.
By Road: A mile from the town centre, off the A429 (Evesham road).
By Rail: Stratford-on-Avon Station (from Birmingham New Street or Leamington Spa) 1 mile.
By Air: Helicopter landing facility by prior arrangement.

TAUNTON (R.H)

N.H. Elongated oval, 1m 2f (8) 150y run-in uphill. Sharp turns, especially after the winning post, with a steady climb from the home bend. Suits the handy sort.
Address: Taunton Racecourse, Orchard Portman, Taunton, Somerset TA3 7BL Tel: 01823 337172
Office Fax: 01823 325881 Website: www.tauntonracecourse.co.uk
Clerk of the Course: Jason Loosemore
General Manager: Bob Young
Going reports: Contact Clerk of the Course as above, or Head Groundsman (after 4.30pm) 07971 695132.
Stabling: 90 boxes allotted on arrival. Advance bookings for long journeys. Apply to the Stable Manager, 01823 337172
By Road: Two miles south of the town on the B3170 (Honiton) road (M5 Junction 25).
By Rail: Taunton Station 2 miles. There are buses and taxis to course.
By Air: Helicopter landing facility by prior arrangement.

THIRSK (L.H)

Flat: Left-handed, oval of 1m 2f with sharp turns and an undulating run-in of 4f. There is a straight 6f track.
Address: The Racecourse, Station Road, Thirsk, North Yorkshire YO7 1QL Tel: 01845 522276
Fax: 01845 525353. Website: www.thirskracecourse.net
Clerk of the Course & Managing Director: James Sanderson
Going reports: Contact main office or Clerk of the Course as above
Stabling: 110 boxes. For stabling and accommodation apply to the Racecourse Tel: 01845 522096
By Road: West of the town on the A61. Free car park adjacent to the course for buses and cars.
By Rail: Thirsk Station (from King's Cross). ½ mile from the course.
By Air: Helicopters can land by prior arrangement. Tel: Racecourse 01845 522276. Fixed wing aircraft can land at RAF Leeming. Tel: 01677 423041. Light aircraft at Bagby. Tel: 01845 597385 or 01845 537555.

TOWCESTER (R.H)

N.H. Square, 1m 6f (10) 200y run-in uphill. The final six furlongs are uphill. One of the most testing tracks in the country with the emphasis purely on stamina.
Address: The Racecourse, Easton Neston, Towcester, Northants NN12 7HS Tel: 01327 353414
Fax: 01327 358534 Website: www.towcester-racecourse.co.uk
Clerk of the Course: Robert Bellamy 07836 241458
General Manager: Kevin Ackerman.
Going Reports: Tel: 01327 353414 or contact Clerk of the Course as above.
Stabling: 101 stables in a new block. Allocated on arrival. Please contact racecourse in advance for overnight stabling / accommodation 01327 350200.
By Road: 1 mile southeast of the town on the A5 (Milton Keynes road). M1 (Junction 15a).
By Rail: Northampton Station (Euston) 9 miles, buses to Towcester; or Milton Keynes (Euston) 12 miles, taxis available.
By Air: Helicopters can land by prior arrangement with the Racecourse Manager.

UTTOXETER (L.H)

N.H. Oval, 1m 2f (8) 170y run-in. A few undulations, easy bends and fences and a flat home straight of over half a mile. Suits front-runners, especially on the 2m hurdle course.
Address: The Racecourse, Wood Lane, Uttoxeter, Staffordshire ST14 8BD Tel: 01889 562561
Fax: 01889 562786 Website: www.uttoxeter-racecourse.co.uk
Clerk of the Course: Charlie Moore 07764 255500
General Manager: David MacDonald
Going Reports: Contact main office or Clerk of the Course as above.
Stabling: 102 boxes, allotted on arrival. Tel: 01889 562561. Overnight and Accommodation requirements must be notified in advance as no hostel at course.
By Road: South-East of the town off the B5017 (Marchington Road).
By Rail: Uttoxeter Station (Crewe-Derby line) adjoins the course.
By Air: Helicopters can land by prior arrangement with the raceday office.

WARWICK (L.H)

Flat: Left-handed, sharp, level track of 1m 6f 32y in circumference, with a run-in of two and a half furlongs.
N.H. Circular, 1m 6f (10) 240y run-in. Undulating with tight bends, five quick fences in the back straight and a short home straight, Warwick favours handiness and speed rather than stamina.
Address: Warwick Racecourse, Hampton Street, Warwick CV34 6HN Tel: 01926 491553
Fax: 01926 403223 Website: www.warwickracecourse.co.uk
Regional Director: Ian Renton
Clerk of the Course: Sulekha Varma
Managing Director: Huw Williams
Going Reports: Contact main office or Clerk of the Course as above.
Stabling: 117 boxes allocated on arrival or by reservation 01926 491553.
By Road: West of the town on the B4095 adjacent to Junction 15 of the M40.
By Rail: Warwick or Warwick Parkway Stations.
By Air: Helicopters can land by prior arrangement with the Clerk of the Course.

WETHERBY (L.H)

N.H. Oval, 1m 4f (9) 200y run-in slightly uphill. A flat, very fair course which suits the long-striding galloper.
Address: The Racecourse, York Road, Wetherby, LS22 5EJ Tel: 01937 582035 Fax: 01937 588021
Website: www.wetherbyracing.co.uk
Clerk of the Course & Chief Executive: Jonjo Sanderson 07831 437453
Going reports: Tel: 01937 582035, or Head Groundsman: 07880 722586
Stabling: 91 boxes allocated on arrival. Accommodation available. Tel: 01937 582035 or from 2pm the day before racing 01937 582074.
By Road: East of the town off the B1224 (York Road). Adjacent to the A1. Excellent bus and coach facilities. Car park free.
By Rail: Leeds Station 12 miles. Buses to Wetherby.
By Air: Helicopters can land by prior arrangement

WINCANTON (R.H)

N.H. Rectangular, 1m 3f (9) 200y run-in. Good galloping course where the going rarely becomes heavy. The home straight is mainly downhill.
Address: Wincanton Racecourse, Wincanton, Somerset BA9 8BJ Tel: 01963 32344 Fax: (01963) 34668
Website: www.wincantonracecourse.co.uk
Regional Director: Ian Renton
Clerk of the Course: Barry Johnson 07976 791578
General Manager: Steve Parlett
Going Reports: Contact Racecourse Office as above.
Stabling: 94 boxes allocated on arrival, overnight accommodation must be booked in advance. Apply to the Stable Manager, Wincanton Racecourse. Tel: 01963 32344.
By Road: 1 mile north of the town on the B3081.
By Rail: Gillingham Station (from Waterloo) or Castle Cary Station (from Paddington). Buses and taxis to the course.
By Air: Helicopter landing area is situated in the centre of the course.

WINDSOR (Fig. 8)

Flat: Figure of eight track of 1m 4f 110y. The course is level and sharp with a long run-in. The 6f course is essentially straight.
Address: Royal Windsor Racecourse, Maidenhead Road, Windsor, Berkshire SL4 5JJ Tel: 01753 498400
Fax: 01753 830156. Website: www.windsor-racecourse.co.uk
Clerk of the Course: Jeff Green
Executive Director: Stuart Dorn
Going Reports: Contact Clerk of the Course as above.
Stabling: 114 boxes available. Reservation required for overnight stay and accommodation only.
Tel: 07825 603236 or 01753 498405 (racedays).
By Road: North of the town on the A308 (M4 Junction 6).
By Rail: Windsor Central Station (from Paddington) or Windsor & Eton Riverside Station (from Waterloo).
By Air: London (Heathrow) Airport 15 minutes. Also White Waltham Airport (West London Aero Club) 15 minutes.
River Bus: Seven minutes from Barry Avenue promenade at Windsor.

WOLVERHAMPTON (L.H)

Flat: Left-handed oval Polytrack of 1m, with a run-in of 380y. A level track with sharp bends.
Address: Wolverhampton Racecourse, Dunstall Park, Gorsebrook Road, Wolverhampton WV6 0PE
Tel: 01902 390000 Fax: 01902 421621 Website: www.wolverhampton-racecourse.co.uk
Clerk of the Course: Fergus Cameron 07971 531162
General Manager: Dave Roberts
Going Reports: Contact Main Office as above
Stabling: Applications for lads and lasses, and overnight stables must be made to Racecourse by noon on the day before racing. Tel: 07971 531162. Fax: 01902 421621.
By Road: 1 mile north of the city on the A449 (M54 Junction 2 or M6 Junction 12). Car parking free of charge.
By Rail: Wolverhampton Station (from Euston) 1 mile.
By Air: Halfpenny Green Airport 8 miles.

WORCESTER (L.H)

N.H. Elongated oval, 1m 5f (9) 220y run-in. Flat with easy turns, Worcester is a very fair, galloping track.
Address: Worcester Racecourse, Pitchcroft, Worcester WR1 3EJ Tel: 01905 25364 Fax: 01905 617563
Website: www.worcester-racecourse.co.uk
Clerk of the Course: Keith Ottesen
Managing Director: Dave Roberts 01905 25364.
Going Reports: Contact Clerk of the Course as above, or 01905 25364 (racedays).
Stabling: 97 boxes allotted on arrival. Overnight accommodation for lads and lasses in Worcester.
Tel: 01905 25364 Fax: 01905 617563.
By Road: West of the city off the A449 (Kidderminster road) (M5 Junction 8).
By Rail: Foregate Street Station, Worcester (from Paddington) ¾ mile.
By Air: Helicopter landing facility in the centre of the course, by prior arrangement only.

YARMOUTH (L.H)

Flat: Left-handed, level circuit of 1m 4f, with a run-in of 5f. The straight course is 1m long.
Address: The Racecourse, Jellicoe Road, Great Yarmouth, Norfolk NR30 4AU Tel: 01493 842527
Fax: 01493 843254 Website: www.greatyarmouth-racecourse.co.uk
Clerk of the Course: Richard Aldous 07738 507643
General Manager: Glenn Tubby
Going Reports: Contact Main Office or Clerk of the Course as above
Stabling: 127 boxes available. Allocated on arrival. Tel: 01493 855651 (racedays only) or racecourse office.
By Road: 1 mile east of town centre (well signposted from A47 & A12).
By Rail: Great Yarmouth Station (1 mile). Bus service to the course.
By Air: Helicopter landing available by prior arrangement with Racecourse Office

YORK (L.H)

Flat: Left-handed, level, galloping track, with a straight 6f. There is also an adjoining course of 6f 214y.
Address: The Racecourse, York YO23 1EX Tel: 01904 683932 Fax: 01904 611071 Website:
www.yorkracecourse.co.uk
Clerk of the Course & Chief Executive: William Derby 07812 961176
Assistant Clerk of the Course: Anthea Morshead
Going Reports: Contact 01904 683932 or Clerk of the Course as above.
Stabling: 177 boxes available Tel: 01904 706317 (Racedays) or 07712 676434.
By Road: 1 mile southeast of the city on the A1036.
By Rail: 1½ miles York Station (from King's Cross). Special bus service from station to the course.
By Air: Light aircraft and helicopter landing facilities available at Rufforth aerodrome (5,000ft tarmac
runway). £20 landing fee - transport arranged to course. Leeds Bradford airport (25 miles).

THE INVESTEC DERBY STAKES (GROUP 1), EPSOM DOWNS SATURDAY 7TH JUNE 2014

SECOND ENTRIES BY NOON APRIL 8TH; SUPPLEMENTARY ENTRIES BY NOON JUNE 2ND.

HORSE	TRAINER	HORSE	TRAINER
ABSOLUTE (IRE)	Marco Botti	CLUB WEXFORD (IRE)	J. S. Bolger, Ireland
ADELAIDE (IRE)	Aidan O'Brien, Ireland	COUNTY WEXFORD (IRE)	J. S. Bolger, Ireland
ADJUSTED (IRE)	Aidan O'Brien, Ireland	CRY JOY (USA)	Charlie Appleby
AFFAIRS OF STATE (IRE)	Aidan O'Brien, Ireland	DALAROSSO	Ed Dunlop
AFFINISEA (IRE)	John M. Oxx, Ireland	DAMASCENE	Marco Botti
AGAMON LAKE (FR)	G. Henrot, France	DANJEU (IRE)	John Gosden
AGE OF DISCOVERY	Ed McMahon	DARK DAYS	Paul Cole
AGE OF INNOCENCE	A. Fabre, France	DAURAN (IRE)	A. de Royer Dupre, France
AGENA (IRE)	Aidan O'Brien, Ireland	DEADLY APPROACH	Charlie Appleby
A GREATER FORCE (FR)	Aidan O'Brien, Ireland	DEINONYCHUS	
AL FATIH (IRE)	M. Delzangles, France	DESERT TIGER (IRE)	Aidan O'Brien, Ireland
ALIGHIERI (IRE)	David Lanigan	DICKIEBIRD (IRE)	Declan Carroll
ALMERZEM (USA)	Saeed bin Suroor	DIEGO VELAZQUEZ (IRE)	David O'Meara
ALMUHALAB	Charles Hills	DOWN HOUSE	Aidan O'Brien, Ireland
ALMUHEET	Sir Michael Stoute	DRACO'S CODE	Gary Moore
ALTAAYIL (IRE)	Sir Michael Stoute	DYNAMO (IRE)	Aidan O'Brien, Ireland
ALTRUISTIC (IRE)	J. P. Murtagh, Ireland	EAGLE TOP	John Gosden
ALYASAN (IRE)	John M. Oxx, Ireland	EARL OF MENTEITH (IRE)	Charlie Appleby
ALZAMMAAR (USA)	Charles Hills	EBANORAN (IRE)	John M. Oxx, Ireland
ANGLO IRISH	John Gosden	EBASANI (IRE)	John M. Oxx, Ireland
ANJIN (IRE)	Sir Mark Prescott Bt	EBN NAAS	Saeed bin Suroor
ANNUS MIRABILIS (IRE)	Aidan O'Brien, Ireland	EDKHAN (IRE)	A. de Royer Dupre, France
ARAB DAWN	Hughie Morrison	ELJADDAAF (IRE)	Saeed bin Suroor
ARABIAN REVOLUTION	Saeed bin Suroor	ELUSIVE GUEST (FR)	George Margarson
ARBAAB	Sir Michael Stoute	EMIRATI SPIRIT	Roger Varian
ARMOURER (IRE)	William R. Muir	ENTIQAAM	D. K. Weld, Ireland
AROD (IRE)	Peter Chapple-Hyam	ENZANI (IRE)	John M. Oxx, Ireland
ARQUIMEDES (IRE)		EVASON	J. S. Bolger, Ireland
ASPIRING ARTIST	A. Fabre, France	FAIR WIND	Aidan O'Brien, Ireland
ASTRONEREUS (IRE)	Amanda Perrett	FALKIRK (IRE)	Aidan O'Brien, Ireland
ASTRONOMOS	John Gosden	FAMOUS KID (USA)	Saeed bin Suroor
AUSTRALIA (IRE)	Aidan O'Brien, Ireland	FAST DELIVERY	Saeed bin Suroor
AUTHENTICITY	John Butler	FAUVE (IRE)	Aidan O'Brien, Ireland
AWESOME STAR (IRE)	John M. Oxx, Ireland	FELIX MENDELSSOHN (IRE)	Aidan O'Brien, Ireland
AYRAD (IRE)	Roger Varian	FESTIVAL THEATRE (IRE)	Sir Michael Stoute
BASEM	Saeed bin Suroor	FIERY PHOENIX (GER)	
BATTERSEA	Roger Varian	FINAL ATTACK (IRE)	Saeed bin Suroor
BAZAAR (IRE)	Aidan O'Brien, Ireland	FISCAL FOCUS (IRE)	J. S. Bolger, Ireland
BE MY SEA (IRE)	John M. Oxx, Ireland	FIVE STAR GENERAL	Aidan O'Brien, Ireland
BE READY (IRE)	Saeed bin Suroor	FLAG WAR (GER)	Saeed bin Suroor
BEACHY HEAD (IRE)		FLIGHT OFFICER	Saeed bin Suroor
BELISARIUS (IRE)	Aidan O'Brien, Ireland	FOG OF WAR	G. M. Lyons, Ireland
BELROG	Ralph Beckett	FOREVER NOW	John Gosden
BERKSHIRE (IRE)	Paul Cole	FORT DE FRANCE (IRE)	Aidan O'Brien, Ireland
BEYOND THE MOON (IRE)	John Gosden	FOUR CARAT (GER)	Aidan O'Brien, Ireland
BLUE ARMY	Saeed bin Suroor	FRANCISTOWN (IRE)	Charlie Appleby
BLUE HUSSAR (IRE)	Aidan O'Brien, Ireland	FRAZIER (IRE)	
BORN IN BOMBAY	Andrew Balding	FREE EAGLE (IRE)	D. K. Weld, Ireland
BUONARROTI (IRE)	Aidan O'Brien, Ireland	FREEMASON	Sir Michael Stoute
BURNING DESIRE (IRE)	T. Stack, Ireland	FRENCH PAINTER (IRE)	R. Collet, France
CARLO BUGATTI (IRE)	Aidan O'Brien, Ireland	FRIENDSHIP (IRE)	Aidan O'Brien, Ireland
CASTLE COMBE (IRE)	Marcus Tregoning	FUN MAC (GER)	Hughie Morrison
CENTURY (IRE)	Aidan O'Brien, Ireland	GALLANTE (IRE)	A. Fabre, France
CHAOTIC CARNIVAL	Dominique Sepulchre, France	GEOFFREY CHAUCER (USA)	Aidan O'Brien, Ireland
CHEEKY CHAPPIE (IRE)	David Wachman, Ireland	GEORGE HERBERT	
CHIEF BARKER (IRE)	Richard Hannon	GHAAWY	Sir Michael Stoute
CLASSIC DEVOTION (USA)	Charlie Appleby	GHAFAAN (IRE)	M. Delzangles, France
CLASSICAL DUET (USA)		GLORIOUS SUN	Ed Walker
CLOUDSCAPE (IRE)	John Gosden	GOD'S SPEED (IRE)	Rae Guest

HORSE	TRAINER
GOLD RUN	Olly Stevens
GOLD STRUCK	John Gosden
GOLD TRAIL (IRE)	Charlie Appleby
GOTHIC	Sir Michael Stoute
GOVERNMENT HOUSE (USA)	Aidan O'Brien, Ireland
GRAND MEISTER	Michael Bell
GRANDDUKEOFTUSCANY (IRE)	Aidan O'Brien, Ireland
GRANDEST	John Gosden
GREENSIDE	Henry Candy
GUARD OF HONOUR (IRE)	Aidan O'Brien, Ireland
GULF WIND (IRE)	
GYPSY KING (IRE)	Aidan O'Brien, Ireland
HAAYIL	Jassim Ghazali, Qatar
HANDASY	Francois Rohaut, France
HARDSTONE (USA)	J. P Murtagh, Ireland
HAWASH	Ismail Mohammed
HIGHPLAINS DRIFTER (IRE)	David Lanigan
HOIST THE COLOURS (IRE)	David Lanigan
HOMESTRETCH	Mick Channon
HORSEGUARDSPARADE	Aidan O'Brien, Ireland
HOUSEHOLD CAVALRY	Aidan O'Brien, Ireland
HYDROGEN	Peter Chapple-Hyam
HYMENAIOS (IRE)	Richard Hannon
IAN'S MEMORY (USA)	Jeremy Noseda
ICONIC ARTIST (USA)	Graham Motion, USA
IDDER (IRE)	Roger Varian
IL GRAN CAPO (IRE)	Roger Ingram
ILLUSIVE (IRE)	Aidan O'Brien, Ireland
IMPULSIVE MOMENT (IRE)	Andrew Balding
INDIAN MAHARAJA (IRE)	Aidan O'Brien, Ireland
INFANTRY	Mme C. Head-Maarek, France
INIESTA (IRE)	Aidan O'Brien, Ireland
INVINCIBLE FRESH (IRE)	James Fanshawe
ISTIMRAAR (IRE)	
JEFFERSON CITY (IRE)	John Gosden
JOHANN STRAUSS	Aidan O'Brien, Ireland
JOHN CONSTABLE (IRE)	Aidan O'Brien, Ireland
JUNIPER TREE (IRE)	Aidan O'Brien, Ireland
JUPITER AND MARS (IRE)	John M. Oxx, Ireland
KAHYL (IRE)	M. Delzangles, France
KALIDJAR (FR)	M. Delzangles, France
KARAKONTIE (JPN)	J. E. Pease, France
KARRAAR	Richard Hannon
KATILAN (IRE)	John M. Oxx, Ireland
KIFAAH	Jean Claude Rouget, France
KINEMA (IRE)	Ed Walker
KINGFISHER (IRE)	Aidan O'Brien, Ireland
KINGS FETE	Sir Michael Stoute
KING'S LAND	Saeed bin Suroor
KINSHASA	Luca Cumani
KISANJI	Mick Channon
KNIFE POINT (GER)	Hugo Palmer
LABAIK (FR)	J. E. Hammond, France
LACAN (IRE)	Clive Cox
LAMUBAALY (IRE)	F. Head, France
LATE NIGHT MARK (IRE)	Charles Hills
LEGAL SHARK (IRE)	Sir Mark Prescott Bt
LELIANI (IRE)	John M. Oxx, Ireland
LESSAADY (IRE)	A. de Royer Dupre, France
LIGHT OF ASIA (IRE)	Ed Dunlop
LIGNEROLLES (FR)	M. Delzangles, France
LORD OF THE NILE (IRE)	David O'Meara
LUNASEA (IRE)	Luca Cumani
MAHSOOB	John Gosden
MAJESTIC SUN (IRE)	Peter Chapple-Hyam
MANALI (FR)	A. de Royer Dupre, France
MANSION HOUSE (IRE)	David Wachman, Ireland

HORSE	TRAINER
MARAKOUSH (IRE)	John M. Oxx, Ireland
MARITAL (IRE)	J. P Murtagh, Ireland
MAXIE T	Mark Johnston
MEADOW CREEK	A. Fabre, France
MEKONG RIVER (IRE)	Aidan O'Brien, Ireland
MEMORIAL DAY (IRE)	Saeed bin Suroor
METEOROID (USA)	Lady Cecil
MIHANY (IRE)	John Gosden
MIN ALEMARAT (IRE)	Marco Botti
MINER'S LAMP (IRE)	Charlie Appleby
MISTER OK	M. Delzangles, France
MIZZOU (IRE)	Luca Cumani
MONOCEROS (USA)	P. Bary, France
MOONFAARID	M. F. de Kock, South Africa
MORNING WATCH (IRE)	Lady Cecil
MR ROCK (IRE)	David Wachman, Ireland
MR SMITH	John Gosden
MUJAAHER (IRE)	Saeed bin Suroor
MUNAASER	Sir Michael Stoute
MUNATAS	Roger Varian
MUNJAZ	John Gosden
MUSTAJEEB	D. K. Weld, Ireland
MUTAKAYYEF	William Haggas
MYMATECHRIS (IRE)	Andrew Balding
MYSTIC BLUE	M. Delzangles, France
MYTHICAL MADNESS	
NEVER TO BE (USA)	John Gosden
NICO DE BOREPAIR (FR)	
NORAB (GER)	Marco Botti
NORTHERN SOLSTICE	
NOS GALAN (IRE)	
OASIS FANTASY (IRE)	Ed Dunlop
OBSERVATIONAL	Roger Charlton
OKLAHOMA CITY	Aidan O'Brien, Ireland
ORACLE BOY	William R. Muir
ORCHESTRA (IRE)	Aidan O'Brien, Ireland
ORIENTEER	A. Fabre, France
ORKNEY ISLAND	
PANTOLONI	Charlie Appleby
PEARL SPECTRE (USA)	Andrew Balding
PERSONAL OPINION	Charlie Appleby
PICK POCKETT	Luca Cumani
PINZOLO	Charlie Appleby
PONCE DE LEON	M. Delzangles, France
PONFEIGH (IRE)	John M. Oxx, Ireland
PRAIRIE DALE (FR)	A. de Royer Dupre, France
PRIMOGENITURE (IRE)	John M. Oxx, Ireland
PROMETHEUS (IRE)	M. Delzangles, France
PROPHETS THUMB (IRE)	Martyn Meade
QUEBEC	A. Fabre, France
RAGGED ROBBIN (FR)	David Lanigan
RANDWICK (IRE)	Charles Hills
RAPPROCHEMENT (IRE)	Charlie Appleby
RAZOR WIND (IRE)	
RED ROCKS POINT (IRE)	Aidan O'Brien, Ireland
REKN (IRE)	A. de Royer Dupre, France
REMBRANDT VAN RIJN (IRE)	David Lanigan
RESILIENCY (IRE)	David Wachman, Ireland
RIJM	Luca Cumani
RIPPLES EFFECT	John M. Oxx, Ireland
RIVER GLASS (IRE)	
ROGUE AGENT (IRE)	A. Fabre, France
ROSKILLY (IRE)	Andrew Balding
ROYAL BATTALION	Olly Stevens
ROYAL HISTORY	Saeed bin Suroor
SAARREM (USA)	John Gosden
SALVADORI (IRE)	Ahmed bin Harmash, UAE

HORSE	TRAINER
SANATI (FR)	M. Delzangles, France
SANPEDER (IRE)	S. Botti, Italy
SARPECH (IRE)	Sir Mark Prescott Bt
SATELLITE (IRE)	William Haggas
SAVANT (IRE)	Sir Michael Stoute
SCURBATT	S. Botti, Italy
SEA HERE	Ralph Beckett
SEAGULL STAR	William Haggas
SEA'S ARIA (IRE)	John M. Oxx, Ireland
SHANKLY	Clive Cox
SHARP SWORD (IRE)	Saeed bin Suroor
SHOKUNIN (IRE)	Francis-Henri Graffard, France
SIGNAL	Andrew Balding
SIGNPOSTED (IRE)	Andrew Balding
SINAKAR (IRE)	A. de Royer Dupre, France
SINDARBAN (IRE)	John M. Oxx, Ireland
SINKAL (USA)	John M. Oxx, Ireland
SKY JOCKEY	
SNOW SKY	Sir Michael Stoute
SNOWMANE (IRE)	G. M. Lyons, Ireland
SOLAR ECLIPSE	Aidan O'Brien, Ireland
SONG OF NAMIBIA (IRE)	Sir Michael Stoute
SPIRIT OR SOUL (FR)	Marco Botti
SPRING FOCUS (IRE)	J. S. Bolger, Ireland
ST PETER'S SQUARE (IRE)	David Wachman, Ireland
STAMPEDE (IRE)	Sir Michael Stoute
STAY DE NIGHT (IRE)	D. K. Weld, Ireland
STERLING RUN (IRE)	M. Delzangles, France
STREETCAR TO STARS	John M. Oxx, Ireland
SUDDEN WONDER (IRE)	Charlie Appleby
SUNDARA (IRE)	J. S. Bolger, Ireland
SURACON (GER)	A. Wohler, Germany
TABJEEL	Saeed bin Suroor
TACTICUS (USA)	Lady Cecil
TAGHREEB	Brian Meehan
TAHADEE (IRE)	Mick Channon
TALL SHIP (IRE)	Sir Michael Stoute
TAP YOUR TOES (IRE)	Luca Cumani
TAQNEEN (IRE)	Ed Dunlop
TARABIYN (IRE)	John M. Oxx, Ireland
TARRAFAL (IRE)	Mark Johnston
TATOOINE (FR)	P. Bary, France
TEAM WORK	Saeed bin Suroor
TELETEXT (USA)	P. Bary, France
TERCEL (IRE)	Sir Michael Stoute
THE NEW PHARAOH (IRE)	Chris Wall
THE PEOPLES CHOICE (FR)	Francis-Henri Graffard, France
THEOPHILUS (IRE)	J. S. Bolger, Ireland
THINK AHEAD	Saeed bin Suroor
THOMAS WEDGWOOD (IRE)	Aidan O'Brien, Ireland
TIGRIS RIVER (IRE)	Aidan O'Brien, Ireland
TIME AND SPACE	J. E. Pease, France
TIMIYAN (USA)	John M. Oxx, Ireland
TIZLOVE REGARDLESS (USA)	Mark Johnston
TOUCH THE SKY	Lady Cecil
TOUR DE FORCE (IRE)	Aidan O'Brien, Ireland
TRUE STORY	Saeed bin Suroor
UP THE JUNCTION	Luca Cumani
URBAN MOON (IRE)	J. P Murtagh, Ireland
VENEZIA (IRE)	Martyn Meade
VENT DE FORCE	Hughie Morrison
VEYA (USA)	R. Ribaudo, U.S.A.
VICEROYALTY	
VOLARE (IRE)	
WARRIOR OF LIGHT (IRE)	David Lanigan
WEDNAAN	M. F. de Kock, South Africa
WELD ARAB (IRE)	D. K. Weld, Ireland

HORSE	TRAINER
WENGEN	Luca Cumani
WESTERN HYMN	John Gosden
WEXFORD TOWN (IRE)	J. S. Bolger, Ireland
WHAT MATTERS NOW (USA)	P. Bary, France
WILD AT SEA (IRE)	John M. Oxx, Ireland
WINTER THUNDER	Saeed bin Suroor
WRANGLER	William Haggas
ZEE ZEELY	William Haggas
ZEPHYR	Karl Burke
ZERFAAL	John Gosden
ZILBER (GER)	Ed Dunlop
ZIRIYAN (FR)	M. Delzangles, France
EX BOWSTRING (IRE)	Michael Bell
EX KOTDIJI	Michael Bell
EX RIVERINE	Hughie Morrison
EX TROPICAL LADY (IRE)	J. S. Bolger, Ireland
EX WITHORWITHOUTYOU (IRE)	Aidan O'Brien, Ireland

THE CSP
EUROPEAN FREE HANDICAP
NEWMARKET CRAVEN MEETING 2014
(ON THE ROWLEY MILE COURSE)
WEDNESDAY APRIL 16TH

The CSP European Free Handicap (Class 1) (Listed race) with total prize fund of £37,000 for two-year-olds only of 2013 which are included in the European 2-y-o Thoroughbred Rankings or which, in 2013, either ran in Great Britain or ran for a trainer who at the time was licensed by the British Horseracing Authority, and are Rated 100 or above; lowest weight 8st; highest weight 9st 7lbs.

Penalty for a winner after December 31st 2013, 5 lbs. Seven furlongs.

Rating		st	lb	Rating		st	lb
122	TOORMORE (IRE)	9	7	110	MEKONG RIVER (IRE)	8	9
120	KINGSTON HILL (GB)	9	5	110	MUSTAJEEB (GB)	8	9
119	NO NAY NEVER (USA)	9	4	110	PRIORE PHILIP (ITY)	8	9
119	WAR COMMAND (USA)	9	4	110	SHINING EMERALD (GB)	8	9
118	KARAKONTIE (JPN)	9	3	110	SUPPLICANT (GB)	8	9
117	AUSTRALIA (GB)	9	2	110	THE GREY GATSBY (IRE)	8	9
117	CHRISELLIAM (IRE)	9	2	109	NIGHT OF THUNDER (IRE)	8	8
117	OUTSTRIP (GB)	9	2	109	OKLAHOMA CITY (GB)	8	8
116	NOOZHOH CANARIAS (SPA)	9	1	109	SANDIVA (IRE)	8	8
116	SUDIRMAN (USA)	9	1	108	JUSTICE DAY (IRE)	8	7
115	ECTOT (GB)	9	0	108	LUCKY KRISTALE (GB)	8	7
115	GIOVANNI BOLDINI (USA)	9	0	108	SAAYERR (GB)	8	7
114	ASTAIRE (IRE)	8	13	107	AL THAKHIRA (IRE)	8	6
114	BIG TIME (IRE)	8	13	107	BUNKER (IRE)	8	6
114	CABLE BAY (IRE)	8	13	107	COACH HOUSE (IRE)	8	6
114	VORDA (FR)	8	13	107	COME TO HEEL (IRE)	8	6
113	BERKSHIRE (IRE)	8	12	107	DOROTHY B (IRE)	8	6
113	CHARM SPIRIT (IRE)	8	12	107	FIGURE OF SPEECH (IRE)	8	6
113	EARNSHAW (USA)	8	12	107	GOOD BOY LUKEY (GB)	8	6
113	PRINCE GIBRALTAR (FR)	8	12	107	GREEN DOOR (IRE)	8	6
113	RIZEENA (IRE)	8	12	107	IHTIMAL (IRE)	8	6
112	DECATHLETE (USA)	8	11	107	SHAMSHON (IRE)	8	6
112	GEOFFREY CHAUCER (USA)	8	11	107	TRUTH OR DARE (GB)	8	6
112	HOT STREAK (IRE)	8	11	106	ALTRUISTIC (IRE)	8	5
112	INDONESIENNE (IRE)	8	11	106	DOLCE N KARAMA (IRE)	8	5
112	MISS FRANCE (IRE)	8	11	106	MUSICAL COMEDY (GB)	8	5
112	PRESTIGE VENDOME (FR)	8	11	106	QUEEN CATRINE (IRE)	8	5
112	SOMEWHAT (USA)	8	11	106	SIR JACK LAYDEN (GB)	8	5
112	TAPESTRY (USA)	8	11	105	AMAZING MARIA (IRE)	8	4
112	WILSHIRE BOULEVARD (IRE)	8	11	105	ANTICIPATED (IRE)	8	4
111	ANJAAL (GB)	8	10	105	GOD WILLING (GB)	8	4
111	BE READY (IRE)	8	10	105	RUFFORD (IRE)	8	4
111	BROWN SUGAR (IRE)	8	10	105	SHIFTING POWER (GB)	8	4
111	JALLOTA (GB)	8	10	105	SPEEDFIEND (GB)	8	4
111	JOHANN STRAUSS (GB)	8	10	105	WASHAAR (GB)	8	4
111	KINGMAN (GB)	8	10	105	WONDERFULLY (IRE)	8	4
111	KIRAM (FR)	8	10	104	EMIRATES FLYER (GB)	8	3
111	KIYOSHI (GB)	8	10	104	JOYEUSE (GB)	8	3
111	PARBOLD (IRE)	8	10	104	MIRACLE OF MEDINAH (GB)	8	3
111	PRINCESS NOOR (IRE)	8	10	104	SIR JOHN HAWKINS (USA)	8	3
110	BARLEY MOW (IRE)	8	9	103	AMBIANCE (IRE)	8	2
110	CRAFTSMAN (IRE)	8	9	103	CHIEF BARKER (IRE)	8	2
110	ELLIPTIQUE (IRE)	8	9	103	HAIKBIDIAC (IRE)	8	2
110	LESSTALK IN PARIS (IRE)	8	9	103	HARTNELL (GB)	8	2
110	LIGHTNING THUNDER (GB)	8	9	103	MORNING POST (GB)	8	2

Rating		st	lb
103	**MUSIC THEORY** (IRE)	8	2
103	**STUBBS** (IRE)	8	2
102	**DOUBLE POINT** (IRE)	8	1
102	**EXTORTIONIST** (IRE)	8	1
102	**FOUNTAIN OF YOUTH** (IRE)	8	1
102	**LANGAVAT** (IRE)	8	1
102	**MY CATCH** (IRE)	8	1
102	**STRATEGICAL** (USA)	8	1
102	**TOAST OF NEW YORK** (USA)	8	1
101	**AEOLUS** (GB)	8	0

Rating		st	lb
101	**PENIAPHOBIA** (IRE)	8	0
101	**SLEEPER KING** (IRE)	8	0
101	**THUNDER STRIKE** (GB)	8	0
100	**BLOCKADE** (IRE)	7	13
100	**HEART FOCUS** (IRE)	7	13
100	**MUSHIR** (GB)	7	13
100	**QAWAASEM** (IRE)	7	13
100	**SWEET ACCLAIM** (IRE)	7	13
100	**TRUE STORY** (GB)	7	13
100	**WIND FIRE** (USA)	7	13

LONGINES WORLD'S BEST RACEHORSE RANKINGS AND EUROPEAN THOROUGHBRED RANKINGS 2013

for three-year-olds rated 115 or greater by the IFHA World's Best Racehorse Rankings Conference. Horses rated 114-110 by the European Thoroughbred Rankings Conference do not constitute a part of the World's Best Racehorse Rankings. Those ratings were compiled on behalf of the European Pattern Committee

Rating		Trained
130	TREVE (FR)	FR
125	OLYMPIC GLORY (IRE)	GB
125	TORONADO (IRE)	GB
124	DAWN APPROACH (IRE)	IRE
124	INTELLO (GER)	GB
124	MAGICIAN (IRE)	GB
124	WILL TAKE CHARGE (USA)	USA
122	RULER OF THE WORLD (IRE)	GB
121	BEHOLDER (USA)	USA
121	KIZUNA (JPN)	JPN
120	FLINTSHIRE (GB)	FR
120	ORB (USA)	USA
120	PRINCESS OF SYLMAR (USA)	USA
120	TRADING LEATHER (IRE)	GB
119	GOLDENCENTS (USA)	USA
119	PALACE MALICE (USA)	USA
119	SKY LANTERN (IRE)	GB
119	VERRAZANO (USA)	USA
118	EPIPHANEIA (JPN)	JPN
118	HILLSTAR (GB)	GB
118	LEADING LIGHT (IRE)	GB
118	OXBOW (USA)	USA
118	PENGLAI PAVILION (USA)	FR
118	SHAMUS AWARD (AUS)	AUS
118	TOP NOTCH TONTO (IRE)	GB
117	BATTLE OF MARENGO (IRE)	IRE
117	FIXADOR (BRZ)	BRZ
117	KINGSBARNS (IRE)	IRE
117	LOGOTYPE (JPN)	JPN
117	MARS (IRE)	GB
117	MORENO (USA)	USA
117	POLANSKI (AUS)	AUS
117	ZOUSTAR (AUS)	AUS
116	DENIM AND RUBY (JPN)	JPN
116	DREAMING OF JULIA (USA)	USA
116	ECOLOGO (ARG)	ARG
116	FLOTILLA (FR)	FR
116	GALILEO ROCK (IRE)	GB
116	LIBERTARIAN (GB)	GB
116	OCOVANGO (GB)	GB
116	VANCOUVERITE (GB)	FR
115	APOLLO SONIC (USA)	JPN
115	AYAHUASCA (USA)	PER
115	BIZ THE NURSE (IRE)	ITY
115	CHICQUITA (IRE)	GB
115	CHOPIN (GER)	GER
115	CLOSE HATCHES (USA)	USA
115	COMPLACENT (AUS)	AUS
115	ESOTERIQUE (IRE)	GB
115	GALE FORCE TEN (GB)	IRE
115	GARSWOOD (GB)	GB
115	GOLDEN SOUL (USA)	USA

Rating		Trained
115	GUELPH (AUS)	AUS
115	IHTSAHYMN (AUS)	AUS
115	INTEGRAL (GB)	GB
115	ITSMYLUCKYDAY (USA)	USA
115	LONG JOHN (AUS)	AUS
115	LUCKY SPEED (IRE)	GER
115	MEISHO MAMBO (JPN)	JPN
115	MIDNIGHT LUCKY (USA)	USA
115	MORANDI (FR)	FR
115	NO JET LAG (USA)	USA
115	PEPTIDE AMAZON (JPN)	JPN
115	SKY HUNTER (GB)	FR
115	SPOSITO (CHI)	CHI
115	STYLE VENDOME (FR)	GB
115	TELESCOPE (IRE)	GB
115	TRES BLUE (IRE)	FR
115	UNLIMITED BUDGET (USA)	USA
115	VIOLENCE (USA)	USA
115	WINSILI (GB)	GB
114	DARWIN (USA)	GB
114	DASTARHON (IRE)	FR
114	DUNDONNELL (USA)	GB
114	FESTIVE CHEER (FR)	GB
114	MANNDAWI (FR)	GB
114	MONTIRIDGE (IRE)	GB
114	MSHAWISH (USA)	FR
114	RECKLESS ABANDON (GB)	GB
114	SECRET NUMBER (GB)	GB
114	TALENT (GB)	GB
114	TASADAY (USA)	FR
114	TRIPLE THREAT (FR)	GB
113	ALTERITE (FR)	FR
113	CAPE PERON (GB)	GB
113	EMPOLI (GER)	GER
113	HAVANA GOLD (IRE)	GB
113	IVANHOWE (GER)	GER
113	JUST PRETENDING (USA)	GB
113	MAPUTO (GB)	GB
113	MOVIESTA (USA)	GB
113	PILOTE (IRE)	FR
113	SEEK AGAIN (USA)	GB
113	TAWHID (GB)	GB
113	VENUS DE MILO (IRE)	GB
112	CAP O'RUSHES (GB)	GB
112	COUNT OF LIMONADE (IRE)	GB
112	EYE OF THE STORM (IRE)	GB
112	FOUNDRY (IRE)	GB
112	GLORY AWAITS (IRE)	GB
112	LINES OF BATTLE (USA)	GB
112	NORDVULKAN (GER)	GER
112	PACIFIC RIM (IRE)	GB
112	PEACE AT LAST (IRE)	GB

Rating	Trained
112 PEARL FLUTE (IRE)	GB
112 QUINZIEME MONARQUE (USA)	GER
112 SAN MARINO GREY (FR)	FR
112 SCINTILLULA (IRE)	GB
112 SUGAR BOY (IRE)	IRE
112 ZHIYI (USA)	GB
111 ANODIN (IRE)	GB
111 CHALNETTA (FR)	FR
111 CHARITY LINE (IRE)	ITY
111 DUTCH MASTERPIECE (GB)	GB
111 EBIYZA (IRE)	FR
111 GENGIS (FR)	FR
111 GLOBAL BANG (GER)	GER
111 HOT SNAP (GB)	GB
111 KENHOPE (FR)	GB
111 LOCH GARMAN (IRE)	IRE
111 NICHOLS CANYON (GB)	GB
111 NICOLOSIO (IRE)	GER
111 PEACE BURG (FR)	GB
111 PENELOPA (GB)	GER
111 RED LIPS (GER)	GER
111 REMOTE (GB)	GB
111 RIPOSTE (GB)	GB
111 SEUSSICAL (IRE)	GB

Rating	Trained
111 SILASOL (IRE)	FR
111 SPARKLING BEAM (IRE)	GB
111 SRUTHAN (IRE)	IRE
111 TABLEAUX (USA)	GB
111 VALIRANN (FR)	FR
111 VIF MONSIEUR (GER)	GER
111 VIZTORIA (IRE)	IRE
110 ADOYA (GER)	GER
110 BALTIC KNIGHT (IRE)	GB
110 BRAVODINO (USA)	GB
110 FLYING THE FLAG (IRE)	GB
110 JUST THE JUDGE (IRE)	GB
110 LIMARIO (GER)	GER
110 MONTCLAIR (IRE)	GB
110 ORION LOVE (GB)	GB
110 PARK REEL (FR)	FR
110 POMOLOGY (USA)	GB
110 SARATINO (GER)	GER
110 SAY (IRE)	GB
110 SHIKARPOUR (IRE)	GB
110 SINGING (FR)	FR
110 SUPERPLEX (FR)	GER
110 TOPAZE BLANCHE (IRE)	FR

OLDER HORSES 2013

for four-year-olds and up rated 115 or greater by the IFHA World's Best Racehorse Rankings Conference. Horses rated 114-110 by the European Thoroughbred Rankings Conference do not constitute a part of the World's Best Racehorse Rankings. Those ratings were compiled on behalf of the European Pattern Committee

Rating		Age	Trained	Rating		Age	Trained
130	BLACK CAVIAR (AUS)	7	AUS	119	SEA MOON (GB)	5	AUS
129	ORFEVRE (JPN)	5	JPN	119	SHEA SHEA (SAF)	6	UAE
129	WISE DAN (USA)	6	USA	119	SHONAN MIGHTY (JPN)	5	JPN
128	LORD KANALOA (JPN)	5	JPN	119	STRADA COLORATO (IRE)	4	HK
128	NOVELLIST (IRE)	4	GER	119	TOSEN JORDAN (JPN)	7	JPN
125	ANIMAL KINGDOM (USA)	5	USA	119	TOSEN RA (JPN)	5	JPN
125	MUCHO MACHO MAN (USA)	5	USA	118	BOBAN (AUS)	4	AUS
124	AL KAZEEM (GB)	5	GB	118	BUFFERING (AUS)	6	AUS
124	AMBITIOUS DRAGON (NZ)	7	HK	118	DUNBOYNE EXPRESS (IRE)	5	HK
124	DECLARATION OF WAR (USA)	4	IRE	118	GORDON LORD BYRON (IRE)	5	IRE
124	FARRH (GB)	5	GB	118	HAPPY TRAILS (AUS)	6	AUS
124	FORT LARNED (USA)	5	USA	118	HEAVY METAL (SAF)	5	SAF
124	GAME ON DUDE (USA)	6	USA	118	LITTLE MIKE (USA)	6	USA
124	GOLD SHIP (JPN)	4	JPN	118	REYNALDOTHEWIZARD (USA)	7	UAE
124	RAVE (IRE)	4	HK	118	SILENTIO (USA)	4	USA
124	ST NICHOLAS ABBEY (IRE)	6	IRE	118	SUCCESSFUL DAN (USA)	7	USA
123	CIRRUS DES AIGLES (FR)	7	FR	118	SUPER COOL (AUS)	4	AUS
123	JUST A WAY (JPN)	4	JPN	118	TIME AFTER TIME (AUS)	6	HK
123	MOONLIGHT CLOUD (GB)	5	FR	118	VAGABOND SHOES (IRE)	6	USA
123	POINT OF ENTRY (USA)	5	USA	118	VERY NICE NAME (FR)	4	QTR
123	THE FUGUE (GB)	4	GB	118	VEYRON (NZ)	8	NZ
122	ALL TOO HARD (AUS)	4	AUS	117	ADMIRE RAKTI (JPN)	5	JPN
122	ATLANTIC JEWEL (AUS)	5	AUS	117	ALTANO (GER)	7	GER
122	MAXIOS (GB)	5	FR	117	ARASIN (IRE)	6	HK
122	MUKHADRAM (GB)	4	GB	117	BEATEN UP (GB)	5	AUS
122	OCEAN PARK (NZ)	5	NZ	117	BEL SPRINTER (AUS)	6	AUS
122	PIERRO (AUS)	4	AUS	117	BOISTEROUS (USA)	6	USA
122	RELIABLE MAN (GB)	5	AUS	117	CAMELOT (GB)	4	IRE
122	RON THE GREEK (USA)	6	USA	117	DANK (GB)	4	GB
121	DUNDEEL (NZ)	4	NZ	117	DANON BALLADE (JPN)	5	JPN
121	FENOMENO (JPN)	4	JPN	117	DANON SHARK (JPN)	5	JPN
121	GLORIOUS DAYS (AUS)	6	HK	117	DUNADEN (FR)	7	FR
121	INDY POINT (ARG)	4	USA	117	ELUSIVE KATE (USA)	4	GB
121	LETHAL FORCE (GB)	4	GB	117	ENDOWING (IRE)	6	HK
121	OBVIOUSLY (IRE)	5	USA	117	FIVEANDAHALFSTAR (AUS)	4	AUS
121	PASTORIUS (GER)	4	GER	117	GENTILDONNA (JPN)	4	JPN
120	AKEED MOFEED (GB)	4	HK	117	GRANDEUR (IRE)	4	GB
120	EPAULETTE (AUS)	4	AUS	117	HAWKSPUR (AUS)	4	AUS
120	LUCKY NINE (IRE)	6	HK	117	HOKKO TARUMAE (JPN)	4	JPN
120	RED CADEAUX (GB)	7	GB	117	HUNTER'S LIGHT (IRE)	5	GB
120	SAHARA SKY (USA)	5	USA	117	JOY AND FUN (NZ)	10	HK
120	SOFT FALLING RAIN (SAF)	4	GB	117	MANDOUR (USA)	4	GB
120	VARIETY CLUB (SAF)	5	SAF	117	MOMENT OF CHANGE (AUS)	5	AUS
120	WHAT A WINTER (SAF)	6	SAF	117	MUFHASA (NZ)	9	NZ
120	ZA APPROVAL (USA)	5	USA	117	NEATICO (GER)	6	GER
119	AFRICAN STORY (GB)	6	UAE	117	PLANTEUR (IRE)	6	UAE
119	AL REP (IRE)	5	HK	117	POINTS OFFTHEBENCH (USA)	4	USA
119	BIG BLUE KITTEN (USA)	5	USA	117	RAIN AFFAIR (AUS)	6	AUS
119	CROSS TRAFFIC (USA)	4	USA	117	SAJJHAA (GB)	6	GB
119	DOMINANT (IRE)	5	HK	117	SHOOT OUT (AUS)	7	AUS
119	EISHIN FLASH (JPN)	6	JPN	117	SILVER MAX (USA)	4	USA
119	FIORENTE (IRE)	5	AUS	117	SOCIETY ROCK (IRE)	6	GB
119	FLAT OUT (USA)	7	USA	117	SOLZHENITSYN (NZ)	5	AUS
119	GRAYDAR (USA)	4	USA	117	SOY CARAMBOLO (ARG)	6	ARG
119	MENTAL (AUS)	5	UAE	117	STEINBECK (IRE)	6	HK
119	PORTUS BLENDIUM (USA)	7	HK	117	TAC DE BOISTRON (FR)	6	GB
119	ROYAL DELTA (USA)	5	USA	117	THE APACHE (SAF)	6	UAE
119	SAMAREADY (AUS)	4	AUS	117	TOKEI HALO (JPN)	4	JPN

Rating	Age	Trained
117 TWILIGHT ECLIPSE (USA)	4	USA
117 VOLEUSE DE COEURS (IRE)	4	GB
117 XTENSION (IRE)	6	HK
117 YOUR SONG (AUS)	4	AUS
116 AFSARE (GB)	6	GB
116 ALJAMAAHEER (IRE)	4	GB
116 ALPHA (USA)	4	USA
116 BELSHAZZAR (JPN)	5	JPN
116 DAIWA MAGGIORE (JPN)	4	JPN
116 DATA LINK (USA)	5	USA
116 EARL OF TINSDAL (GER)	5	GER
116 EKTIHAAM (IRE)	4	GB
116 ERNEST HEMINGWAY (IRE)	4	GB
116 FEUERBLITZ (GER)	4	GB
116 FORETELLER (GB)	6	AUS
116 GRAPE BRANDY (JPN)	5	JPN
116 JACKSON (SAF)	5	SAF
116 JERANIMO (USA)	7	USA
116 JOSHUA TREE (IRE)	6	GB
116 JUSTIN PHILLIP (USA)	5	USA
116 LAST GUNFIGHTER (USA)	4	USA
116 LELOUCH (JPN)	5	JPN
116 MARKETING MIX (CAN)	5	USA
116 MONTON (AUS)	7	AUS
116 MOURAYAN (AUS)	7	AUS
116 NASHVILLE (NZ)	5	NZ
116 PACKING COMMANDER (AUS)	7	HK
116 PRIVATE ZONE (CAN)	4	USA
116 REAL SOLUTION (USA)	5	USA
116 REAL SPECIALIST (NZ)	6	HK
116 ROYAL DESCENT (AUS)	4	AUS
116 SEAL OF APPROVAL (GB)	4	GB
116 SECRET CIRCLE (USA)	5	USA
116 STREAMA (AUS)	5	AUS
116 SUPER EASY (NZ)	5	SIN
116 TAKE CHARGE INDY (USA)	4	USA
116 THOMAS CHIPPENDALE (IRE)	4	GB
116 ULTIMATE EAGLE (USA)	4	USA
116 WILD COCO (GER)	5	GB
116 WIN VARIATION (JPN)	5	JPN
115 AEROSOL (BRZ)	4	BRZ
115 AMIRA'S PRINCE (IRE)	4	USA
115 APPEARANCE (AUS)	5	AUS
115 ARTE POP (ARG)	4	ARG
115 AWAIT THE DAWN (USA)	6	UAE
115 BALMONT MAST (IRE)	5	IRE
115 BETTER LUCKY (USA)	4	USA
115 BLAZING SPEED (GB)	4	HK
115 BOURBON COURAGE (USA)	4	USA
115 BRENDAN BRACKAN (IRE)	4	IRE
115 BRIGHT THOUGHT (USA)	4	USA
115 CAZALS (IRE)	5	HK
115 CENTRE COURT (USA)	4	USA
115 CLUSTER OF STARS (USA)	4	USA
115 COIL (USA)	5	USA
115 DALKALA (USA)	4	FR
115 DANDINO (GB)	6	GB
115 DANLEIGH (AUS)	10	AUS
115 DARK COVE (USA)	6	USA
115 DI GIORGIO (ARG)	4	ARG
115 DISCREET DANCER (USA)	4	USA
115 DREAM VALENTINO (JPN)	6	JPN
115 DUX SCHOLAR (GB)	5	UAE/CHR
115 EAGLE REGIMENT (AUS)	6	HK
115 EGG DROP (USA)	4	USA
115 ESPOIR CITY (JPN)	8	JPN
115 FINAL TOUCH (NZ)	6	NZ

Rating	Age	Trained
115 FONTELINA (AUS)	5	AUS
115 FORTE DEI MARMI (GB)	7	CAN
115 GREGORIAN (IRE)	4	GB
115 GROUPIE DOLL (USA)	5	USA
115 HAKUSAN MOON (JPN)	4	JPN
115 JAKKALBERRY (IRE)	7	GB
115 JIMMY CREED (USA)	4	USA
115 JOYFUL VICTORY (CAN)	5	USA
115 KELINNI (IRE)	5	AUS
115 LAUGH TRACK (USA)	4	USA
115 LAUGHING (IRE)	5	USA
115 LES BEAUFS (FR)	4	FR
115 LINTON (AUS)	7	AUS
115 LUCKYGRAY (AUS)	6	AUS
115 MANIGHAR (FR)	7	AUS
115 MAWINGO (GER)	5	SIN
115 MIZDIRECTION (USA)	5	USA
115 MORE JOYOUS (NZ)	7	AUS
115 MOUNT ATHOS (IRE)	6	GB
115 MR BIG (AUS)	5	SIN
115 MUSHREQ (AUS)	5	UAE
115 NORZITA (NZ)	4	AUS
115 PAYNTER (USA)	4	USA
115 PROISIR (AUS)	4	AUS
115 PUISSANCE DE LUNE (IRE)	5	AUS
115 REBEL DANE (AUS)	4	AUS
115 RED TRACER (AUS)	6	AUS
115 SACRED FALLS (NZ)	4	AUS
115 SAGA DREAM (FR)	7	FR
115 SANGSTER (NZ)	5	NZ
115 SEISMOS (IRE)	5	GER
115 SESSIONS (AUS)	4	AUS
115 SHAMEXPRESS (NZ)	4	GB
115 SIDE GLANCE (GB)	6	GB
115 SLADE POWER (IRE)	4	GB
115 SLIM SHADEY (GB)	5	USA
115 SOLE POWER (GB)	6	IRE
115 STEPHANIE'S KITTEN (USA)	4	USA
115 SUGGESTIVE BOY (ARG)	5	USA
115 SUMMER FRONT (USA)	4	USA
115 SUPER NINETYSEVEN (AUS)	4	SIN
115 SURVIVED (NZ)	4	NZ
115 TIGHTEND TOUCHDOWN (USA)	4	USA
115 TIZ FLIRTATIOUS (USA)	5	USA
115 TOYDINI (AUS)	4	AUS
115 TRADE STORM (GB)	5	GB
115 UNBRIDLED COMMAND (USA)	4	USA
115 UNIVERSAL (IRE)	4	GB
115 WINNING PRIZE (ARG)	4	USA
115 WONDER ACUTE (JPN)	7	JPN
115 XANADU (NZ)	5	NZ
114 CAMBORNE (GB)	5	GB
114 DANADANA (IRE)	5	GB
114 DOMESIDE (GB)	7	SPA
114 DON BOSCO (FR)	6	FR
114 FIESOLANA (IRE)	4	IRE
114 GIROLAMO (GER)	4	GER
114 JACK DEXTER (GB)	4	GB
114 JWALA (GB)	4	GB
114 KRYPTON FACTOR (USA)	5	UAE
114 LOST IN THE MOMENT (IRE)	6	GB
114 MAAREK (GB)	6	IRE
114 MEANDRE (FR)	5	CHR
114 MULL OF KILLOUGH (IRE)	7	GB
114 NYMPHEA (IRE)	4	GER
114 ORSINO (GER)	6	GER
114 ROMANTICA (GB)	4	FR

Rating	Age	Trained	Rating	Age	Trained
114 ROYAL DIAMOND (IRE)	7	IRE	111 EMIRATES QUEEN (GB)	4	GB
114 SIMENON (IRE)	6	GB	111 FITFUL SKIES (IRE)	4	FR
114 THISTLE BIRD (GB)	5	GB	111 HIGHLAND COLORI (IRE)	5	GB
114 TROPICS (USA)	5	GB	111 KINGSGATE NATIVE (IRE)	8	GB
113 AHZEEMAH (IRE)	4	GB	111 LA COLLINA (IRE)	4	IRE
113 BROWN PANTHER (GB)	5	GB	111 LA POMME D'AMOUR (GB)	5	FR
113 CATCALL (FR)	4	FR	111 LAST TRAIN (GB)	4	FR
113 CHIGUN (GB)	4	GB	111 MAIN SEQUENCE (USA)	4	GB
113 CITY STYLE (USA)	7	GB	111 MAINSAIL (GB)	4	FR
113 DAVID LIVINGSTON (IRE)	4	GB	111 MELEAGROS (IRE)	4	GB
113 GIANT SANDMAN (IRE)	6	GB	111 MYASUN (FR)	6	FR
113 GLEN'S DIAMOND (GB)	5	GB	111 NOBLE MISSION (GB)	4	GB
113 HAMISH MCGONAGALL (GB)	8	GB	111 PREMIO LOCO (USA)	9	GB
113 HARRIS TWEED (GB)	6	GB	111 SHAMALGAN (FR)	6	FR
113 IVORY LAND (FR)	6	FR	111 SOFAST (FR)	4	FR
113 MIBLISH (GB)	4	GB	111 SOVEREIGN DEBT (IRE)	4	GB
113 NORSE KING (FR)	4	FR	111 SUN CENTRAL (IRE)	4	GB
113 NOW WE CAN (GB)	4	FR	111 VEDELAGO (IRE)	4	ITY
113 OPPOSITE (IRE)	4	FR	111 VEREMA (FR)	4	FR
113 PARISH HALL (IRE)	4	IRE	111 WALDPARK (GER)	5	GER
113 PENITENT (GB)	7	GB	111 WILD WOLF (GB)	4	ITY
113 PETIT CHEVALIER (FR)	5	GER	111 WILLING FOE (USA)	6	GB
113 SEA SIREN (AUS)	5	IRE	111 ZAZOU (GER)	6	GER
113 SLOW PACE (USA)	5	FR	110 ADRIANA (GER)	5	GER
113 TOP TRIP (GB)	4	FR	110 AMERICAN DEVIL (FR)	4	FR
113 ZINABAA (FR)	8	FR	110 ANSGAR (IRE)	5	GB
112 ALONG CAME CASEY (IRE)	5	GB	110 BIOGRAPHER (GB)	4	GB
112 AMARILLO (IRE)	4	GER	110 CASPAR NETSCHER (GB)	4	GB
112 AMARON (GB)	4	GER	110 CAUCUS (GB)	6	GB
112 COMBAT ZONE (IRE)	7	GER	110 DESERT BLANC (GB)	5	FR
112 ESTIMATE (IRE)	4	GB	110 EDUCATE (GB)	4	GB
112 ETON FOREVER (IRE)	6	GB	110 FORGOTTEN VOICE (IRE)	8	GB
112 FELICIAN (GER)	5	GER	110 GIFTED GIRL (IRE)	4	GB
112 FENCING (USA)	4	GB	110 GLOBAL THRILL (GB)	4	GER
112 FRENCH NAVY (GB)	5	GB	110 GUEST OF HONOUR (IRE)	4	GB
112 GEREON (GER)	5	GER	110 HAYA LANDA (FR)	5	FR
112 GIOFRA (GB)	5	FR	110 HEERAAT (GB)	4	GB
112 GOING SOMEWHERE (BRZ)	4	FR	110 HIGH JINX (IRE)	5	GB
112 GRACE LADY (FR)	4	FR	110 INIS MEAIN (USA)	6	GB
112 LOCKWOOD (GB)	4	GB	110 LILY'S ANGEL (IRE)	4	GB
112 PINTURICCHIO (IRE)	5	FR	110 PEARL SECRET (GB)	4	GB
112 REMUS DE LA TOUR (FR)	4	FR	110 PIRIKA (FR)	5	FR
112 ROYAL EMPIRE (IRE)	4	GB	110 POLLYANA (IRE)	4	FR
112 SADDLER'S ROCK (IRE)	5	IRE	110 PRINCE BISHOP (IRE)	6	GB
112 STELLAR WIND (JPN)	4	JPN	110 PRODUCER (GB)	4	GB
112 TIMES UP (GB)	7	GB	110 RICH COAST (GB)	5	GB
112 TRUMPET MAJOR (IRE)	4	GB	110 ROMANTIC WAVE (IRE)	4	ITY
112 WIGMORE HALL (IRE)	6	GB	110 SMOKING SUN (USA)	4	FR
111 BELLE DE CRECY (IRE)	4	IRE	110 SOMMERABEND (GB)	6	GER
111 COLOUR VISION (FR)	5	GB	110 SPIRIT QUARTZ (IRE)	5	GB
111 DANCE MOVES (GB)	5	FR	110 STIPULATE (GB)	4	GB
111 DUNTLE (IRE)	4	IRE	110 SWISS SPIRIT (GB)	4	GB

RACEFORM CHAMPIONS 2013
THREE-YEAR-OLDS AND UP

5f-6f

BLACK CAVIAR	129	GORDON LORD BYRON	121
LORD KANALOA	129	LUCKY NINE	121
LETHAL FORCE	124	MENTAL	121
SHEA SHEA	123	BUFFERING	120
SOCIETY ROCK	122	GOLDENCENTS	120
BEL SPRINTER	121	JOY AND FUN	120
EPAULETTE	121	SOLE POWER	120

7f-9f

TORONADO	129	FARHH	126
DAWN APPROACH	128	CROSS TRAFFIC	125
FORT LARNED	128	MOONLIGHT CLOUD	125
MUCHO MACHO MAN	128	SOFT FALLING RAIN	125
WILL TAKE CHARGE	128	POINT OF ENTRY	124
GAME ON DUDE	127	SUCCESSFUL DAN	124
OLYMPIC GLORY	127	VERRAZANO	124

10f-12f

TREVE	131	ST NICHOLAS ABBEY	126
FARHH	128	INTELLO	125
GAME ON DUDE	128	MUCHO MACHO MAN	125
NOVELLIST	128	ORFEVRE	125
AL KAZEEM	126	RULER OF THE WORLD	125
CIRRUS DES AIGLES	126	ANIMAL KINGDOM	124
GOLD SHIP	126	DECLARATION OF WAR	124
RON THE GREEK	126	WILL TAKE CHARGE	124

13+f

FENOMENO	123	HARRIS TWEED	118
RED CADEAUX	119	LEADING LIGHT	118
TAC DE BOISTRON	119	LES BEAUFS	118
EPIPHANEIA	118	VOLEUSE DE COEURS	118

RACEFORM CHAMPIONS 2013
TWO-YEAR-OLDS

5f-6f

NO NAY NEVER	117
ASTAIRE	116
HOT STREAK	115
SUDIRMAN	115
WAR COMMAND	115

BIG TIME	113
KIRAM	113
NOOZHOH CANARIAS	113
VORDA	113

7f+

TOORMORE	122
KINGSTON HILL	119
AUSTRALIA	118
WAR COMMAND	118
KARAKONTIE	115
OUTSTRIP	115

CABLE BAY	115
GIOVANNI BOLDINI	115
NOOZHOH CANARIAS	115
PRINCE GIBRALTAR	115
SUDIRMAN	115

NOW PRECISELY TWICE AS GOOD AS ANY OTHER BETTING APP

That's just cold hard maths.
The Racing Post Mobile App
now gives you the power to
place a bet through *Ladbrokes*
as well as *William Hill*.
That's two great bookies,
in one great app.

RACING POST

MEDIAN TIMES 2013

The following Raceform median times are used in the calculation of the Split Second speed figures. They represent a true average time for the distance, which has been arrived at after looking at the winning times for all races over each distance within the past five years, except for those restricted to two or three-year-olds.

Some current race distances have been omitted as they have not yet had a sufficient number of races run over them to produce a reliable average time.

ASCOT

5f 1m 0.50	1m Straight 1m 40.80	2m 3m 29.00
6f 1m 14.50	1m 2f 2m 7.40	2m 4f 4m 24.80
7f 1m 27.60	1m 4f 2m 32.50	2m 5f 159y 4m 49.40
1m Round 1m 40.70		

AYR

5f 59.40	1m 1m 43.80	1m 5f 13y 2m 54.00
6f 1m 12.40	1m 1f 20y 1m 57.50	1m 7f 3m 20.40
7f 50y 1m 33.40	1m 2f 2m 12.00	1m 1f 105y 3m 59.70

BATH

5f 11y 1m 2.50	1m 2f 46y 2m 11.00	1m 5f 22y 2m 52.00
5f 161y 1m 11.20	1m 3f 144y 2m 30.60	2m 1f 34y 3m 51.90
1m 5y 1m 40.80		

BEVERLEY

5f 1m 3.50	1m 100y 1m 47.60	1m 4f 16y 2m 39.80
7f 100y 1m 33.80	1m 1f 207y 2m 7.00	2m 35y 3m 39.80

BRIGHTON

5f 59y 1m 2.30	6f 209y 1m 23.10	1m 1f 209y 2m 3.60
5f 213y 1m 10.20	7f 214y 1m 36.00	1m 3f 196y 2m 32.70

CARLISLE

5f 1m 0.80	7f 200y 1m 40.00	1m 6f 32y 3m 7.50
5f 193y 1m 13.70	1m 1f 61y 1m 57.60	2m 1f 52y 3m 53.00
6f 192y 1m 27.10	1m 3f 107y 2m 23.10	

CATTERICK

5f 59.80	7f 1m 27.00	1m 5f 175y 3m 3.60
5f 212y 1m 13.60	1m 3f 214y 2m 38.90	1m 7f 177y 3m 32.00

CHEPSTOW

5f 16y 59.30	1m 14y 1m 36.20	2m 49y 3m 38.90
6f 16y 1m 12.00	1m 2f 36y 2m 10.60	2m 2f 4m 3.60
7f 16y 1m 23.20	1m 4f 23y 2m 39.00	

CHESTER

5f 16y 1m 1.00	7f 122y 1m 33.80	1m 5f 89y 2m 52.70
5f 110y 1m 6.20	1m 2f 75y 2m 11.20	1m 6f 91y 3m 7.00
6f 18y 1m 13.80	1m 3f 79y 2m 24.80	1m 7f 195y 3m 28.00
7f 2y 1m 26.50	1m 4f 66y 2m 38.50	2m 2f 147y 4m 4.80

DONCASTER

5f 1m 0.50	7f 1m 26.30	1m 4f 2m 34.90
5f 140y 1m 8.80	1m Straight 1m 39.30	1m 6f 132y 3m 7.40
6f 1m 13.60	1m Round 1m 39.70	2m 110y 3m 40.40
6f 110y 1m 19.90	1m 2f 60y 2m 9.40	2m 2f 3m 55.00

EPSOM

5f 55.70	7f 1m 23.30	1m 2f 18y 2m 9.70
6f 1m 9.40	1m 114y 1m 46.10	1m 4f 10y 2m 38.90

FFOS LAS

5f 58.30	1m 2f 2m 9.40	1m 6f 3m 3.80
6f 1m 10.00	1m 4f 2m 37.40	2m 3m 30.00
1m 1m 41.00		

GOODWOOD

5f 1m 0.20	1m 1f 1m 56.30	1m 6f 3m 3.60
6f 1m 12.20	1m 1f 192y 2m 8.10	2m 3m 29.00
7f 1m 27.00	1m 3f 2m 26.50	2m 5f 4m 31.00
1m 1m 39.90	1m 4f 2m 38.40	

HAMILTON

5f 4y 4m 31.00	1m 1f 36y 1m 59.70	1m 4f 17y 2m 38.60
6f 5y 1m 12.20	1m 3f 16y 2m 25.60	1m 5f 9y 2m 53.90
1m 65y 1m 48.40		

HAYDOCK

5f 1m 0.80	7f 1m 30.70	1m 3f 200y 2m 33.80
5fl 1m 0.80	1m 1m 43.70	1m 6f 3m 2.00
6f 1m 13.80	1m 2f 95y 2m 15.50	2m 45y 3m 34.30
6fl 1m 13.80		

KEMPTON (A.W)

5f 1m 0.50	1m 1m 39.80	1m 4f 2m 34.50
6f 1m 13.10	1m 2f 2m 8.00	2m 3m 30.10
7f 1m 26.00	1m 3f 2m 21.90	

LEICESTER

5f 2y 3m 30.10	7f 9y 1m 26.20	1m 1f 218y 2m 7.90
5f 218y 1m 13.00	1m 60y 1m 45.10	1m 3f 183y 2m 33.90

LINGFIELD

5f 58.20	7f 140y 1m 32.30	1m 3f 106y 2m 31.50
6f 1m 11.20	1m 1f 1m 56.60	1m 6f 3m 10.00
7f 1m 23.30	1m 2f 2m 10.50	2m 3m 34.80

LINGFIELD (A.W)

5f 58.80	1m 1m 38.20	1m 5f 2m 46.00
6f 1m 11.90	1m 2f 2m 6.60	2m 3m 25.70
7f 1m 24.80	1m 4f 2m 33.00	

MUSSELBURGH

5f 1m 0.40	1m 1f 1m 53.90	1m 6f 3m 5.30
5f 30y 1m 29.00	1m 4f 100y 2m 42.00	2m 3m 33.50
1m 1m 41.20	1m 5f 2m 52.00	

NEWBURY

5f 34y 1m 1.40	1m Straight 1m 39.70	1m 3f 5y 2m 21.20
6f 8y 1m 13.00	1m 7y Round 1m 38.70	1m 4f 5y 2m 35.50
7f 110y 1m 19.30	1m 1f 1m 55.50	1m 5f 61y 2m 52.00
7f Straight 1m 25.70	1m 2f 6y 2m 8.80	2m 3m 32.00

NEWCASTLE

5f 1m 1.10	1m Round 1m 45.30	1m 4f 93y 2m 45.60
6f 1m 14.60	1m 3y Straight 1m 43.40	1m 6f 97y 3m 11.30
7f 1m 27.80	1m 2f 32y 2m 11.90	2m 19y 3m 39.40

NEWMARKET (ROWLEY MILE)

5f...............59.10	1m 1f...............1m 51.70	1m 6f...............2m 57.00
6f...............1m 12.20	1m 2f...............2m 5.80	2m...............3m 30.50
7f...............1m 25.40	1m 4f...............2m 32.00	2m 2f...............3m 52.00
1m...............1m 38.60		

NEWMARKET (JULY COURSE)

5f...............59.10	1m...............1m 40.00	1m 5f...............2m 44.00
6f...............1m 12.50	1m 2f...............2m 5.50	1m 6f 175y...............3m 8.40
7f...............1m 25.70	1m 4f...............2m 32.90	2m 24y...............3m 27.00

NOTTINGHAM

5f 13y...............1m 1.50	1m 75yl...............1m 49.00	1m 6f 15y...............3m 7.00
5f 13yl...............1m 1.50	1m 2f 50y...............2m 14.30	1m 6f 15yl...............3m 7.00
6f 15y...............1m 14.70	1m 2f 50yl...............2m 14.30	2m 9y...............3m 34.50
1m 75y...............1m 49.00		

PONTEFRACT

5f...............1m 3.30	1m 2f 6y...............2m 13.70	2m 1f 216y...............3m 56.20
6f...............1m 16.90	1m 4f 8y...............2m 40.80	2m 5f 122y...............4m 51.00
1m 4y...............1m 45.90	2m 1f 22y...............3m 44.60	

REDCAR

5f...............58.60	1m...............1m 36.60	1m 2f...............2m 7.10
6f...............1m 11.80	1m Round...............1m 36.60	1m 6f 19y...............3m 4.70
7f...............1m 24.50	1m 1f...............1m 53.00	2m 4y...............3m 31.40

RIPON

5f...............3m 31.40	1m 1f...............1m 54.70	1m 4f 10y...............2m 36.702m
6f...............1m 13.00	1m 1f 170y...............2m 5.40	3m 31.80
1m...............1m 41.40		

SALISBURY

5f...............1m 1.00	1m...............1m 43.50	1m 4f...............2m 38.00
6f...............1m 14.80	1m 1f 198y...............2m 9.90	1m 6f 21y...............3m 7.40
6f 212y...............1m 28.60		

SANDOWN

5f 6y...............1m 1.60	1m 1f...............1m 55.70	1m 6f...............3m 4.50
7f 16y...............1m 29.50	1m 2f 7y...............2m 10.50	2m 78y...............3m 38.70
1m 14y...............1m 43.30		

SOUTHWELL (A.W)

5f...............59.70	1m...............1m 43.70	1m 6f...............3m 8.30
6f...............1m 16.50	1m 3f...............2m 28.00	2m...............3m 45.50
7f...............1m 30.30	1m 4f...............2m 41.00	

THIRSK

5f...............59.60	7f...............1m 27.20	1m 4f...............2m 36.20
6f...............1m 12.70	1m...............1m 40.10	2m...............3m 28.30

WARWICK

5f...............59.60	7f 26y...............1m 24.60	1m 4f 134y...............2m 44.60
5f 110y...............1m 5.90	1m 22y...............1m 41.00	1m 6f 213y...............3m 19.00
6f...............1m 11.80	1m 2f 188y...............2m 21.10	

WINDSOR

5f 10y...............1m 0.30	1m 67y...............1m 44.70	1m 3f 135y...............2m 29.50
6f...............1m 13.00	1m 2f 7y...............2m 8.70	

WOLVERHAMPTON (A.W)

5f 20y................1m 2.30	1m 141y................1m 50.50	1m 5f 194y................3m 6.00
5f 216y................1m 15.00	1m 1f 103y................2m 1.70	2m 119y................3m 41.80
7f 32y................1m 29.60	1m 4f 50y................2m 41.10	

YARMOUTH

5f 43y................1m 2.70	1m 3y................1m 40.60	1m 3f 101y................2m 28.70
6f 3y................1m 14.40	1m 1f................1m 55.80	1m 6f 17y................3m 7.60
7f 3y................1m 26.60	1m 2f 21y................2m 10.50	2m................3m 32.40

YORK

5f................59.30	1m................1m 39.00	1m 6f................3m 0.20
5f 89y................1m 4.10	1m 208y................1m 52.00	2m 88y................3m 34.50
6f................1m 11.90	1m 2f 88y................2m 12.50	2m 2f................3m 55.40
7f................1m 25.30	1m 4f................2m 33.20	

MULTIPLE
MULTIPLE
MULTIPLE
MULTIPLE
MULTIPLE
MULTIPLE
MULTIPLE
MULTIPLE
MULTIPLE
MULTIPLE
MULTIPLE
MULTIPLE
MULTIPLE
BETS

SAMSUNG

RACING POST MOBILE APP

You asked for it, so we're giving it to you — multiple bets on the Racing Post Mobile App with William Hill and Ladbrokes.

With a multitude of multiples to choose from, the chance for a bigger payout has never been so close to hand.

RACING POST

RACEFORM RECORD TIMES (FLAT)

ASCOT

DISTANCE	TIME	AGE	WEIGHT	GOING	HORSE	DATE		
5f	58.80 secs	2	9-1	Good To Firm	**NO NAY NEVER**	Jun	20	2013
5f	57.44 secs	6	9-1	Good To Firm	**MISS ANDRETTI**	Jun	19	2007
6f	1m 12.46	2	9-1	Good To Firm	**HENRYTHENAVIGATOR**	Jun	19	2007
6f	1m 11.50	3	9-10	Good To Firm	**MINCE**	Aug	11	2012
7f	1m 27.9	2	7-12	Good To Firm	**RELATIVE ORDER**	Aug	11	2007
7f	1m 24.28	4	8-11	Good To Firm	**GALICIAN**	July	27	2013
1m (Rnd)	1m 39.55	2	8-12	Good	**JOSHUA TREE**	Sep	26	2009
1m (Rnd)	1m 38.32	3	9-0	Good	**GHANAATI**	Jun	19	2009
1m (Str)	1m 37.16	5	9-0	Good To Firm	**INVISIBLE MAN**	Jun	16	2010
1m 2f	2m 02.52	5	9-3	Good	**CIRRUS DES AIGLES**	Oct	15	2011
1m 4f	2m 24.60	4	9-7	Good	**NOVELLIST**	July	27	2013
2m	3m 24.13	3	9-1	Good	**HOLBERG**	May	2	2007
2m 4f	4m 16.92	6	9-2	Good To Firm	**RITE OF PASSAGE**	Jun	17	2010
2m 5f 159y	4m 47.79	7	9-2	Good To Firm	**BERGO**	Jun	19	2010

AYR

DISTANCE	TIME	AGE	WEIGHT	GOING	HORSE	DATE		
5f	56.9 secs	2	8-11	Good	**BOOGIE STREET**	Sep	18	2003
5f	55.68 secs	3	8-11	Good To Firm	**LOOK BUSY**	Jun	21	2008
6f	1m 09.7	2	7-10	Good	**SIR BERT**	Sep	17	1969
6f	1m 08.37	5	8-6	Good To Firm	**MAISON DIEU**	Jun	21	2008
7f 50y	1m 28.9	2	9-0	Good	**TAFAAHUM**	Sep	19	2003
7f 50y	1m 28.07	5	9-0	Good To Firm	**GINGER JACK**	May	30	2012
1m	1m 39.2	2	9-0	Good To Firm	**KRIBENSIS**	Sep	17	1986
1m	1m 36.0	4	7-13	Firm	**SUFI**	Sep	16	1959
1m 1f 20y	1m 50.3	4	9-3	Good	**RETIREMENT**	Sep	19	2003
1m 2f	2m 04.0	4	9-9	Good	**ENDLESS HALL**	July	17	2000
1m 5f 13y	2m 45.8	4	9-7	Good To Firm	**EDEN'S CLOSE**	Sep	18	1993
1m 7f	3m 13.1	3	9-4	Good	**ROMANY RYE**	Sep	19	1991
2m 1f 105y	3m 45.0	4	6-13	Good	**CURRY**	Sep	16	1955

BATH

DISTANCE	TIME	AGE	WEIGHT	GOING	HORSE	DATE		
5f 11y	59.50 secs	2	9-2	Firm	**AMOUR PROPRE**	July	24	2008
5f 11y	58.75 secs	3	8-12	Firm	**ENTICING**	May	1	2007
5f 161y	1m 08.7	2	8-12	Firm	**QALAHARI**	July	24	2008
5f 161y	1m 08.1	6	9-0	Firm	**MADRACO**	May	22	1989
1m 5y	1m 39.7	2	8-9	Firm	**CASUAL LOOK**	Sep	16	2002
1m 5y	1m 37.2	5	8-12	Good To Firm	**ADOBE**	Jun	17	2000
1m 5y	1m 37.2	3	8-7	Firm	**ALASHA**	Aug	18	2012
1m 2f 46y	2m 05.6	3	9-0	Good To Firm	**CONNOISSEUR BAY**	May	29	1998
1m 3f 144y	2m 25.74	3	9-0	Hard	**TOP OF THE CHARTS**	Sep	8	2005
1m 5f 22y	2m 47.2	4	10-0	Firm	**FLOWN**	Aug	13	1991
2m 1f 34y	3m 43.4	6	7-9	Firm	**YAHESKA**	Jun	14	2003

BEVERLEY

DISTANCE	TIME	AGE	WEIGHT	GOING	HORSE	DATE		
5f	1m 00.89	2	8-12	Good To Firm	LANGAVAT	Jun	8	2013
5f	1m 00.1	4	9-5	Firm	PIC UP STICKS	Apr	16	2003
7f 100y	1m 31.1	2	9-0	Firm	MAJAL	July	30	1991
7f 100y	1m 29.5	3	7-8	Firm	WHO'S TEF	July	30	1991
1m 100y	1m 43.3	2	9-0	Firm	ARDEN	Sep	24	1986
1m 100y	1m 42.2	3	8-4	Firm	LEGAL CASE	Jun	14	1989
1m 1f 207y	2m 01.00	3	9-7	Good To Firm	EASTERN ARIA	Aug	29	2009
1m 4f 16y	2m 34.88	6	10-0	Firm	WEE CHARLIE CASTLE	Aug	30	2009
2m 35y	3m 29.5	4	9-2	Good To Firm	RUSHEN RAIDER	Aug	14	1996

BRIGHTON

DISTANCE	TIME	AGE	WEIGHT	GOING	HORSE	DATE		
5f 59y	1m.00.1	2	9-0	Firm	BID FOR BLUE	May	6	1993
5f 59y	59.3 secs	3	8-9	Firm	PLAY HEVER GOLF	May	26	1993
5f 213y	1m 08.1	2	8-9	Firm	SONG MIST	July	16	1996
5f 213y	1m 07.3	3	8-9	Firm	THIRD PARTY	Jun	3	1997
5f 213y	1m 07.3	5	9-1	Good To Firm	BLUNDELL LANE	May	4	2000
7f 214y	1m 32.8	2	9-7	Firm	ASIAN PETE	Oct	3	1989
7f 214y	1m 30.5	5	8-11	Firm	MYSTIC RIDGE	May	27	1999
1m 1f 209y	2m 04.7	2	9-0	Good To Soft	ESTEEMED MASTER	Nov	2	2001
1m 1f 209y	1m 57.2	3	9-0	Firm	GET THE MESSAGE	Apr	30	1984
1m 3f 196y	2m 25.8	4	8-2	Firm	NEW ZEALAND	July	4	1985

CARLISLE

DISTANCE	TIME	AGE	WEIGHT	GOING	HORSE	DATE		
5f	1m 00.1	2	8-5	Firm	LA TORTUGA	Aug	2	1999
5f	58.8 secs	3	9-8	Good To Firm	ESATTO	Aug	21	2002
5f 193y	1m 12.45	2	9-6	Good To Firm	MUSICAL GUEST	Sep	11	2005
5f 193y	1m 10.83	4	9-0	Good To Firm	BO MCGINTY	Sep	11	2005
6f 192y	1m 24.3	3	8-9	Good To Firm	MARJURITA	Aug	21	2002
7f 200y	1m 37.34	5	9-7	Good To Firm	HULA BALLEW	Aug	17	2005
1m 1f 61y	1m 53.8	3	9-0	Firm	LITTLE JIMBOB	Jun	14	2004
1m 3f 107y	2m 22.00	7	9-5	Good To Firm	TARTAN GIGHA	Jun	4	2012
1m 3f 206y	2m 29.13	5	9-8	Good To Firm	TEMPSFORD	Sep	19	2005
1m 6f 32y	3m 02.2	6	8-10	Firm	EXPLOSIVE SPEED	May	26	1994

CATTERICK

DISTANCE	TIME	AGE	WEIGHT	GOING	HORSE	DATE		
5f	57.6 secs	2	9-0	Firm	H HARRISON	Oct	8	2002
5f	57.1 secs	4	8-7	Firm	KABCAST	July	7	1989
5f 212y	1m 11.4	2	9-4	Firm	CAPTAIN NICK	July	11	1978
5f 212y	1m 09.8	9	8-13	Good To Firm	SHARP HAT	May	30	2003
7f	1m 24.1	2	8-11	Firm	LINDA'S FANTASY	Sep	18	1982
7f	1m 22.5	6	8-7	Firm	DIFFERENTIAL	May	31	2003
1m 3f 214y	2m 30.5	3	8-8	Good To Firm	RAHAF	May	30	2003
1m 5f 175y	2m 54.8	3	8-5	Firm	GERYON	May	31	1984
1m 7f 177y	3m 20.8	4	7-11	Firm	BEAN BOY	July	8	1982

CHEPSTOW

DISTANCE	TIME	AGE	WEIGHT	GOING	HORSE	DATE	
5f 16y	57.6 secs	2	8-11	Firm	MICRO LOVE	July	8	1986
5f 16y	56.8 secs	3	8-4	Firm	TORBAY EXPRESS	Sep	15	1979
6f 16y	1m 08.5	2	9-2	Firm	NINJAGO	July	27	2012
6f 16y	1m 08.1	3	9-7	Firm	AMERICA CALLING	Sep	18	2001
7f 16y	1m 20.8	2	9-0	Good To Firm	ROYAL AMARETTO	Sep	12	1996
7f 16y	1m 19.3	3	9-0	Firm	TARANAKI	Sep	18	2001
1m 14y	1m 33.1	2	8-11	Good To Firm	SKI ACADEMY	Aug	28	1995
1m 14y	1m 31.6	3	8-13	Firm	STOLI	Sep	18	2001
1m 2f 36y	2m 04.1	5	8-9	Hard	LEONIDAS	July	5	1983
1m 2f 36y	2m 04.1	7-8		Good To Firm	IT'S VARADAN	Sep	9	1989
1m 2f 36y	2m 04.1	3	8-5	Good To Firm	ELA ATHENA	July	23	1999
1m 4f 23y	2m 31.0	3	8-9	Good To Firm	SPRITSAIL	July	13	1989
1m 4f 23y	2m 31.0	7	9-6	Hard	MAINTOP	Aug	27	1984
2m 49y	3m 27.7	4	9-0	Good To Firm	WIZZARD ARTIST	July	1	1989
2m 2f	3m 56.4	5	8-7	Good To Firm	LAFFAH	July	8	2000

CHESTER

DISTANCE	TIME	AGE	WEIGHT	GOING	HORSE	DATE	
5f 16y	59.94 secs	2	9-2	Good To Firm	LEIBA LEIBA	Jun	26	2010
5f 16y	59.2 secs	3	10-0	Firm	ALTHREY DON	July	10	1964
5f 110y	1m 7.48	2	9-0	Good	BUBBLY BALLERINA	Sep	10	2011
5f 110y	1m 5.28	3	9-1	Good To Firm	MAPPIN TIME	Aug	20	2011
6f 18y	1m 12.85	2	8-11	Good To Firm	FLYING EXPRESS	Aug	31	2002
6f 18y	1m 12.78	3	8-3	Good To Firm	PLAY HEVER GOLF	May	4	1993
6f 18y	1m 12.78	6	9-2	Good	STACK ROCK	Jun	23	1993
7f 2y	1m 25.29	2	9-0	Good To Firm	DUE RESPECT	Sep	25	2002
7f 2y	1m 23.75	5	8-13	Good To Firm	THREE GRACES	July	9	2005
7f 122y	1m 32.29	2	9-0	Good To Firm	BIG BAD BOB	Sep	25	2002
7f 122y	1m 30.91	3	8-12	Good To Firm	CUPID'S GLORY	Aug	18	2005
1m 2f 75y	2m 7.15	3	8-8	Good To Firm	STOTSFOLD	Sep	23	2006
1m 3f 79y	2m 22.17	3	8-12	Good To Firm	PERFECT TRUTH	May	6	2009
1m 4f 66y	2m 33.7	3	8-10	Good To Firm	FIGHT YOUR CORNER	May	7	2002
1m 5f 89y	2m 45.4	5	8-11	Firm	RAKAPOSHI KING	May	7	1987
1m 7f 195y	3m 20.33	4	9-0	Good To Firm	GRAND FROMAGE	July	13	2002
2m 2f 147y	3m 58.59	7	9-2	Good To Firm	GREENWICH MEANTIME	May	9	2007

DONCASTER

DISTANCE	TIME	AGE	WEIGHT	GOING	HORSE	DATE	
5f	58.1 secs	2	9-5	Good To Firm	SAND VIXEN	Sep	11	2009
5f	57.2 secs	6	9-12	Good To Firm	CELTIC MILL	Sep	9	2004
5f 140y	1m 07.26	2	9-0	Good To Firm	CARTOGRAPHY	Jun	29	2003
5f 140y	1m 05.6	9	9-10	Good	HALMAHERA	Sep	8	2004
5f	1m 09.6	2	8-11	Good	CAESAR BEWARE	Sep	8	2004
5f	1m 09.56	3	8-10	Good To Firm	PROCLAIM	May	30	2009
5f 110y	1m 17.22	2	8-3	Good To Firm	SWILLY FERRY	Sep	10	2009
7f	1m 22.6	2	9-1	Good To Firm	LIBRETTIST	Sep	8	2004
7f	1m 21.6	3	9-4	Good To Firm	PASTORAL PURSUITS	Sep	9	2004
1m Str	1m 36.5	2	8-6	Good To Firm	SINGHALESE	Sep	9	2004
1m Rnd	1m 35.4	2	9-0	Good To Firm	PLAYFUL ACT	Sep	9	2004
1m Str	1m 34.95	6	8-9	Firm	QUICK WIT	July	18	2013
1m Rnd	1m 34.46	4	8-12	Good To Firm	STAYING ON	Apr	18	2009
1m 2f 60y	2m 13.4	2	8-8	Good	YARD BIRD	Nov	6	1981
1m 2f 60y	2m 04.81	4	8-13	Good To Firm	RED GALA	Sep	12	2007
1m 4f	2m 27.48	3	8-4	Good To Firm	SWIFT ALHAARTH	Sep	11	2011
1m 6f 132y	3m 00.44	3	9-0	Good To Firm	MASKED MARVEL	Sep	10	2011
2m 110y	3m 34.4	4	9-12	Good To Firm	FARSI	Jun	12	1992
2m 2f	3m 48.41	4	9-4	Good To Firm	SEPTIMUS	Sep	14	2007

EPSOM

DISTANCE	TIME	AGE	WEIGHT	GOING	HORSE	DATE		
5f	55.0 secs	2	8-9	Good To Firm	PRINCE ASLIA	Jun	9	1995
5f	53.6 secs	4	9-5	Firm	INDIGENOUS	Jun	2	1960
6f	1m 07.8	2	8-11	Good To Firm	SHOWBROOK	Jun	5	1991
6f	1m 07.21	5	9-13	Good To Firm	MAC GILLE EOIN	July	2	2009
7f	1m 21.3	2	8-9	Good To Firm	RED PEONY	July	29	2004
7f	1m 20.1	4	8-7	Firm	CAPISTRANO	Jun	7	1972
1m 114y	1m 42.8	2	8-5	Good To Firm	NIGHTSTALKER	Aug	30	1988
1m 114y	1m 40.7	3	8-6	Good To Firm	SYLVA HONDA	Jun	5	1991
1m 2f 18y	2m 03.5	5	7-13	Good	CROSSBOW	Jun	7	1967
1m 4f 10y	2m 31.3	3	9-0	Good To Firm	WORKFORCE	Jun	5	2010

FFOS LAS

DISTANCE	TIME	AGE	WEIGHT	GOING	HORSE	DATE		
5f	57.06 secs	2	9-3	Good To Firm	MR MAJEIKA	May	5	2011
5f	56.35 secs	5	8-8	Good	HAAJES	Sep	12	2009
6f	1m 9.93	2	9-0	Good To Firm	LUNAR DEITY	May	26	2010
6f	1m 7.80	8	8-4	Good To Firm	THE JAILER	May	5	2011
1m	1m 39.36	2	9-2	Good To Firm	HALA HALA	Sep	2	2013
1m	1m 37.12	5	9-0	Good To Firm	ZEBRANO	May	5	2011
1m 2f	2m 04.85	8	8-12	Good To Firm	PELHAM CRESCENT	May	5	2011
1m 4f	2m 31.58	4	8-9	Good To Firm	MEN DON'T CRY	July	23	2013
1m 6f	2m 58.61	4	9-7	Good To Firm	LADY ECLAIR	July	12	2010
2m	3m 29.58	4	8-9	Good To Firm	ANNALUNA	July	1	2013

GOODWOOD

DISTANCE	TIME	AGE	WEIGHT	GOING	HORSE	DATE		
5f	57.51 secs	2	9-0	Good	REQUINTO	July	26	2011
5f	56.0 secs	5	9-0	Good To Firm	RUDI'S PET	July	27	1999
6f	1m 09.8	2	8-11	Good To Firm	BACHIR	July	28	1999
6f	1m 09.1	6	9-0	Good To Firm	TAMAGIN	Sep	12	2009
7f	1m 24.9	2	8-11	Good To Firm	EKRAAR	July	29	1999
7f	1m 23.8	3	8-7	Firm	BRIEF GLIMPSE	July	25	1995
1m	1m 37.21	2	9-0	Good	CALDRA	Sep	9	2006
1m	1m 35.61	4	8-9	Good To Firm	SPECTAIT	Aug	4	2006
1m 1f	1m 56.27	2	9-3	Good To Firm	DORDOGNE	Sep	22	2010
1m 1f	1m 52.8	3	9-6	Good	VENA	July	27	1995
1m 1f 192y	2m 02.81	3	9-3	Good To Firm	ROAD TO LOVE	Aug	3	2006
1m 3f	2m 23.0	3	8-8	Good To Firm	ASIAN HEIGHTS	May	22	2001
1m 4f	2m 31.5	3	8-10	Firm	PRESENTING	July	25	1995
1m 6f	2m 57.61	4	9-6	Good To Firm	MEEZNAM	July	28	2011
2m	3m 21.55	5	9-10	Good To Firm	YEATS	Aug	3	2006
2m 4f	4m 11.7	3	7-10	Firm	LUCKY MOON	Sep	2	1990

HAMILTON

DISTANCE	TIME	AGE	WEIGHT	GOING	HORSE	DATE		
5f 4y	57.95 secs	2	8-8	Good To Firm	ROSE BLOSSOM	May	29	2009
6f 5y	1m 10.0	2	8-12	Good To Firm	BREAK THE CODE	Aug	24	1999
6f 5y	1m 09.3	4	8-7	Firm	MARCUS GAME	July	11	1974
1m 65y	1m 45.8	2	8-11	Firm	HOPEFUL SUBJECT	Sep	24	1973
1m 65y	1m 42.7	6	7-7	Firm	CRANLEY	Sep	25	1972
1m 1f 36y	1m 53.6	5	9-6	Good To Firm	REGENT'S SECRET	Aug	10	2005
1m 3f 16y	2m 19.32	3	8-1	Good To Firm	CAPTAIN WEBB	May	16	2008
1m 4f 17y	2m 30.52	5	9-10	Good To Firm	RECORD BREAKER	Jun	10	2009
1m 5f 9y	2m 45.1	6	9-6	Firm	MENTALASANYTHIN	Jun	14	1995

HAYDOCK

DISTANCE	TIME	AGE	WEIGHT	GOING	HORSE	DATE		
5f	58.56 secs	2	8-2	Good To Firm	BARRACUDA BOY	Aug	11	2012
5f	56.39 secs	5	9-4	Firm	BATED BREATH	May	26	2012
5f (Inner)	59.66 secs	2	8-12	Good	DEEDS NOT WORDS	Sep	27	2013
5f (Inner)	57.67 secs	4	9-4	Good To Firm	SOLE POWER	May	21	2011
6f	1m 10.72	2	9-2	Good To Firm	EASY TICKET	Sep	27	2013
6f	1m 09.9	4	9-0	Good To Firm	IKTAMAL	Sep	7	1996
6f (Inner)	1m 09.40	7	9-3	Good To Firm	MARKAB	Sep	4	2010
7f	1m 27.62	2	9-4	Good	TICKLE TIME	Aug	10	2012
7f	1m 25.95	7	9-9	Good To Firm	SET THE TREND	Jul	20	2013
1m	1m 39.02	3	8-11	Good	LADY MACDUFF	Aug	10	2012
1m 2f 95y	2m 08.25	3	9-0	Good To Firm	PRUSSIAN	Sep	7	2012
1m 3f 200y	2m 25.53	4	8-12	Good To Firm	NUMBER THEORY	May	24	2012
1m 6f	2m 55.20	5	9-9	Good To Firm	HUFF AND PUFF	Sep	7	2012
2m 45y	3m 26.98	5	8-13	Good To Firm	DE RIGUEUR	Jun	8	2013

KEMPTON (A.W)

DISTANCE	TIME	AGE	WEIGHT	GOING	HORSE	DATE		
5f	58.96	2	8-6	Standard	GLAMOROUS SPIRIT	Nov	28	2008
5f	58.33	3	9-1	Standard	EXCEEDANCE	May	7	2012
6f	1m 11.44	2	9-5	Standard	SIGNS IN THE SAND	Oct	6	2010
6f	1m 10.77	7	9-7	Standard	CAPONE	Nov	1	2012
7f	1m 23.95	2	8-10	Standard	TAMARKUZ	Oct	10	2012
7f	1m 23.29	5	8-11	Standard	PRIMAEVAL	Nov	16	2011
1m	1m 37.50	2	9-4	Standard	I'M BACK	Oct	3	2012
1m	1m 35.73	3	8-9	Standard	WESTERN ARISTOCRAT	Sep	5	2011
1m 2f	2m 3.77	6	8-13	Standard	KANDIDATE	Mar	29	2008
1m 3f	2m 16.98	5	9-6	Standard	IRISH FLAME	Nov	10	2011
1m 4f	2m 28.99	6	9-3	Standard	SPRING OF FAME	Nov	7	2012
2m	3m 21.50	4	8-12	Standard	COLOUR VISION	May	2	2012

LEICESTER

DISTANCE	TIME	AGE	WEIGHT	GOING	HORSE	DATE		
5f 2y	58.4 secs	2	9-0	Firm	CUTTING BLADE	Jun	9	1986
5f 2y	57.85 secs	5	9-5	Good To Firm	THE JOBBER	Sep	18	2006
5f 218y	1m 09.99	2	9-0	Good	EL MANATI	Aug	1	2012
5f 218y	1m 09.12	6	8-12	Good To Firm	PETER ISLAND	Apr	25	2009
7f 9y	1m 22.6	2	9-0	Good To Firm	MARIE DE MEDICI	Oct	6	2009
7f 9y	1m 20.8	3	8-7	Firm	FLOWER BOWL	Jun	9	1986
1m 60y	1m 44.05	2	8-11	Good To Firm	CONGRESSIONAL	Sep	6	2005
1m 60y	1m 41.89	5	9-7	Good To Firm	VAINGLORY	Jun	18	2009
1m 1f 218y	2m 05.3	9	9-1	Good To Firm	WINDSOR CASTLE	Oct	14	1996
1m 1f 218y	2m 02.4	3	8-11	Firm	EFFIGY	Nov	4	1985
1m 1f 218y	2m 02.4	4	9-6	Good To Firm	LADY ANGHARAD	Jun	18	2000
1m 3f 183y	2m 27.1	5	8-12	Good To Firm	MURGHEM	Jun	18	2000

LINGFIELD (TURF)

DISTANCE	TIME	AGE	WEIGHT	GOING	HORSE	DATE		
5f	57.07 secs	2	9-0	Good To Firm	QUITE A THING	Jun	11	2011
5f	56.09 secs	3	9-4	Good To Firm	WHITECREST	Sep	16	2011
6f	1m 08.36	2	8-12	Good To Firm	FOLLY BRIDGE	Sep	8	2009
6f	1m 08.13	6	9-8	Firm	CLEAR PRAISE	Aug	10	2013
7f	1m 20.55	2	8-11	Good To Firm	HIKING	Aug	17	2013
7f	1m 20.05	3	8-5	Good To Firm	PERFECT TRIBUTE	May	7	2011
7f 140y	1m 29.32	2	9-3	Good To Firm	DUNDONNELL	Aug	4	2012
7f 140y	1m 26.7	3	8-6	Good To Firm	HIAAM	Jul	11	1987
1m 1f	1m 52.4	4	9-2	Good To Firm	QUANDARY	July	15	1995
1m 2f	2m 04.6	3	9-3	Firm	USRAN	July	15	1989
1m 3f 106y	2m 23.9	3	8-5	Firm	NIGHT-SHIRT	July	14	1990
1m 6f	2m 59.1	5	9-5	Firm	IBN BEY	July	1	1989
2m	3m 23.7	3	9-5	Good To Firm	LAURIES CRUSADOR	Aug	13	1988

LINGFIELD (A.W)

DISTANCE	TIME	AGE	WEIGHT	GOING	HORSE	DATE		
5f	58.29 secs	2	8-8	Standard	SMOKEY RYDER	Dec	14	2008
5f	56.67 secs	5	8-12	Standard	LADIES ARE FOREVER	Mar	16	2013
6f	1m 09.99	2	8-12	Standard	SWISS DIVA	Nov	19	2008
6f	1m 08.75	7	9-2	Standard	TAROOQ	Dec	18	2013
7f	1m 22.67	2	9-3	Standard	COMPLICIT	Nov	23	2013
7f	1m 22.19	4	8-7	Standard	RED SPELL	Nov	19	2005
1m	1m 36.33	2	9-7	Standard	YARROOM	Dec	5	2012
1m	1m 34.77	4	9-3	Standard	BAHARAH	Oct	30	2008
1m 2f	2m 00.99	5	9-0	Standard	FARRAAJ	Mar	16	2013
1m 4f	2m 27.97	4	9-3	Standard	MIDSUMMER SUN	Apr	14	2012
1m 5f	2m 41.08	3	8-8	Standard	MISCHIEF MAKER	Oct	30	2008
2m	3m 16.73	5	9-2	Standard	ARCH VILLAIN	Jan	22	2014

MUSSELBURGH

DISTANCE	TIME	AGE	WEIGHT	GOING	HORSE	DATE		
5f	57.7 secs	2	8-2	Firm	ARASONG	May	16	1994
5f	57.3 secs	3	8-12	Firm	CORUNNA	Jun	3	2000
7f 30y	1m 27.46	2	8-8	Good	DURHAM REFLECTION	Sep	14	2009
7f 30y	1m 26.30	3	9-5	Firm	WALTZING WIZARD	Aug	22	2002
1m	1m 40.3	2	8-12	Good To Firm	SUCCESSION	Sep	26	2004
1m	1m 36.83	3	9-5	Good To Firm	GINGER JACK	July	13	2010
1m 1f	1m 50.42	8	8-11	Good To Firm	DHAULAR DHAR	Sep	3	2010
1m 4f 100y	2m 36.80	3	8-3	Good To Firm	HARRIS TWEED	Jun	5	2010
1m 5f	2m 46.41	3	9-5	Good To Firm	ALCAEUS	Sep	29	2013
1m 6f	2m 59.2	3	9-7	Firm	FORUM CHRIS	July	3	2000
2m	3m 26.20	5	9-6	Good To Firm	JACK DAWSON	Jun	1	2002

NEWBURY

DISTANCE	TIME	AGE	WEIGHT	GOING	HORSE	DATE		
5f 34y	59.1 secs	2	8-6	Good To Firm	SUPERSTAR LEO	July	22	2000
5f 34y	59.2 secs	3	9-5	Good To Firm	THE TRADER	Aug	18	2001
6f 8y	1m 11.07	2	8-4	Good To Firm	BAHATI	May	30	2009
6f 8y	1m 09.42	3	8-11	Good To Firm	NOTA BENE	May	13	2005
7f	1m 24.1	2	8-11	Good To Firm	HAAFHD	Aug	15	2003
7f	1m 21.5	3	8-4	Good To Firm	THREE POINTS	July	21	2000
1m	1m 37.5	2	9-1	Good To Firm	WINGED CUPID	Sep	16	2005
1m	1m 33.59	6	9-0	Firm	RAKTI	May	14	2005
1m 1f	1m 49.6	3	8-0	Good To Firm	HOLTYE	May	21	1995
1m 2f 6y	2m 1.2	3	8-7	Good To Firm	WALL STREET	July	20	1996
1m 3f 5y	2m 16.5	3	8-9	Good To Firm	GRANDERA	Sep	22	2001
1m 4f 5y	2m 28.26	4	9-7	Good To Firm	AZAMOUR	July	23	2005
1m 5f 61y	2m 44.9	5	10-0	Good To Firm	MYSTIC HILL	July	20	1996
2m	3m 25.4	8	9-12	Good To Firm	MOONLIGHT QUEST	July	19	1996

NEWCASTLE

DISTANCE	TIME	AGE	WEIGHT	GOING	HORSE	DATE		
5f	58.8 secs	2	9-0	Firm	ATLANTIC VIKING	Jun	4	1997
5f	58.0 secs	4	9-2	Firm	PRINCESS OBERON	July	23	1994
6f	1m 11.98	2	9-3	Good	PEARL ARCH	Sep	6	2010
6f	1m 10.58	4	9-9	Good To Firm	JONNY MUDBALL	Jun	26	2010
7f	1m 24.2	2	9-0	Good To Firm	ISCAN	Aug	31	1998
7f	1m 23.3	4	9-2	Good To Firm	QUIET VENTURE	Aug	31	1998
1m 3y	1m 37.1	2	8-3	Good To Firm	HOH STEAMER	Aug	31	1998
1m 3y	1m 37.3	3	8-8	Good To Firm	IT'S MAGIC	May	27	1999
1m 1f 9y	2m 03.2	2	8-13	Soft	RESPONSE	Oct	30	1993
1m 1f 9y	1m 58.4	3	8-8	Good To Firm	INTRODUCING	Aug	6	2003
1m 2f 32y	2m 06.5	3	8-11	Firm	MISSIONARY RIDGE	July	29	1990
1m 4f 93y	2m 36.9	4	9-3	Good To Firm	LIVIA'S DREAM	Jul	27	2013
1m 6f 97y	3m 06.4	3	9-6	Good To Firm	ONE OFF	Aug	6	2003
2m 19y	3m 24.3	4	8-10	Good	FAR CRY	Jun	26	1999

NEWMARKET (ROWLEY MILE)

DISTANCE	TIME	AGE	WEIGHT	GOING	HORSE	DATE		
5f	58.76 secs	2	8-5	Good To Firm	VALIANT ROMEO	Oct	3	2002
5f	56.8 secs	6	9-2	Good To Firm	LOCHSONG	Apr	30	1994
6f	1m 09.56	2	8-12	Good To Firm	BUSHRANGER	Oct	3	2008
7f	1m 22.39	2	8-12	Good To Firm	ASHRAM	Oct	2	2008
7f	1m 22.18	3	9-0	Good To Firm	CODEMASTER	May	14	2011
1m	1m 35.67	2	8-12	Good	STEELER	Sep	29	2012
1m	1m 34.07	4	9-0	Good To Firm	EAGLE MOUNTAIN	Oct	3	2008
1m 1f	1m 47.26	5	8-12	Good To Firm	MANDURO	Apr	19	2007
1m 2f	2m 04.6	2	9-4	Good	HIGHLAND CHIEFTAIN	Nov	2	1985
1m 2f	2m 00.13	3	8-12	Good	NEW APPROACH	Oct	18	2008
1m 4f	2m 26.07	3	8-9	Good To Firm	MOHEDIAN LADY	Sep	22	2011
1m 6f	2m 51.59	3	8-7	Good	ART EYES	Sep	29	2005
2m	3m 18.64	5	9-6	Good To Firm	TIMES UP	Sep	22	2011
2m 2f	3m 47.5	3	7-12	Hard	WHITEWAY	Oct	15	1947

NEWMARKET (JULY COURSE)

DISTANCE	TIME	AGE	WEIGHT	GOING	HORSE	DATE		
5f	58.5 secs	2	8-10	Good	SEDUCTRESS	July	10	1990
5f	56.09 secs	6	9-11	Good	BORDERLESCOTT	Aug	22	2008
6f	1m 10.35	2	8-11	Good	ELNAWIN	Aug	22	2008
6f	1m 09.11	4	9-5	Good To Firm	LETHAL FORCE	July	13	2013
7f	1m 23.57	3	9-5	Good To Firm	LIGHT UP MY LIFE	Aug	18	2012
7f	1m 22.5	3	9-7	Firm	HO LENG	July	9	1998
1m	1m 37.47	2	8-13	Good	WHIPPERS LOVE	Aug	28	2009
1m	1m 35.5	3	8-6	Good To Firm	LOVERS KNOT	July	8	1998
1m 2f	2m 00.91	3	9-5	Good To Firm	MAPUTO	July	11	2013
1m 4f	2m 25.11	3	8-11	Good	LUSH LASHES	Aug	22	2008
1m 5f	2m 42.01	3	9-0	Good	KITE WOOD	July	9	2009
1m 6f 175y	3m 04.2	3	8-5	Good	ARRIVE	July	11	2001
2m 24y	3m 20.2	7	9-10	Good	YORKSHIRE	July	11	2001

NOTTINGHAM

DISTANCE	TIME	AGE	WEIGHT	GOING	HORSE	DATE		
5f 13y (Inner)	1m 00.17	2	9-3	Good	ENDERBY SPIRIT	Oct	1	2008
5f 13y (Inner)	59.44 secs	9	9-3	Good To Firm	RACCOON	Apr	18	2009
5f 13y	57.9 secs	2	8-9	Firm	HOH MAGIC	May	13	1994
5f 13y	57.71secs	4	8-11	Good To Firm	DINKUM DIAMOND	Aug	14	2002
6f 15y	1m 11.4	2	8-11	Firm	JAMEELAPI	Aug	8	1983
6f 15y	1m 10.0	4	9-2	Firm	AJANAC	Aug	8	1988
1m 75y	1m 45.23	2	9-0	Good To Firm	TACTFULLY	Sep	28	2011
1m 75y	1m 42.25	5	9-1	Good To Firm	RIO DE LA PLATA	Jun	2	2010
1m 2f 50y	2m 07.13	5	9-8	Good To Firm	VASILY	July	19	2013
1m 2f 50y (Inner)	2m 06.66	2	9-3	Soft	LETHAL GLAZE	Oct	1	2008
1m 2f 50y (Inner)	2m 09.4	3	9-5	Good	CENTURIUS	Apr	20	2013
1m 6f 15y	2m 57.8	3	8-10	Firm	BUSTER JO	Oct	1	1985
2m 9y	3m 25.25	3	9-5	Good	BULWARK	Sep	27	2005

PONTEFRACT

DISTANCE	TIME	AGE	WEIGHT	GOING	HORSE	DATE		
5f	1m 01.1	2	9-0	Firm	GOLDEN BOUNTY	Sep	20	2001
5f	1m 00.8	4	8-9	Firm	BLUE MAEVE	Sep	29	2004
6f	1m 14.0	2	9-3	Firm	FAWZI	Sep	6	1983
6f	1m 12.6	3	7-13	Firm	MERRY ONE	Aug	29	1970
1m 4y	1m 42.8	2	9-13	Firm	STAR SPRAY	Sep	6	1970
1m 4y	1m 42.80	2	9-0	Firm	ALASIL	Sep	26	2002
1m 4y	1m 40.6	4	9-10	Good To Firm	ISLAND LIGHT	Apr	13	2002
1m 2f 6y	2m 12.8	2	9-0	Good To Firm	WARBROOK	Oct	2	1995
1m 2f 6y	2m 08.2	4	7-8	Hard	HAPPY HECTOR	July	9	1979
1m 4f 8y	2m 33.72	3	8-7	Firm	AJAAN	Aug	8	2007
2m 1f 22y	3m 40.67	4	8-7	Good To Firm	PARADISE FLIGHT	Jun	6	2005
2m 1f 216y	3m 51.1	3	8-8	Firm	KUDZ	Sep	9	1986
2m 5f 122y	4m 47.8	4	8-4	Firm	PHYSICAL	May	14	1984

REDCAR

DISTANCE	TIME	AGE	WEIGHT	GOING	HORSE	DATE		
5f	56.9 secs	2	9-0	Firm	**MISTER JOEL**	Oct	24	1995
5f	56.01 secs	10	9-3	Firm	**HENRY HALL**	Sep	20	2006
6f	1m 08.8	2	8-3	Good To Firm	**OBE GOLD**	Oct	2	2004
6f	1m 08.6	3	9-2	Good To Firm	**SIZZLING SAGA**	Jun	21	1991
7f	1m 21.28	2	9-3	Firm	**KAROO BLUE**	Sep	20	2006
7f	1m 21.0	3	9-1	Firm	**EMPTY QUARTER**	Oct	3	1995
1m	1m 34.37	2	9-0	Firm	**MASTERSHIP**	Sep	20	2006
1m	1m 32.42	4	10-0	Firm	**NANTON**	Sep	20	2006
1m 1f	1m 52.4	2	9-0	Firm	**SPEAR**	Sep	13	2004
1m 1f	1m 48.5	5	8-12	Firm	**MELLOTTIE**	July	25	1990
1m 2f	2m 10.1	2	8-11	Good	**ADDING**	Nov	10	1989
1m 2f	2m 01.4	5	9-2	Firm	**ERADICATE**	May	28	1990
1m 3f	2m 17.2	3	8-9	Firm	**PHOTO CALL**	Aug	7	1990
1m 6f 19y	2m 59.81	4	9-1	Good To Firm	**ESPRIT DE CORPS**	Sep	11	2006
2m 4y	3m 24.9	3	9-3	Firm	**SUBSONIC**	Oct	8	1991

RIPON

DISTANCE	TIME	AGE	WEIGHT	GOING	HORSE	DATE		
5f	57.8 secs	2	8-8	Firm	**SUPER ROCKY**	July	5	1991
5f	57.6 secs	5	8-5	Good	**BROADSTAIRS BEAUTY**	May	21	1995
6f	1m 10.9	2	9-2	Good	**CUMBRIAN VENTURE**	Aug	17	2002
6f	1m 09.72	4	8-9	Good	**BACCARAT**	Aug	17	2013
1m	1m 38.77	2	9-4	Good	**GREED IS GOOD**	Sep	28	2013
1m	1m 36.62	4	8-11	Good To Firm	**GRANSTON**	Aug	29	2005
1m 1f	1m 49.97	6	9-3	Good To Firm	**GINGER JACK**	Jun	20	2013
1m 2f	2m 02.6	3	9-4	Firm	**SWIFT SWORD**	July	20	1990
1m 4f 10y	2m 31.40	4	8-8	Good To Firm	**DANDINO**	Apr	16	2011
2m	3m 27.07	5	9-12	Good To Firm	**GREENWICH MEANTIME**	Aug	30	2005

SALISBURY

DISTANCE	TIME	AGE	WEIGHT	GOING	HORSE	DATE		
5f	59.3 secs	2	9-0	Good To Firm	**AJIGOLO**	May	12	2005
6f	1m 12.1	2	8-0	Good To Firm	**PARISIAN LADY**	Jun	10	1997
6f	1m 11.09	3	9-0	Firm	**L'AMI LOUIS**	May	1	2011
6f 212y	1m 25.9	2	9-0	Firm	**MORE ROYAL**	Jun	29	1995
6f 212y	1m 24.91	3	9-4	Firm	**CHILWORTH LAD**	May	1	2011
1m	1m 40.48	2	8-13	Firm	**CHOIR MASTER**	Sep	17	2002
1m	1m 38.29	3	8-7	Good To Firm	**LAYMAN**	Aug	11	2005
1m 1f 198y	2m 04.81	3	8-5	Good To Firm	**PRIMEVERE**	Aug	10	2011
1m 4f	2m 31.6	3	9-5	Good To Firm	**ARRIVE**	Jun	27	2001
1m 6f 21y	3m 0.84	8	8-12	Firm	**KANGAROO COURT**	May	24	2012

SANDOWN

DISTANCE	TIME	AGE	WEIGHT	GOING	HORSE	DATE		
5f 6y	59.4 secs	2	9-3	Firm	TIMES TIME	July	22	1982
5f 6y	58.8 secs	6	8-9	Good To Firm	PALACEGATE TOUCH	Sep	17	1996
7f 16y	1m 26.56	2	9-0	Good To Firm	RAVEN'S PASS	Sep	1	2007
7f 16y	1m 26.3	3	9-0	Firm	MAWSUFF	Jun	14	1983
1m 14y	1m 41.1	2	8-11	Firm	REFERENCE POINT	Sep	23	1986
1m 14y	1m 38.87	7	9-10	Good To Firm	PRINCE OF JOHANNE	July	6	2013
1m 1f	1m 54.6	2	8-8	Good To Firm	FRENCH PRETENDER	Sep	20	1988
1m 1f	1m 52.4	7	9-3	Good To Firm	BOURGAINVILLE	Aug	11	2005
1m 2f 7y	2m 02.1	4	8-11	Firm	KALAGLOW	May	31	1982
1m 6f	2m 56.9	4	8-7	Good To Firm	LADY ROSANNA	July	19	1989
2m 78y	3m 29.38	6	9-0	Good To Firm	CAUCUS	July	6	2013

SOUTHWELL (TURF)

DISTANCE	TIME	AGE	WEIGHT	GOING	HORSE	DATE		
6f	1m 15.03	2	9-3	Good	TREPA	Sep	6	2006
6f	1m 13.48	4	8-10	Good	PARIS BELL	Sep	6	2006
7f	1m 27.56	2	9-7	Good	HART OF GOLD	Sep	6	2006
7f	1m 25.95	4	9-0	Good	AEROPLANE	Sep	6	2006
1m 2f	2m 7.47	3	8-11	Good To Firm	DESERT AUTHORITY	Sep	7	2006
1m 3f	2m 20.13	4	9-12	Good	SANCHI	Sep	6	2006
1m 4f	2m 34.4	5	9-3	Good To Firm	CORN LILY	Aug	10	1991
2m	3m 34.1	5	9-1	Good To Firm	TRIPLICATE	Sep	20	1991

SOUTHWELL (A.W)

DISTANCE	TIME	AGE	WEIGHT	GOING	HORSE	DATE		
5f	57.85 secs	2	9-3	Standard	ARCTIC FEELING	Mar	31	2010
5f	56.80 secs	5	9-7	Standard	GHOSTWING	Jan	3	2012
6f	1m 14.0	2	8-5	Standard	PANALO	Nov	8	1989
6f	1m 13.3	3	9-2	Standard	RAMBO EXPRESS	Dec	18	1990
7f	1m 27.1	2	8-12	Standard	WINGED ICARUS	Aug	28	2012
7f	1m 26.8	5	8-4	Standard	AMENABLE	Dec	13	1990
1m	1m 38.0	2	8-9	Standard	ALPHA RASCAL	Nov	13	1990
1m	1m 38.0	2	8-10	Standard	ANDREW'S FIRST	Dec	30	1989
1m	1m 37.2	3	8-6	Standard	VALIRA	Nov	3	1990
1m 3f	2m 21.5	4	9-7	Standard	TEMPERING	Dec	5	1990
1m 4f	2m 33.9	4	9-12	Standard	FAST CHICK	Nov	8	1989
1m 6f	3m 01.6	3	7-7	Standard	QUALITAIR AVIATOR	Dec	1	1989
1m 6f	3m 01.6	3	7-8	Standard	EREVNON	Dec	29	1990
2m	3m 37.6	9	8-12	Standard	OLD HUBERT	Dec	5	1990

THIRSK

DISTANCE	TIME	AGE	WEIGHT	GOING	HORSE	DATE		
5f	57.2 secs	2	9-7	Good To Firm	PROUD BOAST	Aug	5	2000
5f	56.1 secs	7	8-0	Firm	SIR SANDROVITCH	Jun	26	2003
6f	1m 09.2	2	9-6	Good To Firm	WESTCOURT MAGIC	Aug	25	1995
6f	1m 08.8	6	9-4	Firm	JOHAYRO	July	23	1999
7f	1m 23.7	2	8-9	Firm	COURTING	July	23	1999
7f	1m 22.8	4	8-5	Firm	SILVER HAZE	May	21	1988
1m	1m 37.9	2	9-0	Good To Firm	SUNDAY SYMPHONY	Sep	4	2004
1m	1m 34.8	4	8-13	Firm	YEARSLEY	May	5	1990
1m 4f	2m 29.9	5	9-12	Firm	GALLERY GOD	Jun	4	2001
2m	3m 22.3	3	8-10	Firm	TOMASCHEK	Aug	1	1964

WARWICK

DISTANCE	TIME	AGE	WEIGHT	GOING	HORSE	DATE		
5f	57.95 secs	2	8-9	Good To Firm	**AMOUR PROPRE**	Jun	26	2008
5f	57.7 secs	4	9-6	Good To Firm	**LITTLE EDWARD**	July	7	2002
5f 110y	1m 03.6	5	8-6	Good To Firm	**DIZZY IN THE HEAD**	Jun	27	2004
6f	1m 10.70	2	9-5	Good To Firm	**GREEB**	Aug	21	2013
6f	1m 09.36	8	9-5	Good To Firm	**FATHSTA**	Aug	21	2013
7f 26y	1m 22.74	2	9-0	Good To Firm	**CHRISELLIAM**	July	11	2013
7f 26y	1m 21.2	3	8-11	Good To Firm	**LUCKY SPIN**	Jun	19	2004
1m 22y	1m 37.1	3	8-11	Firm	**ORINOCOVSKY**	Jun	26	2002
1m 2f 188y	2m 14.98	4	8-12	Good To Firm	**RONALDSAY**	Jun	16	2008
1m 4f 134y	2m 39.5	3	8-13	Good To Firm	**MAIMANA**	Jun	22	2002
1m 6f 135y	3m 07.5	3	9-7	Good To Firm	**BURMA BABY**	July	2	1999
2m 39y	3m 27.9	3	8-1	Firm	**DECOY**	Jun	26	2002

WINDSOR

DISTANCE	TIME	AGE	WEIGHT	GOING	HORSE	DATE		
5f 10y	58.69 secs	2	9-0	Good To Firm	**CHARLES THE GREAT**	May	23	2011
5f 10y	58.08 secs	5	8-13	Good To Firm	**TAURUS TWINS**	Apr	4	2011
6f	1m 10.5	2	9-5	Good To Firm	**CUBISM**	Aug	17	1998
6f	1m 09.89	4	9-0	Good To Firm	**BATED BREATH**	May	23	2011
1m 67y	1m 42.46	2	8-9	Good To Firm	**TIGER CUB**	Oct	10	2011
1m 67y	1m 39.81	5	9-7	Good	**FRENCH NAVY**	Jun	29	2013
1m 2f 7y	2m 02.44	3	9-1	Good To Firm	**CAMPANOLOGIST**	Aug	29	2009
1m 3f 135y	2m 21.5	3	9-2	Firm	**DOUBLE FLORIN**	May	19	1980

WOLVERHAMPTON (A.W)

DISTANCE	TIME	AGE	WEIGHT	GOING	HORSE	DATE		
5f 20y	1m 00.96	2	9-3	Standard	**MOVIESTA**	Sep	17	2012
5f 20y	59.79 secs	7	9-7	Standard	**WOOLFALL SOVEREIGN**	Jan	1	2013
5f 216y	1m 12.61	2	9-0	Standard To Fast	**PRIME DEFENDER**	Nov	8	2006
7f 32y	1m 27.7	2	9-5	Standard	**BILLY DANE**	Aug	14	2006
7f 32y	1m 26.42	7	8-12	Standard	**PRIME EXHIBIT**	Sep	8	2012
1m 141y	1m 47.68	2	9-3	Standard	**GLORY CITY**	Dec	26	2012
1m 141y	1m 46.07	5	9-0	Standard	**ALFRED HUTCHINSON**	Jan	1	2013
1m 1f 103y	2m 00.74	2	8-4	Standard	**LUCY BEE**	Dec	3	2012
1m 1f 103y	1m 57.34	4	8-13	Standard	**BAHAR SHUMAAL**	Oct	28	2006
1m 4f 50y	2m 34.75	5	8-13	Standard To Fast	**FANTOCHE**	May	3	2007
1m 5f 194y	2m 58.68	3	9-2	Standard	**INSTRUMENTALIST**	Oct	9	2012
2m 119y	3m 35.85	5	8-11	Standard To Fast	**MARKET WATCHER**	Nov	21	2006

YARMOUTH

DISTANCE	TIME	AGE	WEIGHT	GOING	HORSE	DATE		
5f 43y	1m 00.4	2	8-6	Good To Firm	**EBBA**	July	26	1999
5f 43y	59.80 secs	4	8-13	Good To Firm	**ROXANNE MILL**	Aug	25	2002
6f 3y	1m 10.4	2	9-0	Firm	**LANCHESTER**	Aug	15	1988
6f 3y	1m 9.90	4	8-9	Firm	**MALHUB**	Jun	13	2002
7f 3y	1m 22.2	2	9-0	Good To Firm	**WARRSHAN**	Sep	14	1988
7f 3y	1m 22.12	4	9-4	Good To Firm	**GLENBUCK**	Apr	26	2007
1m 3y	1m 36.3	2	8-2	Good To Firm	**OUTRUN**	Sep	15	1988
1m 3y	1m 33.9	3	8-8	Firm	**BONNE ETOILE**	Jun	27	1995
1m 1f	1m 52.00	3	9-5	Good To Firm	**TOUCH GOLD**	July	5	2012
1m 2f 21y	2m 02.83	3	8-9	Firm	**REUNITE**	July	18	2006
1m 3f 101y	2m 23.1	3	8-9	Firm	**RAHIL**	July	1	1993
1m 6f 17y	2m 57.8	3	8-2	Good To Firm	**BARAKAT**	July	24	1990
2m	3m 26.7	4	8-2	Good To Firm	**ALHESN**	July	26	1999

YORK

DISTANCE	TIME	AGE	WEIGHT	GOING	HORSE	DATE		
5f 3y	58.47 secs	2	8-11	Good To Firm	HOWICK FALLS	Aug	20	2003
5f 3y	56.20 secs	3	9-9	Good To Firm	OASIS DREAM	Aug	21	2003
5f 89y	1m 3.20	2	9-3	Good To Firm	THE ART OF RACING	Sep	12	2012
5f 89y	1m 1.72	4	9-7	Good To Firm	BOGART	Aug	21	2013
6f	1m 9.28	2	8-12	Good To Firm	SHOWCASING	Aug	19	2009
6f	1m 08.23	3	8-11	Good To Firm	MINCE	Sep	19	2012
7f	1m 22.45	2	9-0	Good To Firm	ELUSIVE PIMPERNEL	Aug	18	2009
7f	1m 21.83	4	9-8	Good To Firm	DIMENSION	July	28	2012
1m	1m 39.20	2	8-1	Good To Firm	MISSOULA	Aug	31	2005
1m	1m 35.14	6	9-11	Good To Firm	THE RECTIFIER	Jul	13	2013
1m 205y	1m 52.4	2	8-1	Good To Firm	ORAL EVIDENCE	Oct	6	1988
1m 208y	1m 46.76	5	9-8	Good To Firm	ECHO OF LIGHT	Sep	5	2007
1m 2f 88y	2m 05.29	3	8-11	Good To Firm	SEA THE STARS	Aug	18	2009
1m 3f 198y	2m 27.4	4	9-4	Good To Firm	ISLINGTON	Aug	20	2003
1m 6f	2m 54.96	4	9-0	Good To Firm	TACTIC	May	22	2010
1m 7f 195y	3m 18.4	3	8-0	Good To Firm	DAM BUSTERS	Aug	16	1988
2m 88y	3m 30.01	4	8-6	Good To Firm	FLASHMAN	July	27	2013

TOP FLAT JOCKEYS IN BRITAIN 2013

(JANUARY 1ST - DECEMBER 31ST)

W-R	%	JOCKEY	2ND	3RD	TOTAL PRIZE	WIN PRIZE
208-1010	21%	RICHARD HUGHES	171	135	4,143,975	3,116,549
194-899	22%	RYAN MOORE	135	135	4,478,997	2,946,909
168-1022	16%	ADAM KIRBY	138	138	1,688,198	1,289,577
168-1406	12%	LUKE MORRIS	161	190	1,023,148	613,205
160-821	19%	SILVESTRE DE SOUSA	107	86	2,710,532	2,139,287
156-1180	13%	JOE FANNING	158	152	1,606,138	1,016,495
137-910	15%	JIM CROWLEY	113	107	1,471,027	780,959
127-1098	12%	GRAHAM LEE	124	127	1,437,214	803,052
120-815	15%	ANDREA ATZENI	133	90	1,613,313	1,107,080
116-658	18%	WILLIAM BUICK	97	75	2,560,329	1,409,176
109-716	15%	GEORGE BAKER	111	78	1,057,599	763,773
108-723	15%	PAUL HANAGAN	91	81	1,858,853	972,824
107-653	16%	JAMIE SPENCER	99	82	2,012,337	876,064
106-659	16%	NEIL CALLAN	87	85	1,219,045	887,675
103-788	13%	MARTIN HARLEY	110	104	1,109,719	640,395
100-575	17%	DANIEL TUDHOPE	61	86	836,931	513,516
98-703	14%	GRAHAM GIBBONS	96	68	812,427	525,898
98-753	13%	ROBERT WINSTON	78	85	878,030	611,103
82-602	14%	JAMES DOYLE	79	78	1,761,235	1,201,136
82-634	13%	DAVID PROBERT	93	81	726,943	385,801
80-579	14%	FRANNY NORTON	78	73	745,535	474,700
79-655	12%	SHANE KELLY	71	73	538,704	279,463
79-697	11%	TOM QUEALLY	67	83	1,434,087	985,839
77-525	15%	SEB SANDERS	67	73	568,769	381,554
76-515	15%	DANE O'NEILL	62	65	685,274	401,239
76-996	8%	TOM EAVES	107	103	582,556	330,445
74-358	21%	MICKAEL BARZALONA	55	47	1,144,154	636,827
68-797	9%	LIAM KENIRY	65	98	578,732	397,231
66-531	12%	PAUL MULRENNAN	64	57	731,180	497,602
65-486	13%	RICHARD KINGSCOTE	60	61	814,910	545,101
65-553	12%	SEAN LEVEY	56	58	481,178	266,911
62-538	12%	KIEREN FALLON	73	56	1,162,452	566,938
62-538	12%	FREDERIK TYLICKI	47	77	435,034	260,889
61-518	12%	ROBERT TART	72	69	448,921	292,452
61-549	11%	ROBERT HAVLIN	78	72	564,547	379,654
61-565	11%	P J MCDONALD	65	65	369,494	233,404
60-448	13%	HAYLEY TURNER	59	61	405,556	263,836
58-517	11%	TONY HAMILTON	64	70	712,166	439,508
57-590	10%	MARTIN LANE	74	49	586,331	412,130
55-505	11%	ANDREW MULLEN	46	59	321,257	219,024
55-647	9%	JIMMY QUINN	47	63	333,701	181,356
54-738	7%	WILLIAM CARSON	72	84	334,891	182,452
51-287	18%	THOMAS BROWN	33	33	302,321	223,791
51-384	13%	JASON HART	45	36	295,959	194,610
51-436	12%	LIAM JONES	45	50	507,933	368,393
47-424	11%	PAT DOBBS	50	32	455,472	282,437
47-473	10%	WILLIAM TWISTON-DAVIES	62	57	346,533	192,197
47-536	9%	MARTIN DWYER	59	49	384,186	221,245
46-432	11%	TED DURCAN	42	48	323,342	179,557
43-458	9%	CHRIS CATLIN	26	42	250,114	177,246

TOP FLAT TRAINERS IN BRITAIN 2013

TRAINER	LEADING HORSE	W-R	2ND	3RD	4TH	TOTAL PRIZE	WIN PRIZE
RICHARD HANNON	Olympic Glory	235-1412	180	169	138	4,532,464	3,137,720
A P O'BRIEN	Ruler Of The World	13-80	11	9	9	3,819,986	2,700,649
MARK JOHNSTON	Universal	216-1557	200	190	158	2,743,581	1,826,629
SAEED BIN SUROOR	Farhh	106-523	87	67	46	2,665,780	1,934,401
RICHARD FAHEY	Heaven's Guest	164-1287	162	156	136	2,455,584	1,588,826
JOHN GOSDEN	The Fugue	108-525	98	66	55	2,033,077	1,263,914
WILLIAM HAGGAS	Mukhadram	107-503	87	74	58	1,896,067	1,133,364
SIR MICHAEL STOUTE	Hillstar	87-398	53	67	35	1,687,826	1,167,720
KEVIN RYAN	Astaire	94-781	86	73	73	1,588,817	1,067,445
ANDREW BALDING	Highland Colori	99-713	93	104	70	1,356,742	873,940
ROGER VARIAN	Kingston Hill	89-402	62	52	38	1,332,296	921,239
CHARLES HILLS	Cable Bay	68-547	82	67	65	1,244,948	584,244
DAVID O'MEARA	Mont Ras	136-905	85	109	79	1,159,386	777,659
RALPH BECKETT	Talent	73-418	60	49	41	1,117,771	645,013
ROGER CHARLTON	Al Kazeem	43-256	33	39	29	1,115,140	804,499
MARCO BOTTI	Masamah	89-541	92	84	52	1,076,761	642,596
CLIVE COX	Lethal Force	37-325	37	37	40	1,012,149	821,854
LUCA CUMANI	Postponed	69-333	58	42	39	1,008,042	580,473
J S BOLGER	Dawn Approach	2-19	4	0	3	995,905	425,325
CHARLIE APPLEBY	Wedding Ring	60-304	43	33	39	970,334	693,520
DAVID SIMCOCK	Moment In Time	84-490	70	61	45	892,801	494,790
JAMES FANSHAWE	Seal Of Approval	39-208	23	32	20	867,909	552,839
MICK CHANNON	Elidor	75-865	116	116	100	829,821	369,350
LADY CECIL	Tiger Cliff	36-173	36	19	23	817,023	603,265
TIM EASTERBY	Ventura Mist	68-868	79	79	79	786,997	470,015
BRIAN ELLISON	Top Notch Tonto	62-510	69	58	43	784,997	319,660
DAVID BARRON	Bertiewhittle	63-342	43	32	21	703,627	427,173
MRS K BURKE	Libertarian	35-272	54	42	29	701,878	235,603
EDWARD LYNAM	Slade Power	4-14	1	3	1	696,810	497,077
ED DUNLOP	Times Up	45-349	49	35	35	688,978	351,820
A WOHLER	Novellist	1-6	0	1	0	624,136	603,961
DAVID EVANS	Forest Edge	116-880	96	134	81	562,496	371,616
MICHAEL BELL	The Lark	51-476	63	56	45	558,252	243,809
TOM DASCOMBE	Brown Panther	56-378	60	54	34	517,567	336,479
JIM GOLDIE	Jack Dexter	34-359	33	45	41	455,159	210,354
CLIVE BRITTAIN	Rizeena	21-221	26	27	26	437,297	223,204
JEREMY NOSEDA	Grandeur	51-242	39	22	26	436,674	284,293
ROBERT COWELL	Jwala	19-264	22	22	29	429,968	297,234
BRIAN MEEHAN	Correspondent	33-310	40	36	32	408,337	188,00
JAMES TATE	Blockade	62-298	50	52	24	401,536	255,38
DAVID NICHOLLS	Rodrigo De Torres	55-503	62	45	43	399,153	212,364
IAN WILLIAMS	Genzy	44-315	32	38	42	377,810	219,32
MICHAEL DODS	Mass Rally	41-362	42	34	39	373,208	212,784
DEAN IVORY	Tropics	39-239	21	21	17	367,125	304,765
MICHAEL EASTERBY	Hoof It	47-478	51	34	30	360,013	212,772
HENRY CANDY	Treaty Of Paris	29-213	27	22	32	344,171	157,854
DAVID WACHMAN	Galileo Rock	1-10	0	5	1	343,410	77,372
MME C BARANDE-BARBE	Cirrus Des Aigles	0-2	1	0	1	336,584	
BRYAN SMART	Moviesta	31-327	33	35	35	336,030	208,97
MICHAEL APPLEBY	Demora	61-443	53	54	53	334,736	230,74

TOP FLAT OWNERS IN BRITAIN IN 2013

OWNER	LEADING HORSE	W-R	2ND	3RD	4TH	TOTAL PRIZE	WIN PRIZE
GODOLPHIN	FARHH	170-843	133	102	88	4,197,745	3,063,273
HAMDAN AL MAKTOUM	MUKHADRAM	107-616	106	73	68	1,643,897	824,256
MRS JOHN MAGNIER & MICHAEL TABOR & DERRICK SMITH	RULER OF THE WORLD	4-28	3	5	4	1,442,706	932,785
SHEIKH HAMDAN BIN MOHAMMED AL MAKTOUM	SCATTER DICE	104-719	96	88	65	1,322,275	954,677
K ABDULLAH	WINSILI	84-351	51	50	38	1,135,477	780,548
HE SH JOAAN BIN HAMAD AL THANI	OLYMPIC GLORY	9-29	5	1	5	1,099,329	922,891
DERRICK SMITH & MRS JOHN MAGNIER & MICHAEL TABOR	LEADING LIGHT	5-31	5	2	2	1,046,541	855,708
DR MARWAN KOUKASH	AREA FIFTY ONE	70-557	79	72	59	951,906	560,492
MRS J MAGNIER, MICHAEL TABOR, DERRICK SMITH & JOSEPH ALLEN	DECLARATION OF WAR	2-5	1	1	0	752,690	623,810
D J DEER	AL KAZEEM	8-61	9	12	4	681,371	574,004
CHEVELEY PARK STUD	KINGSGATE NATIVE	47-227	35	31	26	659,971	421,042
QATAR RACING LIMITED	HOT STREAK	34-231	32	30	29	625,391	283,436
B KESWICK	SKY LANTERN	3-6	2	0	0	625,044	568,064
DR CHRISTOPH BERGLAR	NOVELLIST	1-1	0	0	0	603,961	603,961
ALAN G CRADDOCK	LETHAL FORCE	4-13	3	2	2	599,892	572,598
MRS S POWER	SLADE POWER	3-10	3	2	1	595,512	440,367
SAEED MANANA	VAN DER NEER	48-319	47	55	36	542,038	291,558
SHEIKH MOHAMMED OBAID AL MAKTOUM	POSTPONED	21-78	12	8	8	489,885	293,250
SALEH AL HOMAIZI & IMAD AL SAGAR	DANCHAI	25-108	21	16	10	473,922	285,984
J L ROWSELL & M H DIXON	TALENT	2-4	1	1	0	450,438	264,410
HRH PRINCESS HAYA OF JORDAN	GREGORIAN	22-88	17	16	9	438,736	264,094
MRS J S BOLGER	TRADING LEATHER	0-10	3	0	1	430,277	0
HUBERT JOHN STRECKER	LIBERTARIAN	2-7	1	1	1	390,866	90,240
SHEIKH JUMA DALMOOK AL MAKTOUM	HAIKBIDIAC	22-131	20	24	10	379,313	244,347
MICHAEL TABOR & DERRICK SMITH & MRS JOHN MAGNIER	BATTLE OF MARENGO	2-23	3	3	4	376,728	76,558
THE QUEEN	ESTIMATE	17-101	12	16	10	374,768	340,452
SIR ROBERT OGDEN	THOMAS CHIPPENDALE	16-81	13	5	9	360,420	273,022
LADY ROTHSCHILD	THISTLE BIRD	19-97	21	14	7	356,157	170,573
ANDREW TINKLER	ROYAL DIAMOND	11-90	12	13	6	340,256	154,602
JEAN-CLAUDE-ALAIN DUPOUY	CIRRUS DES AIGLES	0-2	1	0	1	336,584	0
T R G VESTEY	SEAL OF APPROVAL	4-7	1	0	0	334,621	333,273
KEITH BROWN	TOP NOTCH TONTO	8-38	3	2	4	322,837	83,618
SHEIKH AHMED AL MAKTOUM	FARRAAJ	22-101	14	16	8	314,956	263,600
SIR EVELYN DE ROTHSCHILD	HILLSTAR	3-16	2	3	1	312,935	128,395
J ALLEN/MRS J MAGNIER/M TABOR/D SMITH	WAR COMMAND	2-2	0	0	0	296,593	296,593
MRS ANGIE BAILEY	ASTAIRE	7-26	1	1	1	287,451	284,280
SIMON GIBSON	SOCIETY ROCK	2-14	2	0	2	278,573	63,068
N H PONSONBY	TIGER CLIFF	7-63	7	10	7	276,918	212,628
JOHNNIE DELTA RACING	JACK DEXTER	7-102	9	17	12	273,997	88,049
ABDULLA AL MANSOORI	UNIVERSAL	13-59	4	6	7	266,438	187,508
LORD LLOYD-WEBBER	THE FUGUE	1-4	0	1	0	254,695	200,895
SULTAN ALI	EDUCATE	11-49	4	6	5	253,408	172,581
MRS FITRI HAY	NO HERETIC	20-128	20	23	13	247,218	132,724
MATT & LAUREN MORGAN	MORNING POST	3-54	8	4	5	238,238	179,797
C SMITH	HIGHLAND KNIGHT	10-119	19	10	8	228,826	116,957
CHARLES WENTWORTH	LEVITATE	10-58	9	12	9	225,133	114,847
MICHAEL O'FLYNN	GALILEO ROCK	0-3	0	3	0	224,830	0
GIULIANO MANFREDINI	HASOPOP	12-46	7	10	2	209,236	135,378
R H SULTAN AHMAD SHAH	BERKSHIRE	17-85	6	10	13	204,717	179,228
K SHANNON & M A SCAIFE	HEAVEN'S GUEST	4-21	1	2	4	196,617	177,656

TOP FLAT HORSES IN BRITAIN 2013

HORSE (AGE)	WIN & PLACE £	W-R	TRAINER	OWNER	BREEDER
RULER OF THE WORLD (3)	956,220	2-3	A P O'Brien	Mrs John Magnier & Michael Tabor & Derrick Smith	Southern Bloodstock
FARHH (5)	847,389	2-2	Saeed bin Suroor	Godolphin	Darley
DECLARATION OF WAR (4)	752,690	2-5	A P O'Brien	Mrs J Magnier & Michael Tabor & Derrick Smith & Joseph Allen	Joseph Allen
AL KAZEEM (5)	639,293	3-4	Roger Charlton	D J Deer	D J And Mrs Deer
OLYMPIC GLORY (3)	635,152	2-2	Richard Hannon	HE Sh Joaan Bin Hamad Al Thani	Denis McDonnell
SKY LANTERN (3)	625,044	3-6	Richard Hannon	B Keswick	Tally-Ho Stud
NOVELLIST (4)	603,961	1-1	A Wohler	Dr Christoph Berglar	Christoph Berglar
LETHAL FORCE (4)	590,029	2-4	Clive Cox	Alan G Craddock	Declan Johnson
DAWN APPROACH (3)	546,641	2-5	J S Bolger	Godolphin	J S Bolger
TALENT (3)	450,438	2-4	Ralph Beckett	J L Rowsell & M H Dixon	Ashbrittle Stud & M H Dixon
TRADING LEATHER (3)	422,475	0-3	J S Bolger	Mrs J S Bolger	J S Bolger
LIBERTARIAN (3)	422,208	2-5	Charlie Appleby	Godolphin	Serpentine Bloodstock Ltd
LEADING LIGHT (3)	382,792	2-2	A P O'Brien	Derrick Smith & Mrs John Magnier & Michael Tabor	Lynch-Bages Ltd
CIRRUS DES AIGLES (7)	336,584	0-2	Mme C Barande-Barbe	Jean-Claude-Alain Dupouy	M Yvon Lelimouzin & M Benoit Deschamps
SEAL OF APPROVAL (4)	330,686	3-4	James Fanshawe	T R G Vestey	T R G Vestey
SLADE POWER (4)	315,406	1-5	Edward Lynam	Mrs S Power	Mrs S Power
TORONADO (3)	310,971	2-5	Richard Hannon	HE Sh Joaan Bin Hamad Al Thani	Paul Nataf
TOP NOTCH TONTO (3)	303,291	3-10	Brian Ellison	Keith Brown	Seamus Finucane
WAR COMMAND (2)	296,593	2-2	A P O'Brien	J Allen/Mrs J Magnier/ M Tabor/D Smith	Joseph Allen
SOLE POWER (6)	280,106	2-5	Edward Lynam	Mrs S Power	G Russell
OKLAHOMA CITY (2)	279,150	1-2	A P O'Brien	Derrick Smith & Mrs John Magnier & Michael Tabor	Meon Valley Stud
HILLSTAR (3)	278,941	1-6	Sir Michael Stoute	Sir Evelyn De Rothschild	Southcourt Stud
MUKHADRAM (4)	278,936	2-5	William Haggas	Hamdan Al Maktoum	Wardall Bloodstock
SOCIETY ROCK (6)	275,481	1-3	James Fanshawe	Simon Gibson	San Gabriel Investments
THE FUGUE (4)	254,695	1-3	John Gosden	Lord Lloyd-Webber	Watership Down Stud
ASTAIRE (2)	249,383	4-5	Kevin Ryan	Mrs Angie Bailey	John O'Connor
ESTIMATE (4)	232,511	2-3	Sir Michael Stoute	The Queen	His Highness The Aga Khan's Studs S C
WEDDING RING (2)	231,987	3-6	Charlie Appleby	Godolphin	Swettenham Stud
UNIVERSAL (4)	219,724	4-7	Mark Johnston	Abdulla Al Mansoori	Grangecon Stud
GALILEO ROCK (3)	219,450	0-3	David Wachman	Michael O'Flynn	Rockfield Farm
ST NICHOLAS ABBEY (6)	198,485	1-1	A P O'Brien	Derrick Smith & Mrs John Magnier & Michael Tabor	Barton Bloodstock & Villiers Synd
MORNING POST (2)	197,286	1-9	Kevin Ryan	Matt & Lauren Morgan	T J Cooper
JWALA (4)	194,849	2-7	Robert Cowell	Manor Farm Stud & Miss S Hoare	Manor Farm Stud (Rutland)
HEAVEN'S GUEST (3)	191,753	4-11	Richard Fahey	J K Shannon & M A Scaife	Yeomanstown Stud
JACK DEXTER (4)	190,361	3-8	Jim Goldie	Johnnie Delta Racing	Jim Goldie
TIGER CLIFF (4)	185,484	2-4	Alan King	W H Ponsonby	Mrs Clodagh McStay
GORDON LORD BYRON (5)	180,050	1-4	T Hogan	Morgan J Cahalan	Roland H Alder
HAIKBIDIAC (2)	177,101	2-7	William Haggas	Sheikh Juma Dalmook Al Maktoum	Silk Fan Syndicate
KINGSTON HILL (2)	176,926	3-3	Roger Varian	Paul Smith	Ridgecourt Stud

TOP NH JOCKEYS IN BRITAIN 2012/13

W-R	%	JOCKEY	2ND	3RD	TOTAL PRIZE
185-848	22%	A P MCCOY	139	91	1,734,591
144-747	19%	JASON MAGUIRE	128	91	1,033,535
133-830	16%	RICHARD JOHNSON	137	117	1,241,996
89-575	15%	AIDAN COLEMAN	77	79	795,143
87-615	14%	SAM TWISTON-DAVIES	84	65	1,020,575
85-546	16%	TOM SCUDAMORE	68	59	849,379
73-419	17%	DARYL JACOB	64	45	816,162
70-457	15%	TOM O'BRIEN	59	52	519,269
66-505	13%	NICK SCHOLFIELD	55	64	550,646
64-389	16%	NOEL FEHILY	50	46	675,758
63-457	14%	PADDY BRENNAN	61	67	623,381
60-517	12%	PAUL MOLONEY	60	66	674,545
57-211	27%	R WALSH	37	32	1,769,831
57-225	25%	BARRY GERAGHTY	39	20	1,916,082
53-471	11%	DOUGIE COSTELLO	62	62	445,788
50-397	13%	DENIS O'REGAN	51	58	531,552
47-477	10%	JAMIE MOORE	57	48	514,410
46-322	14%	JAMES REVELEY	39	36	282,454
44-455	10%	BRIAN HUGHES	55	59	296,000
38-304	13%	WAYNE HUTCHINSON	40	32	735,317
38-383	10%	LUCY ALEXANDER	29	41	215,482
36-236	15%	MICHEAL NOLAN	29	37	193,180
36-288	13%	ROBERT THORNTON	43	48	385,505
35-336	10%	BRENDAN POWELL	34	44	315,301
34-295	12%	HENRY BROOKE	34	26	196,016
32-236	14%	LEIGHTON ASPELL	43	31	225,246
32-318	10%	ANDREW THORNTON	30	42	231,785
31-230	13%	TIMMY MURPHY	30	20	278,318
31-298	10%	PETER BUCHANAN	32	25	254,911
31-325	10%	TOM CANNON	34	37	243,914
30-214	14%	DANNY COOK	33	20	255,076
29-183	16%	DAVID BASS	13	21	229,303
28-197	14%	JOE TIZZARD	18	27	565,672
28-253	11%	DOMINIC ELSWORTH	34	28	231,947
28-255	11%	ANDREW TINKLER	20	31	262,780
28-261	11%	BRIAN HARDING	22	24	175,635
27-196	14%	LIAM TREADWELL	22	14	295,592
27-313	9%	RYAN MANIA	36	32	753,647
26-287	9%	WILSON RENWICK	22	32	173,952
24-170	14%	GAVIN SHEEHAN	15	16	129,798
23-184	13%	CONOR O'FARRELL	27	23	208,092
21-165	13%	MARC GOLDSTEIN	17	24	113,825
21-174	12%	ANDREW GLASSONBURY	14	15	114,078
21-236	9%	JAMES BEST	29	28	173,690
20-208	10%	ADAM WEDGE	21	19	163,104
20-259	8%	RICHIE MCLERNON	18	21	205,558
19-198	10%	MICHAEL BYRNE	30	30	123,016
18-134	13%	JOSHUA MOORE	16	12	143,730
18-167	11%	ALAIN CAWLEY	20	19	130,694
18-181	10%	JAKE GREENALL	19	19	92,741
18-249	7%	RICHIE MCGRATH	17	22	120,949

TOP NH TRAINERS IN BRITAIN 2012/13

TRAINER	LEADING HORSE	W-R	2ND	3RD	4TH	TOTAL PRIZE	WIN PRIZE
NICKY HENDERSON	SPRINTER SACRE	125-509	79	56	33	2,924,917	2,220,033
PAUL NICHOLLS	ZARKANDAR	131-565	107	72	53	2,375,585	1,553,145
DAVID PIPE	DYNASTE	104-624	72	64	76	1,142,418	702,610
ALAN KING	GODSMEJUDGE	60-419	68	68	54	1,066,685	565,939
NIGEL TWISTON-DAVIES	THE NEW ONE	75-542	69	69	64	1,026,314	575,290
DONALD McCAIN	ACROSS THE BAY	141-726	116	95	61	990,645	617,741
VENETIA WILLIAMS	KATENKO	90-532	76	65	39	966,433	639,354
PHILIP HOBBS	WISHFUL THINKING	68-503	75	59	45	902,487	449,681
SUE SMITH	AURORAS ENCORE	31-215	30	34	26	822,155	699,165
COLIN TIZZARD	CUE CARD	43-311	29	44	29	812,834	577,391
EVAN WILLIAMS	CAPPA BLEU	57-506	63	64	59	703,297	307,858
W P MULLINS	HURRICANE FLY	6-51	4	5	3	688,530	444,745
JONJO O'NEILL	HOLYWELL	88-689	57	64	60	683,402	457,635
REBECCA CURTIS	AT FISHERS CROSS	49-210	33	28	13	562,662	342,483
TOM GEORGE	OLOFI	39-243	39	30	30	478,434	307,846
TIM VAUGHAN	HAWKHILL	83-633	103	92	73	471,406	259,070
LUCINDA RUSSELL	TAP NIGHT	59-478	68	64	54	408,617	239,804
GARY MOORE	SIRE DE GRUGY	33-273	35	22	25	395,439	284,514
PETER BOWEN	BUACHAILL ALAINN	48-363	53	42	30	378,662	242,272
BRIAN ELLISON	FLEET DAWN	39-265	41	30	27	335,339	220,608
CHARLIE LONGSDON	PETE THE FEAT	51-385	45	44	29	330,311	215,131
NICK WILLIAMS	REVE DE SIVOLA	20-120	13	17	12	327,699	184,931
HARRY FRY	ROCK ON RUBY	19-70	11	9	4	274,359	152,750
GORDON ELLIOTT	CAUSE OF CAUSES	17-91	19	5	9	263,623	199,150
MALCOLM JEFFERSON	CAPE TRIBULATION	23-151	22	18	17	251,068	167,950
C BYRNES	SOLWHIT	3-11	2	0	1	245,602	234,721
JOHN QUINN	COUNTRYWIDE FLAME	20-69	8	9	6	236,480	163,957
DR RICHARD NEWLAND	BOBOWEN	35-146	26	18	13	228,254	151,566
HENRY DALY	QUENTIN COLLONGES	20-174	18	22	19	227,659	178,668
EMMA LAVELLE	HIGHLAND LODGE	12-171	25	26	12	222,445	105,278
M F MORRIS	FIRST LIEUTENANT	1-6	3	1	0	216,994	84,477
MARTIN KEIGHLEY	CHAMPION COURT	29-194	24	23	21	210,841	128,581
JEREMY SCOTT	MELODIC RENDEZVOUS	30-211	32	33	22	196,907	122,263
KIM BAILEY	HARRY TOPPER	27-240	31	37	18	188,946	119,133
KEITH REVELEY	BRAVE SPARTACUS	34-153	21	17	12	184,166	130,870
OLIVER SHERWOOD	PUFFIN BILLY	25-161	29	15	12	181,654	108,603
D T HUGHES	OUR CONOR	2-21	3	4	0	179,894	78,349
JOHN FERGUSON	COTTON MILL	23-124	17	17	18	166,916	89,083
DAVID BRIDGWATER	THE GIANT BOLSTER	16-101	20	13	10	165,217	73,623
FERGAL O'BRIEN	BRADLEY	28-227	36	25	21	162,422	92,045
NICK GIFFORD	FAIRY RATH	10-99	9	14	10	161,073	121,066
STEVE GOLLINGS	CONQUISTO	16-69	10	5	9	158,168	116,694
NICKY RICHARDS	MISTER MARKER	25-154	19	18	17	157,963	86,707
TIM EASTERBY	TRUSTAN TIMES	16-97	10	12	10	151,710	111,247
RICHARD LEE	SIMPLY WINGS	21-161	17	20	22	151,508	95,959
HENRY DE BROMHEAD	SIZING EUROPE	1-8	1	1	0	145,937	62,189
PAUL WEBBER	ALASI	18-193	21	17	26	137,837	80,834
CHRIS GRANT	ULYSSE COLLONGES	20-213	30	30	19	134,290	75,687
JOHN WADE	BLAZING BULL	24-226	20	26	33	133,789	86,951
N W ALEXANDER	ISLA PEARL FISHER	28-184	21	16	13	131,807	91,156

TOP NH OWNERS IN BRITAIN IN 2012/13

OWNER	LEADING HORSE	W-R	2ND	3RD	4TH	TOTAL PRIZE	WIN PRIZE
JOHN P MCMANUS	At Fishers Cross	95-585	69	57	60	1,143,289	816,433
D PRYDE,J BEAUMONT & DP VAN DER HOEVEN	Auroras Encore	1-6	0	0	1	551,543	547,267
CHRIS GILES & POTENSIS LIMITED	Zarkandar	8-15	3	1	1	516,108	462,904
MRS CAROLINE MOULD	Sprinter Sacre	4-20	3	1	0	466,840	429,101
THE NOT AFRAID PARTNERSHIP	Bobs Worth	2-2	0	0	0	398,650	398,650
GIGGINSTOWN HOUSE STUD	First Lieutenant	2-38	7	3	6	376,225	95,152
MRS JEAN R BISHOP	Cue Card	5-19	3	3	1	350,428	295,091
MRS DIANA L WHATELEY	Wishfull Thinking	12-55	13	7	5	347,658	130,992
ROBERT WALEY-COHEN	Long Run	5-23	3	3	2	287,553	181,077
MR & MRS WILLIAM RUCKER	Cappa Bleu	10-57	12	9	5	286,475	37,095
TREVOR HEMMINGS	Carrickboy	25-178	25	21	12	275,006	195,950
SIMON MUNIR	Raya Star	11-51	11	4	3	268,623	159,174
ANDREA & GRAHAM WYLIE	Back In Focus	10-42	11	3	3	264,016	175,038
GEORGE CREIGHTON & MRS ROSE BOYD	Hurricane Fly	1-1	0	0	0	227,800	227,800
TOP OF THE HILL SYNDICATE	Solwhit	2-2	0	0	0	224,136	224,136
J HALES	Al Ferof	5-15	0	3	4	179,296	166,924
POTENSIS LIMITED & CHRIS GILES	For Non Stop	4-26	3	4	4	171,997	74,991
FAVOURITES RACING	Godsmejudge	5-55	14	2	7	168,536	119,370
J MARTIN	Overturn	19-99	20	11	12	169,604	92,548
BLOOMFIELDS	Cotton Mill	22-118	17	17	16	165,054	87,437
WALTERS PLANT HIRE LTD	Oscar Whisky	14-63	10	6	11	161,371	116,052
P J MARTIN	Conquisto	16-72	10	7	11	160,397	116,694
JOHN WADE	Benny Be Good	23-229	23	26	30	155,173	95,319
MCNEILL FAMILY	Walkon	2-21	5	1	1	153,492	60,848
BROCADE RACING	Golden Chieftain	10-52	5	6	2	152,964	123,918
J A TWISTON-DAVIES	Hello Bud	14-104	9	16	9	149,067	115,942
MRS S SUCH	The New One	5-10	2	0	0	149,044	100,233
MRS GAY SMITH	Holywell	8-64	5	6	8	144,792	88,814
S BROOKHOUSE	Goulanes	12-68	16	2	9	142,767	93,080
TERRY WARNER	Oiseau De Nuit	9-35	0	4	2	140,317	119,554
THE STEWART FAMILY	Celestial Halo	7-48	3	2	7	138,924	44,646
THE JOHNSON & STEWART FAMILIES	Salubrious	6-19	2	4	2	129,586	83,282
MICHAEL BUCKLEY	Minella Forfitness	7-41	8	5	2	129,243	59,287
J BROOKS	Katenko	8-34	4	4	3	128,048	105,839
EXORS OF THE LATE D A JOHNSON	The Package	7-32	3	2	4	126,707	75,284
437	Teaforthree	0-5	1	1	0	124,105	0
NEVILLE STATHAM & FAMILY	Quentin Collonges	3-15	1	1	1	121,237	119,864
A BARTLETT	Simonsig	4-12	1	1	1	121,197	120,128
STIO PINNACLE RACING	Countrywide Flame	1-8	2	2	2	116,844	58,520
J WHITE	Dynaste	4-5	1	0	0	113,423	92,053
THE FESTIVAL GOERS	Rock On Ruby	1-4	1	1	0	109,960	10,570
PIERMORE STUD	Captain Conan	7-11	0	0	0	110,174	106,492
WAYNE CLIFFORD	Shoegazer	15-73	9	10	5	103,307	79,234
DAVID ABELL	Cape Tribulation	2-10	0	1	0	100,653	80,735
PAUL DUFFY DIAMOND PARTNERSHIP	Reve De Sivola	2-6	1	0	1	98,509	76,372
MEFORM BETFAIR RACING CLUB LTD	Cause Of Causes	1-7	0	1	0	95,395	84,405
MRS S SMITH	Mwaleshi	10-114	10	17	10	95,377	59,410
MRS JANET DAVIES	Court Minstrel	6-49	6	6	4	91,245	65,963
THE OLD BETFAIRIANS	Big Occasion	1-8	2	3	1	89,263	45,560
PRISM BLOODSTOCK	Fleet Dawn	8-30	5	3	3	88,145	78,454

TOP NH HORSES IN BRITAIN 2012/13

HORSE (AGE)	WIN & PLACE £	W-R	TRAINER	OWNER	BREEDER
AURORAS ENCORE (11)	551,543	1-9	Sue Smith	D Pryde,J Beaumont & DP Van Der Hoeven	Mountarmstrong Stud
SPRINTER SACRE (7)	429,101	4-4	Nicky Henderson	Mrs Caroline Mould	Christophe Masle
BOBS WORTH (8)	398,650	2-2	Nicky Henderson	The Not Afraid Partnership	Mrs L Eadie
CUE CARD (7)	324,903	3-5	Colin Tizzard	Mrs Jean R Bishop	R T Crellin
ZARKANDAR (6)	274,811	4-5	Paul Nicholls	Chris Giles & Potensis Ltd	His Highness The Aga Khan's Studs S C
HURRICANE FLY (9)	227,800	1-1	W P Mullins	George Creighton & Mrs Rose Boyd	Agricola Del Parco
SOLWHIT (9)	224,136	2-2	C Byrnes	Top Of The Hill Syndicate	Haras De Preaux
CAPPA BLEU (11)	217,327	0-3	Evan Williams	Mr & Mrs William Rucker	Thomas O'Connor
LONG RUN (8)	215,150	1-3	Nicky Henderson	Robert Waley-Cohen	Mrs Marie-Christine Gabeur
SILVINIACO CONTI (7)	211,105	3-5	Paul Nicholls	Chris Giles & Potensis Ltd	Patrick Joubert
AT FISHERS CROSS (6)	171,703	6-6	Rebecca Curtis	John P McManus	Liam O'Regan
FIRST LIEUTENANT (8)	159,295	1-3	M F Morris	Gigginstown House Stud	Mrs Mary O'Connor
MY TENT OR YOURS (6)	158,537	4-6	Nicky Henderson	John P McManus	F Dunne
THE NEW ONE (5)	146,445	4-6	Nigel Twiston-Davies	Mrs S Such	R Brown & Ballylinch Stud
GODSMEJUDGE (7)	137,646	3-7	Alan King	Favourites Racing	Cecil And Martin McCracken
TEAFORTHREE (9)	124,105	0-5	Rebecca Curtis	T437	M O'Sullivan
WISHFULL THINKING (10)	123,032	2-6	Philip Hobbs	Mrs Diana L Whateley	Cobhall Court Stud
SIMONSIG (7)	118,417	3-3	Nicky Henderson	R A Bartlett	Simon Tindall
QUENTIN COLLONGES (9)	117,915	2-4	Henry Daly	Neville Statham & Family	G A E C Delorme Freres
SIR DES CHAMPS (7)	117,535	0-1	W P Mullins	Gigginstown House Stud	Dominique Clayeux
COUNTRYWIDE FLAME (5)	115,337	1-5	John Quinn	Estio Pinnacle Racing	Michael Clarke
DYNASTE (7)	113,423	4-5	David Pipe	A J White	Paul Chartier
CAPTAIN CHRIS (9)	110,385	1-4	Philip Hobbs	Mrs Diana L Whateley	Mrs Noreen Walsh
ROCK ON RUBY (8)	109,960	1-3	Harry Fry	The Festival Goers	John O'Dwyer
CAPTAIN CONAN (6)	103,481	4-5	Nicky Henderson	Triermore Stud	Woodcote Stud Limited
CAPE TRIBULATION (8)	100,395	2-5	Malcolm Jefferson	J David Abell	Taker Bloodstock
REVE DE SIVOLA (8)	98,509	2-4	Nick Williams	Paul Duffy Diamond P'ship	Gilles Trapenard & Thomas Trapenard
OSCAR WHISKY (8)	96,845	2-5	Nicky Henderson	Walters Plant Hire Ltd	Stephanie Hanly
HOLYWELL (6)	96,287	1-6	Jonjo O'Neill	Mrs Gay Smith	Patrick Doyle
CAUSE OF CAUSES (5)	95,395	1-6	Gordon Elliott	Timeform Betfair RC Ltd	Flaxman Holdings Ltd
AL FEROF (7)	91,120	1-1	Paul Nicholls	J Hales	J Rauch & G Chenu
BIG OCCASION (6)	89,263	1-8	David Pipe	The Old Betfairians	Swettenham Stud & Ben Sangster
MONBEG DUDE (8)	87,755	2-5	Michael Scudamore	Oydunow	Hilary O'Connor
LORD WINDERMERE (7)	85,425	1-1	J H Culloty	Dr R Lambe	Edmond Coleman
FOR NON STOP (8)	84,051	1-5	Nick Williams	Potensis Ltd & Chris Giles	Raymond O'Rourke
WALKON (8)	83,414	0-5	Alan King	McNeill Family	Marquise Soledad De Moratall
MEDINAS (6)	82,661	2-6	Alan King	Mr & Mrs F D Bell	Mme Laurence Gagneux
UNIONISTE (5)	81,994	3-5	Paul Nicholls	J Hales	Haras De Saint-Voir Et Al
SAME DIFFERENCE (8)	80,363	2-8	Nigel Twiston-Davies	Mrs R Vaughan	Mrs Marie Fenlon
SIRE DE GRUGY (7)	80,079	4-6	Gary Moore	The Preston Family & Friends Ltd	La Grugerie
SIZING EUROPE (11)	78,162	0-1	Henry De Bromhead	Ann & Alan Potts P'ship	Mrs Angela Bracken
OISEAU DE NUIT (11)	78,044	2-7	Colin Tizzard	Terry Warner	Guy Cherel
MENORAH (8)	76,840	1-6	Philip Hobbs	Mrs Diana L Whateley	Mrs E Grant & Miss Anna Brislane
L'UNIQUE (4)	74,501	3-4	Alan King	Denis J Barry	S A R L Ecurie D
TRIOLO D'ALENE (6)	73,146	1-5	Nicky Henderson	Mr & Mrs Sandy Orr	Louis Couteaudier
GOLDEN CHIEFTAIN (8)	71,997	2-8	Colin Tizzard	Brocade Racing	Robert Donaldson
OPENING BATSMAN (7)	70,846	3-7	Harry Fry	The Twelfth Man P'ship	A Cogley
KATENKO (7)	70,324	2-4	Venetia Williams	A Brooks	S C P Haras Des Coudraie
CARRICKBOY (9)	69,094	2-7	Venetia Williams	Trevor Hemmings	B & I McClelland

LEADING SIRES OF 2013 IN GREAT BRITAIN AND IRELAND

STALLION	BREEDING	RNRS	WNRS	WINS	WIN MONEY	PLACES	PLACE MONEY	TOTAL
GALILEO (IRE)	by Sadler's Wells (USA)	228	107	162	2639588	371	2093634	4733222
DUBAWI (IRE)	by Dubai Millennium (GB)	113	47	74	1571227	186	956288	2527515
OASIS DREAM (GB)	by Green Desert (USA)	180	96	151	1742656	388	686497	2429152
TEOFILO (IRE)	by Galileo (IRE)	128	53	83	1352092	243	984834	2336926
DANSILI (GB)	by Danehill (USA)	139	71	106	1691672	245	570236	2261907
PIVOTAL (GB)	by Polar Falcon (USA)	156	72	101	1531851	302	440211	1972062
NEW APPROACH (IRE)	by Galileo (IRE)	88	38	50	1079226	131	838530	1917757
DARK ANGEL (IRE)	by Acclamation (GB)	86	46	84	1217908	237	504131	1722039
MONTJEU (IRE)	by Sadler's Wells (USA)	105	33	46	1199457	176	434158	1632616
ACCLAMATION (GB)	by Royal Applause (GB)	197	94	134	945503	424	610392	1555895
INVINCIBLE SPIRIT (IRE)	by Green Desert (USA)	220	96	142	831559	375	694383	1525941
DANEHILL DANCER (IRE)	by Danehill (USA)	155	64	82	785397	277	676739	1462137
CAPE CROSS (IRE)	by Green Desert (USA)	167	74	130	1039623	298	397463	1437086
SHAMARDAL (USA)	by Giant's Causeway (USA)	143	67	108	830843	281	553524	1384367
DUTCH ART (GB)	by Medicean (GB)	120	53	91	912657	191	470125	1382782
WAR FRONT (USA)	by Danzig (USA)	10	5	11	1059364	12	197827	1257192
EXCEED AND EXCEL (AUS)	by Danehill (USA)	175	81	118	808732	346	401400	1210132
KYLLACHY (GB)	by Pivotal (GB)	146	66	100	727575	335	478870	1206446
AUTHORIZED (IRE)	by Montjeu (IRE)	105	39	58	856396	135	250328	1106724
CHOISIR (AUS)	by Danehill Dancer (IRE)	78	30	45	860074	157	226820	1086894
HOLY ROMAN EMPEROR (IRE)	by Danehill (USA)	140	62	87	604509	280	452033	1056542
ROCK OF GIBRALTAR (IRE)	by Danehill (USA)	132	44	71	443575	226	574599	1018174
MONSUN (GER)	by Konigsstuhl (GER)	26	12	16	907832	30	99732	1007563
IFFRAAJ (GB)	by Zafonic (USA)	111	40	64	590192	197	351144	941336
RED CLUBS (IRE)	by Red Ransom (USA)	78	25	53	744943	167	173970	918914

LEADING SIRES OF 2013
(GREAT BRITAIN, IRELAND AND OVERSEAS)

STALLION	BREEDING	DOMESTIC WNRS	WINS	WIN MONEY	OVERSEAS WNRS	WINS	WIN MONEY	TOTAL
GALILEO (IRE)	by Sadler's Wells (USA)	107	162	2639588	35	52	2790708	5430296
DANSILI (GB)	by Danehill (USA)	71	106	1691672	65	109	3655212	5346884
DUBAWI (IRE)	by Dubai Millenium (GB)	47	74	1571227	51	94	3650379	5221605
MONSUN (GER)	by Konigsstuhl (GER)	12	16	907832	16	31	3702495	4610326
ORATORIO (IRE)	by Danehill (USA)	53	88	528693	89	168	3870072	4398764
MONTJEU (IRE)	by Sadler's Wells (USA)	33	46	1198457	40	46	2787421	3985878
MOTIVATOR (GB)	by Montjeu (IRE)	26	37	201702	39	71	3421735	3623436
KING'S BEST (USA)	by Kingmambo (USA)	20	39	442362	33	55	2918749	3361111
OASIS DREAM (GB)	by Green Desert (USA)	96	151	1742656	72	126	1300452	3043107
SHAMARDAL (USA)	by Giant's Causeway (USA)	67	108	830843	67	111	2038667	2869510
PIVOTAL (GB)	by Polar Falcon (USA)	72	101	1531851	52	107	1187921	2719773
HOLY ROMAN EMPEROR (IRE)	by Danehill (USA)	62	87	604509	84	152	2018873	2623382
FOOTSTEPSINTHESAND (GB)	by Giant's Causeway (USA)	60	94	577176	84	140	1818852	2396028
TEOFILO (IRE)	by Galileo (IRE)	53	83	1352092	43	67	969811	2321903
CAPE CROSS (IRE)	by Green Desert (USA)	74	130	1039623	45	74	1266488	2306112
DANEHILL DANCER (IRE)	by Danehill (USA)	64	82	785397	50	75	1494130	2279527
INVINCIBLE SPIRIT (IRE)	by Green Desert (USA)	96	142	831559	53	84	1397350	2228909
DUTCH ART (GB)	by Medicean (GB)	53	91	912657	30	76	998405	1911061
WAR FRONT (USA)	by Danzig (USA)	5	11	1059364	2	2	742950	1802314
EXCEED AND EXCEL (AUS)	by Danehill (USA)	81	118	808732	40	80	990674	1799406
ROCK OF GIBRALTAR (IRE)	by Danehill (USA)	44	71	443575	79	121	1299667	1743242
ACCLAMATION (GB)	by Royal Applause (GB)	94	134	945503	46	87	756682	1702185
DARK ANGEL (IRE)	by Acclamation (IRE)	46	84	1217908	20	37	297509	1515416
CHOISIR (AUS)	by Danehill Dancer (IRE)	30	45	860074	34	56	647746	1507820
SINGSPIEL (IRE)	by In The Wings	35	49	296285	57	98	1199002	1495287

LEADING TWO-YEAR-OLD SIRES OF 2013 IN GREAT BRITAIN AND IRELAND

STALLION	BREEDING	RNRS	WNRS	WINS	WIN MONEY	PLACES	PLACE MONEY	TOTAL
OASIS DREAM (GB)	by Green Desert (USA)	43	22	30	726111	60	180917	907028
ACCLAMATION (GB)	by Royal Applause (GB)	65	29	38	371597	121	267414	639011
IFFRAAJ (GB)	by Zafonic (GB)	44	13	21	383805	60	202905	586710
GALILEO (IRE)	by Sadler's Wells (USA)	58	21	30	385288	53	190928	576216
KODIAC (GB)	by Danehill (USA)	63	33	48	369218	137	171504	540722
INVINCIBLE SPIRIT (IRE)	by Green Desert (USA)	82	34	39	194595	118	309416	504011
MASTERCRAFTSMAN (IRE)	by Danehill Dancer (IRE)	55	21	29	358188	86	143570	501759
DUBAWI (IRE)	by Dubai Millenium (GB)	55	20	29	233631	62	254186	487817
INTENSE FOCUS (USA)	by Giant's Causeway (USA)	51	16	23	336242	86	107621	443863
WAR FRONT (USA)	by Danzig (USA)	6	3	7	398244	4	36553	434797
HOLY ROMAN EMPEROR (IRE)	by Danehill (USA)	51	21	26	180358	93	195383	375741
DANDY MAN (IRE)	by Mozart (IRE)	46	18	22	246385	74	123390	369775
PASTORAL PURSUITS (GB)	by Bahamian Bounty (GB)	48	17	27	213391	78	139632	353023
HENRYTHENAVIGATOR (USA)	by Kingmambo (USA)	18	7	10	243451	25	82695	326145
EXCEED AND EXCEL (AUS)	by Danehill (USA)	67	26	33	178352	84	141549	319901
BAHAMIAN BOUNTY (GB)	by Cadeaux Genereux	51	19	28	209369	83	109150	318519
CLODOVIL (IRE)	by Danehill (USA)	28	13	18	151659	69	162871	314529
SHAMARDAL (USA)	by Giant's Causeway (USA)	53	16	20	157936	75	116236	274172
CAMACHO (GB)	by Danehill (USA)	39	12	18	155844	87	104060	259904
FOOTSTEPSINTHESAND (GB)	by Giant's Causeway (USA)	48	16	21	142967	78	89320	232287
KHELEYF (USA)	by Green Desert (USA)	42	17	28	111430	71	115683	227113
ROYAL APPLAUSE (GB)	by Waajib	55	23	31	128872	95	77405	206278
KYLLACHY (GB)	by Pivotal (GB)	27	11	14	98119	42	105588	203707
BUSHRANGER (IRE)	by Danetime (IRE)	76	15	19	82163	91	105716	187879
DARK ANGEL (IRE)	by Acclamation (IRE)	21	11	15	88711	39	91171	179881

LEADING FIRST CROP SIRES OF 2013 IN GREAT BRITAIN AND IRELAND

STALLION	BREEDING	RNRS	WNRS	WINS	WIN MONEY	PLACES	PLACE MONEY	TOTAL
MASTERCRAFTSMAN (IRE)	by Danehill Dancer (IRE)	55	21	29	358188	86	143570	501759
INTENSE FOCUS (USA)	by Giant's Causeway (USA)	51	16	23	336242	86	107621	443863
DANDY MAN (IRE)	by Mozart (IRE)	46	18	22	246385	74	123390	369775
BUSHRANGER (IRE)	by Danetime (IRE)	76	15	19	82163	91	105716	187879
SEA THE STARS (IRE)	by Cape Cross (IRE)	35	8	10	84849	35	30487	115336
CAPTAIN GERRARD (IRE)	by Oasis Dream (GB)	42	13	22	59661	65	47211	106872
CHAMPS ELYSEES (GB)	by Danehill (USA)	28	9	10	64894	27	37934	102828
AQLAAM (GB)	by Oasis Dream (GB)	18	7	8	60779	20	20454	81233
MAJOR CADEAUX (GB)	by Cadeaux Genereux	21	5	8	40565	24	17052	57618
ART CONNOISSEUR (IRE)	by Lucky Story (USA)	23	6	8	25229	38	21001	46231
ARCHIPENKO (USA)	by Kingmambo (USA)	11	4	7	20482	6	3472	23953
THE CARBON UNIT (USA)	by Catienus (USA)	2	0	0	0	5	16019	16019
SOLDIER OF FORTUNE (IRE)	by Galileo (IRE)	3	1	2	11968	7	3303	15272
THEWAYYOUARE (USA)	by Kingmambo (USA)	2	2	4	10325	2	2503	12828
WINKER WATSON (GB)	by Piccolo (GB)	10	1	1	2911	23	9069	11980
YEATS (IRE)	by Sadler's Wells (USA)	11	1	1	3235	8	5984	9219
NAAQOOS (GB)	by Oasis Dream (GB)	5	1	1	6469	3	2647	9116
VIRTUAL (GB)	by Pivotal (GB)	14	1	1	2588	6	4601	7188
CREACHADOIR (IRE)	by King's Best (USA)	2	1	1	3235	2	1352	4586
ADMIRALOFTHEFLEET (USA)	by Danehill (USA)	1	1	1	3881	1	558	4439
DUNKERQUE (FR)	by Highest Honor (FR)	1	1	1	1941	3	1566	3507
U S RANGER (USA)	by Danzig (USA)	4	0	0	0	5	2778	2778
IALYSOS (GR)	by So Factual (USA)	2	0	0	0	2	2310	2310
REBELLION (GB)	by Mozart (IRE)	2	0	0	0	2	962	962
LE HAVRE (IRE)	by Noverre (USA)	1	0	0	0	1	241	241

LEADING MATERNAL GRANDSIRES OF 2013 IN GREAT BRITAIN AND IRELAND

STALLION	BREEDING	RNRS	WNRS	WINS	WIN MONEY	PLACES	PLACE MONEY	TOTAL
DARSHAAN	by Shirley Heights	166	76	126	2275203	279	1019235	3294438
SADLER'S WELLS (USA)	by Northern Dancer	385	151	222	2214394	670	856222	3070616
DANEHILL (USA)	by Danzig (USA)	269	116	175	1565775	510	1027830	2593605
RAINBOW QUEST (USA)	by Blushing Groom (FR)	201	79	121	1133068	311	642566	1775634
INDIAN RIDGE	by Ahonoora	162	78	118	1144158	316	513441	1657598
KINGMAMBO (USA)	by Mr Prospector (USA)	82	37	58	1117843	164	423582	1541425
GALILEO (IRE)	by Sadler's Wells (USA)	104	46	64	786715	152	488031	1274746
GREEN DESERT (USA)	by Danzig (USA)	211	75	108	697340	360	552281	1249621
PIVOTAL (GB)	by Polar Falcon (GB)	163	76	117	919567	280	313073	1232640
SINNDAR (IRE)	by Grand Lodge (USA)	27	10	14	693850	42	531838	1225689
SELKIRK (USA)	by Sharpen Up	159	68	105	749669	324	451220	1200890
ALZAO (USA)	by Lyphard (USA)	98	33	55	828288	144	235671	1063959
RAHY (USA)	by Blushing Groom (FR)	50	16	25	743839	101	257699	1001538
MACHIAVELLIAN (USA)	by Mr Prospector (USA)	125	46	76	628946	236	354268	983213
LANDO (GER)	by Acatenango (GER)	12	4	7	890138	18	27860	917998
DESERT STYLE (IRE)	by Green Desert (USA)	30	10	17	784226	56	125964	910190
KEY OF LUCK (USA)	by Chief's Crown (USA)	42	18	31	507446	67	401061	908506
MARK OF ESTEEM (IRE)	by Darshaan	81	27	46	450334	154	379081	829415
DANSILI (GB)	by Danehill (USA)	73	33	51	691633	125	130114	821748
SHAREEF DANCER (USA)	by Northern Dancer	38	7	12	659485	62	151891	811375
CADEAUX GENEREUX	by Young Generation	127	46	70	385910	237	420575	806485
PEINTRE CELEBRE (USA)	by Nureyev (USA)	55	25	32	444008	97	354615	798623
NIGHT SHIFT (USA)	by Northern Dancer	151	53	80	445650	337	332116	777766
BARATHEA (IRE)	by Sadler's Wells (USA)	147	54	85	362562	290	403376	765938
GONE WEST (USA)	by Mr Prospector (USA)	71	31	47	615435	111	144818	760253

FLAT STALLIONS' EARNINGS FOR 2013

(includes every stallion who sired a winner on the Flat in Great Britain and Ireland in 2013)

STALLIONS	RNRS	STARTS	WNRS	WINS	PLACES	TOTAL (£)
ACCLAMATION (GB)	197	1182	94	134	424	1555895.34
ACCORDION	7	15	2	2	3	13083.34
ACT ONE (GB)	17	96	6	10	30	80061.84
ADMIRALOFTHEFLEET (USA)	1	4	1	1	1	4439.36
AD VALOREM (USA)	43	212	15	20	66	117629.77
ALDEBARAN (USA)	2	20	1	2	9	37819.53
ALDERBROOK (GB)	1	1	1	1	0	4487.80
ALHAARTH (IRE)	39	170	11	17	41	99725.61
ALJABR (USA)	3	13	1	1	4	3584.60
ALMATY (IRE)	1	14	1	2	4	5503.85
ALMUTAWAKEL (GB)	3	19	1	2	5	5669.52
AMADEUS WOLF (GB)	76	349	19	29	93	278174.61
AMERICAN POST (GB)	4	26	1	2	8	8561.45
ANABAA (USA)	10	69	5	7	15	41668.72
ANTONIUS PIUS (USA)	53	303	20	34	92	180552.97
A P INDY (USA)	3	9	1	1	6	6444.30
AQLAAM (GB)	18	64	7	8	20	81233.26
ARAAFA (IRE)	27	112	8	10	30	56860.93
ARAGORN (IRE)	2	17	1	2	10	8588.70
ARAKAN (USA)	21	110	5	10	32	317262.21
ARCH (USA)	33	131	14	22	54	238508.24
ARCHIPENKO (USA)	11	33	4	7	6	23953.31
ARKADIAN HERO (USA)	4	17	1	2	5	6600.40
ART CONNOISSEUR (IRE)	23	92	6	8	38	46230.53
ASHKALANI (IRE)	2	13	1	2	4	13983.75
ASSERTIVE (GB)	31	163	10	13	55	81361.69
ATRAF (GB)	6	31	2	2	9	7840.26
AUCTION HOUSE (USA)	21	114	7	7	24	34521.00
AUSSIE RULES (USA)	52	334	19	36	120	446787.82
AUTHORIZED (IRE)	105	419	39	58	135	1106724.22
AVERTI (IRE)	4	25	2	2	6	8235.75
AVONBRIDGE (GB)	68	373	17	24	110	194217.27
AZAMOUR (IRE)	63	262	19	30	85	506392.36
BACHELOR DUKE (USA)	28	161	11	12	37	76305.08
BAHAMIAN BOUNTY (GB)	149	870	51	74	273	756906.31
BAHRI (USA)	9	28	2	2	7	9158.99
BALLET MASTER (USA)	4	53	3	6	17	21949.80
BALMONT (USA)	12	73	6	9	25	73609.14
BALTIC KING (GB)	28	177	9	16	60	134550.57
BARATHEA (IRE)	33	166	10	14	44	99356.82
BEAT ALL (USA)	10	75	5	11	26	97714.95
BEAT HOLLOW (GB)	54	284	21	31	88	260776.26
BEAUCHAMP KING (GB)	1	7	1	1	4	4333.25
BENEFICIAL (GB)	9	27	1	2	8	19105.65
BERNARDINI (USA)	18	57	5	6	21	63482.09
BERNSTEIN (USA)	11	73	5	9	28	94055.22
BERTOLINI (USA)	88	540	25	41	157	231412.2
BEST OF THE BESTS (IRE)	4	30	1	1	9	5678.4
BIG BAD BOB (IRE)	30	138	8	11	31	215034.44
BIG BROWN (USA)	1	3	1	2	1	46382.1
BLACK SAM BELLAMY (IRE)	6	26	2	2	10	10257.3
BLUE DAKOTA (IRE)	2	16	1	2	6	7955.2
BOB AND JOHN (USA)	1	2	1	2	0	8733.1
BOB BACK (USA)	1	3	1	1	1	4382.1
BOLD EDGE (GB)	5	47	2	4	14	13142.5
BOLD FACT (USA)	4	31	2	2	10	7993.7
BOLLIN ERIC (GB)	6	29	1	1	12	8981.9
BROKEN VOW (USA)	4	16	2	3	4	23923.5

STALLIONS	RNRS	STARTS	WNRS	WINS	PLACES	TOTAL (£)
BUSHRANGER (IRE)	76	277	15	19	91	187879.02
BYRON (GB)	95	657	47	79	206	707468.14
CACIQUE (IRE)	2	16	1	1	6	4065.55
CADEAUX GENEREUX	28	190	12	16	67	151598.96
CAMACHO (GB)	64	382	25	37	162	452183.14
CANDY RIDE (ARG)	2	7	1	1	2	3742.40
CAPE CROSS (IRE)	167	837	74	130	298	1437086.41
CAPE TOWN (IRE)	3	16	1	4	2	11222.22
CAPTAIN GERRARD (IRE)	42	207	13	22	65	106872.22
CAPTAIN MARVELOUS (IRE)	22	113	9	14	23	75559.43
CAPTAIN RIO (GB)	84	492	33	52	143	392398.51
CARNEGIE (IRE)	1	19	1	4	6	10631.50
CATCHER IN THE RYE (IRE)	17	73	2	2	18	16152.02
CELTIC SWING (GB)	27	134	9	14	37	169717.06
CENTRAL PARK (IRE)	5	30	1	4	5	13328.15
CHAMPS ELYSEES (GB)	28	82	9	10	27	102827.95
CHEROKEE RUN (USA)	2	13	1	3	4	9670.25
CHEVALIER (IRE)	23	148	10	15	51	130230.56
CHINEUR (FR)	36	264	14	23	83	193087.90
CHOISIR (AUS)	78	489	30	45	157	1086893.71
CITY ON A HILL (USA)	2	12	1	1	4	4803.86
CITY ZIP (USA)	4	11	2	3	6	72874.00
CLODOVIL (IRE)	87	551	46	63	200	826849.37
COCKNEY REBEL (IRE)	37	168	8	11	50	67917.93
COMPTON ADMIRAL (GB)	3	18	1	2	1	4178.20
COMPTON PLACE (GB)	115	663	41	67	185	435806.01
CONSOLIDATOR (USA)	1	9	1	1	4	12134.15
CRAIGSTEEL (GB)	1	14	1	1	5	6252.01
CREACHADOIR (IRE)	2	6	1	1	2	4586.16
CURLIN (USA)	3	15	1	2	6	17657.85
DAAHER (CAN)	5	23	1	2	7	17216.86
DAGGERS DRAWN (USA)	4	19	2	3	5	8045.95
DALAKHANI (IRE)	117	477	33	47	180	662945.86
DANBIRD (AUS)	14	108	5	8	36	45417.97
DANDY MAN (IRE)	46	193	18	22	74	369774.92
DANEHILL (USA)	4	12	1	7	1	15253.30
DANEHILL DANCER (IRE)	155	732	64	82	277	1462136.92
DANETIME (IRE)	17	169	7	10	52	127825.46
DANROAD (AUS)	10	63	4	5	19	29168.73
DANSILI (GB)	139	609	71	106	245	2261907.15
DARK ANGEL (IRE)	86	622	46	84	237	1722038.72
DASHING BLADE	1	5	1	1	3	20746.10
DAYLAMI (IRE)	9	51	5	5	17	24479.18
DEFINITE ARTICLE (GB)	6	13	2	3	1	12476.65
DELLA FRANCESCA (USA)	2	15	1	2	4	7212.93
DELTA DANCER (GB)	4	15	1	2	10	10400.75
DENOUNCE (GB)	4	13	1	1	1	3103.45
DEPLOY	2	8	1	2	2	19890.25
DEPORTIVO (GB)	6	48	4	7	11	62926.05
DESERT KING (IRE)	4	15	1	1	3	4565.60
DESERT MILLENNIUM (IRE)	4	23	2	2	4	5998.70
DESERT PRINCE (IRE)	10	69	4	5	21	27047.57
DESERT STYLE (IRE)	15	77	4	5	25	48303.88
DESERT SUN (GB)	5	25	2	3	4	13365.22
DIAMOND GREEN (FR)	55	286	15	22	71	164919.97
DIESIS	7	45	2	4	12	38604.77
DIKTAT (GB)	27	184	8	19	38	161071.11
DILSHAAN (GB)	6	32	1	3	3	8319.20
DISCREET CAT (USA)	3	10	1	1	1	12834.80
DISTANT MUSIC (USA)	9	64	3	8	19	47743.57
DISTORTED HUMOR (USA)	17	68	8	11	29	144958.49
DIXIE UNION (USA)	9	35	3	4	15	34116.75
DOCKSIDER (USA)	3	29	1	1	8	15599.95

STALLIONS	RNRS	STARTS	WNRS	WINS	PLACES	TOTAL (£)
DOMEDRIVER (IRE)	4	21	1	1	4	8920.96
DONERAILE COURT (USA)	1	21	1	5	10	16817.95
DOYEN (IRE)	22	131	9	17	47	182581.77
DR FONG (USA)	38	205	11	25	58	173243.37
DR MASSINI (IRE)	7	13	1	1	0	4488.60
DUBAI DESTINATION (USA)	65	391	24	39	157	379882.57
DUBAWI (IRE)	113	490	47	74	186	2527514.98
DUKE OF MARMALADE (IRE)	84	377	35	56	131	599123.22
DUNKERQUE (FR)	1	5	1	1	3	3507.00
DUTCH ART (GB)	120	594	53	91	191	1382781.66
DYLAN THOMAS (IRE)	87	408	36	62	142	461589.72
DYNAFORMER (USA)	26	103	15	20	41	298383.96
ECHO OF LIGHT (GB)	36	162	12	17	45	210120.01
E DUBAI (USA)	4	33	2	4	8	18755.33
EFISIO	6	31	2	2	12	38044.42
ELMAAMUL (USA)	1	7	1	2	3	7334.80
ELNADIM (USA)	53	312	18	26	97	222024.74
EL PRADO (IRE)	5	24	1	1	8	5963.93
ELUSIVE CITY (USA)	96	546	36	63	168	539493.21
ELUSIVE QUALITY (USA)	53	321	28	41	105	521686.36
EMPIRE MAKER (USA)	12	36	5	6	12	36256.25
ENCOSTA DE LAGO (AUS)	4	13	1	1	2	3512.69
ENGLISH CHANNEL (USA)	7	25	2	3	9	18368.71
EUROSILVER (USA)	1	16	1	2	6	12469.22
EXCEED AND EXCEL (AUS)	175	970	81	118	346	1210132.24
EXCELLENT ART (GB)	114	570	46	63	186	573187.92
EXCHANGE RATE (USA)	10	41	3	4	18	41804.37
FAIR MIX (IRE)	6	36	2	2	21	13865.05
FALBRAV (IRE)	5	42	1	2	12	11977.20
FALCO (USA)	2	9	1	2	3	15499.07
FANTASTIC LIGHT (USA)	21	181	10	17	64	158073.85
FASLIYEV (USA)	29	228	7	15	69	102968.72
FASTNET ROCK (AUS)	13	31	5	5	13	72027.97
FATH (USA)	20	156	7	11	37	65747.67
FIREBREAK (GB)	45	243	14	22	77	157255.64
FIRST DEFENCE (USA)	8	17	4	5	10	53724.30
FIRST SAMURAI (USA)	7	29	2	2	11	23019.75
FIRST TRUMP (GB)	4	25	2	2	5	5298.00
FIVE STAR DAY (USA)	1	12	1	2	7	142577.62
FOOTSTEPSINTHESAND (GB)	121	701	60	94	271	904362.96
FOREST DANGER (USA)	1	9	1	2	2	9211.38
FORESTRY (USA)	2	15	2	3	7	12213.65
FOXHOUND (USA)	4	31	2	2	8	12834.30
FRAAM (GB)	11	82	5	9	24	109612.33
GALILEO (IRE)	228	874	107	162	371	4733221.73
GENEROUS (IRE)	10	35	1	1	8	111127.86
GENTLEMAN'S DEAL (IRE)	7	63	3	4	31	25755.95
GENTLEWAVE (IRE)	5	26	1	1	9	74399.90
GHOSTZAPPER (USA)	2	5	1	1	0	7292.68
GIANT'S CAUSEWAY (USA)	36	170	16	22	62	321932.74
GOLAN (IRE)	12	40	3	4	13	70652.96
GOLD AWAY (IRE)	7	34	5	10	11	56946.48
GOLDEN SNAKE (USA)	4	18	2	4	7	32243.87
GONE WEST (USA)	3	15	1	3	4	82312.12
GOOD REWARD (USA)	1	16	1	1	5	4621.60
GOODRICKE (GB)	2	6	1	1	1	6391.75
GOVERNOR BROWN (USA)	1	4	1	1	1	4967.48
GRAND LODGE (USA)	3	19	1	4	4	12396.35
GRAPE TREE ROAD (GB)	3	15	2	4	7	12884.89
GREAT EXHIBITION (USA)	10	45	1	1	5	9295.66
GREEN DESERT (USA)	52	350	28	42	99	328343.10
HAAFHD (GB)	78	489	33	59	163	493855.94
HAATEF (USA)	36	191	15	21	62	256484.38

STALLIONS	RNRS	STARTS	WNRS	WINS	PLACES	TOTAL (£)
HALLING (USA)	96	479	30	46	149	381791.65
HANNOUMA (IRE)	2	11	1	1	4	9873.96
HARD SPUN (USA)	28	135	13	19	55	206599.76
HAT TRICK (JPN)	2	13	1	1	5	3988.20
HAWK WING (USA)	40	231	11	15	69	162668.89
HELIOSTATIC (IRE)	4	12	1	1	3	5086.35
HELISSIO (FR)	6	27	2	3	7	29223.59
HENNY HUGHES (USA)	6	22	2	2	2	6189.47
HENRYTHENAVIGATOR (USA)	40	190	18	26	72	495586.03
HERNANDO (FR)	38	197	15	29	69	359333.42
HERON ISLAND (IRE)	3	9	1	2	2	66353.66
HIGH CHAPARRAL (IRE)	114	462	36	49	155	823710.24
HOLD THAT TIGER (USA)	3	18	1	1	2	4298.77
HOLY ROMAN EMPEROR (IRE)	140	777	62	87	280	1056542.43
HURRICANE RUN (IRE)	63	274	26	36	93	319755.28
ICEMAN (GB)	43	307	18	23	99	170300.10
IFFRAAJ (GB)	111	621	40	64	197	941336.25
IMPERIAL BALLET (IRE)	6	18	1	1	6	6349.58
IMPERIAL DANCER (GB)	9	61	4	8	16	27030.64
INCHINOR (GB)	3	17	1	1	5	33033.40
INCLUDE (USA)	2	10	1	1	3	3274.30
INDESATCHEL (IRE)	37	199	10	13	51	76999.71
INDIAN CHARLIE (USA)	3	14	1	1	5	8590.65
INDIAN DANEHILL (IRE)	3	26	2	4	5	12211.37
INDIAN HAVEN (GB)	30	166	14	19	57	134057.94
INDIAN RIDGE	16	131	5	11	50	146430.49
INDIAN ROCKET (GB)	2	7	1	1	4	9548.78
INTENSE FOCUS (USA)	51	216	16	23	86	443862.90
IN THE WINGS	3	9	1	2	1	4726.90
INTIKHAB (USA)	57	323	24	33	100	277032.34
INVASOR (ARG)	9	48	3	5	19	32071.88
INVINCIBLE SPIRIT (IRE)	220	1058	96	142	375	1525941.11
IRON MASK (USA)	4	35	1	1	14	11489.37
ISHIGURU (USA)	52	384	22	35	122	273787.15
IVAN DENISOVICH (IRE)	18	125	6	8	45	66876.45
JAMMAAL (GB)	1	8	1	1	1	4837.40
JAZIL (USA)	7	30	2	2	9	16578.40
JELANI (IRE)	1	8	1	1	5	5346.70
JEREMY (USA)	66	348	23	29	121	292138.55
JOHANNESBURG (USA)	30	196	8	17	49	186742.86
JOHAR (USA)	2	18	1	3	5	40500.00
JOSR ALGARHOUD (IRE)	12	56	2	3	13	12860.50
KALANISI (IRE)	14	68	2	3	26	37114.91
KALLISTO (GER)	1	6	1	1	1	5028.45
KAYF TARA (GB)	7	24	3	7	7	29019.07
KEY OF LUCK (USA)	12	73	3	5	20	76886.20
KHELEYF (USA)	150	937	55	89	297	671785.35
KING CHARLEMAGNE (USA)	4	27	1	1	3	3191.60
KINGMAMBO (USA)	5	11	1	1	4	18985.40
KINGSALSA (USA)	4	43	2	3	18	28491.06
KING'S BEST (USA)	51	326	20	39	113	584474.33
KING'S THEATRE (IRE)	8	22	1	1	8	18243.24
KIRKWALL (GB)	5	26	1	1	10	13584.09
KITTEN'S JOY (USA)	12	66	5	12	23	61066.86
KODIAC (GB)	106	597	49	71	221	789753.97
KONIGSTIGER (GER)	2	6	1	1	1	2876.20
KYLLACHY (GB)	146	950	66	100	335	1206445.76
LAHIB (USA)	6	22	1	1	5	11905.83
LANDO (GER)	7	36	2	2	11	21152.40
LANGFUHR (CAN)	6	22	2	3	9	39681.27
LATENT HEAT (USA)	2	13	1	2	2	4262.32
LAWMAN (FR)	88	431	30	45	152	722154.22
LAYMAN (USA)	5	14	1	1	3	5241.70

STALLIONS	RNRS	STARTS	WNRS	WINS	PLACES	TOTAL (£)
LEMON DROP KID (USA)	19	80	6	7	33	50763.20
LEND A HAND (GB)	3	19	2	2	4	9010.37
LEROIDESANIMAUX (BRZ)	4	19	1	2	7	9169.78
LE VIE DEI COLORI (GB)	15	135	4	10	50	188262.82
LIBRETTIST (USA)	22	133	9	15	42	108314.47
LIL'S BOY (USA)	4	15	2	2	4	13418.70
LINNGARI (IRE)	2	10	1	1	3	10494.50
LION HEART (USA)	4	22	2	2	6	11099.35
LOMITAS (GB)	7	48	2	2	17	87293.44
LUCARNO (GB)	8	33	2	3	6	37280.05
LUCKY OWNERS (NZ)	3	20	2	2	7	15312.79
LUCKY STORY (USA)	50	259	19	29	78	332363.29
LUJAIN (USA)	10	68	3	5	23	37473.18
MACHIAVELLIAN (USA)	8	76	5	7	18	75826.35
MAJESTIC MISSILE (IRE)	32	220	14	29	65	193113.37
MAJOR CADEAUX (GB)	21	98	5	8	24	57617.52
MAKBUL	5	45	4	6	14	41288.15
MALINAS (GER)	1	1	1	1	0	7012.20
MANDURO (GER)	86	352	31	38	127	587923.17
MARJU (IRE)	53	243	19	28	74	312288.31
MARK OF ESTEEM (IRE)	12	88	6	10	32	51105.81
MARTALINE (GB)	2	8	1	2	4	37719.51
MARTINO ALONSO (IRE)	1	9	1	1	3	8559.80
MASTERCRAFTSMAN (IRE)	55	204	21	29	86	501758.51
MASTERFUL (USA)	2	12	1	3	2	9887.55
MEDAGLIA D'ORO (USA)	23	109	7	12	49	149742.80
MEDECIS (GB)	14	73	3	5	20	62515.08
MEDICEAN (GB)	113	636	48	75	212	784945.03
MIDNIGHT LEGEND (GB)	2	18	2	6	4	14433.27
MIESQUE'S SON (USA)	2	15	1	1	5	6425.99
MILK IT MICK (GB)	15	94	6	9	26	99773.20
MILLKOM (GB)	4	29	2	4	16	24410.80
MINASHKI (IRE)	1	2	1	2	0	3881.40
MIND GAMES (GB)	13	75	7	9	23	52125.12
MISU BOND (IRE)	25	153	10	23	45	92798.40
MIZZEN MAST (USA)	27	134	13	15	47	125158.56
MODIGLIANI (USA)	11	54	4	11	13	92701.87
MONASHEE MOUNTAIN (USA)	5	33	2	2	9	15293.72
MONSIEUR BOND (IRE)	44	314	19	33	101	424733.74
MONSUN (GER)	26	91	12	16	30	1007563.05
MONTJEU (IRE)	105	428	33	46	176	1632615.65
MORE THAN READY (USA)	12	70	7	15	18	55271.66
MOSS VALE (IRE)	51	317	15	28	91	189043.43
MOST WELCOME	1	10	1	1	1	5621.35
MOTIVATOR (GB)	66	327	26	37	118	385003.78
MOUNTAIN HIGH (IRE)	2	4	1	1	0	3926.83
MOUNT NELSON (GB)	61	269	20	35	89	368267.82
MOZART (IRE)	3	25	1	3	8	20067.61
MR GREELEY (USA)	25	107	6	10	44	157632.30
MTOTO	4	18	1	1	6	8185.52
MUHAYMIN (USA)	1	6	1	1	0	5609.76
MUHTARRAM (USA)	4	24	3	4	6	22761.20
MUHTATHIR (GB)	11	64	4	6	30	58097.55
MUJADIL (USA)	27	181	10	16	57	169340.30
MUJAHID (USA)	14	102	6	7	25	34572.37
MULL OF KINTYRE (USA)	11	38	3	3	11	70793.60
MULTIPLEX (GB)	45	238	13	19	63	74275.85
MUTAKDDIM (USA)	1	8	1	1	1	2626.4?
MYBOYCHARLIE (IRE)	28	110	8	10	41	62763.0?
NAAQOOS (GB)	5	7	1	1	3	9115.6?
NAMID (GB)	35	267	12	20	72	131576.8?
NATIONAL ASSEMBLY (CAN)	1	3	1	1	1	72539.0?
NAYEF (USA)	98	416	34	40	131	308286.3?

STALLIONS	RNRS	STARTS	WNRS	WINS	PLACES	TOTAL (£)
NEEDWOOD BLADE (GB)	42	292	14	22	81	102998.37
NEW APPROACH (IRE)	88	320	38	50	131	1917756.53
NIGHT SHIFT (USA)	10	70	4	6	20	97854.96
NORSE DANCER (IRE)	13	53	2	4	9	43136.96
NORTH LIGHT (IRE)	4	18	1	1	1	2731.90
NOTNOWCATO (GB)	48	184	16	20	60	261462.87
NOVERRE (USA)	23	179	11	21	56	146024.35
NUMEROUS (USA)	2	17	1	3	3	7846.75
OASIS DREAM (GB)	180	1019	96	151	388	2429152.16
OBSERVATORY (USA)	22	90	6	9	20	39133.52
OFFICER (USA)	4	36	3	6	7	16490.21
OLDEN TIMES (GB)	5	28	1	1	9	77524.00
OLMODAVOR (USA)	1	10	1	1	2	2662.50
ONE COOL CAT (USA)	33	219	9	12	67	160660.53
ORATORIO (IRE)	123	681	53	88	234	755613.59
ORIENTATE (USA)	4	28	3	4	8	36349.35
ORIENTOR (GB)	8	33	2	5	6	195559.26
ORPEN (USA)	13	45	2	2	9	112775.43
OSCAR (IRE)	6	12	1	2	2	8914.63
OSORIO (GER)	4	18	1	2	4	12715.57
PAIRUMANI STAR (IRE)	1	21	1	2	4	16414.64
PAPAL BULL (GB)	30	125	4	6	35	65447.31
PARIS HOUSE (GB)	10	36	1	3	13	19645.90
PASSING GLANCE (GB)	13	38	1	1	9	5430.61
PASTORAL PURSUITS (GB)	120	659	39	67	221	604181.45
PEARL OF LOVE (IRE)	2	13	2	3	5	10417.55
PEINTRE CELEBRE (USA)	30	135	10	14	44	117726.54
PELDER (IRE)	1	5	1	2	0	12060.97
PENTIRE (GB)	2	16	1	2	8	9396.05
PETIONVILLE (USA)	2	31	2	4	11	12092.73
PHOENIX REACH (IRE)	23	103	4	5	28	43194.43
PICCOLO (GB)	79	568	32	60	188	335113.67
PILSUDSKI (IRE)	1	5	1	1	1	4126.02
PIVOTAL (GB)	156	868	72	101	302	1972062.23
PLEASANTLY PERFECT (USA)	2	17	2	4	3	15793.95
PRESENTING (GB)	8	21	2	3	2	24285.06
PRESIDIUM	6	26	1	2	4	6062.55
PRIMARY (USA)	4	17	1	1	3	6343.82
PRIMO VALENTINO (IRE)	12	75	2	4	12	18929.98
PRIZED (USA)	1	9	1	1	5	58954.00
PROCLAMATION (IRE)	40	187	10	19	54	96209.40
PROUD CITIZEN (USA)	14	72	7	11	18	57889.19
PULPIT (USA)	4	20	2	3	5	15388.01
PURSUIT OF LOVE (GB)	2	7	2	4	1	13186.92
PYRUS (USA)	16	107	4	9	25	56251.38
RAHY (USA)	8	61	6	8	22	121323.13
RAIL LINK (GB)	57	259	23	37	84	198557.63
RAINBOW QUEST (USA)	7	19	2	4	7	38527.23
RAKTI (GB)	18	114	6	11	24	50183.56
RAMONTI (FR)	8	37	2	4	11	123782.43
RAVEN'S PASS (USA)	54	213	26	35	95	353808.87
REDBACK (GB)	35	219	9	16	57	97383.43
RED CLUBS (IRE)	78	511	25	53	167	918913.79
REDOUTE'S CHOICE (AUS)	5	57	3	6	24	153593.18
RED RANSOM (USA)	25	146	7	12	40	56275.95
REFUSE TO BEND (IRE)	82	506	32	51	148	365068.75
REPENT (USA)	1	3	1	1	0	5175.20
RESET (AUS)	11	81	6	9	34	54107.94
RESPLENDENT GLORY (IRE)	7	43	2	3	11	13005.52
REVOQUE (IRE)	3	9	1	2	2	21414.22
RICHTER SCALE (USA)	1	7	1	1	2	2373.60
ROB ROY (USA)	2	10	1	1	3	2517.90
ROCK HARD TEN (USA)	5	20	1	1	9	14395.38

STALLIONS	RNRS	STARTS	WNRS	WINS	PLACES	TOTAL (£)
ROCK OF GIBRALTAR (IRE)	132	692	44	71	226	1018174.16
ROCKPORT HARBOR (USA)	2	7	1	1	0	1940.70
ROMAN RULER (USA)	3	32	1	2	11	7249.60
ROSSINI (USA)	2	6	1	1	1	13848.00
ROYAL APPLAUSE (GB)	167	958	68	94	318	741689.35
SADLER'S WELLS (USA)	27	102	5	6	30	129975.00
SAKHEE (USA)	60	301	22	34	102	266906.74
SAKHEE'S SECRET (GB)	86	468	29	41	166	372366.13
SAMPOWER STAR (GB)	2	22	1	1	7	10726.66
SAMUM (GER)	5	22	4	5	8	20325.50
SCAT DADDY (USA)	4	10	1	1	2	46967.20
SEA THE STARS (IRE)	35	72	8	10	35	115336.39
SECOND EMPIRE (IRE)	1	19	1	2	10	11489.10
SELKIRK (USA)	61	269	23	33	80	452163.46
SEPTIEME CIEL (USA)	5	33	2	3	6	10607.52
SHAMARDAL (USA)	143	749	67	108	281	1384366.96
SHINKO FOREST (IRE)	7	59	5	8	13	42364.30
SHIROCCO (GER)	47	191	16	22	63	264957.57
SHOLOKHOV (IRE)	3	14	1	2	2	5924.30
SILVER DEPUTY (CAN)	3	30	2	8	7	22949.42
SILVER PATRIARCH (IRE)	7	19	1	1	9	6947.50
SINGSPIEL (IRE)	81	427	35	49	168	534817.15
SINNDAR (IRE)	15	43	2	2	15	46633.67
SIR PERCY (GB)	66	296	27	39	96	348747.16
SIX SENSE (JPN)	2	10	1	2	4	35874.59
SIXTIES ICON (GB)	24	158	13	20	61	141463.17
SKY MESA (USA)	2	20	1	3	9	19645.67
SLEEPING INDIAN (GB)	84	481	29	58	159	368019.89
SMART STRIKE (CAN)	20	63	7	9	22	67928.91
SOLDIER HOLLOW (GB)	4	9	1	1	2	18997.50
SOLDIER OF FORTUNE (IRE)	3	13	1	2	7	15271.55
SONGANDAPRAYER (USA)	2	16	1	2	4	11374.20
SOVIET STAR (USA)	22	133	7	12	44	94492.09
SPARTACUS (IRE)	9	50	1	1	14	12545.56
SPECTRUM (IRE)	2	20	1	2	8	5932.87
SPEIGHTSTOWN (USA)	27	167	15	25	49	263890.59
SPINNING WORLD (USA)	6	60	2	3	14	24096.10
STARBOROUGH (GB)	1	11	1	2	4	6513.70
STARCRAFT (NZ)	10	55	2	3	21	21114.02
STATUE OF LIBERTY (USA)	26	120	9	14	33	87851.67
STEPPE DANCER (IRE)	2	9	1	1	6	4154.10
STONESIDER (USA)	1	4	1	1	1	3733.30
STORM CAT (USA)	2	19	1	1	10	7315.05
STORMING HOME (GB)	15	89	7	11	24	43810.77
STORMY ATLANTIC (USA)	10	63	4	6	19	33714.23
STRATEGIC PRINCE (GB)	46	295	19	31	91	316864.36
STRAVINSKY (USA)	4	30	1	2	5	24526.02
STREET BOSS (USA)	8	37	4	5	9	18410.58
STREET CRY (IRE)	79	389	45	68	153	601934.72
STREET SENSE (USA)	13	58	5	6	12	60067.24
STRIKING AMBITION (GB)	11	73	6	10	17	57169.40
SUCCESSFUL APPEAL (USA)	2	9	1	1	3	8250.42
SUGARFOOT (GB)	1	6	1	2	2	5086.25
SULAMANI (IRE)	18	130	9	18	47	101108.75
SUPERIOR PREMIUM (GB)	6	35	3	6	9	32922.81
SUPREME SOUND (GB)	1	10	1	2	3	6168.80
SWAIN (IRE)	3	18	2	2	1	21150.60
SYSTEMATIC (GB)	1	8	1	1	3	2977.50
TAGULA (IRE)	55	370	20	32	118	248108.18
TAKE RISKS (FR)	2	3	1	1	1	26208.00
TALAASH (IRE)	1	6	1	2	0	4667.50
TALE OF THE CAT (USA)	11	66	1	1	23	46676.75
TALKIN MAN (CAN)	2	6	1	2	0	15056.91

STALLIONS	RNRS	STARTS	WNRS	WINS	PLACES	TOTAL (£)
TAMAYUZ (GB)	65	310	18	26	117	236638.10
TAMURE (IRE)	3	18	1	1	4	5605.85
TAPIT (USA)	6	24	2	3	8	24527.22
TAU CETI (GB)	2	7	1	1	0	1871.70
TENDULKAR (USA)	1	7	1	1	2	2277.40
TEOFILO (IRE)	128	571	53	83	243	2336926.47
THEATRICAL	5	12	1	2	3	6730.10
THEWAYYOUARE (USA)	2	9	2	4	2	12827.92
THOUSAND WORDS (GB)	25	148	10	13	53	376358.50
THREE VALLEYS (USA)	47	175	12	13	48	83952.69
THUNDER GULCH (USA)	2	18	1	2	3	4936.30
TIGER HILL (IRE)	75	338	18	27	94	392314.73
TILLERMAN (GB)	5	18	1	2	1	4835.35
TITUS LIVIUS (FR)	17	96	6	7	32	43379.53
TIZNOW (USA)	2	13	1	1	5	4607.80
TOBOUGG (IRE)	60	260	12	16	76	141837.96
TOMBA (GB)	10	47	3	6	13	39919.66
TRADE FAIR (GB)	36	243	14	22	72	173333.16
TRADITIONALLY (USA)	7	55	1	1	20	22179.90
TRANS ISLAND (GB)	13	88	4	6	26	81567.67
TREMPOLINO (USA)	3	15	1	1	6	3755.25
TURTLE BOWL (IRE)	1	5	1	1	0	1940.70
UMISTIM (GB)	2	11	1	1	5	5950.40
UNBRIDLED'S SONG (USA)	2	7	1	1	3	9782.99
UNFUWAIN (USA)	1	6	1	2	2	5288.10
URGENT REQUEST (IRE)	2	9	1	2	4	4664.40
VAL ROYAL (FR)	23	141	10	16	34	77114.47
VAN NISTELROOY (USA)	5	23	2	2	11	15613.24
VERGLAS (IRE)	130	672	47	73	221	674290.51
VETTORI (IRE)	7	31	1	2	7	20461.85
VIKING RULER (AUS)	4	14	1	1	2	5926.82
VINDICATION (USA)	1	22	1	2	6	9760.16
VINNIE ROE (IRE)	2	9	2	2	3	24197.16
VIRTUAL (GB)	14	32	1	1	6	7188.14
VISION OF NIGHT (GB)	1	19	1	2	13	18175.92
VITAL EQUINE (IRE)	6	28	1	3	6	24523.52
VITA ROSA (JPN)	6	27	3	5	11	17798.20
WAKY NAO (GB)	3	14	1	1	3	2924.40
WAR CHANT (USA)	12	56	2	6	17	80160.14
WAR FRONT (USA)	10	32	5	11	12	1257191.51
WEET-A-MINUTE (IRE)	1	14	1	1	6	4290.30
WESTERNER (GB)	9	38	3	5	9	24868.17
WHERE OR WHEN (IRE)	9	62	4	6	22	33815.02
WHIPPER (USA)	50	253	18	28	91	271551.46
WINDSOR KNOT (IRE)	20	98	4	11	28	134157.95
WINGED LOVE (IRE)	3	10	1	2	3	20845.53
WINKER WATSON (GB)	10	56	1	1	23	11979.86
WISEMAN'S FERRY (USA)	3	10	1	1	5	8520.26
WITH APPROVAL (CAN)	12	44	5	6	11	20828.47
XAAR (GB)	9	56	2	2	20	15829.51
YANKEE GENTLEMAN (USA)	4	19	3	3	7	21254.40
YEATS (IRE)	11	26	1	1	8	9218.61
ZAFEEN (FR)	19	99	8	13	32	106802.39
ZAHA (CAN)	1	5	1	1	2	3252.90
ZAMINDAR (USA)	51	220	14	21	67	171954.30
ZAVATA (USA)	1	11	1	3	7	9912.30

BY KIND PERMISSION OF WEATHERBYS

NH STALLIONS' EARNINGS FOR 2012/13

(includes every stallion who sired a winner over jumps in Great Britain and Ireland in 2012/13)

STALLIONS	RNRS	STARTS	WNRS	WINS	PLACES	TOTAL (£)
AAHSAYLAD	6	27	1	1	6	8565.05
ABOO HOM (GB)	5	23	1	1	5	6079.53
ACAMBARO (GER)	3	13	1	1	6	5848.56
ACATENANGO (GER)	5	11	2	2	3	8371.02
ACCESS SKI	4	11	1	1	2	8546.50
ACCLAMATION (GB)	14	74	4	7	26	50726.61
ACCORDION	81	336	25	38	130	446927.69
ACT ONE (GB)	19	57	3	4	14	24213.86
AD VALOREM (USA)	8	34	1	1	8	14078.87
AGENT BLEU (FR)	3	21	3	5	11	205772.34
AGNES WORLD (USA)	1	2	1	1	1	5052.30
AKBAR (IRE)	3	15	1	1	3	8145.94
ALAMO BAY (USA)	2	7	1	1	2	7104.17
ALBANO (IRE)	4	23	3	6	9	37773.57
ALBERTO GIACOMETTI (IRE)	2	9	1	2	3	25165.00
ALDERBROOK (GB)	103	430	28	48	120	461431.31
ALEXIUS (IRE)	5	13	1	2	3	11766.66
ALFLORA (IRE)	157	586	41	53	193	506266.25
ALHAARTH (IRE)	36	144	11	12	53	120606.07
ALJABR (USA)	3	16	1	2	7	36455.00
ALKALDE (GER)	3	13	3	4	4	35983.28
ALMUTAWAKEL (GB)	3	15	3	3	2	16756.15
AL NAMIX (FR)	6	20	2	2	11	60403.07
ALWUHUSH (USA)	2	17	1	1	11	7481.19
ALZAO (USA)	1	6	1	2	1	6537.42
AMERICAN POST (GB)	2	15	2	2	7	19807.54
AMILYNX (FR)	16	49	2	3	10	14571.85
ANABAA (USA)	10	53	2	3	21	27805.23
AND BEYOND (IRE)	16	47	1	1	3	4510.80
ANSHAN	103	403	24	30	122	317805.51
ANTARCTIQUE (IRE)	7	29	4	7	10	70204.50
ANTONIUS PIUS (USA)	27	99	6	6	33	41026.08
APPLE TREE (FR)	1	9	1	1	5	6619.65
APRIL NIGHT (FR)	13	57	4	5	23	40973.02
ARAAFA (IRE)	8	21	1	1	8	6655.99
ARAKAN (USA)	13	60	6	8	25	64452.49
ARCADIO (GER)	1	2	1	1	0	4487.80
ARCH (USA)	8	30	3	6	6	17225.37
ARCTIC LORD	7	21	1	1	5	4954.71
ARTAN (IRE)	3	10	1	1	2	5506.29
ARVICO (FR)	2	12	1	4	4	148170.77
ARZANNI	2	8	1	1	3	20282.56
ASIAN HEIGHTS (GB)	1	2	1	1	1	1954.80
ASSESSOR (IRE)	7	26	3	6	10	143393.73
ASTARABAD (USA)	14	50	4	7	22	55385.72
ATRAF (GB)	10	28	1	2	6	7273.41
AUSSIE RULES (USA)	11	30	3	3	8	12143.77
AUTHORIZED (IRE)	12	40	3	4	18	33828.88
AVONBRIDGE (GB)	12	44	4	4	17	33361.51
AZAMOUR (IRE)	22	82	8	13	32	365047.55
BABY TURK	2	7	1	1	3	3785.22
BACH (IRE)	67	236	11	17	50	127506.60
BACHELOR DUKE (USA)	16	58	1	1	18	28928.90
BADOLATO (USA)	1	9	1	1	4	3250.98
BAHAMIAN BOUNTY (GB)	9	21	1	2	3	5087.22
BAHHARE (USA)	9	47	2	4	10	15430.38
BAHRI (USA)	16	51	1	1	16	10777.36
BALAKHERI (IRE)	5	19	1	2	4	6210.22
BAL HARBOUR (GB)	4	22	1	1	8	7683.78
BALKO (FR)	2	11	1	1	7	15699.06

STALLIONS	RNRS	STARTS	WNRS	WINS	PLACES	TOTAL (£)
BALLINGARRY (IRE)	13	55	4	8	17	47080.13
BANDARI (IRE)	3	7	1	1	2	5253.04
BANDMASTER (USA)	6	22	1	2	8	15640.57
BANYUMANIK (IRE)	1	9	1	2	5	35465.78
BARATHEA (IRE)	25	101	5	10	29	91165.34
BARYSHNIKOV (AUS)	13	50	1	4	15	26390.63
BASANTA (IRE)	10	34	2	3	8	39190.64
BEAT ALL (USA)	81	247	11	15	64	87917.89
BEAT HOLLOW (GB)	37	189	15	25	66	260437.46
BEAT OF DRUMS (GB)	2	13	1	1	5	4895.22
BEAUCHAMP KING (GB)	6	12	2	2	6	6546.96
BENEFICIAL (GB)	347	1519	116	183	458	1933847.31
BENNY THE DIP (USA)	2	6	1	1	4	16395.08
BERING	8	39	2	2	10	29377.75
BERNARDINI (USA)	2	6	1	1	1	4203.00
BERNEBEAU (FR)	4	12	2	3	5	15310.33
BERTOLINI (USA)	21	52	2	2	12	19789.83
BEST OF THE BESTS (IRE)	7	30	1	1	10	13969.24
BIENAMADO (USA)	14	55	1	4	20	24721.90
BIEN BIEN (USA)	2	6	1	1	2	3066.66
BISHOP OF CASHEL (GB)	26	76	3	5	17	128580.89
BLACK SAM BELLAMY (IRE)	10	46	2	2	23	88869.32
BLUE OCEAN (GB)	2	14	2	4	6	58502.74
BLUEPRINT (IRE)	32	129	12	19	36	100794.22
BOB BACK (USA)	88	373	33	50	117	1069687.70
BOB'S RETURN (IRE)	50	221	18	23	76	294703.50
BOLLIN ERIC (GB)	29	90	6	10	19	48343.35
BRAVEFOOT (GB)	8	23	1	1	6	6676.02
BRIAN BORU (GB)	79	305	18	26	84	224779.33
BRIER CREEK (USA)	11	46	3	4	17	26503.25
BROADWAY FLYER (USA)	22	68	7	12	20	65789.75
BROKEN HEARTED	14	52	2	2	13	21397.59
BULINGTON (FR)	5	19	1	1	10	11836.44
BUSY FLIGHT (GB)	6	16	2	3	2	11493.07
BYRON (GB)	11	30	1	1	3	5503.57
CABALLO RAPTOR (CAN)	4	20	2	6	7	44347.16
CACIQUE (IRE)	3	15	1	1	5	6118.24
CADOUDAL (FR)	12	43	5	7	18	314792.40
CALIFET (FR)	5	15	1	1	9	14016.13
CANYON CREEK (IRE)	1	3	1	1	1	2067.48
CAPE CROSS (IRE)	38	135	11	16	44	139027.05
CAPTAIN RIO (GB)	14	50	3	4	13	72266.46
CARROLL HOUSE	31	126	5	5	35	59215.31
CARROWKEEL (IRE)	2	7	1	1	2	3671.92
CATCHER IN THE RYE (IRE)	69	260	14	21	72	162113.77
CELTIC SWING (GB)	14	61	3	3	12	22963.83
CENTRAL PARK (IRE)	24	70	4	5	19	29511.97
CHARENTE RIVER (IRE)	5	30	3	3	12	19389.86
CHARMING GROOM (FR)	3	5	1	1	3	4043.88
CHEF DE CLAN (FR)	1	9	1	2	4	7399.80
CHEVALIER (IRE)	24	61	3	4	16	38061.13
CHICHICASTENANGO (FR)	1	1	1	1	0	2534.22
CHINEUR (FR)	7	15	1	1	0	5677.08
CHOCOLAT DE MEGURO (USA)	1	9	1	2	3	7797.99
CHOISIR (AUS)	13	43	4	7	10	40763.49
CITY HONOURS (USA)	22	83	6	9	24	83740.83
CITY ON A HILL (USA)	2	8	1	1	1	4895.83
CLASSIC CLICHE (IRE)	56	178	11	11	59	77176.29
CLERKENWELL (USA)	6	21	2	5	4	21108.56
CLETY (FR)	1	2	1	1	0	3119.04
CLODOVIL (IRE)	9	25	2	3	8	18700.88
CLOSE CONFLICT (USA)	21	66	2	3	17	38366.33
CLOUDINGS (IRE)	74	285	20	26	86	212204.55
COCKNEY REBEL (IRE)	3	9	2	4	3	40176.39

STALLIONS	RNRS	STARTS	WNRS	WINS	PLACES	TOTAL (£)
COIS NA TINE (IRE)	3	17	2	3	6	15961.10
COLONEL COLLINS (USA)	2	12	2	5	4	55119.33
COMMANCHE RUN	7	35	2	5	16	26135.88
COMPTON PLACE (GB)	9	20	2	3	3	9407.10
COUNTRY REEL (USA)	1	3	1	1	2	2757.18
COURT CAVE (IRE)	56	200	18	25	65	234094.68
CRAIGSTEEL (GB)	58	210	11	18	59	132026.01
CROCO ROUGE (IRE)	23	76	5	6	24	36670.43
CURTAIN TIME (IRE)	9	25	1	2	4	54080.90
CYBORG (FR)	6	24	2	4	7	14876.07
DAGGERS DRAWN (USA)	6	21	1	1	5	7678.69
DAI JIN (GB)	1	3	1	2	1	71630.65
DALAKHANI (IRE)	30	101	9	14	28	89239.17
DALIAPOUR (IRE)	5	28	3	4	12	65928.76
DANCING SPREE (USA)	3	15	1	1	4	4154.90
DANEHILL DANCER (IRE)	40	143	7	10	38	112156.87
DANETIME (IRE)	3	13	1	1	3	14391.67
DANO-MAST (GB)	3	14	1	7	0	24963.68
DANSILI (GB)	37	152	15	22	48	98827.40
DARK MOONDANCER (GB)	10	37	6	7	16	28253.74
DAYLAMI (IRE)	28	129	11	19	42	134673.99
DEFINITE ARTICLE (GB)	154	467	38	52	139	376907.98
DELLA FRANCESCA (USA)	5	15	3	3	4	35265.05
DENEL (FR)	4	20	1	1	6	7264.34
DENHAM RED (FR)	2	4	1	2	1	16329.56
DENON (USA)	1	7	1	1	2	18229.68
DEPLOY	28	105	4	5	29	69862.61
DESERT KING (IRE)	20	50	4	4	13	13496.32
DESERT PRINCE (IRE)	18	74	6	10	23	215751.71
DESERT STYLE (IRE)	9	48	1	2	18	16611.49
DESERT SUN (GB)	5	19	1	1	2	3937.14
DESIDERATUM (GB)	3	12	1	1	5	4095.25
DIESIS	6	21	1	1	8	8501.03
DIKTAT (GB)	17	95	5	9	28	44021.08
DILSHAAN (GB)	13	41	1	1	13	8641.87
DISCOVER D'AUTEUIL (FR)	10	38	4	4	14	39593.66
DISTANT MUSIC (USA)	5	16	1	1	4	7904.16
DOCKSIDER (USA)	2	9	1	1	3	5633.91
DOLPOUR	6	16	1	1	4	6507.34
DOM ALCO (FR)	28	108	14	30	45	684140.79
DOMEDRIVER (IRE)	6	24	2	2	6	14668.68
DOUBLE ECLIPSE (IRE)	9	47	1	1	25	61834.15
DOUBLETOUR (USA)	2	12	1	2	6	10103.38
DOUBLE TRIGGER (IRE)	35	124	8	9	39	141291.79
DOYEN (IRE)	34	103	6	11	30	116928.79
DREAM WELL (FR)	5	28	3	5	9	18290.75
DR FONG (USA)	25	89	8	13	23	64899.20
DR MASSINI (IRE)	124	495	36	54	141	406000.41
DUBAI DESTINATION (USA)	44	170	12	14	58	78120.87
DUBAWI (IRE)	19	74	8	13	33	133216.47
DUSHYANTOR (USA)	55	240	20	30	82	221682.40
DUTCH ART (GB)	2	10	1	1	3	4955.42
DYLAN THOMAS (IRE)	13	42	4	5	13	35272.87
DYNAFORMER (USA)	17	97	12	22	26	257511.55
E DUBAI (USA)	1	2	1	1	1	3754.32
ELMAAMUL (USA)	4	23	1	2	7	8803.35
EL PRADO (IRE)	4	11	1	1	4	3684.49
ELUSIVE CITY (USA)	12	34	1	1	3	4645.47
ELUSIVE QUALITY (USA)	2	10	1	1	3	19534.56
EMPIRE MAKER (USA)	2	5	1	1	0	6498.00
ENCOSTA DE LAGO (AUS)	2	9	1	2	0	6368.04
ENDOLI (USA)	5	33	3	4	8	13951.68
ENRIQUE (GB)	11	32	2	3	16	73622.25
ENVIRONMENT FRIEND (GB)	11	29	1	1	4	4028.23

STALLIONS	RNRS	STARTS	WNRS	WINS	PLACES	TOTAL (£)
EPALO (GER)	7	20	2	2	6	81082.25
EPISTOLAIRE (IRE)	2	20	2	4	9	74464.15
EQUERRY (USA)	5	17	2	2	4	9870.60
ERHAAB (USA)	22	56	4	5	14	17340.69
EVENING WORLD (FR)	1	7	1	2	4	78044.00
EXCEED AND EXCEL (AUS)	6	21	2	2	12	15423.97
EXCELLENT ART (GB)	3	8	1	3	4	32545.45
EXIT TO NOWHERE (USA)	88	300	19	24	95	189200.09
EXPELLED (USA)	4	11	1	1	3	6558.33
FADO (FR)	3	11	1	1	3	4169.16
FAIR MIX (IRE)	55	157	9	12	46	187312.75
FANTASTIC LIGHT (USA)	22	95	7	10	21	61296.72
FANTASTIC QUEST (IRE)	3	20	2	3	4	10160.80
FASLIYEV (USA)	9	41	2	3	11	16129.68
FATH (USA)	9	34	1	1	5	8636.94
FLEETWOOD (IRE)	14	50	5	5	14	35857.10
FLEMENSFIRTH (USA)	303	1162	90	127	390	1605387.24
FOOTSTEPSINTHESAND (GB)	10	37	2	3	10	17129.15
FOURSTARS ALLSTAR (USA)	13	38	1	2	4	13227.67
FRAAM (GB)	14	66	5	6	16	32630.76
FRAGRANT MIX (IRE)	8	40	4	7	17	44165.63
FREDDIE'S STAR	1	3	1	1	1	3392.10
FRENCH GLORY	1	2	1	1	1	13941.36
FRUITS OF LOVE (USA)	44	163	10	12	39	78647.97
FUNNY BABY (FR)	2	8	1	1	2	5840.82
GALILEO (IRE)	66	259	19	28	90	308608.93
GAMUT (IRE)	25	81	4	6	17	47579.90
GARDE ROYALE	2	16	1	1	3	2719.89
GARUDA (IRE)	7	29	1	1	10	11159.65
GENEROUS (IRE)	91	322	24	41	88	272508.20
GERMANY (USA)	7	27	3	3	10	88244.53
GIANT'S CAUSEWAY (USA)	14	47	3	4	17	40533.67
GLACIAL STORM (USA)	11	34	2	3	10	9873.78
GOLAN (IRE)	64	185	14	23	48	177181.67
GOLDEN LARIAT (USA)	1	3	1	1	0	3926.83
GOLDEN TORNADO (IRE)	15	62	2	3	18	39722.32
GOLDMARK (USA)	20	65	7	7	25	39660.92
GOLDNEYEV (USA)	3	14	1	1	6	50364.46
GOLD WELL (GB)	35	117	7	11	51	231139.48
GOOFALIK (USA)	2	2	1	1	0	4679.25
GOVERNOR BROWN (USA)	2	5	1	3	1	13661.46
GRAND LODGE (USA)	7	49	1	1	13	10358.38
GRAND SEIGNEUR (FR)	1	7	1	2	2	6088.50
GRAPE TREE ROAD (GB)	37	105	6	7	21	25338.20
GREAT EXHIBITION (USA)	7	25	1	2	5	14366.68
GREAT PALM (USA)	71	226	12	14	51	130419.98
GREAT PRETENDER (IRE)	4	16	3	5	7	45300.34
GREEN TUNE (USA)	5	20	2	2	10	18101.48
GREY RISK (FR)	3	18	1	1	10	111475.55
GROOM DANCER (USA)	8	38	2	2	9	23478.86
GULLAND (GB)	6	31	2	3	6	43098.78
GUNNER B	4	8	1	1	3	3849.81
HAAFHD (GB)	21	82	6	8	33	176791.04
HALLING (USA)	23	86	6	10	26	52285.91
HAMAS (IRE)	5	18	1	2	6	11421.78
HAWK WING (USA)	46	156	8	11	53	71807.64
HELIOSTATIC (IRE)	2	12	1	1	8	6042.15
HELISSIO (FR)	33	114	8	9	32	47589.19
HERNANDO (FR)	35	140	13	20	58	237922.38
HERON ISLAND (IRE)	105	343	20	31	117	320203.32
HIGH CHAPARRAL (IRE)	57	204	11	15	50	142861.24
HIGHEST HONOR (FR)	7	23	2	2	4	7850.73
HIGH-RISE (IRE)	17	41	2	2	12	14629.98
HIGH ROLLER (IRE)	6	18	1	1	3	5960.98

STALLIONS	RNRS	STARTS	WNRS	WINS	PLACES	TOTAL (£)
HIGH YIELD (USA)	2	9	1	1	4	8318.48
HOLY BULL (USA)	1	9	1	1	2	2695.28
HOLY ROMAN EMPEROR (IRE)	9	31	1	2	7	10608.23
HOUMAYOUN (FR)	3	7	1	1	1	2587.44
HUBBLY BUBBLY (USA)	17	61	4	7	14	33714.24
HUMBEL (USA)	9	23	2	3	5	10825.01
HUNTING LION (IRE)	2	2	1	1	0	2534.22
HURRICANE RUN (IRE)	21	63	4	5	23	30383.14
HUSHANG (IRE)	1	13	1	1	3	11509.55
ICEMAN (GB)	13	43	2	3	18	28605.20
IFFRAAJ (GB)	11	33	3	3	7	15259.95
IKTIBAS (GB)	5	16	1	1	3	4976.46
IMPERIAL BALLET (IRE)	12	66	4	5	24	80938.08
IMPERIAL DANCER (GB)	13	50	4	7	14	26706.27
INDESATCHEL (IRE)	4	10	2	3	4	11564.48
INDIAN CREEK (GB)	2	8	1	1	3	3291.90
INDIAN DANEHILL (IRE)	50	157	7	13	38	104841.84
INDIAN RIDGE	11	37	2	3	6	11036.93
INSAN (USA)	10	22	1	1	7	9594.45
INSATIABLE (IRE)	12	39	3	4	13	55536.99
IN THE WINGS	13	60	5	7	17	39050.62
INTIKHAB (USA)	10	40	2	3	12	17884.48
INVINCIBLE SPIRIT (IRE)	15	41	2	2	14	26390.46
IN YARAK (GB)	1	3	1	1	0	4312.00
ISLAND HOUSE (IRE)	1	3	1	1	2	28285.60
IVAN DENISOVICH (IRE)	9	23	2	3	5	32619.95
JACKSON'S DRIFT (USA)	1	6	1	2	4	33113.02
JADE ROBBERY (USA)	4	22	2	2	5	5307.75
JAMMAAL (GB)	5	19	2	2	8	47075.43
JENDALI (USA)	2	11	1	1	3	3575.43
JEREMY (USA)	7	29	3	8	14	190234.11
JIMBLE (FR)	10	41	2	5	6	20580.41
JOHANNESBURG (USA)	9	35	2	3	13	12133.52
JOHANN QUATZ (FR)	2	14	1	2	6	16431.41
JOSR ALGARHOUD (IRE)	14	37	2	2	11	9961.83
JURADO (USA)	1	3	1	1	2	63672.78
KADALKO (FR)	4	11	1	1	7	28007.12
KADASTROF (FR)	13	40	4	5	12	19499.60
KAHYASI	34	119	9	14	54	217714.63
KALANISI (IRE)	34	110	8	11	28	84359.98
KALDOUNEVEES (FR)	3	14	2	2	3	8349.73
KALMOSS (FR)	1	10	1	1	6	9313.34
KAPGARDE (FR)	31	150	16	20	54	180798.70
KARINGA BAY	123	486	43	64	147	426513.56
KASAKOV (GB)	2	21	2	5	4	48377.26
KAYF TARA (GB)	166	553	53	75	216	694854.29
KENDOR (FR)	3	10	1	1	6	64149.31
KEY OF LUCK (USA)	16	72	2	2	18	23316.18
KHALKEVI (IRE)	2	10	2	3	4	22942.26
KHELEYF (USA)	6	23	2	2	6	12488.48
KIER PARK (IRE)	3	9	1	3	3	11201.12
KING CHARLEMAGNE (USA)	6	24	1	1	10	6559.95
KING CUGAT (USA)	1	2	1	1	0	13541.67
KINGSALSA (USA)	6	38	4	8	11	126429.81
KING'S BEST (USA)	44	189	17	25	75	200580.97
KING'S THEATRE (IRE)	234	926	77	128	332	1794018.41
KIRKWALL (GB)	10	42	2	4	10	11886.10
KODIAC (GB)	6	31	2	3	10	13034.70
KOTASHAAN (FR)	7	24	1	3	5	14470.84
KRIS KIN (USA)	26	85	5	7	19	34154.55
KYLLACHY (GB)	15	41	1	1	20	19201.05
LAHIB (USA)	44	165	6	7	46	62696.40
LANDO (GER)	16	63	7	10	18	107821.74
LAVERON (GB)	24	110	9	19	22	160115.50

STALLIONS	RNRS	STARTS	WNRS	WINS	PLACES	TOTAL (£)
LAVIRCO (GER)	19	97	9	23	31	326019.03
LAWMAN (FR)	6	11	1	2	0	5848.20
LEADING COUNSEL (USA)	6	29	2	4	8	146916.00
LE BALAFRE (FR)	4	18	1	2	4	20631.84
LECROIX (GER)	2	8	1	1	2	3952.45
LE FOU (IRE)	6	38	3	6	17	80462.35
LEMON DROP KID (USA)	9	32	3	3	15	23750.64
LEND A HAND (GB)	7	30	4	4	10	31371.35
LIBRETTIST (USA)	8	17	1	2	0	12671.10
LIMNOS (JPN)	6	15	1	1	4	12038.87
LINAMIX (FR)	15	64	1	1	15	16962.61
LION HEART (USA)	2	11	1	2	1	8924.40
LITTLE BIGHORN	2	5	1	2	0	3638.88
LOMITAS (GB)	16	51	3	4	18	60307.67
LONE BID (FR)	1	8	1	1	5	28637.60
LORD AMERICO	49	225	18	26	69	180549.27
LORD OF APPEAL (GB)	17	62	2	2	13	11252.23
LORD OF ENGLAND (GER)	2	8	1	2	2	19188.50
LOST WORLD (IRE)	13	58	6	8	11	104450.67
LOUP SOLITAIRE (USA)	3	8	1	1	2	12087.00
LOXIAS (FR)	3	6	1	1	1	1628.96
LUCKY OWNERS (NZ)	5	28	1	1	8	5492.53
LUSO (GB)	103	366	26	36	104	310403.51
LUTE ANTIQUE (FR)	2	7	1	2	1	4598.58
MAD TAX (USA)	2	7	1	1	0	3249.00
MAKBUL	6	28	4	4	7	15143.38
MALINAS (GER)	9	43	6	12	20	169621.84
MANSONNIEN (FR)	9	46	4	8	19	39557.83
MARCHAND DE SABLE (USA)	1	7	1	1	2	4316.42
MARESCA SORRENTO (FR)	6	27	2	4	9	43054.39
MARIGNAN (USA)	18	66	3	8	14	51978.71
MARJU (IRE)	23	104	8	10	36	93541.32
MARK OF ESTEEM (IRE)	13	69	6	10	17	49457.73
MARTALINE (GB)	25	90	11	19	30	276233.02
MASTER WILLIE	1	4	1	1	0	3378.96
MEDALLIST (USA)	1	9	1	1	2	4030.20
MEDECIS (GB)	4	10	1	1	2	3528.20
MEDICEAN (GB)	42	192	12	19	62	144515.42
MIDNIGHT LEGEND (GB)	95	382	36	54	130	353313.49
MILAN (GB)	290	1099	103	160	341	1377992.07
MILLENARY (GB)	26	86	4	6	11	26090.49
MINSTER SON	14	48	3	4	16	16733.77
MISTER BAILEYS (GB)	2	12	1	3	3	22355.19
MISTER MAT (FR)	4	16	2	2	6	17663.80
MISTERNANDO (GB)	4	20	2	5	8	40229.21
MONSUN (GER)	12	43	4	4	22	37735.04
MONTJEU (IRE)	67	287	25	43	88	868849.03
MONTJOY (USA)	1	7	1	2	1	20044.00
MOONAX (IRE)	9	25	2	5	6	29218.47
MOROZOV (USA)	16	64	8	16	25	153222.28
MORPETH (GB)	9	38	1	4	11	15190.45
MOSCOW SOCIETY (USA)	72	291	20	24	89	186770.98
MOTIVATOR (GB)	23	87	7	15	28	91716.16
MR COMBUSTIBLE (IRE)	21	78	4	7	26	174417.35
MR DINOS (IRE)	3	11	1	1	0	6170.73
MR GREELEY (USA)	8	25	3	4	5	14142.87
MTOTO	8	47	7	10	12	28964.24
MUHTARRAM (USA)	16	78	6	14	26	67885.56
MUHTATHIR (GB)	9	32	4	8	11	128453.40
MUJAHID (USA)	12	42	2	2	15	31650.81
MULL OF KINTYRE (USA)	13	52	3	3	11	28214.53
MULTIPLEX (GB)	7	21	2	4	4	15161.88
MURMURE (FR)	1	7	1	1	1	3037.53
MY RISK (FR)	1	6	1	4	2	80079.18

STALLIONS	RNRS	STARTS	WNRS	WINS	PLACES	TOTAL (£)
NAHEEZ (USA)	11	44	1	2	14	13380.54
NASHAMAA	2	7	1	1	3	4272.18
NAYEF (USA)	34	114	7	10	38	74670.58
NEEDLE GUN (IRE)	32	109	6	8	29	90662.90
NEEDWOOD BLADE (GB)	23	66	2	3	18	20086.21
NETWORK (GER)	17	72	9	19	30	638754.94
NEW FRONTIER (IRE)	17	85	4	7	27	69950.34
NEXT DESERT (IRE)	3	18	3	6	8	35392.05
NICOBAR (GB)	1	4	1	2	2	7140.96
NIKOS	13	53	2	5	19	82922.47
NOMADIC WAY (USA)	18	66	2	4	18	21073.83
NONONITO (FR)	3	9	1	1	4	3490.59
NORWICH	42	169	11	13	48	122157.17
NOVERRE (USA)	20	79	4	5	19	31189.40
OASIS DREAM (GB)	14	42	2	2	12	9531.38
OBSERVATORY (USA)	12	51	4	7	12	26968.88
OKAWANGO (USA)	3	15	2	3	6	17280.05
OLD VIC	239	922	73	102	306	952109.69
ONE COOL CAT (USA)	14	70	4	4	23	40011.79
ORATORIO (IRE)	17	42	2	7	6	23495.67
ORIENTATE (USA)	1	5	1	1	1	3697.38
ORPEN (USA)	16	40	1	2	9	12817.86
OSCAR (IRE)	364	1338	99	158	420	1902490.17
OSCAR SCHINDLER (IRE)	28	105	2	2	20	29105.01
OVERBURY (IRE)	105	387	26	35	112	248058.55
PANORAMIC	7	31	4	6	14	70790.14
PAOLINI (GER)	2	6	1	1	0	19932.50
PARTHIAN SPRINGS (GB)	8	26	1	1	7	7099.61
PASSING GLANCE (GB)	12	46	5	8	16	41088.09
PASSING SALE (FR)	14	44	4	6	13	69701.78
PASTERNAK (GB)	19	76	4	6	10	60108.86
PASTORAL PURSUITS (GB)	5	15	1	1	4	10521.96
PEACOCK JEWEL (GB)	1	2	1	1	0	1317.20
PEINTRE CELEBRE (USA)	12	30	1	1	6	4281.89
PELDER (IRE)	6	26	1	2	12	36275.98
PENNEKAMP (USA)	1	2	1	1	0	1364.58
PENTIRE (GB)	4	14	1	1	2	8508.40
PERPENDICULAR (GB)	1	5	1	2	3	19431.36
PHANTOM BREEZE	1	5	1	2	2	6601.56
PHOENIX REACH (IRE)	7	37	3	4	16	18894.55
PIERRE (GB)	21	70	6	9	16	64810.39
PILSUDSKI (IRE)	33	104	8	9	21	52937.64
PISTOLET BLEU (IRE)	22	61	3	8	21	477783.30
PIVOTAL (GB)	34	127	9	13	33	92430.57
PLEASANTLY PERFECT (USA)	1	3	1	1	0	4747.50
PLEASANT TAP (USA)	1	7	1	3	4	45119.10
POLIGLOTE (GB)	16	61	7	14	23	168292.27
POLISH PRECEDENT (USA)	7	31	2	4	7	51302.13
POLISH SUMMER (GB)	3	16	2	3	8	29855.09
POLTARF (USA)	1	5	1	1	1	4747.96
PORT LYAUTEY (FR)	3	13	2	2	7	19663.45
PORTRAIT GALLERY (IRE)	31	105	9	14	30	97529.61
POSIDONAS (GB)	8	24	1	1	8	7555.57
PRESENTING (GB)	357	1284	91	122	401	1289936.35
PRIMITIVE RISING (USA)	3	12	2	2	4	38713.62
PRIMO VALENTINO (IRE)	4	12	2	2	3	6547.56
PRINCE DANIEL (USA)	4	17	1	2	2	5317.20
PRIOLO (USA)	3	15	1	1	8	15884.66
PROCLAMATION (IRE)	12	44	1	3	12	17710.46
PROTEKTOR (GER)	1	5	1	1	0	1819.44
PROUD CITIZEN (USA)	2	14	1	1	7	4597.71
PUBLISHER (USA)	7	27	3	4	6	23101.12
PURSUIT OF LOVE (GB)	7	40	4	5	10	24636.78
PUSHKIN (IRE)	5	12	1	1	3	7320.83

STALLIONS	RNRS	STARTS	WNRS	WINS	PLACES	TOTAL (£)
PUTRA SANDHURST (IRE)	1	5	1	2	1	12083.33
PYRUS (USA)	13	49	3	3	15	19558.21
QUWS (GB)	18	76	4	4	31	39262.60
RAGMAR (FR)	10	44	4	5	9	62829.57
RAINBOW HIGH (GB)	9	42	3	4	11	27803.70
RAINBOW QUEST (USA)	12	22	3	3	7	20555.45
RAISE A GRAND (IRE)	11	56	3	7	23	43148.51
RAKAPOSHI KING	12	50	2	2	14	10594.33
RAKTI (GB)	10	38	1	1	13	9534.24
RAMBLING BEAR (GB)	2	12	2	4	4	14726.50
RANSOM O'WAR (USA)	1	4	1	1	2	11312.60
RASHAR (USA)	30	102	5	7	27	42490.21
REDBACK (GB)	13	36	2	3	10	29819.47
RED CLUBS (IRE)	12	32	5	8	8	30263.05
RED RANSOM (USA)	29	104	7	9	33	128818.67
REEFSCAPE (GB)	2	5	1	3	1	74501.30
REFUSE TO BEND (IRE)	33	107	7	11	22	55674.58
RELIEF PITCHER	6	18	1	1	7	7151.49
RELIGIOUSLY (USA)	5	26	2	3	3	32161.39
REPRIMAND	1	6	1	1	2	2929.64
RESET (AUS)	10	35	2	3	19	13630.20
REVOQUE (IRE)	67	207	11	16	59	188541.25
RIGHT WIN (IRE)	3	8	2	2	1	18732.50
ROBELLINO (USA)	5	39	4	7	13	36175.50
ROBERTICO (USA)	3	13	1	2	3	9427.64
ROBIN DES CHAMPS (FR)	23	96	12	22	28	594311.66
ROBIN DES PRES (FR)	10	45	5	9	18	125005.81
ROCK HOPPER	7	28	2	4	7	26476.76
ROCK OF GIBRALTAR (IRE)	35	128	8	12	39	103520.01
ROI DE ROME (USA)	7	25	2	2	8	19115.10
ROMAN SADDLE (IRE)	1	4	1	1	1	4451.22
ROSSINI (USA)	4	21	1	1	5	10006.56
ROYAL ANTHEM (USA)	16	40	3	4	10	37149.28
ROYAL APPLAUSE (GB)	28	105	7	8	35	49619.49
RUDIMENTARY (USA)	37	167	6	8	50	105784.64
RUNYON (IRE)	8	44	4	7	11	25615.15
SABIANGO (GER)	3	9	1	3	2	5216.94
SADDLERS' HALL (IRE)	82	348	18	22	116	262617.58
SADLER'S WELLS (USA)	63	296	22	33	90	345343.57
SAFETY CATCH (USA)	6	20	1	1	6	4403.43
SAFFRON WALDEN (FR)	21	77	4	4	27	32417.70
SAGACITY (FR)	10	39	1	1	13	13466.55
SAGAMIX (FR)	5	22	2	2	4	23882.66
SAHM (USA)	1	4	1	1	2	7018.29
SAINT DES SAINTS (FR)	16	69	8	13	26	245179.63
SAINT PREUIL (FR)	6	22	2	2	8	10936.31
SAKHEE (USA)	24	68	7	9	16	61672.91
SAMRAAN (USA)	8	27	1	2	6	12768.73
SAMUM (GER)	5	19	2	3	2	13187.70
SASSANIAN (USA)	10	45	2	3	15	84254.56
SAUMAREZ	1	6	1	1	4	8371.60
SAYARSHAN (FR)	7	24	1	1	6	7140.70
SCRIBANO (GB)	6	31	3	3	12	18506.20
SCRIBE (IRE)	1	5	1	1	1	2707.62
SEA FREEDOM (GB)	1	7	1	2	5	6914.01
SEA RAVEN (IRE)	5	35	2	4	16	62137.75
SEATTLE DANCER (USA)	1	10	1	3	4	23954.20
SECOND EMPIRE (IRE)	7	30	2	2	8	574244.33
SELKIRK (USA)	25	93	6	9	27	47959.08
SHAANMER (IRE)	10	39	2	4	13	84275.55
SHAHRASTANI (USA)	6	33	3	4	14	33007.24
SHAMARDAL (USA)	9	44	1	1	11	10350.13
SHANTOU (USA)	62	201	19	28	73	303224.64
SHEER DANZIG (IRE)	2	13	1	2	2	13591.66

STALLIONS	RNRS	STARTS	WNRS	WINS	PLACES	TOTAL (£)
SHERNAZAR	30	119	7	12	36	68603.61
SHEYRANN	3	7	1	1	4	5853.42
SHINKO FOREST (IRE)	3	15	1	2	2	7605.18
SHIROCCO (GER)	19	66	8	16	18	144955.20
SHOLOKHOV (IRE)	8	40	5	8	15	65836.00
SILVANO (GER)	2	11	1	2	5	7426.00
SILVER PATRIARCH (IRE)	69	248	19	24	77	240392.49
SIMON DU DESERT (FR)	2	5	1	1	2	11769.00
SIMPLY GREAT (FR)	6	31	2	4	6	24613.67
SINGSPIEL (IRE)	22	69	3	4	22	46238.62
SIN KIANG (FR)	1	5	1	2	2	10837.70
SINNDAR (IRE)	10	32	3	6	9	96444.75
SIR HARRY LEWIS (USA)	66	265	21	32	83	190264.40
SKY CLASSIC (CAN)	1	7	1	1	2	4472.64
SLEEPING CAR (FR)	19	67	5	8	18	48271.80
SLICKLY (FR)	3	13	2	2	4	63813.35
SMADOUN (FR)	14	66	5	10	33	177384.61
SMART STRIKE (CAN)	3	17	2	3	4	11843.52
SNOW CAP (FR)	1	7	1	3	2	44638.69
SNURGE	38	175	12	20	65	184322.55
SOLON (GER)	2	7	1	3	2	241835.69
SON OF SHARP SHOT (IRE)	3	19	1	1	7	6004.41
SONUS (IRE)	15	50	4	4	11	33935.48
SOVEREIGN WATER (FR)	7	17	4	5	5	20613.48
SOVIET STAR (USA)	14	49	4	5	16	62497.84
SPADOUN (FR)	14	78	5	7	31	63696.33
SPARTACUS (IRE)	18	81	4	8	17	37737.34
SPECTRUM (IRE)	7	36	2	5	8	38347.89
SPINNING WORLD (USA)	4	12	1	1	3	10311.20
STARDAN (IRE)	3	16	1	1	5	7329.16
STATUE OF LIBERTY (USA)	13	48	3	5	14	39992.00
STORMIN FEVER (USA)	2	9	1	1	3	5807.58
STORMING HOME (GB)	15	47	5	7	15	28329.28
STORMY RIVER (FR)	3	8	1	1	1	6110.61
STOWAWAY (GB)	37	154	15	26	46	377759.40
STRATEGIC CHOICE (USA)	8	40	5	9	9	81685.69
STRATEGIC PRINCE (GB)	6	21	2	2	4	8214.63
STRAVINSKY (USA)	2	4	1	1	0	4487.80
STREET CRY (IRE)	16	61	7	8	23	41353.66
SUBTLE POWER (IRE)	17	67	4	6	22	62965.85
SULAMANI (IRE)	29	102	11	15	44	160481.38
SUNDAY BREAK (JPN)	1	3	1	1	1	15791.60
SUNSHINE STREET (USA)	6	23	2	3	7	27789.83
SUPREME LEADER	31	149	6	9	38	136885.61
SUPREME SOUND (GB)	12	43	2	3	8	20177.94
SYNEFOS (USA)	1	5	1	1	1	10270.83
SYSTEMATIC (GB)	3	8	1	1	3	5984.85
TAGULA (IRE)	8	27	1	1	5	15250.29
TAIPAN (IRE)	14	51	4	6	12	38211.49
TAJRAASI (USA)	4	13	1	1	3	10802.08
TALAASH (IRE)	1	8	1	1	4	4804.02
TALKIN MAN (CAN)	15	43	3	3	14	21214.88
TAMAYAZ (CAN)	29	106	4	7	22	46773.18
TAMURE (IRE)	24	80	5	9	28	52758.45
TEL QUEL (FR)	12	42	1	1	7	6002.36
TENDULKAR (USA)	5	29	1	1	11	7899.61
TEN MOST WANTED (USA)	1	9	1	2	1	10376.10
TERIMON	22	94	5	8	32	49860.43
TERTULLIAN (USA)	5	33	3	6	11	31701.42
TIDARO (USA)	2	5	1	1	0	8625.00
TIGER HILL (IRE)	53	173	14	18	52	194851.86
TIKKANEN (USA)	45	163	9	14	35	132562.20
TILLERMAN (GB)	12	39	2	3	9	21057.54
TIPSY CREEK (USA)	4	22	1	1	10	7797.97

STALLIONS	RNRS	STARTS	WNRS	WINS	PLACES	TOTAL (£)
TIRAAZ (USA)	6	19	2	3	7	61730.90
TOBOUGG (IRE)	50	187	9	13	54	97730.42
TOMBA (GB)	4	12	1	1	4	14420.73
TOPANOORA	9	51	2	3	19	86086.07
TRADE FAIR (GB)	21	80	4	6	26	41029.03
TRADITIONALLY (USA)	9	42	5	7	8	47331.43
TRAGIC ROLE (USA)	4	23	4	7	7	37223.03
TRANS ISLAND (GB)	19	53	3	4	14	63368.54
TREMPOLINO (USA)	14	57	4	6	17	45372.30
TURGEON (USA)	37	162	15	30	70	231403.34
TURTLE ISLAND (IRE)	59	238	13	17	79	181626.30
UN DESPERADO (FR)	4	16	1	2	8	18564.62
UNGARO (GER)	10	40	4	6	19	37646.36
URBAN OCEAN (FR)	6	27	1	1	9	8287.28
USEFUL (FR)	7	27	2	2	7	10460.23
VALANJOU (FR)	1	10	1	1	4	8875.40
VAL ROYAL (FR)	26	60	2	2	12	33248.81
VALSEUR (USA)	1	7	1	2	3	28036.00
VERGLAS (IRE)	20	73	2	3	24	25059.75
VERTICAL SPEED (FR)	6	27	3	4	7	32236.39
VETTORI (IRE)	10	37	2	4	9	16174.42
VIDEO ROCK (FR)	12	47	4	6	19	41248.76
VIKING RULER (AUS)	11	40	4	5	11	36615.66
VILLEZ (USA)	5	24	2	3	9	67829.33
VINNIE ROE (IRE)	63	243	21	32	70	236886.53
VISIONARY (FR)	3	15	2	2	8	67589.93
VOIX DU NORD (FR)	13	44	4	7	17	78011.36
WAKY NAO (GB)	10	29	3	3	6	24001.13
WAR CHANT (USA)	7	21	1	1	9	8671.17
WAREED (IRE)	14	58	3	7	12	34245.02
WAVENEY (UAE)	1	7	1	1	2	5221.33
WEET-A-MINUTE (IRE)	2	14	1	2	5	5102.16
WELL CHOSEN (GB)	9	42	2	7	10	31335.56
WESTERNER (GB)	116	366	32	44	110	320129.06
WHERE OR WHEN (IRE)	21	42	2	6	7	54034.09
WHIPPER (USA)	19	81	5	10	39	92266.39
WHITMORE'S CONN (USA)	14	40	1	2	10	39126.76
WIMBLEBALL	1	6	1	1	1	4948.20
WINDSOR CASTLE (GB)	10	33	2	2	6	9556.44
WINDSOR KNOT (IRE)	1	5	1	2	2	59160.47
WINGED LOVE (IRE)	80	336	19	33	111	369237.19
WITH APPROVAL (CAN)	5	20	1	1	4	5223.62
WITH THE FLOW (USA)	3	11	1	1	3	71951.59
WITNESS BOX (USA)	69	289	18	25	89	514518.21
WIZARD KING (GB)	19	69	1	1	16	19138.54
WOODMAN (USA)	1	7	1	1	3	4090.62
WOODS OF WINDSOR (USA)	4	29	1	2	11	59608.28
XAAR (GB)	18	67	2	4	20	25268.36
ZAFEEN (FR)	14	25	1	1	3	3219.24
ZAFFARAN (USA)	10	31	2	2	9	18848.88
ZAGREB (USA)	58	233	11	13	86	120562.48
ZAHA (CAN)	7	21	1	1	5	7252.07
ZAMINDAR (USA)	8	23	2	4	9	25217.58
ZINAAD (GB)	2	6	1	2	2	27375.45
ZINDABAD (FR)	1	7	1	2	3	5547.49

BY KIND PERMISSION OF WEATHERBYS

HIGH-PRICED YEARLINGS OF 2013 AT TATTERSALLS SALES
The following yearlings realised 77,000 Guineas and over at Tattersalls Sales in 2013:-

Name and Breeding	Purchaser	Guineas
B F GALILEO (IRE) - ALLURING PARK (IRE)	AL SHAQAB RACING	5000000
B C GALILEO (IRE) - SHASTYE (IRE)	MV MAGNIER	3600000
AL RIFAI (IRE) B C GALILEO (IRE) - LAHALEEB (IRE)	VENDOR	1200000
ALKHAYYAM (IRE) B C OASIS DREAM (GB) - TARIYSHA (IRE)	SHADWELL ESTATE COMPANY	1100000
B C OASIS DREAM (GB) - DAR RE MI (GB)	C GORDON-WATSON BS	850000
B F GALILEO (IRE) - FRAPPE (IRE)	MV MAGNIER	775000
B C MONTJEU (IRE) - FIRST BREEZE (USA)	JOHN WARREN	650000
CH C GALILEO (IRE) - FIELD OF HOPE (IRE)	BLANDFORD BS	650000
B C OASIS DREAM (GB) - BRIOLETTE (IRE)	JOHN FERGUSON BS	650000
B C DUBAWI (IRE) - DEMISEMIQUAVER (GB)	JOHN FERGUSON BS	650000
B C OASIS DREAM (GB) - ANNABELLE'S CHARM (IRE)	JOHN FERGUSON BS	625000
B F GALILEO (IRE) - BRIGID (USA)	FORM BS	600000
B F GALILEO (IRE) - TYRANNY (GB)	VENDOR	600000
B F INVINCIBLE SPIRIT (IRE) - ROMIE'S KASTETT (GER)	AL SHAQAB RACING	600000
B C EXCEED AND EXCEL (AUS) - AYMARA (GB)	MV MAGNIER	600000
B C MONTJEU (IRE) - MADEIRA MIST (IRE)	AL SHAQAB RACING	600000
FIESOLE (GB) B C MONTJEU (IRE) - FORGOTTEN DREAMS (IRE)	VENDOR	575000
B C SEA THE STARS (IRE) - MOOD SWINGS (IRE)	AL SHAQAB RACING	550000
BARTHOLOMEW FAIR (GB) B C DANSILI (GB) - REBECCA SHARP (GB)	JOHN WARREN BS	525000
PRANCE (IRE)B F DANEHILL DANCER (IRE) - CABARET (IRE)	FLAXMAN STABLES IRELAND	525000
B C GALILEO (IRE) - MAURALAKANA (FR)	MV MAGNIER	525000
B F GALILEO (IRE) - SINGING DIVA (IRE)	BADGERS BS	525000
B C RAVEN'S PASS (USA) - PALATIAL (GB)	AL SHAQAB RACING	525000
CH F GALILEO (IRE) - RIVER BELLE (GB)	MLW BELL RACING	500000
BR C TEOFILO (IRE) - NEVERLETME GO (IRE)	JOHN FERGUSON BS	500000
B C GALILEO (IRE) - FUNSIE (FR)	VENDOR	500000
BR C SEA THE STARS (IRE) - GLOBAL WORLD (GER)	SACKVILLEDONALD	460000
B C GALILEO (IRE) - HVEGER (AUS)	J WARREN BS	460000
RAGGETY ANN (IRE) B F GALILEO (IRE) - SASSENACH (IRE)	MCCALMONT BS	450000
SPIRITING (IRE) B C INVINCIBLE SPIRIT (IRE) - GOLD BUBBLES (USA)	C GORDON-WATSON BS	450000
GR F DALAKHANI (IRE) - NEARTICA (FR)	TONY NERSES	450000
B C MONTJEU (IRE) - ATTRACTION (GB)	JS COMPANY	450000
B F NEW APPROACH (IRE) - PATACAKE PATACAKE (USA)	AL SHAQAB RACING	450000
LADY OF DUBAI (GB) B F DUBAWI (IRE) - LADY OF EVEREST (IRE)	C GORDON-WATSON BS	450000
B C NEW APPROACH (IRE) - SANDTIME (IRE)	JOHN FERGUSON BS	440000
B C MONTJEU (IRE) - LA SYLVIA (IRE)	MV MAGNIER	420000
B C RIP VAN WINKLE (IRE) - STEEL PRINCESS (IRE)	DAVID REDVERS BS	400000
B C GALILEO (IRE) - BLUE SYMPHONY (GB)	DAVID REDVERS BS	400000
B C GALILEO (IRE) - SO SQUALLY (GER)	FIONA SHAW	400000
B C GALILEO (IRE) - ALEXANDER GOLDRUN (IRE)	VENDOR	400000
BAQQA (IRE) B F SHAMARDAL (USA) - LOVE EXCELLING (FR)	SHADWELL ESTATE COMPANY	400000
B C SEA THE STARS (IRE) - OUT WEST (USA)	AL SHAQAB RACING	400000
SHURFAH (IRE) CH F SEA THE STARS (IRE) - CAP COZ (IRE)	SHADWELL ESTATE COMPANY	400000
ABHAJAT (IRE) B F LOPE DE VEGA (IRE) - STARRY MESSENGER (GB)	SHADWELL ESTATE COMPANY	400000
B F GALILEO (IRE) - SECRET GARDEN (IRE)	HUGO LASCELLES BS	380000
B C SEA THE STARS (IRE) - THREE MOONS (IRE)	AL SHAQAB RACING	380000
B C MONTJEU (IRE) - ECOUTILA (USA)	JOHN WARREN	375000
B F GALILEO (IRE) - SPECIFICALLY (USA)	DAVID REDVERS BS	375000
B C OASIS DREAM (GB) - SPLASHDOWN (GB)	ROB SPEERS	370000
CH C NEW APPROACH (IRE) - CHEERLEADER (GB)	JOHN FERGUSON BS	360000
B C SEA THE STARS (IRE) - QUE PUNTUAL (ARG)	JOHN FERGUSON BS	360000
B F GALILEO (IRE) - DEVOTED TO YOU (IRE)	C GORDON-WATSON BS	350000
GR F GALILEO (IRE) - HOTELGENIE DOT COM (GB)	FORM BS	350000
B F DANEHILL DANCER (IRE) - YUMMY MUMMY (GB)	MV MAGNIER	350000
ALLO GALANTE (GB) CH C GALILEO (IRE) - SPACIOUS (GB)	JEREMY BRUMMITT	350000
C GALILEO (IRE) - KENTUCKY WARBLER (GB)	FORM BS	340000
AYALEE (IRE) B F LAWMAN (FR) - RED FEATHER (IRE)	SHADWELL ESTATE COMPANY	340000
C EXCEED AND EXCEL (AUS) - WISE MELODY (GB)	AL SHAQAB RACING	320000
C TEOFILO (IRE) - NENUPHAR (IRE)	JOHN FERGUSON BS	320000
F MOTIVATOR (GB) - ELEGANT BEAUTY (GB)	PETER & ROSS DOYLE BS	320000
H F PIVOTAL (GB) - VASSIANA (FR)	JOHN FERGUSON BS	320000
H C EXCEED AND EXCEL (AUS) - ONE GIANT LEAP (IRE)	AL SHAQAB RACING	320000
F MONTJEU (IRE) - ARBELLA (GB)	DAVID REDVERS BS	300000
C OASIS DREAM (GB) - LOVE DIVINE (GB)	JOHN FERGUSON BS	300000
NGLAND ROSE (GB) B F DANSILI (GB) - VENTURA HIGHWAY (GB)	KOJI MAEDA	300000
BR F GALILEO (IRE) - HOITY TOITY (GB)	ANTHONY STROUD BS	300000
F DUBAWI (IRE) - MUCH FASTER (IRE)	JOHN FERGUSON BS	300000
C RIP VAN WINKLE (IRE) - YARIA (IRE)	MV MAGNIER	300000

Name and Breeding	Purchaser	Guineas
WELL OFF (GER) B C MONSUN (GER) - WELLS PRESENT (GER)	JOHN FERGUSON BS	300000
MR QUICKSILVER (GB) GR C DANSILI (GB) - LAST SECOND (IRE)	NORRIS/HUNTINGDON	300000
MUSHARRIF (GB) B C ARCANO (IRE) - CEFIRA (USA)	SHADWELL ESTATE COMPANY	300000
B C MONTJEU (IRE) - BONNIE BYERLY (USA)	VENDOR	300000
MURAHANA (IRE) B F INVINCIBLE SPIRIT (IRE) - BY REQUEST (GB)	SHADWELL ESTATE COMPANY	300000
MONOTYPE (IRE) B C MAKFI (GB) - MILL GUINEAS (USA)	JOHN WARREN BS	300000
CH C RAVEN'S PASS (USA) - GENEROUS LADY (GB)	PHILIP ROBINSON	300000
CAVANAUGH PARK (IRE) B F GALILEO (IRE) - ICE MINT (USA)	D WACHMAN	300000
IJMAALY (IRE) CH C MAKFI (GB) - WEDDING GOWN (GB)	SHADWELL ESTATE COMPANY	300000
B/BR C STREET CRY (IRE) - LADY DARSHAAN (IRE)	JOHN FERGUSON BS	300000
B F DUBAWI (IRE) - SUGAR FREE (IRE)	JOHN FERGUSON BS	300000
B G HIGH CHAPARRAL (IRE) - URSULA MINOR (IRE)	HONG KONG JOCKEY CLUB	290000
CH C MASTERCRAFTSMAN (IRE) - DUNDEL (IRE)	MV MAGNIER	290000
B C SHAMARDAL (USA) - TWYLA THARP (IRE)	VENDOR	290000
B F INVINCIBLE SPIRIT (IRE) - DANCE TROUPE (GB)	C GORDON-WATSON BS	280000
B C SHAMARDAL (USA) - DEVERON (USA)	JOHN FERGUSON BS	280000
BR C LAWMAN (FR) - FONDA (USA)	TONY NERSES	280000
B C HIGH CHAPARRAL (IRE) - WANNA (IRE)	FORM BS	280000
CH F LOPE DE VEGA (IRE) - DANIELLI (IRE)	JOHN FERGUSON BS	280000
B C HIGH CHAPARRAL (IRE) - MIDDLE PERSIA (GB)	MV MAGNIER	275000
B F FASTNET ROCK (AUS) - HAWALA (IRE)	BBA IRELAND	270000
CH C DUTCH ART (GB) - BROOKLYN'S SKY (GB)	BRIAN CASSIDY	270000
B C NEW APPROACH (IRE) - CARO GEORGE (USA)	JOHN FERGUSON BS	270000
BIG BLUE (GB) CH C GALILEO (IRE) - BOARD MEETING (IRE)	VENDOR	270000
QUAKE (GB) B F DUBAWI (IRE) - POLITESSE (USA)	VENDOR	260000
B F SHAMARDAL (USA) - SADIMA (IRE)	JOHN FERGUSON BS	260000
AZMAAM (IRE) GR C DARK ANGEL (IRE) - MISS INDIGO (GB)	SHADWELL ESTATE COMPANY	260000
B F MEDICEAN (GB) - DISTINCTIVE LOOK (USA)	DEMI O'BYRNE	260000
CH F GALILEO (IRE) - FLAMINGO SEA (USA)	VENDOR	260000
B/BR F DANSILI (GB) - LADEENA (IRE)	SIR ROBERT OGDEN	260000
POUR DEUX (IRE) B F DANSILI (GB) - GAGNOA (IRE)	VENDOR	260000
B F CAPE CROSS (IRE) - QUEEN OF MEAN (GB)	TONY NERSES	260000
CH C TEOFILO (IRE) - TASHA'S DREAM (USA)	SHADWELL ESTATE COMPANY	250000
B C SHAMARDAL (USA) - PIONEER BRIDE (USA)	JOHN FERGUSON BS	250000
HORSESHOE BAY (IRE) B C ARCH (USA) - SWEEPSTAKE (IRE)	J WARREN BS	250000
CH C RAVEN'S PASS (USA) - OLYMPIC MEDAL (USA)	AL SHAQAB RACING	250000
GRAND INQUISITOR (GB) B C DANSILI (GB) - DUSTY ANSWER (GB)	J WARREN BS	250000
WHITE LAKE (GB) B C PIVOTAL (GB) - WHITE PALACE (IRE)	C GORDON-WATSON BS	240000
B C LAWMAN (FR) - WHOLE GRAIN (GB)	C GORDON-WATSON BS	240000
SUNSHINE REGAE (IRE) B F CAPE CROSS (IRE) - SLINK (IRE)	C GORDON-WATSON BS	240000
CH C NEW APPROACH (IRE) - COLORADO DAWN (GB)	C GORDON-WATSON BS	240000
CH C RAVEN'S PASS (USA) - SENSATIONALLY (GB)	JOHN FERGUSON BS	240000
B F WAR FRONT (USA) - DAWN CHORUS (USA)	CHINA HORSE CLUB	240000
B F GALILEO (IRE) - PHOTOPHORE (IRE)	AL SHAQAB RACING	240000
B F INVINCIBLE SPIRIT (IRE) - DRESS UNIFORM (USA)	VENDOR	240000
ARCHERY SUMMIT (GB) B C ARCH (USA) - COME TOUCH THE SUN (IRE)	MCCALMONT BS	235000
B C RIP VAN WINKLE (IRE) - SHANGHAI LILY (IRE)	PAUL SMITH	230000
B C MAKFI (GB) - MAIDIN MAITH (IRE)	TONY NERSES	230000
B C FASTNET ROCK (AUS) - KUSHNARENKOVO (GB)	C GORDON-WATSON BS	220000
B C ZEBEDEE (GB) - KEENES ROYALE (GB)	MRS A SKIFFINGTON	220000
FADHAYYIL (IRE) B F TAMAYUZ (GB) - ZIRIA (IRE)	SHADWELL ESTATE COMPANY	220000
B C INVINCIBLE SPIRIT (IRE) - MANOEUVRE (IRE)	VENDOR	220000
GR F IFFRAAJ (GB) - WRONG ANSWER (GB)	YES/AL SHAHANIA STUD	220000
B F DANEHILL DANCER (IRE) - MENNETOU (IRE)	AL SHAQAB RACING	220000
B C EXCEED AND EXCEL (AUS) - PICKLE (GB)	JOHN FERGUSON BS	220000
B C OASIS DREAM (GB) - ENTENTE CORDIALE (IRE)	NORRIS/HUNTINGDON	220000
B F GALILEO (IRE) - BLUE RHAPSODY (GB)	BLANDFORD BS	210000
INSHAA (GB) B C DANSILI (GB) - HIDDEN BRIEF (GB)	SHADWELL ESTATE COMPANY	210000
B C BIG BAD BOB (IRE) - SCRUMPTIOUS (GB)	PETER & ROSS DOYLE BS	210000
B C ARCH (USA) - WILKI (FR)	VENDOR	210000
JOYFUL HOPE (GB) CH F SHAMARDAL (USA) - CLABA DI SAN JORE (IRE)	VENDOR	210000
B F TEOFILO (IRE) - WADAAT (GB)	PAUL WEBBER RACING	205000
CH C DUBAWI (IRE) - TIME HONOURED (GB)	FORM BS	200000
B F MOTIVATOR (GB) - CLASSIC REMARK (IRE)	DAVID REDVERS BS	200000
B C MASTERCRAFTSMAN (IRE) - SPLASH MOUNTAIN (IRE)	SUZANNE ROBERTS	200000
B C GALILEO (IRE) - DHANYATA (IRE)	VENDOR	200000
CH C DUBAWI (IRE) - REBELLINE (IRE)	JOHN FERGUSON BS	200000
B C DANSILI (GB) - GALAXY HIGHFLYER (GB)	BADGERS FOR A NEZHENETS	200000
B C BERNARDINI (USA) - CLOUD CASTLE (GB)	BADGERS FOR A NEZHENETS	200000
B F INVINCIBLE SPIRIT (IRE) - WHITE AND RED (IRE)	C GORDON-WATSON BS	200000
B F DANEHILL DANCER (IRE) - NOAHS ARK (IRE)	D WACHMAN	200000

Name and Breeding	Purchaser	Guineas
CH C EXCEED AND EXCEL (AUS) - DEAREST DAISY (GB)	PHILIP ROBINSON	200000
B C RIP VAN WINKLE (IRE) - AURELIA (GB)	BBA IRELAND	200000
B C GALILEO (IRE) - APPROACH (GB)	DAVID REDVERS BS	190000
BLACK N BLUE (GB) CH C GALILEO (IRE) - COYOTE (GB)	MARK JOHNSTON RACING	190000
B C DARK ANGEL (IRE) - COVER GIRL (IRE)	VENDOR	190000
GOLDEN HORN (GB) B C CAPE CROSS (IRE) - FLECHE D'OR (GB)	VENDOR	190000
B F GALILEO (IRE) - LADY LAHAR (GB)	J O'BYRNE	185000
B C EXCEED AND EXCEL (AUS) - MAGGIE LOU (IRE)	VENDOR	185000
B F PIVOTAL (GB) - PORTAL (GB)	EMERALD BS	180000
CH C NEW APPROACH (IRE) - PURPLE GLOW (IRE)	JOHN FERGUSON BS	180000
B C FASTNET ROCK (AUS) - GREEN CASTLE (IRE)	C GORDON-WATSON BS	180000
CH C KYLLACHY (GB) - NAIZAK (GB)	SHADWELL ESTATE COMPANY	180000
B F SEA THE STARS (IRE) - MAMONTA (GB)	JOHN FERGUSON BS	180000
CH C SHAMARDAL (USA) - TRULY YOURS (IRE)	JOHN FERGUSON BS	180000
B C HENRYTHENAVIGATOR (USA) - SHERMEEN (IRE)	AL SHAQAB RACING	180000
B C SHAMARDAL (USA) - TIME AWAY (IRE)	JOHN FERGUSON BS	180000
SULAALAAT (GB) B F NEW APPROACH (IRE) - DANEHILL DREAMER (USA)	SHADWELL ESTATE COMPANY	180000
SAMEEK (IRE) B C ACCLAMATION (GB) - VARENKA (IRE)	SHADWELL ESTATE COMPANY	175000
CH C EXCEED AND EXCEL (AUS) - SHARP TERMS (GB)	JOHN FERGUSON BS	175000
B C LAWMAN (FR) - ON MY KNESS (FR)	PETER & ROSS DOYLE BS	170000
GR F DUKE OF MARMALADE (IRE) - DOOKUS (IRE)	DAVID REDVERS BS	170000
BR C KODIAC (GB) - SUNBLUSH (UAE)	VENDOR	170000
ISAMOL (GB) B C INTIKHAB (USA) - UVINZA (GB)	PETER & ROSS DOYLE BS	170000
BARSANTI (IRE) B C CHAMPS ELYSEES (GB) - SILVER STAR (GB)	C GORDON-WATSON BS	170000
LACING (GB) B F EQUIANO (FR) - LACEWORK (GB)	CHEVELEY PARK STUD	170000
B C RIP VAN WINKLE (IRE) - HAVE FAITH (IRE)	PETER & ROSS DOYLE BS	170000
CH C TEOFILO (IRE) - RIBOT'S GUEST (IRE)	PETER & ROSS DOYLE BS	170000
CH F BAHAMIAN BOUNTY (GB) - REVEUSE DE JOUR (IRE)	BBA IRELAND	170000
B F DANSILI (GB) - CUT SHORT (USA)	JEREMY BRUMMITT	160000
B C ACCLAMATION (GB) - ANNEE LUMIERE (IRE)	C GORDON-WATSON BS	160000
CH C IFFRAAJ (GB) - PRINCESS MOOD (GER)	HONG KONG JOCKEY CLUB	160000
B C NEW APPROACH (IRE) - FASLEN (USA)	JOHN FERGUSON BS	160000
CH C NEW APPROACH (IRE) - WOSAITA (GB)	ANDREW BALDING	160000
B C OASIS DREAM (GB) - LONGING TO DANCE (GB)	FEDERICO BARBERINI, AGENT	160000
GR F GALILEO (IRE) - FAMOUS (IRE)	VENDOR	160000
B C INTIKHAB (USA) - DON'T TELL MUM (IRE)	HAPPY VALLEY RACING	160000
CH F EXCEED AND EXCEL (AUS) - WELSH DIVA (GB)	KATSUMI YOSHIDA	160000
GR F DARK ANGEL (IRE) - WIN CASH (IRE)	JOHN FERGUSON BS	160000
B F PIVOTAL (GB) - ARABIAN MIRAGE (GB)	BLANDFORD BS	160000
B C DANEHILL DANCER (IRE) - GILDED VANITY (IRE)	JOHN WARREN BS	155000
B F OASIS DREAM (GB) - SWEET STREAM (ITY)	VENDOR	155000
B C ACCLAMATION (GB) - MUSICAL TREAT (GB)	PETER & ROSS DOYLE BS	150000
B C OASIS DREAM (GB) - VICTORIA CROSS (IRE)	BBA IRELAND	150000
B G FASTNET ROCK (AUS) - MOHICAN PRINCESS (GB)	ANTHONY STROUD BS (P.S.)	150000
MUNFARRID (GB) BR C SHOWCASING (GB) - THANKFUL (GB)	PETER & ROSS DOYLE BS	150000
B C EXCEED AND EXCEL (AUS) - WELSH CAKE (GB)	AL SHAQAB RACING	150000
B F VALE OF YORK (IRE) - AHLA WASAHL (GB)	WILLIAM HAGGAS	150000
TAJATHUB (GB) GR/RO C BAHAMIAN BOUNTY (GB) - GALAPAGAR (USA)	SHADWELL ESTATE COMPANY	150000
HOLLAND PARK (GB) B C MORE THAN READY (USA) - B BERRY BRANDY (USA)	PETER & ROSS DOYLE BS	150000
BERMONDSEY (GB) B C GALILEO (IRE) - BARTER (GB)	VENDOR	150000
B F NEW APPROACH (IRE) - PARK TWILIGHT (IRE)	JOHN FERGUSON BS	150000
B C ACCLAMATION (GB) - GREEN POPPY (GB)	HIGHFIELD FARM LLP	150000
KHAREER (IRE) B C ACCLAMATION (GB) - FANTASTIC ACCOUNT (GB)	SHADWELL ESTATE COMPANY	150000
B C FASTNET ROCK (AUS) - SALONTASCHE (GER)	TINA RAU BS	150000
B F DANSILI (GB) - LANDELA (GB)	MRS A SKIFFINGTON	150000
B F OASIS DREAM (GB) - MOLOMO (GB)	VENDOR	150000
B C SHAMARDAL (USA) - DISCREET BRIEF (IRE)	JOHN FERGUSON BS	150000
B C RIP VAN WINKLE (IRE) - VAS Y CARLA (USA)	PAUL SMITH	150000
B F IFFRAAJ (GB) - PRINCESS SPEEDFIT (FR)	ARMANDO DUARTE	150000
B C DUTCH ART (GB) - COMMON CONSENT (IRE)	HONG KONG JOCKEY CLUB	150000
B C DUTCH ART (GB) - ARCULINGE (GB)	RUSSELL MCNABB	150000
B C HIGH CHAPARRAL (IRE) - GALLIVANT (GB)	PETER & ROSS DOYLE BS	150000
B F SHAMARDAL (USA) - NASHMIAH (IRE)	JOHN FERGUSON BS	150000
GR C LOPE DE VEGA (IRE) - MUNDUS NOVUS (USA)	JOHN WARREN BS	150000
B C IFFRAAJ (GB) - BAHIA BREEZE (GB)	SHADWELL ESTATE COMPANY	150000
B F EXCEED AND EXCEL (AUS) - DAME BLANCHE (IRE)	HUGO MERRY BS	145000
B/BR C STREET CRY (IRE) - GLOWING (IRE)	JOHN FERGUSON BS	145000
B F LOPE DE VEGA (IRE) - HIGHER LOVE (IRE)	VENDOR	145000
B F LOPE DE VEGA (IRE) - WANA DOO (USA)	ANTHONY STROUD BS	140000
B C DARK ANGEL (IRE) - WINESONG (IRE)	SEAMUS DURACK	140000

Name and Breeding	Purchaser	Guineas
B F FASTNET ROCK (AUS) - FIG TREE DRIVE (USA)	FORM BS	140000
CH F GALILEO (IRE) - BARAKA (IRE)	BBA IRELAND	140000
B C KODIAC (GB) - CASSAVA (IRE)	DAVID REDVERS BS	140000
B F DALAKHANI (IRE) - CLAXON (GB)	MARK JOHNSTON RACING	140000
B C ACCLAMATION (GB) - DORELIA (IRE)	DAVID REDVERS BS	140000
CH C NEW APPROACH (IRE) - GLEAM OF LIGHT (IRE)	JOHN FERGUSON BS	140000
B C EQUIANO (FR) - MAIL THE DESERT (IRE)	PETER & ROSS DOYLE BS	140000
B F SEA THE STARS (IRE) - LION FOREST (USA)	SACKVILLEDONALD	140000
CH F SHAMARDAL (USA) - DUBAI SURPRISE (IRE)	VENDOR	140000
B F ROYAL APPLAUSE (GB) - POLISH BELLE (GB)	TINA RAU BS	135000
CH F MASTERCRAFTSMAN (IRE) - KHIBRAAT (GB)	ANTHONY STROUD BS	135000
B C DANEHILL DANCER (IRE) - TITIVATION (GB)	J WARREN BS	135000
B F INVINCIBLE SPIRIT (IRE) - ATTASLIYAH (IRE)	FORM BS (P.S.)	135000
B C INVINCIBLE SPIRIT (IRE) - ERMINE AND VELVET (GB)	MCCALMONT BS	135000
B F GALILEO (IRE) - ARTFUL (IRE)	DAVID REDVERS BS	135000
B C KODIAC (GB) - RIGHT AFTER MOYNE (IRE)	TONY NERSES	130000
B C ACCLAMATION (GB) - CURSORY (GB)	VENDOR	130000
MISTERIOSO (IRE) B C IFFRAAJ (GB) - ROYSTONEA (GB)	PETER & ROSS DOYLE BS	130000
B C ACCLAMATION (GB) - ABERAVON (GB)	HONG KONG JOCKEY CLUB	130000
B C RIP VAN WINKLE (IRE) - WIND SURF (USA)	C GORDON-WATSON BS	130000
ROCK KRISTAL (IRE) B F FASTNET ROCK (AUS) - PELLINORE (USA)	DENFORD STUD	130000
MOHTAFAL (GB) B C DUTCH ART (GB) - VIVE LES ROUGES (GB)	SHADWELL ESTATE COMPANY	130000
CH C EXCEED AND EXCEL (AUS) - MONNAVANNA (IRE)	HAPPY VALLEY RACING	130000
BR/GR F ZEBEDEE (GB) - FUERTA VENTURA (IRE)	JEREMY NOSEDA AGENT	120000
B/GR C RAVEN'S PASS (USA) - KAPRIA (IRE)	JOHN FERGUSON BS	120000
KWEEN MARMALADE (GB) BR/GR F DUKE OF MARMALADE (IRE) - KASSIYRA (IRE)	GESTUT BRUMMERHOF	120000
SARHAAN (GB) B C NEW APPROACH (IRE) - COVETED (GB)	SHADWELL ESTATE COMPANY	120000
B C PIVOTAL (GB) - FONDLED (GB)	J NOSEDA AGENT	120000
RISING SUN (IRE) B C IFFRAAJ (GB) - ROLLY POLLY (IRE)	DAVID REDVERS BS	120000
B C MAKFI (GB) - DANCEABOUT (GB)	WILLIE BROWNE	120000
B F SHAMARDAL (USA) - KARMIFIRA (FR)	VENDOR	120000
DALAMAR (GB) B F MONTJEU (IRE) - DALASYLA (IRE)	VENDOR	120000
B C INVINCIBLE SPIRIT (IRE) - IN THE LIGHT (GB)	THE CHANNEL CONSIGNMENT	120000
SERAFIGLIO (GB) B C TEOFILO (IRE) - SERADIM (GB)	JOHN FERGUSON BS	120000
B F DANEHILL DANCER (IRE) - ARDBRAE LADY (GB)	J O'BYRNE	120000
MUKHAYYAM (GB) B C DARK ANGEL (IRE) - CASTER SUGAR (USA)	SHADWELL ESTATE COMPANY	120000
B C LAWMAN (FR) - KERIYKA (IRE)	JOHN FERGUSON BS	120000
B C DANSILI (GB) - PENANG PEARL (FR)	VENDOR	120000
B C THEWAYYOUARE (USA) - COZZENE'S PRIDE (USA)	JAMIE OSBORNE	120000
B C HOLY ROMAN EMPEROR (IRE) - COUVERTURE (USA)	STEPHEN HILLEN BS	120000
B C ARCANO (IRE) - TARBELA (IRE)	JOHN FERGUSON BS	120000
B C MASTERCRAFTSMAN (IRE) - CHANTER (GB)	STEPHEN HILLEN BS	120000
B C TEOFILO (IRE) - HENTIES BAY (IRE)	JOHN FERGUSON BS	120000
B C SEA THE STARS (IRE) - SPEED SONG (GB)	FEDERICO BARBERINI, AGENT	115000
B F INVINCIBLE SPIRIT (IRE) - SNOW CRYSTAL (IRE)	KATSUMI YOSHIDA	115000
B F IFFRAAJ (GB) - RAJA (IRE)	DAVID REDVERS BS	115000
B F RIP VAN WINKLE (IRE) - RAMONA (GB)	VENDOR	115000
B C HIGH CHAPARRAL (IRE) - HADARAMA (IRE)	STEPHEN HILLEN BS	115000
FIVE OF DIAMONDS (FR) B F PEINTRE CELEBRE (USA) - GIVE ME FIVE (GER)	ROGER P VARIAN	115000
B C DARK ANGEL (IRE) - SASSARI (IRE)	SACKVILLEDONALD	115000
B C HENRYTHENAVIGATOR (USA) - SAINTLY SPEECH (USA)	BLANDFORD BS	115000
B C RIP VAN WINKLE (IRE) - AINE (IRE)	GERARD BUTLER	115000
CH C STARSPANGLEDBANNER (AUS) - PINA COLADA (GB)	TONY NERSES	110000
B C INVINCIBLE SPIRIT (IRE) - TEMPLE STREET (IRE)	JS COMPANY	110000
MUMFORD (GB) B C STIMULATION (IRE) - NOBLE NOVA (GB)	PETER & ROSS DOYLE BS	110000
B C EXCEED AND EXCEL (AUS) - SENSIBLE (GB)	SHADWELL ESTATE COMPANY	110000
MUSTAQQIL (IRE) B C INVINCIBLE SPIRIT (IRE) - CAST IN GOLD (USA)	SHADWELL ESTATE COMPANY	110000
ACCLIMATISATION (IRE) B F ACCLAMATION (GB) - TAHARA (IRE)	DENFORD STUD	110000
B C INVINCIBLE SPIRIT (IRE) - PRECIOUS SPRING (IRE)	VENDOR	110000
B C HIGH CHAPARRAL (IRE) - MUSIQUE MAGIQUE (GB)	PETER & ROSS DOYLE BS	110000
MAISRAH (IRE) B C INVINCIBLE SPIRIT (IRE) - VIRGINIA ROSE (IRE)	SHADWELL ESTATE COMPANY	110000
ATAMAN (IRE) B C SHOLOKHOV (IRE) - DIORA (IRE)	MRS A SKIFFINGTON	110000
B C KYLLACHY (GB) - SOMETHING BLUE (GB)	SACKVILLEDONALD	110000
B F INVINCIBLE SPIRIT (IRE) - ALLANNAH ABU (GB)	VENDOR	110000
B C INVINCIBLE SPIRIT (IRE) - URGELE (FR)	SACKVILLEDONALD (P.S.)	110000
TAFAHOM (IRE) B C ACCLAMATION (GB) - DANCE SET (GB)	HUGO MERRY BS	110000
B F SEA THE STARS (IRE) - MISS RIVIERA GOLF (GB)	GILL RICHARDSON BS	110000
B F SHOWCASING (GB) - CLINCHER CLUB (GB)	OLIVER ST LAWRENCE BS	110000
B C ROCK OF GIBRALTAR (IRE) - SERENA'S STORM (IRE)	W SWINBURN	110000
CH C IFFRAAJ (GB) - ALEXANDER YOUTH (IRE)	JOHN FERGUSON BS	110000
B F MONTJEU (IRE) - O' BELLA BALLERINA (USA)	RACHEL SANSON	105000

Name and Breeding	Purchaser	Guineas
B C GALILEO (IRE) - NAUSICAA (USA)	OLIVER ST LAWRENCE BS	105000
B/BR C INVINCIBLE SPIRIT (IRE) - PHILLIPPA (GB)	JAMIE LLOYD	105000
CH C EXCEED AND EXCEL (AUS) - KANGRA VALLEY (GB)	JOHN FERGUSON BS	105000
B C DUTCH ART (GB) - POPOCATEPETL (FR)	SACKVILLEDONALD	105000
LITTLE PRAIRIE (GB) CH F EXCEED AND EXCEL (AUS) - CHETWYND (IRE)	ANTHONY STROUD BS	105000
B C CHAMPS ELYSEES (GB) - MILLISTAR (GB)	FIONA SHAW	105000
GR C MASTERCRAFTSMAN (IRE) - TWICE THE EASE (GB)	BBA IRELAND	105000
PROFUSION (GB) B C DANSILI (GB) - RED BLOOM (GB)	VENDOR	105000
B F EQUIANO (FR) - STONEACRE SARAH (GB)	PETER & ROSS DOYLE BS	105000
B F EQUIANO (FR) - LUANSHYA (GB)	MCKEEVER BS	105000
B F FASTNET ROCK (AUS) - CRINOLETTE (IRE)	WILLIE BROWNE	105000
B C TEOFILO (IRE) - HENTIES BAY (IRE)	VENDOR	100000
B C IFFRAAJ (GB) - BALLADONIA (GB)	BBA IRELAND	100000
B C PACO BOY (IRE) - WILAYA (USA)	JS COMPANY	100000
B F IFFRAAJ (GB) - GIFT OF SPRING (USA)	SACKVILLEDONALD	100000
B C IFFRAAJ (GB) - MISS LACEY (IRE)	LI FUNG LOK (P.S.)	100000
B C DANEHILL DANCER (IRE) - ROSE CUT (IRE)	JOHN WARREN BS	100000
B C PIVOTAL (GB) - TOWARDS (USA)	VENDOR	100000
B F INVINCIBLE SPIRIT (IRE) - FINCHLEY (GB)	FLOORS STUD	100000
RED TYCOON (IRE) B C ACCLAMATION (GB) - RUGGED UP (IRE)	C GORDON-WATSON BS	100000
B C TAMAYUZ (GB) - CARIOCA (IRE)	PETER & ROSS DOYLE BS	100000
B C IFFRAAJ (GB) - ARTISTI (GB)	JOHN FERGUSON BS	100000
CH C ARCANO (IRE) - WESTERN SKY (GB)	SEAMUS DURACK	100000
B C IFFRAAJ (GB) - WHAZZIS (GB)	ANTHONY STROUD BS	100000
ALLUMAGE (GB) B F MONTJEU (IRE) - ALAIA (IRE)	BBA IRELAND (P.S.)	100000
B C DANSILI (GB) - SAGACIOUS (IRE)	GEORGE BOLTON	100000
B F NEW APPROACH (IRE) - SUPERSTITIOUS (USA)	YES/AL SHAHANIA STUD	100000
B F KODIAC (GB) - OPERISSIMO (GB)	BBA IRELAND	100000
MUHAAFIZ (IRE) BR G LORD SHANAKILL (USA) - YASMIN SATINE (IRE)	SHADWELL ESTATE COMPANY	100000
B F DANEHILL DANCER (IRE) - FOOLISH ACT (USA)	VENDOR	100000
B C IFFRAAJ (GB) - FOREVER TIMES (GB)	C GORDON-WATSON BS	100000
CH F TEOFILO (IRE) - FRAGRANCY (IRE)	MARK JOHNSTON RACING	100000
CH C EXCEED AND EXCEL (AUS) - MUFFLED (USA)	SHADWELL ESTATE COMPANY	100000
B C INVINCIBLE SPIRIT (IRE) - SERRES (IRE)	VENDOR	100000
B C DANSILI (GB) - BRISEIDA (GB)	VENDOR	100000
BE JAZZY (IRE) B F TEOFILO (IRE) - SUGAR MINT (IRE)	VENDOR	100000
MORGENLICHT (GER) B F SHOLOKHOV (IRE) - MONBIJOU (GER)	VENDOR	100000
CH C BAHAMIAN BOUNTY (GB) - TOUCHING (GB)	RABBAH BS	100000
B F ACCLAMATION (GB) - SECRET HISTORY (USA)	MARCO BOTTI	100000
CALIMA BREEZE (GB) B F OASIS DREAM (GB) - PARIS WINDS (IRE)	BBA IRELAND	100000
B F EXCEED AND EXCEL (AUS) - REFLECTED IMAGE (IRE)	VENDOR	100000
B F NEW APPROACH (IRE) - JOUET (GB)	J O'BYRNE	95000
B C FASTNET ROCK (AUS) - SLOW SAND (USA)	CORMAC MCCORMACK BS	95000
B/GR F ACCLAMATION (GB) - RED BOOTS (IRE)	JOHN WARREN BS	95000
DIAMOND BLAISE (GB) B F IFFRAAJ (GB) - SEE YOU LATER (GB)	H SLADE	95000
B C KYLLACHY (GB) - CONSTITUTE (USA)	DAVID REDVERS BS	95000
CH C MEDICEAN (GB) - BLUE ROCKET (IRE)	WILL EDMEADES BS	95000
B F MONTJEU (IRE) - BATIK (IRE)	VENDOR	95000
B F SHAMARDAL (USA) - BADEE'A (IRE)	BLANDFORD BS	95000
B F LAWMAN (FR) - LUNDUV (IRE)	OLIVER ST LAWRENCE BS	95000
LITTLE TREASURE (ITY) B F INVINCIBLE SPIRIT (IRE) - DOREGAN (IRE)	WILLIE BROWNE	95000
B C INVINCIBLE SPIRIT (IRE) - DANI RIDGE (IRE)	CLIVE COX RACING	95000
B C HIGH CHAPARRAL (IRE) - COOL CATENA (GB)	AB RACING	95000
HEART OF THE SEA (IRE) B F RIP VAN WINKLE (IRE) - LANGOUSTINE (USA)	C GORDON-WATSON BS	92000
B/BR C HIGH CHAPARRAL (IRE) - FINAL LEGACY (USA)	DAVID REDVERS BS	92000
B C MARJU (IRE) - CELESTIAL DREAM (IRE)	VENDOR	92000
SEARCHING (IRE) B C MASTERCRAFTSMAN (IRE) - MIRACOLIA (IRE)	ROGER P VARIAN	90000
DUFOOF (IRE) B F SHAMARDAL (USA) - EVENSONG (GER)	SHADWELL ESTATE COMPANY	90000
MONT D'ARGENT (GB) GR C MONTJEU (IRE) - AYLA (GB)	MARK JOHNSTON (P.S.)	90000
B C KODIAC (GB) - CALLANISH (GB)	DAVID REDVERS BS	90000
B F GALILEO (IRE) - ALTA ANNA (FR)	ANTHONY STROUD BS	90000
ROCKING THE BOAT (IRE) B F ZEBEDEE (GB) - ROCKING (GB)	BBA IRELAND	90000
B C ACCLAMATION (GB) - TATIANA ROMANOVA (USA)	SHADWELL ESTATE COMPANY	90000
B C EXCEED AND EXCEL (AUS) - IMPERIAL QUEST (GB)	PETER & ROSS DOYLE BS	90000
B F INVINCIBLE SPIRIT (IRE) - TOWANDA (GB)	J WARREN BS	90000
CH C DUTCH ART (GB) - VALENTINA GUEST (IRE)	HIGHFIELD FARM LLP	90000
B C DANEHILL DANCER (IRE) - ALTHEA ROSE (IRE)	ANTHONY STROUD BS	90000
B C SHAMARDAL (USA) - SOLAIA (USA)	GILL RICHARDSON BS	90000
B C ZEBEDEE (GB) - ROMANY PRINCESS (IRE)	SHADWELL ESTATE COMPANY	90000
WINTERVAL (GB) B C DUBAWI (IRE) - FESTIVALE (IRE)	C GORDON-WATSON BS	90000
B F SEA THE STARS (IRE) - PARACEL (USA)	MARK JOHNSTON RACING	90000

Name and Breeding	Purchaser	Guineas
B C EQUIANO (FR) - MERLE (GB)	VENDOR	90000
GOLDMETAL JACKET (IRE) B C ACCLAMATION (GB) - TWINSPOT (USA)	CHANTILLY BS AGENCY	90000
CH C RIP VAN WINKLE (IRE) - NIGHT HAVEN (GB)	STEPHEN HILLEN BS	90000
B C SHAMARDAL (USA) - NANTYGLO (GB)	JOHN FERGUSON BS	90000
B F ROYAL APPLAUSE (GB) - PARISIAN ELEGANCE (GB)	KERN LILLINGSTON	90000
B C FASTNET ROCK (AUS) - BUTTERFLY BLUE (GB)	VENDOR	90000
B C ACCLAMATION (GB) - OBSARA (GB)	JOHN WARREN BS	90000
TIGRILLA (IRE) GR F CLODOVIL (IRE) - LISIEUX ORCHID (IRE)	CHEVELEY PARK STUD	90000
CH C GALILEO (IRE) - NATIVE FORCE (IRE)	BBA IRELAND	90000
B C EXCEED AND EXCEL (AUS) - PERSEFONA (IRE)	VENDOR	90000
B F DANSILI (GB) - RUBIES FROM BURMA (USA)	FEDERICO BARBERINI, AGENT	88000
CH C SELKIRK (USA) - RYELLA (USA)	PETER & ROSS DOYLE BS	88000
OPEN THE RED (GB) B C LAWMAN (FR) - ACQUAINTED (GB)	PETER & ROSS DOYLE BS	87000
AMERICAN ARTIST (IRE) CH C DANEHILL DANCER (IRE) - AMERICAN ADVENTURE (USA)...	WILL EDMEADES BS	86000
B C DARK ANGEL (IRE) - CHINCOTEAGUE (USA)	PETER & ROSS DOYLE BS	85000
GIPSY DOLL (GB) B F DANSILI (GB) - GIPSY MOTH (GB)	PFI COLE	85000
CH F DUTCH ART (GB) - PINK STONE (FR)	SHADWELL ESTATE COMPANY	85000
B C DANEHILL DANCER (IRE) - PHRASE (GB)	BLANDFORD BS	85000
B/BR F U S RANGER (USA) - SAUDIA (USA)	RABBAH BS	85000
CH C EQUIANO (FR) - CLASSICAL DANCER (GB)	CLIVE COX RACING	85000
BR F MASTERCRAFTSMAN (IRE) - DAMA'A (IRE)	MARGARET O'TOOLE (IRE)	85000
MUFFRI'HA (IRE) B F IFFRAAJ (GB) - GRECIAN DANCER (GB)	RABBAH BS	85000
BIG MCINTOSH (IRE) B C BUSHRANGER (IRE) - THREE DECADES (IRE)	JOHN RYAN RACING	85000
B C MYBOYCHARLIE (IRE) - BECUILLE (IRE)	PETER & ROSS DOYLE BS	82000
WAR PAINT (IRE) BR F EXCELLENT ART (GB) - STAIRWAY TO GLORY (IRE)	SACKVILLEDONALD	82000
DARK RED (IRE) GR C DARK ANGEL (IRE) - ESSEXFORD (IRE)	C GORDON-WATSON BS	82000
B C LAWMAN (FR) - SPESIALTA (IRE)	D WACHMAN	82000
B C FAST COMPANY (IRE) - LOST SHILLING (IRE)	DAVID REDVERS BS	82000
QAARIB (IRE) B C EXCEED AND EXCEL (AUS) - NO COMPLAINING (IRE)	PETER & ROSS DOYLE BS	82000
MUNTAZAH (IRE) B C MOUNT NELSON (GB) - TRISHULI (GB)	SHADWELL ESTATE COMPANY	82000
SKYLIGHT (IRE) B F ACCLAMATION (GB) - SWINGSKY (IRE)	CHEVELEY PARK STUD	82000
DECISIVE (IRE) CH F IFFRAAJ (GB) - GUARANTIA (IRE)	CHEVELEY PARK STUD	80000
CH C EXCEED AND EXCEL (AUS) - LUDYNOSA (USA)	KUBLER RACING	80000
POETIC LICENSE (IRE) B C DYLAN THOMAS (IRE) - BRIGHT BANK (IRE)	JEREMY BRUMMITT	80000
B F EXCEED AND EXCEL (AUS) - FINAL DYNASTY (GB)	NIGEL TINKLER BS	80000
TOWN CRIER (IRE) B C ACCLAMATION (GB) - MISS DELA (IRE)	VENDOR	80000
B C KYLLACHY (GB) - LABISA (IRE)	SHADWELL ESTATE COMPANY	80000
CH C PACO BOY (IRE) - INTERCHANGE (IRE)	J WARREN BS	80000
B F SHAMARDAL (USA) - SUMMERS LEASE (GB)	JOHN FERGUSON BS	80000
VIXEN HILL (GB) B F ACCLAMATION (GB) - HECKLE (GB)	BBA IRELAND	80000
B F LAWMAN (FR) - TROPICAL LADY (IRE)	OLIVER ST LAWRENCE BS	80000
ATLETICO (IRE) B C KODIAC (GB) - QUEENOFTHEFAIRIES (GB)	ROGER P VARIAN	80000
B C IFFRAAJ (GB) - NIGHT SPHERE (IRE)	R O'RYAN / R FAHEY	80000
B C DANSILI (GB) - HIGH HEELED (IRE)	VENDOR	80000
B F SIR PERCY (GB) - PIVOTTING (GB)	SC WILLIAMS	80000
SINGAPORE DREAM (IRE) B C TEOFILO (IRE) - RAINBOW DESERT (USA)	HIGHFLYER BS	80000
B C DARK ANGEL (IRE) - BOX OF FROGS (IRE)	SHANE DONOHOE	80000
THE TIN MAN (GB) B C EQUIANO (FR) - PERSARIO (GB)	ANTHONY STROUD BS	80000
SUDDEN CAUSE (USA) CH C GIANT'S CAUSEWAY (USA) - SOUDANAISE (IRE)	HIGHFLYER BS	80000
B C DANEHILL DANCER (IRE) - CELTIC HEROINE (IRE)	STEPHEN HILLEN BS	80000
B F EQUIANO (FR) - CHRISTMAS TART (IRE)	MIDDLEHAM PARK RACING	80000
B C ACCLAMATION (GB) - WELSH MIST (GB)	JAMIE LLOYD	80000
IMMORTAL LIFE (IRE) B F IFFRAAJ (GB) - PURSUIT OF LIFE (GB)	KERN LILLINGSTON	80000
PRIORS GATE (IRE) B C ACCLAMATION (GB) - KEY ROSE (IRE)	PETER & ROSS DOYLE BS	80000
KIFAAYA (GB) B C INTIKHAB (USA) - JUNIPER GIRL (IRE)	SHADWELL ESTATE COMPANY	80000
TAKAFOL (IRE) B C FAST COMPANY (IRE) - JAMARY (IRE)	SHADWELL ESTATE COMPANY	80000
B C AUTHORIZED (IRE) - SABLONNE (USA)	DWAYNE WOODS	80000
B F EXCELLENT ART (GB) - MEEK APPEAL (USA)	MICHAEL ENRIGHT	80000
CH C APPROVE (IRE) - ZABADANI (GB)	SHADWELL ESTATE COMPANY	80000
SHAAKIS (IRE) BR/GR C DARK ANGEL (IRE) - CURIOUS LASHES (IRE)	SHADWELL ESTATE COMPANY	80000
B/BR C DANEHILL DANCER (IRE) - ABSOLUTE MUSIC (USA)	SUZANNE ROBERTS	80000
MARAAKIB (IRE) B C DARK ANGEL (IRE) - MRS CEE (IRE)	SHADWELL ESTATE COMPANY	80000
B F NAYEF (USA) - SHIBINA (IRE)	MIDDLEHAM PARK RACING	80000
B F RAVEN'S PASS (USA) - MULTICOLOUR WAVE (IRE)	PETER & ROSS DOYLE BS	80000
SKYE MORNING (GB) B F INVINCIBLE SPIRIT (IRE) - BRIGHT MORNING (USA)	VENDOR	80000
FRANKLIN D (GB) CH C PIVOTAL (GB) - SABREON (GB)	WJ GREDLEY (P.S.)	80000
B F KODIAC (GB) - TIP THE SCALE (USA)	WILLIE BROWNE	80000
NAVAL ACTION (GB) B C LAWMAN (FR) - DANCE OF THE SEA (IRE)	JEREMY BRUMMITT	80000
TADARROJ (GB) B C EXCEED AND EXCEL (AUS) - QUINTRELL (GB)	SHADWELL ESTATE COMPANY	78000
B C INTENSE FOCUS (USA) - BIASCA (GB)	PAUL D'ARCY	77000

HIGH-PRICED YEARLINGS OF 2013 AT GOFFS
The following yearlings realised 52,000 euros and over at Goffs Sales in 2013:-

Name and Breeding	Purchaser	Euros
B C MONTJEU (IRE) - FINSCEAL BEO (IRE)	M V MAGNIER	2850000
B F GALILEO (IRE) - GREEN ROOM (USA)	M V MAGNIER	680000
B F ACCLAMATION (GB) - GALISTIC (IRE)	PETER & ROSS DOYLE	580000
MESADAH (IRE) B F RAVEN'S PASS (USA) - ALBISOLA (IRE)	SHADWELL ESTATE COMPANY	520000
NOZHAR (IRE) B F IFFRAAJ (GB) - GIVE A WHISTLE (IRE)	SHADWELL ESTATE COMPANY	500000
DON'T TRY (IRE) B F GALILEO (IRE) - BONHEUR (IRE)	DAVID REDVERS	480000
B C GALILEO (IRE) - SAOIRE (GB)	M V MAGNIER	425000
B F FASTNET ROCK (AUS) - FLASHING GREEN (GB)	M V MAGNIER	420000
MAJESTIC POWER (IRE) B F DALAKHANI (IRE) - INCHMAHOME (GB)	DAVID WACHMAN	380000
B F DUBAWI (IRE) - WATERSHIP CRYSTAL (IRE)	JOHN FERGUSON	380000
B F INVINCIBLE SPIRIT (IRE) - LETHAL QUALITY (IRE)	TONY NERSES	375000
B C HENRYTHENAVIGATOR (USA) - ANTONIETTE (USA)	J WARREN BS	340000
B F INVINCIBLE SPIRIT (IRE) - IDILIC CALM (IRE)	PETER & ROSS DOYLE	320000
JOHNNY BARNES (IRE) B C ACCLAMATION (GB) - MAHALIA (IRE)	J WARREN BS	310000
GR C DARK ANGEL (IRE) - GOLDTHROAT (IRE)	HUGO MERRY BS	310000
IRISH HAWKE (IRE) B C MONTJEU (IRE) - AHDAAB (USA)	MCCALMONT BS	280000
B F INVINCIBLE SPIRIT (IRE) - PROPAGANDA (IRE)	PETER & ROSS DOYLE	280000
CH C GALILEO (IRE) - MAINE LOBSTER (USA)	FORM BS	280000
B C RIP VAN WINKLE (IRE) - SAHARA SKY (IRE)	MCCALMONT BS	280000
B F FASTNET ROCK (AUS) - ALSHARQ (IRE)	BBA IRELAND	280000
GR F GALILEO (IRE) - ALTITUDE (GB)	BLANDFORD BS	280000
B C SHAMARDAL (USA) - WEDDING GIFT (FR)	MC KEEVER BS	260000
CH C GALILEO (IRE) - KINDLING (GB)	FORM BS	260000
B C GALILEO (IRE) - BELESTA	HORSE FRANCE	260000
MUSICAL BEAT (IRE) B F ACCLAMATION (GB) - MUSICAL BAR (IRE)	CHEVELEY PARK STUD LTD	250000
B C GALILEO (IRE) - ST ROCH (IRE)	MCCALMONT BS	250000
B C GALILEO (IRE) - AKDARENA (GB)	PETER & ROSS DOYLE	250000
B F MOTIVATOR (GB) - ISRAAR (GB)	DAVID REDVERS	240000
CH C DUTCH ART (GB) - BALTIC PRINCESS (FR)	STEPHEN HILLEN	240000
B F DUKE OF MARMALADE (IRE) - GUANTANAMERA (IRE)	DAVID REDVERS	240000
BOCCA BACIATA (IRE) B/BR F BIG BAD BOB (IRE) - SOVANA (IRE)	FLAXMAN STABLES	230000
LILIAN BAYLIS (IRE) B F SHAMARDAL (USA) - KIYRA WELLS (IRE)	J WARREN BS	230000
B C TEOFILO (IRE) - QUIXOTIC (GB)	HUGO MERRY BS	230000
B F GALILEO (IRE) - PISTE NOIRE (USA)	CREGG CASTLE STUD	220000
CH C EXCELLENT ART (GB) - ULIANA (USA)	HONG KONG JOCKEY CLUB	210000
B G ACCLAMATION (GB) - EMMA'S STAR (ITY)	HONG KONG JOCKEY CLUB	210000
B C PIVOTAL (GB) - DANELETA (IRE)	JOHN FERGUSON	210000
GR F DARK ANGEL (IRE) - THE HERMITAGE (IRE)	SACKVILLEDONALD	210000
B C CAPE CROSS (IRE) - LADY SLIPPERS (IRE)	JAMIE LLOYD	210000
B/BR F KODIAC (GB) - SPECIAL DANCER (GB)	JEREMY NOSEDA	210000
B C MASTERCRAFTSMAN (IRE) - FLAMENCO RED (GB)	HONG KONG JOCKEY CLUB	200000
B C ACCLAMATION (GB) - CHAMPION PLACE (IRE)	J WARREN BS	200000
B C DUBAWI (IRE) - SPECIOSA (IRE)	JOHN FERGUSON	200000
B F HENRYTHENAVIGATOR (USA) - SWEET TEMPER (USA)	J WARREN BS	190000
B C PACO BOY (IRE) - SOLOLA (GER)	PETER & ROSS DOYLE	190000
B F HIGH CHAPARRAL (IRE) - DANEHILL'S DREAM (IRE)	PETER & ROSS DOYLE	185000
BOUNDING AWAY (IRE) B F GALILEO (IRE) - FLEETING SPIRIT (IRE)	GORDIAN TROELLER BS	180000
SANDBELL (IRE) B F ACCLAMATION (GB) - DULCIAN (IRE)	J WARREN BS	175000
B C TEOFILO (IRE) - ZEITING (IRE)	HILLEN/MERRY	170000
B F INVINCIBLE SPIRIT (IRE) - SHAMWARI LODGE (IRE)	FIONA SHAW	170000
B C HIGH CHAPARRAL (IRE) - CIVILITY CAT (USA)	M V MAGNIER	170000
B C CAPE CROSS (IRE) - SNIPPETS (IRE)	JOHN FERGUSON	160000
B H C SEA THE STARS (IRE) - EMPRESS OF FRANCE (USA)	CHARLES GORDON-WATSON	160000
B F NEW APPROACH (IRE) - AUSPICIOUS (GB)	JOHN FERGUSON	160000
B H C IFFRAAJ (GB) - ALEXANDER YOUTH (IRE)	ANTHONY STROUD BS	160000
ASEEHA (IRE) CH F TEOFILO (IRE) - TURKANA GIRL (GB)	SHADWELL ESTATE COMPANY	160000
CH F DUTCH ART (GB) - THE FAIRIES DID IT (USA)	TONY NERSES	160000
B C GALILEO (IRE) - BEAUTY BRIGHT (IRE)	GARY MOORE RACING (P.S.)	150000
B H C NEW APPROACH (IRE) - LADY MILETRIAN (IRE)	CHARLES GORDON-WATSON	150000
MARIE CELESTE (IRE) B F GALILEO (IRE) - KINCOB (USA)	DAVID REDVERS	150000
B/RO C HENRYTHENAVIGATOR (USA) - EIGHTYFIVEBROADST (USA)	TONY NERSES	150000
B C SEA THE STARS (IRE) - REZYANA (AUS)	JOHN FERGUSON	150000
B C FAST COMPANY (IRE) - HI KATRIONA (IRE)	BOBBY O'RYAN/DERRINSTOWN	150000
B F DARK ANGEL (IRE) - STARTARETTE (USA)	BBA IRELAND	150000
SENSE OF VICTORY (IRE) B F MONTJEU (IRE) - SHAANARA (IRE)	DAVID REDVERS	150000
B C GALILEO (IRE) - ELLETELLE (IRE)	BBA IRELAND	145000
GEORGIE HYDE (GB) B F YEATS (IRE) - EDABIYA (IRE)	J.S. BOLGER	145000

Name and Breeding	Purchaser	Guineas
B C KYLLACHY (GB) - FLUTTERING ROSE (GB)	STEPHEN HILLEN	140000
B C ELUSIVE QUALITY (USA) - MO CHEOIL THU (IRE)	JOHN FERGUSON	140000
B C ROCK OF GIBRALTAR (IRE) - ASHEYANA (IRE)	MICHAEL HOUSE	140000
BR C AUTHORIZED (IRE) - ELLASHA (GB)	JOHN FERGUSON	135000
CH/GR F GALILEO (IRE) - ROSA GRACE (GB)	FRANK BARRY	130000
STARS AND STRIPES (GB) CH C SELKIRK (USA) - CAPANNINA (GB)	J WARREN BS	130000
B F CAMACHO (GB) - AMBER TIDE (IRE)	DAVID REDVERS	130000
CH F GIANT'S CAUSEWAY (USA) - A MIND OF HER OWN (IRE)	JIM & SUSAN HILL	130000
BOUNCING CZECH (GB) B C DANDY MAN (IRE) - CORRELANDIE (USA)	PETER & ROSS DOYLE	130000
DUTCH PARTY (GB) B F DUTCH ART (GB) - THIRD PARTY (GB)	CHEVELEY PARK STUD LTD	130000
B C HIGH CHAPARRAL (IRE) - COOL CATENA (GB)	JIM & SUSAN HILL	125000
B F SEA THE STARS (IRE) - BITOOH (GB)	RABBAH BS LTD	125000
CH C EXCEED AND EXCEL (AUS) - LIFE RELY (USA)	BALLYHANE STUD	120000
B C HOLY ROMAN EMPEROR (IRE) - SOUFFLE (GB)	SACKVILLEDONALD	120000
B G INVINCIBLE SPIRIT (IRE) - MY RENEE (IRE)	HONG KONG JOCKEY CLUB	120000
SEAWORTHY (IRE) B F SEA THE STARS (IRE) - NIGHT FAIRY (IRE)	AIRLIE STUD	120000
CH F FAST COMPANY (IRE) - ELEGANT RIDGE (IRE)	ANNE COUGHLAN	120000
B F DUKE OF MARMALADE (IRE) - PALANCA (GB)	J WARREN BS	120000
B C EXCEED AND EXCEL (AUS) - DIXIE BELLE (GB)	HONG KONG JOCKEY CLUB	120000
B C EXCELLENT ART (GB) - STARFISH (IRE)	DAVID REDVERS	120000
CH F IFFRAAJ (GB) - SLIEVE MISH (IRE)	RABBAH BS LTD	120000
B C ARCANO (IRE) - SERAPHINA (IRE)	J WARREN BS	115000
SPIRIT OF XIAN (IRE) B F KODIAC (GB) - GOLD AGAIN (USA)	SACKVILLEDONALD	115000
CH C RIP VAN WINKLE (IRE) - FOR EVVA SILCA (GB)	PETER & ROSS DOYLE	110000
SAVOY SHOWGIRL (IRE) CH F KYLLACHY (GB) - THE STRAND (GB)	RICHARD FRISBY BS	110000
CELESTIAL PATH B/BR C FOOTSTEPSINTHESAND (GB) - MISS KITTYHAWK (IRE)	JEREMY BRUMMITT	110000
MOONADEE (IRE) GR C HAATEF (USA) - AGAIN ROYALE (IRE)	SHADWELL ESTATE COMPANY	110000
B C FASTNET ROCK (AUS) - SUPER GIFT (IRE)	SACKVILLEDONALD	110000
CH C DUTCH ART (GB) - HIGHLAND STARLIGHT (USA)	TICK TOCK BS	105000
B C DARK ANGEL (IRE) - GLISTEN (GB)	KERRI RADCLIFFE BS	105000
B C FASTNET ROCK (AUS) - NANCY SPAIN (IRE)	STEPHEN HILLEN	105000
CH G LEMON DROP KID (USA) - PIN TURN (GB)	HONG KONG JOCKEY CLUB	105000
SHADOW ROCK (IRE) GR C VERGLAS (IRE) - ICE ROCK (IRE)	PETER & ROSS DOYLE	100000
CH F DANEHILL DANCER (IRE) - TWINKLING ICE (USA)	BBA IRELAND	100000
CH F SEA THE STARS (IRE) - GIROUETTE (IRE)	YOICHI AOYAMA	100000
B F FASTNET ROCK (AUS) - WINGED HARRIET (IRE)	BADGERS BS	100000
B C INVINCIBLE SPIRIT (IRE) - PHARMACIST (IRE)	STEPHEN HILLEN	100000
GR/RO C MASTERCRAFTSMAN (IRE) - CAPRIOLE (GB)	BLANDFORD BS	100000
DON RICARDO (IRE) B C ACCLAMATION (GB) - CITY DANCER (IRE)	NORMAN STEEL	100000
B C HOLY ROMAN EMPEROR (IRE) - TRALANZA (IRE)	HONG KONG JOCKEY CLUB	100000
B C KYLLACHY (GB) - SWINGLE (GB)	BOBBY O'RYAN/DK WELD	100000
CH F DANEHILL DANCER (IRE) - NASANICE (IRE)	BBA IRELAND	100000
B F FAST COMPANY (IRE) - NOVA TOR (IRE)	JOHN FERGUSON	100000
B F ZEBEDEE (GB) - NIGHT OF JOY (IRE)	PETER & ROSS DOYLE	100000
B C LAWMAN (FR) - KATE THE GREAT (GB)	JOHN FERGUSON	100000
B C DUTCH ART (GB) - JUNCEA (GB)	MCBLOODSTOCK	100000
FROZEN LAKE (USA) B C ELUSIVE QUALITY (USA) - CREATIVE DESIGN (USA)	JOHN OXX	95000
B F DANEHILL DANCER (IRE) - BEYOND BELIEF (IRE)	VENDOR	95000
B C DARK ANGEL (IRE) - SPRING VIEW (GB)	JIM & SUSAN HILL	90000
BARNACLE BILL (IRE) GR C BIG BAD BOB (IRE) - KATCH ME KATIE (GB)	BBA IRELAND	90000
RO C CLODOVIL (IRE) - SUNDAE GIRL (USA)	STEPHEN HILLEN	90000
MAKIN A STATEMENT (IRE) B C BAHAMIAN BOUNTY (GB) - STAR NOW (GB)	PETER & ROSS DOYLE	90000
CH F IFFRAAJ (GB) - BRATISLAVA (GB)	RABBAH BS LTD	88000
ALLEY (IRE) B F ROCK OF GIBRALTAR (IRE) - ALLEVIATE (IRE)	SEELAND INT.	85000
B C LAWMAN (FR) - TRULY MAGNIFICENT (USA)	BBA IRELAND	85000
CEASELESS (IRE) B F IFFRAAJ (GB) - SHEER BLISS (IRE)	RABBAH BS LTD	85000
B C FOOTSTEPSINTHESAND (GB) - GWYLLION (USA)	NORMAN STEEL	85000
STINKY SOCKS (IRE) B F FOOTSTEPSINTHESAND (GB) - CITY OF CITIES (IRE)	BBA IRELAND	85000
B C DUKE OF MARMALADE (IRE) - WRONG KEY (IRE)	DAVID REDVERS	85000
CH C EQUIANO (FR) - FAME IS THE SPUR (GB)	DAVID REDVERS	82000
SYDNEY HEIGHTS (IRE) CH C LORD SHANAKILL (USA) - ASHDALI (IRE)	BBA IRELAND	82000
B C ACCLAMATION (GB) - DIXIE EYES BLAZING (USA)	J WARREN BS	82000
CH F LOPE DE VEGA (IRE) - INDIAN EXPRESS (GB)	JOHN O'BYRNE	80000
B C INVINCIBLE SPIRIT (IRE) - AGUINAGA (IRE)	HIGHFIELD FARM LLP	80000
B C MAKFI (GB) - LIBERTY CHERY (GB)	DAVID REDVERS	80000
B C ROCK OF GIBRALTAR (IRE) - BEAN UASAL (IRE)	J WARREN BS	80000
B/BR F INVINCIBLE SPIRIT (IRE) - MALYANA (GB)	DAVID REDVERS	80000
B F AZAMOUR (IRE) - BOO BOO BEAR (IRE)	JIM & SUSAN HILL	80000
B C FASTNET ROCK (AUS) - AMETHYST (IRE)	BBA IRELAND	8000
CH/RO C MASTERCRAFTSMAN (IRE) - CATCH THE BLUES (IRE)	FEDERICO BARBERINI	7800
B C WAR CHANT (USA) - ROSE RED (USA)	JIM RYAN	7700

Name and Breeding	Purchaser	Guineas
B F MUJADIL (USA) - SINEGRONTO (IRE)	GILL RICHARDSON BS LTD	75000
BR F SEA THE STARS (IRE) - INDEPANDANT (GB)	RABBAH BS LTD	75000
CH C FOOTSTEPSINTHESAND (GB) - KOOYONG (IRE)	IVA	75000
B F ZEBEDEE (GB) - EXPONENT (GB)	CORMAC MCCORMACK BS	70000
B C RIP VAN WINKLE (IRE) - COLD COLD WOMAN (GB)	PETER & ROSS DOYLE	70000
CH F TAMAYUZ (GB) - SHEER GLAMOUR (USA)	LARS KELP	70000
B C INVINCIBLE SPIRIT (IRE) - INTERPOSE (GB)	VENDOR	70000
B F ACCLAMATION (GB) - MOVIE QUEEN (GB)	CHEVELEY PARK STUD LTD	70000
CH/RO C PICCOLO (GB) - CHERRYCOMBE-ROW (GB)	SACKVILLEDONALD	70000
B C RIP VAN WINKLE (IRE) - SET FIRE (IRE)	ALBERTO PANETTA	68000
B F FASTNET ROCK (AUS) - CAPE VINTAGE (IRE)	PAUL GAFFNEY	68000
B C LOPE DE VEGA (IRE) - ROSCOFF (IRE)	VENDOR	65000
BR C DANEHILL DANCER (IRE) - CHATURANGA (GB)	FEDERICO BARBERINI	65000
B F DUKE OF MARMALADE (IRE) - REPRISE (GB)	BBA IRELAND	65000
B C LORD SHANAKILL (USA) - TITIAN QUEEN (GB)	BBA IRELAND	65000
B C CAPE CROSS (IRE) - ALTRUISTE (USA)	RICHARD KNIGHT BS	65000
BR C DANEHILL DANCER (IRE) - OBSESSIVE (USA)	MARK JOHNSTON RACING	65000
NEXT GENERATION (IRE) B F ROYAL APPLAUSE (GB) - GAZEBO (GB)	DAVID REDVERS	65000
B F FASTNET ROCK (AUS) - CHRISALICE (GB)	WILLIE BROWNE	65000
B C NAAQOOS (GB) - NAADRAH (GB)	GILL RICHARDSON BS LTD	65000
B C HENRYTHENAVIGATOR (USA) - LA TRAVIATA (USA)	BLANDFORD BS	65000
B C BIG BAD BOB (IRE) - CHICA ROCA (USA)	PETER & ROSS DOYLE	62000
B C FAST COMPANY (IRE) - SPINNING RUBY (GB)	GROVE STUD	62000
B F BIG BAD BOB (IRE) - ULANOVA (IRE)	BBA IRELAND	62000
BALLYNANTY (IRE) BR C YEATS (IRE) - REINA BLANCA (GB)	RICHARD WILMOT-SMITH	62000
CH C STARSPANGLEDBANNER (AUS) - HIGHINDI (GB)	JOHNNY MURTAGH	62000
B C EXCELLENT ART (GB) - GENTLE NIGHT (GB)	MOTONARI MITSUYAMA	62000
B C ACCLAMATION (GB) - EASTER HEROINE (IRE)	RABBAH BS (P.S.)	60000
B C ACCLAMATION (GB) - SOCIETY GAL (IRE)	SACKVILLEDONALD	60000
CH F TEOFILO (IRE) - QUEEN OF LYONS (USA)	DAVID WACHMAN	60000
C FASTNET ROCK (AUS) - QUIET MOUSE (USA)	WILLIE BROWNE	60000
EXINGTON TIMES (IRE) B C PACO BOY (IRE) - FUAIGH MOR (IRE)	PETER & ROSS DOYLE	60000
CH C COMPTON PLACE (GB) - CORRYVRECKAN (IRE)	PETER & ROSS DOYLE	60000
C F RIP VAN WINKLE (USA) - CLAND DI SAN JORE (IRE)	PETER & ROSS DOYLE	60000
ONNYTHENAVIGATOR (USA) B/BR C HENRYTHENAVIGATOR (USA) - LADY SIMPSON (GB)	BLANDFORD BS	60000
MAKIN TROUBLE (IRE) B C LAWMAN (FR) - CRAFTY NOTION (GB)	PETER & ROSS DOYLE	60000
C ALFRED NOBEL (IRE) - SANDBOX TWO (USA)	SACKVILLEDONALD	60000
C BUSHRANGER (IRE) - BOSTON IVY (USA)	STEPHEN HILLEN	60000
F ACCLAMATION (GB) - CHURCH MELODY (GB)	ARAN BS	60000
F FASTNET ROCK (AUS) - DREAM TIME (GB)	JIM & SUSAN HILL (P.S.)	59000
R C ACCLAMATION (GB) - CRADLE BRIFF (GB)	ANTHONY STROUD BS LTD	59000
R C ZEBEDEE (GB) - IDLE FANCY (GB)	MARGARET O'TOOLE	58000
C KODIAC (GB) - DANCING PRIZE (IRE)	R FAHEY/R O'RYAN	57000
F AZAMOUR (IRE) - MOURIYANA (IRE)	FOX COVERT STUD	56000
F ACCLAMATION (GB) - MISS TANGO HOTEL (GB)	DAVID REDVERS	55000
F EXCELLENT ART (GB) - ZIGARRA (GB)	G BUTLER	55000
C KODIAC (GB) - REALITY CHECK (IRE)	GILL RICHARDSON BS LTD	55000
R C DALAKHANI (IRE) - RIYNAAZ (IRE)	LARRY STRATTON	55000
I C INTIKHAB (USA) - CAYMAN SUNRISE (IRE)	J WARREN BS	55000
C ARCANO (IRE) - STARCHY (GB)	IVA	55000
RD OF DUBLIN (IRE) B C LORD SHANAKILL (USA) - IMELDA (USA)	BENT OLSEN	55000
F FAST COMPANY (GB) - EVENING TIME (IRE)	MC KEEVER BS	55000
C MAJESTIC MISSILE (IRE) - XENA (GB)	RON HARRIS	55000
C KODIAC (GB) - REFUSE TO GIVE UP (IRE)	SACKVILLEDONALD	55000
C LAWMAN (FR) - ENIGMA (GER)	JOHN QUINN	55000
F RAVEN'S PASS (USA) - DARK INDIAN (IRE)	JOHN FERGUSON BS	55000
C AMADEUS WOLF (GB) - ROSE DE FRANCE (IRE)	PAUL GAFFNEY	54000
C ACCLAMATION (GB) - COACHHOUSE LADY (USA)	HORSE PARK STUD	52000
F ARCANO (IRE) - OH NELLIE (USA)	CORMAC MCCORMACK BS	52000
F AZAMOUR (IRE) - CAUSEWAY QUEEN (IRE)	ANTHONY STROUD BS LTD	52000
C LAWMAN (FR) - HALICARDIA (GB)	PETER & ROSS DOYLE	52000
R C MORE THAN READY (USA) - BALLETOMAINE (IRE)	STANLEY MOORE	52000
C PACO BOY (IRE) - SNOWDROPS (GB)	PFI COLE	52000
SIR PERCY (GB) - HEAT OF THE NIGHT (GB)	BADGERS BS	52000
DARK ANGEL (IRE) - DIVINE DESIGN (IRE)	SACKVILLEDONALD	52000
ACCLAMATION (GB) - FULLY FASHIONED (GB)	STANLEY MOORE	52000
HIGH CHAPARRAL (IRE) - BILLET (IRE)	GILL RICHARDSON BS LTD	52000
GR F ACCLAMATION (GB) - DANAMIGHT (IRE)	DAVID MARNANE RACING	52000

HIGH-PRICED YEARLINGS OF 2013 AT DONCASTER

The following yearlings realised 34,285 Guineas and over at Doncaster Sales in 2013:-

Name and Breeding	Purchaser	Guineas
B C LAWMAN (FR) - ZUNIGA'S DATE (USA)	A SKIFFINGTON	204761
B C FAST COMPANY (IRE) - TAWAAFUR (GB)	MANDORE INTERNATIONAL	200000
ESTIDHKAAR (IRE) B C DARK ANGEL (IRE) - DANETIME OUT (IRE)	PETER & ROSS DOYLE BS	190476
MARKAZ (IRE) GR C DARK ANGEL (IRE) - FOLGA (GB)	SHADWELL ESTATE CO. LTD	190476
BR C KODIAC (GB) - TOWN AND GOWN (GB)	BLANDFORD BS	152380
B C ACCLAMATION (GB) - DANCE HALL GIRL (IRE)	T NERSES	152380
CH F MAKFI (GB) - AUNTY MARY (GB)	BBA IRELAND LTD	147619
TOP OF THE ART (IRE) GR F DARK ANGEL (IRE) - THAWRAH (IRE)	D REDVERS	123809
MUTAFARREJ (GB) B C PACO BOY (IRE) - CRINKLE (IRE)	SHADWELL ESTATE CO. LTD	123809
BRUSH STROKE (GB) B F DUTCH ART (GB) - PETONG'S PET (GB)	BBA IRELAND LTD	114285
HAYDAR (IRE) B C MAKFI (GB) - WAVEBAND (GB)	SHADWELL ESTATE CO. LTD	104761
ALAKHTAL (IRE) BR C LORD SHANAKILL (USA) - DEFINITE OPINION (IRE)	SHADWELL ESTATE CO. LTD	100000
ST GEORGES ROCK (IRE) B C CAMACHO (GB) - RADIO WAVE (GB)	CLIVE COX RACING LTD	100000
SAWAAHEL (GB) B C PASTORAL PURSUITS (GB) - SHEER INDULGENCE (FR)	PETER & ROSS DOYLE BS	95238
B C DANDY MAN (IRE) - LUCAYAN BEAUTY (IRE)	HIGHFIELD FARM LLP	95238
KIBAAR (GB) B C PASTORAL PURSUITS (GB) - ASHES (GB)	SHADWELL ESTATE CO. LTD	95238
B C RIP VAN WINKLE (IRE) - MAID TO DREAM (GB)	D O'BYRNE	85714
B F INVINCIBLE SPIRIT (IRE) - CEDAR SEA (IRE)	VENDOR	85714
MUTANAAWAL (GB) CH C INTIKHAB (USA) - PIKABOO (GB)	SHADWELL ESTATE CO. LTD	85714
B C IFFRAAJ (GB) - GO LOVELY ROSE (IRE)	D REDVERS	83809
B F MOUNT NELSON (GB) - SAKHEE'S SONG (IRE)	T NERSES	80952
THE TEMPEST (GB) B F MASTERCRAFTSMAN (IRE) - VIRGINIA HALL (GB)	SIR R OGDEN	80952
AWJAB (IRE) B C BAHAMIAN BOUNTY (GB) - APPLAUSE (IRE)	SHADWELL ESTATE CO. LTD	76190
PASTORAL GIRL (GB) B F PASTORAL PURSUITS (GB) - TALAMPAYA (USA)	A STROUD BS	76190
MALJAA (GB) CH C PACO BOY (IRE) - KERRY'S DREAM (GB)	SHADWELL ESTATE CO. LTD	76190
ERTIDAAD (IRE) B C KODIAC (GB) - LITTLE SCOTLAND (GB)	SHADWELL ESTATE CO. LTD	76190
MUBTAGHAA (IRE) B C ACCLAMATION (GB) - MABALANE (IRE)	SHADWELL ESTATE CO. LTD	76190
B F APPROVE (IRE) - MISS CORINNE (GB)	D REDVERS	74285
ARTISTIC FLARE (GB) CH F DUTCH ART (GB) - PANTILE (GB)	MCKEEVER BS	71428
RISE UP LOTUS (IRE) GR F ZEBEDEE (GB) - FACE THE STORM (IRE)	SHADWELL ESTATE CO. LTD	71428
B F FASTNET ROCK (AUS) - CARN LADY (IRE)	OLIVER ST LAWRENCE BS	68571
B F ACCLAMATION (GB) - ART WORK (GB)	MANDORE INTERNATIONAL	66666
B C CAMACHO (GB) - TIDES (GB)	A SKIFFINGTON	66666
B F MASTERCRAFTSMAN (IRE) - MARKET DAY (GB)	BLANDFORD BS	64761
B F KHELEYF (USA) - EASY TO IMAGINE (USA)	RABBAH BS LTD	64761
SAMEER (IRE) CH C APPROVE (IRE) - BRAZILIAN FLAME (IRE)	SHADWELL ESTATE CO. LTD	61904
B F ZEBEDEE (GB) - SONNY SUNSHINE (GB)	T NERSES	61904
B C MAJESTIC MISSILE (IRE) - QUEEN OF SILK (IRE)	E LYNAM	59047
MUZARKASH (GB) B C KYLLACHY (GB) - QUINZEY'S BEST (IRE)	SHADWELL ESTATE CO. LTD	59047
CH C SHAMARDAL (USA) - ANSE VICTORIN (USA)	SACKVILLEDONALD	57142
MULAASEQ (GB) B C SHOWCASING (GB) - LONELY HEART (GB)	SHADWELL ESTATE CO. LTD	57142
DAWN'S EARLY LIGHT (IRE) GR C STARSPANGLEDBANNER (AUS) - SKY RED (GB)	SACKVILLEDONALD	57142
MUKHMAL (IRE) CH C BAHAMIAN BOUNTY (GB) - MAY DAY QUEEN (IRE)	SHADWELL ESTATE CO. LTD	57142
B C BUSHRANGER (IRE) - NOYELLES (GB)	BBA IRELAND LTD	57142
B C KYLLACHY (GB) - MARLIANA (IRE)	PETER & ROSS DOYLE BS	57142
B F MASTERCRAFTSMAN (IRE) - FACT (GB)	BBA IRELAND LTD	55238
DARK WAR (IRE) B C DARK ANGEL (IRE) - WAROONGA (IRE)	A STROUD BS	55238
B C ARCANO (IRE) - AQUATINT (GB)	GEOFFREY HOWSON BS	55238
B F ARCANO (IRE) - LYCA BALLERINA (GB)	PETER & ROSS DOYLE BS	55238
BLUESBREAKER (IRE) B C FASTNET ROCK (AUS) - JALISCO (IRE)	PETER & ROSS DOYLE BS	53333
MAGIC FLORENCE (IRE) CH F ZEBEDEE (GB) - LADY SHANGHAI (IRE)	A STROUD BS	53333
B C MYBOYCHARLIE (IRE) - LOQUACITY (GB)	WILL EDMEADES BS LTD	53333
B C DUKE OF MARMALADE (IRE) - PRIMISSIMA (GER)	SACKVILLEDONALD	52380
B C DARK ANGEL (IRE) - CUTE ASS (IRE)	HIGH HOPES FARM	52380
SILKY SANDS (GB) B C KYLLACHY (GB) - CHOOSEY GIRL (IRE)	A STROUD BS	52380
B C SHOWCASING (GB) - RAGGLE TAGGLE (IRE)	D REDVERS	51428
B C EXCEED AND EXCEL (AUS) - INAMINUTE (IRE)	D SHAW	49523
B C EQUIANO (FR) - MILLY-M (GB)	HIGHFIELD FARM LLP	49523
B C PACO BOY (IRE) - KEY LIGHT (IRE)	J WARREN BS	49523
CH F ARCANO (IRE) - GREAT JOY (IRE)	PETER & ROSS DOYLE BS	47619
B F FASTNET ROCK (AUS) - SPEAK SOFTLY TO ME (USA)	COLES RACING LTD	47619
ITS GONNA BE ME (IRE) B C ZEBEDEE (GB) - DORN HILL (GB)	SHADWELL ESTATE CO. LTD	47619
SHARAASA (IRE) B F APPROVE (IRE) - RUMLINE (GB)	SHADWELL ESTATE CO. LTD	47619
B F DUTCH ART (GB) - SIENA GOLD (GB)	E LYNAM	47619
GR C ZEBEDEE (GB) - ROAD TO REALITY (IRE)	SACKVILLEDONALD	47619
MURTASSIM (IRE) B C TAMAYUZ (GB) - MEANYA (IRE)	SHADWELL ESTATE CO. LTD	47619
B C KODIAC (GB) - GOLDEN SHADOW (IRE)	A DUARTE	47619

Name and Breeding	Purchaser	Guineas
CH C LORD SHANAKILL (USA) - NO GREATER LOVE (USA)	SACKVILLEDONALD	47619
STEAL THE SCENE (IRE) B C LORD SHANAKILL (USA) - NAMOOS (USA)	PETER & ROSS DOYLE BS	47619
QATAR SUCCESS (GB) B F KYLLACHY (GB) - CHEROKEE STREAM (IRE)	SACKVILLEDONALD	47619
MUTARAKEZ (IRE) CH C FAST COMPANY (IRE) - NIGHTSWIMMER (IRE)	SHADWELL ESTATE CO. LTD	47619
B C ACCLAMATION (GB) - RED SHAREEF (GB)	SACKVILLEDONALD	47619
B C FIREBREAK (GB) - CHARLIE GIRL (GB)	RABBAH BS LTD	47619
BUSHEPHALUS (IRE) GR C DARK ANGEL (IRE) - WHITE DAFFODIL (IRE)	SACKVILLEDONALD (P.S.)	45714
B F DUTCH ART (GB) - CLASSIC LASS (GB)	W BROWNE	45714
ZIGGURAT (IRE) GR C TAGULA (IRE) - VISUAL ELEMENT (USA)	A SKIFFINGTON	45714
CH C COMPTON PLACE (GB) - LADY DARAYNA (GB)	PETER & ROSS DOYLE BS	45714
B C DARK ANGEL (IRE) - MONSUSU (IRE)	MCKEEVER BS	45714
B/BR C FOOTSTEPSINTHESAND (GB) - SHAGADELLIC (USA)	HUGO MERRY BS	45714
F APPROVE (IRE) - GRANDEL (GB)	RABBAH BS LTD	45714
F DANDY MAN (IRE) - KISS AND DON'TELL (USA)	BBA IRELAND LTD	45714
F SHOWCASING (GB) - DOWAGER (GB)	A DUARTE	45714
CH C DUTCH ART (GB) - TWENTY SEVEN (IRE)	C MARNANE	44761
C IFFRAAJ (GB) - ELUTRAH (GB)	BBA IRELAND LTD	44761
C FAST COMPANY (IRE) - KIVA (GB)	B SMART	44761
H C STARSPANGLEDBANNER (AUS) - LULAWIN (GB)	A SKIFFINGTON	43809
H C CAPTAIN GERRARD (IRE) - ELEGANT LADY (GB)	GILL RICHARDSON BS LTD	43809
OLETTE (GB) CH F AQLAAM (GB) - VIOLETTE (GB)	JAMIE LLOYD BS	42857
F HOLY ROMAN EMPEROR (IRE) - QUEEN PADME (IRE)	A SKIFFINGTON	42857
H C AMERICAN POST (GB) - FAIRY SHOES (GB)	R O'RYAN	42857
F EXCEED AND EXCEL (AUS) - CHILDREY (USA)	HILLWOOD BS	42857
F PACO BOY (IRE) - XTRASENSORY (USA)	HILLEN & RYAN	42857
C KHELEYF (USA) - MISS MCGUIRE (GB)	RABBAH BS LTD	42857
C MONSIEUR BOND (IRE) - ASHTAROUTE (USA)	E LYNAM	41904
R C MARJU (IRE) - RADHA (GB)	BBA IRELAND LTD	40952
F CAMACHO (GB) - STATELY PRINCESS (GB)	E O'GORMAN	40000
H C ZEBEDEE (GB) - FLORIDA CITY (IRE)	MCKEEVER BS	40000
H C FAST COMPANY (IRE) - TITIAN SAGA (IRE)	MCKEEVER BS	40000
R C DUTCH ART (GB) - JILLOLINI (GB)	PETER & ROSS DOYLE BS	40000
LACKFOOT BRAVE (IRE) CH C IFFRAAJ (GB) - BEATRIX POTTER (IRE)	M DODS	40000
C HOLY ROMAN EMPEROR (IRE) - SHARPVILLE (USA)	D WACHMAN	40000
FLATION (GB) B C STIMULATION (IRE) - MISS POPPY (GB)	PETER & ROSS DOYLE BS	40000
GGY WIGGY (IRE) B F KODIAC (GB) - KHELEYF'S SILVER (IRE)	PETER & ROSS DOYLE BS	39047
C TAGULA (IRE) - COME APRIL (GB)	PETER & ROSS DOYLE BS	39047
C COMPTON PLACE (GB) - REALLY RANSOM (GB)	MCKEEVER BS	39047
CKS THE BOXES (IRE) CH C FAST COMPANY (IRE) - SWAN SEA (USA)	CLIVE COX RACING LTD	38095
/RO C COMPTON PLACE (GB) - DICTATRIX (GB)	B O'RYAN	38095
C LOPE DE VEGA (IRE) - DEHBANU (IRE)	D REDVERS	38095
C LOPE DE VEGA (IRE) - PIVOTAL ROLE (IRE)	G MULLINS	38095
C KYLLACHY (GB) - ALCHEMY (IRE)	D BROWN	38095
C JEREMY (USA) - ABSOLUTELY COOL (IRE)	PETER & ROSS DOYLE BS	38095
C SAKHEE'S SECRET (GB) - CHARLOTTE POINT (USA)	B O'RYAN	38095
C APPROVE (IRE) - MISS ASSERTIVE (GB)	MCKEEVER BS	38095
C DANDY MAN (IRE) - BALANCE THE BOOKS (GB)	HIGHFIELD FARM LLP	38095
C ACCLAMATION (GB) - FAVORITELY (USA)	BBA IRELAND LTD	38095
C EQUIANO (FR) - KHYBER KNIGHT (IRE)	HIGHFIELD FARM LLP	38095
F DUTCH ART (GB) - SEMPLICITA (IRE)	HUGO MERRY BS	36190
C KYLLACHY (GB) - MAMOUNIA (IRE)	PETER & ROSS DOYLE BS	36190
RRY HURRICANE (GB) B C KODIAC (GB) - EOLITH (GB)	GEORGE BAKER RACING LTD	36190
C SAKHEE'S SECRET (GB) - CORTON CHARLEMAGNE (IRE)	PETER & ROSS DOYLE BS	36190
C EQUIANO (FR) - PRETTY GIRL (IRE)	D SHAW	36190
C EQUIANO (FR) - ZIA (GER)	ANTHONY STROUD BS LTD	36190
AZED KNEES (IRE) B C MAJESTIC MISSILE (IRE) - CARPET LOVER (IRE)	D BROWN	36190
EN WILL IT END (IRE) B C KODIAC (GB) - ALEXANDER DUCHESS (IRE)	PETER & ROSS DOYLE BS	35238
C BAHAMIAN BOUNTY (GB) - RAINBOW END (GB)	HILLEN & RYAN	35238
C TOBOUGG (IRE) - ROSEUM (GB)	D REDVERS	34285
APPROVE (IRE) - FRENCH FERN (IRE)	PETER & ROSS DOYLE BS	34285
ACCLAMATION (GB) - VENUS RISING (GB)	WILL EDMEADES BS LTD	34285

HIGH-PRICED YEARLINGS OF 2012 AT TATTERSALLS IRELAND SALES

The following yearlings realised 21,000 euros and over at Tattersalls Ireland Sales in 2013:-

Name and Breeding	Purchaser	Euros
B C YEATS (IRE) - LAURENTINE (USA)	LILY CORPORATION	180000
CH C TAMAYUZ (GB) - SANDY LADY (IRE)	LILY CORPORATION	110000
B C MOUNT NELSON (GB) - ALEXIA REVEUSE (IRE)	DAVID MARNANE RACING	85000
BR G PRESENTING (GB) - DARE TO VENTURE (IRE)	JOHN O'BYRNE	70000
B G ROBIN DES CHAMPS (FR) - DAWN COURT (GB)	MRS C BAILEY	65000
B C ROBIN DES CHAMPS (FR) - JOHN'S ELIZA (IRE)	HIGHFLYER BS	60000
GR C DARK ANGEL (IRE) - KAYOKO (IRE)	GER LYONS	55000
DUKE ELLINGTON (IRE) B C ROCK OF GIBRALTAR (IRE) - CRYSTAL VIEW (IRE)	WILLIAM MCCREERY	52000
B C EXCEED AND EXCEL (AUS) - JERITZA (GB)	CON MARNANE	52000
B C IFFRAAJ (GB) - DANCE OF LIGHT (USA)	GER LYONS	52000
B C PICCOLO (GB) - CAPE WOOD (GB)	GER LYONS	50000
B G STOWAWAY (GB) - ALLY ROSE (IRE)	JOHN O'BYRNE	46000
B G KING'S THEATRE (IRE) - SYMPHONICA (IRE)	ALAN HARTE BS	45000
B C DARK ANGEL (IRE) - THINK (FR)	LILY CORPORATION	44000
BR G MIDNIGHT LEGEND (GB) - SHATABDI (IRE)	DAI WALTERS	44000
B C DANDY MAN (IRE) - WHITEGATE WAY (GB)	WILLIE BROWNE	43000
EL ROULI (FR) CH G MARESCA SORRENTO (FR) - CYBERTINA (FR)	HAROLD KIRK	42000
CLOUDS AT NIGHT (IRE) B C ELNADIM (USA) - TRULLITTI (IRE)	BELIAR BS	42000
CH C ZEBEDEE (GB) - PLAYFUL (GB)	SACKVILLEDONALD	42000
B G STOWAWAY (GB) - FITANGA (FR)	HAROLD KIRK	42000
MIGNOLINO (IRE) B C KODIAC (GB) - CATERINA DI CESI (GB)	HARROWGATE BS	40000
B C DANDY MAN (IRE) - COCKALEEKIE (USA)	GER LYONS	4000
B C ROBIN DES CHAMPS (FR) - FALCONS GIFT (IRE)	EDDIE HARTY	4000
B F CAMACHO (GB) - BELLE OF THE BLUES (IRE)	DAVID REDVERS	4000
GR C DANDY MAN (IRE) - ON THIN ICE (IRE)	SACKVILLEDONALD	4000
CRYSTAL MALT (IRE) B F INTIKHAB (USA) - ELEGANTLY (IRE)	VENDOR	4000
CH/GR C MASTERCRAFTSMAN (IRE) - GLEAMING SILVER (IRE)	A&E BS	4000
B G YEATS (IRE) - OLIGARCH SOCIETY (IRE)	A MURPHY	4000
B C AZAMOUR (IRE) - JINSKYS GIFT (GB)	MILLTOWN STUD	3800
B C APPROVE (IRE) - ANNE BONNEY (GB)	JC BS	3700
STELLAR JET (IRE) CH F INTENSE FOCUS (USA) - RAISE YOUR SPIRITS (IRE)	LODGE FARM STUD	3700
B F DARK ANGEL (IRE) - LINE AHEAD (IRE)	GER LYONS	3600
GR C VERGLAS (IRE) - FINE DAY (GB)	JOHN M OXX	3600
B F KODIAC (GB) - SINGINGINTHERAIN (IRE)	RABBAH BS LTD	3500
B F EQUIANO (FR) - LA TINTORETTA (IRE)	SACKVILLEDONALD	3500
CH C ZEBEDEE (GB) - POLLY JONES (USA)	PETER & ROSS DOYLE BS	3500
CH G BALLINGARRY (IRE) - MISS POUTINE (FR)	TOWER VIEW STABLES	3500
LADY D'S ROCK (IRE) GR F AUSSIE RULES (USA) - ZA ZA (GB)	CLIVE COX RACING	3400
BR G GETAWAY (GER) - ANDALUSIA (GER)	MARGARET O'TOOLE	3400
CH C APPROVE (IRE) - GLYNDEBOURNE (USA)	HARROWGATE BS	3300
B G OSCAR (IRE) - AFROSTAR (IRE)	JOHN O'BYRNE	3300
B F APPROVE (IRE) - MATHOOL (IRE)	LILY CORPORATION	320
B F HOLY ROMAN EMPEROR (IRE) - CAROLXAAR (IRE)	A&E BS	320
B F PASTORAL PURSUITS (GB) - CAROLLAN (IRE)	HAPPY VALLEY RACING	320
CH C MEDICEAN (GB) - INTREPID QUEEN (IRE)	LILY CORPORATION	320
B C KODIAC (GB) - BELMORA (USA)	CLIVE COX RACING	320
B C FOOTSTEPSINTHESAND (GB) - SAMPERS (IRE)	BBA IRELAND	320
B C CAPE CROSS (IRE) - ZAHOO (IRE)	GER LYONS RACING	320
GR C JEREMY (USA) - INDUS RIDGE (IRE)	MILLTOWN STUD	320
CH C INTENSE FOCUS (USA) - KAYAK (GB)	HARROWGATE BS	320
B F MAKFI (GB) - RUSSIAN EMPRESS (IRE)	LILY CORPORATION	320
CH C CHAMPS ELYSEES (GB) - VIVIANNA (GB)	D ELSWORTH	320
B G ARCADIO (GER) - MA DOUCE (IRE)	KEVIN ROSS BS	320
B F TAGULA (IRE) - FATHOMING (USA)	EDWARD LYNAM	310
B G YEATS (IRE) - SHE'S OUR MARE (IRE)	VENDOR	310
GAELIC PRINCE (FR) B C MARTALINE (GB) - GAELIC JANE (FR)	B MURPHY	310
GR C DARK ANGEL (IRE) - CAPE COD (IRE)	GER LYONS	300
CH F EQUIANO (FR) - STAVINSKY'S GAL (USA)	MIDDLEHAM PARK RACING	300
B F FAST COMPANY (IRE) - CONSENSUS (IRE)	LADYSWOOD STUD	300
SISTER OF MERCY (IRE) B F AZAMOUR (IRE) - GREEN TAMBOURINE (GB)	PETER & ROSS DOYLE BS	300
KRISTJANO (GER) B C NAYEF (USA) - KALAHARI DANCER (GB)	MICHAEL HALFORD	300
B G NOTNOWCATO (GB) - GILAH (IRE)	ANDREW HOLLINSHEAD	300
B F MASTERCRAFTSMAN (IRE) - EL SOPRANO (IRE)	WILLIE BROWNE	300
B G INTIKHAB (USA) - ULTIMATE BEAT (USA)	KEVIN O'BRIEN	300
B C ARCANO (IRE) - MOON UNIT (IRE)	A C BS	29
B G SCORPION (IRE) - PAIRTREE (GB)	JOHN O'BYRNE	29
B F ACCLAMATION (GB) - BOWNESS (GB)	MARCO BOTTI	28

Name and Breeding	Purchaser	Euros
GR C SILVER FROST (IRE) - DESERT NIGHTS (IRE)	GER LYONS	28000
RO F DARK ANGEL (IRE) - CAPPELLA (IRE)	D SHAW	28000
B G JEREMY (USA) - GET A FEW BOB BACK (IRE)	IAN FERGUSON	28000
GR C AUSSIE RULES (USA) - MY AMERICAN BEAUTY (GB)	CLIVE COX RACING	27000
DIAZ (IRE) B C AZAMOUR (IRE) - NEW GIRLFRIEND (IRE)	MARK JOHNSTON	27000
B F ORATORIO (IRE) - ARIONELLA (GB)	FOZZY STACK	27000
B C FAST COMPANY (IRE) - GOLDEN ORA (ITY)	DAVID MARNANE RACING	27000
B F ACCLAMATION (GB) - PETITE SPECTRE (GB)	YEOMANSTOWN STUD	27000
B G YEATS (IRE) - SHE'S A VENTURE (GB)	NIALL HANNITY	27000
CH C SIR PERCY (GB) - SUERTUDA (GB)	RICHARD KNIGHT BS	26000
B F EXCELLENT ART (GB) - MAYBE GRACE (IRE)	GROVE STUD	26000
B C FOOTSTEPSINTHESAND (GB) - PEPS (IRE)	KEVIN ROSS BS	26000
PASSIONATE SPIRIT (IRE) GR C ZEBEDEE (GB) - EL MOROCCO (USA)	SACKVILLEDONALD	26000
B/BR G STOWAWAY (GB) - CORRIE HALL (IRE)	MICHAEL TALLON	26000
B C ASK (GB) - LA PROTAGONISTA (IRE)	BRENDAN BASHFORD BS	26000
B G SCORPION (IRE) - WATERMELON (GB)	SAPNESS FARM	26000
CH C DUKE OF MARMALADE (IRE) - TAKING LIBERTIES (GB)	SHEIKH ABDULLAH AL THANI	25000
B/BR C BIG BAD BOB (IRE) - DAFTARA (IRE)	A&E BS	25000
B/BR C HENRYTHENAVIGATOR (USA) - DAMINI (USA)	SACKVILLEDONALD	25000
B F APPROVE (IRE) - BAKEWELL TART (IRE)	SACKVILLEDONALD	25000
B C STRATEGIC PRINCE (GB) - IVY QUEEN (IRE)	KEVIN ROSS BS	25000
B F SIR PERCY (GB) - PAYPHONE (IRE)	KEN CONDON	25000
BR F EXCELLENT ART (GB) - OPEN BOOK (GB)	FRANK BARRY	25000
C CAMACHO (GB) - SPRING OPERA (IRE)	JOHNNY LEVINS	25000
C HOLY ROMAN EMPEROR (IRE) - BIG SWIFTY (GB)	HARROWGATE BS	25000
G ROBIN DES CHAMPS (FR) - SILKY STREAM (IRE)	RICHARD FRISBY	25000
CH C ELNADIM (USA) - ALMUROOJ (GB)	FRANK BARRY	24000
G MAHLER (GB) - MIRANDA'S LACE (IRE)	BRYAN MURPHY	24000
DIVINE LAW (GB) CH C MAJOR CADEAUX (GB) - YANOMAMI (USA)	PETER & ROSS DOYLE BS	24000
C DARK ANGEL (IRE) - SHOWERPROOF (GB)	MARK FLANNERY	24000
BR C MASTERCRAFTSMAN (IRE) - TITANS CLASH (IRE)	VENDOR	24000
CH C NAYEF (USA) - I HEARYOU KNOCKING (IRE)	BELIAR BS	24000
F PACO BOY (IRE) - MOUNT LAVINIA (IRE)	BOTTI	24000
C IFFRAAJ (GB) - DOROTHY DENE (GB)	LADYSWOOD STUD	24000
G STOWAWAY (GB) - ALLY ROSE (IRE)	A MURPHY	24000
C EXCELLENT ART (GB) - TEDDY BEARS PICNIC (GB)	D SHAW	23000
CH F MASTERCRAFTSMAN (IRE) - LA LUNETE (GB)	AMANDA SKIFFINGTON	23000
BR C WINDSOR KNOT (GB) - BROGELLA (IRE)	CRAMPSCASTLE BS	23000
THE EYES HAVE IT (IRE) BR C ARCANO (IRE) - ALEXANDER ICEQUEEN (IRE)	A OLIVER	23000
CH G GETAWAY (GB) - MISS HOLSTEN (USA)	HAROLD KIRK	22000
CH C OBSERVATORY (USA) - BETRAY (GB)	PETER & ROSS DOYLE BS	22000
C JEREMY (USA) - ARCHETYPAL (IRE)	MARK O'HARE (P.S.)	22000
G OSCAR (IRE) - TOP HER UP (IRE)	FABRICATED PRODUCTS LTD	22000
F KING'S THEATRE (IRE) - PORTRYAN NATIVE (IRE)	RATHBARRY STUD	22000
C MASTERCRAFTSMAN (IRE) - LAKE LADOGA (GB)	SACKVILLEDONALD	22000
G PRESENTING (GB) - ZARINAVA (IRE)	VENDOR	22000
G FLEMENSFIRTH (USA) - PETITE BALLERINA (IRE)	FUTURERATE LIMITED	22000
C SINNDAR (IRE) - HARRANDA (GB)	5 STAR	21000
PEAKY VOICE (IRE) B F VOCALISED (USA) - LAVENDER BLUE (GB)	BBA IRELAND	21000
F KODIAC (GB) - MEAON (IRE)	P D EVANS	21000
AIR VENTURE (IRE) B G INTIKHAB (USA) - AQUA VITAE (IRE)	M DODS	21000
C HALLING (USA) - SEEKING SOLACE (GB)	JANDA BS	21000
G APPROVE (IRE) - CLASSIC STYLE (IRE)	EMMA O' GORMAN	21000
C HOLY ROMAN EMPEROR (IRE) - LOVE VALENTINE (IRE)	JOHNNY MURTAGH	21000
G PRESENTING (GB) - SHUIL DEARG (IRE)	MARGARET O'TOOLE	21000
F ACCLAMATION (GB) - PERSE (GB)	BOTTI BS	21000
BR C ZAMINDAR (USA) - SHEBOYGAN (IRE)	VENDOR	21000
C CAPTAIN RIO (GB) - THE OLDLADYSAYS NO (IRE)	MIDDLEHAM PARK RACING	21000
G KALANISI (IRE) - RENVYLE SOCIETY (IRE)	A & P MORRIS	21000
C CAPTAIN RIO (GB) - DAFTIYNA (IRE)	TADGH RYAN	21000
F ACCLAMATION (GB) - PRAESEPE (GB)	BRYAN SMART	21000
G SHIROCCO (GER) - LADY EMILY (GB)	MICHAEL MCDONAGH	21000

2000 GUINEAS STAKES (3y) Newmarket-1 mile

Year	Owner	Winner and Price	Jockey	Trainer	Second	Third	Ran	Time
1972	Sir J Thom's	HIGH TOP (85/40)	W Carson	R Van Cutsem	Roberto	Sun Prince	12	1 40.82
1973	Mrs B Davis's	MON FILS (50/1)	F Durr	R Van Cutsem	Noble Decree	Sharp Edge	18	1 42.97
1974	Mme M Berger's	NONOALCO (19/2)	Y Saint Martin	F Boutin	Giacometti	Apalache	12	1 39.53
1975	C d'Alessio's	BOLKONSKI (33/1)	G Dettori	H Cecil	Grundy	Dominion	24	1 39.53
1976	C d'Alessio's	WOLLOW (evens)	G Dettori	H Cecil	Vitiges	Thieving Demon	17	1 38.09
1977	N Schibbye's	NEBBIOLO (20/1)	G Curran	K Prendergast	Tachypous	The Minstrel	18	1 38.54
1978	J Hayter's	ROLAND GARDENS (28/1)	F Durr	D Sasse	Remainder Man	Weth Nan	19	1 47.33
1979	A Shead's	TAP ON WOOD (20/1)	S Cauthen	B Hills	Kris	Young Generation	20	1 43.60
1980	K Abdulla's	KNOWN FACT (14/1)	W Carson	J Tree	Posse	Night Alert	14	1 40.46
(Nureyev finished first but was disqualified)								
1981	Mrs A Muinos's	TO-AGORI-MOU (5/2)	G Starkey	G Harwood	Mattaboy	Bel Bolide	19	1 41.43
1982	G Oldham's	ZINO (8/1)	F Head	F Boutin	Wind and Wuthering	Tender King	26	1 37.13
1983	R Sangster's	LOMOND (9/1)	Pat Eddery	V O'Brien	Tolomeo	Muscatite	16	1 43.87
1984	R Sangster's	EL GRAN SENOR (15/8)	Pat Eddery	V O'Brien	Chief Singer	Lear Fan	9	1 37.41
1985	Maktoum Al Maktoum's	SHADEED (4/5)	L Piggott	M Stoute	Bairn	Supreme Leader	14	1 37.41
1986	K Abdulla's	DANCING BRAVE (15/8)	G Starkey	G Harwood	Green Desert	Huntingdale	15	1 40.00
1987	J Horgan's	DON'T FORGET ME (9/1)	W Carson	R Hannon	Bellotto	Midyan	13	1 36.74
1988	H H Aga Khan's	DOYOUN (4/5)	W R Swinburn	M Stoute	Charmer	Bellfella	13	1 41.73
1989	Hamdan Al-Maktoum's	NASHWAN (3/1)	W Carson	R Hern	Exbourne	Danehill	14	1 36.44
1990	John Horgan's	TIROL (9/1)	M Kinane	R Hannon	Machiavellian	Anshan	14	1 35.84
1991	Lady Beaverbrook's	MYSTIKO (13/2)	M Roberts	C Brittain	Lycius	Ganges	14	1 37.83
1992	R Sangster's	RODRIGO DE TRIANO (6/1)	L Piggott	P Chapple-Hyam	Lucky Lindy	Pursuit of Love	16	1 38.37
1993	K Abdulla's	ZAFONIC (5/6)	Pat Eddery	A Fabre	Barathea	Bin Ajwaad	14	1 35.32
1994	G R Bailey Ltd's	MISTER BAILEYS (16/1)	J Weaver	M Johnston	Grand Lodge	Colonel Collins	23	1 35.08
1995	Sheikh Mohammed's	PENNEKAMP (9/2)	T Jarnet	A Fabre	Celtic Swing	Bahri	11	1 35.16
1996	Godolphin's	MARK OF ESTEEM (8/1)	L Dettori	S bin Suroor	Even Top	Bijou D'Inde	13	1 37.59
1997	M Tabor & Mrs J Magnier's	ENTREPRENEUR (11/2)	M Kinane	M Stoute	Revoque	Poteen	16	1 35.64
1998	M Tabor & Mrs J Magnier's	KING OF KINGS (7/2)	M Kinane	A O'Brien	Lend A Hand	Border Arrow	18	1 39.25
1999	Godolphin's	ISLAND SANDS (10/1)	L Dettori	S Bin Suroor	Enrique	Mujahid	16	1 37.14
(Run on July Course)								
2000	Saeed Suhail's	KING'S BEST (13/2)	K Fallon	Sir M Stoute	Giant's Causeway	Barathea Guest	27	1 37.77
2001	Lord Weinstock's	GOLAN (11/1)	K Fallon	Sir M Stoute	Tamburlaine	Frenchmans Bay	18	1 37.48
2002	Sir A Ferguson & Mrs J Magnier's	ROCK OF GIBRALTAR (9/1)	J Murtagh	A O'Brien	Hawk Wing	Redback	22	1 36.50
2003	Moyglare Stud Farm's	REFUSE TO BEND (9/2)	P J Smullen	D Weld	Zafeen	Norse Dancer	20	1 37.98
2004	Hamdan Al Maktoum's	HAAFHD (11/2)	R Hills	B Hills	Snow Ridge	Azamour	14	1 36.60
2005	Mr M Tabor & Mrs John Magnier's	FOOTSTEPSINTHESAND (13/2)	K Fallon	A O'Brien	Rebel Rebel	Kandidate	19	1 36.10
2006	Mrs J Magnier, Mr M Tabor & Mr D Smith's	GEORGE WASHINGTON (6/4)	K Fallon	A O'Brien	Sir Percy	Olympian Odyssey	14	1 36.80
2007	P Cunningham's	COCKNEY REBEL (25/1)	O Peslier	G Huffer	Vital Equine	Dutch Art	24	1 35.28
2008	Mrs J Magnier's	HENRYTHENAVIGATOR (11/1)	J Murtagh	A O'Brien	New Approach	Stubbs Art	15	1 39.14
2009	C Tsui's	SEA THE STARS (8/1)	M Kinane	J Oxx	Delegator	Gan Amhras	19	1 35.88
2010	K Abdulla's	MAKFI (33/1)	T Queally	M Delzangles	Dick Turpin	Canford Cliffs	19	1 36.35
2011	K Abdulla's	FRANKEL (1/2)	T Queally	H Cecil	Dubawi Gold	Native Khan	13	1 37.30
2012	D Smith, Mrs J Magnier &	CAMELOT (15/8)	J O'Brien	A O'Brien	French Fifteen	Herival	18	1 42.46

Year	Owner	Winner and Price	Jockey	Trainer	Second	Third	Ran	Time
1971	F Hue-Williams's	ALTESSE ROYALE (25/1)	Y Saint Martin	N Murless	Super Honey	Catherine Wheel	10	1 40.90
1972	Mrs R Stanley's	WATERLOO (8/1)	E Hide	J W Watts	Marisela	Rose Dubarry	18	1 39.49
1973	R Pople's	MYSTERIOUS (11/1)	G Lewis	N Murless	Jacinth	Shellshock	14	1 42.12
1974	The Queen's	HIGHCLERE (12/1)	J Mercer	R Hern	Polygamy	Mrs Twiggywinkle	15	1 40.32
1975	Mrs D O'Kelly's	NOCTURNAL SPREE (14/1)	J Roe	S Murless	Girl Friend	Joking Apart	16	1 41.65
1976	D Wildenstein's	FLYING WATER (2/1)	Y Saint Martin	A Penna	Konata	Kesar Queen	25	1 37.83
1977	Mrs E Kettlewell's	MRS MCARDY (16/1)	E Hide	M W Easterby	Freeze the Secret	Sanedtki	18	1 40.07
1978	R Bonnycastle's	ENSTONE SPARK (35/1)	E Johnson	B Hills	Fair Salinia	Seraghima	16	1 41.56
1979	Helena Springfield Ltd's	ONE IN A MILLION (evens)	J Mercer	H Cecil	Abbeydale	Yanuka	17	1 43.06
1980	O Phipps's	QUICK AS LIGHTNING (12/1)	B Rouse	J Dunlop	Our Home	Mrs Penny	23	1 41.89
1981	H Joel's	FAIRY FOOTSTEPS (6/4)	L Piggott	H Cecil	Tolmi	Go Leasing	14	1 40.43
1982	Sir P Oppenheimer's	ON THE HOUSE (33/1)	J Reid	H Wragg	Time Charter	Dione	15	1 40.45
1983	M Lemos's	MA BICHE (5/2)	F Head	Mme C Head	Favoridge	Habibti	18	1 40.71
1984	Maktoum Al-Maktoum's	PEBBLES (8/1)	P Robinson	C Brittain	Meis El-Reem	Desirable	15	1 38.18
1985	Sheikh Mohammed's	OH SO SHARP (2/1)	S Cauthen	H Cecil	Al Bahathri	Bella Colora	15	1 36.85
1986	H Ranier's	MIDWAY LADY (10/1)	R Cochrane	B Hanbury	Maysoon	Sonic Lady	15	1 41.54
1987	S Niarchos's	MESQUE (15/8)	F Head	F Boutin	Milligram	Interval	14	1 38.48
1988	E Aland's	RAVINELLA (4/5)	G W Moore	Mme C Head	Dabaweyaa	Diminuendo	12	1 40.88
1989	Sheikh Mohammed's	MUSICAL BLISS (7/2)	W R Swinburn	M Stoute	Kerrera	Aldbourne	7	1 42.69
1990	Hamdan Al-Maktoum's	SALSABIL (6/4)	W Carson	J Dunlop	Heart of Joy	Negligent	10	1 38.06
1991	Hamdan Al-Maktoum's	SHADAYID (4/6)	W Carson	J Dunlop	Kooyonga	Crystal Gazing	14	1 38.18
1992	Maktoum Al-Maktoum's	HATOOF (5/1)	W R Swinburn	Mme C Head	Marling	Kenbu	14	1 39.45
1993	Mohamed Obaid's	SAYYEDATI (4/1)	W R Swinburn	C Brittain	Niche	Aljaan	12	1 37.34
1994	R Sangster's	LAS MENINAS (12/1)	J Reid	T Stack	Balanchine	Coup de Genie	15	1 36.71
1995	Hamdan Al-Maktoum's	HARAYIR (5/1)	R Hills	Major W R Hern	Aqaarid	Moonshell	14	1 36.72
1996	Walic Said's	BOSRA SHAM (10/11)	Pat Eddery	H Cecil	Matiya	Bint Shadayid	13	1 37.75
1997	Greenay Stables Ltd's	SLEEPYTIME (4/1)	K Fallon	H Cecil	Oh Nellie	Dazzle	15	1 37.66
1998	Godolphin's	CAPE VERDI (100/30)	L Dettori	S Bin Suroor	Shahtoush	Exclusive	16	1 37.86
1999	K Abdulla's	WINCE (4/1)	K Fallon	H Cecil	Wannabe Grand	Valentine Waltz	22	1 37.91

(Run on July Course)

Year	Owner	Winner and Price	Jockey	Trainer	Second	Third	Ran	Time
2000	Hamdan Al-Maktoum's	LAHAN (14/1)	R Hills	J Gosden	Princess Ellen	Petrushka	18	1 36.38
2001	Sheikh Ahmed Al Maktoum's	AMEERAT (11/1)	P Robinson	J Jarvis	Muwakleh	Toroca	15	1 36.36
2002	Godolphin's	KAZZIA (11/1)	L Dettori	S Bin Suroor	Snowfire	Alasha	17	1 37.85
2003	Cheveley Park Stud's	RUSSIAN RHYTHM (12/1)	K Fallon	Sir M Stoute	Six Perfections	Intercontinental	19	1 38.43
2004	Duke of Roxburghe's	ATTRACTION (11/2)	K Darley	M Johnston	Sundrop	Hathrah	16	1 36.70
2005	Mrs John Magnier & Mr M Tabor's	VIRGINIA WATERS (12/1)	K Fallon	A O'Brien	Maids Causeway	Vista Bella	20	1 36.50
2006	Mr Sly, Dr Davies & Mrs P Sly's	SPECIOSA (10/1)	M Fenton	Mrs P Sly	Confidential Lady	Nasheej	13	1 40.50
2007	M Ryan's	FINSCEAL BEO (5/4)	K Manning	J Bolger	Arch Swing	Simply Perfect	21	1 34.94
2008	S Fitborg's	NATAGORA (20/1)	C Lemaire	P Bary	Spacious	Saoirse Abu	15	1 38.99
2009	Hamdan Al-Maktoum's	GHANAATI (20/1)	R Hills	B Hills	Cuis Ghaire	Super Sleuth	14	1 34.22
2010	K Abdulla's	SPECIAL DUTY (9/2)	S Pasquier	Mme C Head-Maarek	Jacqueline Quest	Gile Na Greine	17	1 39.66

(The first two placings were reversed by the Stewards)

Year	Owner	Winner and Price	Jockey	Trainer	Second	Third	Ran	Time
2011	Godolphin's	BLUE BUNTING (16/1)	L Dettori	M Al Zarooni	Together	Maqaasid	18	1 39.27
2012	Mrs John Magnier, M Tabor & D Smith's	HOMECOMING QUEEN (25/1)	R Moore	A O'Brien	Starscope	Maybe	17	1 40.45
2013	B Keswick's	SKY LANTERN (9/1)	R Hughes	R Hannon	Just The Judge	Moth	15	1 36.38

OAKS STAKES (3y fillies) Epsom-1 mile 4 furlongs 10 yards

Year	Owner	Winner and Price	Jockey	Trainer	Second	Third	Ran	Time
1976	D Wildenstein's	PAWNEESE (6/5)	Y Saint Martin	A Penna	Roses for the Star	African Dancer	14	2 35.25
1977	The Queen's	DUNFERMLINE (6/1)	W Carson	R Hern	Freeze the Secret	Vaguely Deb	13	2 36.53
1978	S Hanson's	FAIR SALINIA (8/1)	G Starkey	M Stoute	Dancing Maid	Suni	15	2 36.82
1979	J Morrison's	SCINTILLATE (20/1)	Pat Eddery	J Tree	Bonnie Isle	Britannia's Rule	14	2 43.74
1980	R Hollingsworth's	BIREME (9/2)	W Carson	R Hern	Vielle	The Dancer	11	2 34.33
1981	Mrs B Firestone's	BLUE WIND (3/1)	L Piggott	D Weld	Madam Gay	Leap Lively	12	2 40.93
1982	R Barnett's	TIME CHARTER (12/1)	W Newnes	H Candy	Slightly Dangerous	Last Feather	13	2 34.21
1983	Sir M Sobell's	SUN PRINCESS (6/1)	W Carson	R Hern	Acclimatise	New Coins	15	2 40.98
1984	Sir R McAlpine's	CIRCUS PLUME (4/1)	L Piggott	J Dunlop	Media Luna	Poquito Queen	15	2 38.97
1985	Sheikh Mohammed's	OH SO SHARP (6/4)	S Cauthen	H Cecil	Triptych	Dubian	12	2 41.37
1986	H Ranier's	MIDWAY LADY (15/8)	R Cochrane	B Hanbury	Untold	Maysoon	15	2 35.60
1987	Sheikh Mohammed's	UNITE (11/1)	W R Swinburn	M Stoute	Bourbon Girl	Three Tails	11	2 38.17
1988	Sheikh Mohammed's	DIMINUENDO (7/4)	S Cauthen	H Cecil	Sudden Love	Animatrice	11	2 35.02
1989	Saeed Maktoum Al Maktoum's	SNOW BRIDE (13/2)	S Cauthen	H Cecil	Roseate Tern	Mamaluna	9	2 34.22
		(Aliysa finished first but was disqualified)						
1990	Hamdan Al-Maktoum's	SALSABIL (2/1)	W Carson	J Dunlop	Game Plan	Knight's Baroness	8	2 38.70
1991	Maktoum Al-Maktoum's	JET SKI LADY (50/1)	C Roche	J Bolger	Shamshir	Shadayid	7	2 37.30
1992	W J Gredley's	USER FRIENDLY (5/1)	G Duffield	C Brittain	All At Sea	Pearl Angel		2 39.77
1993	Sheikh Mohammed's	INTREPIDITY (5/1)	M Roberts	A Fabre	Royal Ballerina	Oakmead	14	2 34.19
1994	Godolphin's	BALANCHINE (3/1)	L Dettori	H Ibrahim	Wind in Her Hair	Hawajiss	10	2 40.37
1995	Maktoum Al Maktoum/ Godolphin's	MOONSHELL (3/1)	L Dettori	S Bin Suroor	Dance A Dream	Pure Grain	10	2 35.44
1996	Watic Said's	LADY CARLA (100/30)	Pat Eddery	H Cecil	Pricket	Mezzogiorno	11	2 35.55
1997	K Abdulla's	REAMS OF VERSE (5/6)	K Fallon	H Cecil	Gazelle Royale	Crown of Light	12	2 35.59
1998	Mrs D Nagle & Mrs J Magnier's	SHAHTOUSH (12/1)	K Kinane	A O'Brien	Bahr	Midnight Line	8	2 38.23
1999	F Salman's	RAMRUMA (11/4)	K Fallon	H Cecil	Noushkey	Zahrat Dubai	10	2 38.72
2000	Lordship Stud's	LOVE DIVINE (9/4)	T Quinn	H Cecil	Kalypso Katie	Melikah	16	2 43.11
2001	Mrs D Nagle & Mrs J Magnier's	IMAGINE (100/30)	M Kinane	A O'Brien	Flight Of Fancy	Relish The Thought	14	2 36.70
2002	Godolphin's	KAZZIA (100/30)	L Dettori	S Bin Suroor	Quarter Moon	Shadow Dancing	14	2 44.52
2003	W S Farish III's	CASUAL LOOK (10/1)	M Dwyer	A Balding	Yesterday	Summitville	15	2 38.07
2004	Lord Derby's	OUIJA BOARD (7/2)	K Fallon	E Dunlop	All Too Beautiful	Punctilious	7	2 35.40
2005	Hamdan Al Maktoum's	ESWARAH (11/4)	R Hills	M Jarvis	Something Exciting	Pictavia	12	2 39.00
2006	Mrs J Magnier, Mr M Tabor & Mr D Smith's	ALEXANDROVA (9/4)	K Fallon	A O'Brien	Rising Cross	Short Skirt	10	2 37.70
2007	Niarchos Family's	LIGHT SHIFT (13/2)	T Durcan	H Cecil	Peeping Fawn	All My Loving	14	2 40.38
2008	J H Richmond-Watson's	LOOK HERE (33/1)	S Sanders	R Beckett	Moonstone	Katiyra	16	2 36.89
2009	Lady Bamford's	SARISKA (9/4)	J Spencer	M Bell	Midday	High Heeled	10	2 35.28
2010	Anamoine Ltd's	SNOW FAIRY (9/1)	R Moore	E Dunlop	Remember When	Rumoush	15	2 35.77
		(Meezah finished second but was disqualified)						
2011	M J & L A Taylor's	DANCING RAIN (20/1)	J Murtagh	W Haggas	Wonder of Wonders	Izzi Top	13	2 41.73
2012	D Smith, Mrs J Magnier & M Tabor's	WAS (20/1)	S Heffernan	A O'Brien	Shirocco Star	The Fugue	12	2 38.68
2013	J L Rowsell & M H Dixon's	TALENT (20/1)	R Hughes	R Beckett	Secret Gesture	The Lark	11	2 42.00

DERBY STAKES (3y) Epsom-1 mile 4 furlongs 10 yards

Year	Owner	Winner and Price	Jockey	Trainer	Second	Third	Ran	Time
1975	Dr C Vittadini's	GRUNDY (5/1)	Pat Eddery	P Walwyn	Nobiliary	Hunza Dancer	18	2 35.35
1976	N B Hunt's	EMPERY (10/1)	L Piggott	M Zilber	Relkino	Oats	23	2 35.69
1977	R Sangster's	THE MINSTREL (5/1)	L Piggott	V O'Brien	Hot Grove	Blushing Groom	22	2 36.44
1978	Lord Halifax's	SHIRLEY HEIGHTS (8/1)	G Starkey	J Dunlop	Hawaiian Sound	Remainder Man	25	2 35.30
1979	Sir M Sobell's	TROY (6/1)	W Carson	R Hern	Dickens Hill	Northern Baby	23	2 36.59
1980	Mrs A Plesch's	HENBIT (7/1)	W Carson	R Hern	Master Willie	Rankin	24	2 34.77
1981	H H Aga Khan's	SHERGAR (10/11)	W Swinburn	M Stoute	Glint of Gold	Scintillating Air	18	2 44.21
1982	R Sangster's	GOLDEN FLEECE (3/1)	Pat Eddery	V O'Brien	Touching Wood	Silver Hawk	18	2 34.27
1983	E Moller's	TEENOSO (9/1)	L Piggott	G Wragg	Carlingford Castle	Shearwalk	21	2 49.07
1984	L Miglitt's	SECRETO (14/1)	C Roche	D O'Brien	El Gran Senor	Mighty Flutter	17	2 39.12
1985	Lord H. de Walden's	SLIP ANCHOR (9/4)	S Cauthen	H Cecil	Law Society	Damister	14	2 36.23
1986	H H Aga Khan's	SHAHRASTANI (11/2)	W Swinburn	M Stoute	Dancing Brave	Mashkour	17	2 37.13
1987	L Freedman's	REFERENCE POINT (6/4)	S Cauthen	H Cecil	Most Welcome	Bellotto	19	2 33.90
1988	H H Aga Khan's	KAHYASI (11/1)	R Cochrane	L Cumani	Glacial Storm	Doyoun	14	2 33.84
1989	Hamdan Al-Maktoum's	NASHWAN (5/4)	W Carson	R Hern	Terimon	Cacoethes	12	2 34.90
1990	K Abdulla's	QUEST FOR FAME (7/1)	Pat Eddery	R Charlton	Blue Stag	Elmaamul	18	2 37.26
1991	F Salman's	GENEROUS (9/1)	A Munro	P Cole	Marju	Star of Gdansk	13	2 34.00
1992	Sidney H Craig's	DR DEVIOUS (8/1)	J Reid	C Chapple-Hyam	St Jovite	Silver Wisp	18	2 36.19
1993	K Abdulla's	COMMANDER IN CHIEF (15/2)	M Kinane	H Cecil	Blue Judge	Blues Traveller	16	2 34.51
1994	Hamdan Al-Maktoum's	ERHAAB (7/2)	W Carson	J Dunlop	King's Theatre	Colonel Collins	25	2 34.16
1995	Saeed Maktoum Al Maktoum's	LAMMTARRA (14/1)	W Swinburn	S Bin Suroor	Tamure	Presenting	15	2 32.31
1996	K Dasmal's	SHAAMIT (12/1)	M Hills	W Haggas	Dushyantor	Shantou	20	2 35.05
1997	L Knight's	BENNY THE DIP (11/1)	W Ryan	J Gosden	Silver Patriarch	Romanov	13	2 35.77
1998	Sheikh Mohammed & Obaid Al Maktoum's	HIGH-RISE (20/1)	O Pesller	L Cumani	City Honours	Border Arrow	15	2 33.88
1999	The Thoroughbred Corporation's	OATH (13/2)	K Fallon	H Cecil	Daliapour	Beat All	16	2 37.43
2000	H H Aga Khan's	SINNDAR (7/1)	J Murtagh	J Oxx	Sakhee	Beat Hollow	15	2 36.75
2001	M Tabor & Mrs J Magnier's	GALILEO (11/4)	M Kinane	A O'Brien	Golan	Tobougg	12	2 33.27
2002	M Tabor & Mrs J Magnier's	HIGH CHAPARRAL (7/2)	J Murtagh	A O'Brien	Hawk Wing	Moon Ballad	12	2 39.45
2003	Saeed Suhail's	KRIS KIN (6/1)	K Fallon	Sir M Stoute	The Great Gatsby	Alamshar	20	2 33.35
2004	Ballymacoll Stud's	NORTH LIGHT (7/2)	K Fallon	Sir M Stoute	Rule Of Law	Let The Lion Roar	14	2 33.70
2005	The Royal Ascot Racing Club's	MOTIVATOR (3/1)	J Murtagh	M Bell	Walk In The Park	Dubawi	13	2 33.60
2006	A E Pakenham's	SIR PERCY (6/1)	M Dwyer	M Tregoning	Dragon Dancer	Dylan Thomas	18	2 35.60
2007	Saleh Al Homaiz & Imad Al Sagar's	AUTHORIZED (5/4)	L Dettori	P Chapple-Hyam	Eagle Mountain	Aqaleem	17	2 34.77
2008	HRH Princess Haya of Jordan's	NEW APPROACH (5/1)	K Manning	J Bolger	Tartan Bearer	Casual Conquest	16	2 36.50
2009	C Tsui's	SEA THE STARS (11/4)	M Kinane	J Oxx	Fame And Glory	Masterofthehorse	12	2 36.74
2010	K Abdulla's	WORKFORCE (6/1)	R Moore	Sir M Stoute	At First Sight	Rewilding	12	2 31.33
2011	Mrs John Magnier, M Tabor & D Smith's	POUR MOI (4/1)	M Barzalona	A Fabre	Treasure Beach	Carlton House	13	2 34.54
2012	D Smith, Mrs J Magnier & M Tabor's	CAMELOT (8/13)	J O'Brien	A O'Brien	Main Sequence	Astrology	9	2 33.90
2013	Mrs John Magnier, Michael Tabor & Derrick Smith's	RULER OF THE WORLD (7/1)	R Moore	A O'Brien	Libertarian	Galileo Rock	12	2 39.06

ST LEGER STAKES (3y) Doncaster-1 mile 6 furlongs 132 yards

Year	Owner	Winner and Price	Jockey	Trainer	Second	Third	Ran	Time
1972	O Phipps's	BOUCHER (3/1)	L Piggott	V O'Brien	Our Mirage	Ginevra	7	3 28.71
1973	W Behrens's	PELEID (28/1)	F Durr	W Elsey	Buoy	Duke of Ragusa	13	3 8.21
1974	Lady Beaverbrook's	BUSTINO (11/10)	J Mercer	W Hern	Giacometti	Riboson	10	3 9.02
1975	C St George's	BRUNI (9/1)	A Murray	R Price	King Pellinore	Libra's Rib	12	3 9.02
1976	D Wildenstein's	CROW (6/1)	Y Saint-Martin	A Penna	Secret Man	Scallywag	15	3 13.17
1977	The Queen's	DUNFERMLINE (10/1)	W Carson	R Hern	Alleged	Classic Example	13	3 5.17
1978	M Lemos's	JULIO MARINER (28/1)	E Hide	C Brittain	Le Moss	M-Lolshan	14	3 4.94
1979	A Rolland's	SON OF LOVE (20/1)	A Lequeux	R Collet	Soleil Noir	Niniski	17	3 9.02
1980	H Joel's	LIGHT CAVALRY (3/1)	J Mercer	H Cecil	Water Mill	World Leader	7	3 11.48
1981	Sir J Astor's	CUT ABOVE (28/1)	J Mercer	H Cecil	Glint of Gold	Bustomi	7	3 11.60
1982	Maktoum Al Maktoum's	TOUCHING WOOD (7/1)	P Cook	R Hern	Zilos	Diamond Shoal	15	3 3.53
1983	Sir M Sobell's	SUN PRINCESS (11/8)	W Carson	H Cecil	Esprit du Nord	Carlingford Castle	10	3 16.65
1984	I Allan's	COMMANCHE RUN (7/4)	L Piggott	L Cumani	Baynoun	Alphabatim	11	3 9.93
1985	Sheikh Mohammed's	OH SO SHARP (8/11)	S Cauthen	H Cecil	Phardante	Lanfranco	6	3 7.13
1986	Duchess of Norfolk's	MOON MADNESS (9/2)	Pat Eddery	J Dunlop	Celestial Storm	Untold	8	3 5.03
1987	L Freedman's	REFERENCE POINT (4/11)	S Cauthen	H Cecil	Mountain Kingdom	Dry Dock	7	3 5.91
1988	Lady Beaverbrook's	MINSTER SON (15/2)	W Carson	N A Graham	Diminuendo	Sheriff's Star	8	3 6.80
1989	C St George's	MICHELOZZO (6/4)	S Cauthen	H Cecil	Sapience	Roseate Tern	8	3 20.72
		(Run at Ayr)						
1990	M Arbib's	SNURGE (7/2)	T Quinn	P Cole	Hellenic	River God	8	3 8.78
1991	K Abdulla's	TOULON (5/2)	Pat Eddery	A Fabre	Saddlers' Hall	Michelletti	13	3 5.48
1992	W J Gredley's	USER FRIENDLY (7/4)	G Duffield	M Tompkins	Sonus	Bonny Scot	10	3 5.73
1993	Mrs G A E Smith's	BOB'S RETURN (3/1)	P Robinson	B Hills	Armiger	Edbaysaan	9	3 7.85
1994	Sheikh Mohammed's	MOONAX (40/1)	Pat Eddery	S Bin Suroor	Broadway Flyer	Double Trigger	8	3 4.19
1995	Godolphin's	CLASSIC CLICHE (100/30)	L Dettori	S Bin Suroor	Minds Music	Istidaad	10	3 9.74
1996	Sheikh Mohammed's	SHANTOU (8/1)	L Dettori	J Dunlop	Dushyantor	Samraan	11	3 5.10
1997	P Winfield's	SILVER PATRIARCH (5/4)	Pat Eddery	J Dunlop	Vertical Speed	The Fly	9	3 6.92
1998	Godolphin's	NEDAWI (5/2)	J Reid	S Bin Suroor	High and Low	Sunshine Street	9	3 5.61
1999	Godolphin's	MUTAFAWEQ (11/2)	R Hills	S Bin Suroor	Ramruma	Adair	9	3 2.75
2000	N Jones's	MILLENARY (11/4)	T Quinn	J Dunlop	Air Marshall	Chimes At Midnight	11	3 2.58
2001	M Tabor & Mrs J Magnier's	MILAN (13/8)	M Kinane	A O'Brien	Demophilos	Mr Combustible	11	3 5.16
2002	Sir Neil Westbrook's	BOLLIN ERIC (7/1)	K Darley	T Easterby	Highest	Bandari	8	3 2.92
2003	Mrs J Magnier's	BRIAN BORU (5/4)	J P Spencer	A O'Brien	High Accolade	Phoenix Reach	12	3 4.64
2004	Godolphin's	RULE OF LAW (3/1)	K McEvoy	S Bin Suroor	Quiff	Tycoon	9	3 6.20
2005	Mrs J Magnier & M Tabor's	SCORPION (10/11)	L Dettori	A O'Brien	The Geezer	Tawqeet	6	3 19.00
2006	Mrs S Roy's	SIXTIES ICON (11/8)	L Dettori	J Noseda	The Last Drop	Red Rocks	11	2 57.20
		(Run at York)						
2007	G Strawbridge's	LUCARNO (7/2)	J Fortune	J Gosden	Mahler	Honolulu	10	3 1.90
2008	Ballymacoll Stud's	CONDUIT (14/1)	L Dettori	Sir M Stoute	Unsung Heroine	Look Here	14	3 7.92
2009	Godolphin's	MASTERY (14/1)	T Durcan	S Bin Suroor	Kite Wood	Monitor Closely	8	3 4.81
2010	Ms R Hood & R R Geffen's	ARCTIC COSMOS (12/1)	W Buick	J Gosden	Midas Touch	Corsica	10	3 3.12
2011	B Nielsen's	MASKED MARVEL (15/2)	W Buick	J Gosden	Brown Panther	Sea Moon	9	3 0.44
2012	Godolphin's	ENCKE (25/1)	M Barzalona	M Al Zarooni	Camelot	Michelangelo	9	3 3.81
2013	Derek Smith & Mrs John Magnier & M Tabor's	LEADING LIGHT (7/2)	J O'Brien	A O'Brien	Talent	Galileo Rock	11	3 9.20

KING GEORGE VI AND QUEEN ELIZABETH STAKES Ascot-1 mile 4 furlongs

Year	Owner	Winner and Price	Jockey	Trainer	Second	Third	Ran	Time
1974	N B Hunt's	DAHLIA 4-9-4 (15/8)	L Piggott	M Zilber	Highclere	Dankaro	10	2 33.03
1975	D r C Vittadini's	GRUNDY 3-8-7 (4/5)	P Eddery	P Walwyn	Bustino	Dahlia	11	2 26.98
1976	D Wildenstein's	PAWNEESE 3-8-5 (9/4)	Y Saint Martin	A Penna	Bruni	Orange Bay	10	2 29.36
1977	R Sangster's	THE MINSTREL 3-8-8 (7/4)	L Piggott	V O'Brien	Orange Bay	Exceller	11	2 30.48
1978	D McCall's	ILE DE BOURBON 3-8-8 (12/1)	J Reid	F Houghton	Hawaiian Sound	Montcontour	14	2 30.53
1979	Sir M Sobell's	TROY 3-8-8 (2/5)	W Carson	R Hern	Gay Mecene	Ela-Mana-Mou	7	2 33.75
1980	S Weinstock's	ELA-MANA-MOU 4-9-7 (11/4)	W Carson	R Hern	Mrs Penny	Gregorian	10	2 35.39
1981	H H Aga Khan's	SHERGAR 3-8-8 (2/5)	W Swinburn	M Stoute	Madam Gay	Fingals Cave	7	2 35.40
1982	G Ward's	KALAGLOW 4-9-7 (13-2)	G Starkey	G Harwood	Assert	Glint of Gold	9	2 31.58
1983	R Barnett's	TIME CHARTER 4-9-4 (5/1)	J Mercer	H Candy	Diamond Shoal	Sun Princess	9	2 30.78
1984	E Moller's	TEENOSO 4-9-7 (13/2)	L Piggott	G Wragg	Sadler's Wells	Tolomeo	13	2 27.95
1985	Lady Beaverbrook's	PETOSKI 3-8-8 (12/1)	W Carson	R Hern	On So Sharp	Rainbow Quest	12	2 27.61
1986	K Abdulla's	DANCING BRAVE 3-8-8 (6/4)	Pat Eddery	G Harwood	Shardari	Triptych	9	2 29.49
1987	L Freedman's	REFERENCE POINT 3-8-8 (11/10)	S Cauthen	H Cecil	Celestial Storm	Triptych	9	2 34.63
1988	Sheikh Ahmed Al Maktoum	MTOTO 5-9-7 (4/1)	M Roberts	A C Stewart	Unfuwain	Tony Bin	10	2 37.33
1989	Hamdan Al-Maktoum's	NASHWAN 3-8-8 (2/9)	W Carson	R Hern	Cacoethes	Top Class	7	2 32.27
1990	Sheikh Mohammed's	BELMEZ 3-8-9 (15/2)	M Kinane	H Cecil	Old Vic	Assatis	11	2 30.76
1991	F Salman's	GENEROUS 3-8-9 (4/6)	A Munro	P Cole	Sanglamore	Rock Hopper	9	2 28.99
1992	Mrs V K Payson's	ST JOVITE 3-8-9 (4/5)	S Craine	J Bolger	Sadlers' Hall	Opera House	8	2 30.85
1993	Sheikh Mohammed's	OPERA HOUSE 5-9-7 (8/1)	M Roberts	M Stoute	White Muzzle	Commander in Chief	10	2 33.94
1994	Sheikh Mohammed's	KING'S THEATRE 3-8-9 (12/1)	M Kinane	H Cecil	White Muzzle	Wagon Master	12	2 28.92
1995	Saeed Maktoum Al Maktoum's	LAMMTARRA 3-8-9 (9/4)	L Dettori	S Bin Suroor	Pentire	Strategic Choice	7	2 31.01
1996	Mollers Racing's	PENTIRE 4-9-7 (100/30)	M Hills	G Wragg	Classic Cliche	Shaamit	8	2 28.11
1997	Godolphin's	SWAIN 5-9-7 (11/2)	J Reid	S Bin Suroor	Pilsudski	Helissio	8	2 36.45
1998	Godolphin's	SWAIN 6-9-7 (11/2)	L Dettori	S Bin Suroor	High-Rise	Royal Anthem	8	2 29.06
1999	Godolphin's	DAYLAMI 5-9-7 (3/1)	L Dettori	S Bin Suroor	Nedawi	Fruits of Love	8	2 29.35
2000	M Tabor's	MONTJEU 4-9-7 (1/3)	M Kinane	J Hammond	Fantastic Light	Daliapour	7	2 29.98
2001	Mrs J Magnier & M Tabor's	GALILEO 3-8-9 (1/2)	M Kinane	A O'Brien	Fantastic Light	Hightori	12	2 29.70
2002	Exors of the late Lord Weinstock's	GOLAN 4-9-7 (11/2)	K Fallon	Sir M Stoute	Nayef	Zindabad	9	2 29.70
2003	H H Aga Khan	ALAMSHAR 3-8-9 (13/2)	J Murtagh	J Oxx	Sulamani	Black Sam Bellamy	12	2 33.26
2004	Godolphin's	DOYEN 4-9-7 (11/10)	L Dettori	S Bin Suroor	Hard Buck	Sulamani	11	2 33.10
2005	H H Aga Khan's	AZAMOUR 4-9-7 (5/2)	M Kinane	J Oxx	Norse Dancer	Bago	12	2 28.20
2006	M Tabor's (Run at Newbury)	HURRICANE RUN 4-9-7 (5/6)	C Soumillon	A Fabre	Electrocutionist	Heart's Cry	6	2 30.20
2007	Mrs J Magnier & M Tabor's	DYLAN THOMAS 4-9-7 (5/4)	J Murtagh	A O'Brien	Youmzain	Maraahel	7	2 31.10
2008	Mrs J Magnier & M Tabor's	DUKE OF MARMALADE 4-9-7 (4/6)	J Murtagh	A O'Brien	Papal Bull	Youmzain	9	2 27.91
2009	Ballymacoll Stud's	CONDUIT 4-9-7 (13/8)	R Moore	Sir M Stoute	Tartan Bearer	Ask	9	2 28.73
2010	Highclere Thoroughbred Racing (Adm. Rous)'s	HARBINGER 4-9-7 (4/1)	O Peslier	Sir M Stoute	Cape Blanco	Youmzain	6	2 26.78
2011	Lady Rothschild's	NATHANIEL 3-8-8 (11/2)	W Buick	J Gosden	Workforce	St Nicholas Abbey	5	2 35.07
2012	Gestut Burg Eberstein & Teruya Yoshida's	DANEDREAM 4-9-4 (9/1)	A Starke	P Schiergen	Nathaniel	St Nicholas Abbey	10	2 31.62
2013	Dr Christophe Berglar's	NOVELLIST 4-9-7 (13/2)	J Murtagh	A Wohler	Trading Leather	Hillstar	8	2 24.60

PRIX DE L'ARC DE TRIOMPHE Longchamp-1 mile 4 furlongs

Year	Owner	Winner and Price	Jockey	Trainer	Second	Third	Ran	Time
1973	H Zeisel's	RHEINGOLD 4-9-6 (77/10)	L Piggott	B Hills	Allez France	Hard to Beat	27	2 35.80
1974	D Wildenstein's	ALLEZ FRANCE 4-9-3 (1/2)	Y Saint Martin	A Penna	Comtesse de Loir	Margouillat	20	2 36.90
1975	W Zeitelhack's	STAR APPEAL 5-9-6 (119/1)	G Starkey	T Grieper	On My Way	Comtesse de Loir	24	2 33.60
1976	W Wertheimer's	IVANJICA 4-9-1 (71/10)	F Head	A Head	Crow	Youth	20	2 33.40
1977	R Sangster's	ALLEGED 3-8-11 (38/10)	L Piggott	V O'Brien	Balmerino	Crystal Palace	26	2 30.60
1978	R Sangster's	ALLEGED 4-9-4 (7/5)	L Piggott	V O'Brien	Trillon	Dancing Maid	18	2 36.10
1979	Mme G Head's	THREE TROIKAS 3-8-8 (88/10)	F Head	Mme C Head	Le Marmot	Troy	22	2 28.90
1980	R Sangster's	DETROIT 3-8-8 (67/10)	Pat Eddery	O Douieb	Argument	Ela-Mana-Mou	20	2 28.00
1981	J Wertheimer's	GOLD RIVER 4-9-1 (53/1)	G W Moore	A Head	Bikala	April Run	24	2 35.20
1982	H H Aga Khan's	AKIYDA 3-8-8 (43/4)	Y Saint Martin	F Mathet	Ardross	Awaasif	17	2 37.00
1983	D Wildenstein's	ALL ALONG 4-9-1 (173/10)	W Swinburn	P Biancone	Sun Princess	Luth Enchantee	26	2 28.10
1984	D Wildenstein's	SAGACE 4-9-4 (29/10)	Y Saint Martin	P Biancone	Northern Trick	All Along	22	2 39.10
1985	K Abdulla's	RAINBOW QUEST 3-8-8 (71/10)	Pat Eddery	J Tree	Sagace	Kozana	15	2 29.50
	(The first two placings were reversed by the Stewards)							
1986	K Abdulla's	DANCING BRAVE 3-8-11 (11/10)	Pat Eddery	G Harwood	Bering	Triptych	15	2 27.70
1987	P de Moussac's	TREMPOLINO 3-8-11 (20/1)	Pat Eddery	A Fabre	Tony Bin	Triptych	11	2 26.30
1988	Mrs V Gaucci del Bono's	TONY BIN 5-9-4 (14/1)	J Reid	L Camici	Mtoto	Boyatino	24	2 27.30
1989	A Balzarini's	CARROLL HOUSE 4-9-4 (19/1)	M Kinane	M Jarvis	Behera	Saint Andrews	19	2 30.80
1990	B McNall's	SAUMAREZ 3-8-11 (15/1)	G Mosse	N Clement	Epervier Bleu	Snurge	21	2 29.80
1991	A Chalhoub's	SUAVE DANCER 3-8-11 (37/10)	C Asmussen	J Hammond	Magic Night	Pistolet Bleu	14	2 31.40
1992	O Lecerf's	SUBOTICA 4-9-4 (88/10)	T Jarnet	A Fabre	User Friendly	Vert Amande	18	2 39.00
1993	D Tsui's	URBAN SEA 4-9-1 (37/1)	E Saint Martin	J Lesbordes	White Muzzle	Opera House	23	2 37.90
1994	Sheikh Mohammed's	CARNEGIE 3-8-11 (3/1)	T Jarnet	A Fabre	Hernando	Apple Tree	20	2 31.10
1995	Saeed Maktoum Al Maktoum's	LAMMTARRA 3-8-11 (2/1)	L Dettori	S Bin Suroor	Freedom Cry	Swain	16	2 31.80
1996	E Sarasola's	HELISSIO 3-8-11 (22/10)	O Peslier	E Lellouche	Pilsudski	Oscar Schindler	16	2 29.40
1997	D Wildenstein's	PEINTRE CELEBRE 3-8-11 (22/10)	O Peslier	A Fabre	Pilsudski	Borgia	18	2 24.60
1998	J-L Lagardere's	SAGAMIX 3-8-11 (5/2)	O Peslier	A Fabre	Leggera	Tiger Hill	14	2 34.50
1999	M Tabor's	MONTJEU 3-8-11 (6/4)	M Kinane	J Oxx	El Condor Pasa	Croco Rouge	14	2 38.50
2000	H H Aga Khan's	SINNDAR 3-8-11 (6/4)	J Murtagh	S Bin Suroor	Egyptband	Volvoreta	10	2 25.80
2001	Godolphin's	SAKHEE 4-9-5 (22/10)	L Dettori	S Bin Suroor	Aquarelliste	Sagacity	17	2 36.10
2002	Godolphin's	MARIENBARD 5-9-5 (158/10)	L Dettori	S Bin Suroor	Sulamani	High Chaparral	16	2 36.40
2003	H H Aga Khan's	DALAKHANI 3-8-11 (9/4)	C Soumillon	A De Royer-Dupre	Mubtaker	High Chaparral	13	2 32.30
2004	Niarchos Family's	BAGO 3-8-11 (11/4)	T Gillet	J E Pease	Cherry Mix	Ouija Board	13	2 32.50
2005	M Tabor's	HURRICANE RUN 3-8-11 (11/4)	K Fallon	A Fabre	Westerner	Bago	15	2 27.40
2006	K Abdulla's	RAIL LINK 3-8-11 (8/1)	S Pasquier	A Fabre	Pride	Hurricane Run	8	2 26.30
	(Deep Impact disqualified from third place)							
2007	Mrs J Magnier & M Tabor's	DYLAN THOMAS 4-9-5 (11/2)	K Fallon	A O'Brien	Youmzain	Sagara	12	2 28.50
2008	H H Aga Khan's	ZARKAVA 3-8-8 (13/8)	C Soumillon	A De Royer-Dupre	Youmzain	Soldier of Fortune/It's Gino	16	2 28.80
2009	C Tsui's	SEA THE STARS 3-8-11 (4/6)	M Kinane	J Oxx	Youmzain	Cavalryman	19	2 26.30
2010	K Abdulla's	WORKFORCE 3-8-11 (6/1)	R Moore	Sir M Stoute	Nakayama Festa	Sarafina	18	2 35.30
2011	Gestut Burg Eberstain & T Yoshida's	DANEDREAM 3-8-8 (20/1)	A Starke	P Schiergen	Shareta	Snow Fairy	16	2 24.49
2012	Wertheimer & Frere's	SOLEMIA 4-9-2 (33/1)	O Peslier	C Laffon-Parias	Orfevre	Masterstroke	18	2 37.68
2013	Al Thani's	TREVE 3-8-8 (9/2)	T Jarnet	Mme C Head-Maarek	Orfevre	Intello	17	2 32.04

GRAND NATIONAL STEEPLECHASE Aintree-4m 3f 110y (4m 4f before 2013)

Year	Winner and Price	Age & Weight	Jockey	Second	Third	Ran	Time
1968	RED ALLIGATOR (100/7)	9 10 4	B Fletcher	Moidore's Token	Different Class	45	9 28.60
1969	HIGHLAND WEDDING (100/9)	12 10 4	E Harty	Steel Bridge	Rondetto	30	9 30.80
1970	GAY TRIP (15/1)	8 11 5	P Taaffe	Vulture	Miss Hunter	28	9 38.00
1971	SPECIFY (28/1)	9 10 13	J Cook	Black Secret	Astbury	38	9 34.20
1972	WELL TO DO (14/1)	9 10 1	G Thorner	Gay Trip	Black Secret/General Symons	42	10 08.40
1973	RED RUM (9/1)	8 10 5	B Fletcher	Crisp	L'Escargot	38	9 01.90
1974	RED RUM (11/1)	9 12 0	B Fletcher	L'Escargot	Charles Dickens	42	9 20.30
1975	L'ESCARGOT (13/2)	12 11 3	T Carberry	Red Rum	Spanish Steps	31	9 31.10
1976	RAG TRADE (14/1)	10 10 12	J Burke	Red Rum	Eyecatcher	32	9 20.90
1977	RED RUM (9/1)	12 11 8	T Stack	Churchtown Boy	Eyecatcher	42	9 30.30
1978	LUCIUS (14/1)	9 10 9	B R Davies	Sebastian V	Drumroan	37	9 33.90
1979	RUBSTIC (25/1)	10 10 0	M Barnes	Zongalero	Rough and Tumble	34	9 52.90
1980	BEN NEVIS (40/1)	12 10 12	Mr C Fenwick	Rough and Tumble	The Pilgarlic	30	10 17.40
1981	ALDANITI (10/1)	11 10 13	B Champion	Spartan Missile	Royal Mail	39	9 47.20
1982	GRITTAR (7/1)	9 11 5	Mr C Saunders	Hard Outlook	Loving Words	39	9 12.60
1983	CORBIERE (13/1)	8 11 4	B de Haan	Greasepaint	Yer Man	41	9 47.04
1984	HALLO DANDY (13/1)	10 10 2	N Doughty	Greasepaint	Corbiere	40	9 21.04
1985	LAST SUSPECT (50/1)	11 10 5	H Davies	Mr Snugfit	Corbiere	40	9 42.70
1986	WEST TIP (15/2)	9 10 11	R Dunwoody	Young Driver	Classified	40	9 33.00
1987	MAORI VENTURE (28/1)	11 10 13	S Knight	The Tsarevich	Lean Ar Aghaidh	40	9 19.30
1988	RHYME 'N' REASON (10/1)	9 11 0	B Powell	Durham Edition	Monanore	40	9 53.50
1989	LITTLE POLVEIR (28/1)	12 10 3	J Frost	West Tip	The Thinker	40	10 06.80
1990	MR FRISK (16/1)	11 10 6	Mr M Armytage	Durham Edition	Rinus	38	8 47.80
1991	SEAGRAM (12/1)	11 10 6	N Hawke	Garrison Savannah	Auntie Dot	40	9 29.90
1992	PARTY POLITICS (14/1)	8 10 7	C Llewellyn	Romany King	Laura's Beau	40	9 06.30
1993	Race Void - false start						
1994	MIINNEHOMA (16/1)	11 10 8	R Dunwoody	Just So	Moorcroft Boy	36	10 18.80
1995	ROYAL ATHLETE (40/1)	12 10 6	J Titley	Party Politics	Over The Deel	35	9 04.00
1996	ROUGH QUEST (7/1)	10 10 7	M Fitzgerald	Encore Un Peu	Superior Finish	27	9 00.80
1997	LORD GYLLENE (14/1)	9 10 0	A Dobbin	Suny Bay	Camelot Knight	36	9 05.80
1998	EARTH SUMMIT (7/1)	10 10 5	C Llewellyn	Suny Bay	Samlee	37	10 51.40
1999	BOBBYJO (10/1)	9 10 0	P Carberry	Blue Charm	Call It A Day	32	9 14.00
2000	PAPILLON (10/1)	9 10 12	R Walsh	Mely Moss	Niki Dee	40	9 09.70
2001	RED MARAUDER (33/1)	11 10 11	R Guest	Smarty	Blowing Wind	40	11 00.10
2002	BINDAREE (20/1)	8 10 4	J Culloty	What's Up Boys	Blowing Wind	40	9 09.00
2003	MONTY'S PASS (16/1)	10 10 7	B J Geraghty	Supreme Glory	Amberleigh House	40	9 09.70
2004	AMBERLEIGH HOUSE (16/1)	12 10 10	G Lee	Clan Royal	Lord Atterbury	39	9 20.30
2005	HEDGEHUNTER (7/1)	9 11 1	R Walsh	Royal Auclair	Simply Gifted	40	9 20.80
2006	NUMBERSIXVALVERDE (11/1)	10 10 8	N Madden	Hedgehunter	Clan Royal	40	9 41.00
2007	SILVER BIRCH (33/1)	10 10 6	R M Power	McKelvey	Slim Pickings	40	9 13.60
2008	COMPLY OR DIE (7/1)	9 10 9	T Murphy	King Johns Castle	Snowy Morning	40	9 16.60
2009	MON MOME (100/1)	9 11 0	L Treadwell	Comply Or Die	My Will	40	9 32.30
2010	DON'T PUSH IT (10/1)	10 11 5	A P McCoy	Black Apalachi	State Of Play	40	9 04.60
2011	BALLABRIGGS (14/1)	10 11 0	J Maguire	Oscar Time	Don't Push It	40	9 01.20
2012	NEPTUNE COLLONGES (33/1)	11 11 6	D Jacob	Sunnyhillboy	Seabass	40	9 05.10
2013	AURORAS ENCORE (66/1)	11 11 0	R Mania	Cappa Bleu	Teaforthree	40	9 12.00

WINNERS OF GREAT RACES

LINCOLN HANDICAP
Doncaster-1m

2004	**BABODANA** 4-9-10	24
2005	**STREAM OF GOLD** 4-9-10	22
*2006	**BLYTHE KNIGHT** 6-8-10	30
*2007	**VERY WISE** 5-8-11	20
2008	**SMOKEY OAKEY** 4-8-9	21
2009	**EXPRESSO STAR** 4-8-12	20
2010	**PENITENT** 4-9-2	21
2011	**SWEET LIGHTNING** 6-9-4	21
2012	**BRAE HILL** 6-9-1	22
2013	**LEVITATE** 5-8-4	22

*Run at Redcar
*Run at Newcastle

GREENHAM STAKES (3y)
Newbury-7f

2004	**SALFORD CITY** 9-0	10
2005	**INDESATCHEL** 9-0	9
2006	**RED CLUBS** 9-0	5
2007	**MAJOR CADEAUX** 9-0	6
2008	**PACO BOY** 9-0	8
2009	**VOCALISED** 9-0	8
2010	**DICK TURPIN** 9-0	5
2011	**FRANKEL** 9-0	6
2012	**CASPAR NETSCHER** 9-0	5
2013	**OLYMPIC GLORY** 9-0	5

EUROPEAN FREE HANDICAP (3y)
Newmarket-7f

2004	**BRUNEL** 8-13	11
2005	**KAMAKIRI** 8-10	8
2006	**MISU BOND** 8-13	8
2007	**PRIME DEFENDER** 9-5	7
2008	**STIMULATION** 9-3	11
2009	**OUQBA** 8-9	7
2010	**RED JAZZ** 9-6	7
2011	**PAUSANIAS** 8-12	6
2012	**TELWAAR** 8-11	7
2013	**GARSWOOD** 9-0	10

CRAVEN STAKES (3y)
Newmarket-1m

2004	**HAAFHD** 8-9	5
2005	**DEMOCRATIC DEFICIT** 8-12	8
2006	**KILLYBEGS** 8-12	9
2007	**ADAGIO** 8-12	8
2008	**TWICE OVER** 8-12	10
2009	**DELEGATOR** 8-12	7
2010	**ELUSIVE PIMPERNEL** 8-12	9
2011	**NATIVE KHAN** 8-12	6
2012	**TRUMPET MAJOR** 9-1	12
2013	**TORONADO** 9-1	4

JOCKEY CLUB STAKES
Newmarket-1m 4f

2004	**GAMUT** 5-8-9	7
2005	**ALKAASED** 5-8-9	5
2006	**SHIROCCO** 5-9-3	7
2007	**SIXTIES ICON** 4-9-3	5
2008	**GETAWAY** 5-9-1	10
2009	**BRONZE CANNON** 4-8-12	3

2010	**JUKEBOX JURY** 4-9-3	5
2011	**DANDINO** 4-8-11	6
2012	**AL KAZEEM** 4-8-12	8
2013	**UNIVERSAL** 4-8-12	4

SANDOWN MILE
Sandown-1m

2004	**HURRICANE ALAN** 4-9-0	10
2005	**HURRICANE ALAN** 5-9-0	8
2006	**ROB ROY** 4-9-0	8
2007	**JEREMY** 4-9-0	9
2008	**MAJOR CADEAUX** 4-9-0	8
2009	**PACO BOY** 4-9-6	7
2010	**PACO BOY** 5-9-0	9
2011	**DICK TURPIN** 4-9-0	5
2012	**PENITENT** 6-9-0	6
2013	**TRUMPET MAJOR** 4-9-0	7

CHESTER VASE (3y)
Chester-1m 4f 66yds

2004	**RED LANCER** 8-10	6
2005	**HATTAN** 8-10	5
2006	**PAPAL BULL** 8-12	5
2007	**SOLDIER OF FORTUNE** 9-2	4
2008	**DOCTOR FREMANTLE** 8-12	8
2009	**GOLDEN SWORD** 8-12	8
2010	**TED SPREAD** 8-12	7
2011	**TREASURE BEACH** 8-12	5
2012	**MICKDAAM** 8-12	5
2013	**RULER OF THE WORLD** 8-12	4

CHESTER CUP
Chester-2m 2f 147yds

2004	**ANAK PEKAN** 4-8-2	17
2005	**ANAK PEKAN** 5-9-6	17
2006	**ADMIRAL** 5-8-1	17
2007	**GREENWICH MEANTIME** 7-9-2	17
2008	**BULWARK** 6-9-4	17
2009	**DARAAHEM** 4-9-0	17
2010	**MAMLOOK** 6-8-12	17
2011	**OVERTURN** 7-8-13	17
2012	**ILE DE RE** 6-8-11	16
2013	**ADDRESS UNKNOWN** 6-9-0	17

OAKS TRIAL (3y fillies)
Lingfield-1m 3f 106yds

2004	**BARAKA** 8-8	5
2005	**CASSYDORA** 8-10	6
2006	**SINDIRANA** 8-10	10
2007	**KAYAH** 8-12	7
2008	**MIRACLE SEEKER** 8-12	6
2009	**MIDDAY** 8-12	5
2010	**DYNA WALTZ** 8-12	9
2011	**ZAIN AL BOLDAN** 8-12	9
*2012	**VOW** 8-12	8
2013	**SECRET GESTURE** 8-12	7

*Run over 1m4f on Polytrack

DERBY TRIAL (3y)
Lingfield-1m 3f 106yds

2004	**PERCUSSIONIST** 8-7	4
2005	**KONG** 8-10	6
2006	**LINDA'S LAD** 9-3	5
2007	**AQALEEM** 8-12	7

2008	**ALESSANDRO VOLTA** 8-12	5
2009	**AGE OF AQUARIUS** 8-12	5
2010	**BULLET TRAIN** 8-12	7
2011	**DORDOGNE** 8-12	6
*2012	**MAIN SEQUENCE** 8-12	8
2013	**NEVIS** 8-12	4

*Run over 1m4f on Polytrack

MUSIDORA STAKES (3y fillies)
York-1m 2f 85yds

2004	**PUNCTILIOUS** 8-8	6
2005	**SECRET HISTORY** 8-10	6
2006	**SHORT SKIRT** 8-12	6
2007	**PASSAGE OF TIME** 9-1	5
2008	**LUSH LASHES** 8-12	8
2009	**SARISKA** 8-12	6
2010	**AVIATE** 8-12	8
2011	**JOVIALITY** 8-12	5
2012	**THE FUGUE** 8-12	6
2013	**LIBER NAUTICUS** 8-12	6

DANTE STAKES (3y)
York-1m 2f 88yds

2004	**NORTH LIGHT** 8-11	10
2005	**MOTIVATOR** 8-11	6
2006	**SEPTIMUS** 9-0	6
2007	**AUTHORIZED** 9-0	6
2008	**TARTAN BEARER** 9-0	6
2009	**BLACK BEAR ISLAND** 9-0	10
2010	**CAPE BLANCO** 9-0	5
2011	**CARLTON HOUSE** 9-0	6
2012	**BONFIRE** 9-0	7
2013	**LIBERTARIAN** 9-0	8

MIDDLETON STAKES
(fillies and mares)
York-1m 2f 88yds

2004	**CRIMSON PALACE** 5-8-9	6
2005	**ALL TOO BEAUTIFUL** 4-8-9	5
2006	**STRAWBERRY DALE** 4-8-12	7
2007	**TOPATOO** 5-8-12	7
2008	**PROMISING LEAD** 4-8-12	5
2009	**CRYSTAL CAPELLA** 4-9-2	5
2010	**SARISKA** 4-8-12	4
2011	**MIDDAY** 5-9-3	8
2012	**IZZI TOP** 4-8-12	9
2013	**DALKALA** 4-9-0	8

YORKSHIRE CUP
York-1m 6f (1m 5f 194yds before 2007)

2004	**MILLENARY** 7-8-13	10
2005	**FRANKLINS GARDENS** 5-8-10	9
2006	**PERCUSSIONIST** 5-8-12	7
2007	**SERGEANT CECIL** 8-9-3	10
2008	**GEORDIELAND** 7-8-12	5
2009	**ASK** 6-8-13	8
2010	**MANIFEST** 4-8-12	5
2011	**DUNCAN** 6-9-2	8
2012	**RED CADEAUX** 6-9-0	8
2013	**GLEN'S DIAMOND** 5-9-0	8

DUKE OF YORK STAKES
York-6f

2004	**MONSIEUR BOND** 4-9-2	15
2005	**THE KIDDYKID** 5-9-2	11
2006	**STEENBERG** 7-9-2	16
2007	**AMADEUS WOLF** 4-9-2	17
2008	**ASSERTIVE** 5-9-7	17
2009	**UTMOST RESPECT** 5-9-7	16

2010	**PRIME DEFENDER** 6-9-7	12
2011	**DELEGATOR** 5-9-7	14
2012	**TIDDLIWINKS** 6-9-7	13
2013	**SOCIETY ROCK** 6-9-13	17

LOCKINGE STAKES
Newbury-1m

2004	**RUSSIAN RHYTHM** 4-8-11	15
2005	**RAKTI** 6-9-0	8
2006	**PEERESS** 5-8-11	9
2007	**RED EVIE** 4-8-11	8
2008	**CREACHADOIR** 4-9-0	11
2009	**VIRTUAL** 4-9-0	11
2010	**PACO BOY** 5-9-0	9
2011	**CANFORD CLIFFS** 4-9-0	7
2012	**FRANKEL** 4-9-0	6
2013	**FARHH** 5-9-0	12

HENRY II STAKES
Sandown-2m 78yds

2004	**PAPINEAU** 4-8-12	9
2005	**FIGHT YOUR CORNER** 6-9-0	16
2006	**TUNGSTEN STRIKE** 5-9-2	7
2007	**ALLEGRETTO** 4-9-0	7
2008	**FINALMENTE** 6-9-2	8
2009	**GEORDIELAND** 8-9-2	7
2010	**AKMAL** 4-9-0	9
2011	**BLUE BAJAN** 9-9-2	8
2012	**OPINION POLL** 6-9-4	10
2013	**GLOOMY SUNDAY** 4-8-11	10

TEMPLE STAKES
Haydock-5f
(Run at Sandown before 2008)

*2004	**NIGHT PROSPECTOR** 4-9-4	12
2005	**CELTIC MILL** 7-9-4	13
2006	**REVERENCE** 4-9-4	12
2007	**SIERRA VISTA** 7-9-1	8
2008	**FLEETING SPIRIT** 3-8-11	12
2009	**LOOK BUSY** 4-9-1	8
2010	**KINGSGATE NATIVE** 5-9-4	9
2011	**SOLE POWER** 4-9-4	12
2012	**BATED BREATH** 5-9-4	12
2013	**KINGSGATE NATIVE** 8-9-4	10

*Run at Epsom

BRIGADIER GERARD STAKES
Sandown-1m 2f 7yds

2004	**BANDARI** 5-8-10	9
2005	**NEW MORNING** 4-8-7	5
2006	**NOTNOWCATO** 4-9-3	5
2007	**TAKE A BOW** 6-9-0	5
2008	**SMOKEY OAKEY** 4-9-0	14
2009	**CIMA DE TRIOMPHE** 4-9-0	6
2010	**STOTSFOLD** 7-9-0	8
2011	**WORKFORCE** 4-9-7	8
2012	**CARLTON HOUSE** 4-9-0	6
2013	**MUKHADRAM** 4-9-0	6

CORONATION CUP
Epsom-1m 4f 10yds

2004	**WARRSAN** 6-9-0	1
2005	**YEATS** 4-9-0	6
2006	**SHIROCCO** 5-9-0	6
2007	**SCORPION** 5-9-0	6
2008	**SOLDIER OF FORTUNE** 4-9-0	1
2009	**ASK** 6-9-0	6
2010	**FAME AND GLORY** 4-9-0	6
2011	**ST NICHOLAS ABBEY** 4-9-0	8

2012	**ST NICHOLAS ABBEY** 5-9-0	6
2013	**ST NICHOLAS ABBEY** 6-9-0	5

SPRINT TROPHY HANDICAP (3y)
York-6f

2004	**TWO STEP KID** 8-9	20
2005	**TAX FREE** 8-9	20
2006	**PRINCE TAMINO** 8-13	18
2007	ABANDONED	
2008	**BRAVE PROSPECTOR** 9-0	19
2009	**SWISS DIVA** 9-1	20
2010	**VICTOIRE DE LYPHAR** 8-7	20
2011	**LEXI'S HERO** 8-11	20
2012	**SHOLAAN** 8-9	17
2013	**BODY AND SOUL** 8-11	19

QUEEN ANNE STAKES
Ascot-1m (st)

2004	**REFUSE TO BEND** 4-9-0	16
*2005	**VALIXIR** 4-9-0	7
2006	**AD VALOREM** 4-9-0	7
2007	**RAMONTI** 5-9-0	8
2008	**HARADASUN** 5-9-0	11
2009	**PACO BOY** 4-9-0	9
2010	**GOLDIKOVA** 5-8-11	10
2011	**CANFORD CLIFFS** 4-9-0	7
2012	**FRANKEL** 4-9-0	11
2013	**DECLARATION OF WAR** 4-9-0	13

*Run at York

PRINCE OF WALES'S STAKES
Ascot-1m 2f

2004	**RAKTI** 5-9-0	10
*2005	**AZAMOUR** 4-9-0	8
2006	**OUIJA BOARD** 5-8-11	7
2007	**MANDURO** 5-9-0	6
2008	**DUKE OF MARMALADE** 4-9-0	12
2009	**VISION D'ETAT** 4-9-0	8
2010	**BYWORD** 4-9-0	12
2011	**REWILDING** 4-9-0	7
2012	**SO YOU THINK** 6-9-0	11
2013	**AL KAZEEM** 5-9-0	11

*Run at York

ST JAMES'S PALACE STAKES (3y)
Ascot-1m (rnd)

2004	**AZAMOUR** 9-0	11
*2005	**SHAMARDAL** 9-0	8
2006	**ARAAFA** 9-0	11
2007	**EXCELLENT ART** 9-0	8
2008	**HENRYTHENAVIGATOR** 9-0	8
2009	**MASTERCRAFTSMAN** 9-0	10
2010	**CANFORD CLIFFS** 9-0	9
2011	**FRANKEL** 9-0	9
2012	**MOST IMPROVED** 9-0	16
2013	**DAWN APPROACH** 9-0	9

*Run at York

COVENTRY STAKES (2y)
Ascot-6f

2004	**ICEMAN** 8-12	13
*2005	**RED CLUBS** 8-12	14
2006	**HELLVELYN** 9-1	21
2007	**HENRYTHENAVIGATOR** 9-1	20
2008	**ART CONNOISSEUR** 9-1	18
2009	**CANFORD CLIFFS** 9-1	13
2010	**STRONG SUIT** 9-1	13
2011	**POWER** 9-1	23

2012	**DAWN APPROACH** 9-1	22
2013	**WAR COMMAND** 9-1	15

*Run at York

KING EDWARD VII STAKES (3y)
Ascot-1m 4f

2004	**FIVE DYNASTIES** 8-11	5
*2005	**PLEA BARGAIN** 8-11	5
2006	**PAPAL BULL** 8-12	9
2007	**BOSCOBEL** 8-12	9
2008	**CAMPANOLOGIST** 8-12	9
2009	**FATHER TIME** 8-12	12
2010	**MONTEROSSO** 8-12	8
2011	**NATHANIEL** 8-12	10
2012	**THOMAS CHIPPENDALE** 8-12	5
2013	**HILLSTAR** 8-12	8

*Run at York

JERSEY STAKES (3y)
Ascot-7f

2004	**KHELEYF** 8-10	15
*2005	**PROCLAMATION** 8-13	21
2006	**JEREMY** 9-1	14
2007	**TARIQ** 9-1	15
2008	**AQLAAM** 9-1	16
2009	**OUQBA** 9-1	16
2010	**RAINFALL** 8-12	13
2011	**STRONG SUIT** 9-6	9
2012	**ISHVANA** 8-12	22
2013	**GALE FORCE TEN** 9-1	21

*Run at York

DUKE OF CAMBRIDGE STAKES
(fillies & mares)
Ascot-1m (st)
(Windsor Forest Stakes before 2013)

2004	**FAVOURABLE TERMS** 4-8-12	10
*2005	**PEERESS** 4-8-9	8
2006	**SOVIET SONG** 6-8-12	10
2007	**NANNINA** 4-8-12	9
2008	**SABANA PERDIDA** 5-8-12	13
2009	**SPACIOUS** 4-8-12	9
2010	**STRAWBERRYDAIQUIRI** 4-8-12	10
2011	**LOLLY FOR DOLLY** 4-8-12	13
2012	**JOVIALITY** 4-8-12	13
2013	**DUNTLE** 4-8-12	9

*Run at York

QUEEN MARY STAKES (2y fillies)
Ascot-5f

2004	**DAMSON** 8-10	17
*2005	**FLASHY WINGS** 8-10	17
2006	**GILDED** 8-12	15
2007	**ELLETELLE** 8-12	21
2008	**LANGS LASH** 8-12	17
2009	**JEALOUS AGAIN** 8-12	13
2010	**MAQAASID** 8-12	18
2011	**BEST TERMS** 8-12	14
2012	**CEILING KITTY** 8-12	27
2013	**RIZEENA** 8-12	23

*Run at York

CORONATION STAKES (3y fillies)
Ascot-1m (rnd)

2004	**ATTRACTION** 9-0	11
*2005	**MAIDS CAUSEWAY** 9-0	10
2006	**NANNINA** 9-0	15
2007	**INDIAN INK** 9-0	13

2008	**LUSH LASHES** 9-0	11
2009	**GHANAATI** 9-0	10
2010	**LILLIE LANGTRY** 9-0	13
2011	**IMMORTAL VERSE** 9-0	12
2012	**FALLEN FOR YOU** 9-0	10
2013	**SKY LANTERN** 9-0	17

*Run at York

ROYAL HUNT CUP
Ascot-1m (st)

2004	**MINE** 6-9-5	31
*2005	**NEW SEEKER** 5-9-0	22
2006	**CESARE** 5-8-8	30
2007	**ROYAL OATH** 4-9-0	26
2008	**MR AVIATOR** 4-9-5	29
2009	**FORGOTTEN VOICE** 4-9-1	25
2010	**INVISIBLE MAN** 4-8-9	29
2011	**JULIENAS** 4-8-8	28
2012	**PRINCE OF JOHANNE** 6-9-3	30
2013	**BELGIAN BILL** 5-8-11	28

*Run at York

QUEEN'S VASE (3y)
Ascot-2m

2004	**DUKE OF VENICE** 8-11	10
*2005	**MELROSE AVENUE** 8-11	10
2006	**SOAPY DANGER** 9-1	11
2007	**MAHLER** 9-1	15
2008	**PATKAI** 9-1	12
2009	**HOLBERG** 9-1	14
2010	**MIKHAIL GLINKA** 9-1	12
2011	**NAMIBIAN** 9-1	11
2012	**ESTIMATE** 8-12	10
2013	**LEADING LIGHT** 9-4	15

*Run at York

DIAMOND JUBILEE STAKES
Ascot-6f
(Run as Golden Jubilee Stakes before 2012)

2004	**FAYR JAG** 5-9-4	14
*2005	**CAPE OF GOOD HOPE** 7-9-4	15
2006	**LES ARCS** 6-9-4	18
2007	**SOLDIER'S TALE** 6-9-4	21
2008	**KINGSGATE NATIVE** 3-8-11	17
2009	**ART CONNOISSEUR** 3-8-11	14
2010	**STARSPANGLEDBANNER** 4-9-4	24
2011	**SOCIETY ROCK** 4-9-4	16
2012	**BLACK CAVIAR** 6-9-1	14
2013	**LETHAL FORCE** 4-9-4	18

*Run at York

NORFOLK STAKES (2y)
Ascot-5f

2004	**BLUE DAKOTA** 8-12	9
*2005	**MASTA PLASTA** 8-12	12
2006	**DUTCH ART** 9-1	11
2007	**WINKER WATSON** 9-1	11
2008	**SOUTH CENTRAL** 9-1	11
2009	**RADIOHEAD** 9-1	11
2010	**APPROVE** 9-1	12
2011	**BAPAK CHINTA** 9-1	15
2012	**RECKLESS ABANDON** 9-1	11
2013	**NO NAY NEVER** 9-1	14

*Run at York

GOLD CUP
Ascot-2m 4f

2004	**PAPINEAU** 4-9-0	13
*2005	**WESTERNER** 6-9-2	17

2006	**YEATS** 5-9-2	12
2007	**YEATS** 6-9-2	14
2008	**YEATS** 7-9-2	10
2009	**YEATS** 8-9-2	9
2010	**RITE OF PASSAGE** 6-9-2	12
2011	**FAME AND GLORY** 5-9-2	15
2012	**COLOUR VISION** 4-9-0	9
2013	**ESTIMATE** 4-8-11	14

*Run at York

RIBBLESDALE STAKES (3y fillies)
Ascot-1m 4f

2004	**PUNCTILIOUS** 8-11	9
*2005	**THAKAFAAT** 8-11	9
2006	**MONT ETOILE** 8-12	11
2007	**SILKWOOD** 8-12	12
2008	**MICHITA** 8-12	9
2009	**FLYING CLOUD** 8-12	10
2010	**HIBAAYEB** 8-12	11
2011	**BANIMPIRE** 8-12	12
2012	**PRINCESS HIGHWAY** 8-12	14
2013	**RIPOSTE** 8-12	9

*Run at York

HARDWICKE STAKES
Ascot-1m 4f

2004	**DOYEN** 4-8-9	6
*2005	**BANDARI** 6-8-9	6
2006	**MARAAHEL** 5-9-0	8
2007	**MARAAHEL** 6-9-0	7
2008	**MACARTHUR** 4-9-0	9
2009	**BRONZE CANNON** 4-9-3	9
2010	**HARBINGER** 4-9-0	11
2011	**AWAIT THE DAWN** 4-9-0	9
2012	**SEA MOON** 4-9-0	12
2013	**THOMAS CHIPPENDALE** 4-9-0	8

*Run at York

WOKINGHAM STAKES
Ascot-6f

2004	**LAFI** 5-8-13	29
*2005	**IFFRAAJ** 4-9-6	17
2006	**BALTIC KING** 6-9-10	28
2007	**DARK MISSILE** 4-8-6	26
2008	**BIG TIMER** 4-9-2	27
2009	**HIGH STANDING** 4-8-12	26
2010	**LADDIES POKER TWO** 5-8-11	27
2011	**DEACON BLUES** 4-8-13	25
2012	**DANDY BOY** 6-9-8	28
2013	**YORK GLORY** 5-9-2	26

*Run at York

KING'S STAND STAKES
Ascot-5f

2004	**THE TATLING** 7-9-2	19
*2005	**CHINEUR** 4-9-2	16
2006	**TAKEOVER TARGET** 7-9-7	28
2007	**MISS ANDRETTI** 6-9-1	20
2008	**EQUIANO** 3-8-12	13
2009	**SCENIC BLAST** 5-9-4	15
2010	**EQUIANO** 5-9-4	12
2011	**PROHIBIT** 6-9-4	19
2012	**LITTLE BRIDGE** 6-9-4	22
2013	**SOLE POWER** 6-9-4	19

*Run at York

NORTHUMBERLAND PLATE
Newcastle-2m 19yds
2004	**MIRJAN** 8-8-3	19
2005	**SERGEANT CECIL** 6-8-8	20
2006	**TOLDO** 4-8-2	20
2007	**JUNIPER GIRL** 4-8-11	20
2008	**ARC BLEU** 7-8-2	18
2009	**SOM TALA** 4-8-8	17
2010	**OVERTURN** 6-8-7	19
2011	**TOMINATOR** 4-8-5	19
2012	**ILE DE RE** 6-9-3	16
2013	**TOMINATOR** 6-9-10	18

ECLIPSE STAKES
Sandown-1m 2f 7yds
2004	**REFUSE TO BEND** 4-9-7	12
2005	**ORATORIO** 3-8-10	7
2006	**DAVID JUNIOR** 4-9-7	9
2007	**NOTNOWCATO** 5-9-7	8
2008	**MOUNT NELSON** 4-9-7	8
2009	**SEA THE STARS** 3-8-10	10
2010	**TWICE OVER** 5-9-7	5
2011	**SO YOU THINK** 5-9-7	5
2012	**NATHANIEL** 4-9-7	9
2013	**AL KAZEEM** 5-9-7	7

LANCASHIRE OAKS (fillies and mares)
Haydock-1m 3f 200yds
2004	**PONGEE** 4-9-3	8
2005	**PLAYFUL ACT** 3-8-5	8
2006	**ALLEGRETTO** 3-8-6	8
2007	**TURBO LINN** 4-9-5	12
2008	**ANNA PAVLOVA** 5-9-8	9
2009	**BARSHIBA** 5-9-5	8
2010	**BARSHIBA** 6-9-5	10
2011	**GERTRUDE BELL** 4-9-5	7
2012	**GREAT HEAVENS** 3-8-6	9
2013	**EMIRATES QUEEN** 4-9-5	8
Run at Newmarket

DUCHESS OF CAMBRIDGE STAKES (2y fillies)
Newmarket-6f
(Prior to 2013 Cherry Hinton Stakes)
2004	**JEWEL IN THE SAND** 8-9	10
2005	**DONNA BLINI** 8-9	8
2006	**SANDER CAMILLO** 8-12	10
2007	**YOU'RESOTHRILLING** 8-12	14
2008	**PLEASE SING** 8-12	8
2009	**MISHEER** 8-12	10
2010	**MEMORY** 8-12	7
2011	**GAMILATI** 8-12	11
2012	**SENDMYLOVETOROSE** 8-12	10
2013	**LUCKY KRISTALE** 8-12	8

BUNBURY CUP
(Run as 32Red Trophy in 2010)
Newmarket-7f
2004	**MATERIAL WITNESS** 7-9-3	19
2005	**MINE** 7-9-9	18
2006	**MINE** 8-9-10	19
2007	**GIGANTICUS** 4-8-8	18
2008	**LITTLE WHITE LIE** 4-9-0	18
2009	**PLUM PUDDING** 6-9-10	19
2010	**ST MORITZ** 4-9-1	19
2011	**BRAE HILL** 5-9-1	20
2012	**BONNIE BRAE** 5-9-9	15
2013	**FIELD OF DREAM** 6-9-7	19

PRINCESS OF WALES'S STAKES
Newmarket-1m 4f
2004	**BANDARI** 5-9-2	8
2005	**GAMUT** 6-9-2	5
2006	**SOAPY DANGER** 3-8-3	4
2007	**PAPAL BULL** 4-9-2	12
2008	**LUCARNO** 4-9-7	6
2009	**DOCTOR FREMANTLE** 4-9-2	9
2010	**SANS FRONTIERES** 4-9-2	8
2011	**CRYSTAL CAPELLA** 6-8-13	8
2012	**FIORENTE** 4-9-2	7
2013	**AL KAZEEM** 4-9-5	6

JULY STAKES (2y)
Newmarket-6f
2004	**CAPTAIN HURRICANE** 8-10	7
2005	**IVAN DENISOVICH** 8-10	11
2006	**STRATEGIC PRINCE** 8-12	9
2007	**WINKER WATSON** 9-1	13
2008	**CLASSIC BLADE** 8-12	7
2009	**ARCANO** 8-12	11
2010	**LIBRANNO** 8-12	5
2011	**FREDERICK ENGELS** 8-12	7
2012	**ALHEBAYEB** 8-12	7
2013	**ANJAAL** 8-12	11

FALMOUTH STAKES (fillies & mares)
Newmarket-1m
2004	**SOVIET SONG** 4-9-1	7
2005	**SOVIET SONG** 5-9-1	7
2006	**RAJEEM** 3-8-10	7
2007	**SIMPLY PERFECT** 3-8-10	7
2008	**NAHOODH** 3-8-10	11
2009	**GOLDIKOVA** 4-9-5	8
2010	**MUSIC SHOW** 3-8-10	8
2011	**TIMEPIECE** 4-9-5	11
2012	**GIOFRA** 4-9-5	10
2013	**ELUSIVE KATE** 4-9-5	4

SUPERLATIVE STAKES (2y)
Newmarket-7f
2004	**DUBAWI** 8-11	12
2005	**HORATIO NELSON** 8-11	11
2006	**HALICARNASSUS** 8-11	7
2007	**HATTA FORT** 9-0	10
2008	**FIRTH OF FIFTH** 9-0	9
2009	**SILVER GRECIAN** 9-0	8
2010	**KING TORUS** 9-0	6
2011	**RED DUKE** 9-0	11
2012	**OLYMPIC GLORY** 9-0	9
2013	**GOOD OLD BOY LUKEY** 9-0	8

JULY CUP
Newmarket-6f
2004	**FRIZZANTE** 5-9-2	20
2005	**PASTORAL PURSUITS** 4-9-5	19
2006	**LES ARCS** 6-9-5	15
2007	**SAKHEE'S SECRET** 3-8-13	18
2008	**MARCHAND D'OR** 5-9-5	13
2009	**FLEETING SPIRIT** 4-9-2	13
2010	**STARSPANGLEDBANNER** 4-9-5	14
2011	**DREAM AHEAD** 3-8-13	16
2012	**MAYSON** 4-9-5	12
2013	**LETHAL FORCE** 4-9-5	11

WEATHERBYS SUPER SPRINT (2y)

Newbury-5f 34 yds

2004	SIENA GOLD 8-1	24
2005	LADY LIVIUS 8-5	25
2006	ELHAMRI 9-4	23
2007	ABANDONED	
2008	JARGELLE 8-6	23
2009	MONSIEUR CHEVALIER 8-12	20
2010	TEMPLE MEADS 8-6	24
2011	CHARLES THE GREAT 8-11	25
2012	BODY AND SOUL 7-12	22
2013	PENIAPHOBIA 8-8	24

SUMMER MILE

Ascot-1m (rnd)

2007	CESARE 6-9-1	9
2008	ARCHIPENKO 4-9-6	7
2009	AQLAAM 4-9-1	7
2010	PREMIO LOCO 6-9-1	8
2011	DICK TURPIN 4-9-4	5
2012	FANUNALTER 6-9-1	8
2013	ALJAMAAHEER 4-9-1	11

PRINCESS MARGARET STAKES (2y fillies)

Ascot-6f

2004	SOAR 8-9	6
*2005	MIXED BLESSING 8-9	12
2006	SCARLET RUNNER 8-12	10
2007	VISIT 8-12	13
2008	AFRICAN SKIES 8-12	16
2009	LADY OF THE DESERT 8-12	9
2010	SORAAYA 8-12	11
2011	ANGELS WILL FALL 8-12	7
2012	MAUREEN 8-12	6
2013	PRINCESS NOOR 8-12	10

*Run at Newbury

LENNOX STAKES

Goodwood-7f

2004	BYRON 3-8-7	8
2005	COURT MASTERPIECE 5-9-0	14
2006	IFFRAAJ 5-9-4	10
2007	TARIQ 3-8-9	13
2008	PACO BOY 3-8-9	9
2009	FINJAAN 3-8-9	8
2010	LORD SHANAKILL 4-9-2	12
2011	STRONG SUIT 3-8-9	9
2012	CHACHAMAIDEE 5-8-13	7
2013	GARSWOOD 3-8-9	10

STEWARDS' CUP

Goodwood-6f

2004	PIVOTAL POINT 4-8-11	28
2005	GIFT HORSE 5-9-7	27
2006	BORDERLESCOTT 4-9-5	27
2007	ZIDANE 5-9-1	27
2008	CONQUEST 4-8-9	27
2009	GENKI 5-9-1	26
2010	EVENS AND ODDS 6-8-10	28
2011	HOOF IT 4-10-0	27
2012	HAWKEYETHENOO 6-9-9	27
2013	REX IMPERATOR 4-9-4	27

GORDON STAKES (3y)

Goodwood-1m 4f

2004	MARAAHEL 8-10	8
2005	THE GEEZER 8-10	5

2006	SIXTIES ICON 9-0	7
2007	YELLOWSTONE 9-0	9
2008	CONDUIT 9-0	6
2009	HARBINGER 9-0	9
2010	REBEL SOLDIER 9-0	10
2011	NAMIBIAN 9-3	10
2012	NOBLE MISSION 9-0	7
2013	CAP O'RUSHES 9-0	7

VINTAGE STAKES (2y)

Goodwood-7f

2004	SHAMARDAL 8-11	10
2005	SIR PERCY 8-11	7
2006	STRATEGIC PRINCE 9-3	10
2007	RIO DE LA PLATA 9-0	7
2008	ORIZABA 9-0	9
2009	XTENSION 9-0	10
2010	KING TORUS 9-3	7
2011	CHANDLERY 9-0	7
2012	OLYMPIC GLORY 9-3	10
2013	TOORMORE 9-0	12

SUSSEX STAKES

Goodwood-1m

2004	SOVIET SONG 4-9-4	11
2005	PROCLAMATION 3-8-13	12
2006	COURT MASTERPIECE 6-9-7	7
2007	RAMONTI 5-9-7	8
2008	HENRYTHENAVIGATOR 3-8-13	6
2009	RIP VAN WINKLE 3-8-13	7
2010	CANFORD CLIFFS 3-8-13	7
2011	FRANKEL 3-8-13	4
2012	FRANKEL 4-9-7	4
2013	TORONADO 3-8-13	7

RICHMOND STAKES (2y)

Goodwood-6f

2004	MONTGOMERY'S ARCH 8-11	8
2005	ALWAYS HOPEFUL 8-11	6
2006	HAMOODY 9-0	7
2007	STRIKE THE DEAL 9-0	9
2008	PROLIFIC 9-0	12
2009	DICK TURPIN 9-0	9
2010	LIBRANNO 9-3	6
2011	HARBOUR WATCH 9-0	10
2012	HEAVY METAL 9-0	8
2013	SAAYERR 9-0	10

KING GEORGE STAKES

Goodwood-5f

2004	RINGMOOR DOWN 5-8-11	13
2005	FIRE UP THE BAND 6-9-0	12
2006	LA CUCARACHA 5-8-11	18
2007	MOORHOUSE LAD 4-9-0	12
2008	ENTICING 4-8-11	12
2009	KINGSGATE NATIVE 4-9-0	15
2010	BORDERLESCOTT 8-9-0	15
2011	MASAMAH 5-9-0	17
2012	ORTENSIA 7-9-5	17
2013	MOVIESTA 3-8-12	14

GOODWOOD CUP

Goodwood-2m

2004	DARASIM 6-9-4	1
2005	DISTINCTION 6-9-5	1
2006	YEATS 5-9-10	1
2007	ALLEGRETTO 4-9-5	1
2008	YEATS 7-9-12	1
2009	SCHIAPARELLI 6-9-7	1

2010	**ILLUSTRIOUS BLUE** 7-9-7	10
2011	**OPINION POLL** 5-9-7	15
2012	**SADDLER'S ROCK** 4-9-7	14
2013	**BROWN PANTHER** 5-9-7	10

MOLECOMB STAKES (2y)
Goodwood-5f

2004	**TOURNEDOS** 8-12	13
2005	**STRIKE UP THE BAND** 9-1	15
2006	**ENTICING** 8-11	13
2007	**FLEETING SPIRIT** 8-11	16
2008	**FINJAAN** 9-0	11
2009	**MONSIEUR CHEVALIER** 9-0	11
2010	**ZEBEDEE** 9-0	12
2011	**REQUINTO** 9-0	13
2012	**BUNGLE INTHEJUNGLE** 9-0	10
2013	**BROWN SUGAR** 9-0	8

NASSAU STAKES (fillies and mares)
Goodwood-1m 1f 192yds

2004	**FAVOURABLE TERMS** 4-9-2	6
2005	**ALEXANDER GOLDRUN** 4-9-3	11
2006	**OUIJA BOARD** 5-9-5	7
2007	**PEEPING FAWN** 3-8-10	8
2008	**HALFWAY TO HEAVEN** 3-8-10	9
2009	**MIDDAY** 3-8-10	7
2010	**MIDDAY** 4-9-6	7
2011	**MIDDAY** 5-9-6	6
2012	**THE FUGUE** 3-8-11	8
2013	**WINSILI** 3-8-11	14

HUNGERFORD STAKES
Newbury-7f

2004	**CHIC** 4-8-11	13
2005	**SLEEPING INDIAN** 4-9-0	10
2006	**WELSH EMPEROR** 7-9-3	7
2007	**RED EVIE** 4-9-4	10
2008	**PACO BOY** 3-9-0	9
2009	**BALTHAZAAR'S GIFT** 6-9-3	9
2010	**SHAKESPEAREAN** 3-8-11	7
2011	**EXCELEBRATION** 3-8-13	9
2012	**LETHAL FORCE** 3-8-12	9
2013	**GREGORIAN** 4-9-3	5

GEOFFREY FREER STAKES
Newbury-1m 5f 61yds

2004	**MUBTAKER** 7-9-3	4
2005	**LOCHBUIE** 4-9-3	5
2006	**ADMIRAL'S CRUISE** 4-9-3	5
2007	**PAPAL BULL** 4-9-7	5
2008	**SIXTIES ICON** 5-9-5	10
2009	**KITE WOOD** 3-8-8	8
2010	**SANS FRONTIERES** 4-9-8	8
2011	**CENSUS** 3-8-6	10
2012	**MOUNT ATHOS** 5-9-4	6
2013	**ROYAL EMPIRE** 4-9-4	10

INTERNATIONAL STAKES
York-1m 2f 88yds

2004	**SULAMANI** 5-9-5	9
2005	**ELECTROCUTIONIST** 4-9-5	7
2006	**NOTNOWCATO** 4-9-5	7
2007	**AUTHORIZED** 3-8-11	7
2008	**DUKE OF MARMALADE** 4-9-5	9
2009	**SEA THE STARS** 3-8-11	9
2010	**RIP VAN WINKLE** 4-9-5	9
2011	**TWICE OVER** 6-9-5	5

| 2012 | **FRANKEL** 4-9-5 | 9 |
| 2013 | **DECLARATION OF WAR** 4-9-5 | 6 |
*Run at Newmarket over 1m 2f

GREAT VOLTIGEUR STAKES (3y)
York-1m 4f

2004	**RULE OF LAW** 8-9	7
2005	**HARD TOP** 8-9	6
2006	**YOUMZAIN** 8-12	10
2007	**LUCARNO** 8-12	9
*2008	**CENTENNIAL** 8-12	5
2009	**MONITOR CLOSELY** 8-12	7
2010	**REWILDING** 8-12	10
2011	**SEA MOON** 8-12	8
2012	**THOUGHT WORTHY** 8-12	6
2013	**TELESCOPE** 8-12	7
*Run at Goodwood

LOWTHER STAKES (2y fillies)
York-6f

2004	**SOAR** 9-0	8
2005	**FLASHY WINGS** 9-2	6
2006	**SILK BLOSSOM** 8-12	7
2007	**NAHOODH** 8-12	10
*2008	**INFAMOUS ANGEL** 8-12	10
2009	**LADY OF THE DESERT** 8-12	12
2010	**HOORAY** 8-12	8
2011	**BEST TERMS** 9-1	10
2012	**ROSDHU QUEEN** 8-12	11
2013	**LUCKY KRISTALE** 9-1	9
*Run at Newmarket (July)

YORKSHIRE OAKS (fillies and mares)
York-1m 4f

2004	**QUIFF** 3-8-8	8
2005	**PUNCTILIOUS** 4-9-4	11
2006	**ALEXANDROVA** 3-8-11	6
2007	**PEEPING FAWN** 3-8-11	7
*2008	**LUSH LASHES** 3-8-11	6
2009	**DAR RE MI** 4-9-7	6
2010	**MIDDAY** 4-9-7	8
2011	**BLUE BUNTING** 3-8-11	8
2012	**SHARETA** 4-9-7	6
2013	**THE FUGUE** 4-9-7	7
*Run at Newmarket

EBOR HANDICAP
York-1m 6f (1m 5f 194yds before 2007)

2004	**MEPHISTO** 5-9-4	19
2005	**SERGEANT CECIL** 6-8-12	20
2006	**MUDAWIN** 5-8-4	19
2007	**PURPLE MOON** 4-9-4	19
*2008	**ALL THE GOOD** 5-9-0	20
2009	**SESENTA** 5-8-8	19
2010	**DIRAR** 5-9-1	20
2011	**MOYENNE CORNICHE** 6-8-10	19
2012	**WILLING FOE** 5-9-2	19
2013	**TIGER CLIFF** 4-9-0	14
*Run as Newburgh Handicap at Newbury over 1m 5f 61yds

GIMCRACK STAKES (2y)
York-6f

2004	**TONY JAMES** 8-11	11
2005	**AMADEUS WOLF** 8-11	13
2006	**CONQUEST** 8-12	8
2007	**SIR GERRY** 8-12	8
*2008	**SHAWEEL** 8-12	12
2009	**SHOWCASING** 8-12	9
2010	**APPROVE** 9-1	11

2011	**CASPAR NETSCHER** 8-12	9
2012	**BLAINE** 8-12	8
2013	**ASTAIRE** 8-12	7

*Run at Newbury

NUNTHORPE STAKES
York-5f

2004	**BAHAMIAN PIRATE** 9-9-11	12
2005	**LA CUCARACHA** 4-9-8	16
2006	**REVERENCE** 5-9-11	14
2007	**KINGSGATE NATIVE** 2-8-1	16
*2008	**BORDERLESCOTT** 6-9-11	14
2009	**BORDERLESCOTT** 7-9-11	16
2010	**SOLE POWER** 3-9-9	12
2011	**MARGOT DID** 3-9-6	15
2012	**ORTENSIA** 7-9-8	19
2013	**JWALA** 4-9-8	17

*Run at Newmarket

LONSDALE CUP
York-2m 88y (1m 7f 198y before 2006)

2004	**FIRST CHARTER** 5 9-1	10
2005	**MILLENARY** 8 9-4	8
2006	**SERGEANT CECIL** 7 9-1	11
2007	**SEPTIMUS** 4 9-1	9
2008	ABANDONED	
2009	**ASKAR TAU** 4 9-1	5
2010	**OPINION POLL** 4 9-1	8
2011	**OPINION POLL** 5 9-4	10
2012	**TIMES UP** 6 9-1	11
2013	**AHZEEMAH** 4 9-3	7

PRESTIGE STAKES (2y fillies)
Goodwood-7f

2004	**DUBAI SURPRISE** 8-9	12
2005	**NANNINA** 8-9	9
2006	**SESMEN** 9-0	10
2007	**SENSE OF JOY** 9-0	7
2008	**FANTASIA** 9-0	10
2009	**SENT FROM HEAVEN** 9-0	8
2010	**THEYSKENS' THEORY** 9-0	7
2011	**REGAL REALM** 9-0	6
2012	**OLLIE OLGA** 9-0	8
2013	**AMAZING MARIA** 9-0	7

CELEBRATION MILE
Goodwood-1m

2004	**CHIC** 4-8-12	7
2005	**CHIC** 5-8-12	8
2006	**CARADAK** 5-9-1	6
2007	**ECHELON** 5-8-12	8
2008	**RAVEN'S PASS** 3-8-9	5
2009	**DELEGATOR** 3-8-9	7
2010	**POET'S VOICE** 3-8-9	4
2011	**DUBAWI GOLD** 3-8-9	7
2012	**PREMIO LOCO** 8-9-1	5
2013	**AFSARE** 6-9-1	8

SOLARIO STAKES (2y)
Sandown-7f 16yds

2004	**WINDSOR KNOT** 8-11	8
2005	**OPERA CAPE** 8-11	7
2006	**DRUMFIRE** 9-0	8
2007	**RAVEN'S PASS** 9-0	9
2008	**SRI PUTRA** 9-0	11
2009	**SHAKESPEAREAN** 9-0	8
2010	**NATIVE KHAN** 9-0	6
2011	**TALWAR** 9-0	4

2012	**FANTASTIC MOON** 9-0	7
2013	**KINGMAN** 9-0	4

SPRINT CUP
Haydock-6f

2004	**TANTE ROSE** 4-8-11	19
2005	**GOODRICKE** 3-8-12	17
2006	**REVERENCE** 5-9-3	11
2007	**RED CLUBS** 4-9-3	14
*2008	**AFRICAN ROSE** 3-8-12	15
2009	**REGAL PARADE** 5-9-3	14
2010	**MARKAB** 7-9-3	13
2011	**DREAM AHEAD** 3-9-1	16
2012	**SOCIETY ROCK** 5-9-3	13
2013	**GORDON LORD BYRON** 5-9-3	13

*Run at Doncaster

SEPTEMBER STAKES
Kempton-1m 4f Polytrack
(run on turf before 2006)

2004	**MAMOOL** 5-9-3	4
*2005	**IMPERIAL STRIDE** 4-9-8	6
2006	**KANDIDATE** 4-9-4	6
2007	**STEPPE DANCER** 4-9-4	7
2008	**HATTAN** 6-9-7	12
2009	**KIRKLEES** 5-9-9	10
2010	**LAAHEB** 4-9-4	9
2011	**MODUN** 4-9-4	7
2012	**DANDINO** 5-9-4	9
2013	**PRINCE BISHOP** 6-9-4	10

*Run at Newmarket

MAY HILL STAKES (2y fillies)
Doncaster-1m

2004	**PLAYFUL ACT** 8-10	8
2005	**NASHEEJ** 8-13	8
*2006	**SIMPLY PERFECT** 8-12	9
2007	**SPACIOUS** 8-12	12
2008	**RAINBOW VIEW** 9-1	7
2009	**POLLENATOR** 8-12	7
2010	**WHITE MOONSTONE** 8-12	7
2011	**LYRIC OF LIGHT** 8-12	8
2012	**CERTIFY** 8-12	7
2013	**IHTIMAL** 8-12	7

*Run at York

PORTLAND HANDICAP
Doncaster-5f 140yds

2004	**HALMAHERA** 9-9-10	22
2005	**OUT AFTER DARK** 4-8-12	21
*2006	**FANTASY BELIEVER** 8-8-13	19
2007	**FULLANDBY** 5-8-13	21
2008	**HOGMANEIGH** 5-9-6	21
2009	**SANTO PADRE** 5-9-1	22
2010	**POET'S PLACE** 5-9-3	22
2011	**NOCTURNAL AFFAIR** 5-9-5	21
2012	**DOC HAY** 5-8-11	20
2013	**ANGELS WILL FALL** 4-9-2	21

*Run at York over 5f 89yds

PARK HILL STAKES (fillies and mares)
Doncaster-1m 6f 132yds

2004	**ECHOES IN ETERNITY** 4-9-3	1
2005	**SWEET STREAM** 5-9-3	1
*2006	**RISING CROSS** 3-8-7	1
2007	**HI CALYPSO** 3-8-7	1

2008 **ALLEGRETTO** 5-9-4 8
2009 **THE MINIVER ROSE** 3-8-6 9
2010 **EASTERN ARIA** 4-9-4 12
2011 **MEEZNAH** 4-9-4 7
2012 **WILD COCO** 4-9-4 9
2013 **THE LARK** 3-8-6 9
*Run at York

DONCASTER CUP
Doncaster-2m 2f
2004 **MILLENARY** 7-9-4 dead heated with
       KASTHARI 5-9-1 8
2005 **MILLENARY** 8-9-4 7
*2006 **SERGEANT CECIL** 7-9-4 8
2007 **SEPTIMUS** 3-9-4 8
2008 **HONOLULU** 4-9-1 9
2009 **ASKAR TAU** 4-9-4 9
2010 **SAMUEL** 6-9-1 10
2011 **SADDLER'S ROCK** 3-8-1 7
2012 **TIMES UP** 6-9-1 10
2013 **TIMES UP** 7-9-3 7
*Run at York

CHAMPAGNE STAKES (2y)
Doncaster-7f
2004 **ETLAALA** 8-10 10
2005 **CLOSE TO YOU** 8-10 dead heated with
       SILENT TIMES 8-10 7
*2006 **VITAL EQUINE** 8-12 8
2007 **MCCARTNEY** 8-12 10
2008 **WESTPHALIA** 8-12 7
2009 **POET'S VOICE** 8-12 7
2010 **SAAMIDD** 8-12 6
2011 **TRUMPET MAJOR** 8-12 5
2012 **TORONADO** 8-12 5
2013 **OUTSTRIP** 8-12 4
*Run at York

PARK STAKES
Doncaster-7f
2004 **PASTORAL PURSUITS** 3-8-10 8
2005 **IFFRAAJ** 4-9-0 11
2006 **IFFRAAJ** 5-9-6 9
2007 **ARABIAN GLEAM** 3-8-12 6
2008 **ARABIAN GLEAM** 4-9-4 9
2009 **DUFF** 6-9-4 6
2010 **BALTHAZAR'S GIFT** 7-9-4 12
2011 **PREMIO LOCO** 7-9-4 5
2012 **LIBRANNO** 4-9-4 8
2013 **VIZTORIA** 3-8-11 9

FLYING CHILDERS STAKES (2y)
Doncaster-5f
2004 **CHATEAU ISTANA** 8-12 11
2005 **GODFREY STREET** 8-12 9
2006 **WI DUD** 9-0 9
2007 **FLEETING SPIRIT** 8-11 8
2008 **MADAME TROP VITE** 8-11 12
2009 **SAND VIXEN** 8-11 10
2010 **ZEBEDEE** 9-0 12
2011 **REQUINTO** 9-0 10
2012 **SIR PRANCEALOT** 9-0 9
2013 **GREEN DOOR** 9-0 7
*Run at York

AYR GOLD CUP
Ayr-6f
2004 **FUNFAIR WANE** 5-8-6 24
2005 **PRESTO SHINKO** 4-9-2 27

2006 **FONTHILL ROAD** 6-9-2 23
2007 **ADVANCED** 4-9-9 28
2008 **REGAL PARADE** 4-8-10 27
2009 **JIMMY STYLES** 5-9-2 26
2010 **REDFORD** 5-9-2 26
2011 **OUR JONATHAN** 4-9-6 26
2012 **CAPTAIN RAMIUS** 6-9-0 26
2013 **HIGHLAND COLORI** 5-8-13 26

MILL REEF STAKES (2y)
Newbury-6f 8yds
2004 **GALEOTA** 8-12 13
2005 **COOL CREEK** 8-12 13
2006 **EXCELLENT ART** 9-1 6
2007 **DARK ANGEL** 9-1 6
2008 **LORD SHANAKILL** 9-1 9
2009 **AWZAAN** 9-1 7
2010 **TEMPLE MEADS** 9-1 7
2011 **CASPAR NETSCHER** 9-4 9
2012 **MOOHAAJIM** 9-1 8
2013 **SUPPLICANT** 9-1 7

ROYAL LODGE STAKES (2y)
Newmarket-1m (run at Ascot before 2011)
2004 **PERFECTPERFORMANCE** 8-11 8
*2005 **LEO** 8-11 8
2006 **ADMIRALOFTHEFLEET** 8-12 7
2007 **CITY LEADER** 8-12 11
2008 **JUKEBOX JURY** 8-12 8
2009 **JOSHUA TREE** 8-12 10
2010 **FRANKEL** 8-12 5
2011 **DADDY LONG LEGS** 8-12 6
2012 **STEELER** 8-12 8
2013 **BERKSHIRE** 8-12 5
*Run at Newmarket

CHEVELEY PARK STAKES (2y fillies)
Newmarket-6f
2004 **MAGICAL ROMANCE** 8-11 7
2005 **DONNA BLINI** 8-11 10
2006 **INDIAN INK** 8-12 11
2007 **NATAGORA** 8-12 14
2008 **SERIOUS ATTITUDE** 8-12 16
2009 **SPECIAL DUTY** 8-12 8
2010 **HOORAY** 8-12 11
2011 **LIGHTENING PEARL** 8-12 9
2012 **ROSDHU QUEEN** 8-12 11
2013 **VORDA** 8-12 7

SUN CHARIOT STAKES
(fillies and mares)
Newmarket-1m
2004 **ATTRACTION** 3-8-11 5
2005 **PEERESS** 4-9-0 10
2006 **SPINNING QUEEN** 3-8-12 5
2007 **MAJESTIC ROI** 3-8-13 9
2008 **HALFWAY TO HEAVEN** 3-8-13 10
2009 **SAHPRESA** 4-9-2 8
2010 **SAHPRESA** 5-9-2 11
2011 **SAHPRESA** 6-9-3 8
2012 **SIYOUMA** 4-9-3 8
2013 **SKY LANTERN** 3-8-13 7

CAMBRIDGESHIRE
Newmarket-1m 1f
2004 **SPANISH DON** 6-8-7 32
2005 **BLUE MONDAY** 4-9-3 30
2006 **FORMAL DECREE** 3-8-9 33
2007 **PIPEDREAMER** 3-8-12 34

2008 **TAZEEZ** 4-9-2.................................28
2009 **SUPASEUS** 6-9-1............................32
2010 **CREDIT SWAP** 7-8-7.......................35
2011 **PRINCE OF JOHANNE** 5-8-9...........32
2012 **BRONZE ANGEL** 3-8-8.....................33
2013 **EDUCATE** 4-9-9..............................31

CUMBERLAND LODGE STAKES
Ascot-1m 4f
2004 **HIGH ACCOLADE** 4-9-0......................9
*2005 **MUBTAKER** 8-9-0..............................6
2006 **YOUNG MICK** 4-9-0............................8
2007 **ASK** 4-9-3...8
2008 **SIXTIES ICON** 5-9-3...........................5
2009 **MAWATHEEQ** 4-9-0..........................12
2010 **LAAHEB** 4-9-3...................................6
2011 **QUEST FOR PEACE** 3-8-7..................7
2012 **HAWAAFEZ** 4-8-11...........................6
2013 **SECRET NUMBER** 3-8-7......................7
*Run at Newmarket

FILLIES' MILE (2y fillies)
Newmarket-1m (run at Ascot before 2011)
2004 **PLAYFUL ACT** 8-10...........................9
*2005 **NANNINA** 8-10..................................6
2006 **SIMPLY PERFECT** 8-12......................7
2007 **LISTEN** 8-12....................................8
2008 **RAINBOW VIEW** 8-12........................8
2009 **HIBAAYEB** 8-12................................9
2010 **WHITE MOONSTONE** 8-12..................5
2011 **LYRIC OF LIGHT** 8-12........................8
2012 **CERTIFY** 8-12...................................8
2013 **CHRISELLIAM** 8-12............................8
*Run at Newmarket

MIDDLE PARK STAKES (2y)
Newmarket-6f
2004 **AD VALOREM** 8-11.............................9
2005 **AMADEUS WOLF** 8-11........................6
2006 **DUTCH ART** 8-12...............................6
2007 **DARK ANGEL** 8-12.............................9
2008 **BUSHRANGER** 8-12............................9
2009 **AWZAAN** 8-12...................................5
2010 **DREAM AHEAD** 8-12..........................8
2011 **CRUSADE** 8-12................................16
2012 **RECKLESS ABANDON** 8-12................10
2013 **ASTAIRE** 9-0....................................9

CHALLENGE STAKES
Newmarket-7f
2004 **FIREBREAK** 5-9-4.............................12
2005 **LE VIE DEI COLORI** 5-9-0.................15
2006 **SLEEPING INDIAN** 5-9-3...................16
2007 **MISS LUCIFER** 3-8-12.......................15
2008 **STIMULATION** 3-9-1..........................15
2009 **ARABIAN GLEAM** 5-9-3......................9
2010 **RED JAZZ** 3-9-1...............................14
2011 **YOUNG SUIT** 3-9-5............................9
2012 **FULBRIGHT** 3-9-1.............................11
2013 **FIESOLANA** 4-9-0..............................9

DEWHURST STAKES (2y)
Newmarket-7f
2004 **SHAMARDAL** 9-0................................9
2005 **SIR PERCY** 9-0..................................8
2006 **TEOFILO** 9-1....................................15
2007 **NEW APPROACH** 9-1.........................10
2008 **INTENSE FOCUS** 9-1.........................13

2009 **BEETHOVEN** 9-1...............................15
2010 **FRANKEL** 9-1.....................................6
2011 **PARISH HALL** 9-1...............................9
2012 **DAWN APPROACH** 9-1........................6
2013 **WAR COMMAND** 9-1...........................6

CESAREWITCH
Newmarket-2m 2f
2004 **CONTACT DANCER** 5-8-2...................34
2005 **SERGEANT CECIL** 6-9-8.....................34
2006 **DETROIT CITY** 4-9-1..........................31
2007 **LEG SPINNER** 6-8-11........................33
2008 **CARACCIOLA** 11-9-6..........................32
2009 **DARLEY SUN** 3-8-6...........................32
2010 **AAIM TO PROSPER** 6-7-13.................32
2011 **NEVER CAN TELL** 4-8-11....................33
2012 **AAIM TO PROSPER** 8-9-10.................34
2013 **SCATTER DICE** 4-8-8........................33

ROCKFEL STAKES (2y fillies)
Newmarket-7f
2004 **MAIDS CAUSEWAY** 8-12......................8
2005 **SPECIOSA** 8-9..................................14
2006 **FINSCEAL BEO** 9-2...........................14
2007 **KITTY MATCHAM** 8-12.......................10
2008 **LAHALEEB** 8-12................................15
2009 **MUSIC SHOW** 8-12...........................11
2010 **CAPE DOLLAR** 8-12..........................10
2011 **WADING** 8-12....................................9
2012 **JUST THE JUDGE** 8-12......................11
2013 **AL THAKHIRA** 8-12.............................8

QIPCO BRITISH CHAMPIONS SPRINT STAKES
Ascot-6f
(run as Diadem Stakes before 2011)
2011 **DEACON BLUES** 4-9-0.......................16
2012 **MAAREK** 5-9-0..................................15
2013 **SLADE POWER** 4-9-0.........................14

QUEEN ELIZABETH II STAKES (BRITISH CHAMPIONS MILE)
Ascot-1m (st - rnd before 2011)
2004 **RAKTI** 5-9-1.....................................11
*2005 **STARCRAFT** 5-9-1..............................6
2006 **GEORGE WASHINGTON** 3-8-13............8
2007 **RAMONTI** 5-9-3..................................7
2008 **RAVEN'S PASS** 3-8-13........................7
2009 **RIP VAN WINKLE** 3-8-13.....................4
2010 **POET'S VOICE** 3-8-13.........................8
2011 **FRANKEL** 3-9-0..................................8
2012 **EXCELEBRATION** 4-9-3.......................8
2013 **OLYMPIC GLORY** 3-9-0.......................12
*Run at Newmarket

QIPCO BRITISH CHAMPIONS LONG DISTANCE CUP
(formerly Jockey Club Cup, run at Newmarket before 2011)
Ascot-2m
2011 **FAME AND GLORY** 5-9-0.....................10
2012 **RITE OF PASSAGE** 8-9-7.....................9
2013 **ROYAL DIAMOND** 7-9-7......................12

QIPCO BRITISH CHAMPIONS FILLIES' AND MARES' STAKES
(formerly Pride Stakes, run at Newmarket before 2011)
Ascot-1m 4f
2011 **DANCING RAIN** 3-8-10................................10
2012 **SAPPHIRE** 4-9-3.....................................10
2013 **SEAL OF APPROVAL** 4-9-3.........................8

QIPCO CHAMPION STAKES (BRITISH CHAMPIONS MIDDLE DISTANCE)
Ascot-1m 2f
(run at Newmarket before 2011)
2004 **HAAFHD** 3-8-11.....................................11
2005 **DAVID JUNIOR** 3-8-11............................15
2006 **PRIDE** 6-9-0...8
2007 **LITERATO** 3-8-12...................................12
2008 **NEW APPROACH** 3-8-12.........................11
2009 **TWICE OVER** 4-9-3..................................14
2010 **TWICE OVER** 5-9-3..................................10
2011 **CIRRUS DES AIGLES** 5-9-3.......................12
2012 **FRANKEL** 4-9-3..6
2013 **FARHH** 5-9-3...10

CORNWALLIS STAKES (2y)
Ascot-5f
*2004 **CASTELLETTO** 8-9..................................11
*2005 **HUNTER STREET** 8-12............................12
2006 **ALZERRA** 8-1...10
2007 **CAPTAIN GERRARD** 9-0............................12
2008 **AMOUR PROPRE** 9-0................................19
2009 **OUR JONATHAN** 9-0.................................17
2010 **ELECTRIC WAVES** 8-11.............................14
2011 **PONTY ACCLAIM** 8-11.............................16
2012 **BUNGLE INTHEJUNGLE** 9-3.......................6
2013 **HOT STREAK** 9-0.....................................12
Run at Newmarket
Run at Salisbury

TWO-YEAR-OLD TROPHY (2y)
Redcar-6f
2004 **OBE GOLD** 8-3..24
2005 **MISU BOND** 9-0......................................24
2006 **DANUM DANCER** 8-3................................24
2007 **DUBAI DYNAMO** 9-2................................23
2008 **TOTAL GALLERY** 8-9................................22

2009 **LUCKY LIKE** 8-6......................................22
2010 **LADIES ARE FOREVER** 7-12......................22
2011 **BOGART** 8-12...22
2012 **BODY AND SOUL** 8-1...............................21
2013 **VENTURA MIST** 8-7.................................23

HORRIS HILL STAKES (2y)
Newbury-7f
2004 **CUPID'S GLORY** 8-9................................13
2005 **HURRICANE CAT** 8-9...............................13
2006 **DIJEERR** 8-12..10
2007 **BEACON LODGE** 8-12..............................11
2008 **EVASIVE** 8-12..13
2009 **CARNABY STREET** 8-12...........................14
2010 **KLAMMER** 8-12.....................................10
2011 **TELL DAD** 8-12......................................14
2012 **TAWHID** 8-12..8
2013 **PIPING ROCK** 8-12.................................11

RACING POST TROPHY (2y)
Doncaster-1m
2004 **MOTIVATOR** 9-0.......................................8
2005 **PALACE EPISODE** 9-0...............................7
*2006 **AUTHORIZED** 9-0..................................14
2007 **IBN KHALDUN** 9-0.................................12
2008 **CROWDED HOUSE** 9-0............................15
2009 **ST NICHOLAS ABBEY** 9-0.........................11
2010 **CASAMENTO** 9-0....................................10
2011 **CAMELOT** 9-0..5
2012 **KINGSBARNS** 9-0.....................................7
2013 **KINGSTON HILL** 9-0................................11
*Run at Newbury

NOVEMBER HANDICAP
Doncaster-1m 4f
2004 **CARTE DIAMOND** 3-9-6............................24
2005 **COME ON JONNY** 3-8-0............................21
*2006 **GROUP CAPTAIN** 4-9-5...........................20
2007 **MALT OR MASH** 3-8-10............................21
2008 **TROPICAL STRAIT** 5-8-13.........................21
2009 **CHARM SCHOOL** 4-8-12..........................23
2010 **TIMES UP** 4-8-13....................................22
2011 **ZUIDER ZEE** 4-8-13................................23
2012 **ART SCHOLAR** 5-8-7...............................23
2013 **CONDUCT** 6-9-2.....................................23
*Run at Windsor

WINNERS OF PRINCIPAL RACES IN IRELAND

IRISH 2000 GUINEAS (3y)
The Curragh-1m
2004	BACHELOR DUKE 9-0	8
2005	DUBAWI 9-0	8
2006	ARAAFA 9-0	11
2007	COCKNEY REBEL 9-0	12
2008	HENRYTHENAVIGATOR 9-0	5
2009	MASTERCRAFTSMAN 9-0	9
2010	CANFORD CLIFFS 9-0	13
2011	RODERIC O'CONNOR 9-0	8
2012	POWER 9-0	10
2013	MAGICIAN 9-0	10

TATTERSALLS GOLD CUP
The Curragh-1m 2f 110yds
2004	POWERSCOURT 4-9-0	6
2005	GREY SWALLOW 4-9-0	6
2006	HURRICANE RUN 4-9-0	3
2007	NOTNOWCATO 5-9-0	9
2008	DUKE OF MARMALADE 4-9-0	6
2009	CASUAL CONQUEST 4-9-0	5
2010	FAME AND GLORY 4-9-0	6
2011	SO YOU THINK 5-9-1	5
2012	SO YOU THINK 6-9-1	5
2013	AL KAZEEM 5-9-3	4

IRISH 1000 GUINEAS (3y fillies)
The Curragh-1m
2004	ATTRACTION 9-0	15
2005	SAOIRE 9-0	18
2006	NIGHTIME 9-0	15
2007	FINSCEAL BEO 9-0	11
2008	HALFWAY TO HEAVEN 9-0	13
2009	AGAIN 9-0	16
2010	BETHRAH 9-0	19
2011	MISTY FOR ME 9-0	15
2012	SAMITAR 9-0	8
2013	JUST THE JUDGE 9-0	15

IRISH DERBY (3y)
The Curragh-1m 4f
2004	GREY SWALLOW 9-0	10
2005	HURRICANE RUN 9-0	9
2006	DYLAN THOMAS 9-0	8
2007	SOLDIER OF FORTUNE 9-0	11
2008	FROZEN FIRE 9-0	11
2009	FAME AND GLORY 9-0	11
2010	CAPE BLANCO 9-0	10
2011	TREASURE BEACH 9-0	8
2012	CAMELOT 9-0	5
2013	TRADING LEATHER 9-0	9

PRETTY POLLY STAKES
(fillies and mares)
Curragh-1m 2f
2004	CHORIST 5-9-7	6
2005	ALEXANDER GOLDRUN 4-9-7	10
2006	ALEXANDER GOLDRUN 5-9-8	7
2007	PEEPING FAWN 3-8-11	9
2008	PROMISING LEAD 4-9-9	9
2009	DAR RE MI 4-9-9	7

IRISH OAKS (3y fillies)
The Curragh-1m 4f
2004	OUIJA BOARD 9-0	7
2005	SHAWANDA 9-0	13
2006	ALEXANDROVA 9-0	6
2007	PEEPING FAWN 9-0	12
2008	MOONSTONE 9-0	14
2009	SARISKA 9-0	10
2010	SNOW FAIRY 9-0	15
2011	BLUE BUNTING 9-0	9
2012	GREAT HEAVENS 9-0	7
2013	CHICQUITA 9-0	7

PHOENIX STAKES (2y)
The Curragh-6f
2004	DAMSON 8-11	6
2005	GEORGE WASHINGTON 9-0	7
2006	HOLY ROMAN EMPEROR 9-1	7
2007	SAOIRSE ABU 8-12	6
2008	MASTERCRAFTSMAN 9-1	5
2009	ALFRED NOBEL 9-1	8
2010	ZOFFANY 9-1	7
2011	LA COLLINA 8-12	9
2012	PEDRO THE GREAT 9-3	6
2013	SUDIRMAN 9-3	5

MATRON STAKES (fillies and mares)
Leopardstown-1m
2004	SOVIET SONG 4-9-2	6
2005	ATTRACTION 4-9-2	9
2006	RED EVIE 3-8-12	8
2007	ECHELON 5-9-3	9
2008	LUSH LASHES 3-8-12	10
2009	RAINBOW VIEW 3-8-12	7
2010	LILLIE LANGTRY 3-8-12	6
2011	EMULOUS 4-9-5	8
*2012	CHACHAMAIDEE 5-9-5	11
2013	LA COLLINA 4-9-5	12
*Duntle disqualified from first place

IRISH CHAMPION STAKES
Leopardstown-1m
2004	AZAMOUR 3-8-11	8
2005	ORATORIO 3-8-11	10
2006	DYLAN THOMAS 3-9-0	5
2007	DYLAN THOMAS 4-9-7	6
2008	NEW APPROACH 3-9-0	6
2009	SEA THE STARS 3-9-0	6
2010	CAPE BLANCO 3-9-0	6
2011	SO YOU THINK 5-9-7	6
2012	SNOW FAIRY 5-9-4	6
2013	THE FUGUE 4-9-4	6

IRISH CAMBRIDGESHIRE
The Curragh-1m
2004	**DUE RESPECT** 4-8-10	18
2005	**KESTREL CROSS** 3-9-1	20
2006	**QUINMASTER** 4-10-1	22
2007	**JALMIRA** 6-8-13	24
2008	**TIS MIGHTY** 5-8-1	21
2009	**POET** 4-9-9	27
2010	**HUJAYLEA** 7-8-3	25
2011	**CASTLE BAR SLING** 6-8-11	21
2012	**PUNCH YOUR WEIGHT** 3-8-6	18
2013	**MORAN GRA** 6-8-13	20

MOYGLARE STUD STAKES (2y fillies)
The Curragh-7f
2004	**CHELSEA ROSE** 8-11	12
2005	**RUMPLESTILTSKIN** 8-11	9
2006	**MISS BEATRIX** 8-12	12
2007	**SAOIRSE ABU** 8-12	9
2008	**AGAIN** 8-12	12
2009	**TERMAGANT** 8-12	7
2010	**MISTY FOR ME** 8-12	12
2011	**MAYBE** 9-1	8
2012	**SKY LANTERN** 9-0	13
2013	**RIZEENA** 9-0	7

VINCENT O'BRIEN (NATIONAL) STAKES (2y)
The Curragh-7f
2004	**DUBAWI** 9-0	7
2005	**GEORGE WASHINGTON** 9-0	7
2006	**TEOFILO** 9-1	6
2007	**NEW APPROACH** 9-1	9
2008	**MASTERCRAFTSMAN** 9-1	7
2009	**KINGSFORT** 9-1	6
2010	**PATHFORK** 9-1	9
2011	**POWER** 9-1	9
2012	**DAWN APPROACH** 9-3	7
2013	**TOORMORE** 9-3	5

IRISH ST LEGER
The Curragh-1m 6f
2004	**VINNIE ROE** 6-9-8	13
2005	**COLLIER HILL** 7-9-8	8
2006	**KASTORIA** 5-9-7	8
2007	**YEATS** 6-9-11	9
2008	**SEPTIMUS** 5-9-11	9
2009	**ALANDI** 4-9-11	8
2010	**SANS FRONTIERES** 4-9-11	8
2011	**DUNCAN** 6-9-11 dead heated with	6
	JUKEBOX JURY 5-9-11	6
2012	**ROYAL DIAMOND** 6-9-11	9
2013	**VOLEUSE DE COEURS** 4-9-8	10

IRISH CESAREWITCH
The Curragh-2m
2004	**ESSEX** 4-7-9	20
2005	**CLARA ALLEN** 7-8-0	17
2006	**IKTITAF** 5-8-8	16
2007	**SANDYMOUNT EARL** 4-9-3	21

2008	**SUAILCE** 3-8-1	28
2009	**DANI CALIFORNIA** 5-8-0	29
2010	**BRIGHT HORIZON** 3-8-7	23
2011	**MINSK** 3-8-9	19
2012	**VOLEUSE DE COEURS** 3-9-1	27
2013	**MONTEFELTRO** 5-9-4	30

BOYLESPORTS.COM HURDLE
Leopardstown-2m
(Pierse Hurdle before 2010)
(MCR Hurdle in 2011)
2005	**ESSEX** 5-10-8	21
2006	**STUDMASTER** 6-10-3	27
2007	**SPRING THE QUE** 8-10-3	30
2008	**BARKER** 7-10-6	28
2009	**PENNY'S BILL** 7-9-9	29
2010	**PUYOL** 8-10-10	30
2011	**FINAL APPROACH** 5-10-9	26
2012	**CITIZENSHIP** 6-10-3	30
2013	**ABBEY LANE** 8-10-8	28
2014	**GILGAMBOA** 6-10-9	24

IRISH CHAMPION HURDLE
Leopardstown-2m
2005	**MACS JOY** 6-11-10	6
2006	**BRAVE INCA** 8-11-10	7
2007	**HARDY EUSTACE** 10-11-10	8
2008	**SIZING EUROPE** 6-11-10	6
2009	**BRAVE INCA** 11-11-10	9
2010	**SOLWHIT** 6-11-10	7
2011	**HURRICANE FLY** 7-11-10	5
2012	**HURRICANE FLY** 8-11-10	5
2013	**HURRICANE FLY** 9-11-10	5
2014	**HURRICANE FLY** 10-11-10	4

HENNESSY GOLD CUP
Leopardstown-3m
2005	**RULE SUPREME** 9-11-12	7
2006	**BEEF OR SALMON** 10-11-12	7
2007	**BEEF OR SALMON** 11-11-12	5
2008	**THE LISTENER** 9-11-10	8
2009	**NEPTUNE COLLONGES** 8-11-10	6
2010	**JONCOL** 7-11-10	7
2011	**KEMPES** 8-11-10	9
2012	**QUEL ESPRIT** 8-11-10	7
2013	**SIR DES CHAMPS** 7-11-10	4
2014	**LAST INSTALMENT** 9-11-10	7

IRISH GRAND NATIONAL
Fairyhouse-3m 5f
2004	**GRANIT D'ESTRUVAL** 10-10-0	28
2005	**NUMBERSIXVALVERDE** 9-10-1	26
2006	**POINT BARROW** 8-10-8	26
2007	**BUTLER'S CABIN** 7-10-4	28
2008	**HEAR THE ECHO** 7-10-0	23
2009	**NICHE MARKET** 8-10-5	30
2010	**BLUESEA CRACKER** 8-10-4	26
2011	**ORGANISEDCONFUSION** 6-9-13	25
2012	**LION NA BEARNAI** 10-10-5	29
2013	**LIBERTY COUNSEL** 10-9-5	28

WINNERS OF PRINCIPAL RACES IN FRANCE

PRIX GANAY
Longchamp-1m 2f 110yds
2004	**EXECUTE** 7-9-2	8
2005	**BAGO** 4-9-2	9
2006	**CORRE CAMINOS** 4-9-2	7
2007	**DYLAN THOMAS** 4-9-2	8
2008	**DUKE OF MARMALADE** 4-9-2	6
2009	**VISION D'ETAT** 4-9-2	8
2010	**CUTLASS BAY** 4-9-2	9
2011	**PLANTEUR** 4-9-2	7
2012	**CIRRUS DES AIGLES** 6-9-2	6
2013	**PASTORIUS** 4-9-2	9

POULE D'ESSAI DES POULAINS (3y)
Longchamp-1m
2004	**AMERICAN POST** 9-2	7
2005	**SHAMARDAL** 9-2	15
2006	**AUSSIE RULES** 9-2	11
2007	**ASTRONOMER ROYAL** 9-2	14
2008	**FALCO** 9-2	19
2009	**SILVER FROST** 9-2	6
2010	**LOPE DE VEGA** 9-2	15
2011	**TIN HORSE** 9-2	14
2012	**LUCAYAN** 9-2	12
2013	**STYLE VENDOME** 9-2	18

POULE D'ESSAI DES POULICHES (3y fillies)
Longchamp-1m
2004	**TORRESTRELLA** 9-0	13
2005	**DIVINE PROPORTIONS** 9-0	8
*2006	**TIE BLACK** 9-0	13
2007	**DARJINA** 9-0	14
2008	**ZARKAVA** 9-0	13
2009	**ELUSIVE WAVE** 9-0	11
**2010	**SPECIAL DUTY** 9-0	10
2011	**GOLDEN LILAC** 9-0	16
2012	**BEAUTY PARLOUR** 9-0	13
2013	**FLOTILLA** 9-0	20

*Price Tag disqualified from first place
**Liliside disqualified from first place

PRIX SAINT-ALARY (3y fillies)
Longchamp-1m 2f
2004	**ASK FOR THE MOON** 9-0	7
2005	**VADAWINA** 9-0	8
2006	**GERMANCE** 9-0	8
2007	**COQUERELLE** 9-0	6
2008	**BELLE ET CELEBRE** 9-0	7
2009	**STACELITA** 9-0	8
2010	**SARAFINA** 9-0	9
2011	**WAVERING** 9-0	12
2012	**SAGAWARA** 9-0	8
2013	**SILASOL** 9-0	8

PRIX JEAN PRAT (3y)
Chantilly-1m (1m 1f before 2005)
2004	**BAGO** 9-2	8
2005	**TURTLE BOWL** 9-2	8
2006	**STORMY RIVER** 9-2	11
2007	**LAWMAN** 9-2	7
2008	**TAMAYUZ** 9-2	16
2009	**LORD SHANAKILL** 9-2	9
2010	**DICK TURPIN** 9-2	8
2011	**MUTUAL TRUST** 9-2	7
2012	**AESOP'S FABLES** 9-2	8
2013	**HAVANA GOLD** 9-2	12

PRIX D'ISPAHAN
Longchamp-1m 1f 55yds
2004	**PRINCE KIRK** 4-9-2	5
2005	**VALIXIR** 4-9-2	8
2006	**LAVEROCK** 4-9-2	11
2007	**MANDURO** 5-9-2	5
2008	**SAGEBURG** 4-9-2	6
2009	**NEVER ON SUNDAY** 4-9-2	9
2010	**GOLDIKOVA** 5-8-13	8
2011	**GOLDIKOVA** 6-8-13	8
2012	**GOLDEN LILAC** 4-8-13	9
2013	**MAXIOS** 5-9-2	7

PRIX DU JOCKEY CLUB (3y)
Chantilly-1m 2f 110yds (1m 4f before 2005)
2004	**BLUE CANARI** 9-2	15
2005	**SHAMARDAL** 9-2	17
2006	**DARSI** 9-2	15
2007	**LAWMAN** 9-2	20
2008	**VISION D'ETAT** 9-2	20
2009	**LE HAVRE** 9-2	17
2010	**LOPE DE VEGA** 9-2	22
2011	**RELIABLE MAN** 9-2	16
2012	**SAONOIS** 9-2	20
2013	**INTELLO** 9-2	19

PRIX DE DIANE (3y fillies)
Chantilly-1m 2f 110yds
2004	**LATICE** 9-0	17
2005	**DIVINE PROPORTIONS** 9-0	10
2006	**CONFIDENTIAL LADY** 9-0	16
2007	**WEST WIND** 9-0	14
2008	**ZARKAVA** 9-0	12
2009	**STACELITA** 9-0	12
2010	**SARAFINA** 9-0	9
2011	**GOLDEN LILAC** 9-0	11
2012	**VALYRA** 9-0	12
2013	**TREVE** 9-0	11

GRAND PRIX DE PARIS (3y)
Longchamp-1m 4f (1m 2f before 2005)
2004	**BAGO** 9-2	4
2005	**SCORPION** 9-2	9
2006	**RAIL LINK** 9-2	9
2007	**ZAMBEZI SUN** 9-2	7
2008	**MONTMARTRE** 9-2	13
2009	**CAVALRYMAN** 9-2	9
2010	**BEHKABAD** 9-2	9
2011	**MEANDRE** 9-2	7
2012	**IMPERIAL MONARCH** 9-2	9
2013	**FLINTSHIRE** 9-2	8

GRAND PRIX DE SAINT-CLOUD
Saint-Cloud-1m 4f
2004 **GAMUT** 5-9-9..................................10
2005 **ALKAASED** 5-9-2..............................11
2006 **PRIDE** 6-8-13...................................6
2007 **MOUNTAIN HIGH** 5-9-2.....................6
2008 **YOUMZAIN** 5-9-2.............................9
2009 **SPANISH MOON** 5-9-2.....................10
2010 **PLUMANIA** 4-8-13............................7
2011 **SARAFINA** 4-8-13.............................5
2012 **MEANDRE** 4-9-2................................4
2013 **NOVELLIST** 4-9-2.............................11

PRIX MAURICE DE GHEEST
Deauville-6f 110yds
2004 **SOMNUS** 4-9-2...............................18
2005 **WHIPPER** 4-9-2..............................13
2006 **MARCHAND D'OR** 3-8-11....................17
2007 **MARCHAND D'OR** 4-9-2....................13
2008 **MARCHAND D'OR** 5-9-2....................16
2009 **KING'S APOSTLE** 5-9-2....................12
2010 **REGAL PARADE** 6-9-2......................15
2011 **MOONLIGHT CLOUD** 3-8-8..................13
2012 **MOONLIGHT CLOUD** 4-8-13..................9
2013 **MOONLIGHT CLOUD** 5-8-13.................14

PRIX JACQUES LE MAROIS
Deauville-1m
2004 **WHIPPER** 3-8-11.............................10
2005 **DUBAWI** 3-8-11...............................6
2006 **LIBRETTIST** 4-9-4...........................10
2007 **MANDURO** 5-9-4..............................6
2008 **TAMAYUZ** 3-8-11.............................8
2009 **GOLDIKOVA** 4-9-0...........................9
2010 **MAKFI** 3-8-11.................................8
2011 **IMMORTAL VERSE** 3-8-8...................12
2012 **EXCELEBRATION** 4-9-4....................11
2013 **MOONLIGHT CLOUD** 5-9-1.................13

PRIX MORNY (2y)
Deauville-6f
2004 **DIVINE PROPORTIONS** 8-11................9
2005 **SILCA'S SISTER** 8-11.......................7
2006 **DUTCH ART** 9-0...............................7
2007 **MYBOYCHARLIE** 8-13........................6
2008 **BUSHRANGER** 9-0...........................14
2009 **ARCANO** 9-0....................................5
2010 **DREAM AHEAD** 9-0..........................11
2011 **DABIRSIM** 9-0..................................7
2012 **RECKLESS ABANDON** 9-0..................11
2013 **NO NAY NEVER** 9-0..........................10

PRIX DU MOULIN DE LONGCHAMP
Longchamp-1m
2004 **GREY LILAS** 3-8-8...........................11
2005 **STARCRAFT** 5-9-2............................9
2006 **LIBRETTIST** 4-9-2............................8
2007 **DARJINA** 3-8-8................................9
2008 **GOLDIKOVA** 3-8-8..........................11
2009 **AQLAAM** 4-9-2.................................9
2010 **FUISSE** 4-9-2.................................6
2011 **EXCELEBRATION** 3-8-11....................8
2012 **MOONLIGHT CLOUD** 4-8-13.................4
2013 **MAXIOS** 5-9-2.................................7

CRITERIUM INTERNATIONAL (2y)
Saint-Cloud-1m
2004 **HELIOS QUERCUS** 9-0......................8
2005 **CARLOTAMIX** 9-0.............................6
2006 **MOUNT NELSON** 9-0........................10
2007 **THEWAYYOUARE** 9-0........................6
2008 **ZAFISIO** 9-0...................................11
2009 **JAN VERMEER** 9-0...........................7
2010 **RODERIC O'CONNOR** 9-0.................10
2011 **FRENCH FIFTEEN** 9-0......................11
2012 **LOCH GARMAN** 9-0...........................6
2013 **ECTOT** 9-0......................................4

PRIX VERMEILLE (fillies and mares)
Longchamp-1m 4f
2004 **SWEET STREAM** 4-9-2......................13
2005 **SHAWANDA** 3-8-7.............................6
2006 **MANDESHA** 3-8-7............................11
2007 **MRS LINDSAY** 3-8-9.........................10
2008 **ZARKAVA** 3-8-8...............................12
*2009 **STACELITA** 3-8-8............................12
2010 **MIDDAY** 4-9-3.................................12
2011 **GALIKOVA** 3-8-8...............................6
2012 **SHARETA** 4-9-2..............................13
2013 **TREVE** 3-8-8..................................10
*Dar Re Mi disqualified from first place

PRIX DU CADRAN
Longchamp-2m 4f
2004 **WESTERNER** 5-9-6............................8
2005 **REEFSCAPE** 4-9-2...........................10
2006 **SERGEANT CECIL** 7-9-2.....................7
2007 **LE MIRACLE** 6-9-2............................6
2008 **BANNABY** 5-9-2..............................11
2009 **ALANDI** 4-9-2.................................12
2010 **GENTOO** 6-9-2.................................8
2011 **KASBAH BLISS** 9-9-2.......................10
2012 **MOLLY MALONE** 4-8-13....................10
2013 **ALTANO** 7-9-2................................10

PRIX DE L'ABBAYE DE LONGCHAMP
Longchamp-5f
2004 **VAR** 5-9-11.....................................15
2005 **AVONBRIDGE** 5-9-11.........................17
2006 **DESERT LORD** 6-9-11.......................14
2007 **BENBAUN** 6-9-11.............................17
*2008 **MARCHAND D'OR** 5-9-11..................17
2009 **TOTAL GALLERY** 3-9-11....................16
2010 **GILT EDGE GIRL** 4-9-7.....................21
2011 **TANGERINE TREES** 6-9-11.................15
2012 **WIZZ KID** 4-9-7...............................18
2013 **MAAREK** 6-9-11...............................20
* re-run; Overdose won void first running

PRIX MARCEL BOUSSAC (2y fillies)
Longchamp-1m
2004 **DIVINE PROPORTIONS** 8-11................10
2005 **RUMPLESTILTSKIN** 8-11....................15
2006 **FINSCEAL BEO** 8-11.........................13
2007 **ZARKAVA** 8-11................................10
2008 **PROPORTIONAL** 8-11........................16
2009 **ROSANARA** 8-11.............................11
2010 **MISTY FOR ME** 8-11..........................8
2011 **ELUSIVE KATE** 8-11..........................5
2012 **SILASOL** 8-11..................................9
2013 **INDONESIENNE** 8-11........................12

PRIX JEAN-LUC LAGARDERE (2y)
Longchamp-7f
2004	**ORATORIO** 9-0	6
2005	**HORATIO NELSON** 9-0	6
2006	**HOLY ROMAN EMPEROR** 9-0	9
2007	**RIO DE LA PLATA** 9-0	8
2008	**NAAQOOS** 9-0	7
2009	**SIYOUNI** 9-0	7
2010	**WOOTTON BASSETT** 9-0	9
2011	**DABIRSIM** 9-0	7
2012	**OLYMPIC GLORY** 9-0	8
2013	**KARAKONTIE** 9-0	8

PRIX DE LA FORET
Longchamp-7f
2004	**SOMNUS** 4-9-2	7
2005	**COURT MASTERPIECE** 5-9-2	8
2006	**CARADAK** 5-9-3	14
2007	**TOYLSOME** 8-9-2	13
2008	**PACO BOY** 3-9-0	8
2009	**VARENAR** 3-9-0	14
2010	**GOLDIKOVA** 5-8-13	10
2011	**DREAM AHEAD** 3-9-0	8
2012	**GORDON LORD BYRON** 4-9-2	11
2013	**MOONLIGHT CLOUD** 5-8-13	11

PRIX ROYAL-OAK
Longchamp-1m 7f 110yds
2004	**WESTERNER** 5-9-4	8
2005	**ALCAZAR** 10-9-4	11
2006	**MONTARE** 4-9-1	10
2007	**ALLEGRETTO** 4-9-1	11
2008	**YEATS** 7-9-4	11
2009	**ASK** 6-9-4	9
2010	**GENTOO** 6-9-4	10
2011	**BE FABULOUS** 4-9-1	14
2012	**LES BEAUFS** 3-8-9	9
2013	**TAC DE BOISTRON** 6-9-4	15

CRITERIUM DE SAINT-CLOUD (2y)
Saint-Cloud-1m 2f
2004	**PAITA** 8-11	7
2005	**LINDA'S LAD** 9-0	5
2006	**PASSAGE OF TIME** 8-11	13
2007	**FULL OF GOLD** 9-0	6
2008	**FAME AND GLORY** 9-0	11
2009	**PASSION FOR GOLD** 9-0	9
2010	**RECITAL** 9-0	9
2011	**MANDAEAN** 9-0	8
2012	**MORANDI** 9-0	8
2013	**PRINCE GIBRALTAR** 9-0	12

WINNERS OF OTHER OVERSEAS RACES

DUBAI WORLD CUP
Meydan-1m 2f Tapeta
(Run at Nad Al Sheba over 1m 2f on dirt before 2010)
2004	**PLEASANTLY PERFECT** 6-9-0	12
2005	**ROSES IN MAY** 5-9-0	12
2006	**ELECTROCUTIONIST** 5-9-0	11
2007	**INVASOR** 5-9-0	7
2008	**CURLIN** 4-9-0	12
2009	**WELL ARMED** 6-9-0	14
2010	**GLORIA DE CAMPEAO** 7-9-0	14
2011	**VICTOIRE PISA** 4-9-0	14
2012	**MONTEROSSO** 5-9-0	13
2013	**ANIMAL KINGDOM** 5-9-0	13

KENTUCKY DERBY
Churchill Downs-1m 2f dirt
2004	**SMARTY JONES** 9-0	18
2005	**GIACOMO** 9-0	20
2006	**BARBARO** 9-0	20
2007	**STREET SENSE** 9-0	20
2008	**BIG BROWN** 9-0	20
2009	**MINE THAT BIRD** 9-0	19
2010	**SUPER SAVER** 9-0	20
2011	**ANIMAL KINGDOM** 9-0	19
2012	**I'LL HAVE ANOTHER** 9-0	20
2013	**ORB** 9-0	19

BREEDERS' CUP TURF
Various courses-1m 4f
2004	**BETTER TALK NOW** 5-9-0	8
2005	**SHIROCCO** 4-9-0	13
2006	**RED ROCKS** 3-8-10	11
2007	**ENGLISH CHANNEL** 5-9-0	8
2008	**CONDUIT** 3-8-9	11
2009	**CONDUIT** 4-9-0	7
2010	**DANGEROUS MIDGE** 4-9-0	7
2011	**ST NICHOLAS ABBEY** 4-9-0	12
2012	**LITTLE MIKE** 5-9-0	12
2013	**MAGICIAN** 3-8-10	12

BREEDERS' CUP CLASSIC
Various courses-1m 2f dirt/pro-ride
2004	**GHOSTZAPPER** 4-9-0	13
2005	**SAINT LIAM** 5-9-0	13
2006	**INVASOR** 4-9-0	13
2007	**CURLIN** 3-8-9	9
2008	**RAVEN'S PASS** 3-8-9	12
2009	**ZENYATTA** 5-8-11	12
2010	**BLAME** 4-9-0	12
2011	**DROSSELMEYER** 4-9-0	12
2012	**FORT LARNED** 4-9-0	12
2013	**MUCHO MACHO MAN** 5-9-0	11

MELBOURNE CUP
Flemington-2m
2004	**MAKYBE DIVA** 5-8-11	24
2005	**MAKYBE DIVA** 6-9-2	24
2006	**DELTA BLUES** 5-8-11	23
2007	**EFFICIENT** 4-8-8	21
2008	**VIEWED** 5-8-5	24
2009	**SHOCKING** 4-8-0	23
2010	**AMERICAIN** 5-8-8	23
2011	**DUNADEN** 5-8-8	23
2012	**GREEN MOON** 5-8-6	24
2013	**FIORENTE** 5-8-9	24

JAPAN CUP
Tokyo-1m 4f

2004	**ZENNO ROB ROY** 4-9-0	16
2005	**ALKAASED** 5-9-0	18
2006	**DEEP IMPACT** 4-9-0	11
2007	**ADMIRE MOON** 4-9-0	18
2008	**SCREEN HERO** 4-9-0	17
2009	**VODKA** 5-8-10	18
*2010	**ROSE KINGDOM** 3-8-9	18
2011	**BUENA VISTA** 5-8-9	16
2012	**GENTILDONNA** 3-8-5	17
2013	**GENTILDONNA** 4-8-9	17

*Buena Vista disqualified from first place

WINNERS OF PRINCIPAL NATIONAL HUNT RACES

PADDY POWER GOLD CUP (HANDICAP CHASE)
Cheltenham-2m 4f 110yds

2004	**CELESTIAL GOLD** 6-10-2	14
2005	**OUR VIC** 7-11-7	18
2006	**EXOTIC DANCER** 6-11-2	16
2007	**L'ANTARTIQUE** 7-10-13	20
2008	**IMPERIAL COMMANDER** 7-10-7	19
2009	**TRANQUIL SEA** 7-10-13	16
2010	**LITTLE JOSH** 8-10-5	18
2011	**GREAT ENDEAVOUR** 7-10-3	20
2012	**AL FEROF** 7-11-8	18
2013	**JOHNS SPIRIT** 6-10-2	20

BETFAIR CHASE
Haydock-3m

2005	**KINGSCLIFF** 8-11-8	7
2006	**KAUTO STAR** 6-11-8	6
2007	**KAUTO STAR** 7-11-7	7
2008	**SNOOPY LOOPY** 10-11-7	6
2009	**KAUTO STAR** 9-11-7	7
2010	**IMPERIAL COMMANDER** 9-11-7	7
2011	**KAUTO STAR** 11-11-7	6
2012	**SILVINIACO CONTI** 6-11-7	5
2013	**CUE CARD** 7-11-7	8

HENNESSY GOLD CUP HANDICAP CHASE
Newbury-3m 2f 110yds

2004	**CELESTIAL GOLD** 6-10-5	14
2005	**TRABOLGAN** 7-11-12	19
2006	**STATE OF PLAY** 6-11-4	16
2007	**DENMAN** 7-11-12	18
2008	**MADISON DU BERLAIS** 7-11-4	15
2009	**DENMAN** 9-11-12	19
2010	**DIAMOND HARRY** 7-10-0	20
2011	**CARRUTHERS** 8-10-4	18
2012	**BOBS WORTH** 7-11-6	19
2013	**TRIOLO D'ALENE** 6-11-1	21

TINGLE CREEK CHASE
Sandown-2m

2004	**MOSCOW FLYER** 10-11-7	7
2005	**KAUTO STAR** 5-11-7	7
2006	**KAUTO STAR** 6-11-7	7
2007	**TWIST MAGIC** 5-11-7	8
2008	**MASTER MINDED** 5-11-7	7
2009	**TWIST MAGIC** 7-11-7	5
2010	**MASTER MINDED** 7-11-7	9
2011	**SIZING EUROPE** 9-11-7	7

2012	**SPRINTER SACRE** 6-11-7	7
2013	**SIRE DE GRUGY** 7-11-7	9

*Run at Cheltenham over 2m 110yds

CHRISTMAS HURDLE
Kempton-2m

2004	**HARCHIBALD** 5-11-7	7
*2005	**FEATHARD LADY** 5-11-0	7
2006	**JAZZ MESSENGER** 6-11-7	7
2007	**STRAW BEAR** 6-11-7	6
2008	**HARCHIBALD** 9-11-7	7
2009	**GO NATIVE** 6-11-7	7
**2010	**BINOCULAR** 7-11-7	6
2011	**BINOCULAR** 7-11-7	5
2012	**DARLAN** 5-11-7	7
2013	**MY TENT OR YOURS** 6-11-7	6

*Run at Sandown
**Run in January 2011

KING GEORGE VI CHASE
Kempton-3m

2004	**KICKING KING** 6-11-10	13
*2005	**KICKING KING** 7-11-10	9
2006	**KAUTO STAR** 6-11-10	9
2007	**KAUTO STAR** 7-11-10	7
2008	**KAUTO STAR** 8-11-10	9
2009	**KAUTO STAR** 9-11-10	13
**2010	**LONG RUN** 6-11-10	9
2011	**KAUTO STAR** 11-11-10	9
2012	**LONG RUN** 7-11-10	9
2013	**SILVINIACO CONTI** 7-11-10	9

*Run at Sandown
**Run in January 2011

WELSH GRAND NATIONAL (HANDICAP CHASE)
Chepstow-3m 5f 110yds

2004	**SILVER BIRCH** 7-10-5	17
2005	**L'AVENTURE** 6-10-4	18
2006	**HALCON GENELARDAIS** 6-11-3	18
2007	**MIKO DE BEAUCHENE** 7-10-5	18
2008	**NOTRE PERE** 7-11-0	20
2009	**DREAM ALLIANCE** 8-10-8	18
*2010	**SYNCHRONISED** 8-11-6	18
2011	**LE BEAU BAI** 8-10-1	20
**2012	**MONBEG DUDE** 8-10-1	17
2013	**MOUNTAINOUS** 8-10-0	20

*Run in January 2011
**Run in January 2013

CLARENCE HOUSE CHASE
(Victor Chandler Chase before 2014)
(Handicap before 2008)
Ascot-2m 1f (2m before 2008)
*2005	WELL CHIEF 6-11-10	10
**2006	TYSOU 9-11-2	10
2007	ABANDONED	
2008	TAMARINBLEU 8-11-7	7
2009	MASTER MINDED 6-11-7	5
2010	TWIST MAGIC 8-11-7	7
2011	MASTER MINDED 8-11-7	9
2012	SOMERSBY 8-11-7	8
*2013	SPRINTER SACRE 7-11-7	7
2014	SIRE DE GRUGY 8-11-7	7

*Run at Cheltenham over 2m 110yds
**Run at Sandown over 2m

BETFAIR H'CAP HURDLE
Newbury-2m 4yds
(Totesport Trophy 2005-2011)
2005	ESSEX 5-11-6	25
2006	ABANDONED	
2007	HEATHCOTE 5-10-6	20
2008	WINGMAN 6-10-0	24
2009	ABANDONED	
2010	GET ME OUT OF HERE 6-10-6	23
2011	RECESSION PROOF 5-10-8	15
2012	ZARKANDAR 5-11-1	20
2013	MY TENT OR YOURS 6-11-2	21
2014	SPLASH OF GINGE 6-10-3	20

SUPREME NOVICES' HURDLE
Cheltenham-2m 110yds
2004	BRAVE INCA 6-11-7	19
2005	ARCALIS 5-11-7	20
2006	NOLAND 5-11-7	20
2007	EBAZIYAN 6-11-7	22
2008	CAPTAIN CEE BEE 7-11-7	22
2009	GO NATIVE 6-11-7	20
2010	MENORAH 5-11-7	18
2011	AL FEROF 6-11-7	15
2012	CINDERS AND ASHES 5-11-7	19
2013	CHAMPAGNE FEVER 6-11-7	12

ARKLE CHALLENGE TROPHY (NOVICES' CHASE)
Cheltenham-2m
2004	WELL CHIEF 5-11-3	16
2005	CONTRABAND 7-11-7	19
2006	VOY POR USTEDES 5-11-2	14
2007	MY WAY DE SOLZEN 7-11-7	13
2008	TIDAL BAY 7-11-7	14
2009	FORPADYDEPLASTERER 7-11-7	17
2010	SIZING EUROPE 8-11-7	12
2011	CAPTAIN CHRIS 7-11-7	10
2012	SPRINTER SACRE 6-11-7	6
2013	SIMONSIG 7-11-7	7

CHAMPION HURDLE
Cheltenham-2m 110yds
2004	HARDY EUSTACE 7-11-10	14
2005	HARDY EUSTACE 8-11-10	14
2006	BRAVE INCA 8-11-10	18
2007	SUBLIMITY 7-11-10	10
2008	KATCHIT 5-11-10	15
2009	PUNJABI 6-11-10	23
2010	BINOCULAR 6-11-10	12
2011	HURRICANE FLY 7-11-10	11

2012	ROCK ON RUBY 7-11-10	10
2013	HURRICANE FLY 9-11-10	9

QUEEN MOTHER CHAMPION CHASE
Cheltenham-2m
2004	AZERTYUIOP 7-11-10	8
2005	MOSCOW FLYER 11-11-10	8
2006	NEWMILL 8-11-10	12
2007	VOY POR USTEDES 6-11-10	10
2008	MASTER MINDED 5-11-10	8
2009	MASTER MINDED 6-11-10	12
2010	BIG ZEB 9-11-10	9
2011	SIZING EUROPE 9-11-10	11
2012	FINIAN'S RAINBOW 9-11-10	8
2013	SPRINTER SACRE 7-11-10	6

NEPTUNE INVESTMENT MANAGEMENT NOVICES' HURDLE
(Royal & SunAlliance Hurdle until 2007,
Ballymore Hurdle 2008-9)
Cheltenham-2m 5f
2004	FUNDAMENTALIST 6-11-7	15
2005	NO REFUGE 5-11-7	20
2006	NICANOR 5-11-7	15
2007	MASSINI'S MAGUIRE 6-11-7	15
2008	FIVEFORTHREE 6-11-7	15
2009	MIKAEL D'HAGUENET 5-11-7	14
2010	PEDDLERS CROSS 5-11-7	17
2011	FIRST LIEUTENANT 6-11-7	12
2012	SIMONSIG 6-11-7	17
2013	THE NEW ONE 5-11-7	8

RSA CHASE
(Royal & SunAlliance Chase before 2009)
(Cheltenham-3m
2004	RULE SUPREME 8-11-4	10
2005	TRABOLGAN 7-11-4	9
2006	STAR DE MOHAISON 5-10-8	15
2007	DENMAN 7-11-4	17
2008	ALBERTAS RUN 7-11-4	15
2009	COOLDINE 7-11-4	15
2010	WEAPON'S AMNESTY 7-11-4	9
2011	BOSTONS ANGEL 7-11-4	12
2012	BOBS WORTH 7-11-4	9
2013	LORD WINDERMERE 7-11-4	11

WORLD HURDLE
(Stayers' Hurdle before 2005)
Cheltenham-3m
2004	IRIS'S GIFT 7-11-10	10
2005	INGLIS DREVER 6-11-10	12
2006	MY WAY DE SOLZEN 6-11-10	20
2007	INGLIS DREVER 8-11-10	14
2008	INGLIS DREVER 9-11-10	14
2009	BIG BUCK'S 6-11-10	14
2010	BIG BUCK'S 7-11-10	14
2011	BIG BUCK'S 8-11-10	13
2012	BIG BUCK'S 9-11-10	9
2013	SOLWHIT 9-11-10	13

TRIUMPH HURDLE (4y)
Cheltenham-2m 1f
2004	MADE IN JAPAN 11-0	23
2005	PENZANCE 11-0	23
2006	DETROIT CITY 11-0	23
2007	KATCHIT 11-0	23
2008	CELESTIAL HALO 11-0	18
2009	ZAYNAR 11-0	18
2010	SOLDATINO 11-0	17

2011	**ZARKANDAR** 11-0	23
2012	**COUNTRYWIDE FLAME** 11-0	20
2013	**OUR CONOR** 11-0	17

CHELTENHAM GOLD CUP
Cheltenham-3m 2f 110yds

2004	**BEST MATE** 9-11-10	10
2005	**KICKING KING** 7-11-10	15
2006	**WAR OF ATTRITION** 7-11-10	22
2007	**KAUTO STAR** 7-11-10	18
2008	**DENMAN** 8-11-10	12
2009	**KAUTO STAR** 9-11-10	16
2010	**IMPERIAL COMMANDER** 9-11-10	11
2011	**LONG RUN** 6-11-0	13
2012	**SYNCHRONISED** 9-11-10	14
2013	**BOBS WORTH** 8-11-10	9

RYANAIR CHASE (FESTIVAL TROPHY)
Cheltenham-2m 5f

2005	**THISTHATANDTHOTHER** 9-11-3	12
2006	**FONDMORT** 10-11-0	11
2007	**TARANIS** 6-11-0	9
2008	**OUR VIC** 10-11-10	9
2009	**IMPERIAL COMMANDER** 8-11-10	10
2010	**ALBERTAS RUN** 9-11-10	13
2011	**ALBERTAS RUN** 10-11-10	11
2012	**RIVERSIDE THEATRE** 8-11-10	12
2013	**CUE CARD** 7-11-10	8

BETFRED BOWL CHASE
(Martell Cup Chase before 2005)
(Betfair Bowl Chase 2005-8)
(Totesport Bowl Chase 2009-11)
Aintree-3m 1f

2004	**TIUTCHEV** 11-11-12	8
2005	**GREY ABBEY** 11-11-12	8
2006	**CELESTIAL GOLD** 8-11-8	9
2007	**EXOTIC DANCER** 7-11-12	5
2008	**OUR VIC** 10-11-10	5
2009	**MADISON DU BERLAIS** 8-11-10	10
2010	**WHAT A FRIEND** 7-11-7	5
2011	**NACARAT** 11-11-7	6
2012	**FOLLOW THE PLAN** 9-11-7	11
2013	**FIRST LIEUTENANT** 8-11-7	8

MELLING CHASE
Aintree-2m 4f

2004	**MOSCOW FLYER** 10-11-10	7
2005	**MOSCOW FLYER** 11-11-10	6
2006	**HI CLOY** 9-11-10	11

2007	**MONET'S GARDEN** 9-11-10	6
2008	**VOY POR USTEDES** 7-11-10	6
2009	**VOY POR USTEDES** 8-11-10	10
2010	**ALBERTAS RUN** 9-11-10	11
2011	**MASTER MINDED** 8-11-10	10
2012	**FINIAN'S RAINBOW** 9-11-10	8
2013	**SPRINTER SACRE** 7-11-10	6

AINTREE HURDLE
Aintree-2m 4f

2004	**RHINESTONE COWBOY** 8-11-7	11
2005	**AL EILE** 5-11-7	9
2006	**ASIAN MAZE** 7-11-0	9
2007	**AL EILE** 7-11-7	11
2008	**AL EILE** 8-11-7	9
2009	**SOLWHIT** 5-11-7	16
2010	**KHYBER KIM** 8-11-7	7
2011	**OSCAR WHISKY** 6-11-7	8
2012	**OSCAR WHISKY** 7-11-7	5
2013	**ZARKANDAR** 6-11-7	9

SCOTTISH GRAND NATIONAL (H'CAP CHASE)
Ayr-4m 110 yds (4m 1f before 2007)

2004	**GREY ABBEY** 10-11-12	28
2005	**JOES EDGE** 8-9-11	20
2006	**RUN FOR PADDY** 10-10-2	30
2007	**HOT WELD** 8-9-9	23
2008	**IRIS DE BALME** 8-9-7	24
2009	**HELLO BUD** 11-10-9	17
2010	**MERIGO** 9-10-0	30
2011	**BESHABAR** 9-10-4	28
2012	**MERIGO** 11-10-2	24
2013	**GODSMEJUDGE** 7-11-3	24

BET365 GOLD CUP (H'CAP CHASE)
(Betfred Gold Cup 2004-7)
Sandown-3m 5f 110yds

2004	**PUNTAL** 8-11-4	18
2005	**JACK HIGH** 10-10-0	19
2006	**LACDOUDAL** 7-11-5	18
2007	**HOT WELD** 8-10-0	10
2008	**MONKERHOSTIN** 11-10-13	19
2009	**HENNESSY** 8-10-7	14
2010	**CHURCH ISLAND** 11-10-5	19
2011	**POKER DE SIVOLA** 8-10-12	18
2012	**TIDAL BAY** 11-11-12	19
2013	**QUENTIN COLLONGES** 9-10-12	19

DISTANCE CONVERSION

5f	1,000m	10f	2,000m	15f	3,000m	20f	4,000m
6f	1,200m	11f	2,200m	16f	3,200m	21f	4,200m
7f	1,400m	12f	2,400m	17f	3,400m	22f	4,400m
8f	1,600m	13f	2,600m	18f	3,600m		
9f	1,800m	14f	2,800m	19f	3,800m		

LEADING TRAINERS ON THE FLAT: 1898-2013

1898 R Marsh	1937 C Boyd-Rochfort	1976 H Cecil
1899 J Porter	1938 C Boyd-Rochfort	1977 M V O'Brien
1900 R Marsh	1939 J L Jarvis	1978 H Cecil
1901 J Huggins	1940 F Darling	1979 H Cecil
1902 R S Sievier	1941 F Darling	1980 W Hern
1903 G Blackwell	1942 F Darling	1981 M Stoute
1904 P P Gilpin	1943 W Nightingall	1982 H Cecil
1905 W T Robinson	1944 Frank Butters	1983 W Hern
1906 Hon G Lambton	1945 W Earl	1984 H Cecil
1907 A Taylor	1946 Frank Butters	1985 H Cecil
1908 C Morton	1947 F Darling	1986 M Stoute
1909 A Taylor	1948 C F N Murless	1987 H Cecil
1910 A Taylor	1949 Frank Butters	1988 H Cecil
1911 Hon G Lambton	1950 C H Semblat	1989 M Stoute
1912 Hon G Lambton	1951 J L Jarvis	1990 H Cecil
1913 R Wootton	1952 M Marsh	1991 P Cole
1914 A Taylor	1953 J L Jarvis	1992 R Hannon Snr
1915 P P Gilpin	1954 C Boyd-Rochfort	1993 H Cecil
1916 R C Dawson	1955 C Boyd-Rochfort	1994 M Stoute
1917 A Taylor	1956 C F Elsey	1995 J Dunlop
1918 A Taylor	1957 C F N Murless	1996 Saeed bin Suroor
1919 A Taylor	1958 C Boyd-Rochfort	1997 M Stoute
1920 A Taylor	1959 C F N Murless	1998 Saeed bin Suroor
1921 A Taylor	1960 C F N Murless	1999 Saeed bin Suroor
1922 A Taylor	1961 C F N Murless	2000 Sir M Stoute
1923 A Taylor	1962 W Hern	2001 A O'Brien
1924 R C Dawson	1963 P Prendergast	2002 A O'Brien
1925 A Taylor	1964 P Prendergast	2003 Sir M Stoute
1926 F Darling	1965 P Prendergast	2004 Saeed bin Suroor
1927 Frank Butters	1966 M V O'Brien	2005 Sir M Stoute
1928 Frank Butters	1967 C F N Murless	2006 Sir M Stoute
1929 R C Dawson	1968 C F N Murless	2007 A O'Brien
1930 H S Persse	1969 A M Budgett	2008 A O'Brien
1931 J Lawson	1970 C F N Murless	2009 Sir M Stoute
1932 Frank Butters	1971 I Balding	2010 R Hannon Snr
1933 F Darling	1972 W Hern	2011 R Hannon Snr
1934 Frank Butters	1973 C F N Murless	2012 J Gosden
1935 Frank Butters	1974 P Walwyn	2013 R Hannon Snr
1936 J Lawson	1975 P Walwyn	

CHAMPION JOCKEYS ON THE FLAT: 1896-2013

1896 M Cannon	164	1918 S Donoghue	66	1939 G Richards	15
1897 M Cannon	145	1919 S Donoghue	129	1940 G Richards	6
1898 O Madden	161	1920 S Donoghue	143	1941 H Wragg	7
1899 S Loates	160	1921 S Donoghue	141	1942 G Richards	6
1900 L Reiff	143	1922 S Donoghue	102	1943 G Richards	6
1901 O Madden	130	1923 S Donoghue	89	1944 G Richards	8
1902 W Lane	170	C Elliott	89	1945 G Richards	1C
1903 O Madden	154	1924 C Elliott	106	1946 G Richards	2
1904 O Madden	161	1925 G Richards	118	1947 G Richards	26
1905 E Wheatley	124	1926 T Weston	95	1948 G Richards	22
1906 W Higgs	149	1927 G Richards	164	1949 G Richards	22
1907 W Higgs	146	1928 G Richards	148	1950 G Richards	2C
1908 D Maher	139	1929 G Richards	135	1951 G Richards	2
1909 F Wootton	165	1930 F Fox	129	1952 G Richards	2
1910 F Wootton	137	1931 G Richards	145	1953 G Richards	1
1911 F Wootton	187	1932 G Richards	190	1954 D Smith	1
1912 F Wootton	118	1933 G Richards	259	1955 D Smith	1
1913 D Maher	115	1934 G Richards	212	1956 D Smith	1
1914 S Donoghue	129	1935 G Richards	217	1957 A Breasley	1
1915 S Donoghue	62	1936 G Richards	174	1958 D Smith	1
1916 S Donoghue	43	1937 G Richards	216	1959 D Smith	1
1917 S Donoghue	42	1938 G Richards	206	1960 L Piggott	1

1961 A Breasley 171	1979 J Mercer 164	1997 K Fallon 196
1962 A Breasley 179	1980 W Carson 166	1998 K Fallon 185
1963 A Breasley 176	1981 L Piggott 179	1999 K Fallon 200
1964 L Piggott 140	1982 L Piggott 188	2000 K Darley 152
1965 L Piggott 160	1983 W Carson 159	2001 K Fallon 166
1966 L Piggott 191	1984 S Cauthen 130	2002 K Fallon 144
1967 L Piggott 117	1985 S Cauthen 195	2003 K Fallon 208
1968 L Piggott 139	1986 Pat Eddery 176	2004 L Dettori 192
1969 L Piggott 163	1987 S Cauthen 197	2005 J Spencer 163
1970 L Piggott 162	1988 Pat Eddery 183	2006 R Moore 180
1971 L Piggott 162	1989 Pat Eddery 171	2007 S Sanders 190
1972 W Carson 132	1990 Pat Eddery 209	J Spencer 190
1973 W Carson 164	1991 Pat Eddery 165	2008 R Moore 186
1974 Pat Eddery 148	1992 M Roberts 206	2009 R Moore 174
1975 Pat Eddery 164	1993 Pat Eddery 169	2010 P Hanagan 191
1976 Pat Eddery 162	1994 L Dettori 233	2011 P Hanagan 165
1977 Pat Eddery 176	1995 L Dettori 211	2012 R Hughes 172
1978 W Carson 182	1996 Pat Eddery 186	2013 R Hughes 203

CHAMPION APPRENTICES ON THE FLAT 1980-2013

1980 P Robinson 59	1992 D Harrison 56	2005 S Golam 44
1981 B Crossley 45	1993 D Harrison 40	H Turner 44
1982 W Newnes 57	1994 S Davies 45	2006 S Donohoe 44
1983 M Hills 39	1995 S Sanders 61	2007 G Fairley 65
1984 T Quinn 62	1996 D O'Neill 79	2008 W Buick 50
1985 G Carter 37	1997 R Ffrench 77	D Probert 50
W Ryan 37	1998 C Lowther 72	2009 F Tylicki 60
1986 G Carter 34	1999 R Winston 49	2010 M Lane 41
1987 G Bardwell 27	2000 L Newman 87	2011 M Harley 57
1988 G Bardwell 39	2001 C Catlin 71	2012 A Ryan 40
1989 L Dettori 71	2002 P Hanagan 81	2013 J Hart 51
1990 J Fortune 46	2003 R Moore 52	
1991 D Holland 79	2004 T Queally 59	

LEADING OWNERS ON THE FLAT: 1895-2013

1895 Ld de Rothschild	1924 H.H. Aga Khan	1953 Sir Victor Sassoon
1896 Ld de Rothschild	1925 Ld Astor	1954 Her Majesty
1897 Mr J Gubbins	1926 Ld Woolavington	1955 Lady Zia Wernner
1898 Ld de Rothschild	1927 Ld Derby	1956 Maj L B Holliday
1899 Duke of Westminster	1928 Ld Derby	1957 Her Majesty
1900 H.R.H. The Prince of Wales	1929 H.H. Aga Khan	1958 Mr J McShain
1901 Sir G Blundell Maple	1930 H.H. Aga Khan	1959 Prince Aly Khan
1902 Mr R S Sievier	1931 Mr J A Dewar	1960 Sir Victor Sassoon
1903 Sir James Miller	1932 H.H. Aga Khan	1961 Maj L B Holliday
1904 Sir James Miller	1933 Ld Derby	1962 Maj L B Holliday
1905 Col W Hall Walker	1934 H.H. Aga Khan	1963 Mr J R Mullion
1906 Ld Derby (late)	1935 H.H. Aga Khan	1964 Mrs H E Jackson
1907 Col W Hall Walker	1936 Ld Astor	1965 M J Ternynck
1908 Mr J B Joel	1937 H.H. Aga Khan	1966 Lady Zia Wernher
1909 Mr "Fairie"	1938 Ld Derby	1967 Mr H J Joel
1910 Mr "Fairie"	1939 Ld Rosebery	1968 Mr Raymond R Guest
1911 Ld Derby	1940 Lord Rothermere	1969 Mr D Robinson
1912 Mr T Pilkington	1941 Ld Glanely	1970 Mr C Engelhard
1913 Mr J B Joel	1942 His Majesty	1971 Mr P Mellon
1914 Mr J B Joel	1943 Miss D Paget	1972 Mrs J Hislop
1915 Mr L Neumann	1944 H.H. Aga Khan	1973 Mr N B Hunt
1916 Mr E Hulton	1945 Ld Derby	1974 Mr N B Hunt
1917 Mr "Fairie"	1946 H.H. Aga Khan	1975 Dr C Vittadini
1918 Lady James Douglas	1947 H.H. Aga Khan	1976 Mr D Wildenstein
1919 Ld Glanely	1948 H.H. Aga Khan	1977 Mr R Sangster
1920 Sir Robert Jardine	1949 H.H. Aga Khan	1978 Mr R Sangster
1921 Mr S B Joel	1950 M M Boussac	1979 Sir M Sobell
1922 Ld Woolavington	1951 M M Boussac	1980 S Weinstock
1923 Ld Derby	1952 H. H. Aga Khan	1981 H.H. Aga Khan

1982 Mr R Sangster	1993 Sheikh Mohammed	2004 Godolphin
1983 Mr R Sangster	1994 Mr Hamdan Al-Maktoum	2005 Mr Hamdan Al-Maktoum
1984 Mr R Sangster	1995 Mr Hamdan Al-Maktoum	2006 Godolphin
1985 Sheikh Mohammed	1996 Godolphin	2007 Godolphin
1986 Sheikh Mohammed	1997 Sheikh Mohammed	2008 HRH Princess Haya of Jordan
1987 Sheikh Mohammed	1998 Godolphin	2009 Mr Hamdan Al-Maktoum
1988 Sheikh Mohammed	1999 Godolphin	2010 K Abdullah
1989 Sheikh Mohammed	2000 H.H. Aga Khan	2011 K Abdullah
1990 Mr Hamdan Al-Maktoum	2001 K Abdullah	2012 Godolphin
1991 Sheikh Mohammed	2002 Mr Hamdan Al-Maktoum	2013 Godolphin
1992 Sheikh Mohammed	2003 K Abdullah	

LEADING SIRES ON THE FLAT: 1895-2013

1895 St Simon	1935 Blandford	1975 Great Nephew
1896 St Simon	1936 Fairway	1976 Wolver Hollow
1897 Kendal	1937 Solario	1977 Northern Dancer
1898 Galopin	1938 Blandford	1978 Mill Reef (USA)
1899 Orme	1939 Fairway	1979 Petingo
1900 St Simon	1940 Hyperion	1980 Pitcairn
1901 St Simon	1941 Hyperion	1981 Great Nephew
1902 Persimmon	1942 Hyperion	1982 Be My Guest (USA)
1903 St Frusquin	1943 Fairway	1983 Northern Dancer
1904 Gallinule	1944 Fairway	1984 Northern Dancer
1905 Gallinule	1945 Hyperion	1985 Kris
1906 Persimmon	1946 Hyperion	1986 Nijinsky (CAN)
1907 St Frusquin	1947 Nearco	1987 Mill Reef (USA)
1908 Persimmon	1948 Big Game	1988 Caerleon (USA)
1909 Cyllene	1949 Nearco	1989 Blushing Groom (FR)
1910 Cyllene	1950 Fair Trial	1990 Sadler's Wells (USA)
1911 Sundridge	1951 Nasrullah	1991 Caerleon (USA)
1912 Persimmon	1952 Tehran	1992 Sadler's Wells (USA)
1913 Desmond	1953 Chanteur II	1993 Sadler's Wells (USA)
1914 Polymelus	1954 Hyperion	1994 Sadler's Wells (USA)
1915 Polymelus	1955 Alycidon	1995 Sadler's Wells (USA)
1916 Polymelus	1956 Court Martial	1996 Sadler's Wells (USA)
1917 Bayardo	1957 Court Martial	1997 Sadler's Wells (USA)
1918 Bayardo	1958 Mossborough	1998 Sadler's Wells (USA)
1919 The Tetrarch	1959 Petition	1999 Sadler's Wells (USA)
1920 Polymelus	1960 Aureole	2000 Sadler's Wells (USA)
1921 Polymelus	1961 Aureole	2001 Sadler's Wells (USA)
1922 Lemberg	1962 Never Say Die	2002 Sadler's Wells (USA)
1923 Swynford	1963 Ribot	2003 Sadler's Wells (USA)
1924 Son-in-Law	1964 Chamossaire	2004 Sadler's Wells (USA)
1925 Phalaris	1965 Court Harwell	2005 Danehill (USA)
1926 Hurry On	1966 Charlottesville	2006 Danehill (USA)
1927 Buchan	1967 Ribot	2007 Danehill (USA)
1928 Phalaris	1968 Ribot	2008 Galileo (IRE)
1929 Tetratema	1969 Crepello	2009 Danehill Dancer (IRE)
1930 Son-in-Law	1970 Northern Dancer	2010 Galileo (IRE)
1931 Pharos	1971 Never Bend	2011 Galileo (IRE)
1932 Gainsborough	1972 Queen's Hussar	2012 Galileo (IRE)
1933 Gainsborough	1973 Vaguely Noble	2013 Galileo (IRE)
1934 Blandford	1974 Vaguely Noble	

LEADING BREEDERS ON THE FLAT: 1911-2013

1911 Ld Derby (late)	1919 Ld Derby	1927 Ld Derby
1912 Col. W Hall Walker	1920 Ld Derby	1928 Ld Derby
1913 Mr J B Joel	1921 Mr S B Joel	1929 Ld Derby
1914 Mr J B Joel	1922 Ld Derby	1930 Ld Derby
1915 Mr L Neumann	1923 Ld Derby	1931 Ld Dewar
1916 Mr E Hulton	1924 Lady Sykes	1932 H.H. Aga Khan
1917 Mr "Fairie"	1925 Ld Astor	1933 Sir Alec Black
1918 Lady James Douglas	1926 Ld Woolavington	1934 H.H. Aga Khan

1935 H.H. Aga Khan	1961 Eve Stud Ltd	1988 H. H. Aga Khan
1936 Ld Astor	1962 Maj L B Holliday	1989 Mr Hamdan Al- Maktoum
1937 H.H. Aga Khan	1963 Mr H F Guggenheim	1990 Capt. Macdonald- Buchanan
1938 Ld Derby	1964 Bull Run Stud	1991 Barronstown Stud
1939 Ld Rosebery	1965 Mr J Ternynck	1992 Swettenham Stud
1940 Mr H E Morriss	1966 Someries Stud	1993 Juddmonte Farms
1941 Ld Glanely	1967 Mr H J Joel	1994 Shadwell Farm & Estate Ltd
1942 National Stud	1968 Mill Ridge Farm	1995 Shadwell Farm & Estate Ltd
1943 Miss D Paget	1969 Lord Rosebery	1996 Sheikh Mohammed
1944 Ld Rosebery	1970 Mr E P Taylor	1997 Sheikh Mohammed
1945 Ld Derby	1971 Mr P Mellon	1998 Sheikh Mohammed
1946 Lt- Col H Boyd-Rochfort	1972 Mr J Hislop	1999 H. H. The Aga Khan's Studs
1947 H.H. Aga Khan	1973 Claiborne Farm	2000 H. H. The Aga Khan's Studs
1948 H.H. Aga Khan	1974 Mr N B Hunt	2001 Shadwell Farm & Estate Ltd
1949 H.H. Aga Khan	1975 Overbury Stud	2002 Gainsborough Stud
1950 M M Boussac	1976 Dayton Ltd	2003 Juddmonte
1951 M M Boussac	1977 Mr E P Taylor	2004 Juddmonte
1952 H. H. Aga Khan	1978 Cragwood Estates Inc	2005 Shadwell Farm & Estate Ltd
1953 Mr F Darling	1979 Ballymacoll Stud	2006 Darley
1954 Maj L B Holliday	1980 P Clarke	2007 Darley
1955 Someries Stud	1981 H.H. Aga Khan	2008 Darley
1956 Maj L B Holliday	1982 Someries Stud	2009 Darley
1957 Eve Stud	1983 White Lodge Stud	2010 Juddmonte
1958 Mr R Ball	1984 Mr E P Taylor	2011 Juddmonte
1959 Prince Aly Khan and the late	1985 Dalham Stud Farms	2012 Juddmonte
H.H. Aga Khan	1986 H.H. Aga Khan	2013 Darley
1960 Eve Stud Ltd	1987 Cliveden Stud	

LEADING TRAINERS OVER JUMPS: 1946-2013

1946-47 F T T Walwyn	1969-70 T F Rimell	1992-93 M C Pipe
1947-48 F T T Walwyn	1970-71 F T Winter	1993-94 D Nicholson
1948-49 F T T Walwyn	1971-72 F T Winter	1994-95 D Nicholson
1949-50 P V F Cazalet	1972-73 F T Winter	1995-96 M C Pipe
1950-51 T F Rimell	1973-74 F T Winter	1996-97 M C Pipe
1951-52 N Crump	1974-75 F T Winter	1997-98 M C Pipe
1952-53 M V O'Brien	1975-76 T F Rimell	1998-99 M C Pipe
1953-54 M V O'Brien	1976-77 F T Winter	1999-00 M C Pipe
1954-55 H R Price	1977-78 F T Winter	2000-01 M C Pipe
1955-56 W Hall	1978-79 M H Easterby	2001-02 M C Pipe
1956-57 N Crump	1979-80 M H Easterby	2002-03 M C Pipe
1957-58 F T T Walwyn	1980-81 M H Easterby	2003-04 M C Pipe
1958-59 H R Price	1981-82 M W Dickinson	2004-05 M C Pipe
1959-60 P V F Cazalet	1982-83 M W Dickinson	2005-06 P F Nicholls
1960-61 T F Rimell	1983-84 M W Dickinson	2006-07 P F Nicholls
1961-62 H R Price	1984-85 F T Winter	2007-08 P F Nicholls
1962-63 K Piggott	1985-86 N J Henderson	2008-09 P F Nicholls
1963-64 F T T Walwyn	1986-87 N J Henderson	2009-10 P F Nicholls
1964-65 P V F Cazalet	1987-88 D R C Elsworth	2010-11 P F Nicholls
1965-66 H R Price	1988-89 M C Pipe	2010-11 P F Nicholls
1966-67 H R Price	1989-90 M C Pipe	2011-12 P F Nicholls
1967-68 Denys Smith	1990-91 M C Pipe	2012-13 N J Henderson
1968-69 T F Rimell	1991-92 M C Pipe	

CHAMPION JOCKEYS OVER JUMPS: 1900-2013

Prior to the 1925-26 season the figure relates to racing between January and December

1900	Mr H Sidney	53	1907	F Mason	59	1914	Mr J R Anthony	60
1901	F Mason	58	1908	P Cowley	65	1915	E Piggott	44
1902	F Mason	67	1909	R Gordon	45	1916	C Hawkins	17
1903	P Woodland	54	1910	E Piggott	67	1917	W Smith	15
1904	F Mason	59	1911	W Payne	76	1918	G Duller	17
1905	F Mason	73	1912	I Anthony	78	1919	Mr H Brown	48
1906	F Mason	58	1913	E Piggott	60	1920	F B Rees	64

1921	F B Rees	65	1951-52	T Moloney	99	P Scudamore	120

1921 F B Rees.....................65	1951-52 T Moloney 99	P Scudamore.......120
1922 J Anthony....................78	1952-53 F Winter....................121	1982-83 J Francome 106
1923 F B Rees.....................64	1953-54 F Francis 76	1983-84 J Francome 131
1924 F B Rees....................108	1954-55 T Moloney 67	1984-85 J Francome 101
1925 E Foster......................76	1955-56 F Winter.....................74	1985-86 P Scudamore..............91
1925-26 T Leader..................61	1956-57 F Winter.....................80	1986-87 P Scudamore.............123
1926-27 F B Rees..................59	1957-58 F Winter.....................82	1987-88 P Scudamore.............132
1927-28 W Stott....................88	1958-59 T Brookshaw 83	1988-89 P Scudamore.............221
1928-29 W Stott....................65	1959-60 S Mellor.....................68	1989-90 P Scudamore.............170
1929-30 W Stott....................77	1960-61 S Mellor...................118	1990-91 P Scudamore.............141
1930-31 W Stott....................81	1961-62 S Mellor.....................80	1991-92 P Scudamore.............175
1931-32 W Stott....................77	1962-63 J Gifford....................70	1992-93 R Dunwoody..............173
1932-33 G Wilson..................61	1963-64 J Gifford....................94	1993-94 R Dunwoody..............197
1933-34 G Wilson..................56	1964-65 T Biddlecombe 114	1994-95 R Dunwoody..............160
1934-35 G Wilson..................73	1965-66 T Biddlecombe 102	1995-96 A P McCoy................175
1935-36 G Wilson..................57	1966-67 J Gifford..................122	1996-97 A P McCoy................190
1936-37 G Wilson..................45	1967-68 J Gifford....................82	1997-98 A P McCoy................253
1937-38 G Wilson..................59	1968-69 B R Davies.................77	1998-99 A P McCoy................186
1938-39 T F Rimell.................61	T Biddlecombe 77	1999-00 A P McCoy................245
1939-40 T F Rimell.................24	1969-70 B R Davies.................91	2000-01 A P McCoy................191
1940-41 G Wilson..................22	1970-71 G Thorner..................74	2001-02 A P McCoy................289
1941-42 R Smyth...................12	1971-72 B R Davies.................89	2002-03 A P McCoy................256
1942-43 No racing	1972-73 R Barry 125	2003-04 A P McCoy................209
1943-44 No racing	1973-74 R Barry 94	2004-05 A P McCoy................200
1944-45 H Nicholson...............15	1974-75 T Stack 82	2005-06 A P McCoy................178
T F Rimell.........................15	1975-76 J Francome.................96	2006-07 A P McCoy................184
1945-46 T F Rimell.................54	1976-77 T Stack 97	2007-08 A P McCoy................140
1946-47 J Dowdeswell............58	1977-78 J J O'Neill 149	2008-09 A P McCoy................186
1947-48 B Marshall................66	1978-79 J Francome.................95	2009-10 A P McCoy................195
1948-49 T Moloney.................60	1979-80 J J O'Neill 117	2010-11 A P McCoy................218
1949-50 T Moloney.................95	1980-81 J Francome................105	2011-12 A P McCoy................199
1950-51 T Moloney.................83	1981-82 J Francome................120	2012-13 A P McCoy................185

LEADING OWNERS OVER JUMPS: 1946-2013

(Please note that prior to the 1994-95 season the leading owner was determined by win prizemoney only)

1946-47 Mr J J McDowell	1969-70 Mr E R Courage	Racing Stables Ltd
1947-48 Mr J Proctor	1970-71 Mr F Pontin	1992-93 Mrs J Mould
1948-49 Mr W F Williamson	1971-72 Capt T A Forster	1993-94 Pell-Mell Partners
1949-50 Mrs L Brotherton	1972-73 Mr N H Le Mare	1994-95 Roach Foods Limited
1950-51 Mr J Royle	1973-74 Mr N H Le Mare	1995-96 Mr A T A Wates
1951-52 Miss D Paget	1974-75 Mr R Guest	1996-97 Mr R Ogden
1952-53 Mr J H Griffin	1975-76 Mr P B Raymond	1997-98 Mr D A Johnson
1953-54 Mr J H Griffin	1976-77 Mr N H Le Mare	1998-99 Mr J P McManus
1954-55 Mrs W H E Welman	1977-78 Mrs O Jackson	1999-00 Mr R Ogden
1955-56 Mrs L Carver	1978-79 Snailwell Stud Co Ltd	2000-01 Sir R Ogden
1956-57 Mrs Geoffrey Kohn	1979-80 Mr H J Joel	2001-02 Mr D A Johnson
1957-58 Mr D J Coughlan	1980-81 Mr R J Wilson	2002-03 Mr D A Johnson
1958-59 Mr J E Bigg	1981-82 Sheikh Ali Abu Khamsin	2003-04 Mr D A Johnson
1959-60 Miss W H Wallace	1982-83 Sheikh Ali Abu Khamsin	2004-05 Mr D A Johnson
1960-61 Mr C Vaughan	1983-84 Sheikh Ali Abu Khamsin	2005-06 Mr J P McManus
1961-62 Mr N Cohen	1984-85 T Kilroe and Son Ltd	2006-07 Mr J P McManus
1962-63 Mr P B Raymond	1985-86 Sheikh Ali Abu Khamsin	2007-08 Mr D A Johnson
1963-64 Mr J K Goodman	1986-87 Mr H J Joel	2008-09 Mr J P McManus
1964-65 Mrs M Stephenson	1987-88 Miss Juliet E Reed	2009-10 Mr J P McManus
1965-66 Duchess of Westminster	1988-89 Mr R Burridge	2010-11 Mr T Hemmings
1966-67 Mr C P T Watkins	1989-90 Mrs Harry J Duffey	2011-12 Mr J P McManus
1967-68 Mr H S Alper	1990-91 Mr P Piller	2012-13 Mr J P McManus
1968-69 Mr B P Jenks	1991-92 Whitcombe Manor	

LEADING AMATEUR RIDERS OVER JUMPS: 1947-201~~3~~

1947-48 Ld Mildmay..................22	1951-52 Mr C Straker...............19	1955-56 Mr R McCreery............
1948-49 Ld Mildmay..................30	1952-53 Mr A H Moralee 22	Mr A H Moralee ....
1949-50 Ld Mildmay..................38	1953-54 Mr A H Moralee 22	1956-57 Mr R McCreery............
1950-51 Mr P Chisman.............13	1954-55 Mr A H Moralee 16	1957-58 Mr J Lawrence............

1958-59 Mr J Sutcliffe	18	
1959-60 Mr G Kindersley	22	
1960-61 Sir W Pigott-Brown	28	
1961-62 Mr A Biddlecombe	30	
1962-63 Sir W Pigott-Brown	20	
1963-64 Mr S Davenport	32	
1964-65 Mr M Gifford	15	
1965-66 Mr C Collins	24	
1966-67 Mr C Collins	33	
1967-68 Mr R Tate	30	
1968-69 Mr R Tate	17	
1969-70 Mr M Dickinson	23	
1970-71 Mr J Lawrence	17	
1971-72 Mr W Foulkes	26	
1972-73 Mr R Smith	56	
1973-74 Mr A Webber	21	
1974-75 Mr R Lamb	22	
1975-76 Mr P Greenall	25	
Mr G Jones	25	

1976-77 Mr P Greenall	27
1977-78 Mr G Sloan	23
1978-79 Mr T G Dun	26
1979-80 Mr O Sherwood	29
1980-81 Mr P Webber	32
1981-82 Mr D Browne	28
1982-83 Mr D Browne	33
1983-84 Mr S Sherwood	28
1984-85 Mr S Sherwood	30
1985-86 Mr T Thomson Jones	25
1986-87 Mr T Thomson Jones	19
1987-88 Mr T Thomson Jones	15
1988-89 Mr P Fenton	18
1989-90 Mr P McMahon	15
1990-91 Mr K Johnson	24
1991-92 Mr M P Hourigan	24
1992-93 Mr A Thornton	26
1993-94 Mr J Greenall	21
1994-95 Mr D Parker	16

1995-96 Mr J Culloty	40
1996-97 Mr R Thornton	30
1997-98 Mr S Durack	41
1998-99 Mr A Dempsey	47
1999-00 Mr P Flynn	41
2000-01 Mr T Scudamore	24
2001-02 Mr D Crosse	19
2002-03 Mr C Williams	23
2003-04 Mr O Nelmes	14
2004-05 Mr T Greenall	31
2005-06 Mr T O'Brien	32
2006-07 Mr T Greenall	31
2007-08 Mr T Greenall	23
2008-09 Mr O Greenall	23
2009-10 Mr O Greenall	41
2010-11 Mr R Mahon	19
2011-12 Miss E Sayer	11
2012-13 Mr N de Boinville	16

LEADING SIRES OVER JUMPS: 1986-2013

1986 Deep Run	1995-96 Strong Gale	2005-06 Supreme Leader
1987 Deep Run	1996-97 Strong Gale	2006-07 Presenting
1988 Deep Run	1997-98 Strong Gale	2007-08 Old Vic
1989 Deep Run	1998-99 Strong Gale	2008-09 Presenting
1989-90 Deep Run	1999-00 Strong Gale	2009-10 Presenting
1990-91 Deep Run	2000-01 Be My Native (USA)	2010-11 Presenting
1991-92 Deep Run	2001-02 Be My Native (USA)	2011-12 King's Theatre
1992-93 Deep Run	2002-03 Be My Native (USA)	2012-13 Beneficial
1993-94 Strong Gale	2003-04 Be My Native (USA)	
1994-95 Strong Gale	2004-05 Supreme Leader	

JOCKEYS' AGENTS

Jockeys' Agents and their Contact Details

Agent	Telephone	Mobile/Email	Fax
NICKY ADAMS	01488 72004/72964	07796 547659 nickadams1961@hotmail.co.uk	
NEIL ALLAN	01243 543870	07985 311141/07825 549081 aneil@aol.com	
NIGEL BAXTER	01942 269972	07973 561521 nigelbaxter@blueyonder.co.uk	
PAUL BRIERLEY	01434 608212	07824 828750 bbjockeys@hotmail.co.uk	
CHRIS BROAD	01452 760482/447	07836 622858 chrisd.broad@yahoo.co.uk	01452 760394
ADAM BROOK	01422 378597	07757 968824 agent@adambrook.co.uk	
PAUL CLARKE	01638 660804	07885 914306 paul.clarke79@btinternet.com	
RAY COCHRANE	01223 812008	07798 651247 ray@raysagency.co.uk	
DANIEL CREIGHTON		07597 945219 danielcreighton@hotmail.com	
SIMON DODDS	01509 852344/852254	07974 924735 simon.dodds@btinternet.com	
JACQUI DOYLE	01488 72788	07831 880678 doyleracing@yahoo.co.uk	
SHIPPY ELLIS	01638 668484	07860 864864 shippysjockeys@btconnect.com	01638 660946

Agent	Telephone	Mobile/Email	Fax
TONY ELVES	01638 454012	07969 051306 tony.elves@yahoo.co.uk	
JOHN W FORD	01954 261122	07830 294210 john.ford47@btinternet.com	
MARK FURNASS	01347 824633	07988 203831 jockeysagent@gmail.com	
MARK GILCHRIST		07810 821787 shaz.gilly@hotmail.co.uk	
JAYNE GOLLINGS	01507 343204	07836 711122 jaynemgollings@aol.com	
PAUL GRUNDY	01845 597850	07760 993936 pg2960@btinternet.com	
MICHAEL HAGGAS	01638 660811	07740 624550 mhaggas@ntlworld.com	
RICHARD HALE	01768 88699	07909 520542 richardhale77@hotmail.co.uk	
HELEN HAMILTON	01653 697882	07908 860239 tony@thamilton.orangehome.co.uk	
DAVID HARRISON	01614 087888	07592 767206 davidpharrison@hotmail.com	
ALAN HARRISON	01969 625006	07846 187991 ahjockagent60@yahoo.co.uk	0560 2729293
TONY HIND	01638 724997	07807 908599 tonyhind@jockeysagent.com	
GAVIN HORNE	01392 423352	07914 897170 gavin.horne@hotmail.co.uk	
JO HUGHES	01488 71103	07900 680189 johughes3@aol.co.uk	01488 71444

Agent	Telephone	Mobile/Email	Fax
RUSS JAMES	01653 699466	07947 414001 russjames2006@btinternet.com	01653 699581
BRUCE JEFFREY	01750 21521	07747 854684 brucejeffrey@live.co.uk	
GUY JEWELL	01672 861231	07765 248859 guyjewell@btconnect.com	01672 861231
ANDREW LEWIS	01908 473812	07838 506594 andrew.lewis11@sky.com	
JESSIE LODGE	01635 281166	07887 870389 jessie.lodge@btinternet.com	
DAVID LYONS	0117 3730674	07861 500508 davidly0ns@live.co.uk	
NICK MCKEE		07554 867209 nbmckee30@googlemail.com	
SARA-LOUISE METCALFE	01635 298067	07900 207018 troopersjockeys@hotmail.co.uk	
LOUISE MILLMAN	01884 266620	07740 932791 rod.millman@ic24.net	
PHILIP MITCHELL	01367 820299	07836 231462 philipmitchell48@gmail.com	
LEE NEWTON	01302 376370	07710 422437 newton808@btinternet.com	
TERRY NORMAN	01279 419395	07900 525033 tj.norman@hotmail.co.uk	01279 432619
JAMES O'FARRELL		07821 617976/07741 264475 jpfarrello@hotmail.com	
GARETH OWEN	01603 569390	07958 335206 gareth@willowracing.com	

Agent	Telephone	Mobile/Email	Fax
SHASHI RIGHTON	01353 688081	07825 381350 slasher74@aol.com	
DAVE ROBERTS	01737 761369	07860 234342 daveroberts.racing@nhworld.com	
MICHELLE SMITH	01638 668509	07860 467220 michelle@safetyrelease.co.uk	
SAM STRONGE	01488 72818	07775 727778 sam.stronge@virgin.net	01488 670378
GARY THOMSON	01642 873152	07986 607014 garythomson73@me.com	
JENNIFER WALSH	00353 45883704	00353 872528025 jennifer@ruby-walsh.com	00353 45871929
IAN WARDLE	01793 688858	07831 865974 ian.wardlex@googlemail.com	
LAURA WAY	01704 834488	07775 777494 laura.way@btconnect.com	
IAN WOOD	01488 72324	07733 156380 ianwood@chase3c.com	

MULTIPLE
MULTIPLE
MULTIPLE
MULTIPLE
MULTIPLE
MULTIPLE
MULTIPLE
MULTIPLE
MULTIPLE
MULTIPLE
MULTIPLE
MULTIPLE
MULTIPLE
BETS

You asked for it, so we're givin it to you — multiple bets on th Racing Post Mobile App with William Hill and Ladbrokes.

With a multitude of multiples to choose from, the chance for a bigger payout has never been so close to hand.

RACING POST

FLAT JOCKEYS

Riding weights and contact details

An index of agents appears on page 712

AHMED AJTEBI	8 - 7	07771 777010
DAVID ALLAN	8 - 7	Mr G. R. Owen
PADDY ASPELL	8 - 9	Mr R. A. Hale
ANDREA ATZENI	8 - 0	Mr Paul Clarke
AMY BAKER	7 - 12	0781 0723342
GEORGE BAKER	9 - 0	Mr G. D. Jewell
MICKAEL BARZALONA	8 - 5	Mr R. Cochrane
HARRY BENTLEY	8 - 2	Mr T. J. Norman
ADAM BESCHIZZA	8 - 4	Mr John W. Ford
WILLIAM BUICK	8 - 6	Mr M. R. Haggas
DONNA CALDWELL	7 - 12	Mr Paul Brierley
NEIL CALLAN	8 - 7	Mr S. T. Dodds
DECLAN CANNON	7 - 13	Mr Alan Harrison
WILLIAM CARSON	8 - 2	Mr Neil Allan
ADAM CARTER	8 - 6	Mr Alan Harrison
CHRIS CATLIN	8 - 3	Mr N. M. Adams
AIDAN COLEMAN	9 - 0	Mr S. Stronge
PAT COSGRAVE	8 - 8	Mr N. M. Adams
DOUGIE COSTELLO	8 - 10	Mr Dave Roberts
MARK COUMBE	8 - 4	Mr Mark Gilchrist
STEPHEN CRAINE	8 - 11	Mr Mark Gilchrist
JIM CROWLEY	8 - 7	Mr G. D. Jewell
BEN CURTIS	8 - 2	Mr S. T. Dodds
RAUL DA SILVA	7 - 11	Mr M. Furnass
MATTHEW DAVIES	8 - 10	07702 359356
SILVESTRE DE SOUSA	7 - 12	Mr G. R. Owen
FRANKIE DETTORI	8 - 7	Mr R. Cochrane
PAT DOBBS	8 - 7	Mr Tony Hind
PATRICK DONAGHY	8 - 6	07864 006781
STEVIE DONOHOE	8 - 6	Mr L. R. James
BRETT DOYLE	8 - 6	07445 202925
JAMES DOYLE	8 - 7	Mr M. R. Haggas
STEVE DROWNE	8 - 7	Mr I. P. Wardle
TED DURCAN	8 - 6	Mr David Harrison
MARTIN DWYER	8 - 4	Mr S. T. Dodds
NATASHA EATON	7 - 10	Mr A. D. Lewis
TOM EAVES	8 - 6	Mr R. A. Hale
ANDREW ELLIOTT	8 - 4	Mr N. A. Baxter
JOHN FAHY	8 - 4	Mr N. M. Adams
KIEREN FALLON	8 - 6	Mr G. R. Owen
JOE FANNING	8 - 2	Mr W. P. Grundy
DURAN FENTIMAN	8 - 0	Mr Alan Harrison
MICKY FENTON	8 - 8	07841 829419
JENNIFER FERGUSON	7 - 12	01622 880767
ROYSTON FFRENCH	8 - 4	Mr R. A. Hale
ROBBIE FITZPATRICK	8 - 6	Mr S. M. Righton
JIMMY FORTUNE	8 - 9	Mr Tony Hind
DOMINIC FOX	8 - 2	07856 666234
KIEREN FOX	8 - 2	Mr Mark Gilchrist
CATHY GANNON	7 - 12	Mr Neil Allan
NATALIA GEMELOVA	7 - 9	Mr John W. Ford
GRAHAM GIBBONS	8 - 6	Mrs L. H. Way
SALEEM GOLAM	8 - 5	Mr Paul Clarke
RACHAEL GREEN	9 - 7	01308 868272
J.-P. GUILLAMBERT	8 - 9	07789 172956
MARC HALFORD	8 - 7	Mr Ian Wood
TONY HAMILTON	8 - 7	Mrs H. Hamilton
PAUL HANAGAN	8 - 0	Mr R. A. Hale
MARTIN HARLEY	8 - 9	Mr Neil Allan
ROBERT HAVLIN	8 - 6	Mr I. P. Wardle
SAM HITCHCOTT	8 - 5	Mr N. M. Adams
BRIAN HUGHES	9 - 7	Mr R. A. Hale
RICHARD HUGHES	8 - 7	Mr Tony Hind
LIAM JONES	8 - 2	Mr Paul Clarke
SHANE KELLY	8 - 7	Mrs L. H. Way
LIAM KENIRY	8 - 6	Mr N. M. Adams
RUSS KENNEMORE	8 - 7	Mr L. R. James
RICHARD KINGSCOTE	8 - 5	Mr G. D. Jewell
ADAM KIRBY	8 - 12	Mr N. M. Adams
RACHEAL KNELLER	8 - 0	07828 961415
MARTIN LANE	8 - 0	Mr S. T. Dodds
GRAHAM LEE	8 - 9	Mr R. A. Hale
SEAN LEVEY	8 - 10	Mr Tony Hind
JAMIE MACKAY	8 - 0	Mr M. Furnass
NICKY MACKAY	8 - 0	Mr Paul Clarke
PHILLIP MAKIN	8 - 9	Mr R. A. Hale
JEMMA MARSHALL	8 - 0	01273 620405
PATRICK MATHERS	8 - 2	Mr A. T. Brook
FRANKIE MCDONALD	7 - 13	Mr N. M. Adams
P. J. MCDONALD	8 - 4	Mr R. A. Hale
BARRY MCHUGH	8 - 4	Mr R. A. Hale
TOM MCLAUGHLIN	8 - 10	Mr G. J. Horne
KIRSTY MILCZAREK	8 - 2	Mr M. Furnass
JACK MITCHELL	8 - 6	Mr Philip Mitchell
RYAN MOORE	8 - 7	Mr Tony Hind
LUKE MORRIS	8 - 0	Mr Neil Allan
ANDREW MULLEN	8 - 0	Mr S. M. Righton
PAUL MULRENNAN	8 - 6	Mr R. A. Hale
ADRIAN NICHOLLS	8 - 1	Mr S. M. Righton
DAVID NOLAN	8 - 13	Mr R. A. Hale
FRANNY NORTON	8 - 0	Mr I. P Wardle
MICHAEL O'CONNELL	8 - 8	07981 686503
DARAGH O'DONOHOE	8 - 5	07718 086654
CONOR O'FARRELL	9 - 7	Mr Dave Roberts\
		Mr J. P O'Farrell
SLADE O'HARA	8 - 8	Mr A. T. Brook\
		Mr L. Newton
KIERAN O'NEILL	7 - 12	Mr G. D. Jewell
SIMON PEARCE	7 - 13	Mr N. M. Adams
PAUL PICKARD	8 - 5	Mr A. D. Lewis
LAURA PIKE	8 - 4	Mr L. R. James
I. POULLIS	8 - 8	07708 376642
HARRY POULTON	8 - 9	Mr Ian Wood
RYAN POWELL	7 - 12	Mr N. M. Adams
DAVID PROBERT	8 - 2	Miss S. L. Metcalfe
TOM QUEALLY	8 - 7	Mr T. Elves
AMIR QUINN	8 - 11	Mr L. R. James
JIMMY QUINN	7 - 12	Mr G. J. Horne
PAUL QUINN	7 - 12	Mr S. M. Righton
WILSON RENWICK	9 - 0	Mr R. A. Hale
AMY RYAN	8 - 2	Mr R. A. Hale
SEB SANDERS	8 - 7	Mr I. P. Wardle
VICTOR SANTOS	7 - 12	Mr A. D. Lewis
KATIA SCALLAN	7 - 7	07585 802986
AMY SCOTT	7 - 13	07894 018259
PAOLO SIRIGU	7 - 12	Mr S. M. Righton

J. D. SMITH	8 - 10		Mr D. P. J. Lyons
RENATO SOUZA	8 - 5		Mr A. T. Brook\
			Mr L. Newton
JAMIE SPENCER	8 - 6		07879 478158
MICHAEL STAINTON	8 - 10		01638 665511
ANN STOKELL	8 - 7		07814 579982
JAMES SULLIVAN	8 - 0		Mr R. A. Hale
FERGUS SWEENEY	8 - 9		Mr G. D. Jewell
DALE SWIFT	8 - 7		Mr R. A. Hale
RICHARD THOMAS	8 - 2		Mr I. P. Wardle

LEE TOPLISS	8 - 10		Mr R. A. Hale
LIAM TREADWELL	9 - 6		Mr Dave Roberts\
			Mr Mark Gilchrist
DANIEL TUDHOPE	8 - 8		Mrs L. H. Way
HAYLEY TURNER	8 - 2		Mr G. D. Jewell
FREDERIK TYLICKI	8 - 6		Mrs L. H. Way
CHARLIE WALLIS	9 - 5		Mr L. R. James
GARRY WHILLANS	8 - 7		Mr Alan Harrison
ROBERT WINSTON	8 - 7		Mr L. Newton

Only riders we have contact details for are included
in this section.

Are your details missing or incorrect?
Please update us by email:
richard.lowther@racingpost.co.uk
Or leave a message on 0500 007071

APPRENTICES

Riding weights and contact details

An index of agents appears on page 712

SINEAD ALDERMAN (Roger Teal)	8 - 2	Mr A. D. Lewis
LUCY ALEXANDER (N. W. Alexander)	9 - 0	c/o 07831 488210
NATHAN ALISON (William Haggas)	7 - 12	Mr Paul Clarke
ROSS ATKINSON (Roger Varian)	8 - 4	Mr N. M. Adams
LAURA BARRY (Tony Coyle)	8 - 4	Mr R. A. Hale
DECLAN BATES (David Evans)	8 - 5	Mr L. R. James
JOSH BAUDAINS (Dominic Ffrench Davis)	8 - 3	Mr L. R. James
GEORGINA BAXTER (Kristin Stubbs)	8 - 0	Mr A. D. Lewis
CONNOR BEASLEY (Michael Dods)	8 - 0	Mr R. A. Hale
SAMANTHA BELL (Richard Fahey)	7 - 10	Mr R. A. Hale
CHARLIE BENNETT (Hughie Morrison)	7 - 12	Mr G. J. Thomson
SHELLEY BIRKETT (Julia Feilden)	7 - 12	Mr John W. Ford
CHARLES BISHOP (Olly Stevens)	8 - 6	Jessie Lodge\Mr G. D. Jewell
AIDEN BLAKEMORE (Tony Carroll)	8 - 4	c/o 01386 861020
PAIGE BOLTON (Lee Carter)	8 - 2	c/o 01372 740878
PAUL BOOTH (Dean Ivory)	8 - 5	Mr L. R. James
BRADLEY BOSLEY (Ed Walker)	7 - 12	Mr L. R. James
DANNY BROCK (Marco Botti)	8 - 0	Mr Ian Wood
THOMAS BROWN (Andrew Balding)	8 - 7	Mr David Harrison
GEORGE BUCKELL (David Simcock)	8 - 2	Mrs Michelle Smith
JULIE BURKE (David O'Meara)	7 - 13	Mr R. A. Hale
HARRY BURNS (Jo Hughes)	8 - 0	c/o 07900 680189
JACOB BUTTERFIELD (Ollie Pears)	8 - 7	c/o 07760 197103
DARYL BYRNE (Ronald Harris)	8 - 3	Mr Neil Allan
EIREANN CAGNEY (Richard Fahey)	8 - 4	c/o 01653 698915
GEORGE CHALONER (Richard Fahey)	8 - 1	Mr R. A. Hale
RYAN CLARK (Jeremy Gask)	8 - 6	Mr A. D. Lewis
TIM CLARK (Alan Bailey)	8 - 2	Mr G. J. Horne\Mr N. M. Adams
SAMUEL CLARKE (Chris Wall)	8 - 1	c/o 01638 661999
JAMIE COATES (William Knight)	8 - 2	c/o 01903 871188
GRANT COCKBURN (Lucinda Russell)	9 - 1	Mr Paul Brierley
MATTHEW COSHAM (Nikki Evans)	7 - 7	c/o 07977 753437
JOSH CRANE (Chris Dwyer)	9 - 0	Mr L. R. James
BILLY CRAY (Garry Moss)	8 - 2	Mr L. Newton
MATTHEW COSHAM (Mick Channon)	8 - 0	Mr I. P. Wardle
HECTOR CROUCH (Gary Moore)	7 - 5	c/o 01403 891912
NICOLA CURRIE (Lucinda Russell)	8 - 2	c/o 01577 865512
NED CURTIS (Jonathan Portman)	8 - 9	Mr N. M. Adams
ROBERT DODSWORTH (Mel Brittain)	7 - 9	c/o 01759 371472
GEORGE DOWNING (Ian Williams)	8 - 8	Mr Ian Wood
JOE DOYLE (John Quinn)	7 - 7	Mr M. Furnass
JOSH DOYLE (David O'Meara)	7 - 12	c/o 01439 771400
JACK DUERN (Andrew Hollinshead)	8 - 2	Mr L. Newton
JANE ELLIOTT (Ralph Beckett)	8 - 3	c/o 01264 772278
JONATHAN ENGLAND (Sue Smith)	9 - 3	Mr J. B. Jeffrey
RICHARD EVANS (David Evans)	9 - 5	c/o 01873 890837
NEIL FARLEY (Declan Carroll)	7 - 12	c/o 07801 553779
JAYNE FARWELL (Gary Moore)	8 - 4	c/o 01403 891912
JOB J FITZPATRICK (K. R. Burke)	8 - 0	Mr N. A. Baxter
CRISTY FRENCH (J. S. Moore)	7 - 7	c/o 01488 73887
JOEL GARBUTT (Hugo Palmer)	7 - 2	Mr L. R. James
ELLIE GARNER (Martin Keighley)	9 - 1	Mr L. R. James
THOMAS GARNER (Oliver Sherwood)	9 - 3	Mr Dave Roberts\Mr A. T. Brook
JACK GARRITTY (Andrew Balding)	7 - 5	Mr Mark Gilchrist
JACK GILLIGAN (Sir Mark Prescott Bt)	8 - 2	c/o 01638 662117
JOSEPHINE GORDON (Jo Hughes)	8 - 0	c/o 07900 680189
RACHAEL GRANT (Jim Goldie)	8 - 0	c/o 0411 936989
SHANE GRAY (Kevin Ryan)	7 - 13	Mr R. A. Hale

NICOLA GRUNDY (Alan Berry)	7 - 12	c/o 07880 553515
LAUREN HAIGH (Clive Brittain)	8 - 4	c/o 01638 664347
NATALIE HAMBLING-YATES (Alan McCabe)	8 - 3	c/o 07766 302092
CAMERON HARDIE (Richard Hannon)	7 - 7	Mr Tony Hind
TOMAS HARRIGAN (Gay Kelleway)	8 - 2	c/o 07974 948768
JASON HART (Declan Carroll)	8 - 2	Mr Alan Harrison
JOEY HAYNES (K. R. Burke)	7 - 10	Mr S. T. Dodds
THOMAS HEMSLEY (Michael Bell)	8 - 1	Mr Mark Gilchrist
ANNA HESKETH (David Nicholls)	7 - 13	c/o 01845 501470
JORDAN HIBBERD (Alan Berry)	7 - 9	c/o 07880 553515
RYAN HOLMES (Barry Leavy)	7 - 10	c/o 07540 806915.
MATTHEW HOPKINS (Scott Dixon)	8 - 0	Mr A. D. Lewis
ALEX HOPKINSON (Shaun Harris)	8 - 1	c/o 07768 950460
ROB HORNBY (Andrew Balding)	7 - 10	Mr G. D. Jewell
CHLOE INGRAM (Tim Vaughan)	7 - 10	c/o 01446 771626
RHIAIN INGRAM (Roger Ingram)	7 - 10	c/o 07773 665980
SAM JAMES (David O'Meara)	8 - 4	Mr R. A. Hale
CHARLOTTE JENNER (Mark Usher)	8 - 1	Mr M. Furnass
ROSIE JESSOP (Sir Mark Prescott Bt)	7 - 12	Mr G. R. Owen
STEPHANIE JOANNIDES (William Haggas)	7 - 6	c/o 07860 282281
AARON JONES (Alan McCabe)	8 - 0	Mr A. D. Lewis
CAROLINE KELLY (John Ryan)	7 - 13	c/o 01638 664172
DAVID KENNY (Amy Weaver)	8 - 5	Mr L. R. James
STACEY KIDD (Paul D'Arcy)	8 - 0	c/o 01638 662000
APRIL KITCHENER (Jim Best)	8 - 6	c/o 01435 882073
JOHN LAWSON (Jamie Osborne)	8 - 2	Mr A. D. Lewis
MATTHEW LAWSON (Jonathan Portman)	8 - 3	Mr G. J. Horne\Mr A. T. Brook
LUKE LEADBITTER (Declan Carroll)	8 - 0	Mr Alan Harrison
KEVIN LUNDIE (Brian Ellison)	8 - 0	Mr A. D. Lewis
GARY MAHON (Richard Hannon)	7 - 7	Mr S. M. Righton
EILISH MCCALL (Graeme McPherson)	7 - 6	c/o 07815 887360
CIARAN MCKEE (John O'Shea)	9 - 2	Mr Dave Roberts
ADAM MCLEAN (Derek Shaw)	7 - 13	Mr John W. Ford
JORDON MCMURRAY (John Ryan)	8 - 1	Mr A. D. Lewis
JAMES MERRETT (Charles Hills)	8 - 2	c/o 07774 474969
SIOBHAN MILLER (David Simcock)	8 - 2	c/o 07808 954109
PAT MILLMAN (Rod Millman)	8 - 10	Mr Ian Wood
DANIELLE MOONEY (Michael Easterby)	7 - 12	c/o 01347 878368
ASHLEY MORGAN (Chris Wall)	8 - 5	Mr Mark Gilchrist
EVA MOSCROP (Philip Kirby)	7 - 10	c/o 01969 624400
PAULA MUIR (Mark Johnston)	8 - 0	c/o 01969 622237
MICHAEL J. M. MURPHY (Mark Johnston)	8 - 2	Mr S. T. Dodds
OISIN MURPHY (Andrew Balding)	7 - 11	Miss S. L. Metcalfe
CLAIRE MURRAY (David Brown)	8 - 4	c/o 07889 132931
DANIEL MUSCUTT (Andrew Balding)	8 - 0	Miss S. L. Metcalfe
ADAM NICOL (Philip Kirby)	9 - 4	Mr Paul Brierley\Mr R. A. Hale
PATRICK O'DONNELL (Ralph Beckett)	8 - 0	c/o 01264 772278
JACK OSBORN (Gary Harrison)	8 - 1	Mr A. D. Lewis
DAVID PARKES (Jeremy Gask)	8 - 6	Mr A. T. Brook\Miss S. L. Metcalfe
PHILIP PRINCE (Liam Corcoran)	8 - 6	Mr Mark Gilchrist
JOSH QUINN (Richard Fahey)	8 - 2	c/o 01653 698915
SOPHIE RALSTON (Pat Phelan)	7 - 12	c/o 07917 762781
PAIGE RANGER (David Simcock)	7 - 12	c/o 07808 954109
ALI RAWLINSON (Michael Appleby)	8 - 6	Mr S. M. Righton
RACHEL RICHARDSON (Tim Easterby)	7 - 10	Mr Alan Harrison
SOPHIE ROBERTSON (Jim Goldie)	8 - 3	c/o 0411 936989
GARY RUTHERFORD (Stuart Coltherd)	9 - 2	Mr J. B. Jeffrey
STEVIE SANDERS (J. R. Jenkins)	9 - 0	c/o 01763 241147
TYLER SAUNDERS (J. W. Hills)	8 - 0	c/o 01488 731447
EMMA SAYER (Dianne Sayer)	8 - 7	c/o 07980 295316
ROWAN SCOTT (Ann Duffield)	7 - 7	c/o 07802 49633
CALLUM SHEPHERD (Charles Hills)	7 - 13	c/o 07774 474960
KIERAN SHOEMARK (Andrew Balding)	7 - 12	c/o 01635 298213
ROSS SMITH (Linda Perratt)	8 - 7	c/o 07931 306149
LOUIS STEWARD (Michael Bell)	8 - 0	c/o 07802 26451
LEWIS STONES (Michael Mullineaux)	9 - 2	c/o 07753 650263
KEVIN STOTT (Kevin Ryan)	8 - 0	Mr R. A. Hale
ROBERT TART (Alan Bailey)	8 - 2	Mr A. D. Lewis

RYAN TATE (Clive Cox)	7 - 13	Mr G. D. Jewell
SHIRLEY TEASDALE (David Nicholls)	7 - 9	Mr M. Furnass
MELISSA THOMPSON (Richard Guest)	8 - 2	c/o 01937 587552
BRIAN TOOMEY (Kevin Guest)	9 - 3	c/o 01845 597622
BRIAN TREANOR (K. R. Burke)	8 - 2	Mr J. B. Jeffrey
GEMMA TUTTY (Karen Tutty)	7 - 12	Mr M. Furnass
WILLIAM TWISTON-DAVIES (Nigel Twiston-Davies)	8 - 9	Mr C. D. Broad\Mr Tony Hind
JORDAN VAUGHAN (George Margarson)	8 - 0	Mr S. T. Dodds
EOIN WALSH (David Evans)	8 - 4	Mr L. R. James
LEWIS WALSH (David Simcock)	8 - 2	c/o 07808 954109
ALFIE WARWICK (Tobias B. P Coles)	8 - 3	Mr A. D. Lewis
KATIE WATSON (Mark Usher)	8 - 3	c/o 07831 873531
RYAN WHILE (Bill Turner)	8 - 6	c/o 07932 100173
CASEY WILCOX (Richard Whitaker)	8 - 8	c/o 01132 892265
JONATHAN WILLETTS (Andrew Balding)	8 - 0	Mr Mark Gilchrist
ROBERT WILLIAMS (Bernard Llewellyn)	8 - 13	Mr Mark Gilchrist
DANIEL WRIGHT (Kevin Ryan)	7 - 13	c/o 01845 597622

Only riders we have contact details for are included in this section.

Are your details missing or incorrect?
Please update us by email:
richard.lowther@racingpost.co.uk
Or leave a message on 0500 007071

JUMP JOCKEYS

Riding weights and contact details

An index of agents appears on page 712

CONDITIONALS

Their employer and contact details

An index of agents appears on page 712

NATHAN ADAMS (Laura Mongan)	9 - 7	Mr L. R. James
JOSEPH AKEHURST (Gary Moore)	10 - 0	Mr Paul Brierley
TOM BELLAMY (David Pipe)	10 - 0	Mr Dave Roberts
JAMES BEST (Philip Hobbs)	10 - 0	Mr Dave Roberts
CALLUM BEWLEY (Sue Smith)	9 - 7	Mr J. B. Jeffrey
JONATHON BEWLEY (George Bewley)	9 - 12	c/o 07704 924783
PAUL BOHAN (Steve Gollings)	9 - 10	Mrs Jayne M. Gollings
DARAGH BOURKE (Stuart Coltherd)	9 - 10	Mr J. B. Jeffrey
PADDY BRADLEY (Pat Phelan)	9 - 0	c/o 07917 762781
ELLIOT BROOKBANKS (Keith Reveley)	9 - 7	c/o 01287 650456
MICHAEL BYRNE (Tim Vaughan)	10 - 2	c/o 01446 771626
PETER CARBERRY (Nicky Henderson)	9 - 6	Mr Dave Roberts
ALEX CHADWICK (Paul Nicholls)	9 - 9	c/o 01749 860656
HARRY CHALLONER (Venetia Williams)	9 - 6	c/o 07770 627108
THOMAS CHEESMAN (Philip Hobbs)	9 - 10	Mr Dave Roberts
RYAN D. CLARK (Ben Haslam)	9 - 5	c/o 01969 624351
GRANT COCKBURN (Lucinda Russell)	9 - 7	Mr Paul Brierley
JOE COLLIVER (Micky Hammond)	9 - 12	Mr R. A. Hale
ED COOKSON (Kim Bailey)	9 - 11	c/o 01242 890241
JAMES CORBETT (Susan Corbett)	9 - 0	c/o 07713 651215
PATRICK CORBETT (Rebecca Curtis)	9 - 7	Mr Dave Roberts
JOE CORNWALL (John Cornwall)	8 - 12	c/o 07939 557091
JAMES COWLEY (Donald McCain)	9 - 7	Mr R. A. Hale
PATRICK COWLEY (Jonjo O'Neill)	9 - 5	c/o 01386 584209
MATT CRAWLEY (Lucy Wadham)	10 - 0	c/o 07980 545776
JOHN DAWSON (John Wade)	10 - 0	Mr Paul Brierley
NICO DE BOINVILLE (Nicky Henderson)	9 - 7	Mr Dave Roberts
HARRY DERHAM (Paul Nicholls)	9 - 7	Mr C. D. Broad
GARY DERWIN (Harry Fry)	9 - 7	Mr Dave Roberts
CHARLIE DEUTSCH (Charlie Longsdon)	9 - 5	Mr Dave Roberts
SHAUN DOBBIN (Rose Dobbin)	9 - 12	Mr R. A. Hale
KIERON EDGAR (David Pipe)	9 - 7	c/o 01884 840715
JONATHAN ENGLAND (Sue Smith)	9 - 7	Mr J. B. Jeffrey
WILLIAM FEATHERSTONE (Warren Greatrex)	10 - 0	Mr C. D. Broad
BEN FFRENCH DAVIS (Charlie Mann)	9 - 6	c/o 01488 71717
ANTHONY FOX (David Pipe)	10 - 4	c/o 01884 840715
DEREK FOX (Lucinda Russell)	10 - 0	Mr R. A. Hale
CRAIG GALLAGHER (Brian Ellison)	9 - 0	Mr R. A. Hale
OLLIE GARNER (Martin Keighley)	9 - 0	Mr L. R. James
THOMAS GARNER (Oliver Sherwood)	9 - 0	Mr Dave Roberts\Mr A. T. Brook
ZACHERY-JAMES GAUGHAN (Sue Smith)	9 - 5	c/o 01274 564930
LEWIS GORDON (Colin Tizzard)	9 - 10	c/o 07976 778656
JAKE GREENALL (Henry Daly)	10 - 0	Mr Dave Roberts
MATT GRIFFITHS (Jeremy Scott)	10 - 0	Mr Dave Roberts
ANDRIAS GUERIN (Paul Nicholls)	9 - 7	c/o 01749 860656
JOSH HAMER (Tony Carroll)	10 - 0	Mr C. D. Broad
MIKEY HAMILL (Sean Curran)	9 - 10	Mr Dave Roberts
RYAN HATCH (Nigel Twiston-Davies)	9 - 10	Mr C. D. Broad
GILES HAWKINS (Bob Buckler)	10 - 0	Mr L. R. James
DANIEL HISKETT (Richard Phillips)	9 - 7	Mr Dave Roberts
JAKE HODSON (David Bridgwater)	9 - 10	Mr Dave Roberts
JAKE HOLLIDAY (Malcolm Jefferson)	10 - 2	c/o 07710 502044
JAMES HUXHAM (Jonjo O'Neill)	9 - 7	Mr S. Stronge
LUKE INGRAM (Lucy Wadham)	9 - 0	c/o 07980 545776
DALE IRVING (James Ewart)	9 - 7	Mr J. B. Jeffrey
ALAN JOHNS (Tim Vaughan)	9 - 12	c/o 01446 771626
KEVIN JONES (Seamus Mullins)	9 - 10	Mr L. R. James
TONY KELLY (Rebecca Menzies)	10 - 0	c/o 07843 169217

JASON KIELY (Tim Vaughan)	9 - 10	Mr Dave Roberts
GARRY LAVERY (Brian Ellison)	9 - 7	Mr J. B. Jeffrey
MAURICE LINEHAN (Jonjo O'Neill)	9 - 7	Mr Dave Roberts
RYAN LYNAM (Ben Case)	9 - 7	c/o 07808 061223
MARK MARRIS (Anthony Middleton)	10 - 4	Mr L. R. James
COLM MCCORMACK (Keith Reveley)	10 - 2	Mr Paul Brierley\Mr R. A. Hale
DYLAN MCDONAGH (Simon West)	9 - 0	c/o 07855 924529
JEREMIAH MCGRATH (Nicky Henderson)	10 - 0	Mr Dave Roberts
MARTIN MCINTYRE (Harry Fry)	9 - 10	Mr C. D. Broad
CIARAN MCKEE (John O'Shea)	9 - 2	Mr Dave Roberts
CHRIS MEEHAN (Jeremy Scott)	9 - 0	Mr Dave Roberts
JOSHUA MOORE (Gary Moore)	10 - 0	Mr Dave Roberts
KILLIAN MOORE (Graeme McPherson)	9 - 9	Mr Dave Roberts
NATHAN MOSCROP (Brian Ellison)	10 - 4	Mr J. B. Jeffrey
STEPHEN MULQUEEN (Maurice Barnes)	9 - 7	Mr G. J. Thomson
LOUIS MUSPRATT (Chris Gordon)	9 - 4	c/o 07713 082392
CRAIG NICHOL (Lucinda Russell)	9 - 9	Mr R. A. Hale
RYAN NICHOL (Donald Whillans)	10 - 0	c/o 07771 550556
ADAM NICOL (Philip Kirby)	9 - 4	Mr Paul Brierley\Mr R. A. Hale
MICHEAL NOLAN (Philip Hobbs)	10 - 0	Mr Dave Roberts
PAUL O'BRIEN (Rebecca Curtis)	9 - 10	Mr Dave Roberts
TOMMIE M. O'BRIEN (Jonjo O'Neill)	10 - 0	c/o 01386 584209
RICHARD O'DEA (Emma Lavelle)	10 - 0	c/o 01264 735412
DIARMUID O'REGAN (Chris Grant)	9 - 4	c/o 07860 577998
LEE OSWIN (Gary Moore)	10 - 7	c/o 01403 891912
JOSEPH PALMOWSKI (Robin Dickin)	9 - 4	c/o 07979 518593
JON PARK (Kevin Bishop)	9 - 9	c/o 07816 837610
BEN POSTE (Tom Symonds)	9 - 7	Mr Dave Roberts
DEAN PRATT (John Quinn)	10 - 0	Mr Paul Brierley
PHILIP PRINCE (Liam Corcoran)	8 - 6	Mr Mark Gilchrist
JACK QUINLAN (John Ferguson)	9 - 11	Mr Dave Roberts
GERALD QUINN (Claire Dyson)	9 - 7	Mr C. D. Broad
CONOR RING (Evan Williams)	9 - 7	Mr C. D. Broad
STEVIE SANDERS (J. R. Jenkins)	9 - 4	c/o 01763 241141
JACK SAVAGE (Jo Davis)	9 - 7	c/o 07879 811535
EMMA SAYER (Dianne Sayer)	8 - 7	c/o 07980 295316
GAVIN SHEEHAN (Warren Greatrex)	9 - 7	Mr C. D. Broad
JACK SHERWOOD (Paul Nicholls)	9 - 7	Mr Dave Roberts
CONOR SHOEMARK (Fergal O'Brien)	9 - 7	Mr Dave Roberts
NICK SLATTER (Donald McCain)	9 - 7	c/o 01829 720352
JOHN STOREY (J. R. Jenkins)	9 - 6	c/o 01763 241141
GEMMA TUTTY (Karen Tutty)	7 - 12	Mr M. Furnass
JOSH WALL (Trevor Wall)	9 - 10	Mr L. R. James
CHRISTOPHER WARD (Dr Richard Newland)	9 - 7	Mr Dave Roberts
LUKE WATSON (Paul Webber)	9 - 4	c/o 01295 750226
GRAHAM WATTERS (Lucinda Russell)	9 - 7	Mr R. A. Hale
ADAM WEDGE (Evan Williams)	9 - 11	Mr Dave Roberts
TREVOR WHELAN (Neil King)	9 - 7	Mr Dave Roberts
RYAN WHILE (Bill Turner)	8 - 8	c/o 07932 100173
CALLUM WHILLANS (Venetia Williams)	9 - 7	Mr S. Stronge\Mr Dave Roberts
ROBERT WILLIAMS (Bernard Llewellyn)	9 - 5	Mr Mark Gilchrist
KIELAN WOODS (Charlie Longsdon)	9 - 11	Mr C. D. Broad

AMATEUR RIDERS

Riding weights and contact details

An index of agents appears on page 712

ADDIS, T. 10 - 0 .... 07956 155651
ALEXANDER, C. 9 - 12 .... 07799 191093
ALEXANDER, J. F. 11 - 7 .... 0131 3328850
ALLAN, V. L. 9 - 2 .... 07703 355870
ANDREWS, B. E. 9 - 0 .... Mr Dave Roberts
ANDREWS, D. I. J. 10 - 7 .... 07817 322974
ANDREWS, G. 9 - 9 .... Mr C. D. Broad
ASQUITH, R. 9 - 10 .... 07592 990461
BAILEY, J. 10 - 8 .... 07813 994980
BAKER, J. L. 9 - 8 .... 07900 980915
BAKER, Z. C. N. 9 - 12 .... 07769 531572
BALL, G. 9 - 10 .... 07977 113512
BANNISTER, H. A. A. 9 - 5 .... Mr C. D. Broad
BANNON, K. 8 - 2 .... 07944 415554
BARBER, C. R. 8 - 0 .... 07747 021213
BARBER, J. 10 - 9 .... 07904 185720
BARBER, M. 10 - 5 .... Mr L. R. James
BARFOOT-SAUNT, G. C. 10 - 9 ...... 01684 833227
BARGARY, J. P. 9 - 6 .... 07793 462688
BARRATT, RAY 8 - 12 .... 07505 508740
BARRETT, E. 9 - 7 .... 07805 683189
BARTLEY, C. A. 9 - 0 .... 07734 303862
BEAUMONT, G. 9 - 7 .... 07807 695195
BEGLEY, K. F. 9 - 0 .... 01544 267672
BESWICK, H. 9 - 7 .... 07792 472302
BETHELL, H. 9 - 8 .... 07733 424242
BIDDICK, W. E. T. 11 - 0 .... 07976 556823
BIRKETT, R. A. 10 - 0 .... 07855 065036
BISHOP-PECK, M. 8 - 6 .... 07717 268782
BLAGG, P. 11 - 3 .... 07946 605987
BOWEN, S. L. 9 - 5 .... 07718 069485
BOWEN, S. P. 8 - 7 .... 07896 272599
BOXALL, C. E. 9 - 3 .... 01472 388438
BRANTON, G. J. 9 - 10 .... 07742 260231
BRISBOURNE, R. M. 9 - 0 .... 07854 516497
BROOKE, L. 9 - 3 .... 07786 962911
BROTHERTON, J. L. 10 - 5 .... 01386 710772
BROTHERTON, S. 8 - 12 .... 07740 257110
BRYANT, M. P. 9 - 9 .... 07976 217542
BRYSON, K. A. 9 - 10 .... 07851 921496
BUCK, J. M. 9 - 10 .... 01984 667229
BULLOCK, E. 7 - 9 .... 07593 951904
BURCHELL, D. G. 10 - 7 .... 07824 332899
BURKE, T. 9 - 7 ....
BUSHBY, S. 8 - 2 .... 07561 887128
BUTTERWORTH, E. 9 - 4 .... 07917 717346
CAMPBELL, B. H. 9 - 0 .... Mr Paul Brierley
CARSON, G. 9 - 7 .... 07525 370078
CHADWICK, A. 8 - 11 .... 07712 473615
CHANIN, I. 10 - 6 .... 01258 817271
CHANIN, T. 10 - 12 .... 07815 431533
CHAPMAN, R. 9 - 2 .... 07805 213851
CHATFEILD-ROBERTS, T. 10 - 4 ..... 07794 743577
CHENERY, M. 11 - 7 .... 07967 911360
CHESHIRE, N. P. T. 9 - 9 .... 07531 002966
CHUGG, C. J. 10 - 0 .... 07854 306645
COLLEY, R. 10 - 4 .... Mr L. R. James
COLLINGTON, P. P. M. 9 - 3 .... Mr Paul Clarke

COLLINS, D. S. 11 - 0 .... 07891 882932
COOPER, C. 9 - 10 .... 07969 668909
COSTELLO, D 9 - 6 .... Mr Paul Brierley
COTTLE, D. G. G. 9 - 7 .... Mr A. D. Lewis
COULSON, J. T. 10 - 2 .... 07412 083704
COWARD, J. M. 10 - 0 .... 07919 477619
COX, G. J. 8 - 0 .... 07807 442009
CRATE, G. D. 8 - 12 .... Mr G. J. Horne
CROMBEZ, A. S. P. 8 - 10 .... 07974 948768
CROW, G. M. 10 - 7 .... 01928 740555
CUTHBERT, H. E. 9 - 0 .... 01228 560700
DALTON, A. 9 - 6 .... 07787 501331
DAVID, E. 10 - 2 .... 07500 383138
DAVID, T. R. 10 - 0 .... 07866 775562
DAVIDSON, J. T. 11 - 5 .... 07789 684290
DAVIDSON, Z. 9 - 12 .... 07584 422286
DAVIES, J. 9 - 0 .... 07713 140840
DAVIES, V. G. 9 - 5 .... 07786 925756
DAVIES-THOMAS, S. 11 - 0 .... 07769 337473
DAVIS, F. B. 8 - 6 .... Mr L. R. James
DAVIS, S. 9 - 0 .... 07960 101204
DAWSON, C. T. 11 - 5 .... 07796 530084
DAY, R. D. 9 - 7 .... 07568 557591
DEAN, A. S. 9 - 2 .... 07540 106050
DEBENHAM, I. 7 - 0 .... 07798 526745
DEFAGO, R. P. 10 - 3 .... 07515 390341
DEGNAN, W. 10 - 0 .... 07400 626696
DEMPSTER, L. 8 - 11 .... 07975 794119
DENIEL, A. 8 - 10 .... 01302 861000
DENNIS, P. 8 - 10 .... Mr R. A. Hale
DIXON, J. 9 - 7 .... 07761 998988
DOOLAN, S. M. 9 - 7 .... 07975 736480
DOYLE, A. 10 - 5 .... 07941 986549
DOYLE, H. 7 - 0 .... Mr L. R. James
DRINKWATER, S. W. 10 - 5 .... 07747 444633
DROWNE, L. 10 - 5 .... 07506 871171
DUKES, H. R. 9 - 0 .... 07758 518483
DUNN, A. 8 - 7 .... 07738 512924
DUNNING, M. 10 - 4 .... 07739 455378
DUNSDON, D. 10 - 6 .... 07885 110826
EASTERBY, W. H. 9 - 2 .... 07772 216507
EATON, S. T. 8 - 9 .... 07852 128013
EDDEN, M. L. 9 - 0 .... 07792 025352
EDWARDS, A. W. 10 - 0 .... 07590 683295
EDWARDS, D. M. 11 - 0 .... 07811 898002
EDWARDS, S. 8 - 0 .... 07517 109537
EGERTON, L. 9 - 0 .... 07900 458666
ELLINGHAM, C. 9 - 10 .... 0151 5260095
ELLIS, J. B. 8 - 5 .... 07810 723235
ELLIS, T. 10 - 10 .... 01926 632770
EVANS, C. 9 - 0 .... 07970 704456
FELD, P. 8 - 5 .... 07718 175095
FERGUSON, A. R. D. 7 - 12 ....
FERGUSON, J. 10 - 4 .... 07825 563773
FOX, STEVEN 10 - 5 .... Mr Paul Brierley
FRENCH, A. 8 - 13 .... 07776 306588
FROST, B. 10 - 0 .... 07861 814643
FULLER, P. 9 - 7 .... 07876 473926

FURNIVAL, B. A. 10 - 0 .... 07702 273729
GANNON, D. C. 9 - 4 .... 07595 4067539
GARDNER, L. 10 - 0 .... 07814 979699
GARNETT, M. B. 10 - 7 .... 01539 624314
GERETY, P. H. 10 - 8 .... 00353 852160097
GETHINGS, C. 10 - 0 .... 07873 255422
GIBBS, B. 10 - 7 .... 07818 407883
GILLAM, J. 9 - 7 .... 07847 607391
GOLDIE, I. C. 9 - 7 .... 07815 516499
GOLDSTEIN, K. A. 8 - 5 .... 07976 516318
GORMAN, G. 9 - 5 .... 07429 557863
GOSS, J. R. 10 - 0 .... 07747 514321
GRANT, C. 10 - 3 .... 07415 896552
GREENALL, O. C. 11 - 0 .... 07771 571000
GREENWAY, C. A. 9 - 5 .... 07526 923647
GREENWOOD, T. O. M. 9 - 10 .... 07904 889779
GRIFFITHS, L. C. 8 - 6 .... 01367 820280
HALL, L. 10 - 0 .... 07972 136644
HALL, P. G. 11 - 7 .... 01892 553160
HAMILTON, J. 8 - 10 .... Mr R. A. Hale
HAMILTON, T. 9 - 2 .... Mr J. B. Jeffrey
HAMPSON, B. 9 - 0 .... 07825 585218
HAMPTON, M. L. 10 - 7 .... 07515 269391
HANSON, S. P. 9 - 4 .... 07817 275107
HARBOUR, E. 10 - 0 .... 07814 646230
HARDING, J. 9 - 4 .... N. B. McKee
HARDY, P. 9 - 0 .... 07949 198410
HARGREAVES, I. 10 - 10 .... 07917 288810
HARPER, H. 9 - 2 .... 07765 494447
HARRIS, M. M. H. 8 - 0 .... 07823 554701
HART, C. V. 10 - 0 .... 07808 511705
HAWKER, C. R. 9 - 0 .... 07825 210749
HAWKER, R. 10 - 7 .... 07891 960365
HAYDON, C. M. E. 10 - 7 .... 07775 517129
HAYES, N. M. 8 - 9 .... Mr A. D. Lewis
HEAL, H. 8 - 0 .... 07890 260919
HEARD, M. R. 9 - 7 .... 07720 972159
HENDERSON, C. P. 9 - 0 .... 07796 844170
HENDERSON, G. L. 8 - 8 .... 07864 036893
HENDERSON, R. G. 9 - 7 .... 07789 332185
HEPTONSTALL, R. 9 - 0 .... 07725 185506
HICKMAN, F. J. 8 - 12 .... 07972 186098
HILL, J. P. 11 - 7 .... 07584 373313
HOGG, R. C. 10 - 0 .... 07548 934272
HOGG, W. S. 10 - 0 .... 01969 622237
HOLMES, D. T. R. 11 - 0 .... 0191 2847093
HOWDEN, K. 9 - 1 .... 07765 228349
HUGHES, J. 9 - 7 .... 07884 432672
HUGHES, J. 9 - 0 .... Mrs Joanna Hughes
INSOLE, J. J. 9 - 0 .... 07891 775449
JAMES, A. M. 9 - 4 .... 07932 479035
JARRETT, R. N. 10 - 7 .... 07527 034069
JEAVONS, J. 9 - 5 .... Mr Paul Brierley
JEFFREY, P. 8 - 10 .... 07591 478991
JOHN, P. 9 - 7 .... Mr L. R. James
JOHNSON, M. 10 - 10 .... 07788 138634
JOHNSON, M. S. 9 - 5 .... 07816 609314
JONES, E. J. 9 - 3 .... 07775 846925
JONES, L. J. 9 - 9 .... 07973 689040
JORDAN, J. 11 - 3 .... 07725 913220
KELLY, E. 10 - 3 .... 07724 839047
KEMP, D. J. 11 - 0 .... 07771 857493
KENDRICK, M. J. P. 9 - 0 .... 07798 724268
KERR, M. 9 - 0 ....
KERSWELL, S. L. 9 - 7 .... 07799 235969
KILGARRIFF, L. 9 - 0 .... Mr A. D. Lewis
KING, A. M. 9 - 0 .... 07710 406834
KING, R. 8 - 5 .... 07845 700971

KINGSLEY, E. P. 10 - 0 .... 07989 572413
KITCHMAN, W. 10 - 7 .... 07415 888662
KNOX, J. S. 10 - 7 .... 07792 196146
LAMBERT, J. 9 - 4 .... 07581 139101
LEGG, M. D. 9 - 7 .... 07590 690898
LEVEY, D. 10 - 0 .... Mr Paul Brierley\Mr Tony Hind
LEWIS, H. M. 9 - 2 .... 01451 850182
LEWIS, S. 9 - 3 .... 07701 071974
LEYSHON, R. 8 - 9 .... 07977 545239
LILLY, Z. 9 - 4 .... 01488 73311
LINDSAY, R. W. 10 - 0 .... Mr J. B. Jeffrey
LOCKING, K. P. 9 - 0 .... 07835 360125
LORDAN, D. 9 - 10 .... 00353 862537135
LYONS, K. 9 - 7 .... Mr Paul Brierley
LYTTLE, J. 10 - 9 .... 07774 060675
MABON, K. 8 - 7 .... 07565 331808
MACMAHON, E. E. 9 - 7 .... 07747 857950
MAHOT, J. H. M. 10 - 12 .... 07779 797079
MANN, P. R. 11 - 7 .... 07929 535608
MARETT, T. 9 - 6 .... 07580 241302
MARGARSON, K. L. 9 - 0 .... Mr Paul Brierley
MARTIN, C. J. 9 - 12 .... Mr Ian Wood
MARTIN, J. I. 10 - 4 .... 07807 139763
MASKILL, A. P. 9 - 3 .... 07594 478006
MASKILL, W. G. C. 10 - 5 .... 07833 937472
MASON, J. L. 8 - 12 .... 07816 453613
MASON, P. W. 11 - 0 .... 07921 707292
MAXWELL, D. 11 - 0 .... 0207 5292323
MCCAFFREY, N. A. 8 - 0 ....
MCCANN, N. 8 - 11 .... 07951 110806
MCDONALD, R. M. 9 - 7 .... 07713 113393
MCENTEE, J. A. 9 - 9 .... 07751 198496
MCGREGOR, A. L. 9 - 7 .... Mr J. B. Jeffrey
MEEK, N. 9 - 5 .... 07876 505442
MELBOURN, E. 9 - 3 .... 07765 415011
MILLER, C. 10 - 0 .... 07817 455592
MILLER, H. G. 10 - 0 .... 07825 750836
MILLS, A. 8 - 10 .... Mr L. R. James
MITCHELL, F. 9 - 7 .... Mr Philip Mitchell\Mr Dave Roberts
MOORE, H. J. 9 - 0 .... 07736 149669
MORRIS, J. 9 - 6 .... 07825 599426
MULLINEAUX, M. 8 - 7 .... 01829 261440
MURPHY, A. L. 9 - 4 .... 07711 992500
MURPHY, M. J. J. 9 - 5 .... Mr A. D. Lewis
MURPHY, O. J. 10 - 0 .... 07774 233222
MURRAY, S. 10 - 7 .... 07813 459374
NEWMAN, J. 9 - 7 .... 07920 464705
NICHOLLS, M. 8 - 4 .... 07792 440002
NIXON, J. 10 - 4 .... 07837 467167
NOONAN, D. G. 9 - 5 .... 07572 244576
NUGENT, H. F. 9 - 7 .... 07868 146696
NUTTALL, J. 9 - 7 .... 07597 481944
O'MAHONY, C. M. 10 - 0 .... 00353 876881653
ORPWOOD, N. 10 - 9 .... 07831 836626
PAINTING, S. W. 10 - 0 .... 07919 454844
PALMER, M. 9 - 2 .... 07415 799212
PARKER, N. L. 9 - 7 .... 07877 151521
PATRICK, R. P. 9 - 8 .... 07891 968199
PAYTER, L. R. 10 - 3 .... 07709 671375
PEARCE, J. 9 - 5 .... 07538 110484
PENFORD, F. 9 - 0 .... 07927 371083
PETTIS, W. 9 - 7 .... 07930 469256
PILLEY, P. 7 - 0 .... 07951 147448
PIMLOTT, O. 9 - 8 .... 07969 216409
PONTING, J. A. 10 - 7 .... 07500 847821
POOLES, R. L. 10 - 4 .... 07766 244716
POTTER, R. D. 10 - 7 .... 07921 761114
POTTER, W. E. 10 - 5 .... 07872 933534

POWELL, J. M. 8 - 2 .... 07785 113422
PRICE, M. R. 10 - 7 .... 07765 490190
PRICHARD, C. 9 - 0 .... 07928 670424
RANDALL, K. A. 8 - 6 .... 07951 952650
RAYBOULD, P. S. G. 9 - 7 .... 07761 058988
REDDINGTON, J. J. 11 - 6 .... 07766 767464
REED, W. H. R. 9 - 4 ....
RICHARDS, J. R. 9 - 0 .... Mr G. J. Thomson
RIDLEY, J. M. 10 - 0 .... 07557 879646
ROBERTS, M. 9 - 7 .... 01305 782218
ROBINSON, I. P. B. 9 - 2 .... 07581 361986
ROBINSON, S. C. 12 - 0 .... 01424 204190
ROBINSON, S. J. 11 - 3 .... 07850 640067
RUSSELL, J. J. 11 - 0 .... 07717 558257
SANGSTER, O. R. J. 9 - 0 .... 07787 745046
SCOTT, C. M. 9 - 4 .... 01638 722100
SHEPPARD, S. 9 - 0 ....
SHORT, C. E. 9 - 6 .... 07904 409937
SMITH, C. 10 - 0 .... 07702 034401
SMITH, D. J. 10 - 0 .... 07718 275288
SMITH, D. R. 10 - 0 .... 07826 392286
SMITH, E. J. 9 - 0 .... 07790 507410
SMITH, G. R. 10 - 2 .... 07748 064384
SMITH, J. 9 - 7 .... 07562 137956
SMITH, R. 9 - 0 .... 07716 919975
SOLE, J. D. 10 - 4 .... 07968 947091
SPEKE, T. 10 - 0 .... 07870 813256
SPENCER, S. 10 - 7 .... 07790 060050
SQUIRE, T. D. 10 - 5 .... 07990 964850
STANLEY, M. T. 9 - 5 .... 07967 548373
STIRLING, A. E. 10 - 0 .... 07557 952057
STOCK, H. 9 - 3 .... 07887 850816
STRAWSON, T. R. F. 11 - 7 .... 07809 444373
SUTTON, D. 9 - 7 .... 07850 106068
SWAN, G. 9 - 7 .... 07966 801736
TAYLOR, A. 8 - 2 .... 01638 664700
TEAL, J. 9 - 7 .... 07984 649070
TELFER, W. 11 - 0 .... 01793 762232
TETT, F. 9 - 4 .... Mr C. D. Broad
TICKLE, L. 9 - 12 .... 07769 183447
TODD, E. L. 9 - 7 .... 01347 878382
TORBITT, L. 10 - 0 .... 07983 446567

TRAINOR, M. 9 - 12 .... 07554 992851
TREACY, G. 10 - 7 .... 07901 199386
TUDOR, J. E. 11 - 5 .... 07950 381227
TURNER, D. I. 9 - 3 .... 01264 353242
TURNER, L. M. 10 - 0 .... 07984 531836
TUTTY, P. L. 9 - 0 .... 07815 798222
WADE, V. L. 9 - 9 .... 07772 925721
WAGGOTT, J. J. 9 - 7 .... 07789 465482
WALEY-COHEN, S. B. 10 - 3 .... 07887 848425
WALKER, K. 9 - 0 .... 07875 738696
WALKER, S. A. 9 - 7 .... Mr S. T. Dodds
WALL, M. 8 - 9 .... 07837 517094
WALL, M. J. 10 - 7 .... 07990 995053
WALTON, C. M. 9 - 4 .... Mr Paul Brierley
WALTON, J. 9 - 10 .... 07955 260235
WALTON, M. 10 - 10 .... 07717 024223
WATSON, H. 9 - 0 .... 07974 442856
WEDMORE, O. Z. F. 9 - 11 .... 07806 517766
WELTON, S. 9 - 7 .... 07738 209316
WEST, C. 10 - 7 .... 07826 236919
WESTON, T. H. 10 - 7 .... 07752 313698
WHEELER, G. F. 11 - 3 .... 07778 157245
WHEELER, T. W. 9 - 7 .... 07432 095447
WILKINSON, D. S. 8 - 0 .... 01969 640223
WILLEY, J. P. 9 - 6 .... Mr A. D. Lewis
WILLIAMS, C. 10 - 0 ....
WILLIAMS, D. 10 - 8 .... 07743 206572
WILLIAMS, J. C. 9 - 4 .... 07841 576651
WILLIAMS, L. 8 - 5 .... 07871 448437
WILLS, C. L. 10 - 0 .... 07791 846383
WILSON, A. 10 - 0 .... 07816 669962
WILSON, L. J. 8 - 10 .... Mr L. R. James
WILSON, R. 9 - 12 .... Mr J. B. Jeffrey
WILSON, R. E. 9 - 0 .... 07770 732007
WINKS, R. P. 9 - 10 .... 01226 340011
WOOD, K. 10 - 0 .... 07429 078066
WOOD, V. L. 8 - 8 .... 07985 709609
WOODWARD, M. J. 10 - 10 .... 07724 627766
WORSLEY, T. 9 - 7 .... 07825 067820
YORK, P. 10 - 7 .... 07774 962168
YOUNG, K. 8 - 7 .... 07784 942377

NOTES

NOTES

NOTES

NOTES

NOTES

NOTES

NOTES

NOTES

Equine Veterinary Excellence

Rossdales is the largest specialist equine veterinary practice in the UK, providing high quality first opinion and referral services to the Thoroughbred community for more than 50 years.

Local ambulatory service (24 hours)
- Dedicated veterinary team for Horses in Training

State-of-the-art Equine Hospital & Diagnostic Centre
- RCVS and European recognised Specialists
- Advanced diagnostics, all types of surgery, specialist treatment and care
- Lameness/poor performance and medical investigations

Advisory and veterinary services at major Thoroughbred sales

Specialised equine reproduction services and neonatology

ROSSDALES EQUINE PRACTICE
01638 663150

ROSSDALES EQUINE HOSPITAL & DIAGNOSTIC CENTRE
01638 577754

www.rossdales.com

Animal *Health* Trust

ANIMAL HEALTH TRUST

Supporting the Thoroughbred industry

The AHT works behind the scenes to constantly monitor equine disease, identify threats to the British Thoroughbred population and to put in place robust plans to head off infectious disease.

The Thoroughbred world needs the AHT.

The AHT needs your support.

DONATE NOW
help us to keep helping you

Registered charity no 209642

www.aht.org.uk